2024
STANDARD POSTAGE
STAMP CATALOGUE

ONE HUNDRED AND EIGHTIETH EDITION IN SIX VOLUMES

Volume 2B

Cyp-F

EDITOR-IN-CHIEF	Jay Bigalke
EDITOR-AT-LARGE	Donna Houseman
CONTRIBUTING EDITOR	Charles Snee
EDITOR EMERITUS	James E. Kloetzel
SENIOR EDITOR /NEW ISSUES AND VALUING	Martin J. Frankevicz
ADMINISTRATIVE ASSISTANT/CATALOGUE LAYOUT	Eric Wiessinger
PRINTING AND IMAGE COORDINATOR	Stacey Mahan
SENIOR GRAPHIC DESIGNER	Cinda McAlexander
SALES DIRECTOR	David Pistello
SALES DIRECTOR	Eric Roth
SALES DIRECTOR	Brenda Wyen
SALES REPRESENTATIVE	Julie Dahlstrom

Released May 2023

Includes New Stamp Listings through the March 2023 *Linn's Stamp News Monthly* Catalogue Update

AMOS MEDIA

1660 Campbell Road, Suite A, Sidney, OH 45365

Publishers of *Linn's Stamp News, Linn's Stamp News Monthly, Coin World* and *Coin World Monthly.*

Table of contents

See the following volumes for other country listings:
Volume 1A: United States, United Nations, Abu Dhabi-Australia; Volume 1B: Austria-B
Volume 2A: C-Cur
Volume 3A: G; Volume 3B: H-I
Volume 4A: J-L; Volume 4B: M
Volume 5A: N-Phil; Volume 5B: Pit-Sam
Volume 6A: San-Tete; Volume 6B: Thai-Z

Scott Catalogue Mission Statement

The Scott Catalogue Team exists to serve the recreational,
educational and commercial hobby needs of stamp collectors and dealers.

We strive to set the industry standard for philatelic information and products by developing and
providing goods that help collectors identify, value, organize and present their collections.

Quality customer service is, and will continue to be, our highest priority.
We aspire toward achieving total customer satisfaction.

Nos. 329-330 (2)	5.25	2.00
Nos. 1108-1109 (2)	.50	.50
Nos. 528-529 (2)	.60	.60
Nos. 523-524 (2)	.90	.75
Nos. 469-471 (3)	.90	1.20
Nos. 866-867 (2)	15.00	2.40
Nos. 504-505 (2)	1.20	.95
Nos. 604-605 (2)	4.00	1.80
Nos. 1170-1172 (3)	13.00	2.15
Nos. 802-803 (2)	1.00	.60
No. 1753 (1)	.35	.25
Nos. 580-581 (2)	1.55	.60
Nos. 1935-1936 (2)	4.15	2.25
Nos. 1138-1139 (2)	1.15	1.10
Set total (46) Stamps	88.15	40.05

Europa, 2000

CD17

2000

Albania	2621-2622
Andorra, French	522
Andorra, Spanish	262
Armenia	610-611
Austria	1814
Azerbaijan	698-699
Belarus	350
Belgium	1818
Bosnia & Herzegovina (Moslem)	358
Bosnia & Herzegovina (Serb)	111-112
Croatia	428-429
Cyprus	959
Czech Republic	3120
Denmark	1189
Estonia	394
Faroe Islands	376
Finland	1129
Aland Islands	166
France	2771
Georgia	228-229
Germany	2086-2087
Gibraltar	837-840
Great Britain (Jersey)	935-936
Great Britain (Isle of Man)	883
Greece	1959
Greenland	363
Hungary	3699-3700
Iceland	910
Ireland	1230-1231
Italy	2349
Latvia	504
Liechtenstein	1178
Lithuania	668
Luxembourg	1035
Macedonia	187
Malta	1011-1012
Moldova	355
Monaco	2161-2162
Poland	3519
Portugal	2358
Portugal (Azores)	455
Portugal (Madeira)	208
Romania	4370
Russia	6589
San Marino	1480
Slovakia	355
Slovenia	424
Spain	3036
Sweden	2394
Switzerland	1074
Turkey	2762
Turkish Rep. of Northern Cyprus	500
Ukraine	379
Vatican City	1152

Nos. 2621-2622 (2)	9.50	9.50
No. 522 (1)	2.00	1.00
No. 262 (1)	1.75	.80
Nos. 610-611 (2)	4.75	4.75
No. 1814 (1)	1.25	1.25
Nos. 698-699 (2)	6.00	6.00
No. 350 (1)	1.75	1.75
No. 1818 (1)	1.40	.60
No. 358 (1)	4.75	4.75
Nos. 111-112 (2)	110.00	110.00
Nos. 428-429 (2)	6.25	6.25
No. 959 (1)	2.10	1.40
No. 3120 (1)	1.20	.40
No. 1189 (1)	3.50	2.25
No. 394 (1)	1.25	1.25
No. 376 (1)	2.40	2.40
No. 1129 (1)	2.00	.60
No. 166 (1)	1.10	1.20
No. 2771 (1)	1.25	.40
Nos. 228-229 (2)	9.00	9.00
Nos. 2086-2087 (2)	4.35	2.10
Nos. 837-840 (4)	5.50	5.30

Nos. 935-936 (2)	2.40	2.40
No. 883 (1)	1.75	1.75
No. 363 (1)	1.90	1.90
Nos. 3699-3700 (2)	6.50	2.50
No. 910 (1)	1.60	1.60
Nos. 1230-1231 (2)	4.35	4.35
No. 2349 (1)	1.50	.40
No. 504 (1)	5.00	2.40
No. 1178 (1)	2.25	1.75
No. 668 (1)	1.50	1.50
No. 1035 (1)	1.40	.85
No. 187 (1)	3.00	3.00
Nos. 1011-1012 (2)	4.35	4.35
No. 355 (1)	3.50	3.50
Nos. 2161-2162 (2)	2.80	1.40
No. 3519 (1)	1.25	.75
No. 2358 (1)	1.25	.65
No. 455 (1)	1.25	.50
No. 208 (1)	1.25	.50
No. 4370 (1)	2.50	1.25
No. 6589 (1)	4.00	.85
No. 1480 (1)	1.00	1.00
No. 355 (1)	1.60	.80
No. 424 (1)	3.25	3.25
No. 3036 (1)	1.00	.40
No. 2394 (1)	3.00	1.50
No. 1074 (1)	2.10	1.05
No. 2762 (1)	2.75	2.00
No. 500 (1)	2.50	2.50
No. 379 (1)	4.50	3.00
No. 1152 (1)	1.75	1.75
Set total (68) Stamps	261.80	228.35

The Gibraltar stamps are similar to the stamp illustrated, but none have the design shown above. All other sets listed above include at least one stamp with the design shown, but some include stamps with entirely different designs. Bulgaria Nos. 4131-4132, Guernsey Nos. 802-803 and Yugoslavia Nos. 2485-2486 are Europa stamps with completely different designs.

PORTUGAL & COLONIES
Vasco da Gama

Fleet Departing
CD20

Fleet Arriving at
Calicut — CD21

Embarking at
Rastello
CD22

Muse of
History
CD23

San Gabriel,
da Gama and
Camoens
CD24

Archangel
Gabriel, the
Patron Saint
CD25

Flagship San
Gabriel — CD26

Vasco da
Gama — CD27

Fourth centenary of Vasco da Gama's discovery of the route to India.

1898

Azores	93-100
Macao	67-74
Madeira	37-44
Portugal	147-154
Port. Africa	1-8
Port. Congo	75-98
Port. India	189-196
St. Thomas & Prince Islands	170-193
Timor	45-52

Nos. 93-100 (8)	113.50	73.50
Nos. 67-74 (8)	138.75	91.75
Nos. 37-44 (8)	60.55	37.25
Nos. 147-154 (8)	155.00	50.25
Nos. 1-8 (8)	35.00	23.50
Nos. 75-98 (24)	52.15	41.65
Nos. 189-196 (8)	25.25	15.50
Nos. 170-193 (24)	56.30	43.00
Nos. 45-52 (8)	39.75	27.25
Set total (104) Stamps	676.25	403.65

Pombal
POSTAL TAX
POSTAL TAX DUES

Marquis de
Pombal — CD28

Planning
Reconstruction
of Lisbon,
1755 — CD29

Pombal Monument,
Lisbon — CD30

Sebastiao Jose de Carvalho e Mello, Marquis de Pombal (1699-1782), statesman, rebuilt Lisbon after earthquake of 1755. Tax was for the erection of Pombal monument. Obligatory on all mail on certain days throughout the year. Postal Tax Dues are inscribed "Multa."

1925

Angola	RA1-RA3, RAJ1-RAJ3
Azores	RA9-RA11, RAJ2-RAJ4
Cape Verde	RA1-RA3, RAJ1-RAJ3
Macao	RA1-RA3, RAJ1-RAJ3
Madeira	RA1-RA3, RAJ1-RAJ3
Mozambique	RA1-RA3, RAJ1-RAJ3
Nyassa	RA1-RA3, RAJ1-RAJ3
Portugal	RA11-RA13, RAJ2-RAJ4
Port. Guinea	RA1-RA3, RAJ1-RAJ3
Port. India	RA1-RA3, RAJ1-RAJ3
St. Thomas & Prince Islands	RA1-RA3, RAJ1-RAJ3
Timor	RA1-RA3, RAJ1-RAJ3

Nos. RA1-RA3,RAJ1-RAJ3 (6)	6.60	6.60
Nos. RA9-RA11,RAJ2-RAJ4 (6)	6.60	6.60
Nos. RA1-RA3,RAJ1-RAJ3 (6)	7.80	7.65
Nos. RA1-RA3,RAJ1-RAJ3 (6)	21.25	13.20
Nos. RA1-RA3,RAJ1-RAJ3 (6)	7.95	14.70
Nos. RA1-RA3,RAJ1-RAJ3 (6)	2.40	2.55
Nos. RA1-RA3,RAJ1-RAJ3 (6)	63.00	63.00
Nos. RA11-RA13,RAJ2-RAJ4 (6)	5.95	5.20
Nos. RA1-RA3,RAJ1-RAJ3 (6)	5.10	4.65
Nos. RA1-RA3,RAJ1-RAJ3 (6)	3.45	3.45
Nos. RA1-RA3,RAJ1-RAJ3 (6)	4.50	4.50
Nos. RA1-RA3,RAJ1-RAJ3 (6)	2.10	3.90
Set total (72) Stamps	136.70	136.00

Vasco da Gama
CD34

Mousinho de
Albuquerque
CD35

Dam
CD36

Prince Henry
the Navigator
CD37

Affonso de
Albuquerque
CD38

Plane over
Globe
CD39

1938-39

Angola	274-291, C1-C9
Cape Verde	234-251, C1-C9
Macao	289-305, C7-C15
Mozambique	270-287, C1-C9
Port. Guinea	233-250. C1-C9
Port. India	439-453, C1-C8
St. Thomas & Prince Islands	302-319, 323-340, C1-C18
Timor	223-239, C1-C9

Nos. 274-291,C1-C9 (27)	129.40	22.85
Nos. 234-251,C1-C9 (27)	122.40	38.30
Nos. 289-305,C7-C15 (26)	495.70	149.20
Nos. 270-287,C1-C9 (27)	63.45	11.20
Nos. 233-250,C1-C9 (27)	130.20	49.15
Nos. 439-453,C1-C8 (23)	82.75	30.95
Nos. 302-319,323-340,C1-C18 (54)	467.70	244.80
Nos. 223-239,C1-C9 (26)	193.55	94.50
Set total (237) Stamps	1,685.	640.95

Lady of Fatima

Our Lady of the
Rosary, Fatima,
Portugal — CD40

1948-49

Angola	315-318
Cape Verde	266
Macao	336
Mozambique	325-328
Port. Guinea	271
Port. India	480
St. Thomas & Prince Islands	351
Timor	254

Nos. 315-318 (4)	68.00	17.25
No. 266 (1)	8.50	9.00
No. 336 (1)	42.50	12.00
Nos. 325-328 (4)	73.25	16.85
No. 271 (1)	6.50	3.50
No. 480 (1)	4.50	3.00
No. 351 (1)	8.50	7.00
No. 254 (1)	6.00	6.00
Set total (14) Stamps	217.75	74.60

A souvenir sheet of 9 stamps was issued in 1951 to mark the extension of the 1950 Holy Year. The sheet contains: Angola No. 316, Cape Verde No. 266, Macao No. 336, Mozambique No. 325, Portuguese Guinea No. 271, Portuguese India Nos. 480, 485, St. Thomas & Prince Islands No. 351, Timor No. 254. The sheet also contains a portrait of Pope Pius XII and is inscribed "Encerramento do

Ano Santo, Fatima 1951." It was sold for 11 escudos.

Holy Year

Church Bells and Dove CD41   Angel Holding Candelabra CD42

Holy Year, 1950.

1950-51

Angola	331-332
Cape Verde	268-269
Macao	339-340
Mozambique	330-331
Port. Guinea	273-274
Port. India	490-491, 496-503
St. Thomas & Prince Islands	353-354
Timor	258-259

Nos. 331-332 (2)	7.60	1.35
Nos. 268-269 (2)	7.35	4.75
Nos. 339-340 (2)	60.00	14.00
Nos. 330-331 (2)	3.00	1.10
Nos. 273-274 (2)	11.25	3.50
Nos. 490-491,496-503 (10)	10.40	4.95
Nos. 353-354 (2)	7.75	4.90
Nos. 258-259 (2)	8.00	4.00
Set total (24) Stamps	115.35	38.55

A souvenir sheet of 8 stamps was issued in 1951 to mark the extension of the Holy Year. The sheet contains: Angola No. 331, Cape Verde No. 269, Macao No. 340, Mozambique No. 331, Portuguese Guinea No. 275, Portuguese India No. 490, St. Thomas & Prince Islands No. 354, Timor No. 258, some with colors changed. The sheet contains doves and is inscribed 'Encerramento do Ano Santo, Fatima 1951.' It was sold for 17 escudos.

Holy Year Conclusion

Our Lady of Fatima — CD43

Conclusion of Holy Year. Sheets contain alternate vertical rows of stamps and labels bearing quotation from Pope Pius XII, different for each colony.

1951

Angola	357
Cape Verde	270
Macao	352
Mozambique	356
Port. Guinea	275
Port. India	506
St. Thomas & Prince Islands	355
Timor	270

No. 357 (1)	5.25	1.50
No. 270 (1)	1.75	1.25
No. 352 (1)	45.00	10.00
No. 356 (1)	2.25	1.00
No. 275 (1)	1.75	.90
No. 506 (1)	2.50	1.00
No. 355 (1)	3.00	2.00
No. 270 (1)	5.75	2.40
Set total (8) Stamps	67.25	20.05

Medical Congress

CD44

First National Congress of Tropical Medicine, Lisbon, 1952. Each stamp has a different design.

1952

Angola	358
Cape Verde	287
Macao	364

Mozambique	359
Port. Guinea	276
Port. India	516
St. Thomas & Prince Islands	356
Timor	271

No. 358 (1)	1.50	.50
No. 287 (1)	.95	.75
No. 364 (1)	10.00	6.00
No. 359 (1)	1.25	.55
No. 276 (1)	1.00	.45
No. 516 (1)	5.50	2.00
No. 356 (1)	.35	.30
No. 271 (1)	2.50	1.30
Set total (8) Stamps	23.05	11.85

Postage Due Stamps

CD45

1952

Angola	J37-J42
Cape Verde	J31-J36
Macao	J53-J58
Mozambique	J51-J56
Port. Guinea	J40-J45
Port. India	J47-J52
St. Thomas & Prince Islands	J52-J57
Timor	J31-J36

Nos. J37-J42 (6)	4.30	2.55
Nos. J31-J36 (6)	2.80	2.30
Nos. J53-J58 (6)	17.45	6.85
Nos. J51-J56 (6)	1.80	1.55
Nos. J40-J45 (6)	2.55	2.55
Nos. J47-J52 (6)	6.10	6.10
Nos. J52-J57 (6)	3.85	3.85
Nos. J31-J36 (6)	6.20	3.50
Set total (48) Stamps	45.05	29.25

Sao Paulo

Father Manuel da Nobrega and View of Sao Paulo — CD46

Founding of Sao Paulo, Brazil, 400th anniv.

1954

Angola	385
Cape Verde	297
Macao	382
Mozambique	395
Port. Guinea	291
Port. India	530
St. Thomas & Prince Islands	369
Timor	279

No. 385 (1)	.80	.50
No. 297 (1)	.95	.80
No. 382 (1)	15.00	6.00
No. 395 (1)	.40	.30
No. 291 (1)	.35	.25
No. 530 (1)	.80	.40
No. 369 (1)	.70	.50
No. 279 (1)	3.00	1.25
Set total (8) Stamps	22.00	10.00

Tropical Medicine Congress

CD47

Sixth International Congress for Tropical Medicine and Malaria, Lisbon, Sept. 1958. Each stamp shows a different plant.

1958

Angola	409
Cape Verde	303
Macao	392
Mozambique	404
Port. Guinea	295
Port. India	569
St. Thomas & Prince Islands	371

Timor	289

No. 409 (1)	3.50	1.10
No. 303 (1)	6.75	3.25
No. 392 (1)	10.00	5.00
No. 404 (1)	2.50	.85
No. 295 (1)	3.00	1.10
No. 569 (1)	1.75	.75
No. 371 (1)	2.75	2.00
No. 289 (1)	3.50	2.75
Set total (8) Stamps	33.75	16.80

Sports

CD48

Each stamp shows a different sport.

1962

Angola	433-438
Cape Verde	320-325
Macao	394-399
Mozambique	424-429
Port. Guinea	299-304
St. Thomas & Prince Islands	374-379
Timor	313-318

Nos. 433-438 (6)	5.50	3.20
Nos. 320-325 (6)	16.05	7.40
Nos. 394-399 (6)	68.65	14.60
Nos. 424-429 (6)	5.70	2.45
Nos. 299-304 (6)	6.00	3.00
Nos. 374-379 (6)	6.75	3.20
Nos. 313-318 (6)	9.15	5.05
Set total (42) Stamps	117.80	38.90

Anti-Malaria

Anopheles Funestus and Malaria Eradication Symbol — CD49

World Health Organization drive to eradicate malaria.

1962

Angola	439
Cape Verde	326
Macao	400
Mozambique	430
Port. Guinea	305
St. Thomas & Prince Islands	380
Timor	319

No. 439 (1)	1.75	.90
No. 326 (1)	1.90	1.60
No. 400 (1)	7.00	2.25
No. 430 (1)	1.40	.40
No. 305 (1)	1.25	.45
No. 380 (1)	2.25	1.25
No. 319 (1)	1.50	1.00
Set total (7) Stamps	17.05	7.85

Airline Anniversary

Map of Africa, Super Constellation and Jet Liner — CD50

Tenth anniversary of Transportes Aereos Portugueses (TAP).

1963

Angola	490
Cape Verde	327
Mozambique	434
Port. Guinea	318
St. Thomas & Prince Islands	381

No. 490 (1)	1.00	.35
No. 327 (1)	1.50	1.10
No. 434 (1)	.40	.25

No. 318 (1)	.65	.35
No. 381 (1)	.80	.50
Set total (5) Stamps	4.35	2.55

National Overseas Bank

Antonio Teixeira de Sousa — CD51

Centenary of the National Overseas Bank of Portugal.

1964, May 16

Angola	509
Cape Verde	328
Port. Guinea	319
St. Thomas & Prince Islands	382
Timor	320

No. 509 (1)	.90	.30
No. 328 (1)	1.50	1.30
No. 319 (1)	.65	.40
No. 382 (1)	.70	.50
No. 320 (1)	1.50	.85
Set total (5) Stamps	5.25	3.35

ITU

ITU Emblem and the Archangel Gabriel — CD52

International Communications Union, Cent.

1965, May 17

Angola	511
Cape Verde	329
Macao	402
Mozambique	464
Port. Guinea	320
St. Thomas & Prince Islands	383
Timor	321

No. 511 (1)	1.25	.65
No. 329 (1)	2.90	2.25
No. 402 (1)	6.00	2.25
No. 464 (1)	.45	.25
No. 320 (1)	1.90	.75
No. 383 (1)	2.00	1.00
No. 321 (1)	1.50	.90
Set total (7) Stamps	16.00	8.05

National Revolution

CD53

40th anniv. of the National Revolution. Different buildings on each stamp.

1966, May 28

Angola	525
Cape Verde	338
Macao	403
Mozambique	465
Port. Guinea	329
St. Thomas & Prince Islands	392
Timor	322

No. 525 (1)	.50	.25
No. 338 (1)	.85	.75
No. 403 (1)	9.00	2.25
No. 465 (1)	.50	.30
No. 329 (1)	.55	.35
No. 392 (1)	.80	.50
No. 322 (1)	1.75	.95
Set total (7) Stamps	13.95	5.35

Navy Club

CD54

Centenary of Portugal's Navy Club. Each stamp has a different design.

1967, Jan. 31

Angola	527-528
Cape Verde	339-340
Macao	412-413
Mozambique	478-479
Port. Guinea	330-331
St. Thomas & Prince Islands	393-394
Timor	323-324

Nos. 527-528 (2)	1.75	.75
Nos. 339-340 (2)	2.70	2.30
Nos. 412-413 (2)	11.25	4.00
Nos. 478-479 (2)	1.40	.65
Nos. 330-331 (2)	1.20	.90
Nos. 393-394 (2)	3.30	1.30
Nos. 323-324 (2)	4.65	1.90
Set total (14) Stamps	26.25	11.80

Admiral Coutinho

CD55

Centenary of the birth of Admiral Carlos Viegas Gago Coutinho (1869-1959), explorer and aviation pioneer. Each stamp has a different design.

1969, Feb. 17

Angola	547
Cape Verde	355
Macao	417
Mozambique	484
Port. Guinea	335
St. Thomas & Prince Islands	397
Timor	335

No. 547 (1)	.85	.35
No. 355 (1)	.60	.25
No. 417 (1)	5.00	1.75
No. 484 (1)	.25	.25
No. 335 (1)	.35	.25
No. 397 (1)	.60	.35
No. 335 (1)	2.50	1.05
Set total (7) Stamps	10.15	4.25

Administration Reform

Luiz Augusto Rebello da Silva — CD56

Centenary of the administration reforms of the overseas territories.

1969, Sept. 25

Angola	549
Cape Verde	357
Macao	419
Mozambique	491
Port. Guinea	337
St. Thomas & Prince Islands	399
Timor	338

No. 549 (1)	.35	.25
No. 357 (1)	.65	.40
No. 419 (1)	6.00	1.00
No. 491 (1)	.25	.25
No. 337 (1)	.25	.25
No. 399 (1)	.45	.45
No. 338 (1)	1.25	.50
Set total (7) Stamps	9.20	3.10

Marshal Carmona

CD57

Birth centenary of Marshal Antonio Oscar Carmona de Fragoso (1869-1951), President of Portugal. Each stamp has a different design.

1970, Nov. 15

Angola	563
Cape Verde	359
Macao	422
Mozambique	493
Port. Guinea	340
St. Thomas & Prince Islands	403
Timor	341

No. 563 (1)	.45	.25
No. 359 (1)	.70	.50
No. 422 (1)	2.00	1.00
No. 493 (1)	.40	.25
No. 340 (1)	.35	.25
No. 403 (1)	.75	.40
No. 341 (1)	1.00	.35
Set total (7) Stamps	5.65	3.00

Olympic Games

CD59

20th Olympic Games, Munich, Aug. 26-Sept. 11. Each stamp shows a different sport.

1972, June 20

Angola	569
Cape Verde	361
Macao	426
Mozambique	504
Port. Guinea	342
St. Thomas & Prince Islands	408
Timor	343

No. 569 (1)	.65	.25
No. 361 (1)	.85	.40
No. 426 (1)	4.25	1.00
No. 504 (1)	.30	.25
No. 342 (1)	.45	.25
No. 408 (1)	.45	.25
No. 343 (1)	1.60	.80
Set total (7) Stamps	8.55	3.20

Lisbon-Rio de Janeiro Flight

CD60

50th anniversary of the Lisbon to Rio de Janeiro flight by Arturo de Sacadura and Coutinho, March 30-June 5, 1922. Each stamp shows a different stage of the flight.

1972, Sept. 20

Angola	570
Cape Verde	362
Macao	427
Mozambique	505
Port. Guinea	343
St. Thomas & Prince Islands	409
Timor	344

No. 570 (1)	.35	.25
No. 362 (1)	.85	.40
No. 427 (1)	22.50	8.50
No. 505 (1)	.25	.25
No. 343 (1)	.25	.25
No. 409 (1)	.50	.25
No. 344 (1)	1.40	.60
Set total (7) Stamps	26.10	10.50

WMO Centenary

WMO Emblem — CD61

Centenary of international meterological cooperation.

1973, Dec. 15

Angola	571
Cape Verde	363
Macao	429
Mozambique	509
Port. Guinea	344
St. Thomas & Prince Islands	410

Timor	345

No. 571 (1)	.45	.25
No. 363 (1)	.85	.40
No. 429 (1)	6.00	1.75
No. 509 (1)	.30	.25
No. 344 (1)	.45	.35
No. 410 (1)	.60	.50
No. 345 (1)	4.25	2.50
Set total (7) Stamps	12.90	6.00

FRENCH COMMUNITY

Upper Volta can be found under
Burkina Faso in Vol. 1
Madagascar can be found under
Malagasy in Vol. 3

Colonial Exposition

People of French Empire CD70

Women's Heads CD71

France Showing Way to Civilization CD72

"Colonial Commerce" CD73

International Colonial Exposition, Paris.

1931

Cameroun	213-216
Chad	60-63
Dahomey	97-100
Fr. Guiana	152-155
Fr. Guinea	116-119
Fr. India	100-103
Fr. Polynesia	76-79
Fr. Sudan	102-105
Gabon	120-123
Guadeloupe	138-141
Indo-China	140-142
Ivory Coast	92-95
Madagascar	169-172
Martinique	129-132
Mauritania	65-68
Middle Congo	61-64
New Caledonia	176-179
Niger	73-76
Reunion	122-125
St. Pierre & Miquelon	132-135
Senegal	138-141
Somali Coast	135-138
Togo	254-257
Ubangi-Shari	82-85
Upper Volta	66-69
Wallis & Futuna Isls.	85-88

Nos. 213-216 (4)	23.00	18.25
Nos. 60-63 (4)	22.00	22.00
Nos. 97-100 (4)	26.00	26.00
Nos. 152-155 (4)	22.00	22.00
Nos. 116-119 (4)	19.75	19.75
Nos. 100-103 (4)	18.00	18.00
Nos. 76-79 (4)	30.00	30.00
Nos. 102-105 (4)	19.00	19.00
Nos. 120-123 (4)	17.50	17.50
Nos. 138-141 (4)	19.00	19.00
Nos. 140-142 (4)	12.00	11.50
Nos. 92-95 (4)	22.50	22.50
Nos. 169-172 (4)	9.25	6.50
Nos. 129-132 (4)	21.00	21.00
Nos. 65-68 (4)	22.00	22.00
Nos. 61-64 (4)	20.00	18.50
Nos. 176-179 (4)	24.00	24.00
Nos. 73-76 (4)	20.50	20.50
Nos. 122-125 (4)	22.00	22.00
Nos. 132-135 (4)	24.00	24.00
Nos. 138-141 (4)	20.00	20.00
Nos. 135-138 (4)	22.00	22.00
Nos. 254-257 (4)	22.00	22.00

Nos. 82-85 (4)	21.00	21.00
Nos. 66-69 (4)	19.00	19.00
Nos. 85-88 (4)	31.00	35.00
Set total (103) Stamps	548.50	543.00

Paris International Exposition Colonial Arts Exposition

"Colonial Resources"
CD74   CD77

Overseas Commerce CD75

Exposition Building and Women CD76

"France and the Empire" CD78

Cultural Treasures of the Colonies CD79

Souvenir sheets contain one imperf. stamp.

1937

Cameroun	217-222A
Dahomey	101-107
Fr. Equatorial Africa	27-32, 73
Fr. Guiana	162-168
Fr. Guinea	120-126
Fr. India	104-110
Fr. Polynesia	117-123
Fr. Sudan	106-112
Guadeloupe	148-154
Indo-China	193-199
Inini	41
Ivory Coast	152-158
Kwangchowan	132
Madagascar	191-197
Martinique	179-185
Mauritania	69-75
New Caledonia	208-214
Niger	77-83
Reunion	167-173
St. Pierre & Miquelon	165-171
Senegal	172-178
Somali Coast	139-145
Togo	258-264
Wallis & Futuna Isls.	89

Nos. 217-222A (7)	18.80	20.30
Nos. 101-107 (7)	23.60	27.60
Nos. 27-32, 73 (7)	28.10	32.10
Nos. 162-168 (7)	22.50	24.50
Nos. 120-126 (7)	24.00	28.00
Nos. 104-110 (7)	21.15	36.50
Nos. 117-123 (7)	58.50	75.00
Nos. 106-112 (7)	23.60	27.60
Nos. 148-154 (7)	19.55	21.05
Nos. 193-199 (7)	17.70	19.70
No. 41 (1)	21.00	27.50
Nos. 152-158 (7)	22.20	26.20
No. 132 (1)	9.25	11.00
Nos. 191-197 (7)	19.25	21.75
Nos. 179-185 (7)	19.95	21.70
Nos. 69-75 (7)	20.50	24.50
Nos. 208-214 (7)	39.00	50.50
Nos. 73-83 (11)	40.60	45.10
Nos. 167-173 (7)	21.70	23.20
Nos. 165-171 (7)	49.60	64.00
Nos. 172-178 (7)	21.00	23.80
Nos. 139-145 (7)	25.60	32.60
Nos. 258-264 (7)	20.40	20.40
No. 89 (1)	19.00	37.50
Set total (154) Stamps	606.55	742.10

Curie

Pierre and
Marie Curie
CD80

40th anniversary of the discovery of radium.
The surtax was for the benefit of the Intl. Union
for the Control of Cancer.

1938

Cameroun	B1
Cuba	B1-B2
Dahomey	B2
France	B76
Fr. Equatorial Africa	B1
Fr. Guiana	B3
Fr. Guinea	B2
Fr. India	B6
Fr. Polynesia	B5
Fr. Sudan	B1
Guadeloupe	B3
Indo-China	B14
Ivory Coast	B2
Madagascar	B2
Martinique	B2
Mauritania	B3
New Caledonia	B4
Niger	B1
Reunion	B4
St. Pierre & Miquelon	B3
Senegal	B3
Somali Coast	B2
Togo	B1

No. B1 (1)	10.00	10.00
Nos. B1-B2 (2)	12.00	3.35
No. B2 (1)	9.50	9.50
No. B76 (1)	21.00	12.50
No. B1 (1)	24.00	24.00
No. B3 (1)	13.50	13.50
No. B2 (1)	8.75	8.75
No. B6 (1)	10.00	10.00
No. B5 (1)	20.00	20.00
No. B1 (1)	12.50	12.50
No. B3 (1)	11.00	10.50
No. B14 (1)	12.00	12.00
No. B2 (1)	11.00	7.50
No. B2 (1)	11.00	11.00
No. B2 (1)	13.00	13.00
No. B3 (1)	7.75	7.75
No. B4 (1)	16.50	17.50
No. B1 (1)	16.50	16.50
No. B4 (1)	14.00	14.00
No. B3 (1)	21.00	22.50
No. B3 (1)	10.50	10.50
No. B2 (1)	7.75	7.75
No. B1 (1)	20.00	20.00
Set total (24) Stamps	313.25	294.60

Caillie

Rene Caillie and Map of Northwestern
Africa — CD81

Death centenary of Rene Caillie (1799-
1838), French explorer. All three denominations exist with colony name omitted.

1939

Dahomey	108-110
Fr. Guinea	161-163
Fr. Sudan	113-115
Ivory Coast	160-162
Mauritania	109-111
Niger	84-86
Senegal	188-190
Togo	265-267

Nos. 108-110 (3)	1.20	3.60
Nos. 161-163 (3)	1.20	3.20
Nos. 113-115 (3)	1.20	3.20
Nos. 160-162 (3)	1.05	2.55
Nos. 109-111 (3)	1.05	3.80
Nos. 84-86 (3)	2.35	2.35
Nos. 188-190 (3)	1.05	2.90
Nos. 265-267 (3)	1.05	3.30
Set total (24) Stamps	10.15	24.90

New York World's Fair

Natives
and New
York
Skyline
CD82

1939

Cameroun	223-224
Dahomey	111-112
Fr. Equatorial Africa	78-79
Fr. Guiana	169-170
Fr. Guinea	164-165
Fr. India	111-112
Fr. Polynesia	124-125
Fr. Sudan	116-117
Guadeloupe	155-156
Indo-China	203-204
Inini	42-43
Ivory Coast	163-164
Kwangchowan	133-134
Madagascar	209-210
Martinique	186-187
Mauritania	112-113
New Caledonia	215-216
Niger	87-88
Reunion	174-175
St. Pierre & Miquelon	205-206
Senegal	191-192
Somali Coast	179-180
Togo	268-269
Wallis & Futuna Isls.	90-91

Nos. 223-224 (2)	2.80	2.40
Nos. 111-112 (2)	1.60	3.20
Nos. 78-79 (2)	1.60	3.20
Nos. 169-170 (2)	2.60	2.60
Nos. 164-165 (2)	1.60	3.20
Nos. 111-112 (2)	3.00	8.00
Nos. 124-125 (2)	4.80	4.80
Nos. 116-117 (2)	1.60	3.20
Nos. 155-156 (2)	2.50	2.50
Nos. 203-204 (2)	2.05	2.05
Nos. 42-43 (2)	7.50	9.00
Nos. 163-164 (2)	1.50	3.00
Nos. 133-134 (2)	2.50	2.50
Nos. 209-210 (2)	1.50	2.50
Nos. 186-187 (2)	2.35	2.35
Nos. 112-113 (2)	1.40	2.80
Nos. 215-216 (2)	3.35	3.35
Nos. 87-88 (2)	1.60	2.80
Nos. 174-175 (2)	2.80	2.80
Nos. 205-206 (2)	4.80	6.00
Nos. 191-192 (2)	1.40	2.80
Nos. 179-180 (2)	1.40	2.80
Nos. 268-269 (2)	1.40	2.80
Nos. 90-91 (2)	5.00	6.00
Set total (48) Stamps	62.65	86.65

French Revolution

Storming of
the Bastille
CD83

French Revolution, 150th anniv. The surtax
was for the defense of the colonies.

1939

Cameroun	B2-B6
Dahomey	B3-B7
Fr. Equatorial Africa	B4-B8, CB1
Fr. Guiana	B4-B8, CB1
Fr. Guinea	B3-B7
Fr. India	B7-B11
Fr. Polynesia	B6-B10, CB1
Fr. Sudan	B2-B6
Guadeloupe	B4-B8
Indo-China	B15-B19, CB1
Inini	B1-B5
Ivory Coast	B3-B7
Kwangchowan	B1-B5
Madagascar	B3-B7, CB1
Martinique	B3-B7
Mauritania	B4-B8
New Caledonia	B5-B9, CB1
Niger	B2-B6
Reunion	B5-B9, CB1
St. Pierre & Miquelon	B4-B8
Senegal	B4-B8, CB1
Somali Coast	B3-B7
Togo	B2-B6
Wallis & Futuna Isls.	B1-B5

Nos. B2-B6 (5)	60.00	60.00
Nos. B3-B7 (5)	47.50	47.50
Nos. B4-B8,CB1 (6)	120.00	120.00
Nos. B4-B8,CB1 (6)	79.50	79.50
Nos. B3-B7 (5)	47.50	47.50
Nos. B7-B11 (5)	28.75	32.50
Nos. B6-B10,CB1 (6)	122.50	122.50
Nos. B2-B6 (5)	50.00	50.00
Nos. B4-B8 (5)	50.00	50.00
Nos. B15-B19,CB1 (6)	85.00	85.00
Nos. B1-B5 (5)	80.00	100.00
Nos. B3-B7 (5)	43.75	43.75
Nos. B1-B5 (5)	46.25	46.25
Nos. B3-B7,CB1 (6)	65.50	65.50
Nos. B3-B7 (5)	52.50	52.50
Nos. B4-B8 (5)	42.50	42.50
Nos. B5-B9,CB1 (6)	101.50	101.50
Nos. B2-B6 (5)	60.00	60.00
Nos. B5-B9,CB1 (6)	87.50	87.50
Nos. B4-B8 (5)	67.50	72.50
Nos. B4-B8,CB1 (6)	56.50	56.50
Nos. B3-B7 (5)	45.00	45.00
Nos. B2-B6 (5)	42.50	42.50
Nos. B1-B5 (5)	80.00	110.00
Set total (128) Stamps	1,562.	1,621.

Plane over
Coastal
Area
CD85

All five denominations exist with colony
name omitted.

1940

Dahomey	C1-C5
Fr. Guinea	C1-C5
Fr. Sudan	C1-C5
Ivory Coast	C1-C5
Mauritania	C1-C5
Niger	C1-C5
Senegal	C12-C16
Togo	C1-C5

Nos. C1-C5 (5)	4.00	4.00
Nos. C1-C5 (5)	4.00	4.00
Nos. C1-C5 (5)	4.00	4.00
Nos. C1-C5 (5)	3.80	3.80
Nos. C1-C5 (5)	3.50	3.50
Nos. C1-C5 (5)	3.50	3.50
Nos. C12-C16 (5)	3.50	3.50
Nos. C1-C5 (5)	3.15	3.15
Set total (40) Stamps	29.45	29.45

Defense of the Empire

Colonial
Infantryman — CD86

1941

Cameroun	B13B
Dahomey	B13
Fr. Equatorial Africa	B8B
Fr. Guiana	B10
Fr. Guinea	B13
Fr. India	B13
Fr. Polynesia	B12
Fr. Sudan	B12
Guadeloupe	B10
Indo-China	B19B
Inini	B7
Ivory Coast	B13
Kwangchowan	B7
Madagascar	B9
Martinique	B9
Mauritania	B14
New Caledonia	B11
Niger	B12
Reunion	B11
St. Pierre & Miquelon	B8B
Senegal	B14
Somali Coast	B9
Togo	B10B
Wallis & Futuna Isls.	B7

No. B13B (1)	1.60
No. B13 (1)	1.20
No. B8B (1)	3.50
No. B10 (1)	1.40
No. B13 (1)	1.40
No. B13 (1)	1.25
No. B12 (1)	3.50
No. B12 (1)	1.40
No. B10 (1)	1.00
No. B19B (1)	3.00
No. B7 (1)	1.75
No. B13 (1)	1.25
No. B7 (1)	.85

No. B9 (1)	1.50
No. B9 (1)	1.40
No. B14 (1)	.95
No. B12 (1)	1.40
No. B11 (1)	1.60
No. B8B (1)	4.50
No. B14 (1)	1.25
No. B9 (1)	1.60
No. B10B (1)	1.10
No. B7 (1)	1.75
Set total (23) Stamps	40.15

Each of the CD86 stamps listed above is
part of a set of three stamps. The designs of
the other two stamps in the set vary from
country to country. Only the values of the
Common Design stamps are listed here.

Colonial Education Fund

CD86a

1942

Cameroun	CB3
Dahomey	CB4
Fr. Equatorial Africa	CB5
Fr. Guiana	CB4
Fr. Guinea	CB4
Fr. India	CB3
Fr. Polynesia	CB4
Fr. Sudan	CB4
Guadeloupe	CB3
Indo-China	CB5
Inini	CB3
Ivory Coast	CB4
Kwangchowan	CB4
Malagasy	CB5
Martinique	CB3
Mauritania	CB4
New Caledonia	CB4
Niger	CB4
Reunion	CB4
St. Pierre & Miquelon	CB3
Senegal	CB5
Somali Coast	CB3
Togo	CB3
Wallis & Futuna	CB3

No. CB3 (1)	1.10	
No. CB4 (1)	.80	5.50
No. CB5 (1)	.80	
No. CB4 (1)	1.10	
No. CB4 (1)	.40	5.50
No. CB3 (1)	.90	
No. CB4 (1)	2.00	
No. CB4 (1)	.40	5.50
No. CB3 (1)	1.10	
No. CB5 (1)	2.00	
No. CB3 (1)	1.25	
No. CB4 (1)	1.00	5.50
No. CB4 (1)	1.00	
No. CB5 (1)	.65	
No. CB3 (1)	1.00	
No. CB4 (1)	.80	
No. CB4 (1)	2.25	
No. CB4 (1)	.35	
No. CB4 (1)	.90	
No. CB3 (1)	7.00	
No. CB5 (1)	.80	6.50
No. CB3 (1)	.70	
No. CB3 (1)	.35	
No. CB3 (1)	2.00	
Set total (24) Stamps	30.65	28.50

Cross of
Lorraine &
Four-motor
Plane
CD87

1941-5

Cameroun	C1-C7
Fr. Equatorial Africa	C17-C23
Fr. Guiana	C9-C10
Fr. India	C1-C6
Fr. Polynesia	C3-C9
Fr. West Africa	C1-C3
Guadeloupe	C1-C2
Madagascar	C37-C43

Martinique		C1-C2
New Caledonia		C7-C13
Reunion		C18-C24
St. Pierre & Miquelon		C1-C7
Somali Coast		C1-C7

Nos. C1-C7 (7)	6.30	6.30
Nos. C17-C23 (7)	10.40	6.35
Nos. C9-C10 (2)	3.80	3.10
Nos. C1-C6 (6)	9.30	15.00
Nos. C3-C9 (7)	13.75	10.00
Nos. C1-C3 (3)	9.50	3.90
Nos. C1-C2 (2)	3.75	2.50
Nos. C37-C43 (7)	5.60	3.80
Nos. C1-C2 (2)	3.00	1.60
Nos. C7-C13 (7)	8.85	7.30
Nos. C18-C24 (7)	7.05	5.00
Nos. C1-C7 (7)	11.60	9.40
Nos. C1-C7 (7)	13.95	11.10
Set total (71) Stamps	106.85	85.35

Somali Coast stamps are inscribed "Djibouti".

Transport Plane CD88

Caravan and Plane CD89

1942

Dahomey		C6-C13
Fr. Guinea		C6-C13
Fr. Sudan		C6-C13
Ivory Coast		C6-C13
Mauritania		C6-C13
Niger		C6-C13
Senegal		C17-C25
Togo		C6-C13

Nos. C6-C13 (8)	7.15
Nos. C6-C13 (8)	5.75
Nos. C6-C13 (8)	8.00
Nos. C6-C13 (8)	11.15
Nos. C6-C13 (8)	9.75
Nos. C6-C13 (8)	6.20
Nos. C17-C25 (9)	9.45
Nos. C6-C13 (8)	6.75
Set total (65) Stamps	64.20

Red Cross

Marianne CD90

The surtax was for the French Red Cross and national relief.

1944

Cameroun		B28
Fr. Equatorial Africa		B38
Fr. Guiana		B12
Fr. India		B14
Fr. Polynesia		B13
Fr. West Africa		B1
Guadeloupe		B12
Madagascar		B15
Martinique		B11
New Caledonia		B13
Reunion		B15
St. Pierre & Miquelon		B13
Somali Coast		B13
Wallis & Futuna Isls.		B9

No. B28 (1)	2.00	1.60
No. B38 (1)	1.60	1.20
No. B12 (1)	1.75	1.25
No. B14 (1)	1.50	1.25
No. B13 (1)	2.00	1.60
No. B1 (1)	6.50	4.75
No. B12 (1)	1.40	1.00
No. B15 (1)	.90	.90
No. B11 (1)	1.20	1.20
No. B13 (1)	1.50	1.50
No. B15 (1)	1.60	1.10
No. B13 (1)	2.60	2.60
No. B13 (1)	1.75	2.00
No. B9 (1)	3.00	3.00
Set total (14) Stamps	29.30	24.95

Eboue

CD91

Felix Eboue, first French colonial administrator to proclaim resistance to Germany after French surrender in World War II.

1945

Cameroun		296-297
Fr. Equatorial Africa		156-157
Fr. Guiana		171-172
Fr. India		210-211
Fr. Polynesia		150-151
Fr. West Africa		15-16
Guadeloupe		187-188
Madagascar		259-260
Martinique		196-197
New Caledonia		274-275
Reunion		238-239
St. Pierre & Miquelon		322-323
Somali Coast		238-239

Nos. 296-297 (2)	2.40	1.95
Nos. 156-157 (2)	2.55	2.00
Nos. 171-172 (2)	2.45	2.00
Nos. 210-211 (2)	2.20	1.95
Nos. 150-151 (2)	3.60	2.85
Nos. 15-16 (2)	2.40	2.40
Nos. 187-188 (2)	2.05	1.60
Nos. 259-260 (2)	2.00	1.45
Nos. 196-197 (2)	2.05	1.55
Nos. 274-275 (2)	3.40	3.00
Nos. 238-239 (2)	2.40	2.00
Nos. 322-323 (2)	4.40	3.45
Nos. 238-239 (2)	2.45	2.10
Set total (26) Stamps	34.35	28.30

Victory

Victory — CD92

European victory of the Allied Nations in World War II.

1946, May 8

Cameroun		C8
Fr. Equatorial Africa		C24
Fr. Guiana		C11
Fr. India		C7
Fr. Polynesia		C10
Fr. West Africa		C4
Guadeloupe		C3
Indo-China		C19
Madagascar		C44
Martinique		C3
New Caledonia		C14
Reunion		C25
St. Pierre & Miquelon		C8
Somali Coast		C8
Wallis & Futuna Isls.		C1

No. C8 (1)	1.60	1.20
No. C24 (1)	1.60	1.25
No. C11 (1)	1.75	1.25
No. C7 (1)	1.00	4.00
No. C10 (1)	2.75	2.00
No. C4 (1)	1.60	1.20
No. C3 (1)	1.25	1.00
No. C19 (1)	1.00	.55
No. C44 (1)	1.00	.35
No. C3 (1)	1.30	1.00
No. C14 (1)	1.50	1.25
No. C25 (1)	1.10	.90
No. C8 (1)	2.10	2.10
No. C8 (1)	1.75	1.40
No. C1 (1)	2.25	1.90
Set total (15) Stamps	23.55	21.35

Chad to Rhine

Leclerc's Departure from Chad — CD93

Battle at Cufra Oasis — CD94

Tanks in Action, Mareth — CD95

Normandy Invasion — CD96

Entering Paris — CD97

Liberation of Strasbourg — CD98

"Chad to the Rhine" march, 1942-44, by Gen. Jacques Leclerc's column, later French 2nd Armored Division.

1946, June 6

Cameroun		C9-C14
Fr. Equatorial Africa		C25-C30
Fr. Guiana		C12-C17
Fr. India		C8-C13
Fr. Polynesia		C11-C16
Fr. West Africa		C5-C10
Guadeloupe		C4-C9
Indo-China		C20-C25
Madagascar		C45-C50
Martinique		C4-C9
New Caledonia		C15-C20
Reunion		C26-C31
St. Pierre & Miquelon		C9-C14
Somali Coast		C9-C14
Wallis & Futuna Isls.		C2-C7

Nos. C9-C14 (6)	12.05	9.70
Nos. C25-C30 (6)	14.70	10.80
Nos. C12-C17 (6)	12.65	10.35
Nos. C8-C13 (6)	12.80	15.00
Nos. C11-C16 (6)	17.55	13.40
Nos. C5-C10 (6)	16.05	11.95
Nos. C4-C9 (6)	12.00	9.60
Nos. C20-C25 (6)	6.40	6.40
Nos. C45-C50 (6)	10.30	8.40
Nos. C4-C9 (6)	8.85	7.30
Nos. C15-C20 (6)	13.40	11.90
Nos. C26-C31 (6)	10.25	6.55
Nos. C9-C14 (6)	17.30	14.35

Nos. C9-C14 (6)	18.10	12.65
Nos. C2-C7 (6)	13.75	10.45
Set total (90) Stamps	196.15	158.80

UPU

French Colonials, Globe and Plane — CD99

Universal Postal Union, 75th anniv.

1949, July 4

Cameroun		C29
Fr. Equatorial Africa		C34
Fr. India		C17
Fr. Polynesia		C20
Fr. West Africa		C15
Indo-China		C26
Madagascar		C55
New Caledonia		C24
St. Pierre & Miquelon		C18
Somali Coast		C18
Togo		C18
Wallis & Futuna Isls.		C10

No. C29 (1)	8.00	4.75
No. C34 (1)	16.00	12.00
No. C17 (1)	11.50	8.75
No. C20 (1)	20.00	15.00
No. C15 (1)	12.00	8.75
No. C26 (1)	4.75	4.00
No. C55 (1)	4.00	2.75
No. C24 (1)	7.50	5.00
No. C18 (1)	20.00	12.00
No. C18 (1)	14.00	10.50
No. C18 (1)	8.50	7.00
No. C10 (1)	11.00	8.25
Set total (12) Stamps	137.25	98.75

Tropical Medicine

Doctor Treating Infant CD100

The surtax was for charitable work.

1950

Cameroun		B29
Fr. Equatorial Africa		B39
Fr. India		B15
Fr. Polynesia		B14
Fr. West Africa		B3
Madagascar		B17
New Caledonia		B14
St. Pierre & Miquelon		B14
Somali Coast		B14
Togo		B11

No. B29 (1)	7.25	5.50
No. B39 (1)	7.25	5.50
No. B15 (1)	6.00	4.00
No. B14 (1)	10.50	8.00
No. B3 (1)	9.50	7.25
No. B17 (1)	5.50	5.50
No. B14 (1)	6.75	5.25
No. B14 (1)	16.00	15.00
No. B14 (1)	7.75	6.25
No. B11 (1)	5.00	3.50
Set total (10) Stamps	81.50	65.75

Military Medal

Medal, Early Marine and Colonial Soldier — CD101

Centenary of the creation of the French Military Medal.

1952

Cameroun		322
Comoro Isls.		39
Fr. Equatorial Africa		186

Fr. India 233
Fr. Polynesia 179
Fr. West Africa 57
Madagascar..............................286
New Caledonia..........................295
St. Pierre & Miquelon...............345
Somali Coast............................267
Togo...327
Wallis & Futuna Isls. 149

No. 322 (1)	7.25	3.25
No. 39 (1)	45.00	37.50
No. 186 (1)	8.00	8.00
No. 233 (1)	5.50	7.00
No. 179 (1)	13.50	10.00
No. 57 (1)	8.75	6.50
No. 286 (1)	3.75	2.50
No. 295 (1)	6.50	6.00
No. 345 (1)	16.00	15.00
No. 267 (1)	9.00	8.00
No. 327 (1)	5.50	4.75
No. 149 (1)	7.25	7.25
Set total (12) Stamps	136.00	113.25

Liberation

Allied Landing, Victory Sign and Cross of Lorraine — CD102

Liberation of France, 10th anniv.

1954, June 6

Cameroun..................................C32
Comoro Isls. C4
Fr. Equatorial Africa C38
Fr. India C18
Fr. Polynesia C22
Fr. West Africa C17
Madagascar..............................C57
New Caledonia..........................C25
St. Pierre & Miquelon...............C19
Somali Coast............................C19
Togo...C19
Wallis & Futuna Isls. C11

No. C32 (1)	7.25	4.75
No. C4 (1)	32.50	19.00
No. C38 (1)	12.00	8.00
No. C18 (1)	11.00	8.00
No. C22 (1)	10.00	8.00
No. C17 (1)	12.00	5.50
No. C57 (1)	3.25	2.00
No. C25 (1)	7.50	5.00
No. C19 (1)	19.00	12.00
No. C19 (1)	10.50	8.50
No. C19 (1)	7.00	5.50
No. C11 (1)	11.00	8.25
Set total (12) Stamps	143.00	94.50

FIDES

Plowmen
CD103

Efforts of FIDES, the Economic and Social Development Fund for Overseas Possessions (Fonds d' Investissement pour le Developpement Economique et Social). Each stamp has a different design.

1956

Cameroun.........................326-329
Comoro Isls. 43
Fr. Equatorial Africa 189-192
Fr. Polynesia 181
Fr. West Africa 65-72
Madagascar.....................292-295
New Caledonia..........................303
St. Pierre & Miquelon...............350
Somali Coast....................268-269
Togo...331

Nos. 326-329 (4)	6.90	3.20
No. 43 (1)	2.25	1.60
Nos. 189-192 (4)	3.20	1.65
No. 181 (1)	4.00	2.00
Nos. 65-72 (8)	16.00	6.35
Nos. 292-295 (4)	2.25	1.20
No. 303 (1)	1.90	1.10
No. 350 (1)	6.00	4.00

Nos. 268-269 (2)	5.35	3.15
No. 331 (1)	4.25	2.10
Set total (27) Stamps	52.10	26.35

Flower

CD104

Each stamp shows a different flower.

1958-9

Cameroun..................................333
Comoro Isls. 45
Fr. Equatorial Africa 200-201
Fr. Polynesia 192
Fr. So. & Antarctic Terr. 11
Fr. West Africa 79-83
Madagascar.....................301-302
New Caledonia..................304-305
St. Pierre & Miquelon...............357
Somali Coast............................270
Togo.................................348-349
Wallis & Futuna Isls. 152

No. 333 (1)	1.60	.80
No. 45 (1)	5.25	4.25
Nos. 200-201 (2)	3.60	1.60
No. 192 (1)	6.50	4.00
No. 11 (1)	8.75	7.50
Nos. 79-83 (5)	10.45	5.60
Nos. 301-302 (2)	1.60	.60
Nos. 304-305 (2)	8.00	3.00
No. 357 (1)	4.50	2.25
No. 270 (1)	4.25	1.40
Nos. 348-349 (2)	1.10	.50
No. 152 (1)	3.25	3.25
Set total (20) Stamps	58.85	34.75

Human Rights

Sun, Dove and U.N. Emblem
CD105

10th anniversary of the signing of the Universal Declaration of Human Rights.

1958

Comoro Isls. 44
Fr. Equatorial Africa 202
Fr. Polynesia 191
Fr. West Africa 85
Madagascar..............................300
New Caledonia..........................306
St. Pierre & Miquelon...............356
Somali Coast............................274
Wallis & Futuna Isls. 153

No. 44 (1)	9.00	9.00
No. 202 (1)	2.40	1.25
No. 191 (1)	13.00	8.75
No. 85 (1)	2.40	2.00
No. 300 (1)	.80	.40
No. 306 (1)	2.00	1.50
No. 356 (1)	3.50	2.50
No. 274 (1)	3.50	2.10
No. 153 (1)	4.50	4.50
Set total (9) Stamps	41.10	32.00

C.C.T.A.

CD106

Commission for Technical Cooperation in Africa south of the Sahara, 10th anniv.

1960

Cameroun..................................339
Cent. Africa 3
Chad...66
Congo, P.R. 90
Dahomey...................................138
Gabon.......................................150
Ivory Coast 180
Madagascar..............................317

Mali..9
Mauritania.................................117
Niger...104
Upper Volta.................................89

No. 339 (1)	1.60	.75
No. 3 (1)	1.60	.75
No. 66 (1)	1.75	.50
No. 90 (1)	1.00	1.00
No. 138 (1)	.50	.25
No. 150 (1)	1.25	1.10
No. 180 (1)	1.10	.50
No. 317 (1)	.60	.30
No. 9 (1)	1.20	.50
No. 117 (1)	.75	.40
No. 104 (1)	.85	.45
No. 89 (1)	.65	.40
Set total (12) Stamps	12.85	6.90

Air Afrique, 1961

Modern and Ancient Africa, Map and Planes — CD107

Founding of Air Afrique (African Airlines).

1961-62

Cameroun..................................C37
Cent. Africa C5
Chad...C7
Congo, P.R. C5
Dahomey...................................C17
Gabon.......................................C5
Ivory Coast C18
Mauritania.................................C17
Niger...C22
Senegal C31
Upper Volta.................................C4

No. C37 (1)	1.00	.50
No. C5 (1)	1.00	.65
No. C7 (1)	1.00	.25
No. C5 (1)	1.75	.90
No. C17 (1)	.80	.40
No. C5 (1)	11.00	6.00
No. C18 (1)	2.00	1.25
No. C17 (1)	2.40	1.25
No. C22 (1)	1.75	.90
No. C31 (1)	.80	.30
No. C4 (1)	3.50	1.75
Set total (11) Stamps	27.00	14.15

Anti-Malaria

CD108

World Health Organization drive to eradicate malaria.

1962, Apr. 7

Cameroun..................................B36
Cent. Africa B1
Chad...B1
Comoro Isls. B1
Congo, P.R. B3
Dahomey...................................B15
Gabon.......................................B4
Ivory Coast B15
Madagascar..............................B19
Mali..B1
Mauritania.................................B16
Niger...B14
Senegal B16
Somali Coast............................B15
Upper Volta.................................B1

No. B36 (1)	1.00	.45
No. B1 (1)	1.40	1.40
No. B1 (1)	1.00	.50
No. B1 (1)	3.50	3.50
No. B3 (1)	1.40	1.00
No. B15 (1)	.75	.75
No. B4 (1)	1.00	1.00
No. B15 (1)	1.25	1.25
No. B19 (1)	.75	.50
No. B1 (1)	1.25	.60
No. B16 (1)	.50	.50
No. B14 (1)	.75	.75

No. B16 (1)	1.10	.65
No. B15 (1)	7.00	7.00
No. B1 (1)	.75	.70
Set total (15) Stamps	23.40	20.55

Abidjan Games

CD109

Abidjan Games, Ivory Coast, Dec. 24-31, 1961. Each stamp shows a different sport.

1962

Cent. Africa 19-20, C6
Chad..................................83-84, C8
Congo, P.R. 103-104, C7
Gabon.............................163-164, C6
Niger.......................................109-111
Upper Volta.............................103-105

Nos. 19-20, C6 (3)	4.15	2.85
Nos. 83-84, C8 (3)	5.80	1.55
Nos. 103-104, C7 (3)	3.85	1.80
Nos. 163-164, C6 (3)	5.00	3.00
Nos. 109-111 (3)	2.60	1.25
Nos. 103-105 (3)	2.80	1.75
Set total (18) Stamps	24.20	12.20

African and Malagasy Union

Flag of Union
CD110

First anniversary of the Union.

1962, Sept. 8

Cameroun..................................373
Cent. Africa 21
Chad...85
Congo, P.R. 105
Dahomey...................................155
Gabon.......................................165
Ivory Coast 198
Madagascar..............................332
Mauritania.................................170
Niger...112
Senegal 211
Upper Volta................................106

No. 373 (1)	2.00	.75
No. 21 (1)	1.25	.75
No. 85 (1)	1.25	.25
No. 105 (1)	1.50	.50
No. 155 (1)	1.25	.90
No. 165 (1)	1.60	1.25
No. 198 (1)	2.10	.75
No. 332 (1)	.80	.80
No. 170 (1)	.75	.50
No. 112 (1)	.80	.50
No. 211 (1)	.80	.50
No. 106 (1)	1.10	.75
Set total (12) Stamps	15.20	8.20

Telstar

Telstar and Globe Showing Andover and Pleumeur-Bodou — CD111

First television connection of the United States and Europe through the Telstar satellite, July 11-12, 1962.

1962-63

Andorra, French 154
Comoro Isls. C7
Fr. Polynesia C29
Fr. So. & Antarctic Terr. C5
New Caledonia..........................C33
St. Pierre & Miquelon...............C26
Somali Coast............................C31
Wallis & Futuna Isls. C17

No. 154 (1)	2.00	1.60
No. C7 (1)	4.50	2.75
No. C29 (1)	11.50	8.00

No. C5 (1)	29.00	21.00
No. C33 (1)	25.00	18.50
No. C26 (1)	7.25	4.50
No. C31 (1)	1.00	1.00
No. C17 (1)	3.75	3.75
Set total (8) Stamps	84.00	61.10

Freedom From Hunger

World Map and Wheat Emblem CD112

U.N. Food and Agriculture Organization's "Freedom from Hunger" campaign.

1963, Mar. 21

Cameroun	B37-B38
Cent. Africa	B2
Chad	B2
Congo, P.R.	B4
Dahomey	B16
Gabon	B5
Ivory Coast	B16
Madagascar	B21
Mauritania	B17
Niger	B15
Senegal	B17
Upper Volta	B2

Nos. B37-B38 (2)	2.25	.75
No. B2 (1)	1.25	1.25
No. B2 (1)	1.10	.50
No. B4 (1)	1.40	1.00
No. B16 (1)	.80	.80
No. B5 (1)	1.00	1.00
No. B16 (1)	1.50	1.50
No. B21 (1)	.60	.45
No. B17 (1)	.60	.60
No. B15 (1)	.75	.75
No. B17 (1)	.80	.50
No. B2 (1)	.75	.70
Set total (13) Stamps	12.80	9.80

Red Cross Centenary

CD113

Centenary of the International Red Cross.

1963, Sept. 2

Comoro Isls.	55
Fr. Polynesia	205
New Caledonia	328
St. Pierre & Miquelon	367
Somali Coast	297
Wallis & Futuna Isls.	165

No. 55 (1)	7.50	6.00
No. 205 (1)	15.00	12.00
No. 328 (1)	8.00	6.75
No. 367 (1)	12.00	5.50
No. 297 (1)	6.25	6.25
No. 165 (1)	4.00	4.00
Set total (6) Stamps	52.75	40.50

African Postal Union, 1963

UAMPT Emblem, Radio Masts, Plane and Mail CD114

Establishment of the African and Malagasy Posts and Telecommunications Union.

1963, Sept. 8

Cameroun	C47
Cent. Africa	C10
Chad	C9
Congo, P.R.	C13

Dahomey	C19
Gabon	C13
Ivory Coast	C25
Madagascar	C75
Mauritania	C22
Niger	C27
Rwanda	36
Senegal	C32
Upper Volta	C9

No. C47 (1)	2.25	1.00
No. C10 (1)	1.90	.90
No. C9 (1)	1.80	.60
No. C13 (1)	1.40	.75
No. C19 (1)	.75	.25
No. C13 (1)	1.90	.80
No. C25 (1)	2.50	1.50
No. C75 (1)	1.25	.80
No. C22 (1)	1.50	.60
No. C27 (1)	1.25	.60
No. 36 (1)	1.10	.75
No. C32 (1)	1.75	.50
No. C9 (1)	1.50	.75
Set total (13) Stamps	20.85	9.80

Air Afrique, 1963

Symbols of Flight — CD115

First anniversary of Air Afrique and inauguration of DC-8 service.

1963, Nov. 19

Cameroun	C48
Chad	C10
Congo, P.R.	C14
Gabon	C18
Ivory Coast	C26
Mauritania	C26
Niger	C35
Senegal	C33

No. C48 (1)	1.25	.40
No. C10 (1)	1.80	.60
No. C14 (1)	1.60	.60
No. C18 (1)	1.25	.65
No. C26 (1)	1.00	.50
No. C26 (1)	.70	.25
No. C35 (1)	1.00	.55
No. C33 (1)	2.00	.65
Set total (8) Stamps	10.60	4.20

Europafrica

Europe and Africa Linked — CD116

Signing of an economic agreement between the European Economic Community and the African and Malagasy Union, Yaounde, Cameroun, July 20, 1963.

1963-64

Cameroun	402
Cent. Africa	C12
Chad	C11
Congo, P.R.	C16
Gabon	C19
Ivory Coast	217
Niger	C43
Upper Volta	C11

No. 402 (1)	2.25	.60
No. C12 (1)	2.50	1.75
No. C11 (1)	1.60	.50
No. C16 (1)	1.60	1.00
No. C19 (1)	1.25	.75
No. 217 (1)	1.10	.35
No. C43 (1)	.85	.50
No. C11 (1)	1.50	.80
Set total (8) Stamps	12.65	6.25

Human Rights

Scales of Justice and Globe CD117

15th anniversary of the Universal Declaration of Human Rights.

1963, Dec. 10

Comoro Isls.	56
Fr. Polynesia	206
New Caledonia	329
St. Pierre & Miquelon	368
Somali Coast	300
Wallis & Futuna Isls.	166

No. 56 (1)	7.50	6.00
No. 205 (1)	15.00	12.00
No. 329 (1)	7.00	6.00
No. 368 (1)	7.00	3.50
No. 300 (1)	8.50	8.50
No. 166 (1)	7.00	7.00
Set total (6) Stamps	52.00	43.00

PHILATEC

Stamp Album, Champs Elysees Palace and Horses of Marly CD118

Intl. Philatelic and Postal Techniques Exhibition, Paris, June 5-21, 1964.

1963-64

Comoro Isls.	60
France	1078
Fr. Polynesia	207
New Caledonia	341
St. Pierre & Miquelon	369
Somali Coast	301
Wallis & Futuna Isls.	167

No. 60 (1)	4.00	3.50
No. 1078 (1)	.25	.25
No. 206 (1)	15.00	10.00
No. 341 (1)	6.50	6.50
No. 369 (1)	11.00	8.00
No. 301 (1)	7.75	7.75
No. 167 (1)	3.00	3.00
Set total (7) Stamps	47.50	39.00

Cooperation

CD119

Cooperation between France and the French-speaking countries of Africa and Madagascar.

1964

Cameroun	409-410
Cent. Africa	39
Chad	103
Congo, P.R.	121
Dahomey	193
France	1111
Gabon	175
Ivory Coast	221
Madagascar	360
Mauritania	181
Niger	143
Senegal	236
Togo	495

Nos. 409-410 (2)	2.50	.50
No. 39 (1)	.90	.50
No. 103 (1)	1.00	.25
No. 121 (1)	.90	.35
No. 193 (1)	.80	.35
No. 1111 (1)	.25	.25
No. 175 (1)	.90	.60
No. 221 (1)	1.10	.35
No. 360 (1)	.60	.25
No. 181 (1)	.60	.35
No. 143 (1)	.80	.40
No. 236 (1)	1.60	.85
No. 495 (1)	.70	.25
Set total (14) Stamps	12.65	5.25

ITU

Telegraph, Syncom Satellite and ITU Emblem CD120

Intl. Telecommunication Union, Cent.

1965, May 17

Comoro Isls.	C14
Fr. Polynesia	C33
Fr. So. & Antarctic Terr.	C8
New Caledonia	C40
New Hebrides	124-125
St. Pierre & Miquelon	C29
Somali Coast	C36
Wallis & Futuna Isls.	C20

No. C14 (1)	18.00	9.00
No. C33 (1)	80.00	52.50
No. C8 (1)	200.00	160.00
No. C40 (1)	10.00	8.00
Nos. 124-125 (2)	32.25	27.25
No. C29 (1)	24.00	11.50
No. C36 (1)	15.00	9.00
No. C20 (1)	16.00	16.00
Set total (9) Stamps	395.25	293.25

French Satellite A-1

Diamant Rocket and Launching Installation — CD121

Launching of France's first satellite, Nov. 26, 1965.

1965-66

Comoro Isls.	C16a
France	1138a
Reunion	359a
Fr. Polynesia	C41a
Fr. So. & Antarctic Terr.	C10a
New Caledonia	C45a
St. Pierre & Miquelon	C31a
Somali Coast	C40a
Wallis & Futuna Isls.	C23a

No. C16a (1)	9.00	9.00
No. 1138a (1)	.65	.65
No. 359a (1)	3.50	3.00
No. C41a (1)	14.00	14.00
No. C10a (1)	29.00	24.00
No. C45a (1)	7.00	7.00
No. C31a (1)	14.50	14.50
No. C40a (1)	7.00	7.00
No. C23a (1)	8.50	8.50
Set total (9) Stamps	93.15	87.65

French Satellite D-1

D-1 Satellite in Orbit — CD122

Launching of the D-1 satellite at Hammaguir, Algeria, Feb. 17, 1966.

1966

Comoro Isls.	C17
France	1148

Fr. Polynesia	C42
Fr. So. & Antarctic Terr.	C11
New Caledonia	C46
St. Pierre & Miquelon	C32
Somali Coast	C49
Wallis & Futuna Isls.	C24

No. C17 (1)	4.00	4.00
No. 1148 (1)	.25	.25
No. C42 (1)	7.00	4.75
No. C11 (1)	57.50	40.00
No. C46 (1)	2.25	2.00
No. C32 (1)	9.00	6.00
No. C49 (1)	4.25	2.75
No. C24 (1)	3.50	3.50
Set total (8) Stamps	87.75	63.25

Air Afrique, 1966

Planes and Air Afrique Emblem — CD123

Introduction of DC-8F planes by Air Afrique.

1966

Cameroun	C79
Cent. Africa	C35
Chad	C26
Congo, P.R.	C42
Dahomey	C42
Gabon	C47
Ivory Coast	C32
Mauritania	C57
Niger	C63
Senegal	C47
Togo	C54
Upper Volta	C31

No. C79 (1)	.80	.25
No. C35 (1)	1.00	.50
No. C26 (1)	.85	.25
No. C42 (1)	1.00	.25
No. C42 (1)	.75	.25
No. C47 (1)	.90	.35
No. C32 (1)	1.00	.60
No. C57 (1)	.60	.30
No. C63 (1)	.70	.35
No. C47 (1)	.80	.30
No. C54 (1)	.80	.50
No. C31 (1)	.75	.50
Set total (12) Stamps	9.95	4.15

African Postal Union, 1967

Telecommunications Symbols and Map of Africa — CD124

Fifth anniversary of the establishment of the African and Malagasy Union of Posts and Telecommunications, UAMPT.

1967

Cameroun	C90
Cent. Africa	C46
Chad	C37
Congo, P.R.	C57
Dahomey	C61
Gabon	C58
Ivory Coast	C34
Madagascar	C85
Mauritania	C65
Niger	C75
Rwanda	C1-C3
Senegal	C60
Togo	C81
Upper Volta	C50

No. C90 (1)	2.40	.65
No. C46 (1)	2.25	.85
No. C37 (1)	2.00	.60
No. C57 (1)	1.60	.60
No. C61 (1)	1.75	.95
No. C58 (1)	2.00	.85
No. C34 (1)	3.50	1.50
No. C85 (1)	1.25	.60
No. C65 (1)	1.25	.60
No. C75 (1)	1.40	.60

Nos. C1-C3 (3)	2.05	1.25
No. C60 (1)	1.75	.50
No. C81 (1)	1.90	.30
No. C50 (1)	1.80	.70
Set total (16) Stamps	26.90	10.55

Monetary Union

Gold Token of the Ashantis, 17-18th Centuries — CD125

West African Monetary Union, 5th anniv.

1967, Nov. 4

Dahomey	244
Ivory Coast	259
Mauritania	238
Niger	204
Senegal	294
Togo	623
Upper Volta	181

No. 244 (1)	.65	.65
No. 259 (1)	.85	.40
No. 238 (1)	.45	.25
No. 204 (1)	.55	.25
No. 294 (1)	.60	.25
No. 623 (1)	.60	.25
No. 181 (1)	.65	.35
Set total (7) Stamps	4.35	2.40

WHO Anniversary

Sun, Flowers and WHO Emblem CD126

World Health Organization, 20th anniv.

1968, May 4

Afars & Issas	317
Comoro Isls.	73
Fr. Polynesia	241-242
Fr. So. & Antarctic Terr.	31
New Caledonia	367
St. Pierre & Miquelon	377
Wallis & Futuna Isls.	169

No. 317 (1)	3.00	3.00
No. 73 (1)	2.40	1.75
Nos. 241-242 (2)	22.00	12.75
No. 31 (1)	62.50	47.50
No. 367 (1)	4.00	2.25
No. 377 (1)	12.00	9.00
No. 169 (1)	5.75	5.75
Set total (8) Stamps	111.65	82.00

Human Rights Year

Human Rights Flame — CD127

1968, Aug. 10

Afars & Issas	322-323
Comoro Isls.	76
Fr. Polynesia	243-244
Fr. So. & Antarctic Terr.	32
New Caledonia	369
St. Pierre & Miquelon	382
Wallis & Futuna Isls.	170

Nos. 322-323 (2)	6.75	4.00
No. 76 (1)	3.25	3.25
Nos. 243-244 (2)	24.00	14.00
No. 32 (1)	55.00	47.50
No. 369 (1)	2.75	1.50
No. 382 (1)	8.00	5.50
No. 170 (1)	3.25	3.25
Set total (9) Stamps	103.00	79.00

2nd PHILEXAFRIQUE

CD128

Opening of PHILEXAFRIQUE, Abidjan, Feb. 14. Each stamp shows a local scene and stamp.

1969, Feb. 14

Cameroun	C118
Cent. Africa	C65
Chad	C48
Congo, P.R.	C77
Dahomey	C94
Gabon	C82
Ivory Coast	C38-C40
Madagascar	C92
Mali	C65
Mauritania	C80
Niger	C104
Senegal	C68
Togo	C104
Upper Volta	C62

No. C118 (1)	3.25	1.25
No. C65 (1)	1.75	1.75
No. C48 (1)	2.40	1.00
No. C77 (1)	2.00	1.75
No. C94 (1)	2.25	2.25
No. C82 (1)	2.00	2.00
Nos. C38-C40 (3)	14.50	14.50
No. C92 (1)	1.75	.85
No. C65 (1)	1.75	1.00
No. C80 (1)	1.90	.75
No. C104 (1)	3.00	1.90
No. C68 (1)	2.00	1.40
No. C104 (1)	2.25	.45
No. C62 (1)	4.00	3.25
Set total (16) Stamps	44.80	34.10

Concorde

Concorde in Flight CD129

First flight of the prototype Concorde supersonic plane at Toulouse, Mar. 1, 1969.

1969

Afars & Issas	C56
Comoro Isls.	C29
France	C42
Fr. Polynesia	C50
Fr. So. & Antarctic Terr.	C18
New Caledonia	C63
St. Pierre & Miquelon	C40
Wallis & Futuna Isls.	C30

No. C56 (1)	26.00	16.00
No. C29 (1)	18.00	12.00
No. C42 (1)	.75	.35
No. C50 (1)	55.00	35.00
No. C18 (1)	55.00	37.50
No. C63 (1)	27.50	20.00
No. C40 (1)	32.50	11.00
No. C30 (1)	15.00	10.00
Set total (8) Stamps	229.75	141.85

Development Bank

Bank Emblem — CD130

African Development Bank, fifth anniv.

1969

Cameroun	499
Chad	217
Congo, P.R.	181-182

Ivory Coast	281
Mali	127-128
Mauritania	267
Niger	220
Senegal	317-318
Upper Volta	201

No. 499 (1)	.80	.25
No. 217 (1)	.90	.25
Nos. 181-182 (2)	1.00	.50
No. 281 (1)	.70	.40
Nos. 127-128 (2)	1.00	.50
No. 267 (1)	.60	.25
No. 220 (1)	.70	.30
Nos. 317-318 (2)	1.55	.50
No. 201 (1)	.65	.30
Set total (12) Stamps	7.90	3.25

ILO

ILO Headquarters, Geneva, and Emblem — CD131

Intl. Labor Organization, 50th anniv.

1969-70

Afars & Issas	337
Comoro Isls.	83
Fr. Polynesia	251-252
Fr. So. & Antarctic Terr.	35
New Caledonia	379
St. Pierre & Miquelon	396
Wallis & Futuna Isls.	172

No. 337 (1)	2.75	2.00
No. 83 (1)	1.25	.75
Nos. 251-252 (2)	24.00	12.50
No. 35 (1)	15.00	10.00
No. 379 (1)	2.25	1.10
No. 396 (1)	10.00	5.50
No. 172 (1)	2.75	2.75
Set total (8) Stamps	58.00	34.60

ASECNA

Map of Africa, Plane and Airport CD132

10th anniversary of the Agency for the Security of Aerial Navigation in Africa and Madagascar (ASECNA, Agence pour la Securite de la Navigation Aerienne en Afrique et a Madagascar).

1969-70

Cameroun	500
Cent. Africa	119
Chad	222
Congo, P.R.	197
Dahomey	269
Gabon	260
Ivory Coast	287
Mali	130
Niger	221
Senegal	321
Upper Volta	204

No. 500 (1)	2.00	.60
No. 119 (1)	2.00	.80
No. 222 (1)	1.00	.25
No. 197 (1)	2.00	.40
No. 269 (1)	.90	.55
No. 260 (1)	1.75	.75
No. 287 (1)	.90	.40
No. 130 (1)	.90	.40
No. 221 (1)	1.40	.70
No. 321 (1)	1.60	.50
No. 204 (1)	1.75	1.00
Set total (11) Stamps	16.20	6.35

U.P.U. Headquarters

CD133

New Universal Postal Union headquarters, Bern, Switzerland.

1970

Afars & Issas	.342
Algeria	.443
Cameroun	.503-504
Cent. Africa	.125
Chad	.225
Comoro Isls.	.84
Congo, P.R.	.216
Fr. Polynesia	.261-262
Fr. So. & Antarctic Terr.	.36
Gabon	.258
Ivory Coast	.295
Madagascar	.444
Mali	.134-135
Mauritania	.283
New Caledonia	.382
Niger	.231-232
St. Pierre & Miquelon	.397-398
Senegal	.328-329
Tunisia	.535
Wallis & Futuna Isls.	.173

No. 342 (1)	2.50	1.40
No. 443 (1)	1.10	.40
Nos. 503-504 (2)	2.60	.55
No. 125 (1)	1.75	.70
No. 225 (1)	1.20	.25
No. 84 (1)	5.50	2.00
No. 216 (1)	1.00	.25
Nos. 261-262 (2)	20.00	10.00
No. 36 (1)	40.00	27.50
No. 258 (1)	.90	.55
No. 295 (1)	1.10	.50
No. 444 (1)	.55	.25
Nos. 134-135 (2)	1.05	.50
No. 283 (1)	.60	.30
No. 382 (1)	3.00	1.50
Nos. 231-232 (2)	1.50	.60
Nos. 397-398 (2)	34.00	16.25
Nos. 328-329 (2)	1.55	.55
No. 535 (1)	.60	.25
No. 173 (1)	3.25	3.25
Set total (26) Stamps	123.75	67.55

De Gaulle

CD134

First anniversary of the death of Charles de Gaulle, (1890-1970), President of France.

1971-72

Afars & Issas	.356-357
Comoro Isls.	.104-105
France	.1325a
Fr. Polynesia	.270-271
Fr. So. & Antarctic Terr.	.52-53
New Caledonia	.393-394
Reunion	.380a
St. Pierre & Miquelon	.417-418
Wallis & Futuna Isls.	.177-178

Nos. 356-357 (2)	12.50	7.50
Nos. 104-105 (2)	9.00	5.75
No. 1325a (1)	3.00	2.50
Nos. 270-271 (2)	51.50	29.50
Nos. 52-53 (2)	40.00	29.50
Nos. 393-394 (2)	23.00	11.75
No. 380a (1)	9.25	8.00
Nos. 417-418 (2)	56.50	31.00
Nos. 177-178 (2)	20.00	16.25
Set total (16) Stamps	224.75	141.75

African Postal Union, 1971

UAMPT Building, Brazzaville, Congo — CD135

10th anniversary of the establishment of the African and Malagasy Posts and Telecommunications Union, UAMPT. Each stamp has a different native design.

1971, Nov. 13

Cameroun	C177
Cent. Africa	C89
Chad	C94

Congo, P.R.	C136
Dahomey	C146
Gabon	C120
Ivory Coast	C47
Mauritania	C113
Niger	C164
Rwanda	C8
Senegal	C105
Togo	C166
Upper Volta	C97

No. C177 (1)	2.00	.50
No. C89 (1)	2.25	.85
No. C94 (1)	1.50	.50
No. C136 (1)	1.60	.75
No. C146 (1)	1.75	.80
No. C120 (1)	1.75	.70
No. C47 (1)	2.00	1.00
No. C113 (1)	1.10	.65
No. C164 (1)	1.25	.60
No. C8 (1)	2.75	2.50
No. C105 (1)	1.60	.50
No. C166 (1)	1.25	.40
No. C97 (1)	1.50	.70
Set total (13) Stamps	22.30	10.45

West African Monetary Union

African Couple, City, Village and Commemorative Coin — CD136

West African Monetary Union, 10th anniv.

1972, Nov. 2

Dahomey	.300
Ivory Coast	.331
Mauritania	.299
Niger	.258
Senegal	.374
Togo	.825
Upper Volta	.280

No. 300 (1)	.65	.25
No. 331 (1)	1.00	.50
No. 299 (1)	.75	.25
No. 258 (1)	.65	.30
No. 374 (1)	.50	.30
No. 825 (1)	.60	.25
No. 280 (1)	.60	.25
Set total (7) Stamps	4.75	2.10

African Postal Union, 1973

Telecommunications Symbols and Map of Africa — CD137

11th anniversary of the African and Malagasy Posts and Telecommunications Union (UAMPT).

1973, Sept. 12

Cameroun	.574
Cent. Africa	.194
Chad	.294
Congo, P.R.	.289
Dahomey	.311
Gabon	.320
Ivory Coast	.361
Madagascar	.500
Mauritania	.304
Niger	.287
Rwanda	.540
Senegal	.393
Togo	.849
Upper Volta	.297

No. 574 (1)	1.75	.40
No. 194 (1)	1.25	.75
No. 294 (1)	1.75	.40
No. 289 (1)	1.60	.50
No. 311 (1)	1.25	.55
No. 320 (1)	1.40	.75
No. 361 (1)	2.50	1.00
No. 500 (1)	1.10	.35
No. 304 (1)	1.10	.40
No. 287 (1)	.90	.60
No. 540 (1)	3.00	2.00
No. 393 (1)	1.60	.50

No. 849 (1)	1.00	.35
No. 297 (1)	1.25	.70
Set total (14) Stamps	21.45	9.25

Philexafrique II — Essen

CD138

CD139

Designs: Indigenous fauna, local and German stamps. Types CD138-CD139 printed horizontally and vertically se-tenant in sheets of 10 (2x5). Label between horizontal pairs alternately commemorates Philexafrique II, Libreville, Gabon, June 1978, and 2nd International Stamp Fair, Essen, Germany, Nov. 1-5.

1978-1979

Benin	C286a
Central Africa	C201a
Chad	C239a
Congo Republic	C246a
Djibouti	C122a
Gabon	C216a
Ivory Coast	C65a
Mali	C357a
Mauritania	C186a
Niger	C292a
Rwanda	C13a
Senegal	C147a
Togo	C364a

No. C286a (1)	9.00	8.50
No. C201a (1)	7.50	7.50
No. C239a (1)	7.50	4.00
No. C246a (1)	7.00	7.00
No. C122a (1)	6.50	6.50
No. C216a (1)	6.50	4.00
No. C65a (1)	9.00	9.00
No. C357a (1)	5.00	3.00
No. C186a (1)	5.50	3.00
No. C292a (1)	6.00	6.00
No. C13a (1)	4.00	4.00
No. C147a (1)	10.00	4.00
No. C364a (1)	3.00	1.50
Set total (13) Stamps	86.50	70.00

BRITISH COMMONWEALTH OF NATIONS

The listings follow established trade practices when these issues are offered as units by dealers. The Peace issue, for example, includes only one stamp from the Indian state of Hyderabad. The U.P.U. issue includes the Egypt set. Pairs are included for those varieties issued with bilingual designs se-tenant.

Silver Jubilee

Windsor Castle and King George V CD301

Reign of King George V, 25th anniv.

1935

Antigua	.77-80
Ascension	.33-36
Bahamas	.92-95
Barbados	.186-189
Basutoland	.11-14

Bechuanaland Protectorate	.117-120
Bermuda	.100-103
British Guiana	.223-226
British Honduras	.108-111
Cayman Islands	.81-84
Ceylon	.260-263
Cyprus	.136-139
Dominica	.90-93
Falkland Islands	.77-80
Fiji	.110-113
Gambia	.125-128
Gibraltar	.100-103
Gilbert & Ellice Islands	.33-36
Gold Coast	.108-111
Grenada	.124-127
Hong Kong	.147-150
Jamaica	.109-112
Kenya, Uganda, Tanzania	.42-45
Leeward Islands	.96-99
Malta	.184-187
Mauritius	.204-207
Montserrat	.85-88
Newfoundland	.226-229
Nigeria	.34-37
Northern Rhodesia	.18-21
Nyasaland Protectorate	.47-50
St. Helena	.111-114
St. Kitts-Nevis	.72-75
St. Lucia	.91-94
St. Vincent	.134-137
Seychelles	.118-121
Sierra Leone	.166-169
Solomon Islands	.60-63
Somaliland Protectorate	.77-80
Straits Settlements	.213-216
Swaziland	.20-23
Trinidad & Tobago	.43-46
Turks & Caicos Islands	.71-74
Virgin Islands	.69-72

The following have different designs but are included in the omnibus set:

Great Britain	.226-229
Offices in Morocco (Sp. Curr.)	.67-70
Offices in Morocco (Br. Curr.)	.226-229
Offices in Morocco (Fr. Curr.)	.422-425
Offices in Morocco (Tangier)	.508-510
Australia	.152-154
Canada	.211-216
Cook Islands	.98-100
India	.142-148
Nauru	.31-34
New Guinea	.46-49
New Zealand	.199-201
Niue	.67-69
Papua	.114-117
Samoa	.163-165
South Africa	.68-71
Southern Rhodesia	.33-36
South-West Africa	.121-124

Nos. 77-80 (4)	20.25	23.25
Nos. 33-36 (4)	58.50	127.50
Nos. 92-95 (4)	25.00	46.00
Nos. 186-189 (4)	30.00	50.30
Nos. 11-14 (4)	11.60	21.25
Nos. 117-120 (4)	15.75	36.00
Nos. 100-103 (4)	16.80	58.50
Nos. 223-226 (4)	22.35	35.50
Nos. 108-111 (4)	15.25	16.35
Nos. 81-84 (4)	21.60	24.50
Nos. 260-263 (4)	10.40	21.60
Nos. 136-139 (4)	39.75	34.40
Nos. 90-93 (4)	18.85	19.85
Nos. 77-80 (4)	55.00	14.75
Nos. 110-113 (4)	20.25	34.00
Nos. 125-128 (4)	13.05	25.25
Nos. 100-103 (4)	28.75	42.75
Nos. 33-36 (4)	36.80	67.00
Nos. 108-111 (4)	25.75	78.10
Nos. 124-127 (4)	16.70	40.60
Nos. 147-150 (4)	73.75	20.75
Nos. 109-112 (4)	24.20	50.50
Nos. 42-45 (4)	10.25	11.75
Nos. 96-99 (4)	35.75	49.60
Nos. 184-187 (4)	22.00	33.70
Nos. 204-207 (4)	44.60	58.25
Nos. 85-88 (4)	10.25	30.25
Nos. 226-229 (4)	17.50	12.05
Nos. 34-37 (4)	17.50	73.00
Nos. 18-21 (4)	17.00	15.00
Nos. 47-50 (4)	43.50	82.50
Nos. 111-114 (4)	31.15	36.50
Nos. 72-75 (4)	11.80	18.65
Nos. 91-94 (4)	16.00	20.80
Nos. 134-137 (4)	9.45	21.25
Nos. 118-121 (4)	15.75	40.00
Nos. 166-169 (4)	23.60	50.35
Nos. 60-63 (4)	29.00	38.00
Nos. 77-80 (4)	17.00	48.25
Nos. 213-216 (4)	15.00	25.10
Nos. 20-23 (4)	8.90	18.25
Nos. 43-46 (4)	18.60	37.50
Nos. 71-74 (4)	9.90	14.50
Nos. 69-72 (4)	25.00	55.25
Nos. 226-229 (4)	5.15	9.90

Nos. 67-70 (4) 13.60 30.70
Nos. 226-229 (4) 16.30 56.00
Nos. 422-425 (4) 9.35 3.95
Nos. 508-510 (3) 26.00 33.50
Nos. 152-154 (3) 49.50 45.35
Nos. 211-216 (6) 23.85 13.35
Nos. 98-100 (3) 9.65 12.00
Nos. 142-148 (7) 28.85 14.00
Nos. 31-34 (4) 12.35 13.15
Nos. 46-47 (2) 4.35 1.70
Nos. 199-201 (3) 23.00 28.50
Nos. 67-69 (3) 19.25 31.00
Nos. 114-117 (4) 9.20 17.50
Nos. 163-165 (3) 4.40 6.50
Nos. 68-71 (4) 57.50 153.00
Nos. 33-36 (4) 27.75 45.25
Nos. 121-124 (4) 13.00 36.10
Set total (245) Stamps 1,401. 2,231.

Coronation

Queen Elizabeth and King George VI CD302

1937

Aden 13-15
Antigua 81-83
Ascension 37-39
Bahamas 97-99
Barbados 190-192
Basutoland 15-17
Bechuanaland Protectorate 121-123
Bermuda 115-117
British Guiana 227-229
British Honduras 112-114
Cayman Islands 97-99
Ceylon 275-277
Cyprus 140-142
Dominica 94-96
Falkland Islands 81-83
Fiji 114-116
Gambia 129-131
Gibraltar 104-106
Gilbert & Ellice Islands 37-39
Gold Coast 112-114
Grenada 128-130
Hong Kong 151-153
Jamaica 113-115
Kenya, Uganda, Tanzania 60-62
Leeward Islands 100-102
Malta 188-190
Mauritius 208-210
Montserrat 89-91
Newfoundland 230-232
Nigeria 50-52
Northern Rhodesia 22-24
Nyasaland Protectorate 51-53
St. Helena 115-117
St. Kitts-Nevis 76-78
St. Lucia 107-109
St. Vincent 138-140
Seychelles 122-124
Sierra Leone 170-172
Solomon Islands 64-66
Somaliland Protectorate 81-83
Straits Settlements 235-237
Swaziland 24-26
Trinidad & Tobago 47-49
Turks & Caicos Islands 75-77
Virgin Islands 73-75

The following have different designs but are included in the omnibus set:

Great Britain 234
Offices in Morocco (Sp. Curr.) 82
Offices in Morocco (Fr. Curr.) 439
Offices in Morocco (Tangier) 514
Canada 237
Cook Islands 109-111
Nauru 35-38
Newfoundland 233-243
New Guinea 48-51
New Zealand 223-225
Niue 70-72
Papua 118-121
South Africa 74-78
Southern Rhodesia 38-41
South-West Africa 125-132

Nos. 13-15 (3) 2.70 5.65
Nos. 81-83 (3) 1.85 8.00
Nos. 37-39 (3) 2.75 2.75
Nos. 97-99 (3) 1.05 3.05
Nos. 190-192 (3) 1.10 1.95
Nos. 15-17 (3) 1.15 3.00
Nos. 121-123 (3) .95 3.35
Nos. 115-117 (3) 1.25 5.00
Nos. 227-229 (3) 1.45 3.05
Nos. 112-114 (3) 1.20 2.40
Nos. 97-99 (3) 1.10 2.70
Nos. 275-277 (3) 8.25 10.35

Nos. 140-142 (3) 3.75 6.50
Nos. 94-96 (3) .85 2.40
Nos. 81-83 (3) 2.90 2.30
Nos. 114-116 (3) 1.35 5.75
Nos. 129-131 (3) .85 3.95
Nos. 104-106 (3) 2.25 6.45
Nos. 37-39 (3) .85 2.15
Nos. 112-114 (3) 3.10 10.00
Nos. 128-130 (3) 1.00 .85
Nos. 151-153 (3) 17.00 17.75
Nos. 113-115 (3) 1.25 1.25
Nos. 60-62 (3) 1.25 2.35
Nos. 100-102 (3) 1.55 4.00
Nos. 188-190 (3) 1.25 1.60
Nos. 208-210 (3) 1.75 3.50
Nos. 89-91 (3) 1.00 3.35
Nos. 230-232 (3) 7.00 2.80
Nos. 50-52 (3) 3.25 8.50
Nos. 22-24 (3) .95 2.25
Nos. 51-53 (3) 1.05 1.30
Nos. 115-117 (3) 1.45 2.05
Nos. 76-78 (3) .95 2.15
Nos. 107-109 (3) 1.05 2.05
Nos. 138-140 (3) .80 4.75
Nos. 122-124 (3) 1.20 1.90
Nos. 170-172 (3) 1.95 5.65
Nos. 64-66 (3) .90 2.00
Nos. 81-83 (3) 1.10 3.50
Nos. 235-237 (3) 3.25 1.60
Nos. 24-26 (3) .75 2.70
Nos. 47-49 (3) 1.10 3.20
Nos. 75-77 (3) 1.25 3.95
Nos. 73-75 (3) 2.20 6.90

No. 234 (1) .30 .25
No. 82 (1) .80 .60
No. 439 (1) .50 .25
No. 514 (1) 1.25 .50
No. 237 (1) .35 .25
Nos. 109-111 (3) .85 .80
Nos. 35-38 (4) 1.25 5.50
Nos. 233-243 (11) 41.90 30.40
Nos. 48-51 (4) 1.40 7.90
Nos. 223-225 (3) 1.75 2.25
Nos. 70-72 (3) .90 2.05
Nos. 118-121 (4) 1.60 5.25
Nos. 74-78 (5) 7.60 9.35
Nos. 38-41 (4) 3.55 15.50
Nos. 125-132 (8) 5.00 8.40
Set total (189) Stamps 165.95 268.90

Peace

King George VI and Parliament Buildings, London CD303

Return to peace at the close of World War II.

1945-46

Aden 28-29
Antigua 96-97
Ascension 50-51
Bahamas 130-131
Barbados 207-208
Bermuda 131-132
British Guiana 242-243
British Honduras 127-128
Cayman Islands 112-113
Ceylon 293-294
Cyprus 156-157
Dominica 112-113
Falkland Islands 97-98
Falkland Islands Dep. 1L9-1L10
Fiji 137-138
Gambia 144-145
Gibraltar 119-120
Gilbert & Ellice Islands 52-53
Gold Coast 128-129
Grenada 143-144
Jamaica 136-137
Kenya, Uganda, Tanzania 90-91
Leeward Islands 116-117
Malta 206-207
Mauritius 223-224
Montserrat 104-105
Nigeria 71-72
Northern Rhodesia 46-47
Nyasaland Protectorate 82-83
Pitcairn Islands 9-10
St. Helena 128-129
St. Kitts-Nevis 91-92
St. Lucia 127-128
St. Vincent 152-153
Seychelles 149-150
Sierra Leone 186-187
Solomon Islands 80-81
Somaliland Protectorate 108-109
Trinidad & Tobago 62-63
Turks & Caicos Islands 90-91
Virgin Islands 88-89

The following have different designs but are included in the omnibus set:

Great Britain 264-265

Offices in Morocco (Tangier)....523-524
Aden
  Kathiri State of Seiyun 12-13
  Qu'aiti State of Shihr and Mukalla .....
  12-13
Australia 200-202
Basutoland 29-31
Bechuanaland Protectorate 137-139
Burma 66-69
Cook Islands 127-130
Hong Kong 174-175
India 195-198
  Hyderabad 51-53
New Zealand 247-257
Niue 90-93
Pakistan-Bahawalpur O16
Samoa 191-194
South Africa 100-102
Southern Rhodesia 67-70
South-West Africa 153-155
Swaziland 38-40
Zanzibar 222-223

Nos. 28-29 (2) .95 2.50
Nos. 96-97 (2) .50 .80
Nos. 50-51 (2) .80 2.00
Nos. 130-131 (2) .50 1.40
Nos. 207-208 (2) .50 1.10
Nos. 131-132 (2) .55 .55
Nos. 242-243 (2) 1.05 1.40
Nos. 127-128 (2) .50 .50
Nos. 112-113 (2) .80 .80
Nos. 293-294 (2) .60 2.10
Nos. 156-157 (2) .90 .70
Nos. 112-113 (2) .50 .50
Nos. 97-98 (2) .90 1.35
Nos. 1L9-1L10 (2) 1.30 1.00
Nos. 137-138 (2) .75 1.75
Nos. 144-145 (2) .50 .95
Nos. 119-120 (2) .75 1.00
Nos. 52-53 (2) .50 1.10
Nos. 128-129 (2) 1.85 3.75
Nos. 143-144 (2) .50 .95
Nos. 136-137 (2) 2.00 13.50
Nos. 90-91 (2) .65 .85
Nos. 116-117 (2) .50 1.50
Nos. 206-207 (2) .65 2.00
Nos. 223-224 (2) .50 1.05
Nos. 104-105 (2) .50 .50
Nos. 71-72 (2) .70 2.75
Nos. 46-47 (2) 1.25 2.00
Nos. 82-83 (2) .55 .60
Nos. 9-10 (2) 1.40 .60
Nos. 128-129 (2) .65 .70
Nos. 91-92 (2) .50 .50
Nos. 127-128 (2) .50 .60
Nos. 152-153 (2) .50 .50
Nos. 149-150 (2) .55 .50
Nos. 186-187 (2) .50 .50
Nos. 80-81 (2) .50 1.50
Nos. 108-109 (2) .70 .50
Nos. 62-63 (2) .75 1.85
Nos. 90-91 (2) .50 .50
Nos. 88-89 (2) .50 .50

Nos. 264-265 (2) .50 .50
Nos. 523-524 (2) 2.00 2.55
Nos. 12-13 (2) .50 .90
Nos. 12-13 (2) .50 1.25
Nos. 200-202 (3) 1.60 1.25
Nos. 29-31 (3) 2.10 2.60
Nos. 137-139 (3) 2.05 4.75
Nos. 66-69 (4) 1.50 1.25
Nos. 127-130 (4) 2.00 1.85
Nos. 174-175 (2) 6.75 2.75
Nos. 195-198 (4) 5.60 5.50
Nos. 51-53 (3) 1.50 1.70
Nos. 247-257 (11) 3.35 3.65
Nos. 90-93 (4) 1.70 2.20
No. O16 (1) 15.00 10.00
Nos. 191-194 (4) 2.05 1.00
Nos. 100-102 (3) 1.00 3.25
Nos. 67-70 (4) 1.40 1.75
Nos. 153-155 (3) 1.85 3.25
Nos. 38-40 (3) 2.40 5.50
Nos. 222-223 (2) .65 1.00
Set total (151) Stamps 86.05 118.15

Silver Wedding

King George VI and Queen Elizabeth
CD304 CD305

1948-49

Aden 30-31
  Kathiri State of Seiyun 14-15
  Qu'aiti State of Shihr and Mukalla .....
  14-15

Antigua 98-99
Ascension 52-53
Bahamas 148-149
Barbados 210-211
Basutoland 39-40
Bechuanaland Protectorate 147-148
Bermuda 133-134
British Guiana 244-245
British Honduras 129-130
Cayman Islands 116-117
Cyprus 158-159
Dominica 114-115
Falkland Islands 99-100
Falkland Islands Dep. 1L11-1L12
Fiji 139-140
Gambia 146-147
Gibraltar 121-122
Gilbert & Ellice Islands 54-55
Gold Coast 142-143
Grenada 145-146
Hong Kong 178-179
Jamaica 138-139
Kenya, Uganda, Tanzania 92-93
Leeward Islands 118-119
Malaya
  Johore 128-129
  Kedah 55-56
  Kelantan 44-45
  Malacca 1-2
  Negri Sembilan 36-37
  Pahang 44-45
  Penang 1-2
  Perak 99-100
  Perlis 1-2
  Selangor 74-75
  Trengganu 47-48
Malta 223-224
Mauritius 229-230
Montserrat 106-107
Nigeria 73-74
North Borneo 238-239
Northern Rhodesia 48-49
Nyasaland Protectorate 85-86
Pitcairn Islands 11-12
St. Helena 130-131
St. Kitts-Nevis 93-94
St. Lucia 129-130
St. Vincent 154-155
Sarawak 174-175
Seychelles 151-152
Sierra Leone 188-189
Singapore 21-22
Solomon Islands 82-83
Somaliland Protectorate 110-111
Swaziland 48-49
Trinidad & Tobago 64-65
Turks & Caicos Islands 92-93
Virgin Islands 90-91
Zanzibar 224-225

The following have different designs but are included in the omnibus set:

Great Britain 267-268
  Offices in Morocco (Sp. Curr.) 93-94
  Offices in Morocco (Tangier) 525-526
Bahrain 62-63
Kuwait 82-83
Oman 25-26
South Africa 106
South-West Africa 159

Nos. 30-31 (2) 40.40 56.50
Nos. 14-15 (2) 17.85 16.00
Nos. 14-15 (2) 18.55 12.50
Nos. 98-99 (2) 13.55 15.75
Nos. 52-53 (2) 55.55 50.45
Nos. 148-149 (2) 45.25 40.30
Nos. 210-211 (2) 18.35 13.55
Nos. 39-40 (2) 52.80 55.25
Nos. 147-148 (2) 42.85 47.75
Nos. 133-134 (2) 47.75 55.25
Nos. 244-245 (2) 24.25 28.45
Nos. 129-130 (2) 25.25 53.20
Nos. 116-117 (2) 25.25 33.50
Nos. 158-159 (2) 58.50 78.05
Nos. 114-115 (2) 25.25 32.75
Nos. 99-100 (2) 112.10 76.10
Nos. 1L11-1L12 (2) 4.25 6.00
Nos. 139-140 (2) 18.20 11.50
Nos. 146-147 (2) 21.25 21.25
Nos. 121-122 (2) 61.00 78.00
Nos. 54-55 (2) 14.25 26.25
Nos. 142-143 (2) 35.25 48.25
Nos. 145-146 (2) 21.75 21.75
Nos. 178-179 (2) 329.00 106.75
Nos. 138-139 (2) 30.35 75.25
Nos. 92-93 (2) 51.00 68.00
Nos. 118-119 (2) 7.00 8.25
Nos. 128-129 (2) 29.25 53.25
Nos. 55-56 (2) 35.25 50.25
Nos. 44-45 (2) 35.75 62.75
Nos. 1-2 (2) 35.40 49.75
Nos. 36-37 (2) 28.10 38.20
Nos. 44-45 (2) 28.00 38.05
Nos. 1-2 (2) 40.50 37.80

Nos. 99-100 (2)	27.80	37.75
Nos. 1-2 (2)	33.50	58.00
Nos. 74-75 (2)	30.25	25.30
Nos. 47-48 (2)	32.75	61.75
Nos. 223-224 (2)	40.55	45.25
Nos. 229-230 (2)	19.25	45.25
Nos. 106-107 (2)	8.75	17.25
Nos. 73-74 (2)	17.85	22.80
Nos. 238-239 (2)	35.30	45.75
Nos. 48-49 (2)	100.30	90.25
Nos. 85-86 (2)	18.25	35.25
Nos. 11-12 (2)	44.50	54.00
Nos. 130-131 (2)	32.80	42.80
Nos. 93-94 (2)	13.25	10.50
Nos. 129-130 (2)	22.25	40.25
Nos. 154-155 (2)	27.75	30.25
Nos. 174-175 (2)	52.80	67.80
Nos. 151-152 (2)	16.25	48.25
Nos. 188-189 (2)	25.25	29.75
Nos. 21-22 (2)	116.00	45.40
Nos. 82-83 (2)	13.40	13.40
Nos. 110-111 (2)	8.40	8.75
Nos. 48-49 (2)	40.30	47.75
Nos. 64-65 (2)	31.80	50.25
Nos. 92-93 (2)	16.25	22.75
Nos. 90-91 (2)	16.25	22.25
Nos. 224-225 (2)	29.60	38.00
Nos. 267-268 (2)	30.40	25.25
Nos. 93-94 (2)	17.10	25.75
Nos. 525-526 (2)	22.90	32.75
Nos. 62-63 (2)	38.50	57.75
Nos. 82-83 (2)	69.50	45.50
Nos. 25-26 (2)	41.00	42.50
No. 106 (1)	.80	1.00
No. 159 (1)	1.10	.35
Set total (136) Stamps	2,542.	2,754.

U.P.U.

Mercury and Symbols of
Communications — CD306

Plane, Ship and
Hemispheres — CD307

Mercury
Scattering
Letters over
Globe
CD308

U.P.U.
Monument,
Bern
CD309

Universal Postal Union, 75th anniversary.

1949

The following have different designs but are
included in the omnibus set:

Nos. 32-35 (4)	5.85	8.45
Nos. 16-19 (4)	2.75	16.00
Nos. 16-19 (4)	2.60	8.00
Nos. 100-103 (4)	3.60	7.70
Nos. 57-60 (4)	11.10	9.00
Nos. 150-153 (4)	5.35	9.30
Nos. 212-215 (4)	4.40	14.85
Nos. 41-44 (4)	4.75	10.00
Nos. 149-152 (4)	3.35	7.25
Nos. 138-141 (4)	4.75	6.15
Nos. 246-249 (4)	2.75	4.20
Nos. 137-140 (4)	3.30	6.35
Nos. 79-82 (4)	9.50	8.45
Nos. 118-121 (4)	3.60	7.25
Nos. 160-163 (4)	4.60	10.70
Nos. 116-119 (4)	2.30	5.65
Nos. 103-106 (4)	14.00	17.10
Nos. 1L14-1L17 (4)	14.60	14.50
Nos. 141-144 (4)	3.35	15.75
Nos. 148-151 (4)	2.75	7.10
Nos. 123-126 (4)	5.90	8.75
Nos. 56-59 (4)	4.30	13.00
Nos. 144-147 (4)	2.55	10.35
Nos. 147-150 (4)	2.15	3.55
Nos. 180-183 (4)	66.75	19.95
Nos. 142-145 (4)	2.50	2.45
Nos. 94-97 (4)	2.90	4.00
Nos. 126-129 (4)	3.05	9.60
Nos. 151-154 (4)	4.70	8.90
Nos. 57-60 (4)	4.80	12.00
Nos. 46-49 (4)	4.25	12.65
Nos. 18-21 (4)	4.25	17.30
Nos. 59-62 (4)	3.50	10.75
Nos. 46-49 (4)	3.00	7.25
Nos. 23-26 (4)	5.10	11.75
Nos. 101-104 (4)	3.65	10.75
Nos. 3-6 (4)	3.95	14.25
Nos. 76-79 (4)	4.90	12.30
Nos. 49-52 (4)	5.55	12.25
Nos. 225-228 (4)	4.50	4.85
Nos. 231-234 (4)	3.70	7.05
Nos. 108-111 (4)	3.30	4.35
Nos. 62-65 (4)	1.60	4.25
Nos. 79-82 (4)	15.40	22.00

Nos. 75-78 (4)	2.80	9.25
Nos. 240-243 (4)	7.15	6.50
Nos. 50-53 (4)	5.00	6.50
Nos. 87-90 (4)	4.55	6.60
Nos. 13-16 (4)	15.05	14.25
Nos. 132-135 (4)	4.85	7.10
Nos. 95-98 (4)	4.35	5.55
Nos. 131-134 (4)	2.55	3.85
Nos. 170-173 (4)	2.20	5.05
Nos. 176-179 (4)	13.40	13.35
Nos. 153-156 (4)	3.00	5.15
Nos. 190-193 (4)	2.90	9.15
Nos. 23-26 (4)	19.00	13.70
Nos. 84-87 (4)	4.05	4.90
Nos. 112-115 (4)	3.95	9.95
Nos. 71-72 (4)	1.95	2.25
Nos. 50-53 (4)	2.80	4.65
Nos. 87-90 (4)	3.00	5.25
Nos. 66-69 (4)	3.55	6.80
Nos. 101-104 (4)	3.05	8.90
Nos. 92-95 (4)	2.60	5.90
Nos. 226-229 (4)	4.95	13.50
Nos. 276-279 (4)	1.35	1.00
Nos. 546-549 (4)	2.60	16.00
No. 223 (1)	.40	.40
Nos. 68-71 (4)	4.75	16.50
Nos. 116-121 (6)	7.30	5.35
Nos. 304-306 (3)	3.35	4.25
Nos. 281-283 (3)	5.75	2.70
Nos. 223-226 (4)	27.25	10.50
Nos. 89-92 (4)	6.10	10.25
Nos. 31-34 (4)	8.00	15.75
Nos. 26-29, O25-O28 (8)	2.40	44.00
Nos. 109-111 (3)	2.00	2.70
Nos. 160-162 (3)	3.00	5.50
Set total (313) Stamps	466.45	741.05

University

Arms of
University
College
CD310

Alice, Princess
of Athlone
CD311

1948 opening of University College of the
West Indies at Jamaica.

1951

Nos. 104-105 (2)	1.35	3.75
Nos. 228-229 (2)	1.75	2.65
Nos. 250-251 (2)	1.10	1.25
Nos. 141-142 (2)	1.40	2.20
Nos. 120-121 (2)	1.40	1.75
Nos. 164-165 (2)	1.20	1.60
Nos. 146-147 (2)	1.05	.70
Nos. 130-131 (2)	1.35	4.00
Nos. 112-113 (2)	.85	2.00
Nos. 105-106 (2)	1.40	2.25
Nos. 149-150 (2)	1.40	1.50
Nos. 174-175 (2)	1.00	2.15
Nos. 70-71 (2)	1.00	4.20
Nos. 96-97 (2)	1.50	3.75
Set total (28) Stamps	17.75	33.75

Coronation

Queen Elizabeth
II — CD312

1953

The following have different designs but are
included in the omnibus set:

No. 47 (1)	1.25	1.25
No. 28 (1)	.75	1.50
No. 28 (1)	1.10	.60
No. 106 (1)	.40	.75
No. 61 (1)	1.25	2.75
No. 157 (1)	1.40	.25
No. 234 (1)	1.00	.25
No. 45 (1)	.50	.60
No. 153 (1)	.50	.35
No. 142 (1)	.85	.50
No. 252 (1)	.45	.25
No. 143 (1)	.60	.40
No. 150 (1)	.40	1.75
No. 167 (1)	1.60	.75
No. 141 (1)	.40	.40
No. 121 (1)	.90	1.50
No. 1L18 (1)	1.80	1.40
No. 145 (1)	1.00	.60
No. 152 (1)	.50	.50
No. 131 (1)	.50	.50
No. 60 (1)	.65	2.25
No. 160 (1)	1.00	.25

No. 170 (1)	.30	.25
No. 184 (1)	3.00	.30
No. 153 (1)	.70	.25
No. 101 (1)	.40	.25
No. 132 (1)	1.00	2.25
No. 155 (1)	1.40	.30
No. 82 (1)	2.25	.60
No. 71 (1)	1.60	1.60
No. 27 (1)	1.10	1.50
No. 63 (1)	1.40	.65
No. 71 (1)	2.25	.25
No. 27 (1)	1.75	.30
No. 126 (1)	1.60	.25
No. 28 (1)	1.75	4.00
No. 101 (1)	1.75	.25
No. 74 (1)	1.50	1.00
No. 241 (1)	.50	.25
No. 250 (1)	1.10	.25
No. 127 (1)	.60	.45
No. 77 (1)	.75	.60
No. 79 (1)	.40	.25
No. 260 (1)	1.75	1.00
No. 60 (1)	.70	.25
No. 96 (1)	.75	.75
No. 19 (1)	2.00	3.50
No. 139 (1)	1.25	1.25
No. 119 (1)	.35	.25
No. 156 (1)	.70	.35
No. 185 (1)	.50	.30
No. 196 (1)	1.75	1.75
No. 172 (1)	.80	.80
No. 194 (1)	.40	.40
No. 27 (1)	2.50	.40
No. 88 (1)	1.00	1.00
No. 127 (1)	.40	.25
No. 54 (1)	.30	.25
No. 84 (1)	.30	.25
No. 13 (1)	1.00	1.75
No. 118 (1)	.40	1.10
No. 114 (1)	.40	1.00
Nos. 313-316 (4)	11.40	4.05
Nos. 579-582 (4)	10.90	5.30
Nos. 259-261 (3)	3.60	2.75
Nos. 92-95 (4)	15.25	12.75
No. 330 (1)	.30	.25
No. 317 (1)	1.40	.25
Nos. 145-146 (2)	2.65	2.65
Nos. 113-116 (4)	16.00	8.50
Nos. 280-284 (5)	3.30	4.55
Nos. 104-105 (2)	2.25	1.50
Nos. 52-55 (4)	14.25	6.50
Nos. 214-215 (2)	2.50	.80
No. 192 (1)	.45	.30
No. 80 (1)	7.25	7.25
Nos. 244-248 (5)	3.00	2.35
No. 4 (1)	2.75	2.75
Set total (106) Stamps	160.40	114.75

Separate designs for each country for the visit of Queen Elizabeth II and the Duke of Edinburgh.

Royal Visit 1953

1953

Aden		62
Australia		267-269
Bermuda		163
Ceylon		318
Fiji		146
Gibraltar		146
Jamaica		154
Kenya, Uganda, Tanzania		102
Malta		242
New Zealand		286-287

No. 62 (1)	.65	4.00
Nos. 267-269 (3)	2.75	2.05
No. 163 (1)	.50	.25
No. 318 (1)	1.00	.25
No. 146 (1)	.65	.35
No. 146 (1)	.50	.30
No. 154 (1)	.50	.25
No. 102 (1)	.50	.25
No. 242 (1)	.35	.25
Nos. 286-287 (2)	.50	.50
Set total (13) Stamps	7.90	8.45

West Indies Federation

Map of the Caribbean CD313

Federation of the West Indies, April 22, 1958.

1958

Antigua		122-124
Barbados		248-250
Dominica		161-163
Grenada		184-186
Jamaica		175-177
Montserrat		143-145
St. Kitts-Nevis		136-138
St. Lucia		170-172

St. Vincent		198-200
Trinidad & Tobago		86-88

Nos. 122-124 (3)	5.80	3.80
Nos. 248-250 (3)	1.60	2.90
Nos. 161-163 (3)	1.95	1.85
Nos. 184-186 (3)	1.50	1.20
Nos. 175-177 (3)	2.65	3.45
Nos. 143-145 (3)	2.35	1.35
Nos. 136-138 (3)	3.00	3.10
Nos. 170-172 (3)	2.05	2.80
Nos. 198-200 (3)	1.50	1.75
Nos. 86-88 (3)	2.40	2.35
Set total (30) Stamps	24.80	24.55

Freedom from Hunger

Protein Food CD314

U.N. Food and Agricultural Organization's "Freedom from Hunger" campaign.

1963

Aden		65
Antigua		133
Ascension		89
Bahamas		180
Basutoland		83
Bechuanaland Protectorate		194
Bermuda		192
British Guiana		271
British Honduras		179
Brunei		100
Cayman Islands		168
Dominica		181
Falkland Islands		146
Fiji		198
Gambia		172
Gibraltar		161
Gilbert & Ellice Islands		76
Grenada		190
Hong Kong		218
Malta		291
Mauritius		270
Montserrat		150
New Hebrides, British		93
North Borneo		296
Pitcairn Islands		35
St. Helena		173
St. Lucia		179
St. Vincent		201
Sarawak		212
Seychelles		213
Solomon Islands		109
Swaziland		108
Tonga		127
Tristan da Cunha		68
Turks & Caicos Islands		138
Virgin Islands		140
Zanzibar		280

No. 65 (1)	1.50	1.75
No. 133 (1)	.35	.35
No. 89 (1)	1.00	.50
No. 180 (1)	.65	.65
No. 83 (1)	.50	.25
No. 194 (1)	.50	.50
No. 192 (1)	1.00	.50
No. 271 (1)	.45	.25
No. 179 (1)	.60	.25
No. 100 (1)	3.25	2.25
No. 168 (1)	.55	.30
No. 181 (1)	.30	.30
No. 146 (1)	10.50	2.50
No. 198 (1)	3.50	2.25
No. 172 (1)	.50	.25
No. 161 (1)	4.00	2.25
No. 76 (1)	1.40	.40
No. 190 (1)	.30	.25
No. 218 (1)	37.50	5.00
No. 291 (1)	2.00	2.00
No. 270 (1)	.45	.25
No. 150 (1)	.55	.35
No. 93 (1)	.60	.25
No. 296 (1)	1.90	.75
No. 35 (1)	3.50	1.50
No. 173 (1)	2.25	1.10
No. 179 (1)	.40	.40
No. 201 (1)	.90	.50
No. 212 (1)	1.60	1.00
No. 213 (1)	.85	.35
No. 109 (1)	3.00	.85
No. 108 (1)	.50	.50
No. 68 (1)	.60	.35
No. 68 (1)	.75	.35
No. 138 (1)	.30	.25
No. 140 (1)	.50	.50
No. 280 (1)	1.50	.80
Set total (37) Stamps	90.50	32.80

Red Cross Centenary

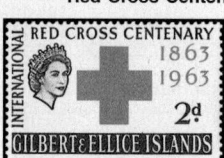

Red Cross and Elizabeth II CD315

1963

Antigua		134-135
Ascension		90-91
Bahamas		183-184
Basutoland		84-85
Bechuanaland Protectorate		195-196
Bermuda		193-194
British Guiana		272-273
British Honduras		180-181
Cayman Islands		169-170
Dominica		182-183
Falkland Islands		147-148
Fiji		203-204
Gambia		173-174
Gibraltar		162-163
Gilbert & Ellice Islands		77-78
Grenada		191-192
Hong Kong		219-220
Jamaica		203-204
Malta		292-293
Mauritius		271-272
Montserrat		151-152
New Hebrides, British		94-95
Pitcairn Islands		36-37
St. Helena		174-175
St. Kitts-Nevis		143-144
St. Lucia		180-181
St. Vincent		202-203
Seychelles		214-215
Solomon Islands		110-111
South Arabia		1-2
Swaziland		109-110
Tonga		134-135
Tristan da Cunha		69-70
Turks & Caicos Islands		139-140
Virgin Islands		141-142

Nos. 134-135 (2)	1.00	2.00
Nos. 90-91 (2)	6.75	3.35
Nos. 183-184 (2)	2.30	2.80
Nos. 84-85 (2)	1.20	.90
Nos. 195-196 (2)	.95	.85
Nos. 193-194 (2)	3.00	2.80
Nos. 272-273 (2)	.85	.60
Nos. 180-181 (2)	1.00	2.50
Nos. 169-170 (2)	1.10	3.00
Nos. 182-183 (2)	.70	1.05
Nos. 147-148 (2)	18.00	5.50
Nos. 203-204 (2)	3.25	2.80
Nos. 173-174 (2)	.75	1.00
Nos. 162-163 (2)	6.25	5.40
Nos. 77-78 (2)	2.00	3.50
Nos. 191-192 (2)	.80	.50
Nos. 219-220 (2)	18.75	7.35
Nos. 203-204 (2)	.75	1.65
Nos. 292-293 (2)	2.50	4.75
Nos. 271-272 (2)	.85	.50
Nos. 151-152 (2)	1.00	.75
Nos. 94-95 (2)	1.00	.50
Nos. 36-37 (2)	2.50	4.00
Nos. 174-175 (2)	1.70	2.30
Nos. 143-144 (2)	.90	.90
Nos. 180-181 (2)	1.25	1.25
Nos. 202-203 (2)	.90	.90
Nos. 214-215 (2)	1.00	1.50
Nos. 110-111 (2)	1.25	1.15
Nos. 1-2 (2)	1.25	1.25
Nos. 109-110 (2)	1.10	1.10
Nos. 134-135 (2)	1.00	1.25
Nos. 69-70 (2)	1.15	.80
Nos. 139-140 (2)	.55	1.00
Nos. 141-142 (2)	.80	1.25
Set total (70) Stamps	90.10	72.70

Shakespeare

Shakespeare Memorial Theatre, Stratford-on-Avon — CD316

400th anniversary of the birth of William Shakespeare.

1964

Antigua		151
Bahamas		201
Bechuanaland Protectorate		197
Cayman Islands		171

Dominica		184
Falkland Islands		149
Gambia		192
Gibraltar		164
Montserrat		153
St. Lucia		196
Turks & Caicos Islands		141
Virgin Islands		143

No. 151 (1)	.35	.25
No. 201 (1)	.60	.35
No. 197 (1)	.35	.35
No. 171 (1)	.35	.30
No. 184 (1)	.35	.35
No. 149 (1)	1.60	.50
No. 192 (1)	.35	.25
No. 164 (1)	.65	.55
No. 153 (1)	.35	.25
No. 196 (1)	.45	.25
No. 141 (1)	.30	.25
No. 143 (1)	.45	.45
Set total (12) Stamps	6.15	4.10

ITU

ITU Emblem CD317

Intl. Telecommunication Union, cent.

1965

Antigua		153-154
Ascension		92-93
Bahamas		219-220
Barbados		265-266
Basutoland		101-102
Bechuanaland Protectorate		202-203
Bermuda		196-197
British Guiana		293-294
British Honduras		187-188
Brunei		116-117
Cayman Islands		172-173
Dominica		185-186
Falkland Islands		154-155
Fiji		211-212
Gibraltar		167-168
Gilbert & Ellice Islands		87-88
Grenada		205-206
Hong Kong		221-222
Mauritius		291-292
Montserrat		157-158
New Hebrides, British		108-109
Pitcairn Islands		52-53
St. Helena		180-181
St. Kitts-Nevis		163-164
St. Lucia		197-198
St. Vincent		224-225
Seychelles		218-219
Solomon Islands		126-127
Swaziland		115-116
Tristan da Cunha		85-86
Turks & Caicos Islands		142-143
Virgin Islands		159-160

Nos. 153-154 (2)	1.45	1.35
Nos. 92-93 (2)	1.90	1.30
Nos. 219-220 (2)	1.35	1.50
Nos. 265-266 (2)	1.50	1.25
Nos. 101-102 (2)	.85	.65
Nos. 202-203 (2)	1.10	.75
Nos. 196-197 (2)	2.15	2.25
Nos. 293-294 (2)	.50	.50
Nos. 187-188 (2)	.75	.75
Nos. 116-117 (2)	1.75	1.75
Nos. 172-173 (2)	1.00	.85
Nos. 185-186 (2)	.55	.55
Nos. 154-155 (2)	6.75	3.15
Nos. 211-212 (2)	2.00	1.05
Nos. 167-168 (2)	9.00	5.95
Nos. 87-88 (2)	.85	.60
Nos. 205-206 (2)	.50	.50
Nos. 221-222 (2)	10.50	4.75
Nos. 291-292 (2)	1.10	.50
Nos. 157-158 (2)	1.05	1.15
Nos. 108-109 (2)	.65	.50
Nos. 52-53 (2)	1.65	1.90
Nos. 180-181 (2)	.80	.60
Nos. 163-164 (2)	.60	.60
Nos. 197-198 (2)	1.25	1.25
Nos. 224-225 (2)	.80	.90
Nos. 218-219 (2)	.75	.60
Nos. 126-127 (2)	.70	.55
Nos. 115-116 (2)	.70	.70
Nos. 85-86 (2)	1.00	.65
Nos. 142-143 (2)	.50	.50
Nos. 159-160 (2)	.85	.85
Set total (64) Stamps	56.85	40.70

Intl. Cooperation Year

ICY Emblem CD318

1965

Antigua	155-156
Ascension	94-95
Bahamas	222-223
Basutoland	103-104
Bechuanaland Protectorate	204-205
Bermuda	199-200
British Guiana	295-296
British Honduras	189-190
Brunei	118-119
Cayman Islands	174-175
Dominica	187-188
Falkland Islands	156-157
Fiji	213-214
Gibraltar	169-170
Gilbert & Ellice Islands	104-105
Grenada	207-208
Hong Kong	223-224
Mauritius	293-294
Montserrat	176-177
New Hebrides, British	110-111
New Hebrides, French	126-127
Pitcairn Islands	54-55
St. Helena	182-183
St. Kitts-Nevis	165-166
St. Lucia	199-200
Seychelles	220-221
Solomon Islands	143-144
South Arabia	17-18
Swaziland	117-118
Tristan da Cunha	87-88
Turks & Caicos Islands	144-145
Virgin Islands	161-162

Nos. 155-156 (2)	.55	.50
Nos. 94-95 (2)	1.30	1.40
Nos. 222-223 (2)	.65	1.90
Nos. 103-104 (2)	.75	.85
Nos. 204-205 (2)	.85	1.00
Nos. 199-200 (2)	2.05	1.25
Nos. 295-296 (2)	.55	.50
Nos. 189-190 (2)	.60	.55
Nos. 118-119 (2)	.85	.85
Nos. 174-175 (2)	1.00	.75
Nos. 187-188 (2)	.55	.55
Nos. 156-157 (2)	6.00	1.65
Nos. 213-214 (2)	1.95	1.25
Nos. 169-170 (2)	1.25	2.75
Nos. 104-105 (2)	.85	.60
Nos. 207-208 (2)	.50	.50
Nos. 223-224 (2)	11.00	3.50
Nos. 293-294 (2)	.65	.50
Nos. 176-177 (2)	.80	.65
Nos. 110-111 (2)	.50	.50
Nos. 126-127 (2)	12.00	12.00
Nos. 54-55 (2)	1.60	1.85
Nos. 182-183 (2)	.95	.50
Nos. 165-166 (2)	.80	.60
Nos. 199-200 (2)	.55	.55
Nos. 220-221 (2)	.80	.60
Nos. 143-144 (2)	.70	.60
Nos. 17-18 (2)	1.20	.50
Nos. 117-118 (2)	.75	.75
Nos. 87-88 (2)	1.05	.65
Nos. 144-145 (2)	.50	.50
Nos. 161-162 (2)	.65	.50
Set total (64) Stamps	54.75	41.60

Churchill Memorial

Winston Churchill and St. Paul's, London, During Air Attack CD319

1966

Antigua	157-160
Ascension	96-99
Bahamas	224-227
Barbados	281-284
Basutoland	105-108
Bechuanaland Protectorate	206-209
Bermuda	201-204
British Antarctic Territory	16-19
British Honduras	191-194
Brunei	120-123
Cayman Islands	176-179
Dominica	189-192
Falkland Islands	158-161
Fiji	215-218

Gibraltar	171-174
Gilbert & Ellice Islands	106-109
Grenada	209-212
Hong Kong	225-228
Mauritius	295-298
Montserrat	178-181
New Hebrides, British	112-115
New Hebrides, French	128-131
Pitcairn Islands	56-59
St. Helena	184-187
St. Kitts-Nevis	167-170
St. Lucia	201-204
St. Vincent	241-244
Seychelles	222-225
Solomon Islands	145-148
South Arabia	19-22
Swaziland	119-122
Tristan da Cunha	89-92
Turks & Caicos Islands	146-149
Virgin Islands	163-166

Nos. 157-160 (4)	3.05	3.05
Nos. 96-99 (4)	10.00	6.40
Nos. 224-227 (4)	2.30	3.20
Nos. 281-284 (4)	3.00	4.95
Nos. 105-108 (4)	2.80	3.25
Nos. 206-209 (4)	2.50	2.50
Nos. 201-204 (4)	4.00	4.75
Nos. 16-19 (4)	41.20	18.00
Nos. 191-194 (4)	2.45	1.30
Nos. 120-123 (4)	7.65	6.55
Nos. 176-179 (4)	3.10	3.65
Nos. 189-192 (4)	1.15	1.15
Nos. 158-161 (4)	12.75	9.55
Nos. 215-218 (4)	4.40	3.00
Nos. 171-174 (4)	3.05	5.30
Nos. 106-109 (4)	1.50	1.30
Nos. 209-212 (4)	1.10	1.10
Nos. 225-228 (4)	52.50	11.40
Nos. 295-298 (4)	3.70	3.75
Nos. 178-181 (4)	1.60	1.55
Nos. 112-115 (4)	2.30	1.00
Nos. 128-131 (4)	8.35	8.35
Nos. 56-59 (4)	4.45	6.10
Nos. 184-187 (4)	1.85	1.95
Nos. 167-170 (4)	1.50	1.70
Nos. 201-204 (4)	1.50	1.50
Nos. 241-244 (4)	1.50	1.75
Nos. 222-225 (4)	3.20	4.35
Nos. 145-148 (4)	1.50	1.60
Nos. 19-22 (4)	2.95	2.20
Nos. 119-122 (4)	1.70	2.55
Nos. 89-92 (4)	5.95	2.70
Nos. 146-149 (4)	1.60	1.75
Nos. 163-166 (4)	1.90	1.90
Set total (136) Stamps	204.05	135.10

Royal Visit, 1966

Queen Elizabeth II and Prince Philip CD320

Caribbean visit, Feb. 4 - Mar. 6, 1966.

1966

Antigua	161-162
Bahamas	228-229
Barbados	285-286
British Guiana	299-300
Cayman Islands	180-181
Dominica	193-194
Grenada	213-214
Montserrat	182-183
St. Kitts-Nevis	171-172
St. Lucia	205-206
St. Vincent	245-246
Turks & Caicos Islands	150-151
Virgin Islands	167-168

Nos. 161-162 (2)	3.50	2.60
Nos. 228-229 (2)	3.05	3.05
Nos. 285-286 (2)	3.00	2.00
Nos. 299-300 (2)	2.35	.85
Nos. 180-181 (2)	3.45	1.80
Nos. 193-194 (2)	3.00	.60
Nos. 213-214 (2)	.80	.50
Nos. 182-183 (2)	2.00	1.00
Nos. 171-172 (2)	.90	.75
Nos. 205-206 (2)	1.50	1.35
Nos. 245-246 (2)	2.75	1.35
Nos. 150-151 (2)	1.00	.50
Nos. 167-168 (2)	1.75	1.75
Set total (26) Stamps	29.05	18.10

World Cup Soccer

Soccer Player and Jules Rimet Cup CD321

World Cup Soccer Championship, Wembley, England, July 11-30.

1966

Antigua	163-164
Ascension	100-101
Bahamas	245-246
Bermuda	205-206
Brunei	124-125
Cayman Islands	182-183
Dominica	195-196
Fiji	219-220
Gibraltar	175-176
Gilbert & Ellice Islands	125-126
Grenada	230-231
New Hebrides, British	116-117
New Hebrides, French	132-133
Pitcairn Islands	60-61
St. Helena	188-189
St. Kitts-Nevis	173-174
St. Lucia	207-208
Seychelles	226-227
Solomon Islands	167-168
South Arabia	23-24
Tristan da Cunha	93-94

Nos. 163-164 (2)	.80	.85
Nos. 100-101 (2)	2.50	2.00
Nos. 245-246 (2)	.65	.65
Nos. 205-206 (2)	1.75	1.75
Nos. 124-125 (2)	1.30	1.25
Nos. 182-183 (2)	.75	.65
Nos. 195-196 (2)	1.20	.75
Nos. 219-220 (2)	1.70	.60
Nos. 175-176 (2)	1.85	1.75
Nos. 125-126 (2)	.70	.60
Nos. 230-231 (2)	.65	.95
Nos. 116-117 (2)	1.00	1.00
Nos. 132-133 (2)	7.00	7.00
Nos. 60-61 (2)	2.00	2.00
Nos. 188-189 (2)	1.25	.60
Nos. 173-174 (2)	.85	.80
Nos. 207-208 (2)	1.15	.90
Nos. 226-227 (2)	.85	.75
Nos. 167-168 (2)	1.10	1.10
Nos. 23-24 (2)	1.90	.55
Nos. 93-94 (2)	1.25	.80
Set total (42) Stamps	32.20	27.30

WHO Headquarters

World Health Organization Headquarters, Geneva — CD322

1966

Antigua	165-166
Ascension	102-103
Bahamas	247-248
Brunei	126-127
Cayman Islands	184-185
Dominica	197-198
Fiji	224-225
Gibraltar	180-181
Gilbert & Ellice Islands	127-128
Grenada	232-233
Hong Kong	229-230
Montserrat	184-185
New Hebrides, British	118-119
New Hebrides, French	134-135
Pitcairn Islands	62-63
St. Helena	190-191
St. Kitts-Nevis	177-178
St. Lucia	209-210
St. Vincent	247-248
Seychelles	228-229
Solomon Islands	169-170
South Arabia	25-26
Tristan da Cunha	99-100

Nos. 165-166 (2)	1.15	.55
Nos. 102-103 (2)	6.60	3.35
Nos. 247-248 (2)	.80	.80
Nos. 126-127 (2)	1.35	1.35
Nos. 184-185 (2)	2.25	1.20
Nos. 197-198 (2)	.75	.75
Nos. 224-225 (2)	4.70	3.30
Nos. 180-181 (2)	6.50	4.50
Nos. 127-128 (2)	.80	.70
Nos. 232-233 (2)	.80	.50
Nos. 229-230 (2)	11.25	2.30
Nos. 184-185 (2)	1.00	1.00
Nos. 118-119 (2)	.75	.50
Nos. 134-135 (2)	8.50	8.50
Nos. 62-63 (2)	5.50	7.00
Nos. 190-191 (2)	3.50	1.50
Nos. 177-178 (2)	.60	.60
Nos. 209-210 (2)	.80	.80
Nos. 247-248 (2)	1.15	1.05
Nos. 228-229 (2)	1.25	.65
Nos. 169-170 (2)	.95	.80

Nos. 25-26 (2)	2.10	.70
Nos. 99-100 (2)	1.90	1.25
Set total (46) Stamps	64.95	43.65

UNESCO Anniversary

"Education" — CD323

"Science" (Wheat ears & flask enclosing globe). "Culture" (lyre & columns). 20th anniversary of the UNESCO.

1966-67

Antigua	183-185
Ascension	108-110
Bahamas	249-251
Barbados	287-289
Bermuda	207-209
Brunei	128-130
Cayman Islands	186-188
Dominica	199-201
Gibraltar	183-185
Gilbert & Ellice Islands	129-131
Grenada	234-236
Hong Kong	231-233
Mauritius	299-301
Montserrat	186-188
New Hebrides, British	120-122
New Hebrides, French	136-138
Pitcairn Islands	64-66
St. Helena	192-194
St. Kitts-Nevis	179-181
St. Lucia	211-213
St. Vincent	249-251
Seychelles	230-232
Solomon Islands	171-173
South Arabia	27-29
Swaziland	123-125
Tristan da Cunha	101-103
Turks & Caicos Islands	155-157
Virgin Islands	176-178

Nos. 183-185 (3)	1.90	2.50
Nos. 108-110 (3)	11.00	5.80
Nos. 249-251 (3)	2.35	2.35
Nos. 287-289 (3)	2.35	2.15
Nos. 207-209 (3)	3.80	3.90
Nos. 128-130 (3)	4.65	5.40
Nos. 186-188 (3)	2.50	1.50
Nos. 199-201 (3)	1.60	.75
Nos. 183-185 (3)	6.50	3.25
Nos. 129-131 (3)	2.50	2.45
Nos. 234-236 (3)	1.10	1.20
Nos. 231-233 (3)	49.50	24.00
Nos. 299-301 (3)	2.10	1.50
Nos. 186-188 (3)	2.40	2.40
Nos. 120-122 (3)	1.90	1.50
Nos. 136-138 (3)	7.75	7.75
Nos. 64-66 (3)	4.05	4.00
Nos. 192-194 (3)	5.25	3.65
Nos. 179-181 (3)	.90	.90
Nos. 211-213 (3)	1.15	1.15
Nos. 249-251 (3)	2.30	1.35
Nos. 230-232 (3)	2.40	2.40
Nos. 171-173 (3)	2.00	1.50
Nos. 27-29 (3)	5.50	5.50
Nos. 123-125 (3)	1.40	1.40
Nos. 101-103 (3)	2.00	1.40
Nos. 155-157 (3)	1.15	1.20
Nos. 176-178 (3)	1.40	1.30
Set total (84) Stamps	133.40	94.55

Silver Wedding, 1972

Queen Elizabeth II and Prince Philip — CD324

Designs: borders differ for each country.

1972

Anguilla	161-162
Antigua	295-296
Ascension	164-165
Bahamas	344-345
Bermuda	296-297
British Antarctic Territory	43-44
British Honduras	306-307
British Indian Ocean Territory	48-49

Brunei	186-187
Cayman Islands	304-305
Dominica	352-353
Falkland Islands	223-224
Fiji	328-329
Gibraltar	292-293
Gilbert & Ellice Islands	206-207
Grenada	466-467
Hong Kong	271-272
Montserrat	286-287
New Hebrides, British	169-170
New Hebrides, French	188-189
Pitcairn Islands	127-128
St. Helena	271-272
St. Kitts-Nevis	257-258
St. Lucia	328-329
St. Vincent	344-345
Seychelles	309-310
Solomon Islands	248-249
South Georgia	35-36
Tristan da Cunha	178-179
Turks & Caicos Islands	257-258
Virgin Islands	241-242

Nos. 161-162 (2)	1.10	1.50
Nos. 295-296 (2)	.50	.50
Nos. 164-165 (2)	.70	.70
Nos. 344-345 (2)	.60	.60
Nos. 296-297 (2)	.50	.65
Nos. 43-44 (2)	6.50	5.65
Nos. 306-307 (2)	.80	.80
Nos. 48-49 (2)	2.00	1.00
Nos. 186-187 (2)	.70	.70
Nos. 304-305 (2)	.75	.75
Nos. 352-353 (2)	.65	.65
Nos. 223-224 (2)	1.00	1.15
Nos. 328-329 (2)	.70	.70
Nos. 292-293 (2)	.50	.50
Nos. 206-207 (2)	.50	.50
Nos. 466-467 (2)	.70	.70
Nos. 271-272 (2)	1.70	1.50
Nos. 286-287 (2)	.50	.50
Nos. 169-170 (2)	.50	.50
Nos. 188-189 (2)	1.25	1.25
Nos. 127-128 (2)	.90	.85
Nos. 271-272 (2)	.60	1.20
Nos. 257-258 (2)	.65	.50
Nos. 328-329 (2)	.75	.75
Nos. 344-345 (2)	.55	.55
Nos. 309-310 (2)	.90	.90
Nos. 248-249 (2)	.50	.50
Nos. 35-36 (2)	1.40	1.40
Nos. 178-179 (2)	.70	.70
Nos. 257-258 (2)	.50	.50
Nos. 241-242 (2)	.50	.50
Set total (62) Stamps	30.10	29.15

Princess Anne's Wedding

Princess Anne and Mark Phillips — CD325

Wedding of Princess Anne and Mark Phillips, Nov. 14, 1973.

1973

Anguilla	179-180
Ascension	177-178
Belize	325-326
Bermuda	302-303
British Antarctic Territory	60-61
Cayman Islands	320-321
Falkland Islands	225-226
Gibraltar	305-306
Gilbert & Ellice Islands	216-217
Hong Kong	289-290
Montserrat	300-301
Pitcairn Islands	135-136
St. Helena	277-278
St. Kitts-Nevis	274-275
St. Lucia	349-350
St. Vincent	358-359
St. Vincent Grenadines	1-2
Seychelles	311-312
Solomon Islands	259-260
South Georgia	37-38
Tristan da Cunha	189-190
Turks & Caicos Islands	286-287
Virgin Islands	260-261

Nos. 179-180 (2)	.55	.55
Nos. 177-178 (2)	.60	.60
Nos. 325-326 (2)	1.10	.50
Nos. 302-303 (2)	.50	.50
Nos. 60-61 (2)	1.10	1.10
Nos. 320-321 (2)	.50	.50

Nos. 225-226 (2)	.70	.60
Nos. 305-306 (2)	.55	.55
Nos. 216-217 (2)	.50	.50
Nos. 289-290 (2)	2.65	2.00
Nos. 300-301 (2)	.55	.55
Nos. 135-136 (2)	.70	.60
Nos. 277-278 (2)	.50	.50
Nos. 274-275 (2)	.50	.50
Nos. 349-350 (2)	.50	.50
Nos. 358-359 (2)	.50	.50
Nos. 1-2 (2)	.50	.50
Nos. 311-312 (2)	.65	.65
Nos. 259-260 (2)	.70	.70
Nos. 37-38 (2)	.75	.75
Nos. 189-190 (2)	.50	.50
Nos. 286-287 (2)	.50	.50
Nos. 260-261 (2)	.50	.50
Set total (46) Stamps	16.10	14.65

Elizabeth II Coronation Anniv.

CD326

CD327

CD328

Designs: Royal and local beasts in heraldic form and simulated stonework. Portrait of Elizabeth II by Peter Grugeon. 25th anniversary of coronation of Queen Elizabeth II.

1978

Ascension	229
Barbados	474
Belize	397
British Antarctic Territory	71
Cayman Islands	404
Christmas Island	87
Falkland Islands	275
Fiji	384
Gambia	380
Gilbert Islands	312
Mauritius	464
New Hebrides, British	258
New Hebrides, French	278
St. Helena	317
St. Kitts-Nevis	354
Samoa	472
Solomon Islands	368
South Georgia	51
Swaziland	302
Tristan da Cunha	238
Virgin Islands	337

No. 229 (1)	2.00	2.00
No. 474 (1)	1.35	1.35
No. 397 (1)	4.50	5.00
No. 71 (1)	6.00	6.00
No. 404 (1)	2.00	2.00
No. 87 (1)	3.50	4.00
No. 275 (1)	4.00	5.50
No. 384 (1)	1.75	1.75
No. 380 (1)	1.50	1.50
No. 312 (1)	1.25	1.25
No. 464 (1)	2.10	2.10
No. 258 (1)	1.75	1.75
No. 278 (1)	3.50	3.50
No. 317 (1)	1.75	1.75
No. 354 (1)	1.00	1.00
No. 472 (1)	2.10	2.10
No. 368 (1)	2.50	2.50
No. 51 (1)	3.00	3.00
No. 302 (1)	1.60	1.60
No. 238 (1)	1.50	1.50
No. 337 (1)	1.80	1.80
Set total (21) Stamps	50.45	52.95

Queen Mother Elizabeth's 80th Birthday

CD330

Designs: Photographs of Queen Mother Elizabeth. Falkland Islands issued in sheets of 50; others in sheets of 9.

1980

Ascension	261
Bermuda	401
Cayman Islands	443
Falkland Islands	305
Gambia	412
Gibraltar	393
Hong Kong	364
Pitcairn Islands	193
St. Helena	341
Samoa	532
Solomon Islands	426
Tristan da Cunha	277

No. 261 (1)	.40	.40
No. 401 (1)	.45	.75
No. 443 (1)	.40	.40
No. 305 (1)	.40	.40
No. 412 (1)	.40	.50
No. 393 (1)	.35	.35
No. 364 (1)	1.10	1.25
No. 193 (1)	.60	.60
No. 341 (1)	.50	.50
No. 532 (1)	.55	.55
No. 426 (1)	.50	.50
No. 277 (1)	.45	.45
Set total (12) Stamps	6.10	6.65

Royal Wedding, 1981

CD331a

Prince Charles and Lady Diana — CD331

Wedding of Charles, Prince of Wales, and Lady Diana Spencer, St. Paul's Cathedral, London, July 29, 1981.

1981

Antigua	623-627
Ascension	294-296
Barbados	547-549
Barbuda	497-501
Bermuda	412-414
Brunei	268-270
Cayman Islands	471-473
Dominica	701-705
Falkland Islands	324-326
Falkland Islands Dep.	1L59-1L61
Fiji	442-444
Gambia	426-428
Ghana	759-764
Grenada	1051-1055
Grenada Grenadines	440-443
Hong Kong	373-375
Jamaica	500-503
Lesotho	335-337
Maldive Islands	906-909
Mauritius	520-522
Norfolk Island	280-282
Pitcairn Islands	206-208
St. Helena	353-355
St. Lucia	543-549
Samoa	558-560
Sierra Leone	509-518
Solomon Islands	450-452
Swaziland	382-384
Tristan da Cunha	294-296
Turks & Caicos Islands	486-489
Caicos Island	8-11
Uganda	314-317
Vanuatu	308-310
Virgin Islands	406-408

Nos. 623-627 (5)	6.55	2.55
Nos. 294-296 (3)	1.00	1.00

Nos. 547-549 (3)	.90	.90
Nos. 497-501 (5)	10.95	10.95
Nos. 412-414 (3)	2.00	2.00
Nos. 268-270 (3)	2.15	4.50
Nos. 471-473 (3)	1.20	1.30
Nos. 701-705 (5)	8.35	2.35
Nos. 324-326 (3)	1.65	1.70
Nos. 1L59-1L61 (3)	1.45	1.45
Nos. 442-444 (3)	1.35	1.35
Nos. 426-428 (3)	.80	.80
Nos. 759-764 (9)	6.20	6.20
Nos. 1051-1055 (5)	9.85	1.85
Nos. 440-443 (3)	2.35	2.35
Nos. 373-375 (3)	3.05	2.85
Nos. 500-503 (4)	1.45	1.35
Nos. 335-337 (3)	.90	.90
Nos. 906-909 (3)	1.55	1.55
Nos. 520-522 (3)	2.15	2.15
Nos. 280-282 (3)	1.75	1.75
Nos. 206-208 (3)	1.20	1.10
Nos. 353-355 (3)	.85	.85
Nos. 543-549 (5)	7.00	7.00
Nos. 558-560 (3)	.85	.85
Nos. 509-518 (10)	15.50	15.50
Nos. 450-452 (3)	1.25	1.25
Nos. 382-384 (3)	1.30	1.25
Nos. 294-296 (3)	.90	.90
Nos. 486-489 (4)	2.20	2.20
Nos. 8-11 (4)	5.00	5.00
Nos. 314-317 (4)	3.10	3.00
Nos. 308-310 (3)	1.15	1.15
Nos. 406-408 (3)	1.10	1.10
Set total (131) Stamps	109.00	92.95

Princess Diana

CD332

CD333

Designs: Photographs and portrait of Princess Diana, wedding or honeymoon photographs, royal residences, arms of issuing country. Portrait photograph by Clive Friend. Souvenir sheet margins show family tree, various people related to the princess. 21st birthday of Princess Diana of Wales, July 1.

1982

Antigua	663-666
Ascension	313-316
Bahamas	510-513
Barbados	585-588
Barbuda	544-547
British Antarctic Territory	92-95
Cayman Islands	486-489
Dominica	773-776
Falkland Islands	348-351
Falkland Islands Dep.	1L72-1L75
Fiji	470-473
Gambia	447-450
Grenada	1101A-1105
Grenada Grenadines	485-491
Lesotho	372-375
Maldive Islands	952-955
Mauritius	548-551
Pitcairn Islands	213-216
St. Helena	372-375
St. Lucia	591-594
Sierra Leone	531-534
Solomon Islands	471-474
Swaziland	406-409
Tristan da Cunha	310-313
Turks and Caicos Islands	531-534
Virgin Islands	430-433

Nos. 663-666 (4)	8.25	7.35
Nos. 313-316 (4)	3.50	3.50
Nos. 510-513 (4)	6.00	3.85
Nos. 585-588 (4)	3.40	3.25
Nos. 544-547 (4)	9.75	7.70
Nos. 92-95 (4)	4.25	3.45
Nos. 486-489 (4)	4.75	2.70
Nos. 773-776 (4)	7.05	7.00
Nos. 348-351 (4)	2.95	2.95
Nos. 1L72-1L75 (4)	2.50	2.60
Nos. 470-473 (4)	3.25	2.95
Nos. 447-450 (4)	2.85	2.85
Nos. 1101A-1105 (7)	16.05	15.55

Nos. 485-491 (7)	17.65	17.65
Nos. 372-375 (4)	4.00	4.00
Nos. 952-955 (4)	5.50	3.90
Nos. 548-551 (4)	5.00	5.00
Nos. 213-216 (4)	1.90	1.85
Nos. 372-375 (4)	2.00	2.00
Nos. 591-594 (4)	8.70	8.70
Nos. 531-534 (4)	7.20	7.20
Nos. 471-474 (4)	2.90	2.90
Nos. 406-409 (4)	3.85	2.25
Nos. 310-313 (4)	3.65	1.45
Nos. 486-489 (4)	2.20	2.20
Nos. 430-433 (4)	3.00	3.00
Set total (110) Stamps	142.10	127.85

250th anniv. of first edition of Lloyd's List (shipping news publication) & of Lloyd's marine insurance.

CD335

Designs: First page of early edition of the list; historical ships, modern transportation or harbor scenes.

1984

Ascension	351-354	
Bahamas	555-558	
Barbados	627-630	
Cayes of Belize	10-13	
Cayman Islands	522-526	
Falkland Islands	404-407	
Fiji	509-512	
Gambia	519-522	
Mauritius	587-590	
Nauru	280-283	
St. Helena	412-415	
Samoa	624-627	
Seychelles	538-541	
Solomon Islands	521-524	
Vanuatu	368-371	
Virgin Islands	466-469	

Nos. 351-354 (4)	2.90	2.55
Nos. 555-558 (4)	4.15	2.95
Nos. 627-630 (4)	6.10	5.15
Nos. 10-13 (4)	4.85	4.85
Nos. 522-526 (5)	9.30	8.45
Nos. 404-407 (4)	3.50	3.65
Nos. 509-512 (4)	5.30	4.90
Nos. 519-522 (4)	4.20	4.30
Nos. 587-590 (4)	9.40	9.40
Nos. 280-283 (4)	2.40	2.35
Nos. 412-415 (4)	2.40	2.40
Nos. 624-627 (4)	2.55	2.35
Nos. 538-541 (4)	5.00	5.00
Nos. 521-524 (4)	4.65	3.95
Nos. 368-371 (4)	1.85	1.85
Nos. 466-469 (4)	4.25	4.25
Set total (65) Stamps	72.80	68.35

Queen Mother 85th Birthday

CD336

Designs: Photographs tracing the life of the Queen Mother, Elizabeth. The high value in each set pictures the same photograph of the Queen Mother holding the infant Prince Henry.

1985

Ascension	372-376	
Bahamas	580-584	
Barbados	660-664	
Bermuda	469-473	
Falkland Islands	420-424	
Falkland Islands Dep.	1L92-1L96	
Fiji	531-535	
Hong Kong	447-450	
Jamaica	599-603	
Mauritius	604-608	
Norfolk Island	364-368	
Pitcairn Islands	253-257	
St. Helena	428-432	
Samoa	649-653	

Seychelles	567-571	
Zil Elwannyen Sesel	101-105	
Solomon Islands	543-547	
Swaziland	476-480	
Tristan da Cunha	372-376	
Vanuatu	392-396	

Nos. 372-376 (5)	4.65	4.65
Nos. 580-584 (5)	7.70	6.45
Nos. 660-664 (5)	8.00	6.70
Nos. 469-473 (5)	9.40	9.40
Nos. 420-424 (5)	7.35	6.65
Nos. 1L92-1L96 (5)	8.00	8.00
Nos. 531-535 (5)	6.15	6.15
Nos. 447-450 (4)	9.50	8.50
Nos. 599-603 (5)	6.15	7.00
Nos. 604-608 (5)	11.30	11.30
Nos. 364-368 (5)	5.00	5.00
Nos. 253-257 (5)	5.30	5.95
Nos. 428-432 (5)	5.25	5.25
Nos. 649-653 (5)	8.40	7.55
Nos. 567-571 (5)	8.70	8.70
Nos. 101-105 (5)	6.60	6.60
Nos. 543-547 (5)	3.95	3.95
Nos. 476-480 (5)	7.75	7.25
Nos. 372-376 (5)	5.40	5.40
Nos. 392-396 (5)	5.25	5.25
Set total (99) Stamps	139.80	135.70

Queen Elizabeth II, 60th Birthday

CD337

1986, April 21

Ascension	389-393	
Bahamas	592-596	
Barbados	675-679	
Bermuda	499-503	
Cayman Islands	555-559	
Falkland Islands	441-445	
Fiji	544-548	
Hong Kong	465-469	
Jamaica	620-624	
Kiribati	470-474	
Mauritius	629-633	
Papua New Guinea	640-644	
Pitcairn Islands	270-274	
St. Helena	451-455	
Samoa	670-674	
Seychelles	592-596	
Zil Elwannyen Sesel	114-118	
Solomon Islands	562-566	
South Georgia	101-105	
Swaziland	490-494	
Tristan da Cunha	388-392	
Vanuatu	414-418	
Zambia	343-347	

Nos. 389-393 (5)	2.80	3.30
Nos. 592-596 (5)	2.75	3.70
Nos. 675-679 (5)	3.25	3.10
Nos. 499-503 (5)	4.65	5.15
Nos. 555-559 (5)	4.55	5.60
Nos. 441-445 (5)	3.95	4.95
Nos. 544-548 (5)	3.00	3.00
Nos. 465-469 (5)	8.75	6.75
Nos. 620-624 (5)	2.75	2.70
Nos. 470-474 (5)	2.25	2.10
Nos. 629-633 (5)	3.50	3.50
Nos. 640-644 (5)	4.10	4.10
Nos. 270-274 (5)	2.80	2.70
Nos. 451-455 (5)	2.50	3.05
Nos. 670-674 (5)	2.55	2.55
Nos. 592-596 (5)	2.70	2.70
Nos. 114-118 (5)	2.15	2.15
Nos. 562-566 (5)	2.90	2.90
Nos. 101-105 (5)	3.30	3.65
Nos. 490-494 (5)	2.15	2.15
Nos. 388-392 (5)	3.00	3.00
Nos. 414-418 (5)	3.10	3.10
Nos. 343-347 (5)	1.65	1.60
Set total (115) Stamps	75.10	77.50

Royal Wedding

Marriage of Prince Andrew and Sarah Ferguson
CD338

1986, July 23

Ascension	399-400	
Bahamas	602-603	
Barbados	687-688	

Cayman Islands	560-561	
Jamaica	629-630	
Pitcairn Islands	275-276	
St. Helena	460-461	
St. Kitts	181-182	
Seychelles	602-603	
Zil Elwannyen Sesel	119-120	
Solomon Islands	567-568	
Tristan da Cunha	397-398	
Zambia	348-349	

Nos. 399-400 (2)	1.60	1.60
Nos. 602-603 (2)	2.75	2.75
Nos. 687-688 (2)	2.00	1.25
Nos. 560-561 (2)	1.70	2.35
Nos. 629-630 (2)	1.35	1.35
Nos. 275-276 (2)	2.40	2.40
Nos. 460-461 (2)	1.05	1.05
Nos. 181-182 (2)	1.50	2.25
Nos. 602-603 (2)	2.50	2.50
Nos. 119-120 (2)	2.30	2.30
Nos. 567-568 (2)	1.00	1.00
Nos. 397-398 (2)	1.40	1.40
Nos. 348-349 (2)	1.10	1.30
Set total (26) Stamps	22.65	23.50

Queen Elizabeth II, 60th Birthday

Queen Elizabeth II & Prince Philip, 1947 Wedding Portrait — CD339

Designs: Photographs tracing the life of Queen Elizabeth II.

1986

Anguilla	674-677	
Antigua	925-928	
Barbuda	783-786	
Dominica	950-953	
Gambia	611-614	
Grenada	1371-1374	
Grenada Grenadines	749-752	
Lesotho	531-534	
Maldive Islands	1172-1175	
Sierra Leone	760-763	
Uganda	495-498	

Nos. 674-677 (4)	8.00	8.00
Nos. 925-928 (4)	5.50	6.20
Nos. 783-786 (4)	23.15	23.15
Nos. 950-953 (4)	7.25	7.25
Nos. 611-614 (4)	8.25	7.90
Nos. 1371-1374 (4)	6.80	6.80
Nos. 749-752 (4)	6.75	6.75
Nos. 531-534 (4)	5.25	5.25
Nos. 1172-1175 (4)	6.25	6.25
Nos. 760-763 (4)	5.25	5.25
Nos. 495-498 (4)	8.50	8.50
Set total (44) Stamps	90.95	91.30

Royal Wedding, 1986

CD340

Designs: Photographs of Prince Andrew and Sarah Ferguson during courtship, engagement and marriage.

1986

Antigua	939-942	
Barbuda	809-812	
Dominica	970-973	
Gambia	635-638	
Grenada	1385-1388	
Grenada Grenadines	758-761	
Lesotho	545-548	
Maldive Islands	1181-1184	
Sierra Leone	769-772	
Uganda	510-513	

Nos. 939-942 (4)	7.00	8.75
Nos. 809-812 (4)	14.55	14.55
Nos. 970-973 (4)	7.25	7.25
Nos. 635-638 (4)	7.80	7.80
Nos. 1385-1388 (4)	8.30	8.30
Nos. 758-761 (4)	9.00	9.00

Nos. 545-548 (4)	7.45	7.45
Nos. 1181-1184 (4)	8.45	8.45
Nos. 769-772 (4)	5.35	5.35
Nos. 510-513 (4)	9.25	10.00
Set total (40) Stamps	84.40	86.90

Lloyds of London, 300th Anniv.

CD341

Designs: 17th century aspects of Lloyds, representations of each country's individual connections with Lloyds and publicized disasters insured by the organization.

1986

Ascension	454-457	
Bahamas	655-658	
Barbados	731-734	
Bermuda	541-544	
Falkland Islands	481-484	
Liberia	1101-1104	
Malawi	534-537	
Nevis	571-574	
St. Helena	501-504	
St. Lucia	923-926	
Seychelles	649-652	
Zil Elwannyen Sesel	146-149	
Solomon Islands	627-630	
South Georgia	131-134	
Trinidad & Tobago	484-487	
Tristan da Cunha	439-442	
Vanuatu	485-488	

Nos. 454-457 (4)	5.00	5.00
Nos. 655-658 (4)	8.90	4.95
Nos. 731-734 (4)	12.50	8.35
Nos. 541-544 (4)	8.00	6.60
Nos. 481-484 (4)	5.45	3.85
Nos. 1101-1104 (4)	4.25	4.25
Nos. 534-537 (4)	11.00	7.85
Nos. 571-574 (4)	8.35	8.35
Nos. 501-504 (4)	8.70	7.15
Nos. 923-926 (4)	8.80	8.80
Nos. 649-652 (4)	12.85	12.85
Nos. 146-149 (4)	11.25	11.25
Nos. 627-630 (4)	7.00	4.45
Nos. 131-134 (4)	6.30	3.70
Nos. 484-487 (4)	10.25	6.35
Nos. 439-442 (4)	7.60	7.60
Nos. 485-488 (4)	4.85	4.85
Set total (68) Stamps	141.05	116.20

Moon Landing, 20th Anniv.

CD342

Designs: Equipment, crew photographs, spacecraft, official emblems and report profiles created for the Apollo Missions. Two stamps in each set are square in format rather than like the stamp shown; see individual country listings for more information.

1989

Ascension	468-472	
Bahamas	674-678	
Belize	916-920	
Kiribati	517-521	
Liberia	1125-1129	
Nevis	586-590	
St. Kitts	248-252	
Samoa	760-764	
Seychelles	676-680	
Zil Elwannyen Sesel	154-158	
Solomon Islands	643-647	
Vanuatu	507-511	

Nos. 468-472 (5)	9.40	8.60
Nos. 674-678 (5)	23.00	19.70
Nos. 916-920 (5)	29.25	21.60
Nos. 517-521 (5)	12.50	12.50
Nos. 1125-1129 (5)	8.50	8.50
Nos. 586-590 (5)	7.50	7.50

Nos. 248-252 (5)	8.00	8.25
Nos. 760-764 (5)	9.85	9.30
Nos. 676-680 (5)	16.05	16.05
Nos. 154-158 (5)	26.85	26.85
Nos. 643-647 (5)	9.00	6.75
Nos. 507-511 (5)	8.60	8.60
Set total (60) Stamps	168.50	154.20

Queen Mother, 90th Birthday

CD343   CD344

Designs: Portraits of Queen Elizabeth, the Queen Mother. See individual country listings for more information.

1990

Ascension	491-492
Bahamas	698-699
Barbados	782-783
British Antarctic Territory	170-171
British Indian Ocean Territory	106-107
Cayman Islands	622-623
Falkland Islands	524-525
Kenya	527-528
Kiribati	555-556
Liberia	1145-1146
Pitcairn Islands	336-337
St. Helena	532-533
St. Lucia	969-970
Seychelles	710-711
Zil Elwannyen Sesel	171-172
Solomon Islands	671-672
South Georgia	143-144
Swaziland	565-566
Tristan da Cunha	480-481

Nos. 491-492 (2)	4.75	4.75
Nos. 698-699 (2)	5.25	5.25
Nos. 782-783 (2)	4.00	3.70
Nos. 170-171 (2)	6.00	6.00
Nos. 106-107 (2)	18.00	18.50
Nos. 622-623 (2)	4.00	5.50
Nos. 524-525 (2)	4.75	4.75
Nos. 527-528 (2)	6.05	6.05
Nos. 555-556 (2)	4.75	4.75
Nos. 1145-1146 (2)	3.25	3.25
Nos. 336-337 (2)	4.25	4.25
Nos. 532-533 (2)	5.25	5.25
Nos. 969-970 (2)	4.60	4.60
Nos. 710-711 (2)	6.60	6.60
Nos. 171-172 (2)	8.25	8.25
Nos. 671-672 (2)	5.00	5.30
Nos. 143-144 (2)	5.50	6.50
Nos. 565-566 (2)	4.10	4.10
Nos. 480-481 (2)	5.60	5.60
Set total (38) Stamps	109.95	112.95

Queen Elizabeth II, 65th Birthday, and Prince Philip, 70th Birthday

CD345

CD346

Designs: Portraits of Queen Elizabeth II and Prince Philip differ for each country. Printed in sheets of 10 + 5 labels (3 different) between. Stamps alternate, producing 5 different triptychs.

1991

Ascension	506a
Bahamas	731a
Belize	970a
Bermuda	618a
Kiribati	572a
Mauritius	734a
Pitcairn Islands	349a
St. Helena	555a
St. Kitts	319a
Samoa	791a
Seychelles	724a
Zil Elwannyen Sesel	178a
Solomon Islands	689a
South Georgia	150a
Swaziland	587a
Vanuatu	541a

No. 506a (1)	3.50	3.75
No. 731a (1)	4.00	4.00
No. 970a (1)	4.25	4.25
No. 618a (1)	3.50	4.00
No. 572a (1)	4.00	4.00
No. 734a (1)	4.00	4.00
No. 349a (1)	3.25	3.25
No. 555a (1)	2.75	2.75
No. 319a (1)	3.00	3.00
No. 791a (1)	3.75	3.75
No. 724a (1)	5.00	5.00
No. 178a (1)	6.25	6.25
No. 689a (1)	3.75	3.75
No. 150a (1)	4.75	7.00
No. 587a (1)	4.00	4.00
No. 541a (1)	2.50	2.50
Set total (16) Stamps	62.25	65.25

Royal Family Birthday, Anniversary

CD347

Queen Elizabeth II, 65th birthday, Charles and Diana, 10th wedding anniversary: Various photographs of Queen Elizabeth II, Prince Philip, Prince Charles, Princess Diana and their sons William and Henry.

1991

Antigua	1446-1455
Barbuda	1229-1238
Dominica	1328-1337
Gambia	1080-1089
Grenada	2006-2015
Grenada Grenadines	1331-1340
Guyana	2440-2451
Lesotho	871-875
Maldive Islands	1533-1542
Nevis	666-675
St. Vincent	1485-1494
St. Vincent Grenadines	769-778
Sierra Leone	1387-1396
Turks & Caicos Islands	913-922
Uganda	918-927

Nos. 1446-1455 (10)	21.70	20.05
Nos. 1229-1238 (10)	125.00	119.50
Nos. 1328-1337 (10)	30.20	30.20
Nos. 1080-1089 (10)	24.65	24.40
Nos. 2006-2015 (10)	25.45	22.10
Nos. 1331-1340 (10)	23.85	23.35
Nos. 2440-2451 (12)	21.40	21.15
Nos. 871-875 (5)	13.55	13.55
Nos. 1533-1542 (10)	28.10	28.10
Nos. 666-675 (10)	23.65	23.65
Nos. 1485-1494 (10)	26.75	25.90
Nos. 769-778 (10)	25.40	25.40
Nos. 1387-1396 (10)	26.35	26.35
Nos. 913-922 (10)	27.50	25.30
Nos. 918-927 (10)	17.65	17.65
Set total (147) Stamps	461.20	446.65

Queen Elizabeth II's Accession to the Throne, 40th Anniv.

CD348

Various photographs of Queen Elizabeth II with local Scenes.

1992

Antigua	1513-1518
Barbuda	1306-1311
Dominica	1414-1419
Gambia	1172-1177
Grenada	2047-2052
Grenada Grenadines	1368-1373
Lesotho	881-885
Maldive Islands	1637-1642
Nevis	702-707
St. Vincent	1582-1587
St. Vincent Grenadines	829-834
Sierra Leone	1482-1487
Turks and Caicos Islands	978-987
Uganda	990-995
Virgin Islands	742-746

Nos. 1513-1518 (6)	15.00	15.10
Nos. 1306-1311 (6)	125.25	83.65
Nos. 1414-1419 (6)	12.50	12.50
Nos. 1172-1177 (6)	14.95	14.85
Nos. 2047-2052 (6)	15.95	15.95
Nos. 1368-1373 (6)	17.00	15.35
Nos. 881-885 (5)	11.90	11.90
Nos. 1637-1642 (6)	17.55	17.55
Nos. 702-707 (6)	13.55	13.55
Nos. 1582-1587 (6)	14.40	14.40
Nos. 829-834 (6)	19.65	19.65
Nos. 1482-1487 (6)	22.50	22.50
Nos. 913-922 (10)	27.50	25.30
Nos. 990-995 (6)	19.50	19.50
Nos. 742-746 (5)	15.50	15.50
Set total (92) Stamps	362.70	317.25

CD349

1992

Ascension	531-535
Bahamas	744-748
Bermuda	623-627
British Indian Ocean Territory	119-123
Cayman Islands	648-652
Falkland Islands	549-553
Gibraltar	605-609
Hong Kong	619-623
Kenya	563-567
Kiribati	582-586
Pitcairn Islands	362-366
St. Helena	570-574
St. Kitts	332-336
Samoa	805-809
Seychelles	734-738
Zil Elwannyen Sesel	183-187
Solomon Islands	708-712
South Georgia	157-161
Tristan da Cunha	508-512
Vanuatu	555-559
Zambia	561-565

Nos. 531-535 (5)	6.10	6.10
Nos. 744-748 (5)	6.90	4.70
Nos. 623-627 (5)	7.40	7.55
Nos. 119-123 (5)	22.75	19.25
Nos. 648-652 (5)	7.60	6.60
Nos. 549-553 (5)	5.95	5.90
Nos. 605-609 (5)	5.15	5.50
Nos. 619-623 (5)	5.10	5.25
Nos. 563-567 (5)	7.80	7.75
Nos. 582-586 (5)	3.85	3.85
Nos. 362-366 (5)	5.35	5.35
Nos. 570-574 (5)	5.70	5.70
Nos. 332-336 (5)	6.60	5.50
Nos. 805-809 (5)	7.85	5.90
Nos. 734-738 (5)	10.55	10.55
Nos. 183-187 (5)	9.40	9.40
Nos. 708-712 (5)	5.00	5.30
Nos. 157-161 (5)	5.60	5.90
Nos. 508-512 (5)	8.75	8.30
Nos. 555-559 (5)	3.10	3.10
Nos. 561-565 (5)	5.20	5.15
Set total (105) Stamps	151.70	142.60

Royal Air Force, 75th Anniversary

CD350

1993

Ascension	557-561
Bahamas	771-775
Barbados	842-846
Belize	1003-1008
Bermuda	648-651
British Indian Ocean Territory	136-140
Falkland Is.	573-577
Fiji	687-691
Montserrat	830-834
St. Kitts	351-355

Nos. 557-561 (5)	15.60	14.60
Nos. 771-775 (5)	24.65	21.45
Nos. 842-846 (5)	14.15	12.85
Nos. 1003-1008 (6)	21.15	16.50
Nos. 648-651 (4)	9.65	10.45
Nos. 136-140 (5)	16.10	16.10
Nos. 573-577 (5)	10.85	10.85
Nos. 687-691 (5)	17.75	17.40
Nos. 830-834 (5)	14.10	14.10
Nos. 351-355 (5)	22.80	23.55
Set total (50) Stamps	166.80	157.85

Royal Air Force, 80th Anniv.

Design CD350 Re-inscribed

1998

Ascension	697-701
Bahamas	907-911
British Indian Ocean Terr	198-202
Cayman Islands	754-758
Fiji	814-818
Gibraltar	755-759
Samoa	957-961
Turks & Caicos Islands	1258-1265
Tuvalu	763-767
Virgin Islands	879-883

Nos. 697-701 (5)	16.10	16.10
Nos. 907-911 (5)	13.60	12.65
Nos. 136-140 (5)	16.10	16.10
Nos. 754-758 (5)	15.25	15.25
Nos. 814-818 (5)	14.00	12.75
Nos. 755-759 (5)	9.70	9.70
Nos. 957-961 (5)	15.70	14.90
Nos. 1258-1265 (2)	27.50	27.50
Nos. 763-767 (5)	7.75	7.75
Nos. 879-883 (5)	15.00	15.00
Set total (47) Stamps	150.70	147.70

End of World War II, 50th Anniv.

CD351

CD352

1995

Ascension	613-617
Bahamas	824-828
Barbados	891-895
Belize	1047-1050
British Indian Ocean Territory	163-167
Cayman Islands	704-708
Falkland Islands	634-638
Fiji	720-724
Kiribati	662-668
Liberia	1175-1179
Mauritius	803-805
St. Helena	646-654
St. Kitts	389-393
St. Lucia	1018-1022
Samoa	890-894
Solomon Islands	799-803
South Georgia	198-200
Tristan da Cunha	562-566

Nos. 613-617 (5)	21.50	21.50

Nos. 824-828 (5)	22.00	18.70
Nos. 891-895 (5)	14.20	11.90
Nos. 1047-1050 (4)	8.25	5.90
Nos. 163-167 (5)	16.25	16.25
Nos. 704-708 (5)	17.65	13.95
Nos. 634-638 (5)	18.65	17.15
Nos. 720-724 (5)	17.50	14.50
Nos. 662-668 (7)	12.55	12.55
Nos. 1175-1179 (5)	15.25	11.15
Nos. 803-805 (3)	7.50	7.50
Nos. 646-654 (9)	26.10	26.10
Nos. 389-393 (5)	16.40	16.40
Nos. 1018-1022 (5)	12.25	10.15
Nos. 890-894 (5)	15.25	14.50
Nos. 799-803 (5)	14.75	14.75
Nos. 198-200 (3)	14.50	15.50
Nos. 562-566 (5)	20.10	20.10
Set total (91) Stamps	290.65	268.55

UN, 50th Anniv.

CD353

1995

Bahamas	839-842
Barbados	901-904
Belize	1055-1058
Jamaica	847-851
Liberia	1187-1190
Mauritius	813-816
Pitcairn Islands	436-439
St. Kitts	398-401
St. Lucia	1023-1026
Samoa	900-903
Tristan da Cunha	568-571
Virgin Islands	807-810

Nos. 839-842 (4)	7.15	6.40
Nos. 901-904 (4)	7.00	5.75
Nos. 1055-1058 (4)	6.80	4.70
Nos. 847-851 (5)	5.40	5.45
Nos. 1187-1190 (4)	10.90	10.90
Nos. 813-816 (4)	4.55	4.55
Nos. 436-439 (4)	8.15	8.15
Nos. 398-401 (4)	6.15	7.15
Nos. 1023-1026 (4)	7.50	7.25
Nos. 900-903 (4)	9.35	8.20
Nos. 568-571 (4)	13.50	13.50
Nos. 807-810 (4)	7.45	7.45
Set total (49) Stamps	93.90	89.45

Queen Elizabeth, 70th Birthday

CD354

1996

Ascension	632-635
British Antarctic Territory	240-243
British Indian Ocean Territory	176-180
Falkland Islands	653-657
Pitcairn Islands	446-449
St. Helena	672-676
Samoa	912-916
Tokelau	223-227
Tristan da Cunha	576-579
Virgin Islands	824-828

Nos. 632-635 (4)	5.30	5.30
Nos. 240-243 (4)	9.45	8.15
Nos. 176-180 (5)	11.50	11.50
Nos. 653-657 (5)	13.55	11.20
Nos. 446-449 (4)	8.60	8.60
Nos. 672-676 (5)	12.45	12.70
Nos. 912-916 (5)	10.50	10.50
Nos. 223-227 (5)	10.50	10.50
Nos. 576-579 (4)	8.35	8.35
Nos. 824-828 (5)	11.30	11.30
Set total (46) Stamps	101.50	98.10

Diana, Princess of Wales (1961-97)

CD355

1998

Ascension	696
Bahamas	901A-902
Barbados	950
Belize	1091
Bermuda	753
Botswana	659-663
British Antarctic Territory	258
British Indian Ocean Terr.	197
Cayman Islands	752A-753
Falkland Islands	694
Fiji	819-820
Gibraltar	754
Kiribati	719A-720
Namibia	909
Niue	706
Norfolk Island	644-645
Papua New Guinea	937
Pitcairn Islands	487
St. Helena	711
St. Kitts	437A-438
Samoa	955A-956
Seychelles	802
Solomon Islands	866-867
South Georgia	220
Tokelau	252B-253
Tonga	980
Niuafo'ou	201
Tristan da Cunha	618
Tuvalu	762
Vanuatu	718A-719
Virgin Islands	878

No. 696 (1)	5.25	5.25
Nos. 901A-902 (2)	5.30	5.30
No. 950 (1)	6.25	6.25
No. 1091 (1)	10.00	10.00
No. 753 (1)	5.00	5.00
Nos. 659-663 (5)	8.25	8.80
No. 258 (1)	5.50	5.50
No. 197 (1)	5.50	5.50
Nos. 752A-753 (3)	7.40	7.40
No. 694 (1)	5.00	5.00
Nos. 819-820 (2)	5.25	5.25
No. 754 (1)	4.75	4.75
Nos. 719A-720 (2)	4.60	4.60
No. 909 (1)	1.75	1.75
No. 706 (1)	5.50	5.50
Nos. 644-645 (2)	5.60	5.60
No. 937 (1)	6.25	6.25
No. 487 (1)	4.75	4.75
No. 711 (1)	4.25	4.25
Nos. 437A-438 (2)	5.15	5.15
Nos. 955A-956 (2)	7.00	7.00
No. 802 (1)	6.25	6.25
Nos. 866-867 (2)	5.40	5.40
No. 220 (1)	4.50	5.00
Nos. 252B-253 (2)	6.00	6.00
No. 980 (1)	4.00	4.00
No. 201 (1)	6.50	6.50
No. 618 (1)	5.00	5.00
No. 762 (1)	3.50	3.50
Nos. 718A-719 (2)	8.00	8.00
No. 878 (1)	4.50	4.50
Set total (46) Stamps	171.95	173.00

Wedding of Prince Edward and Sophie Rhys-Jones

CD356

1999

Ascension	729-730
Cayman Islands	775-776
Falkland Islands	729-730
Pitcairn Islands	505-506
St. Helena	733-734
Samoa	971-972
Tristan da Cunha	636-637

Virgin Islands	908-909

Nos. 729-730 (2)	4.50	4.50
Nos. 775-776 (2)	4.95	4.95
Nos. 729-730 (2)	14.00	14.00
Nos. 505-506 (2)	7.00	7.00
Nos. 733-734 (2)	5.00	5.00
Nos. 971-972 (2)	5.00	5.00
Nos. 636-637 (2)	7.50	7.50
Nos. 908-909 (2)	7.50	7.50
Set total (16) Stamps	55.45	55.45

1st Manned Moon Landing, 30th Anniv.

CD357

1999

Ascension	731-735
Bahamas	942-946
Barbados	967-971
Bermuda	778
Cayman Islands	777-781
Fiji	853-857
Jamaica	889-893
Kirbati	746-750
Nauru	465-469
St. Kitts	460-464
Samoa	973-977
Solomon Islands	875-879
Tuvalu	800-804
Virgin Islands	910-914

Nos. 731-735 (5)	12.80	12.80
Nos. 942-946 (5)	14.10	14.10
Nos. 967-971 (5)	9.45	8.25
No. 778 (1)	9.00	9.00
Nos. 777-781 (5)	9.25	9.25
Nos. 853-857 (5)	9.25	8.45
Nos. 889-893 (5)	8.30	7.18
Nos. 746-750 (5)	8.60	8.60
Nos. 465-469 (5)	7.55	7.10
Nos. 460-464 (5)	11.35	11.65
Nos. 973-977 (5)	12.60	12.45
Nos. 875-879 (5)	7.50	7.50
Nos. 800-804 (5)	6.75	6.75
Nos. 910-914 (5)	11.75	11.75
Set total (66) Stamps	138.25	134.83

Queen Mother's Century

CD358

1999

Ascension	736-740
Bahamas	951-955
Cayman Islands	782-786
Falkland Islands	734-738
Fiji	858-862
Norfolk Island	688-692
St. Helena	740-744
Samoa	978-982
Solomon Islands	880-884
South Georgia	231-235
Tristan da Cunha	638-642
Tuvalu	805-809

Nos. 736-740 (5)	15.50	15.50
Nos. 951-955 (5)	13.75	12.65
Nos. 782-786 (5)	8.35	8.35
Nos. 734-738 (5)	30.00	28.25
Nos. 858-862 (5)	12.80	13.25
Nos. 688-692 (5)	9.50	9.50
Nos. 740-744 (5)	16.15	16.15
Nos. 978-982 (5)	12.50	12.10
Nos. 880-884 (5)	7.50	7.00
Nos. 231-235 (5)	29.75	30.00
Nos. 638-642 (5)	18.00	18.00
Nos. 805-809 (5)	7.00	7.00
Set total (60) Stamps	180.80	177.75

Prince William, 18th Birthday

CD359

2000

Ascension	755-759
Cayman Islands	797-801
Falkland Islands	762-766
Fiji	889-893
South Georgia	257-261
Tristan da Cunha	664-668
Virgin Islands	925-929

Nos. 755-759 (5)	15.50	15.50
Nos. 797-801 (5)	11.15	10.90
Nos. 762-766 (5)	24.60	22.50
Nos. 889-893 (5)	12.90	12.90
Nos. 257-261 (5)	29.00	28.75
Nos. 664-668 (5)	21.50	21.50
Nos. 925-929 (5)	14.50	14.50
Set total (35) Stamps	129.15	126.55

Reign of Queen Elizabeth II, 50th Anniv.

CD360

2002

Ascension	790-794
Bahamas	1033-1037
Barbados	1019-1023
Belize	1152-1156
Bermuda	822-826
British Antarctic Territory	307-311
British Indian Ocean Territory	239-243
Cayman Islands	844-848
Falkland Islands	804-808
Gibraltar	896-900
Jamaica	952-956
Nauru	491-495
Norfolk Island	758-762
Papua New Guinea	1019-1023
Pitcairn Islands	552
St. Helena	788-792
St. Lucia	1146-1150
Solomon Islands	931-935
South Georgia	274-278
Swaziland	706-710
Tokelau	302-306
Tonga	1059
Niuafo'ou	239
Tristan da Cunha	706-710
Virgin Islands	967-971

Nos. 790-794 (5)	14.10	14.10
Nos. 1033-1037 (5)	15.25	15.25
Nos. 1019-1023 (5)	12.90	12.90
Nos. 1152-1156 (5)	17.10	15.10
Nos. 822-826 (5)	18.00	18.00
Nos. 307-311 (5)	23.00	23.00
Nos. 239-243 (5)	19.40	19.40
Nos. 844-848 (5)	13.25	13.25
Nos. 804-808 (5)	23.00	22.00
Nos. 896-900 (5)	6.65	6.65
Nos. 952-956 (5)	16.65	16.65
Nos. 491-495 (5)	17.75	17.75
Nos. 758-762 (5)	15.90	15.90
Nos. 1019-1023 (5)	14.50	14.50
No. 552 (1)	8.50	8.50
Nos. 788-792 (5)	19.75	19.75
Nos. 1146-1150 (5)	12.25	12.25
Nos. 931-935 (5)	12.40	12.40
Nos. 274-278 (5)	28.00	28.50
Nos. 706-710 (5)	12.50	12.50
Nos. 302-306 (5)	14.50	14.50
No. 1059 (1)	8.00	8.00
No. 239 (1)	8.75	8.75
Nos. 706-710 (5)	18.50	18.50
Nos. 967-971 (5)	16.50	16.50
Set total (113) Stamps	387.10	384.60

Queen Mother Elizabeth (1900-2002)

CD361

2002

Ascension		799-801
Bahamas		1044-1046
Bermuda		834-836
British Antarctic Territory		312-314
British Indian Ocean Territory		245-247
Cayman Islands		857-861
Falkland Islands		812-816
Nauru		499-501
Pitcairn Islands		561-565
St. Helena		808-812
St. Lucia		1155-1159
Seychelles		830
Solomon Islands		945-947
South Georgia		281-285
Tokelau		312-314
Tristan da Cunha		715-717
Virgin Islands		979-983

Nos. 799-801 (3)	8.85	8.85
Nos. 1044-1046 (3)	9.10	9.10
Nos. 834-836 (3)	12.25	12.25
Nos. 312-314 (3)	18.75	18.75
Nos. 245-247 (3)	17.35	17.35
Nos. 857-861 (5)	15.00	15.00
Nos. 812-816 (5)	28.50	28.50
Nos. 499-501 (3)	14.00	14.00
Nos. 561-565 (5)	15.25	15.25
Nos. 808-812 (5)	12.00	12.00
Nos. 1155-1159 (5)	12.00	12.00
No. 830 (1)	6.50	6.50
Nos. 945-947 (3)	9.25	9.25
Nos. 281-285 (5)	19.50	19.50
Nos. 312-314 (3)	11.85	11.85
Nos. 715-717 (3)	16.25	16.25
Nos. 979-983 (5)	23.50	23.50
Set total (63) Stamps	249.90	249.90

Head of Queen Elizabeth II

CD362

2003

Ascension		822
Bermuda		865
British Antarctic Territory		322
British Indian Ocean Territory		261
Cayman Islands		878
Falkland Islands		828
St. Helena		820
South Georgia		294
Tristan da Cunha		731
Virgin Islands		1003

No. 822 (1)	12.50	12.50
No. 865 (1)	50.00	50.00
No. 322 (1)	9.50	9.50
No. 261 (1)	11.00	11.00
No. 878 (1)	14.00	14.00
No. 828 (1)	9.00	9.00
No. 820 (1)	9.00	9.00
No. 294 (1)	8.50	8.50
No. 731 (1)	10.00	10.00
No. 1003 (1)	10.00	10.00
Set total (10) Stamps	143.50	143.50

Coronation of Queen Elizabeth II, 50th Anniv.

CD363

2003

Ascension		823-825

Bahamas		1073-1075
Bermuda		866-868
British Antarctic Territory		323-325
British Indian Ocean Territory		262-264
Cayman Islands		879-881
Jamaica		970-972
Kiribati		825-827
Pitcairn Islands		577-581
St. Helena		821-823
St. Lucia		1171-1173
Tokelau		320-322
Tristan da Cunha		732-734
Virgin Islands		1004-1006

Nos. 823-825 (3)	12.50	12.50
Nos. 1073-1075 (3)	13.00	13.00
Nos. 866-868 (2)	14.25	14.25
Nos. 323-325 (3)	23.00	23.00
Nos. 262-264 (3)	28.00	28.00
Nos. 879-881 (3)	19.25	19.25
Nos. 970-972 (3)	10.00	10.00
Nos. 825-827 (3)	13.00	13.00
Nos. 577-581 (5)	14.40	14.40
Nos. 821-823 (3)	7.25	7.25
Nos. 1171-1173 (3)	8.75	8.75
Nos. 320-322 (3)	17.25	17.25
Nos. 732-734 (3)	16.75	16.75
Nos. 1004-1006 (3)	25.00	25.00
Set total (43) Stamps	222.40	222.40

Prince William, 21st Birthday

CD364

2003

Ascension		826
British Indian Ocean Territory		265
Cayman Islands		882-884
Falkland Islands		829
South Georgia		295
Tokelau		323
Tristan da Cunha		735
Virgin Islands		1007-1009

No. 826 (1)	7.25	7.25
No. 265 (1)	8.00	8.00
Nos. 882-884 (3)	6.95	6.95
No. 829 (1)	13.50	13.50
No. 295 (1)	8.50	8.50
No. 323 (1)	7.25	7.25
No. 735 (1)	6.00	6.00
Nos. 1007-1009 (3)	10.00	10.00
Set total (12) Stamps	67.45	67.45

CYPRUS

'sī-prəs

LOCATION — An island in the Mediterranean Sea off the coast of Turkey
GOVT. — Republic
AREA — 3,572 sq. mi.
POP. — 754,064 (1999 est.)
CAPITAL — Nicosia

The British Crown Colony of Cyprus became a republic in 1960. Turkey invaded Cyprus in 1974 resulting in the the northern 40% of the island becoming the Turkish Republic of Northern Cyprus. No other country recognizes this division of the island. See Turkey in Volume 6.

12 Pence = 1 Shilling
40 Paras = 1 Piaster
9 Piasters = 1 Shilling
20 Shillings = 1 Pound
1000 Milliemes = 1 Pound (1955)
100 Cents = 1 Cyprus Pound (1983)
100 Cents = 1 Euro (2008)

> Catalogue values for unused stamps in this country are for Never Hinged items, beginning with Scott 156 in the regular postage section and Scott RA1 in the postal tax section.

Values for unused stamps are for examples with original gum as defined in the catalogue introduction. Very fine examples of Nos. 1, 2 and 7-10 will have perforations touching the design on at least one or more sides due to the narrow spacing of the stamps on the plates and to imperfect perforation methods. Stamps with perfs clear on all four sides are scarce and will command higher prices.

Watermark

Wmk. 344 — Map of Cyprus and KC/K Delta

 Queen Victoria — A1

A2 A3
A4 A5
A6 A7

Various Watermarks as in Great Britain (#20, 23, 25, 27 & 29)

1880		Typo.		Perf. 14
1	A1	½p rose (P 15)	125.00	115.00
		Plate 12	240.00	300.00
		Plate 19	5,750.	950.00

---

b.		Double overprint (P 15)		45,000.
2	A2	1p red (P 216)	24.00	55.00
		Plate 217	24.00	60.00
		Plate 174	1,500.	1,500.
		Plate 181	525.00	210.00
		Plate 184	22,000.	3,500.
		Plate 193	840.00	
		Plate 196	725.00	
		Plate 201	27.50	57.50
		Plate 205	90.00	57.50
		Plate 208	135.00	65.00
		Plate 215	24.00	57.50
		Plate 218	32.50	65.00
		Plate 220	550.00	475.00
b.		Double overprint (P 218)	5,400.	
		Double overprint (P 208)	27,500.	
c.		Pair, one without ovpt. (P 208)	27,500.	
3	A3	2½p claret (P 14)	4.50	19.00
		Plate 15	8.00	50.00
4	A4	4p lt ol grn (P 16)	150.00	240.00
5	A5	6p ol gray (P 16)	575.00	750.00
6	A6	1sh green (P 13)	900.00	525.00

Black Surcharge

7	A7	30 paras on 1p red (P 216)	150.00	95.00
		Plate 201	180.00	110.00
		Plate 217	210.00	210.00
		Plate 220	175.00	190.00
b.		Dbl. surch., one invtd. (P 220)	2,000.	1,500.
		Dbl. surch., one invtd. (P 216)	7,750.	

No. 2 Surcharged

18mm Long

1881				
8	A2	½p on 1p (205, 216)	82.50	100.00
		Plate 201	250.00	400.00
		Plate 181	225.00	260.00
		Plate 201	115.00	140.00
		Plate 205	85.00	100.00
		Plate 208	225.00	375.00
		Plate 215	840.00	1,000.
		Plate 217	1,000.	900.00
		Plate 218	550.00	675.00
		Plate 220	325.00	450.00

16mm Long

9	A2	½p on 1p (P 201)	140.00	190.00
		Plate 216	400.00	460.00
		Plate 218		17,500.
a.		Double surcharge (P 201, 216)	3,750.	3,000.

13mm Long

10	A2	½p on 1p red (P 215)	52.50	75.00
		Plate 205	425.00	
		Plate 217	175.00	110.00
		Plate 218	90.00	125.00
c.		Double surcharge (P 215)	550.00	700.00
		Double surcharge (P 205)	875.00	
e.		Triple surcharge (P 215)	875.00	
		Triple surcharge (P 205)	4,750.	
		Triple surcharge (P 217)	—	
		Triple surcharge (P 218)	4,750.	
h.		Quadruple surch. (P 205, 215)	7,500.	
j.		"CYPRUS" double (P 218)	6,000.	

A8

1881, July		Typo.		Wmk. 1
11	A8	½pi emer grn	210.00	52.50
12	A8	1pi rose	425.00	37.50
13	A8	2pi ultramarine	525.00	37.50
14	A8	4pi olive green	1,050.	325.00
15	A8	6pi olive gray	1,900.	500.00

Postage and revenue stamps of Cyprus with "J.A.B." (the initials of Postmaster J.A. Bulmer) in manuscript, or with "POSTAL SURCHARGE" (with or without "J. A. B.") were not Postage Due stamps but were employed for accounting purposes between the chief PO at Larnaca and the sub-offices.
See Nos. 19-25, 28-37. For surcharges see Nos. 16-18, 26-27.

Nos. 1881-1894 Surcharged in Black

1882				Wmk. 1
16	A8	½pi on ½pi grn	750.00	92.50
17	A8	30pa on 1pi rose	1,750.	140.00
a.		Double surcharge, one inverted	1,400.	850.00

1884				Wmk. 2
18	A8	½pi on ½pi grn	190.00	10.00
a.		Double surcharge	3,200.	

See Nos. 26, 27.

1882-94				Die B

For description of Dies A and B see "Dies of British Colonial Stamps" in Table of Contents.

19	A8	½pi green	16.00	2.50
20	A8	30pa violet	12.50	14.00
21	A8	1pi rose	15.50	11.00
22	A8	2pi blue	15.50	2.10
23	A8	4pi pale ol grn	20.00	42.50
24a	A8	6pi	275.00	800.00
25a	A8	12pi	190.00	450.00
		Nos. 19-25a (7)	544.50	1,322.

Die A

19a	A8	½pi	25.00	3.25
b.		½pi emerald	6,000.	525.00
20a	A8	30pa lilac	85.00	30.00
21a	A8	1pi	110.00	4.50
22a	A8	2pi	170.00	4.00
23a	A8	4pi	375.00	40.00
24	A8	6pi olive gray	75.00	21.00
25	A8	12pi brown org	225.00	45.00
		Nos. 19a-25 (7)	1,065.	147.75

Nos. 1881-1894 Surcharged in Black

Type I — Figures "½" 8mm apart.
Type II — Figures "½" 6mm apart.
The space between the fraction bars varies from 5½ to 8½mm but is usually 6 or 8mm.

Black Surcharge Type I

1886				Wmk. 2
26	A8	½pi on ½pi grn	525.00	17.50
a.		Type II	325.00	100.00
b.		Double surcharge, type II		

				Wmk. 1
27	A8	½pi on ½pi grn	8,750.	500.00
a.		Type II	24,000.	

No. 27a probably is a proof.

1894-96				Wmk. 2
28	A8	½pi grn & car rose	5.25	1.75
29	A8	30pa violet & green	5.75	6.00
30	A8	1pi rose & ultra	8.50	1.75
31	A8	2pi ultra & mar	19.00	1.75
32	A8	4pi ol green & vio	22.50	17.50
33	A8	6pi ol gray & grn	22.50	40.00
34	A8	9pi brown & rose	29.00	40.00
35	A8	12pi brn org & blk	25.00	72.50
36	A8	18pi slate & brown	60.00	62.50
37	A8	45pi dk vio & ultra	125.00	165.00
		Nos. 28-37 (10)	322.50	408.75

King Edward VII — A12

1903				Typo.
38	A12	½pi grn & car rose	16.00	1.40
39	A12	30pa violet & green	26.00	5.50
40	A12	1pi car rose & ultra	42.50	7.50
41	A12	2pi ultra & mar	90.00	18.00
42	A12	4pi ol grn & vio	62.50	27.50
43	A12	6pi ol brn & car	52.50	145.00
44	A12	9pi brn & car rose	200.00	275.00
45	A12	12pi org brn & blk	37.50	87.50
46	A12	18pi blk & brn	100.00	175.00
47	A12	45pi dk vio & ultra	250.00	600.00
		Nos. 38-47 (10)	802.00	1,342.

1904-07				Wmk. 3
48	A12	5pa bis & blk ('07)	1.25	2.00
49	A12	10pa org & grn ('07)	6.00	1.90
50	A12	½pi grn & car rose	12.00	1.60
51	A12	30pa redsh vio & grn	21.50	2.75
52	A12	1pi car rose & ultra	17.50	1.10
53	A12	2pi ultra & mar	20.00	2.00
54	A12	4pi ol grn & red vio	32.50	20.00
55	A12	6pi ol brn & grn	32.50	17.00
56	A12	9pi brn & car rose	52.50	9.75
57	A12	12pi org brn & blk	40.00	67.50
58	A12	18pi blk & brn	55.00	15.00
59	A12	45pi dk vio & ultra	120.00	175.00
		Nos. 48-59 (12)	410.75	315.60

King George V — A13

1912

61a	A13	10pa org yel & br grn ('15)	2.75	1.60
62	A13	½pi grn & car rose	2.90	.35
63	A13	30pa vio & grn	3.25	2.40
64	A13	1pi car & ultra	5.75	1.90
65	A13	2pi ultra & mar	8.50	2.25
66	A13	4pi ol grn & red vio	5.50	5.25
67	A13	6pi ol brn & grn	6.00	11.50
68	A13	9pi brn & car rose	42.50	28.00
69	A13	12pi org brn & blk	25.00	57.50
70	A13	18pi blk & brn	50.00	50.00
71	A13	45pi dl vio & ultra	130.00	170.00
		Nos. 61a-71 (11)	282.15	330.75

1921-23   Wmk. 4

72	A13	10pa org & grn	16.00	13.50
73	A13	10pa gray & yel	16.00	9.50
74	A13	30pa violet & grn	3.75	2.00
75	A13	30pa green	9.00	1.75
76	A13	1pi rose & ultra	26.00	45.00
77	A13	1pi violet & car	4.00	5.00
78	A13	1½pi org & blk	12.50	7.25
79	A13	2pi ultra & red vio	35.00	25.00
80	A13	2pi rose & ultra	16.00	27.50
81	A13	2¾pi ultra & red vio	11.00	12.00
82	A13	4pi ol grn & red vio	19.00	26.00
83	A13	6pi ol brn & grn	37.50	80.00
84	A13	9pi brn & car	47.50	95.00
85	A13	18pi black & brn	90.00	175.00
86	A13	45pi dl vio & ultra	275.00	325.00
		Nos. 72-86 (15)	618.25	849.50

Wmk. 3

87	A13	10sh grn & red, yel	425.00	900.00
88	A13	£1 vio & blk, red	1,400.	3,250.

Years of issue: Nos. 73, 75, 77-78, 80-81, 87-88, 1923; others, 1921.

A14

1924-28   Chalky Paper   Wmk. 4

89	A14	¼pi gray & brn org	2.10	.55
90	A14	½pi gray blk & blk	6.25	14.50
91	A14	½pi grn & dp grn ('25)	2.50	1.10
92	A14	¾pi grn & dp grn	4.25	1.10
93	A14	¾pi gray blk & blk ('25)	4.50	1.10
94	A14	1pi brn vio & org brn	2.40	2.10
95	A14	1½pi org & blk	3.50	14.50
96	A14	1½pi car ('25)	5.25	1.60
97	A14	2pi car & grn	4.25	21.00
98	A14	2pi org & blk ('25)	15.00	4.25
99	A14	2½pi ultra ('25)	9.00	1.90
100	A14	2¾pi ultra & dl vio	3.75	5.00
101	A14	4pi ap grn & vio	5.25	5.25
102	A14	4½pi blk & yel, emer	4.00	5.25
103	A14	6pi grn ol & grn	5.25	9.00
104	A14	9pi brn & dk vio	9.00	5.75
105	A14	12pi org brn & blk	14.50	65.00
106	A14	18pi blk & org	29.00	5.75
		Revenue cancel		1.00
107	A14	45pi gray vio & ultra	65.00	45.00
		Revenue cancel		1.50
108	A14	90pi grn & red, yel	125.00	270.00
		Revenue cancel		3.75
109	A14	£5 blk, yel ('28)	3,750.	8,000.
		On cover (overfranked)		275.00

	Revenue cancel		275.00

Wmk. 3

110	A14	£1 vio & blk, red	350.00	900.00
		Revenue cancel		12.50
		Nos. 89-108 (20)	319.75	479.70

Nos. 96 and 99 are on ordinary paper.

Silver Coin of Amathus A15

Philosopher Zeno A16

Map of Cyprus A17

Discovery of Body of St. Barnabas A18

Cloisters of Bella Paise Monastery A19

Badge of the Colony A20

Hospice of Umm Haram at Larnaca A21

Statue of Richard Coeur de Lion, London A22

St. Nicholas Cathedral, Famagusta A23

King George V A24

1928, Feb. 1   Engr.   Perf. 12   Wmk. 4

114	A15	¾pi dark violet	3.75	1.60
115	A16	1pi Prus bl & blk	4.00	2.00
116	A17	1½pi red	7.50	2.25
117	A18	2½pi ultramarine	4.75	2.75
118	A19	4pi dp red brown	9.50	9.50
119	A20	6pi dark blue	14.00	32.50
120	A21	9pi violet brown	11.00	17.50
121	A22	18pi dk brn & blk	30.00	35.00
122	A23	45pi dp blue & vio	52.50	62.50
123	A24	£1 brn & dp blue	275.00	400.00
		Nos. 114-123 (10)	412.00	565.60

50th year of Cyprus as a British colony.

Peristerona Church — A27

Soli Theater — A28

Kyrenia Castle and Harbor — A29

Kolossi Castle — A30

St. Sophia Cathedral A31

Bairakdar Mosque A32

Queen's Window, St. Hilarion Castle — A33

Buyuk Khan, Nicosia — A34

Forest Scene — A35

1934, Dec. 1   Engr.   Perf. 12½

125	A25	¼pi yel brn & ultra	1.40	1.10
		Never hinged	2.10	
a.		Vert. pair, imperf. between	52,500.	35,000.
126	A26	½pi green	1.90	1.25
		Never hinged	2.10	
a.		Vert. pair, imperf. between	18,000.	20,000.
127	A27	¾pi vio & blk	3.50	.45
		Never hinged	4.50	
a.		Vert. pair, imperf. between	52,500.	
128	A28	1pi brn & blk	3.00	2.50
		Never hinged	4.50	
a.		Vert. pair, imperf. between	26,000.	26,000.
b.		Horiz. pair, imperf. btwn.	19,000.	
129	A29	1½pi rose red	4.00	2.10
		Never hinged	6.00	
130	A30	2½pi dk ultra	5.25	2.40
		Never hinged	7.75	
131	A31	4½pi dk car & blk	5.25	5.00
		Never hinged	14.00	
132	A32	6pi blue & blk	12.50	20.00
		Never hinged	26.00	
133	A33	9pi dl vio & blk brn	20.00	8.50
		Never hinged	32.50	
134	A34	18pi ol grn & blk	55.00	50.00
		Never hinged	120.00	
135	A35	45pi blk & emer	120.00	85.00
		Never hinged	225.00	
		Nos. 125-135 (11)	231.80	178.30
		Set, never hinged	405.00	

Common Design Types pictured following the introduction.

Silver Jubilee Issue
Common Design Type

1935, May 6   Perf. 11x12

136	CD301	¾pi gray blk & ultra	4.25	1.50
137	CD301	1½pi car & dk bl	6.25	3.00
138	CD301	2½pi ultra & brn	5.25	1.90
139	CD301	9pi brn vio & ind	24.00	28.00
		Nos. 136-139 (4)	39.75	34.40
		Set, never hinged	60.00	

Coronation Issue
Common Design Type

1937, May 12   Perf. 11x11½

140	CD302	¾pi dark gray	1.00	1.00
141	CD302	1½pi dark car	1.25	2.50
142	CD302	2½pi deep ultra	1.50	3.00
		Nos. 140-142 (3)	3.75	6.50
		Set, never hinged	7.75	

Ruins of Vouni Palace — A36

Columns at Salamis — A37

Peristerona Church — A38

Soli Theater — A39

Kyrenia Castle and Harbor — A40

Kolossi Castle — A41

Map of Cyprus A42

Bairakdar Mosque A43

Citadel, Famagusta A44

Buyuk Khan A45

Forest Scene A46

King George VI A47

1938-44   Wmk. 4   Perf. 12½

143	A36	¼pi yel brn & ultra	.60	.60
144	A37	½pi green	.80	.50
145	A38	¾pi violet & blk	7.25	1.75
146	A39	1pi orange	.90	.40
a.		Perf. 13½x12½ ('44)	375.00	30.00
		Never hinged	575.00	
147	A40	1½pi rose car	3.25	2.00
147A	A40	1½pi lt vio ('43)	.90	.75
147B	A38	2pi car & blk	.90	.45
c.		Perf. 12½x13½ ('44)	2.00	12.50
		Never hinged	3.25	
148	A42	2½pi ultramarine	15.00	4.50
148A	A41	3pi dp ultra ('42)	1.25	.60
149	A42	4½pi gray	.90	.40
150	A43	6pi blue & blk	1.25	1.10
151	A44	9pi ol vio & blk	1.00	.80
152	A45	18pi ol grn & blk	5.00	1.75
153	A46	45pi blk & emer	16.00	5.00
154	A47	90pi blk & brt vio	21.00	8.00
155	A47	£1 ind & dl red	45.00	32.50
		Nos. 143-155 (16)	121.00	61.10
		Set, never hinged	275.00	

See Nos. 164-166.

Peace Issue
Common Design Type
1946, Oct. 21 Engr. Perf. 13½x14
156	CD303	1½pi purple	.45	.25
157	CD303	3pi deep blue	.45	.45

Silver Wedding Issue
Common Design Types
1948, Dec. 20 Photo. Perf. 14x14½
158	CD304	1½pi purple	1.00	.55

Engr.; Name Typo.
Perf. 11½x11
159	CD305	£1 dark blue	57.50	77.50

UPU Issue
Common Design Types
Perf. 13½, 11x11½
			Wmk. 4	
160	CD306	1½pi violet	.65	1.60
161	CD307	2pi deep carmine	1.75	1.60
162	CD308	3pi indigo	1.10	1.50
163	CD309	9pi rose violet	1.10	6.00
		Nos. 160-163 (4)	4.60	10.70

Types of 1938-43
1951, July 2 Engr. Perf. 12½
164	A37	½pi purple	3.75	.45
165	A40	1½pi deep green	6.25	1.25
166	A41	4pi deep ultra	6.75	1.40
		Nos. 164-166 (3)	16.75	3.40

Coronation Issue
Common Design Type
1953, June 2 Perf. 13½x13
167	CD312	1½pi brt grn & black	1.60	.75

Carobs
A48

Copper Pyrites
Mine
A49

Coin of Paphos
— A49a

St. Hilarion
Castle — A50

Queen Elizabeth II
and Cyprian Coin
Devices — A51

Designs: 3m, Grapes. 5m, Oranges. 15m, Troodos forest. 20m, Aphrodite beach. 30m, Kyrenia. 35m, Harvest in Mesaoria. 40m, Famagusta harbor. 100m, Hala Sultan Tekke. 250m, Kanakaria church. £1, Queen Elizabeth II and devices of Byzantium, Lusignan, Ottoman Empire and Venice.

Perf. 11½
1955, Aug. 1 Engr. Wmk. 4
168	A48	2m chocolate	.25	.50
169	A48	3m violet blue	.25	.25
170	A48	5m orange	1.00	.25
171	A49	10m gray grn & chocolate	1.25	.25
172	A49	15m indigo & olive	3.50	.50
173	A49	20m ultra & brown	1.25	.25
174	A49a	25m aquamarine	3.25	.70
175	A49	30m carmine & blk	3.00	.25
176	A49	35m aqua & org brn	1.25	.50
177	A49	40m brn & dk grn	2.00	.75

Perf. 13½
178	A50	50m red brn & aqua	2.10	.30
179	A50	100m bl green & mag	13.00	.60
180	A50	250m vio brn & dk blue gray	16.00	13.00

Perf. 11x11½
181	A51	500m lilac rose & grnsh gray	37.50	15.00
182	A51	£1 grnsh gray & brn red	30.00	52.50
		Revenue cancel		1.00
		Nos. 168-182 (15)	115.60	85.60

Republic

Nos. 168-182 Overprinted
in Dark Blue

1960, Aug. 16 Ovpt. 10x6½mm
183	A48	2m chocolate	.25	.75
184	A48	3m violet blue	.25	.25
185	A48	5m orange	.25	.25

Overprint 12½x11mm
186	A49	10m gray grn & choc	1.00	.25
187	A49	15m indigo & ol	3.25	.30
188	A49	20m ultra & brn	1.75	1.50
a.		Double overprint		12,000.
189	A49	25m aquamarine	1.75	1.75
190	A49	30m car & black	1.75	.30
a.		Double overprint		45,000.
191	A49	35m aqua & org	1.75	.70
192	A49	40m choc & dk grn	2.00	2.50

2-line overprint 2½mm apart
193	A50	50m red brown & aqua	2.00	.75
194	A50	100m bl grn & mag	9.00	2.50
195	A50	250m vio brn & dk blue gray	30.00	5.50

2-line overprint 22mm
apart

196	A51	500m lil rose & grnsh gray	45.00	27.00
197	A51	£1 grnsh gray & brn red	50.00	62.50
		Nos. 183-197 (15)	152.00	106.80

The overprint, in Greek and Turkish, reads "Republic of Cyprus."

Map of
Cyprus — A52

Wmk. 314
1960, Aug. 16 Engr. Perf. 11½
198	A52	10m brown & green	.25	.25
199	A52	30m blue & brown	.80	.70
200	A52	100m purple & black	2.40	2.25
		Nos. 198-200 (3)	3.45	3.20

Independence of Republic of Cyprus.

Europa Issue

Nineteen Doves
Flying as
One — CD4

Perf. 14x13½
1962, Mar. 19 Litho. Unwmk.
201	CD4	10m lilac	.30	.25
202	CD4	40m deep ultra	.90	.35
203	CD4	100m emerald	.90	.60
		Nos. 201-203 (3)	2.10	1.20

Admission of Cyprus to Council of Europe.

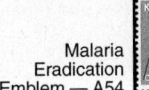

Malaria
Eradication
Emblem — A54

1962, May 14 Perf. 14x13½
204	A54	10m gray green & black	.25	.25
205	A54	30m red brown & black	.45	.25

WHO drive to eradicate malaria.

Iron Age
Jug — A55

St. Barnabas
Church,
Salamis — A56

Designs: 5m, Grapes. 10m, Head of Apollo. 15m, St. Sophia Church, Nicosia. 30m, Temple of Apollo. 35m, Head of Aphrodite. 40m, Skiing on Mt. Troodos. 50m, Ruins of Gymnasium, Salamis. 100m, Hala Sultan Tekke (sheep, Salt Lake Larnaca and tomb). 250m, Bella Paise Monastery. 500m, Cyprus mouflon. £1, St. Hilarion Castle.

Perf. 13½x14, 14x13½
1962, Sept. 17 Wmk. 344
206	A55	3m dk brn & sal	.25	.30
207	A55	5m dull green & red lilac	.25	.25
208	A55	10m dk slate grn & yel green	.25	.25
209	A55	15m dk brn & rose vio	.40	.25
210	A56	25m salmon & brn	.45	.25
211	A56	30m lt bl & dk bl	.25	.25
212	A56	35m dk bl & pale grn	.45	.25
213	A56	40m vio bl & dk bl	1.50	1.75
214	A56	50m olive bis & dk grn	.60	.25
215	A55	100m brn & yel brn	4.25	.30
216	A56	250m tan & black	11.00	2.40
217	A55	500m brown & olive	21.00	9.00
218	A56	£1 gray & green	22.50	30.00
		Nos. 206-218 (13)	63.15	45.50

Wmk. 344 is found in two positions: normal or inverted on vertical stamps, and reading up or down on horizontal stamps.
For overprints see Nos. 232-236, 265-268. For surcharge see No. 273.

Europa Issue, 1962
Common Design Type
Perf. 14x13½
1963, Jan. 28 Wmk. 344
Size: 36x20mm
219	CD5	10m ultra & black	3.75	.25
220	CD5	40m red & black	15.00	1.50
221	CD5	150m green & black	57.50	5.00
		Nos. 219-221 (3)	76.25	6.75

Cypriot Farm Girl — A57

75m, Statue of Demeter, goddess of agriculture.

1963, Mar. 21 Perf. 13½x14
222	A57	25m blk, ultra & ocher	.50	.45
223	A57	75m dk car, gray & blk	3.25	2.25

FAO "Freedom from Hunger" campaign.

Cub Scout and
Tents — A58

20m, Sea Scout. 150m, Boy Scout & mouflon.

1963, Aug. 21 Wmk. 344
224	A58	3m multicolored	.25	.25
225	A58	20m multicolored	.40	.25
226	A58	150m multicolored	2.00	2.50
a.		Souvenir sheet of 3	120.00	175.00
		Nos. 224-226 (3)	2.65	3.00

Boy Scout movement in Cyprus, 50th anniv. No. 226a contains 3 imperf. stamps similar to Nos. 224-226 with simulated perforations. Sold for 250m.

Red Cross
Nurse
A59

Children's Home,
Kyrenia
A60

Perf. 13½x14, 14x13½
1963, Sept. 9 Litho. Wmk. 344
227	A59	10m multicolored	.75	.25
228	A60	100m multicolored	3.50	4.25

Intl. Red Cross, cent.

Europa Issue

Stylized Links,
Symbolizing
Unity — CD6

1963, Nov. 4 Perf. 14x13½
229	CD6	20m multicolored	6.50	.70
230	CD6	30m multicolored	7.50	.70
231	CD6	150m multicolored	50.00	8.00
		Nos. 229-231 (3)	64.00	9.40

Nos. 208, 211, 213-215
Overprinted in
Ultramarine

1964, May 5　Perf. 13½x14, 14x13½
232 A55　10m dk sl grn & yel
　　　　　　grn　　　　　　　.25　.25
233 A55　30m lt blue & dk blue　.25　.25
234 A55　40m vio bl & dull bl　.40　.30
235 A55　50m ol bis & dk grn　.30　.35
236 A55　100m dk brn & brown　.40　.75
　　Nos. 232-236 (5)　　　1.60　1.90

Decision by the UN and its Security Council
to help restore the country to normality and to
seek a solution of its problems.

Clay Mask and
Soli
Theater — A62

Designs: 35m, Curium theater. 50m, Salamis theater. 100m, Performance of "Othello" in
front of Othello Tower.

1964, June 15　　　　Perf. 13½x14
237 A62　15m multicolored　.45　.25
238 A62　35m multicolored　.45　.25
239 A62　50m multicolored　.45　.25
240 A62　100m multicolored　1.75　2.25
　　Nos. 237-240 (4)　　　3.10　3.00

400th anniversary of Shakespeare's birth.

Boxers — A63

14th century B.C. art: 10m, Runners, vert.
75m, Chariot.

1964, July 6　Perf. 13½x14, 14x13½
241 A63　10m brn, bis & blk　.25　.25
242 A63　25m gray bl, bl & brn　.30　.25
243 A63　75m brick red, blk &
　　　　　　brn　　　　　　　.65　.80
a.　Souvenir sheet of 3　8.00　15.00
　　Nos. 241-243 (3)　　　1.20　1.30

18th Olympic Games, Tokyo, Oct. 10-25,
1964. No. 243a contains three imperf. stamps
similar to Nos. 241-243 with gray marginal
inscription. Sheet sold for 250m; the difference
between face value and selling price went for
the promotion of classical athletics in Cyprus.

Europa Issue

Symbolic Daisy — CD7

Perf. 13½x14
1964, Sept. 14　Litho.　Wmk. 344
244 CD7　20m bis brn & red
　　　　　　brn　　　　　　　2.25　.30
245 CD7　30m lt blue & dk blue　3.00　.30
246 CD7　150m grn & ol grn　27.00　4.50
　　Nos. 244-246 (3)　　　32.25　5.10

CEPT, 5th anniv. The 22 petals of the flower
symbolize the 22 members of the
organization.

Satyr
Drinking
Wine, 5th
Century
B.C.
Statuette
A65

Modern Winery
A66

Cypriot Wine Industry: 10m, Dionysus and
Acme drinking wine, 3rd century mosaic. 50m,
Commandaria wine, Knight Templar and
Kolossi Castle.

Perf. 14x13½, 13½x14
1964, Oct. 26　　　　Wmk. 344
247 A66　10m multicolored　.45　.25
248 A65　40m multicolored　.80　1.00
249 A65　50m multicolored　.80　.30
250 A66　100m multicolored　1.75　2.00
　　Nos. 247-250 (4)　　　3.80　3.55

Pres. John F.
Kennedy (1917-
1963)
A67

Perf. 14x13½
1965, Feb. 15　Litho.　Wmk. 344
251 A67　10m violet blue　.25　.25
252 A67　40m green　　　.35　.35
253 A67　100m rose claret　.45　.35
a.　Souvenir sheet of 3　4.00　7.00
　　Nos. 251-253 (3)　　　1.05　.95

No. 253a contains 3 imperf. stamps similar
to Nos. 251-253 with simulated perforations.
Sold for 250m, 100m going to charitable organizations in Cyprus.

Old Couple
A68

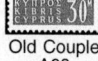

Mother and
Children by
A. Diamantis
A69

45m, Man with broken leg (accident
insurance).

1965, Apr. 12　　　　Perf. 13½x14
254 A68　30m dull green & tan　.25　.25
255 A68　45m dk vio bl, bl & gray　.40　.30

Perf. 13½x12½
256 A69　75m buff & red brown　1.25　1.75
　　Nos. 254-256 (3)　　　1.90　2.30

Introduction of Social Insurance Law.

ITU Emblem, Old
and New
Communication
Equipment — A70

1965, May 17　Litho.　Perf. 14x13½
257 A70　15m brn, yel & blk　.65　.25
258 A70　60m grn, lt grn & blk　7.00　3.25
259 A70　75m dk & lt bl & blk　8.00　4.75
　　Nos. 257-259 (3)　　　15.65　8.25

ITU, cent.

ICY
Emblem — A71

1965, May 17　　　　Wmk. 344
260 A71　50m multicolored　.90　.25
261 A71　100m multicolored　1.60　.75

International Cooperation Year.

Europa Issue

Leaves and
Fruit — CD8

Perf. 14x13½
1965, Sept. 27　Litho.　Wmk. 344
262 CD8　5m org, org brn &
　　　　　　black　　　　　　1.10　.25
263 CD8　45m lt grn, org brn
　　　　　　& black　　　　　5.25　1.75
264 CD8　150m gray, org brn &
　　　　　　black　　　　　　19.00　4.00
　　Nos. 262-264 (3)　　　25.35　6.00

Nos. 206, 208, 211 and
216 Overprinted in Dark
Blue

1966, Jan. 31　Perf. 13½x14, 14x13½
265 A55　3m dk brn & salmon　.35　.40
266 A55　10m dk sl grn & yel
　　　　　　green　　　　　　.40　.25
267 A56　30m lt bl & dk blue　.40　.25
268 A56　250m tan & black　1.35　2.25
　　Nos. 265-268 (4)　　　2.50　3.15

UN General Assembly's resolution to medi-
ate the dispute between Greeks and Turks on
Cyprus, Dec. 18, 1965.

St. Barnabas,
Ancient
Icon — A73

Chapel over Tomb of
St. Barnabas — A74

Bishop Anthemios of Constantine
Dreaming of St. Barnabas, Discovering
Tomb, etc. — A75

Design: 15m, Discovery of body of St. Barnabas (scene as in type A18).

Perf. 13x14, 14x13
1966, Apr. 25　Litho.　Wmk. 344
269 A73　15m multicolored　.25　.25
270 A74　25m multicolored　.25　.25
271 A73　100m multicolored　.65　2.00

Size: 110x91mm
Imperf
272 A75　250m multicolored　5.25　11.00
　　Nos. 269-272 (4)　　　6.40　13.50

1900th anniv. of the death of St. Barnabas.

No. 206 Surcharged with New Value
and Three Bars

Perf. 13½x14
1966, May 30　Litho.　Wmk. 344
273 A55　5m on 3m dk brn & sal　.45　.25

Gen. K. S.
Thimayya — A76

1966, June 6　　　　Perf. 14x13½
274 A76　50m tan & black　.35　.25

In memory of Gen. Kodendera Subayya
Thimayya (1906-1965), commander of the UN
Peace-keeping Force on Cyprus.

Europa Issue

Symbolic Sailboat — CD9

Perf. 13½x14
1966, Sept. 26　Litho.　Wmk. 344
275 CD9　20m multicolored　.50　.25
276 CD9　30m multicolored　.50　.25
277 CD9　150m multicolored　3.75　2.25
　　Nos. 275-277 (3)　　　4.75　2.75

Stavrovouni
Monastery
A78

St. Nicholas
Cathedral,
Famagusta
A79

Ingot Bearer, Bronze
Age — A80

Designs: 5m, St. James' Church, Tricomo,
vert. 10m, Zeno of Citium, marble bust, vert.
15m, Ship from 7th cent. BC vase, horiz. 20m,
Silver coin, 4th cent. BC (head of Hercules
with lion skin). 25m, Sleeping Eros (1st cent.
marble statue; horiz.). 35m, Hawks on 11th
cent. gold and enamel scepter from Curium.
40m, Marriage of David (7th cent. silver disc).
50m, Silver coin of Alexander the Great showing Hercules and Zeus, horiz. 100m, Bird
catching fish on 7th cent. BC jug. 500m, The
Rape of Ganymede (3rd cent. mosaic). £1,
Aphrodite (1st cent. marble statue).

Perf. 12x12½, 12½x12
1966, Nov. 21　Litho.　Wmk. 344
278 A78　3m bl, dl yel, grn &
　　　　　　black　　　　　　.40　.25
279 A78　5m dk bl, ol & blk　.25　.25
280 A78　10m olive & black　.25　.25

Perf. 14x13½, 13½x14
281 A79　15m org brn, blk &
　　　　　　red brn　　　　　.25　.25
282 A79　20m red brn & blk　1.25　1.25
283 A79　25m red brn, gray &
　　　　　　black　　　　　　.40　.25
284 A79　30m aqua, tan & blk　.60　.30
285 A79　35m dk car, yel &
　　　　　　blk　　　　　　　.60　.45
286 A79　40m brt bl, gray &
　　　　　　blk　　　　　　　.80　.45
287 A79　50m org brn, gray &
　　　　　　blk　　　　　　　1.10　.25
288 A79　100m gray, buff, blk &
　　　　　　red　　　　　　　4.00　.25

Perf. 13x14
289 A80　250m dull yel, grn &
　　　　　　blk　　　　　　　1.10　.50
290 A80　500m multicolored　3.00　.90
291 A80　£1 gray, lt gray &
　　　　　　black　　　　　　2.50　6.75
　　Nos. 278-291 (14)　　16.50　12.35

Electric Power Station,
Limassol — A81

Arghaka-Maghounda Dam — A82

Designs: 35m, Troodos Highway. 50m, Cyprus Hilton Hotel. 100m, Ships in Famagusta Harbor.

Perf. 14x13½, 13½x14
1967, Apr. 10   Litho.   Wmk. 344
292	A81	10m lt brn, dark brn & yellow	.25 .25
293	A82	15m lt bl, bl & grn	.25 .25
294	A82	35m dark gray, indigo & dark grn	.30 .25
295	A82	50m gray, olive & blue	.30 .25
296	A82	100m gray, ind & bl	.30 1.00
		Nos. 292-296 (5)	1.40 2.00

1st development program, 1962-66, completion.

Europa Issue, 1967
Common Design Type
1967, May 2   Perf. 13x14
Size: 21x37mm
297	CD10	20m yel grn & olive	.50 .25
298	CD10	30m rose vio & pur	.50 .25
299	CD10	150m pale brn & brn	3.25 2.00
		Nos. 297-299 (3)	4.25 2.50

Javelin Thrower, Map of Eastern Mediterranean and "Victory" — A83

Map of Eastern Mediterranean, Victory Statue and: 35m, Runner. 100m, High jumper. 250m, Amphora, map of Eastern Mediterranean and Victory statue.

Perf. 13½x13
1967, Sept. 4   Litho.   Wmk. 344
300	A83	15m multicolored	.25 .25
301	A83	35m multicolored	.25 .30
302	A83	100m multicolored	.60 1.00
Size: 97x77mm
Imperf
303	A83	250m multicolored	2.50 6.50
		Nos. 300-303 (4)	3.60 8.05

Cyprus-Crete-Salonika Athletic Games.

A84

ITY Emblem and: 10m, Marble Forum at Salamis, Church of St. Barnabas and Bellapais Abbey. 40m, Famagusta Beach. 50m, Plane and Nicosia International Airport. 100m, Youth Hostel and skiing on Mt. Troodos.

Perf. 13½x13
1967, Oct. 16   Litho.   Wmk. 344
304	A84	10m multicolored	.25 .25
305	A84	40m multicolored	.25 1.00
306	A84	50m multicolored	.25 .25
307	A84	100m multicolored	.25 1.00
		Nos. 304-307 (4)	1.00 2.50

Intl. Tourist Year, 1967.

St. Andrew, 6th Century Mosaic A85

Crucifixion, 15th Century A86

The Three Kings, 15th Century Fresco — A87

1967, Nov. 8   Perf. 13x13½
308	A85	25m multicolored	.25 .25
309	A86	50m multicolored	.25 .25
310	A87	75m multicolored	.25 .25
		Nos. 308-310 (3)	.75 .75

St. Andrew's Monastery, cent. (25m); Exhibition of Art of Cyprus, Paris, Nov. 7, 1967-Jan. 3, 1968 (50m); 20th anniv. of UNESCO (75m).

Human Rights Flame and Stars — A88

Designs: 90m, Human Rights flame and UN emblem. 250m, Scroll showing Article One of the Declaration of Human Rights.

Perf. 13½x14
1968, Mar. 18   Litho.   Wmk. 344
311	A88	50m multicolored	.25 .25
312	A88	90m multicolored	.25 .70
Size: 110x90mm
Imperf
313	A88	250m multicolored	1.25 4.75
		Nos. 311-313 (3)	1.75 5.70

Intl. Human Rights Year.

Europa Issue, 1968
Common Design Type
1968, Apr. 29   Perf. 14x13½
314	CD11	20m multicolored	.40 .25
315	CD11	30m dk car rose, gray brn & blk	.50 .25
316	CD11	150m multicolored	2.00 2.00
		Nos. 314-316 (3)	2.90 2.50

Boy Holding Milk, UNICEF Emblem A89

Aesculapius and WHO Emblem A90

Perf. 14x13½, 13½x14
1968, Sept. 2   Wmk. 344
317	A89	35m dk red, lt brn & blk	.25 .25
318	A90	50m gray ol, blk & grn	.25 .25

21st anniv. of UNICEF (No. 317), 20th anniv. of the WHO (No. 318).

Discus Thrower — A91

25m, Runners. 100m, Stadium, Mexico City.

Perf. 13½x14, 14x13½
1968, Oct. 24   Litho.
319	A91	10m multicolored	.25 .25
320	A91	25m vio blue & multi	.25 .25
321	A91	100m blue & multi, horiz.	.25 1.25
		Nos. 319-321 (3)	.75 1.75

19th Olympic Games, Mexico City, 10/12-27.

ILO Emblem — A92

Perf. 12x13½
1969, Mar. 3   Wmk. 344
322	A92	50m bl, vio bl & org brn	.25 .25
323	A92	90m gray, blk & org brn	.25 .55

ILO, 50th anniv.

Ancient Map of Cyprus — A93

Design: 50m, Medieval map of Cyprus.

Perf. 13½x13
1969, Apr. 7   Wmk. 344
324	A93	35m multicolored	.25 .30
325	A93	50m olive & multi	.25 .30

1st Intl. Congress of Cypriot Studies.

Europa Issue

"EUROPA" and "CEPT" — CD12

1969, Apr. 28   Litho.   Perf. 14x13½
326	CD12	20m bl, blk & gray	.55 .25
327	CD12	30m cop red, blk & ocher	.55 .25
328	CD12	150m grn, blk & yel	1.90 1.75
		Nos. 326-328 (3)	3.00 2.25

CEPT, 10th anniv.

European Roller — A95

Birds: 15m, Audouin's gull. 20m, Cyprus warbler. 30m, Eurasian jay, vert. 40m, Hoopoe, vert. 90m, Eleonora's falcon, vert.

Perf. 13½x12, 12x13½
1969, July 7   Wmk. 344
329	A95	5m multicolored	.45 .25
330	A95	15m multicolored	.60 .25
331	A95	20m multicolored	.60 .25
332	A95	30m multicolored	.65 .25
333	A95	40m multicolored	.75 .30
334	A95	90m multicolored	1.90 4.00
		Nos. 329-334 (6)	4.95 5.30

Nativity, Mural, 1192 — A96

Christmas: 45m, Nativity, mural in Church of Ayios Nicolaos tis Steghis, 14th century. 250m, Virgin and Child between Archangels Michael and Gabriel, mosaic in Church of Panayia Angeloktistos, 6th-7th centuries. Design of 20m is a mural in Church of Panayia tou Arakos, Lagoudhera.

1969, Nov. 24   Litho.   Perf. 13½x13
335	A96	20m multicolored	.25 .25
336	A96	45m multicolored	.25 .25
Size: 109x89mm
Imperf
337	A96	250m dk blue & multi	5.00 12.00
		Nos. 335-337 (3)	5.50 12.50

Mahatma Gandhi — A97

1970, Jan. 26   Perf. 14x13½
338	A97	25m multicolored	.35 .35
339	A97	75m multicolored	1.40 1.50

Birth cent. of Mohandas K. Gandhi (1869-1948), leader in India's struggle for independence.

Europa Issue

Interwoven Threads — CD13

1970, May 4   Litho.   Wmk. 344
340	CD13	20m brn, yel & org	.40 .25
341	CD13	30m brt bl, yel & org	.40 .25
342	CD13	150m brt rose lil, yel & orange	1.90 2.25
		Nos. 340-342 (3)	2.70 2.75

Landscape with Flowers — A99

Designs: Various landscapes with flowers.

Perf. 13x14
1970, Aug. 3   Litho.   Wmk. 344
343	A99	10m multicolored	.25 .25
344	A99	50m multicolored	.25 .25
345	A99	90m multicolored	.60 1.25
		Nos. 343-345 (3)	1.10 1.75

European Nature Conservation Year.

Education Year Emblem A100

Grapes and Partridge (Mosaic) A101

UN Emblem, Dove, Globe and Wheat — A102

Perf. 13x14, 14x13
1970, Sept. 7   Litho.   Wmk. 344
346	A100	5m tan, blk & brn	.25 .25
347	A101	15m multicolored	.25 .25
348	A102	75m multicolored	.25 .75
		Nos. 346-348 (3)	.75 1.25

Intl. Education Year (No. 346); 50th General Assembly of the Intl. Vine and Wine Office (No. 347); 25th anniv. of the UN (No. 348).

Virgin and Child, Mural from Podhithou Church, 16th Century A103

Perf. 14x14½
1970, Nov. 23   Photo.   Unwmk.
349	A103	Strip of three	.45 .55
a.		25m Left angel	.25 .25
b.		25m Virgin and Child	.25 .25
c.		25m Right angel	.25 .25
350	A103	75m multicolored	.35 .35

Christmas.
Design of No. 349 is same as No. 350, but divided by perforation into 3 stamps with 25m denomination each. Size of No. 349: 71x46mm; size of No. 350: 42x31mm.

Cotton Napkin A104

Festive Costume A105

Drinking Cup, 7th Cent. B.C. — A106

Mouflon from Mosaic Pavement, 3rd Century — A107

Cypriot Art: 5m, St. George, bas-relief on pine board, 19th cent. 20m, kneeling donors, painting, Church of St. Mamas, 1465. 25m, Mosaic head, 5th cent. A.D. 30m, Athena mounting horse-drawn chariot, terracotta figurine, 5th cent. B.C. 40m, Shepherd playing pipe, 14th cent. fresco. 50m, Woman's head, limestone, 3rd cent. B.C. 75m, Angel, mosaic, 6th cent. 90m, Mycenaean silver bowl, 14th cent. B.C. 500m, Woman and tree, decoration from amphora, 7th-6th cent. B.C. £1, God statue (horned helmet), from Enkomi, 12th cent. B.C., vert.

Perf. 12½x13½ (A104), 13x14 (A105), 14x13 (A106), 13½x13, 13x13½ (A107)

1971, Feb. 22		Litho.	Wmk. 344	
351	A104	3m blk, red & brn	.35	.50
352	A104	5m citron, red brn & black	.25	.25
353	A105	10m multicolored	.25	.30
354	A106	15m bister brn, blk & slate	.25	.25
355	A105	20m slate, red brn & black	.40	.50
356	A105	25m multicolored	.30	.25
357	A106	30m multicolored	.30	.25
358	A105	40m gray & multi	1.10	1.10
359	A105	50m bl, bis & blk	.90	.25
360	A105	75m cit & multi	2.00	1.25
361	A106	90m multicolored	2.25	2.50
362	A107	250m lt red brn, brn & black	1.75	.40
363	A107	500m tan & multi	.90	.50
364	A107	£1 multicolored	1.75	.75
		Nos. 351-364 (14)	12.75	9.05

For surcharges & overprints see Nos. 403, 424-427, 444, RA1.

Europa Issue

"Fraternity, Co-operation, Common Effort" — CD14

1971, May 3		Litho.	*Perf. 14x13½*	
		Size: 36½x23½mm		
365	CD14	1m lt bl, vio bl & blk	.30	.25
366	CD14	30m brt yel grn, grn & blk	.30	.25
367	CD14	150m yel, grn & blk	2.00	2.75
		Nos. 365-367 (3)	2.60	3.25

Archbishop Kyprianos, 1821 — A109

Paintings: 30m, Young Greek Taking Oath, horiz. 100m, Bishop Germanòs of Patras Declaring Greek Independence.

Perf. 13x13½, 13½x13

1971, July 9			Wmk. 344	
368	A109	15m multicolored	.25	.25
369	A109	30m multicolored	.25	.25
370	A109	100m multicolored	.25	.50
		Nos. 368-370 (3)	.75	1.00

150th anniversary of Greek independence.

Arch and Castle — A110

Tourist Publicity: 25m, Decorated gourd and sun over shore, vert. 60m, Mountain road, vert. 100m, Village church.

Perf. 13½x13, 13x13½

1971, Sept. 20				
371	A110	15m vio bl & multi	.25	.25
372	A110	25m ocher & multi	.25	.25
373	A110	60m green & multi	.25	.60
374	A110	100m blue & multi	.25	.65
		Nos. 371-374 (4)	1.00	1.75

Virgin and Child — A111

1971, Nov. 22			*Perf. 13½x14*	
375	A111	10m shown	.25	.35
376	A111	50m The Three Kings	.25	.35
377	A111	100m Shepherds	.25	.35
a.		Strip of 3, Nos. 375-377	.65	.95

Christmas.

Heart and Electrocardiogram A112

1972, Apr. 11			*Perf. 13½x12½*	
378	A112	15m bister & multi	.25	.25
379	A112	50m brown & multi	.25	.45

"Your heart is your health," World Health Day.

Europa Issue

Sparkles, Symbolic of Communications CD15

1972, May 22			*Perf. 12½x13½*	
380	CD15	20m brn, org & fawn	.60	.30
381	CD15	30m pur, org & lilac	.60	.45
382	CD15	150m dk ol, org & brt green	4.75	3.50
		Nos. 380-382 (3)	5.95	4.25

Archery, Olympic and Motion Emblems — A114

1972, July 24			*Perf. 14x13½*	
383	A114	10m shown	.25	.25
384	A114	40m Wrestling	.35	.25
385	A114	100m Soccer	.65	1.75
		Nos. 383-385 (3)	1.25	2.25

20th Olympic Games, Munich, 8/26-9/11.

Apollo, Silver Stater, Marion, 5th Century B.C. — A115

Silver Staters of Cyprus: 30m, Eagle's head, Paphos, c. 460 B.C. 40m, Pallas Athena, Lapithos, 388-387 B.C. 100m, Sphinx (obverse) and lotus flower (reverse), Idalion, c. 460 B.C.

1972, Sept. 25		Litho.	Wmk. 344	
		Coins in Silver		
386	A115	20m lt grnsh bl & blk	.25	.25
387	A115	30m pale bl & silver	.25	.25
388	A115	40m ol bister & black	.25	.30
389	A115	100m pale brn & blk	.75	1.00
		Nos. 386-389 (4)	1.50	1.80

Bathing the Christ Child — A116

Christmas: 20m, The Three Kings. 100m, Nativity. 250m, The Nativity, 1466, mural in Church of the Holy Cross, Platanistasa. The designs of the 10m, 20m, 100m, show details from mural shown entirely on 250m.

1972, Nov. 20		Litho.	*Perf. 13½x14*	
390	A116	10m multicolored	.25	.25
391	A116	20m multicolored	.25	.25
392	A116	100m multicolored	.25	.40
		Size: 110x90mm		
		Imperf		
393	A116	250m multicolored	1.75	4.25
		Nos. 390-393 (4)	2.50	5.15

Landscape, Troodos Mountains A117

100m, FIS Congress emblem and map of Cyprus.

Perf. 14x13½

1973, Mar. 13			Wmk. 344	
394	A117	20m blue & multi	.25	.25
395	A117	100m blue & multi	.25	.40

29th Meeting of the Intl. Ski Fed. (FIS), Nicosia, June 1973.

Europa Issue

Post Horn of Arrows — CD16

1973, May 7			*Size: 37x21mm*	
396	CD16	20m dl bl & multi	.50	.25
397	CD16	30m multicolored	.50	.35
398	CD16	150m multicolored	3.25	3.25
		Nos. 396-398 (3)	4.25	3.85

Archbishop's Palace, Nicosia — A119

Traditional Architecture: 30m, Konak, Nicosia, 18th century, vert. 50m, House, Gourri, 1850, vert. 100m, House, Rizokarpaso, 1772.

1973, July 23			*Perf. 14x13, 13x14*	
399	A119	20m multicolored	.25	.25
400	A119	30m multicolored	.25	.25
401	A119	50m multicolored	.25	.25
402	A119	100m multicolored	.25	.85
		Nos. 399-402 (4)	1.00	1.60

No. 354 Surcharged

1973, Sept. 24			*Perf. 14x13*	
403	A106	20m on 15m multi	.35	.35

Cyprus Scout Emblem A120

EEC Emblem A121

Cyprus Airways Emblem — A122

35m, FAO emblem. 100m, INTERPOL emblem.

Archangel Gabriel A123

Virgin and Child A124

1973, Sept. 24		*Perf. 13x14, 14x13*		
404	A120	10m brn ol, ol & buff	.30	.30
405	A121	25m pur, ol & multi	.30	.30
406	A121	35m grn, gray grn & citron	.30	.30
407	A122	50m black & blue	.30	.30
408	A120	100m brown & fawn	.40	.80
		Nos. 404-408 (5)	1.60	2.00

60th anniv. of Cyprus Boy Scout Organ.; association of Cyprus with EEC; 10th anniv. of FAO; 25th anniv. of Cyprus Airways; 50th anniv. of Intl. Criminal Police Organization.

Christmas: 100m, Panaya tou Araka Church, horiz. Designs of 10m, 20m are from wall paintings in Arakas Church.

1973, Nov. 26			Wmk. 344	
409	A123	10m multicolored	.25	.25
410	A124	20m multicolored	.25	.25
411	A124	100m multicolored	.25	.75
		Nos. 409-411 (3)	.75	1.25

Grapes — A125

1974, Mar. 18		Litho.	*Perf. 13x14*	
412	A125	25m shown	.25	.25
413	A125	50m Grapefruit	.25	.60
414	A125	50m Oranges	.25	.60
415	A125	50m Lemons	.25	.60
a.		Strip of 3, #413-415	1.00	2.00
		Nos. 412-415 (4)	1.00	2.05

Europa Issue

Rape of Europa — A126

Design shows a silver stater of Marion, second half of 5th century B.C.

1974, Apr. 29				
416	A126	10m org brn & multi	.60	.30
417	A126	40m multicolored	.60	.60
418	A126	150m dk car & multi	2.75	2.75
		Nos. 416-418 (3)	3.95	3.65

Solon, 3rd Century Mosaic — A127

Designs: 10m, Front page of "History of Cyprus," by Archimandrite Kyprianos, 1788, vert. 100m, St. Neophytos, mural, vert. 250m, Maps of Cyprus and Greek Islands, by Abraham Ortelius, 1584.

1974, July 22		Litho.	Wmk. 344	
419	A127	10m multicolored	.25	.25
420	A127	25m multicolored	.25	.25
421	A127	100m multicolored	.30	.85
		Size: 110x90mm		
		Imperf		
422	A127	250m multicolored	2.25	4.75
		Nos. 419-422 (4)	3.05	6.10

2nd Intl. Congress of Cypriot Studies, Nicosia, Sept. 15-21. No. 422 has simulated perforations.

Nos. 353, 358-359, 362
Overprinted

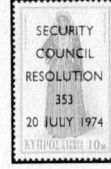

Perf. 13x14, 13½x13

1974, Oct. 14   **Litho.**
424	A105	10m multicolored	.25	.25
425	A105	40m multicolored	.35	.50
426	A105	50m multicolored	.35	.35
427	A107	250m multicolored	.70	2.75
		Nos. 424-427 (4)	1.65	3.85

UN Security Council Resolution No. 353 to end hostilities on Cyprus. Overprint is in 3 lines on No. 427.

Virgin and Child, 1466
A129

Adoration of the Kings, c. 1500
A130

Christmas: 100m, Flight into Egypt, mural, Monastery Church of Ayios Neophytos, c. 1500. (50m is from same church). Mural on 10m is in Church of Stavros tou Agiasmati.

Perf. 14x13, 13x14

1974, Dec. 2   **Wmk. 344**
429	A129	10m multicolored	.25	.25
430	A130	50m multicolored	.25	.25
431	A129	100m multicolored	.25	.45
		Nos. 429-431 (3)	.75	.95

Disabled Persons, Emblem
A131

Council of Europe Flag
A132

1975, Feb. 17   **Unwmk.**   *Perf. 14½*
432	A131	30m ocher & ultra	.25	.25
433	A132	100m multicolored	.55	1.25

8th European Meeting of the Intl. Society for the Rehabilitation of Disabled Persons (30m; design shows society's emblem); 25th anniv. of Council of Europe (100m).

First Mail Coach in Cyprus — A133

1975, Feb. 17
434	A133	20m multicolored	.25	.25
435	A133	50m ultra & multi	.80	.40

Centenary (in 1974) of UPU.

The Distaff, by Michael Kashalos — A134

Europa (Paintings): 30m, Still Life, by Christoforos Savva. 150m, Virgin and Child of Liopetri, by Georghios P. Georghiou.

Perf. 13½x14½

1975, Apr. 28   **Photo.**
436	A134	20m multicolored	.25	.25
437	A134	30m multicolored	.30	.25
438	A134	150m multicolored	.80	.60
a.		Strip of 3, #436-438	1.40	1.60

Red Cross Flag over Cyprus
A135

Nurse and Nurses Emblem
A136

Steatite Female Figure, c. 3000 B.C. — A137

Perf. 12½x13½, 13½x12½

1975, Aug. 4   **Litho.**   **Wmk. 344**
439	A135	25m blue green & red	.25	.25
440	A136	30m dp blue & lt grn	.25	.25
441	A137	75m multicolored	.25	.85
		Nos. 439-441 (3)	.75	1.35

Cyprus Red Cross, 25th anniv.; Intl. Nurses' Day 1975; IWY.

Submarine Cable
A138

International Telephone
A139

Perf. 12½x13½, 13½x12½

1975, Oct. 13   **Litho.**
442	A138	50m multicolored	.30	.25
443	A139	100m purple & org	.60	.85

Telecommunications achievements.

No. 351 Surcharged

1976, Jan. 5   *Perf. 12½x13½*
444	A104	10m on 3m multi	.45	.90

Vessel in Shape of Woman, 19th Century
A140

Composite Vessel, 2100-2000 B.C.
A141

Europa: 100m, Byzantine goblet, 15th cent.

Perf. 13x14

1976, May 3   **Wmk. 344**
445	A140	20m violet & multi	.35	.25
446	A141	60m gray & multi	.80	.70
447	A140	100m brown & multi	1.60	1.60
		Nos. 445-447 (3)	2.75	2.55

Self-help Housing — A142

Cyprus Airways Jet — A143

Designs: 25m, Women sewing in front of tents. 30m, Aforestation.

Terracotta Statue, 7th-6th Centuries B.C.
A144

Bronze Plate with Inscription, Idalion, 5th Century B.C.
A145

Designs: 10m, Limestone head of bearded man, 5th cent. B.C. 20m, Gold necklace, Lamboussa, 6th cent. A.D. 25m, Terracotta warrior on horseback, 7th cent. B.C. 30m, Limestone figure, priest of Aphrodite, 5th cent. B.C. 50m, Mycenaean crater, 13th cent. B.C. 60m, Limestone sarcophagus, Amathus, 550-500 B.C. 100m, Gold bracelet, Lamboussa, 6th cent. A.D. 250m, Silver dish, Lamboussa, 6th cent. A.D. 500m, Bronze stand, 12th cent. B.C. £1, Marble statue of Artemis, Larnaca, 4th cent. B.C.

Perf. 12x13½

1976, June 7   **Wmk. 344**

Size: 22x33mm
452	A144	5m brn & multi	.25	.75
453	A144	10m gray & multi	.25	.65

Size: 24x37mm, 37x24mm

Perf. 13x14, 14x13
454	A144	20m red & multi	.25	.60
455	A144	25m lt brn & blk	.25	.25
456	A144	30m green & multi	.25	.25
457	A145	40m bis gray & blk	.25	.60
458	A145	50m brn & multi	.25	.25
459	A145	60m dk brn & multi	.25	.25
460	A145	100m crim & multi	.40	.60

Size: 28x40mm

Perf. 13x12½
461	A144	250m dk bl & multi	.50	1.60
462	A144	500m yel & multi	1.00	1.75
463	A144	£1 slate & multi	2.10	2.50
		Nos. 452-463 (12)	6.00	10.05

George Washington — A146

1976, July 5   *Perf. 13x13½*
464	A146	100m multicolored	.50	.40

American Bicentennial.

Montreal Olympic Games Emblem
A147

Various Sports
A148

100m, like 60m, with different sports.

1976, July 5   **Unwmk.**   *Perf. 14*
465	A147	20m yel, blk & dk car	.25	.25
466	A148	60m ultra & multi	.25	.30
467	A148	100m lilac & multi	.35	.40
		Nos. 465-467 (3)	.85	.95

21st Olympic Games, Montreal, Canada, July 17-Aug. 1.

Children in Library
A149

Low-cost Housing Development
A150

Hands Shielding Eye — A151

Perf. 13½x14, 13x13½

1976, Sept. 27   **Litho.**   **Wmk. 344**
468	A149	40m black & multi	.25	.25
469	A150	50m multicolored	.25	.25
470	A151	80m ultra & multi	.35	.55
		Nos. 468-470 (3)	.85	1.05

Books for Children (40m); Habitat, UN Conference on Human Settlements, Vancouver, Canada, May 31-June 11 (50m); World Health Day: Foresight prevents blindness (80m).

Archangel Michael — A152

Christmas: 15m, Archangel Gabriel. 150m, Nativity. Icons in Ayios Neophytos Monastery, 16th century.

1976, Nov. 15   **Unwmk.**   *Perf. 12½*
471	A152	10m multicolored	.25	.25
472	A152	15m multicolored	.25	.25
473	A152	150m multicolored	.30	.80
		Nos. 471-473 (3)	.80	1.30

Landscape, by A. Diamantis
A154

Europa (Paintings): 60m, Trees and Meadow, by T. Kanthos. 120m, Harbor, by V. Ioannides.

Perf. 13½x13

1977, May 2   **Litho.**   **Unwmk.**
475	A154	20m multicolored	.30	.25
476	A154	60m multicolored	.70	.40
477	A154	120m multicolored	1.25	2.00
		Nos. 475-477 (3)	2.25	2.65

Cyprus No. 196 — A155

Perf. 13x13½

1977, June 13   **Litho.**   **Wmk. 344**
478	A155	120m multicolored	.40	.40

25th anniv. of reign of Queen Elizabeth II.

Silver Tetradrachm of Demetrios Poliorcetes
A156

Ancient Coins of Cyprus: 10m, Bronze coin of Emperor Trajan. 60m, Silver Tetradrachm of Ptolemy VIII. 100m, Gold octadrachm of Arsinoe II.

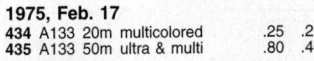

1977, June 13   **Unwmk.**   *Perf. 14*
479	A156	10m multicolored	.25	.25
480	A156	40m multicolored	.30	.25
481	A156	60m multicolored	.35	.30
482	A156	100m multicolored	.50	.85
		Nos. 479-482 (4)	1.40	1.65

Archbishop Makarios (1913-1977), Pres. of Cyprus — A157

20m, Archbishop in full vestments. 250m, Head.

Perf. 13x14
1977, Sept. 10   **Litho.**   **Unwmk.**
483	A157	20m multicolored	.25	.25
484	A157	60m multicolored	.25	.25
485	A157	250m multicolored	.60	1.00
		Nos. 483-485 (3)	1.10	1.50

Handicrafts A158

Sputnik over Earth A159

Designs: 40m, Map of the Mediterranean Sea. 60m, Gold medals and sports emblems.

Perf. 13½x12
1977, Oct. 17   **Wmk. 344**
486	A158	20m multicolored	.25	.25
487	A158	40m multicolored	.25	.25
488	A158	60m multicolored	.25	.25
489	A159	80m multicolored	.25	.75
		Nos. 486-489 (4)	1.00	1.50

Revitalization of handicrafts (20m); Man and the biosphere (40m); Gold medals won by secondary school students in France for long jump and 200 meter race (60m); 60th anniv. of Bolshevik Revolution (80m).

Nativity — A160

Christmas (Children's Drawings): 10m, Three Kings following the star. 150m, Flight into Egypt.

Perf. 14x13½
1977, Nov. 21   **Litho.**   **Unwmk.**
490	A160	10m multicolored	.25	.25
491	A160	40m multicolored	.25	.25
492	A160	150m multicolored	.25	.70
		Nos. 490-492 (3)	.75	1.20

Demetrios Lipertis (1866-1937) A161

150m, Vasilis Michaelides (1849-1917).

1978, Mar. 6   **Wmk. 344**   **Perf. 14x13**
493	A161	40m bister & olive	.25	.25
494	A161	150m gray, ver & blk	.35	.70

Cypriot poets.

Chrysorrhogiatissa Monastery — A162

Europa: 75m, Kolossi Castle. 125m, Municipal Library, Paphos.

Perf. 14½x13
1978, Apr. 24   **Litho.**   **Unwmk.**
495	A162	25m multicolored	.30	.25
496	A162	75m multicolored	.80	.40
497	A162	125m multicolored	1.40	1.40
		Nos. 495-497 (3)	2.50	2.05

Makarios as Archbishop 1950-1977 — A163

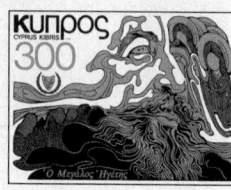

"The Great Leader" A164

Archbishop Makarios: 25m, Exiled, Seychelles, 1956-1957. 50m, President of Cyprus, 1960-1977. 75m, Soldier of Christ. 100m, Freedom fighter.

Perf. 14x14½
1978, Aug. 3   **Litho.**   **Unwmk.**
498	A163	15m multicolored	.25	.25
499	A163	25m multicolored	.25	.25
500	A163	50m multicolored	.25	.25
501	A163	75m multicolored	.25	.35
502	A163	100m multicolored	.25	.35
a.		Strip of 5, #498-502	1.25	1.50

Size: 110x80mm
Imperf
503	A164	300m multicolored	2.00	2.50
		Nos. 498-503 (6)	3.25	3.95

Archbishop Makarios, President of Cyprus.

Blood Cells with Low Hemoglobin A165

Bust of Aristotle A166

Heads and Human Rights Emblem — A167

Wilbur and Orville Wright, Flyer I — A168

Perf. 13x14, 14x13
1978, Oct. 23   **Unwmk.**   **Litho.**
504	A165	15m multicolored	.25	.25
505	A166	35m multicolored	.25	.25
506	A167	75m black	.25	.35
507	A168	125m multicolored	.35	.70
		Nos. 504-507 (4)	1.10	1.55

Anemia prevention (15m); 2300th death anniv. of Aristotle (35m); 30th anniv. of Universal Declaration of Human Rights (75m); 75th anniv. of first powered flight (125m).

Kiti Icon Stand — A169

Christmas: 35m, Athienou icon stand. 150m, Omodhos icon stand.

1978, Dec. 4   **Perf. 14x14½**
508	A169	15m multicolored	.25	.25
509	A169	35m multicolored	.25	.25
510	A169	150m multicolored	.40	.70
		Nos. 508-510 (3)	.90	1.20

Venus Statue from Soli — A170

125m, Birth of Venus, by Botticelli (detail).

1979, Mar. 12   **Litho.**   *Perf. 14x13½*
511	A170	75m multicolored	.30	.25
512	A170	125m multicolored	.50	.40

Mail Coach, Envelope and Truck — A171

Europa: 75m, Old telephone, dish antenna and satellite. 125m, Steamship, jet and envelopes.

1979, Apr. 30   **Litho.**   *Perf. 14x13½*
513	A171	25m multicolored	.55	.25
514	A171	75m multicolored	.95	.40
515	A171	125m multicolored	2.75	1.25
		Nos. 513-515 (3)	4.25	1.90

Peacock Wrasse — A172

Designs: 50m, Black partridge, vert. 75m, Cyprus cedar, vert. 125m, Mule.

Perf. 13½x12½, 12½x13½
1979, June 25   **Litho.**
516	A172	25m multicolored	.25	.25
517	A172	50m multicolored	.40	.55
518	A172	75m multicolored	.40	.35
519	A172	125m multicolored	.60	1.10
		Nos. 516-519 (4)	1.65	2.25

Children Holding Globe, UNESCO Emblem A173

Dove, Magnifying Glass, Album A174

Lord Kitchener, Map of Cyprus — A175

Smiling Child, IYC Emblem — A176

Soccer A177

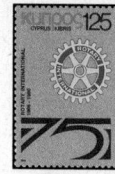

Rotary Emblem A178

1979, Oct. 1   **Litho.**   *Perf. 12½*
520	A173	15m multicolored	.25	.25
521	A174	25m multicolored	.25	.25
522	A175	50m multicolored	.25	.25
523	A176	75m multicolored	.25	.25
524	A177	100m multicolored	.25	.35
525	A178	125m multicolored	.25	.70
		Nos. 520-525 (6)	1.50	2.05

Intl. Bureau of Education, Geneva, 50th anniv.; Cyprus Philatelic Society, 20th anniv.; Horatio Herbert Kitchener's survey of Cyprus, cent.; IYC; European Soccer Assoc., 25th anniv.; Rotary Club of Cyprus, 75th anniv.

Jesus, Icon, 12th Century — A179

Christmas (Icons): 35m, Nativity, 16th cent. 150m, Virgin and Child, 12th cent.

Perf. 13½x14, 13x14
1979, Nov. 5   **Litho.**
Sizes: 24x37mm; 27x40mm (35m)
526	A179	15m multicolored	.25	.25
527	A179	35m multicolored	.25	.25
528	A179	150m multicolored	.25	.45
		Nos. 526-528 (3)	.75	.95

Cyprus No. 1, Nicosia Cancel — A180

Cyprus Stamp Centenary: 125m, #3, Kyrenia cancel. 175m, #6, Larnaca cancel. 500m, #1-6.

1980, Mar. 17   **Litho.**   *Perf. 14x13*
529	A180	40m multicolored	.25	.25
530	A180	125m multicolored	.25	.25
531	A180	175m multicolored	.50	.50

Size: 105x85mm
Imperf
532	A180	500m multicolored	1.40	1.40
		Nos. 529-532 (4)	2.40	2.40

Holy Cross, St. Barnabas Church, Agiasmati — A181

Europa: 125m, Zeno of Citium, Ny Carsberg Glyptothek, Copenhagen.

1980, Apr. 28   *Perf. 12½*
533	A181	40m multicolored	.25	.25
534	A181	125m multicolored	.45	.30

Sailing, Moscow '80 Emblem — A182

1980, June 23   **Litho.**   *Perf. 14x13*
535	A182	40m shown	.25	.25
536	A182	125m Swimming	.25	.25
537	A182	200m Gymnast	.40	.40
		Nos. 535-537 (3)	.90	.90

22nd Summer Olympic Games, Moscow, July 19-Aug. 3.

Gold Necklace A183

Clay Amphora A184

Archaeological finds on Cyprus, 12th cent. B.C. to 3rd cent. A.D. 15m, 40m, 150m, 500m, horiz.

Perf. 13½x14, 14x13½
1980, Sept. 15   **Litho.**   **Wmk. 344**
538	A183	10m shown	.30	.90
539	A184	15m Bronze cow	.30	.90
540	A184	25m shown	.30	.30
541	A184	40m Lion, gold ring	.40	.65
542	A184	50m Bronze cauldron	.40	.25
543	A184	75m Stele	1.10	1.40
544	A184	100m Clay jug	.80	.25

545	A184	125m	Warrior, terracotta bust	.80	*.90*
546	A184	150m	Lions attacking bull	1.25	.25
547	A184	175m	Faience and enamel vase	.90	*1.25*
548	A184	200m	Warrior god, bronze	.90	.40
549	A184	500m	Stone bowl	.90	*1.50*
550	A183	£1	Ivory plaque	1.10	*1.25*
551	A183	£2	Leda and the swan, mosaic	1.90	*2.25*
			Nos. 538-551 (14)	11.35	12.45

For surcharges see Nos. 584, 600-611.

Cyprus Flag
A185

Archbishop
Makarios
A187

Treaty Signing
Establishing
Republic, 20th
Anniversary
A186

1980, Oct. 1   Perf. 13½x14, 14x13

552	A185	40m	multicolored	.25	.25
553	A186	125m	multicolored	.25	.25
554	A187	175m	multicolored	.35	.35
			Nos. 552-554 (3)	.85	.85

Dove and
Woman — A188

Perf. 14x13

1980, Nov. 29   Litho.   Wmk. 344

555	A188	40m	shown	.25	.25
556	A188	125m	Dove and man	.40	.40
a.			Pair, #555-556	.65	.65

Intl. Palestinian Solidarity Day.

Pulpit, Ayios Lazaros
Church, Larnaca — A189

Christmas: 25m, Pulpit, Tripiotis Church, Nicosia. 100m, Iconostatis (Holy Door), Panayia Church, Paralimni.

1980, Nov. 29   Perf. 13½x14

557	A189	25m	multicolored	.25	.25

Size: 24x37mm

558	A189	100m	multicolored	.25	.25

Size: 21x37mm

559	A189	125m	multicolored	.25	.25
			Nos. 557-559 (3)	.75	.75

Europa Issue

Folk Dance — A190

1981, May 4   Photo.   Perf. 14

560	A190	40m	shown	*.30*	.25
561	A190	175m	Dance, diff.	*.65*	*.50*

Self-portrait, by
Leonardo Da
Vinci — A191

The Last
Supper, by
Da Vinci
A192

Perf. 13½x14, 12½x13½

1981, June 15   Wmk. 344   Litho.

562	A191	50m	shown	.35	.30
563	A192	125m	shown	.75	.50
564	A191	175m	Lace pattern, Milan Cathedral	.90	.70
			Nos. 562-564 (3)	2.00	1.50

Da Vinci's visit to Cyprus, 500th anniv.

Ophrys Kotschyi — A193

Orchids: 50m, Orchis puntulata. 75m, Ophrys argolica elegantis. 150m, Epipactis veratrifolia.

1981, July 6   Perf. 13½x14

565	A193	25m	shown	.30	.30
566	A193	50m	multi	.55	.55
567	A193	75m	multi	.90	.90
568	A193	150m	multi	1.50	1.50
a.			Block of 4, #565-568	3.25	3.25
			Nos. 565-568 (4)	3.25	3.25

Prince Charles
and Lady Diana,
St. Paul's
Cathedral
A194

Perf. 14x13

1981, Sept. 28   Wmk. 344

569	A194	200m	multicolored	.70	*.80*

Royal wedding.

Heinrich von
Stephan (1831-
1897), UPU
Founder
A195

World Food Day
(Oct. 16) — A196

Intl. Year of the
Disabled
A197

European
Campaign for
Urban
Renaissance
A198

1981, Sept. 28

570	A195	25m	multicolored	.25	.25
571	A196	40m	multicolored	.25	.25
572	A197	125m	multicolored	.30	.30
573	A198	150m	multicolored	.35	.35
			Nos. 570-573 (4)	1.15	1.15

Our Lady of the
Angels,
Transfiguration
Church,
Palekhori — A199

Christmas (Frescoes): 100m, Christ, Madonna of Arakas Church, Lagoudera, vert. 125m, Baptism of Christ, Our Lady of Assinou Church, Nikitari.

1981, Nov. 16   Perf. 12½

574	A199	25m	multicolored	.25	.25
575	A199	100m	multicolored	.60	.35
576	A199	125m	multicolored	.70	.45
			Nos. 574-576 (3)	1.55	1.05

Bathing Aphrodite,
Sculpture, Soloi, 250
B.C. — A200

Design: 175m, Aphrodite Emerging from the Water, by Titian, 16th cent.

Perf. 13½x14

1982, Apr. 12   Litho.   Wmk. 344

577	A200	125m	multicolored	.70	.50
578	A200	175m	multicolored	.90	.70

Europa Issue

Liberation by
Emperor
Nicephorus II
Phocas, 965
A.D. — A201

175m, Conversion of Sergius Paulus, 45 A.D.

Perf. 12½

1982, May 3   Photo.   Unwmk.

579	A201	40m	shown	*.45*	.25
580	A201	175m	multi	*.80*	1.75

Mosaic
Chrismon — A202

Cultural Heritage: 125m, King of Palaepaphos (High Priest of Aphrodite), sculpture, vert. 225m, Theseus Struggling with the Minotaur, mosaic.

1982, July 5   Litho.   Wmk. 344

581	A202	50m	multicolored	.25	.25
582	A202	125m	multicolored	.55	.55
583	A202	225m	multicolored	1.00	1.00
			Nos. 581-583 (3)	1.80	1.80

No. 543 Surcharged

1982, Sept. 6   Litho.   Perf. 13½x14

584	A184	100m	on 75m multi	.55	.55

Scouting Year — A203

Perf. 13½x12½, 12½x13½

1982, Nov. 8   Wmk. 344

585	A203	100m	Emblem, horiz.	.40	.40
586	A203	125m	Baden-Powell	.50	.50
587	A203	175m	Camp site, horiz.	.60	*.90*
			Nos. 585-587 (3)	1.50	1.80

A203a

Christmas — A204

Designs: 25m, 250m, Christ Giving Holy Communion (bread, 25m: wine, 250m) to the Apostles, St. Neophytos Monastery Church, Paphos. 100m, Chalice, Church of St. Savvas, Nicosia.

Perf. 12½, 13½x14 (100m)

1982, Dec. 6

588	A203a	25m	multicolored	.25	.25
589	A204	100m	multicolored	.40	.35
590	A203a	250m	multicolored	.85	*1.50*
			Nos. 588-590 (3)	1.50	2.10

A204a

50m, Cyprus Forest Industries, Ltd. 125m, Mosaic, 3rd cent. 150m, Dancers. 175m, Royal Exhibition Building, Melbourne.

1983, Mar. 14   Perf. 14x13½

591	A204a	50m	multi	.25	.25
592	A204a	125m	multi	.25	.25
593	A204a	150m	multi	.25	.35
594	A204a	175m	multi	.25	*.45*
			Nos. 591-594 (4)	1.00	1.30

Commonwealth Day.

Europa — A205

50m, Cyprosyllabic script funerary stele, 6th cent. B.C. 200m, Copper ore, Enkomi ingot, 1400-1250 BC, bronze jug, 2nd cent.

1983, May 3   Photo.   Perf. 14½x14

595	A205	50m	multicolored	*.25*	.25
596	A205	200m	multicolored	*.75*	1.75

Local
Butterflies — A206

60m, Pararge aegeria. 130m, Aricia medon. 250m, Glaucopsyche paphos.

Wmk. 344

1983, June 28   Litho.   Perf. 12½

597	A206	60m	multi	.35	.30
598	A206	130m	multi	.75	.50
599	A206	250m	multi	1.40	*2.00*
			Nos. 597-599 (3)	2.50	2.80

Nos. 538-549 Surcharged

Perf. 13½x14, 14x13½

1983, Oct. 3   Litho.   Wmk. 344

600	A183	1c	on 10m multi	.25	*.90*
601	A184	2c	on 15m multi	.25	*1.10*
602	A184	3c	on 25m multi	.25	*.90*
603	A184	4c	on 40m multi	.25	*.90*
604	A184	5c	on 50m multi	.40	.40
605	A184	6c	on 75m multi	.40	.40
606	A184	10c	on 100m multi	.55	.50
607	A184	13c	on 125m multi	.65	.60
608	A184	15c	on 150m multi	.65	.70
609	A184	20c	on 200m multi	.70	*.80*
610	A184	25c	on 175m multi	1.10	*1.25*
611	A184	50c	on 500m multi	1.90	*2.25*
			Nos. 600-611 (12)	7.35	11.20

Electricity
Authority of
Cyprus, 30th
Anniv.
A207

World
Communications Year
A208

Intl. Maritime
Org., 25th
Anniv.
A209

Universal
Declaration
of Human
Rights, 35th
Anniv.
A210

Nicos
Kazantzakis,
100th Birth
Anniv.
A211

Archbishop
Makarios III,
70th Birth
Anniv.
A212

1983, Oct. 27   Litho.   Perf. 13½x14

612	A207	3c multicolored	.25	.25
613	A208	6c multicolored	.25	.25
614	A209	13c multicolored	.25	.25
615	A210	15c multicolored	.25	.25
616	A211	20c multicolored	.30	.75
617	A212	25c multicolored	.30	.80
		Nos. 612-617 (6)	1.60	2.55

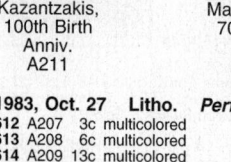
Christmas — A213

Designs: 4c, Belfry, St. Lazaros Church,
Larnaca. 13c, Belfry, St. Varvara Church,
Kaimakli, Nicosia. 20c, Belfry, St. Ioannis
Church, Larnaca.

1983, Dec. 12   Perf. 12½x14

618	A213	4c multicolored	.25	.25
619	A213	13c multicolored	.60	.60
620	A213	20c multicolored	.85	1.40
		Nos. 618-620 (3)	1.70	2.25

Waterside Cafe
at the Marina,
Larnaca — A214

19th Century engravings. Size of 6c:
41x27mm; 75c, 110x85mm.

Perf. 14½x14 (6c), 14, Imperf. (75c)
1984, Mar. 6

621	A214	6c shown	.25	.25
622	A214	20c Bazaar, Larnaca	.40	.75
623	A214	30c East Gate, Nicosia	.65	1.40
624	A214	75c St. Lazarus Church Interior, Larnaca	1.50	2.10
		Nos. 621-624 (4)	2.80	4.50

Europa (1959-
1984)
A215

1984, Apr. 30   Wmk. 344   Perf. 12½

625	A215	6c multicolored	.40	.25
626	A215	15c multicolored	.90	1.75

1984 Summer
Olympics
A216

1984, June 18   Litho.   Perf. 14

627	A216	3c Running	.25	.25
628	A216	4c Olympic column	.25	.25
629	A216	13c Swimming	.50	.75
630	A216	20c Gymnastics	.70	1.40
		Nos. 627-630 (4)	1.70	2.65

Turkish Invasion,
10th
Anniv. — A217

15c, Prisoners, barbed wire. 20c, Map.

1984, July 20   Litho.   Perf. 14x13½

631	A217	15c multicolored	.45	.45
632	A217	20c multicolored	.60	.60

Cyprus
Philatelic
Society, 25th
Anniv.
A218

Cyprus Soccer
Assoc., 50th Anniv.
A219

George
Papanicolaou
(1883-1962),
Cancer
Researcher
A220

Medieval Map
A221

1984, Oct. 15   Wmk. 344   Perf. 12½

633	A218	6c multicolored	.25	.25
634	A219	10c multicolored	.40	.40
635	A220	15c multicolored	.70	.70
636	A221	25c multicolored	1.25	2.00
		Nos. 633-636 (4)	2.60	3.35

Intl. Symposium of Cyprus Cartography and
First Intl. Symposium on Medieval Paleogra-
phy (25c).

Christmas — A222

4c, St. Mark. 13c, Gospel page (St. Mark).
20c, St. Luke.

1984, Nov. 26   Litho.   Perf. 12½

637	A222	4c multicolored	.30	.30
638	A222	13c multicolored	.90	.90
639	A222	20c multicolored	1.40	2.00
		Nos. 637-639 (3)	2.60	3.20

Landscapes
A223

1c, Autumn at Platania. 2c, Ayia Napa
Monastery. 3c, Phine Village. 4c, Kykko
Monastery. 5c, Beach at Makronissos. 6c, Village Street, Omodhos, vert. 10c, Sea view.
13c, Water sports. 15c, Beach at Protaras.
20c, Forestry, vert. 25c, Sunrise at Protaras,
vert. 30c, Village houses, Pera Orinis. 50c,
Apollo Hylates Sanctuary. £1, Troodos Mountain, vert. £5, Personification of Autumn,
Dionyssos House, vert.

Perf. 15x14, 14x15
1985, Mar. 18   Litho.

640	A223	1c multicolored	.25	.65
641	A223	2c multicolored	.25	.65
642	A223	3c multicolored	.25	.65

643	A223	4c multicolored	.25	.35
644	A223	5c multicolored	.25	.25
645	A223	6c multicolored	.25	.25
646	A223	10c multicolored	.30	.30
647	A223	13c multicolored	.40	.30
648	A223	15c multicolored	.45	.35
649	A223	20c multicolored	.50	.50
650	A223	25c multicolored	.80	.90
651	A223	30c multicolored	1.10	1.10
652	A223	50c multicolored	2.25	2.75
653	A223	£1 multicolored	5.00	3.00
654	A223	£5 multicolored	18.00	16.00
		Nos. 640-654 (15)	30.30	28.00

For surcharges see Nos. 684-685, 712.

Europa — A224

6c, Ceramic figures playing the double flute,
lyre and tambourine, 7th-6th cent. B.C. 15c,
Cypriot violin, lute, flute, the Fourth Women's
Dance from the Cyprus Suite.

1985, May 6   Litho.   Perf. 12½

655	A224	6c multicolored	.40	.40
656	A224	15c multicolored	1.10	2.00

Republic of
Cyprus,
25th Anniv.
A225

UN 40th
Anniv.
A229

Natl. Liberation
Movement, 30th
Anniv. — A226

Intl. Youth
Year — A227

Solon
Michaelides
(1905-1979),
Conductor,
European Music
Year — A228

Perf. 14½ (#657), 14½x14, 15 (#661)
1985, Sept. 23   Litho.

657	A225	4c multicolored	.25	.25
658	A226	6c multicolored	.25	.25
659	A227	13c multicolored	.55	1.10
660	A228	15c multicolored	.90	1.25
661	A229	20c multicolored	.50	1.75
		Nos. 657-661 (5)	2.45	4.60

Christmas — A230

Murals of the St. Ioannis Lampadistis
Monastery, Kalopanyiotis: 4c, Virgin Mary's
Visit to Elizabeth. 13c, The Nativity. 20c, The
Candlemas, Church of Our Lady of Assinous,
Nikitari.

1985, Nov. 18   Litho.   Perf. 12½

662	A230	4c multicolored	.25	.25
663	A230	13c multicolored	.50	.50
664	A230	20c multicolored	.85	7.50
		Nos. 662-664 (3)	1.60	8.25

Hellenistic
Platinum
Spoon — A231

Designs: 20c, Ionian helmet, foot of a sculpture. 25c, Union of Eros and Intellect personi-
fied, abstract. 30c, Statue profile.

1986, Feb. 17   Perf. 15x14

665	A231	15c multicolored	.70	.70
666	A231	20c multicolored	.95	.95
667	A231	25c multicolored	1.20	1.20
668	A231	30c multicolored	1.50	1.50
a.		Souv. sheet of 4, #665-668	15.00	17.00
		Nos. 665-668 (4)	4.35	4.35

Construction of the New Archaeological
Museum, Nicosia. Department of Antiquities,
50th anniv. No. 668a sold for £1.

Europa Issue

Mouflon, Cedar
Trees — A232

17c, Flamingos, Larnaca Salt Lake.

1986, Apr. 28   Litho.   Perf. 14x13

669	A232	7c shown	.40	.35
670	A232	17c multicolored	1.50	2.50

Seashells — A233

1986, July 1   Perf. 14x13½

671	A233	5c Chlamys pesfelis	.35	.35
672	A233	7c Charonia variegata	.40	.40
673	A233	18c Murex brandaris	1.00	1.00
674	A233	25c Cypraea spurca	1.30	2.00
		Nos. 671-674 (4)	3.05	3.75

Overseas
Cypriots
Year — A234

Halley's
Comet — A235

Anniversaries and events: No. 677, Comet
tail, Edmond Halley.

Perf. 13½x13
1986, Oct. 13   Litho.   Wmk. 344

675	A234	15c multicolored	1.10	.75
676	A235	18c shown	1.60	2.00
677	A235	18c multicolored	1.60	2.00
a.		Pair, #676-677	3.25	4.00
		Nos. 675-677 (3)	4.30	4.75

No. 677a has continuous design.

Road
Safety — A236

5c, Pedestrian crossing. 7c, Helmet, motorcycle controls. 18c, Seatbelt, rearview mirror.

1986, Nov. 10   Perf. 14x13

678	A236	5c multicolored	.60	.50
679	A236	7c multicolored	1.00	.50
680	A236	18c multicolored	2.40	3.00
		Nos. 678-680 (3)	4.00	4.00

Intl. Peace Year, Christmas — A237

Nativity frescoes (details): 5c, Church of Panayia tou Araka. 15c, Church of Panayia tou Moutoulla. 17c, Church of St. Nicholaos tis Steyis.

1986, Nov. 24   **Perf. 13½x14**

681	A237	5c multicolored	.40	.30
682	A237	15c multicolored	1.25	.60
683	A237	17c multicolored	1.60	2.00
		Nos. 681-683 (3)	3.25	2.90

Nos. 645 and 647 Surcharged
Perf. 14x15, 15x14

1986, Oct. 13   **Litho.**   **Wmk. 344**

684	A223	7c on 6c multi	.90	.50
685	A223	18c on 13c multi	1.75	1.00

Miniature Sheet

Troodos Churches on UNESCO World Heritage List — A238

Churches and frescoes: a, Assinou, Nikitari. b, Moutoulla, Moutoullas. c, Podithou, Galata. d, Ayios Ioannis Lampadistis, Kalopanayiotis. e, Timios Stavros, Pelentri. f, Stavros Ayiasmati, Platanistasa. g, Archangelos Pedoula, Pedoulas. h, Ayios Nicolaos tis Steyis, Kakopetria. i, Araka, Lagoudera.

Perf. 12½

1987, Apr. 22   **Photo.**   **Unwmk.**

686	A238	Sheet of 9	10.00	10.00
a.-i.		15c any single	1.00	1.00

Europa Issue

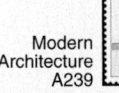

Modern Architecture A239

7c, Central Bank of Cyprus. 18c, Cyprus Communications Authority.

Perf. 14x13½

1987, May 11   **Litho.**   **Wmk. 344**

687	A239	7c multicolored	.50	.40
688	A239	18c multicolored	1.00	1.75

Ships Named Kyrenia — A240

2c, The Kyrenia, Kyrenia Castle. 3c, Kyrenia II, Perama Shipyard. 5c, Kyrenia II, Paphos. 17c, Kyrenia II, NY Harbor.

1987, Oct. 3

689	A240	2c multicolored	.45	.30
690	A240	3c multicolored	.60	.75
691	A240	5c multicolored	.80	.50
692	A240	17c multicolored	1.75	1.25
		Nos. 689-692 (4)	3.60	2.80

Blood Donation Coordinating Committee, 10th Anniv. — A241

European Campaign for Countryside A242

TROODOS '87 — A243

Perf. 14x13½

1987, Nov. 2   **Litho.**   **Wmk. 344**

693	A241	7c multicolored	.60	.55
694	A242	15c multicolored	1.40	1.25
695	A243	20c multicolored	2.00	2.75
		Nos. 693-695 (3)	4.00	4.55

Christmas A244

1987, Nov. 30   **Perf. 14**

696	A244	5c Babe in a manger	.35	.35
697	A244	15c Ornament	1.25	1.25
698	A244	17c Fruit bowl	1.50	2.00
		Nos. 696-698 (3)	3.10	3.60

Cyprus Customs Union in Cooperation with the EEC — A245

15c, Natl. and EEC flags. 18c, Maps.

Perf. 13x13½

1988, Jan. 11   **Wmk. 344**

699	A245	15c multicolored	1.25	1.60
700	A245	18c multicolored	1.60	1.60

A246

Europa (Communication and transportation): No. 701, Electronic mail (Intelpost). No. 702, Cellular telephone system. No. 703, Cyprus Airways, technology vs. ecology (jet, 3 flamingos). No. 704, Cyprus Airways (jet, 4 flamingos).

1988, May 9   **Perf. 14x14½**

701	A246	7c multicolored	.65	1.00
702	A246	7c multicolored	.65	1.00
a.		Pair, #701-702	1.30	2.00
703	A246	18c multicolored	2.25	3.00
704	A246	18c multicolored	2.25	3.00
a.		Pair, #703-704	6.50	6.00
		Nos. 701-704 (4)	5.80	8.00

1988 Summer Olympics, Seoul — A247

Unwmk.

1988, June 27   **Photo.**   **Perf. 12**
Granite Paper

705	A247	5c Sailing	.40	.30
706	A247	7c Track	.45	.45
707	A247	10c Marksmanship	.50	.70
708	A247	20c Judo	1.10	1.50
		Nos. 705-708 (4)	2.45	2.95

Non-Aligned Foreign Minister's Conference A248

Designs: 10c, Natl. coat of arms. 50c, Jawaharlal Nehru, Tito, Gamal Abdel Nasser and Makarios III (1913-77).

No. 643 Srchd.

1988, Sept. 5   **Litho.**   **Wmk. 344**

709	A248	1c shown	.25	.25
710	A248	10c multicolored	.65	.65
711	A248	50c multicolored	3.00	3.00
		Nos. 709-711 (3)	3.90	3.90

1988, Oct. 3   **Litho.**   **Perf. 15x14**

712	A223	15c on 4c multi	1.75	1.40

Christmas — A249

5c, Candlemas. 15c, Madonna and child. 17c, Adoration of the Magi.

Perf. 13½x14

1988, Nov. 28   **Litho.**   **Wmk. 344**

713	A249	5c multicolored	.40	.25
714	A249	15c multicolored	.85	.30
715	A249	17c multicolored	1.30	1.75
		Nos. 713-715 (3)	2.55	2.30

A250

1988, Dec. 10

716	A250	25c lt ultra & int blue	1.40	1.40

UN Declaration of Human Rights, 40th anniv.

3rd Games of Small European States, Nicosia — A251

Perf. 13½

1989, Apr. 10   **Litho.**   **Unwmk.**

717	A251	1c Discus	.40	.30
718	A251	5c Javelin	.40	.30
719	A251	15c Wrestling	.90	.50
720	A251	18c Running	1.10	1.10

Size: 110x80mm
Imperf

721	A251	£1 Nike, laurel, bird	7.50	7.50
		Nos. 717-721 (5)	10.30	9.70

Various Children's Games — A252

Perf. 13x13½

1989, May 8   **Litho.**   **Unwmk.**

722	A252	7c multi (5 boys)	.85	.75
723	A252	7c multi (6 boys)	.85	.75
a.		Pair, #722-723	1.90	1.90
724	A252	18c multi (6 boys)	1.25	1.10
725	A252	18c multi (5 boys)	1.25	1.10
a.		Pair, #724-725	2.75	2.75
		Nos. 722-725 (4)	4.20	3.70

Europa.

French Revolution, Bicent. A253

Perf. 11½

1989, July 7   **Litho.**   **Unwmk.**
Granite Paper

726	A253	18c multicolored	1.40	1.00

A254   A255

1989, Sept. 4   **Perf. 13½**

727	A254	15c multicolored	.65	.65
728	A255	30c multicolored	1.40	1.40

15c for Interparliamentary Union, cent. 30c for 9th Non-Aligned Summit Conf., Belgrade.

Apiculture — A256

3c, Honeycomb and bees. 10c, Gathering nectar on pink flower. 15c, Gathering nectar on white flower. 18c, Queen, worker bees.

1989, Oct. 15   **Perf. 13½x14**

729	A256	3c multicolored	.50	.30
730	A256	10c multicolored	.90	.60
731	A256	15c multicolored	1.10	.60
732	A256	18c multicolored	1.25	1.75
		Nos. 729-732 (4)	3.75	3.25

Annivs. & Events — A257

Designs: 3c, Armenian earthquake. 5c, Cyprus Philatelic Society. 7c, European Cancer Year. 17c, World Food Day.

1989, Nov. 13

733	A257	3c multicolored	.35	1.10
734	A257	5c multicolored	.50	.30
735	A257	7c multicolored	.85	1.40
736	A257	17c multicolored	1.25	1.40
		Nos. 733-736 (4)	2.95	4.20

A258   A259

Mosaics, 3rd-5th Cent. — A260

Details: 1c, Winter, from *The Four Seasons*, House of Dionysos. 2c, Personification of Crete, from *Theseus Slaying the Minotaur*, Villa of Theseus. 3c, Centaur and Maenad, from *The Dionysiac Procession*, House of Aion, vert. 4c, *Poseidon and Amymone*, House of Dionysos. 5c, Leda, from *Leda and the Swan*, House of Aion. 7c, Apollon, from *Apollo and Marsyas*, House of Aion. 10c, Hermes and Dionysos, from *Hermes Presenting Dionysos to Tropheus*, House of Aion. 15c, Cassiopeia, from *Cassiopeia and the Nereids*, House of Aion. 18c, Orpheus Playing the Lyre, House of Orpheus. 20c, Nymphs preparing bath, from *Hermes Presenting Dionysos to Tropheus*, vert. 25c, Amazon holding double ax and reins, House of Orpheus, vert. 40c, Doris, one of 3 Nereids in *Cassiopeia and the Nereids*, vert. 50c, Hercules and the lion, from *The First Labor of Hercules*, House of Orpheus. £1, *Apollon and Daphne*, House of Dionysos. £3, Cupid hunting, Villa of Theseus.

Perf. 13, 13x13½ (2c, 4c, 18c, 40c),
13½x13 (3c, 10c, 20c, 25c)
1989, Dec. 29
737	A258	1c multicolored	.50	1.50
738	A259	2c multicolored	.50	1.50
739	A259	3c multicolored	.65	1.50
740	A259	4c multicolored	.85	1.50
741	A258	5c multicolored	.85	.30
742	A258	7c multicolored	1.10	.35
743	A259	10c multicolored	1.30	.40
744	A258	15c multicolored	2.10	.65
745	A258	18c multicolored	2.10	.70
746	A259	20c multicolored	2.50	.90
747	A259	25c multicolored	2.50	.90
748	A259	40c multicolored	3.75	2.00

Perf. 13½x14
749	A260	50c multicolored	2.75	2.00
750	A260	£1 multicolored	6.25	3.75
751	A260	£3 multicolored	13.00	14.00
		Nos. 737-751 (15)	40.70	31.95

UNESCO World
Literacy
Year — A261

83rd
Interparliamentary
Conference,
Nicosia — A262

Lions Europa
Forum — A263

Anniversaries & events.

1990, Apr. 3   *Perf. 14x13½*
752	A261	15c multicolored	.80	.80
753	A262	17c multicolored	.95	.95
754	A263	18c multicolored	1.25	1.25
		Nos. 752-754 (3)	3.00	3.00

Europa — A264

Post Offices: 7c, Paphos. 18c, Limassol City
Center.

1990, May 10   Litho.   *Perf. 13x13½*
755	A264	7c multicolored	1.00	.45
756	A264	18c multicolored	1.75	2.50

European Year of Tourism — A265

Designs: 5c, Hotel and Catering Institute,
25th anniv. 7c, Holy Church of St. Lazarus,
1100th anniv. 15c, Female silhouette, butterflies. 18c, Male silhouette, birds.

1990, July 9   *Perf. 14*
757	A265	5c multicolored	.60	.60
758	A265	7c multicolored	.75	.75
759	A265	15c multicolored	2.10	1.75
760	A265	18c multicolored	2.40	3.75
		Nos. 757-760 (4)	5.85	6.85

Republic of Cyprus,
30th Anniv. — A266

1990, Sept. 29   Photo.   *Perf. 11½*
761	A266	15c Sun	.75	.60
762	A266	17c shown	.95	.70
763	A266	18c Fish	1.25	.80
764	A266	40c Birds, flowers	3.00	5.00

Size: 90x90mm
Imperf
765	A266	£1 Stylized bird	6.50	6.50
		Nos. 761-765 (5)	12.45	13.60

Flowers — A267

2c, Chionodoxa lochiae. 3c, Pancrayium
maritimum. 5c, Paeonia mascula. 7c, Cyclamen cyprium. 15c, Tulipa cypria. 18c, Crocus
cyprius.

1990, Nov. 5   Litho.   *Perf. 13½x13*
766	A267	2c multicolored	.40	1.50
767	A267	3c multicolored	.60	1.50
768	A267	5c multicolored	.85	.65
769	A267	7c multicolored	1.10	1.00
770	A267	15c multicolored	2.25	2.25
771	A267	18c multicolored	2.40	3.50
		Nos. 766-771 (6)	7.60	10.40

Christmas — A268

1990, Dec. 3   *Perf. 13½x14*
772	A268	5c Nativity	.90	.30
773	A268	15c Virgin and Child	1.90	.45
774	A268	17c Nativity, diff.	2.25	3.00
		Nos. 772-774 (3)	5.05	3.75

Mosaics From
Kanakaria
Church — A269

1991, Mar. 28   Photo.   *Perf. 12*
Granite Paper
775	A269	5c Archangel	.80	.25
776	A269	15c Christ Child	.85	.75
777	A269	17c St. James	1.60	1.75
778	A269	18c St. Matthew	1.75	2.25
		Nos. 775-778 (4)	5.00	5.00

Europa — A270

1991, May 6   Litho.   *Perf. 13x13½*
779	A270	7c Spacecraft Ulysses	.75	.40
780	A270	18c Spacecraft Giotto	1.60	2.25

Oenanthe Cypriaca
(Cyprus
Wheatear) — A271

1991, July 4   Litho.   *Perf. 13½*
781	A271	5c Juvenile bird	1.10	.50
782	A271	7c Autumn plumage	1.25	.50
783	A271	15c Male bird	1.50	.75
784	A271	30c Female bird	2.40	3.75
		Nos. 781-784 (4)	6.25	5.50

UN High
Commissioner for
Refugees, 40th
Anniv. — A272

1991, Oct. 7   Litho.   *Perf. 14x13½*
785	A272	5c shown	.35	.25
786	A272	15c Legs	1.40	.75
787	A272	18c Faces	1.75	2.25
		Nos. 785-787 (3)	3.50	3.25

Christmas — A273

1991, Nov. 25   Litho.   *Perf. 13½*
788	A273	5c Nativity scene	.35	.25
789	A273	15c St. Basil	.85	.85
790	A273	17c Baptism of Jesus	1.10	1.50
a.		Strip of 3, #788-790	2.75	2.75

Strips of 3 are from sheets of 9.

A274

1992, Apr. 3   Litho.   *Perf. 12*
Granite Paper
791	A274	10c Swimming	1.10	.60
792	A274	20c Long jump	1.50	1.00
793	A274	30c Running	2.25	2.25
794	A274	35c Discus	2.50	2.50
		Nos. 791-794 (4)	7.35	6.35

1992 Summer Olympics, Barcelona.

Expo '92,
Seville — A275

10th Youth Under
16 European
Soccer
Tournament
A276

Opening of
University of
Cyprus — A277

1992, Apr. 20   Litho.   *Perf. 14*
795	A275	20c multicolored	2.00	.95
796	A276	25c multicolored	2.10	1.25
797	A277	30c multicolored	2.10	2.75
		Nos. 795-797 (3)	6.20	4.95

Discovery of
America, 500th
Anniv. — A278

No. 798, Map. No. 799, Embarkation at
Palos. No. 800, Three ships. No. 801,
Columbus.

1992, May 29   Litho.   *Perf. 13x13½*
798	A278	10c multicolored	1.00	.90
799	A278	10c multicolored	1.00	.90
a.		Pair, #798-799	2.25	2.25
800	A278	30c multicolored	1.50	1.25
801	A278	30c multicolored	1.50	1.25
a.		Pair, #800-801	3.25	3.25
		Nos. 798-801 (4)	5.00	4.30

Europa.

Reptiles — A279

Designs: 7c, Chamaeleo chamaeleon. 10c,
Lacerta laevis troodica. 15c, Mauremys cas-
pica. 20c, Coluber cypriensis.

1992, Sept. 14   Litho.   *Perf. 14x13½*
802	A279	7c multicolored	1.00	.40
803	A279	10c multicolored	1.10	.65
804	A279	15c multicolored	1.60	1.10
805	A279	20c multicolored	2.10	2.50
		Nos. 802-805 (4)	5.80	4.65

Intl. Maritime
and Shipping
Conference
A280

Unwmk.
1992, Nov. 9   Litho.   *Perf. 14*
806	A280	50c multicolored	4.00	4.00

Christmas — A281

Church wall paintings: 7c, "Virgin Mary
Greeting Elizabeth," Church of Timios Stavros,
Pelendri. 15c, "The Virgin and Child," Church
of Panayia tou Araka. 20c, "Holy Mother Odigitria," Church of Ayios Nicolaos tis Steyis.

1992, Nov. 9   *Perf. 13½x14*
807	A281	7c multicolored	.65	.35
808	A281	15c multicolored	1.00	.75
809	A281	20c multicolored	1.60	2.25
		Nos. 807-809 (3)	3.25	3.35

A282

1993, Feb. 15   Litho.   *Perf. 14*
810	A282	10c multicolored	1.00	.80

Pancyprian Gymnasium, cent.

A283

Europa: 10c, Bronze sculpture, Motherhood,
by N. Dymiotis (1930-1990). 30c, Applique,
Motherhood, by Savva (1924-1968), horiz.

1993, Apr. 3   *Perf. 13½x14, 14x13½*
811	A283	10c multicolored	.90	.65
812	A283	30c multicolored	1.60	2.00

13th European Cup
for Women Athletes
A284

Scouting in
Cyprus, 80th
Anniv.
A285

Water Skiing
Moufflon
Encouragement
Cup — A286

Archbishop
Makarios III, 80th
Anniv. of
Birth — A287

Perf. 13½x14, 14x13½

1993, May 24   **Litho.**
813	A284	7c multicolored	.50	.40
814	A285	10c multicolored	.70	.55
815	A286	20c multicolored	1.25	1.25
a.		Inscribed "MUFFLON"	13.00	
816	A287	25c multicolored	1.75	2.25
		Nos. 813-816 (4)	4.20	4.45

Fish — A288

1993, Sept. 6   **Litho.**   *Perf. 14x13½*
817	A288	7c Holocentrus ruber	.60	.35
818	A288	15c Scorpaena scrofa	.90	.70
819	A288	20c Serranus scriba	1.00	1.00
820	A288	30c Balistes capriscus	2.00	2.40
		Nos. 817-820 (4)	4.50	4.45

Maritime Cyprus — A289

1993, Oct. 4   *Perf. 14*
821	A289	25c multicolored	2.25	2.25

12th Commonwealth Summit Conference A290

1993, Oct. 4   *Perf. 14x13½*
822	A290	35c red brown & tan	2.10	2.10
823	A290	40c olive brown & tan	2.75	2.75

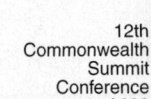

Christmas — A291

7c, Carved wooden cross, Stavrovouni Monastery. 20c, Crucifixion, cross from Lefkara Church. 25c, Nativity, cross from Pedoulas Church.

1993, Nov. 22   **Litho.**   *Perf. 13½x14*
824	A291	7c multicolored	.40	.30
825	A291	20c multicolored	.95	.95

Perf. 14x13½
826	A291	25c multi, horiz.	1.40	2.00
		Nos. 824-826 (3)	2.75	3.25

Copper Industry — A292

Europa: 10c, Early smelting of copper. 30c, Map, boat, copper ingot.

1994, Mar. 1   **Litho.**   *Perf. 13x13½*
827	A292	10c multicolored	.70	.70
828	A292	30c multicolored	1.25	1.75

Persons with Special Needs A293

Intl. Olympic Committee, Cent. A294

World Gymnasiade, Nicosia A295

Intl. Year of the Family A296

1994, May 9   **Litho.**   *Perf. 13*
829	A293	7c multicolored	.55	.35
830	A294	15c multicolored	1.00	.65
831	A295	20c multicolored	1.25	1.25
832	A296	25c multicolored	1.50	2.00
		Nos. 829-832 (4)	4.30	4.25

Turkish Invasion and Occupation of Cyprus, 20th Anniv. — A297

1994, June 27   **Litho.**   *Perf. 14*
833	A297	10c Human rights	.80	.40
834	A297	50c Cultural heritage	3.25	3.25

Trees — A298

7c, Pinus nigra. 15c, Cedrus libani. 20c, Quercus alnifolia. 30c, Arbutus andrachne.

1994, Oct. 10   **Litho.**   *Perf. 13½*
835	A298	7c multicolored	.70	.40
836	A298	15c multicolored	1.10	.80
837	A298	20c multicolored	1.25	1.25
838	A298	30c multicolored	1.90	2.50
		Nos. 835-838 (4)	4.95	4.95

ICAO, 50th Anniv. — A299

1994, Nov. 21   **Litho.**   *Perf. 14*
839	A299	30c multicolored	3.25	3.25

Christmas — A300

Designs: 7c, Virgin Mary (Vlahernitissa). 20c, Nativity. 25c, Archangel Michael.

1994, Nov. 21   *Perf. 13½*
840	A300	7c multicolored	.80	.50
841	A300	20c multicolored	1.90	1.00
842	A300	25c multicolored	2.50	3.00
		Nos. 840-842 (3)	5.20	4.50

Traditional Costumes — A301

Costumes: 1c, Female, Phapos. 2c, Bridal, Karpess. 3c, Female, Phapos, diff. 5c, Female, Messaoria. 7c, Bridegroom's. 10c, Shepherd's, Messaoria. 15c, Festive female, Nicosia. 20c, Festive female, Karpass. 25c, Female, Mountain-Pitsillia. 30c, Festive female, Karpass, diff. 35c, Rural male. 40c, Plain festive male, Messaoria. 50c, Urban male. £1, Urban festive female, Sarka.

1994, Dec. 27   **Litho.**   *Perf. 13½x13*
843	A301	1c multicolored	.40	.40
844	A301	2c multicolored	.60	.60
845	A301	3c multicolored	.65	.65
846	A301	5c multicolored	.80	.80

847	A301	7c multicolored	.85	.85
848	A301	10c multicolored	1.25	1.25
849	A301	15c multicolored	2.10	2.10
850	A301	20c multicolored	2.10	2.10
851	A301	25c multicolored	2.40	2.40
852	A301	30c multicolored	2.40	2.40
853	A301	35c multicolored	2.40	2.40
854	A301	40c multicolored	2.75	2.75
855	A301	50c multicolored	3.50	3.50
856	A301	£1 multicolored	6.00	6.00
a.		Inscribed "1998"	6.00	6.00
		Nos. 843-856 (14)	28.20	28.20

Third Intl. Congress of Cypriot Studies — A302

Excavations: 20c, Hearth room, Ashlar building, Paliotaverna. 30c, Hall, Agios Demetrios area, Kalavasos. £1, Old Nicosia Archbishopric building, 18th cent.

1995, Feb. 27   *Perf. 13½*
859	A302	20c multicolored	1.25	1.25
860	A302	30c multicolored	1.90	1.90

Size: 107x71mm
Imperf
861	A302	£1 multicolored	6.25	6.25
		Nos. 859-861 (3)	9.40	9.40

A303

Liberation Monument, Nicosia: a, People walking left. b, Statue of Liberty, prisoners leaving prison. c, People walking right.

1995, Mar. 31   **Litho.**   *Perf. 13x14*
862		Strip of 3	4.25	4.25
a.-c.		A303 20c any single	1.35	1.35

No. 862 is a continuous design.
Formation of EOKA (Natl. Organization of Cypriot Struggle), 40th anniv.

Europa — A304

10c, Concentration camp prisoners, dove, rainbow, map of Europe. 30c, Prisoner, dove.

1995, May 8   **Litho.**   *Perf. 13½*
863	A304	10c multicolored	1.00	.75
864	A304	30c multicolored	2.00	3.00

Liberation of the concentration camps, 50th anniv.

Health — A305

7c, Proper nutrition, exercise. 10c, Fight against AIDS. 15c, Fight against illegal drugs. 20c, Stop smoking campaign.

1995, June 26   **Litho.**   *Perf. 13½*
865	A305	7c multi, vert.	.35	.30
866	A305	10c multi	.75	.75
867	A305	15c multi	.80	.80
868	A305	20c multi, vert.	1.10	1.50
		Nos. 865-868 (4)	3.00	3.35

European Cultural Month — A306

25c, Map of Europe, building.

1995, Sept. 18   **Litho.**   *Perf. 13x13½*
869	A306	20c shown	.85	.85
870	A306	25c multicolored	1.10	1.25

Souvenir Sheet

Europhilex '95 — A307

Designs: a, Dove carrying letter, stars. b, Stars, exhibition emblem.

1995, Sept. 18   **Litho.**   *Perf. 14*
871	A307	Sheet of 2	8.75	8.75
a.-b.		50c any single	4.00	4.00

A limited number were surcharged £5 on each stamp and sold at "Europhilex '95" on Oct. 27 and 28, 1995.

UN, 50th Anniv. — A308

Volleyball, Cent. — A309

European Conservation Year — A310

World Clay Target Shooting Championships A311

Perf. 13x13½, 13½x13

1995, Oct. 24   **Litho.**
872	A308	10c multicolored	.65	.65
873	A309	15c multicolored	1.00	.75
874	A310	20c multicolored	1.40	1.10
875	A311	25c multicolored	1.60	2.25
		Nos. 872-875 (4)	4.65	4.75

Christmas — A312

Various reliquaries, Kykko Monastery.

1995, Nov. 27   **Litho.**   *Perf. 13½x13*
876	A312	7c multicolored	.60	.45
877	A312	20c multicolored	1.40	1.10
878	A312	25c multicolored	1.75	2.25
		Nos. 876-878 (3)	3.75	3.80

A313

A314

A315

Anniversaries and
Events — A316

1996, Jan. 4   Litho.   Perf. 13½x13
879 A313 10c multicolored   .90 .65
880 A314 20c multicolored   1.50 1.10
881 A315 35c multicolored   2.25 2.25
882 A316 40c multicolored   2.25 2.75
   Nos. 879-882 (4)   6.90 6.75

Pancyprian Organization of Large Families,
25th anniv. (No. 879). Motion pictures, cent.
(NO. 880). UNICEF, 50th anniv. (No. 881).
13th Conf. of Commonwealth Speakers and
Presiding Officers (No. 882).

Portraits of Women
A317   A318

1996, Apr. 8   Litho.   Perf. 14
883 A317 10c multicolored   1.10 .50
884 A318 30c multicolored   2.40 2.75

       Europa.

1996 Summer
Olympics,
Atlanta — A319

1996, June 10   Litho.   Perf. 13
885 A319 10c High jump   .90 .35
886 A319 20c Javelin   1.25 .70
887 A319 25c Wrestling   1.75 1.10
888 A319 30c Swimming   2.10 2.50
   Nos. 885-888 (4)   6.00 4.65

Mills of
Cyprus — A320

1996, Sept. 23   Litho.   Perf. 13
889 A320 10c Watermill   .95 .70
890 A320 15c Olivemill   1.40 1.00
891 A320 20c Windmill   1.50 1.40
892 A320 25c Handmill   2.00 2.00
   Nos. 889-892 (4)   5.85 5.10

Icons, Religious
Landmarks — A321

Designs: No. 893, Icon of Our Lady of
Iberia, Moscow. No. 894, Holy Monastery of
Stavrovouni, Cyprus. No. 895, Icon of St.
Nicholas, Cyprus. No. 896, Iveron Mother of
God Resurrection Gate, Moscow.

1996, Nov. 13   Litho.   Perf. 11½
893 A321 30c multicolored   2.10 2.10
894 A321 30c multicolored   2.10 2.10
895 A321 30c multicolored   2.10 2.10
896 A321 30c multicolored   2.10 2.10
a. Block of 4, #893-896   9.00 9.00

See Russia No. 6356.

Christmas
A322

Paintings from Church of the Virgin of Asi-
nou: 7c, Detail from Nativity. 20c, Virgin Mary
between Archangels Gabriel and Michael.
25c, Christ bestowing blessings, vert.

1996, Dec. 2   Perf. 13x13½, 13½x13
897 A322 7c multicolored   .90 .50
898 A322 20c multicolored   2.00 1.25
899 A322 25c multicolored   2.40 2.75
   Nos. 897-899 (3)   5.30 4.50

Easter — A323

1997, Mar. 24   Litho.   Perf. 13x13½
900 A323 15c The Last Supper   1.25 .75
901 A323 25c The Crucifixion   1.75 1.75

A324

1997, Mar. 24   Perf. 13½x13
902 A324 30c multicolored   4.25 3.75
European Men's Clubs Basketball Cup finals.

A325

Europa (Stories and Legends): 30c, Man in
red cape fighting Death, eagle above.

1997, May 5   Litho.   Perf. 13½x13
903 A325 15c shown   1.10 .50
904 A325 30c multicolored   2.10 2.50

Insects — A326

10c, Oedipoda miniata. 15c, Acherontia
atropos. 25c, Daphnis nerii. 35c, Ascalaphus
macaronius.

1997, June 30   Litho.   Perf. 13x13½
905 A326 10c multicolored   1.00 .40
906 A326 15c multicolored   1.50 .60
907 A326 25c multicolored   2.00 1.25
908 A326 35c multicolored   2.50 2.50
   Nos. 905-908 (4)   7.00 4.75

Archbishop
Makarios III
(1913-77), 1st
Pres. of Cyprus
Republic — A327

1997, Aug. 1   Litho.   Perf. 13x13½
909 A327 15c multicolored   1.50 1.00

Christmas — A328

Frescoes from Church of Ayios Ioannis
Lambadestis: 10c, Nativity. 25c, Magi on way
to Bethlehem. 30c, Flight into Egypt.

1997, Nov. 17   Litho.   Perf. 13½x13
910 A328 10c multicolored   .95 .65
911 A328 25c multicolored   2.40 1.40
912 A328 30c multicolored   2.75 2.75
   Nos. 910-912 (3)   6.10 4.80

Minerals — A329

1998, Mar. 9   Litho.   Perf. 13x13½
913 A329 10c Green jasper   .55 .40
914 A329 15c Iron pyrite   .80 .65
915 A329 25c Gypsum   1.30 1.30
916 A329 30c Chalcedony   1.60 1.60
   Nos. 913-916 (4)   4.25 3.95

1998 World Cup
Soccer
Championships,
France — A330

1998, May 4   Litho.   Perf. 14
917 A330 35c multicolored   2.75 1.75

Europa — A331

Festivals, holidays: 15c, "Katakklysmos"
Larnaca. 30c, People watching proclamation
of independence, 1960.

1998, May 4
918 A331 15c multicolored   1.10 .55
919 A331 30c multicolored   2.40 1.60

Ovis Gmelini
Ophion — A332

World Wildlife Fund: No. 920, Male, female,
calf. No. 921, Group running. No. 922, Male
up close. No. 923, Male with front legs up on
rock, one grazing.

1998, June 22   Litho.   Perf. 13x13½
920 A332 25c multicolored   1.50 1.50
921 A332 25c multicolored   1.50 1.50
922 A332 25c multicolored   1.50 1.50
923 A332 25c multicolored   1.50 1.50
a. Block of 4, #920-923   6.00 6.00

   Issued in sheets of 16.

World Stamp
Day — A333

1998, Oct. 9   Litho.   Perf. 14
924 A333 30c multicolored   2.75 2.75
a. Booklet pane of 8   22.00
   Complete booklet, #924a   25.00

A334

1998, Oct. 9
925 A334 50c multicolored   2.00 2.00
Universal Declaration of Human Rights,
50th anniv.

A335

Christmas (Scenes from paintings in the
Church of the Virgin of Théosképasti,
Kalopanayiotis): 10c, The Annunciation. 25c,
The Nativity. 30c, Baptism of Christ.

1998, Nov. 16   Litho.   Perf. 14
926 A335 10c multicolored   .35 .35
927 A335 25c multicolored   .90 .90
928 A335 30c multicolored   2.75 2.75
a. Souvenir sheet, #926-928   4.00 4.00
   Nos. 926-928 (3)   4.00 4.00

Mushrooms — A336

10c, Pleurotus eryngii. 15c, Lactarius deliciosus. 25c, Sparassis crispa. 30c, Morchella
elata.

1999, Mar. 4   Litho.   Perf. 13½x13
929 A336 10c multicolored   .50 .50
930 A336 15c multicolored   1.00 .60
931 A336 25c multicolored   1.50 1.50
932 A336 30c multicolored   1.60 2.50
   Nos. 929-932 (4)   4.60 5.10

Natl. Parks and
Nature Preserves
A337

1999, May 6   Litho.   Perf. 14
933 A337 15c Tripylos Reserve   .90 .50
934 A337 30c Lara Reserve   1.60 2.10
a. Booklet pane, 4 each #933-934 11.00
   Complete booklet, #934a   12.00

       Europa.

Council of
Europe, 50th
Anniv. — A338

1999, May 6
935 A338 30c multicolored   2.10 2.10

4000 Years of Hellenism — A339

a, Sanctuary of Apollo Hylates, Kourion. b,
Mycenaean "Krater of the Warriors," Athens. c,
Mycenaean amphoral krater, Cyprus Museum.
d, Sanctuary of Apollo Epikourios, Delphi.

1999, June 28   Litho.   Perf. 13½x13
936 A339 25c Block of 4, #a.-d. 6.25 6.25
   See Greece No. 1938.

UPU, 125th
Anniv. — A340

1999, Sept. 30   Litho.   Perf. 14
937 A340 15c shown   1.00   .90
938 A340 35c "125"   2.50 2.00

Souvenir Sheet

Maritime Cyprus Shipping
Conference — A341

Cyprus flag and: a, Container ship. b, Binoculars, chart, cap. c, Ship with yellow stripe on tower. d, Tanker.

1999, Sept. 30
939 A341 25c Sheet of 4, #a.-d.   5.00 5.00

Souvenir Sheet

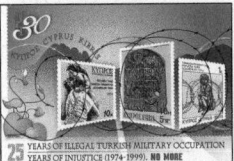

Turkish
Invasion
of
Cyprus,
25th
Anniv.
A342

1999, Nov. 11   Litho.   Imperf.
940 A342 30c multicolored   2.50 2.50

A343

1999, Nov. 11   Perf. 14
941 A343 10c Angel   .70   .55
942 A343 25c Magi   1.40 1.25
943 A343 30c Madonna and child 1.60 1.60
     Nos. 941-943 (3)   3.70 3.40

Christmas.

Souvenir Sheet

A344

Miss Universe 2000: a, 15c, Woman, stars. b, 35c, Armless nude statue of woman.

2000, Mar. 30   Litho.   Perf. 13¼x13
944 A344 Sheet of 2, #a.-b.   3.00 3.00

Jewelry — A345

Various pieces of jewelry. Nos. 945-952 vert.

2000, Mar. 30   Litho.   Perf. 14
945 A345 10c multi   .45   .45
946 A345 15c multi   .60   .60
947 A345 20c multi   .80   .80
948 A345 25c multi   1.00 1.00
949 A345 30c multi   1.25 1.25
950 A345 35c multi   1.40 1.40
951 A345 40c multi   1.60 1.60
952 A345 50c multi   2.25 2.25
953 A345 75c multi   3.00 3.00
954 A345 £1 multi   4.00 4.00
955 A345 £2 multi   7.50 7.50
956 A345 £3 multi   11.00 11.00
     Nos. 945-956 (12)   34.85 34.85

Cyprus Red
Cross, 50th
Anniv. — A346

2000, May 9   Litho.   Perf. 13x13¼
957 A346 15c multi   2.25 2.25

Memorial to Heroes of
1955-59 Independence
Struggle — A347

2000, May 9   Perf. 13¼x13
958 A347 15c multi   2.40 2.40

Europa, 2000
Common Design Type

2000, May 9   Perf. 14
959 CD17 30c multi   2.10 1.40

World
Meteorological
Org., 50th
Anniv. — A348

2000, May 9
960 A348 30c multi   2.25 2.25

European
Convention of
Human Rights,
50th
Anniv. — A349

2000, June 29   Litho.   Perf. 13x13¼
961 A349 30c multi   3.00 3.00

Churches
Damaged Under
Turkish
Occupation
A350

Designs: 10c, Monastery of Antifonitis, Kalograia, vert. 15c, Church of St. Themonianos, Lysi, vert. 25c, Church of Panagia Kanakaria, Lytrhagkomi. 30c, Avgasida Monastery Church, Milia.

Perf. 13¼x13, 13x13¼
2000, June 29
962 A350 10c multi   1.10   .60
963 A350 15c multi   1.50   .80
964 A350 25c multi   2.00 1.60
965 A350 30c multi   2.40 2.40
     Nos. 962-965 (4)   7.00 5.40

2000 Summer
Olympics,
Sydney — A351

Designs: 10c, Archery. 15c, Pommel horse. 25c, Diving. 35c, Trampoline.

2000, Sept. 14   Litho.   Perf. 13x13½
966-969 A351 Set of 4   6.00 6.00

Christmas — A352

Gospel covers: 10c, Annunciation. 25c, Nativity. 30c, Baptism of Jesus.

2000, Nov. 2   Perf. 13½x13
970-972 A352 Set of 3   5.00 5.00

Pavlos Liasides (1901-
85), Poet — A353

2001, Mar. 12   Litho.   Perf. 13¼x13
973 A353 13c multi   1.25   .65

Commonwealth
Day, 25th
Anniv. — A354

2001, Mar. 12   Perf. 13x13¼
974 A354 30c multi   2.75 2.75

UN High
Commissioner for
Refugees, 50th
Anniv. — A355

2001, Mar. 12
975 A355 30c multi   2.50 2.50

Europa — A356

Designs: 20c, Bridge over Diarizos River. 30c, Akaki River.

2001, May 3
976-977 A356 Set of 2   4.00 2.00
977a   Booklet pane, 4 each
              #976-977   17.00
            Booklet, #977a   19.00

Crabs — A357

Designs: 13c, Parthenope massena. 20c, Calappa granulata. 25c, Ocypode cursor. 30c, Pagurus bernhardus.

2001, June 7
978-981 A357 Set of 4   9.00 9.00

Loukis Akritas (1909-65),
Writer — A358

2001, Oct. 25   Litho.   Perf. 13½x13
982 A358 20c multi   2.50 1.25

Christmas — A359

Holy Monastery of Macheras, 800th anniv.: 13c, Icon of Madonna. 25c, Monastery building. 30c, Crucifix.

2001, Oct. 25
983-985 A359 Set of 3   5.00 5.00

Cats
A360

No. 986, 20c: a, Red brown panel. b, Green panel.
No. 987, 25c: a, Dark brown panel. b, Orange brown panel.

2002, Mar. 21   Litho.   Perf. 13x13½
Horiz. Pairs, #a-b
986-987 A360 Set of 2   7.00 7.00

Europa — A361

Designs: 20c, Equestrian act. 30c, Tightrope walker.

2002, May 9   Perf. 13½x13
988-989 A361 Set of 2   4.00 2.00
a.   Booklet pane, 4 each #988-989   17.00 —
       Booklet, #989a   19.00

Medicinal
Plants — A362

Designs: 13c, Myrtus communis. 20c, Lavandula stoechas. 25c, Capparis spinosa. 30c, Ocimum basilicum.

2002, June 13   Perf. 13x13½
990-993 A362 Set of 4   7.00 7.00

Mother Teresa (1910-
97) — A363

2002, Sept. 12   Litho.   Perf. 13½x13
994 A363 40c multi   4.00 4.00

Intl. Teachers' Day — A364

No. 995: a, 13c, Blackboard and teachers. b, 30c, Computer and teachers.

2002, Sept. 12   Perf. 13x13½
995 A364 Horiz. pair, #a-b   3.75 3.75

Cyprus-Europhilex
02 Philatelic
Exhibition — A365

No. 996: a, Seal, 490-470 B.C. (red brown background). b, Silver coin of Timoharis, 5th-4th cent B.C. (blue background) c, Silver coin of Stasioikos, 449 B.C. (yellow background).
No. 997: a, Clay oil lamp, 2nd cent. A.D. (olive green background). b, Clay statue of Europa on a bull, 7th-6th cent. B.C. (yellow background). c, Clay oil lamp, 1st cent. B.C. (lilac background)
No. 998: a, 15th cent. map of eastern Crete and western Cyprus, and statue of Aphrodite, 1st cent. B.C. b, Map of eastern Cyprus, and Abduction of Europe, by Francesco di Giorgio.

2002, Sept. 22
996   Horiz. strip of 3   4.50 4.50
a.-c. A365 20c Any single   1.50 1.50
997   Horiz. strip of 3   6.75 6.75
a.-c. A365 30c Any single   2.25 2.25

Souvenir Sheet
998   Sheet of 2, #a-b   9.50 9.50
a.-b. A365 50c Any single   3.75 3.75

Christmas — A366

Wall painting in Church of Metamorphosis Sotiros, Palechori: 13c, Nativity, detail. 25c,

Angels, detail. 30c, Entire painting (37x37mm).

Perf. 13x13½, 13¾ (30c)
2002, Nov. 21
999-1001 A366 Set of 3 5.75 5.75

Antique Automobiles A367

No. 1002: a, 20c, 1946 Triumph Roadster 1800. b, 25c, 1917 Ford Model T. c, 30c, 1932 Baby Ford.
2003, Mar. 20 Litho. Perf. 13x13½
1002 A367 Vert. strip of 3, #a-c 6.50 6.50

Europa — A368

2003, May 8 Perf. 13½x13
Color of Triangles
1003 A368 20c yellow 1.00 .65
  a.   Perf. 13½x13¾ on 3 sides 1.75 1.10
1004 A368 30c red 1.60 1.00
  a.   Perf. 13½x13¾ on 3 sides 3.00 1.60
  b.   Booklet pane, 4 each #1003a-1004a 20.00
        Complete booklet, #1004b 24.00

European Ministers of Education, 7th Conference — A369

2003, June 12 Litho. Perf. 13½x13
1005 A369 30c multi 2.25 2.25

Worldwide Fund for Nature (WWF) — A370

Mediterranean horseshoe bat: a, In flight. b, Close-up. c, Hanging from rock. d, With open mouth.
2003, June 12 Perf. 13x13½
1006 A370 25c Block of 4, #a-b 7.00 7.00

Birds of Prey A371

No. 1007, 20c: a, Eleonora's falcon. b, Eleonora's falcons in flight.
No. 1008, 25c: a, Head of Imperial eagle. b, Imperial eagles in flight.
No. 1009, 30c: a, Owl on branch. b, Owl in flight, eggs.
2003, Sept. 25 Litho. Perf. 14
Horiz. pairs, #a-b
1007-1009 A371 Set of 3 9.50 9.50

Famous Men — A372

Designs: No. 1010, 5c, Constantinos Spyridakis (1903-76), Education minister. No. 1011, 5c, Tefkros Anthias (1903-68), poet (23x31mm).
Perf. 13x13¼, 13¼x13
2003, Nov. 13
1010-1011 A372 Set of 2 1.25 1.25

Christmas — A373

Details of Nativity icon from church in Kourdali: 13c, Angels. 30c, Three Magi on horses. 40c, Entire icon (37x60mm).
Perf. 13¾x13¼, 13¾x14 (40c)
2003, Nov. 13
1012-1014 A373 Set of 3 5.50 5.50

FIFA (Fédération Internationale de Football Association), Cent. — A374

Perf. 13¼x13¾
2004, Mar. 11 Litho.
1015 A374 30c multi 2.25 2.25

UEFA (European Soccer Union), 50th Anniv. — A375

2004, Mar. 11 Perf. 13¼x13
1016 A375 30c multi 2.25 2.25

Yiannos Kranidiotis (1947-99), Politician — A376

2004, May 1 Perf. 13¼x13½
1017 A376 20c multi 1.10 1.10

Admission to European Union — A377

2004, May 1 Perf. 14¼x14
1018 A377 30c multi 2.25 2.25

Europa — A378

Cliff and: 20c, Amphitheater, ship. 30c, Family at seashore, sculpture
2004, May 1 Perf. 13¾x13¼
1019 A378 20c multi 1.25 .60
  a.   Perf. 13¾ on 3 sides 1.50 .70
1020 A378 30c multi 1.75 .90
  a.   Perf. 13¾ on 3 sides 2.00 1.10
  b.   Booklet pane, 4 each #1019a, 1020a 16.00
        Complete booklet, #1020b 18.00

2004 Summer Olympics, Athens — A379

Designs: 13c, Equestrian. 20c, Runners. 30c, Swimmers. 40c, Athletes, man in robe.
2004, June 10 Litho. Perf. 13¼x13
1021-1024 A379 Set of 4 5.75 5.75

Mammals — A380

No. 1025, 20c — Tursiops truncatus: a, Blue background. b, White background.
No. 1026, 30c — Vulpes vulpes indutus: a, Green background. b, White background.
No. 1027, 40c, Lepus europaeus cyprium: a, Orange brown background. b, White background.
2004, Sept. 9 Litho. Perf. 13¾x13½
Horiz. Pairs, #a-b
1025-1027 A380 Set of 3 13.00 13.00

Georgios Philippou Pierides (1904-99), Writer A381

Emilios Chourmouzios (1904-73), Writer A382

2004, Nov. 11 Perf. 13¼x13
1028 A381 5c multi .65 .65
1029 A382 5c multi .65 .65

Christmas — A383

Details from icon depicting the birth of Christ, Monastery of Chrysoroyiatissa: 13c, Angels. 30c, Magi on horseback. 40c, Annunciation, vert. (37x60mm). £1, Adoration of the Shepherds.
Perf. 13¾x13¼, 13¾x14 (40c)
2004, Nov. 11
1030-1032 A383 Set of 3 6.00 6.00
Souvenir Sheet
Perf. 13¾ on 3 Sides
1033 A383 £1 multi 6.75 6.75
No. 1033 contains one 37x38mm stamp.

Carolina Pelendritou, Swimming Gold Medalist at 2004 Paralympics — A384

2005, Mar. 3 Litho. Perf. 13¼x13¾
1034 A384 20c multi 1.50 1.50

Rotary International, Cent. — A385

2005, Mar. 3
1035 A385 40c multi 2.50 2.50

Natl. Organization of Cypriot Struggle (EOKA), 50th Anniv. — A386

2005, Mar. 3
1036 A386 50c multi 3.00 3.00

Europa — A387

Table with food and: 20c, Purple grapes, sailboat. 30c, Green grapes, steamship.
2005, May 5 Perf. 13½x13
White Frame All Around
1037 A387 20c multi .90 .90
1038 A387 30c multi 1.40 1.40

Booklet Stamps
White Frame on 3 Sides
Perf. 13½ on 3 Sides
1039 A387 20c multi 1.25 .75
1040 A387 30c multi 1.75 1.25
  a.   Horiz. pair, #1039-1040 3.25 2.25
  b.   Booklet pane, 4 #1040a 13.50
        Complete booklet, #1040b 15.00
        Nos. 1037-1040 (4) 5.30 4.30

Dogs — A388

Designs: 13c, German shepherd. 20c, Hungarian vizsla. 30c, Labrador retriever. 40c, Dalmatian.
2005, June 16 Litho. Perf. 13¼
1041-1044 A388 Set of 4 8.00 8.00
1044a Booklet pane, #1041-1044 8.50
       Complete booklet, #1044a 8.50

Christmas — A389

Icons: 13c, Annunciation to the Shepherds. 30c, Adoration of the Magi. 40c, Madonna and Child, vert. (38x60mm).
Perf. 13¼, 13¾x14 (40c)
2005, Nov. 10 Litho.
1045-1047 A389 Set of 3 4.25 4.25

Souvenir Sheet

Europa Stamps, 50th Anniv. A390

No. 1048: a, Cyprus #246. b, Cyprus #202. c, Cyprus #220. d, Cyprus #231.
2006, Feb. 23 Litho. Perf. 13¾
1048 A390 30c Sheet of 4, #a-d 7.00 7.00

Postal Museum, 25th Anniv. — A391

2006, Mar. 30   *Perf. 13¾x13¼*
1049 A391 25c multi   1.75 1.75

Rembrandt (1606-69), Painter — A392

2006, Mar. 30
1050 A392 40c multi   3.00 3.00

2006 World Cup Soccer Championships, Germany — A393

2006, Mar. 30   *Perf. 13¼x13¾*
1051 A393 50c multi   3.25 3.25

Souvenir Sheet

Folk Dances A394

No. 1052 — Folk dancers from: a, Cyprus. b, India.

2006, Apr. 12   *Perf. 13x13½*
1052 A394 40c Sheet of 2, #a-b   5.50 5.50
    See India No. 2151.

Europa — A395

2006, May 4   *Perf. 13½x13*
1053 A395 30c grn & multi   1.60 1.60
   a.   Perf. 13½x13¾ on 3 sides   1.60 1.60
1054 A395 40c red & multi   2.10 2.10
   a.   Perf. 13½x13¾ on 3 sides   2.10 2.10
   b.   Booklet pane, 4 each #1053a-1054a   15.50 —
    Complete booklet, #1054b   15.50

Organ Transplantation A396

2006, June 15   **Litho.**   *Perf. 13¼*
1055 A396 13c multi   .90 .90

Fruit — A397

Designs: 20c, Elaeagnus angustifolia. 25c, Mespilus germanica, horiz. 60c, Opuntia ficus barbarica.

Perf. 13¼x13½, 13½x13¼
2006, June 15
1056-1058 A397   Set of 3   6.75 6.75

Fire Trucks — A398

Designs: 13c, Bedford water carrier. 20c, Hino pump water tender. 50c, Bedford ladder truck.

2006, Sept. 14   *Perf. 13¾x13¼*
1059-1061 A398   Set of 3   6.25 6.25

Nicos Nicolaides (1884-1956), Writer — A399

2006, Nov. 16   **Litho.**   *Perf. 13½x13*
1062 A399 5c multi   .60 .60

Christmas — A400

Items from Agiou Eleftheriou Church: 13c, Carved wood iconostasis. 30c, Cross. 40c, Bas-relief of cross, spear and sponge.

2006, Nov. 16   *Perf. 13¼x13¾*
1063-1065 A400   Set of 3   4.75 4.75

St. Xenon, the Postman A401

Litho. & Embossed
2007, Feb. 8   *Imperf.*
1066 A401 £1 multi   8.00 8.00

Echinoderms A402

No. 1067: a, Antedon mediterranea. b, Centrostephanus longispinus. c, Astropecten jonstoni. d, Ophioderma longicadum.

2007, Feb. 8   **Litho.**   *Perf. 13¾x13¼*
1067   Horiz. strip of 4   6.50 6.50
   a.-d.   A402 25c Any single   1.60 1.60

Motorcycles A403

Designs: 13c, 1972 Triumph Daytona. 20c, 1941 Matchless. 40c, 1940 BSA. 60c, 1939 Ariel Red Hunter.

2007, Mar. 15
1068-1071 A403   Set of 4   7.25 7.25

Treaty of Rome, 50th Anniv. — A404

2007, May 3   *Perf. 13¼x13¾*
1072 A404 30c multi   1.60 1.60

Europa — A405

Scouting emblem in gold, knot in: 30c, Light blue. 40c, Buff.

Litho. & Embossed With Foil Application
2007, May 3
1073-1074 A405   Set of 2   3.25 3.25
1074a   Booklet pane, 4 each #1073-1074, perf. on 3 sides   13.00 —
    Complete booklet, #1074a   13.00
    Scouting, cent.

Social Insurance, 50th Anniv. — A406

No. 1075: a, Text in Greek. b, Text in English.

2007, June 14   **Litho.**   *Perf. 13x13¼*
1075 A406 40c Horiz. pair, #a-b   4.00 4.00

Miniature Sheet

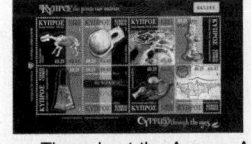

Cyprus Throughout the Ages — A407

No. 1076: a, Skeleton of pygmy hippopotamus, 10,000 B.C. b, Stone vessel, 7000 B.C. c, Choirokoitia Settlement, 7000 B.C. d, Female terracotta figurine, 3000 B.C. e, Terracotta vessel, 2000 B.C. f, Greek inscriptions on bronze skewer, 1000 B.C. g, Bird-shaped vessel, 800 B.C. h, Map of ancient kingdoms of Cyprus.

2007, Oct. 2   *Perf. 13¾*
1076 A407 25c Sheet of 8, #a-h   12.00 12.00
    See Nos. 1101, 1116, 1138.

Neoclassical Buildings — A408

Designs: 13c, Limassol District Administration Building. 15c, National Bank of Greece Building, Nicosia. 20c, Archaeological Research Unit Building, Nicosia. 30c, National Art Gallery, Nicosia. 40c, Paphos Municipal Library. 50c, A. G. Leventis Foundation Office Building, Nicosia. £1, Limassol Municipal Library. £3, Phaneromeni Gymnasium, Nicosia.

2007, Oct. 2   *Perf. 13¾x13½*
1077 A408 13c multi   .65 .65
1078 A408 15c multi   .75 .75
1079 A408 20c multi   1.00 1.00
1080 A408 30c multi   1.50 1.50
1081 A408 40c multi   2.00 2.00
1082 A408 50c multi   2.40 2.40
1083 A408 £1 multi   5.00 5.00
1084 A408 £3 multi   14.50 14.50
    Nos. 1077-1084 (8)   27.80 27.80

Christmas — A409

Murals from Chapel of St. Themonianus, Lysi: 13c, Virgin Mary. 30c, Archangel Gabriel. 40c, Christ Pantocrator (35x45mm).

Perf. 14x13¾, 13¾ (40c)
2007, Nov. 15
1085-1087 A409   Set of 3   4.75 4.75

100 Cents = 1 Euro
Souvenir Sheet

Introduction of Euro Currency — A410

No. 1088: a, Statue of Aphrodite, map of Cyprus. b, Sleeping Lady statue.

2008, Jan. 1   **Litho.**   *Perf. 13¾*
1088 A410 €1 Sheet of 2, #a-b   5.50 5.50
    See Malta No. 1329.

Anemone Flowers — A411

Variously colored Anemone coronaria flowers with background colors of: 26c, Blue. 34c, Red. 51c, Green. 68c, Yellow orange.

2008, Mar. 6   *Perf. 13¼x13¾*
1089-1092 A411   Set of 4   6.25 6.25

Europa — A412

Designs: 51c, Closed and open envelopes. 68c, Envelopes and mail boxes.

2008, May 2   **Litho.**   *Perf. 13¼x13¾*
1093-1094 A412   Set of 2   3.75 3.75
1094a   Booklet pane, 4 each #1093-1094, perf. 13¼x13¾ on 3 sides   15.00 —
    Complete booklet, #1094a   15.00

Souvenir Sheet

Fourth Intl. Congress of Cypriot Studies, Nicosia — A413

2008, May 2   *Perf. 13¾ on 3 Sides*
1095 A413 85c multi   3.50 3.50

12th Francophone Summit, Quebec — A414

2008, June 5   Litho.   Perf. 13¾
1096 A414 85c multi   3.25 3.25

2008 Summer Olympics, Beijing — A415

Designs: 22c, Sailboarding. 34c, High jump. 43c, Tennis. 51c, Shooting.

2008, June 5   Perf. 13x13¼
1097-1100 A415 Set of 4   4.75 4.75

Cyprus Throughout the Years Type of 2007
Miniature Sheet

No. 1101: a, Coin from Archaic period, 750 B.C.-480 B.C. b, Ship from Archaic period. c, Bust of Kimon the Athenian and ship, Classical period, 480 B.C.-310 B.C. d, Tomb of the Kings, Hellenistic period, 310 B.C.-30 B.C. e, Coin from Hellenistic period. f, Painting of St. Paul from Roman period, 30 B.C.-A.D. 324. g, Bust of Septimus Severus from Roman period. h, Granting of church privileges from Early Byzantine period, 324-841.

2008, Oct. 2   Litho.   Perf. 13¾
1101 A407 43c Sheet of 8, #a-h   12.00 12.00

Christmas — A416

Icons from church, Pelendri: 22c, Archangel Gabriel. 51c, Archangel Michael. 68c, Madonna and Child.

2008, Nov. 13   Perf. 13¼x13
1102-1104 A416 Set of 3   4.75 4.75

Cooperative Movement, Cent. — A417

2009, Mar. 12   Litho.   Perf. 13¾
1105 A417 26c multi   1.00 1.00

Louis Braille (1809-52), Educator of the Blind — A418

2009, Mar. 12   Litho. & Embossed
1106 A418 68c multi   2.50 2.50

Introduction of the Euro, 10th Anniv. — A419

Reverse of Cyprus: 51c, Cent coin. 68c, 2-euro coin.

2009, Mar. 12   Litho.
1107-1108 A419 Set of 2   4.75 4.75

Intl. Year of Planet Earth A420

No. 1109: a, Western Hemisphere. b, Eastern Hemisphere.

2009, May 4   Litho.   Perf. 13x13¼
1109 A420 51c Horiz. pair, #a-b   3.75 3.75

Europa — A421

Constellations: 51c, Cassiopeia. 68c, Andromeda.

2009, May 4   Perf. 13¼x13¾
1110-1111 A421 Set of 2   3.75 3.75
1111a   Booklet pane of 8, 4 each
        #1110-1111, perf.
        13¼x13¾ on 3 sides   15.00   —
        Complete booklet, #1111a   15.00

Intl. Year of Astronomy.

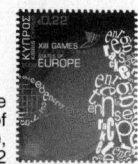

18th Games of the Small States of Europe, Cyprus — A422

Designs: 22c, Tennis. 34c, Sailing. 43c, Cycling.

2009, June 1   Litho.   Perf. 13¼x13¾
1112-1114 A422 Set of 3   3.50 3.50

Souvenir Sheet

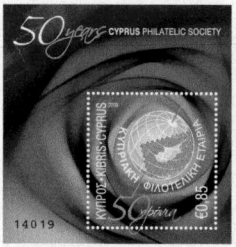

Cyprus Philatelic Society, 50th Anniv. A423

Litho. & Embossed With Foil Application
2009, June 1   Perf. 13¾
1115 A423 85c multi   3.25 3.25

Cyprus Throughout the Years Type of 2007
Miniature Sheet

No. 1116: a, St. Paraskevi Church, 9th cent. b, Monastery of St. John Chrysostom, 1090-1100. c, Lusignan coat of arms, 1192-1489. d, Chronicle of Leontios Machairas, 15th cent. e, Queen Caterina Cornaro cedes Cyprus to Venice, 1489. f, Venetian Walls, Nicosia, 1567-70. g, Ottoman siege of Nicosia, 1570. h, Larnaca Aqueduct, 18th cent.

2009, Sept. 10   Litho.   Perf. 13¾
1116 A407 43c Sheet of 8, #a-h   14.00 14.00

Domesticated Birds — A424

Designs: 22c, Pigeon. 34c, Turkey. 43c, Rooster. 51c, Duck.

2009, Sept. 10   Perf. 13¾x13¼
1117-1120 A424 Set of 4   5.75 5.75

European Court of Human Rights, 50th Anniv. — A425

2009, Nov. 12   Litho.   Perf. 13x13¼
1121 A425 51c multi   2.00 2.00

A426

Christmas — A427

Perf. 13¼x13¾
2009, Nov. 12   Litho.
1122 A426 22c shown   .75   .75
Litho. & Embossed With Foil Application
Perf. 13¾
1123 A427 51c shown   1.75 1.75
1124 A427 68c Solid silver star   2.75 2.75
       Nos. 1122-1124 (3)   5.25 5.25

Republic of Cyprus, 50th Anniv. — A428

Denomination color: 68c, Bister. 85c, Blue.

Litho. & Embossed With Foil Application
2010, Jan. 27   Perf. 13¾x13¼
1125-1126 A428 Set of 2   5.25 5.25

Expo 2010, Shanghai — A429

2010, Mar. 17   Litho.   Perf. 13x13¼
1127 A429 51c multi   1.60 1.60

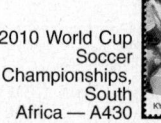

2010 World Cup Soccer Championships, South Africa — A430

2010, Mar. 17   Perf. 13¾
1128 A430 €1.71 multi   5.75 5.75

Barnyard Animals — A431

Designs: 22c, Pig. 26c, Sheep. 34c, Goat. 43c, Cow. €1.71, Rabbit.

2010, Mar. 17   Perf. 13¾x13¼
1129-1133 A431 Set of 5   10.00 10.00

Europa A432

No. 1134 — Stack of books and: a, Sun, flowers, tree, snails, bees. b, Tree, bees.

2010, May 5   Perf. 13¼x13¾
1134 A432 51c Horiz. pair, #a-b   3.25 3.25
   c.   Booklet pane of 8, 4 each
        #1134a-1134b, perf.
        13¼x13¾ on 3 sides   13.00   —
        Complete booklet, #1134c   13.00

Visit of Pope Benedict XVI — A433

2010, June 4   Perf. 13¾x14¼
1135 A433 51c multi   1.60 1.60

Cyprus Railway A434

No. 1136 — Locomotive with denomination in: a, Black. b, White.
85c, Train, map of stations.

2010, June 4   Perf. 13¾x13¼
1136 A434 43c Pair, #a-b   2.75 2.75

Souvenir Sheet
1137 A434 85c multi   3.00 3.00

Cyprus Through the Ages Type of 2007
Miniature Sheet

No. 1138: a, Treaties of Sevres, 1920, and Lausanne, 1923. b, Burnt Government House, 1931. c, Imprisoned graves, 1955-59. d, Statue of Gregoris Afxentiou (1928-57), anti-colonialist leader. e, Presidential Palace, 1960. f, Black Summer 1974, painting by Telemachos Kanthos. g, Pres. Tassos Papadopoulos signing Treaty of Accession to the European Union, 2004. h, Flag of Cyprus.

2010, Oct. 1   Litho.   Perf. 13¾
1138 A407 43c Sheet of 8, #a-h   11.00 11.00

Souvenir Sheet

Viticulture — A435

No. 1139: a, Wine barrels, wine glass. b, Grapes, pitcher.

Perf. 14 on 3 Sides
2010, Nov. 10   Litho.
1139 A435 51c Sheet of 2, #a-b   3.25 3.25
       See Romania Nos. 5216-5217.

Nativity A436

Christmas Ornament A437

Perf. 13¼x13¾
2010, Nov. 10   Litho.
1140 A436 22c shown   .65   .65
Litho. & Embossed With Foil Application
Perf. 13¾
1141 A437 51c shown   1.50 1.50
1142 A437 68c Ornament, diff.   2.10 2.10
       Nos. 1140-1142 (3)   3.90 3.90

Anorthosis Ammochostos Soccer Team, Cent. — A438

2011, Jan. 28   Litho.   Perf. 13¾
1143 A438 34c multi   .95 .95

Composers A439

No. 1144: a, Johann Sebastian Bach (1685-1750). b, Wolfgang Amadeus Mozart (1756-91). c, Ludwig van Beethoven (1770-1827).

2011, Jan. 28   Perf. 13¾x14¼
1144   Horiz. strip of 3   4.25 4.25
  a.-c.   A439 51c Any single   1.40 1.40

Lace — A440

Lace with: 26c, Floral pattern. 43c, Diamonds and squares pattern.

2011, Mar. 23   Perf. 13¾x14
1145-1146 A440 Set of 2   2.00 2.00

Rosa Damascena A441

2011, Mar. 23   Perf. 13¾
1147 A441 34c shown   1.00 1.00
Souvenir Sheet
1148 A441 85c Roses, diff.   2.50 2.50

Nos. 1147-1148 are impregnated with a rose scent.

Europa — A442

2011, May 4   Perf. 14
1149 A442 51c Blue forest   1.50 1.50
  a.   Perf. 13x13½ on 3 sides   1.50
1150 A442 68c Green forest   2.00 2.00
  a.   Perf. 13x13½ on 3 sides   2.00 2.00
  b.   Booklet pane of 8, 4 each
        #1149a-1150a   14.00   —
        Complete booklet, #1150b   14.00

Intl. Year of Forests.

Lighthouses — A443

Map and: 34c, Paphos Lighthouse. 43c, Cape Greco Lighthouse. €1.71 Cape Kiti Lighthouse.

2011, May 4   Perf. 14
1151-1152 A443 Set of 2   3.00 3.00
Souvenir Sheet
Perf. 13½x13¼
1153 A443 €1.71 multi   6.00 6.00
Booklet Stamp
Self-Adhesive
Die Cut Perf. 13¼x13
1153A A443 43c multi (RA28Ab)   1.50 1.50

No. 1153 contains one 27x35mm stamp.

Christopher A. Pissarides, 2010 Nobel Laureate in Economics A444

2011, June 8   Perf. 14x14¼
1154 A444 €1.71 multi   5.00 5.00

Tall Ships — A445

Designs: 22c, Galleon. 43c, Caravel. 85c, Brig.

2011, June 8   Perf. 13¾
1155-1157 A445 Set of 3   4.25 4.25

The Hare and the Tortoise A446

No. 1158: a, Hare. b, Tortoise. c, Tortoise passing sleeping hare, horiz. d, Hare running. e, Tortoise crossing finish line.

Die Cut Perf. 11½x12, 12x11½
2011, Oct. 5   Litho.
Self-Adhesive
1158 A446 34c Booklet pane of
            5, #a-e   4.75 4.75

Nativity A447

Christmas Ornament A448

Perf. 13¼x13¾
2011, Nov. 11   Litho.
1159 A447 22c shown   .60 .60
Litho. & Embossed With Foil Application
Perf. 13¾
1160 A448 51c shown   1.40 1.40
1161 A448 68c Ornament, diff.   1.90 1.90
    Nos. 1159-1161 (3)   3.90 3.90

Horses — A449

Various horses: 26c, 34c, 51c, 85c.

2012, Jan. 31 Litho. Perf. 13¾x13¼
1162-1165 A449 Set of 4   6.50 6.50

2012 Summer Olympics, London — A450

Designs: 22c, Men's gymnastics. 26c, Men's tennis. 34c, Men's high jump. 43c, Shooting.

Litho. With Foil Application
2012, Mar. 21   Perf. 14
1166-1169 A450 Set of 4   4.00 4.00

Souvenir Sheet

Soccer A451

2012, Mar. 21   Litho.   Perf.
1170 A451 €1.71 multi   5.50 5.50

Jasminum Grandiflorum A452

2012, May 2   Perf. 13¾
1171 A452 34c shown   1.10 1.10
Souvenir Sheet
1172 A452 85c Flowers, diff. 2.60 2.60

Nos. 1171-1172 are impregnated with a jaasmine scent.

Europa — A453

Various Cyprus tourist attractions and silhouette of: 51c, Family. 68c, Man and woman with bicycles.

2012, May 2   Perf. 13¾x13½
1173-1174 A453 Set of 2   3.25 3.25
  1174a   Booklet pane of 8, 4 each
           #1173-1174, perf.
           13¾x13½ on 3 sides   13.00   —
           Complete booklet, #1174a 13.00

Cyprus Presidency of European Union Council — A454

Litho. With Foil Application
2012, July 1   Perf. 13¾
1175 A454 51c multi   1.75 1.75
Souvenir Sheet
1176 A454 €10 multi   28.00 28.00

The Cricket and the Ant — A455

No. 1177: a, Cricket with fiddle, sun. b, Ant with seeds. c, Ant carrying seeds. d, Cricket fiddling under tree. e, Cricket outside in winter, ant at door.

2012, Oct. 3   Die Cut Perf. 11¼x12
Self-Adhesive
1177 A455 34c Booklet pane of
            5, #a-e   5.25 5.25

Pavlos Kontides, Silver Medalist in Sailing at 2012 Summer Olympics — A456

Litho. With Foil Application
2012, Nov. 14   Perf. 14
1178 A456 34c multi   .90 .90

Christmas — A457

Icons from: 22c, Madonna and Child, Christ Antiphonitis Church. 51c, Madonna and Child, Panayia Church, Lysi. 68c, Madonna and Child Enthroned Between St. George and St. Nicholas, St. George's Church, Vatyli.

Perf. 13¼x13¾
2012, Nov. 12   Litho.
1179 A457 22c multi   .60 .60
1180 A457 51c multi   1.40 1.40
Size: 65x65mm
Imperf
1181 A457 68c multi   1.75 1.75

Admission of Cyprus Red Cross to International Red Cross, 1st Anniv. — A458

2013, Jan. 30   Perf. 14¼x13¾
1182 A458 22c multi   .80 .80

Cyprus Scouts Association, Cent. — A459

2013, Jan. 30   Perf. 13¾
1183 A459 43c multi   1.40 1.40

Archbishop Makarios (1913-77), President of Cyprus — A460

2013, Jan. 30   Perf. 14
1184 A460 85c multi   2.60 2.60

Easter — A461

Icons depicting: 26c, Christ's entry into Jerusalem. 34c, Crucifixion. €1.71, Resurrection (27x40mm).

2013, Apr. 3   Perf. 14x14¼
1185-1187 A461 Set of 3   6.50 6.50

Origanum Dubium — A462

2013, May 2   Perf. 13¾
1188 A462 22c shown   .75 .75
Souvenir Sheet
1189 A462 85c Flowers, diff. 2.75 2.75

Nos. 1188-1189 are impregnated with an oregano scent.

Europa — A463

Mailbox and postal vehicles: 34c, Automobile, van and airplane. 51c, Automobile.

2013, May 2   **Perf. 14**
1190-1191 A463   Set of 2   2.50 2.50
1191a   Booklet pane of 8, 4 each
   #1190-1191, perf. 14 on
   3 sides   10.00   —
   Complete booklet, #1191a   10.00

Marine
Life — A464

Designs: 34c, Seahorse. 43c, Sea anemone. €1.71, Sea fan coral.

2013, June 5   **Perf. 13¾**
1192-1194 A464   Set of 3   7.50 7.50
For surcharge, see No. 1225.

Cypriot Folk Tale "Spanos and the
Forty Dragons"
A465

No. 1195: a, Spanos in cloud near dragon. b, Boar chasing Spanos up a tree, vert. c, Spanos, river, woman holding flowers. d, Spanos sitting near dragon. e, Spanos pouring water on dragon.

Die Cut Perf. 13x13½, 13½x13
2013, Nov. 13   **Litho.**
Self-Adhesive
1195 A465 34c Booklet pane of
   5, #a-e   5.75 5.75

Christmas
A466

Winning art in children's stamp design contest: 22c, Santa Claus and Christmas tree. 34c, Snowman, Christmas trees and houses. 85c, Christmas tree and gifts, vert.

Perf. 14¼x14, 14x14¼
2013, Nov. 13   **Litho.**
1196-1198 A466   Set of 3   4.75 4.75

Olive Production
A467

Designs: 34c, Olive tree and grove.
No. 1200: a, Olives. b, Olives, container of olive oil.

2014, Jan. 30   **Litho.**   **Perf. 14**
1199 A467 34c multi   1.00 1.00
1200 A467 51c Horiz. pair, #a-b   3.00 3.00

Four
Seasons — A468

Designs: 22c, Child under umbrella (winter). 43c, Girl wearing butterfly costume standing in flowers (spring). 85c, Girl with balloons, fish and dolphins (summer). €1.71, Child holding fallen leaf in front of face (autumn).

2014, Mar. 12   **Litho.**   **Perf. 13¾**
1201-1204 A468   Set of 4   9.00 9.00
For surcharges, see Nos. 1212-1214.

Europa — A469

Musicians with instruments: 34c, Cyprus flute. 51c, Lute.

2014, May 2   **Litho.**   **Perf. 14**
1205-1206 A469   Set of 2   2.40 2.40
1206a   Booklet pane of 8, 4 each
   #1205-1206, perf. 14 on 3
   sides   9.75   —
   Complete booklet, #1206a   9.75

Famous
Men — A470

Designs: 41c, El Greco (1541-1614), painter. 50c, Michelangelo (1475-1564), painter and sculptor. 64c, Galileo Galilei (1564-1642), astronomer. 75c, Henri de Toulouse-Lautrec (1864-1901), painter.

2014, June 30   **Litho.**   **Perf. 14**
1207-1210 A470   Set of 4   6.25 6.25

Euromed Postal
Emblem and
Mediterranean
Sea — A471

2014, July 9   **Litho.**   **Perf. 14**
1211 A471 60c multi   1.60 1.60

Nos. 1201, 1202
and 1204
Surcharged

Methods and Perfs. As Before
2014, Aug. 1
1212 A468   4c on 22c #1201   .25 .25
1213 A468   €1 on 43c #1202   2.75 2.75
1214 A468   €1.88 on €1.71
   #1204   5.00 5.00
   Nos. 1212-1214 (3)   8.00 8.00

Famous
People
A472

No. 1215: a, Theodoulos Kallinikos (1904-2004), cantor and musicologist. b, Stylianos Hourmouzios (1850-1937), cantor and journalist.
No. 1216: a, Sozos Tombolis (1914-2002), cantor and music professor. b, Achilleas Lymbourides (1917-2008), composer.
No. 1217: a, Telemachos Kanthos (1910-93), painter. b, Loukia Nicolaidou (1909-94), painter.
No. 1218: a, George Pol Georgiou (1901-72), painter. b, Michael Kashalos (1885-1974), painter.
No. 1219: a, Kypros Chrysanthis (1915-98), writer. b, Antis Pernaris (1903-80), writer.
No. 1220: a, Glafkos Alithersis (1897-1965), writer. b, Costas Montis (1914-2004), writer.

2014, Oct. 10   **Litho.**   **Perf. 14**
1215 A472   Horiz. pair   .25 .25
  a.-b.   4c Either single   .25 .25
1216 A472   Horiz. pair   1.75 1.75
  a.-b.   34c Either single   .85 .85
1217 A472   Horiz. pair   2.00 2.00
  a.-b.   41c Either single   1.00 1.00
1218 A472   Horiz. pair   2.50 2.50
  a.-b.   50c Either single   1.25 1.25
1219 A472   Horiz. pair   3.25 3.25
  a.-b.   64c Either single   1.60 1.60
1220 A472   Horiz. pair   4.25 4.25
  a.-b.   85c Either single   2.10 2.10
   Nos. 1215-1220 (6)   14.00 14.00

See Nos. 1226-1231.

Cypriot Folk Tale "The Prince of
Venice"
A473

No. 1221: a, Prince carried by angel. b, Angel carrying sword, vert. c, Woman with veil, vert. d, Angel and woman, vert. e, Ship at sea.

Die Cut Perf. 13½
2014, Nov. 24   **Litho.**
Self-Adhesive
1221 A473   Booklet pane of 5   5.00
  a.-e.   41c Any single   1.00 1.00

Christmas — A474

Icons depicting: 41c, Nativity. 64c, Madonna and Child. 75c, Nativity, diff.

2014, Nov. 24   **Litho.**   **Perf. 14**
1222-1224 A474   Set of 3   4.50 4.50

No. 1193
Surcharged

Method and Perf. As Before
2015, Feb. 4
1225 A464 34c on 43c #1193   .75 .75

Famous People Type of 2014
No. 1226: a, Adamantios Diamantis (1900-94), painter. b, Theodosis Pierides (1908-68), poet.
No. 1227: a, Maria Rousia (1894-1957), writer. b, Melis Nicolaides (1892-1979), writer.
No. 1228: a, Kyriakos Hadjioannou (1909-97), folklorist. b, Polyxeni Loizia (1855-1942), educator.
No. 1229: a, Loizos Philippou (1895-1950), newspaper editor. b, Persefoni Papadopoulou (1888-1948), educator.
No. 1230: a, Georgios Frangoudes (1869-1939), politician. b, Porfyrios Dikaios (1904-71), archaeologist.
No. 1231: a, Nicos Pantelides (1906-84), actor. b, Pavlos Xioutas (1908-91), folklorist.

2015, Feb. 4   **Litho.**   **Perf. 14**
1226 A472   Horiz. pair   .25 .25
  a.-b.   4c Either single   .25 .25
1227 A472   Horiz. pair   2.25 2.25
  a.-b.   50c Either single   1.10 1.10
1228 A472   Horiz. pair   2.80 2.80
  a.-b.   60c Either single   1.40 1.40
1229 A472   Horiz. pair   3.50 3.50
  a.-b.   75c Either single   1.75 1.75
1230 A472   Horiz. pair   4.50 4.50
  a.-b.   €1 Either single   2.25 2.25
1231 A472   Horiz. pair   7.00 7.00
  a.-b.   €1.50 Either single   3.50 3.50
   Nos. 1226-1231 (6)   20.30 20.30

Melkonian
Orphanage
A475

2015, Apr. 2   **Litho.**   **Perf. 13¾x14¼**
1232 A475 64c multi   1.40 1.40
See Armenia No. 1034.

Preserved
Fruit — A476

Designs: 34c, Bitter orange. 41c, Bitter orange, diff. €1.88, Cherry.

2015, Apr. 2   **Litho.**   **Perf. 13¾**
1233-1235 A476   Set of 3   5.75 5.75

Souvenir Sheet

Independence Struggle of National
Organization of Cypriot Fighters, 60th
Anniv. — A477

**Litho., Sheet Margin Litho. With Foil
Application**
2015, Apr. 2   **Perf. 13¾**
1236 A477 €2 multi   4.50 4.50

Europa — A478

Children and: 34c, Top. 64c, Marbles.

2015, May 5   **Litho.**   **Perf. 14**
1237-1238 A478   Set of 2   2.25 2.25
1238a   Booklet pane of 8, 4 each
   #1237-1238, perf. 14 on 3
   sides   9.00   —
   Complete booklet, #1238a   9.00

Map of
Mediterranean
Sea and Cypriot
Boats — A479

2015, July 9   **Litho.**   **Perf. 14**
1239 A479 75c multi   1.75 1.75

Akamas Peninsula   Avakas
A480   Gorge
                  A481

2015, July 9   **Litho.**   **Perf. 14**
1240 A480 34c multi   .75 .75
1241 A481 64c multi   1.40 1.40

International Telecommunication
Union, 150th Anniv. — A482

2015, Sept. 14   **Litho.**   **Perf. 14**
1242 A482 64c multi   1.50 1.50

Castles — A483

Designs: 4c, Buffavento Castle. 34c, Kantara Castle. 41c, Agios Ilarionas (St. Hilarion) Castle. 75c, Kyrenia Castle.

Perf. 13¾x13½

2015, Sept. 14   **Litho.**
1243-1246 A483   Set of 4   3.50 3.50

Handicrafts — A484

No. 1247: a, Carved wooden chair. b, Decorated gourds.
No. 1248: a, Silver merrecha. b, Clay vessels.

2015, Sept. 14   **Litho.**   **Perf. 14**
1247 A484   Pair   1.50 1.50
   a.-b.   34c Either single   .75 .75
1248 A484   Pair   3.00 3.00
   a.-b.   64c Either single   1.50 1.50

A485   A486

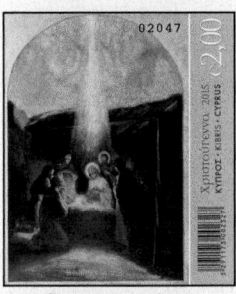

Christmas — A487

Designs: 34c, Girl burning olive leaves. 41c, Madonna and Child icon. 64c, Child mailing letter to Santa Claus. €2, Nativity.

2015, Nov. 19   **Litho.**   **Perf. 14**
1249 A485   34c multi   .75 .75
1250 A486   41c multi   .90 .90
1251 A485   64c multi   1.40 1.40
   Nos. 1249-1251 (3)   3.05 3.05

Imperf

1252 A487   €2 multi   4.25 4.25

Traditional
Crafts — A488

Designs: 41c, Basket weaving. 64c, Wood carving.

2016, Mar. 10   **Litho.**   **Perf. 14**
1253-1254 A488   Set of 2   2.40 2.40

2016
Summer
Olympics,
Rio de
Janeiro
A489

Designs: 34c, Taekwondo. 41c, Tennis. 64c, High jump. 75c, Sprinter.

2016, Apr. 11   **Litho.**   **Perf. 13¾**
1255-1258 A489   Set of 4   5.00 5.00

No. 1258 is a square stamp.

A490

Europa — A491

2016, May 9   **Litho.**   **Perf. 14**
1259 A490   34c multi   .80 .80
1260 A491   64c multi   1.50 1.50
   a.   Booklet pane of 8, 4 each
       #1259-1260, perf. 14 on 3
       sides   9.25 —

Think Green Issue.
No. 1260a was sold with but unattached to a booklet cover.

A492

Winning Art in "Principles
and Values of the
European Union"
Children's Stamp Design
Contest
A493   A494

2016, May 9   **Litho.**   **Perf. 14**
1261 A492   34c multi   .75 .75
1262 A493   41c multi   .95 .95
1263 A494   64c multi   1.50 1.50
   Nos. 1261-1263 (3)   3.20 3.20

Montage of Fish of
the Mediterranean
Sea — A495

2016, July 8   **Litho.**   **Perf. 14**
1264 A495   €1.88 multi   4.25 4.25

Fountains — A496

Designs: 34c, Children at Panayla Fountain, Paphos. 41c, Woman carrying water jug, Pegeia Fountain, Pegia.

2016, July 8   **Litho.**   **Perf. 14**
1265-1266 A496   Set of 2   1.75 1.75

Stelios   Georgios
Joannou   Paraskevaides
(1915-99),   (1916-2007),
Businessman   Businessman
and   and
Philanthropist   Philanthropist
A497   A498

Anastasios Georgios
Leventis (1902-78),
Businessman and
Philanthropist — A499

2016, Oct. 17   **Litho.**   **Perf. 14**
1267 A497   34c multi   .75 .75
1268 A498   34c multi   .75 .75
1269 A499   34c multi   .75 .75
   Nos. 1267-1269 (3)   2.25 2.25

Cyprus
Chairmanship of
the Council of
Europe — A500

2016, Nov. 17   **Litho.**   **Perf. 13¾**
1270 A500   €1 multi   2.25 2.25

A501   Christmas — A502

Designs: 34c, String of Christmas lights. 41c, Christmas tree. 64c, Adoration of the Magi icon.

2016, Nov. 17   **Litho.**   **Perf. 14**
1271 A501   34c multi   .75 .75
1272 A501   41c multi   .90 .90
1273 A502   64c multi   1.40 1.40
   Nos. 1271-1273 (3)   3.05 3.05

Flowers — A503

Designs; 34c, Crocus hartmannianus. 41c, Carlina pygmaea. 64c, Centaurea akamantis. €1, Tulipa cypria.

2017, Feb. 16   **Litho.**   **Perf. 14**
1274-1277 A503   Set of 4   5.00 5.00

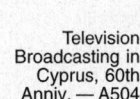

Television
Broadcasting in
Cyprus, 60th
Anniv. — A504

2017, Mar. 24   **Litho.**   **Perf. 14**
1278 A504   34c multi   .75 .75

Cyprus Medical
Association, 50th
Anniv. — A505

2017, Mar. 24   **Litho.**   **Perf. 14**
1279 A505   41c multi   .90 .90

Lions Clubs
International,
Cent. — A506

2017, Mar. 24   **Litho.**   **Perf. 14**
1280 A506   64c multi   1.40 1.40

Paphos, 2017
European Capital
of
Culture — A507

No. 1281: a, Aphrodite's Rock. b, Emblem. c, Pillars of House of Theseus.

2017, Mar. 24   **Litho.**   **Perf. 14**
1281   Horiz. strip of 3   4.25 4.25
   a.-c.   A507 64c Any single   1.40 1.40

International Year
of Sustainable
Tourism for
Development
A508

2017, May 4   **Litho.**   **Perf. 14**
1282 A508   64c multi   1.50 1.50

Europa — A509

Designs: 41c, Larnaca Castle. 64c, Paphos Castle.

2017, May 4   **Litho.**   **Perf. 14**
1283-1284 A509   Set of 2   2.40 2.40
   1284a   Booklet pane of 8, 4 each
       #1283-1284, perf. 14 on 3
       sides   9.75 —
       Complete booklet, #1284a   9.75

Stylized Tree — A510

2017, July 10   **Litho.**   **Perf. 14**
1285 A510   64c multi   1.50 1.50

Triptych From Church of Our Lady
Chryseleousa Strovolos — A511

Children
Opening
Gift
A512

Boy Writing Letter to
Santa Claus — A513

No. 1286: a, St. Minas the Egyptian (carmine panel at left). b, Madonna and Child, ship (carmine panel at bottom). c, St. Spyridon (carmine panel at right).
No. 1287: a, Child in red and white striped shirt, Santa Claus and reindeer. b, Child in green shirt.

2017, Nov. 24   **Litho.**   **Perf. 14**
1286 A511   34c Horiz. strip of 3,
       #a-c   2.50 2.50
1287 A512   41c Horiz. pair, #a-b   2.00 2.00
1288 A513   64c multi   1.60 1.60
   Nos. 1286-1288 (3)   6.10 6.10

Christmas.

Souvenir Sheet

St. Andrew the Apostle Monastery,
Rizokarpaso, 150th Anniv. — A514

Litho. With Foil Application
2017, Nov. 30   *Perf. 13¼x13*
1289 A514 €10 sil & multi   24.00 24.00

Flowers — A515

Designs: 34c, Allium sphaerocephalon. 41c, Anthemis tricolor. 64c, Onobrychis venosa. €1.88, Tragopogon porrifolius.

   Perf. 13¼x13½
2018, Feb. 12   Litho.
1290-1293 A515   Set of 4   8.00 8.00

Halloumi Cheese — A516

2018, Mar. 28   Litho.   *Perf. 14*
1294 A516 41c multi   1.00 1.00

2018 World Cup Soccer Championships, Russia — A517

2018, Mar. 28   Litho.   *Perf. 14*
1295 A517 64c multi   1.60 1.60

Marios Tokas (1954-2008), Composer — A518

2018, Apr. 27   Litho.   *Perf. 13¾x14¼*
1296 A518 64c multi   1.60 1.60

Europa — A519

Designs: 34c, Kelefos Bridge. 64c, Akapnou Bridge.

2018, May 2   Litho.   *Perf. 14*
1297-1298 A519   Set of 2   2.40 2.40
1298a   Booklet pane of 8, 4 each
    #1297-1298, perf. 14 on 3
    sides   9.75
    Complete booklet, #1298a   9.75

Houses, Lefkosa — A520

2018, July 9   Litho.   *Perf. 14*
1299 A520 64c multi   1.50 1.50

Interparliamentary Assembly on Orthodoxy, 25th Anniv. — A521

2018, July 9   Litho.   *Perf. 13¾x14¼*
1300 A521 64c multi   1.50 1.50

Birds — A522

Designs: 34c, Carduelis carduelis. 64c, Chloris chloris. €1, Fringilla coelebs.

2018, Sept. 27   Litho.   *Perf. 14*
1301-1303 A522   Set of 3   4.75 4.75

Children and Snowman A523   Nativity Icon, Panagia Odigitria Church, Galata A524

Children Singing Carols A525

No. 1306: a, Girl with triangle at left. b, Boy with drum at left.

   Perf. 14¼x14, 14 (41c)
2018, Nov. 8   Litho.
1304 A523 34c multi   .80 .80
1305 A524 41c multi   .95 .95
1306 A525 64c Horiz. pair, #a-b   3.00 3.00
    Nos. 1304-1306 (3)   4.75 4.75

Carnival — A526

Carnival revelers wearing: 41c, Clown and Native American costumes. 50c, Pirate and witch costumes.

   Perf. 13¾x13½
2019, Feb. 20   Litho.
1307-1308 A526   Set of 2   2.10 2.10

Old Trees — A527

Designs: 34c, 800-year old Platanus orientalis. 41c, 700-year old Cupressus sempervirens. 64c, 1500-year old Pistacia atlantica.

2019, Mar. 28   Litho.   *Perf. 13¾x14*
1309-1311 A527   Set of 3   3.25 3.25

Pres. Glafcos Clerides (1919-2013) — A528

2019, Apr. 20   Litho.   *Perf. 13¼*
1312 A528 €1 multi   2.25 2.25

Europa — A529

Birds: 41c, Gyps fulvus. 64c, Aquila fasciata.

2019, May 2   Litho.   *Perf. 13½*
1313-1314 A529   Set of 2   2.40 2.40
1314a   Booklet pane of 8, 4 each
    #1313-1314, perf. 13½ on
    3 sides   9.75
    Complete booklet, #1314a   9.75

Traditional Costumes of Men and Women of Cyprus — A530

2019, July 9   Litho.   *Perf. 13¼x13¾*
1315 A530 €1.88 multi   4.25 4.25

Miniature Sheet

Athletic Associations — A531

No. 1316 — Organization and year of establishment: a, Olympia Athletic Association, 1892. b, Pancypria Athletic Association, 1894. c, Zenon Athletic Association, 1896. d, Korivos Athletic Association, 1898. e, Evagoras Athletic Association of Ammochostos, 1903. f, Praxandros Athletic Association, 1919.

2019, July 9   Litho.   *Perf. 13¾x13¼*
1316 A531 34c Sheet of 6, #a-f   4.50 4.50

Council of Europe, 70th Anniv. — A532

   Perf. 13¾x13¼
2019, Sept. 10   Litho.
1317 A532 34c multi   .75 .75

International Civil Aviation Organization, 75th Anniv. — A533

   Perf. 13¾x13¼
2019, Sept. 10   Litho.
1318 A533 41c multi   .90 .90

Express Mail Service, 20th Anniv. — A534

   Perf. 13¾x13¼
2019, Sept. 10   Litho.
1319 A534 64c multi   1.40 1.40

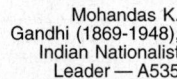

Mohandas K. Gandhi (1869-1948), Indian Nationalist Leader — A535

2019, Sept. 10   Litho.   *Perf. 13½*
1320 A535 75c multi   1.75 1.75

Angel — A536

Snowman A537   Painting of Our Lady of Araka A538

   Perf. 13¾x13¼
2019, Nov. 14   Litho.
1321 A536 34c multi   .75 .75
1322 A537 41c multi   .90 .90

   Perf. 13¼x13¾
1323 A538 64c multi   1.40 1.40
    Nos. 1321-1323 (3)   3.05 3.05
    Christmas.

Dams — A539

Designs: 50c, Asprokremmos Dam. €1, Kouris Dam.

   Perf. 13¼x13½
2020, Feb. 12   Litho.
1324-1325 A539   Set of 2   3.50 3.50

Butterflies A540

Designs: 34c, Aporia crataegi. 41c, Papilio machaon. 64c, Cigaritis acamas cypriaca.

   Perf. 13¼x13½
2020, Feb. 12   Litho.
1326-1328 A540   Set of 3   3.25 3.25

Stelios Kyriakides (1910-87), Marathon Runner and Humanitarian — A541

No. 1329 — Kyriakides: a, Wearing victory wreath on head. b, Running.

2020, Mar. 19   Litho.   *Perf. 13¼*
1329 A541 34c Pair, #a-b   1.50 1.50

2020 Olympic Games, Tokyo — A542

Designs: 34c, Gymnastics. 41c, Discus. 64c, High jump. 75c, Runner crossing finish line.

   Perf. 13½x13¼
2020, Mar. 19   Litho.
1330-1333 A542   Set of 4   4.75 4.75
   The 2020 Summer Olympics was postponed because of the coronavirus pandemic.

Florence Nightingale (1820-1910), Nurse — A543

2020, May 4   Litho.   *Perf. 13¾x13¼*
1334 A543 34c multi   .75 .75
   International Year of the Nurse and Midwife.

Europa — A544

Map of Cyprus postal routes with background color of: 34c, Olive green. 64c, Blue.

2020, May 4   Litho.   Perf. 13¾x13¼
1335-1336 A544   Set of 2   2.25 2.25
1336a   Booklet pane of 8, 4 each
                #1335-1336, perf.
                13¾x13¼ on 3 sides   9.00 —
                Complete booklet, #1336a 9.00

National Organization of Cypriot Fighters, 65th Anniv. — A545

2020, July 9   Litho.   Perf. 13¾x14
1337 A545 34c multi   .80 .80

National Organization of Cypriot Fighters House, 25th Anniv. — A546

2020, July 9   Litho.   Perf. 13¾x14
1338 A546 41c multi   1.00 1.00

Employers and Industrialists Federation, 60th Anniv. — A547

2020, July 9   Litho.   Perf. 13¾x13¼
1339 A547 41c multi   1.00 1.00

Kolokasi (Taro Stew) — A548

2020, July 9   Litho.   Perf. 13¼x13¾
1340 A548 64c multi   1.50 1.50

Famous People — A549

Designs: No. 1341, 34c, Nearchos Clerides (1892-1969), writer. No. 1342, 34c, Stella Soulioti (1920-2012), Attorney General. No. 1343, 34c, Vassos Lyssaridis, physician and politician.

Perf. 13¾x13¼
2020, Sept. 17   Litho.
1341-1343 A549 Set of 3   2.40 2.40
100th birthday of Lyssaridis.

Wreath of Christmas Cookies — A550

Christmas Cookies and Cakes — A551

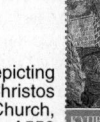

Fresco Depicting Nativity, Christos Antifonitis Church, Kalograia — A552

Perf. 13½x13¼
2020, Nov. 19   Litho.
1344 A550 34c multi   .85 .85
1345 A551 41c multi   1.00 1.00
Perf. 13¼x13¾
1346 A552 64c multi   1.60 1.60
Nos. 1344-1346 (3)   3.45 3.45

Famous Airplanes
A553

Designs: 34c, Wright Flyer, 1903. 75c, Spirit of St. Louis, 1927. €1, Bell X-1, 1947.

Perf. 13¾x13¼
2021, Feb. 18   Litho.
1347-1349 A553 Set of 3   5.00 5.00

Cyprus Cancer Association, 50th Anniv. — A554

Perf. 13¾x13¼
2021, Mar. 24   Litho.
1350 A554 34c multi   .80 .80

Cyprus Telecommunications Authority, 60th Anniv. — A555

Perf. 13¾x13¼
2021, Mar. 24   Litho.
1351 A555 41c multi   1.00 1.00

A556

Greek Revolution, 200th Anniv. — A557

Designs: 34c, Monument of Cypriot Fighters, Missolonghi, and Greek flag. 64c, Mausoleum of the Cypriot Martyrs of July 9, 1821, Nicosia, and Greek flag.
€1, The Bishop of Old Patras Germanos Blesses the Flag of Revolution, painting by Theodoros Vryzakis (1819-78).

Perf. 13¼x13¾
2021, Mar. 24   Litho.
1352-1353 A556   Set of 2   2.40 2.40
Souvenir Sheet
Litho. Sheet Margin Litho. With Foil Application
1354 A557 €1 multi   2.40 2.40

Efrosini Proestou (1903-93), Midwife Who Fed and Protected Soldiers Trapped in Cave — A558

2021, May 6   Litho.   Perf. 13¾x13¼
1355 A558 34c multi   .85 .85

Endangered Animals — A559

Designs: 34c, Apis mellifera cypria. 64c, Monachus monachus.

2021, May 6   Litho.   Perf. 13¾
1356-1357 A559 Set of 2   2.40 2.40
Europa.

14th-13th Cent. B.C. Gold Pendant — A560

2021, July 8   Litho.   Perf. 13¾x13¼
1358 A560 64c multi   1.60 1.60

Miniature Sheet

Natura 2000 Network of Protected Natural Areas — A561

No. 1359: a, Flamingos at Oroklini Lake. b, Mouflon in forest near Paphos. c, Snow crane on Akamas Peninsula. d, Caretta caretta and posidonia oceanica underwater.

2021, July 8   Litho.   Perf. 13½
1359 A561 34c Sheet of 4, #a-d 3.25 3.25

Cyprus Theater Organization, 50th Anniv. — A562

Perf. 13¼x13¾
2021, Sept. 17   Litho.
1360 A562 34c multi   .80 .80

Confucius (c. 551-479 B.C.) and Zenon of Citium (c. 334-262 B.C.), Philosophers
A563

Perf. 13¼x13¾
2021, Sept. 17   Litho.
1361 A563 75c multi   1.75 1.75
Diplomatic relations between Cyprus and People's Republic of China, 50th anniv.

Cats — A564

Cat: 34c, Facing forward. 41c, Sleeping. 50c, Facing left. 64c, Licking its paw.

Perf. 13¾x13¼
2021, Sept. 17   Litho.
1362-1365 A564 Set of 4   4.50 4.50

A565

Embroidered Christmas Ornaments A566

Nativity A567

Perf. 13¾x13¼
2021, Nov. 18   Litho.
1366 A565 34c multi   .80 .80
1367 A566 41c multi   .95 .95
Perf. 13¼x13¾
1368 A567 64c multi   1.50 1.50
Nos. 1366-1368 (3)   3.25 3.25
Christmas.

Human Rights Commission, 30th Anniv. — A568

Perf. 13¼x13½
2021, Dec. 10   Litho.
1369 A568 34c multi   .80 .80

Owls — A569

Designs: 34c, Tyto alba. 64c, Otus cyprius.

2022, Feb. 18   Litho.   Perf. 13¼
1370-1371 A569 Set of 2   2.25 2.25

Pancyprian Organization of Large Families, 50th Anniv. — A570

Perf. 13½x13¼
2022, Mar. 23   Litho.
1372 A570 34c multi   .75 .75

World Autism Awareness Day — A571

Perf. 13½x13¼

2022, Mar. 23   Litho.
1373 A571 41c multi   .90   .90

Limassol Chamber
of Commerce and
Industry, 60th
Anniv. — A572

Perf. 13½x13¼

2022, Mar. 23   Litho.
1374 A572 50c multi   1.10 1.10

Europa — A573

Designs: 34c, Legend of the Secret Treasure of Regina. 64c, Legend of Digenis
Akritas.

2022, May 6 Litho. Perf. 13¼x13¾
1375-1376 A573 Set of 2   2.10 2.10
1376a   Booklet pane of 8, 4 each
            #1375-1376, perf.
            13¼x13¾ on 3 sides   8.50   —
          Complete booklet, #1376a   8.50

Office of the
Commissioner for
Electronic
Communications and
Postal Regulation, 20th
Anniv. — A574

Perf. 13¼x13¾

2022, June 17   Litho.
1377 A574 64c multi   1.40 1.40

Maritime Link
Between Cyprus
and
Greece — A575

Perf. 13¾x13¼

2022, June 17   Litho.
1378 A575 64c multi   1.40 1.40

7th Century B.C.
Stone Vase
From Acropolis
of Amathunta
A576

2022, July 11 Litho. Perf. 13¾x13¼
1379 A576 64c multi   1.30 1.30

POSTAL TAX STAMPS

Catalogue values for unused
stamps in this section are for
Never Hinged items.

Unless otherwise stated, Cyprus postal tax stamps are for the Refugee
Fund.

No. 352 Surcharged

Perf. 12x12½

1974, Dec. 2   Wmk. 344
RA1 A104 10m on 5m multi   .70   .70

Old Woman and
Child — PT1

1974, Oct. 1   Perf. 12½x13½
RA2 PT1 10m gray & black   .60   .60

Child and Barbed
Wire — PT2

Perf. 13x12½

1977, Jan. 10 Litho. Wmk. 344
RA3 PT2 10m black   .60   .60

Inscribed 1984

1984, June 18   Perf. 13x12½
RA4 PT2 1c black   .60   .60
    There are two types of No. RA4.

Inscribed 1988 — PT3

1988-2007   Perf. 13x12½
Design Size 22x28mm
RA5 PT3 1c black & pale
            gray   .60   .60
Perf. 11½x12
RA6 PT3 1c Inscribed 1989   .60   .60
RA7 PT3 1c Inscribed 1990   .60   .60
Unwmk.
Perf. 13
RA8 PT3 1c Inscribed 1991   .60   .60
RA9 PT3 1c Inscribed 1992   .60   .60
RA10 PT3 1c Inscribed 1993   .60   .60
RA11 PT3 1c Inscribed 1994   .60   .60
Perf. 14½x13¾
Design Size 21x24.5mm
RA12 PT3 1c Inscribed 1995   .60   .60
RA13 PT3 1c Inscribed 1996   .60   .60
RA14 PT3 1c Inscribed 1997   .60   .60
RA15 PT3 1c Inscribed 1998   .60   .60
RA16 PT3 1c Inscribed 1999   .60   .60
RA17 PT3 1c Inscribed 2000   .60   .60
RA18 PT3 1c Inscribed 2001   .60   .60
Size: 22x27mm
Perf. 12¾
RA19 PT3 1c Inscribed 2002   .60   .60
RA20 PT3 1c Inscribed 2003   .60   .60
Perf. 12¾x13
RA21 PT3 1c Inscribed 2004   .60   .60
RA22 PT3 1c Inscribed 2005   .60   .60
RA23 PT3 1c Inscribed 2006   .60   .60
Perf. 13½x14
RA24 PT3 1c Inscribed 2007   .50   .50
    Nos. RA5-RA24 (20)   11.90 11.90

Issued: No. RA5, 9/12/88; No. RA6, 9/4/89;
No. RA7, 9/29/90; No. RA8, 10/7/91; No. RA9,
11/9/92; No. RA10, 1993; No. RA11, 11/21/94;
No. RA12, 10/24/95; No. RA13, 6/10/96; No.
RA14, 6/30/97; No. RA15, 1998; No. RA16,
1999; No. RA17, 2000; No. RA18, 2001. No.
RA19, 2002. No. RA19, 2003. No. RA20,
2003. No. RA21, 11/11/04. No. RA22, 6/16/05.
No. RA23, 5/4/06. No. RA24, 3/15/07.

Child and Barbed Wire
With Denomination in
Euro Currency — PT4

2008-21 Litho. Perf. 13½x14
RA25 PT4 2c dk gray & gray   .50   .50
Inscribed "2009"
RA26 PT4 2c blk & lilac gray .50   .50
Inscribed "2010"
RA27 PT4 2c blk & tan   .50   .50
Inscribed "2011"
RA28 PT4 2c blk & lt green   .50   .50

Booklet Stamp
Self-Adhesive
Die Cut Perf. 13½x14¼
RA28A PT4 2c blk & lt grn   .50   .50
    b.   Booklet pane of 12, 6 each
          #1153A, RA28A   18.00
Inscribed "2012"
Perf. 13½
RA29 PT4 2c blk & lt blue   .50   .50
Inscribed "2013"
RA30 PT4 2c blk & dull org   .50   .50
Inscribed "2014"
RA31 PT4 2c blk & gray   .50   .50
Inscribed "2015"
RA32 PT4 2c blk & bl gray   .50   .50
Inscribed "2016"
RA33 PT4 2c ol gray & lt
            brnish gray   .50   .50
Inscribed "2017"
Perf. 13½x14
RA34 PT4 2c blk & bl gray   .50   .50
Inscribed "2018"
Perf. 13½
RA35 PT4 2c blk & grnsh gray .25   .25
Inscribed "2019"
Perf. 13x13¼
RA36 PT4 2c blk & olive grn .25   .25
Inscribed "2020"
Perf. 12¾x13¼
RA37 PT4 2c blk & gray   .25   .25
Inscribed "2021"
RA38 PT4 2c black & buff   .25   .25

Issued: Nos. RA28, RA28A, 5/4/11; No.
RA29, 1/31/12; No. RA30, 1/30/13; No. RA31,
3/12/14; No. RA32, 4/2/15; No. RA33, 3/10/16;
No. RA34, 2/16/17; No. RA35, 2/12/18; No.
RA36, 2/20/19; No. RA37, 2/12/20; No. RA38,
2/18/21.

CYRENAICA

ˌsir-ə-ˈnā-ə-kə

LOCATION — In northern Africa bor-
dering on the Mediterranean Sea
GOVT. — Italian colony
AREA — 75,340 sq. mi.
POP. — 225,000 (approx. 1934)
CAPITAL — Bengasi (Benghazi)

Cyrenaica was an Italian Colony. In
1949 Great Britain granted the Amir of
Cyrenaica autonomy in internal affairs.
Cyrenaica was incorporated into the
kingdom of Libya in 1951.

100 Centesimi = 1 Lira
1000 Milliemes = 1 Pound (1950)

Catalogue values for unused
stamps in this country are for
Never Hinged items, beginning
with Scott 65 in the regular postage section, Scott J1 in the postage due section.

Used values in italics are for postally used stamps. CTO's sell for
about the same as unused, hinged
stamps.

Watermark

Wmk. 140 — Crown

Propaganda of the Faith Issue
Italy Nos. 143-146 Overprinted

1923, Oct. 24   Wmk. 140   Perf. 14
1 A68 20c ol grn & brn
          org   8.00 35.00
2 A68 30c claret & brn
          org   8.00 35.00
3 A68 50c violet & brn org 5.00 40.00
4 A68 1 l blue & brn org 10.00 60.00
    Nos. 1-4 (4)   31.00 170.00
    Set, never hinged   65.00

Fascisti Issue

Italy Nos. 159-164
Overprinted in Red or
Black

1923, Oct. 29   Unwmk.   Perf. 14
5 A69 10c dk grn (R)   9.00 13.00
6 A69 30c dk vio (R)   9.00 13.00
7 A69 50c brn car   9.00 17.50
Wmk. 140
8 A70 1 l blue   9.00 32.50
9 A70 2 l brown   9.00 37.50
10 A71 5 l blk & bl (R)   9.00 60.00
    Nos. 5-10 (6)   54.00 173.50
    Set, never hinged   112.50

Manzoni Issue

Italy Nos. 165-
170 Ovptd. in
Red

1924, Apr. 1   Perf. 14
11 A72 10c brn red &
          blk   9.00 45.00
12 A72 15c bl grn & blk 9.00 45.00
13 A72 30c blk & slate   9.00 45.00
14 A72 50c org brn &
          blk   9.00 45.00
15 A72 1 l blk & blk   55.00 275.00
    a. Double overprint 825.00
        Never hinged   1,250.
16 A72 5 l vio & blk   350.00 2,250.
    Nos. 11-16 (6)   441.00 2,705.
    Set, never hinged   930.00

Vertical overprints on Nos. 11-14 are
essays. On Nos. 15-16 the overprint is vertical
at the left.
All examples of No. 15a are poorly
centered.

Victor Emmanuel Issue

Italy Nos. 175-177
Overprinted

1925-26   Unwmk.   Perf. 11
17 A78 60c brn car   1.35   7.25
18 A78 1 l dark blue   1.35   7.25
19 A78 1.25 l dk bl ('26) 3.75 10.00
    a. Perf. 13½   360.00 1,000.
        Never hinged   900.00
    Nos. 17-19 (3)   6.45 24.50
    Set, never hinged   16.00

Issue dates: Nov. 1925, July 1926.

Saint Francis of Assisi Issue

Italian Stamps of
1926 Ovptd.

1926, Apr. 12   Wmk. 140   Perf. 14
20 A79 20c gray green   2.00   8.50
21 A80 40c dark violet   2.00   8.50
22 A81 60c red brown   2.00 15.00

Ovptd. in Red

Unwmk.

23	A82	1.25 l dk bl, perf. 11	2.00	20.00
24	A83	5 l + 2.50 l ol grn	4.50	42.50
		Nos. 20-24 (5)	12.50	94.50
		Set, never hinged	31.50	

Volta Issue

Type of Italy 1927, Overprinted

1927, Oct. 10   Wmk. 140   Perf. 14

25	A84	20c purple	4.50	23.00
26	A84	50c dp org	5.50	16.00
27	A84	1.25 l brt bl	9.50	37.50
		Nos. 25-27 (3)	19.50	76.50
		Set, never hinged	35.00	

Monte Cassino Issue

Types of 1929 Issue of Italy, Ovptd. in Red or Blue

1929, Oct. 14

28	A96	20c dk grn (R)	4.50	12.75
29	A96	25c red org (Bl)	4.50	12.75
30	A98	50c + 10c crim (Bl)	4.50	13.50
31	A98	75c + 15c ol brn (R)	4.50	13.50
32	A96	1.25 l + 25c dk vio (R)	9.00	25.00
33	A98	5 l + 1 l saph (R)	9.00	27.50

Overprinted in Red

Unwmk.

34	A100	10 l + 2 l gray brn	9.00	40.00
		Nos. 28-34 (7)	45.00	145.00
		Set, never hinged	114.00	

Royal Wedding Issue

Type of Italian Stamps of 1930 Overprinted

1930, Mar. 17   Wmk. 140

35	A101	20c yel grn	2.25	5.50
36	A101	50c + 10c dp org	1.60	7.25
37	A101	1.25 l + 25c rose red	1.60	11.00
		Nos. 35-37 (3)	5.45	23.75
		Set, never hinged	13.75	

Ferrucci Issue

Types of Italian Stamps of 1930, Ovptd. in Red or Blue

1930, July 26

38	A102	20c violet (R)	5.50	4.50
39	A103	25c dk grn (R)	5.50	4.50
40	A103	50c black (R)	5.50	10.00
41	A103	1.25 l dp bl (R)	5.50	16.00
42	A104	5 l + 2 l dp car	12.00	35.00
		Nos. 38-42 (5)	34.00	70.00
		Set, never hinged	84.00	

Virgil Issue

Italian Stamps of 1930 Ovptd. in Red or Blue

1930, Dec. 4

43	A106	15c vio blk	.75	7.00
44	A106	20c org brn (Bl)	.75	2.75
45	A106	25c dk grn	.75	2.75
46	A106	30c lt brn (Bl)	.75	2.75
47	A106	50c dl vio	.75	2.75
48	A106	75c rose red (Bl)	.75	5.50
49	A106	1.25 l gray blk	.75	6.75

Unwmk.

50	A106	5 l + 1.50 l dk vio	2.75	27.50
51	A106	10 l + 2.50 l ol brn (Bl)	2.75	42.50
		Nos. 43-51 (9)	10.75	100.25
		Set, never hinged	26.00	

Saint Anthony of Padua Issue

Italian Stamps of 1931 Ovptd. in Blue or Red

1931, May 7   Wmk. 140

52	A116	20c brown (Bl)	1.10	13.75
53	A116	25c green (R)	1.10	5.50
54	A118	30c gray brn (Bl)	1.10	5.50
55	A118	50c dl vio (Bl)	1.10	5.50
56	A120	1.25 l slate bl (R)	1.10	13.75

Overprinted like Nos. 23-24 in Red or Black

Unwmk.

57	A121	75c black (R)	1.10	25.00
58	A122	5 l + 2.50 l dk brn	8.25	50.00
		Nos. 52-58 (7)	14.85	119.00
		Set, never hinged	37.50	

Carabineer — A1

1934, Oct. 16   Photo.   Wmk. 140

59	A1	5c dk ol grn & brn	4.00	12.75
60	A1	10c brn & blk	4.00	12.75
61	A1	20c scar & indigo	4.00	11.50
62	A1	50c pur & brn	4.00	11.50
63	A1	60c org brn & ind	4.00	16.00
64	A1	1.25 l dk bl & grn	4.00	27.50
		Nos. 59-64 (6)	24.00	92.00
		Set, never hinged	60.00	

2nd Colonial Art Exhibition held at Naples. See Nos. C24-C29.

> **Catalogue values for unused stamps in this section, from this point to the end of the section, are for Never Hinged items.**

Autonomous State

Senussi Warrior
A2   A3

Perf. 12½

1950, Jan. 16   Unwmk.   Engr.

65	A2	1m dark brown	.65	2.25
66	A2	2m rose car	.85	2.00
67	A2	3m orange	.85	2.00
68	A2	4m dark green	4.25	3.25
69	A2	5m gray	1.10	1.25
70	A2	8m red orange	1.25	1.50
71	A2	10m purple	1.25	1.50
72	A2	12m red	1.25	1.50
73	A2	20m deep blue	1.25	1.50
74	A3	50m choc & ultra	6.75	8.50
75	A3	100m bl blk & car rose	21.00	42.50
76	A3	200m vio & pur	25.00	67.50
77	A3	500m dk grn & org	110.00	135.00
		Nos. 65-77 (13)	175.45	270.25

SEMI-POSTAL STAMPS

Many issues of Italy and Italian Colonies include one or more semipostal

denominations. To avoid splitting sets, these issues are generally listed as regular postage unless all values carry a surtax.

Holy Year Issue
Italian Semi-Postal Stamps of 1924 Overprinted in Black or Red

1925, June 1   Wmk. 140   Perf. 12

B1	SP4	20c + 10c dk grn & brn	2.25	14.00
B2	SP4	30c + 15c dk brn & brn	2.25	15.00
B3	SP4	50c + 25c vio & brn	2.25	14.00
B4	SP4	60c + 30c dp rose & brn	2.25	18.00
B5	SP8	1 l + 50c dp bl & vio (R)	2.25	22.50
B6	SP8	5 l + 2.50 l org brn & vio (R)	2.25	35.00
		Nos. B1-B6 (6)	13.50	118.50
		Set, never hinged	34.50	

Colonial Institute Issue

"Peace" Substituting Spade for Sword — SP1

1926, June 1   Typo.   Perf. 14

B7	SP1	5c + 5c brown	.75	5.50
B8	SP1	10c + 5c olive grn	.75	5.50
B9	SP1	20c + 5c blue grn	.75	5.50
B10	SP1	40c + 5c brown red	.75	5.50
B11	SP1	60c + 5c orange	.75	5.50
B12	SP1	1 l + 5c blue	.75	11.50
		Nos. B7-B12 (6)	4.50	39.00
		Set, never hinged	10.50	

Surtax for Italian Colonial Institute.

Types of Italian Semi-Postal Stamps of 1926 Overprinted like Nos. 17-19
1927, Apr. 21   Unwmk.   Perf. 11

B13	SP10	40c + 20c dk brn & blk	2.20	25.00
B14	SP10	60c + 30c brn red & ol brn	2.20	25.00
B15	SP10	1.25 l + 60c dp bl & blk	2.20	37.50
a.		Double overprint	1,450.	
		Never hinged	2,200.	
B16		5 l + 2.50 l dk grn & blk	3.75	57.50
		Nos. B13-B16 (4)	10.35	145.00
		Set, never hinged	21.00	

The surtax on these stamps was for the charitable work of the Voluntary Militia for Italian National Defense.

Allegory of Fascism and Victory — SP2

1928, Oct. 15   Wmk. 140   Perf. 14

B17	SP2	20c + 5c bl grn	2.25	8.25
B18	SP2	30c + 5c red	2.25	8.25
B19	SP2	50c + 10c purple	2.25	14.00
B20	SP2	1.25 l + 20c dk bl	2.75	18.00
		Nos. B17-B20 (4)	9.50	48.50
		Set, never hinged	24.50	

46th anniv. of the Societa Africana d'Italia. The surtax aided that society.

1926 Italian Semi-Postal Types Overprinted in Red or Black

1929, Mar. 4   Unwmk.   Perf. 11

B21	SP10	30c + 10c red & blk (Bk)	2.75	16.00
B22	SP10	50c + 20c vio & blk	2.75	17.50
B23	SP10	1.25 l + 50c brn & bl	4.25	30.00
B24	SP10	5 l + 2 l ol grn & blk	4.25	60.00
		Nos. B21-B24 (4)	14.00	123.50
		Set, never hinged	35.50	

Surtax for the charitable work of the Voluntary Militia for Italian Natl. Defense.

Types of Italian Semi-Postal Stamps of 1926 Overprinted in Black or Red like Nos. 52-56
1930, Oct. 20   Perf. 14

B25	SP10	30c + 10c dk grn & bl (Bk)	25.00	55.00
B26	SP10	50c + 10c dk grn & vio	25.00	80.00
B27	SP10	1.25 l + 30c ol brn & red brn	25.00	80.00
B28	SP10	5 l + 1.50 l ind & grn	100.00	215.00
		Nos. B25-B28 (4)	175.00	430.00
		Set, never hinged	438.00	

Surtax for the charitable work of the Voluntary Militia for Italian Natl. Defense.

Sower — SP3

1930, Nov. 27   Photo.   Wmk. 140

B29	SP3	50c + 20c ol brn	2.75	16.00
B30	SP3	1.25 l + 20c dp bl	2.75	16.00
B31	SP3	1.75 l + 20c green	2.75	18.00
B32	SP3	2.55 l + 50c purple	8.25	27.50
B33	SP3	5 l + 1 l dp car	8.25	42.50
		Nos. B29-B33 (5)	24.75	120.00
		Set, never hinged	67.00	

25th anniv. of the Italian Colonial Agricultural Institute. The surtax was for the aid of that institution.

AIR POST STAMPS

Air Post Stamps of Tripolitania, 1931, Overprinted in Blue like Nos. 38-42

1932, Jan. 7   Wmk. 140   Perf. 14

C1	AP1	50c rose car	1.00	.25
C2	AP1	60c dp org	4.00	9.00
C3	AP1	80c dl vio	4.00	14.00
		Nos. C1-C3 (3)	9.00	23.25
		Set, never hinged	22.50	

Air Post Stamps of Tripolitania, 1931, Overprinted in Blue

1932, May 12

C4	AP1	50c rose car	1.00	1.20
C5	AP1	80c dull violet	4.50	17.50
		Set, never hinged	14.00	

This overprint was also applied to the 60c, Tripolitania No. C9. The overprinted stamp was never used in Cyrenaica, but was sold at Rome in 1943 by the Postmaster General for the Italian Colonies. Value $10.

Arab on Camel   Airplane in Flight
AP2   AP3

1932, Aug. 8   **Photo.**

C6	AP2	50c purple	11.00	.25
C7	AP2	75c brn rose	11.00	10.00
C8	AP2	80c deep blue	11.00	19.00
C9	AP3	1 l black	4.50	.25
C10	AP3	2 l green	4.50	11.50
C11	AP3	5 l deep car	7.70	22.50
		Nos. C6-C11 (6)	49.70	63.50
		Set, never hinged	124.50	

For surcharges and overprint see Nos. C20-C23.

Graf Zeppelin Issue

Zeppelin and Clouds forming Pegasus — AP4

Zeppelin and Ancient Galley — AP5

Zeppelin and Giant Bowman — AP6

1933, Apr. 15

C12	AP4	3 l dk brn	10.00	72.50
C13	AP5	5 l purple	10.00	72.50
C14	AP6	10 l dp grn	10.00	135.00
C15	AP5	12 l deep blue	10.00	150.00
C16	AP4	15 l carmine	10.00	150.00
C17	AP6	20 l black	10.00	200.00
		Nos. C12-C17 (6)	60.00	780.00
		Set, never hinged	150.00	

North Atlantic Crossing Issue

Airplane Squadron and Constellations AP7

1933, June 1

C18	AP7	19.75 l grn & dp bl	13.75	375.00
C19	AP7	44.75 l red & indigo	14.00	375.00
		Set, never hinged	70.00	

Type of 1932 Ovptd. and Srchd.

1934, Jan. 20

C20	AP3	2 l on 5 l org brn	3.25	55.00
C21	AP3	3 l on 5 l yel grn	3.25	55.00
C22	AP3	5 l ocher	3.25	65.00
C23	AP3	10 l on 5 l rose	4.50	65.00
		Nos. C20-C23 (4)	14.25	240.00
		Set, never hinged	35.50	

For use on mail to be carried on a special flight from Rome to Buenos Aires.

Transport Plane — AP8

Venus of Cyrene — AP9

1934, Oct. 9

C24	AP8	25c sl bl & org red	4.00	13.00
C25	AP8	50c dk grn & ind	4.00	11.50
C26	AP8	75c dk brn & org red	4.00	11.50
a.		Imperf.	3,000.	
		Never hinged	4,500.	

C27	AP9	80c org brn & ol grn	4.00	12.50
C28	AP9	1 l scar & ol grn	4.00	16.00
C29	AP9	2 l dk bl & brn	4.00	27.50
		Nos. C24-C29 (6)	24.00	92.00
		Set, never hinged	60.00	

2nd Colonial Arts Exhib. held at Naples.

AIR POST SEMI-POSTAL STAMPS

King Victor Emmanuel III — SPAP1

Wmk. 104

1934, Nov. 5   **Photo.**   *Perf. 14*

CB1	SPAP1	25c + 10c gray grn	9.00	16.00
CB2	SPAP1	50c + 10c brn	9.00	16.00
CB3	SPAP1	75c + 15c rose red	9.00	16.00
CB4	SPAP1	80c + 15c brn blk	9.00	16.00
CB5	SPAP1	1 l + 20c red brn	9.00	16.00
CB6	SPAP1	2 l + 20c brt bl	9.00	16.00
CB7	SPAP1	3 l + 25c pur	22.50	72.50
CB8	SPAP1	5 l + 25c org	22.50	72.50
CB9	SPAP1	10 l + 30c dp vio	22.50	72.50
CB10	SPAP1	25 l + 2 l dp grn	22.50	72.50
		Nos. CB1-CB10 (10)	144.00	386.00
		Set, never hinged	365.00	

65th birthday of King Victor Emmanuel III and the non-stop flight, Rome-Mogadiscio.

AIR POST SEMI-POSTAL OFFICIAL STAMP

Type of Air Post Semi-Postal Stamps, 1934, Overprinted Crown and "SERVIZIO DI STATO" in Black

1934, Nov. 5   **Wmk. 140**   *Perf. 14*

CBO1	SPAP1	25 l + 2 l cop red		1,500.

POSTAGE DUE STAMPS

> Catalogue values for unused stamps in this section are for Never Hinged items.

D1

Perf. 12½

1950, July 1   **Unwmk.**   **Engr.**

J1	D1	2m dark brown	77.50	110.00
J2	D1	4m deep green	77.50	110.00
J3	D1	8m scarlet	77.50	110.00
J4	D1	10m vermilion	77.50	120.00
J5	D1	20m orange yel	77.50	120.00
J6	D1	40m deep blue	77.50	160.00
J7	D1	100m dark gray	77.50	250.00
		Nos. J1-J7 (7)	542.50	980.00

CZECHOSLOVAKIA

ˌche-kə-slō-'vä-kē-ə

LOCATION — Central Europe
GOVT. — Republic
AREA — 49,355 sq. mi.

POP. — 15,395,970 (1983 est.)
CAPITAL — Prague

The Czechoslovakian Republic consists of Bohemia, Moravia and Silesia, Slovakia and Ruthenia (Carpatho-Ukraine). In March 1939, a German protectorate was established over Bohemia and Moravia, as well as over Slovakia which had meanwhile declared its independence. Ruthenia was incorporated in the territory of Hungary. These territories were returned to the Czechoslovak Republic in 1945, except for Ruthenia, which was ceded to Russia. Czechoslovakia became a federal state on Jan. 2, 1969. On Jan. 1, 1993 Czechoslovakia separated into Slovakia and the Czech Republic. See Volume 5 for the stamps of Slovakia.

100 Haleru = 1 Koruna

> Catalogue values for unused stamps in this country are for Never Hinged items, beginning with Scott 142 in the regular postage section, B144 in the semi-postal section, Scott C19 in the air post section, Scott EX1 in the personal delivery section, and Scott J58 in the postage due section, Scott O1 int he officials section, and Scott P14 in the newspaper section.

Watermarks

Wmk. 107 — Linden Leaves (Vertical)

Wmk. 135 — Crown in Oval or Circle, Sideways

Wmk. 136

Wmk. 136a

Wmk. 341 — Striped Ovals

Stamps of Austria overprinted "Ceskoslovenska Republika," lion and "Cesko Slovensky Stat," "Provisorni Ceskoslovenska Vlada" and Arms, and "Ceskoslovenska Statni Posta" and Arms were made privately. A few of them were passed through the post but all have been pronounced unofficial and unauthorized by the Postmaster General.

During the occupation of part of Northern Hungary by the Czechoslovak forces, stamps of Hungary were overprinted "Cesko Slovenska Posta," "Ceskoslovenska Statni Posta" and Arms, and "Slovenska Posta" and Arms. These stamps were never officially issued though examples have passed the post.

Hradcany at Prague — A1

1918-19   **Unwmk.**   **Typo.**   *Imperf.*

1	A1	3h red violet	.25	.25
2	A1	5h yellow green	.25	.25
3	A1	10h rose	.25	.25
4	A1	20h bluish green	.25	.25
5	A1	25h deep blue	.25	.25
6	A1	30h bister	.35	.25
7	A1	40h red orange	.35	.25
8	A1	100h brown	.75	.25
9	A1	200h ultra	1.50	.25
10	A1	400h purple	3.00	.25

On the 3h-40h "Posta Ceskoslovenska" is in white on a colored background; on the higher values the words are in color on a white background.

No. 5c was not valid for postage.

Nos. 1-6 exist as tete-beche gutter pairs.

See Nos. 368, 1554, 1600. For surcharges see Nos. B130, C1, C4, J15, J19-J20, J22-J23, J30.

Perf. 11½, 13½

13	A1	5h yellow green	.60	.25
a.		Perf. 11½x10¾	3.00	.45
14	A1	10h rose	.35	.25
15	A1	20h bluish green	.35	.25
a.		Perf. 11½	.35	.25
16	A1	25h deep blue	.75	.35
a.		Perf. 11½	1.50	.35
20	A1	200h ultra	6.00	.25
		Nos. 1-10,13-16,20 (15)	15.25	3.85

All values of this issue exist with various private perforations and examples have been used on letters.

The 3h, 30h, 40h, 100h and 400h formerly listed are now known to have been privately perforated.

For overprints see Eastern Silesia Nos. 2, 5, 7-8, 14, 16, 18, 30.

A2

Type II

Type III

Type IV

Type II — Sun behind cathedral. Colorless foliage in foreground.
Type III — Without sun. Shaded foliage in foreground.
Type IV — No foliage in foreground. Positions of buildings changed. Letters redrawn.

1919   *Imperf.*

23	A2	1h dark brown (II)	.25	.25
25	A2	5h blue green (IV)	.35	.25
27	A2	15h red (IV)	.35	.25
29	A2	25h dull violet (IV)	.65	.25
30	A2	50h dull violet (II)	.40	.25
31	A2	50h dark blue (IV)	.35	.25
32	A2	60h orange (III)	1.50	.25
33	A2	75h slate (IV)	1.10	.25
34	A2	80h olive grn (III)	.75	.25
36	A2	120h gray black (IV)	2.25	.25
38	A2	300h dark green (III)	7.00	.35
39	A2	500h red brown (IV)	7.00	.25
40	A2	1000h violet (III)	15.00	1.10
a.		1000h bluish violet	35.00	2.25
		Nos. 23-40 (13)	36.95	4.20

For overprints see Eastern Silesia Nos. 1, 3-4, 6, 9-13, 15, 17, 20-21.

1919-20   *Perf. 11½, 13¾, 13¾x11½*

41	A2	1h dk brown (II)	.25	.25
42	A2	5h blue grn (IV),		
		perf. 13½	.60	.25
a.		Perf. 11½	25.00	5.00
43	A2	10h yellow grn (IV)	.35	.25
a.		Imperf.	17.50	14.00
b.		Perf. 11¾	10.00	1.00
44	A2	15h brick red (IV)	.35	.25
a.		Perf. 11½x10¾	27.50	5.00
b.		Perf. 11¾x13¾	75.00	22.50
c.		Perf. 13¾x10¾	100.00	22.50
45	A2	20h rose (IV)	.60	.25
a.		Imperf.	90.00	85.00
46	A2	25h dull vio (IV),		
		perf. 11½	.65	.25
a.		Perf. 11½x10¾	4.50	1.10
b.		Perf. 13¾x10¾	150.00	37.50
47	A2	30h red violet (IV)	.35	.25
a.		Imperf.	150.00	175.00
b.		Perf. 13¾x13½	450.00	175.00
c.		30h deep violet	.60	.25
d.		As "c," perf. 13¾x13½	525.00	190.00
e.		As "c," imperf.	150.00	160.00
50	A2	60h orange (III)	.40	.25
a.		Imperf.	15.00	4.50
53	A2	120h gray black (IV)	4.00	1.00
		Nos. 41-53 (9)	7.55	3.00

Nos. 43a, 45a, 47a and 47e were imperforate by accident and not issued in quantities as were Nos. 23 to 40.

Rouletted stamps of the preceding issues are said to have been made by a postmaster in a branch post office at Prague, or by private firms, but without authority from the Post Office Department.

The 50, 75, 80, 300, 500 and 1000h have been privately perforated.

Unlisted color varieties of types A1 and A2 were not officially released, and some are printer's waste.

For surcharges and overprints see Nos. B131, C2-C3, C5-C6, J16-J18, J21, J24-J29, J31, J42-J43, Eastern Silesia 22-29.

Pres. Thomas Garrigue
Masaryk — A4

1920   *Perf. 13½*

61	A4	125h gray blue	1.50	1.00
a.		125h ultramarine	20.00	19.00
62	A4	500h slate, *grysh*	2.50	1.50
63	A4	1000h blk brn, *brnsh*	6.50	3.00
		Nos. 61-63 (3)	10.50	4.75

Nos. 61, 61a, 63 imperf. were not regularly issued. Values: unused singles, No. 61 $30; No. 61a $150; No. 63 $40.

For surcharge and overprints, see Nos. B131, Eastern Silesia 31-32.

Carrier Pigeon with
Letter — A5

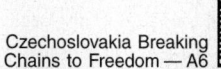

Czechoslovakia Breaking
Chains to Freedom — A6

Hussite
Priest
A7

Agriculture
and Science
A8

	Type I	Type II

Two types of 40h:
Type I: 9 leaves by woman's hip.
Type II: 10 leaves by woman's hip.

1920   *Perf. 14*

65	A5	5h dark blue	.25	.25
a.		Perf. 13¾	275.00	150.00
66	A5	10h blue green	.25	.25
a.		Perf. 13¾	125.00	110.00
67	A5	15h red brown	.25	.25
68	A6	20h rose	.25	.25
69	A6	25h lilac brown	.25	.25
70	A6	30h red violet	.25	.25

71	A6	40h red brown (I)	.50	.25
a.		As "b," tête bêche pair	2.50	1.50
b.		Perf. 13½	.60	.25
c.		Type II	.25	.25
72	A6	50h carmine	.35	.25
73	A6	60h dark blue	.35	.25
a.		As "b," tête bêche pair	3.50	3.50
b.		Perf. 13½	.35	1.50

Photo.

74	A7	80h purple	.25	.25
75	A7	90h black brown	.30	.25

Typo.
Perf. 13¾

76	A8	100h dark green	.50	.25
77	A8	200h violet	.75	.25
78	A8	300h vermilion	1.50	.25
a.		Perf. 13¾x13½	4.50	.35
79	A8	400h brown	3.50	.45
80	A8	500h deep green	3.50	.45
a.		Perf. 13¾x13½	40.00	5.50
81	A8	600h deep violet	4.50	.45
a.		Perf. 13¾x13½	125.00	7.00
		Nos. 65-81 (17)	17.50	4.85

No. 69 has background of horizontal lines. Imperfs. were not regularly issued.

Nos. 71 and 73 exist as tête-beche gutter pairs.

For surcharges and overprint see Nos. C7-C9, J44-J56.

Type I	Type II

Two types of 20h:
Type I: Base of 2 is long, interior of 0 is angular.
Type II: Base of 2 is short, interior of 0 is an oval.

Type I	Type II

Two types of 25h:
Type I: Top of 2 curves up.
Type II: Top of 2 curves down.

1920-25   *Perf. 14*

82	A5	5h violet	.25	.25
a.		As "b," tête bêche pair	2.00	1.00
b.		Perf. 13½	1.00	.35
83	A5	10h olive bister	.25	.25
a.		As "b," tête bêche pair	2.00	1.50
b.		Perf. 13½	.60	.35
84	A5	20h deep orange (II)	.25	.25
a.		As "b," tête bêche pair	14.00	15.00
b.		Perf. 13½	3.50	.60
c.		Type I	—	—
85	A5	25h blue green (I)	.25	.25
a.		Type II	.25	.25
86	A5	30h deep violet ('25)	3.00	.25
87	A6	50h yellow green	.60	.25
a.		As "b," tête bêche pair	27.50	27.50
b.		Perf. 13½	7.50	2.00
88	A6	100h dark brown	1.00	.25
a.		Perf. 13½	15.00	.30
89	A6	150h rose	2.00	.50
a.		Perf. 13½	35.00	2.00
90	A6	185h orange	1.50	.30
91	A6	250h dark green	2.25	.50
		Nos. 82-91 (10)	11.35	3.05

Imperfs. were not regularly issued.
Nos. 82-84, 87 exist as tête-beche gutter pairs.

Type of 1920 Issue Redrawn

Type I	Type II	Type III

Type I — Rib of leaf below "O" of POSTA is straight and extends to tip. White triangle above book is entirely at left of twig. "P" has a stubby, abnormal appendage.
Type II — Rib is extremely bent; does not reach tip. Triangle extends at right of twig. "P" like Type I.
Type III — Rib of top left leaf is broken in two. Triangle like Type II. "P" has no appendage.

1923   *Perf. 13¾, 13¾x13½*

92	A8	100h red, *yellow*, III,		
		perf. 14x13½	.75	.50
a.		Type I, perf. 13¾	1.00	.25
b.		Type I, perf. 13¾x13½	.75	.25
c.		Type II, perf. 13¾	1.25	.25
d.		Type II, perf. 13¾x13½	1.10	.25
e.		Type III, perf. 13¾	7.50	.25

93	A8	200h blue, *yellow*, II,		
		perf. 13¾	10.00	.30
a.		Type II, perf. 13¾x13½	10.00	.30
b.		Type III, perf. 13¾	6.50	.30
c.		Type III, perf. 13¾x13½	45.00	.30
94	A8	300h violet, *yellow*, I,		
		perf. 13¾	4.50	.25
a.		Type II, perf. 13¾	35.00	.35
b.		Type II, perf. 13¾x13½	50.00	.50
c.		Type III, perf. 13¾x13½	6.00	.25
d.		Type III, perf. 13¾	27.50	.35
		Nos. 92-94 (3)	15.25	1.05

President Masaryk
A9   A10

Perf. 13¾x13½, 13¾

1925   **Photo.**   **Wmk. 107**
Size: 19½x23mm

95	A9	40h brown orange	.75	.25
96	A9	50h olive green	1.50	.25
97	A9	60h red violet	1.75	.25
		Nos. 95-97 (3)	4.00	.75

Distinctive Marks of the Engravings.
I, II, III — Background of horizontal lines in top and bottom tablets. Inscriptions in Roman letters with serifs.
IV — Crossed horizontal and vertical lines in the tablets. Inscriptions in Antique letters without serifs.
I, II, IV — Shading of crossed diagonal lines on the shoulder at the right.
III — Shading of single lines only.
I — "T" of "Posta" over middle of "V" of "Ceskoslovenska." Three short horizontal lines in lower part of "A" of "Ceskoslovenska."
II — "T" over right arm of "V." One short line in "A."
III — "T" as in II. Blank space in lower part of "A."
IV — "T" over left arm of "V."

Wmk. Horizontally (107)
Engr.
I. First Engraving
Size: 19¾x22½mm

98	A10	1k carmine	.85	.25
99	A10	2k deep blue	1.75	.35
100	A10	3k brown	3.75	.65
101	A10	5k blue green	1.25	.35
		Nos. 98-101 (4)	7.60	1.60

Wmk. Vertically (107)
Size: 19¼x23mm

101A	A10	1k carmine	60.00	3.50
101B	A10	2k deep blue	60.00	12.50
101C	A10	3k brown	150.00	12.50
101D	A10	5k blue green	3.50	.60
		Nos. 101A-101D (4)	273.50	29.10

II. Second Engraving
Wmk. Horizontally (107)
Size: 19x21½mm

102	A10	1k carmine	35.00	.60
103	A10	2k deep blue	3.50	.30
104	A10	3k brown	4.50	.35
		Nos. 102-104 (3)	43.00	1.25

III. Third Engraving
Size: 19-19½x21½-22mm
Perf. 10

105	A10	1k carmine rose	.75	.25
a.		Perf. 14	6.00	.25

IV. Fourth Engraving
Size: 19x22mm

1926   *Perf. 10*

106	A10	1k carmine rose	1.00	.25

Perf. 14

108	A10	3k brown	4.50	.25

There is a 2nd type of No. 106: with long mustache. Same values. See No. 130, design SP3.

Karlstein Castle — A11

1926, June 1   **Engr.**   *Perf. 10*

109	A11	1.20k red violet	.50	.30
110	A11	1.50k car rose	.35	.25
111	A11	2.50k dark blue	3.25	.35
		Nos. 109-111 (3)	4.10	.90

See Nos. 133, 135.

Karlstein
Castle
A12

Pernstein
Castle
A13

Orava
Castle
A14

Masaryk
A15

Strahov
Monastery
A16

Hradcany at
Prague
A17

Great Tatra — A18

Short Mustache   Long, Wavy
Mustache

1926-27   **Engr.**   **Wmk. 107**

114	A13	30h gray green	1.25	.25
115	A14	40h red brown	.50	.25
116	A15	50h deep green	.50	.25
117	A15	60h red vio, *lil*	.85	.25
118	A16	1.20k red violet	4.00	1.50

Perf. 13½

119	A17	2k blue	1.00	.25
a.		2k ultramarine	6.00	.75
120	A17	3k deep red	1.25	.25
121	A18	4k brn vio ('27)	4.50	.60
122	A18	5k dk grn ('27)	14.00	3.00
		Nos. 114-122 (9)	27.85	6.60

No. 116 exists in two types. The one with short, straight mustache at left sells for several times as much as that with longer wavy mustache.

See Nos. 137-140.

Coil Stamps
Perf. 10 Vertically

123	A12	20h brick red	.50	.40
a.		Vert. pair, imperf. horiz.	100.00	
124	A13	30h gray green	.35	.25
a.		Vert. pair, imperf. horiz.	100.00	
125	A15	50h deep green	.25	.25
		Nos. 123-125 (3)	1.10	.90

See No. 141.

Short Mustache   Long, Wavy Mustache

		1927-31	**Unwmk.**	**Perf. 10**
126	A13	30h gray green	.25	.25
127	A14	40h deep brown	.70	.25
128	A15	50h deep green	.25	.25
129	A15	60h red violet	.70	.25
130	A10	1k carmine rose	1.10	.25
131	A15	1k deep red	.75	.25
132	A16	1.20k red violet	.40	.25
133	A11	1.50k carmine ('29)	.55	.25
134	A13	2k dp grn ('29)	.50	.25
135	A11	2.50k dark blue	5.50	.30
136	A14	3k red brown ('31)	.60	.25
		Nos. 126-136 (11)	11.30	2.80

No. 130 exists in two types. The one with longer mustache at right sells for several times as much as that with the short mustache.

		1927-28		**Perf. 13½**
137	A17	2k ultra	.85	.25
138	A17	3k deep red ('28)	1.90	.65
139	A18	4k brown violet ('28)	6.00	1.00
140	A18	5k dark green ('28)	6.25	.50
		Nos. 137-140 (4)	15.00	2.40

Coil Stamp

		1927	**Perf. 10 Vertically**	
141	A12	20h brick red	.50	.25

> **Catalogue values for unused stamps in this section, from this point to the end of the section, are for Never Hinged items.**

  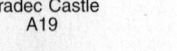

Hradec Castle   Brno
A19   Cathedral
               A25

Masaryk — A27

10th anniv. of Czech. independence: 40h, Town Hall, Levoca. 50h, Telephone exchange, Prague. 60h, Town of Jasina. 1k, Hluboka Castle. 1.20k, Pilgrims' House, Velehrad. 2.50k, Great Tatra. 5k, Old City Square, Prague.

		1928, Oct. 22		**Perf. 13½**
142	A19	30h black	.25	.25
143	A19	40h red brown	.25	.25
144	A19	50h dark green	.25	.25
145	A19	60h orange red	.25	.25
146	A19	1k carmine	.30	.25
147	A19	1.20k brown vio	1.00	.45
148	A25	2k ultra	1.00	.75
149	A19	2.50k dark blue	3.00	2.50
150	A27	3k dark brown	1.50	1.25
151	A25	5k deep violet	3.00	3.00
		Nos. 142-151 (10)	10.80	9.20

From one to three sheets each of Nos. 142-148, perf 12½, appeared on the market in the early 1950's.

Coat of Arms — A29

		1929-37		**Perf. 10**
152	A29	5h dark ultra ('31)	.25	.25
153	A29	10h bister brn ('31)	.25	.25
154	A29	20h red	.25	.25
155	A29	25h green	.25	.25
156	A29	30h red violet	.25	.25
157	A29	40h dk brown ('37)	1.60	.25
a.		40h red brown ('29)	.80	.25
		Nos. 152-157 (6)	2.85	1.50

Coil Stamp
Perf. 10 Vertically

158	A29	20h red	.25	.25

For overprints, see Bohemia and Moravia Nos. 1-5, Slovakia Nos. 2-6.

St.   Founding
Wenceslas   St. Vitus'
A30   Cathedral
               A31

Design: 3k, 5k, St. Wenceslas martyred.

		1929, May 14		**Perf. 13½**
159	A30	50h gray green	.30	.25
160	A30	60h slate violet	.45	.25
161	A31	2k dull blue	1.10	.30
162	A30	3k brown	1.50	.35
163	A30	5k brown violet	5.50	3.50
		Nos. 159-163 (5)	8.85	4.65

Millenary of the death of St. Wenceslas.

Statue of St. Wenceslas and National Museum, Prague — A33

		1929		**Perf. 10**
164	A33	2.50k deep blue	2.00	.25

Brno   Tatra
Cathedral   Mountain
A34   Scene
               A35

Design: 5k, Old City Square, Prague.

		1929, Oct. 15		**Perf. 13½**
165	A34	3k red brown	3.00	.25
166	A35	4k indigo	6.75	.25
167	A35	5k gray green	12.00	.30
		Nos. 165-167 (3)	21.75	.80

See No. 183.

A37

Type I

Type II

Two types of 50h:

I — A white space exists across the bottom of the vignette between the coat, shirt and tie and the "HALERU" frame panel.

II — An extra frame line has been added just above the "HALERU" panel which finishes off the coat and tie shading evenly.

		1930, Jan. 2		**Perf. 10**
168	A37	50h myrtle green (II)	.25	.25
a.		Type I	1.10	.25
169	A37	60h brown violet	1.00	.25
170	A37	1k brown red	.40	.25
		Nos. 168-170 (3)	1.65	.75

See No. 234.

Coil Stamp

		1931	**Perf. 10 Vertically**	
171	A37	1k brown red	1.50	.60

President Masaryk — A38

		1930, Mar. 1		**Perf. 13½**
175	A38	2k gray green	1.50	.35
176	A38	3k red brown	2.25	.35
177	A38	5k slate blue	6.00	1.50
178	A38	10k gray black	16.00	3.50
		Nos. 175-178 (4)	25.75	5.70

Eightieth birthday of President Masaryk. Nos. 175-178 were each issued in sheets with ornamental tabs at the bottom. Value, set with tabs $65.50.

St. Nicholas' Church, Prague — A39

		1931, May 15		
183	A39	10k black violet	11.00	1.10

  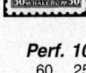

Krivoklat   Krumlov
Castle   Castle
A40   A42

Design: 4k, Orlik Castle.

		1932, Jan. 2		**Perf. 10**
184	A40	3.50k violet	5.00	1.10
185	A40	4k deep blue	4.00	.60
186	A42	5k gray green	7.00	.60
		Nos. 184-186 (3)	16.00	2.30

A43   A44

		1932, Mar. 16		
187	A43	50h yellow green	.35	.25
188	A43	1k brown carmine	1.10	.25
189	A44	2k dark blue	9.00	.35
190	A44	3k red brown	19.00	.35
		Nos. 187-190 (4)	29.45	1.20

Miroslav Tyrs — A45

		1933, Feb. 1		
191	A45	60h dull violet	.60	.25

Miroslav Tyrs (1832-84), founder of the Sokol movement; and the 9th Sokol Congress (Nos. 187-190).

First Christian Church at Nitra

A46   A47

		1933, June 20		
192	A46	50h yellow green	.75	.25
193	A47	1k carmine rose	7.00	.25

Prince Pribina who introduced Christianity into Slovakia and founded there the 1st Christian church in A.D. 833.

All gutter pairs are vertical. Values unused: No. 192 $300; No. 193 $15,000.

Bedrich Smetana, Czech Composer and Pianist, 50th Death Anniv. — A48

		1934, Mar. 26	**Engr.**	**Perf. 10**
194	A48	50h yellow green	.60	.25

Consecration of Legion Colors at Kiev, Sept. 21, 1914 — A49

Ensign   Legionnaires
Heyduk with   A52
Colors
A51

1k, Legion receiving battle flag at Bayonne.

		1934, Aug. 15		**Perf. 10**
195	A49	50h green	.35	.25
196	A49	1k rose lake	.50	.25
197	A51	2k deep blue	2.75	.25
198	A52	3k red brown	4.50	.45
		Nos. 195-198 (4)	8.10	1.20

20th anniv. of the Czechoslovakian Legion which fought in WWI.

Antonin Dvorák, (1841-1904), Composer — A53

		1934, Nov. 22		
199	A53	50h green	.60	.25

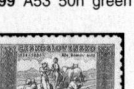

Pastoral Scene — A54

		1934, Dec. 17		**Perf. 10**
200	A54	1k claret	.60	.25
a.		Souv. sheet of 15, perf. 13½	160.00	250.00
b.		As "a," single stamp	10.00	12.50
201	A54	2k blue	1.75	.45
a.		Souv. sheet of 15, perf. 13½	850.00	900.00
b.		As "a," single stamp	50.00	27.50

Centenary of the National Anthem.

Nos. 200-201 were each issued in sheets of 100 stamps and 12 blank labels. Value, set with attached labels: mint $21; used $7.

Nos. 200a & 201a have thick paper, darker shades, no gum. Forgeries exist.

A55

President
Masaryk — A56

1935, Mar. 1

202	A55	50h green, *buff*	.35	.25
203	A55	1k claret, *buff*	.35	.25
204	A56	2k gray blue, *buff*	.50	.60
205	A56	3k brown, *buff*	3.00	.50
		Nos. 202-205 (4)	4.20	1.60

85th birthday of President Masaryk.
Nos. 204-205 were each issued in sheets of 100 stamps and 12 blank labels. Value with attached labels: mint $30; used $30.
See No. 235.

Monument to Czech
Heroes at Arras,
France — A57

1935, May 4

206	A57	1k rose	.35	.25
207	A57	2k dull blue	1.50	.45

20th anniversary of the Battle of Arras.
Nos. 206-207 were each issued in sheets of 100 stamps and 12 blank labels. Value, set with attached labels: mint $8; used $8.

Gen. Milan Stefánik — A58

1935, May 18

208	A58	50h green	.25	.25

Sts. Cyril and
Methodius — A59

1935, June 22

209	A59	50h green	.25	.25
210	A59	1k claret	.45	.25
211	A59	2k deep blue	1.50	.25
		Nos. 209-211 (3)	2.20	.75

Millenary of the arrival in Moravia of the Apostles Cyril and Methodius.

Masaryk — A60

1935, Oct. 20   **Perf. 12½**

212	A60	1k rose lake	.25	.25

No. 212 exists imperforate. See Bohemia and Moravia No. 1A. For overprints see Bohemia and Moravia Nos. 9-10, Slovakia 12.

Statue of Macha,
Prague — A61

1936, Apr. 30

213	A61	50h deep green	.25	.25
214	A61	1k rose lake	.40	.25

Karel Hynek Macha (1810-1836), Bohemian poet.
Nos. 213-214 were each issued in sheets of 100 stamps and 12 blank labels. Value, set with attached labels: mint $1; used 75c.

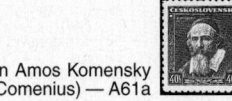

Jan Amos Komensky
(Comenius) — A61a

Pres.
Eduard
Benes
A62

Gen. Milan
Stefánik
A63

1936

215	A61a	40h dark blue	.25	.25
216	A62	50h dull green	.25	.25
217	A63	60h dull violet	.75	.75
		Nos. 215-217 (3)		

See no. 252, Slovakia 23A. For overprints see Bohemia and Moravia Nos. 6, 8, Slovakia 7, 9-11.

Castle
Palanok
near
Mukacevo
A64

Castle at
Zvikov
A66

Castle at
Cesky Raj
A68

Statue of King
George of
Podebrad
A70

Castle Ruins at
Bratislava — A72

Town of
Banska
Bystrica
A65

Ruins of
Castle at
Strecno
A67

Palace at
Slavkov
(Austerlitz)
A69

Town Square
at Olomouc
A71

1936, Aug. 1

218	A64	1.20k rose lilac	.25	.25
219	A65	1.50k carmine	.25	.25
220	A66	2k dark blue green	.25	.25
221	A67	2.50k dark blue	.25	.25
222	A68	3k brown	.25	.25
223	A69	3.50k dark violet	1.50	.25
224	A70	4k dark violet	.60	.25
225	A71	5k green	.60	.25
226	A72	10k blue	1.00	.25
		Nos. 218-226 (9)	4.95	2.25

Nos. 224-226 were each issued in sheets of 100 stamps and 12 blank labels. Value, with attached labels: mint $6; used $6.
For overprints and surcharge see Nos. 237-238, 254A, Bohemia and Moravia 11-12, 14-19, Slovakia 13-14, 16-23.

President Benes — A73

1937, Apr. 26   Unwmk.   Perf. 12½

227	A73	50h deep green	.25	.25

For overprints see Nos. 236, Slovakia 8.

Soldiers of the Czech
Legion — A74

1937, June 15

228	A74	50h deep green	.25	.25
229	A74	1k rose lake	.30	.25

20th anniv. of the Battle of Zborov.
Nos. 228-229 were each issued in sheets of 100 stamps and 12 blank labels. Value, set with attached labels: mint $2; used $1.50.

Cathedral at
Prague — A75

1937, July 1

230	A75	2k green	.90	.25
231	A75	2.50k blue	1.40	.25

Founding of the "Little Entente," 16th anniv.
Nos. 230-231 were each issued in sheets with blank labels. Value, set with attached labels: mint $17.50; used $9.

Jan Evangelista
Purkyne — A76

1937, Sept. 2

232	A76	50h slate green	.25	.25
233	A76	1k dull rose	.30	.25

150th anniv. of the birth of Purkyne, Czech physiologist.
Nos. 232-233 were printed in sheets of 100 with 12 decorated labels. Value, set with labels, $2.50.

Masaryk Types of 1930-35
1937, Sept.   **Perf. 12½**

234	A37	50h black	.25	.25

With date "14.IX. 1937" in design

235	A56	2k black	.30	.25

Death of former President Thomas G. Masaryk on Sept. 14, 1937.
No. 235 was issued in sheets of 100 stamps and 12 inscribed labels. Value, with attached label: mint $3.50; used $3.50.

International Labor Bureau Issue

Stamps of 1936-37
Overprinted in Violet or
Black

1937, Oct. 6   **Perf. 12½**

236	A73	50h dp green (Bk)	.35	.35
237	A65	1.50k carmine (V)	.35	.35
238	A66	2k dp green (V)	.70	.35
		Nos. 236-238 (3)	1.40	1.05

Bratislava Philatelic Exhibition Issue
Souvenir Sheet

A77

1937, Oct. 24   **Perf. 12½**

239	A77	Sheet of 2	2.50	*2.75*
a.		50h dark blue	.80	1.20
b.		1k brown carmine	.80	1.20

The stamps show a view of Poprad Lake (50h) and the tomb of General Milan Stefanik (1k).
No. 239 overprinted with the Czechoslovak arms and "Czecho-Slovak Participation New York World's Fair 1939 and 1940, Czecho-Slovak Pavilion" were privately produced to finance Czechoslovak participation in the exhibition. The overprint exists in black, green, red, blue, gold and silver.
No. 239 overprinted "Liberation de la Tchechoslovaquie, 28-X-1945" etc., was sold at a philatelic exhibition in Brussels, Belgium.

St. Barbara's Church,
Kutna Hora — A79

1937, Dec. 4

240	A79	1.60k olive green	.25	.25

For overprints see Bohemia and Moravia Nos. 13, Slovakia 15.

Peregrine Falcon, Sokol
Emblem — A80

1938, Jan. 21

241	A80	50h deep green	.25	.25
242	A80	1k rose lake	.25	.25

10th Intl. Sokol Games.
Nos. 241-242 were each issued in sheets of 100 stamps and 12 inscribed labels. Value, set with attached labels: mint $1.50; used $2.50.
Imperf. examples of No. 242 are essays.

Legionnaires
A81   A82

Legionnaire — A83

1938

243	A81	50h deep green	.25	.25
244	A82	50h deep green	.25	.25
245	A83	50h deep green	.25	.25
		Nos. 243-245 (3)	.75	.75

20th anniv. of the Battle of Bachmac, Vouziers and Doss Alto.

Nos. 243-245 were each issued in sheets of 100 stamps and 12 inscribed labels. Value, set with attached labels $2, mint or used.

Jindrich Fügner, Co-
Founder of Sokol
Movement — A84

1938, June 18   *Perf. 12½*

246	A84	50h deep green	.25	.25
247	A84	1k rose lake	.25	.25
248	A84	2k slate blue	.40	.40
		Nos. 246-248 (3)	.90	.75

10th Sokol Summer Games.

Nos. 246-248 were each issued in sheets of 100 stamps and 12 inscribed labels. Value, set with attached labels: mint $2.50; used $2.

View of Pilsen — A85

1938, June 24

249	A85	50h deep green	.25	.25

Provincial Economic Council meeting, Pilsen.

No. 249 was issued in sheets of 150 stamps and 10 labels depicting a flower within a cogwheel. Value, with attached label $1, mint or used.

For overprint see Bohemia & Moravia No. 7.

Cathedral of Kosice — A86

1938, July 15   *Perf. 12½*

250	A86	50h deep green	.25	.25

Kosice Cultural Exhibition.

No. 250 was issued in sheets of 150 stamps and 10 labels depicting grapes. Value, with attached label $1, $7.50 mint, $4.50 used.

Prague Philatelic Exhibition Issue
Souvenir Sheet

Vysehrad Castle — Hradcany — A87

1938, June 26   *Perf. 12½*

251	A87	Sheet of 2	5.00	5.00
a.		50h dark blue	1.50	1.50
b.		1k deep carmine	1.50	1.50

See No. 3036.

Stefánik Type of 1936

1938, Nov. 21

252	A63	50h deep green	.25	.25

Allegory of the Republic
— A89

1938, Dec. 19   **Unwmk.**

253	A89	2k lt ultra	.30	.25
254	A89	3k pale brown	.50	.40

20th anniv. of Independence.

Nos. 253-254 were each issued in sheets of 100 stamps and 12 blank labels. Value, set with attached labels $2, mint or used.

See No. B153.

"Wir sind frei!"

Stamps of Czechoslovakia, 1918-37, overprinted with a swastika in black or red and "Wir sind frei!" were issued locally and unofficially in 1938 as Czech authorities were evacuating and German authorities arriving. They appeared in the towns of Asch, Karlsbad, Reichenberg-Maffersdorf, Rumburg, etc.

The overprint, sometimes including a surcharge or the town name (as in Karlsbad), exists on many values of postage, air post, semi-postal, postage due and newspaper stamps.

No. 226 Surcharged
in Orange Red

1939, Jan. 18   **Unwmk.**   *Perf. 12½*

254A	A72	300h on 10k blue	1.25	1.75

Opening of the Slovakian Parliament.

No. 254A was issued in sheets of 100 stamps with 12 blank labels. Value with attached labels, mint $4.

The stamp formerly listed as No. 254B is now listed as Carpatho-Ukraine No. 1 in Vol. 2 of the *Scott Standard Postage Stamp Catalogue*.

The stamps formerly listed as Czechoslovakia Nos. 255, 256 and C18 are now listed with Bohemia and Moravia and Slovakia. No. 255 is now Slovakia No. 23A. No. 256 and C18 are now listed as Bohemia and Moravia 1A and C1, respectively.

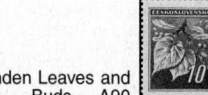

Linden Leaves and
Buds — A90

Closed Buds

Open Buds

1945   **Photo.**   *Perf. 14*

256A	A90	10h black	.25	.25
257	A90	30h yellow brown	.25	.25
258	A90	50h dark green	.25	.25
258A	A90	60h dark blue	.25	.25

Engr.
(Buds Open)
Perf. 12½

259	A90	60h blue	.25	.25
259A	A90	80h orange ver	.25	.25
260	A90	1.20k rose	.25	.25
261	A90	3k violet brown	.25	.25
262	A90	5k green	.25	.25
		Nos. 256A-262 (9)	2.25	2.25

Compare with Bohemia-Moravia type A1.

Thomas G.
Masaryk — A91

1945-46   **Photo.**   *Perf. 12*

262A	A91	5h dull violet ('46)	.25	.25
262B	A91	10h orange yel ('46)	.25	.25
262C	A91	20h dk brown ('46)	.25	.25
263	A91	50h brt green	.25	.25
264	A91	1k orange red	.25	.25
265	A91	2k chalky blue	.25	.25
		Nos. 262A-265 (6)	1.50	1.50

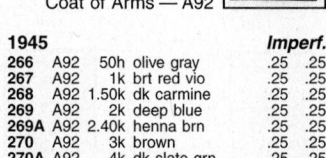

Coat of Arms — A92

1945   *Imperf.*

266	A92	50h olive gray	.25	.25
267	A92	1k brt red vio	.25	.25
268	A92	1.50k dk carmine	.25	.25
269	A92	2k deep blue	.25	.25
269A	A92	2.40k henna brn	.25	.25
270	A92	3k brown	.25	.25
270A	A92	4k dk slate grn	.25	.25
271	A92	6k violet blue	.25	.25
271A	A92	10k sepia	.25	.25
		Nos. 266-271A (9)	2.25	2.25

Nos. 266, 268, 269, 270 and 271 exist in 2 printings. Stamps of the 1st printing have a coarse impression and are on thin, hard paper in sheets of 100; all values exist in the 2nd printing, with fine impressions on thick, soft wove paper in sheets of 200. Values are the same.

Staff Capt.
Ridky
(British
Army)
A93

Capt.
Otakar
Jaros
(Russian
Army)
A95

2nd Lt. Jiri
Kral
(French Air
Force)
A97

Staff Capt. Alois Vasatko
(Royal Air Force)
A99

Dr.
Miroslav
Novak
(French
Army)
A94

Staff Capt.
Stanislav
Zimprich
(Foreign
Legion)
A96

Josef
Gabcik
(Parachutist)
A98

Private Frantisek Adamek
(British Colonial Service)
A100

1945, Aug. 18   **Engr.**   *Perf. 11½x12½*

272	A93	5h intense blue	.25	.25
273	A94	10h dark brown	.25	.25
274	A95	20h brick red	.25	.25
275	A96	25h rose red	.25	.25
276	A97	30h purple	.25	.25
277	A98	40h sepia	.25	.25
278	A99	50h dark olive	.25	.25
279	A100	60h violet	.25	.25
280	A93	1k carmine	.25	.25
281	A94	1.50k lake	.25	.25
282	A95	2k ultra	.25	.25
283	A96	2.50k deep violet	.25	.25
284	A97	3k sepia	.25	.25
285	A98	4k rose lilac	.25	.25
286	A99	5k myrtle green	.25	.25
287	A100	10k brt ultra	.65	.25
		Nos. 272-287 (16)	4.40	4.00

Flags of Russia,
Great Britain,
US and
Czechoslovakia
A101

View of
Banská
Bystrica
A102

Patriot
Welcoming
Russian
Soldier,
Turciansky
A103

Ruins of Castle
at Sklabina
A104

Czech Patriot,
Strecno — A105

1945, Aug. 29   **Photo.**   *Perf. 10*

288	A101	1.50k brt carmine	.25	.25
289	A102	2k brt blue	.25	.25
290	A103	4k dark brown	.25	.25
291	A104	4.50k purple	.25	.30
292	A105	5k deep green	.50	.50
		Nos. 288-292 (5)	1.50	1.55

National uprising against the Germans.

A card contains one each of Nos. 288-292 on thin cardboard, ungummed. Size: 148x210mm. Sold for 50k. Value, $20 unused, $120 used. Forged cancellations exist.

Stefánik
A106

Benes
A107

Masaryk — A108

1945-47   **Engr.**   *Perf. 12, 12½*

293	A106	30h rose violet	.25	.25
294	A107	60h blue	.25	.25
294A	A106	1k red org ('47)	.25	.25
295	A108	1.20k car rose	.25	.25
295A	A108	1.20(k) rose lil ('46)	.25	.25
296	A106	2.40(k) rose	.25	.25
297	A107	3k red violet	.25	.25
297A	A108	4k dark blue ('46)	.25	.25
298	A108	5k Prus green	.25	.25
299	A107	7k gray	.25	.25
300	A106	10k gray blue	.30	.25
300A	A106	20k sepia ('46)	.30	.25
		Nos. 293-300A (12)	3.10	3.00

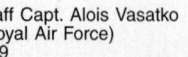

1945 Photo. Perf. 14
301	A108	50h brown	.25	.25
302	A106	80h dark green	.25	.25
303	A107	1.60(k) olive green	.25	.25
304	A108	15k red violet	.30	.25
	Nos. 301-304 (4)		1.05	1.00

Statue of Kozina and Chod Castle, Domazlice — A109

1945, Nov. 28 Engr. Perf. 12½
305	A109	2.40k rose carmine	.25	.25
306	A109	4k blue	.25	.25

250th anniv. of the death of Jan Sladky Kozina, peasant leader.

Nos. 305-306 were issued in sheets of 100 stamps with 12 blank labels. Value, set with attached labels, mint $6.

Red Army Soldier — A110

1945, Mar. 26 Litho. Imperf.
307	A110	2k crimson rose	.40	.40
308	A110	5k slate black	1.10	1.10
309	A110	6k ultramarine	1.10	1.10
	Nos. 307-309 (3)		2.60	2.60

Souvenir Sheet
1945, July 16 Gray Burelage
310		Sheet of 3	4.00	4.00
a.	A110 2k crimson rose		.75	.75
b.	A110 5k slate black		.75	.75
c.	A110 6k ultramarine		.75	.75

Return of Pres. Benes, Apr., 1945.

Clasped Hands — A112

1945 Rouletted 12½
311	A112	1.50k brown red	1.50	1.50
312	A112	9k red orange	.35	.35
313	A112	13k orange brown	.65	.65
314	A112	20k blue	1.50	1.50
	Nos. 311-314 (4)		4.00	4.00

Karel Havlícek Borovsky — A113

1946, July 5 Engr. Perf. 12½
315	A113	1.20k gray black	.25	.25

Borovsky (1821-56), editor and writer. Issued in sheets of 100 stamps and 12 inscribed labels. Value with attached label: $1.25.

Old Town Hall, Brno A114   Hodonin Square A115

Perf. 12½x12, 12x12½
1946, Aug. 3 Engr. Unwmk.
316	A114	2.40k deep rose	.25	.25
317	A115	7.40k dull violet	.25	.25

See No. B159.

President Eduard Benes — A116

1946, Oct. 28
318	A116	60h indigo	.25	.25
319	A116	1.60k dull green	.25	.25
320	A116	3k red lilac	.25	.25
321	A116	8k sepia	.25	.25
	Nos. 318-321 (4)		1.00	1.00

Flag, Symbols — A117

1947, Jan. 1 Perf. 12½
322	A117	1.20k Prus green	.25	.25
323	A117	2.40k deep rose	.25	.25
324	A117	4k deep blue	.45	.25
	Nos. 322-324 (3)		.95	.75

Czechoslovakia's two-year reconstruction and rehabilitation program.

Nos. 322-324 each issued in sheets of 100 stamps and 12 inscribed labels. Value, set with attached labels, $3.

Saint Adalbert — A118

1947, Apr. 23
326	A118	1.60k gray	.75	.60
327	A118	2.40k rose carmine	.90	.60
328	A118	5k blue green	1.10	.45
	Nos. 326-328 (3)		2.75	1.65

950th anniv. of the death of Saint Adalbert, Bishop of Prague.

Nos. 326-328 each issued in sheets of 100 stamps and 12 monogrammed labels. Value, set with attached labels, $35.

Grief A119   Allegorical Figure A120

1947, June 10 Engr.
329	A119	1.20k black	.40	.25
330	A119	1.60k slate black	.45	.45
331	A120	2.40k brown violet	.45	.45
	Nos. 329-331 (3)		1.30	1.15

Destruction of Lidice, 5th anniversary.

Nos. 329-331 each issued in sheets of 100 stamps and 12 inscribed labels. Value, set with attached labels, $15.

World Federation of Youth Symbol — A121

1947, July 20
332	A121	1.20k violet brown	.50	.35
333	A121	4k slate	.50	.35

World Youth Festival held in Prague, July 20-Aug. 17.

Thomas G. Masaryk — A122

1947, Sept. 14
334	A122	1.20k gray blk, *buff*	.25	.25
335	A122	4k blue blk, *cream*	.30	.25

Death of Masaryk, 10th anniv.

Nos. 334-335 each issued in sheets of 100 stamps and 12 inscribed labels. Value, set with attached labels, $5.

Msgr. Stefan Moyses — A123

1947, Oct. 19
336	A123	1.20k rose violet	.25	.25
337	A123	4k deep blue	.25	.25

150th anniversary of the birth of Stefan Moyses, first Slovakian chairman of the Slavic movement.

Each issued in sheets of 100 stamps and 12 labels with "MOYSES" and floral decoration. Value, set with attached labels, $7.50.

"Freedom from Social Oppression" — A124

1947, Oct. 26 Photo. Perf. 14
338	A124	2.40k brt carmine	.40	.30
339	A124	4k brt ultra	.50	.25

Russian revolution of Oct., 1917, 30th anniv.

Benes — A125

1948, Feb. 15 Photo.
Size: 17½x21½mm
340	A125	1.50k brown	.25	.25

Size: 19x23mm
341	A125	2k deep plum	.25	.25
342	A125	5k brt ultra	.25	.25
	Nos. 340-342 (3)		.75	.75

"Czechoslovakia" Greeting Sokol Marchers — A126

1948, Mar. 7 Engr. Perf. 12½
343	A126	1.50k brown	.25	.25
344	A126	3k rose carmine	.25	.25
345	A126	5k blue	.50	.25
	Nos. 343-345 (3)		1.00	.75

The 11th Sokol Congress.

Nos. 343-345 each issued in sheets of 100 stamps and 12 labels depicting dates and bouquet. Values, set with attached labels: mint $4.50; used $3.75.

King Charles IV — A127   St. Wenceslas, King Charles IV — A128

1948, Apr. 7
346	A127	1.50k black brown	.25	.25
347	A128	2k dark brown	.25	.25
348	A128	3k brown red	.25	.25
349	A127	5k dark blue	.25	.25
	Nos. 346-349 (4)		1.00	1.00

600th anniv. of the foundation of Charles University, Prague.

Nos. 346-349 each issued in sheets of 100 stamps and 12 inscribed labels. Value, set with attached labels, $4.50.

Czech Peasants in Revolt — A129

Unwmk.
1948, May 14 Photo. Perf. 14
350	A129	1.50k dk olive brown	.25	.25

Centenary of abolition of serfdom.

Jindrich Vanicek — A130

Designs: 1.50k, 2k, Josef Scheiner.

1948, June 10 Engr. Perf. 12½
351	A130	1k dark green	.25	.25
352	A130	1.50k sepia	.25	.25
353	A130	2k gray blue	.25	.25
354	A130	3k claret	.25	.25
	Nos. 351-354 (4)		1.00	1.00

11th Sokol Congress, Prague, 1948.

Nos. 351-354 each issued in sheets of 100 stamps and 12 labels depicting a sunflower. Values, set with attached labels: $3.75 mint; $3 used.

Frantisek Palacky & F. L. Rieger — A131

1948, June 20 Unwmk.
355	A131	1.50k gray	.25	.25
356	A131	3k brown carmine	.25	.25

Constituent Assembly at Kromeriz, cent.

Nos. 355-356 each issued in sheets of 100 stamps and 12 labels depicting a wreath. Value, set with attached labels, $1.50.

Miloslav Josef Hurban — A132

3k, Ludovit Stur. 5k, Michael M. Hodza.

1948, Aug. 27 Perf. 12½
357	A132	1.50k dark brown	.25	.25
358	A132	3k carmine lake	.25	.25
359	A132	5k indigo	.25	.25
	Nos. 357-359 (3)		.75	.75

Cent. of 1848 insurrection against Hungary.

Nos. 357-359 each issued in sheets of 100 stamps and 12 labels depicting signatures. Values, set with attached labels: mint $5; used $3.50.

Eduard Benes — A133

1948, Sept. 28
360	A133	8k black	.25	.25

President Eduard Benes, 1884-1948.

Czechoslovak Family — A134

1948, Oct. 28 Perf. 12½x12
361	A134	1.50k deep blue	.25	.25
362	A134	3k rose carmine	.25	.25

Czechoslovakia's Independence, 30th anniv.

Nos. 361-362 each issued in sheets of 100 stamps and 12 labels depicting dates, leaves. Value, set with attached labels, $2.

Pres. Klement Gottwald — A135

1948-49 Perf. 12½
Size: 18½x23½mm
363	A135	1.50k dk brown	.25	.25
364	A135	2k car rose	.30	.25
a.	3k rose brown		1.00	.25
365	A135	5k gray blue	.25	.25

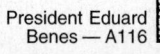

Size: 23½x29mm

366	A135	20k purple	.90	.25
		Nos. 363-366 (4)	1.70	1.00

No. 366 was issued in sheets of 100 stamps and 12 monogrammed labels. Value, with attached label, $3.50.
See Nos. 373, 564, 600-604.

Souvenir Sheet

1948, Nov. 23   Unwmk.   *Imperf.*

367	A135	30k rose brown	4.25	3.00

52nd birthday of Pres. Klement Gottwald (1896-1953).

Hradcany Castle Type of 1918
Souvenir Sheet

1948, Dec. 18

368	A1	10k dk blue violet	3.00	2.40

1st Czech postage stamp, 30th anniv.

Czechoslovak and Russian Workmen Shaking Hands — A138

1948, Dec. 12   *Perf. 12½*

369	A138	3k rose carmine	.25	.25

5th anniv. of the treaty of alliance between Czechoslovakia and Russia.
No. 369 issued in sheets of 100 stamps and 12 labels depicting Czech and Soviet flags. Value with attached label 60c.

Lenin — A139

1949, Jan. 21   Engr.   *Perf. 12½*

370	A139	1.50k violet brown	.30	.25
371	A139	5k deep blue	.30	.30

25th anniversary of the death of Lenin.
Nos. 370-371 each issued in sheets of 100 stamps and 12 labels depicting torch. Value, set with attached labels: mint $1.75; used $1.50.

Gottwald Type of 1948 Inscribed: "UNOR 1948" and

Gottwald Addressing Meeting — A140

1949, Feb. 25   Photo.   *Perf. 14*

372	A140	3k red brown	.25	.25

Perf. 12½
Engr.
Size: 23½x29mm

373	A135	10k deep green	.40	.25

1st anniv. of Gottwald's speech announcing the appointment of a new government. No. 372 exists in a souvenir sheet of 1. It was not sold to the public.
No. 373 issued in sheets of 100 stamps and 12 inscribed labels. Values with attached label: mint $2.50; used $1.50.

A141

Writers: 50h, P. O. Hviezdoslav. 80h, V. Vancura. 1k, J. Sverma. 2k, Julius Fucik. 4k, Jiri Wolker. 8k, Alois Jirasek.

1949   Photo.   *Perf. 14*

374	A141	50h violet brown	.25	.25
375	A141	80h scarlet	.25	.25
376	A141	1k dk olive green	.25	.25
377	A141	2k brt blue	.40	.25

Perf. 12½
Engr.

378	A141	4k violet brown	.40	.25
379	A141	8k brown black	.50	.25
		Nos. 374-379 (6)	2.05	1.50

A142

3k, Stagecoach and Train. 5k, Postrider and post bus. 13k, Sailing ship and plane.

1949, May 20

380	A142	3k brown carmine	1.50	1.50
381	A142	5k deep blue	1.00	.45
382	A142	13k deep green	1.50	1.00
		Nos. 380-382 (3)	4.00	2.95

75th anniv. of the UPU.

Reaping   Communist
A143   Emblem and
               Workers
               A144

Workman, Symbol of Industry — A145

Perf. 12½x12, 12x12½

1949, May 24   Unwmk.

383	A143	1.50k deep green	.50	.45
384	A144	3k brown carmine	.50	.45
385	A145	5k deep blue	.50	.45
		Nos. 383-385 (3)	1.50	1.35

No. 384 for the 9th meeting of the Communist Party of Czechoslovakia, 5/25/49.
Nos. 383-385 each issued in sheets of 100 stamps and 12 inscribed labels. Value, set with attached labels, $12.

Bedrich Smetana and Natl. Theater, Prague — A146

1949, June 4   *Perf. 12½x12*

386	A146	1.50k dull green	.25	.25
387	A146	5k deep blue	.75	.25

Birth of Bedrich Smetana, composer, 125th anniv.

Aleksander Pushkin — A147

1949, June 6   *Perf. 12x12½*

388	A147	2k olive gray	.25	.25

Birth of Aleksander S. Pushkin, 150th anniv.

Frederic Chopin and Conservatory, Warsaw — A148

1949, June 24   *Perf. 12½x12*

389	A148	3k dark red	.40	.25
390	A148	8k violet brown	.75	.50

Cent. of the death of Frederic F. Chopin.

Globe and Ribbon — A149

1949, Aug. 20   *Perf. 12½x12*

391	A149	1.50k violet brown	.35	.35
392	A149	5k ultra	.90	.90

50th Prague Sample Fair, Sept. 11-18, 1949.

Starting in October, 1949, some commemorative sets included one "blocked" value, which could be obtained only by purchasing the complete set. These restricted values were printed in smaller quantities than other stamps in the set and were typically sold for more than face value.

Zvolen Castle — A150

1949, Aug. 28   *Perf. 12½*

393	A150	10k rose lake	.75	.25

Early Miners   Miner of
A151   Today
               A152

Design: 5k, Mining Machine.

1949, Sept. 11   *Perf. 12½*

394	A151	1.50k sepia	.70	.50
395	A152	3k carmine rose	5.50	2.00
396	A151	5k deep blue	4.00	1.50
		Nos. 394-396 (3)	10.20	4.00

700th anniv. of the Czechoslovak mining industry; 150th anniv. of the miner's laws.

Construction Workers — A153

1949, Dec. 11   *Perf. 12½*

397	A153	1k shown	3.00	1.40
398	A153	2k Machinist	2.00	.70

2nd Trade Union Congress, Prague, 1949.

Joseph V. Stalin — A154

Design: 3k, Stalin facing left.

Cream Paper

1949, Dec. 21   Unwmk.

399	A154	1.50k greenish gray	.75	.35
400	A154	3k claret	4.50	1.75

70th birthday of Joseph V. Stalin.

Skier   Efficiency
A155   Badge
            A156

Engr., Photo. (3k)

1950, Feb. 15   *Perf. 12½, 13½*

401	A155	1.50k gray blue	2.75	1.50
402	A156	3k vio brn, *pale org*	2.75	1.50
403	A155	5k ultramarine	2.00	1.10
		Nos. 401-403 (3)	7.50	4.10

51st Ski Championship for the Tatra cup, Feb. 15-26, 1950.

Vladimir V. Mayakovsky, Poet, 20th Death Anniv. — A157

1950, Apr. 14   Engr.   *Perf. 12½*

404	A157	1.50k dark brown	2.25	1.10
405	A157	3k brown red	2.25	1.10

See Nos. 414-417, 422-423, 432-433, 464-465, 477-478.

Soviet Tank Soldier and Hradcany A158

2k, Hero of Labor medal. 3k, Two workers (militiamen) and Town Hall, Prague. 5k, Text of government program and heraldic lion.

1950, May 5

406	A158	1.50k gray green	.35	.25
407	A158	2k dark brown	1.00	1.00
408	A158	3k brown red	.25	.25
409	A158	5k dark blue	.50	.25
		Nos. 406-409 (4)	2.10	1.75

5th anniv. of the Czechoslovak People's Democratic Republic.

Factory and Young Couple with Tools — A159

Designs: 2k, Steam shovel. 3k, Farmer and farm scene. 5k, Three workers leaving factory.

1950, May 9   Engr.

410	A159	1.50k dark green	1.75	.85
411	A159	2k dark brown	1.75	.85
412	A159	3k rose red	1.00	.35
413	A159	5k deep blue	1.00	.35
		Nos. 410-413 (4)	5.50	2.40

Canceled to Order

The government philatelic department started about 1950 to sell canceled sets of new issues. Values in the second ("used") column are for these canceled-to-order stamps. Postally used stamps are worth more.

Portrait Type of 1950

Design: S. K. Neumann.

1950, June 5   Unwmk.   *Perf. 12½*

414	A157	1.50k deep blue	.35	.25
415	A157	3k violet brown	1.10	1.00

Stanislav Kostka Neumann (1875-1947), journalist and poet.

1950, June 21

Design: Bozena Nemcova.

416	A157	1.50k deep blue	1.25	.75
417	A157	7k dark brown	.30	.25

Bozena Nemcova (1820-1862), writer.

Liberation of Colonies — A160

Designs: 2k, Allegory, Fight for Peace. 3k, Group of Students. 5k, Marching Students with flags.

1950, Aug. 14

418	A160	1.50k dark green	.25	.25
419	A160	2k sepia	.25	.25
420	A160	3k rose carmine	.25	.25
421	A160	5k ultra	.60	.45
		Nos. 418-421 (4)	1.35	1.20

2nd International Students World Congress, Prague, Aug. 12-24, 1950.

Portrait Type of 1950

Design: Zdenek Fibich.

1950, Oct. 15
| 422 | A157 | 3k rose brown | .90 | .55 |
| 423 | A157 | 8k gray green | .35 | .25 |

Zdenek Fibich, musician, birth centenary.

Miner, Soldier and Farmer — A161

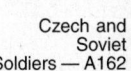

Czech and Soviet Soldiers — A162

1950, Oct. 6
| 424 | A161 | 1.50k slate | .35 | .35 |
| 425 | A162 | 3k carmine rose | .35 | .35 |

Issued to publicize Czech Army Day.

Prague Castle, 16th Century — A163

Prague, 1493 — A164

3k, Prague, 1606. 5k, Prague, 1794.

1950, Oct. 21   *Perf. 14*
426	A163	1.50k black	4.50	2.25
427	A164	2k chocolate	4.50	2.25
428	A164	3k brown car	4.50	2.25
429	A164	5k gray	4.50	2.25
a.		Block of 4, #426-429	25.00	15.00

See Nos. 434-435.

Communications Symbols — A165

1950, Oct. 25   *Perf. 12½*
| 430 | A165 | 1.50k chocolate | .35 | .25 |
| 431 | A165 | 3k brown carmine | .75 | .60 |

1st anniv. of the foundation of the Intl. League of P.T.T. Employees.

Portrait Type of 1950

Design: J. Gregor Tajovsky.

1950, Oct. 26
| 432 | A157 | 1.50k brown | 1.00 | .75 |
| 433 | A157 | 5k deep blue | 1.00 | .75 |

10th anniversary of the death of J. Gregor Tajovsky (1874-1940), Slovakian writer.

Scenic Type of 1950

Design: Prague, 1950.

1950, Oct. 28
434	A164	1.50k indigo	.35	.25
a.		Souvenir sheet of 4, imperf.	30.00	11.00
435	A164	3k brown car	.90	.50

Czech and Soviet Steel Workers — A166

1950, Nov. 4   *Unwmk.*
| 436 | A166 | 1.50k chocolate | .45 | .30 |
| 437 | A166 | 5k deep blue | .90 | .60 |

Issued to publicize the 2nd meeting of the Union of Czechoslovak-Soviet Friendship.

Dove by Picasso — A167

1951, Jan. 20   Photo.   *Perf. 14*
| 438 | A167 | 2k deep blue | 6.00 | 4.50 |
| 439 | A167 | 3k rose brown | 4.00 | 1.50 |

1st Czechoslovak Congress of Fighters for Peace, held in Prague.

Julius Fucik — A168

1951, Feb. 17   Engr.   *Perf. 12½*
| 440 | A168 | 1.50k gray | .75 | .75 |
| 441 | A168 | 5k gray blue | 1.50 | 1.50 |

No. 441 exists in a sheet of 12. Value, $500.

Drop Hammer A169   Installing Gear A170

1951, Feb. 24
442	A169	1.50k gray blk	.25	.25
443	A170	3k violet brn	.25	.25
444	A169	4k gray blue	.60	.50
		Nos. 442-444 (3)	1.10	1.00

Women Machinists — A171

Designs: 3k, Woman tractor operator. 5k, Women of different races.

1951, Mar. 8   Photo.   *Perf. 14*
445	A171	1.50k olive brown	.40	.30
446	A171	3k brown car	1.40	1.00
447	A171	5k blue	.70	.40
		Nos. 445-447 (3)	2.50	1.70

International Women's Day, Mar. 8.

Apprentice Miners — A172

1951, Apr. 12   Engr.   *Perf. 12½*
| 448 | A172 | 1.50k gray | .55 | .50 |
| 449 | A172 | 3k red brown | .25 | .25 |

Plowing A173   Collective Cattle Breeding A174

1951, Apr. 28   Photo.   *Perf. 14*
| 450 | A173 | 1.50k brown | .70 | .70 |
| 451 | A174 | 2k dk green | 1.40 | 1.40 |

Tatra Mountain Recreation Center — A175

Mountain Recreation Centers: 2k, Beskydy (Beskids). 3k, Krkonose (Carpathians).

1951, May 5   Engr.   *Perf. 12½*
452	A175	1.50k deep green	.25	.25
453	A175	2k dark brown	1.00	.25
454	A175	3k rose brown	.25	.25
		Nos. 452-454 (3)	1.50	1.25

Issued to publicize the summer opening of trade union recreation centers.

Klement Gottwald and Joseph Stalin A176   Factory Militiaman A177

Red Army Soldier and Partisan A178   Marx, Engels, Lenin and Stalin A179

1951   Unwmk.   *Perf. 12½*
455	A176	1.50k olive gray	.75	.25
456	A177	2k red brown	.35	.25
457	A178	3k rose brown	.35	.25
458	A176	5k deep blue	1.40	1.00
459	A179	8k gray	.70	.25
		Nos. 455-459 (5)	3.55	2.00

30th anniv. of the founding of the Czechoslovak Communist Party.

A180

Design: 1k, 2k, Antonin Dvorák. 1.50k, 3k, Bedrich Smetana.

1951, May 30
460	A180	1k redsh brown	.35	.25
461	A180	1.50k olive gray	1.40	.70
462	A180	2k dk redsh brn	1.40	.70
463	A180	3k rose brown	.35	.25
		Nos. 460-463 (4)	3.50	1.90

International Music Festival, Prague.
Nos. 461 and 462 were each issued in sheets of 10 stamps. Value, $700 for 461, $600 for 462.

Portrait Type of 1950

Portrait: Bohumir Smeral (facing right).

1951, June 21
| 464 | A157 | 1.50k dark gray | .75 | .50 |
| 465 | A157 | 3k rose brown | .35 | .25 |

10th anniv. of the death of Bohumir Smeral, political leader.

A181

1951, June 21
466	A181	1k shown	.75	.35
467	A181	1.50k Discus	.75	.35
468	A181	3k Soccer	1.50	.35
469	A181	5k Skier	3.50	1.50
		Nos. 466-469 (4)	6.50	2.55

Issued to honor the 9th Congress of the Czechoslovak Sokol Federation.

Scene from "Fall of Berlin" — A182

Scene from "The Great Citizen" — A183

1951, July 14
470	A182	80h rose brown	.35	.35
471	A183	1.50k dark gray	.35	.35
472	A182	4k gray blue	1.40	1.10
		Nos. 470-472 (3)	2.10	1.80

Intl. Film Festival, Karlovy Vary, July 14-29.

Alois Jirásek A184   "Fables and Fate" A185

Design: 4k, Scene from "Reign of Tabor."

1951, Aug. 23   Engr.   *Perf. 12½*
| 473 | A184 | 1.50k gray | .35 | .25 |
| 474 | A184 | 5k dark blue | 2.10 | .80 |

    Photo.   *Perf. 14*
475	A185	3k dark red	.50	.25
476	A185	4k dark brown	.50	.25
		Nos. 473-476 (4)	3.45	1.55

Cent. of the birth of Alois Jirásek, author.
No. 474 was issued in a sheet of 10 stamps. Value: mint *$1,000.*

Portrait Type of 1950

Design: Josef Hybes (1850-1921), cofounder of Czech Communist Party.

1951, July 21   Engr.
| 477 | A157 | 1.50k chocolate | .35 | .25 |
| 478 | A157 | 2k rose brown | .75 | .40 |

"Ostrava Region" A186   Mining Iron Ore A187

1951, Sept. 9
479	A186	1.50k dk brown	.25	.25
480	A187	3k rose brown	.25	.25
481	A186	5k deep blue	1.00	.65
		Nos. 479-481 (3)	1.50	1.15

Miner's Day, Sept. 9, 1951.

Soldiers on Parade — A188

1k, Gunner and field gun. 1.50k, Klement Gottwald. 3k, Tankman and tank. 5k, Aviators.

Photo. (80h, 5k), Engr.
1951, Oct. 6   *Perf. 14 (80h, 5k), 12½*
Inscribed: "Den CS Armady 1951"
482	A188	80h olive brown	.35	.30
483	A188	1k dk olive grn	.35	.30
484	A188	1.50k sepia	.35	.30
485	A188	3k claret	.75	.35
486	A188	5k blue	1.75	.75
		Nos. 482-486 (5)	3.55	2.00

Issued to publicize Army Day, Oct. 6, 1951.

Stalin and Gottwald A189   Lenin, Stalin and Soldiers A190

1951, Nov. 3   **Engr.**   **Perf. 12½**
487 A189 1.50k sepia   .25 .25
488 A190 2k red brown   .25 .25
489 A189 4k deep blue   1.00 .45
    Nos. 487-489 (3)   1.50 .95

Issued to publicize the month of Czechoslovak-Soviet friendship, 1951.

Peter Jilemnicky — A191

1951, Dec. 5   **Unwmk.**
491 A191 1.50k redsh brown   .25 .25
492 A191 2k dull blue   .80 .30

Peter Jilemnicky (1901-1949), writer.

Ladislav Zapotocky — A192

1952, Jan. 12   **Perf. 11½**
493 A192 1.50k brown red   .25 .25
494 A192 4k gray   1.00 .45

Centenary of the birth of Ladislav Zapotocky, Bohemian socialist pioneer.

Jan Kollar — A193

1952, Jan. 30   **Unwmk.**   **Perf. 11½**
495 A193 3k dark carmine   .25 .25
496 A193 5k violet blue   1.10 .60

Jan Kollar (1793-1852), poet.

Lenin and Lenin Hall — A194

1952, Jan. 30   **Perf. 12½**
497 A194 1.50k rose carmine   .30 .25
498 A194 5k deep blue   1.10 .75

6th All-Russian Party Conf., 40th anniv.

Emil Holub and African — A195

1952, Feb. 21   **Perf. 11½**
499 A195 3k red brown   .35 .25
500 A195 5k gray   1.50 .90

Death of Emil Holub, explorer, 50th anniv.

Gottwald Metallurgical Plant — A196

Designs: 2k, Foundry. 3k, Chemical plant.

1952, Feb. 25   **Photo.**   **Perf. 14**
501 A196 1.50k sepia   .25 .25
502 A196 2k red brown   1.50 .60
503 A196 3k scarlet   .25 .25
    Nos. 501-503 (3)   2.00 1.10

Student, Soldier and Miner A197   Youths of Three Races A198

1952, Mar. 21   **Unwmk.**   **Perf. 14**
504 A197 1.50k blue   .25 .25
505 A198 2k olive black   .25 .25
506 A197 3k lake   1.00 .50
    Nos. 504-506 (3)   1.50 1.00

International Youth Day, Mar. 25, 1952.

Similar to Type of 1951

Portrait: Otakar Sevcik.

1952, Mar. 22   **Engr.**   **Perf. 12½**
507 A184 2k choc, cr   .80 .35
508 A184 3k rose brn, cr   .25 .25

Otakar Sevcik, violinist, birth cent.

Jan A. Komensky — A199

1952, Mar. 28
509 A199 1.50k dk brown, cr   1.50 .65
510 A199 11k dk blue, cr   .35 .25

360th anniv. of the birth of Jan Amos Komensky (Comenius), teacher and philosopher.

Industrial and Farm Women — A200

1952, Mar. 8
511 A200 1.50k dp blue, cr   1.20 .50

International Women's Day Mar. 8, 1952.

Woman and Children — A201

1952, Apr. 12
512 A201 2k chocolate, cr   1.60 1.00
513 A201 3k dp claret, cr   .25 .25

Intl. Conf. for the Protection of Children, Vienna, Apr. 12-16, 1952.

Antifascist — A202

1952, Apr. 11   **Photo.**   **Perf. 14**
514 A202 1.50k red brown   .25 .25
515 A202 2k ultra   1.10 .60

Day of International Solidarity of Fighters against Fascism, Apr. 11, 1952.

Harvester — A203

Design: 3k, Tractor and Seeders.

1952, Apr. 30
516 A203 1.50k deep blue   2.10 1.20
517 A203 2k brown   .30 .30
518 A203 3k brown red   .30 .30
    Nos. 516-518 (3)   2.70 1.80

Youths Carrying Flags — A204

1952, May 1
519 A204 3k brown red   .35 .25
520 A204 4k dk red brown   1.40 1.25

Issued to publicize Labor Day, May 1, 1952.

Crowd Cheering Soviet Soldiers A205

1952, May 9
521 A205 1.50k dark red   .55 .45
522 A205 5k deep blue   2.25 1.25

Liberation of Czechoslovakia from German occupation, 7th anniversary.

Children — A206

Design: 3k, "Pioneer" teaching children.

1952, May 31   **Engr.**   **Perf. 12½**
523 A206 1.50k dk brn, cr   .25 .25
524 A206 2k Prus grn, cr   1.50 .60
525 A206 3k rose brn, cr   .25 .25
    Nos. 523-525 (3)   2.00 1.10

International Children's Day May 31, 1952.

J. V. Myslbek — A207

Design: 8k, Allegory, "Music."

1952, June 2
526 A207 1.50k red brown   .30 .25
527 A207 2k dark brown   1.25 .90
528 A207 8k gray green   .25 .25
    Nos. 526-528 (3)   1.80 1.40

Joseph V. Myslbek (1848-1922), sculptor.

Beethoven A208   House of Artists A209

1952, June 7   **Unwmk.**   **Perf. 11½**
529 A208 1.50k sepia   .35 .25
530 A209 3k red brown   .35 .25
531 A208 5k indigo   1.40 1.10
    Nos. 529-531 (3)   2.10 1.60

International Music Festival, Prague, 1952.

Lidice, Symbol of a New Life — A210

1952, June 10   **Perf. 12½**
532 A210 1.50k dk violet brn   .25 .25
533 A210 5k dark blue   1.00 .60

Destruction of Lidice, 10th anniversary.

Jan Hus A211   Bethlehem Chapel A212

1952, July 5
534 A211 1.50k brown   .25 .25
535 A212 3k red brown   .25 .25
536 A211 5k black   1.10 .65
    Nos. 534-536 (3)   1.60 1.15

550th anniv. of the installation of Jan Hus as pastor of Bethlehem Chapel, Prague.

Doctor Examining Patient — A213

2k, Doctor, Nurse, Mother and child.

1952, July 31
537 A213 1.50k dark brown   1.40 .80
538 A213 2k blue violet   .35 .25
539 A213 3k rose brown   .35 .25
    Nos. 537-539 (3)   2.10 1.30

Czechoslovakia's Unified Health Service.

A214   United Physical Education Program — A214a

1952, Aug. 2   **Perf. 11½**
540 A214 1.50k Relay race   .95 .60
541 A214a 2k Canoeing   2.50 1.10
542 A214a 3k Cycling   .60 .55
543 A214a 4k Hockey   3.25 3.00
    Nos. 540-543 (4)   7.30 5.25

Issued to publicize Czechoslovakia's Unified Physical Education program.

F. L. Celakovski — A215

1952, Aug. 5   **Perf. 12½**
544 A215 1.50k dark brown   .25 .25
545 A215 2k dark green   1.40 .90

Centenary of the death of Frantisek L. Celakovski, poet and writer.

Mikulas Ales — A216

Perf. 11x11½
1952, Aug. 30   **Engr.**   **Unwmk.**
546 A216 1.50k dk gray grn   .45 .35
547 A216 6k red brown   3.00 2.25

Birth centenary of Mikulas Ales, painter.

17th Century Mining Towers — A217

Designs: 1.50k, Coal Excavator. 2k, Peter Bezruc mine. 3k, Automatic coaling crane.

1952, Sept. 14   Perf. 12½
548 A217   1k sepia   1.25   .45
549 A217   1.50k dark blue   .25   .25
550 A217   2k olive gray   .25   .25
551 A217   3k violet brown   .25   .25
   Nos. 548-551 (4)   2.00 1.20

Miners' Day, Sept. 14, 1952. No. 550 also for the 85th anniv. of the birth of Peter Bezruc (Vladimir Vasek), poet.

Jan Zizka — A218

Designs: 2k, Fraternization with Russians. 3k, Marching with flag.

Inscribed: ". . . . Armady 1952,"

1952, Oct. 5   Engr.   Perf. 11½
552 A218   1.50k rose lake   .25   .25
553 A218   2k olive bister   .25   .25
554 A218   3k dk car rose   .25   .25
555 A218   4k gray   1.50   .45
   Nos. 552-555 (4)   2.25 1.20

Issued to publicize Army Day, Oct. 5, 1952.

Souvenir Sheet

Statues to Bulgarian Partisans and to Soviet Army — A219

1952, Oct. 18   Unwmk.   Perf. 12½
556 A219   Sheet of 2   85.00 16.00
  a.   2k deep carmine   35.00   7.50
  b.   3k ultramarine   35.00   7.50

National Philatelic Exhibition, Bratislava, Oct. 18-Nov. 2, 1952.

Danube River, Bratislava — A220

1952, Oct. 18
557 A220   1.50k dark brown   .25   .25

National Philatelic Exhibition, Bratislava.

Conference with Lenin and Stalin — A221

1952, Nov. 7
558 A221   2k brown black   1.40   .95
559 A221   3k carmine   .25   .25

35th anniv. of the Russian Revolution and to publicize Czechoslovak-Soviet friendship.

Worker and Nurse Holding Dove and Olive Branch — A222

1952, Nov. 15   Photo.   Perf. 14
560 A222   2k brown   1.40   .80
561 A222   3k red   .25   .25

Issued to publicize the first State Congress of the Czechoslovak Red Cross.

Matej Louda, Hussite Leader, Painted by Mikulas Ales — A223

3k, Dragon-killer Trutnov, painted by Ales.

1952, Nov. 18   Engr.   Perf. 11½
562 A223   2k red brown   .35   .25
563 A223   3k grnsh gray   .75   .25

Mikulas Ales, painter, birth cent.

Gottwald Type of 1948-49

1952, June 2   Unwmk.   Perf. 12½
Size: 19x24mm
564 A135 1k dark green   .60   .25

"Peace" Flags — A224

1952, Dec. 12   Photo.   Perf. 14
565 A224 3k red brown   .35   .25
566 A224 4k deep blue   .75 1.00

Issued to publicize the Congress of Nations for Peace, Vienna, Dec. 12-19, 1952.

Dove by Picasso — A225

Design: 4k, Czech Family.

1953, Jan. 17
567 A225 1.50k dark brown   .25   .25
568 A225   4k slate blue   .65   .30

2nd Czechoslovak Peace Congress.

Smetana Museum — A226

Design: 4k, Jirásek Museum.

1953, Feb. 10   Engr.   Perf. 11½
569 A226 1.50k dk violet brn   .25   .25
570 A226   4k dark gray   1.50   .75

Prof. Zdenek Nejedly, 75th birth anniv.

Martin Kukucin A227   Jaroslav Vrchlicky A228

Designs: 2k, Karel Jaromir Erben. 3k, Vaclav Matej Kramerius. 5k, Josef Dobrovsky.

1953, Feb. 28
571 A227 1k gray   .25   .25
572 A228 1.50k olive   .25   .25
573 A228 2k rose lake   .25   .25
574 A228 3k lt brown   .50   .25
575 A228 5k slate blue   1.50   .75
   Nos. 571-575 (5)   2.75 1.75

Issued to honor Czech writers and poets: 1k, 25th anniv. of death of Kukucin. 1.50k, birth cent. of Vrchlicky. 2k, cent. of completion of "Kytice" by Erben. 3k, birth bicent. of Kramerius. 5k, birth bicent. of Dobrovsky.

Militia A229   Gottwald A230

Design: 8k, Portraits of Stalin and Gottwald and Peoples Assembly.

Perf. 13½x14

1953, Feb. 25   Photo.   Unwmk.
576 A229 1.50k deep blue   .25   .25
577 A230 3k red   .25   .25
578 A229 8k dark brown   2.10   .75
   Nos. 576-578 (3)   2.60 1.25

5th anniv. of the defeat of the attempt to reinstate capitalism.

Book and Torch — A231

Design: 3k, Bedrich Vaclavek.

1953, Mar. 5   Engr.   Perf. 11½
579 A231 1k sepia   1.50   .60
580 A231 3k orange brown   .25   .25

Bedrich Vaclavek (1897-1943), socialist writer.

Stalin Type of 1949
Inscribed "21 XII 1879-5 III 1953"
1953, Mar. 12
581 A154 1.50k black   .35   .25

Death of Joseph Stalin, Mar. 5, 1953.

Mother and Child A232   Girl Revolutionist A233

1953, Mar. 8
582 A232 1.50k ultra   .25   .25
583 A233 2k brown red   1.25   .60

International Women's Day.

Klement Gottwald — A234

1953, Mar. 19
584 A234 1.50k black   .25   .25
585 A234 3k black   .25   .25

Souvenir Sheet
Imperf
586 A234 5k black   5.00 4.00

Death of Pres. Klement Gottwald, 3/14/53.

Josef Pecka, Ladislav Zapotocky and Josef Hybes — A236

1953, Apr. 7   Unwmk.   Perf. 11½
587 A236 2k lt violet brn   .25   .25

75th anniversary of the first congress of the Czech Social Democratic Party.

Cyclists — A237

1953, Apr. 29
588 A237 3k deep blue   .75   .35

6th International Peace Bicycle Race, Prague-Berlin-Warsaw.

Medal of "May 1, 1890" — A238

Designs: 1.50k, Lenin and Stalin. 3k, May Day Parade. 8k, Marx and Engels.

Engraved and Photogravure
1953, Apr. 30   Perf. 11½x11, 14
589 A238 1k chocolate   1.40   .35
590 A238 1.50k dark gray   .25   .25
591 A238 3k carmine lake   .25   .25
592 A238 8k dk gray green   .30   .25
   Nos. 589-592 (4)   2.20 1.10

Issued to publicize Labor Day, May 1, 1953.

Sowing Grain — A239

1953, May 8   Photo.   Perf. 14
593 A239 1.50k shown   .35   .25
594 A239 7k Reaper   1.60 1.40

Socialization of the village.

Dam A240   Welder A241

Design: 3k, Iron works.

1953, May 8   Perf. 11½
595 A240 1.50k gray   1.10   .30
596 A241 2k blue gray   .25   .25
597 A240 3k red brown   .25   .25
   Nos. 595-597 (3)   1.60   .80

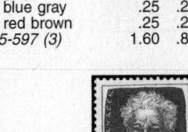

Josef Slavik A242   Leos Janacek A243

1953, June 19   Photo.
598 A242 75h dp gray blue   .75   .25
599 A243 1.60k dark brown   1.00   .25

Issued on the occasion of the International Music Festival, Prague, 1953.

Gottwald Type of 1948-49
Perf. 12½ (15h, 1k), 11½ (20h, 3k)
1953
600 A135 15h yellow green   .35   .25
601 A135 20h dk violet brn   .45   .25
602 A135 1k purple   1.10   .25
603 A135 3k brown car   .25   .25
604 A135 3k gray   .75   .25
   Nos. 600-604 (5)   2.90 1.25

Nos. 600-604 vary slightly in size.

Pres. Antonin Zapotocky — A244

1953, June 19   *Perf. 14*
605 A244 30h violet blue   .75 .25
606 A244 60h cerise   1.00 .25

Julius Fucik
A245

Book and Carnation
A246

1953, Sept. 8   **Engr.**   *Perf. 12½*
607 A245 40h dk violet brn   .30 .25
608 A246 60h pink   .50 .30

10th anniv. of the death of Julius Fucik, Communist leader executed by the Nazis.

Miner and Flag — A247

Design: 60h, Oil field and workers.

1953, Sept. 10   *Perf. 11½*
609 A247 30h gray   .30 .25
610 A247 60h brown vio   1.25 .50

Miner's Day, Sept. 10, 1953.

Volleyball Game
A248

Motorcyclist
A249

Design: 60h, Woman throwing javelin.

1953, Sept. 15
611 A248 30h brown red   4.50 1.50
612 A249 40h dk violet brn   2.75 .85
613 A248 60h rose violet   2.50 .85
    Nos. 611-613 (3)   9.75 3.20

Hussite Warrior — A250

Designs: 60h, Soldier presenting arms. 1k, Red army soldiers.

1953, Oct. 8
614 A250 30h brown   .30 .25
615 A250 60h rose lake   .35 .25
616 A250 1k brown red   1.50 1.25
    Nos. 614-616 (3)   2.15 1.75

Issued to publicize Army Day, Oct. 3, 1953.

Pres. Antonin Zapotocky — A251

1953   **Unwmk.**   *Perf. 11½, 12½*
617 A251 30h violet blue   .50 .25
618 A251 60h carmine rose   .80 .25

No. 617 is perf. 11½ & measures 19x23mm, No. 618 perf. 12½ & 18½x23½mm. See No. 780.

Charles Bridge and Prague Castle — A252

1953, Aug. 15   **Engr.**   *Perf. 11½*
619 A252 5k gray   4.00 .25

Korean and Czech Girls — A253

1953, Oct. 11   *Perf. 11x11½*
620 A253 30h dark brown   2.40 1.50

Czechoslovakia's friendship with Korea.

Flags, Hradcany Castle and Kremlin
A254

Designs: 60h, Lomonosov University, Moscow. 1.20k, Lenin Ship Canal.

1953, Nov. 7
621 A254 30h dark gray   .75 .50
622 A254 60h dark brown   1.10 .85
623 A254 1.20k ultra   3.00 1.90
    Nos. 621-623 (3)   4.85 3.25

Czechoslovak-Soviet friendship month.

Emmy Destinn, Opera Singer
A255

National Theater, Prague
A256

Portrait: 2k, Eduard Vojan, actor.

1953, Nov. 18   *Perf. 14*
624 A255 30h blue black   1.10 .75
625 A256 60h brown   .35 .35
626 A255 2k sepia   2.75 1.10
    Nos. 624-626 (3)   4.20 2.20

Natl. Theater founding, 70th anniv.
Nos. 624 and 626 each were issued in sheets of 10. Values: No. 624, $100; No. 626, $75.

Josef Manes — A257

1953, Nov. 28   *Perf. 11x11½*
627 A257 60h brown carmine   .35 .25
628 A257 1.20k deep blue   1.50 .90

Issued to honor Josef Manes, painter.

Vaclav Hollar — A258

Portrait: 1.20k, Head framed, facing right.

1953, Dec. 5
629 A258 30h brown black   .35 .25
630 A258 1.20k dark brown   1.50 .65

Vaclav Hollar, artist and etcher.

Leo N. Tolstoy — A259

1953, Dec. 29   **Unwmk.**
631 A259 60h dark green   .35 .25
632 A259 1k chocolate   1.50 .50

Leo N. Tolstoi, 125th birth anniv.

Locomotive
A260

Design: 1k, Plane loading mail.

Engraved, Center Photogravure
1953, Dec. 29   *Perf. 11½x11*
633 A260 60h brn org & gray vio   1.50 .45
634 A260 1k org brn & brt bl   3.50 1.10

Lenin — A261

Lenin Museum, Prague
A262

1954, Jan. 21   **Engr.**   *Perf. 11½*
635 A261 30h dark brown   .45 .25
636 A262 1.40k chocolate   1.50 .65

30th anniversary of the death of Lenin.

Klement Gottwald — A263

Design: 2.40k, Revolutionist with flag.

1954, Feb. 18   *Perf. 11x11½, 14x13½*
637 A263 60h dark brown   .30 .25
638 A263 2.40k rose lake   3.50 1.50

25th anniversary of the fifth congress of the Communist Party in Czechoslovakia.
No. 638 was issued in a sheet of 10 stamps. Value, $90.

Gottwald Mausoleum, Prague — A264

Gottwald and Stalin — A265

1.20k, Lenin & Stalin mausoleum, Moscow.

1954, Mar. 5   *Perf. 11½, 14x13½*
639 A264 30h olive brown   .35 .25
640 A265 60h deep ultra   .35 .25
641 A264 1.20k rose brown   2.25 1.00
    Nos. 639-641 (3)   2.95 1.50

1st anniv. of the deaths of Stalin and Gottwald.
No. 641 was issued in a sheet of 10 stamps. Value, $120.

Two Runners
A266

Group of Hikers
A267

Design: 1k, Woman swimmer.

1954, Apr. 24   *Perf. 11¼, 13¾ (#643)*
642 A266 30h dark brown   2.10 1.10
643 A267 80h dark green   7.00 3.50
644 A266 1k dk violet blue   1.75 .75
    Nos. 642-644 (3)   10.85 5.35

No. 643 was issued in a sheet of 10 stamps. Value, $350.

Nurse — A268

Designs: 15h, Construction worker. 40h, Postwoman. 45h, Ironworker. 50h, Soldier. 75h, Lathe operator. 80h, Textile worker. 1k, Farm woman. 1.20k, Scientist and microscope. 1.60k, Miner. 2k, Physician and baby. 2.40k, Engineer. 3k, Chemist.

1954   *Perf. 12½x12, 11½x11*
645 A268 15h dark green   .35 .25
646 A268 20h lt violet   .40 .25
647 A268 40h dark brown   .50 .25
648 A268 45h dk gray blue   .40 .25
649 A268 50h dk gray green   .50 .25
650 A268 75h deep blue   .50 .25
651 A268 80h violet brown   .50 .25
652 A268 1k green   .80 .25
653 A268 1.20k dk violet blue   .50 .25
654 A268 1.60k brown blk   1.20 .25
655 A268 2k orange brown   1.60 .25
656 A268 2.40k violet blue   1.60 .25
657 A268 3k carmine   1.60 .25
    Nos. 645-657 (13)   10.45 3.25

Antonin Dvorák — A269

40h, Leos Janacek. 60h, Bedrich Smetana.

1954, May 22   *Perf. 11x11½*
658 A269 30h violet brown   2.25 .25
659 A269 40h brick red   3.00 .35
660 A269 60h dark blue   .90 .25
    Nos. 658-660 (3)   6.15 .85

"Year of Czech Music," 1954.

Prokop Divis — A270

1954, June 15
661 A270 30h gray   .35 .25
662 A270 1.20k violet brown   1.40 .50

200th anniv. of the invention of a lightning conductor by Prokop Divis.

Slovak Insurrectionist — A271

Design: 1.20k, Partisan woman.

1954, Aug. 28   *Perf. 11½*
663 A271 30h brown orange   .25 .25
664 A271 1.20k dark blue   .85 .50

Slovak national uprising, 10th anniv.

Anton P. Chekhov — A272

1954, Sept. 24
665 A272 30h dull gray grn   .30 .25
666 A272 45h dull gray grn   1.10 .50

50th anniv. of the death of Chekhov, writer.

Soviet Representative Giving Agricultural Instruction
A273

Designs: 60h, Soviet industrial instruction. 2k, Dancers (cultural collaboration).

1954, Nov. 6   *Perf. 11½x11*
667 A273 30h yellow brown .25 .25
668 A273 60h dark blue .25 .25
669 A273 2k vermilion 1.40 .90
   Nos. 667-669 (3) 1.90 1.40

Czechoslovak-Soviet friendship month.

Jan Neruda — A274

60h, Janko Jesensky. 1.60k, Jiri Wolker.

1954, Nov. 25   *Perf. 11x11½*
670 A274 30h dark blue .85 .25
671 A274 60h dull red 1.40 .50
672 A274 1.60k sepia .35 .25
   Nos. 670-672 (3) 2.60 1.00

Issued to honor Czechoslovak poets.

View of
Telc — A275

Views: 60h, Levoca. 3k, Ceske Budejovice.

1954, Dec. 10   **Engr. & Photo.**
673 A275 30h black & bis .70 .25
674 A275 60h brown & bis .80 .25
675 A275 3k black & bis 2.50 1.25
   Nos. 673-675 (3) 4.00 1.75

Pres. Antonin
Zapotocky — A276

1954, Dec. 18   **Engr.**   *Perf. 11½*
676 A276 30h black brown .50 .25
677 A276 60h dark blue .55 .25

Souvenir Sheet
Imperf

678 A276 2k deep claret 15.00 6.00

70th birthday of Pres. Antonin Zapotocky.
See Nos. 829-831.

Attacking
Soldiers — A278

Design: 2k, Soldier holding child.

1954, Oct. 3   *Perf. 11½*
679 A278 30h dark green .30 .25
680 A278 2k dark brown 1.40 1.25

Army Day, Oct. 6, 1954.

Woman Holding
Torch — A279

Design: 45h, Ski jumper.

1955, Jan. 20   **Engr.**
681 A279 30h red 2.10 .50

Engraved and Photogravure

682 A279 45h black & blue 3.50 .50

First National Spartacist Games, 1955.

Comenius University
Building — A280

Design: 75h, Jan A. Komensky medal.

1955, Jan. 28   **Engr.**   *Perf. 11½*
683 A280 60h deep green .30 .25
684 A280 75h chocolate 1.40 .65

35th anniversary of the founding of Comenius University, Bratislava.

Czechoslovak
Automobile — A281

60h, Textile worker. 75h, Lathe operator.

1955, Mar. 15   **Unwmk.**
685 A281 45h dull green 1.40 .30
686 A281 60h dk violet blue .60 .25
687 A281 75h sepia .90 .25
   Nos. 685-687 (3) 2.90 .80

Woman
Decorating
Soviet
Soldier
A282

Stalin Memorial,
Prague
A283

Designs: 35h, Tankman with flowers. 60h,
Children greeting soldier.

1955, May 5   **Engr.**   *Perf. 11½*
688 A282 30h blue .35 .25
689 A282 35h dark brown 1.50 .30
690 A282 60h cerise .35 .25

Photo.

691 A283 60h sepia .35 .25
   Nos. 688-691 (4) 2.55 1.05

10th anniv. of Czechoslovakia's liberation.

Music and
Spring — A284

Design: 1k, Woman with lyre.

1955, May 12   **Engr. & Photo.**
692 A284 30h black & pale blue .35 .25
693 A284 1k black & pale rose 1.40 1.20

International Music Festival, Prague, 1955.

Foundry Worker — A285

Design: 45h, Farm workers.

1955, May 12   **Engr.**
694 A285 30h violet .25 .25
695 A285 45h green 1.20 .60

Issued to publicize the third congress of the
Trade Union Revolutionary Movement.

Woman Athlete — A286

60h, Dancing couple. 1.60k, Athlete.

1955, June 21
696 A286 20h violet blue 1.00 .40
697 A286 60h green .35 .25
698 A286 1.60k red .75 .25
   Nos. 696-698 (3) 2.10 .90

Issued to publicize the first National Spartacist Games, Prague, June-July, 1955.

Jakub Arbes — A287

Portraits: 30h, Jan Stursa. 40h, Elena
Marothy-Soltesova. 60h, Josef Vaclav Sladek.
75h, Alexander Stepanovic Popov. 1.40k, Jan
Holly. 1.60k, Pavel Josef Safarik.

1955
699 A287 20h brown .25 .25
700 A287 30h black .25 .25
701 A287 40h gray green .60 .25
702 A287 60h black .50 .25
703 A287 75h claret 1.75 .25
704 A287 1.40k black, *cr* .50 .25
705 A287 1.60k dark blue .50 .25
   Nos. 699-705 (7) 4.35 1.75

Various anniversaries of prominent Slavs.

Girl and Boy of Two
Races — A288

1955, July 20
706 A288 60h violet blue .75 .25

5th World Festival of Youth in Warsaw, July
31-Aug. 14.

Costume of Ocova,
Slovakia — A289

Regional Costumes: 75h, Detva man,
Slovakia. 1.60k, Chodsko man, Bohemia. 2k,
Hana woman, Moravia.

1955, July 25
Frame and Outlines in Brown
707 A289 60h orange & rose 10.00 7.00
708 A289 75h orange & lilac 4.00 4.00
709 A289 1.60k blue & orange 11.50 7.00
710 A289 2k yellow & rose 11.50 7.00
   Nos. 707-710 (4) 37.00 25.00

Nos. 707-710 were each issued in sheets of
10 stamps. Value, $450.

Carp — A290

Designs: 30h, Beetle. 35h, Gray Partridge.
1.40k, Butterfly. 1.50k, Hare.

1955, Aug. 8   **Engr. & Photo.**
711 A290 20h sepia & lt bl 2.25 .35
712 A290 30h sepia & pink 1.50 .30
713 A290 35h sepia & buff 1.50 .75
714 A290 1.40k sepia & cream 7.50 4.50
715 A290 1.50k sepia & lt grn 2.75 1.10
   Nos. 711-715 (5) 15.50 7.00

Tabor — A291

45h, Prachatice. 60h, Jindrichuv Hradec.

1955, Aug. 26   **Engr.**
716 A291 30h violet brown .50 .25
717 A291 45h rose carmine 2.00 .45
718 A291 60h sage green 1.00 .25
   Nos. 716-718 (3) 3.50 .95

Issued to publicize the architectural beauty
of the towns of Southern Bohemia.

Souvenir Sheet

Various
Views of
Prague
A292

1955, Sept. 10   **Engr.**   *Perf. 14x13½*
719 A292 Sheet of 5 27.50 27.50
   a. 30h gray black 4.75 5.25
   b. 45h gray black 4.75 5.25
   c. 60h rose lake 4.75 5.25
   d. 75h rose lake 4.75 5.25
   e. 1.60k gray black 4.75 5.25

International Philatelic Exhibition, Prague,
Sept. 10-25, 1955. Size: 145x110mm. Exists
imperf., value $47.50.

Motorcyclists — A293

1955, Aug. 28
720 A293 60h violet brown 3.00 .75

30th International Motorcycle Races at
Gottwaldov, Sept. 13-18, 1955.

Workers, Soldier and
Pioneer — A294

Army Day: 60h, Tanks and planes.

1955, Oct. 6   **Unwmk.**   *Perf. 11½*
721 A294 30h violet brown .35 .25
722 A294 60h slate 1.75 .75

Hans Christian
Andersen — A295

Portraits: 40h, Friedrich von Schiller. 60h,
Adam Mickiewicz. 75h, Walt Whitman.

1955, Oct. 27
723 A295 30h brown red .35 .25
724 A295 40h dark blue 2.25 1.00
725 A295 60h deep claret .35 .25
726 A295 75h greenish black .75 .35
   Nos. 723-726 (4) 3.70 1.85

Issued in honor of these four poets and to
mark the 100th anniversary of the publication
of Walt Whitman's "Leaves of Grass."

Railroad
Bridge — A296

30h, Train crossing bridge. 60h, Train
approaching tunnel. 1.60k, Miners' housing
project.

Inscribed: "Stavba Socialismu"

1955, Dec. 15
727 A296 20h dull green .75 .25
728 A296 30h violet brown .75 .25
729 A296 60h slate .75 .25
730 A296 1.60k carmine rose .75 .25
   Nos. 727-730 (4) 3.00 1.00

Issued to publicize socialist public works.

Hydroelectric
Plant — A297

2nd Five Year Plan: 10h, Miner with drill. 25h, Building construction. 30h, Harvester. 60h, Metallurgical plant.

Inscribed: "Druhy Petilety Plan 1956-1960."

1956, Feb. 20　　　　　Perf. 11½x11
731	A297	5h violet brown	.30	.25
732	A297	10h gray black	.30	.25
733	A297	25h dk car rose	.45	.25
734	A297	30h green	.30	.25
735	A297	60h violet blue	.30	.25
		Nos. 731-735 (5)	1.65	1.25

Jewelry — A298

1956, Mar. 17　　　　　Perf. 11x11½
736	A298	30h shown	.45	.25
737	A298	45h Glassware	3.50	1.60
738	A298	60h Ceramics	.45	.25
739	A298	75h Textiles	.45	.30
		Nos. 736-739 (4)	4.85	2.40

Products of Czechoslovakian industries.

Karlovy Vary (Karlsbad) — A299

Various Spas: 45h, Marianske Lazne (Marienbad). 75h, Piestany. 1.20k, Tatry Vysne Ruzbachy (Tatra Mountains).

1956, Mar. 17
740	A299	30h olive green	1.50	.30
741	A299	45h brown	1.10	.30
742	A299	75h claret	6.00	3.00
743	A299	1.20k ultra	.75	.30
		Nos. 740-743 (4)	9.35	3.90

Issued to publicize Czechoslovakian spas.

"We Serve our People" — A300

Designs: 60h, Russian War Memorial, Berlin. 1k, Tank crewman with standard.

1956, Apr. 9　Photo.　Perf. 11x11½
744	A300	30h olive brown	.75	.25
745	A300	60h carmine rose	.75	.25
746	A300	1k ultra	4.50	2.75
		Nos. 744-746 (3)	6.00	3.25

Exhibition: "The Construction and Defense of our Country," Prague, Apr., 1956.

Cyclists
A301

Girl Basketball Players
A302

Athletes and Olympic Rings
A303

Engraved and Photogravure
1956, Apr. 25　Unwmk.　Perf. 11½
747	A301	30h green & lt blue	3.50	.35
748	A302	45h dk blue & car	1.40	.35
749	A303	75h brown & lemon	1.10	.70
		Nos. 747-749 (3)	6.00	1.40

9th Intl. Peace Cycling Race, Warsaw-Berlin-Prague, May 1-15, 1956 (No. 747). 5th European Womens' Basketball Championship (No. 748). Summer Olympics, Melbourne, Nov. 22-Dec. 8, 1956 (No. 749). See No. 765.

Mozart — A304

45h, Josef Myslivecek. 60h, Jiri Benda. 1k, Bertramka House, Prague. 1.40k, Xaver Dusek (1731-99) and wife Josepha. 1.60k, Nostic Theater, Prague.

1956, May 12　　　　　Engr.
Design in Gray Black
750	A304	30h bister	1.50	.35
751	A304	45h gray green	8.50	6.00
752	A304	60h pale rose lilac	1.50	.35
753	A304	1k salmon	1.50	.35
754	A304	1.40k lt blue	4.50	.75
755	A304	1.60k lemon	3.00	.35
		Nos. 750-755 (6)	20.50	8.15

200th anniv. of the birth of Wolfgang Amadeus Mozart and to publicize the International Music Festival in Prague.

Home Guard — A305

1956, May 25
756	A305	60h violet blue	.75	.25

Issued to commemorate the first meeting of the Home Guard, Prague, May 25-27, 1956.

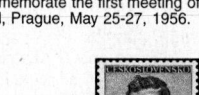

Josef Kajetan Tyl — A306

Portraits: 20h, Ludovit Stur. 30h, Frana Sramek. 1.40k, Karel Havlicek Borovsky.

1956, June 23
757	A306	20h dull purple	.75	.25
758	A306	30h blue	.45	.25
759	A306	60h black	.45	.25
760	A306	1.40k claret	3.00	1.75
		Nos. 757-760 (4)	4.65	2.50

Issued to honor various Czechoslovakian writers. See Nos. 781-784, 873-876.

River Patrol — A307

Design: 60h, Guard and dog.

1956, July 8　　　　　Perf. 11x11½
761	A307	30h ultra	.75	.25
762	A307	60h green	.60	.25

Issued to honor men of Frontier Guard.

Type of 1956 and

Steeplechase — A308

1956, Sept. 8　Unwmk.　Perf. 11½
763	A308	60h indigo & bister	3.00	.75
764	A308	80h brown vio & vio	1.50	.35
765	A303	1.20k slate & orange	3.00	1.50
		Nos. 763-765 (3)	7.50	2.60

Steeplechase, Pardubice, 1956 (No. 763). Marathon race, Kosice, 1956 (No. 764). Olympic Games, Melbourne, Nov. 22-Dec. 8 (No. 765).

Woman Gathering Grapes
A309

Fishermen
A310

35h, Women gathering hops. 95h, Logging.

1956, Sept. 20　　　　　Engr.
766	A309	30h brown lake	.35	.25
767	A309	35h gray green	.35	.25
768	A310	80h dark blue	.75	.25
769	A310	95h chocolate	2.25	1.00
		Nos. 766-769 (4)	3.70	1.75

Issued to publicize natural resources.

European Timetable Conf., Prague, Nov. 9-13 — A311

A312

Locomotives: 10h, 1846. 30h, 1855. 40h, 1945. 45h, 1952. 60h, 1955. 1k, 1954.

1956, Nov. 9　Unwmk.　Perf. 11½
770	A311	10h brown	2.50	.35
771	A312	30h gray	2.50	.35
772	A312	40h green	5.00	.35
773	A312	45h brown car	8.50	5.00
774	A312	60h indigo	2.50	.35
775	A312	1k ultra	6.00	.35
		Nos. 770-775 (6)	27.00	6.75

Costume of Moravia — A313

Regional Costumes (women): 1.20k, Blata, Bohemia. 1.40k, Cicmany, Slovakia. 1.60k, Novohradsko, Slovakia.

1956, Dec. 15　　　　　Perf. 13½
776	A313	30h brn, ultra & car	1.75	1.75
777	A313	1.20k brn, car & ultra	2.75	.40
778	A313	1.40k brn, ocher & ver	10.00	3.25
779	A313	1.60k brn, car & grn	3.50	.80
		Nos. 776-779 (4)	18.00	6.20

See Nos. 832-835.
Nos. 776-779 each were issued in sheets of 10 stamps. Value, $160.

Zapotocky Type of 1953
1956, Oct. 7　Unwmk.　Perf. 12½
780	A251	30h blue	.75	.25

Portrait Type of 1956

15h, Ivan Olbracht. 20h, Karel Toman. 30h, F. X. Salda. 1.60k, Terezia Vansova.

1957, Jan. 18　Engr.　Perf. 11½
781	A306	15h dk red brn, cr	.30	.25
782	A306	20h dk green, cr	.30	.25
783	A306	30h dk brown, cr	.30	.25
784	A306	1.60k dk blue, cr	1.50	1.00
		Nos. 781-784 (4)	1.50	1.00

Issued in honor of Czechoslovakian writers.

Kolin Cathedral
A315

Views: No. 786, Banska Stiavnica. No. 787, Uherske Hradiste. No. 788, Karlstein. No. 789, Charles Bridge, Prague. 1.25k, Moravska Trebova.

1957, Feb. 23
785	A315	30h dk blue gray	.40	.25
786	A315	30h rose violet	.50	.25
787	A315	60h deep rose	.50	.25
788	A315	60h gray green	.50	.25
789	A315	60h brown	.75	.25
790	A315	1.25k gray	3.00	1.50
		Nos. 785-790 (6)	5.65	2.50

Anniversaries of various towns and landmarks.

Komensky Mausoleum, Naarden
A316

Jan A. Komensky
A317

Old Prints: 40h, Komensky teaching. 1k, Sun, moon, stars and earth.

Perf. 11½x11, 14 (A317)
1957, Mar. 28　Engr.　Unwmk.
791	A316	30h pale brown	.45	.25
792	A316	40h dark green	.45	.25
793	A317	60h chocolate	3.00	.75
794	A316	1k carmine rose	.60	.25
		Nos. 791-794 (4)	4.50	1.50

300th anniv. of the publication of "Didactica Opera Omnia" by J. A. Komensky (Comenius). No. 793 issued in sheets of four. Value, $24.

Farm Woman — A318

1957, Mar. 22　　　　　Perf. 11½
795	A318	30h lt blue green	.75	.25

3rd Cong. of Agricultural Cooperatives.

Cyclists — A319

Woman Archer
A320

Boxers
A321

Rescue Team — A322

1957, Apr. 30　Perf. 11½x11, 11x11½
796	A319	30h sepia & ultra	.60	.25
797	A319	60h dull grn & bis	2.25	1.25
798	A320	60h gray & emer	.45	.25

799	A321 60h sepia & org	.45	.25
800	A322 60h violet & choc	.75	.25
	Nos. 796-800 (5)	4.50	2.25

10th Intl. Peace Cycling Race, Prague-Berlin-Warsaw (Nos. 796-797). Intl. Archery Championships (No. 798). European Boxing Championships, Prague (No. 799). Mountain Climbing Rescue Service (No. 800).

Jan V. Stamic — A323

Musicians: No. 802, Ferdinand Laub. No. 803, Frantisek Ondricek. No. 804, Josef B. Foerster. No. 805, Vitezslav Novak. No. 806, Josef Suk.

1957, May 12   *Perf. 11½*

801	A323 60h purple	.35	.25
802	A323 60h black	.35	.25
803	A323 60h slate blue	.35	.25
804	A323 60h brown	.35	.25
805	A323 60h dull red brn	.90	.25
806	A323 60h blue green	.35	.25
	Nos. 801-806 (6)	2.65	1.50

Spring Music Festival, Prague.

Josef Bozek   School of
A324   Engineering
           A325

60h, F. J. Gerstner. 1k, R. Skuhersky.

1957, May 25

807	A324 30h bluish black	.25	.25
808	A324 60h gray brown	.30	.25
809	A324 1k rose lake	.30	.25
810	A325 1.40k blue violet	.65	.25
	Nos. 807-810 (4)	1.50	1.00

School of Engineering in Prague, 250th anniv.

Pioneer and
Philatelic
Symbols — A326

Design: 60h, Girl and carrier pigeon.

Engraved and Photogravure
1957, June 8   *Perf. 11½*

811	A326 30h olive grn & org	.45	.25

         Engr.   *Perf. 13½*

812	A326 60h brn & vio bl	3.00	2.25

Youth Philatelic Exhibition, Pardubice. No. 812 was printed in miniature sheets of 4. Value $12.

"Grief" — A327

Design: 60h, Rose, symbol of new life.

1957, June 10

813	A327 30h black	.35	.25
814	A327 60h blk & rose red	1.25	.35

Destruction of Lidice, 15th anniversary. No. 814 was issued in a sheet of 10 stamps. Value, $28.

Motorcyclists — A328

1957, July 5   *Perf. 11½*

815	A328 60h dk gray & blue	1.50	.30

32nd International Motorcycle Race.

Karel Klic   Josef Ressel
A329   A330

1957, July 5

816	A329 30h gray black	.60	.25
817	A330 60h violet blue	.60	.25

Klic, inventor of photogravure, and Ressel, inventor of the ship screw.

Chamois   Gentian
A331   A332

Designs: 30h, Brown bear. 60h, Edelweiss. 1.25k, Tatra Mountains.

1957, Aug. 28   **Engr.**   *Perf. 11½*

818	A331 20h emer & brnsh gray	1.00	.25
819	A331 30h lt blue & brn	1.00	.25
820	A332 40h gldn brn & vio bl	1.60	.30
821	A332 60h yellow & grn	1.00	.25

        Size: 48x28½mm

822	A332 1.25k ol grn & bis	1.60	.80
	Nos. 818-822 (5)	6.20	1.85

Tatra Mountains National Park.

"Marycka
Magdonova" — A333

Engraved and Photogravure
1957, Sept. 15 Unwmk.   *Perf. 11½*

823	A333 60h black & dull red	.45	.25

90th birthday of Petr Bezruc, poet and author of "Marycka Magdonova."

Man Holding Banner of
Trade Union
Cong. — A334

1957, Sept. 28   **Engr.**

824	A334 75h rose red	.45	.25

4th Intl. Trade Union Cong., Leipzig, 10/4-15.

Television Transmitter
and Antennas — A335

Design: 60h, Family watching television.

1957, Oct. 19   **Engr.**   *Perf. 11½*

825	A335 40h dk blue & car	.30	.25
826	A335 60h redsh brown & emer	.45	.25

Issued to publicize the television industry.

Worker, Globe
and
Lenin — A336

60h, Worker, factory, hammer and sickle.

1957, Nov. 7   *Perf. 12x11½*

827	A336 30h claret	.25	.25
828	A336 60h gray blue	.25	.25

Russian Revolution, 40th anniversary.

Zapotocky Type of 1954 dated: 19 XII 1884-13 XI 1957
1957, Nov. 18 Unwmk.   *Perf. 11½*

829	A276 30h black	.25	.25
830	A276 60h black	.25	.25

Souvenir Sheet
Imperf

831	A276 2k black	5.00	1.25

Death of Pres. Antonin Zapotocky.

Costume Type of 1956

Regional Costumes: 45h, Pilsen woman, Bohemia. 75h, Slovacko man, Moravia. 1.25k, Hana woman, Moravia. 1.95k, Teshinsko woman, Silesia.

1957, Dec. 18   **Engr.**   *Perf. 13½*

832	A313 45h brn, bl & dk red	4.25	1.50
833	A313 75h dk brn, red & grn	3.00	.80
834	A313 1.25k dk brn, scar & ocher	5.25	1.50
835	A313 1.95k sepia, bl & ver	6.00	3.75
	Nos. 832-835 (4)	18.50	7.55

Nos. 832-835 each was issued in sheets of 10 stamps. Value, set $200.

A337   A338

Designs: 30h, Radio telescope and observatory. 45h, Meteorological station in High Tatra. 75h, Sputnik 2 over Earth.

1957, Dec. 20   *Perf. 11½*

836	A337 30h violet brn & yel	1.60	.50
837	A338 45h sepia & lt bl	.65	.30
838	A337 75h claret & blue	2.00	.85
	Nos. 836-838 (3)	4.25	1.65

IGY, 1957-58. No. 838 also for the launching of Sputnik 2, Nov. 3, 1957.

Girl Skater — A339

Designs: 40h, Canoeing. 60h, Volleyball. 80h, Parachutist. 1.60k, Soccer.

1958, Jan. 25   **Engr.**   *Perf. 11½x12*

839	A339 30h rose violet	1.75	.25
840	A339 40h blue	.35	.25
841	A339 60h redsh brown	.35	.25
842	A339 80h violet blue	1.50	.45
843	A339 1.60k brt green	.65	.25
	Nos. 839-843 (5)	4.60	1.45

Issued to publicize various sports championship events in 1958.

Litomysl
Castle — A340

Design: 60h, Bethlehem Chapel.

1958, Feb. 10   *Perf. 11½*

844	A340 30h green	.30	.25
845	A340 60h redsh brown	.30	.25

80th anniversary of the birth of Zdenek Nejedly, restorer of Bethlehem Chapel.

Giant
Excavator — A341

Peace Dove and: 60h, Soldiers, flame and banner, horiz. 1.60k, Harvester and rainbow, horiz.

1958, Feb. 25

846	A341 30h gray violet & yel	.25	.25
847	A341 60h gray brown & car	.25	.25
848	A341 1.60k green & dull yel	.45	.25
	Nos. 846-848 (3)	.95	.75

10th anniv. of the "Victorious February."

Jewelry — A342

Designs: 45h, Dolls. 60h, Textiles. 75h, Kaplan turbine. 1.20k, Glass.

Engraved and Photogravure
1958 Unwmk.   *Perf. 11½*

849	A342 30h rose car & blue	.40	.25
850	A342 45h rose red & pale lil	.40	.25
851	A342 60h violet & aqua	.60	.25
852	A342 75h ultra & salmon	1.50	.35
853	A342 1.20k blue grn & pink	.60	.25
	Nos. 849-853 (5)	3.50	1.75

Issued for the Universal and International Exposition at Brussels.

King George of
Podebrad — A343

Design: 60h, View of Prague, 1628.

1958, May 19   **Engr.**

854	A343 30h carmine rose	.50	.25
855	A343 60h violet blue	.30	.25

Issued to publicize the National Archives Exhibition, Prague, May 15-Aug. 15.

"Towards the   Women of
Stars"   Three Races
A344   A345

Boy, Girl and
Globes — A346

1958, May 26

856	A344 30h carmine rose	.45	.25
857	A345 45h rose violet	.45	.25
858	A346 60h blue	.45	.25
	Nos. 856-858 (3)	1.35	.75

The Soc. for Dissemination of Political and Cultural Knowledge (No. 856). 4th Cong. of the Intl. Democratic Women's Fed. (No. 857).

1st World Trade Union Conf. of Working Youths, Prague, July 14-20 (No. 858).

Grain, Hammer and Sickle — A347

Atomic Reactor — A348

45h, Map of Czechoslovakia, hammer & sickle.

1958, May 26
859	A347	30h dull red	.25	.25
860	A347	45h green	.30	.25
861	A348	60h dark blue	.30	.25
		Nos. 859-861 (3)	.85	.75

11th Congress of the Czech Communist Party and the 15th anniv. of the Russo-Czechoslovakian Treaty.

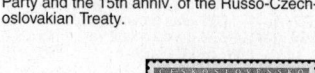

Karlovy Vary — A349

Various Spas: 40h, Podebrady. 60h, Marianske Lazne. 80h, Luhacovice. 1.20k, Strbske Pleso. 1.60k, Trencianske Teplice.

1958, June 25
862	A349	30h rose claret	.45	.25
863	A349	40h redsh brown	.45	.25
864	A349	60h gray green	.30	.25
865	A349	80h sepia	.45	.25
866	A349	1.20k violet blue	.60	.25
867	A349	1.60k lt violet	1.20	.75
		Nos. 862-867 (6)	3.45	2.00

Telephone Operator — A350

Design: 45h, Radio transmitter.

1958, June 20
| 868 | A350 | 30h black & brn org | .40 | .25 |
| 869 | A350 | 45h black & lt grn | .40 | .25 |

Conference of Postal Ministers of Communist Countries, Prague, June 30-July 9.

Pres. Novotny — A351

1958-59   **Perf. 12½**
870	A351	30h brt violet blue	.65	.25
b.		Perf. 11½	.50	.25
870A	A351	30h violet ('59)	4.00	1.75
871	A351	60h carmine rose	.45	.25

Perf. 11½
Redrawn
| 871A | A351 | 60h rose red | .50 | .25 |
| | | Nos. 870-871A (4) | 5.60 | 2.50 |

On No. 871 the top of the "6" turns down; on No. 871A it is open.

Czechoslovak Pavilion, Brussels — A352

1958, July 15   **Engr. & Photo.**
872 A352 1.95k lt blue & bis brn   .90   .25
Czechoslovakia Week at the Universal and International Exhibition at Brussels.

Portrait Type of 1956

30h, Julius Fucik. 45h, G. K. Zechenter 60h, Karel Capek. 1.40k, Svatopluk Cech.

1958, Aug. 20   **Engr.**   **Perf. 11½**
873	A306	30h rose red	.30	.25
874	A306	45h violet	1.50	.25
875	A306	60h dk blue gray	.60	.25
876	A306	1.40k gray	.60	.25
		Nos. 873-876 (4)	3.00	1.00

Death anniversaries of four famous Czechs.

The Artist and the Muse — A353

1958, Aug. 20   **Perf. 14**
877 A353 1.60k black   3.50   1.10
85th birthday of Max Svabinsky, artist and engraver.
No. 877 was printed in miniature sheets of 4. Value $24.

Children's Hospital, Brno — A354

Designs: 60h, New Town Hall, Brno. 1k, St. Thomas Church. 1.60k, View of Brno.

1958, Sept. 6   **Unwmk.**   **Perf. 11½**
       Size: 40x23mm
878	A354	30h violet	.25	.25
879	A354	60h rose red	.25	.25
880	A354	1k brown	.35	.25

       Perf. 14
       Size: 50x28mm
| 881 | A354 | 1.60k dk slate grn | 1.75 | 1.25 |
| | | Nos. 878-881 (4) | 2.60 | 2.00 |

Natl. Phil. Exhib., Brno, Sept. 9.
No. 881 sold for 3.10k, including entrance ticket to exhibition. Issued in sheets of four. Value, $10.

Lepiota Procera — A355

Mushrooms: 40h, Boletus edulis. 60h, Krombholzia rufescens. 1.40k, Amanita muscaria L. 1.60k, Armillariella mellea.

1958, Oct. 6   **Perf. 14**
882	A355	30h dk brn, grn & buff	1.60	.35
883	A355	40h vio brn & brn org	1.60	.35
884	A355	60h black, red & buff	2.40	.35
885	A355	1.40k brown, scar & grn	4.00	1.60
886	A355	1.60k blk, red brn & ol	8.00	4.50
		Nos. 882-886 (5)	17.60	7.15

Nos. 882-886 were each issued in a miniature sheet of 10 stamps. Value, set $275.

Children on Beach — A356

45h, Mother, child and bird. 60h, Skier.

1958, Oct. 24   **Unwmk.**   **Perf. 14**
887	A356	30h blue, yel & red	.35	.25
888	A356	45h ultra & carmine	1.40	.60
889	A356	60h brown, blue & yel	.35	.25
		Nos. 887-889 (3)	2.10	1.10

UNESCO Headquarters in Paris opening, Nov. 3. Nos. 887-889 each were issued in sheets of 10. Value, set $75.

Bozek's Steam Car of 1815 — A357

Designs: 45h, "Präsident" car of 1897. 60h, "Skoda" sports car. 80h, "Tatra" sedan. 1k, "Autocar Skoda" bus. 1.25k, Trucks.

Engraved and Photogravure
1958, Dec. 1   **Perf. 11½x11**
890	A357	30h vio blk & buff	.70	.25
891	A357	45h ol & lt ol grn	.70	.25
892	A357	60h ol gray & sal	1.75	.25
893	A357	80h claret & bl grn	1.10	.25
894	A357	1k brn & lt yel grn	1.40	.30
895	A357	1.25k green & buff	2.10	.45
		Nos. 890-895 (6)	7.75	1.75

Issued to honor the automobile industry.

Stamp of 1918 and Allegory — A358

1958, Dec. 18   **Engr.**   **Perf. 11x11½**
896 A358 60h dark blue gray   .85   .30
1st Czechoslovakian postage stamp, 40th anniv.

Ice Hockey — A359

30h, Girl throwing javelin. 60h, Ice hockey. 1k, Hurdling. 1.60k, Rowing. 2k, High jump.

1959, Feb. 6   **Perf. 11½x11**
897	A359	20h dk brown & gray	.50	.25
898	A359	30h red brn & org brn	.40	.25
899	A359	60h dk bl & pale grn	.65	.25
900	A359	1k maroon & citron	.50	.25
901	A359	1.60k dull vio & lt bl	.80	.25
902	A359	2k red brn & lt bl	1.75	.25
		Nos. 897-902 (6)	4.60	1.50

Congress Emblem — A360

60h, Industrial & agricultural workers, emblem.

1959, Feb. 27   **Perf. 11½**
| 903 | A360 | 30h maroon & lt blue | .45 | .25 |
| 904 | A360 | 60h dk blue & yellow | .45 | .25 |

4th Agricultural Cooperative Cong. in Prague.

"Equality of All Races" — A361

Designs: 1k, "Peace." 2k, Mother and Child: "Freedom for Colonial People."

1959, Mar. 23
905	A361	60h gray green	.30	.25
906	A361	1k gray	.45	.25
907	A361	2k dk gray blue	1.50	.50
		Nos. 905-907 (3)	2.25	1.00

10th anniversary of the signing of the Universal Declaration of Human Rights.

Girl Holding Puppet — A362

40h, Pioneer studying map. 60h, Pioneer with radio. 80h, Girl pioneer planting tree.

1959, Mar. 28   **Engr. & Photo.**
908	A362	30h violet bl & yel	.35	.25
909	A362	40h indigo & ultra	.45	.25
910	A362	60h black & lilac	.35	.25
911	A362	80h brown & lt green	.65	.25
		Nos. 908-911 (4)	1.80	1.00

10th anniv. of the Pioneer organization.

Frederic Joliot Curie — A363

1959, Apr. 17   **Engr.**
912 A363 60h sepia   1.40   .30
Frederic Joliot Curie and the 10th anniversary of the World Peace Movement.

"Reaching for the Moon" — A364

1959, Apr. 17
913 A364 30h violet blue   1.10   .30
2nd Cong. of the Czechoslovak Assoc. for the Propagation of Political and Cultural knowledge.

Town Hall Pilsen — A365

Designs: 60h, Part of steam condenser turbine. 1k, St. Bartholomew's Church, Pilsen. 1.60k, Part of lathe.

1959, May 2
914	A365	30h lt brown	.30	.25
915	A365	60h violet & lt grn	.30	.25
916	A365	1k violet blue	.40	.25
917	A365	1.60k black & yellow	1.10	.50
		Nos. 914-917 (4)	2.10	1.25

2nd Pilsen Stamp Exhib. in connection with the centenary of the Skoda (Lenin) armament works.

Factory and Emblem — A366

Inscribed: "IV Vseodborovy sjezd, 1959"

1959, May 13
918 A366 30h shown .45 .25
919 A366 60h Dam .30 .25
4th Trade Union Congress.

Zvolen Castle — A367

1959, June 13
920 A367 60h gray olive & yel .60 .25
Regional Stamp Exhibition, Zvolen, 1959.

Frantisek Benda A368

Aurel Stodola A369

30h, Vaclav Kliment Klicpera. 60h, Karel V. Rais. 80h, Antonin Slavicek. 1k, Peter Bezruc.

1959, June 22   Perf. 11½x11
921 A368 15h violet blue .25 .25
922 A368 30h orange brown .25 .25
923 A369 40h dull green .25 .25
924 A369 60h dull red brn .35 .25
925 A368 80h dull violet .55 .25
926 A368 1k dark brown .55 .25
Nos. 921-926 (6) 2.20 1.50

View of the Fair Grounds A370

Designs: 60h, Fair emblem and world map. 1.60k, Pavilion "Z."

Inscribed: "Mezinarodni Veletrh Brne 6.-20.IX. 1959"

Engraved and Photogravure
1959, July 20   Unwmk.   Perf. 11½
927 A370 30h lilac & yellow .25 .25
928 A370 60h dull blue .25 .25
929 A370 1.60k dk blue & bister .75 .25
Nos. 927-929 (3) 1.25 .75
International Fair at Brno, Sept. 6-20.

Revolutionist and Flag A371

Slovakian Fighter A372

1.60k, Linden leaves, sun and factory.

Perf. 11½
1959, Aug. 29   Unwmk.   Engr.
930 A371 30h black & rose .25 .25
931 A372 60h carmine rose .25 .25
932 A371 1.60k dk blue & yel .45 .25
Nos. 930-932 (3) .95 .75

Natl. Slovakian revolution, 15th anniv. and Slovakian Soviet Republic, 40th anniv.

Alpine Marmots A373

1959, Sept. 25   Engr. & Photo.
933 A373 30h shown 1.25 .25
934 A373 40h Bison 1.00 .40
935 A373 60h Lynx, vert. 2.60 .30
936 A373 1k Wolf 2.60 1.00
937 A373 1.60k Red deer 2.25 .55
Nos. 933-937 (5) 9.70 2.50
Tatra National Park, 10th anniv.

Lunik 2 Hitting Moon and Russian Flag — A374

1959, Sept. 23   Perf. 11½
938 A374 60h dk red & lt ultra 1.50 .30
Issued to commemorate the landing of the Soviet rocket on the moon, Sept. 13, 1959.

Stamp Printing Works, Peking — A375

1959, Oct. 1
939 A375 30h pale green & red .40 .25
10 years of Czechoslovakian-Chinese friendship.

Haydn — A376

Design: 3k, Charles Darwin.

1959, Oct. 16   Engr.   Perf. 11½
940 A376 60h violet black .50 .25
941 A376 3k dark red brown 1.25 .65
150th death anniv. of Franz Joseph Haydn, Austrian composer, and 150th birth anniv. of Charles Darwin, English naturalist.

Great Spotted Woodpecker — A377

Birds: 30h, Blue tits. 40h, Nuthatch. 60th, Golden oriole. 80h, Goldfinch. 1k, Bullfinch. 1.20k, European kingfisher.

1959, Nov. 16   Perf. 14
942 A377 20h multicolored 1.50 .60
943 A377 30h multicolored 1.50 .60
944 A377 40h multicolored 4.50 1.50
945 A377 60h multicolored 1.50 .60
946 A377 80h multicolored 2.25 .75
947 A377 1k multicolored 2.25 .75
948 A377 1.20k multicolored 3.00 .75
Nos. 942-948 (7) 16.50 5.55

Nos. 942-948 were each issued in miniature sheets of 10. Value, set $275.

Nikola Tesla — A378

Designs: 30h, Alexander S. Popov. 35h, Edouard Branly. 60h, Guglielmo Marconi. 1k, Heinrich Hertz. 2k, Edwin Howard Armstrong and research tower, Alpine, N. J.

Engraved and Photogravure
1959, Dec. 7   Perf. 11½
949 A378 25h black & pink 1.00 .25
950 A378 30h black & orange .25 .25
951 A378 35h black & lt vio .25 .25

952 A378 60h black & blue .25 .25
953 A378 1k black & lt grn .25 .25
954 A378 2k black & bister 1.25 .25
Nos. 949-954 (6) 3.25 1.50
Issued to honor inventors in the fields of telegraphy and radio.

Gymnast — A379

2nd Winter Spartacist Games: 60h, Skier. 1.60k, Basketball players.

1960, Jan. 20   Perf. 11½
955 A379 30h salmon pink & brn 1.00 .25
956 A379 60h lt blue & blk 1.00 .25
957 A379 1.60k bister & brn .85 .25
Nos. 955-957 (3) 2.85 .75

1960, June 15   Unwmk.
Designs: 30h, Two girls in "Red Ball" drill. 60h, Gymnast with stick. 1k, Three girls with hoops.
958 A379 30h lt grn & rose claret .65 .25
959 A379 60h pink & black .50 .25
960 A379 1k ocher & vio bl .85 .25
Nos. 958-960 (3) 2.00 .75
2nd Summer Spartacist Games, Prague, June 23-July 3.

River Dredge Boat — A380

Ships: 60h, River tug. 1k, Tourist steamer. 1.20k, Cargo ship "Lidice."

1960, Feb. 22   Perf. 11½
961 A380 30h slate grn & sal 2.75 .30
962 A380 60h mar & pale bl 1.40 .30
963 A380 1k dk violet & yel 2.50 .30
964 A380 1.20k lilac & pale grn 3.50 .90
Nos. 961-964 (4) 10.15 1.80

Ice Hockey Players A381

Design: 1.80k, Figure skaters.

1960, Feb. 27
965 A381 60h sepia & lt blue 2.00 .40
966 A381 1.80k black & lt green 6.00 1.75
8th Olympic Winter Games, Squaw Valley, Calif., Feb. 18-29, 1960.

1960, June 15   Unwmk.
Designs: 1k, Running. 1.80k, Women's gymnastics. 2k, Rowing.
967 A381 1k black & orange .85 .30
968 A381 1.80k black & sal claret 1.40 .40
969 A381 2k black & blue 2.50 .75
Nos. 967-969 (3) 4.75 1.45
17th Olympic Games, Rome, 8/25-9/11.

Trencin Castle — A382

Castles: 10h, Bezdez. 20h, Kost. 30h, Pernstein. 40h, Kremnica. 50h, Krivoklát castle. 60h, Karlstein. 1k, Smolenice. 1.60k, Kokorin.

1960-63   Engr.   Perf. 11½
970 A382 5h gray violet .30 .25
971 A382 10h black .30 .25
972 A382 20h brown org .35 .25
973 A382 30h green .30 .25
974 A382 40h brown .35 .25
974A A382 50h black ('63) 3.50 .25
975 A382 60h rose red .45 .25

976 A382 1k lilac .45 .25
977 A382 1.60k dark blue .75 .25
Nos. 970-977 (9) 6.75 2.25

1961, Oct.   Wmk. 341
977A A382 30h green 3.00 .40

Lenin — A383

1960, Apr. 22   Unwmk.
978 A383 60h gray olive 1.40 .25
90th anniversary of the birth of Lenin.

Soldier Holding Child — A384

Designs: No. 980, Child eating pie. No. 981, Soldier helping concentration camp victim. No. 982, Welder and factory, horiz. No. 983, Tractor driver and farm, horiz.

1960, May 5   Engr. & Photo.
979 A384 30h maroon & lt blue .35 .25
980 A384 30h dull red .35 .25
981 A384 30h green & dull blue .40 .25
982 A384 60h dk blue & buff .35 .25
983 A384 60h redsh brn & yel grn .40 .25
Nos. 979-983 (5) 1.85 1.25
15th anniversary of liberation.

Steelworker A385

Design: 60h, Farm woman and child.

1960, May 24
984 A385 30h maroon & gray .30 .25
985 A385 60h green & pale blue .30 .25
1960 parliamentary elections.

Red Cross Nurse Holding Dove — A386

Fire Fighters A387

1960, May 26   Unwmk.
986 A386 30h brown car & bl .30 .25
987 A387 60h dk blue & pink .45 .25
3rd Congress of the Czechoslovakian Red Cross (No. 986), and the 2nd Fire Fighters' Congress (No. 987).

Hand of Philatelist with Tongs and Two Stamps — A388

Design: 1k, Globe and 1937 Bratislava stamp (shown in miniature on 60h).

1960, July 11   Perf. 11½
988 A388 60h black & dull yel .75 .25
989 A388 1k black & blue .90 .25
Issued to publicize the National Stamp Exhibition, Bratislava, Sept. 24-Oct. 9. See Nos. C49-C50.

Stalin Mine, Ostrava-Hermanovice
A390

Designs: 20h, Power station, Hodonin. 30h, Gottwald iron works, Kuncice. 40h, Harvester. 60h, Oil refinery.

1960, July 25
992	A390	10h black & pale grn	.30	.25
993	A390	20h maroon & lt bl	.30	.25
994	A390	30h indigo & pink	.30	.25
995	A390	40h green & pale lilac	.30	.25
996	A390	60h dk blue & yel	.30	.25
		Nos. 992-996 (5)	1.50	1.25

Issued to publicize the new five-year plan.

Viktorin Cornelius, Lawyer — A391

Portraits: 20h, Karel Matej Capek-Chod, writer. 30h, Hana Kvapilova, actress. 40h, Oskar Nedbal, composer. 60h, Otakar Ostrcil, composer.

1960, Aug. 23   Engr.
997	A391	10h black	.30	.25
998	A391	20h red brown	.45	.25
999	A391	30h rose red	.55	.25
1000	A391	40h dull green	1.40	.60
1001	A391	60h gray violet	.45	.25
		Nos. 997-1001 (5)	3.15	1.60

See Nos. 1037-1041.

Skoda Sports Plane Flying Upside Down — A392

1960, Aug. 28   Engr. & Photo.
1002 A392 60h violet blue & blue 1.40 .30

1st aerobatic world championships, Bratislava.

Constitution and "Czechoslovakia" — A393

1960, Sept. 18
1003 A393 30h violet bl & pink .40 .25

Proclamation of the new socialist constitution.

Workers Reading Newspaper A394

Man Holding Newspaper A395

1960, Sept. 18
1004	A394	30h slate & ver	.25	.25
1005	A395	60h black & rose	.25	.25

Day of the Czechoslovak Press, Sept. 21, 1960, and 40th anniv. of the Rudé Právo paper.

Globes and Laurel — A396

1960, Sept. 18   Engr.
1006 A396 30h dk blue & bister .40 .25

World Federation of Trade Unions, 15th anniv.

Black-crowned Night Heron — A397

Birds: 30h, Great crested grebe. 40h, Lapwing. 60h, Gray heron. 1k, Graylag goose, horiz. 1.60k, Mallard, horiz.

Engraved and Photogravure
1960, Oct. 24   Unwmk.   Perf. 11½
Designs in Black
1007	A397	25h pale vio blue	.90	.25
1008	A397	30h pale citron	.80	.25
1009	A397	40h pale blue	.90	.25
1010	A397	60h pink	.60	.25
1011	A397	1k pale yellow	1.75	.25
1012	A397	1.60k lt violet	4.50	1.25
		Nos. 1007-1012 (6)	9.45	2.55

Doronicum Clusii (Thistle) — A398

Flowers: 30h, Cyclamen. 40h, Primrose. 60h, Hen-and-chickens. 1k, Gentian. 2k, Pasqueflower.

1960, Nov. 21   Engr.   Perf. 14
1013	A398	20h black, yel & grn	.80	.40
1014	A398	30h black, car rose & grn	.80	.40
1015	A398	40h black, yel & grn	.80	.40
1016	A398	60h black, pink & grn	.80	.40
1017	A398	1k black, bl, vio & grn	2.00	.40
1018	A398	2k black, lil, yel & grn	2.75	1.60
		Nos. 1013-1018 (6)	7.95	3.60

Nos. 1013-1018 were each issued in sheets of 10. Value, set $100.

Alfons Mucha — A399

1960, Dec. 18   Engr.   Perf. 11½x12
1019 A399 60h dk blue gray 3.00 .25

Day of the Czechoslovak Postage Stamp and birth cent. of Alfons Mucha, designer of the 1st Czechoslovakian stamp (Type A1).

Rolling-mill Control Bridge — A400

Designs: 30h, Turbo generator. 60h, Ditch-digging machine.

1961, Jan. 20   Unwmk.   Perf. 11½
1020	A400	20h blue	.30	.25
1021	A400	30h rose	.30	.25
1022	A400	60h brt green	.30	.25
		Nos. 1020-1022 (3)	.90	.75

Third Five-Year Plan.

Athletes with Flags — A401

Designs: No. 1024, Motorcycle race, horiz. 40h, Sculling, horiz. 60h, Ice skater. 1k, Rugby. 1.20k, Soccer. 1.60k, Long-distance runners.

Perf. 11x11½, 11½x11
1961, Feb. 20   Engr. & Photo.
1023	A401	30h rose red & bl	.30	.25
1024	A401	30h dk blue & car	.30	.25
1025	A401	40h dk gray & car	.45	.25
1026	A401	60h lilac & blue	.45	.25
1027	A401	1k ultra & yel	.45	.25
1028	A401	1.20k green & buff	1.10	.25
1029	A401	1.60k sepia & salmon	1.50	.30
		Nos. 1023-1029 (7)	4.55	1.80

Various sports events.

Exhibition Emblem — A402

1961, Mar. 6   Engr.   Perf. 11½
1030 A402 2k dk blue & red 2.25 .25

"Praga 1962" International Stamp Exhibition, Prague, Sept. 1962.

Rocket Launching — A403

30h, Sputnik III, horiz. 40h, As 20h, but inscribed "Start Kosmicke Rakety k Venusi — 12.II.1961". 60h, Luna I, horiz. 1.60k, Interplanetary station, horiz. 2k, Similar to type A404, without commemorative inscription.

1961, Mar. 6   Engr. & Photo.
1031	A403	20h violet & pink	.30	.25
1032	A403	30h dk green & buff	.65	.25
1033	A403	40h dk red & yel grn	.65	.30
1034	A403	60h violet & buff	.80	.25
1035	A403	1.60k dk bl & pale grn	.55	.25
1036	A403	2k mar & pale bl	1.25	.75
		Nos. 1031-1036 (6)	4.20	2.05

Issued to publicize Soviet space research.

Portrait Type of 1960

No. 1037, Jindrich Mosna. No. 1038, Pavol Orszagh Hviezdoslav. No. 1039, Alois Mrstik. No. 1040, Joza Uprka. No. 1041, Josef Hora.

1961, Mar. 27   Perf. 11½
1037	A391	60h green	.30	.25
1038	A391	60h dark blue	.60	.25
a.		"ORSZACH" instead of "ORSZAGH"	175.00	25.00
1039	A391	60h dull claret	.75	.25
1040	A391	60h gray	.55	.25
1041	A391	60h sepia	.30	.25
		Nos. 1037-1041 (5)	2.50	1.25

Man Flying into Space — A404

1961, Apr. 13
1042	A404	60h car & pale bl	.65	.25
1043	A404	3k ultra & yel	2.00	.60

1st man in space, Yuri A. Gagarin, Apr. 12, 1961. See No. 1036.

Flute Player — A405

1961, Apr. 24   Engr.
1044	A405	30h shown	.45	.25
1045	A405	30h Dancer	.45	.25
1046	A405	60h Lyre player	.65	.25
		Nos. 1044-1046 (3)	1.55	.75

Prague Conservatory of Music, 150th anniv.

Blast Furnace and Mine, Kladno — A406

1961, Apr. 24
1047 A406 3k dull red .65 .25

City of Kladno, 400th anniv.

Marching Workers A407

Woman with Hammer and Sickle A408

Klement Gottwald Museum A409

Designs: No. 1050, Lenin Museum. No. 1051, Crowd with flags. No. 1053, Man saluting Red Star.

1961, May 10
1048	A407	30h dull violet	.30	.25
1049	A409	30h dark blue	.30	.25
1050	A409	30h redsh brown	.30	.25
1051	A407	60h vermilion	.30	.25
1052	A408	60h dark green	.30	.25
1053	A408	60h carmine	.30	.25
		Nos. 1048-1053 (6)	1.80	1.50

Czech Communist Party, 40th anniversary.

Puppet — A410

Designs: Various Puppets.

Engraved and Photogravure
1961, June 20   Unwmk.   Perf. 11½
1054	A410	30h ver & yel	.30	.25
1055	A410	40h sepia & bluish grn	.30	.25
1056	A410	60h vio bl & sal	.30	.25
1057	A410	1k green & lt blue	.30	.25
1058	A410	1.60k mar & pale vio	.95	.25
		Nos. 1054-1058 (5)	2.15	1.25

Woman, Map of Africa and Flag of Czechoslovakia A411

1961, June 26
1059 A411 60h red & blue .35 .25

Issued to publicize the friendship between the people of Africa and Czechoslovakia.

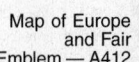

Map of Europe
and Fair
Emblem — A412

Fair emblem and: 60h Horizontal boring
machine, vert. 1k, Scientists' meeting and
nuclear physics emblem.

1961, Aug. 14   *Perf. 11½*

1060	A412	30h dk bl & pale grn	.30 .25
1061	A412	60h green & pink	.30 .25
1062	A412	1k vio brn & lt bl	.60 .25
	Nos. 1060-1062 (3)		1.20 .75

International Trade Fair, Brno, Sept. 10-24.

Sugar Beet, Cup of
Coffee and Bags of
Sugar — A413

1961, Sept. 18   Unwmk.   *Perf. 11½*

1063	A413	20h shown	.25 .25
1064	A413	30h Clover	.25 .25
1065	A413	40h Wheat	.25 .25
1066	A413	60h Hops	.25 .25
1067	A413	1.40k Corn	.30 .25
1068	A413	2k Potatoes	2.00 .35
	Nos. 1063-1068 (6)		3.30 1.60

Charles Bridge, St.
Nicholas Church and
Hradcany — A414

1961, Sept. 25

1069	A414	60h violet bl & car	1.20 .25

26th session of the Governor's Council of
the Red Cross Societies League, Prague.

Orlik Dam and
Kaplan
Turbine — A415

Designs: 30h, View of Prague, flags and
stamps. 40h, Hluboká Castle, river and fish.
60h, Karlovy Vary and cup. 1k, Pilsen and
beer bottle. 1.20k, North Bohemia landscape
and vase. 1.60k, Tatra mountains, boots, ice
pick and rope. 2k, Ironworks, Ostrava Kuncice
and pulley. 3k, Brno and ball bearing. 4k, Bratislava and grapes. 5k, Prague and flags.

1961   Unwmk.   *Perf. 11½*
Size: 41x23mm

1070	A415	20h gray & blue	*1.50* .45
1071	A415	30h vio blue & red	1.50 .75
1072	A415	40h dk blue & lt grn	1.60 .75
1073	A415	60h dk blue & yel	1.10 .75
1074	A415	1k mar & grn	.60 .75
1075	A415	1.20k green & pink	1.60 1.10
1076	A415	1.60k brn & vio bl	1.90 1.10
1077	A415	2k blk & ocher	1.90 .45
1078	A415	3k ultra & yel	2.00 .55
1079	A415	4k purple & sal	2.40 1.10

Perf. 13½
Engr.
Size: 50x29mm

1080	A415	5k multicolored	20.00 20.00
	Nos. 1070-1080 (11)		37.10 27.75

"PRAGA 1962 World Exhib. of Postage
Stamps," Aug. 18-Sept. 2, 1962.
No. 1080 was printed in sheet of 4. Value
$120.

Globe — A416

Engraved and Photogravure
1961, Nov. 27   *Perf. 11½*

1081	A416	60h red & ultra	.50 .25

Issued to publicize the Fifth World Congress
of Trade Unions, Moscow, Dec. 4-16.

Orange Tip
Butterfly — A417

Designs (butterflies): 20h, Zerynthia hyp-
sipyle Sch. 30h, Apollo. 40h, Swallowtail. 60h,
Peacock. 80h, Mourning cloak (Camberwell
beauty). 1k, Underwing (moth). 1.60k, Red
admiral. 2k, Brimstone (sulphur).

1961, Nov. 27   Engr.

1082	A417	15h multicolored	.80 .30
1083	A417	20h multicolored	.80 .30
1084	A417	30h multicolored	.80 .30
1085	A417	40h multicolored	.80 .30
1086	A417	60h multicolored	.80 .30
1087	A417	80h multicolored	2.40 .90
1088	A417	1k multicolored	2.40 .90
1089	A417	1.60k multicolored	2.40 .90
1090	A417	2k multicolored	6.50 3.00
	Nos.1082-1090 (9)		17.70 7.20

Nos.1082-1090 were each issued in sheets
of 10. Value, set $400.

Bicyclists — A418

Sports: 40h, Woman gymnast. 60h, Figure
skaters. 1k, Woman bowler. 1.20k, Goalkeeper, soccer. 1.60k, Discus thrower.

Engraved and Photogravure
1962, Feb. 5   Unwmk.   *Perf. 11½*

1091	A418	30h black & vio bl	.25 .25
1092	A418	40h black & yel	.25 .25
1093	A418	60h slate & grnsh bl	.35 .25
1094	A418	1k black & pink	.35 .25
1095	A418	1.20k black & green	.35 .25
1096	A418	1.60k blk & dull grn	1.50 .45
	Nos. 1091-1096 (6)		3.05 1.70

Various 1962 sports events.
No. 1095 does not have the commemorative
inscription.

Karel
Kovarovic
A419

Frantisek Zaviska
and Karel Petr
A420

20h, Frantisek Skroup. 30h, Bozena
Nemcova. 60h, View of Prague & staff of Aes-
culapius. 1.60k, Ladislav Celakovsky. 1.80k,
Miloslav Valouch & Juraj Hronec.

1962, Feb. 26   Engr.

1097	A419	10h red brown	.25 .25
1098	A419	20h violet blue	.25 .25
1099	A419	30h brown	.25 .25
1100	A420	40h claret	.50 .25
1101	A419	60h black	.25 .25
1102	A419	1.60k slate green	.25 .25
1103	A420	1.80k dark blue	.60 .25
	Nos. 1097-1103 (7)		2.35 1.75

Various cultural personalities and events.

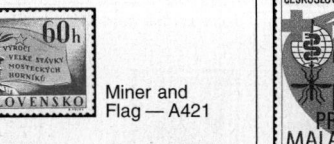

Miner and
Flag — A421

1962, Mar. 19   Engr. & Photo.

1104	A421	60h indigo & rose	.25 .25

30th anniv. of the miners' strike at Most.

"Man Conquering
Space" — A422

Soviet
Spaceship
Vostok
2 — A423

40h, Launching of Soviet space rocket. 80h,
Multi-stage automatic rocket. 1k, Automatic
station on moon. 1.60k, Television satellite.

1962, Mar. 26

1105	A422	30h dk red & lt blue	.35 .25
1106	A422	40h dk blue & sal	.35 .25
1107	A422	60h dk blue & pink	.35 .25
1108	A423	80h rose vio & lt grn	.35 .25
1109	A422	1k indigo & citron	.35 .25
1110	A423	1.60k green & buff	1.90 .25
	Nos. 1105-1110 (6)		3.65 1.50

Issued to publicize space research.

Polar Bear — A424

Zoo Animals: 30h, Chimpanzee. 60h,
Camel. 1k, African and Indian elephants,
horiz. 1.40k, Leopard, horiz. 1.60k, Przewalski
horse, horiz.

1962, Apr. 24   Unwmk.   *Perf. 11½*
Design and Inscriptions in Black

1111	A424	20h grnsh blue	.75 .25
1112	A424	30h violet	.75 .25
1113	A424	60h orange	.75 .25
1114	A424	1k green	.75 .25
1115	A424	1.40k carmine rose	.75 .25
1116	A424	1.60k lt brown	1.90 1.25
	Nos. 1111-1116 (6)		5.65 2.50

Child and Grieving
Mother — A425

60h, Flowers growing from ruins of Lezáky.

1962, June 9   Engr. & Photo.

1118	A425	30h black & red	.45 .25
1119	A425	60h black & dull bl	.75 .25

20th anniversary of the destruction of Lidice
and Lezáky by the Nazis.

Klary's Fountain,
Teplice — A426

1962, June 9

1120	A426	60h dull grn & yel	.40 .25

1,200th anniversary of the discovery of the
medicinal springs of Teplice.

Malaria Eradication
Emblem, Cross and
Dove — A427

3k, Dove and malaria eradication emblem.

1962, June 18

1121	A427	60h black & crimson	.45 .25
1122	A427	3k dk blue & yel	1.10 .35

WHO drive to eradicate malaria.

Soccer
Goalkeeper — A428

1962, June 20   Unwmk.   *Perf. 11½*

1123	A428	1.60k green & yellow	1.50 .25

Czechoslovakia's participation in the World
Cup Soccer Championship, Chile, May 30-
June 17. See No. 1095.

Soldier in Swimming
Relay Race — A429

Designs: 40h, Soldier hurdling. 60h, Soccer
player. 1k, Soldier with rifle in relay race.

1962, July 20

1124	A429	30h green & lt ultra	.25 .25
1125	A429	40h dk purple & yel	.25 .25
1126	A429	60h brown & green	.25 .25
1127	A429	1k dk blue & sal pink	.25 .25
	Nos. 1124-1127 (4)		1.00 1.00

2nd Summer Spartacist Games of Friendly
Armies, Prague, Sept., 1962.

"Agriculture" — A430

Designs: 60h, Astronaut in capsule. 80h,
Boy with flute, horiz. 1k, Workers of three
races, horiz. 1.40k, Children dancing around
tree. 1.60k, Flying bird, horiz. 5k, View of
Prague, horiz.

1962   Engr.   *Perf. 13½*

1128	A430	30h multicolored	1.20 .60
1129	A430	60h multicolored	.60 .30
a.	Miniature sheet of 8		20.00 20.00
1130	A430	80h multicolored	1.75 1.25
1131	A430	1k multicolored	1.75 1.25
1132	A430	1.40k multicolored	1.75 1.25
1133	A430	1.60k multicolored	3.00 2.10
	Nos. 1128-1133 (6)		10.05 6.75

Souvenir Sheet

1134	A430	5k multicolored	13.00 10.00
a.	Imperf.		40.00 35.00

"PRAGA 1962 World Exhib. of Postage
Stamps," 8/18-9/2/62. No. 1133 also for FIP
Day, Sept. 1. Printed in sheets of 10. Value:
Nos. 1128-1133 $150; No. 1134 $80.
No. 1129a contains 4 each of Nos. 1128-
1129 and 2 labels arranged in 2 rows of 2 se-
tenant pairs of Nos. 1128-1129 with label
between. Sold for 5k, only with ticket.
No. 1134 contains one 51x30mm stamp.
Sold only with ticket.

Children in Day
Nursery and Factory
A431

Sailboat and
Trade Union
Rest Home,
Zinkovy
A432

Engraved and Photogravure
1962, Oct. 29   Unwmk.   Perf. 11½
1135 A431 30h black & lt blue   .25   .25
1136 A432 60h brown & yellow   .25   .25

Cruiser "Aurora" — A433

1962, Nov. 7
1137 A433 30h black & gray bl   .25   .25
1138 A433 60h black & pink   .25   .25

Russian October revolution, 45th anniv.

Cosmonaut and Worker A434

Lenin A435

1962, Nov. 7
1139 A434 30h dark red & blue   .25   .25
1140 A435 60h black & dp rose   .25   .25

40th anniversary of the USSR.

Symbolic Crane A436

40h, Agricultural products, vert. 60h, Factories.

1962, Dec. 4
1141 A436 30h dk red & yel   .25   .25
1142 A436 40h gray blue & yel   .25   .25
1143 A436 60h black & dp rose   .30   .25
      Nos. 1141-1143 (3)   .80   .75

Communist Party of Czechoslovakia, 12th cong.

Ground Beetle — A437

Beetles: 30h, Cardinal beetle. 60h, Stag beetle, vert. 1k, Great water beetle. 1.60k, Alpine longicorn, vert. 2k, Ground beetle, vert.

1962, Dec. 15   Engr.   Perf. 14
1144 A437 20h multicolored   .80   .40
1145 A437 30h multicolored   .80   .40
1146 A437 60h multicolored   .80   .40
1147 A437 1k multicolored   1.60   .60
1148 A437 1.60k multicolored   3.25   .60
1149 A437 2k multicolored   4.50   2.00
      Nos. 1144-1149 (6)   11.75   4.40

Nos. 1144-1149 were each printed in sheets of 10. Value, set $225.

Table Tennis — A438

Sports: 60h, Bicyclist. 80h, Skier. 1k, Motorcyclist. 1.20k, Weight lifter. 1.60k, Hurdler.

Engraved and Photogravure
1963, Jan.   Perf. 11½
1150 A438 30h black & dp grn   .25   .25
1151 A438 60h black & orange   .25   .25
1152 A438 80h black & ultra   .25   .25
1153 A438 1k black & violet   .40   .25
1154 A438 1.20k blk & pale brn   .40   .25
1155 A438 1.60k blk & car   .85   .25
      Nos. 1150-1155 (6)   2.40   1.50

Various 1963 sports events.

Industrial Plant, Laurel and Star A439

Symbol of Pioneer Summer Camp A440

Industrial Plant and Symbol of Growth — A441

1963, Feb. 25   Unwmk.   Perf. 11½
1156 A439 30h carmine & lt bl   .25   .25
1157 A440 60h black & car   .25   .25
1158 A441 60h black & red   .25   .25
      Nos. 1156-1158 (3)   .75   .75

15th anniv. of the "Victorious February" and 5th Trade Union Cong.

Artists' Guild Emblem A442

Juraj Jánosik A443

Eduard Urx — A444

National Theater, Prague — A445

No. 1163, Woman reading to children. No. 1164, Juraj Pálkovic. 1.60k, Max Svabinsky.

Engr. & Photo.; Engr. (A444)
1963, Mar. 25   Unwmk.   Perf. 11½
1159 A442 20h black & Prus bl   .25   .25
1160 A443 30h car & lt bl   .25   .25
1161 A444 30h carmine   .25   .25
1162 A445 60h dl red brn & lt
             bl   .25   .25
1163 A444 60h green   .25   .25
1164 A444 60h black   .25   .25
1165 A444 1.60k brown   .50   .25
      Nos. 1159-1165 (7)   2.00   1.75

Various cultural personalities and events.

Boy and Girl with Flag — A446

Engraved and Photogravure
1963, Apr. 18   Perf. 11½
1166 A446 30h slate & rose red   .35   .25

The 4th Congress of Czechoslovak Youth.

Television Transmitter — A447

40h, Television camera, mast and set, horiz.

1963, Apr. 25
1167 A447 40h buff & slate   .40   .25
1168 A447 60h dk red & lt blue   .40   .25

Czechoslovak television, 10th anniversary.

Rocket to the Sun — A448

50h, Rockets & Sputniks leaving Earth. 60h, Spacecraft to & from Moon. 1k, 3k, Interplanetary station & Mars 1. 1.60k, Atomic rocket & Jupiter. 2k, Rocket returning from Saturn.

1963, Apr. 25
1169 A448 30h red brn & buff   .45   .25
1170 A448 50h slate & bluish
             grn   .45   .25
1171 A448 60h dk green & yel   .40   .25
1172 A448 1k dk gray & sal   .65   .25
1173 A448 1.60k gray brn & lt
             grn   .65   .25
1174 A448 2k dk purple &
             yel   1.25   .75
      Nos. 1169-1174 (6)   3.85   2.00

Souvenir Sheet
Imperf
1175 A448 3k Prus grn & org
             red   10.00   5.00

No. 1175 issued for 1st Space Research Exhib., Prague, Apr. 1963.

Studio and Radio — A449

1k, Globe inscribed "Peace" & aerial mast, vert.

1963, May 18   Unwmk.   Perf. 11½
1176 A449 30h choc & pale grn   .40   .25
1177 A449 1k bluish grn & lilac   .40   .25

40th anniversary of Czechoslovak radio.

Tupolev Tu-104B Turbojet — A450

Design: 1.80k, Ilyushin Il-18 Moskva.

1963, May 25
1178 A450 80h violet & lt bl   1.00   .35
1179 A450 1.80k dk blue & lt grn   1.50   .35

40th anniversary of Czechoslovak airlines.

9th Cent. Ring, Map of Moravian Settlements — A451

1.60k, Falconer, 9th cent. silver disk.

1963, May 25
1180 A451 30h lt green & blk   .25   .25
1181 A451 1.60k dull yel & blk   .75   .25

1100th anniversary of Moravian empire.

Woman Singing — A452

1963, May 25   Engr.
1182 A452 30h bright red   .55   .25

60th anniversary of the founding of the Moravian Teachers' Singing Club.

Kromeriz Castle and Barley — A453

Engraved and Photogravure
1963, June 20   Unwmk.   Perf. 11½
1183 A453 30h slate grn & yel   .55   .25

Natl. Agricultural Exhib. and 700th anniv. of Kromeriz.

Centenary Emblem, Nurse and Playing Child — A454

1963, June 20
1184 A454 30h dk gray & car   .50   .25

Centenary of the International Red Cross.

Bee, Honeycomb and Emblem — A455

1963, June 20
1185 A455 1k brown & yellow   .75   .25

19th Intl. Beekeepers Cong., Apimondia, 1963.

Liberec Fair Emblem — A456

1963, July 13
1186 A456 30h black & dp rose   .40   .25

Liberec Consumer Goods Fair.

Town Hall, Brno — A457

Design: 60h, Town Hall tower, Brno.

1963, July 29
1187 A457 30h lt blue & maroon   .35   .25
1188 A457 60h pink & dk blue   .35   .25

International Trade Fair, Brno.

Cave, Moravian Karst — A458

No. 1190, Trout, Hornad Valley. 60h, Great Hawk Gorge. 80h, Macocha mountains.

1963, July 29
1189 A458 30h brown & lt bl   .80   .25
1190 A458 30h dk bl & dull grn   .95   .25
1191 A458 60h green & blue   .80   .25
1192 A458 80h sepia & pink   .80   .25
      Nos. 1189-1192 (4)   3.35   1.00

Blast Furnace — A459

1963, Aug. 15   Unwmk.   Perf. 11½
1193 A459 60h blk & bluish grn   .40   .25

30th Intl. Cong. of Iron Founders, Prague.

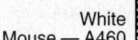

White Mouse — A460

1963, Aug. 15
1194 A460 1k black & carmine .60 .25
2nd Intl. Pharmacological Cong., Prague.

Farm Machinery for Underfed Nations — A461

1963, Aug. 15 **Engr.**
1195 A461 1.60k black .50 .25
FAO "Freedom from Hunger" campaign.

Wooden Toys — A462

Folk Art (Inscribed "UNESCO"): 80h, Cock and flowers. 1k, Flowers in vase. 1.20k, Janosik, Slovak hero. 1.60k, Stag. 2k, Postilion.

1963, Sept. 2 **Engr.** **Perf. 13½**
1196 A462 60h red & vio bl .65 .30
1197 A462 80h multi .65 .30
1198 A462 1k multi .65 .30
1199 A462 1.20k multi .65 .30
1200 A462 1.60k multi .65 .30
1201 A462 2k multi 2.75 1.75
      Nos. 1196-1201 (6) 6.00 3.25

Nos. 1196-1201 were printed in sheets of 10. Value, set $100.

Canoeing — A463

Sports: 40h, Volleyball. 60h, Wrestling. 80h, Basketball. 1k, Boxing. 1.60k, Gymnastics.

Engraved and Photogravure
1963, Oct. 26 **Perf. 11½**
1202 A463 30h indigo & grn .30 .25
1203 A463 40h red brn & lt bl .30 .25
1204 A463 60h brn red & yel .35 .25
1205 A463 80h dk pur & dp org .45 .25
1206 A463 1k ultra & dp rose .60 .35
1207 A463 1.60k vio bl & ultra 2.00 1.00
      Nos. 1202-1207 (6) 4.00 2.35

1964 Olympic Games, Tokyo.

Tree and Star — A464

Design: 60h, Star, hammer and sickle.

1963, Dec. 11 **Unwmk.** **Perf. 11½**
1208 A464 30h bis brn & lt bl .30 .25
1209 A464 60h carmine & gray .30 .25

Russo-Czechoslovakian Treaty, 20th anniv.

Atom Diagrams Surrounding Head — A465

1963, Dec. 12 **Engr.**
1210 A465 60h dark purple .40 .25

3rd Congress of the Association for the Propagation of Scientific Knowledge.

Chamois — A466

40h, Alpine ibex. 60h, Mouflon. 1.20k, Roe deer. 1.60k, Fallow deer. 2k, Red deer.

1963, Dec. 14 **Perf. 14**
1211 A466 30h multi 1.25 .35
1212 A466 40h multi 1.25 .35
1213 A466 60h brn, yel & grn 1.25 .35
1214 A466 1.20k multi 2.00 1.00
1215 A466 1.60k multi 2.50 1.25
1216 A466 2k multi 5.00 2.50
      Nos. 1211-1216 (6) 13.25 5.80

Nos. 1211-1216 were each issued in sheets of 10 stamps. Value, set $400.

Figure Skating — A467

80h, Skiing, horiz. 1k, Field ball player.

Engraved and Photogravure
1964, Jan. 20 **Unwmk.** **Perf. 11½**
1217 A467 30h violet bl & yel .30 .25
1218 A467 80h dk blue & org .45 .25
1219 A467 1k brown & lilac .75 .25
      Nos. 1217-1219 (3) 1.50 .75

Intl. University Games (30h, 80h) and the World Field Ball Championships (1k).

Ice Hockey — A468

1964, Jan. 20
1220 A468 1k shown 1.10 .45
1221 A468 1.80k Toboggan 1.20 .60
1222 A468 2k Ski jump 2.25 1.00
      Nos. 1220-1222 (3) 4.55 2.05

9th Winter Olympic Games, Innsbruck, Jan. 29-Feb. 9, 1964.

Magura Rest Home, High Tatra — A469

Design: 80h, Slovak National Insurrection Rest Home, Low Tatra.

1964, Feb. 19 **Unwmk.** **Perf. 11½**
1223 A469 60h green & yellow .30 .25
1224 A469 80h violet bl & pink .30 .25

Tourism — A470

30h, Skiers at Belianske Tatras mountains. 60h, Automobile camp, Telc. 1k, Fishing, Spis Castle. 1.80k, Lake & boats, Cesky Krumlov.

1964, Feb. 19 **Engr. & Photo.**
1225 A470 30h dk vio brn & bl .40 .25
1226 A470 60h slate & car .45 .25
1227 A470 1k red brn & olive .80 .25
1228 A470 1.80k slate grn & org 1.10 .35
      Nos. 1225-1228 (4) 2.75 1.10

Moses, Day and Night by Michelangelo A471

Designs: 60h, "A Midsummer Night's Dream," by Shakespeare. 1k, Man, telescope and heaven, vert. 1.60k, King George of Podebrad (1420-71).

1964, Mar. 20
1229 A471 40h black & yel grn .35 .25
1230 A471 60h grnsh blk & ce-
           rise .35 .25
1231 A471 1k black & lt blue 1.25 .25
1232 A471 1.60k black & yellow 1.25 .25
    a. Souvenir sheet of 4, imperf.
       ('88) 9.50 6.50
      Nos. 1229-1232 (4) 3.20 1.00

UNESCO issue. 400th anniv. of the death of Michelangelo (40h); 400th anniv. of the birth of Shakespeare (60h); 400th anniv. of the birth of Galileo (1k); 500th anniv. of the pacifist efforts of King George of Podebrad (1.60k).

No. 1232a for PRAGA '88.

Yuri A. Gagarin A472

Astronauts: 60h, Gherman Titov. 80h, John H. Glenn, Jr. 1k, Scott M. Carpenter, vert. 1.20k, Pavel R. Popovich and Andrian G. Nikolayev. 1.40k, Walter M. Schirra, vert. 1.60k, Gordon L. Cooper, vert. 2k, Valentina Tereshkova and Valeri Bykovski, vert.

1964, Apr. 27 **Unwmk.** **Perf. 11½**
Yellow Paper
1233 A472 30h black & vio bl .50 .25
1234 A472 60h dk grn & dk car .50 .25
1235 A472 80h dk car & vio .55 .25
1236 A472 1k ultra & rose vio .75 .25
1237 A472 1.20k ver & ol gray .60 .30
1238 A472 1.40k black & dl grn 1.00 .45
1239 A472 1.60k pale pur & Prus
           grn 2.25 1.50
1240 A472 2k dk blue & red .75 .40
      Nos. 1233-1240 (8) 6.90 3.65

World's first 10 astronauts.

Creeping Bellflower — A473

Flowers: 80h, Musk thistle. 1k, Chicory. 1.20k, Yellow iris. 1.60k, Gentian. 2k, Corn poppy.

1964, June 15 **Engr.** **Perf. 14**
1241 A473 60h dk grn, lil &
           org .75 .25
1242 A473 80h blk, grn & red
           lil 1.10 .25
1243 A473 1k vio bl, grn &
           pink 1.10 .45
1244 A473 1.20k black, yel &
           grn 1.10 .30
1245 A473 1.60k violet & grn 1.10 .40
1246 A473 2k vio, red & grn 4.50 1.50
      Nos. 1241-1246 (6) 9.65 3.15

Nos. 1241-1246 were each issued in sheets of 10. Value, set $250.

Film "Flower" and Karlovy Vary Colonnade — A474

Engraved and Photogravure
1964, June 20 **Unwmk.** **Perf. 13½**
1247 A474 60h black, blue & car 2.00 .50

14th Intl. Film Festival at Karlovy Vary, July 4-19.
Issued in sheets of 10. Value, $80.

Silesian Coat of Arms — A475

1964, June 20 **Perf. 11½**
1248 A475 30h black & yel .30 .25
150th anniv. of the Silesian Museum, Opava.

Young Miner of 1764 — A476

1964, June 20
1249 A476 60h sepia & lt grn .30 .25
Mining School at Banska Stiavnica, bicent.

Skoda Fire Engine — A477

1964, June 20
1250 A477 60h car rose & lt bl 1.00 .25
Voluntary fire brigades in Bohemia, cent.

Gulls, Hradcany Castle, Red Cross — A478

1964, July 10
1251 A478 60h car & bluish gray .55 .25
4th Czechoslovak Red Cross Congress at Prague.

Human Heart — A479

1964, July 10
1252 A479 1.60k ultra & car 1.10 .25
4th European Cardiological Cong. at Prague.

Partisans, Girl and Factories A480

Battle Scene, 1944 A481

Design: No. 1254, Partisans and flame.

Engraved and Photogravure
1964, Aug. 17 **Unwmk.** **Perf. 11½**
1253 A480 30h brown & red .25 .25
1254 A480 60h dk blue & red .25 .25
1255 A481 60h black & red .25 .25
      Nos. 1253-1255 (3) .75 .75

20th anniv. of the Slovak Natl. Uprising; No. 1255, 20th anniv. of the Battles of Dukla Pass.

Hradcany at
Prague — A482

Design: 5k, Charles Bridge and Hradcany.

1964, Aug. 30   *Perf. 11½x12*
1256 A482 60h black & red   .65   .25

Souvenir Sheet
     Engr.   *Imperf.*
1257 A482 5k deep claret   3.50 2.50
Millenium of the Hradcany, Prague.
No. 1257 stamp size: 30x50mm.

Discus Thrower and
Pole Vaulter — A483

Designs: 60h, Bicycling, horiz. 1k, Soccer.
1.20k, Rowing. 1.60k, Swimming, horiz. 2.80k,
Weight lifting, horiz.

Engraved and Photogravure
1964, Sept. 2   *Perf. 13½*
1258 A483   60h multi   .80   .30
1259 A483   80h multi   .80   .30
1260 A483   1k multi   .80   .30
1261 A483   1.20k multi   .80   .30
1262 A483   1.60k multi   .80   .30
1263 A483   2.80k multi   4.00 2.00
    Nos. 1258-1263 (6)   8.00 3.50

Issued to commemorate the 18th Olympic
Games, Tokyo, Oct. 10-25.
Nos. 1258-1263 were issued in sheets of
10. Value, set $125.

Miniature Sheet

Space Ship Voskhod I, Astronauts and
Globe — A484

1964, Nov. 12   *Unwmk.*   *Perf. 11½*
1264 A484 3k dk bl & dl lil, *buff*   5.00 3.50
Russian 3-man space flight of Vladimir M.
Komarov, Boris B. Yegorov and Konstantin
Feoktistov, Oct. 12-13.

Steam Engine   Diesel Engine
and Atomic   "CKD
Power   Praha" — A486
Plant — A485

1964, Nov. 16   *Engr.*
1265 A485 30h dull red brown   .25   .25

Engraved and Photogravure
1266 A486 60h green & salmon   1.00   .25

Traditions and development of engineering;
No. 1265 for 150th anniv. of the First Brno
Engineering Works, No. 1266 for the engineer-
ing concern CKD Praha.

European
Redstart — A487

Birds: 60h, Green woodpecker. 80h, Haw-
finch. 1k, Black woodpecker. 1.20k, European
robin. 1.60k, European roller.

1964, Nov. 16   *Litho.*   *Perf. 10½*
1267 A487   30h multicolored   1.10   .30
1268 A487   60h black & multi   1.10   .30
1269 A487   80h multicolored   1.40   .35
1270 A487   1k multicolored   1.75   .40
1271 A487   1.20k yellow & blk   1.75   .40
1272 A487   1.60k yellow & blk   3.50 1.00
    Nos. 1267-1272 (6)   10.60 2.75

Dancer   "In the Sun"
A488   Pre-school
           Children
           A489

Designs: 60h, "Over the Obstacles," teen-
agers. 1k, "Movement and Beauty," woman
flag twirler. 1.60k, Runners at start.

Engraved and Photogravure
1965   *Unwmk.*   *Perf. 11½*
1273 A488 30h red & lt blue   .25   .25

       Perf. 11½x12
1274 A489   30h vio bl & car   .25   .25
1275 A489   60h brown & ultra   .25   .25
1276 A489   1k black & yellow   .25   .25
1277 A489   1.60k maroon & gray   .60   .25
    Nos. 1273-1277 (5)   1.60 1.25

3rd Natl. Spartacist Games. Issue dates:
No. 1273, Jan. 3; Nos. 1274-1277, May 24.

Mountain Rescue
Service — A490

Designs: No. 1279, Woman gymnast. No.
1280, Bicyclists. No. 1281, Women hurdlers.

1965, Jan. 15   *Unwmk.*   *Perf. 11½*
1278 A490 60h violet & blue   .30   .25
1279 A490 60h maroon & ocher   .30   .25
1280 A490 60h black & carmine   .30   .25
1281 A490 60h green & yellow   .30   .25
    Nos. 1278-1281 (4)   1.20 1.00

Mountain Rescue Service (No. 1278); 1st
World Championship in Artistic Gymnastics,
Prague, Dec. 1965 (No. 1279); World Champi-
onship in Indoor Bicycling, Prague, Oct. 1965
(No. 1280); "Universiada 1965," Brno (No.
1281).

Arms and View,
Beroun — A491

Designs: No. 1283, Town Square, Domazlice. No. 1284, Old and new buildings, Frydek-
Mystek. No. 1285, Arms and view, Lipnik. No.
1286, Fortified wall, City Hall and Arms,
Policka. No. 1287, View and hops, Zatek. No.
1288, Small fortress and rose, Terezin.

1965, Feb. 15
1282 A491   30h vio bl & lt bl   .30   .25
1283 A491   30h dull pur & yel   .30   .25
1284 A491   30h slate & gray   .30   .25
1285 A491   30h green & bis   .30   .25
1286 A491   30h brown & tan   .30   .25
1287 A491   30h dk blue & cit   .30   .25
1288 A491   30h black & rose   .30   .25
    Nos. 1282-1288 (7)   2.10 1.75

Nos. 1282-1287 for 700th anniv. of the
founding of various Bohemian towns; No.
1288 the 20th anniv. of the liberation of the
Theresienstadt (Terezin) concentration camp.

Sun's
Corona — A492

Space Research: 30h, Sun. 60h, Exploration of the Moon. 1k, Twin space craft, vert.
1.40k, Space station. 1.60k, Exploration of
Mars, vert. 2k, USSR and US Meteorological
collaboration.

1965, Mar. 15   *Perf. 12x11½, 11½x12*
1289 A492   20h rose & red lilac   .25   .25
1290 A492   30h rose red & yel   .25   .25
1291 A492   60h bluish blk & yel   .25   .25
1292 A492   1k pur & pale bl   .25   .25
1293 A492   1.40k black & salmon   .35   .25
1294 A492   1.60k black & pink   .50   .25
1295 A492   2k bluish blk & lt bl   1.50 1.00
    Nos. 1289-1295 (7)   3.35 2.50

Space research; Nos. 1289-1290 also for
the Intl. Quiet Sun Year, 1964-65.

Frantisek Ventura,
Equestrian; Amsterdam,
1928 — A493

Czechoslovakian Olympic Victories: 30h,
Discus, Paris, 1900. 60h, Running, Helsinki,
1952. 1k, Weight lifting, Los Angeles, 1932.
1.40k, Gymnastics, Berlin, 1936. 1.60k,
Double sculling, Rome, 1960. 2k, Women's
gymnastics, Tokyo, 1964.

1965, Apr. 16   *Perf. 11½x12*
1296 A493   20h choc & gold   .25   .25
1297 A493   30h indigo & emer   .25   .25
1298 A493   60h ultra & gold   .25   .25
1299 A493   1k red brn & gold   .25   .25
1300 A493   1.40k dk sl grn & gold   1.10   .45
1301 A493   1.60k black & gold   1.10   .45
1302 A493   2k maroon & gold   .55   .30
    Nos. 1296-1302 (7)   3.75 2.20

Astronauts
Virgil
Grissom
and John
Young
A494

Designs: No. 1304, Alexei Leonov floating in
space. No. 1305, Launching pad at Cape Kennedy. No. 1306, Leonov leaving space ship.

1965, Apr. 17   *Perf. 11x11½*
1303 A494   60h slate bl & lil rose   .45   .25
1304 A494   60h vio blk & blue   .45   .25
1305 A494   3k slate bl & lil rose   1.60 1.00
   a.   Pair, #1303, 1305   3.50 1.50
1306 A494   3k vio blk & blue   1.60 1.00
   a.   Pair, #1304, 1306   3.50 1.50
    Nos. 1303-1306 (4)   4.10 2.50

Issued to honor American and Soviet astronauts. Printed in sheets of 25; one sheet contains 20 No. 1303 and 5 No. 1305, the other
sheet contains 20 No. 1304 and 5 No. 1306.
Value, $125 each.

Russian Soldier,
View of Prague
and Guerrilla
Fighters — A495

Designs: No. 1308, Blast furnace, workers
and tank. 60h, Worker and factory. 1k, Worker
and new constructions. 1.60k, Woman farmer,
new farm buildings and machinery.

1965, May 5   *Engr.*   *Perf. 13½*
1307 A495   30h dk red, blk & ol   .35   .25
1308 A495   30h multicolored   .35   .25
1309 A495   60h vio bl, red & blk   .35   .25
1310 A495   1k dp org, blk &
          brn   .50   .25
1311 A495   1.60k yel, red & blk   .55   .25
    Nos. 1307-1311 (5)   2.10 1.25

20th anniv. of liberation from the Nazis.
Nos. 1307-1311 were each printed in sheets
of 10. Value, set $120.

Slovakian Kopov
Dog — A496

Dogs: 40h, German shepherd. 60h, Czech
hunting dog with pheasant. 1k, Poodle. 1.60k,
Czech terrier. 2k, Afghan hound.

1965, June 10   *Perf. 12x11½*
1312 A496   30h black & red org   .45   .25
1313 A496   40h black & yellow   .45   .25
1314 A496   60h black & ver   .70   .25
1315 A496   1k black & dk car
          rose   1.00   .25
1316 A496   1.60k black & orange   1.25   .25
1317 A496   2k black & orange   2.00 1.25
    Nos. 1312-1317 (6)   5.85 2.50

World Dog Show at Brno and the International Dog Breeders Congress, Prague.

UN
Headquarters
Building,
NY — A497

Emblems: 60h, UN & inscription. 1.60k, ICY.

1965, June 24   *Perf. 12x11½*
1318 A497   60h dk red brn &
          yel   .25   .25
1319 A497   1k ultra & lt blue   .65   .25
1320 A497   1.60k gold & dk red   .55   .25
    Nos. 1318-1320 (3)   1.45   .75

20th anniv. of the UN and the ICY, 1965.

Trade Union
Emblem
A498

1965, June 24   *Engr.*
1321 A498 60h dk red & ultra   .40   .25

Intl. Trade Union Federation, 20th anniv.

Women and
Globe — A499

1965, June 24   *Perf. 11½x12*
1322 A499 60h violet blue   .40   .25

20th anniv. of the Intl. Women's Federation.

Children's   Matthias
House   Tower
(Burgraves'   A501
Palace),
Hradcany
A500

1965, June 25   *Perf. 11½*
1323 A500 30h slate green   .30   .25
1324 A501 60h dark brown   .30   .25

Issued to publicize the Hradcany, Prague.

Marx and Lenin — A502

1965, July 1   *Engr. & Photo.*
1325 A502 60h car rose & gold   .40   .25

6th conf. of Postal Ministers of Communist
Countries, Peking, June 21-July 15.

Joseph   Jan Hus
Navratil   A504
A503

Gregor Johann Mendel A505

Costume Jewelry A506

Bohuslav Martinu A507

Seated Woman and University of Bratislava A508

ITU Emblem and Communication Symbols A509

Macromolecular Symposium Emblem A510

Design: No. 1327, Ludovit Stur (diff. frame).

1965		**Unwmk.**	**Perf. 11½**	
1326	A503	30h black & fawn	.25	.25
1327	A503	30h black & dull grn	.25	.25
1328	A504	60h black & crimson	.25	.25
1329	A505	60h vio bl & red	.25	.25
1330	A506	60h purple & gold	.25	.25
1331	A507	60h black & orange	.25	.25
1332	A508	60h brn, yel	.25	.25
1333	A509	1k orange & blue	.35	.25
1334	A510	1k black & dp org	.35	.25
		Nos. 1326-1334 (9)	2.45	2.25

No. 1326, Navratil (1798-1865), painter; No. 1327, Stur (1815-56), Slovak author and historian; No. 1328, the 550th anniv. of the death of Hus, religious reformer; No. 1329, cent. of publication of Mendel's laws of inheritance; No. 1330 publicizes the "Jablonec 1965" costume jewelry exhib.; No. 1331, Martinu (1890-1959), composer; No. 1332, 500th anniv. of the founding of the University of Bratislava as Academia Istropolitana; No. 1333, cent. of the ITU; No. 1334, Intl. Symposium on Macromolecular Chemistry, Prague, Sept. 1-8. Issued: No. 1333, 7/10.

Miniature Sheet

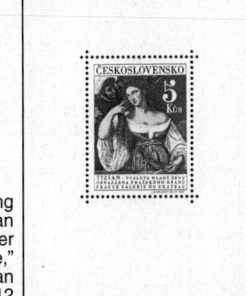
"Young Woman at her Toilette," by Titian A512

1965, Aug. 12
1336 A512 5k multicolored 6.00 4.00
Hradcany Art Gallery. No. 1336 contains one stamp.

Help for Flood Victims A513

Rescue of Flood Victims A514

1965, Sept. 6 **Engr.**
1337 A513 30h violet blue .25 .25
Engraved and Photogravure
1338 A514 2k dk ol grn & ol .65 .45
Help for Danube flood victims in Slovakia.

Dotterel A515

Mountain Birds: 60h, Wall creeper, vert. 1.20k, Lesser redpoll. 1.40k, Golden eagle, vert. 1.60k, Ring ouzel. 2k, Eurasian nutcracker, vert.

1965, Sept. 20 **Litho.** **Perf. 11**
1339	A515	30h multi	.80	.25
1340	A515	60h multi	.80	.25
1341	A515	1.20k multi	.80	.25
1342	A515	1.40k multi	1.50	.25
1343	A515	1.60k multi	1.00	.45
1344	A515	2k multi	4.00	1.75
		Nos. 1339-1344 (6)	8.90	3.20

Levoca — A516

Views of Towns: 10h, Jindrichuv Hradec. 20h, Nitra. 30h, Kosice. 40h, Hradec Králové. 50h, Telc. 60h, Ostrava. 1k, Olomouc. 1.20k, Ceske Budejovice. 1.60k, Cheb. 2k, Brno. 3k, Bratislava. 5k, Prague.

Engraved and Photogravure
1965-66 **Perf. 11½x12**
Size: 23x19mm
1345	A516	5h black & yel	.25	.25
1346	A516	10h ultra & ol bis	.80	.25
1347	A516	20h black & lt bl	.25	.25
1348	A516	30h vio bl & lt grn	.25	.25
1348A	A516	40h dk brn & lt bl ('66)	.25	.25
1348B	A516	50h black & ocher ('66)	.50	.25
1348C	A516	60h red & gray ('66)	1.00	.25
1348D	A516	1k pur & pale grn ('66)	1.00	.25

Perf. 11½x11
Size: 30x23mm
1349	A516	1.20k slate & lt bl	.75	.25
1350	A516	1.60k indigo & yel	.75	.25
1351	A516	2k sl grn & pale yel	.75	.25
1352	A516	3k brn & yel	1.25	.25
1353	A516	5k black & pink	1.75	.25
		Nos. 1345-1353 (13)	9.55	3.25

Medicinal Plants — A517

1965, Dec. 3 **Engr.** **Perf. 14**
1354	A517	30h Coltsfoot	.35	.25
1355	A517	60h Meadow saffron	.35	.25
1356	A517	80h Corn poppy	1.00	.25
1357	A517	1k Foxglove	1.00	.40
1358	A517	1.20k Arnica	1.40	.60
1359	A517	1.60k Cornflower	1.40	.45
1360	A517	2k Dog rose	3.50	1.50
		Nos. 1354-1360 (7)	9.00	3.70

Nos. 1354-1360 were each printed in sheets of 10. Value, set $225.

Strip of "Stamps" A518

Engraved and Photogravure
1965, Dec. 18 **Perf. 11½**
1361 A518 1k dark red & gold 3.50 2.00
Issued for Stamp Day, 1965.

Romain Rolland (1866-1944), French Writer — A519

Portraits: No. 1362, Stanislav Sucharda (1866-1916), sculptor. No. 1363, Ignac Josef Pesina (1766-1808), veterinarian. No. 1365, Donatello (1386-1466), Italian sculptor.

1966, Feb. 14 **Engr.** **Perf. 11½**
1362	A519	30h deep green	.25	.25
1363	A519	30h violet blue	.25	.25
1364	A519	60h rose lake	.25	.25
1365	A519	60h brown	.25	.25
		Nos. 1362-1365 (4)	1.00	1.00

Symbolic Musical Instruments & Names of Composers — A520

1966, Jan. 15 **Engr. & Photo.**
1366 A520 30h black & gold .55 .25
Czech Philharmonic Orchestra, 70th anniv.

Figure Skating Pair — A521

No. 1368, Man skater. No. 1369, Volleyball player, spiking, vert. 1k, Volleyball player, saving, vert. 1.60k, Woman skater. 2k, Figure skating pair.

1966, Feb. 17
1367	A521	30h dk car rose	.30	.25
1368	A521	30h green	.30	.25
1369	A521	60h carmine & buff	.30	.25
1370	A521	1k vio & lt bl	.40	.25
1371	A521	1.60k brown & yellow	.50	.25
1372	A521	2k blue & grnsh bl	2.40	.40
		Nos. 1367-1372 (6)	4.20	1.65

Nos. 1367-1368, 1371-1372 for the European Figure Skating Championships, Bratislava; Nos. 1369-1370 for the World Volleyball Championships.

Souvenir Sheet

Girl Dancing A522

1966, Mar. 21 **Engr.** **Imperf.**
1373 A522 3k slate bl, red & bl 3.50 1.50
Cent. of the opera "The Bartered Bride" by Bedrich Smetana.

"Ajax" 1841 — A523

Locomotives: 30h, "Karlstejn" 1865. 60h, Steam engine, 1946. 1k, Steam engine with tender, 1946. 1.60k, Electric locomotive, 1964. 2k, Diesel locomotive, 1964.

1966, Mar. 21 **Perf. 11½x11**
Buff Paper
1374	A523	20h sepia	1.10	.25
1375	A523	30h dull violet	1.60	.25
1376	A523	60h dull purple	1.10	.25
1377	A523	1k dark blue	1.25	.50
1378	A523	1.60k dk blue grn	1.75	.40
1379	A523	2k dark red	3.25	2.10
		Nos. 1374-1379 (6)	10.05	3.75

European Perch — A524

30h, Brown trout, vert. 1k, Carp. 1.20k, Northern pike. 1.40k, Grayling. 1.60k, Eel.

Perf. 13x13½, 13½x13
1966, Apr. 22 **Litho.** **Unwmk.**
1380	A524	30h multi	.60	.25
1381	A524	60h multi	.60	.25
1382	A524	1k multi	1.25	.25
1383	A524	1.20k multi	.60	.25
1384	A524	1.40k multi	1.10	.50
1385	A524	1.60k multi	2.50	1.00
		Nos. 1380-1385 (6)	6.65	2.50

Intl. Fishing Championships, Svit, Sept. 3-5.

WHO Headquarters, Geneva — A525

Engraved and Photogravure
1966, Apr. 25 **Perf. 12x11½**
1386 A525 1k dk blue & lt blue .35 .25
Opening of the WHO Headquarters, Geneva.

Symbolic Handshake and UNESCO Emblem — A526

1966, Apr. 25 **Perf. 11½**
1387 A526 60h bister & olive gray .45 .25
20th anniv. of UNESCO.

Prague Castle Issue

Belvedere Palace and St. Vitus' Cathedral — A527

Crown of St. Wenceslas, 1346 — A528

Design: 60h, Madonna, altarpiece from St. George's Church.

1966, May 9 **Engr.** **Perf. 11½**
1388 A527 30h dark blue .50 .25
Engraved and Photogravure
1389 A527 60h blk & yel bis .75 .25
Souvenir Sheet
Engr.
1390 A528 5k multi 5.00 2.50
See Nos. 1537-1539.

Tiger Swallowtail A529

Butterflies and Moths: 60h, Clouded sulphur. 80h, European purple emperor. 1k, Apollo. 1.20k, Burnet moth. 2k, Tiger moth.

1966, May 23   Engr.   Perf. 14

1391	A529	30h multi	.90	.25
1392	A529	60h multi	.90	.25
1393	A529	80h multi	1.25	.40
1394	A529	1k multi	1.90	.60
1395	A529	1.20k multi	1.90	.50
1396	A529	2k multi	5.50	2.00
		Nos. 1391-1396 (6)	12.35	4.00

Nos. 1391-1396 were issued in sheets of 10. Value, set $250.

Flags of Russia and Czechoslovakia A530

Designs: 60h, Rays surrounding hammer and sickle "sun." 1.60k, Girl's head and stars.

Engraved and Photogravure

1966, May 31   Perf. 11½

1397	A530	30h dk bl & crim	.25	.25
1398	A530	60h dk bl & red	.25	.25
1399	A530	1.60k red & dk bl	.30	.25
		Nos. 1397-1399 (3)	.80	.75

13th Congress of the Communist Party of Czechoslovakia.

Dakota Chief — A531

Designs: 20h, Indians, canoe and tepee, horiz. 30h, Tomahawk. 40h, Haida totem poles. 60h, Kachina, good spirit of the Hopis. 1k, Indian on horseback hunting buffalo, horiz. 1.20k, Calumet, Dakota peace pipe.

1966, June 20   Size: 23x40mm

1400	A531	20h vio bl & dp org	.25	.25
1401	A531	30h blk & dl org	.25	.25
1402	A531	40h blk & lt bl	.25	.25
1403	A531	60h grn & yel	.25	.25
1404	A531	1k pur & emer	.40	.25
1405	A531	1.20k vio bl & rose lil	.65	.30

Perf. 14
Engr.
Size: 23x37mm

1406	A531	1.40k multi	1.60	.90
		Nos. 1400-1406 (7)	3.65	2.45

Cent. of the Náprstek Ethnographic Museum, Prague, and "The Indians of North America" exhibition.

No. 1406 was issued in sheets of 10. Value, $500.

Model of Molecule — A532

Engraved and Photogravure

1966, July 4   Unwmk.   Perf. 11½

1407	A532	60h blk & lt bl	.50	.25

Czechoslovak Chemical Society, cent.

"Guernica" by Pablo Picasso — A533

1966, July 5   Size: 75x30mm

1408	A533	60h blk & pale bl	2.75	1.40

30th anniversary of International Brigade in Spanish Civil War.

Sheets of 15 stamps and 5 labels inscribed "Picasso-Guernica 1937." Values: with tab attached, $6; sheet $75.

Pantheon, Bratislava — A534

Designs: No. 1410, Devin Castle and Ludovit Stur. No. 1411, View of Nachod. No. 1412, State Science Library, Olomouc.

1966, July 25   Engr.

1409	A534	30h dl pur	.30	.25
1410	A534	60h dk bl	.35	.25
1411	A534	60h green	.35	.25
1412	A534	60h sepia	.30	.25
		Nos. 1409-1412 (4)	1.30	1.00

No. 1409, Russian War Memorial, Bratislava; No. 1410, the 9th cent. Devin Castle as symbol of Slovak nationalism; No. 1411, 700th anniv. of the founding of Nachod; No. 1412, the 400th anniv. of the State Science Library, Olomouc.

Atom Symbol and Sun — A535

Engraved and Photogravure

1966, Aug. 29   Perf. 11½

1413	A535	60h blk & red	.40	.25

Issued to publicize Jachymov (Joachimsthal), where pitchblende was first discovered, "cradle of the atomic age."

Brno Fair Emblem — A536

1966, Aug. 29

1414	A536	60h blk & red	.40	.25

8th International Trade Fair, Brno.

Olympia Coin and Olympic Rings — A537

Design: 1k, Olympic flame, Czechoslovak flag and Olympic rings.

1966, Aug. 29

1415	A537	60h blk & gold	.30	.25
1416	A537	1k dk bl & red	1.10	.30

70th anniv. of the Olympic Committee.

Missile Carrier, Tank and Jet Plane — A538

1966, Aug. 31

1417	A538	60h blk & apple grn	.40	.25

Issued to commemorate the maneuvers of the armies of the Warsaw Pact countries.

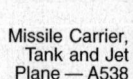

Mercury A539

30h, Moravian silver thaler, 1620, reverse & obverse, vert. 1.60k, Old & new buildings of Brno State Theater. 5k, Intl. Trade Fair Administration Tower & postmark, vert.

1966, Sept. 10

1418	A539	30h dk red & blk	.45	.25
1419	A539	60h org & blk	.45	.25
1420	A539	1.60k blk & brt grn	.75	.25
		Nos. 1418-1420 (3)	1.65	.75

Souvenir Sheet

1421	A539	5k multi	3.00	3.00

Brno Philatelic Exhibition, Sept. 11-25. No. 1421 contains one 30x40mm stamp.

First Meeting in Orbit A540

30h, Photograph of far side of Moon & Russian satellite. 60h, Photograph of Mars & Mariner 4. 80h, Soft landing on Moon. 1k, Satellite, laser beam & binary code. 1.20k, Telstar over Earth & receiving station.

1966, Sept. 26   Perf. 11½

1422	A540	20h vio & lt grn	.25	.25
1423	A540	30h blk & sal pink	.25	.25
1424	A540	60h slate & lilac	.35	.25
1425	A540	80h dk pur & lt bl	.35	.25
1426	A540	1k blk & vio	.40	.25
1427	A540	1.20k red & bl	1.75	.25
		Nos. 1422-1427 (6)	3.35	1.50

Issued to publicize American and Russian achievements in space research.

Badger — A541

Game Animals: 40h, Red deer, vert. 60h, Lynx. 80h, Hare. 1k, Red fox. 1.20k, Brown bear, vert. 2k, Wild boar.

1966, Nov. 28   Litho.   Perf. 13½

1428	A541	30h multi	.60	.25
1429	A541	40h multi	.60	.25
1430	A541	60h multi	.50	.25
1431	A541	80h multi	1.25	.25
		(europaens)		
a.		80h multi (europaeus)	6.00	3.50
1432	A541	1k multi	.90	.30
1433	A541	1.20k multi	1.25	.50
1434	A541	2k multi	3.00	1.25
		Nos. 1428-1434 (7)	8.10	3.05

The sheet of 50 of the 80h contains 40 with misspelling "europaens" and 10 with "europaeus."

"Spring" by Vaclav Hollar, 1607-77 — A542

Paintings: No. 1436, Portrait of Mrs. F. Wussin, by Jan Kupecky (1667-1740). No. 1437, Snow Owl by Karel Purkyne (1834-1868). No. 1438, Tulips by Vaclav Spála (1885-1964). No. 1439, Recruit by Ludovít Fulla (1902-1980).

1966, Dec. 8   Engr.   Perf. 14

1435	A542	1k black	3.75	3.50
1436	A542	1k multicolored	5.25	1.90
1437	A542	1k multicolored	2.40	1.90
1438	A542	1k multicolored	2.40	1.90
1439	A542	1k multicolored	19.00	16.00
		Nos. 1435-1439 (5)	32.80	25.20

Printed in sheets of 4 stamps and 2 labels. The labels in sheet of No. 1435 are inscribed "Vaclav Hollar 1607-1677" in fancy frame. Other labels are blank. Value, set $135.
See No. 1484.

Symbolic Bird A543

Engraved and Photogravure

1966, Dec. 17   Perf. 11½

1440	A543	1k dp blue & yel	1.25	.80

Issued for Stamp Day.

Youth — A544

1967, Jan. 16   Perf. 11½

1441	A544	30h ver & lt bl	.30	.25

5th Cong. of the Czechoslovak Youth Org.

Symbolic Flower and Machinery — A545

1967, Jan. 16

1442	A545	30h carmine & yel	.30	.25

6th Trade Union Congress, Prague.

Parents with Dead Child — A545a

1967, Jan. 16   Perf. 11½

1442A	A545a	60h blk & sal	.30	.25

"Peace and Freedom in Viet Nam."

View of Jihlava and Tourist Year Emblem A546

Views and Tourist Year Emblem: 40h, Spielberg Castle and churches, Brno. 1.20k, Danube, castle and churches, Bratislava. 1.60k, Vlatava River bridges, Hradcany and churches, Prague.

1967, Feb. 13   Engr.   Perf. 11½
Size: 40x23mm

1443	A546	30h brown violet	.25	.25
1444	A546	40h maroon	.25	.25

Size: 75x30mm

1445	A546	1.20k violet blue	.60	.25
1446	A546	1.60k black	2.00	.80
		Nos. 1443-1446 (4)	3.10	1.55

International Tourist Year, 1967.

Black-tailed Godwit — A547

Birds: 40h, Shoveler, horiz. 60h, Purple heron. 80h, Penduline tit. 1k, Avocet. 1.40k, Black stork. 1.60k, Tufted duck, horiz.

1967, Feb. 20   Litho.   Perf. 13½

1447	A547	30h multi	.75	.30
1448	A547	40h multi	.75	.30
1449	A547	60h multi	.75	.30
1450	A547	80h multi	.75	.30
1451	A547	1k multi	.75	.30
1452	A547	1.40k multi	1.40	.60
1453	A547	1.60k multi	2.75	1.20
		Nos. 1447-1453 (7)	7.90	3.30

Solar Research and Satellite A548

Space Research: 40h, Space craft, rocket and construction of station. 60h, Man on moon and orientation system. 1k, Exploration of solar system and rocket. 1.20k, Lunar satellites and moon photograph. 1.60k, Planned lunar architecture and moon landing.

Engraved and Photogravure

1967, Mar. 24			**Perf. 11½**	
1454	A548	30h yel & dk red	.30	.25
1455	A548	40h vio bl & blk	.45	.25
1456	A548	60h lilac & grn	.45	.25
1457	A548	1k brt pink & sl	.45	.25
1458	A548	1.20k lt violet & blk	.70	.25
1459	A548	1.60k brn lake & blk	2.10	.60
		Nos. 1454-1459 (6)	4.45	1.85

Gothic Painting, by Master Theodoric — A549

Designs: 40h, "Burning of Master Hus," from Litomerice Hymnal. 60h, Modern glass sculpture. 80h, "The Shepherdess and the Chimney Sweep," Andersen fairy tale, painting by J. Trnka. 1k, Section of pressure vessel from atomic power station. 1.20k, Three ceramic figurines, by P. Rada. 3k, Montreal skyline and EXPO '67 emblem.

1967, Apr. 10		**Engr.**	**Perf. 14**	
		Size: 37x23mm		
1460	A549	30h multi	.25	.25
1461	A549	40h multi	.25	.25
1462	A549	60h multi	.25	.25
1463	A549	80h multi	.25	.25
1464	A549	1k multi	1.00	.25
1465	A549	1.20k multi	1.25	.60
		Nos. 1460-1465 (6)	3.25	1.85

Souvenir Sheet
Perf. 11½
Size: 40x30mm

1466	A549	3k multi	3.00	2.50

EXPO '67, International Exhibition, Montreal, Apr. 28-Oct. 27, 1967.
Nos. 1460-1465 were each issued in a miniature sheet of 10 stamps. Value, set $50.
Examples of No. 1466 imperf. were not issued.

Canoe Race A550

Women Playing Basketball A551

No. 1468, Wheels, dove & emblems of Warsaw, Berlin, Prague. 1.60k, Canoe slalom.

Perf. 12x11½, 11½x12

1967, Apr. 17		**Engr. & Photo.**		
1467	A550	60h black & brt bl	.25	.25
1468	A550	60h black & salmon	.25	.25
1469	A551	60h blk & grnsh bl	.25	.25
1470	A551	1.60k black & brt vio	1.10	.55
		Nos. 1467-1470 (4)	1.85	1.30

No. 1467, 5th Intl. Wild-Water Canoeing Championships; No. 1468, 20th Warsaw-Berlin-Prague Bicycle Race; No. 1469, Women's Basketball Championships; No. 1470, 10th Intl. Water Slalom Championships.

"Golden Street" — A552

Designs: 60h, Interior of Hall of King Wenceslas. 5k, St. Matthew, from illuminated manuscript, 11th century.

1967, May 9			**Perf. 11½x11**	
1471	A552	30h rose claret	.25	.25
1472	A552	60h bluish black	.50	.25

Souvenir Sheet
Perf. 11½

1473	A552	5k multicolored	2.60	2.40

Issued to publicize the Castle of Prague.

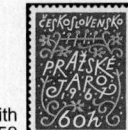

Stylized Lyre with Flowers — A553

1967, May 10			**Perf. 11½**	
1474	A553	60h dull pur & brt grn	.30	.25

Prague Music Festival.

Old-New Synagogue, Prague — A554

30h, Detail from Torah curtain, 1593. 60h, Prague Printer's emblem, 1530. 1k, Mikulov jug, 1804. 1.40k, Memorial for Concentration Camp Victims 1939-45, Pincas Synagogue (menorah & tablet). 1.60k, Tombstone of David Gans, 1613.

1967, May 22			**Perf. 11½**	
1475	A554	30h dull red & lt bl	.30	.25
1476	A554	60h blk & lt grn	.25	.25
1477	A554	1k dk bl & rose lil	.35	.25
1478	A554	1.20k dk brn & mar	.65	.25
1479	A554	1.40k black & yellow	.55	.25
1480	A554	1.60k green & yel	4.50	2.75
		Nos. 1475-1480 (6)	6.60	4.00

Issued to show Jewish relics. The items shown on the 30h, 60h and 1k are from the State Jewish Museum, Prague.

"Lidice" — A555

1967, June 9	**Unwmk.**		**Perf. 11½**	
1481	A555	30h black & brt rose	.30	.25

Destruction of Lidice by the Nazis, 25th anniv.

Prague Architecture — A556

1967, June 10		**Engr. & Photo.**		
1482	A556	1k black & gold	.35	.25

Issued to publicize the 9th Congress of the International Union of Architects, Prague.

Peter Bezruc — A557

1967, June 21				
1483	A557	60h dull rose & blk	.30	.25

Peter Bezruc, poet & writer, birth cent.

Painting Type of 1966

2k, Henri Rousseau (1844-1910), self-portrait.

1967, June 22		**Engr.**	**Perf. 11½**	
1484	A542	2k multicolored	2.00	1.60

Praga 68, World Stamp Exhibition, Prague, June 22-July 7, 1968.
Printed in sheets of 4 stamps (2x2), separated by horizontal gutter with inscription and picture of Natl. Gallery, site of Praga 68. Value, $10.

View of Skalitz — A558

No. 1486, Mining tower & church steeple, Pribram. No. 1487, Hands holding book & view of Presov.

1967, Aug. 21		**Engr.**	**Perf. 11½**	
1485	A558	30h violet blue	.25	.25
1486	A558	30h slate green	.25	.25
1487	A558	30h claret	.25	.25
		Nos. 1485-1487 (3)	.75	.75

Towns of Skalitz, Pribram, Presov, annivs.

Colonnade and Spring, Karlovy Vary and Communications Emblem — A559

1967, Aug. 21		**Engr. & Photo.**		
1488	A559	30h violet bl & gold	.30	.25

5th Sports & Cultural Festival of the Employees of the Ministry of Communications, Karlovy Vary.

Ondrejov Observatory and Galaxy — A560

1967, Aug. 22		**Engr.**		
1489	A560	60h vio bl, rose lil & sil	1.50	.25

13th Cong. of the Intl. Astronomical Union. No. 1489 was issued in a sheet of 10 stamps. Value, set $60.

Orchid — A561

Flowers from the Botanical Gardens: 30h, Cobaea scandens. 40h, Lycaste deppei. 60h, Glottiphyllum davisii. 1k, Anthurium. 1.20k, Rhodocactus. 1.40k, Moth orchid.

1967, Aug. 30		**Litho.**	**Perf. 12½**	
1490	A561	20h multicolored	.30	.25
1491	A561	30h pink & multi	.30	.25
1492	A561	40h multicolored	.45	.25
1493	A561	60h lt blue & multi	.45	.25
1494	A561	1k multicolored	.60	.25
1495	A561	1.20k lt yellow & multi	.65	.30
1496	A561	1.40k multicolored	1.75	.70
		Nos. 1490-1496 (7)	4.50	2.25

Red Squirrel — A562

Animals from the Tatra National Park: 60h, Wild cat. 1k, Ermine. 1.20k, Dormouse. 1.40k, Hedgehog. 1.60k, Pine marten.

Engraved and Photogravure

1967, Sept. 25			**Perf. 11½**	
1497	A562	30h black, yel & org	.35	.25
1498	A562	60h black & buff	.35	.25
1499	A562	1k black & lt blue	.40	.25
1500	A562	1.20k brn, pale grn & yel	.50	.25
1501	A562	1.40k blk, pink & yel	.55	.25
1502	A562	1.60k black, org & yel	2.75	1.25
		Nos. 1497-1502 (6)	4.90	2.50

Rockets and Weapons — A563

1967, Oct. 6		**Engr.**	**Perf. 11½**	
1503	A563	30h slate green	.30	.25

Day of the Czechoslovak People's Army.

Cruiser "Aurora" Firing at Winter Palace — A564

Designs: 60h, Hammer and sickle emblems and Red Star, vert. 1k, Hands reaching for hammer and sickle, vert.

1967, Nov. 7		**Engr. & Photo.**		
1504	A564	30h black & dk car	.25	.25
1505	A564	60h black & dk car	.25	.25
1506	A564	1k black & dk car	.25	.25
		Nos. 1504-1506 (3)	.75	.75

Russian October Revolution, 50th anniv.

The Conjurer, by Frantisek Tichy — A565

Paintings: 80h, Don Quixote, by Cyprian Majernik. 1k, Promenade in the Park, by Norbert Grund. 1.20k, Self-portrait, by Peter J. Brandl. 1.60k, Saints from Jan of Jeren Epitaph, by Czech Master of 1395.

1967, Nov. 13		**Engr.**	**Perf. 11½**	
1507	A565	60h multi	.35	.25
1508	A565	80h multi	.50	.30
1509	A565	1k multi	.75	.50
1510	A565	1.20k multi	.75	.50
1511	A565	1.60k multi	3.25	2.75
		Nos. 1507-1511 (5)	5.60	4.30

Nos. 1507-1511 were issued in sheets of 4. Value, set $24.
See Nos. 1589-1593, 1658-1662, 1711-1715, 1779-1783, 1847-1851, 1908-1913, 2043-2047, 2090-2093, 2147-2151, 2265-2269, 2335-2339, 2386-2390, 2437-2441, 2534-2538, 2586-2590, 2634-2638, 2810-2813, 2843-2847, 2872-2874, 2908-2910, 2936-2938, 2973-2975, 2995, 3001-3002, 3028-3030, 3054-3055, 3075-3076, 3105-3107, 3133-3135, 3160-3162, 3188-3190, 3224-3226, 3233, 3255-3257, 3287-3289, 3323-3325, 3359-3361, 3401-3402, 3435-3436, 3478-3480, 3518-3520, 3552-3553, 3591-3593, 3616, 3618, 3656-3658, 3680, 3690-3692, 3726-3727, 3729, 3774-3776, 3794-3795, 3810-3811, 3828-3830, 3851-3852, 3881-3883, 3917-3918.

Pres. Antonin Novotny — A566

1967, Dec. 9		**Engr.**	**Perf. 11½**	
1512	A566	2k blue gray	1.40	.25
1513	A566	3k brown	1.40	.25

Czechoslovakia Nos. 65, 71 and 81 of 1920 — A567

1967, Dec. 18				
1514	A567	1k maroon & silver	1.60	1.10

Issued for Stamp Day.

Symbolic Flag and Dates — A568

1968, Jan. 15   Engr.   Perf. 11½
1515 A568 30h red, dk bl & ultra   .75   .25

50th anniversary of Czechoslovakia. No. 1515 was issued in a sheet of 10. Value, $30.

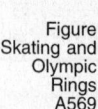

Figure Skating and Olympic Rings A569

Olympic Rings and: 1k, Ski course. 1.60k, Toboggan chute. 2k, Ice hockey.

1968, Jan. 29   Engr. & Photo.
1516 A569 60h blk, yel & ocher   .30   .25
1517 A569 1k ol grn, lt bl & lem   .55   .25
1518 A569 1.60k blk, lil & bl grn   .70   .25
1519 A569 2k blk, ap grn & lt bl   1.10   .30
      Nos. 1516-1519 (4)   2.65   1.00

10th Winter Olympic Games, Grenoble, France, Feb. 6-18.

Factories and Rising Sun — A570

Design: 60h, Workers and banner.

1968, Feb. 25   Perf. 11½x12
1520 A570 30h car & dk bl   .25   .25
1521 A570 60h car & dk bl   .25   .25

20th anniversary of February Revolution.

Map of Battle of Sokolovo A571

Human Rights Flame A572

1968, Mar. 8   Perf. 11½
1522 A571 30h blk, brt bl & car   .40   .25
Engr.
1523 A572 1k rose carmine   1.10   .40

25th anniv. of the Battle of Sokolovo, Mar. 8, 1943, against the German Army, No. 1522; Intl. Human Rights Year, No. 1523.

Janko Kral and Liptovsky Mikulas — A573

Karel Marx A574

Girl's Head A575

Arms and Allegory A576

Head A577

1968, Mar. 25   Engr.
1524 A573 30h green   .30   .25
1525 A574 30h claret   .25   .25
Engraved and Photogravure
1526 A575 30h dk red & gold   .25   .25
1527 A576 30h dk blue & dp org   .25   .25
1528 A577 1k multicolored   .50   .25
      Nos. 1524-1528 (5)   1.55   1.25

The writer Janko Kral and the Slovak town Liptovsky Mikulas (No. 1524); 150th anniv. of the birth of Karl Marx (No. 1525); cent. of the cornerstone laying of the Prague Natl. Theater (No. 1526); 150th anniv. of the Prague Natl. Museum (No. 1527); 20th anniv. of WHO (1k).

Symbolic Radio Waves — A578

No. 1530, Symbolic television screens.

1968, Apr. 29   Perf. 11½
1529 A578 30h blk, car & vio bl   .25   .25
1530 A578 30h blk, car & vio bl   .25   .25

45th anniv. of Czechoslovak broadcasting (No. 1529), 15th anniv. of television (No. 1530).

Olympic Rings, Mexican Sculpture and Diver — A579

Olympic Rings and: 40h, Runner and "The Sanctification of Quetzalcoatl." 60h, Volleyball and Mexican ornaments. 1k, Czechoslovak and Mexican Olympic emblems and carved altar. 1.60k, Soccer and ornaments. 2k, View of Hradcany, weather vane and key.

1968, Apr. 30
1531 A579 30h black, bl & car   .25   .25
1532 A579 40h multi   .25   .25
1533 A579 60h multi   .25   .25
1534 A579 1k multi   .35   .25
1535 A579 1.60k multi   .35   .25
1536 A579 2k black & multi   1.75   .40
      Nos. 1531-1536 (6)   3.20   1.65

19th Olympic Games, Mexico City, 10/12-27.

Prague Castle Types of 1966

Designs: 30h, Tombstone of Bretislav I. 60h, Romanesque door knocker, St. Wenceslas Chapel. 5k, Head of St. Peter, mosaic from Golden Gate of St. Vitus Cathedral.

1968, May 9   Perf. 11½
1537 A527 30h multicolored   .40   .25
1538 A527 60h black, red & cit   .40   .25
Souvenir Sheet
Engr.
1539 A528 5k multicolored   2.75   2.75

Pres. Ludvik Svoboda — A580

1968-70   Engr.   Perf. 11½
1540   A580 30h ultramarine   .25   .25
1540A A580 50h green ('70)   .25   .25
1541   A580 60h maroon   .25   .25
1541A A580 1k rose car ('70)   .30   .25
       Nos. 1540-1541A (4)   1.05   1.00

Shades exist of No. 1541A.

"Business," Sculpture by Otto Gutfreund A581

Cabaret Performer, by Frantisek Kupka A582

Designs (The New Prague): 40h, Broadcasting Corporation Building. 60h, New Parliament. 1.40k, Tapestry by Jan Bauch "Prague 1787." 3k, Presidential standard.

Engr. & Photo.; Engr. (2k)
1968, June 5
1542 A581 30h black & multi   .25   .25
1543 A581 40h black & multi   .25   .25
1544 A581 60h dk brn & multi   .25   .25
1545 A581 1.40k dk brn & multi   .40   .25
1546 A582 2k indigo & multi   .85   .70
1547 A581 3k black & multi   .85   .30
      Nos. 1542-1547 (6)   2.85   2.00

Designs (The Old Prague): 30h, St. George's Basilica. 60h, Renaissance fountain. 1k, Villa America-Dvorak Museum, 18th cent. building. 1.60k, Emblem from the House of Three Violins, 18th cent. 2k, Josefina, by Josef Manes. 3k, Emblem of Prague, 1475.

1968, June 21   Perf. 11½
1548 A581 30h grn, gray & yel   .25   .25
1549 A581 60h dk vio, ap grn & gold   .25   .25
1550 A581 1k blk, lt bl & pink   .30   .25
1551 A581 1.60k slate grn & multi   .55   .25
1552 A582 2k brown & multi   1.25   .60
1553 A581 3k blk, yel, bl & pink   1.25   .60
      Nos. 1548-1553 (6)   3.85   2.20

Nos. 1542-1553 publicized the Praga 68 Philatelic Exhibition. Nos. 1542-1545, 1547-1551, 1553 issued in sheets of 15 + 15 labels with Praga 68 emblem and inscription. Nos. 1546, 1552 issued in sheets of 4 (2x2) with one horizontal label between top and bottom rows showing Praga 68 emblem. Values for sheets of 4, each $8.

Souvenir Sheet

View of Prague and Emblems — A583

Engraved and Photogravure
1968, June 22   Imperf.
1554 A583 10k multicolored   3.25   2.50

Praga 68 and 50th anniv. of Czechoslovak postage stamps. Sold only together with a 5k admission ticket to the Praga 68 philatelic Exhibition. Value $20.

Madonna with the Rose Garlands, by Dürer — A584

1968, July 6   Perf. 11½
1555 A584 5k multicolored   3.75   2.75

FIP Day, July 6. Issued in sheets of 4 (2x2) with one horizontal label between, showing Praga 68 emblem. Value, $20.

Stagecoach on Rails — A585

Design: 1k, Steam and electric locomotives.

1968, Aug. 6
1556 A585 60h multicolored   .45   .25
1557 A585 1k multicolored   1.60   .60

No. 1556: 140th anniv. of the horse-drawn railroad Ceské Budejovice to Linz; No. 1557: cent. of the Ceské Budejovice to Plzen railroad.

6th Intl. Slavonic Cong. in Prague — A586

1968, Aug. 7   Perf. 11½
1558 A586 30h vio blue & car   .40   .25

Ardspach Rocks and Ammonite A587

60h, Basalt formation & frog skeleton fossil. 80h, Rocks, basalt veins & polished agate. 1k, Pelecypoda (fossil shell) & Belanske Tatra mountains. 1.60k, Trilobite & Barrande rock formation.

1968, Aug. 8
1559 A587 30h black & citron   .25   .25
1560 A587 60h black & rose cl   .25   .25
1561 A587 80h blk, lt vio & pink   .30   .25
1562 A587 1k black & lt blue   .40   .25
1563 A587 1.60k black & bister   1.40   .65
      Nos. 1559-1563 (5)   2.60   1.65

Issued to publicize the 23rd International Geological Congress, Prague, Aug. 8-Sept. 3.

Raising Slovak Flag — A588

60h, Slovak partisans, and mountain.

1968, Sept. 9   Engr.   Perf. 11½
1564 A588 30h ultra   .25   .25
1565 A588 60h red   .25   .25

No. 1564 for the Slovak Natl. Council, No. 1565 the 120th anniv. of the Slovak national uprising.

Flowerpot, by Jiri Schlessinger (age 10) — A589

Drawings by Children in Terezin Concentration Camp: 30h, Jew and Guard, by Jiri Beutler (age 10). 60h, Butterflies, by Kitty Brunnerova (age 11).

Engraved and Photogravure

1968, Sept. 30   *Perf. 11½*

Size: 30x23mm

| 1566 | A589 | 30h blk, buff & rose lil | .30 | .25 |
| 1567 | A589 | 60h black & multi | .30 | .25 |

Perf. 12x11½

Size: 41x23mm

| 1568 | A589 | 1k black & multi | .80 | .25 |
| | | Nos. 1566-1568 (3) | 1.40 | .75 |

30th anniversary of Munich Pact.

Arms of Regional Capitals A590

Arms of Prague A591

1968, Oct. 21   *Perf. 11½*

1569	A590	60h Banská Bystrica	.25	.25
1570	A590	60h Bratislava	.25	.25
1571	A590	60h Brno	.25	.25
1572	A590	60h Ceské Budejovice	.25	.25
1573	A590	60h Hradec Králové	.25	.25
1574	A590	60h Kosice	.25	.25
1575	A590	60h Ostrava (horse)	.25	.25
1576	A590	60h Plzen	.25	.25
1577	A590	60h Ustí nad Labem	.25	.25

Perf. 11½x16

| 1578 | A591 | 1k shown | .25 | .25 |
| | | Nos. 1569-1578 (10) | 2.50 | 2.50 |

No. 1578 issued in sheets of 10. Value, $40. See Nos. 1652-1657, 1742-1747, 1886-1888, 2000-2001.

Flag and Linden Leaves — A592

Bohemian Lion Breaking Chains (Type SP1 of 1919) — A593

Design: 60h, Map of Czechoslovakia, linden leaves, Hradcany in Prague and Castle in Bratislava.

1968, Oct. 28   *Perf. 12x11½*

| 1579 | A592 | 30h dp blue & mag | .30 | .25 |
| 1580 | A592 | 60h blk, gold, red & ultra | .30 | .25 |

Souvenir Sheet

Engr.

Perf. 11½x12

| 1581 | A593 | 5k red | | 3.50 | 2.75 |

Founding of Czechoslovakia, 50th anniv.

Ernest Hemingway — A594

Caricatures: 30h, Karel Capek (1890-1938), writer. 40h, George Bernard Shaw. 60h, Maxim Gorki. 1k, Pablo Picasso. 1.20k, Taikan Yokoyama (1868-1958), painter. 1.40k, Charlie Chaplin.

Engraved and Photogravure

1968, Nov. 18   *Perf. 11½x12*

1582	A594	20h black, org & red	.25	.25
1583	A594	30h black & multi	.30	.25
1584	A594	40h blk, lic & car	.30	.25
1585	A594	60h black, sky bl & grn	.25	.25
1586	A594	1k black, brn & yel	.45	.25
1587	A594	1.20k black, dp car & vio	.45	.25
1588	A594	1.40k black, brn & dp org	1.75	.40
		Nos. 1582-1588 (7)	3.75	1.90

Cultural personalities of the 20th cent. and UNESCO. See Nos. 1628-1633.

Painting Type of 1967

Czechoslovakian Art: 60h, Cleopatra II, by Jan Zrzavy (1890-1977). 80h, Black Lake (man and horse), by Jan Preisler (1872-1918). 1.20k, Giovanni Francisci as a Volunteer, by Peter Michal Bohun (1822-1879). 1.60k, Princess Hyacinth, by Alfons Mucha (1860-1939). 3k, Madonna and Child, woodcarving, 1518, by Master Paul of Levoca.

1968, Nov. 29   Engr.   *Perf. 11½*

1589	A565	60h multi	.75	.35
1590	A565	80h multi	.75	.35
1591	A565	1.20k multi	.75	.35
1592	A565	1.60k multi	.75	.35
1593	A565	3k multi	2.50	2.50
		Nos. 1589-1593 (5)	5.50	3.90

Nos. 1589-1593 were issued in sheets of 4. Value, set $25.

Cinderlad — A595

Slovak Fairy Tales: 60h, The Proud Lady. 80h, The Ruling Knight. 1k, Good Day, Little Bench. 1.20k, The Spellbound Castle. 1.80k, The Miraculous Hunter. The designs are from illustrations by Ludovit Fulla for "Slovak Stories."

1968, Dec. 18   Engr. & Photo.

1594	A595	30h multi	.25	.25
1595	A595	60h multi	.25	.25
1596	A595	80h multi	.40	.25
1597	A595	1k multi	.55	.25
1598	A595	1.20k multi	.55	.25
1599	A595	1.80k multi	1.50	.65
		Nos. 1594-1599 (6)	3.50	1.90

Czechoslovakia Nos. 2 and 3 — A596

1968, Dec. 18

| 1600 | A596 | 1k violet bl & gold | .95 | .65 |

50th anniv. of Czechoslovakian postage stamps.

Crescent, Cross and Lion and Sun Emblems — A597

60h, 12 crosses in circles forming large cross.

1969, Jan. 31   *Perf. 11½*

| 1601 | A597 | 60h black, red & gold | .25 | .25 |
| 1602 | A597 | 1k black, ultra & red | .35 | .25 |

No. 1601: 50th anniv. of the Czechoslovak Red Cross. No. 1602: 50th anniv. of the League of Red Cross Societies.

ILO Emblem — A598

1969, Jan. 31

| 1603 | A598 | 1k black & gray | .30 | .25 |

50th anniv. of the ILO.

Cheb Pistol — A599

Historical Firearms: 40h, Italian pistol with Dutch decorations, c. 1600. 60h, Wheellock rifle from Matej Kubik workshop c. 1720. 1k, Flintlock pistol, Devieuxe workshop, Liege, c. 1760. 1.40k, Duelling pistols, from Lebeda workshop, Prague, c. 1835. 1.60k, Derringer pistols, US, c. 1865.

1969, Feb. 18

1604	A599	30h black & multi	.25	.25
1605	A599	40h black & multi	.25	.25
1606	A599	60h black & multi	.25	.25
1607	A599	1k black & multi	.25	.25
1608	A599	1.40k black & multi	.35	.25
1609	A599	1.60k black & multi	1.40	.25
		Nos. 1604-1609 (6)	2.75	1.50

Bratislava Castle, Muse and Book A600

No. 1611, Science symbols & emblem (Brno University). No. 1612, Harp, laurel & musicians' names. No. 1613, Theatrical scene. No. 1614, Arms of Slovakia, banner & blossoms. No. 1615, School, outstretched hands & woman with linden leaves.

1969, Mar. 24   Engr.   *Perf. 11½*

| 1610 | A600 | 60h violet blue | .25 | .25 |

Engraved and Photogravure

1611	A600	60h blk, gold & slate	.25	.25
1612	A600	60h gold, blue, blk & red	.25	.25
1613	A600	60h black & rose red	.25	.25
1614	A600	60h rose red, sil & bl	.25	.25
1615	A600	60h black & gold	.25	.25
		Nos. 1610-1615 (6)	1.50	1.50

50th anniv. of: Komensky University in Bratislava (No. 1610); Brno University (No. 1611); Brno Conservatory of Music (No. 1612); Slovak Natl. Theater (No. 1613); Slovak Soviet Republic (No. 1614); cent. of the Zniev Gymnasium (academic high school) (No. 1615).

Baldachin-top Car and Four-seat Coupé of 1900-1905 — A601

Designs: 1.60k, Laurin & Klement Voiturette, 1907, and L & K touring car with American top, 1907. 1.80k, First Prague bus, 1907, and sectionalized Skoda bus, 1967.

1969, Mar. 25   Engr. & Photo.

1616	A601	30h blk, lil & lt grn	.60	.25
1617	A601	1.60k blk, org brn & lt bl	.75	.25
1618	A601	1.80k multi	1.40	.60
		Nos. 1616-1618 (3)	2.75	1.10

Peace, by Ladislav Guderna A602

1969, Apr. 21   *Perf. 11*

| 1619 | A602 | 1.60k multi | .50 | .35 |

20th anniv. of the Peace Movement. Issued in sheets of 15 stamps and 5 tabs. Stamp with tab $2.50.

Horse and Rider, by Vaclav Hollar — A603

Old Engravings of Horses: 30h, Prancing Stallion, by Hendrik Goltzius, horiz. 80h, Groom Leading Horse, by Matthäus Merian, horiz. 1.80k, Horse and Soldier, by Albrecht Dürer. 2.40k, Groom and Horse, by Johann E. Ridinger.

1969, Apr. 24   *Perf. 11x11½, 11½x11*

Yellowish Paper

1620	A603	30h dark brown	.25	.25
1621	A603	80h violet brown	.25	.25
1622	A603	1.60k slate	.45	.25
1623	A603	1.80k sepia	.50	.25
1624	A603	2.40k multi	2.40	.60
		Nos. 1620-1624 (5)	3.85	1.60

M. R. Stefánik as Astronomy Professor and French General A604

1969, May 4   Engr.   *Perf. 11½*

| 1625 | A604 | 60h rose claret | .40 | .25 |

Gen. Milan R. Stefánik, 50th death anniv.

St. Wenceslas Pressing Wine, Mural by the Master of Litomerice A605

Design: No. 1627, Coronation banner of the Estates, 1723, with St. Wenceslas and coats of arms of Bohemia and Czech Crown lands.

1969, May 9   Engr.   *Perf. 11½*

| 1626 | A605 | 3k multicolored | 2.00 | 1.40 |
| 1627 | A605 | 3k multicolored | 2.00 | 1.40 |

Issued to publicize the art treasures of the Castle of Prague.
Issued in sheets of 4. Value, set $20. See Nos. 1689-1690.

Caricature Type of 1968

Caricatures: 30h, Pavol Orszagh Hviezdoslav (1849-1921), Slovak writer. 40h, Gilbert K. Chesterton (1874-1936), English writer. 60h, Vladimir Mayakovski (1893-1930), Russian poet. 1k, Henri Matisse (1869-1954), French painter. 1.80k, Ales Hrdlicka (1869-1943), Czech-born American anthropologist. 2k, Franz Kafka (1883-1924), Austrian writer.

Engraved and Photogravure

1969, June 17   *Perf. 11½x12*

1628	A594	30h blk, red & bl	.25	.25
1629	A594	40h blk, bl & lt vio	.25	.25
1630	A594	60h blk, rose & yel	.25	.25
1631	A594	1k black & multi	.25	.25
1632	A594	1.80k blk, ultra & ocher	.25	.25
1633	A594	2k blk, yel & brt grn	1.50	.50
		Nos. 1628-1633 (6)	2.75	1.75

Issued to honor cultural personalities of the 20th century and UNESCO.

"Music," by Alfons Mucha — A606

Paintings by Mucha: 60h, "Painting." 1k, "Dance." 2.40k, "Ruby" and "Amethyst."

1969, July 14   Perf. 11½x11
Size: 30x49mm

1634	A606	30h black & multi	.80	.25
1635	A606	60h black & multi	.80	.25
1636	A606	1k black & multi	1.00	.25

Size: 39x51mm

1637	A606	2.40k black & multi	2.00	1.25
		Nos. 1634-1637 (4)	4.60	2.00

Alfons Mucha (1860-1930), painter and stamp designer (Type A1).
No. 1637 was issued in sheets of 4. Value $12.50.

Pres. Svoboda and Partisans — A607

No. 1639, Slovak fighters and mourners.

1969, Aug. 29   Perf. 11

1638	A607	30h ol grn & red, yel	.25	.25
1639	A607	30h vio bl & red, yel	.25	.25

25th anniversary of the Slovak uprising and of the Battle of Dukla.

Tatra Mountain Stream and Gentians A608

Designs: 60h, Various views in Tatra Mountains. No. 1644, Mountain pass and gentians. No. 1645, Houses, Krivan Mountain and autumn crocuses.

1969, Sept. 8   Engr.   Perf. 11
Size: 71x33mm

1640	A608	60h gray	.25	.25
1641	A608	60h dark blue	.25	.25
1642	A608	60h dull gray vio	.25	.25

Perf. 11½
Size: 40x23mm

1643	A608	1.60k multi	.55	.25
1644	A608	1.60k multi	1.25	.50
1645	A608	1.60k multi	.55	.25
		Nos. 1640-1645 (6)	3.10	1.75

20th anniv. of the creation of the Tatra Mountains Natl. Park.
Nos. 1640-1642 are printed in sheets of 15 (3x5) with 5 labels showing mountain plants. Value, set with tabs $2.50.
Nos. 1643-1645 were issued in sheets of 10. Value, $70.

Bronze Belt Ornaments — A609

Archaeological Treasures from Bohemia and Moravia: 30h, Gilt ornament with 6 masks. 1k, Jeweled earrings. 1.80k, Front and back of lead cross with Greek inscription. 2k, Gilt strap ornament with human figure.

Engraved and Photogravure

1969, Sept. 30   Perf. 11½x11

1646	A609	20h gold & multi	.25	.25
1647	A609	30h gold & multi	.25	.25
1648	A609	1k red & multi	.25	.25
1649	A609	1.80k dull org & multi	.45	.25
1650	A609	2k gold & multi	1.75	.25
		Nos. 1646-1650 (5)	2.95	1.25

"Mail Circling the World" — A610

1969, Oct. 1   Engr.   Perf. 12

1651	A610	3.20k multi	.95	.60

16th UPU Cong., Tokyo, Oct. 1-Nov. 14. Issued in sheets of 4. Value $9.

Coat of Arms Type of 1968
Engraved and Photogravure

1969, Oct. 25   Perf. 11½

1652	A590	50h Bardejov	.25	.25
1653	A590	50h Hranice	.25	.25
1654	A590	50h Kezmarok	.25	.25
1655	A590	50h Krnov	.25	.25
1656	A590	50h Litomerice	.25	.25
1657	A590	50h Manetin	.25	.25
		Nos. 1652-1657 (6)	1.50	1.50

Painting Type of 1967

Designs: 60h, Requiem, 1944, by Frantisek Muzika. 1k, Resurrection, 1380, by the Master of the Trebon Altar. 1.60k, Crucifixion, 1950, by Vincent Hloznik. 1.80k, Girl with Doll, 1863, by Julius Bencur. 2.20k, St. Jerome, 1357-67, by Master Theodorik.

1969, Nov. 25   Perf. 11½

1658	A565	60h multi	.75	.25
1659	A565	1k multi	.75	.25
1660	A565	1.60k multi	.75	.40
1661	A565	1.80k multi	.75	.40
1662	A565	2.20k multi	3.00	2.00
		Nos. 1658-1662 (5)	6.00	3.30

Nos. 1658-1662 were each issued in sheets of 4. Value, set $30.

Symbolic Sheet of Stamps A611

1969, Dec. 18   Perf. 11½x12

1663	A611	1k dk brn, ultra & gold	.30	.30

Issued for Stamp Day 1969.

Ski Jump A612

Designs: 60h, Long distance skier. 1k, Ski jump and slope. 1.60k, Woman skier.

1970, Jan. 6   Perf. 11½

1664	A612	50h multi	.25	.25
1665	A612	60h multi	.25	.25
1666	A612	1k multi	.25	.25
1667	A612	1.60k multi	.60	.30
		Nos. 1664-1667 (4)	1.35	1.05

Intl. Ski Championships "Tatra 1970."

Ludwig van Beethoven — A613

Portraits: No. 1669, Friedrich Engels (1820-95), German socialist. No. 1670, Maximilian Hell (1720-92), Slovakian Jesuit and astronomer. No. 1671, Lenin, Russian Communist leader. No. 1672, Josef Manes (1820-71), Czech painter. No. 1673, Comenius (1592-1670), theologian and educator.

1970, Feb. 17   Engr.   Perf. 11x11½

1668	A613	40h multi	.25	.25
1669	A613	40h dull red	.25	.25
1670	A613	40h yellow brn	.25	.25
1671	A613	40h dull red	.25	.25
1672	A613	40h brown	.25	.25
1673	A613	40h dull red	.25	.25
		Nos. 1668-1673 (6)	1.50	1.50

Anniversaries of birth of Beethoven, Engels, Hell, Lenin and Manes, 300th anniv. of the death of Comenius, and to honor UNESCO.

Bells — A614

80h, Machine tools & lathe. 1k, Folklore masks. 1.60k, Angel & Three Wise Men, 17th cent. icon from Koniec. 2k, View of Orlik Castle, 1787, by F. K. Wolf. 3k, "Passing through Koshu down to Mishima" from Hokusai's 36 Views of Fuji.

Engraved and Photogravure

1970, Mar. 13   Perf. 11½x11
Size: 40x23mm

1674	A614	50h multi	.25	.25
1675	A614	80h multi	.25	.25
1676	A614	1k multi	.25	.25

Size: 50x40mm
Perf. 11½

1677	A614	1.60k multi	.35	.30
1678	A614	2k multi	.45	.25
1679	A614	3k multi	2.10	.70
		Nos. 1674-1679 (6)	3.65	2.00

EXPO '70 Intl. Exhib., Osaka, Japan, Mar. 15-Sept. 13, 1970.
Nos. 1674-1676 issued in sheets of 50, Nos. 1677-1679 in sheets of 4. Value, set of 3 sheets, $18.

Kosice Townhall, Laurel and Czechoslovak Arms — A615

1970, Apr. 5   Perf. 11

1680	A615	60h slate, ver & gold	.40	.25

Government's Kosice Program, 25th anniv.

"The Remarkable Horse" by Josef Lada — A616

Paintings by Josef Lada: 60h, Autumn, 1955, horiz. 1.80k, "The Water Sprite." 2.40k, Children in Winter, 1943, horiz.

1970, Apr. 21   Perf. 11½

1681	A616	60h black & multi	.30	.25
1682	A616	1k black & multi	.45	.25
1683	A616	1.80k black & multi	.75	.25
1684	A616	2.40k black & multi	1.50	.25
		Nos. 1681-1684 (4)	3.00	1.00

Lenin — A617

Design: 60h, Lenin without cap, facing left.

1970, Apr. 22

1685	A617	30h dk red & gold	.25	.25
1686	A617	60h black & gold	.25	.25

Lenin (1870-1924), Russian communist leader.

Fighters on the Barricades A618

No. 1688, Lilac, Russian tank and castle.

1970, May 5   Perf. 11x11½

1687	A618	30h dull pur, gold & bl	.25	.25
1688	A618	30h dull grn, gold & red	.25	.25

No. 1687: 25th anniv. of the Prague uprising. No. 1688: 25th anniv. of the liberation of Czechoslovakia from the Germans.

Prague Castle Art Type of 1969

No. 1689, Bust of St. Vitus, 1486. No. 1690, Hermes and Athena, by Bartholomy Spranger (1546-1611), mural from White Tower.

1970, May 7   Engr.   Perf. 11½

1689	A605	3k maroon & multi	1.90	1.25
1690	A605	3k lt blue & multi	1.75	1.00

Nos. 1689-1690 were issued in sheets of 4. Value, set of 2 sheets, $18.

Compass Rose, UN Headquarters and Famous Buildings of the World — A619

Engraved and Photogravure

1970, June 26   Perf. 11

1691	A619	1k black & multi	.40	.25

25th anniv. of the UN. Issued in sheets of 15 (3x5) and 5 labels showing UN emblem. Value of single with tab attached: unused $1; used 75c.

Cannon from 30 Years' War and Baron Munchhausen — A620

Historical Cannons: 60h, Cannon from Hussite war and St. Barbara. 1.20k, Cannon from Prussian-Austrian war, and legendary cannoneer Javurek. 1.80k, Early 20th century cannon and spaceship "La Colombiad" (Jules Verne). 2.40k, World War I cannon and "Good Soldier Schweik."

1970, Aug. 31   Perf. 11½

1692	A620	30h black & multi	.25	.25
1693	A620	60h black & multi	.25	.25
1694	A620	1.20k black & multi	.25	.25
1695	A620	1.80k black & multi	.25	.25
1696	A620	2.40k black & multi	1.25	.25
		Nos. 1692-1696 (5)	2.25	1.25

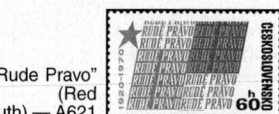

"Rude Pravo" (Red Truth) — A621

1970, Sept. 21   Perf. 11½x11

1697	A621	60h car, gold & blk	.25	.25

50th anniv. of the Rude Pravo newspaper.

"Great Sun" House Sign and Old Town Tower Bridge, Prague — A622

60h, "Blue Lion" & Town Hall Tower, Brno. 1k, Gothic corner stone & Town Hall Tower, Bratislava. 1.40k, Coat of Arms & Gothic Tower, Bratislava, & medallion. 1.60k, Moravian Eagle & Gothic Town Hall Tower, Brno. 1.80k, "Black Sun" & "Green Frog" house signs & New Town Hall, Prague.

1970, Sept. 23   Perf. 11x11½

1698	A622	40h black & multi	.25	.25
1699	A622	60h black & multi	.25	.25
1700	A622	1k black & multi	.25	.25
1701	A622	1.40k black & multi	1.40	.25
1702	A622	1.60k black & multi	.30	.25
1703	A622	1.80k black & multi	.80	.25
		Nos. 1698-1703 (6)	3.25	1.50

Germany-Uruguay Semifinal Soccer Match — A623

Designs: 20h, Sundisk Games' emblem and flags of participating nations. 60h, England-Czechoslovakia match and coats of arms. 1k, Romania-Czechoslovakia match and coats of arms. 1.20k, Brazil-Italy, final match and emblems. 1.80k, Brazil-Czechoslovakia match and emblems.

1970, Oct. 29   *Perf. 11½*
1704	A623	20h blk & multi	.25	.25
1705	A623	40h blk & multi	.25	.25
1706	A623	60h blk & multi	.30	.25
1707	A623	1k blk & multi	.45	.25
1708	A623	1.20k blk & multi	.45	.25
1709	A623	1.80k blk & multi	1.50	.25
		Nos. 1704-1709 (6)	3.20	1.50

9th World Soccer Championships for the Jules Rimet Cup, Mexico City, 5/30-6/21.

Congress Emblem — A624

1970, Nov. 9   **Engr. & Photo.**
1710 A624 30h blk, gold, ultra & red   .25 .25

Congress of the Czechoslovak Socialist Youth Federation.

Painting Type of 1967

Paintings: 1k, Seated Mother, by Mikulas Galanda. 1.20k, Bridesmaid, by Karel Svolinsky. 1.40k, Walk by Night, 1944, by Frantisek Hudecek. 1.80k, Banska Bystrica Market, by Dominik Skutecky. 2.40k, Adoration of the Kings, from the Vysehrad Codex, 1085.

1970, Nov. 27   **Engr.**   *Perf. 11½*
1711	A565	1k multi	.35	.25
1712	A565	1.20k multi	.70	.30
1713	A565	1.40k multi	.35	.30
1714	A565	1.80k multi	.70	.30
1715	A565	2.40k multi	3.00	2.00
		Nos. 1711-1715 (5)	5.10	3.15

Nos. 1711-1715 were each issued in sheets of 4. Value, set $20.

Radar — A625

Designs: 40h, Interkosmos 3, geophysical satellite. 60h, Kosmos meteorological satellite. 1k, Astronaut and Vostok satellite. No. 1720, Interkosmos 4, solar research satellite. No. 1720A, Space satellite (Sputnik) over city. 1.60k, Two-stage rocket on launching pad.

1970-71   **Engr. & Photo.**   *Perf. 11*
1716	A625	20h black & multi	.25	.25
1717	A625	40h black & multi	.25	.25
1718	A625	60h black & multi	.25	.25
1719	A625	1k black & multi	.25	.25
1720	A625	1.20k black & multi	.25	.25
1720A	A625	1.20k black & multi ('71)	.25	.25
1721	A625	1.60k black & multi	.90	.25
		Nos. 1716-1721 (7)	2.40	1.75

"Interkosmos," the collaboration of communist countries in various phases of space research.
Issued: No. 1720A, 11/15/71; others, 11/30/70.

Face of Christ on Veronica's Veil A626

Slovak Ikons, 16th-18th Centuries: 60h, Adam and Eve in the Garden, vert. 2k, St. George and the Dragon. 2.80k, St. Michael, vert.

1970, Dec. 17   **Engr.**   *Perf. 11½*
Cream Paper
1722	A626	60h multi	.70	.35
1723	A626	1k multi	1.00	.35
1724	A626	2k multi	1.00	.70
1725	A626	2.80k multi	2.10	1.40
		Nos. 1722-1725 (4)	4.80	2.80

Nos. 1722-1725 were each issued in sheets of 4. Value, set $22.50.

Carrier Pigeon Type of 1920 A627

Engraved and Photogravure
1970, Dec. 18   *Perf. 11x11½*
1726 A627 1k red, blk & yel grn   .40 .30
Stamp Day.

Song of the Barricades, 1938, by Karel Stika — A628

Czech and Slovak Graphic Art: 50h, Fruit Grower's Barge, 1941, by Cyril Bouda. 60h, Moon (woman) Searching for Lilies of the Valley, 1913, by Jan Zrzavy. 1k, At the Edge of Town (working man and woman), 1931, by Koloman Sokol. 1.60k, Summer, 1641, by Vaclav Hollar. 2k, Gamekeeper and Shepherd of Orava Castle, 1847, by Peter M. Bohun.

Engr. & Photo.; Engr. (40h, 60h, 1k)
1971, Jan. 28   *Perf. 11½*
1727	A628	40h brown	.25	.25
1728	A628	50h black & multi	.25	.25
1729	A628	60h slate	.25	.25
1730	A628	1k black	.30	.25
1731	A628	1.60k black & buff	.30	.25
1732	A628	2k black & multi	1.25	.25
		Nos. 1727-1732 (6)	2.60	1.50

Church of St. Bartholomew, Chrudim A629

Bell Tower, Hronsek A630

Designs: 1k, Roofs and folk art, Horácko. 1.60k, Saris Church. 2.40k, House, Jicin. 3k, House and folk art, Melnik. 5k, Watch Tower, Nachod. 5.40k, Baroque house, Posumavi. 6k, Cottage, Orava. 9k, Cottage, Turnov. 10k, Old houses, Liptov. 14k, House and wayside bell stand. 20k, Houses, Cicmany.

Engraved and Photogravure
1971-72   *Perf. 11½x11, 11x11½*
1733	A630	1k multi	.25	.25
1734	A629	1.60k multi	1.50	.25
1735	A630	2k multi	2.10	.25
1736	A629	2.40k multi	1.10	.25
1736A	A630	3k multi ('72)	2.10	.25
1737	A629	3.60k multi	1.40	.25
1737A	A630	5k multi ('72)	2.10	.25
1738	A630	5.40k multi	.75	.25
1739	A630	6k multi	3.50	.25
1740	A630	9k multi	1.40	.25
1740A	A629	10k multi ('72)	2.10	.25
1741	A629	14k multi	2.25	.25
1741A	A629	20k multi ('72)	2.10	.30
		Nos. 1733-1741A (13)	22.65	3.30

Nos. 1736A, 1738, 1740 are horizontal.
See No. 2870.

Coat of Arms Type of 1968
1971, Mar. 26   *Perf. 11½*
1742	A590	60h Zilina	.25	.25
1743	A590	60h Levoca	.25	.25
1744	A590	60h Ceska Trebova	.25	.25
1745	A590	60h Uhersky Brod	.25	.25
1746	A590	60h Trutnov	.25	.25
1747	A590	60h Karlovy Vary	.25	.25
		Nos. 1742-1747 (6)	1.50	1.50

"Fight of the Communards and Rise of the International" — A631

Design: No. 1749, World fight against racial discrimination, and "UNESCO."

1971, Mar. 18   *Perf. 11*
1748	A631	1k multicolored	.30	.25
1749	A631	1k multicolored	.30	.25

No. 1748 for cent. of the Paris Commune. No. 1749 for the Year against Racial Discrimination. Issued in sheets of 15 stamps and 5 labels. Value for single with attached tab, each $1.

A632

Edelweiss, mountaineering map & equipment.

1971, Apr. 27   *Perf. 11½x11*
1750 A632 30h multicolored   .25 .25
50th anniversary of Slovak Alpine Club.

A633

1971, Apr. 27   *Perf. 11½*
1751 A633 30h Singer   .25 .25
50th anniversary of Slovak Teachers' Choir.

Abbess' Crosier, 16th Century A634

No. 1753, Allegory of Music, 16th cent. mural.

1971, May 9
1752	A634	3k gold & multi	1.90	1.40
1753	A634	3k blk, dk brn & buff	1.90	1.40

Nos. 1752-1753 were each issued in sheets of 4. Value, set $15.
See Nos. 1817-1818, 1884-1885, 1937-1938, 2040-2041, 2081-2082, 2114-2115, 2176-2177, 2238-2239, 2329-2330, 2384-2385, 2420-2421.

Lenin — A635

40h, Hammer & sickle allegory. 60h, Raised fists. 1k, Star, hammer & sickle.

1971, May 14   *Perf. 11*
1754	A635	30h blk, red & gold	.25	.25
1755	A635	40h blk, ultra, red & gold	.25	.25
1756	A635	60h blk, ultra, red & gold	.25	.25
1757	A635	1k blk, ultra, red & gold	.30	.25
		Nos. 1754-1757 (4)	1.05	1.00

Czechoslovak Communist Party, 50th anniv.

Star, Hammer-Sickle Emblems A636

60h, Hammer-sickle emblem, fist & people, vert.

Perf. 11½x11, 11x11½
1971, May 24   **Engr. & Photo.**
1758	A636	30h blk, red, gold & yel	.25	.25
1759	A636	60h blk, red, gold & bl	.25	.25

14th Congress of Communist Party of Czechoslovakia.

Ring-necked Pheasant A637

Designs: 60h, Rainbow trout. 80h, Mouflon. 1k, Chamois. 2k, Stag. 2.60k, Wild boar.

1971, Aug. 17   *Perf. 11½x11*
1760	A637	20h orange & multi	.25	.25
1761	A637	60h lt blue & multi	.25	.25
1762	A637	80h yellow & multi	.25	.25
1763	A637	1k lt green & multi	.30	.25
1764	A637	2k lilac & multi	.40	.25
1765	A637	2.60k bister & multi	2.25	.65
		Nos. 1760-1765 (6)	3.70	1.90

World Hunting Exhib., Budapest, Aug. 27-30.

Diesel Locomotive — A638

1971, Sept. 2   *Perf. 11x11½*
1766 A638 30h lt bl, blk & red   .40 .25
Cent. of CKD, Prague Machine Foundry.

Gymnasts and Banners — A639

1971, Sept. 2   *Perf. 11½x11*
1767 A639 30h red brn, gold & ultra   .25 .25
50th anniversary of Workers' Physical Exercise Federation.

Road Intersections and Bridge — A640

1971, Sept. 2   **Engr. & Photo.**
1768 A640 1k blk, gold, red & bl   .30 .25
14th World Highways and Bridges Congress. Sheets of 25 stamps and 25 labels printed se-tenant with continuous design. Value, single with attached tab, unused 60c; used 30c.

Chinese Fairytale, by Eva Bednarova — A641

Designs: 1k, Tiger and other animals, by Mirko Hanak. 1.60k, The Miraculous Bamboo Shoot, by Yasuo Segawa, horiz.

Perf. 11½x11, 11x11½
1971, Sept. 10
1769	A641	60h multi	.25	.25
1770	A641	1k multi	.30	.25
1771	A641	1.60k multi	.45	.25
		Nos. 1769-1771 (3)	1.00	.75

Bratislava BIB 71 biennial exhibition of illustrations for children's books.

Apothecary Jars and Coltsfoot A642

Intl. Pharmaceutical Cong.: 60h, Jars and dog rose. 1k, Scales and adonis vernalis. 1.20k, Mortars and valerian. 1.80k, Retorts and chicory. 2.40k, Mill, mortar and henbane.

1971, Sept. 20   *Perf. 11½x11*
Yellow Paper

1772	A642	30h multi	.25	.25
1773	A642	60h multi	.25	.25
1774	A642	1k multi	.25	.25
1775	A642	1.20k multi	.25	.25
1776	A642	1.80k multi	.25	.25
1777	A642	2.40k multi	1.25	.25
	Nos. 1772-1777 (6)		2.50	1.50

Painting Type of 1967

Paintings: 1k, "Waiting" (woman's head), 1967, by Imro Weiner-Král. 1.20k, Resurrection, by Master of Vyssi Brod, 14th century. 1.40k, Woman with Pitcher, by Milos Bazovsky. 1.80k, Veruna Cudova (in folk costume), by Josef Mánes. 2.40k, Detail from "Feast of the Rose Garlands," by Albrecht Dürer.

1971, Nov. 27   *Perf. 11½*

1779	A565	1k multi	.30	.30
1780	A565	1.20k multi	.75	.45
1781	A565	1.40k multi	.60	.30
1782	A565	1.80k multi	1.10	.50
1783	A565	2.40k multi	1.75	.75
	Nos. 1779-1783 (5)		4.50	2.30

Nos. 1779-1783 were each issued in sheets of 4. Value, set $25.

Workers Revolt in Krompachy, by Julius Nemcik — A643

1971, Nov. 28   *Perf. 11x11½*
1784 A643 60h multi   .30   .25

History of the Czechoslovak Communist Party.

Wooden Dolls and Birds — A644

Folk Art and UNICEF Emblem: 80h, Jug handles, carved. 1k, Horseback rider. 1.60k, Shepherd carrying lamb. 2k, Easter eggs and rattle. 3k, "Zbojnik," folk hero.

1971, Dec. 11   *Perf. 11½*

1785	A644	60h multi	.40	.25
1786	A644	80h multi	.80	.25
1787	A644	1k multi	.40	.25
1788	A644	1.60k multi	.40	.25
1789	A644	2k multi	.40	.30
1790	A644	3k multi	2.00	.60
	Nos. 1785-1790 (6)		4.40	1.90

25th anniv. of UNICEF.
Nos. 1785-1790 were each issued in sheets of 10. Value, set $45.

Runners, Parthenon, Czechoslovak Olympic Emblem — A645

Designs: 40h, Women's high jump, Olympic emblem and plan for Prague Stadium. 1.60k, Cross-country skiers, Sapporo '72 emblem and ski jump in High Tatras. 2.60k, Discus thrower, Discobolus and St. Vitus Cathedral.

1971, Dec. 16   **Engr. & Photo.**

1791	A645	30h multi	.25	.25
1792	A645	40h multi	.25	.25
1793	A645	1.60k multi	.25	.25
1794	A645	2.60k multi	1.50	.75
	Nos. 1791-1794 (4)		2.25	1.50

75th anniversary of Czechoslovak Olympic Committee (30h, 2.60k); 20th Summer Olympic Games, Munich, Aug. 26-Sept. 10, 1972 (40h); 11th Winter Olympic Games, Sapporo, Japan, Feb. 3-13, 1972 (1.60k).

Post Horns and Lion — A646

1971, Dec. 17   *Perf. 11x11½*
1795 A646 1k blk, gold, car & bl   .30   .25

Stamp Day.

Figure Skating — A647

Olympic Emblems and: 50h, Ski jump. 1k, Ice hockey. 1.60k, Sledding, women's.

1972, Jan. 13   *Perf. 11½*

1796	A647	40h pur, org & red	.25	.25
1797	A647	50h dk bl, org & red	.25	.25
1798	A647	1k mag, org & red	.30	.25
1799	A647	1.60k bl grn, org & red	1.25	.25
	Nos. 1796-1799 (4)		2.05	1.00

11th Winter Olympic Games, Sapporo, Japan, Feb. 3-13.

"Lezáky" — A648

No. 1801, Boy's head behind barbed wire, horiz. No. 1802, Hand rising from ruins. No. 1803, Soldier and banner, horiz.

1972, Feb. 16

1800	A648	30h blk, dl org & red	.25	.25
1801	A648	30h blk & brn org	.25	.25
1802	A648	60h blk, yel & red	.25	.25
1803	A648	60h sl grn & multi	.25	.25
	Nos. 1800-1803 (4)		1.00	1.00

30th anniv. of: destruction of Lezáky (No. 1800) and Lidice (No. 1802); Terezin concentration camp (No. 1801); Czechoslovak Army unit in Russia (No. 1803).

Book Year Emblem — A649

1972, Mar. 17   *Perf. 11½x11*
1804 A649 1k blk & org brn   .30   .25

International Book Year 1972.

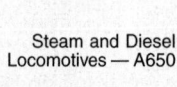

Steam and Diesel Locomotives — A650

1972, Mar. 17   *Perf. 11½x11*
1805 A650 30h multi   .75   .25

Centenary of the Kosice-Bohumin railroad.

"Pasture," by Vojtech Sedlacek — A651

Designs: 50h, Dressage, by Frantisek Tichy. 60th, Otakar Kubin, by Vaclav Fiala. 1k, The Three Kings, by Ernest Zmetak. 1.60k, Woman Dressing, by Ludovit Fulla.

1972, Mar. 27   *Perf. 11½x11*

1806	A651	40h multi	.25	.25
1807	A651	50h multi	.25	.25
1808	A651	60h multi	.25	.25
1809	A651	1k multi	.25	.25
1810	A651	1.60k multi	1.25	.90
	Nos. 1806-1810 (5)		2.25	1.90

Czech and Slovak graphic art.
1.60k issued in sheets of 4. Value $9.
See Nos. 1859-1862, 1921-1924.

Ice Hockey — A652

Design: 1k, Two players.

1972, Apr. 7   *Perf. 11*

1811	A652	60h blk & multi	.25	.25
1812	A652	1k blk & multi	.40	.25

World and European Ice Hockey Championships, Prague.
For overprint see Nos. 1845-1846.

Bicycling, Olympic Rings and Emblem — A653

1972, Apr. 7

1813	A653	50h shown	.25	.25
1814	A653	1.60k Diving	.35	.25
1815	A653	1.80k Canoeing	.55	.25
1816	A653	2k Gymnast	1.10	.25
	Nos. 1813-1816 (4)		2.25	1.00

20th Olympic Games, Munich, 8/26-9/11.

Prague Castle Art Type of 1971

Designs: No. 1817, Adam and Eve, column capital, St. Vitus Cathedral. No. 1818, Czech coat of arms (lion), c. 1500.

1972, May 9   *Perf. 11½*

1817	A634	3k blk & multi	2.10	1.40
1818	A634	3k blk, red, sil & gold	1.40	.85

Nos. 1817-1818 were each issued in sheets of 4. Value, set $15.

Andrej Sladkovic (1820-1872), Poet — A654

No. 1820, Janko Kral (1822-1876), poet. No. 1821, Ludmilla Podjavorinska (1872-1951), writer. No. 1822, Antonin Hudecek (1872-1941), painter. No. 1823, Frantisek Bilek (1872-1941), sculptor. No. 1824, Jan Preisler (1872-1918), painter.

1972, June 14   *Perf. 11*

1819	A654	40h pur, ol & bl	.25	.25
1820	A654	40h dk grn, bl & yel	.25	.25
1821	A654	40h blk & multi	.25	.25
1822	A654	40h brn, lt grn	.25	.25
1823	A654	40h choc, grn & org	.25	.25
1824	A654	40h grn, sl & dp org	.25	.25
	Nos. 1819-1824 (6)		1.50	1.50

Men with Banners — A655

1972, June 14   *Perf. 11x11½*
1825 A655 30h dk vio bl, red & yel   .25   .25

8th Trade Union Congress, Prague.

Art Forms of Wire — A656

Ornamental Wirework: 60h, Plane and rosette. 80h, Four-headed dragon and ornament. 1k, Locomotive and loops. 2.60k, Tray and owl.

1972, Aug. 28   *Perf. 11½x11*

1826	A656	20h sal & multi	.25	.25
1827	A656	60h multi	.25	.25
1828	A656	80h pink & multi	.25	.25
1829	A656	1k multi	.25	.25
1830	A656	2.60k rose & multi	1.40	.25
	Nos. 1826-1830 (5)		2.40	1.25

"Jiskra" — A657

Engr. & Photo.
1972, Sept. 27   *Perf. 11½x11*
Size: 40x22mm
Multicolored Design on Blue Paper

1831	A657	50h shown	.25	.25
1832	A657	60h "Mir"	.25	.25
1833	A657	80h "Republika"	.25	.25

Size: 48x29mm
Perf. 11x11½

1834	A657	1k "Kosice"	.30	.25
1835	A657	1.60k "Dukla"	.45	.25
1836	A657	2k "Kladno"	1.40	.55
	Nos. 1831-1836 (6)		2.90	1.80

Czechoslovak sea-going vessels.

Hussar, 18th Century Tile — A658

60h, Janissary. 80h, St. Martin. 1.60k, St. George. 1.80k, Nobleman's guard. 2.20k, Slovakian horseman.

1972, Oct. 24   *Perf. 11½x11*

1837	A658	30h shown	.25	.25
1838	A658	60h multicolored	.25	.25
1839	A658	80h multicolored	.25	.25
1840	A658	1.60k multicolored	.45	.25
1841	A658	1.80k multicolored	.70	.25
1842	A658	2.20k multicolored	1.25	.25
	Nos. 1837-1842 (6)		3.15	1.50

Horsemen from 18th-19th century tiles or enamel paintings on glass.

Worker, Flag Hoisted on Bayonet A659

Star, Hammer and Sickle — A660

1972, Nov. 7   *Perf. 11x11½*

1843	A659	30h gold & multi	.25	.25
1844	A660	60h rose car & gold	.25	.25

55th anniv. of the Russian October Revolution (30h); 50th anniv. of the Soviet Union (60h).

Nos. 1811-1812 Overprinted in Violet Blue or Black

1972　　　　　　　　　　　*Perf. 11*
1845	A652	60h multi (VBl)	7.00	6.50
1846	A652	1k multi (Bk)	7.00	6.50

Czechoslovakia's victorious ice hockey team. The overprint on the 60h (shown) is in Czech and reads CSSR/MISTREM/SVETA; the overprint on the 1k is in Slovak.

Painting Type of 1967

Designs: 1k, "Nosegay" (nudes and flowers), by Max Svabinsky. 1.20k, Struggle of St. Ladislas with Kuman nomad, anonymous, 14th century. 1.40k, Lady with Fur Hat, by Vaclav Hollar. 1.80k, Midsummer Night's Dream, 1962, by Josef Liesler. 2.40k, Pablo Picasso, self-portrait.

1972, Nov. 27　　**Engr. & Photo.**
1847	A565	1k multi	.85	.40
1848	A565	1.20k multi	.85	.40
1849	A565	1.40k blk & cream	1.10	.40
1850	A565	1.80k multi	.85	.50
1851	A565	2.40k multi	2.10	1.40
	Nos. 1847-1851 (5)		5.75	3.10

Nos. 1847-1851 were each issued in sheets of 4. Value, set $24.

Goldfinch — A661

Songbirds: 60h, Warbler feeding young cuckoo. 80h, Cuckoo. 1k, Black-billed magpie. 1.60k, Bullfinch. 3k, Song thrush.

1972, Dec. 15　　**Size: 30x48½mm**
1852	A661	60h yel & multi	.25	.25
1853	A661	80h multi	.25	.25
1854	A661	1k lt bl & multi	.25	.25

Engr.
Size: 30x23mm
1855	A661	1.60k multi	1.50	.70
1856	A661	2k multi	1.50	.70
1857	A661	3k multi	1.50	.70
	Nos. 1852-1857 (6)		5.25	2.85

Nos. 1855-1857 were each issued in a sheet of 10. Value, set $55.

Post Horn and Allegory A662

1972, Dec. 18　　**Engr. & Photo.**
1858	A662	1k blk, red lil & gold	.30	.30

Stamp Day.

Art Type of 1972

Designs: 30h, Flowers in Window, by Jaroslav Grus. 60h, Quest for Happiness, by Josef Balaz. 1.60k, Balloon, by Kamil Lhotak. 1.80k, Woman with Viola, by Richard Wiesner.

1973, Jan. 25　　*Perf. 11½x11*
1859	A651	30h multi	.25	.25
1860	A651	60h multi	.25	.25
1861	A651	1.60k multi	.30	.25
1862	A651	1.80k multi	.25	.35
	Nos. 1859-1862 (4)		1.05	1.10

Czech and Slovak graphic art.

Tennis Player A663

Figure Skater A664

Torch and Star — A665

1973, Feb. 22　　　　*Perf. 11*
1863	A663	30h vio & multi	.25	.25
1864	A664	60h blk & multi	.25	.25
1865	A665	1k multi	.30	.25
	Nos. 1863-1865 (3)		.80	.75

80th anniversary of the tennis organization in Czechoslovakia (30h); World figure skating championships, Bratislava (60h); 3rd summer army Spartakiad of socialist countries (1k).

Star and Factories A666

Workers' Militia, Emblem and Flag A667

1973, Feb. 23
1866	A666	30h multi	.25	.25
1867	A667	60h multi	.25	.25

25th anniversary of the Communist revolution in Czechoslovakia and of the Militia.

A668

Torch &: 30h, Capt. Jan Nalepka, Major Antonin Sochor and Laurel. 40h, Evzen Rosicky, Mirko Nespor & ivy leaves. 60h, Vlado Clementis, Karol Smidke & linden leaves. 80h, Jan Osoha, Josef Molak & oak leaves. 1k, Marie Kuderikova, Jozka Jaburkova & rose. 1.60k, Vaclav Sinkule, Eduard Urx & palm leaf.

1973, Mar. 20　　*Perf. 11½x11*
Yellow Paper
1868	A668	30h blk, ver & gold	.30	.25
1869	A668	40h blk, ver & grn	.30	.25
1870	A668	60h blk, ver & gold	.30	.25
1871	A668	80h blk, ver & gold	.30	.25
1872	A668	1k blk, ver & grn	.30	.25
1873	A668	1.60k blk, ver & sil	.75	.25
	Nos. 1868-1873 (6)		2.25	1.50

Fighters against and victims of Fascism and Nazism during German Occupation.

Virgil I. Grissom, Edward H. White, Roger B. Chaffee A669

Designs: 20h, Soviet planetary station "Venera." 30h, "Intercosmos" station. 40h, Lunokhod on moon. 3.60k, Vladimir M. Komarov, Georgi T. Dobrovolsky, Vladislav N. Volkov, Victor I. Patsayev. 5k, Yuri A. Gagarin.

Two types of 3.60k: type I, Cosmonaut on background of cross-hatched lines; type 2, Cosmonaut on background of parallel diagonal lines.

1973, Apr. 12　　*Perf. 11½x11*
Size: 40x22mm
1874	A669	20h multi	.25	.25
1875	A669	30h multi	.25	.25
1876	A669	40h multi	.25	.25

Engr.
Perf. 11½
Size: 49x30mm
1877	A669	3k multi	1.00	.50
1878	A669	3.60k multi, type 1	1.00	.75
a.		Type 2	20.00	7.50
1879	A669	5k multi	2.50	2.00
	Nos. 1874-1879 (6)		5.25	4.00

In memory of American and Russian astronauts.

Nos. 1877-1879 were each issued in sheets of 4. Values: set (with No. 1878) $30; mset (with No. 1878a) $90.

Radio A670

Telephone and Map of Czechoslovakia A671

Television — A672

1973, May 1　　*Perf. 11½x11*
1880	A670	30h blk & multi	.25	.25
1881	A671	30h lt bl, pink & blk	.25	.25
1882	A672	30h dp bl & multi	.25	.25
	Nos. 1880-1882 (3)		.75	.75

Czechoslovak anniversaries: 50 years of broadcasting (No. 1880); 20 years of telephone service to all communities (No. 1881); 20 years of television (No. 1882).

Coat of Arms and Linden Branch — A673

1973, May 9　　*Perf. 11x11½*
1883	A673	60h red & multi	.25	.25

25th anniv. of the Constitution of May 9.

Prague Castle Art Type of 1971

No. 1884, Royal Legate, 14th century. No. 1885, Seal of King Charles IV, 1351.

1973, May 9　　*Perf. 11½*
1884	A634	3k blue & multi	1.25	.75
1885	A634	3k gold, grn & dk brn	1.75	1.50

Nos. 1884-1885 were each issued in sheets of 4. Value, set $13.

Coat of Arms Type of 1968

1973, June 20
1886	A590	60h Mikulov	.25	.25
1887	A590	60h Zlutice	.30	.25
1888	A590	60h Smolenice	.35	.25
	Nos. 1886-1888 (3)		.90	.75

Coats of arms of Czechoslovakian cities.

Heraldic Colors of Olomouc and Moravia — A674

1973, Aug. 23　　**Engr. & Photo.**
1889	A674	30h multi	.25	.25

University of Olomouc, 400th anniv.

Flower Show — A675

60h, Tulips (30x50mm). 1k, Rose (30x50mm). 1.60k, Anthurium (23x39mm). 1.80k, Iris (23x39mm). 2k, Chrysanthemum (30x50mm). 3.60k, Cymbidium (23x39mm).

1973, Aug. 23　　*Perf. 11½*
1890	A675	60h multi	.75	.35
1891	A675	1k multi	.75	.35
1892	A675	1.60k shown	.40	.35
1893	A675	1.80k multi	.40	.35
1894	A675	2k multi	1.90	1.00
1895	A675	3.60k multi	.75	.35
	Nos. 1890-1895 (6)		4.95	2.75

Olomouc, Aug. 18-Sept. 2. 60h, 1k, 2k issued in sheets of 4, others in sheets of 10. Value, set $50.

Hunting Dogs — A676

1973, Sept. 5
1896	A676	20h Irish setter	.45	.25
1897	A676	30h Czech terrier	.45	.25
1898	A676	40h Bavarian hunting dog	.55	.25
1899	A676	60h German pointer	.55	.25
1900	A676	1k Cocker spaniel	.85	.25
1901	A676	1.60k Dachshund	2.10	.50
	Nos. 1896-1901 (6)		4.95	1.75

Czechoslovak United Hunting Org., 50th anniv.

St. John, the Baptist, by Svabinsky — A677

Works by Max Svabinsky: 60h, "August Noon" (woman). 80h, "Marriage of True Minds" (artist and muse). 1k, "Paradise Sonata I" (Adam dreaming of Eve). 2.60k, Last Judgment, stained glass window, St. Vitus Cathedral.

1973, Sept. 17　　**Litho. & Engr.**
1902	A677	20h blk & pale grn	.25	.25
1903	A677	60h black & buff	.25	.25

Engr.
1904	A677	80h black	.75	.25
1905	A677	1k slate green	.75	.25
1906	A677	2.60k multi	1.90	1.25
	Nos. 1902-1906 (5)		3.90	2.25

Centenary of the birth of Max Svabinsky (1873-1962), artist and stamp designer. 20h and 60h issued in sheets of 25; 80h and 1k setenant in sheets of 4 checkerwise (value $4); 2.60k in sheets of 4 (value $10).

Trade Union Emblem — A678

1973, Oct. 15　　**Engr. & Photo.**
1907	A678	1k red, bl & yel	.25	.25

8t (valueh Congress of the World Federation of Trade Unions, Varna, Bulgaria.

Painting Type of 1967

1k, Boy from Martinique, by Antonin Pelc. 1.20k, "Fortitude" (mountaineer), by Martin Benka. 1.80k, Rembrandt, self-portrait. 2k, Pierrot, by Bohumil Kubista. 2.40k, Ilona Kubinyiova, by Peter M. Bohun. 3.60k, Virgin and Child (Veveri Madonna), c. 1350.

1973, Nov. 27　　*Perf. 11½*
1908	A565	1k multi, vio bl inscriptions	2.50	1.25
a.		1k multi, black inscriptions	9.00	9.00
1909	A565	1.20k multi	2.50	1.25
1910	A565	1.80k multi	.80	.80
1911	A565	2k multi	.80	.80
1912	A565	2.40k multi	.80	.80
1913	A565	3.60k multi	.80	.80
	Nos. 1908-1913 (6)		8.20	5.70

Nos. 1908-1909 were each issued in sheets of 4. Nos. 1910-1913 were printed se-tenant with gold and black inscription on gutter. Value, sheet $35. No. 1908a in sheet of 4, value $45.

The central background is light bluish green on No. 1908; grayish blue on No. 1908a.

Postilion A679

1973, Dec. 18
1914	A679	1k gold & multi	.30	.25

Stamp Day 1974 and 55th anniversary of Czechoslovak postage stamps. Printed with 2 labels showing telephone and telegraph. Value of single with two labels, $1.75.

"CSSR" — A680

1974, Jan. 1
1915 A680 30h red, gold & ultra .25 .25
5th anniversary of Federal Government in the Czechoslovak Socialist Republic.

Bedrich Smetana A681

Pablo Neruda, Chilean Flag A682

1974, Jan. 4   **Perf. 11x11½**
1916 A681 60h shown .25 .25
1917 A681 60h Josef Suk .25 .25
1918 A682 60h shown .25 .25
    Nos. 1916-1918 (3) .75 .75

Smetana (1824-84), composer; Suk (1874-1935), composer, and Pablo Neruda (Neftali Ricardo Reyes, 1904-73), Chilean poet.

Comecon Building, Moscow — A683

1974, Jan. 23
1919 A683 1k gold, red & vio bl .25 .25
25th anniversary of the Council of Mutual Economic Assistance (COMECON).

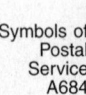

Symbols of Postal Service A684

1974, Feb. 20   **Perf. 11½**
1920 A684 3.60k multi .85 .45
BRNO '74 National Stamp Exhibition, Brno, June 8-23.
No. 1920 was issue both in normal sheets of 25 stamps and in sheets containing 16 stamps se-tenant with 9 labels depicting Brno. Values: single stamp with attached tab unused $2.50; used $2.50; full sheet of 16 stamps and 9 labels $35.

Art Type of 1972
Designs: 60h, Tulips 1973, by Josef Broz. 1k, Structures 1961 (poppy and building), by Orest Dubay. 1.60k, Bird and flowers (Golden Sun-Glowing Day), by Adolf Zabransky. 1.80k, Artificial flowers, by Frantisek Gross.

1974, Feb. 21   **Perf. 11½x11**
1921 A651 60h multi .25 .25
1922 A651 1k multi .30 .25
1923 A651 1.60k multi .40 .25
1924 A651 1.80k multi 1.10 .30
    Nos. 1921-1924 (4) 2.05 1.05
Czech and Slovak graphic art.

Oskar Benes and Vaclav Prochazka A685

40h, Milos Uher, Anton Sedlacek. 60h, Jan Hajecek, Marie Sedlackova. 80h, Jan Sverma, Albin Grznar. 1k, Jaroslav Neliba, Alois Hovorka. 1.60k, Ladislav Exnar, Ludovit Kukorelli.

1974, Mar. 21   **Perf. 11½x11**
1925 A685 30h indigo & multi .25 .25
1926 A685 40h indigo & multi .25 .25
1927 A685 60h indigo & multi .25 .25
1928 A685 80h indigo & multi .25 .25

1929 A685 1k indigo & multi .30 .25
1930 A685 1.60k indigo & multi .85 .25
    Nos. 1925-1930 (6) 2.15 1.50
Partisan commanders and fighters.

"Water, the Source of Energy" — A686

Symbolic Designs: 1k, Importance of water for agriculture. 1.20k, Study of the oceans. 1.60k, "Hydrological Decade." 2k, Struggle for unpolluted water.

1974, Apr. 25   **Engr.**   **Perf. 11½**
1931 A686 60h multi .55 .25
1932 A686 1k multi .55 .25
1933 A686 1.20k multi 1.10 .45
1934 A686 1.60k multi 1.10 .45
1935 A686 2k multi 2.10 1.40
    Nos. 1931-1935 (5) 5.40 2.80
Hydrological Decade (UNESCO), 1965-1974. Nos. 1931-1935 were each issued in sheets of 4. Value $25.

Allegory Holding "Molniya," and Ground Station — A687

1974, Apr. 30   **Engr. & Photo.**
1936 A687 30h vio bl & multi .25 .25
"Intersputnik," first satellite communications ground station in Czechoslovakia.

Prague Castle Art Type of 1971
No. 1937, Golden Cock, 17th century locket. No. 1938, Glass monstrance, 1840.

1974, May 9   **Engr.**   **Perf. 11½**
1937 A634 3k gold & multi 1.50 1.10
1938 A634 3k blk & multi 2.25 1.50
    Nos. 1937-1938 were each issued in sheets of 4. Value, set $15.

Sousaphone — A688

30h, Bagpipe. 40h, Violin, by Martin Benka. 1k, Pyramid piano. 1.60k, Tenor quinton, 1754.

Engraved and Photogravure
1974, May 12   **Perf. 11x11½**
1939 A688 20h shown .25 .25
1940 A688 30h multi .25 .25
1941 A688 40h multi .25 .25
1942 A688 1k multi .25 .25
1943 A688 1.60k multi .80 .25
    Nos. 1939-1943 (5) 1.80 1.25
Prague and Bratislava Music Festivals. The 1.60k also commemorates 25th anniversary of Slovak Philharmonic Orchestra.

Child — A689

1974, June 1   **Perf. 11½**
1944 A689 60h multi .25 .25
Children's Day. Design is from illustration for children's book by Adolf Zabransky.

Globe, People and Exhibition Emblems A690

Design: 6k, Rays and emblems symbolizing "Oneness and Mutuality."

1974, June 1
1945 A690 30h multi .25 .25
1946 A690 6k multi 1.50 .75
BRNO 74 Natl. Stamp Exhib., Brno, June 8-23.
Nos. 2171-2172 were each issued both in sheet of 50 stamps and in sheets of 16 stamps and 14 labels. Values: stamps with attached labels, $1.75; 2 sheets of 16 stamps and 14 labels $35.

Resistance Fighter — A691

1974, Aug. 29   **Perf. 11½**
1947 A691 30h multi .25 .25
Slovak National Uprising, 30th anniversary.

Actress Holding Tragedy and Comedy Masks — A692

1974, Aug. 29
1948 A692 30h red, sil & blk .25 .25
Bratislava Academy of Music and Drama, 25th anniversary.

Slovak Girl with Flower — A693

1974, Aug. 29
1949 A693 30h multi .25 .25
SLUK, Slovak folksong and dance ensemble, 25th anniversary.

Hero and Leander A694

Design: 2.40k, Hero watching Leander swim the Hellespont. No. 1952, Leander reaching shore. No. 1953, Hero mourning over Leander's body. No. 1954, Hermione, Leander's sister. No. 1955, Mourning Cupid. Designs are from 17th century English tapestries in Bratislava Council Palace.

1974-76
1950 A694 2k multi 1.25 1.10
1951 A694 2.40k multi 1.50 1.25
1952 A694 3k multi 1.00 .45
1953 A694 3k multi 1.75 1.75
1954 A694 3.60k multi 2.50 1.10
1955 A694 3.60k multi .85 .60
    Nos. 1950-1955 (6) 8.85 6.25
Issued: Nos. 1950-1951, 9/25/74; Nos. 1952, 1954, 8/29/75; Nos. 1953, 1955, 5/9/76. Nos. 1950-1951 were each issued in sheets of 4, with 2 blank labels; Nos. 1952-1955 were issued in sheets of 4. Value, set $50.

Soldier Standing Guard, Target, 1840 — A695

Painted Folk-art Targets: 60h, Landscape with Pierrot and flags, 1828. 1k, Diana crowning champion marksman, 1832. 1.60k, Still life with guitar, 1839. 2.40k, Salvo and stag in flight, 1834. 3k, Turk and giraffe, 1831.

1974, Sept. 26   **Perf. 11½**
Size: 30x50mm
1956 A695 30h black & multi .25 .25
1957 A695 60h black & multi .25 .25
1958 A695 1k black & multi .30 .25

Engr.
Perf. 12
Size: 40x50mm
1959 A695 1.60k green & multi .50 .45
1960 A695 2.40k sepia & multi .90 .75
1961 A695 3k multi 3.00 3.00
    Nos. 1956-1961 (6) 5.20 4.95
Nos. 1959-1961 were each issued in sheets of 4. Value, set $17.50.

UPU Emblem and Postilion A696

UPU Cent. (UPU Emblem and): 40h, Mail coach. 60h, Railroad mail coach, 1851. 80h, Early mail truck. 1k, Czechoslovak Airlines mail plane. 1.60k, Radar.

Engraved and Photogravure
1974, Oct. 9   **Perf. 11½**
1962 A696 30h multi .25 .25
1963 A696 40h multi .25 .25
1964 A696 60h multi .25 .25
1965 A696 80h multi .40 .25
1966 A696 1k multi .40 .25
1967 A696 1.60k multi 1.25 .25
    Nos. 1962-1967 (6) 2.65 1.50

Sealed Letter A697

Post Rider A698

20h, Post Horn, Old Town Bridge Tower. No. 1971, Carrier pigeon.

1974, Oct. 31   **Perf. 11½x11**
1968 A698 20h multi .25 .25
1969 A697 30h brn, bl & red .25 .25
1970 A698 40h multi .25 .25
1971 A697 60h bl, yel & red .25 .25
    Nos. 1968-1971 (4) 1.00 1.00
Nos. 1968-1971 were reissued in 1979, printed on fluorescent paper. Value, set $15. See No. 2675.

Stylized Bird — A699

No. 1977, Same design as No. 1976. No. 1979, Map of Czechoslovakia with postal code numbers.

Coil Stamps
1975   **Photo.**   **Perf. 14**
1976 A699 30h brt bl .25 .25
1977 A699 60h carmine .25 .25

Postal Code Symbol — A699a

1976 — Perf. 11½

1978	A699a	30h emer	.25 .25
1979	A699a	60h scar	.25 .25

Nos. 1976-1979 have black control number on back of every fifth stamp.

Ludvik Kuba, Self-portrait, 1941 — A700

Paintings: 1.20k, Violinist Frantisek Ondricek, by Vaclav Brozik. 1.60k, Vase with Flowers, by Otakar Kubin. 1.80k, Woman with Pitcher, by Janko Alexy. 2.40k, Bacchanalia, c. 1635, by Karel Skreta.

1974, Nov. 27 — Engr. Perf. 11½

1980	A700	1k multi	.50 .30
1981	A700	1.20k multi	.80 .80
1982	A700	1.60k multi	.80 .60
1983	A700	1.80k multi	1.00 .40
1984	A700	2.40k multi	2.50 1.75
	Nos. 1980-1984 (5)		5.60 3.45

Czech and Slovak art.
Nos. 1980-1984 were each issued in sheets of 4. Value, set $25.
See Nos. 2209-2211, 2678-2682, 2721-2723, 2743, 2766-2768.

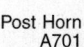

Post Horn A701

Engraved and Photogravure
1974, Dec. 18 — Perf. 11x11½

1985	A701	1k multicolored	.30 .25

Stamp Day.

Still-life with Hare, by Hollar — A702

Designs: 1k, The Lion and the Mouse, by Vaclav Hollar. 1.60k, Deer Hunt, by Philip Galle. 1.80k, Grand Hunt, by Jacques Callot.

1975, Feb. 26 — Perf. 11½x11

1988	A702	60h blk & buff	.25 .25
1989	A702	1k blk & buff	.25 .25
1990	A702	1.60k blk & yel	.25 .25
1991	A702	1.80k blk & buff	1.25 .65
	Nos. 1988-1991 (4)		2.00 1.40

Hunting scenes from old engravings.

Guns Pointing at Family — A703

Designs: 1k, Women and building on fire. 1.20k, People and roses. All designs include names of destroyed villages.

1975, Feb. 26 — Perf. 11

1992	A703	60h multi	.25 .25
1993	A703	1k multi	.25 .25
1994	A703	1.20k multi	.30 .25
	Nos. 1992-1994 (3)		.80 .75

Destruction of 14 villages by the Nazis, 30th anniversary.

Young Woman and Globe — A704

1975, Mar. 7 — Perf. 11½x11

1995	A704	30h red & multi	.25 .25

International Women's Year 1975.

Little Queens, Moravian Folk Custom — A705

Folk Customs: 1k, Straw masks (animal heads and blackened faces), Slovak. 1.40k, The Tale of Maid Dorothea (executioner, girl, king and devil). 2k, Drowning of Morena, symbol of death and winter.

1975, Mar. 26 — Engr. Perf. 11½

1996	A705	60h blk & multi	.45 .25
1997	A705	1k blk & multi	.70 .45
1998	A705	1.40k blk & multi	.85 .60
1999	A705	2k blk & multi	1.00 .75
	Nos. 1996-1999 (4)		3.00 2.05

Nos. 1996-1999 were each issued in sheets of four. Value $12.50.

Coat of Arms Type of 1968
Engraved and Photogravure
1975, Apr. 17 — Perf. 11½

2000	A590	60h Nymburk	.25 .25
2001	A590	60h Znojmo	.25 .25

Coats of arms of Czechoslovakian cities.

Czech May Uprising A706

Liberation by Soviet Army — A707

Czechoslovak-Russian Friendship — A708

Engr. & Photo.; Engr. (A707)
1975, May 9

2002	A706	1k multi	.25 .25
2003	A707	1k multi	.25 .25
2004	A708	1k multi	.25 .25
	Nos. 2002-2004 (3)		.75 .75

30th anniv. of the May uprising of the Czech people and of liberation by the Soviet Army; 5th anniv. of the Czechoslovak-Soviet Treaty of Friendship, Cooperation and Mutual Aid.

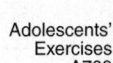

Adolescents' Exercises A709

Designs: 60th, Children's exercises. 1k, Men's and women's exercises.

Engraved and Photogravure
1975, June 15 — Perf. 12x11½

2005	A709	30h lil & multi	.25 .25
2006	A709	60h multi	.25 .25
2007	A709	1k vio & multi	.25 .25
	Nos. 2005-2007 (3)		.75 .75

Spartakiad 1975, Prague, June 26-29. Nos. 2005-2007 each issued in sheets of 30 stamps and 40 labels, showing different Spartakiad emblems. Value, set with tabs, $1.

Datrioides Microlepis and Sea Horse A710

Tropical Fish (Aquarium): 1k, Beta splendens regan and Pterophyllum scalare. 1.20k, Carassius auratus. 1.60k, Amphiprion percula and Chaetodon sp. 2k, Pomacanthodes semicirculatus, Pomacanthus maculosus and Paracanthurus hepatus.

1975, June 27 — Perf. 11½

2008	A710	60h multi	.25 .25
2009	A710	1k multi	.35 .25
2010	A710	1.20k multi	.40 .25
2011	A710	1.60k multi	.55 .25
2012	A710	2k multi	1.75 .50
	Nos. 2008-2012 (5)		3.30 1.50

Pelicans, by Nikita Charushin — A711

Book Illustrations: 30h, The Dreamer, by Lieselotte Schwarz. 40h, Hero on horseback, by Val Munteanau. 60h, Peacock, by Klaus Ensikat. 80h, Woman on horseback, by Robert Dubravec.

1975, Sept. 5

2013	A711	20h multi	.25 .25
2014	A711	30h multi	.25 .25
2015	A711	40h multi	.30 .25
2016	A711	60h multi	.30 .25
2017	A711	80h multi	.60 .25
	Nos. 2013-2017 (5)		1.70 1.25

Bratislava BIB 75 biennial exhibition of illustrations for children's books.
Nos. 2013-2017 issued in sheets of 25 stamps and 15 labels with designs and inscriptions in various languages. Value, set with attached labels, $2.

Strakonice, 1951 — A712

Designs: Motorcycles.

1975, Sept. 29 — Perf. 11½

2018	A712	20h shown	.25 .25
2019	A712	40h Jawa 250, 1945	.25 .25
2020	A712	60h Jawa 175, 1935	.25 .25
2021	A712	1k ITAR, 1921	.25 .25
2022	A712	1.20k ORION, 1903	.25 .25
2023	A712	1.80k Laurin & Klement, 1898	1.40 .40
	Nos. 2018-2023 (6)		2.65 1.65

Study of Shortwave Solar Radiation A713

Soyuz-Apollo Link-up in Space — A714

60h, Study of aurora borealis & Oréol satellite. 1k, Study of ionosphere & cosmic radiation. 2k, Copernicus, radio map of the sun & satellite.

1975, Sept. 30

2024	A713	30h multi	.25 .25
2025	A713	60h yel, rose red & vio	.25 .25
2026	A713	1k bl, yel & vio	.25 .25
2027	A713	2k red, vio & yel	.35 .25

Engr.
2028	A714	5k vio & multi	2.00 1.50
	Nos. 2024-2028 (5)		3.10 2.50

International cooperation in space research. No. 2028 issued in sheets of 4. Value $15. The design of No. 2026 appears to be inverted.

Slovnaft, Petrochemical Plant — A715

Designs: 60h, Atomic power station. 1k, Construction of Prague subway. 1.20k, Construction of Friendship pipeline. 1.40k, Combine harvesters. 1.60k, Apartment house construction.

Engraved and Photogravure
1975, Oct. 28

2029	A715	30h multi	.25 .25
2030	A715	60h multi	.25 .25
2031	A715	1k multi	.25 .25
2032	A715	1.20k multi	.25 .25
2033	A715	1.40k multi	.25 .25
2034	A715	1.60k multi	.75 .30
	Nos. 2029-2034 (6)		2.00 1.55

Socialist construction, 30th anniversary. Nos. 2029-2034 printed se-tenant with labels. Value, set with attached labels, $2.50.

Pres. Gustav Husak — A716

1975, Oct. 28 — Engr.

2035	A716	30h ultra	.25 .25
2036	A716	60h rose red	.25 .25

Prague Castle Art Type of 1971

3k, Gold earring, 9th cent. 3.60k, Arms of Premysl Dynasty & Bohemia from lid of leather case containing Bohemian crown, 14th cent.

1975, Oct. 29

2040	A634	3k blk, grn, pur & gold	.95 .50
2041	A634	3.60k red & multi	2.00 1.60

Nos. 2040-2041 each issued in sheets of 4. Value $12.50.

Miniature Sheet

Ludvik Svoboda, Map of Journey from Buzuluk to Prague, Carnations — A717

1975, Nov. 25

2042	A717	10k multi	9.00 7.00

Pres. Ludvik Svoboda, 80th birthday. Exists imperf. Value, $40 unused, $25 used.

Painting Type of 1967

Paintings: 1k, "May 1975" (Woman and doves for 30th anniv. of peace), by Zdenek Sklenar. 1.40k, Woman in national costume, by Eugen Nevan. 1.80k, "Liberation of Prague," by Alena Cermakova, horiz. 2.40k, "Fire 1938" (woman raising fist), by Josef Capek. 3.40k, Old Prague, 1828, by Vincenc Morstadt.

1975, Nov. 27   Engr.   Perf. 11½
2043 A565   1k blk, buff & brn   .30   .25
2044 A565   1.40k multi   .55   .25
2045 A565   1.80k multi   .55   .30
2046 A565   2.40k multi   1.50   .75
2047 A565   3.40k multi   1.50   1.25
     Nos. 2043-2047 (5)   4.40   2.80

Nos. 2043-2047 were each issued in sheets of 4. Value, set $20.

Carrier
Pigeon
A718

Engraved and Photogravure
1975, Dec. 18   Perf. 11½
2048 A718   1k red & multi   .30   .25

Stamp Day 1975.

Frantisek Halas
A719

Wilhelm
Pieck
A720

Frantisek
Lexa
A721

Jindrich
Jindrich
A722

Ivan Krasko — A723

1976, Feb. 25   Perf. 11½
2049 A719   60h multi   .25   .25
2050 A720   60h multi   .25   .25
2051 A721   60h multi   .25   .25
2052 A722   60h multi   .25   .25
2053 A723   60h multi   .25   .25
     Nos. 2049-2053 (5)   1.25   1.25

Halas (1901-49), poet; Pieck (1876-1960), pres. of German Democratic Republic; Lexa (1876-1960), professor of Egyptology; Jindrich (1876-1967), composer and writer; Krasko (1876-1958), Slovak poet.
No. 2051 printed in sheets of 10, others in sheets of 50. Value, No. 2051 sheet, $4.

Ski Jump,
Olympic
Emblem
A724

Winter Olympic Games Emblem and: 1.40k, Figure skating, women's. 1.60k, Ice hockey.

1976, Mar. 22   Perf. 12x11½
2054 A724   1k gold & multi   .25   .25
2055 A724   1.40k gold & multi   .25   .25
2056 A724   1.60k gold & multi   1.00   .30
     Nos. 2054-2056 (3)   1.50   .80

12th Winter Olympic Games, Innsbruck, Austria, Feb. 4-15.

Javelin and
Olympic
Rings
A725

1976, Mar. 22   Perf. 11½
2057 A725   2k shown   .30   .25
2058 A725   3k Relay race   .45   .25
2059 A725   3.60k Shot put   1.40   .90
     Nos. 2057-2059 (3)   2.15   1.40

21st Olympic Games, Montreal, Canada, July 17-Aug. 1.

Table Tennis — A726

1976, Mar. 22   Perf. 11x12
2060 A726   1k multi   .30   .25

European Table Tennis Championship, Prague, Mar. 26-Apr. 4.

Symbolic of
Communist
Party
A727

Worker,
Derrick,
Emblem
A728

1976, Apr. 12   Perf. 11x12
2061 A727   30h gold & multi   .25   .25
2062 A728   60h gold & multi   .25   .25

15th Congress of the Communist Party of Czechoslovakia.

Radio Prague
Orchestra
A729

Dancer,
Violin, Tragic
Mask
A730

Actors
A731

Folk Dancers
A732

Film Festival — A733

1976, Apr. 26   Perf. 11½
2063 A729   20h gold & multi   .25   .25
2064 A730   20h pink & multi   .25   .25
2065 A731   20h lt bl & multi   .25   .25
2066 A732   30h blk & multi   .25   .25
2067 A733   30h vio bl, rose & grn   .25   .25
     Nos. 2063-2067 (5)   1.25   1.25

Czechoslovak Radio Symphony Orchestra, Prague, 50th anniv. (No. 2063); Academy of Music and Dramatic Art, Prague, 50th anniv. (No. 2064); Nova Scena Theater Co., Bratislava, 30th anniv. (No. 2065); Intl. Folk Song and Dance Festival, Straznice, 30th anniv. (No. 2066); 20th Intl. Film Festival, Karlovy Vary (No. 2067).

Hammer and Sickle
A734   A735

Design: 6k, Hammer and sickle, horiz.

1976, May 14
2068 A734   30h gold, red & dk bl   .25   .25

2069 A735   60h gold, red & dp car   .25   .25

Souvenir Sheet
2070 A735   6k red & multi   2.00   2.00

Czechoslovak Communist Party, 55th anniv. No. 2070 contains a 50x30mm stamp.

Ships in Storm, by
Frans Huys (1522-
1562) — A736

Old Engravings of Ships: 60h, by Václav Hollar (1607-77). 1k, by Regnier Nooms Zeeman (1623-68). 2k, by Francois Chereau (1680-1729).

Engraved and Photogravure
1976, July 21   Perf. 11x11½
2071 A736   40h buff & blk   .25   .25
2072 A736   60h gray, buff & blk   .25   .25
2073 A736   1k lt grn, buff & blk   .25   .25
2074 A736   2k lt bl, buff & blk   1.40   .25
     Nos. 2071-2074 (4)   2.15   1.00

"UNESCO" — A737

1976, July 30   Perf. 11½
2075 A737   2k gray & multi   .35   .30

30th anniversary of UNESCO. Issued in sheets of 10. Value $5.

Souvenir Sheet

Hands Holding Infant, Globe and
Dove — A738

1976, July 30
2076 A738   Sheet of 2   4.00   3.50
     a.   6k multi   2.50   2.00

European Security and Cooperation Conference, Helsinki, Finland, 2nd anniv.

Merino Ram — A739

Designs: 40h, Bern-Hana milk cow. 1.60k, Kladruby stallion Generalissimus XXVII.

1976, Aug. 28   Perf. 11½x12
2077 A739   30h multi   .25   .25
2078 A739   40h multi   .25   .25
2079 A739   1.60k multi   .35   .25
     Nos. 2077-2079 (3)   .85   .75

Bountiful Earth Exhibition, Ceske Budejovice, Aug. 28-Sept. 12.

Couple Smoking,
WHO Emblem and
Skull — A740

1976, Sept. 7   Perf. 12x11½
2080 A740   2k multi   .60   .30

Fight against smoking, WHO drive against drug addiction.
Printed in sheets of 10 (2x5) with WHO emblems and inscription in margin. Value $10.

Prague Castle Art Type of 1971

Designs: 3k, View of Prague Castle, by F. Hoogenberghe, 1572. 3.60k, Faun and Satyr, sculptured panel, 16th century.

1976, Oct. 22   Engr.   Perf. 11½
2081 A634   3k multi   2.50   2.10
2082 A634   3.60k multi   .90   .60

Nos. 2081-2082 were each issued in sheets of 4. Value $15.

Guernica 1937, by
Imro Weiner-
Kral — A741

1976, Oct. 22
2083 A741   5k multi   .80   .40

40th anniv. of the Intl. Brigade in Spain.

Zebras — A742

20h, Elephants. 30h, Cheetah. 40h, Giraffes. 60h, Rhinoceros. 3k, Bongos.

Engraved and Photogravure
1976, Nov. 3   Perf. 11½x11, 11x11½
2084 A742   10h multi   .25   .25
2085 A742   20h multi, vert.   .25   .25
2086 A742   30h multi   .30   .25
2087 A742   40h multi, vert.   .45   .25
2088 A742   60h multi   .45   .25
2089 A742   3k multi, vert.   2.00   .25
     Nos. 2084-2089 (6)   3.70   1.50

African animals in Dvur Kralove Zoo.

Painting Type of 1967

Paintings of Flowers: 1k, by Peter Matejka. 1.40k, by Cyril Bouda. 2k, by Jan Brueghel. 3.60k, J. Rudolf Bys.

1976, Nov. 27   Engr.   Perf. 11½
2090 A565   1k multi   .75   .50
2091 A565   1.40k multi   1.50   .90
2092 A565   2k multi   1.20   .90
2093 A565   3.60k multi   .80   .40
     Nos. 2090-2093 (4)   4.25   2.70

Nos. 2090-2093 were each issued in sheets of 4, with emblem and name of Praga 1978 on horizontal gutter. Value, set $17.50.

Postrider, 17th Century, and Satellites
A743

1976, Dec. 18   Engr. & Photo.
2094 A743   1k multi   .25   .25

Stamp Day 1976.

Ice Hockey — A744

1977, Feb. 11   *Perf. 11½*
2095 A744 60h shown .25 .25
2096 A744 1k Biathlon .25 .25
2097 A744 1.60k Ski jump .85 .25
2098 A744 2k Downhill skiing .25 .25
Nos. 2095-2098 (4) 1.60 1.00

6th Winter Spartakiad of Socialist Countries' Armies.

Arms of Vranov — A745

Coats of Arms of Czechoslovak towns.

1977, Feb. 20
2099 A745 60h shown .25 .25
2100 A745 60h Kralupy nad
Vltavou .25 .25
2101 A745 60h Jicin .25 .25
2102 A745 60h Valasske Mezirici .25 .25
Nos. 2099-2102 (4) 1.00 1.00

See Nos. 2297-2300.

Window, Michna Palace — A746

Prague Renaissance Windows: 30h, Michna Palace. 40h, Thun Palace. 60h, Archbishop's Palace, Hradcany. 5k, St. Nicholas Church.

1977, Mar. 10
2103 A746 20h multi .25 .25
2104 A746 30h multi .25 .25
2105 A746 40h multi .25 .25
2106 A746 60h multi .25 .25
2107 A746 5k multi 1.50 .25
Nos. 2103-2107 (5) 2.50 1.25

PRAGA 1978 International Philatelic Exhibition, Prague, Sept. 8-17, 1978.

Children, Auxiliary Police — A747

1977, Apr. 21   *Perf. 11½*
2108 A747 60h multi .25 .25

Auxiliary Police, 25th anniversary.

Warsaw, Polish Flag, Bicyclists — A748

Designs: 60h, Berlin, DDR flag, bicyclists. 1k, Prague, Czechoslovakian flag, victorious bicyclist. 1.40k, Bicyclists on highways, modern views of Berlin, Prague and Warsaw.

1977, May 7
2109 A748 30h multi .25 .25
2110 A748 60h multi .25 .25
2111 A748 1k multi .60 .25
2112 A748 1.40k multi .40 .25
Nos. 2109-2112 (4) 1.50 1.00

30th International Bicycle Peace Race Warsaw-Prague-Berlin.

Congress Emblem — A749

1977, May 25   *Perf. 11½*
2113 A749 30h car, red & gold .25 .25

9th Trade Union Congress, Prague 1977.

Prague Castle Art Type of 1971

Designs: 3k, Onyx footed bowl, 1350. 3.60k, Bronze horse, 1619.

1977, June 7   Engr.
2114 A634 3k multi 1.25 1.10
2115 A634 3.60k multi 1.10 1.10

Nos. 2114-2115 were each issued in sheets of 4. Value, set $11.

French Postrider, 19th Century, PRAGA '78 Emblem A750

Postal Uniforms: 1k, Austrian, 1838. 2k, Austrian, late 18th century. 3.60k, Germany, early 18th century.

1977, June 8   Engr. & Photo.
2116 A750 60h multi .25 .25
2117 A750 1k multi .25 .25
2118 A750 2k multi .40 .25
2119 A750 3.60k multi 1.50 .35
Nos. 2116-2119 (4) 2.40 1.10

PRAGA 1978 International Philatelic Exhibition, Prague, Sept. 8-17, 1978.
Nos. 2116-2119 were each issued both in sheets of 50 and in sheets of 4 stamps with 4 inscribed labels and 2 blank labels. Value, set of sheets of 4, $10.

Coffeepots, Porcelain Mark — A751

Czechoslovak Porcelain and Porcelain Marks: 30h, Urn. 40h, Vase. 60h, Cup and saucer, jugs. 1k, Candlestick and plate. 3k, Cup and saucer, coffeepot.

1977, June 15
2120 A751 20h multi .25 .25
2121 A751 30h multi .25 .25
2122 A751 40h multi .25 .25
2123 A751 60h multi .25 .25
2124 A751 1k multi .25 .25
2125 A751 3k multi 1.10 .35
Nos. 2120-2125 (6) 2.35 1.60

Mlada Boleslav Costume — A752

PRAGA Emblem and Folk Costumes from: 1.60k, Vazek. 3.60k, Zavadka. 5k, Belkovice.

1977, Aug. 31   Engr.   *Perf. 11½*
2126 A752 1k multi 1.25 .95
2127 A752 1.60k multi 1.25 .95
2128 A752 3.60k multi 1.25 .95
2129 A752 5k multi 1.25 .95
Nos. 2126-2129 (4) 5.00 3.80

Issued in sheets of 10 and in sheets of 8 plus 2 labels showing PRAGA '78 emblem. Value, set: sheets of 10 $50; sheets of 8 $40.

Old Woman, Devil and Spinner, by Viera Bombova A753

Book Illustrations: 60h, Bear and tiger, by Genadij Pavlisin. 1k, Coach drawn by 4 horses (Hans Christian Andersen), by Ulf Lovgren. 2k, Bear and flamingos (Lewis Carroll), by Nicole Claveloux. 3k, King with keys, and toys, by Jiri Trnka.

1977, Sept. 9   Engr. & Photo.
2130 A753 40h multi .25 .25
2131 A753 60h multi .25 .25
2132 A753 1k multi .25 .25
2133 A753 2k multi .25 .25
2134 A753 3k multi 1.00 .35
Nos. 2130-2134 (5) 2.00 1.35

Prize-winning designs, 6th biennial exhibition of illustrations for children's books, Bratislava.

Globe, Violin, Doves, View of Prague — A754

1977, Sept. 28   *Perf. 11½*
2135 A754 60h multi .25 .25

Congress of International Music Council of UNESCO, Prague and Bratislava.

Souvenir Sheets

"For a Europe of Peace" — A755

1.60k, "For a Europe of Cooperation." 2.40k, "For a Europe of Social Progress."

1977, Oct. 3
2136 A755 Sheet of 2 .50 .50
   a. 60h multi .25 .25
2137 A755 Sheet of 2 1.00 1.00
   a. 1.60k multi .25 .25
2138 A755 Sheet of 2 2.00 1.75
   a. 2.40k multi .50 .50

2nd European Security and Cooperation Conference, Belgrade. Nos. 2136-2138 each contain 2 stamps and 2 blue on buff inscriptions and ornaments.
Nos. 2136-2138 were issued imperforate in sheets of 2. Value, $30.
For overprint of No. 2137, see No. 2334.

S. P. Korolev, Sputnik I Emblem — A756

30h, Yuri A. Gagarin & Vostok I. 40h, Alexei Leonov. 1k, Neil A. Armstrong & footprint on moon. 1.60k, Construction of orbital space station.

1977, Oct. 4
2139 A756 20h multi .25 .25
2140 A756 30h multi .25 .25
2141 A756 40h multi .25 .25
2142 A756 1k multi .25 .25
2143 A756 1.60k multi .60 .25
Nos. 2139-2143 (5) 1.60 1.25

Space research, 20th anniv. of 1st earth satellite.

Sailors, Cruiser Aurora — A757

1977, Nov. 7
2144 A757 30h multi .25 .25

60th anniv. of Russian October Revolution.

"Russia," Arms of USSR, Kremlin — A758

1977, Nov. 7
2145 A758 30h multi .25 .25

55th anniversary of the USSR.

"Science" — A759

1977, Nov. 17
2146 A759 3k multi .50 .25

Czechoslovak Academy of Science, 25th anniversary.

Painting Type of 1967

Paintings: 2k, "Fear" (woman), by Jan Mudroch. 2.40k, Jan Francisci, portrait by Peter M. Bohun. 2.60k, Vaclav Hollar, self-portrait, 1647. 3k, Young Woman, 1528, by Lucas Cranach. 5k, Cleopatra, by Rubens.

1977, Nov. 27   Engr.   *Perf. 11½*
2147 A565 2k multi .75 .45
2148 A565 2.40k multi 1.20 .90
2149 A565 2.60k multi 1.20 .90
2150 A565 3k multi .75 .60
2151 A565 5k multi 1.50 1.50
Nos. 2147-2151 (5) 5.40 4.35

Nos. 2147-2151 were each issued in sheets of 4. Value, set $25.

View of Bratislava, by Georg Hoefnagel A760

Design: 3.60k, Arms of Bratislava, 1436.

1977, Dec. 6
2152 A760 3k multi 1.90 1.60
2153 A760 3.60k multi .80 .50

Nos. 2152-21531 were each issued in sheets of 4. Value, set $12.50.
See Nos. 2174-2175, 2270-2271, 2331-2332, 2364-2365, 2422-2423, 2478-2479, 2514-2515, 2570-2571, 2618-2619.

Stamp Pattern and Post Horn A761

1977, Dec. 18   Engr. & Photo.
2154 A761 1k multi .25 .25

Stamp Day.

Zdenek
Nejedly
A762

Karl Marx
A763

1978, Feb. 10   *Perf. 11½*
2155 A762 30h multi   .25 .25
2156 A763 40h multi   .25 .25

Zdenek Nejedly (1878-1962), musicologist and historian; Karl Marx (1818-1883), political philosopher.

Civilians
Greeting
Guardsmen
A764

Intellectual,
Farm Woman
and Steel
Worker,
Flag — A765

1978, Feb. 25
2157 A764 1k gold & multi   .25 .25
2158 A765 1k gold & multi   .25 .25

30th anniv. of "Victorious February" (No. 2157), and Natl. Front (No. 2158).

An imperforate sheet of four of No. 2157 was sold with an admission ticket to PRAGA 78 international philatelic exhibition. Value, $4. See note after 2190.

Yuri A. Gagarin,
Vostok I — A766

Design: 30h, 3.60k, like No. 2140.

Engraved; Overprint Photogravure
(Blue and carmine on 30h, green
and lilac rose on 3.60k)
1978, Mar. 2   *Perf. 11½x12*
2159 A766 30h dk red   .25 .25
2160 A766 3.60k vio bl   2.40 2.40

Capt. V. Remek, 1st Czechoslovakian cosmonaut on Russian spaceship Soyuz 28, Mar. 2-9.

10k Coin, 1964, and
25k Coin, 1965 — A767

40h, Medal for Culture, 1972. 1.40k, Charles University medal, 1948. 3k, Ferdinand I medal, 1568. 5k, Gold florin, 1335.

1978, Mar. 14   **Engr. & Photo.**
2161 A767 20h sil & multi   .25 .25
2162 A767 40h sil & multi   .25 .25
2163 A767 1.40k gold & multi   1.00 .25
2164 A767 3k gold & multi   .35 .25
2165 A767 5k gold & multi   .35 .25
   Nos. 2161-2165 (5)   2.20 1.25

650th anniversary of Kremnica Mint.

Tire Tracks and
Ball — A768

1978, Mar. 15
2166 A768 60h multi   .25 .25

Road safety.

Congress
Emblem — A769

1978, Apr. 16   *Perf. 11½*
2167 A769 1k multi   .25 .25

9th World Trade Union Cong., Prague 1978.

Shot Put and Praha
'78 Emblem — A770

1k, Pole vault. 3.60k, Women runners.

1978, Apr. 26
2168 A770   40h multi   .30 .30
2169 A770   1k multi   .40 .30
2170 A770   3.60k multi   .90 .50
   Nos. 2168-2170 (3)   1.60 1.10

5th European Athletic Championships, Prague 1978.

Ice Hockey
A771

Designs: 30h, Hockey. 2k, Ice hockey play.

1978, Apr. 26
2171 A771 30h multi   .25 .25
2172 A771 60h multi   .35 .25
2173 A771 2k multi   .35 .25
   Nos. 2171-2173 (3)   .95 .75

5th European Ice Hockey Championships and 70th anniversary of Bandy hockey.

Bratislava Type of 1977

Designs: 3k, Bratislava, 1955, by Orest Dubay. 3.60k, Fishpound Square, Bratislava, 1955, by Imro Weiner-Kral.

1978, May 9   **Engr.**   *Perf. 11½*
2174 A760 3k multi   .95 .80
2175 A760 3.60k multi   1.25 .80

Nos. 2174-2175 were each issued in sheets of 4. Value, set $10.

Prague Castle Art Type of 1971

3k, King Ottokar II, detail from tomb. 3.60k, Charles IV, detail from votive panel by Jan Ocka.

1978, May 9
2176 A634 3k multi   .75 .60
2177 A634 3.60k multi   3.50 2.40

Nos. 2176-2177 were each issued in sheets of 4. Value, set $18.

Ministry of Post,
Prague — A772

Engraved and Photogravure
1978, May 29   *Perf. 12x11½*
2178 A772 60h multi   .25 .25

14th session of permanent COMECOM Commission (Ministers of Post and Telecommunications of Socialist Countries).

Palacky
Bridge — A773

Prague Bridges and PRAGA '78 Emblem: 40h, Railroad bridge. 1k, Bridge of May 1. 2k, Manes Bridge. 3k, Svatopluk Cech Bridge. 5.40k, Charles Bridge.

1978, May 30
2179 A773   20h blk & multi   .25 .25
2180 A773   40h blk & multi   .25 .25
2181 A773   1k blk & multi   .25 .25
2182 A773   2k blk & multi   .25 .25
2183 A773   3k blk & multi   .30 .25
2184 A773   5.40k blk & multi   1.40 .25
   Nos. 2179-2184 (6)   2.70 1.50

PRAGA 1978 International Philatelic Exhibition, Prague, Sept. 8-17.

St. Peter and
Apostles, Clock
Tower, and
Emblem — A774

Town Hall Clock, Prague, by Josef Manes, and PRAGA '78 Emblem: 1k, Astronomical clock. 2k, Prague's coat of arms. 3k, Grape harvest (September). 3.60k, Libra. 10k, Arms surrounded by zodiac signs and scenes symbolic of 12 months, horiz. 2k, 3k, 3.60k show details from design of 10k.

1978, June 20   *Perf. 11½x11*
2185 A774   40h multi   .25 .25
2186 A774   1k multi   .25 .25
2187 A774   2k multi   .25 .25
2188 A774   3k multi   1.50 .35
2189 A774   3.60k multi   .55 .25
   Nos. 2185-2189 (5)   2.80 1.35

Souvenir Sheet
Perf. 12x12
2190 A774   10k multi   10.00 7.50

PRAGA '78 Intl. Philatelic Exhibition, Prague, Sept. 8-17. No. 2190 contains one 50x40mm stamp. Sheet exists imperf. Value $27.50.

A non-valid souvenir sheet contains 4 imperf. examples of No. 2157. Sold only with PRAGA ticket.

Folk Dancers — A775

1978, July 7   *Perf. 11½x12*
2191 A775 30h multi   .25 .25

25th Folklore Festival, Vychodna.

Overpass and
PRAGA
Emblem
A776

1k, 2k, Modern office buildings, diff. 6k, Old & new Prague. 20k, Charles Bridge & Old Town, by Vincent Morstadt, 1828.

1978   *Perf. 12x11½*
2192 A776 60h blk & multi   .25 .25
2193 A776 1k blk & multi   .25 .25
2194 A776 2k blk & multi   .25 .25
2195 A776 6k blk & multi   1.50 .75
   Nos. 2192-2195 (4)   2.25 1.50

Souvenir Sheet
Engr.
2196 A776 20k multi   9.50 7.50

PRAGA 1978 Intl. Phil. Exhib., Prague, Sept. 8-17. No. 2196 also for 60th anniv. of

Czechoslovak postage stamps. No. 2196 contains one 61x45mm stamp.
   Issued: Nos. 2192-2195, 9/8; No. 2196, 9/10.

Souvenir Sheet

Titian (1488-1576), Venetian
painter — A777

No. 2197a, Apollo's Companion, by Titian. No. 2197b, King Midas. Stamps show details from "Apollo Flaying Marsya" by Titian.

1978, Sept. 12   *Perf. 11½*
2197 A777   Sheet of 2   11.00 8.75
   a.   10k multi   5.00 4.25
   b.   10k multi   5.00 4.25

No. 2197 with dark blue marginal inscription "FIP" was sold only with entrance ticket to PRAGA Philatelic Exhibition. Value $25.

Exhibition
Hall — A778

Engraved and Photogravure
1978, Sept. 13   *Perf. 11½x11*
2198 A778 30h multi   .25 .25

22nd International Engineering Fair, Brno.

Postal Newspaper
Service — A779

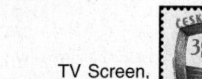

TV Screen,
Headquarters and
Logo — A780

Newspaper,
Microphone — A781

1978, Sept. 21   *Perf. 11½*
2199 A779 30h multi   .25 .25
2200 A780 30h multi   .25 .25
2201 A781 30h multi   .25 .25
   Nos. 2199-2201 (3)   .75 .75

Postal News Service, 25th anniv.; Czechoslovakian television, 25th anniv.; Press, Broadcasting and Television Day.

Sulky
Race — A782

Pardubice Steeplechase: 10h, Falling horses and jockeys at fence. 30h, Race. 40h, Horses passing post. 1.60k, Hurdling. 4.40k, Winner.

1978, Oct. 6   *Perf. 12x11½*
2202 A782 10h multi   .25 .25
2203 A782 20h multi   .25 .25
2204 A782 30h multi   .25 .25
2205 A782 40h multi   .25 .25

CZECHOSLOVAKIA

61

2206 A782 1.60k multi .25 .25
2207 A782 4.40k multi 1.25 .25
   Nos. 2202-2207 (6) 2.50 1.50

Woman Holding Arms of Czechoslovakia A783

1978, Oct. 28 Perf. 11½
2208 A783 60h multi .25 .25

60th anniversary of independence.

Art Type of 1974

2.40k, Flowers, by Jakub Bohdan (1660-1724). 3k, The Dream of Salas, by Ludovit Fulla, horiz. 3.60k, Apostle with Censer, Master of the Spissko Capitals (c. 1480-90).

1978, Nov. 27 Engr.
2209 A700 2.40k multi .90 .45
2210 A700 3k multi 1.00 .75
2211 A700 3.60k multi 2.75 2.25
   Nos. 2209-2211 (3) 4.65 3.45

Slovak National Gallery, 30th anniversary. Nos. 2209-2211 were each issued in sheets of 4. Value, set $20.

Musicians, by Jan Könyves — A784

Slovak Ceramics: 30h, Janosik on Horseback, by Jozef Franko. 40h, Woman in Folk Costume by Michal Polasko. 1k, Three Girls Singing, by Ignac Bizmayer. 1.60k, Janosik Dancing, by Ferdis Kostka.

Engraved and Photogravure
1978, Dec. 5 Perf. 11½x12
2212 A784 20h multi .25 .25
2213 A784 30h multi .25 .25
2214 A784 40h multi .25 .25
2215 A784 1k multi .25 .25
2216 A784 1.60k multi .60 .25
   Nos. 2212-2216 (5) 1.60 1.25

Alfons Mucha and his Design for 1918 Issue A785

1978, Dec. 18 Perf. 11½
2217 A785 1k multi .25 .25

60th Stamp Day.

COMECON Building, Moscow — A786

1979, Jan. 1 Perf. 11½
2218 A786 1k multi .25 .25

Council for Mutual Economic Aid (COMECON), 30th anniversary.

Woman's Head and Grain — A787   **Woman, Workers, Child, Doves — A788**

1979, Jan. 1
2219 A787 30h multi .25 .25
2220 A788 60h multi .25 .25

United Agricultural Production Assoc., 30th anniv. (30h); Czechoslovakian Federation, 10th anniv. (60h).

Soyuz 28, Rockets and Capsule A789

60h, Astronauts Aleksei Gubarev and Vladimir Remek on launching pad, vert. 1.60k, Soviet astronauts J. Romanenko and G. Grecko, Salyut 6 and recovery ship. 2k, Salyut-Soyuz orbital complex, post office in space and Czechoslovakia No. 2153. 4k, Soyuz 28, crew after landing and trajectory map, vert. 10k, Gubarev and Remek, Intercosmos emblem, arms of Czechoslovakia and USSR.

1979, Mar. 2
2221 A789 30h multi .25 .25
2222 A789 60h multi .25 .25
2223 A789 1.60k multi .25 .25
2224 A789 2k multi 1.40 .25
2225 A789 4k multi .60 .25
   Nos. 2221-2225 (5) 2.75 1.25

Souvenir Sheet
2226 A789 10k multi 4.50 2.75

1st anniv. of joint Czechoslovak-Soviet space flight. Size of No. 2226: 76x93mm (stamp 39x55mm). No. 2226 has Cyrillic inscription, No. 2455a does not. No. 2226 exists imperf. Value, $30.

Alpine Bellflowers — A790

Mountain Flowers: 20h, Crocus. 30h, Pinks. 40h, Alpine hawkweed. 3k, Larkspur.

1979, Mar. 23 Perf. 11½
2227 A790 10h multi .25 .25
2228 A790 20h multi .25 .25
2229 A790 30h multi .25 .25
2230 A790 40h multi .25 .25
Perf. 14
2231 A790 3k multi 1.10 .25
   Nos. 2227-2231 (5) 2.10 1.25

Mountain Rescue Service, 25th anniversary. The 3k exists perf. 11½. Value, $20 unused, $10 used. The 3k was issued in sheets of 10. Values: perf 14 (No. 2231), $25; perf 11½, $180.

Stylized Satellite, Dial, Tape — A791

1979, Apr. 2
2232 A791 10h multi .25 .25

Telecommunications research, 30th anniv.

Artist and Model, Dove, Bratislava Castle A792

Cog Wheels, Transformer and Student A793

Musical Instruments, Bratislava Castle — A794

Pioneer Scarf, IYC Emblem A795

Red Star, Man, Child and Doves A796

1979, Apr. 2
2233 A792 20h multi .25 .25
2234 A793 20h multi .25 .25
2235 A794 30h multi .25 .25
2236 A795 30h multi .25 .25
2237 A796 60h multi .25 .25
   Nos. 2233-2237 (5) 1.25 1.25

Fine Arts Academy, Bratislava, 30th anniv.; Slovak Technical University, 40th anniv.; Radio Symphony Orchestra, Bratislava, 30th anniv.; Young Pioneers, 30th anniv. and IYC; Peace Movement, 30th anniversary.

Prague Castle Art Type of 1971

3k, Burial crown of King Ottokar II. 3.60k, Portrait of Mrs. Reitmayer, by Karel Purkyne.

1979, May 9 Perf. 11½
2238 A634 3k multi 1.75 1.10
2239 A634 3.60k multi 1.75 .80

Nos. 2238-2239 were each issued in sheets of 4. Value, set $13.50.

Arms of Vlachovo Brezi, 1538 — A797

Animals in Heraldry: 60h, Jesenik, 1509 (bear and eagle). 1.20k, Vysoke Myto, 1471 (St. George slaying dragon). 1.80k, Martin, 1854 (St. Martin giving coat to beggar). 2k, Zebrak, 1674 (mythological beast).

1979, May 25 Perf. 11½x12
2240 A797 30h multi .25 .25
2241 A797 60h multi .25 .25
2242 A797 1.20k multi .25 .25
2243 A797 1.80k multi 1.00 .25
2244 A797 2k multi .60 .25
   Nos. 2240-2244 (5) 2.35 1.25

Forest, Thriving and Destroyed — A798

Designs: 1.80k, Water. 3.60k, City. 4k, Cattle. All designs show good and bad environment, separated by exclamation point; Man and Biosphere emblem.

1979, June 22 Engr. Perf. 11½
2245 A798 60h multi .25 .25
2246 A798 1.80k multi .25 .25
2247 A798 3.60k multi 1.60 .60
2248 A798 4k multi 1.10 .25
   Nos. 2245-2248 (4) 3.20 1.35

Man and Biosphere Program of UNESCO. Nos. 2245-2248 were each issued in sheets of 10. Value, set $32.50.

Refinery, Smokestacks — A799

Engraved and Photogravure
1979, Aug. 29 Perf. 11x11½
2249 A799 30h multi .25 .25

Slovak National Uprising, 35th anniversary.

Frog and Goat — A800

Book Illustrations (IYC Emblem and): 40h, Knight on horseback. 60h, Maidens. 1k, Boy with sled following rooster. 3k, King riding flying beast.

1979, Apr. 2 Perf. 11½x11
2250 A800 20h multi .25 .25
2251 A800 40h multi .25 .25
2252 A800 60h multi .25 .25
2253 A800 1k multi .25 .25
2254 A800 3k multi 1.10 .25
   Nos. 2250-2254 (5) 2.10 1.25

Prize-winning designs, 7th biennial exhibition of illustrations for children's books, Bratislava; International Year of the Child. Printed with labels showing story characters. Value, set with attached labels, $2.75.

"Bone Shaker" Bicycles, 1870 — A801

Bicycles from: 20h, 1978. 40h, 1910. 60h, 1886. 3.60k, 1820.

1979, Sept. 14 Perf. 12x11½
2255 A801 20h multi .25 .25
2256 A801 40h multi .25 .25
2257 A801 60h multi .25 .25
2258 A801 2k multi .25 .25
2259 A801 3.60k multi 1.50 .30
   Nos. 2255-2259 (5) 2.50 1.30

Bracket Clock, 18th Century — A802

Designs: 18th century clocks.

1979, Oct. 1 Perf. 11½
2260 A802 30h multi .25 .25
2261 A802 60h multi .25 .25
2262 A802 80h multi 1.25 .25
2263 A802 1k multi .25 .25
2264 A802 2k multi .35 .25
   Nos. 2260-2264 (5) 2.35 1.25

Painting Type of 1967

Paintings: 1.60k, Sunday by the River, by Alois Moravec. 2k, Self-portrait, by Gustav Mally. 3k, Self-portrait, by Ilia Yefimovic Repin. 3.60k, Horseback Rider, by Jan Bauch. 5k, Dancing Peasants, by Albrecht Dürer.

1979, Nov. 27 Engr. Perf. 12
2265 A565 1.60k multi .40 .35
2266 A565 2k multi .60 .50
2267 A565 3k multi .60 .50
2268 A565 3.60k multi 2.00 1.75
2269 A565 5k multi 1.60 1.25
   Nos. 2265-2269 (5) 5.20 4.35

Nos. 2265-2269 were each issued in sheets of 4. Value, set $20.

Bratislava Type of 1977

Designs: 3k, Bratislava Castle on the Danube, by L. Janscha, 1787. 3.60k, Bratislava Castle, stone engraving by Wolf, 1815.

1979, Dec. 5
2270 A760 3k multi 1.00 .80
2271 A760 3.60k multi 1.75 1.50

Nos. 2270-2272 were each issued in sheets of 4. Value, set $12.50.

Stamp Day A803

Engraved and Photogravure
1979, Dec. 18 Perf. 11½x12
2272 A803 1k multi .25 .25

Electronic
Circuits — A804

Designs: 50h, Satellite dish. 2k, Airplane. 3k, Computer punch tape.

1979-80		**Photo.**	**Perf. 11½x12**	
Coil Stamps				
2273	A804	50h red	.25	.25
2274	A804	1k brown	.25	.25
2275	A804	2k green ('80)	.30	.25
2276	A804	3k lake ('80)	.45	.25
	Nos. 2273-2276 (4)		1.25	1.00

The 1k comes in two shades.

Runners and
Dove — A805

Engraved and Photogravure

| **1980, Jan. 29** | | | **Perf. 12x11½** | |
| 2289 | A805 | 50h multi | .25 | .25 |

50th Intl. Peace Marathon, Kosice, Oct. 4.

Downhill Skiing — A806

1980, Jan. 29			**Perf. 11½x12**	
2290	A806	1k shown	.30	.25
2291	A806	2k Speed skating	.95	.35
2292	A806	3k Four-man bobsled	.80	.35
	Nos. 2290-2292 (3)		2.05	.95

13th Winter Olympic Games, Lake Placid, NY, Feb. 12-24.

Basketball
A807

1980, Jan. 29			**Perf. 11½**	
2293	A807	40h shown	.25	.25
2294	A807	1k Swimming	.25	.25
2295	A807	2k Hurdles	1.50	.35
2296	A807	3.60k Fencing	1.10	.30
	Nos. 2293-2296 (4)		3.10	1.15

22nd Olympic Games, Moscow, 7/19-8/3.

Arms Type of 1977

No. 2297, Bystrice Nad Pernstejnem. No. 2298, Kunstat. No. 2299, Rozmital Pod Tremsinem. No. 2300, Zlata Idka.

1980, Feb. 20			**Perf. 11½**	
2297	A745	50h multi	.25	.25
2298	A745	50h multi	.25	.25
2299	A745	50h multi	.25	.25
2300	A745	50h multi	.25	.25
	Nos. 2297-2300 (4)		1.00	1.00

Theatrical
Mask
A808

Slovak National
Theater, Actors
A809

1980, Mar. 1				
2301	A808	50h multi	.25	.25
2302	A809	1k multi	.25	.25

50th Jiraskuv Hronov Theatrical Ensemble Review; Slovak National Theater, Bratislava, 60th anniversary.

Mouse in Space,
Satellite — A810

Intercosmos: 1k, Weather map, satellite. 1.60k, Intersputnik television transmission. 4k, Camera, satellite. 5k, Czech satellite station, 1978, horiz. 10k, Intercosmos emblem, horiz.

1980, Apr. 12		**Perf. 11½x12, 12x11½**		
2303	A810	50h multi	.25	.25
2304	A810	1k multi	.25	.25
2305	A810	1.60k multi	1.40	.25
2306	A810	4k multi	1.00	.25
2307	A810	5k multi	1.40	.25
	Nos. 2303-2307 (5)		4.30	1.25

Souvenir Sheet

| 2308 | A810 | 10k multi | 3.50 | 2.50 |

Intercosmos cooperative space program. No. 2305 was issued in a sheet of 10. Value, $25.
No. 2308 exists imperf. Value, $30.

Police Corps Banner,
Emblem — A811

| **1980, Apr. 17** | | | **Perf. 11½** | |
| 2309 | A811 | 50h multi | .25 | .25 |

National Police Corps, 35th anniversary.

Lenin's 110th Birth
Anniversary — A812

Design: No. 2311, Engels's 160th birth anniv.

1980, Apr. 22				
2310	A812	1k tan & brn	.25	.25
2311	A812	1k lt grn & brn	.25	.25

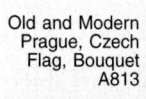
Old and Modern
Prague, Czech
Flag, Bouquet
A813

Boy Writing
"Peace" — A814

Pact Members'
Flags,
Dove — A815

Czech and
Soviet Arms,
Prague and
Moscow
Views — A816

1980, May 6			**Perf. 12x11½**	
2312	A813	50h multi	.25	.25
2313	A814	1k multi	.25	.25
2314	A815	1k multi	.25	.25
2315	A816	1k multi	.25	.25
	Nos. 2312-2315 (4)		1.00	1.00

Liberation by Soviet army, 35th anniv.; Soviet victory in WWII, 35th anniv.; Signing of Warsaw Pact (Bulgaria, Czechoslovakia, German Democratic Rep., Hungary, Poland, Romania, USSR), 25th anniv.; Czechoslovak-Soviet Treaty of Friendship, Cooperation and Mutual Aid, 10th anniv.

Souvenir Sheet

UN, 35th Anniv. — A817

1980, June 3		**Engr.**	**Perf. 12**	
2316	A817	Sheet of 2	3.25	2.50
a.		4k multicolored	1.25	1.25

Athletes Parading Banners in Strahov
Stadium, Prague, Spartakiad
Emblem — A818

Engraved and Photogravure

1980, June 3			**Perf. 12x11½**	
2317	A818	50h shown	.25	.25
2318	A818	1k Gymnast, vert.	.25	.25

Spartakiad 1980, Prague, June 26-29.

Aechmea
Fasciata — A819

Flowers: 50ch, Gerbera Jamesonii. 1k, Aechmea fasciata. 2k, Strelitzia reginae. 4k, Paphiopedilum.

1980, Aug. 13			**Perf. 12**	
2319	A819	50h multicolored	.45	.25
2320	A819	1k multicolored	2.10	.65
2321	A819	2k multicolored	.55	.25
2322	A819	4k multicolored	2.25	.65
	Nos. 2319-2322 (4)		5.35	1.40

Olomouc and Bratislava Flower Shows. Nos. 2319-2322 were each issued in sheets of 10. Values, set: unused, $65; used, $30.

A820

Designs: Folktale character embroideries.

1980, Sept. 24			**Perf. 11½x12**	
2323	A820	50h Chad girl	.25	.25
2324	A820	1k Punch and dog	.25	.25
2325	A820	2k Dandy and Posy	.35	.25
2326	A820	4k Lion and moon	1.30	.75
2327	A820	5k Wallachian dance	.65	.25
	Nos. 2323-2327 (5)		2.80	1.75

National
Census — A821

| **1980, Sept. 24** | | | **Perf. 12x11½** | |
| 2328 | A821 | 1k multi | .25 | .25 |

Prague Castle Type of 1971

Designs: 3k, Old Palace gateway. 4k, Armorial lion, 16th century.

1980, Oct. 28			**Perf. 12**	
2329	A634	3k multi	1.60	1.25
2330	A634	4k multi	1.10	.65

Nos. 2329-2330 were each issued in sheets of 4. Value, set: unused, $12; used, $9.

Bratislava Type of 1977

3k, View across the Danube, by J. Eder, 1810. 4k, The Old Royal Bridge, by J.A. Lantz, 1820.

1980, Oct. 28				
2331	A760	3k multi	1.60	1.40
2332	A760	4k multi	1.25	.80

Nos. 2331-2332 were each issued in sheets of 4. Value, set $16.

10th Anniversary of
Socialist Youth
Federation — A822

| **1980, Nov. 9** | | | **Perf. 12x11½** | |
| 2333 | A822 | 50h multi | .25 | .25 |

**No. 2137 Overprinted 3. /
MEZINARODNI VELETRH ZNAMEK /
ESSEN '80 in Red**

| **1980, Nov. 18** | | | | |
| 2334 | A755 | 1.60k multi | 18.00 | 10.00 |

Czechoslovak Day/ ESSEN '80, 3rd International Stamp Exhibition, No. 2334 has overprinted red marginal inscription.

Painting Type of 1967

Designs: 1k, Pavel Jozef Safarik, by Jozef B. Klemens. 2k, Peasant Revolt mosaic, Anna Podzemna. 3k, St. Lucia, 14th century statue. 4k, Waste Heaps, by Jan Zrzavy, horiz. 5k, Labor, sculpture by Jan Stursa.

1980, Nov. 27		**Engr.**	**Perf. 12**	
2335	A565	1k multi	1.25	1.10
2336	A565	2k multi	1.25	1.10
2337	A565	3k multi	.65	.65
2338	A565	4k multi	.75	.55
2339	A565	5k multi	.75	.55
	Nos. 2335-2339 (5)		4.65	3.75

Nos. 2335-2339 were each issued in sheets of 4. Value, set $27.

Stamp
Day — A823

Engraved and Photogravure

| **1980, Dec. 18** | | | **Perf. 11½x12** | |
| 2340 | A823 | 1k multi | .25 | .25 |

7th Five-year Plan,
1981-1985 — A824

| **1981, Jan. 1** | | | **Perf. 11½** | |
| 2341 | A824 | 50h multi | .25 | .25 |

International Year of
the Disabled — A825

| **1981, Feb. 24** | | | | |
| 2342 | A825 | 1k multi | .25 | .25 |

Landau,
1800 — A826

1k, Mail coach, 1830. 3.60k, Mail sled, 1840. 5k, 4-horse mail coach, 1860. 7k, Open carriage, 1840.

1981, Feb. 25			**Perf. 12x11½**	
2343	A826	50h shown	.25	.25
2344	A826	1k multi	.25	.25
2345	A826	3.60k multi	1.00	.35
2346	A826	5k multi	.75	.45

2347	A826	7k multi	1.10 .75
a.		Sheet of 4	15.00 10.00

Nos. 2343-2347 (5) 3.35 1.85

WIPA '81 Intl. Philatelic Exhibition, Vienna, Austria, May 22-31. No. 2347a issued May 10.

Wolfgang Amadeus Mozart — A827

Famous Men: No. 2348, Josef Hlavka (1831-1908). No. 2349, Juraj Hronec (1881-1959). No. 2350, Jan Sverma (1901-44). No. 2351, Mikulas Schneider-Trnavsky (1881-1958). No. 2352, B. Bolzano (1781-1848). No. 2353, Dimitri Shostakovich, composer. No. 2354, George Bernard Shaw, playwright. No. 2355, Wolfgang Amadeus Mozart.

1981, Mar. 10   *Perf. 11½*

2348	A827	50h multi	.25 .25
2349	A827	50h multi	.25 .25
2350	A827	50h multi	.25 .25
2351	A827	50h multi	.25 .25
2352	A827	1k multi	.45 .25
2353	A827	1k multi	.25 .25
2354	A827	1k multi	.25 .25
2355	A827	1k multi	.25 .25

Nos. 2348-2355 (8) 2.20 2.00

Souvenir Sheet

Yuri Gagarin — A828

1981, Apr. 5   *Perf. 12*

2356	A828	Sheet of 2	4.50 4.00
a.		6k multicolored	2.00 1.60

20th anniv. of 1st manned space flight.

Workers and Banner — A829

1k, Hands holding banner. 4k, Worker holding banner, vert.

1981, Apr. 6   *Perf. 12x11½*

2357	A829	50h shown	.25 .25
2358	A829	1k multi	.25 .25
2359	A829	4k multi	.35 .25

Nos. 2357-2359 (3) .85 .75

Czechoslovakian Communist Party, 60th anniv.

Congress Emblem, View of Prague — A830

1981, Apr. 6

2360	A830	50h shown	.25 .25
2361	A830	1k Bratislava	.25 .25

16th Communist Party Congress.

Agriculture Museum, 90th Anniv. — A831

1981, May 14   *Perf. 11½x12*

2362	A831	1k multi	.25 .25

Natl. Assembly Elections — A832

1981, June 1

2363	A832	50h multi	.25 .25

Bratislava Type of 1977

Designs: 3k, Bratislava Castle, by G.B. Probst, 1760. 4k, Grassalkovic Palace, by C. Bschor, 1815.

1981, June 10   *Perf. 12*

2364	A760	3k multi	1.40 1.25
2365	A760	4k multi	1.00 .75

Nos. 2364-2365 were each issued in sheets of 4. Value, set: unused, $12; used, $9.

Uran and Red October (Health) Resorts — A833

Successes of Socialist Achievements Exhibition: 1k, Brno-Bratislava Highway, Jihlava. 2k, Nuclear power station, Jaslovske Bohunice.

1981, June 10   *Perf. 12x11½*

2366	A833	80h multi	.25 .25
2367	A833	1k multi	.25 .25
2368	A833	2k multi	.25 .25

Nos. 2366-2368 (3) .75 .75

Border Defense Units, 30th Anniv. A834   **Civil Defense, 30th Anniv. A835**

Union for Cooperation with the Army (SVAZARM), 30th Anniv. — A836   **Intl. Youth Character Building Contest, Rysy Mtn., 25th Anniv. — A837**

Engraved and Photogravure

1981, July 11   *Perf. 11½*

2369	A834	40h multi	.25 .25
2370	A835	50h multi	.25 .25
2371	A836	1k multi	.25 .25
2372	A837	3.60k multi	.75 .30

Nos. 2369-2372 (4) 1.50 1.05

30th Natl. Festival of Amateur Puppet Ensembles — A838

1981, July 2   *Perf. 11½*

2373	A838	2k Punch and Devil	.50 .25

Souvenir Sheet

Guernica, by Pablo Picasso — A839

1981, July 2   Engr.   *Perf. 11½x12*

2374	A839	10k multi	3.50 2.50

Picasso's birth centenary; 45th anniv. of Intl. Brigades in Spain.

Cat Holding Flower, by Etienne Delessert — A840

8th Biennial Exhibition of Children's Book Illustrations (Designs by): 50h, Albin Brunovsky, vert. 1k, Adolf Born. 2k, Vive Tolli. 10k, Suekichi Akaba.

Engraved and Photogravure

1981, Sept. 5   *Perf. 11½*

2375	A840	50h multi	.25 .25
2376	A840	1k multi	.25 .25
2377	A840	2k multi	.25 .25
2378	A840	4k multi	.55 .25
2379	A840	10k multi	1.50 .25

Nos. 2375-2379 (5) 2.80 1.25

Prague Zoo, 50th Anniv. A841

1981, Sept. 28   *Perf. 11½x12*

2380	A841	50h Gorillas	.45 .25
2381	A841	1k Lions	.80 .25
2382	A841	7k Przewalski's horses	2.25 .80

Nos. 2380-2382 (3) 3.50 1.30

Anti-smoking Campaign — A842

1981, Oct. 27   *Perf. 12*

2383	A842	4k multi	.85 .45

No. 2383 was issued in sheets of 10, containing 8 stamps and 2 labels. Values: single with label attached, $1.25; sheet, $9.

Prague Castle Art Type of 1971

Designs: 3k, Carved dragon, Palais Lobkovitz, 16th cent. 4k, St. Vitus Cathedral, by J. Sember and G. Dobler, 19th cent.

1981, Oct. 28

2384	A634	3k multi	.75 .45
2385	A634	4k multi	1.75 1.40

Nos. 2384-2385 were each issued in sheets of 4. Value, set $12.

Painting Type of 1967

Designs: 1k, View of Prague, by Vaclav Hollar (1607-1677). 2k, Czechoslovak Academy medallion, engraved by Otakar Spaniel (1881-1955). 3k, Jihoceska Vysivka, by Zdenek Sklenar (b. 1910). 4k, Still Life, by A.M. Gerasimov (1881-1963). 5k, Standing Woman, by Pablo Picasso (1881-1973).

1981, Nov. 27   Engr.   *Perf. 12*

2386	A565	1k multi	2.10 1.40
2387	A565	2k multi	.55 .30
2388	A565	3k multi	.70 .45
2389	A565	4k multi	.85 .45
2390	A565	5k multi	1.40 1.10

Nos. 2386-2390 (5) 5.60 3.70

Nos. 2386-2390 were each issued in sheets of 4. Value, set $27.50.

Sheets of No. 2390 exist with center gutter inscribed with Philexfrance 82 and FIP emblems. Value, $10.

Stamp Day A843

Engraved and Photogravure

1981, Dec. 18   *Perf. 11½x12*

2391	A843	1k Engraver Edward Karel	.25 .25

Russian Workers' Party, Prague Congress, 70th Anniv. — A844

1982, Jan. 18   *Perf. 12*

2392	A844	2k Lenin	.50 .25
a.		Sheet of 4	4.50 4.00

No. 2392 issued in sheet of 8. Value $10.

1982 World Cup Soccer — A845

Designs: Various soccer players.

1982, Jan. 29   *Perf. 12x11½*

2393	A845	1k multi	.25 .25
2394	A845	3.60k multi	.70 .30
2395	A845	4k multi	1.40 .50

Nos. 2393-2395 (3) 2.35 1.05

10th World Trade Union Congress, Havana — A846

1982, Feb. 10   *Perf. 11½*

2396	A846	1k multi	.25 .25

Arms of Hrob — A847

Arms of various cities: No. 2398, Nove Mesto Nad Metuji. No. 2399, Trencin. No. 2400, Mlada Boleslav.

1982, Feb. 10   *Perf. 12x11½*

2397	A847	50h shown	.25 .25
2398	A847	50h multicolored	.25 .25
2399	A847	50h multicolored	.25 .25
2400	A847	50h multicolored	.25 .25

Nos. 2397-2400 (4) 1.00 1.00

See Nos. 2499-2502, 2542-2544, 2595-2597, 2783-2786.

50th Anniv. of the Great Strike at Most — A848

1982, Mar. 23   *Perf. 11½*

2401	A848	1k multi	.25 .25

60th Intl. Railway Union Congress A849

6k, Steam locomotive, 1922, electric, 1982.

1982, Mar. 23   *Perf. 12x11½*

2402	A849	6k multicolored	3.25 .95

10th Workers' Congress, Prague — A850

1982, Apr. 15

2403	A850	1k multi	.25 .25

George Dimitrov — A851

1982, May 1
2404 A851 50h multi　　　　　　　.25　.25

A852

Engravings: 40h, The Muse Euterpe Playing a Flute, by Crispin de Passe (1565-1637). 50h, The Lute Player, by Jacob de Gheyn (1565-1629). 1k, Woman Flautist, by Adriaen Collaert (1560-1618). 2k, Musicians in a Hostel, by Rembrandt (1606-1669). 3k, Hurdy-gurdy Player, by Jacques Callot (1594-1635).

1982, May 18　　　　　**Perf. 11½x12**
2405 A852 40h multi　　　　　　　.25　.25
2406 A852 50h multi　　　　　　　.25　.25
2407 A852 1k multi　　　　　　　.25　.25
2408 A852 2k multi　　　　　　　.30　.25
2409 A852 3k multi　　　　　　　1.10　.60
　　Nos. 2405-2409 (5)　　　　2.15　1.60

10th Lidice Intl. Children's Drawing Contest — A853

1982, May 18
2410 A853 2k multi　　　　　　　1.25　.90
Issued in sheets of 6 with 3 labels. Value $9.

40th Anniv. of Destruction of Lidice and Lezaky — A854

1982, June 4　　　　　**Perf. 11½**
2411 A854 1k Girl, rose　　　　　.45　.25
2412 A854 1k Hands, barbed
　　　　　wire　　　　　　　　.45　.25

Souvenir Sheet

UN Disarmament Conference — A855

1982, June 4　　　　　**Perf. 12**
2413 A855 Sheet of 2　　　　　9.00　7.00
　a.　6k Woman holding doves　4.00　3.00

Souvenir Sheet

2nd UN Conference on Peaceful Uses of Outer Space, Vienna, Aug. 9-21 — A856

1982, Aug. 9　　　　　**Engr. & Photo.**
2414 A856 Sheet of 2　　　　12.50　9.00
　a.　5k multi　　　　　　　4.50　3.50

Krivoklat Castle — A857

1k, Statues (Krivoklat). 2k, Nitra Castle. 3k, Pottery, lock (Nitra).

1982, Aug. 31　　　　**Perf. 12x11½**
2415 A857 50h shown　　　　　　.25　.25
2416 A857 1k multi　　　　　　　.25　.25
2417 A857 2k multi　　　　　　　.30　.25
2418 A857 3k multi　　　　　　　.40　.35
　a.　Souv. sheet of 4, #2415-2418　2.00　1.60
　　Nos. 2415-2418 (4)　　　　1.20　1.10

50th Anniv. of Zizkov Hill Natl. Monument — A858

1982, Sept. 16
2419 A858 1k multi　　　　　　　.25　.25

Prague Castle Art Type of 1971

Designs: 3k, St. George and the Dragon, 1373. 4k, Tomb of King Vratislav I, 10th cent.

1982, Sept. 28　　　　　**Perf. 12**
2420 A634 3k multi　　　　　　1.60　1.25
2421 A634 4k multi　　　　　　　.85　.85
Nos. 2420-2421 were each issued in sheets of 4. Value, set: unused, $11; used, $10.

Bratislava Type of 1977

Designs: 3k, Paddle steamer, Parnik, 1818. 4k, View from Bridge, 19th cent.

1982, Sept. 29
2422 A760 3k multi　　　　　　1.40　1.00
2423 A760 4k multi　　　　　　1.40　1.00
Nos. 2422-2423 were each issued in sheets of 4. Value, set $15.

European Danube Commission A859

3k, Steamer, Bratislava Bridge. 3.60k, Ferry, Budapest.

1982, Sept. 29　　　　**Perf. 11½x12**
2424 A859 3k multi　　　　　　　.65　.25
　a.　Souvenir sheet of 4　　　4.00　3.00
2425 A859 3.60k multi　　　　　.85　.25
　a.　Souvenir sheet of 4　　　6.00　5.00

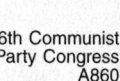

16th Communist Party Congress A860

1982, Oct. 28　　　　**Perf. 12x11½**
2426 A860 20h Agriculture　　　.25　.25
2427 A860 1k Industry　　　　　.25　.25
2428 A860 3k Engineering　　　.25　.25
　　Nos. 2426-2428 (3)　　　　.75　.75

30th Anniv. of Academy of Sciences — A861

1982, Oct. 29　　　　　**Perf. 11½**
2429 A861 6k Emblem　　　　　.90　.35

65th Anniv. of October Revolution A862

Design: 1k, 60th anniv. of USSR.

1982, Nov. 7　　　　**Perf. 12x11½**
2430 A862 50h multi　　　　　　.25　.25
2431 A862 1k multi　　　　　　　.25　.25

Jaroslav Hasek, Writer, Sculpture by Josef Malejovsky — A863

Sculptures: 2k, Jan Zrzavy, painter and graphic artist, by Jan Simota. 4.40k, Leos Janacek, composer, by Milos Axman. 6k, Martin Kukucin, freedom fighter, by Jan Kulich. 7k, Peaceful Work, by Rudolf Pribis.

Engraved and Photogravure

1982, Nov. 26　　　　**Perf. 11½x12**
2432 A863　1k multi　　　　　　.25　.25
2433 A863　2k multi　　　　　　.25　.25
2434 A863 4.40k multi　　　　　.75　.25
2435 A863　6k multi　　　　　　.80　.25
2436 A863　7k multi　　　　　1.20　.50
　　Nos. 2432-2436 (5)　　　　3.25　1.50
Nos. 2432-2436 were each issued in sheets of 4. Value, set $20.

Painting Type of 1967

1k, Revolution in Spain, by Josef Sima (1891-1971). 2k, Woman Dressing, by Rudolf Kremlicka (1886-1932). 3k, The Girl Bride, by Dezider Milly (1906-1971). 4k, Performers, by Jan Zelibsky (b. 1907). 5k, The Complaint of the Birds, by Emil Filla (1882-1953).

1982, Nov. 27　　　　　**Perf. 12**
2437 A565 1k multi　　　　　　.70　.45
2438 A565 2k multi　　　　　1.40　1.00
2439 A565 3k multi　　　　　　.70　.45
2440 A565 4k multi　　　　　　.70　.45
2441 A565 5k multi　　　　　1.40　1.00
　　Nos. 2437-2441 (5)　　　　4.90　3.35
Nos. 2437-2441 were each issued in sheets of 4. Value, set $20.

Stamp Day — A864

1k, Engraver Jaroslav Goldschmied (1890-1977).

1982, Dec. 8　　　　　**Perf. 11½**
2442 A864 1k multicolored　　　.25　.25

A865

1983, Jan. 10　Engr.　Perf. 12x11½
2443 A865 50h dark blue　　　　.25　.25
Pres. Gustav Husak, 70th birthday. See No. 2686.

A866

Designs: 50h, Jaroslav Hasek (1882-1923), writer. 1k, Julius Fucik (1903-1943), antifascist martyr. 2k, Martin Luther (1483-1546). 5k, Johannes Brahms (1833-1897), composer.

1983, Feb. 24　　　　**Engr. & Photo.**
2444 A866 50h multi　　　　　　.25　.25
2445 A866 1k multi　　　　　　.25　.25
2446 A866 2k multi　　　　　　.25　.25
　a.　Souvenir sheet of 4　　24.00　12.50
2447 A866 5k multi　　　　　　.65　.25
　　Nos. 2444-2447 (4)　　　1.40　1.00
Nordposta '83 Intl. Stamp Exhibition, Hamburg.
No. 2446a issued Nov. 1.

Workers Marching A867

Family A868

1983, Feb. 25　　　　　**Perf. 11½**
2448 A867 50h multi　　　　　　.25　.25
2449 A868 1k multi　　　　　　.25　.25
35th anniv. of "Victorious February" (50h), and Natl. Front (1k).

World Communications Year — A869

Perf. 11½, 12x11½ (2k)
1983, Mar. 16
2450 A869　40h multi　　　　　.25　.25
2451 A869　1k multi　　　　　　.25　.25
2452 A869　2k multi　　　　　　.25　.25
2453 A869 3.60k multi　　　　　.40　.25
　　Nos. 2450-2453 (4)　　　1.15　1.00
Various wave patterns. 2k, 40x23mm; 3.60k, 49x19mm.

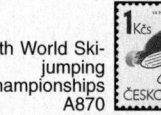

7th World Ski-jumping Championships A870

1983, Mar. 16　　　　　**Perf. 11½**
2454 A870 1k multi　　　　　　.25　.25

Souvenir Sheet

5th Anniv. of Czechoslovak-USSR Intercosmos Cooperative Space Program — A871

1983, Apr. 12　　　　　**Perf. 12**
2455 A871 Sheet of 2　　　　11.00　7.50
　a.　10k multi　　　　　　　3.50　3.50
　　See No. 2226.

Protected Species A872

50h, Butterfly, violets. 1k, Water lilies, frog. 2k, Pine cones, crossbill. 3.60k, Herons. 5k, Gentians, lynx. 7k, Stag.

1983, Apr. 28　　　　**Perf. 12x11½**
2456 A872 50h multi　　　　　　.30　.25
2457 A872 1k multi　　　　　　.65　.25
2458 A872 2k multi　　　　　　.65　.30
2459 A872 3.60k multi　　　　　.80　.35
2460 A872 5k multi　　　　　1.10　.45
2461 A872 7k multi　　　　　2.50　1.00
　　Nos. 2456-2461 (6)　　　6.00　2.60

Soviet Marshals — A873

50h, Ivan S. Konev. 1k, Andrei I. Yeremenko. 2k, Rodion J. Malinovsky.

1983, May 5　　　　　**Perf. 11½**
2462 A873 50h multi　　　　　　.25　.25
2463 A873 1k multi　　　　　　.25　.25
2464 A873 2k multi　　　　　　.25　.25
　　Nos. 2462-2464 (3)　　　　.75　.75
30th anniv. of Czechoslovak-Soviet defense treaty.

A874

1983, July 13 **Perf. 12**
2465 A874 2k multi .35 .25
a. Souvenir sheet of 4 6.50 5.50

World Peace and Life Congress, Prague.
No. 2465 issued in sheets of 8. Value $4.50.

Emperor Rudolf II by
Adrian De Vries
(1560-1626) — A875

Art treasures of the Prague Castle: 5k,
Kinetic relief, Timepiece, Rudolf Svoboda.

1983, Aug. 25 **Perf. 11½**
2466 A875 4k multi .80 .60
2467 A875 5k multi .80 .60

Nos. 2466-2467 were each issued in sheets
of 6. Value, set $12.
See Nos. 2518-2519, 2610-2611, 2654-
2655, 2717-2718, 2744-2745, 2792-2793.

9th Biennial of
Illustrations for
Children and
Youth — A876

Illustrators: 50h, Oleg K. Zotov, USSR. 1k,
Zbigniew Rychlicki, Poland. 4k, Lisbeth
Zwerger, Austria. 7k, Antonio Dominques,
Angola.

1983, Sept. 9 **Engr. & Photo.**
2468 A876 50h multi .25 .25
2469 A876 1k multi .25 .25
2470 A876 4k multi .25 .25
2471 A876 7k multi .50 .25
a. Souv. sheet of 4, #2468-2471 5.00 3.00
Nos. 2468-2471 (4) 1.25 1.00

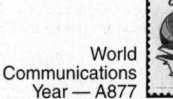

World
Communications
Year — A877

Emblems and aircraft.

1983, Sept. 30 **Perf. 11½**
2472 A877 50h red & black .25 .25
2473 A877 1k red & black, vert. .25 .25
2474 A877 4k red & black .75 .25
Nos. 2472-2474 (3) 1.25 .75

60th anniv. of the Czechoslovak Airlines.

16th Party
Congress
Achievements
A878

1983, Oct. 20 **Perf. 12x11½**
2475 A878 50h Civil engineering
construction .25 .25
2476 A878 1k Chemical industry .25 .25
2477 A878 3k Health services .40 .25
Nos. 2475-2477 (3) .90 .75

Bratislava Type of 1977

Designs: 3k, Two sculptures, Viktor Tilgner
(1844-96). 4k, Mirbachov Palace, 1939, by
Julius Schubert (1888-1947).

1983, Oct. 28 **Perf. 12**
2478 A760 3k multi 1.50 1.25
2479 A760 4k multi 1.25 1.00

Nos. 2478-2479 were each issued in sheets
of 4 stamps. Value $12.

Natl. Theater, Prague,
Centenary — A879

50h, Natl. Theater building. 2k, State Theater, Natl. Theater.

1983, Nov. 8 **Engr.** **Perf. 11½**
2480 A879 50h brown .25 .25
2481 A879 2k green .30 .25

Messenger of
Mourning, by
Mikolas
Ales — A880

Designs: 2k, Genius, theater curtain by
Vojtech Hynais (1854-1925). 3k, Music, Lyric
drawings by Frantisek Zenisek (1849-1916).
4k, Symbolic figure of Prague, by Vaclav
Brozik (1851-1901). 5k, Hradcany Castle, by
Julius Marak (1832-1899).

1983, Nov. 18 **Engr.**
2482 A880 1k multi 1.20 .75
2483 A880 2k multi 1.50 1.10
2484 A880 3k multi .90 .45
2485 A880 4k multi 1.40 .45
2486 A880 5k multi 1.10 .60
Nos. 2482-2486 (5) 6.10 3.35

Nos. 2482-2486 were each issued in sheets
of 4 stamps. Value, set $30.

Warrior with Sword and
Shield, Engraving, 17th
Cent. — A881

Engravings of Costumes: 50h, Bodyguard
of Rudolf II, by Jacob de Gheyn (1565-1629).
1k, Lady with Lace Collar, by Jacques Callot
(1592-1635). 4k, Lady, by Vaclav Hollar (1607-
77). 5k, Man, by Antoine Watteau (1684-
1721).

Engraved and Photogravure
1983, Dec. 2 **Perf. 11½x12**
2487 A881 40h multi .25 .25
2488 A881 50h multi .25 .25
2489 A881 1k multi .25 .25
2490 A881 4k multi .55 .25
2491 A881 5k multi 1.25 .75
Nos. 2487-2491 (5) 2.55 1.75

Stamp Day
A882

1k, Karl Seizinger (1889-1978), #114.

1983, Dec. 18
2492 A882 1k multicolored .25 .25

Czechoslovak
Federation, 15th
Anniv. — A883

50h, Bratislava, Prague Castles.

1984, Jan. 1 **Perf. 11½**
2493 A883 50h multicolored .25 .25

35th Anniv. of
COMECON — A884

1k, Headquarters, Moscow.

1984, Jan. 23
2494 A884 1k dark blue & red
brown .25 .25

1984 Winter
Olympics
A885

1984, Feb. 7 **Perf. 12x11½**
2495 A885 2k Cross-country skiing .40 .25
2496 A885 3k Hockey .50 .25
a. Souvenir sheet of 4 5.00 4.00
2497 A885 5k Biathlon 1.25 .35
Nos. 2495-2497 (3) 2.15 .85

Intl. Olympic Committee, 90th Anniv.
A886

1984, Feb. 7 **Perf. 11½x12**
2498 A886 7k Rings, runners,
torch 1.25 .35

City Arms Type of 1982
1984, Mar. 1 **Perf. 12x11½**
2499 A847 50h Kutna Hora .25 .25
2500 A847 50h Turnov .25 .25
2501 A847 1k Martin .25 .25
2502 A847 1k Milevsko .25 .25
Nos. 2499-2502 (4) 1.00 1.00

Intercosmos Space Program — A887

Various satellites. Nos. 2503-2507 se-tenant with labels showing flags.

1984, Apr. 12 **Perf. 11½x12**
2503 A887 50h multi .30 .25
2504 A887 1k multi .45 .25
2505 A887 2k multi .45 .25
2506 A887 4k multi .75 .25
2507 A887 5k multi .75 .25
Nos. 2503-2507 (5) 2.70 1.25

Resistance
Heroes — A888

Designs: 50h, Vendelin Opatrny (1908-44).
1k, Ladislav Novomesky (1904-76). 2k, Rudolf
Jasiok (1919-44). 4k, Jan Nalepka (1912-43).

1984, May 9 **Perf. 11x11½**
2508 A888 50h multi .25 .25
2509 A888 1k multi .25 .25
2510 A888 2k multi .25 .25
2511 A888 4k multi .25 .25
Nos. 2508-2511 (4) 1.00 1.00

Music Year — A889

1984, May 11 **Perf. 11½**
2512 A889 50h Instruments .25 .25
2513 A889 1k Organ pipes,
vert. .25 .25

Bratislava Type of 1977

Designs: 3k, Vintners' Guild arms, 19th
cent. 4k, View of Bratislava (painting commemorating shooting competition, 1827).

1984, June 1 **Perf. 12**
2514 A760 3k multi 1.10 .85
2515 A760 4k multi 1.60 1.10

Nos. 2514-2515 were each issued in sheets
of 4 stamps. Value $12.

Central
Telecommunications
Building,
Bratislava — A890

1984, June 1 **Perf. 11½**
2516 A890 2k multi .25 .25

A891

1984, June 12 **Perf. 12**
2517 A891 5k UPU emblem,
dove, globe 2.50 2.50

1984 UPU Congress. Issued in sheet of 4
with and without Philatelic Salon text. Values,
$30 with text, $12 without text.

Prague Castle Type of 1983

Designs: 3k, Crowing rooster, St. Vitus
Cathedral, 19th cent. 4k, King David from the
Roundnice, Book of Psalms illuminated manu-
script, Bohemia, 15th cent.

1984, Aug. 9 **Engr. & Photo.**
2518 A875 3k multi .75 .60
2519 A875 4k multi 1.00 .75

Nos. 2518-2519 were each issued in sheets
of 6 stamps. Value, set $10.

Playing Cards — A893

50h, Jack of Spades, 16th cent. 1k, Queen
of spades, 17th cent. 2k, 9 of hearts, 18th
cent. 3k, Jack of clubs, 18th cent. 5k, King of
hearts, 19th cent.

1984, Aug. 28 **Perf. 11½x12**
2520 A893 50h multi .25 .25
2521 A893 1k multi .25 .25
2522 A893 2k multi .25 .25
2523 A893 3k multi .35 .25
2524 A893 5k multi 1.00 .25
Nos. 2520-2524 (5) 2.10 1.25

Slovak Natl.
Uprising, 40th
Anniv. — A894

1984, Aug. 29 **Perf. 12x11½**
2525 A894 50h Family, factories,
flowers .25 .25

Battle of Dukla Pass (Carpathians),
40th Anniv. — A895

1984, Sept. 8 **Perf. 11½x12**
2526 A895 2k Soldiers, flag .40 .25

1984 Summer
Olympics
A896

1984, Sept. 9 **Perf. 12x11½**
2527 A896 1k Pole vault .25 .25
2528 A896 2k Bicycling .40 .25
2529 A896 3k Rowing .60 .35
2530 A896 5k Weight lifting 1.00 .45
a. Souv. sheet of 4, #2527-2530 4.00 3.25
Nos. 2527-2530 (4) 2.25 1.30

16th Party Congress Goals and Projects
A897

1984, Oct. 28   *Perf. 12x11½*
2531 A897 1k Communications .25 .25
2532 A897 2k Transportation .25 .25
2533 A897 3k Transgas pipeline .35 .25
   a. Souvenir sheet of 3 2.00 1.60
   Nos. 2531-2533 (3) .85 .75

Painting Type of 1967

1k, The Milevsky River, by Karel Stehlik (b. 1912). 2k, Under the Trees, by Viktor Barvitius (1834-1902). 3k, Landscape with Flowers, by Zolo Palugyay (1898-1935). 4k, King in Palace, Visehrad Codex miniature, 1085. 5k, View of Kokorin Castles, by Antonin Manes. Nos. 2534-2537 horiz.; issued in sheets of 4.

1984, Nov. 16   *Perf. 11½*
2534 A565 1k multi 1.75 .90
2535 A565 2k multi 1.75 .90
2536 A565 3k multi 1.75 .90
2537 A565 4k multi 2.75 .90
2538 A565 5k multi 3.25 .90
   Nos. 2534-2538 (5) 11.25 4.50

Nos. 2534-2538 were each issued in sheets of 4 stamps. Value, set $45.

Students' Intl., 45th Anniv. — A898

1984, Nov. 17
2539 A898 1k Head, dove .25 .25

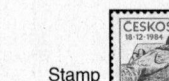

Birth Cent., Antonin Zapotocky — A899

Engr. & Photo.
1984, Dec. 18   *Perf. 11½*
2540 A899 50h multi .25 .25

Stamp Day — A900

1k, Engraver Bohumil Heinz (1894-1940).

1984, Dec. 18   *Perf. 11½x12*
2541 A900 1k multi .25 .25

City Arms Type of 1982
1985, Feb. 5   *Perf. 12x11½*
2542 A847 50h Kamyk nad Vltavou .25 .25
2543 A847 50h Havirov .25 .25
2544 A847 50h Trnava .25 .25
   Nos. 2542-2544 (3) .75 .75

University of Applied Arts, Prague, Centenary — A901

1985, Feb. 6   *Perf. 11½x12*
2545 A901 3k Art and Pleasure, sculpture .40 .25

Trnava University, 350th Anniv. A902

1985, Feb. 6   *Perf. 11½x12*
2546 A902 2k Town of Trnava .40 .25

Military Museum Exposition A903

50h, Armor, crossbow, vert. 1k, Medals, vert. 2k, Biplane, spacecraft.

1985, Feb. 7   *Perf. 11½x12, 12x11½*
2547 A903 50h multi .25 .25
2548 A903 1k multi .25 .25
2549 A903 2k multi .40 .25
   Nos. 2547-2549 (3) .90 .75

Vladimir I. Lenin (1870-1924), 1st Chairman of Russia — A904

1985, Mar. 15   *Engr.*   *Perf. 12*
2550 A904 2k multi .80 .40

No. 2550 printed in sheets of 6 stamps. Value $5.

UN 40th Anniv., Peace Year 1986 — A905

1985, Mar. 15
2551 A905 6k UN, Peace Year emblems 2.75 2.40

Issued in sheets of 4 stamps. Value $12.

Natl. Arms, Twig, Crowd — A906

Engraved and Photogravure
1985, Apr. 5   *Perf. 11½*
2552 A906 4k multicolored .60 .25

Kosice govt. plan, Apr. 5, 1945.

Natl. Arms, Flag, Soldiers — A907

1985, Apr. 5
2553 A907 50h multicolored .25 .25

Natl. Security Forces, 40th anniv.

Halley's Comet, INTERCOSMOS Project Vega — A908

Design: Emblem, space platform, interstellar map, intercept data.

1985, Apr. 12   *Perf. 12x11½*
2554   Sheet of 2 9.00 9.00
   a. A908 5k multicolored 4.00 3.25

Project Vega, a joint effort of the USSR, France, German Democratic Republic, Austria, Poland, Bulgaria and CSSR, was for the geophysical study of Halley's Comet, Dec. 1984-Mar. 1986.

European Ice Hockey Championships, Prague, Apr. 17-May 3 — A909

1985, Apr. 13
2555 A909 1k Hockey players, emblem .25 .25

No. 2555 Ovptd. "CSSR MISTREM SVETA" in Violet Blue
1985, May 31   *Perf. 12x11½*
2556 A909 1k multi 2.00 2.00

Natl. Chess Org., 80th Anniv. — A910

1985, Apr. 13   *Perf. 11½*
2557 A910 6k Emblem, game board, chessmen 1.25 .50

Anniversaries — A911

No. 2558, May Uprising, 1945. No. 2559, Soviet Army in CSSR, 1945. No. 2560, Warsaw Treaty, 1950. No. 2561, Czech-Soviet Treaty, 1970.

1985, May 5   *Perf. 11½x12*
2558 A911 1k multicolored .25 .25
2559 A911 1k multicolored .25 .25
2560 A911 1k multicolored .25 .25
2561 A911 1k multicolored .25 .25
   Nos. 2558-2561 (4) 1.00 1.00

Spartakiad '85, Strahov Stadium, Prague, June 27 — A912

Designs: 50h, Gymnasts warming up with rackets and balls. 1k, Rhythmic gymnastics floor exercise, Prague Castle.

1985, June 3   *Perf. 11½, 11½x12*
2562 A912 50h multi .25 .25

Size: 53x22mm
2563 A912 1k multi .25 .25

WWII Anti-Fascist Political Art — A913

Drawings and caricatures: 50h, Fire, and From the Concentration Camp, by Joseph Capek (1887-1945). 2k, The Conference on Disarmament in Geneva, 1927 and The Prophecy of Three Parrots, 1933, by Frantisek Bidlo (1895-1945). 4k, The Unknown Warrior to Order, 1936, and The Almost Peaceful Dove, 1937, by Antonin Pelc (1895-1967).

1985, June 4   *Perf. 12x11½*
2564 A913 50h multi .25 .25
2565 A913 2k multi .25 .25
2566 A913 4k multi .90 .25
   Nos. 2564-2566 (3) 1.40 .75

Helsinki Conference on European Security and Cooperation, 10th Anniv. — A914

1985, July 1   *Engr. & Photo.*
2567 A914 7k multi 2.25 1.50
   a. Souvenir sheet of 4 9.00 7.00

An imperf. souv. sheet similar to No. 2567a was issued June 1, 1988 for FINLANDIA '88 and PRAGA '88. Value $35.

12th World Youth Festival, Moscow A915

1985, July 2
2568 A915 1k Kremlin, youths .25 .25

A916

1985, Sept. 3   *Perf. 11½*
2569 A916 50h multi .25 .25

Federation of World Trade Unions, 40th anniv.

Bratislava Type of 1977

Designs: 3k, Castle and river, lace embroidery by Elena Holeczyova (1906-1983). 4k, Pottery cups and mugs, 1600-1500 B.C.

1985, Sept. 4   *Engr.*   *Perf. 12*
2570 A760 3k multi 1.60 .45
2571 A760 4k multi 2.10 .60

Nos. 2570-2571 were each issued in sheets of 4 stamps. Value, set $14.

A918

Children's book illustrations: 1k, Rocking Horse, by Kveta Pacovska, USSR. 2k, Fairies, by Gennadij Spirin, USSR. 3k, Butterfly and Girl, by Kaarina Kaila, Finland. 4k, Boy and Animals, by Erick Ingraham, US.

Engraved and Photogravure
1985, Sept. 5   *Perf. 11½*
2572 A918 1k multi .25 .25
2573 A918 2k multi .25 .25
2574 A918 3k multi .70 .25
2575 A918 4k multi .70 .30
   a. Souv. sheet of 4, #2572-2575 4.50 3.00
   Nos. 2572-2575 (4) 1.90 1.05

10th biennial of illustrations.

5-Year Development Plan — A919

50h, Construction machinery. 1k, Prague subway, map. 2k, Modern textile spinning.

1985, Oct. 28   *Perf. 12x11½*
2576 A919 50h multicolored .25 .25
2577 A919 1k multicolored .25 .25
2578 A919 2k multicolored .25 .25
   Nos. 2576-2578 (3) .75 .75

16th Communist Party Congress goals.

Prague Castle — A920

2k, Presidential Palace Gate, 1768. 3k, St. Vitus' Cathedral.

Engr., Engr. & Photo. (3k)
1985, Oct. 28   *Perf. 12*
2579 A920 2k multicolored .40 .40
2580 A920 3k multicolored .50 .50

Nos. 2579-2580 were each issued in sheets of 6 stamps. Value, set $9.

A921

Glassware: 50h, Pitcher, Near East, 4th cent. 1k, Venetian pitcher, 16th cent. 2k, Bohemian goblet, c. 1720. 4k, Harrachov

Bohemian vase, 18th cent. 6k, Jablonec Bohemian vase, c. 1900.

Engraved and Photogravure
1985, Nov. 23   **Perf. 11½x12**
2581	A921	50h multi	.25 .25
2582	A921	1k multi	.25 .25
2583	A921	2k multi	.30 .25
2584	A921	4k multi	.50 .25
2585	A921	6k multi	1.00 .35

Nos. 2581-2585 (5)   2.30 1.35

Arts and Crafts Museum, Prague, cent.

Painting Type of 1967
Designs: 1k, Young Woman in a Blue Gown, by Jozef Ginovsky (1800-1857). 2k, Lenin on the Charles Bridge, Prague, 1952, by Martin Sladky (b. 1920). 3k, Avenue of Poplars, 1935, by Vaclav Rabas (1885-1954). 4k, The Martyrdom of St. Dorothea, 1516, by Hans Baldung Grien (c. 1484-1545). 5k, Portrait of Jasper Schade van Westrum, 1645, by Frans Hals (c. 1581-1666).

1985, Nov. 27   **Engr.**   **Perf. 12**
2586	A565	1k multi	1.60 .80
2587	A565	2k multi	1.10 .35
2588	A565	3k multi	1.50 .35
2589	A565	4k multi	.90 .50
2590	A565	5k multi	.90 .50

Nos. 2586-2590 (5)   6.00 2.50

Nos. 2586-2590 were each issued in sheets of 4 stamps with punched out holes by denomination. Value, set $30.

Bohdan Roule (1921-1960), Engraver — A922

Engraved and Photogravure
1985, Dec. 18   **Perf. 11½x12**
2591 A922 1k multicolored   .25 .25

Stamp Day 1985.

Intl. Peace Year A923

1986, Jan. 2
2592 A923 1k multi   .25 .25

Philharmonic Orchestra, 90th Anniv. — A924

1986, Jan. 2   **Perf. 11½**
2593 A924 1k Victory Statue, Prague   .25 .25

EXPO '86, Vancouver — A925

Design: Z 50 LS monoplane, Cenyerth Prague-Kladno locomotive, Sahara Desert rock drawing, 5th-6th cent. B.C.

1986, Jan. 23   **Perf. 11½**
2594 A925 4k multicolored   .85 .25

City Arms Type of 1982
1986, Feb. 10   **Perf. 12x11½**
Size: 42x54mm
2595	A847	50h Myjava	.25 .25
2596	A847	50h Vodnany	.25 .25
2597	A847	50h Zamberk	.25 .25

Nos. 2595-2597 (3)   .75 .75

17th Natl. Communist Party Congress, Prague, Mar. 24 — A926

1986, Mar. 20   **Perf. 11½**
2598 A926 50h shown   .25 .25
2599 A926 1k Industry   .25 .25

Natl. Communist Party, 65th Anniv. — A927

50h, Star, man, woman. 1k, Hammer, sickle, laborers.

1986, Mar. 20   **Perf. 12x11½**
2600 A927 50h multi   .25 .25
2601 A927 1k multi   .25 .25

Natl. Front Election Program A928

1986, Mar. 28
2602 A928 50h multi   .25 .25

Karlovy Vary Intl. Film Festival, 25th Anniv. — A929

1986, Apr. 3   **Perf. 11½**
2603 A929 1k multi   .25 .25

A930

1986, Apr. 8   **Engr. & Photo.**
2604 A930 1k multi   .25 .25

Spring of Prague Music Festival.

A931

1986, Apr. 25
2605 A931 50h multi   .40 .25

Prague-Moscow air service, 50th anniv.

Intl. Olympic Committee, 90th Anniv. A932

1986, May 12   **Perf. 11½x12**
2606 A932 2k multi   .30 .25

1986 World Cup Soccer Championships, Mexico — A933

1986, May 15   **Perf. 12x11½**
2607 A933 4k multi   .80 .40

Women's World Volleyball Championships, Prague — A934

1986, May 19
2608 A934 1k multi   .25 .25

Souvenir Sheet

Intl. Philatelic Federation, FIP, 60th Anniv. — A935

1986, June 3   **Engr.**   **Perf. 12**
2609 A935 20k multi   6.50 5.00

Exists imperf and with perforations between stamps omitted. Values, $15 and $27.50, respectively.

Prague Castle Type of 1983
Designs: 2k, Jewelled funerary pendant, 9th cent. 3k, Allegory of Blossoms, sculpture by Jaroslav Horejc (1886-1983), St. Vitus' Cathedral.

1986, June 6   **Engr.**   **Perf. 12**
2610 A875 2k multi   .40 .30
2611 A875 3k multi   .70 .45

Nos. 2610-2611 were each issued in sheets of 6 stamps. Value, set $8.

UN Child Survival Campaign — A937

Toys.

Engraved and Photogravure
1986, Sept. 1   **Perf. 11½**
2612	A937	10h Rooster	.25 .25
2613	A937	20h Horse and rider	.25 .25
2614	A937	1k Doll	.25 .25
2615	A937	2k Doll, diff.	.50 .25
2616	A937	3k Tin omnibus, c. 1910	.65 .30

Nos. 2612-2616 (5)   1.90 1.30

UNICEF, 40th anniv.

Registration, Cent. — A938

1986, Sept. 2   **Perf. 11½x12**
2617 A938 4k Label, mail coach   .45 .25

Bratislava Type of 1977
1986, Sept. 11   **Engr.**   **Perf. 12**
2618 A760 3k Sigismund Gate   1.25 .80
2619 A760 4k St. Margaret, bas-relief   1.25 .65

Nos. 2618-2619 were each issued in sheets of 4 stamps. Value, set $12.

Owls — A939

Engraved and Photogravure
1986, Sept. 18   **Perf. 11½**
2620	A939	50h Bubo bubo	.70 .25
2621	A939	2k Asio otus	.85 .25
2622	A939	3k Strix aluco	1.40 .30
2623	A939	4k Tyto alba	1.40 .45
2624	A939	5k Asio flammeus	2.10 .60

Nos. 2620-2624 (5)   6.45 1.85

Souvenir Sheet

Intl. Brigades in Spain — A940

Theater curtain: Woman Savaged by Horses, 1936, by Vladimir Sychra (1903-1963), Natl Gallery, Prague.

1986, Oct. 1   **Engr.**   **Perf. 12**
2625 A940 Sheet of 2   4.50 3.50
a. 5k multi   2.00 1.25

Locomotives and Streetcars A941

Engraved and Photogravure
1986, Oct. 6   **Perf. 12x11½**
2626	A941	50h KT-8	.25 .25
2627	A941	1k E458.1	.25 .25
2628	A941	3k T466.2	.75 .30
2629	A941	5k M152.0	.80 .25

Nos. 2626-2629 (4)   2.05 1.05

Paintings in the Prague and Bratislava Natl. Galleries A942

Designs: 1k, The Circus Rider, 1980, by Jan Bauch (b. 1898). 2k, The Ventriloquist, 1954, by Frantisek Tichy (1896-1961). 3k, In the Circus, 1946, by Vincent Hloznik (b. 1919). 6k, Clown, 1985, by Karel Svolinsky (1896-1986).

1986, Oct. 13   **Engr.**   **Perf. 12**
2630	A942	1k multi	1.25 .65
2631	A942	2k multi	1.60 .85
2632	A942	3k multi	1.60 .85
2633	A942	6k multi	1.10 .95

Nos. 2630-2633 (4)   5.55 3.30

Nos. 2630-2633 were each issued in sheets of 4 stamps. Value, set $25.

Painting Type of 1967
1k, The Czech Lion, May 1918, by Vratislav H. Brunner (1886-1928). 2k, Boy with Mandolin, 1945, by Jozef Sturdik (b. 1920). 3k, Metra Building, 1984, by Frantisek Gross (1909-1985). 4k, Portrait of Maria Maximiliana at Sternberk, 1665, by Karel Skreta (1610-1674). 5k, Adam & Eve, 1538, by Lucas Cranach (1472-1553).

1986, Nov. 3   **Engr.**   **Perf. 12**
2634	A565	1k multi	3.00 2.25
2635	A565	2k multi	3.00 2.25
2636	A565	3k multi	3.00 2.25
2637	A565	4k multi	3.00 2.25
2638	A565	5k multi	3.00 2.25

Nos. 2634-2638 (5)   15.00 11.25

Nos. 2634-2638 were each issued in sheets of 4 stamps. Value, set $75.

Stamp Day A943

Design: V.H. Brunner (1886-1928), stamp designer, and No. 88.

Photo. & Engr.
1986, Dec. 18   **Perf. 11½x12**
2639 A943 1k multicolored   .25 .25

World Cyclocross Championships, Jan. 24-25, Central Bohemia A944

1987, Jan. 22   **Perf. 11½**
2640 A944 6k multi   .80 .25

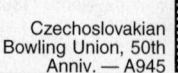

Czechoslovakian
Bowling Union, 50th
Anniv. — A945

1987, Jan. 22   *Perf. 11½*
2641 A945 2k multi   .35   .25

State
Decorations
A946

Designs: 50h, Gold Stars of Socialist Labor and Czechoslovakia. 2k, Order of Klement Gottwald. 3k, Order of the Republic. 4k, Order of Victorious February. 5k, Order of Labor.

1987, Feb. 4   *Perf. 12x11½*
2642 A946 50h multi   .25   .25
2643 A946 2k multi   .25   .25
2644 A946 3k multi   .30   .25
2645 A946 4k multi   .45   .25
2646 A946 5k multi   .60   .40
   Nos. 2642-2646 (5)   1.85 1.40

Butterflies
A947

1k, Limenitis populi. 2k, Smerinthus ocellatus. 3k, Pericallia matronula. 4k, Saturnia pyri.

1987, Mar. 4
2647 A947 1k multi   .65   .25
2648 A947 2k multi   1.00   .25
2649 A947 3k multi   1.25   .35
2650 A947 4k multi   1.60   .35
   Nos. 2647-2650 (4)   4.50 1.20

Natl. Nuclear
Power Industry
A948

1987, Apr. 6
2651 A948 5k multi   .60   .25

11th Revolutionary
Trade Union
Movement Congress,
Apr. 14-17,
Prague — A949

1987, Apr. 7   *Perf. 11½*
2652 A949 1k multi   .25   .25

Souvenir Sheet

INTERCOSMOS, 20th Anniv. — A950

Cosmonauts Alexei Gubarev of the USSR & Vladimir Remek of Czechoslovakia, rocket & emblem.

1987, Apr. 12   **Engr.**   *Perf. 12*
2653 A950 Sheet of 2   6.00 5.00
  a.   10k multi   2.75 1.75
  b.   Souv. sheet of 4, litho. &
      engr., imperf.   9.00 7.00

No. 2653b issued Nov. 15, 1987, and exists in two formats with either exhibition embelm or "Dni Nametove Filatelie" at top.

Prague Castle Type of 1983

Designs: 2k, Three Saints, stained-glass window detail, c. 1870, St. Vitus Cathedral, by Frantisek Sequens (1830-1896). 3k, Coat of Arms, New Land Rolls Hall, 1605.

1987, May 9   *Perf. 11½*
2654 A875 2k multi   .40   .30
2655 A875 3k dk red, slate gray
       & yel org   .60   .45

Nos. 2634-2638 were each issued in sheets of 6 stamps. Value, set $6.

PRAGA
'88 — A951

Photo. & Engr.
1987, May 12   *Perf. 12x11½*
2656 A951 3k Telephone, 1894   .75   .25
2657 A951 3k Postal van, 1924   .75   .30
2658 A951 4k Tender locomotive,
       1907   .75   .30
2659 A951 4k Tram, 1900   .75   .30
2660 A951 5k Steam roller, 1936   .75   .30
   Nos. 2656-2660 (5)   3.75 1.45

Printed in sheets of 8 + 2 labels picturing telephone or vehicles. Value $25.

Nos. 2657-2658 were also printed in sheets of 4 + label picturing vehicles. Value, $30 for both sheets.

Destruction of Lidice
and Lezaky, 45th
Anniv. — A952

Drawings: No. 2661, When the Fighting Ended, 1945, by Pavel Simon. No. 2662, The End of the game, 1945, by Ludmila Jirincova.

1987, June   *Perf. 11½*
2661 A952 1k blk, cerise & vio   .25   .25
2662 A952 1k blk, gold, pale lil &
       cerise   .25   .25

Union of Czechoslovakian
Mathematicians and Physicists, 125th
Anniv. — A953

Designs: No. 2663, Prague Town Hall mathematical clock, Theory of Functions diagram. No. 2664, J.M. Petzval (1807-1891), C. Strouhal (1850-1922) and V. Jarnik (1897-1970). No. 2665, Geographical measurement from A.M. Malletta's book, 1672, earth fold and Brownian motion diagrams.

1987, July 6   *Perf. 11½x12*
2663 A953 50h multi   .25   .25
2664 A953 50h multi   .25   .25
2665 A953 50h multi   .25   .25
   Nos. 2663-2665 (3)   .75   .75

11th Biennial of
Children's Book
Illustration — A954

Award-winning illustrations: 50h, Asun Balzola, Spain. 1k, Frederic Clement, France. 2k, Elzbieta Gaudasinska, Poland. 4k, Marija Lucija Stupica, Yugoslavia.

1987, Sept. 3   *Perf. 11½*
2666 A954 50h multi   .25   .25
2667 A954 1k multi   .25   .25
2668 A954 2k multi   .25   .25
  a.   Souv. sheet of 2 + label   2.00 1.50
2669 A954 4k multi   .55   .35
   Nos. 2666-2669 (4)   1.30 1.10

Sept. 11-Oct. 30, Bratislava.

Eternal Flame,
Flower — A955

1987, Sept. 23
2670 A955 50h multicolored   .25   .25

Theresienstadt Memorial for the victims from 23 European countries who died in the

Small Fortress, Terezin, a Nazi concentration camp.

Socialist
Communications
Organization, 30th
Anniv. — A956

1987, Sept. 23
2671 A956 4k Emblem, satellite,
       dish receiver   .40   .25

Jan Evangelista
Purkyne (1787-1869),
Physiologist — A957

1987, Sept. 30
2672 A957 7k multicolored   .80   .25

Views of
Bratislava
A958

Designs: 3k, Male and female figures supporting an oriel, Arkier Palace, c. 1552. 4k, View of Bratislava from Ware Conterfactur de Stadt Presburg, from an engraving by Hans Mayer, 1563.

1987, Oct. 1   **Engr.**   *Perf. 12*
2673 A958 3k multicolored   .50   .35
2674 A958 4k multicolored   .70   .45

Each printed in sheets of 4 with Bratislava Castle (from Mayer's engraving) between. Value, set $5.

See Nos. 2719-2720, 2763-2764, 2800-2801.

Type of 1974
Photo. & Engr.
1987, Nov. 1   *Perf. 12x11½*
2675 A699 1k Post rider   .25   .25

PRAGA '88, Aug. 26-Sept. 4, 1988. No. 2675 printed se-tenant with label picturing exhibition emblem. Value for single with attached label 40c.

October
Revolution,
Russia, 70th
Anniv. — A959

Establishment
of the Union of
Soviet Socialist
Republics, 65th
Anniv. — A960

1987, Nov. 6   *Perf. 12x11½*
2676 A959 50h multicolored   .25   .25
2677 A960 50h multicolored   .25   .25

Art Type of 1974

Paintings in national galleries: 1k, Enclosure of Dreams, by Kamil Lhotak (b. 1912). 2k, Tulips, by Ester Simerova-Martincekova (b. 1909). 3k, Triptych with Bohemian Landscape, by Josef Lada (1887-1957). 4k, Accordion Player, by Josef Capek (1887-1945). 5k, Self-portrait, by Jiri Trnka (1912-1969).

1987, Nov. 18   **Engr.**   *Perf. 12*
2678 A700 1k multi   3.00   .75
2679 A700 2k multi   3.00 1.60
2680 A700 3k multi   3.00 1.00
2681 A700 4k multi   3.00   .80
2682 A700 5k multi   3.00 1.25
   Nos. 2678-2682 (5)   15.00 5.50

Czech and Slovak art.
Nos. 2678-2682 were each issued in sheets of 4. Value, set $65.

69th Stamp
Day
A961

Portrait of Jacob Obrovsky (1882-1949), stamp designer, Bohemian Lion (Type SP1), sketch of a lion and PRAGA '88 emblem.

Photo. & Engr.
1987, Dec. 18   *Perf. 11½x12*
2683 A961 1k multicolored   .25   .25

No. 2683 printed in sheet of four with eight labels se-tenant with stamps, inscribed "100 Years of the National Philatelic Movement in Czechoslovakia" in Czech. The four labels between the "blocks of six" are blank. Value, sheet $3.

Czechoslovak
Republic, 70th
Anniv. — A962

1k, Woman, natl. arms, linden branch.

1988, Jan. 1   *Perf. 12x11½*
2684 A962 1k multicolored   .25   .25

Natl. Front, 40th
Anniv. — A963

1988, Feb. 25   *Perf. 11½*
2685 A963 50h multicolored   .25   .25

Husak Type of 1983
Photo. & Engr.
1988, Jan. 10   *Perf. 12x11½*
2686 A865 1k brt rose & dk car-
       mine   .25   .25

Olympics
A965

50h, Ski jumping, ice hockey. 1k, Basketball, soccer. 6k, Discus, weight lifting.

1988, Feb. 1   *Perf. 11½x12*
2687 A965 50h multicolored   .25   .25
2688 A965 1k multicolored   .25   .25
2689 A965 6k multicolored   .70   .25
   Nos. 2687-2689 (3)   1.20   .75

Exist in souv. sheets of 2, imperf. between and in souv. sheets of 2, imperf. Value, each set, $16.

Victorious February,
40th Anniv. — A966

Statue of Klement Gottwald by Rudolf Svoboda.

1988, Feb. 25   *Perf. 11½*
2690 A966 50h multicolored   .25   .25

No. 2690 exists in a souvenir sheet of two No. 2690 and two postally invalid imperf impressions of No. 637. Value $5. Sheet exists imperf. Value $9.

Classic
Automobiles
A967

50h, 1914 Laurin & Klement. 1k, 1902 Tatra NW Type B. 2k, 1905 Tatra NW Type E. 3k, 1929 Tatra 12 Normandie. 4k, 1899 Meteor.

1988, Mar. 1   *Perf. 12x11½*
2691 A967 50h multi   .25   .25
2692 A967 1k multi   .25   .25
2693 A967 2k multi   .25   .25
2694 A967 3k multi   .45   .25
2695 A967 4k multi   .75   .25
  a.   Bklt. pane, 2 3k, 3 4k + label   4.00
     Complete booklet, #2695a   5.00
   Nos. 2691-2695 (5)   1.95 1.25

Postal Museum, 70th Anniv. — A968

Praga '88 emblem and: 50h, Postman, Malostranske Namesti Square p.o., Prague, c. 1742, and Velka Javorina television transmitter, 1979. 1k, Telecommunications Center, Mlada Boleslav, 1986, and Carmelite Street p.o., Prague, c. 1792. 2k, Prague 1 (1873) and Bratislava 56 (1984) post offices. 4k, Communications Center, Prachatice (1982), postman and Maltetske Nameski Square p.o., Prague, c. 1622.

1988, Mar. 10

2696	A968	50h multi	.25	.25
2697	A968	1k multi	.25	.25
2698	A968	2k multi	.25	.25
2699	A968	4k multi	.30	.25
a.		Souv. sheet, 2 ea #2698-2699	2.25	1.25
		Nos. 2696-2699 (4)	1.05	1.00

In No. 2699a the top pair of Nos. 2698-2699 is imperf. at top and sides.

A969

1988, Mar. 29   *Perf. 11½*

2700	A969	50h multicolored	.25	.25

Matice Slovenska Cultural Assoc., 125th anniv.

A970

PRAGA '88. (Exhibition emblem and aspects of the Museum of Natl. Literature, Prague): 1k, Gate and distant view of museum. 2k, Celestial globe, illuminated manuscript, bookshelves and ornately decorated ceiling. 5k, Illuminated "B" and decorated binder of a medieval Bible. 7k, Celestial globe, illuminated manuscript, Zodiacal signs (Aries and Leo), view of museum.

1988, May 12   *Photo. & Engr.*

2701	A970	1k multicolored	.30	.25
a.		Souvenir sheet of 4	1.50	1.25
2702	A970	2k multicolored	.55	.25
a.		Souvenir sheet of 4	3.25	2.00
2703	A970	5k multicolored	.80	.30
a.		Souvenir sheet of 4	5.75	4.75
2704	A970	7k multicolored	1.75	.65
a.		Souvenir sheet of 4	11.00	9.00
b.		Souv. sheet of 4, imperf., #2701-2704	3.75	3.00
		Nos. 2701-2704 (4)	3.40	1.45

PRAGA '88 — A971

Exhibition emblem and fountains, Prague.

1988, June 1   *Perf. 11½x12*

2705	A971	1k Waldstein Palace	.30	.25
2706	A971	2k Old town square	.30	.25
2707	A971	3k Charles University	.45	.25
2708	A971	4k Prague Castle	.75	.30
a.		Souv. sheet of 4, #2705-2708	4.00	2.00
		Nos. 2705-2708 (4)	1.80	1.05

Souvenir Sheet

Soviet-US Summit Conference on Arms Reduction, Moscow — A972

Design: The Capitol, Washington, and the Kremlin, Moscow.

1988, June 1   *Perf. 12x11½*

2709	A972	4k blue blk, dark red & gold	2.50	1.50

Exists imperf. Value $7.

PRAGA '88 — A973

Exhibition emblem and modern architecture, Prague: 50h, Trade Unions Central Recreation Center. 1k, Koospol foreign trade company. 2k, Motol Teaching Hospital. 4k, Culture Palace.

1988, July 1   *Perf. 12x11½*

2710	A973	50h multicolored	.25	.25
2711	A973	1k blk, lt blue & bister	.25	.25
2712	A973	2k multicolored	.25	.25
a.		Souv. sheet, 2 1k, 2 2k + 4 labels, imperf.	2.00	1.50
2713	A973	4k multicolored	.25	.25
a.		Souv. sheet, 2 50h, 2 4k + 4 labels, imperf.	2.00	1.50
		Nos. 2710-2713 (4)	1.00	1.00

Souvenir Sheet

PRAGA '88 — A974

Design: Exhibition emblem and Alfons Mucha (1860-1939), designer of first Czech postage stamp.

1988, Aug. 18   *Engr.*   *Perf. 12*

2714	A974	Sheet of 2	5.50	3.25
a.		5k multicolored	2.40	1.25

Czech postage stamps, 70th anniv.

Souvenir Sheets

PRAGA '88 — A975

5k, *Turin, Monte Superga*, by Josef Navratil (1798-1865), Postal Museum, Prague.
Details of *Bacchus and Ariadne*, by Sebastiano Ricci (1659-1734), Natl. Gallery, Prague: No. 2716a, Ariadne. No. 2716b, Bacchus and creatures.

1988

2715	A975	Sheet of 2	5.00	4.00
a.		5k multi	2.50	1.60
2716	A975	Sheet of 2	9.00	6.00
a.-b.		10k any single	4.00	2.40

No. 2716 exists with emblem and inscription "DEN F.I.P. JOURNEE DE LA FEDERATION INTERNATIONALE DE PHILATELIE." Value $12.

Issue dates: 5k, Aug. 19; 10k, Aug. 26.

Prague Castle Type of 1983

2k, Pottery jug, 17th cent. 3k, *St. Catherine with Angel*, 1580, by Paolo Veronese.

1988, Sept. 28   *Engr.*   *Perf. 12*

2717	A875	2k shown	.40	.40
2718	A875	3k multi	.45	.45

Nos. 2717-2718 were each issued in sheets of 6. Value, set $6.

Bratislava Views Type of 1987

3k, *Hlavne Square, circa 1840* an etching by R. Alt-Sandman, 1840. 4k, *Ferdinand House, circa 1850*, a pen-and-ink drawing by V. Reim.

1988, Oct. 19

2719	A958	3k multicolored	.50	.50
2720	A958	4k multicolored	.65	.65

Nos. 2719-2720 were each issued in sheets of 4. Value, set $4.50.

Art Type of 1974

Paintings in natl. galleries: 2k, *With Bundles*, 1931, by Martin Benka (1888-1971). 6k, *Blue Bird*, 1903, by Vojtech Preissig (1873-1944). 7k, *A Jaguar Attacking a Rider*, c. 1850, by Eugene Delacroix (1798-1863).

1988, Nov. 17   *Engr.*   *Perf. 12*

2721	A700	2k multicolored	2.00	1.00
2722	A700	6k multicolored	3.50	1.50
2723	A700	7k multicolored	3.50	1.50
		Nos. 2721-2723 (3)	9.00	4.00

Czech and Slovak art.

Nos. 2721-2723 were each issued in sheets of 4. Value, set $40.

Stamp Day A978

Design: 1k, Jaroslav Benda (1882-1970), illustrator and stamp designer.

1988, Dec. 18   *Photo. & Engr.*   *Perf. 11½x12*

2724	A978	1k multicolored	.25	.25

Paris-Dakar Rally — A979

Trucks: 50h, Earth, Motokov Liaz. 1k, Liaz, globe. 2k, Earth, Motokov Tatra. No. 607. 4k, Map of racecourse, turban, Tatra.

1989, Jan. 2   *Perf. 12x11½*

2725	A979	50h multicolored	.35	.25
2726	A979	1k multicolored	.35	.25
2727	A979	2k multicolored	.45	.25
2728	A979	4k multicolored	.75	.25
		Nos. 2725-2728 (4)	1.90	1.00

Czechoslovakian Federation, 20th Anniv. — A980

1989, Jan. 1

2729	A980	50h multicolored	.25	.25

Jan Botto (1829-1881) A981

Taras Grigorievich Shevchenko (1814-1861) A982

Jean Cocteau (1889-1963) A983

Charlie Chaplin (1889-1977) A984

Jawaharlal Nehru (1889-1964) and "UNESCO" — A985

Famous men: No. 2732, Modest Petrovich Musorgsky (1839-1881).

Photo. & Engr.

1989, Mar. 9   *Perf. 12x11½*

2730	A981	50h brn blk & lt blue green	.25	.25
2731	A982	50h shown	.25	.25
2732	A982	50h multicolored	.25	.25
2733	A983	50h red brn, grnh blk & org brn	.25	.25
2734	A984	50h blk, int blue & dark red	.25	.25
2735	A985	50h brn blk & lt yel green	.25	.25
		Nos. 2730-2735 (6)	1.50	1.50

Shipping Industry — A986

1989, Mar. 27

2736	A986	50h Republika	.25	.25
2737	A986	1k Pionyr, flags	.25	.25
2738	A986	2k Brno, flags	.25	.25
2739	A986	3k Trinec	.35	.25
2740	A986	4k Flags, mast, Orlik	.75	.25
2741	A986	5k Vltava, communication hardware	1.00	.30
		Nos. 2736-2741 (6)	2.85	1.55

Pioneer Organization, 40th Anniv. — A987

Photo. & Engr.

1989, Apr. 20   *Perf. 11½*

2742	A987	50h multi	.25	.25

Art Type of 1974

Details of *Feast of Rose Garlands*, 1506, by Albrecht Durer, Natl. Gallery, Prague: a, Virgin and Child. b, Angel playing mandolin.

1989, Apr. 21   *Engr.*   *Perf. 12*
Miniature Sheet

2743		Sheet of 2	7.50	4.00
a.-b.	A700	10k any single	3.50	2.00

Prague Castle Art Type of 1983

2k, Bas-relief picturing Kaiser Karl IV, from Kralovske tomb by Alexander Colin (c. 1527-1612). 3k, Self-portrait, by V.V. Reiner (1689-1743).

1989, May 9   *Photo. & Engr.*

2744	A875	2k dark red, sepia & buff	.35	.30
2745	A875	3k multi	.50	.40

Nos. 2744-2745 were each issued in sheets of 6. Value, set $6.

Souvenir Sheet

PHILEXFRANCE '89, French Revolution Bicent. — A988

1989, July 14   *Engr.*   *Perf. 12*

2746	A988	5k brt blue, blk & dk red	2.00	1.50

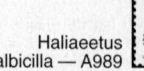

Haliaeetus
albicilla — A989

Photo. & Engr.

1989, July 17 **Perf. 12x11½**
2747 A989 1k multicolored .50 .25

World
Wildlife
Fund
A990

Toads and newts.

1989, July 18 **Perf. 11½x12**
2748 A990 2k Bombina bombina .65 .30
2749 A990 3k Bombina variegata 1.00 .45
2750 A990 4k Triturus alpestris 1.40 .60
2751 A990 5k Triturus mon-
tandoni 1.60 .70
  Nos. 2748-2751 (4) 4.65 2.05

Slovak Folk Art Collective,
40th Anniv. — A991

1989, Aug. 29 **Perf. 12x11½**
2752 A991 50h multicolored .25 .25

Slovak
Uprising,
45th Anniv.
A992

Photo. & Engr.

1989, Aug. 29 **Perf. 11½x12**
2753 A992 1k multicolored .25 .25

A993

Award-winning illustrations: 50h, Hannu
Taina, Finland. 1k, Aleksander Aleksov, Bulga-
ria. 2k, Jurgen Spohn, West Berlin. 4k, Robert
Brun, Czechoslovakia.

1989, Sept. 4 **Perf. 11½**
2754 A993 50h multicolored .25 .25
2755 A993 1k multicolored .25 .25
2756 A993 2k multicolored .25 .25
2757 A993 4k multicolored .60 .25
  a. Souvenir sheet of 2 2.00 .80
  Nos. 2754-2757 (4) 1.35 1.00

12th Biennial of Children's Book Illustration,
Bratislava.

A994

Poisonous mushrooms: 50h, Nolanea
verna. 1k, Amanita phalloides. 2k, Amanita
virosa. 3k, Cortinarius orellanus. 5k, Galerina
marginata.

1989, Sept. 5 **Perf. 11½x12**
2758 A994 50h multicolored .30 .25
2759 A994 1k multicolored .40 .25
2760 A994 2k multicolored .55 .25
2761 A994 3k multicolored .90 .25
2762 A994 5k multicolored 1.00 .25
  Nos. 2758-2762 (5) 3.15 1.25

Nos. 2758-2762 were each issued in sheets
of 10. Value, set $40.

Bratislava Views Type of 1987

Views of Devin, a Slavic castle above the
Danube, Bratislava.

1989, Oct. 16 **Engr.** **Perf. 12**
2763 A958 3k Castle, flower .60 .60
2764 A958 4k Castle, urn .80 .80
  Nos. 2763-2764 were each issued in sheets
of 4. Value, set $6.

Jan Opletal (1915-
39) — A996

Photo. & Engr.

1989, Nov. 17 **Perf. 12x11½**
2765 A996 1k multicolored .25 .25

Intl. Student's Day. Funeral of Opletal, a
Nazi victim, on Nov. 15, 1939, sparked student
demonstrations that resulted in the closing of
all universities in occupied Bohemia and
Moravia.

Art Type of 1974

Paintings in Natl. Galleries: 2k, *Nirvana*, c.
1920, by Anton Jasusch (1882-1965). 4k, *Winter Evening in Town*, c. 1907, by Jakub
Schikaneder (1855-1924), horiz. 5k, *The Bak-
ers*, 1926, by Pravoslav Kotik (1889-1970),
horiz.

1989, Nov. 27 **Engr.** **Perf. 12**
2766 A700 2k multicolored .80 .60
2767 A700 4k multicolored 1.40 1.10
2768 A700 5k multicolored 1.40 1.10
  Nos. 2766-2768 (3) 3.60 2.80

Nos. 2766-2768 were each issued in sheets
of 4. Value, set $15.

Stamp Day
A997

Design: Portrait of Cyril Bouda, stamp
designer, art tools and falcon.

Photo. & Engr.

1989, Dec. 18 **Perf. 11½x12**
2769 A997 1k multicolored .25 .25

A998

Award-winning illustrations

Photo. & Engr.

1990, Jan. 8 **Perf. 11½x12**
2770 A998 50h multicolored .25 .25

UNESCO World Literacy Year. Printed se-
tenant with inscribed label picturing UN and
UNESCO emblems. Value, single with label
attached 75c.

A999

Famous men: No. 2771, Karel Capek,
writer. No. 2772, Thomas G. Masaryk. 1k,
Lenin. 2k, Emile Zola, French writer. 3k, Jaroslav Heyrovsky (1890-1987), chemical physicist. 10k, Bohuslav Martinu (1890-1959),
composer.

1990, Jan. 9 **Perf. 11½**
2771 A999 50h multicolored .25 .25
2772 A999 50h multicolored .25 .25
2773 A999 1k multicolored .25 .25
2774 A999 2k multicolored .30 .25
2775 A999 3k multicolored .50 .30
2776 A999 10k multicolored 1.60 .90
  Nos. 2771-2776 (6) 3.15 2.20

Nos. 2771, 2775-2776 inscribed "UNESCO."

Pres. Vaclav
Havel — A1000

1990, Jan. 9 **Perf. 12x11½**
2777 A1000 50h red, brt vio & bl .30 .25
  See Nos. 2879, 2948.

Handball
Players — A1001

1990, Feb. 1 **Perf. 11½**
2778 A1001 50h multicolored .25 .25

1990 Men's World Handball Championships, Czechoslovakia.

Flora — A1002

Flowers: 50h, Antirrhinum majus. 1k, Zinnia
elegans. 3k, Tigridia pavonia. 5k, Lilium
candidum.

Photo. & Engr.

1990, Mar. 1 **Perf. 11½**
2779 A1002 50h multicolored .55 .25
2780 A1002 1k multicolored .80 .25
2781 A1002 1k multicolored 1.00 .25
  Perf. 12x12½
2782 A1002 5k multicolored 1.40 .60
  Nos. 2779-2782 (4) 3.75 1.35
  No. 2782 was issued in a sheet of 10. Value,
$12.50.

City Arms Type of 1982
Photo. & Engr.

1990, Mar. 28 **Perf. 12x11½**
2783 A847 50h Prostejov .25 .25
2784 A847 50h Bytca .25 .25
2785 A847 50h Sobeslav .25 .25
2786 A847 50h Podebrady .25 .25
  Nos. 2783-2786 (4) 1.00 1.00

A1003

1990, Apr. 16 **Perf. 11½x12**
2787 A1003 1k brn vio, rose &
buff .60 .25
  Visit of Pope John Paul II.

World War II
Liberation — A1004

Photo. & Engr.

1990, May 5 **Perf. 11½**
2788 A1004 1k multicolored .25 .25

Souvenir Sheet

150th
Anniv. of
the
Postage
Stamp
A1005

1990, May 6 **Engr.** **Perf. 12**
2789 A1005 7k multicolored 4.00 1.50
  Stamp World London 90.

A1006

Photo. & Engr.

1990, May 8 **Perf. 11½**
2790 A1006 1k multicolored .60 .25

World Cup Soccer Championships, Italy.

Free
Elections — A1007

1990, June 1
2791 A1007 1k multicolored .60 .25

Prague Castle Type of 1983

2k, Gold and jeweled hand. 3k, King Otakar
II's Seal.

1990, June 6, 1990 **Engr.**
2792 A875 2k multicolored .55 .30
2793 A875 3k multicolored .80 .40

Art treasures of Prague Castle.

Nos. 2792-2793 were each issued in sheets
of 6. Value, set $9.

Helsinki
Conference,
15th
Anniv. — A1008

Photo & Engr.

1990, June 21 **Perf. 12x11½**
2794 A1008 7k multicolored .90 .40

Dr. Milada
Horakova
A1009

1990, June 25 **Perf. 12x11½**
2795 A1009 1k multicolored .30 .25

Intercanis Dog
Show,
Brno — A1010

Designs: 50h, Poodles. 1k, Afghan hound.
Irish wolfhound, greyhound. 4k, Czech terrier,
bloodhound, Hannoverian hound. 7k, Cavalier
King Charles Spaniel, cocker spaniel, American cocker spaniel.

1990, July 2
2796 A1010 50h multicolored .50 .25
2797 A1010 1k multicolored .75 .25
2798 A1010 4k multicolored 1.25 .30
2799 A1010 7k multicolored 1.75 .65
  Nos. 2796-2799 (4) 4.25 1.45

Bratislava Art Type of 1987

1990 **Engr.** **Perf. 12**
2800 A958 3k Ancient Celtic coin .65 .40
2801 A958 4k Gen. Milan
Stefanik .65 .45

Issue dates: 3k, Sept. 29. 4k, July 21.
Nos. 2800-2801 were each issued in sheets
of 4. Value, set $6.

Grand
Pardubice
Steeplechase,
Cent. — A1011

Photo. & Engr.

1990, Sept. 7 **Perf. 12x11½**
2802 A1011 50h multicolored .25 .25
2803 A1011 4k multi, diff. .50 .25

Protected Animals A1012

Litho. & Engr.

1990, Oct. 1   *Perf. 12x11*
2804	A1012	50h	Marmota marmota	1.00 .25
2805	A1012	1k	Felis silvestris	1.00 .25
2806	A1012	4k	Castor fiber	1.75 .30
2807	A1012	5k	Plecotus auritus	1.75 .75
		Nos. 2804-2807 (4)		5.50 1.55

Conf. of Civic Associations, Helsinki A1013

Litho. & Engr.

1990, Oct. 15   *Perf. 12x11½*
2808 A1013 3k blue, gold & yel   .50 .30

Christmas — A1014

Photo. & Engr.

1990, Nov. 15   *Perf. 11½x12*
2809 A1014 50h multicolored   .25 .25

Painting Type of 1967

Works of art: 2k, Krucemburk by Jan Zrzavy (1890-1977), horiz. 3k, St. Agnes of Bohemia from the St. Wenceslas Monument, Prague by Josef V. Myslbek (1848-1922). 4k, The Slavs in their Homeland by Alfons Mucha (1860-1939). 5k, St. John the Baptist by Auguste Rodin (1840-1917).

1990, Nov. 27   Engr.   *Perf. 11½*
2810	A565	2k	multicolored	1.25 .50
2811	A565	3k	multicolored	1.25 .60
2812	A565	4k	multicolored	2.10 .60
2813	A565	5k	multicolored	2.10 .60
		Nos. 2810-2813 (4)		6.70 2.30

Nos. 2810-2813 were each issued in sheets of 4. Value, set $30.

Karel Svolinsky (1896-1986), Vignette from No. 1182 — A1016

1990, Dec. 18   Photo. & Engr.
2814 A1016 1k multicolored   .25 .25

Stamp Day.

A1017

1991, Jan. 10   *Perf. 11½*
2815 A1017 1k multicolored   .30 .25

European Judo Championships, Prague.

A1018

Design: A. B. Svojsik (1876-1938), Czech Scouting Founder.

1991, Jan. 10
2816 A1018 3k multicolored   .75 .30

Scouting in Czechoslovakia, 80th Anniv.

Bethlehem Chapel, Prague, 600th Anniv. — A1019

1991, Feb. 4   *Perf. 12x11½*
2817 A1019 50h multicolored   .25 .25

Wolfgang Amadeus Mozart (1756-1791), Old Theatre A1020

1991, Feb. 4
2818 A1020 1k multicolored   .25 .25

Steamship Bohemia, 150th Anniv. A1021

1991, Feb. 4   *Perf. 11½x12*
2819 A1021 5k multicolored   .85 .30

Famous Men — A1022

Designs: No. 2820, Antonin Dvorak (1841-1904), composer. No. 2821, Andrej Kmet (1841-1908), botanist. No. 2822, Jaroslav Seifert (1901-1986), poet, Nobel laureate for Literature. No. 2823, Jan Masaryk (1886-1948), diplomat. No. 2824, Alois Senefelder (1771-1834), lithographer.

1991, Feb. 18   *Perf. 12x11½*
2820	A1022	1k	multicolored	.25 .25
2821	A1022	1k	multicolored	.25 .25
2822	A1022	1k	multicolored	.25 .25
2823	A1022	1k	multicolored	.25 .25
2824	A1022	1k	multicolored	.25 .25
		Nos. 2820-2824 (5)		1.25 1.25

Nos. 2820-2824 printed with se-tenant labels. See No. 2831.

Europa — A1023

Photo. & Engr.

1991, May 6   *Perf. 11½x12*
2825 A1023 6k blk, bl & red   2.00 .60

A1024

Photo. & Engr.

1991, May 10   *Perf. 11½x12*
2826 A1024 1k multicolored   .25 .25

General Exhibition in Prague, cent.

Antarctic Treaty, 30th Anniv. — A1025

1991, May 20   *Perf. 12x11½*
2827 A1025 8k multicolored   1.75 .60

Castles — A1026

1991, June 3   *Perf. 11½*
2828	A1026	50h	Blatna	.25 .25
2829	A1026	1k	Bouzov	.40 .25
2830	A1026	3k	Kezmarok	.60 .25
		Nos. 2828-2830 (3)		1.25 .75

Famous Men Type

Design: Jan Palach (1948-1969), Student.

Photo. & Engr.

1991, Aug. 9   *Perf. 12x11½*
2831 A1022 4k black   2.00 .30

Printed se-tenant with label.

Scenic Views — A1027

Photo. & Engr.

1991, Aug. 28   *Perf. 11½*
2832	A1027	4k	Krivan mountains	1.00 .60
2833	A1027	4k	Rip mountain	1.00 .60

A1028

Illustrations by: 1k, Binette Schroeder, Germany. 2k, Stasys Eidrigevicius, Poland.

Photo. & Engr.

1991, Sept. 2   *Perf. 11½*
2834	A1028	1k	multicolored	.25 .25
2835	A1028	2k	multicolored	.35 .25

13th Biennial Exhibition of Children's Book Illustrators, Bratislava.

A1029

Design: Father Andrej Hlinka (1864-1938), Slovak nationalist.

1991, Sept. 27   Engr.   *Perf. 11½*
2836 A1029 10k blue black   1.40 .30

Art of Prague and Bratislava — A1030

Designs: No. 2837, Holy Infant of Prague. No. 2838, Blue Church of Bratislava.

1991, Sept. 30
2837	A1030	3k	multicolored	1.25 .50
2838	A1030	3k	multicolored	1.25 .50

Nos. 2837-2838 were each issued in sheets of 8. Value, set $15.

Flowers — A1031

1k, Gagea bohemica. 2k, Aster alpinus. 5k, Fritillaria meleagris. 11k, Daphne cneorum.

Photo. & Engr.

1991, Nov. 3   *Perf. 12x11½*
2839	A1031	1k	multicolored	.60 .25
2840	A1031	2k	multicolored	.85 .25
2841	A1031	5k	multicolored	1.25 .30
2842	A1031	11k	multicolored	2.50 .45
		Nos. 2839-2842 (4)		5.20 1.25

Painting Type of 1967

Paintings: 2k, Everyday Homelife by Max Ernst. 3k, Lovers by Auguste Renoir. 4k, Head of Christ by El Greco. 5k, Coincidence by Ladislav Guderna. 7k, Two Maidens by Utamaro.

1991, Nov. 3   Engr.   *Perf. 11½*
2843	A565	2k	multicolored	1.25 .60
2844	A565	3k	multicolored	1.25 .60
2845	A565	4k	multicolored	1.25 .75
2846	A565	5k	multicolored	1.75 1.25
2847	A565	7k	multicolored	1.75 1.25
		Nos. 2843-2847 (5)		7.25 4.45

Nos. 2843-2847 were each issued in sheets of 4. Value, set $30.

Christmas — A1033

1991, Nov. 19
2848 A1033 50h multicolored   .30 .25

Stamp Day A1034

Martin Benka (1888-1971), stamp engraver.

Photo. & Engr.

1991, Dec. 18   *Perf. 11½x12*
2849 A1034 2k multicolored   .45 .25

1992 Winter Olympics, Albertville — A1035

1992, Jan. 6   *Perf. 11½*
2850 A1035 1k Biathlon   .25 .25

Photo. & Engr.

1992, May 21   *Perf. 11½*
2851 A1035 2k Tennis   .30 .25

1992 Summer Olympics, Barcelona.

Souvenir Sheet

Jan Amos Komensky (Comenius), Educator — A1036

1992, Mar. 5   Engr.
2852 A1036 10k multicolored   4.00 3.50

World Ice Hockey Championships, Prague and Bratislava — A1037

1992, Mar. 31   Photo. & Engr.
2853 A1037 3k multicolored   .75 .25

Traffic Safety — A1038

1992, Apr. 2
2854 A1038 2k multicolored .50 .25

Expo '92, Seville — A1039

1992, Apr. 2
2855 A1039 4k multicolored .75 .25

Discovery of America, 500th Anniv. — A1040

1992, May 5 **Engr.**
2856 A1040 22k multicolored 2.00 2.00
Europa. Printed in sheets of 8. Value $18.

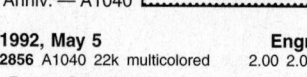

Czechoslovak Military Actions in WWII — A1041

Designs: 1k, J. Kubis and J. Gabcik, assassins of Reinhard Heydrich, 1942. 2k, Pilots flying for France and Great Britain. 3k, Defense of Tobruk. 6k, Capture of Dunkirk, 1944-45.

1992, May 21 **Engr.** **Perf. 12x11½**
2857 A1041 1k multicolored .50 .25
2858 A1041 2k multicolored .60 .25
2859 A1041 3k multicolored .75 .25
2860 A1041 6k multicolored 1.60 .35
    Nos. 2857-2860 (4) 3.45 1.10

A1042

Photo. & Engr.
1992, June 10 **Perf. 11½**
2861 A1042 2k multicolored .30 .25
Czechoslovakian Red Cross.

A1043

1992, June 30
2862 A1043 1k multicolored .30 .25
Junior European Table Tennis Championships, Topolcany.

Beetles — A1044

1992, July 15
2863 A1044 1k Polyphylla fullo .65 .25
2864 A1044 2k Ergates faber .90 .25
2865 A1044 3k Meloe violaceus 1.90 .45
2866 A1044 4k Dytiscus latissimus 1.90 .45
    Nos. 2863-2866 (4) 5.35 1.40
The 1k exists with denomination omitted.

Troja Castle A1045

1992, Aug. 28 **Engr.** **Perf. 11½**
2867 A1045 6k shown 2.60 1.00
2868 A1045 7k Statue of St. Martin, vert. 3.00 1.10
2869 A1045 8k Lednice Castle 3.50 1.25
    Nos. 2867-2869 (3) 9.10 3.35
Nos. 2867-2869 were each issued in sheets of 8. Value $75.

Chrudim Church Type of 1971
Photo. & Engr.
1992, Aug. 28 **Perf. 11½x11**
2870 A629 50h multicolored .75 .25

Postal Bank — A1045a

Photo. & Engr.
1992, Aug. 28 **Perf. 11½x12**
2870A A1045a 20k multicolored 2.00 .75

Antonius Bernolak, Georgius Fandly — A1046

Photo. & Engr.
1992, Oct. 6 **Perf. 12x11½**
2871 A1046 5k multicolored .75 .30
Slovakian Educational Society, bicent.

Cesky Krumlov — A1046a

Photo. & Engr.
1992, Oct. 19 **Perf. 11½x12**
2871A A1046a 3k brick red & brn .75 .25
    See No. 2890.

Painting Type of 1967
6k Old Man on a Raft, by Koloman Sokol. 7k, Still Life of Grapes and Raisins, by Georges Braque, horiz. 8k, Abandoned Corset, by Toyen.

Perf. 11½x12, 12x11½
1992, Nov. 2 **Engr.**
2872 A565 6k multicolored 2.00 .95
2873 A565 7k multicolored 3.25 1.10
2874 A565 8k multicolored 3.25 1.25
    Nos. 2872-2874 (3) 8.50 3.30
Nos. 2872-2874 were each issued in sheets of 4. Value, set $37.50.

Christmas — A1047

Photo. & Engr.
1992, Nov. 9 **Perf. 12x11½**
2875 A1047 2k multicolored .75 .25

Jindra Schmidt (1897-1984), Graphic Artist and Engraver — A1048

Photo. & Engr.
1992, Dec. 18 **Perf. 11½x12**
2876 A1048 2k multicolored .75 .25
    Stamp Day.

On January 1, 1993, Czechoslovakia split into Czech Republic and Slovakia. Czech Republic listings continue here. Slovakia can be found in Volume 5.

CZECH REPUBLIC
AREA — 30,449 sq. mi.
POP. — 10,280,513 (1999 est.)

Natl. Arms — A1049

Photo. & Engr.
1993, Jan. 20 **Perf. 11**
2877 A1049 3k multicolored .40 .25

1993 World Figure Skating Championships, Prague — A1050

1993, Feb. 25 **Perf. 11½x11**
2878 A1050 2k multicolored .30 .25

Havel Type of 1990 Inscribed "Ceska Republika"
Photo. & Engr.
1993, Mar. 2 **Perf. 12x11½**
2879 A1000 2k vio, vio brn & blue .30 .25

St. John Nepomuk, Patron Saint of Czechs, 600th Death Anniv. — A1051

1993, Mar. 11
2880 A1051 8k multicolored 1.00 .35
See Germany No. 1776; Slovakia No. 158.

Holy Hunger, by Mikulas Medek — A1052

1993, Mar. 11 **Perf. 11½**
2881 A1052 14k multicolored 3.75 2.00
    Europa.
Issued in sheets of 4. Value $16.

Sacred Heart Church, Prague A1053

1993, Mar. 30 **Engr.** **Perf. 11½**
2882 A1053 5k multicolored 1.00 .50
Issued in sheets of 8. Value $10.

Brevnov Monastery, 1000th Anniv. — A1054

Litho. & Engr.
1993, Apr. 12 **Perf. 12x11½**
2883 A1054 4k multicolored .55 .25

1993 Intl. Junior Weight Lifting Championships, Cheb — A1055

Photo. & Engr.
1993, May 12 **Perf. 11½**
2884 A1055 6k multicolored 1.00 .35

Clock Tower and Church, Brno — A1056

1993, June 16 **Engr.** **Perf. 12x11½**
2885 A1056 8k multicolored 1.50 1.50
Brno, 750th anniv.
Issued in sheets of 8. Value, $12.

Arrival of St. Cyril and St. Methodius, 1130th Anniv. — A1057

1993, June 22 **Photo. & Engr.**
2886 A1057 8k multicolored 1.00 .50
    See Slovakia No. 167.

Souvenir Sheet

State Arms — A1058

1993, June 22 **Perf. 11½**
2887 A1058 8k Sheet of 2 2.60 2.60

Architecture Type of 1992 Inscribed "Ceska Republika" and

A1059

Cities: 1k, Ceske Budejovice. 2k, Usti Nad Labem. No. 2890, like #2871A. No. 2891, Brno. 5k, Plzen. 6k, Slany. 7k, Ostrava. 8k, Olomouc. 10k, Hradec Kralove. 20k, Prague. 50k, Opava.

Perf. 12x11½, 11½x12
1993-94 **Photo. & Engr.**
2888 A1059 1k dp cl & org .25 .25
2889 A1059 2k red vio & bl .25 .25
2890 A1046a 3k gray bl & red .25 .25
    Complete booklet, 5
    #2890 4.50
2891 A1059 3k dk bl & red .25 .25
    Complete booklet, 5
    #2891 3.75
2892 A1059 5k bluish green & brn .25 .25
2893 A1059 6k grn & org yel 1.00 .30
2894 A1059 7k blk brn & grn 1.00 .30
2895 A1059 8k dp vio & yel .80 .30
2896 A1059 10k olive gray & red .90 .40
2897 A1059 20k red & blue 2.50 .75
2898 A1059 50k brn & grn 4.75 1.75
    Nos. 2888-2898 (11) 12.20 5.05

Issued: No. 2891, 3/30/94; 6k, 10/1/94; 7k, 11/23/94; others, 7/1/93.

World Rowing Championships, Racice — A1060

Photo. & Engr.

1993, Aug. 18   *Perf. 11½*
2901 A1060 3k multicolored   .40 .25

A1061

Famous men: 2k, August Sedlacek (1843-1926), historian. 3k, Eduard Cech (1893-1960), mathematician.

1993, Aug. 26   *Perf. 12x11½*
2902 A1061 2k multicolored   .40 .25
2903 A1061 3k multicolored   .55 .25

Trees — A1062

1993, Oct. 26   *Perf. 11½*
2904 A1062 5k Quercus robur   .60 .30
2905 A1062 7k Carpinus betulus   .80 .40
2906 A1062 9k Pinus silvestris   1.25 .50
   Nos. 2904-2906 (3)   2.65 1.20

See Slovakia Nos. 160-162.

Christmas — A1063

Photo. & Engr.

1993, Nov. 8   *Perf. 11½*
2907 A1063 2k multicolored   .30 .25

Painting Type of 1967 Inscribed "ČESKA REPUBLIKA"

Paintings: 9k, Strahovska Madonna, by "Bohemian Master" in the year 1350. 11k, Composition, by Miro, horiz. 14k, Field of Green, by Van Gogh, horiz.

1993   *Engr.*   *Perf. 11½x12*
2908 A565 9k multicolored   2.00 2.00
    Perf. 12x11½
2909 A565 11k multicolored   2.25 2.25
2910 A565 14k multicolored   3.25 3.25
   Nos. 2908-2910 (3)   7.50 7.50

Issued: 11k, 14k, Nov. 8; 9k, Dec. 15.
Nos. 2908-2910 were each issued in sheets of 4. Value, set $30.

Intl. Year of the Family — A1064

Photo. & Engr.

1994, Jan. 19   *Perf. 11½*
2911 A1064 2k multicolored   .30 .25

Jan Kubelik (1880-1940), Composer — A1065

Photo. & Engr.

1994, Jan. 19   *Perf. 11½*
2912 A1065 3k multicolored   .40 .25

UNESCO A1065a

Designs: 2k, Voltaire (1694-1778), philosopher. 6k, Georgius Agricola (1494-1555), mineralogist, humanist.

1994, Feb. 2   *Perf. 12x11½*
2913 A1065a 2k multicolored   .25 .25
2914 A1065a 6k multicolored   .80 .35

1994 Winter Olympics, Lillehammer — A1066

Photo. & Engr.

1994, Feb. 2   *Perf. 11½*
2915 A1066 5k multicolored   .70 .35

A1067

Europa (Marco Polo &): No. 2916, Stylized animals, Chinese woman. No. 2917, Stylized animals.

Photo. & Engr.

1994, May 4   *Perf. 11½*
2916 A1067 14k multicolored   1.75 1.75
2917 A1067 14k multicolored   1.75 1.75
   a.   Pair, #2916-2917   3.50 3.50

Nos. 2916-2917 were issued in sheets of 2 + 2 labels. Value, $8.

Eduard Benes — A1068

1994, May 18
2918 A1068 5k violet & brt purple   .60 .25

Architectural Sights — A1069

UNESCO: 8k, Houses at the square, Telc. 9k, Cubist house designed by Chochol, Prague.

1994, May 18
2919 A1069 8k multicolored   1.25 .75
2920 A1069 9k multicolored   1.25 .75

Issued in sheets of 8. Value, pair of sheets $20.

Children's Day — A1070

Photo. & Engr.

1994, June 1   *Perf. 11½*
2921 A1070 2k multicolored   .40 .25

Dinosaurs A1071

    Perf. 11½x11, 11x11½
1994, June 1   *Litho.*
2922 A1071 2k Stegosaurus   .30 .25
2923 A1071 3k Apatosaurus   .50 .25
2924 A1071 5k Tarbosaurus, vert.   .70 .35
   Nos. 2922-2924 (3)   1.50 .85

A1072

Photo. & Engr.

1994, June 1   *Perf. 11½x11*
2925 A1072 8k multicolored   1.00 .50

1994 World Cup Soccer Championships, US.

A1073

1994, June 15   *Perf. 11x11½*
2926 A1073 2k multicolored   .35 .25

12th Pan-Sokol Rally, Prague.

Intl. Olympic Committee, Cent. — A1074

1994, June 15
2927 A1074 7k multicolored   1.00 .50

UPU, 120th Anniv. — A1075

1994, Aug. 3   *Engr.*   *Perf. 11½*
2928 A1075 11k multicolored   1.40 1.00

Songbirds — A1076

Designs: 3k, Saxicola torquata. 5k, Carpodacus erythrinus. 14k, Luscinia svecica.

Photo. & Engr.

1994, Aug. 24   *Perf. 11x11½*
2929 A1076 3k multicolored   .40 .25
2930 A1076 5k multicolored   .60 .30
2931 A1076 14k multicolored   1.50 .80
   Nos. 2929-2931 (3)   2.50 1.35

Historic Race Cars — A1077

Photo. & Engr.

1994, Oct. 5   *Perf. 11½*
2932 A1077 2k 1900 NW   .25 .25
   Complete booklet, 10 #2932   3.00
2933 A1077 3k 1908 L&K   .45 .25
   Complete booklet, 5 #2933   2.75
2934 A1077 9k 1912 Praga   1.10 .50
   Nos. 2932-2934 (3)   1.80 1.00

Christmas — A1078

Photo. & Engr.

1994, Nov. 9   *Perf. 11½*
2935 A1078 2k multicolored   .45 .25

Painting Type of 1967 Inscribed "ČESKA REPUBLIKA"

Engraving or paintings: 7k, Stary Posetilec A Zena, by Lucas Van Leyden. 10k, Moulin Rouge, by Henri de Toulouse-Lautrec. 14k, St. Vitus Madonna, St. Vitus Cathedral, Prague.

1994, Nov. 9   *Engr.*   *Perf. 12*
2936 A565 7k multicolored   .95 .95
2937 A565 10k multicolored   1.40 1.40
2938 A565 14k multicolored   2.00 2.00
   Nos. 2936-2938 (3)   4.35 4.35

Nos. 2936-2938 were each printed in sheets of 4. Value, set $17.

World Tourism Organization, 20th Anniv. — A1079

Photo. & Engr.

1995, Jan. 2   *Perf. 11x12*
2939 A1079 8k green blue & red   .95 .50

Czech Stamp Production — A1080

1995, Jan. 20
2940 A1080 3k Design N1   .60 .25

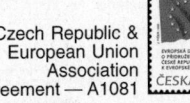

Czech Republic & European Union Association Agreement — A1081

1995, Jan. 20 Litho.   *Perf. 13½x12½*
2941 A1081 8k multicolored   1.20 .65

Famous Men — A1082

Designs: 2k, Johannes Marcus Marci (1595-1667). 5k, Ferdinand Peroutka (1895-1978). 7k, Premysl Pitter (1895-1976).

Photo. & Engr.

1995, Feb. 1   *Perf. 12x11*
2942 A1082 2k multicolored   .30 .25
2943 A1082 5k multicolored   .30 .25
2944 A1082 7k multicolored   .90 .35
   Nos. 2942-2944 (3)   1.50 .85

Theater Personalities — A1083

Designs: No. 2945, Jiri Voskovec (1905-81). No. 2946, Jan Werich (1905-80). No. 2947, Jaroslav Jezek (1906-42). 22k, Caricatures of Voskovec, Werich, and Jezek with piano.

1995   **Photo. & Engr.**   *Perf. 12x11*
2945 A1083 3k multicolored   .35 .25
   Complete booklet, 3 #2945   6.00
2946 A1083 3k multicolored   .35 .25
   Complete booklet, 3 #2946   6.00
2947 A1083 3k multicolored   .35 .25
   Complete booklet, 3 #2947   6.00
   a.   Strip of 3, #2945-2947   1.10 1.10
   Complete booklet, 2 #2947a   9.00
   Nos. 2945-2947 (3)   1.05 .75

Souvenir Sheet
Photo.
    Perf. 12
2947B A1083 22k yellow & black   2.50 2.50

Issued: 3k, 3/15; 22k, 9/20.

Havel Type of 1990 Inscribed "Ceska Republika"
Photo. & Engr.

1995, Mar. 22   *Perf. 12x11½*
2948 A1000 3.60k bl, vio & mag   .45 .25
   Complete booklet, 5 #2948   4.00

Rural Architecture — A1084

1995, Mar. 22   *Perf. 11½*
2949 A1084 40h shown   .25 .25
2950 A1084 60h Homes, diff.   .25 .25

European Nature Conservation Year — A1085

1995, Apr. 12
2951 A1085 3k Bombus terrestris   .55 .30
    Complete booklet, 5 #2951   4.00
2952 A1085 5k Mantis religiosa   .70 .30
    Complete booklet, 5 #2952   4.50
2953 A1085 6k Calopteryx
     splendens   .80 .30
    Complete booklet, 5 #2953   5.00
    Nos. 2951-2953 (3)   2.05 .90

Peace & Freedom A1086

Photo. & Engr.
1995, May 3   *Perf. 11½*
2954 A1086 9k Rose, profiles   1.00 .35
2955 A1086 14k Butterfly, profiles 1.50 .75
     Europa.

Natural Beauties in Czech Republic A1087

Designs: 8k, "Stone Organ" scenic mountain. 9k, Largest sandstone bridge in Europe.

Photo. & Engr.
1995, May 3   *Perf. 11½*
2956 A1087 8k multicolored   .95 .95
2957 A1087 9k multicolored   1.00 1.00
    Nos. 2956-2957 were each issued in sheets of 8. Value, set $16.

Children's Day — A1088

Photo. & Engr.
1995, June 1   *Perf. 11½*
2958 A1088 3.60k multicolored   .60 .25

First Train from Vienna to Prague, 150th Anniv. — A1089

3k, Chocen Tunnel. 9.60k, Entering Prague.

1995, June 21
2959 A1089   3k multicolored   .35 .25
    Complete booklet, 5 #2959   4.00
2960 A1089 9.60k multicolored   1.15 .50

World Wrestling Championships, Prague — A1090

Photo. & Engr.
1995, Sept. 6   *Perf. 11½*
2961 A1090 3k multicolored   .75 .25

Cartoon Characters — A1091

Designs: 3k, Man playing violin, woman washing, by Vladimir Rencin. 3.60k, Angel, naked man, by Vladimir Jiranek. 5k, Circus trainer holding ring for champagne cork to pop through, by Jiri Sliva.

1995, Sept. 6
2962 A1091   3k multicolored   .35 .25
    Complete booklet, 5 #2962   3.50
2963 A1091 3.60k multicolored   .35 .25
    Complete booklet, 5 #2963   3.50
2964 A1091   5k multicolored   .35 .30
    Complete booklet, 5 #2964   3.50
    Nos. 2962-2964 (3)   1.05 .80

A1092

1995, Sept. 20   Litho.   *Perf. 13½x13*
2965 A1092 3k multicolored   .35 .25
    SOS Children's Villages, 25th anniv.

A1093

Designs: 2.40k, Gothic. 3k, Secession. 3.60k, Romance. 4k, Classic portal; 4.60k, Rococo. 9.60k, Renaissance Portal. 12.60k, Cubist. 14k, Baroque.

Photo. & Engr.
1995-97   *Perf. 12x11½*
2966   A1093   2.40k red & green   .30 .25
2967   A1093   3k grn & bl   .35 .25
2967A   A1093   3.60k pur & grn   .45 .25
2968   A1093   4k blue & red   .50 .25
    Complete booklet, 5 #2967A   3.00
2968A   A1093   4.60k multicolored   .55 .25
2969   A1093   9.60k blue & red   1.10 .45
2969A   A1093   12.60k red brn & bl 1.50 .45
2970   A1093   14k grn & pur   1.60 .60
    Nos. 2966-2970 (8)   6.35 2.75

    Issued: 9.60k, 9/27; 2.40k, 14k, 10/11; 3k, 3.60k, 10/25; 4k, 6/12/96; 4.60k, 3/26/97; 12.60k, 6/25/97.

UN, 50th Anniv. — A1094

1995, Oct. 11   Litho.   *Perf. 12x11½*
2971 A1094 14k multicolored   1.60 .80

Wilhelm Röntgen (1845-1923), Discovery of the X-Ray, Cent. — A1095

1995, Oct. 11   Photo. & Engr.
2972 A1095 6k blk, buff & bl vio   .75 .35

Painting Type of 1967 Inscribed "ČESKÁ REPUBLIKA"

Designs: 6k, Parisienne, by Ludek Marold. 9k, Vase of Flowers, by J.K. Hirschely. 14k, Portrait of J. Malinsky, by Antoinín Machek.

1995, Nov. 8   *Perf. 12*
2973 A565   6k multicolored   .95 .45
2974 A565   9k multicolored   1.25 .65
2975 A565 14k multicolored   2.00 1.00
    Nos. 2973-2975 (3)   4.20 2.10

    Nos. 2973-2975 were each printed in sheets of 4. Value, set $13.50.

Christmas — A1096

1995, Nov. 8   *Perf. 11½*
2976 A1096 3k multicolored   .50 .25
    Complete booklet, 5 #2976   3.00

Czech Philharmonic Orchestra, Cent. — A1097

Photo. & Engr.
1996, Jan. 2   *Perf. 12x11½*
2977 A1097 3.60k multicolored   .55 .25

Tradition of Czech Stamp Production — A1098

Photo. & Engr.
1996, Jan. 20   *Perf. 11½x12*
2978 A1098 3.60k Design A5 of
     1920   .55 .25

Vera Mencikova (1906-44), Chess Player — A1099

Photo. & Engr.
1996, Feb. 14   *Perf. 12x11½*
2979 A1099 6k multicolored   .75 .35

Easter — A1100

1996, Mar. 13   *Perf. 11½x12*
2980 A1100 3k multicolored   .45 .25
    Complete booklet, 5 #2980   2.00

Josef Sudek (1896-1976), Photographer A1101

Photo. & Engr.
1996, Mar. 13   *Perf. 11*
2981 A1101 9.60k multicolored   1.10 .60

Rulers from House of Luxembourg — A1102

Designs: a, John of Luxembourg (1296-1346). b, Charles IV (1316-78). c, Wenceslas IV. (1361-1419). d, Sigismund (1368-1437).

1996, Mar. 27   Engr.   *Perf. 11½*
2982 A1102 14k Sheet of 4, #a.-
     d. + label   6.00 6.00

Jiri Guth-Jarkovsky, Participant in First Modern Olympic Games, Athens — A1103

Photo. & Engr.
1996, Mar. 27   *Perf. 11½*
2983 A1103 9.60k multicolored   1.25 .60
    Modern Olympic Games, cent.

World Wildlife Fund — A1104

Designs: a, 3.60k, Eliomys quercinus. b, 5k, Dryomys nitedula. c, 6k, Spermophilus citellus. d, 8k, Sicista betulina.

Photo. & Engr.
1996, Apr. 24   *Perf. 11½x12*
2984 A1104 Block of 4, #a.-d.   2.50 2.50
    Issued in sheets of 8 stamps. Value $5.

Ema Destinnova (1878-1930), Singer — A1105

1996, May 2   *Perf. 11½*
2985 A1105 8k multicolored   .85 .35
    Europa.
    No. 2985 was issued in sheets of 10. Value $8.50.

A1106

Photo. & Engr.
1996, May 15   *Perf. 11x11½*
2986 A1106 12k multicolored   1.20 .65
    Jean Gaspart Deburau (1796-1846), mime.

A1107

1996, May 29
2987 A1107 3k multicolored   .35 .25
    1996 Summmer Olympic Games, Atlanta.

Intl. Children's Day — A1108

Photo. & Engr.
1996, May 29   *Perf. 11½*
2988 A1108 3k multicolored   .35 .25

Architectural Sites — A1109

UNESCO: 8k, St. Nepomuk Church, Zelena Hora. 9k, Loreta Tower, Prague.

1996, June 26   Engr.   Perf. 11½
2989 A1109 8k multicolored   1.00 1.00
2990 A1109 9k multicolored   1.10 1.10
Nos. 2989-2990 were each issued in sheets of 8. Value, set $16.
See Nos. 3056-3057.

UNICEF, 50th Anniv. — A1110

Photo. & Engr.
1996, Sept. 11   Perf. 12x11
2991 A1110 3k multicolored   .35 .25

Horses
A1111   A1112

Photo. & Engr.
1996, Sept. 25   Perf. 11x11½
2992 A1111 3k multicolored   .50 .25
2993 A1112 3k multicolored   .50 .25
a.   Pair, #2992-2993   1.00 .75
     Complete booklet, 3 #2992, 2
     #2993   3.00
     Complete booklet, 2 #2992, 3
     #2993   3.00

Souvenir Sheet

Vaclav Havel, 60th Birthday A1113

1996, Oct. 5
2994 A1113 Sheet of 2   1.25 1.25
a.   6k red & blue   .60 .50

Painting Type of 1967 Inscribed "CESKA REPUBLIKA"
The Baroque Chair, by Endre Nemes (1909-85).

1996, Oct. 5   Engr.   Perf. 11½
2995 A565 20k multicolored   2.00 2.00
No. 2995 was issued in sheets of 4. Value $8.
See Slovakia No. 255; Sweden No. 2199.

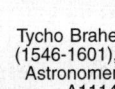

Tycho Brahe (1546-1601), Astronomer A1114

Photo. & Engr.
1996, Oct. 9   Perf. 11½x11
2996 A1114 5k multicolored   .85 .30

Biplanes — A1115

1996, Oct. 9
2997 A1115 7k Letov S1 (1920)   .70 .40
2998 A1115 8k Aero A11 (1925)   .90 .40
2999 A1115 10k Avia BH21
     (1925)   1.00 .50
Nos. 2997-2999 (3)   2.60 1.30

Christmas — A1116

Photo. & Engr.
1996, Nov. 13   Perf. 11½
3000 A1116 3k multicolored   .45 .25
     Complete booklet, 5 #3000   3.50

Painting Type of 1967 Inscribed "CESKA REPUBLIKA"
Designs: 9k, Garden of Eden, by Josef Váchal (1884-1969), horiz. 11k, Breakfast, by Georg Flegel (1566-1638).

1996, Nov. 13   Engr.   Perf. 11½
3001 A565 9k multicolored   1.00 1.00
3002 A565 11k multicolored   1.25 1.25
Nos. 3001-3002 were each issued in sheets of 4. Value, set $10.

Czech Stamp Production — A1117

Photo. & Engr.
1997, Jan. 20   Perf. 11½x12
3003 A1117 3.60k #68, bl & red   .75 .25

Easter — A1118

Photo. & Engr.
1997, Mar. 12   Perf. 11½
3004 A1118 3k multicolored   .75 .25
     Complete booklet, 5 #3004   4.00

Flowers — A1119

3.60k, Erythronium dens-canis. 4k, Calla palustris. 5k, Cypripedium calceolus. 8k, Iris pumila.

1997, Mar. 12   Perf. 11x11½
3005 A1119 3.60k multicolored   .30 .25
     Complete booklet, 5 #3005   2.50
3006 A1119 4k multicolored   .30 .25
     Complete booklet, 5 #3006   2.50
3007 A1119 5k multicolored   .50 .30
     Complete booklet, 5 #3007   3.50
3008 A1119 8k multicolored   .60 .45
     Complete booklet, 5 #3008   5.00
Nos. 3005-3008 (4)   1.70 1.25

A1120

Jewish Monuments in Prague: 8k, Altneus-chul Synagogue. 10k, Tombstone of Rabbi Judah Loew MaHaRaL.

1997, Apr. 30   Perf. 11½
3009 A1120 8k multicolored   .75 .45
3010 A1120 10k multicolored   .90 .55
a.   Sheet, 4 each #3009-3010   7.00 4.00
See Israel Nos. 1302-1303.

Greetings Stamp — A1121

1997, Mar. 26   Litho.   Perf. 13x13½
3011 A1121 4k Girl with cats   .50 .25

A1122

1997, Apr. 23   Engr.   Perf. 11½
3012 A1122 7k deep violet   .95 .40
St. Adalbert (956-97). See Germany No. 1964, Hungary No. 3569, Poland No. 3337, Vatican City No. 1040.
No. 3012 was issued in sheets of 4 + 4 labels. Value, $7.

A1123

Europa (Stories and Legends): No. 3013, Queen, knight with sword, lion, snakes. No. 3014, Man riding in chariot drawn by chickens, King looking through window.

Photo. & Engr.
1997, Apr. 30   Perf. 11½x12
3013 A1123 8k multicolored   1.00 .60
3014 A1123 8k multicolored   1.00 .60
Nos. 3013-3014 were each issued in sheets of 8. Value $16.

Souvenir Sheet

Collections of Rudolf II (1522-1612), Prague Exhibition — A1124

Designs: a, 6k, Musical instruments, flowers, face of bearded man. b, 8k, Rudolf II wearing laurel wreath, holding rose, Muses. c, 10k, Rudolf II, skull, moth's wings, tree, flowers, leaves, fruit.

1997, May 14   Engr.   Perf. 12
3015 A1124 Sheet of 3, #a.-c.   2.25 2.25

Intl. Children's Day — A1125

Photo. & Engr.
1997, May 28   Perf. 11½
3016 A1125 4.60k multicolored   .75 .25

Frantisek Krizik (1847-1941), Electrical Engineer, Inventor of Arc Lamp — A1126

Photo. & Engr.
1997, June 25   Perf. 12x11½
3017 A1126 6k multicolored   .85 .25

European Swimming & Diving Championships, Prague A1127

Photo. & Engr.
1997, Aug. 27   Perf. 11½
3018 A1127 11k multicolored   1.00 .40

"The Good Soldier Schweik," by Jaroslav Hasek, 110th Anniv. — A1128

4k, Mrs. Müller, Schweik in wheelchair. 4.60k, Lt. Lukás, Col. Kraus von Zillergut, dog. 6k, Schweik smoking pipe, winter scene.

Photo. & Engr.
1997, Sept. 10   Perf. 12x11½
3019 A1128   4k multicolored   .50 .25
a.   Booklet pane of 8 + 4 labels   4.50
     Complete booklet, #3019a   4.50
3020 A1128 4.60k multicolored   .50 .25
a.   Booklet pane of 8 + 4 labels   5.00
     Complete booklet, #3020a   5.00
3021 A1128   6k multicolored   .50 .30
a.   Booklet pane of 8 + 4 labels   6.00
     Complete booklet, #3021a   6.00
Nos. 3019-3021 (3)   1.50 .80

Praga 1998, Intl. Stamp Exhibition A1129

No. 3022, Lesser Town, Prague Castle. No. 3023, Old Town, bridges over Vltava River.

Photo. & Engr.
1997, Sept. 24   Perf. 11½
3022 A1129 15k multicolored   1.40 .60
3023 A1129 15k multicolored   1.40 .60
a.   Souvenir sheet, #3022-3023 +
     2 labels   3.75 3.00

Historic Service Vehicles A1130

Designs: 4k, Postal bus, Prague. 4.60k, Sentinel truck, Skoda. 8k, Fire truck, Tatra.

1997, Oct. 8   Perf. 12x11½
3024 A1130   4k multicolored   .30 .25
     Complete booklet, 5 #3024   2.50
3025 A1130 4.60k multicolored   .30 .25
     Complete booklet, 5 #3025   3.50
3026 A1130   8k multicolored   .60 .40
     Complete booklet, 5 #3026   5.00
Nos. 3024-3026 (3)   1.20 .90

A1131

Photo. & Engr.
1997, Nov. 12   Perf. 11½
3027 A1131 4k multicolored   .50 .25
     Complete booklet, 5 #3027   2.75
Christmas.

Painting Type of 1967 Inscribed "ČESKA REPUBLIKA"

7k, Landscape with Chateau in Chantilly, by Antonín Chittussi (1847-91). 12k, The Prophets Came Out of the Desert, by Frantisek Bílek (1872-1941). 1 6k, Parisian Antiquarians, by T. F. Simon (1877-1942).

1997, Nov. 12 **Engr.** **Perf. 12**
3028	A565	7k multi, horiz.	.50	.50
3029	A565	12k multi	1.00	1.00
3030	A565	16k multi	1.50	1.50
		Nos. 3028-3030 (3)	3.00	3.00

Nos. 3028-3030 were each issued in sheets of 4. Value, set $12.

A1132

1998, Jan. 20 **Litho.** **Perf. 11½x12**
3031 A1132 7k multicolored .85 .30

1998 Winter Olympic Games, Nagano.

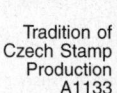

Tradition of Czech Stamp Production A1133

Photo. & Engr.

1998, Jan. 20 **Perf. 12x11½**
3032 A1133 12.60k Type A8 1.25 .55
a. Booklet pane of 8 + 4 labels 12.50
Complete booklet, #3032a 12.50

Pres. Václav Havel — A1134

1998, Jan. 22
3033 A1134 4.60k dark grn & red .85 .25
See No. 3114.

Love — A1135

1998, Feb. 4 **Perf. 11½**
3034 A1135 4k multicolored .50 .50
Complete booklet, 5 #3034 2.50

Skibob World Championship, Spindleruv Mlyn — A1136

1998, Feb. 25
3035 A1136 8k multicolored .85 .35

Prague Philatelic Exhibition Type of 1938
Souvenir Sheet

1998, Feb. 25 **Engr.** **Perf. 12x11½**
3036 A87 Sheet of 2 5.00 5.00
a. 30k like #251a 2.50 2.00

Prague '98, Intl. Philatelic Exhibition.

Easter — A1137

Photo. & Engr.

1998, Mar. 25 **Perf. 11x11½**
3037 A1137 4k multicolored .55 .25
Complete booklet, 5 #3037 2.75

Ondrejov Observatory, Cent. — A1138

1998, Mar. 25 **Perf. 12x11½**
3038 A1138 4.60k multicolored .85 .25

Czech Ice Hockey Team, Gold Medalists at Nagano Winter Olympic Games — A1139

1998, Apr. 1 **Litho.** **Perf. 11½x12**
3039 A1139 23k Dominik Hasek 1.50 1.50

No. 3039 was issued in a sheet with two labels. Value, $2.

Charles University and New Town, Prague, 650th Anniv. — A1140

Designs: a, 15k, Hands forming arch, University seal. b, 22k, Charles IV (1316-78), Holy Roman Emperor, King of Bohemia. c, 23k, Groin vault, St. Vitus Cathedral, Prague.

1998, Apr. 1 **Engr.** **Perf. 12**
3040 A1140 Sheet of 3, #a.-c. 5.50 5.50

World Book and Copyright Day — A1141

1998, Apr. 23 **Litho.** **Perf. 12x11½**
3041 A1141 10k multicolored 1.00 .45

Nature Conservation — A1142

1998, Apr. 23 **Perf. 13x13½**
3042	A1142	4.60k Perdix perdix	.45	.25
3043	A1142	4.60k Lyrurus tetrix	.45	.25
a.		Pair, #3042-3043	1.10	.60
3044	A1142	8k Cervus elaphus	.65	.30
3045	A1142	8k Alces alces	.65	.30
a.		Pair, #3044-3045	1.50	1.10
		Nos. 3042-3045 (4)	2.20	1.10

Natl. Festivals and Holidays A1143

Europa: 11k, King's Ride. 15k, Wearing masks for Carnival.

Litho. & Engr.

1998, May 5 **Perf. 11½**
3046 A1143 11k multicolored .90 .55
3047 A1143 15k multicolored 1.40 .75

Intl. Children's Day — A1144

Designs: 4k, Two satyr musicians. 4.60k, Character riding on fish.

Photo. & Engr.

1998, May 27 **Perf. 11½**
3048	A1144	4k multicolored	.60	.25
a.		Booklet of 6 +4 labels	4.00	
		Complete booklet, #3048a	4.00	
3049	A1144	4.60k multicolored	.60	.25
a.		Booklet of 6 + 4 labels	4.50	
		Complete booklet, #3049a	4.50	

Famous Men — A1145

Designs: 4k, Frantisek Kmoch (1848-1912), bandleader, composer. 4.60k, Frantisek Palacky (1798-1876), historian, politician. 6k, Rafael Kubelík (1914-96), composer, conductor.

1998, May 27 **Perf. 11½x12**
3050 A1145 4k multicolored .35 .25
3051 A1145 4.60k multicolored .45 .25
3052 A1145 6k multicolored .55 .25
Nos. 3050-3052 (3) 1.35 .75

Revolt of 1848, 150th Anniv. — A1146

1998, May 27 **Perf. 12x11½**
3053 A1146 15k multicolored 1.60 .75

Painting Type of 1967 Inscribed "ČESKA REPUBLIKA"

Praga 1998 Intl. Stamp Exhibition, works of art: 22k, Amorfa Dvoubarevna Fuga, by Frantisek Kupka (1871-1957), horiz. 23k, Escape, by Paul Gauguin (1848-1903), horiz.

1998, June 17 **Engr.** **Perf. 12**
3054 A565 22k multicolored 1.75 1.75
3055 A565 23k multicolored 2.25 1.75

Nos. 3054-3055 were each issued in sheets of 4. Value, set $16.

UNESCO World Heritage Sites Type of 1996

8k, St. Barbara Cathedral, Kutná Hora, horiz. 11k, The Chateau of Valtice, horiz.

1998, Oct. 7 **Engr.** **Perf. 11½x12**
3056 A1109 8k multicolored .70 .40
3057 A1109 11k multicolored 1.00 .60

Nos. 3056-3057 were each issued in sheets of 8. Value, set $15.

Czechoslovak Republic, 80th Anniv. — A1147

Designs based on World War I recruitment posters by Vojtech Preissig (1873-1944): 4.60k, Soldiers holding flags, guns. 5k, Three soldiers marching. 12.60k, Flags waving from city buildings.

Perf. 11½x11¾
1998, Oct. 28 **Litho. & Engr.**
3058 A1147 4.60k multicolored .50 .30
3059 A1147 5k multicolored .70 .30
3060 A1147 12.60k multicolored 1.25 .90
Nos. 3058-3060 (3) 2.45 1.50

No. 3060 was issued in sheets of 6+2 labels. Value $25.

Christmas — A1148

Designs: 4k, People following star. 6k, Angel blowing trumpet over town, vert.

Photo. & Engr.

1998, Nov. 18 **Perf. 11½**
3061	A1148	4k multicolored	.45	.25
		Complete booklet, 5 #3061	2.50	
3062	A1148	6k multicolored	.70	.25
		Complete booklet, 5 #3062	4.00	

Signs of the Zodiac — A1149

1998-2003 **Perf. 11¾x11½**
3063	A1149	1k		
3064	A1149	10k Aquarius	.75	.25
3065	A1149	9k Libra	.75	.25
3066	A1149	8k Cancer	.65	.25
3067	A1149	20k Sagittarius	1.60	.45
3068	A1149	5k Taurus	.55	.25
		Booklet, 5 #3068	2.75	
3069	A1149	5.40k Scorpio	.60	.25
		Booklet, 5 #3069	3.00	
3070	A1149	2k Virgo	.25	.25
3071	A1149	40h Pisces	.65	.25
3072	A1149	12k Leo	1.00	.30
3073	A1149	17k Gemini	1.60	.65
3074	A1149	26k Aries	2.40	.95
		Nos. 3063-3074 (12)	11.05	4.35

Issued: 1k, 10k, 11/18; 9k, 5/5/99; 8k, 20k, 9/8/99; 5k, 5.40k, 12/8/99; 2k, 5/9/00. 40h, 1/20/01. 12k, 2/21/01. 17k, 9/1/02. 26k, 2/12/03.

Painting Type of 1967 Inscribed "CESKA REPUBLIKA"

15k, Painting from the Greater Cycle, 1902, by Jan Preisler (1872-1918), horiz. 16k, Spinner, by Josef Navrátil (1798-1865).

1998, Dec. 9 **Perf. 12**
3075 A565 15k multicolored 1.40 1.00
3076 A565 16k multicolored 1.40 1.00

Nos. 3075-3076 were each issued in sheets of 4. Value, set $11.

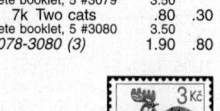

A1150

Photo. & Engr.

1999, Jan. 20 **Perf. 11½x11¾**
3077 A1150 4.60k #164 .85 .25
a. Booklet pane of 8 + 4 labels 5.00
Complete booklet, #3077a 5.50

Tradition of Czech stamp production.

Domestic Cats — A1151

Photo. & Engr.

1999, Feb. 17 **Perf. 11½**
3078	A1151	4.60k shown	.55	.25
		Complete booklet, 5 #3078	3.50	
3079	A1151	5k Adult, kitten	.55	.25
		Complete booklet, 5 #3079	3.50	
3080	A1151	7k Two cats	.80	.30
		Complete booklet, 5 #3080	3.50	
		Nos. 3078-3080 (3)	1.90	.80

Easter — A1152

Photo. & Engr.

1999, Mar. 10 **Perf. 11¼x11½**
3081 A1152 3k multicolored .35 .25

Protected Birds — A1153

No. 3082, Merops apiaster. No. 3083, Upupa epops.

Protected butterflies: No. 3084, Catocala electa. No. 3085, Euphydryas maturna.

Perf. 12¾x13¼

1999, Mar. 10				**Litho.**
3082	A1153	4.60k multicolored	.45	.25
3083	A1153	4.60k multicolored	.45	.25
a.		Pair, #3082-3083	.95	.60
		Complete booklet, 3 #3082, 2 #3083	5.00	
3084	A1153	5k multicolored	.45	.25
3085	A1153	5k multicolored	.45	.25
a.		Pair, #3084-3085	.95	.60
		Complete booklet, 3 #3084, 2 #3085	5.00	

Nature conservation.

Czech Republic's Entry Into NATO — A1154

Photo. & Engr.

1999, Mar. 12			**Perf. 12x11½**	
3086	A1154	4.60k multicolored	.45	.25

Council of Europe, 50th Anniv. — A1155

Photo. & Engr.

1999, Apr. 14			**Perf. 11¾x11¼**	
3087	A1155	7k multicolored	1.20	.40

Natl. Olympic Committee, Cent. — A1156

Design: Josef Rössler-Orovsky (1869-1933), founder of Czech Olympic Committee.

1999, Apr. 14			**Perf. 11¼x11¾**	
3088	A1156	9k multicolored	1.20	.35

Europa A1157

Natl. Parks: 11k, Sumava. 17k, Podyji.

1999, May 5			**Perf. 11¾x11¼**	
3089	A1157	11k multicolored	.90	.40
3090	A1157	17k multicolored	1.40	.65

Nos. 3089-3090 were each issued in sheets of 8. Value, set $27.

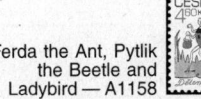

Ferda the Ant, Pytlik the Beetle and Ladybird — A1158

Photo. & Engr.

1999, May 26			**Perf. 11½x11¼**	
3091	A1158	4.60k multicolored	.75	.25
		Complete booklet, 8 #3091	6.00	

Bridges A1159

1999, May 26			**Engr.**	**Perf. 11¾**
3092	A1159	8k Stádlec, vert.	.60	.40
3093	A1159	11k Cernvír	1.00	.60

Nos. 3092-3094 were each issued in sheets of 8. Value, set $13.

Souvenir Sheet

Paleontologist Joachim Barrande (1799-1883) and Trilobite Fossils — A1160

a, 13k, Barrande, fossils. b, 31k, Delphon forbesi, Ophioceras simplex, Carolicrinus barrandei.

1999, June 23		**Engr.**	**Perf. 11¾**	
3094	A1160	Sheet of 2, #a.-b. + 2 labels	4.00	4.00

Jihlava Mining Rights, 750th Anniv. — A1161

Photo. & Engr.

1999, June 23		**Perf. 11¾x11¼**		
3095	A1161	8k multicolored	.95	.35
a.		Bklt. pane of 8 + 4 labels	8.00	
		Complete booklet, #3095a	8.00	

UPU, 125th Anniv. — A1162

Litho. & Engr.

1999, June 23		**Perf. 11¾**		
3096	A1162	9k multicolored	1.00	.40

No. 3096 was issued in sheets of 5 + 10 labels. Value, $6.

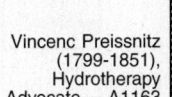

Vincenc Preissnitz (1799-1851), Hydrotherapy Advocate — A1163

Photo. & Engr.

1999, Sept. 8		**Perf. 11¼**		
3097	A1163	4.60k multicolored	.50	.25

UNESCO.

Carved Beehives — A1164

Designs: 4.60k, Woman. 5k, St. Joseph and Infant Jesus. 7k, Chimney sweep.

Photo. & Engr.

1999, Sept. 29		**Perf. 11¼x11½**		
3098	A1164	4.60k multi	.55	.25
		Complete booklet, 5 #3098	2.75	
3099	A1164	5k multi	.60	.25
		Complete booklet, 5 #3099	3.00	
3100	A1164	7k multi	.80	.30
		Complete booklet, 5 #3100	4.00	
		Nos. 3098-3100 (3)	1.95	.80

Cartoons by Miroslav Bartak — A1165

Designs: 4.60k, Doctor in clown mask, infant. 5k, Dog with pipe. 7k, Night seeping through window sill.

1999, Oct. 20				
3101	A1165	4.60k multi	.45	.25
3102	A1165	5k multi	.55	.25
3103	A1165	7k multi	.70	.30
		Nos. 3101-3103 (3)	1.70	.80

Souvenir Sheet

Beuron Art School A1166

Designs: a, 11k, Mater Dei, 1898. b, 13k, Pantocrator, 1911.

Litho. & Engr.

1999, Oct. 20		**Perf. 11¾**		
3104	A1166	Sheet of 2, #a.-b.	2.25	2.25

Painting Type of 1967 Inscribed "CESKA REPUBLIKA"

Designs: 13k, Red Orchid, by Jindrich Styrsky (1899-1942). 17k, Landscape with Marsh, by Julius Marák (1832-99). 26k, Monument, by Frantisek Hudecek (1909-90).

1999, Nov. 10		**Engr.**	**Perf. 11¾**	
3105	A565	13k multi	1.00	1.00
3106	A565	17k multi	1.50	1.50
3107	A565	26k multi	2.50	2.00
		Nos. 3105-3107 (3)	5.00	4.50

Nos. 3105-3107 were each issued in sheets of 4. Value, set $20.

Christmas — A1167

Photo. & Engr.

1999, Nov. 10		**Perf. 11¼x11½**		
3108	A1167	3k multi	.35	.25

A1168

Photo. & Engr.

2000, Jan. 20		**Perf. 11¼x11¾**		
3109	A1168	5.40k #B151	.75	.25
a.		Bklt. pane of 8 + 4 labels	6.00	
		Booklet, #3109a	6.00	

Tradition of Czech stamp production.

Brno 2000 Philatelic Exhibition A1169

Designs: 5k, 1593 view of Brno. 50k, St. James's Church, vert.

2000, Jan. 20		**Perf. 11¾x11¼**		
3110	A1169	5k multi	.60	.25

Souvenir Sheet

		Perf. 11¼x11¾		
3111	A1169	50k multi	5.00	4.25

No. 3110 printed in sheets of 35 stamps and 30 labels.

Kutna Hora Royal Mining Law, 700th Anniv. — A1170

2000, Mar. 1		**Perf. 11¼x11¾**		
3112	A1170	5k multi	.60	.25
a.		Booklet pane of 8 + 4 labels	5.00	
		Booklet, #3112a	5.00	

Souvenir Sheet

Pres. Thomas Garrigue Masaryk (1850-1937) — A1171

2000, Mar. 1		**Engr.**	**Perf. 11¾**	
3113	A1171	17k multi	1.75	1.50

Pres. Havel Type of 1998

Photo. & Engr.

2000, Mar. 1		**Perf. 11¾x11¼**		
3114	A1134	5.40k Prus bl & org brn	.60	.25

Easter — A1172

Photo. & Engr.

2000, Apr. 5		**Perf. 11¼x11½**		
3115	A1172	5k multi	.60	.25

Souvenir Sheet

Prague, 2000 European City of Culture — A1173

No. 3116: a, 9k, Statue of man. b, 11k, Statue of harpist. c, 17k, Statue of King Charles IV.

Litho. & Engr.

2000, Apr. 5		**Perf. 11¾**		
3116	A1173	Sheet of 3, #a-c + 3 labels	4.00	4.00

Souvenir Sheet

Trains
A1174

No. 3117: a, 8k, Train from 1900. b, 15k, Train from 2000.

Litho. & Engr.
2000, May 5			**Perf. 11¾**	
3117	A1174	Sheet of 2, #a-b, +3 labels	3.00	3.00

Czech
Personalities — A1175

5k, Vítezslav Nezval (1900-58), writer. 8k, Gustav Mahler (1860-1911), composer.

Photo. & Engr.
2000, May 5			**Perf. 11¼x11¾**	
3118-3119	A1175	Set of 2	1.40	.50

Europa, 2000
Common Design Type

2000, May 5	**Litho.**		**Perf. 12¾x13¼**	
3120	CD17	9k multi	1.20	.40

Intl. Children's
Year — A1176

Photo. & Engr.
2000, May 31			**Perf. 11½x11¼**	
3121	A1176	5.40k multi	.75	.25
a.		Booklet pane of 8 + 2 labels	6.00	
		Booklet, #3121a	6.00	

1995 Proof of Fermat's Last Theorem by Andrew Wiles — A1177

2000, May 31			**Perf. 11¾x11¼**	
3122	A1177	7k multi	.80	.25

Intl. Mathematics Year.

Prague
Landmarks
A1178

Designs: 9k, Charles Bridge tower. 11k, St. Nicholas's Church. 13k, Town Hall.

2000, June 28	**Engr.**		**Perf. 11¾**	
3123-3125	A1178	Set of 3	3.00	1.10

Issued in sheets of 8. Value, set $24.

Mushrooms
A1179

No. 3126, 5k: a, Geastrum pouzarii. b, Boletus satanoides.
No. 3127, 5.40k: a, Morchella pragensis. b, Verpa bohemica.

Photo. & Engr.
2000, June 28			**Perf. 11¼x11½**	
		Pairs, #a-b		
3126-3127	A1179	Set of 2	2.40	.70
		Booklet, 3 #3126a, 2 #3126b	3.50	
		Booklet, 3 #3127b, 2 #3127a	3.50	

Meeting of Intl. Monetary Fund and World Bank Group, Prague A1180

2000, Aug. 30			**Perf. 11¾x11¼**	
3128	A1180	7k multi	.95	.25

Ancient
Olympics
A1181

2000, Aug. 30				
3129	A1181	9k multi	1.00	.35

2000 Summer Olympics, Sydney A1182

2000, Aug. 30				
3130	A1182	13k multi	1.25	.45

No. 3130 was issued in sheets of 35 + 25 labels. Values: stamp + 1 label, $1.50; stamp + 2 labels, $1.75.

Hunting
A1183

No. 3131: a, 5k, Falconry. b, 5k, Deer at feed trough.
No. 3132: a, 5.40k, Ducks and blind. b, 5.40k, Deer and blind.

Photo. & Engr.
2000, Oct. 4			**Perf. 11¼x11¾**	
		Horiz. Pairs, #a-b		
3131-3132	A1183	Set of 2	2.40	.55
		Booklet, 3 #3131a, 2 #3131b	3.50	
		Booklet, 3 #3132a, 2 #3132b	3.50	

Painting Type of 1967 Inscribed "ČESKA REPUBLIKA"

Designs: 13k, St. Luke the Evangelist, by Master Theodoricus. 17k, Simeon With Infant Jesus, by Petr Jan Brandl. 26k, Brunette, by Alfons Mucha.

2000, Nov. 15	**Engr.**		**Perf. 11¾**	
3133-3135	A565	Set of 3	5.00	4.50

Nos. 3133-3135 were each issued in sheets of 4. Value, set $20.

Christmas — A1184

Photo. & Engr.
2000, Nov. 15			**Perf. 11¼x11½**	
3136	A1184	5k multi	.60	.25

End of
Millennium — A1185

2000, Nov. 22				
3137	A1185	9k multi	1.20	.35

Advent of New
Millennium — A1186

2001, Jan. 2				
3138	A1186	9k multi	1.20	.35

Tradition of Czech Stamp Production — A1187

2001, Jan. 20			**Perf. 11¼x11¾**	
3139	A1187	5.40k #474	.75	.25
a.		Booklet pane of 8 + 4 labels	6.00	
		Booklet, #3139a	6.00	

Jan Amos Komensky (Comenius, 1592-1670), Theologian — A1188

Photo. & Engr.
2001, Mar. 14			**Perf. 11¼x11½**	
3140	A1188	9k red & black	1.10	.35

Souvenir Sheet

Architecture — A1189

No. 3141: a, 13k, Church and decorations, Jakub. b, 17k, Arcade decorations, Bucovice Castle. c, 31k, Dance Hall, Prague.

2001, Mar. 28	**Engr.**	**Perf. 11¾x11½**		
3141	A1189	Sheet of 3, #a-c	6.00	4.50

Easter — A1190

Photo. & Engr.
2001, Mar. 28			**Perf. 11¼x11½**	
3142	A1190	5.40k multi	.75	.25

Souvenir Sheet

Allegory of Art, by Vaclav Vavrinec Reiner A1191

2001, Apr. 18	**Litho. & Engr.**		**Perf. 11¾**	
3143	A1191	50k multi	5.00	4.25

Europa — A1192

Photo. & Engr.
2001, May 9			**Perf. 11¾x11¼**	
3144	A1192	9k pur & lilac	1.20	.35

European Men's Volleyball Championships, Ostrova — A1193

Photo. & Engr.
2001, May 9			**Perf. 11¼x11½**	
3145	A1193	12k multi	1.25	.50

Intl. Children's
Day — A1194

Photo. & Engr.
2001, May 30			**Perf. 11¼x11½**	
3146	A1194	5.40k multi	.60	.25
a.		Booklet pane of 8 + 2 labels	5.00	—
		Booklet, #3146a	5.00	

Famous Men — A1195

Designs: 5.40k, Frantisek Skroup (1801-62), composer. 16k, Frantisek Halas (1901-49), writer.

2001, May 30				
3147-3148	A1195	Set of 2	2.50	.80

Congratulations
A1196

2001, June 20				
3149	A1196	5.40k multi	.75	.25
		Booklet, 5 #3149	4.00	

Dogs — A1197

No. 3150: a, West Highland terrier. b, Beagle.
No. 3151: a, German shepherd. b, Golden retriever.

Photo. & Engr.
2001, June 20			**Perf. 11½x11¼**	
3150		Pair	1.25	1.00
a.-b.	A1197	5.40k Any single	.60	.25
		Booklet, 3 #3150a, 2 #3150b	3.25	
		Booklet, 3 #3150b, 2 #3150a	3.25	
3151		Pair	1.25	1.00
a.-b.	A1197	5.40k Any single	.60	.25
		Booklet, 3 #3151a, 2 #3151b	3.25	

Zoo Animals A1198

No. 3152: a, Pongo pygmaeus. b, Panthera tigris altaica.
No. 3153: a, Ailurus fulgens. b, Fennecus zerda.

Photo. & Engr.
2001, Sept. 5			**Perf. 11¾x11¼**	
3152	A1198	Pair	1.00	1.00
a.-b.		5.40k Any single	.50	.25
		Booklet, 3 #3152b, 2 #3152a	3.25	
3153	A1198	Pair	1.00	1.00
a.-b.		5.40k Any single	.50	.25
		Booklet, 3 #3153b, 2 #3153a	3.25	

UNESCO World Heritage Sites — A1199

Designs: 12k, Kormeríz Castle and Gardens. 14k, Holasovice Historical Village Restoration.

2001, Oct. 9   Engr.   Perf. 11½x11¾
3154-3155 A1199   Set of 2   2.00 1.25
See Nos. 3177-3178, 3267-3268.

Year of Dialogue Among Civilizations — A1200

Photo. & Engr.
2001, Oct. 9   Perf. 11¼x11½
3156 A1200 9k multi   .85 .35

Mills — A1201

Designs: 9k, Windmill. 14.40k, Water mill.

2001, Oct. 9
3157-3158 A1201 Set of 2   2.25 1.00

Christmas — A1202

Photo. & Engr.
2001, Nov. 14   Perf. 11¼x11½
3159 A1202 5.40k multi   .60 .30

Painting Type of 1967 Inscribed "CESKA REPUBLIKA"

Designs: 12k, The Annunciation of the Virgin Mary, by Michael J. Rentz. 17k, The Sans Souci Bar in Nimes, by Cyril Bouda. 26k, The Goose Keeper, by Vaclav Brozík.

2001, Nov. 14   Engr.   Perf. 11¾
3160-3162 A565   Set of 3   4.50 4.25
Nos. 3160-3162 were each issued in sheets of 4. Value, set $18.

Tradition of Czech Stamp Production — A1203

Photo. & Engr.
2002, Jan. 20   Perf. 11¼x11¾
3163 A1203 5.40k Type A89   .75 .25
a. Booklet pane of 8 + 4 labels 5.00 —
    Booklet, #3163a   5.00

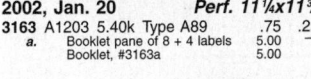

2002 Winter Olympics, Salt Lake City — A1204

2002, Jan. 30   Perf. 11¼
3164 A1204 12k multi   1.25 .45
For overprint, see No. 3168.

2002 Winter Paralympics, Salt Lake City — A1205

2002, Jan. 30   Perf. 11¼x11½
3165 A1205 5.40k multi   .85 .25

Composers Jaromír Vejvoda (1902-88), Josef Poncar (1902-86) and Karel Vacek (1902-82) A1206

2002, Mar. 6   Perf. 11¾x11¼
3166 A1206 9k multi   1.10 .35

Easter — A1207

2002, Mar. 6   Perf. 11¼x11½
3167 A1207 5.40k multi   .85 .25

No. 3164 Overprinted in Blue

Photo. & Engr.
2002, Mar. 8   Perf. 11¼
3168 A1204 12k multi   1.25 .65

Divan, by Vlaho Bukovac (1855-1922) — A1208

Litho. & Engr.
2002, Apr. 23   Perf. 11¾
3169 A1208 17k multi   2.00 1.40
Printed in sheets of 4 + 2 labels. Value $8. See Croatia No. 487.

Europa — A1209

Photo. & Engr.
2002, May 7   Perf. 11¾x11¼
3170 A1209 9k multi   1.20 .35

Souvenir Sheet

Czech Culture and France A1210

No. 3171: a, 23k, Klávesy Piana-Jezero, by Frantisek Kupka. b, 31k, Man with Broken Nose, sculpture by Auguste Rodin.

Perf. 11¾x11½
2002, May 7   Litho. & Engr.
3171 A1210 Sheet of 2, #a-b 5.25 4.00

Intl. Children's Day — A1211

Photo. & Engr.
2002, May 29   Perf. 11¼x11½
3172 A1211 5.40k multi   .60 .25
a. Booklet pane of 8 + 2 labels 5.00 —
    Complete booklet, #3172a   5.00

Margaritifera Margaritifera — A1212

2002, June 6
3173 A1212 9k multi   1.00 .35

Jan Hus (1372-1415), Religious Leader — A1213

2002, June 19
3174 A1213 9k multi + label   1.00 .35

Souvenir Sheet

Worldwide Fund for Nature (WWF) — A1214

Butterflies: a, 5.40k, Maculinea nausithous. b, 5.40k, Maculinea alcon. c, 9k, Maculinea teleius. d, 9k, Maculinea arion.

Litho. & Engr.
2002, June 19   Perf. 11¾
3175 A1214   Sheet of 4, #a-d + 4 labels 3.50 2.75

Pansy — A1215

Photo. & Engr.
2002, Sept. 1   Perf. 11¾x11¼
3176 A1215 6.40k multi   .85 .25
See Nos. 3220-3221, 3262-3263, 3293-3294, 3340, 3345-3347, 3363-3366, 3467-3469, 3500, 3756, 3789.

World Heritage Sites Type of 2001

Designs: 12k, Litomysl Castle. 14k, Holy Trinity Column, Olomouc, vert.

Perf. 11½x11¾, 11¾x11½
2002, Sept. 11   Engr.
3177-3178 A1199   Set of 2   2.75 2.00
Nos. 3177-3178 were each issued in sheets of 8. Value, set $25.

Emil Zátopek (1922-2000), Olympic Long Distance Runner — A1216

Photo. & Engr.
2002, Sept. 11   Perf. 11¼x11¾
3179 A1216 9k multi   1.10 .35

Pres. Havel Type of 1998
Photo. & Engr.
2002, Nov. 6   Perf. 11¾x11½
3180 A1134 6.40k pur & blue   .85 .25

St. Nicholas' Day — A1217

2002, Nov. 6   Perf. 11¼x11½
3181 A1217 6.40k multi   .85 .25
a. Booklet pane of 8 + 2 labels 6.00 —
    Complete booklet, #3181a   6.00

Christmas — A1218

2002, Nov. 13
3182 A1218 6.40k multi   .85 .25

NATO Summit, Prague — A1219

2002, Nov. 14   Perf. 11¼x11¾
3183 A1219 9k multi   1.00 .30

Furniture — A1220

Designs: 6.40k, Armchair, 17th cent. 9k, Sewing table with hemispheric cover, 1820. 12k, Dressing table with mirror, 1860. 17k, Art deco amchair, 1923.

2002, Dec. 11
3184-3187 A1220   Set of 4   4.50 2.25

Painting Type of 1967 Inscribed "CESKA REPUBLIKA"

Designs: 12k, The Abandoned, by Jaroslav Panuska, horiz. 20k, St. Wenceslas, by Mikolás Ales. 26k, Portrait of a Young Man with a Lute, by Jan Petr Molitor.

2002, Dec. 11   Engr.   Perf. 11¾
3188-3190 A565   Set of 3   5.75 3.75
Nos. 3188-3190 were each issued in sheets of 4. Value, set $23.

Souvenir Sheet

Czech Republic, 10th Anniv. A1221

Litho. & Engr.

2003, Jan. 1   **Perf. 11¾**
3191 A1221 25k multi   2.75 1.60

Tradition of Czech Stamp
Production — A1222

Photo. & Engr.

2003, Jan. 20   **Perf. 11¼x11¾**
3192 A1222 6.40k Type A75   .95   .25
a.   Booklet pane of 8 + 2 labels   7.50
      Complete booklet, #3192a   7.50

Famous
Men — A1223

Designs: 6.40k, Jaroslav Vrchlicky (1853-1912), poet. 8k, Josef Thomayer (1853-1927), physician and writer.

2003, Feb. 12   **Perf. 11½x11¼**
3193-3194 A1223 Set of 2   1.75   .50

Easter — A1224

2003, Mar. 26   **Perf. 11¼x11½**
3195 A1224 6.40k multi   .95   .25

Roses
Above
Prague
A1225

Perf. 12¾x13¼

2003, Mar. 26   **Litho.**
3196 A1225 6.40k multi + label   .75   .35
Labels could be personalized.
Issued in sheets of 9 stamps and 12 labels. Value $9.
See No. 3517.

Lace — A1226

Designs: 6.40k, Netted lace. 9k, Bobbin lace.

Photo. & Engr.

2003, Mar. 26   **Perf. 11¼**
3197 A1226 6.40k bl, dk bl & red   .75   .25
a.   Booklet pane of 6 + 4 labels   4.50
      Complete booklet, #3197a   4.50
3198 A1226 9k dk bl, bl & red   1.00   .35
a.   Booklet pane of 6 + 4 labels   6.00
      Complete booklet, #3198a   6.00

Europa — A1227

Litho. & Engr.

2003, May 7   **Perf. 11¾**
3199 A1227 9k multi   1.20   .65

Geologic
Attractions
A1228

Designs: 12k, Sandstone towers, Hrubá Skála Region. 14k, Punkva Caves, Moravian karst area.

2003, May 7   **Engr.**   **Perf. 11½x11¾**
3200-3201 A1228   Set of 2   3.00 2.00
Nos. 3200-3201 were each issued in sheets of 8. Value, set $25.

Mach and Sebestova,
Children's Television
Show
Characters — A1229

Photo. & Engr.

2003, May 28   **Perf. 11¼x11½**
3202 A1229 6.40k multi   .95   .35
a.   Booklet pane of 8 + 2 labels   7.50   —
      Complete booklet #3202a   7.50

First Electric
Railway, Tábor
— Bechyne,
Cent. — A1230

2003, May 28   **Perf. 11¾x11¼**
3203 A1230 10k multi   1.25   .50

A1231

Observation towers: No. 3204, 6.40k, Klet. No. 3205, 6.40k, Slovanka.

2003, May 28   **Perf. 11¼x11½**
3204-3205 A1231   Set of 2   1.50   .50

A1232

2003, June 25   **Perf. 11¾x11¼**
3206 A1232 9k multi   1.25   .35
European Shooting Championships, Plzen and Brno.

A1233

2003, June 25   **Perf. 11¼x11½**
3207 A1233 9k multi   1.20   .35
Josef Dobrovsky (1753-1829), linguist.

Pres. Vaclav
Klaus — A1234

Photo. & Engr.

2003   **Perf. 11¾x11¼**
3208 A1234 6.40k buff, red & vio
bl   .95   .35
3209 A1234 6.50k Prus bl & pur   .95   .35
Issued: 6.40k, 7/30; 6.50k, 11/5.
See No. 3264.

Souvenir Sheet

Tropical
Fish
A1235

No. 3210: a, 12k, Betta splendens (27x44mm). b, 14k, Pterophyllum scalare (27x44mm). c, 16k, Carassius auratus (54x44mm). d, 20k, Symphysodon aequifasciatus (54x44mm).

Litho. & Engr.

2003, Sept. 10   **Perf. 11¾**
3210 A1235   Sheet of 4, #a-d   6.00 5.00
No. 3210 exists in six different varieties, which may be distinguished by the number of horizontal lines in the stone in the bottom sheet margin below the 14k stamp. Values given are for sheets with 1, 2 or 5 lines in the stone; value for sheet with no lines or 3 lines in the stone, $21; value for sheet with 4 lines in the stone, $72.50.

Oriental
Carpets
A1236

Designs: 9k, Turkish prayer carpet, 19th cent. 12k, Turkish carpet, 18th cent.

2003, Oct. 1   **Engr.**   **Perf. 11¾**
3211-3212 A1236   Set of 2   2.50 1.75
Nos. 3211-3212 were each issued in sheets of 4. Value, set $10.

Tympanum,
Porta Coeli
Monastery,
Predklásterí
A1237

Photo. & Engr.

2003, Oct. 15   **Perf. 11¾x11¼**
3213 A1237 6.50k multi   .95   .45
a.   Booklet pane of 8 + 4 labels   7.50   —
      Complete booklet, #3213a   7.50

Birds of Prey — A1238

Designs: 6.50k, Milvus milvus. 8k, Falco peregrinus. 9k, Hieraaetus pennatus.

2003, Oct. 15   **Perf. 11¼x11½**
3214 A1238 6.50k multi   .75   .25
      Booklet, 5 #3214   3.75
3215 A1238   8k multi   .90   .30
      Booklet, 5 #3215   4.50
3216 A1238   9k multi   1.00   .30
      Booklet, 5 #3216   5.00
      Nos. 3214-3216 (3)   2.65   .85

Czech Fire
Fighters, 140th
Anniv. — A1239

Fire engines: 6.50k, Wooden fire engine, 1822. 9k, Motorized fire engine, 1933. 12k, CAS 8/Avia Daewoo fire truck, 2002.

2003, Oct. 15   **Perf. 11¾x11¼**
3217-3219 A1239   Set of 3   3.00 1.50

Flower Type of 2002

Designs: 50h, Cornflower (chrpa). 6.50k, Dahlia (jirina).

2003, Oct. 22
3220 A1215 50h multi   .25   .25
3221 A1215 6.50k multi   .75   .25

**Roses Over Prague Type of 2003
and**

Prague
Castle
Lantern
A1240

2003, Oct. 22 Litho.   Perf. 12¾x13¼
3222 A1225 6.50k multi + label   .75   .25
3223 A1240   9k multi + label   1.00   .30
Labels could be personalized.
Nos. 3222-3223 were each issued in sheets of 9 stamps and 12 labels. Value, set $17.50.

**Painting Type of 1967 Inscribed
"ČESKA REPUBLIKA"**

Designs: 17k, Poor Countryside, by Max Svabinsky, horiz. 20k, Autumn in Veltrusy, by Antonín Slavícek. 26k, Eleanora de Toledo, by Agnolo Bronzino.

2003, Nov. 5   **Engr.**   **Perf. 11¾**
3224-3226 A565   Set of 3   6.50 4.00
Nos. 3224-3226 were each issued in sheets of 4. Value, set $26.

Christmas — A1241

Photo. & Engr.

2003, Nov. 5   **Perf. 11¼x11½**
3227 A1241 6.50k multi   .75   .35

Tradition of Czech
Stamp
Production — A1242

Photo. & Engr.

2004, Jan. 20   **Perf. 11¼x11¾**
3228 A1242 6.50k Vignette of
#1703   .95   .35
a.   Booklet pane of 8 + 4 labels   7.50
      Complete booklet, #3228a   7.50

Church of
the
Assumption
of the
Virgin
Mary, Brno
A1243

2004, Feb. 18   **Engr.**   **Perf. 11¾**
3229 A1243 17k multi   1.90 1.00
Brno 2005 Philatelic Exhibition.
No. 3229 was issued in sheets of 4. Value $8.

Industrial Building
Historical
Preservation
A1244

Designs: 6.50k, Busek's Water Forging Hammer, Lniste. 17k, Iron Furnace, Stará Hut u Adamova.

Photo. & Engr.

2004, Feb. 18   **Perf. 11½x11¼**
3230-3231 A1244   Set of 2   2.40   .90

Easter — A1245

2004, Mar. 17
3232 A1245 6.50k multi .95 .25

Painting Type of 1967 Inscribed "ČESKÁ REPUBLIKA"

Design: Prometheus, by Antonín Procházka.

2004, Mar. 17 Engr. Perf. 11¾
3233 A565 26k multi 2.60 1.60

Brno 2005 Philatelic Exhibition. No. 3233 was issued in sheets of 4. Value $11.

World Ice Hockey Championships, Prague and Ostrava — A1246

Photo. & Engr.
2004, Apr. 14 Perf. 11¼x11¾
3234 A1246 12k multi 1.50 .50

Admission to European Union — A1247

Photo. & Engr.
2004, May 1 Perf. 11¼
3235 A1247 9k multi 1.20 .35

Admission to the European Union — A1248

2004, May 1 Litho. Perf. 11¾x11¼
3236 A1248 9k multi 1.10 .35

No. 3236 was issued in sheets of 10. Value $11.

Europa — A1249

2004, May 5 Perf. 11¼
3237 A1249 9k multi 1.10 .35

Composers of Czech Operas — A1250

Designs: 6.50k, Dalibor, by Bedrich Smetana (1824-84). 8k, Jakobín, by Antonín Dvořák (1841-1904). 10k, Její Pastorkyna, by Leos Janácek (1854-1928).

Photo. & Engr.
2004, May 5 Perf. 11¼x11¾
3238-3240 A1250 Set of 3 2.60 1.10

For Children — A1251

Photo. & Engr.
2004, May 26 Perf. 11½x11¼
3241 A1251 6.50k multi .85 .25
a. Booklet pane of 8 + 2 labels 7.00 —
Complete booklet, #3241a 7.00

Statue of Radegast, by Albín Polásek — A1252

2004, May 26 Perf. 11¼x11½
3242 A1252 6.50k multi .85 .25

Brno 2005 Philatelic Exhibition.

Tourist Attractions A1253

Designs: 12k, Holy Mountain, Príbram. 14k, Holy Shrine, Bystrice pod Hostynem.

2004, May 26 Engr. Perf. 11½x11¾
3243-3244 A1253 Set of 2 2.60 1.50

Nos. 3243-3244 were each issued in sheets of 8. Value, set $24.

A1254

Photo. & Engr.
2004, June 23 Perf. 11¼x11¾
3245 A1254 6.50k multi 1.20 .25

2004 Paralympics, Athens.

A1255

2004, June 23
3246 A1255 9k multi 1.00 .35

2004 Summer Olympics, Athens.

Petrarch (1304-74), Poet — A1256

2004, June 23 Perf. 11¾x11¼
3247 A1256 14k multi 1.40 .60

Famous Trees — A1257

Designs: 6.50k, Singing lime tree, Telecí. 8k, Jan Zizka oak tree, Podhradí.

Photo. & Engr.
2004, Sept. 8 Perf. 11¼x11½
3248 A1257 6.50k multi .75 .25
Complete booklet, 5 #3248 3.75
3249 A1257 8k multi .90 .25
Complete booklet, 5 #3249 4.50

Miniature Sheet

Parrots
A1258

No. 3250: a, 12k, Melopsittacus undulatus. b, 14k, Agapornis personata. c, 16k, Psittacula krameri. d, 20k, Ara chloroptera.

Litho. & Engr.
2004, Sept. 8 Perf. 11¾
3250 A1258 Sheet of 4, #a-d, + 6.00 4.50
4 labels

Compulsory School Attendance, 230th Anniv. — A1259

Photo. & Engr.
2004, Sept. 29 Perf. 11¼x11½
3251 A1259 6.50k multi .85 .25

Baby Carriages — A1260

Carriages made about: 12k, 1880. 14k, 1890. 16k, 1900.

2004, Oct. 20
3252-3254 A1260 Set of 3 4.00 2.00

Painting Type of 1967 Inscribed "ČESKÁ REPUBLIKA"

Designs: 20k, On the Outskirts of the Cesky Ráj Region, by Alois Bubák, horiz. 22k, The Long, the Broad and the Sharpsight, by Hanus Schwaiger. 26k, The Spring, by Vojtěch Hynais.

2004, Nov. 10 Engr. Perf. 11¾
3255-3257 A565 Set of 3 6.50 4.25

Nos. 3255-3257 were each issued in sheets of 4. Value, set $32.

Christmas — A1261

Photo. & Engr.
2004, Nov. 10 Perf. 11¼x11½
3258 A1261 6.50k multi .75 .25

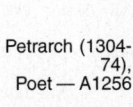

Tradition of Czech Stamp Production — A1262

2005, Jan. 18 Perf. 11¼x11¾
3259 A1262 6.50k Design of .95 .30
#975
a. Booklet pane of 8 + 4 labels 7.50 —
Complete booklet, #3259a 7.50

Peacock and Bugler Portal Decoration A1263

2005, Jan. 18 Litho. Perf. 12¾x13¼
3260 A1263 7.50k multi + label .95 .30

Labels could be personalized for an additional fee.
Issued in sheets of 9 stamps and 12 labels. Value $9.
See Nos. 3372, 3516.

Souvenir Sheet

Moonscape, by Petr Ginz — A1264

Perf. 11¾x11½
2005, Jan. 18 Litho. & Engr.
3261 A1264 31k multi 3.00 2.00

Flower Type of 2002

Designs: 7.50k, Lily (lilie). 19k, Fuchsia (fuchsie).

Photo. & Engr.
2005 Perf. 11¾x11¼
3262 A1215 7.50k multi .85 .30
3263 A1215 19k multi 2.25 .85

Issued: 7.50k, 1/20; 19k, 3/2.

Pres. Vaclav Klaus Type of 2003
2005, Feb. 9
3264 A1234 7.50k claret & red .85 .30

Granny, by Bozena Nemcová, 150th Anniv. of Publication — A1265

2005, Feb. 9 Perf. 11¼x11¾
3265 A1265 7.50k multi .85 .30

Easter — A1266

Photo. & Engr.
2005, Mar. 2 Perf. 11¼x11½
3266 A1266 7.50k multi .85 .30

UNESCO World Heritage Sites Type of 2001

Designs: 14k, St. Prokop's Basilica, Trebíc, vert. 16k, Villa Tugendhat, Brno.

Perf. 11¾x11½, 11½x11¾
2005, Mar. 23   Engr.
3267-3268 A1199   Set of 2   3.25 1.90
Nos. 3267-32682 were each issued in sheets of 8. Value, set $26.

Famous Men — A1267

Designs: 7.50k, Bohuslav Brauner (1855-1935), chemist. 12k, Adalbert Stifter (1805-68), writer, painter. 19k, Mikulás Dacicky of Heslov (1555-1626), poet.

Photo. & Engr.
2005, Apr. 13   Perf. 11¼x11¾
3269-3271 A1267   Set of 3   3.75 1.60

Europa — A1268

2005, May 4   Litho.   Perf. 11¼
3272 A1268 9k multi   1.20 .35
Issued in sheets of 6. Value, $7.50.

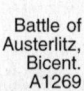

Battle of Austerlitz, Bicent. A1269

Napoleon Before the Battle of Austerlitz, by Louis-François Lejeune — A1270

Photo. & Engr.
2005, May 4   Perf. 11¾x11¼
3273 A1269 19k multi   2.25 .90

Souvenir Sheet
Litho. & Engr.
Perf. 11¾
3274 A1270 30k multi   3.50 2.25
Brno 2005 Stamp Exhibition (No. 3274). No. 3273 was issued in sheets of 40 + 20 labels. Value, one stamp + label $3.25. See France No. 3115.

Kremílek and Vochomurka, by Václav Ctvrtek — A1271

Photo. & Engr.
2005, May 25   Perf. 11¼x11½
3275 A1271 7.50k multi   .85 .30
  a. Booklet pane of 8 + 2 labels   7.00 —
      Complete booklet, #3275a   7.00

Intl. Year of Physics A1272

2005, May 25   Perf. 11¼x11¾
3276 A1272 12k multi   1.40 .75

2005 European Baseball Championships A1273

2005, June 22
3277 A1273 9k multi   1.10 .50

Souvenir Sheet

Protected Flora and Fauna of the Krkonose Mountains — A1274

No. 3278: a, 12k, Viola lutea sudetica, Hedysarum hedysaroides (44x28mm). b, 14k, Cinclus cinclus, Leucojum vernum (44x28mm). c, 15k, Sorex alpinus, Salamandra salamandra, Primula minima (44x54mm). d, 22k, Mt. Snezka, Luscinia svecica svecica, Aeschna coerulea, Pneumonanthe asclepiadea (44x54mm).

Litho. & Engr.
2005, June 22   Perf. 11¾
3278 A1274   Sheet of 4, #a-d, + 4 labels   7.00 4.25

Church Bells — A1275

Bells from: 7.50k, Benesov, 1322, Havlíckuv Brod, 1335. 9k, Dobrs, 1561, 1596. 12k, Olomouc, 1827.

Photo. & Engr.
2005, Sept. 7   Perf. 11½x11¾
3279 A1275 7.50k multi   .80 .30
      Complete booklet, 5 #3279   4.00
3280 A1275 9k multi   .90 .40
      Complete booklet, 5 #3280   4.50
3281 A1275 12k multi   1.20 .50
      Complete booklet, 5 #3281   6.00
      Nos. 3279-3281 (3)   2.90 1.20

Tractors — A1276

Designs: 7.50k, 1923 John Deere 15/27. 9k, 1921 Lanz Bulldog HL-12, 1596. 18k, 1937 Skoda HT 40.

2005, Sept. 21   Perf. 11½x11¼
3282 A1276 7.50k multi   .60 .30
      Complete booklet, 5 #3282   3.50
3283 A1276 9k multi   .90 .35
      Complete booklet, 5 #3283   5.00
3284 A1276 18k multi   1.90 .75
      Complete booklet, 5 #3284   9.50
      Nos. 3282-3284 (3)   3.40 1.40

World Summit on the Information Society, Tunis — A1277

2005, Sept. 21   Perf. 11¼
3285 A1277 9k org & violet   1.10 .35

Curling A1278

Photo. & Engr.
2005, Oct. 12   Perf. 11¾x11¼
3286 A1278 17k multi   2.00 .70

Painting Type of 1967 Inscribed "CĚSKÁ REPUBLIKA"
Designs: 22k, Summer Landscape, by Adolf Kosárek. 25k, Deinotherium, by Zdeněk Burian. 26k, Osiky Near Velké Nemcice, by Alois Kalvoda.

2005, Nov. 9   Engr.   Perf. 11¾
3287-3289 A565   Set of 3   8.00 5.25
Nos. 3287-3289 were each issued in sheets of 4. Value, set $32.50.

A1279

Christmas — A1280

Photo. & Engr.
2005, Nov. 9   Perf. 11¼x11½
3290 A1279 7.50k multi   .85 .30
                            Perf. 11½x11¼
3291 A1280 9k multi   1.00 .35

Tradition of Czech Stamp Production — A1281

Photo. & Engr.
2006, Jan. 20   Perf. 11¼x11¾
3292 A1281 7.50k Portion of #C59   .95 .30
  a. Booklet pane of 8 + 2 labels   7.50
      Complete booklet, #3292a   7.50

Flower Type of 2002
Designs: 11k, Marshmallow (ibisek). 24k, Daffodil (narcis).

2006   Perf. 11¾x11¼
3293 A1215 11k multi   1.25 .45
3294 A1215 24k multi   2.75 1.00
Issued: 11k, 2/1; 24k, 2/22.

Flowers A1282

Flowers, Grapes, Glass of Wine A1283

2006   Litho.   Perf. 12¾x13¼
3295 A1282 10k multi + label   1.10 .60
3296 A1283 12k multi + label   1.40 .75
Issued: 10k, 2/1; 12k, 2/22. Labels could be personalized for an additional fee. Nos. 3295-3296 were issued in sheets of 9 stamps and 12 labels. Value, set $22.50. See No. 3373.

Madonna of Zbraslav A1284

2006, Feb. 8   Engr.   Perf. 11¾
3297 A1284 25k multi   2.50 1.75
Printed in sheets of 4. Value $10.

2006 Winter Paralympics, Turin — A1285

Photo. & Engr.
2006, Feb. 8   Perf. 11¾x11¼
3298 A1285 7.50k multi   .85 .30

2006 Winter Olympics, Turin — A1286

2006   Perf. 11¼x11¾
3299 A1286 9k multi   1.00 .40

With "K. NEUMANNOVA / ZLATA MEDAILE" Overprinted in Red Reading Up
3300 A1286 9k multi   1.10 .40
Issued: No. 3299, 2/8; No. 3300, 3/15.

Famous Men — A1287

Designs: 11k, Frantisek Josef Gerstner (1756-1832), mathematician and educator. 12k, Jaroslav Jezek (1906-42), composer. 19k, Sigmund Freud (1856-1939), psychoanalyst.

2006, Feb. 22   Perf. 11½x11¼
3301-3303 A1287   Set of 3   4.00 1.75

Easter — A1288

2006, Mar. 22   Perf. 11¼x11½
3304 A1288 7.50k multi   1.20 .30

Osek Monastery A1289

Kokorinsko Capstones
A1290

2006, Mar. 22 Engr. Perf. 11½x11¾
3305 A1289 12k multi 1.20 .65
3306 A1290 15k multi 1.40 .85

Nos. 3305-3306 were each issued in sheets of 8. Value, set $22.

Love — A1291

Photo. & Engr.
2006, Apr. 26 Perf. 11¼x11½
3307 A1291 7.50k multi .95 .35
Complete booklet, 5 #3307 4.75

Europa
A1292

Silhouette of person and: 10k, Horse. 20k, Dog.

2006, May 3 Perf. 11¾x11¼
3308-3309 A1292 Set of 2 3.00 1.40

Issued in sheets of 8. Value, set $24.

Rumcajs, Manka and Cipísek, by V. Ctvrtek — A1293

Photo. & Engr.
2006, May 31 Perf. 11¼x11½
3310 A1293 7.50k multi .95 .35
a. Booklet pane of 8 + 2 labels 7.50
Complete booklet, #3310a 7.50

A1294

2006, June 14 Perf. 11¼x11¾
3311 A1294 19k multi 2.00 .90
Kamenice Pass, Czech Switzerland National Park.

A1295

Jewelry with garnets: 15k, Silver brooch with pearl, 1904. 18k, Gold pendant, 1930.

2006, June 14
3312-3313 A1295 Set of 2 3.00 1.75

Miniature Sheet

Bohemian Kings of Premyslid Dynasty — A1296

No. 3314: a, 12k, Otakar I Premysl (c. 1155-1230). b, 14k, Václav (Wenceslas) I (1205-53). c, 15k, Otakar II Premysl (1230-78). d, 22k, Václav (Wenceslas) II (1271-1305). e, 28k, Václav (Wenceslas) III (1289-1306).

2006, June 14 Engr. Perf. 11¾
3314 A1296 Sheet of 5, #a-e, + label 8.25 6.00

Souvenir Sheet

Mosaic of Prague Castle, by Giovanni Castrucci
A1297

Litho. & Engr.
2006, Sept. 13 Perf. 11¾
3315 A1297 35k multi 3.50 2.25

Cacti
A1298

No. 3316: a, Gymnocalycium denudatum. b, Obregonia denegrii.
No. 3317: a, Astrophytum asterias. b, Cintia knizei.

Perf. 11¼x11¾
2006, Sept. 13 Litho.
3316 A1298 7.50k Pair, #a-b 1.50 .90
Complete booklet, 2 #3316a, 3 #3316b 3.50
3317 A1298 10k Pair, #a-b 2.00 1.25
Complete booklet, 2 #3317a, 3 #3317b 5.00

Ecology — A1299

2006, Sept. 27 Perf. 11¾x11¼
3318 A1299 7.50k multi .95 .35

Christmas
A1300

2006, Oct. 11 Perf. 12¾x13¼
3319 A1300 7.50k multi + label 1.10 .35
Printed in sheets of 9 stamps + 12 labels. Labels could be personalized. Value, $11.

Vrtbovská Garden, Prague — A1301

Photo. & Engr.
2006, Oct. 11 Perf. 11½x11¾
3320 A1301 7.50k multi .95 .35
a. Booklet pane of 8 + 4 labels 7.50 —
Complete booklet, #3320a 7.50

Praga 2008 Intl. Philatelic Exhibition, Prague.

Wooden Churches
A1302

Designs: 7.50k, Church of the Virgin Mary, Broumov. 19k, Church of St. Andrew, Hodslavice.

Photo. & Engr.
2006, Oct. 11 Perf. 11¾x11¼
3321-3322 A1302 Set of 2 2.60 1.60

Painting Type of 1967 Inscribed "ČESKÁ REPUBLIKA"

Designs: 22k, Still Life with Fruit, by Jan Davidsz de Heem. 25k, Montenegrin Madonna, by Jaroslav Cermák. 28k, Pod Suchym Skalim, by Frantisek Kaván, horiz.

2006, Nov. 8 Engr. Perf. 11¾
3323-3325 A565 Set of 3 7.00 4.50

Christmas
A1303

Photo. & Engr.
2006, Nov. 8 Perf. 11¾x11½
3326 A1303 7.50k multi .95 .35

Emblem of Praga 2008 Intl. Philatelic Exhibition — A1304

2006, Dec. 1 Litho.
3327 A1304 7.50k multi .95 .35
See Nos. 3341, 3368.

Czech Technical University, Prague, 300th Anniv. — A1305

Photo. & Engr.
2007, Jan. 10 Perf. 11¾x11½
3328 A1305 9k multi 1.10 .50

Famous Men — A1306

Designs: 7.50k, Frána Srámek (1877-1952), writer. 19k, Karel Slavoj Amerling (1807-84), educator.

2007, Jan. 10 Perf. 11½x11¼
3329-3330 A1306 Set of 2 2.50 1.40

Tradition of Czech Stamp Production — A1307

2007, Jan. 20 Perf. 11½x11¾
3331 A1307 7.50k Type A242 .85 .35
a. Booklet pane of 8 + 4 labels 6.75
Complete booklet, #3331a 6.75

Cancer Prevention — A1308

Photo. & Engr.
2007, Feb. 21 Perf. 11¼x11½
3332 A1308 7.50k multi .85 .35

Snake — A1309

Perf. 11¼x11¾
2007, Feb. 21 Litho.
3333 A1309 12k multi 1.20 .70

Oriental Art — A1310

Designs: 12k, Girl with a Puppet, by Kunisawa Utagawa. 24k, Siva, Parvati and Ganesa, 19th cent. Indian glass painting.

Litho. & Engr.
2007, Feb. 21 Perf. 11¾
3334-3335 A1310 Set of 2 3.50 2.10

Easter — A1311

Photo. & Engr.
2007, Mar. 14 Perf. 11¼x11½
3336 A1311 7.50k multi .85 .35

Model of Mala Strana Area of Prague, by Antonín Langweil A1312

2007, Mar. 14 Perf. 11¾x11¼
3337 A1312 7.50k multi .85 .35
a. Booklet pane of 8 + 4 labels 7.00
Complete booklet, #3337a 7.00

Praga 2008 Intl. Philatelic Exhibition, Prague. No. 3337 was issued in sheets of 8 + 4 labels. Value, $10.

Stoclet House, Brussels, Designed by Josef Hoffmann — A1313

Designs: 20k, Building interior. 35k, Building exterior.

2007, Mar. 26   Perf. 11¼x11¾
3338-3339 A1313 Set of 2   5.00 3.25
See Belgium Nos. 2228-2229.

Flowers Type of 2002
Perf. 12¾x13¼
2007, Mar. 26   Litho.
3340 A1282 11k multi + label   1.25 .60
Label could be personalized for an additional fee.

Praga 2008 Emblem Type of 2006
2007, Apr. 4   Perf. 11¾x11½
3341 A1304 11k blue & multi   1.25 .60

Spas — A1314

Designs: 12k, Jurkovic House, Luhacovice. 15k, Gocár Pavillion, Lázne Bohdanec.

2007, Apr. 4   Engr.   Perf. 11½x11¾
3342-3343 A1314 Set of 2   2.50 1.75
Issued in sheets of 8. Value, $20.

Europa — A1315

Photo. & Engr.
2007, May 9   Perf. 11¼
3344 A1315 11k multi   1.25 .60
Scouting, cent.

Flowers Type of 2002
Designs: 1k, Cyclamen (bramborik). 15k, Tropaeolum (lichorerisnice). 23k, Geranium (pelargonie).

Photo. & Engr.
2007   Perf. 11¾x11¼
3345 A1215   1k multi   .25 .25
3346 A1215   15k multi   1.60 .90
3347 A1215   23k multi   2.00 1.25
   Nos. 3345-3347 (3)   3.85 2.40
Issued: 1k, 23k, 5/9. 15k, 9/5.

Fast Arrows, Comic Strip by Jaroslav Foglar — A1316

Photo. & Engr.
2007, May 30   Perf. 11¾x11¼
3348 A1316 7.50k multi   .85 .35
  a.   Booklet pane of 8 + 4 labels   7.00 —
    Complete booklet, #3348a   7.00

Historic Stoves — A1317

Designs: 7.50k, Gothic era stove, Olomouc, and tile. 12k, Renaissance era stove, Rícany u Prahy and tile.

Photo. & Engr.
2007, June 20   Perf. 11½x11¾
3349 A1317 7.50k multi   .70 .35
    Complete booklet, 5 #3349   3.50
3350 A1317   12k multi   1.25 .60
    Complete booklet, 5 #3350   6.25

Souvenir Sheet

Vaclav Hollar (1607-77), Engraver — A1318

Litho. & Engr.
2007, June 20   Perf. 11¾
3351 A1318 35k multi + 2 labels   3.00 2.10

Souvenir Sheet

Charles Bridge, Prague, 650th Anniv. — A1319

2007, June 20
3352 A1319 45k multi   4.50 3.00
Praga 2008 World Philatelic Exhibition.

First Movie Theater in Prague, Cent. — A1320

Photo. & Engr.
2007, Sept. 5   Perf. 11¾x11¼
3353 A1320 7.50k multi   .75 .35

Didactica Opera Omnia, by Comenius, 350th Anniv. — A1321

2007, Sept. 5
3354 A1321 12k multi   1.25 .75

Miniature Sheet

Flora and Fauna of the White Carpathians — A1322

No. 3355: a, 9k, Ophrys holosericea (27x44mm). b, 10k, Colias myrmidone, Anacamptis pyramidalis (27x44mm). c, 11k, Ophrys apifera (27x44mm). d, 12k, Coracias garrulus, Gymnadenia densiflora (54x44mm).

Litho. & Engr.
2007, Sept. 5   Perf. 11¾
3355 A1322   Sheet of 4, #a-d, +   4.25 2.75
    4 labels

Emil Holub (1847-1902), Naturalist A1323

Photo. & Engr.
2007, Oct. 3   Perf. 11¾x11¼
3356 A1323 11k multi   1.25 .65

Water Towers — A1324

Towers in: 7.50k, Karviná. 18k, Plzen.

2007, Oct. 3   Perf. 11¼x11¾
3357-3358 A1324 Set of 2   2.75 1.50

Painting Type of 1967 Inscribed "CESKA REPUBLIKA"

Designs: 22k, Vrbicany Castle, by Amálie Mánesova, horiz. 25k, Way to Bechnye Castle, by Otakar Lebeda, horiz. 28k, Montmartre, by Sobeslav Hippolyt Pinkas, horiz.

2007, Nov. 7   Engr.   Perf. 11¾
3359-3361 A565 Set of 3   7.25 4.50

Christmas — A1325

Photo. & Engr.
2007, Nov. 7   Perf. 11¼x11½
3362 A1325 7.50k multi   .85 .40

Flower Type of 2002
Design: 2.50k, Gaillardia (kokarda); 3k, Azalea (azalka); 10k, Rose (ruze); 21k, Gerbera daisy (gerbera).

Photo. & Engr.
2007-08   Perf. 11¾x11¼
3363 A1215 2.50k multi   .30 .25
3364 A1215   3k multi   .30 .25
3365 A1215   10k multi   1.10 .60
3366 A1215   21k multi   2.00 1.40
   Nos. 3363-3366 (4)   3.70 2.50
Issued: 2.50k, 12/12/07; 3k, 3/19/08; 10k, 1/30/08; 21k, 3/5/08.

Czech Republic's Entry Into Schengen Border-Free Zone — A1326

2007, Dec. 19   Litho.   Perf. 11¼
3367 A1326 10k multi   1.10 .55

Praga 2008 Emblem Type of 2006
2007, Dec. 19   Perf. 11¾x11¼
3368 A1304 18k bl grn & blue   2.00 1.00

Tradition of Czech Stamp Production — A1327

Photo. & Engr.
2008, Jan. 20   Perf. 11¼x11¾
3369 A1327 10k Type A311   .95 .60
  a.   Booklet pane of 8 + 4 labels   8.00
    Complete booklet, #3369a   8.00

Famous Men — A1328

Designs: 11k, Karel Klostermann (1848-1923), writer. 14k, Josef Kajetán Tyl (1808-56), playwright.

2008, Jan. 20   Perf. 11¼x11½
3370-3371 A1328 Set of 2   2.50 1.50

Peacock and Bugler Type of 2005 and Flowers, Grapes and Glass of Wine Type of 2006 Redrawn
2008, Jan. 30 Litho.   Perf. 12¾x13¼
3372 A1263 10k multi + label   1.00 .60
3373 A1283 17k multi + label   1.75 1.00
Nos. 3372-3373 were issued in sheets of 9 stamps and 12 labels. Labels could be personalized for an additional fee.

George of Podebrady (1420-71), King of Bohemia — A1329

Photo. & Engr.
2008, Feb. 20   Perf. 11¼x11¾
3374 A1329 12k multi   1.25 .75
No. 3374 was issued in sheets of 8 + 1 label. Values: single stamp + label, $4; complete sheet, $10.

Intl. Year of Planet Earth — A1330

2008, Feb. 20   Litho.   Perf. 11¼
3375 A1330 18k multi   1.75 1.10

Easter — A1331

Photo. & Engr.
2008, Mar. 5   Perf. 11½x11¼
3376 A1331 10k multi   1.25 .60

Bath Servant Zuzana Carrying King Wenceslas IV Over the Vltava River, by J. Navrátil A1332

2008, Mar. 5   Perf. 11¾x11¼
3377 A1332 10k multi   1.10 .60
  a.   Booklet pane of 8 + 4 labels   9.00
    Complete booklet, #3377a   9.00
Praga 2008 Intl. Philatelic Exhibition, Prague.

Publication of Orbis Pictus, Children's Picture Book, by Comenius, 350th Anniv. — A1333

2008, Mar. 19   Perf. 11¼x11¾
3378 A1333 10k multi   1.25 .60

Mountaintop Hotel With Broadcast Tower, Jested A1334

Hradec Kralové Buildings and Monuments A1335

2008, Mar. 19   Engr.   Perf. 11½
3379 A1334 12k multi   1.10 .75
3380 A1335 15k multi   1.50 .95

Pres. Klaus Type of 2003
Photo. & Engr.
2008, Apr. 2   Perf. 11¾x11¼
3381 A1234 10k multi   1.10 .60

A1336

Items in National Technical Museum: 10k, Reichenbach-Ertel astronomical theodolite, c. 1830. 14k, 1935 Jawa 750 sports car, horiz. 18k, Marky, Bromovsky-Schulz gasoline combustion engine, c. 1889.

Perf. 11¼x11¾, 11¾x11¼
2008, Apr. 16   Photo. & Engr.
3382-3384 A1336 Set of 3   4.25 2.60

National Technical Museum, Prague, cent.

A1337

2008, Apr. 16   Perf. 11¼x11¾
3385 A1337 17k multi   1.75 1.10

Czech Hockey Association, cent.

Europa A1338

2008, May 7 Litho.   Perf. 11¾x11¼
3386 A1338 17k multi   1.75 1.10

The Doggy's and Pussy's Tales, Children's Book by Josef Capek — A1339

Photo. & Engr.
2008, May 28   Perf. 11½x11¼
3387 A1339 10k multi   1.00 .70
a.   Booklet pane of 8 + 2 labels   9.00 —
      Complete booklet, #3387a   9.00

Souvenir Sheet

Ledeburk Gardens, Prague A1340

Litho. & Engr.
2008, May 28   Perf. 11¾
3388 A1340 51k multi   5.50 3.25

Praga 2008 World Philatelic Exhibition.

Miniature Sheet

Flora and Fauna of Trebon Basin UNESCO Biosphere Reservation — A1341

No. 3389: a, 10k, Alcedo atthis (28x44mm). b, 12k, Lutra lutra and Spiraea salicifolia (54x44mm). c, 14k, Haliaeetus albicilla (54x44mm). d, 18k, Netta rufina and Nymphaea alba (54x44mm).

2008, May 28
3389 A1341 Sheet of 4, #a-d, + 3 labels   6.25 3.50

2008 Paralympics, Beijing A1342

Perf. 11¾x11¼
2008, June 18   Litho.
3390 A1342 10k multi   1.10 .70

2008 Summer Olympics, Beijing A1343

2008, June 18
3391 A1343 18k multi   1.75 1.25

Explorers A1344

Designs: 12k, Ferdinand Stolicka (1838-74), explorer of Himalayas. 21k, Alois Musil (1868-1944), explorer of Jordanian desert.

2008, June 18   Photo. & Engr.
3392-3393 A1344 Set of 2   3.25 2.25

Children's Book Illustration by Josef Palacek A1345

2008, Sept. 3 Litho. Perf. 12¾x13¼
3394 A1345 10k multi + label   1.10 .60

Printed in sheets of 9 stamps + 12 labels. Labels could be personalized. Value, $10.

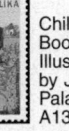

Emmaus Monastery, Prague — A1346

Photo. & Engr.
2008, Sept. 3   Perf. 11¼x11¾
3395 A1346 10k multi   1.00 .60
      Tete-beche pair   2.00 2.00

Praga 2008 World Philatelic Exhibition.

Applied Art Designers' Association, Cent. — A1347

2008, Sept. 3   Perf. 11¾x11¼
3396 A1347 26k multi   2.75 1.60

Karel Plicka (1894-1987), Photographer — A1348

Litho. & Engr.
2008, Sept. 12   Perf. 11¾
3397 A1348 35k multi + 2 labels   4.00 2.10

See Slovakia No. 548.

Souvenir Sheet

Mail Coach A1349

2008, Sept. 12
3398 A1349 35k multi   4.00 2.10

Praga 2008 Intl. Stamp Exhibition, Prague, and 2008 Vienna Intl. Stamp Exhibition. See Austria No. 2172.

Stoves — A1350

Stove from: 10k, Sternberk Castle. 17k, Archbishop's Palace, Prague.

Photo. & Engr.
2008, Oct. 15   Perf. 11¼x11¾
3399 A1350 10k multi   1.00 .55
      Complete booklet, 5 #3399   5.50
3400 A1350 17k multi   1.75 .95
      Complete booklet, 5 #3400   9.50

Painting Type of 1967 Inscribed "CESKA REPUBLIKA"

Designs: 23k, Vltava River at Klecany, by Zdenka Braunerová, horiz. 26k, Autumn Road, by Otakar Nejedly.

2008, Nov. 5   Engr.   Perf. 11¾
3401-3402 A565 Set of 2   5.25 3.00

Issued in sheets of 4. Value, set $21.

Souvenir Sheet

Allegory of Water, by Jan Jakub Hartman A1351

2008, Nov. 5   Litho. & Engr.
3403 A1351 30k multi   3.25 1.75

Basket With Apples — A1352

Winter Scene A1353

Mechanical Christmas Display — A1354

Photo. & Engr.
2008, Nov. 5   Perf. 11¼x11½
3404 A1352 10k multi   .95 .55
Litho.
Perf. 12¾x13¼
3405 A1353 10k multi + label   .95 .55
Souvenir Sheet
Litho. & Engr.
Perf. 11¾
3406 A1354 30k multi   3.25 1.75

Christmas. No. 3405 was printed in sheets of 9 stamps + 12 labels. Value $10. Labels could be personalized.

Czech Republic Presidency of European Union, January to June 2009 — A1355

Perf. 11¾x11¼
2008, Nov. 25   Litho.
3407 A1355 17k multi + label   1.75 .90

No. 3407 was issued in sheets of 30 stamps + 30 labels.

Louis Braille (1809-52), Educator of the Blind — A1356

Charles Darwin (1809-82), Naturalist A1357

2009, Jan. 2   Photo. & Engr.
3408 A1356 10k multi   .95 .55
3409 A1357 12k multi   1.10 .60

Tradition of Czech Stamp Production — A1358

2009, Jan. 20   Perf. 11¼x11¾
3410 A1358 10k Design of #980   1.00 .50
a.   Booklet pane of 8 + 4 labels   8.25
      Complete booklet, #3410a   8.25

Nordic World Skiing Championships, Liberec A1359

Perf. 11¾x11¼
2009, Feb. 11   Litho.
3411 A1359 18k multi   1.25 1.25

Souvenir Sheet

Preservation of Polar Regions and Glaciers — A1360

Litho. & Engr.
2009, Feb. 11 **Perf. 11¾**
3412 A1360 35k multi 3.50 1.90

Easter — A1361

Photo. & Engr.
2009, Mar. 18 **Perf. 11½x11¼**
3413 A1361 10k multi .95 .55

Lu Tung-pin, by Unknown Chinese Artist — A1362

Mythical Beings, by Unknown Balinese Artist — A1363

Litho. & Engr.
2009, Mar. 18 **Perf. 11¾**
3414 A1362 18k multi 1.75 1.00
3415 A1363 24k multi 2.25 1.40

Souvenir Sheet

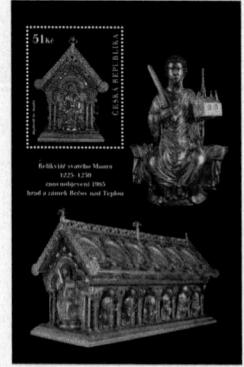

Reliquary of St. Maurus, Becov nad Teplou Castle — A1364

2009, Apr. 8
3416 A1364 51k multi 5.00 3.00

Pardubice to Liberec Rail Line, 150th Anniv. — A1365

Photo. & Engr.
2009, Apr. 22 **Perf. 11¾x11¼**
3417 A1365 10k multi 1.00 .60

Industry and Trade Ministry Building, 75th Anniv. — A1366

Photo. & Engr.
2009, Apr. 22 **Perf. 11¾x11½**
3418 A1366 10k multi 1.00 .60

Europa — A1367

2009, May 6 **Litho.** **Perf. 11¼**
3419 A1367 17k multi 1.75 1.00
Intl. Year of Astronomy.

Buildings — A1368

Designs: 12k, Cistercian Monastery, Vyssí Brod. 14k, Horsovsky Castle, Tyn.

2009, May 6 **Engr.** **Perf. 11¾x11½**
3420-3421 A1368 Set of 2 2.50 1.50
Nos. 3420-3421 also were issued in souvenir sheets of 1. Value, set of two sheets $27.

Marionettes Spejbl and Hurvínek — A1369

Photo. & Engr.
2009, May 27 **Perf. 11¼x11½**
3422 A1369 10k multi 1.10 .60
a. Booklet pane of 8 + 2 labels 9.00 —
Complete booklet, #3422a 9.00

Rabbi Jehuda Löw (c. 1525-1609) — A1370

2009, May 27 **Litho.** **Perf. 11¼x11¾**
3423 A1370 21k multi 2.00 1.25
Printed in sheets of 5 + 4 labels. Value, $10.

Granting of Religious Freedom by Rudolf II, 400th Anniv. — A1371

Photo. & Engr.
2009, June 17 **Perf. 11¼**
3424 A1371 26k multi 2.50 1.50

Intl. Firefighters' Games, Ostrava A1372

Perf. 11¾x11¼
2009, June 17 **Litho.**
3425 A1372 17k multi 1.75 1.00

Miniature Sheet

Krivoklát UNESCO Biosphere Reservation — A1373

No. 3426: a, 10k, Eudia pavonia (44x27mm). b, 12k, Aglia tau, Cervus elaphus (44x54mm). c, 14k, Bubo bubo, Lunaria rediviva, Ciconia nigra (44x54mm). d, 17k, Tyto alba, Krivoklát Castle (44x54mm).

Litho. & Engr.
2009, Sept. 2 **Perf. 11¾**
3426 A1373 Sheet of 4, #a-d, + 4 labels 5.50 4.50

Souvenir Sheet

Bohemian-Moravian Highlands — A1374

2009, Sept. 2
3427 A1374 43k multi 4.00 2.50

Windmill, Ruprechtov A1375

Water Mill, Hoslovice A1376

Photo. & Engr.
2009, Sept. 23 **Perf. 11¼x11½**
3428 A1375 10k multi 1.00 .60
Complete booklet, 5 #3428 5.50
Perf. 11½x11¼
3429 A1376 12k multi 1.25 .70
Complete booklet, 5 #3429 7.00

Czech National Anthem, 175th Anniv. — A1377

2009, Oct. 14 **Perf. 11¼x11¾**
3430 A1377 10k multi 1.00 .60

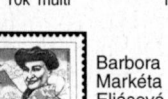

Barbora Markéta Eliásová (1874-1957), Travel Writer — A1378

2009, Oct. 14 **Perf. 11¾x11¼**
3431 A1378 18k multi 1.75 1.10

Stoves — A1379

Designs: 10k, Empire stove, Litomysl Castle. 14k, Biedermeier stove, Vyskov Castle.

2009, Oct. 14 **Perf. 11¼x11¾**
3432 A1379 10k multi 1.00 .60
Complete booklet, 5 #3432 5.50
3433 A1379 14k multi 1.25 .80
Complete booklet, 5 #3433 7.50

Protest Rallies of Nov. 17, 1939, and Nov. 17, 1989 — A1380

2009, Nov. 4 **Litho.**
3434 A1380 14k multi 1.25 .80

Painting Type of 1967 Inscribed "ČESKA REPUBLIKA"

Designs: 24k, Canal Lock in Moret, by Alfred Sisley, horiz. 26k, Alley, by Alfred Justitz, horiz.

2009, Nov. 4 **Engr.** **Perf. 11¾**
3435-3436 A565 Set of 2 5.25 3.00

Souvenir Sheet

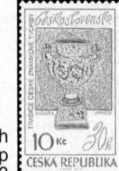

Oldrich and Bozena, by Frantisek Zenísek A1381

Litho. & Engr.
2009, Nov. 4 **Perf. 11¾**
3437 A1381 34k multi 3.50 2.00

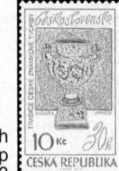

Christmas — A1382

Photo. & Engr.
2009, Nov. 4 **Perf. 11¼x11½**
3438 A1382 10k multi 1.10 .60

Tradition of Czech Stamp Production — A1383

2010, Jan. 20 **Perf. 11¼x11¾**
3439 A1383 10k Vignette of #2121 1.10 .55
a. Booklet pane of 8 + 4 labels 9.00
Complete booklet, #3439a 9.00

Magdalena Dobromila Rettigová (1785-1845), Writer — A1384

2010, Jan. 20 **Perf. 11¾x11¼**
3440 A1384 12k multi 1.25 .65

2010 Winter Olympics,
Vancouver — A1385

2010, Feb. 10   **Perf. 11¼x11¾**
3441 A1385 18k multi   1.25 .95

2010 Winter
Paralympics,
Vancouver — A1386

2010, Feb. 10
3442 A1386 18k multi   1.25 .95

Souvenir Sheet

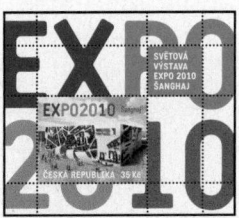

Expo 2010, Shanghai — A1387

2010, Feb. 10   **Litho.**
3443 A1387 35k multi + 3 labels   3.00 1.90

Easter — A1388

Photo. & Engr.
2010, Mar. 10   **Perf. 11½x11¼**
3444 A1388 10k multi   1.10 .55

Martina Sáblíková,
Gold Medalist at 2010
Winter Olympic
Games — A1389

Perf. 11¼x11¾
2010, Mar. 24   **Litho.**
3445 A1389 10k multi   1.10 .55

Souvenir Sheet

Karel Hynek Macha (1810-36),
Writer — A1390

Perf. 11½x11¾
2010, Mar. 10   **Litho. & Engr.**
3446 A1390 43k multi   4.00 2.40

Enrique Stanko
Vráz (1860-
1932), Travel
Writer — A1391

Photo. & Engr.
2010, Apr. 14   **Perf. 11¾x11¼**
3447 A1391 24k multi   2.25 1.25

19th Century
Transcaucasian
Carpets
A1392

Designs: 21k, Kasim Usak carpet. 24k,
Celaberd carpet.

Litho. & Engr.
2010, Apr. 14   **Perf. 11¾**
3448-3449 A1392   Set of 2   4.00 2.40

Ctyrlístek Comic Strip
Character
Fifinka — A1393

Serpentine Die Cut 15x16½
2010, Apr. 28   **Litho.**
Booklet Stamp
Self-Adhesive
3450 A1393 A multi   1.10 .55
   a.   Booklet pane of 10   11.00

No. 3450 sold for 10k on day of issue.

Prague
Castle
A1394

2010, May 5   **Engr.**   **Perf. 11¾**
3451 A1394 17k brown   1.50 .85

Prague Castle in the Art of the Postage
Stamp Exhibition, Prague. Printed in sheets of
4 + label. Value, $6.

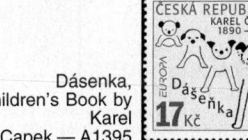

Dásenka,
Children's Book by
Karel
Capek — A1395

2010, May 5   **Litho.**   **Perf. 11¼**
3452 A1395 17k multi   1.50 .85

Europa.

Children's Book
Illustration by Helena
Zmatlíková (1923-
2005) — A1396

Photo. & Engr.
2010, May 26   **Perf. 11¼x11½**
3453 A1396 10k multi   1.10 .50
   a.   Booklet pane of 8 + 2 labels   9.00 —
      Complete booklet, #3453a   9.00

Alphonse Mucha (1860-
1939),
Illustrator — A1397

Designs: E, Gismonda. Z, Zodiac.

Serpentine Die Cut 14¼x14½
2010, May 26   **Litho.**
Booklet Stamps
Self-Adhesive
3454 A1397 E multi   1.60 .80
   a.   Booklet pane of 6   9.75
Size: 43x54mm
Serpentine Die Cut 14½
3455 A1397 Z multi   1.75 .85
   a.   Booklet pane of 6   10.50

No. 3454 sold for 17k and No. 3455 sold for
18k on day of issue.

Zd'árské Hills
Protected
Landscape
A1398

Photo. & Engr.
2010, June 16   **Perf. 11¾x11½**
3456 A1398 10k multi   1.10 .50

Marriage of John of Luxembourg and
Elizabeth of Bohemia, 700th
Anniv. — A1399

Photo. & Engr.
2010, June 16   **Perf. 11¾x11¼**
3457 A1399 17k multi   1.50 .85

Accession to the throne of Bohemia by the
House of Luxembourg. See Luxembourg No.
1292.

No. 3457 was issued in sheets 5 stamps + 4
labels. Values: single stamp + label, $1.75;
complete sheet, $9.

Astronomical
Clock, Prague,
600th
Anniv. — A1400

2010, June 16   **Litho.**
3458 A1400 21k multi   2.25 1.10

Towns — A1401

Designs: 12k, Klatovy. 14k, Stramberk.

2010, June 16   **Engr.**
3459-3460 A1401   Set of 2   2.40 1.25

Czech Republic,
Winners of 2010 World
Ice Hockey
Championships
A1402

Perf. 11¼x11¾
2010, June 23   **Litho.**
3461 A1402 10k multi   1.10 .50

Ctyrlístek Comic Strip Characters
Fifinka, Pind'a, Bobík and Myspulín
A1403

2010, Sept. 1 Litho. Perf. 12¾x13¼
3462 A1403 A multi + label   1.10 .55

No. 3462 was printed in sheets of 9 + 12
labels that could be personalized and had a
franking value of 10k on day of issue.

Children
With
Magnifying
Glass and
Stamp
Album
A1404

Boy
Examining
Stamp
A1405

2010, Sept. 1
3463 A1404 A multi + label   1.10 .55
3464 A1405 E multi + label   2.10 1.10

Nos. 3463-3464 each were printed in sheets
of 9 + 12 labels that could be personalized. On
day of issue, No. 3463 had a franking value of
10k and No. 3464 had a franking value of 20k.

2010 Women's World
Basketball
Championships, Czech
Republic — A1406

2010, Sept. 1   **Perf. 11¼x11¾**
3465 A1406 17k multi   1.75 .90

Miniature Sheet

Flora and Fauna of Lower Morava
UNESCO Biosphere
Reserve — A1407

No. 3466: a, 10k, Tichodroma muraria,
Papilio machaon, Aster amellus (45x55mm).
b, 12k, Saga pedo, Iris variegata (45x27mm).
c, 14k, Lacerta viridis, Pulsatilla grandis
(45x27mm). d, 18k, Upupa epops, Arenaria
grandiflora (45x55mm).

Litho. & Engr.
2010, Sept. 1   **Perf. 11¾**
3466 A1407   Sheet of 4, #a-d, +
      3 labels   6.00 3.00

Flowers Type of 2002

Designs: 4k, Anemone (sasanka). 25k, Iris
(kosatec). 30k, Tulip (tulipán).

Photo. & Engr.

2010   **Perf. 11¾x11¼**
3467 A1215   4k multi   .45   .25
3468 A1215   25k multi   2.00 1.50
3469 A1215   30k multi   2.25 1.75
    Nos. 3467-3469 (3)   4.70 3.50

Issued: 4k, 9/29; 25k, 30k, 9/15.

Austrian Empire
Post Office Sign,
Postal Map,
Dwarves with
Letters,
Handstamp and
Posthorn — A1408

2010, Sept. 29   Litho.   Perf. 11¼
3470 A1408 A multi   1.10   .55
Postal Musuem, Prague. No. 3470 sold for
10k on day of issue.

Famous Men — A1409

Designs: 10k, Adolf Branald (1910-2008),
writer. 12k, Karel Zeman (1910-89), film director and animator.

Photo. & Engr.

2010, Sept. 29   Perf. 11¼x11½
3471-3472 A1409 Set of 2   2.25 1.25

Ctyrlístek Comic Strip
Character
Myspulín — A1410

Serpentine Die Cut 15x16½

2010, Oct. 20   Litho.

Booklet Stamp
Self-Adhesive

3473 A1410 A multi   1.25   .60
  a.   Booklet pane of 10   12.50

No. 3473 sold for 10k on day of issue.

Bridges
A1411

Designs: 10k, Mariánsky Bridge, Ustí nad
Labem. 12k, Stone Bridge, Písek.

Photo. & Engr.

2010, Oct. 20   Perf. 11¾x11¼
3474 A1411 10k multi   1.00   .60
  Complete booklet, 5 #3474   5.50
3475 A1411 12k multi   1.25   .70
  Complete booklet, 5 #3475   7.00

Stoves — A1412

Designs: 10k, Art Nouveau stove. 20k, Art
Deco stove.

2010, Oct. 20   Perf. 11¼x11¾
3476 A1412 10k multi   1.00   .60
  Complete booklet, 5 #3476   6.25
3477 A1412 20k multi   1.75 1.25
  Complete booklet, 5 #3477   12.00

Art Type of 1967 Inscribed "CESKA REPUBLIKA"

Designs: 24k, Paris and Helen, by Karel
Skréta. 26k, Sand Bargemen, by Milos
Jiránek. 30k, Spring, by Karel Spillar, horiz.

Litho. & Engr. (24k), Engr.

2010, Nov. 10   Perf. 11¾
3478-3480 A565 Set of 3   7.50 4.50

Illumination
From 1558
Zlutice Hymn
Book — A1413

Perf. 11¼x11¾
2010, Nov. 10   Litho.
3481 A1413 10k multi   1.10   .55

Christmas.

2011 Census — A1414

2011, Jan. 5
3482 A1414 10k black & green   1.10   .55

Souvenir Sheet

Kaspar Maria von Sternberg (1761-
1838), Paleobotanist — A1415

Perf. 11¾x11½
2011, Jan. 5   Litho. & Engr.
3483 A1415 43k multi   5.00 2.40

Mail Coach on
Charles Bridge,
1966 Envelope
Indicia by Josef
Hercík
A1416

Photo. & Engr.

2011, Jan. 20   Perf. 11¾x11¼
3484 A1416 10k multi   1.10   .55
  a.   Booklet pane of 8 + 4 labels 9.00   —
        Complete booklet, #3484a   9.50

Tradition of Czech stamp production.

St. Agnes of Bohemia
(1211-82) — A1417

2011, Jan. 20   Perf. 11¼x11¾
3485 A1417 12k multi   1.25   .70

Ctyrlístek Comic Strip
Character
Pind'a — A1418

Booklet Stamp
Serpentine Die Cut 15x16½

2011, Feb. 9   Litho.   Self-Adhesive
3486 A1418 A multi   1.10   .55
  a.   Booklet pane of 10   11.00

No. 3486 sold for 10k on day of issue.

Jirí Melantrich of
Aventinum (c. 1511-80),
Printer — A1419

Photo. & Engr.

2011, Feb. 9   Perf. 11¼x11¾
3487 A1419 30k multi   3.00 1.75

Cheb, 950th
Anniv. — A1420

Black Madonna
House, Prague,
Cent. — A1421

2011, Feb. 9   Engr.   Perf. 11¾x11½
3488 A1420 12k multi   1.10   .70

Perf. 11½x11¾
3489 A1421 14k multi   1.40   .80

Visegrád
Group, 20th
Anniv. — A1422

Perf. 11¾x11¼
2011, Feb. 11   Litho.
3490 A1422 20k multi   2.00 1.10

  See Hungary No. 4183, Poland No. 4001,
and Slovakia No. 611.
  No. 3490 was issued in sheets of 8 + 8
labels. Values: single stamp + label, $2.25;
complete sheet, $18.

Architecture — A1423

Designs: A, House gables from Blatensko
region, North Moravia and West Bohemia,
gable shutter from North Bohemia. E, House
gables from North Bohemia and South Bohemia, Wallachian cottage, Central Bohemian
gate. Z, Houses from North Bohemia, West
Bohemia and Wallachia, vert.

Photo. & Engr.

2011   Perf. 11¼x11¾
3491 A1423 A blk, lt bl & bl   1.00   .60
3492 A1423 E blk, beige & brn   2.25 1.25

Perf. 11¾x11¼
3493 A1423 Z blk, gray grn & bl
                          grn   2.25 1.25
    Nos. 3491-3493 (3)   5.50 3.10

Issued: Nos. 3491-3492, 2/23; No. 3493,
5/27. On day of issue Nos. 3491-3493 sold for
10k, 20k and 21k, respectively.
See No. 3559.

Souvenir Sheet

Petr Vok (1539-1611) and Vilém
(1535-92) von Rosenberg,
Aristocrats — A1424

2011, Mar. 9   Engr.   Perf. 11¾
3494 A1424 49k multi   4.50 3.00

Easter — A1425

Perf. 11¼x11¾
2011, Mar. 23   Litho.
3495 A1425 A multi   1.10   .60

No. 3495 sold for 10k on day of issue.

Vlasta Burian
(1891-1962),
Actor — A1426

Photo. & Engr.

2011, Apr. 6   Perf. 11¾x11¼
3496 A1426 10k multi   1.10   .60

Teaching at Prague
Conservatory,
Bicent. — A1427

2011, Apr. 6   Perf. 11¼x11¾
3497 A1427 10k multi   1.10   .60

Ctyrlistek Comic Strip
Character
Bobík — A1428

Booklet Stamp

Serpentine Die Cut 15x16½
2011, May 4   Litho.   Self-Adhesive
3498 A1428 A multi   1.25   .60
  a.   Booklet pane of 10   12.50

No. 3498 sold for 10k on day of issue.

Europa — A1429

2011, May 4   Litho.   Perf. 11¼
3499 A1429 20k multi   2.00 1.25

Intl. Year of Forests.

Flower Type of 2002

Design: 2k,   Chrysanthemum
(chryzantéma).

Photo. & Engr.
2011, May 27   *Perf. 11¾x11¼*
3500 A1215 2k multi   .25 .25

Souvenir Sheet

Johann Gerstner (1851-1939), Violinist — A1430

Litho. & Engr.
2011, May 27   *Perf. 11¾*
3501 A1430 34k multi   3.50 2.10

See Slovenia No. 891.

The Little Witch and Abraxas, the Raven, Animated Characters by Zdenek Smetana — A1431

Photo. & Engr.
2011, June 1   *Perf. 11½x11¼*
3502 A1431 10k multi   1.25 .60
   a.   Booklet pane of 8 + 2 labels   10.00
     Complete booklet, #3502a   10.00

First Public Long-Distance Flight of Jan Kaspar (1883-1927), Cent. — A1432

2011, June 1   *Perf. 11¼x11¾*
3503 A1432 21k multi   2.25 1.25

Execution of 27 Protestant Leaders in Prague, 390th Anniv. A1433

Litho. & Engr.
2011, June 1   *Perf. 11¾*
3504 A1433 26k rose pink & blk   2.50 1.60

Cricetus Cricetus — A1434

Perf. 11¼x11¾
2011, June 15   Litho.
3505 A1434 10k multi   1.10 .60
     Complete booklet, 5 #3505   6.00

Floral Arrangement — A1435

2011, June 15
3506 A1435 25k multi   2.50 1.50

Europa Cup, Championships of European Federation of Professional Florist Associations, Havirov.

Men's European Volleyball Championships, Prague and Karlovy Vary — A1436

Perf. 11¼x11¾
2011, Aug. 31   Litho.
3507 A1436 20k multi   2.25 1.10

Wolfgang Amadeus Mozart (1756-91), Composer A1437

Booklet Stamp
Serpentine Die Cut 11½
2011, Aug. 31   Self-Adhesive
3508 A1437 E multi   2.25 1.10
   a.   Booklet pane of 6   13.50

No. 3508 sold for 20k on day of issue.

Miniature Sheet

Flora and Fauna of Sumava UNESCO Biosphere Reserve — A1438

No. 3509: a, 10k, Turdus torquatus, Erebia euryale, Tetrao urogallus (54x44mm). b, 14k, Dactylorhiza traunsteineri, Colias palaeno (27x44mm). c, 18k, Aeshna juncea, Alces alces, Tetrao tetrix (54x44mm). d, 20k, Lynx lynx, Picoides tridactylus (54x44mm).

Litho. & Engr.
2011, Aug. 31   *Perf. 11¾*
3509 A1438   Sheet of 4, #a-d, +   6.00 3.50
     4 labels

Organ, Church of the Assumption of Our Lady, Plasy — A1439

Perf. 11¼x11¾
2011, Sept. 14   Litho.
3510 A1439 10k multi   1.10 .55

Frantisek Alexander Elstner (1902-74), Travel Writer — A1440

Photo. & Engr.
2011, Sept. 14   *Perf. 11¾x11¼*
3511 A1440 14k multi   1.40 .80

Pat and Mat, Characters From Children's Television Show — A1441

Booklet Stamp
Serpentine Die Cut 15x16½
2011, Oct. 5   Litho.   Self-Adhesive
3512 A1441 A multi   1.10 .55
   a.   Booklet pane of 10   11.00

No. 3512 sold for 10k on day of issue.

World Post Day — A1442

2011, Oct. 5   *Perf. 11¼*
3513 A1442 21k multi   2.25 1.25

Film Posters A1443

Poster for: No. 3514, 10k, Une Femme Douce, 1970. No. 3515, 10k, Markéta Lazarová, 1966.

2011, Oct. 5   Litho.   *Perf. 11¾x11¼*
3514-3515 A1443   Set of 2   2.25 1.10

Peacock & Bugler Type of 2005 and Roses Above Prague Type of 2003
2011, Oct. 27   *Perf. 11¼x11¾*
3516 A1263 A multi + label   1.10 .55
3517 A1225 E multi + label   2.25 1.10

On day of issue, No. 3516 sold for 10k and No. 3517 sold for 20k. Nos. 3516-3517 each were issued in sheets of 9 stamps and 12 labels that could be personalized. Value, $30.

Art Type of 1967 Inscribed "CESKA REPUBLIKA"

Designs: 24k, Lovers, by Jaroslav Vozniak, horiz. 26k, Woman in Corn Field, by Joza Uprka. 30k, Winter Landscape, by August Bedrich Piepenhagen, horiz.

2011, Nov. 9   Engr.   *Perf. 11¾*
3518-3520 A565   Set of 3   8.00 4.50

Christmas — A1444

2011, Nov. 9   Litho.   *Perf. 11¾x11¼*
3521 A1444 A multi   1.10 .55

No. 3521 sold for 10k on day of issue.

House, Vidim — A1445

Photo. & Engr.
2012, Jan. 20   *Perf. 11¼x11¾*
3522 A1445 6k multi   .65 .30

Josef Liesler (1912-2005), Stamp Designer A1446

2012, Jan. 20   *Perf. 11¾x11¼*
3523 A1446 10k multi   1.10 .55
   a.   Booklet pane of 8 + 4 labels   9.00
     Complete booklet, #3523a   9.00

Tradition of Czech stamp production.

Jirí Trnka (1912-69), Film Animator and Director A1447

2012, Feb. 15
3524 A1447 10k multi   1.10 .55

Sokol Movement, 150th Anniv. — A1448

Perf. 11¼x11¾
2012, Feb. 15   Litho.
3525 A1448 14k multi   1.50 .75

Union of Czech Mathematicians and Physicists, 150th Anniv. — A1449

2012, Mar. 7   *Perf. 11¾x11¼*
3526 A1449 10k multi   1.10 .55

Kuks — A1450

Designs: 14k, Buildings in Kuks. 18k, Statue by Matthias B. Braun, vert.

Perf. 11½x11¾, 11¾x11½
2012, Mar. 7   Engr.
3527-3528 A1450   Set of 2   3.00 1.75

Hiker at Signpost A1451

Perf. 11¼x11¾
2012, Mar. 21   Litho.
3529 A1451 A multi + label   1.10 .55

No. 3529 was printed in sheets of 9 + 12 labels that could be personalized and had a franking value of 10k on day of issue.

Gregor Mendel (1822-84), Genetics Pioneer A1452

Photo. & Engr.
2012, Apr. 4   *Perf. 11¾x11¼*
3530 A1452 20k multi   1.90 1.10

First Hebrew Book Printed in Prague, 500th Anniv. — A1453

2012, Apr. 18   Litho.   *Perf. 11¼*
3531 A1453 25k multi   2.40 1.40

Prague Tourist
Attractions — A1454

Photo. & Engr.

2012, May 2   **Perf. 11¼x11¾**
3532 A1454 20k multi   2.00   1.10

Europa.

Scouting in
Czechoslovakia,
Cent. — A1455

2012, May 2   **Litho.**   **Perf. 11¼**
3533 A1455 21k multi   2.00   1.10

Boats on Baťa
Canal — A1456

2012, May 16   **Engr.**   **Perf. 11¾x11¼**

Booklet Stamp

3534 A1456 10k dark blue   1.20   .50
   a.   Booklet pane of 8 + 4 labels   9.50   —
     Complete booklet, #3534a   9.50

The Whipping
of Christ, by
Tintoretto
A1457

2012, May 16   **Perf. 11¾**
3535 A1457 30k multi   3.50   1.50

Art in Prague Castle. See Nos. 3569, 3605,
3642, 3674, 3705, 3755, 3790.

St. Wenceslas (c.
907-35) — A1458

Serpentine Die Cut 11 Syncopated
2012, June 6   **Litho.**

Self-Adhesive

3536 A1458 A multi   1.00   .50

No. 3536 sold for 10k on day of issue. See
No. 3576.

Lezáky
Massacre, 70th
Anniv. — A1459

2012, June 6   **Perf. 11¾x11¼**
3537 A1459 10k multi   1.00   .50

Lidice
Massacre, 70th
Anniv. — A1460

2012, June 6   **Photo. & Engr.**
3538 A1460 20k multi   2.00   1.00

Coronation of Statue of
Our Lady of Hostyn,
Cent. — A1461

Litho. & Engr.

2012, June 20   **Perf. 11¾**
3539 A1461 21k multi   1.90   1.00

No. 3539 was issued in sheets of 8 stamps
+ 1 label. Values: single stamp + label, $2.50;
complete sheet, $16.

A1462   A1463

Personalized
Stamps — A1464

Serpentine Die Cut 11 Syncopated
2012, June 20   **Litho.**

Self-Adhesive

3540 A1462 A multi   .95   .50
3541 A1463 A multi   .95   .50
3542 A1464 E multi   1.90   .95
    Nos. 3540-3542 (3)   3.80   1.95

Nos. 3540-3542 each were printed in sheets
of 25. Vignette portions of each stamp could
be personalized. The generic vignettes of
these stamps are shown. On day of issue, the
franking value of Nos. 3540-3541 each were
10k, and of No. 3542, 20k.

2012 Summer Olympics,
London — A1465

Litho. & Engr.

2012, June 20   **Perf. 11¾**
3543 A1465 20k multi   1.90   .95

No. 3543 was issued in sheets of 3 stamps
+ 2 labels. Values: single stamp + label, $2.25;
complete sheet, $6.

Alberto Vojtech Fric (1882-1944),
Cactus Collector, Botanist and
Ethnographer
A1466

2012, Sept. 5   **Litho.**   **Perf. 11¾x11¼**
3544 A1466 10k multi   1.10   .55

Illustrations of Antique Automobiles by
Václav Zapadlík — A1467

No. 3545: a, 1933 Duesenberg SJ. b, 1931,
Wikov 70. c, 1936 Mercedes-Benz 540. d,
1938 Rolls Royce Phantom III. e, 1934 Bugatti
Royale 41. f, 1929 Isotta Fraschini Tipo 8A.

Serpentine Die Cut 11½
2012, Sept. 5

Self-Adhesive

3545   Booklet pane of 6   13.00
   a.-f.   A1467 E Any single   2.10   1.10

On day of issue, Nos. 3545a-3545f each
sold for 20k. See Nos. 3580-3581, 3610-3611,
3645-3646.

Miniature Sheet

Orchids
A1468

No. 3546: a, 10k, Dendrobium peguanum
(44x27mm). b, 14k, Stanhopea tigrina and
Coryanthes feildingii (44x54mm). c, 18k, Cattleya aclandiae and Cattleya maxima
(44x54mm). d, 20k, Paphiopedilum charles-
worthii, Paphiopedilum insigne, and Paphiopedilum hirsutissimum (44x54mm).

Litho. & Engr.

2012, Sept. 5   **Perf. 11¾**
3546 A1468   Sheet of 4, #a-d, +
          4 labels   6.00   3.25

Souvenir Sheet

Golden
Bull of
Sicily,
800th
Anniv.
A1469

2012, Sept. 19   **Engr.**   **Perf. 11¾**
3547 A1469 49k multi   4.75   2.60

Paphiopedilum Venustum — A1470

2012, Oct. 3   **Litho.**   **Perf. 11¼x11¾**
3548 A1470 A multi + label   1.10   .55

No. 3548 was printed in sheets of 9 + 12
labels that could be personalized. On day of
issue, No. 3548 had a franking value of 10k.

Masaryk Circuit
Racers — A1471

Designs: 18k, Frantisek St'astny (1927-
2000), motorcycle racer. 25k, Louis Chiron
(1899-1979), automobile racer.

2012, Oct. 3   **Photo. & Engr.**
3549-3550   A1471   Set of 2   4.50   2.25

1891 Ericsson
Desk Telephone
A1472

2012, Oct. 3   **Litho.**   **Perf. 11¼**
3551 A1472 26k multi   2.75   1.40

World Post Day.

Art Type of 1967 Inscribed "CESKA
REPUBLIKA" and

Life's Pleasures, by Frantisek
Kupka — A1473

Designs: 26k, A Long-haired Girl, by Kamil
Lhoták. 32k, Self-portrait with Family, by Jan
Kupecky. No. 3554: a, Blonde nude on horse.
b, Brunette nude on pony, vert.

2012, Nov. 7   **Engr.**   **Perf. 11¾**
3552-3553 A565   Set of 2   5.50   3.00

Litho. & Engr.

Souvenir Sheet

3554 A1473 30k Sheet of 2, #a-b   6.00   3.00

Christmas
A1474

2012, Nov. 7   **Litho.**   **Perf. 11¼x11¾**
3555 A1474 A multi + label   1.00   .50

No. 3555 sold for 10k on day of issue and
was printed in sheets of 9 + 12 labels that
could be personalized.

Pinda, Bobik,   Myspulin Taking
Myspulin and   Picture of Bobik,
Fifinka Riding   Fifinka, King
Griffin — A1475   Rudolf II, Aurix
            the Lion and
            Pinda — A1476

Serpentine Die Cut 16½x15
2012, Nov. 7   **Self-Adhesive**

Booklet Stamps

3556 A1475 A multi   1.00   .50
3557 A1476 A multi   1.00   .50
   a.   Booklet pane of 10, 5 each
      #3556-3557   10.00

On day of issue, Nos. 3556-3557 each sold
for 10k.

Architecture Type of 2011 and

Building, Busanovice,
1847 — A1477

Photo. & Engr.

2012   **Perf. 11¼x11¾**
3558 A1477 5k multi   .75   .25
3559 A1423   A black & blue   1.25   .50

Issued: No. 3558, 12/19; No. 3559, 11/8.
No. 3559 sold for 10k on day of issue.
Compare No. 3559 with No. 3491.

Ivan Strnad
(1926-2005),
Stamp Designer
A1478

2013, Jan. 20   **Perf. 11¾x11¼**
3560 A1478 10k multi   1.10 .55
    a.   Booklet pane of 8 + 4 labels   9.00 —
       Complete booklet, #3560a   9.00

Tradition of Czech stamp production.

Bertha von Suttner (1843-1914), 1905 Nobel Peace Laureate — A1479

                 Perf. 11¼x11¾
2013, Feb. 13   **Litho.**
3561 A1479 18k multi   1.90 .95

Cottage, Novy Hrozenkov — A1480

       Photo. & Engr.
2013, Mar. 6   **Perf. 11¾x11¼**
3562 A1480 14k brn & dk brn   1.50 .75

Transportation A1481

No. 3563: a, Aero HC2 Heli Baby helicopter. b, Pécko-18 tugboat.

2013, Mar. 6   **Litho.**
3563 A1481 25k Vert. pair, #a-b   4.50 2.60

Zlatá Koruna Monastery, 750th Anniv. — A1482

2013, Apr. 3   **Engr.**   **Perf. 11¾x11½**
3564 A1482 14k multi   1.40 .70

George Orwell (1903-50), Writer — A1483

       Photo. & Engr.
2013, Apr. 3   **Perf. 11¼x11¾**
3565 A1483 26k multi   2.60 1.40

Pres. Milos Zeman — A1484

2013, Apr. 24   **Perf. 11¾x11¼**
3566 A1484 A red & purple   1.00 .50

No. 3566 sold for 10k on day of issue. See No. 3752.

Europa — A1485

2013, May 2   **Litho.**   **Perf. 11¼**
3567 A1485 25k multi   2.25 1.40

Fláje Dam — A1486

2013, May 15   **Engr.**   **Perf. 11¾x11¼**
3568 A1486 14k green   1.25 .75
    a.   Booklet pane of 8 + 4 labels   10.50 —
       Complete booklet, #3568a   10.50

Art in Prague Castle Type of 2012

Design: 25k, Portrait of Jacob König, Goldsmith and Bookseller, by Paolo Veronese.

2013, May 15   **Engr.**   **Perf. 11¾**
3569 A1457 25k multi   2.25 1.40

Cross of Závis of Falkenstejn — A1487

2013, May 29   **Perf. 11¾**
3570 A1487 26k multi   2.40 1.40

Krtek the Mole — A1488

Serpentine Die Cut 16½x15
2013, May 29   **Litho.**
       Booklet Stamp
       Self-Adhesive
3571 A1488 A multi   1.25 .55
    a.   Booklet pane of 10   12.50
    b.   As No. 3571, serpentine
        die cut 11x11¼ synco-
        pated ('15)   1.50 .55
    c.   Booklet pane of 10 #3571b   15.00

No. 3571 sold for 10k on day of issue. No. 3571b sold for 13k when issued.

Historic Methods of Transportation — A1489

No. 3572: a, Tatra 15/30 automobile. b, Cechie 33 Böhmerland motorcycle.

      Perf. 11¾x11¼
2013, June 12   **Litho.**
3572 A1489 10k Horiz. pair, #a-b   2.40 1.10

Souvenir Sheet

Mission of Sts. Cyril and Methodius to Slavic Lands, 1150th Anniv. — A1490

       Litho. & Engr.
2013, June 12   **Perf. 11¾**
3573 A1490 35k multi   3.75 1.90

See Bulgaria No. 4647, Slovakia No. 666 and Vatican City No. 1536.

Postal Banking Services, 130th Anniv. — A1491

       Perf. 11¾x11¼
2013, June 26   **Litho.**
3574 A1491 20k multi   1.75 1.00

Franz Kafka (1883-1924), Writer — A1492

Serpentine Die Cut 11½
2013, June 26   **Litho.**
       Booklet Stamp
       Self-Adhesive
3575 A1492 E multi   2.00 1.00
    a.   Booklet pane of 6   12.00

No. 3575 sold for 20k on day of issue.

St. Wenceslas Type of 2012

2013, July 31   **Litho.**   **Perf. 11¼x11¾**
3576 A1458 13k multi   1.40 .70

2013 Canoe Slalom World Championships, Prague A1493

       Photo. & Engr.
2013, Sept. 4   **Perf. 11¾x11¼**
3577 A1493 10k multi   1.10 .55

Novy Jicín, 700th Anniv. — A1494

2013, Sept. 4   **Engr.**   **Perf. 11¾**
3578 A1494 20k multi   1.75 1.75

Miniature Sheet

Flora and Fauna of the Karlstejn Region A1495

No. 3579: a, 10k, Dracocephalum austriacum, Chorthippus vagans (27x44mm). b, 14k, Oenanthe oenanthe, Velká Amerika Limestone Quarry (27x44mm). c, 18k, Polyommatus coridon, Pulsatilla pratensis, Colias crocea (54x44mm). d, 20k, Rosa gallica, Karlstejn Castle (54x44mm).

       Litho. & Engr.
2013, Sept. 4   **Perf. 11¾**
3579 A1495   Sheet of 4, #a-d, +   6.00 3.25
             4 labels

Antique Automobiles Type of 2012

Illustrations by Václav Zapadlík: No. 3580, 1930 Skoda 860. No. 3581, 1932 Skoda 645.

Serpentine Die Cut 11¼ Syncopated
2013, Sept. 4   **Litho.**
       Booklet Stamps
       Self-Adhesive
3580 A1467 A multi   1.25 .70
3581 A1467 A multi   1.25 .70
    a.   Booklet pane of 8, 4 each
        #3580-3581   10.00

Nos. 3580-3581 each sold for 13k on day of issue.

A1496

Personalized Stamps — A1497

Serpentine Die Cut 11¼ Syncopated
2013, Sept. 4   **Litho.**
       Booklet Stamps
       Self-Adhesive
3582 A1496 A black   1.50 .70
    a.   Booklet pane of 8   12.00
3583 A1497 E black   3.00 1.25
    a.   Booklet pane of 8   24.00

On day of issue, No. 3582 sold for 13k, and No. 3583 sold for 25k. Nos. 3582 and 3583 could have the image portions of the stamp personalized for an additional fee. The horizontal generic vignettes of these stamps are shown. Nos. 3582a and 3583a contain four stamps with these horizontal generic vignettes and four stamps with similar generic vignettes but with a vertical orientation. Values for Nos. 3582 and Nos. 3583 are for stamps with images with either a horizontal or vertical orientation.

Josef Bican (1913-2001), Soccer Player — A1498

       Photo. & Engr.
2013, Sept. 18   **Perf. 11¼x11¾**
3584 A1498 13k multi   1.25 .70

Horses From Chlumetz Stud Farm — A1499

Design: 13k, Kinsky horse. 17k, Palomino horse.

Perf. 11¼x11¾

2013, Sept. 18   Litho.
3585-3586 A1499 Set of 2   2.75 1.60

Cottage, Salajna — A1500

2013, Oct. 2 Engr. **Perf. 11¼x11¾**
3587 A1500 29k green   2.60 1.60

Souvenir Sheet

Battle of Leipzig, 200th Anniv. A1501

Litho. & Engr.

2013, Oct. 2   **Perf. 11¾**
3588 A1501 53k multi   5.50 3.00

Bible of Kralice, 400th Anniv. — A1502

2013, Oct. 16 Litho. **Perf. 11¼**
3589 A1502 17k multi   1.75 .85

Otto Wichterle (1912-98), Inventor of Soft Contact Lenses — A1503

Photo. & Engr.

2013, Oct. 16   **Perf. 11¼x11¾**
3590 A1503 21k multi   1.90 1.10

Art Type of 1967 Inscribed "CESKA REPUBLIKA"

Designs: 25k, A View of Roman Churches, by Giovanni Battista Piranesi, horiz. 30k, Still Life with the Author, by Bohuslav Reynek. 35k, Round Portrait, by Max Svabinsky.

Engr., Litho & Engr. (30k)

2013, Nov. 27   **Perf. 11¾**
3591-3593 A565 Set of 3   7.50 4.50

Ladislav Jirka (1914-86), Stamp Engraver A1504

2014, Jan. 20 Litho. **Perf. 11¾x11¼**
3594 A1504 13k multi   1.25 .65
   a.   Booklet pane of 8 + 4 labels   10.00 —
       Complete booklet, #3594a   10.00

Tradition of Czech stamp production.

Dog and Four-Leaf Clover A1505

2014, Jan. 20 Litho. **Perf. 11¼x11¾**
3595 A1505 A multi + label   1.25 .65

No. 3595 was printed in sheets of 9 + 12 labels that could be personalized. On day of issue, No. 3595 had a franking value of 13k.

2014 Winter Olympics, Sochi, Russia A1506

2014, Feb. 5 Litho. **Perf. 11¾x11¼**
3596 A1506 25k multi   2.50 1.25

2014 Winter Paralympics, Sochi, Russia — A1507

2014, Feb. 5 Litho. **Perf. 11¾x11¼**
3597 A1507 13k multi   1.25 .70
   a.   Tête-bêche pair   2.50 1.40

Czech Firefighters, 150th Anniv. — A1508

2014, Mar. 5 Litho. **Perf. 11¾x11¼**
3598 A1508 13k multi   1.25 .70

Transportation — A1509

No. 3599: a, Rapid, 1912 airplane of Eugen Cihák. b, Type R1 Prague Metro train.

2014, Mar. 5 Litho. **Perf. 11¾x11¼**
3599 A1509 13k Pair, #a-b   2.25 1.40

Bohumil Hrabal (1914-97), Writer — A1510

Photo. & Engr.

2014, Mar. 26   **Perf. 11¼x11¾**
3600 A1510 17k blk & brn   1.75 .85

Cervená Lhota Castle — A1511

2014, Mar. 26 Engr. **Perf. 11¾**
3601 A1511 17k multi   1.50 .85

Zdenek Kopal (1914-93), Astronomer A1512

Perf. 11¾x11¼

2014, Mar. 26   Litho.
3602 A1512 21k multi   2.10 1.10

Silesian Museum, Opava, 200th Anniv. — A1513

Photo. & Engr.

2014, Apr. 30   **Perf. 11¼x11¾**
3603 A1513 13k multi   1.25 .70

Bagpipes — A1514

Photo. & Engr.

2014, Apr. 30   **Perf. 11¼**
3604 A1514 25k multi   2.10 1.25

Europa.

Art in Prague Castle Type of 2012

Design: 37k, Assembly of Olympian Gods, by Peter Paul Rubens.

Litho. & Engr.

2014, May 28   **Perf. 11¾**
3605 A1457 37k multi   3.75 1.90

No. 3605 was printed in sheets of 2. Value, $7.50.

Paper Mill, Velké Losiny — A1515

Photo. & Engr.

2014, May 28   **Perf. 11¾x11¼**
3606 A1515 13k multi   1.25 .70

Animated Characters Ju and Hele — A1516

Serpentine Die Cut 11 Syncopated
2014, May 28   Litho.
     Booklet Stamp
     Self-Adhesive
3607 A1516 A multi   1.25 .70
   a.   Booklet pane of 10   12.50

No. 3607 sold for 13k on day of issue.

Historic Methods of Transportation — A1517

No. 3608: a, Paddle steamer Franz Joseph I. b, 1936 Zbrojovka Brno Z4 automobile.

Perf. 11¾x11¼

2014, June 11   Litho.
3608 A1517 25k Horiz. pair, #a-b   4.50 2.50

Souvenir Sheet

World War I, Cent. A1518

No. 3609: a, Soldier carrying rifle, mother holding child. b, Soldiers, people falling into pit.

2014, June 11   Litho.   **Perf. 11¾**
3609 A1518 29k Sheet of 2, #a-
       b, + 3 labels   5.00 3.00

Antique Automobiles Type of 2012

Designs: No. 3610, 1938 Skoda Popular Monte Carlo. No. 3611, 1941 Skoda Superb 3000.

Serpentine Die Cut 11¼ Syncopated
2014, Sept. 3   Litho.
     Booklet Stamps
     Self-Adhesive
3610 A1467 A multi   1.10 .60
3611 A1467 A multi   1.10 .60
   a.   Booklet pane of 8, 4 each
       #3610-3611   9.00

Nos. 3610-3611 each sold for 13k on day of issue.

Karel, Elder of Zierotín (1564-1636), Governor of Moravia A1519

Photo. & Engr.

2014, Sept. 3   **Perf. 11¾x11¼**
3612 A1519 29k multi   2.50 1.40

Miniature Sheet

Flora and Fauna of the Beskid Mountains — A1520

No. 3613: a, 13k, Meles meles (44x27mm). b, 17k, Felis silvestris (44x27mm). c, 21k, Ursus arctos, Carabus variolosus (44x54mm). d, 25k, Nucifraga caryocatactes, Canis lupus (44x54mm).

Litho. & Engr.

2014, Sept. 3   **Perf. 11¾**
3613 A1520   Sheet of 4, #a-d, +
       3 labels   7.00 3.50

Flower Bouquet in Wine Bottle A1521

2014, Oct. 15 Litho. Perf. 11¼x11¾
3614 A1521 A multi + label 1.25 .60

No. 3614 was printed in sheets of 9 + 12 labels that could be personalized. On day of issue No. 3614 had a franking value of 13k.

Souvenir Sheet

St. Vitus Cathedral, Prague, 670th Anniv. — A1522

Litho. & Engr.
2014, Oct. 15 Perf. 11¾
3615 A1522 58k multi 5.25 2.60

Art Type of 1967 Inscribed "CESKA REPUBLIKA" and

Solitude and Spectacles, Photograph by Jaromír Funke A1523

Designs: 25k, Street in Winter, by Jakub Schikaneder. 37k, Leda Atomica, by Salvador Dalí.

Engr., Litho. (29k)
2014, Nov. 5 Perf. 11¾
3616 A565 25k multi 2.25 1.10
3617 A1523 29k multi 2.60 1.40
3618 A565 37k multi 3.50 1.75
 Nos. 3616-3618 (3) 8.35 4.25

Historical Events of November 17 — A1524

2014, Nov. 5 Litho. Perf. 11¼x11¾
3619 A1524 13k multi 1.25 .60

Nazi attack on Czech university students, 75th anniv.; start of Velvet Revolution, 25th anniv.

Andreas Vesalius (1514-64), Anatomist — A1525

Photo. & Engr.
2014, Nov. 5 Perf. 11¼x11¾
3620 A1525 25k multi 2.25 1.10

Bethlehem in Winter, by Josef Lada — A1526

2014, Nov. 5 Litho. Perf. 11¾x11¼
3621 A1526 A multi 1.25 .60

Christmas. No. 3621 sold for 13k on day of issue.

A1527 Personalized Stamps — A1528

Serpentine Die Cut Syncopated
2014, Nov. 26 Litho.
Self-Adhesive
3622 A1527 A multi 1.25 .60
3623 A1528 Z multi 2.75 1.40

Nos. 3622-3623 were each printed in sheets of 25. Vignette portions of each stamp could be personalized. The generic vignettes of these stamps are shown. On day of issue, the franking value of No. 3622 was 13k; No. 3623, 30k.

Oldrich Kulhánek (1940-2013), Stamp Designer A1529

Photo. & Engr.
2015, Jan. 20 Perf. 11¾x11¼
3624 A1529 13k multi 1.20 .55
 a. Booklet pane of 8 + 4 labels 9.50 —
 Complete booklet, #3624a 9.50

Vitezslava Kaprálová (1915-40), Composer A1530

2015, Jan. 20 Litho. Perf. 11¾x11¼
3625 A1530 17k multi 1.40 .70

Military Aircraft and Vehicles A1531

Designs: No. 3626, Supermarine Spitfire LF Mk IXE. No. 3627, T-34/76.2 tank. No. 3628, Harley-Davidson motorcycle. No. 3629, Jeep-Ford GPW.

Serpentine Die Cut 11¼ Syncopated
2015, Jan. 20 Litho.
Booklet Stamps
Self-Adhesive
3626 A1531 A multi 1.10 .55
3627 A1531 A multi 1.10 .55
3628 A1531 A multi 1.10 .55
3629 A1531 A multi 1.10 .55
 a. Bookklet pane of 8, 2 each
 #3626-3629 9.00
 Nos. 3626-3629 (4) 4.40 2.20

On day of issue, Nos. 3626-3629 each sold for 13k.

Cartoon Character Vecernícek, 50th Anniv. — A1532

Serpentine Die Cut 11 Syncopated
2015, Feb. 18 Litho.
Self-Adhesive
3630 A1532 A multi 1.10 .55

No. 3630 sold for 13k on day of issue.

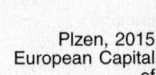

Plzen, 2015 European Capital of Culture — A1533

Photo. & Engr.
2015, Feb. 18 Perf. 11¼
3631 A1533 25k multi 2.00 1.00

Printed in sheets of 3, with 3 labels. Value, $9.50.

Historic Methods of Transportation — A1534

No. 3632: a, Walter 6B automobile. b, Monoplane of Metodej Vlach.

Perf. 11¾x11¼
2015, Feb. 18 Litho.
3632 A1534 13k Horiz. pair, #a-b 2.10 1.10

Easter — A1535

2015, Mar. 4 Litho. Perf. 11¼x11¾
3633 A1535 A multi 1.10 .55

No. 3633 sold for 13k on day of issue.

Postmen on Geese Above Charles Bridge A1536

2015, Mar. 4 Litho. Perf. 11¼x11¾
3634 A1536 A multi + label 1.10 .55

No. 3633 has a franking value of 13k on day of issue and was printed in sheets of 9 + 12 labels that could be personalized.

Souvenir Sheet

The Last Supper, by Leonardo da Vinci — A1537

Perf. 11¼x11¾
2015, Mar. 18 Litho.
3635 A1537 25k multi 2.25 1.00

Expo 2015, Milan.

Church of St. Ignatius and Spejchar Gallery, Chomutov — A1538

Photo. & Engr.
2015, Apr. 15 Perf. 11¼x11¾
3636 A1538 25k multi 2.10 2.10
 a. Booklet pane of 8 + 4 labels 17.00 —
 Complete booklet, #3636a 17.00

Sixth Czech and German Philatelic Exhibition, Chomutov.

2015 Men's Ice Hockey World Championships, Czech Republic A1539

2015, Apr. 15 Litho. Perf. 11¾x11¼
3637 A1539 30k multi 2.50 1.25

Animated Film Characters Bob and Bobek — A1540

Bob and Bobek: No. 3638, Playing ice hockey. No. 3639, Rowing raft.

Serpentine Die Cut 11 Syncopated
2015, Apr. 29 Litho.
Booklet Stamps
Self-Adhesive
3638 A1540 A multi 1.10 .55
3639 A1540 A multi 1.10 .55
 a. Booklet pane of 10, 5 each
 #3638-3639 11.00

Nos. 3638-3639 each sold for 13k on day of issue.

Moldava Railway, 130th Anniv. — A1541

2015, May 6 Engr. Perf. 11¾x11¼
3640 A1541 13k black 1.10 .55
 a. Booklet pane of 8 + 4 labels 9.00 —
 Complete booklet, #3640a 9.00

Europa — A1542

2015, May 6 Litho. Perf. 11¼
3641 A1542 25k multi 2.10 2.10

Art in Prague Castle Type of 2012

Design: 34k, Head of a Woman, by Hans von Aachen.

2015, May 27 Engr. Perf. 11¾
3642 A1457 34k multi 3.00 1.40

Rabí Castle Ruins — A1543

2015, May 27 Engr. Perf. 11¾
3643 A1543 17k multi 1.50 .70

Jan Hus (c. 1370-1415), Church Reformer — A1544

Perf. 11¼x11¾
2015, June 17 Litho.
3644 A1544 13k multi 1.25 .55

Antique Automobiles Type of 2012

Illustrations by Václav Zapadlik: No. 3645, 1955 Skoda 1201. No. 3646, 1947 Skoda Rapid 1500.

Serpentine Die Cut 11¼ Syncopated
2015, Sept. 2   Litho.
Booklet Stamps
Self-Adhesive
3645 A1467 A multi   1.10 .55
3646 A1467 A multi   1.10 .55
   a.   Booklet pane of 8, 4 each
      #3645-3646   9.00

Nos. 3645-3646 each sold for 13k on day of issue.

Sir Nicholas Winton (1909-2015), Rescuer of Jewish Children During World War II — A1545

2015, Sept. 2   Litho.   *Perf. 11¾x11¼*
3647 A1545 13k multi   1.25 .55

Postcrossing — A1546

Serpentine Die Cut 11¼ Syncopated
2015, Sept. 2   Litho.
Self-Adhesive
3648 A1546 E multi   2.50 1.10

No. 3648 sold for 25k on day of issue.

Miniature Sheet

Owls
A1547

No. 3649: a, 13k, Athene noctua (27x44mm). b, 17k, Aegolius funereus (27x44mm). c, 21k, Nyctea scandiaca (27x44mm). d, 25k, Bubo bubo (44x54mm).

Litho. & Engr.
2015, Sept. 2   *Perf. 11¾*
3649 A1547   Sheet of 4, #a-d, +
      4 labels   6.50 3.25

Historic Methods of Transportation A1548

No. 3650: a, Tatra T3 tram, 1960s. b, Primátor Dittrich paddle steamer.

Perf. 11¾x11¼
2015, Sept. 23   Litho.
3650 A1548 25k Vert. pair, #a-b   4.25 2.10

Flag of Czech Republic — A1549

Serpentine Die Cut 11¼ on 1 Side Syncopated
2015, Oct. 14   Litho.
Self-Adhesive
3651 A1549 A multi   1.25 .55

No. 3651 sold for 13k on day of issue.

Organ and Jakub Jan Ryba (1765-1815), Composer — A1550

Photo. & Engr.
2015, Oct. 14   *Perf. 11¼x11¾*
3652 A1550 13k multi   1.25 .55

Wedding of Oldrich and Bozena, Painting From Dalimil's Chronicle A1551

2015, Oct. 14   Litho.   *Perf. 11¾x11¼*
3653 A1551 21k multi   2.00 .85

Souvenir Sheet

World War I, Cent. A1552

No. 3654: a, Unveiling of statue of Jan Hus burning at the stake. b, Soldier carrying dying comrade.

2015, Oct. 14   Litho.   *Perf. 11¾*
3654 A1552 27k Sheet of 2, #a-
      b, + 3 labels   4.50 2.25

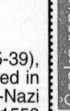

Jan Opletal (1915-39), Medical Student Killed in Anti-Nazi Protests — A1553

Photo. & Engr.
2015, Nov. 11   *Perf. 11¼x11¾*
3655 A1553 13k blue & red   1.25 .55

Art Type of 1967 Inscribed "CESKA REPUBLIKA"

Designs: 27k, The Bride, book illustration by Antonín Strnadel. 30k, Sitting, by Bohumír Matal. 34k, Great Dialogue, sculpture by Karel Nepras, horiz.

Engr., Litho. & Engr. (34k)
2015, Dec. 16   *Perf. 11¾*
3656-3658 A565   Set of 3   8.00 3.75

Postman With Posthorn A1554

2015, Dec. 16   Litho.
3659 A1554 Z multi + label   2.60 1.25

No. 3659 was printed in sheets of 9 + 12 labels that could be personalized. On day of issue, No. 3659 had a franking value of 30k.

Karel Svolinsky (1896-1986), Stamp Designer A1555

2016, Jan. 20   Litho.   *Perf. 11¾x11¼*
3660 A1555 13k multi   1.25 .55
   a.   Booklet pane of 8 + 4 labels   10.00 —
      Complete booklet, #3660a   10.00

Tradition of Czech stamp production.

Jerome of Prague (c. 1378-1416), Church Reformer A1556

2016, Jan. 20   Litho.   *Perf. 11¾x11¼*
3661 A1556 17k multi   1.60 .70

Czech Spotted Dogs — A1557

2016, Feb. 3   Litho.   *Perf. 12*
3662 A1557 13k multi   1.25 .55

Transportation A1558

No. 3663: a, Tatra rail coach M290.0. b, Paddle steamer Vysehrad.

Perf. 11¾x11¼
2016, Feb. 17   Litho.
3663 A1558 27k Pair, #a-b   5.00 2.25

Tomás Bat'a (1876-1932), Shoe Manufacturer — A1559

Photo. & Engr.
2016, Mar. 16   *Perf. 11¼x11¾*
3664 A1559 13k black & red   1.25 .55

Petrín Observation Tower and Funicular, 125th Anniv. — A1560

Photo. & Engr.
2016, Mar. 16   *Perf. 11¼x11¾*
3665 A1560 13k redsh brn &
      cream   1.25 .55
   a.   Booklet pane of 8 + 4 labels   10.00
      Complete booklet, #3665a   10.00

Joint Institute for Nuclear Research, Dubna, Russia, 60th Anniv. — A1561

Perf. 11¾x11¼
2016, Mar. 16   Litho.
3666 A1561 27k multi   2.50 1.10

Buchlov Castle A1562

2016, Apr. 6   Engr.   *Perf. 11½x11¾*
3667 A1562 17k multi   1.50 .75

Czech and Slovak Philatelic Exhibition, Zd'ár nad Sázavou — A1563

2016, Apr. 27   Litho.   *Perf. 11¼x11¾*
3668 A1563 13k multi   1.25 .55
   a.   Booklet pane of 8 + 4 labels   10.00 —
      Complete booklet, #3668a   10.00

Common Yellow Swallowtail Butterflies and Thistles — A1564

2016, Apr. 27   Litho.   *Perf. 12*
3669 A1564 16k multi   1.50 .70

Europa A1565

2016, May 4   Litho.   *Perf. 11¾x11¼*
3670 A1565 27k multi   2.50 1.10

Think Green Issue.
Printed in sheets of 8. Value, $20.

Souvenir Sheet

Holy Roman Emperor Charles IV (1316-78) — A1566

Litho. & Engr.
2016, May 4   *Perf. 11¾*
3671 A1566 54k multi + 2 labels   8.00 5.00

No. 3671 was issued on May 4 with the incorrectly-spelled Latin inscription "Karolus Quatrus" in the sheet margin. Value, $100. The sheet was withdrawn from sale on May 5, and replaced soon thereafter with sheets bearing the correct inscription "Karolus Quartus."

Animated Cartoon Character Amálka the Fairy — A1567

Serpentine Die Cut 11¼ Syncopated
2016, May 18   Litho.
Booklet Stamp
Self-Adhesive
3672 A1567 A multi   1.50 .70
   a.   Booklet pane of 10   15.00

No. 3672 sold for 16k on day of issue.

Premiere of *The Bartered Bride*, by Bedrich Smetana, 150th Anniv. — A1567a

2016, May 18   Litho.   Perf. 11¼x11¾
3673 A1567a 16k multi   1.50 .70

Art in Prague Castle Type of 2012
Design: 38k, Prague Altarpiece detail depicting St. Barbara, by Lucas Cranach the Elder.

2016, May 18   Engr.   *Perf. 11¾*
3674 A1457 38k multi   3.25 1.60

Flower Arrangement A1568

2016, June 8   Litho.   *Perf. 11¾x11¼*
3675 A1568 A multi + label   1.40 .70

No. 3675 was printed in sheets of 9 + 12 labels that could be personalized. On day of issue, No. 3675 had a franking value of 16k.

International Folklore Festival, Strážnice — A1569

Photo. & Engr.
2016, June 22   *Perf. 11¼x11¾*
3676 A1569 20k multi   1.75 .85

Jan Jessenius (1566-1621), Physician and Professor of Anatomy — A1570

Photo. & Engr.
2016, June 22   *Perf. 11¼x11¾*
3677 A1570 27k multi + label   2.50 1.10

See Hungary No. 4393, Poland No. 4232, Slovakia No. 743.

2016 Summer Olympics, Rio de Janeiro A1571

Perf. 11¾x11¼
2016, June 22   Litho.
3678 A1571 32k multi   3.00 1.40

2016 Summer Paralympics, Rio de Janeiro A1572

Perf. 11¾x11¼
2016, June 22   Litho.
3679 A1572 16k multi   1.50 .70

Art Type of 1967 Inscribed "CESKA REPUBLIKA"
Design: Young Woman on a Balcony, by Gerrit Dou.

2016, Sept. 7   Engr.   *Perf. 11¾*
3680 A565 27k multi   2.50 1.10

See Liechtenstein No. 1691.

Tree Frog — A1573

2016, Sept. 7   Litho.   *Perf. 11¾x11¼*
3681 A1573 A multi   1.50 .70

No. 3681 sold for 16k on day of issue.

Dr. Antonín Holy (1936-2012), Developer of Antiretroviral Drugs — A1574

2016, Sept. 7   Litho.   *Perf. 11¼x11¾*
3682 A1574 20k multi   2.00 .85

UNESCO World Heritage Sites in Czech Republic A1575

Designs: 16k, Lednice-Valtice Cultural Landscape. 27k, Historic Center of Prague.

2016, Sept. 7   Litho.   *Perf. 11¼x11¾*
3683-3684 A1575   Set of 2   4.00 1.90

See United Nations Nos. 1142, 1144a, 1144e; Offices in Geneva Nos. 626, 627a, 627e; Offices in Vienna Nos. 594a, 594e.

Miniature Sheet

Animals in Czech Republic Zoos A1576

No. 3685: a, 16k, Panthera uncia, Jihlava Zoo. b, 20k, Oryx gazella gazella, Panthera leo leo, Olomouc Zoo. c, 24k, Diceros bicornis, Lycaon pictus, Dvur Králové Zoo. d, 27k, Equus przewalskii, Prague Zoo.

Litho. & Engr.
2016, Sept. 7   *Perf. 11¾*
3685 A1576   Sheet of 4, #a-d, + 3 labels   8.00 3.75

Historic Methods of Transportation — A1577

No. 3686: a, Tatra 87 automobile. b, Aero Ab-11 biplane.

Perf. 11¾x11¼
2016, Sept. 21   Litho.
3686 A1577 16k Horiz. pair, #a-b 3.00 1.40

Zelezné Hory Protected Landscape Area, 25th Anniv. — A1578

2016, Oct. 12   Litho.   *Perf. 11¾x11¼*
3687 A1578 16k multi   1.50 .70

Bee-eaters — A1579

2016, Oct. 12   Litho.   *Perf. 11¾x11¼*
3688 A1579 20k multi   2.00 .85

Souvenir Sheet

Fight for Czech Statehood — A1580

No. 3689: a, St. Wenceslas, King Ottokar II of Bohemia, Holy Roman Emperor Charles IV, flags, soldiers. b, Grieving widow and children, Austrian imperial eagle.

2016, Oct. 12   Litho.   *Perf. 11¾*
3689 A1580 27k Sheet of 2, #a-b, + 3 labels   5.00 2.25

Art Type of 1967 Inscribed "CESKA REPUBLIKA"
Designs: 27k, Two Women, by Jaroslav Král, horiz. 30k, Girl with Absinthe, sculpture by Bedrich Stefan. 38k, Clown with Monkey, by Frantisek Tichy.

2016, Nov. 9   Litho.   *Perf. 11¾*
3690-3692 A565   Set of 3   8.50 3.75

United Nations Educational, Scientific and Cultural Organization, 70th Anniv. — A1581

2016, Nov. 9   Litho.   *Perf. 12*
3693 A1581 32k multi   2.90 1.40

Oldrich Posmurny (1942-2010), Stamp Designer — A1582

Photo. & Engr.
2017, Jan. 20   *Perf. 11¼x11¾*
3694 A1582 16k multi   1.50 .70
   a.   Booklet pane of 8 + 4 labels   12.00
     Complete booklet, #3694a   12.00

Tradition of Czech stamp production.

Czech Crown Jewels A1583

Serpentine Die Cut 11½ Syncopated
2017, Jan. 20   Litho.
Booklet Stamp
Self-Adhesive
3695 A1583 E multi   2.90 1.40
   a.   Booklet pane of 8   24.00

No. 3695 sold for 32k on day of issue.

Historic Methods of Transportation — A1584

Designs: No. 3696a, Skoda 606DNd postal bus. No. 3696b, Fk-5-1401 railroad mail car. No. 3697, Paddle steamer "Prague." 32k, Aero A-14 biplane.

2017   Litho.   *Perf. 11¾x11¼*
3696 A1584 16k Horiz. pair, #a-b 3.00 1.25
3697 A1584 16k multi   1.50 .65
3698 A1584 32k multi   3.00 1.40
   Nos. 3696-3698 (3)   7.50 3.30

Issued: No. 3696, 2/15; No. 3697, 3/8; No. 3698, 1/20.

Straka Academy, 120th Anniv. — A1585

2017, Mar. 8   Litho.   *Perf. 11¾x11¼*
3699 A1585 24k multi   2.25 .95

Porta Bohemica River Valley — A1586

2017, Apr. 5   Engr.   *Perf. 11¾*
3700 A1586 20k multi   1.75 .85

Prague Airport, 80th Anniv. — A1587

Photo. & Engr.
2017, Apr. 5   *Perf. 11¾x11¼*
3701 A1587 32k multi   2.60 1.40

Vera Cáslavská (1942-2016), Gymnast and President of Czech Olympic Committee — A1588

2017, May 3   Litho.   *Perf. 11¼x11¾*
3702 A1588 16k multi   1.40 .70

Frydlant Castle — A1589

Photo. & Engr.
2017, May 3　　　　　　　Perf. 11¼
3703　A1589　32k multi　　　　2.75 1.40
Europa.

Holy Roman Empress Maria Theresa (1717-80) — A1590

Photo. & Engr.
2017, May 3　　　　　　　Perf. 11¾
3704　A1590　32k multi　　　　2.75 1.40

Art in Prague Castle Type of 2012
No. 3705 — St. Catherine with Angel, by Paolo Veronese: a, Black image. b, Multicolored image.

2017, May 17　　Engr.　　Perf. 11¾
3705　A1457　32k Horiz. pair, #a-b　5.50 2.75
Printed in sheets containing two each of Nos. 3705a-3705b + central label.

Souvenir Sheet

Operation Anthropoid (Assassination of Reinhard Heydrich), 75th Anniv. — A1591

Litho. & Engr.
2017, May 17　　　　　　　Perf. 11¾
3706　A1591　46k multi + 7 labels　4.00 2.00

Josef Kainar (1917-71), Writer — A1592

Photo. & Engr.
2017, June 7　　　　Perf. 11¼x11¾
3707　A1592　16k multi　　　　1.40 .70

Heliodor Píka (1897-1949), General Executed by Communists — A1593

Photo. & Engr.
2017, June 7　　　　Perf. 11¼x11¾
3708　A1593　37k multi　　　　3.25 1.60

Joze Plecnik (1872-1957), Architect — A1594

Perf. 11½x11¾
2017, June 7　　　　Litho. & Engr.
3709　A1594　32k multi　　　　2.75 1.40
No. 3709 was printed in sheets of 2 + central label.

Locomotives — A1595

Designs: No. 3710, Steam locomotive No. 7. No. 3711, Cog locomotive "The Austrian."

Serpentine Die Cut 11½ Syncopated
2017, June 7　　　　　　　　Litho.
Booklet Stamps
Self-Adhesive
3710　A1595　A multi　　　　1.40 .70
3711　A1595　A multi　　　　1.40 .70
　a.　Booklet pane of 8, 4 each
　　　#3710-3711　　　　　11.50
On day of issue, Nos. 3710-3711 each sold for 16k.

Prague Pneumatic Mail System — A1596

2017, June 21　　Litho.　　Perf. 11¼
3712　A1596　A multi　　　　1.40 .70
No. 3712 sold for 16k on day of issue.

Church of the Assumption of Our Lady, Most, 500th Anniv. — A1597

Photo. & Engr.
2017, June 21　　　　Perf. 11¼x11¾
3713　A1597　16k multi　　　　1.40 .70

Moravian Museum, Brno, 200th Anniv. — A1598

Photo. & Engr.
2017, June 21　　　　Perf. 11¾x11¼
3714　A1598　20k multi　　　　1.75 .85

Gas Street Lighting in Prague, 170th Anniv. — A1599

Photo. & Engr.
2017, Sept. 6　　　　Perf. 11¼x11¾
3715　A1599　16k multi　　　　1.50 .75
　a.　Booklet pane of 8 + 4 labels　12.00
　　　Complete booklet, #3715a　12.00

Josef Balabán (1894-1941), Václav Morávek (1904-42), and Josef Masín (1896-1942), Members of "Three Kings" Anti-Nazi Resistance Group — A1600

2017, Sept. 6　Litho.　Perf. 11¾x11¼
3716　A1600　16k multi　　　　1.50 .75

Mauritius No. 2 — A1601

2017, Sept. 6　　Litho.　　Perf. 12
3717　A1601　A multi　　　　1.50 .75
No. 3717 sold for 16k on day of issue.

Worker for Partner Post Office — A1602

2017, Sept. 6　Litho.　Perf. 11¾x11¼
3718　A1602　A multi　　　　1.50 .75
　　　Complete booklet, 5 #3718　7.50
No. 3718 sold for 16k on day of issue.

Miniature Sheet

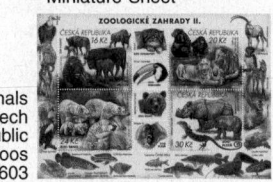

Animals in Czech Republic Zoos — A1603

No. 3719: a, 16k, Bison bonasus, Chomutov Zoo. b, 20k, Pan troglodytes, Panthera leo krugeri, Hodonín Zoo. c, 24k, Ursus maritimus, Brno Zoo. d, 30k, Rhinoceros unicornis, Varanus macraei, Plzen Zoo.

Litho. & Engr.
2017, Sept. 6　　　　　　　Perf. 11¾
3719　A1603　Sheet of 4, #a-d, +
　　　　　　4 labels　　　8.25 4.25
Nature Protection.

Václav Hollar Association of Czech Graphic Artists, Cent. — A1604

Photo. & Engr.
2017, Sept. 20　　　　Perf. 11¼x11¾
3720　A1604　20k multi　　　　1.90 .95

Imperial Austrian Letter Boxes, 200th Anniv. — A1605

Photo. & Engr.
2017, Oct. 4　　　　Perf. 11¼x11¾
3721　A1605　16k multi　　　　1.50 .75
　a.　Booklet pane of 8 + 4 labels　12.00
　　　Complete booklet, #3721a　12.00

Family on Bicycle — A1606

Photo. & Engr.
2017, Oct. 4　　　　Perf. 11½x11¼
3722　A1606　16k blk & red　　1.50 .75

Self-Sculpture of Fictional Character Jára Cimrman, 50th Anniv. — A1607

Serpentine Die Cut 11¼ Syncopated
2017, Oct. 4　　　　　　　　Litho.
Booklet Stamp
Self-Adhesive
3723　A1607　A multi　　　　1.50 .75
　a.　Booklet pane of 8　　　12.00
Jára Cimrman, fictional character created for 1967 Czech radio program, selected as "Greatest Czech" in 2005. No. 3723 sold for 16k on day of issue.

Souvenir Sheet

Fight for Czech Statehood — A1608

No. 3724: a, Soldiers, flag, independence leaders Milan R. Stefánik (1880-1919), Tomás G. Masaryk (1850-1937), and Jan Syrovy (1880-1970). b, Writers Alois Jirásek (1851-1930), and Jaroslav Kvapil (1868-1950) and Manifesto of Czech Writers.

Litho., Sheet Margin Litho. With Foil Application
2017, Oct. 4　　　　　　　Perf. 11¾
3724　A1608　30k Sheet of 2, #a-
　　　　　　b, + 3 labels　　5.50 2.75

Tatra Automobile at Railroad Crossing — A1609

2017, Oct. 18　Litho.　Perf. 11¾x11½
3725　A1609　A multi + label　1.50 .75
No. 3725 was printed in sheets of 9 + 12 labels that could be personalized. On day of issue No. 3725 had a franking value of 16k.

Art Type of 1967 Inscribed "CESKA REPUBLIKA"
Designs: 32k, Cuddled, photograph by Taras Kuscynskyj. 38k, Tempter, painting by Norbert Grund.

Litho. (32k), Engr. (38k)
2017, Nov. 8　　　　　　　Perf. 11¾
3726-3727　A565　Set of 2　6.50 3.25

Czech Astronomical
Society, Cent. — A1610

2017, Nov. 8 Litho. Perf. 11¼x11¾
3728 A1610 16k multi   1.50 .75

**Art Type of 1967 Inscribed "CESKA
REPUBLIKA"**

Design: Winner, by Jaroslava Pesicová.

2017, Dec. 13 Engr. Perf. 11¾
3729 A565 30k multi   3.00 1.50

Souvenir Sheet

Postal
Officials
A1611

No. 3730: a, 32k, Jirí Stríbny (1880-1955),
first Czechoslovakian minister of Posts and
Telegraphs. b, 37k, Maxmilián Fatka (1868-
1962), first director general of Czechoslovak
Post.

Litho. & Engr.
2017, Dec. 13   Perf. 11¾
3730 A1611 Sheet of 2, #a-b   6.50 3.25

Czech Republic, 25th
Anniv. — A1612

2018, Jan. 3 Litho. Perf. 12
3731 A1612 24k multi   2.40 1.25

No. 3731 was printed in sheets of 2 + central label.

2018 Winter
Paralympics,
PyeongChang,
South Korea
A1613

2018 Winter Olympics,
PyeongChang, South
Korea
A1614

2018, Jan. 20 Litho. Perf. 11¾x11¼
3732 A1613 16k multi   1.60 .80
Perf. 11¼x11¾
3733 A1614 37k multi   3.75 1.90

Jirí Bouda
(1934-2015),
Stamp Designer
A1615

Perf. 11¾x11¼
2018, Jan. 20   Litho. & Engr.
3734 A1615 A multi   1.90 .95
  a. Booklet pane of 8 + 4 labels 15.50
      Complete booklet, #3734a   15.50

Tradition of Czech stamp production. No.
3734 sold for 19k on day of issue.

Prague
Castle — A1616

Perf. 11¾x11¼
2018, Feb. 21   Litho.
3735 A1616 A red & indigo + la-
             bel   1.90 .95

No. 3735 was printed in sheets of 9 + 12
labels that could be personalized. On day of
issue, No. 3735 had a franking value of 19k.
See No. 3837.

Person Making
Willow
Whip — A1617

Perf. 11¾x11¼
2018, Feb. 21   Litho.
3736 A1617 A multi   1.90 .95

Easter. On day of issue, No. 3736 sold for
19k.

Prague Municipal
Library — A1618

Perf. 11¼x11¾
2018, Feb. 21   Litho.
3737 A1618 A multi   1.90 .95

On day of issue, No. 3737 sold for 19k.

Silesian
Eagle in
National Coat
of Arms
A1619

Moravian
Eagle in
National
Coat of
Arms
A1620

Presidential
Standard
A1621

National
Seal
A1622

Bohemian
Lion in
National
Coat of
Arms
A1623

National
Flag
A1624

National
Colors
A1625

National
Anthem
A1626

Serpentine Die Cut 11½ Syncopated
2018, Feb. 21   Litho.
Booklet Stamps
Self-Adhesive
3738 A1619 A multi   1.90 .95
3739 A1620 A multi   1.90 .95
3740 A1621 A multi   1.90 .95
3741 A1622 A multi   1.90 .95
3742 A1623 A multi   1.90 .95
3743 A1624 A multi   1.90 .95
3744 A1625 A multi   1.90 .95
3745 A1626 A multi   1.90 .95
  a. Booklet pane of 8, #3738-
      3745   15.50
      Nos. 3738-3745 (8)   15.20 7.60
On day of issue, Nos. 3738-3745 each sold
for 19k.

Dr. Frantisek Hamza
(1868-1930), and
Hamza
Hospital — A1627

Photo. & Engr.
2018, Feb. 21   Perf. 11¼x11¾
3746 A1627 20k blue & claret 1.90 .95

Paddle Steamer
Vltava — A1628

Perf. 11¾x11¼
2018, Mar. 14   Litho.
3747 A1628 A multi   1.90 .95

On day of issue, No. 3747 sold for 19k.

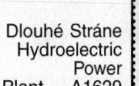

Dlouhé Stráne
Hydroelectric
Power
Plant — A1629

Perf. 11¾x11¼
2018, Mar. 14   Litho.
3748 A1629 23k multi   2.25 1.10

Carriage of
Emperor
Ferdinand I of
Austria
A1630

Carriage of
Princess Pauline
Clémentine von
Metternich-
Sándor
A1631

Postal Coach,
Zamberk
A1632

Carriage of
Johann Adolf II,
Prince of
Schwarzenberg
A1633

Passenger
Coach — A1634

Serpentine Die Cut Syncopated
2018, Mar. 14   Litho.
Self-Adhesive
3749 Strip of 5   17.50 8.75
  a. A1630 E multi   3.50 1.75
  b. A1631 E multi   3.50 1.75
  c. A1632 E multi   3.50 1.75
  d. A1633 E multi   3.50 1.75
  e. A1634 E multi   3.50 1.75

Coaches and carriages from Postal
Museum. Praga 2018 International Philatelic
Exhibition. Nos. 3749a-3749e each sold for
35k on day of issue. Round stamps for the "E"
rate are personalizable.

Eduard Storch
(1878-1959),
Archaeologist
and
Writer — A1635

2018, Apr. 4 Litho. Perf. 11¾x11¼
3750 A1635 19k multi   1.75 .90

Czech National Library Architectural
Design of Jan Kaplicky (1937-2009)
A1636

Photo. & Engr.
2018, Apr. 4   Perf. 11¼x11¾
3751 A1636 E multi   3.25 1.60

No. 3751 sold for 35k on day of issue.

Pres. Zeman Type of 2013
Photo. & Engr.
2018, Apr. 18   Perf. 11¾x11¼
3752 A1484 A red & dk blue   1.75 .90

No. 3752 sold for 19k on day of issue.

Stadlec Bridge and
Podolsko
Bridge — A1637

2018, May 2 Litho. Perf. 11
3753 A1637 E gold & multi   3.25 1.60

Europa. No. 3751 sold for 35k on day of
issue.

Czech Jazz
Music — A1638

2018, May 2 Litho. Perf. 11¼x11¾
3754 A1638 Z multi   3.75 1.90

No. 3754 sold for 41k on day of issue.

Art in Prague Castle Type of 2012

Design: 32k, Sacrifice at the Temple, by
Francesco da Ponte, the Younger.

2018, May 23 Engr. Perf. 11¾
3755 A1457 32k multi   3.00 1.50

Flowers Type of 2002

Design: 1k, Lily of the valley (konvalinka).

Perf. 11¾x11¼
2018, June 20   Litho.
3756 A1215 1k multi   .25 .25

Bentwood Chairs by Factory Established by Michael Thonet (1796-1871) — A1639

Perf. 11¼x11¾

2018, June 20			**Litho.**
3757	A1639	19k multi	1.75	.85
a.		Booklet pane of 8 + 4 labels	14.00	—
		Complete booklet, #3757a	14.00	

Mushrooms — A1640

Designs: No. 3758, Leccinum rufescens. No. 3759, Amanita rubescens.

Serpentine Die Cut 11¼ Syncopated
2018, June 20   Litho.

Booklet Stamps
Self-Adhesive

3758	A1640	A multi	1.75	.85
3759	A1640	A multi	1.75	.85
a.		Booklet pane of 10, 5 each #3758-3759	17.50	

Souvenir Sheet

Czechoslovakian Postage Stamps, Cent. — A1641

No. 3760: a, 27k, Czechoslovakia Nos. B125, P3, 244, P27, 575, 152, 329, 1133. b, 44k, Czech Republic Nos. 3040b, 3210b, 3467, 3567, 3615, 3692.

2018, June 20	**Litho.**	**Perf. 11¾**
3760	A1641	Sheet of 2, #a-b, + 3 labels	6.50	3.25

Souvenir Sheet

Czech Postal Museum, Cent. A1642

Directors: a, 19k, Václav Dragoun (1865-1950). b, 23k, Jirí Karásek (1871-1951). c, 27k, Pavel Ctvrtnik (1947-2008).

Litho. & Engr., Litho. Sheet Margin
2018, Aug. 8	**Perf. 11¾x11½**
3761	A1642	Sheet of 3, #a-c	6.25	3.25

Praga 2018 International Philatelic Exhibition, Prague.

Souvenir Sheet

1850 Cover to Bombay, India From Port Louis, Mauritius A1643

2018, Aug. 8	**Litho.**	**Perf. 11¾**
3762	A1643	59k multi	5.50	2.75

Sale of Bombay Cover to Czech collector. Praga 2018 International Philatelic Exhibition, Prague.

Locomotives — A1644

Designs: No. 3763, 1939 M260001 locomotive. No. 3764, Steam locomotive 365024, 1923.

Serpentine Die Cut 11½ Syncopated
2018, Sept. 5   Litho.

Booklet Stamps
Self-Adhesive

3763	A1644	A multi	1.75	.85
3764	A1644	A multi	1.75	.85
a.		Booklet pane of 8, 4 each #3763-3764	14.00	

On day of issue, Nos. 3763-3764 each sold for 19k.

Miniature Sheet

Animals in Czech Republic Zoos A1645

No. 3765: a, 19k, Ursus arctos horribilis, Decín Zoo. b, 23k, Pongo pygmaeus, Ustí nad Labem Zoo. c, 27k, Loxodonta africana, Zlín Zoo. d, 33k, Cercopithecus diana, Hippopotamus amphibius, Ostrava Zoo.

Litho. & Engr.
	Perf. 11¾
2018, Sept. 5	
3765	A1645	Sheet of 4, #a-d, + 4 labels	9.25	4.75

National Agricultural Museum, Prague, Cent. — A1646

Photo. & Engr.
2018, Sept. 19	**Perf. 11¾x11¼**
3766	A1646	27k multi	2.50	1.25

Souvenir Sheet

Fight for Czech Statehood — A1647

No. 3767 — Flags and: a, Monument to St. Wenceslas, Prague. b, Tomás G. Masaryk (1850-1937), first president of Czechoslovakia.

Litho., Sheet Margin Litho. With Foil Application
2018, Oct. 10	**Perf. 11¾**
3767	A1647	33k Sheet of 2, #a-b, + 3 labels	6.00	3.00

National Museum, Prague, 200th Anniv. — A1648

2018, Oct. 10	**Litho.**	**Perf. 11¼x11¾**
3768	A1648	19k multi	1.75	.85

Goose and Wine Bottle — A1649

2018, Oct. 24	**Litho.**	**Perf. 11¼x11¾**
3769	A1649	A multi	1.75	.85
a.		Booklet pane of 8 + 4 labels	14.00	—
		Complete booklet, #3769a	14.00	
b.		Tete-beche pair	3.50	3.50

St. Martin's Day. No. 3769 sold for 19k on day of issue. No. 3769b is found in No. 3769a.

Miroslav Hornícek (1918-2003), Actor — A1650

Photo. & Engr.
2018, Oct. 24	**Perf. 11¼x11¾**
3770	A1650	19k multi	1.75	.85

Frantisek Ladislav Rieger (1818-1903), Politician — A1651

Photo. & Engr.
2018, Oct. 24	**Perf. 11¼x11¾**
3771	A1651	27k multi	2.40	1.25

Miniature Sheet

Czech Orders and Medals, Cent. A1652

No. 3772: a, 19k, Medal of Merit. b, 23k, Order of Thomas Garrigue Masaryk. c, 27k, Order of the White Lion. d, 33k, Medal for Heroism.

2018, Oct. 24	**Litho.**	**Perf. 12**
3772	A1652	Sheet of 4, #a-d	9.00	4.50

Christmas — A1653

No. 3773: a, Christmas ornament and apple. b, Christmas ornament and cookie.

2018, Oct. 24	**Litho.**	**Perf. 11¾x11¼**
3773	A1653	A Pair, #a-b	3.50	1.75

On day of issue, Nos. 3773a-3773b each sold for 19k.

Art Type of 1967 Inscribed "CESKA REPUBLIKA"

Designs: 27k, The Great Angel's Others I, II, sculpture by Stanislav Libensky. 33k, Birds of Jevis, painting by Vladimir Komárek. 41k, Diego de Guzmán, engraving by Paulus Pontius.

Litho. (27k), Litho. & Engr. (33k), Engr. (41k)
2018, Nov. 14	**Perf. 11¾**
3774-3776	A565	Set of 3	9.00	4.50

Thomas Garrigue Masaryk (1850-1937), First President of Czechoslovakia A1654

Photo. & Engr.
2018, Nov. 14	**Perf. 11¼x11¾**
3777	A1654	A multi	1.75	.85
a.		Souvenir sheet of 1	1.75	.85

No. 3777 sold for 19k on day of issue.

Prague Castle Guard, Cent. — A1655

2018, Dec. 5	**Litho.**	**Perf. 11¼x11¾**
3778	A1655	A multi	1.75	.85
a.		Booklet pane of 8 + 4 labels	14.00	—
		Complete booklet, #3778a	14.00	

No. 3778 sold for 19k on day of issue.

Petr Eben (1929-2007), Composer — A1656

2019, Jan. 20	**Litho.**	**Perf. 11¼x11¾**
3779	A1656	19k multi	1.75	.85

Masaryk University, Brno, Cent. — A1657

2019, Jan. 20 Litho. *Perf. 11¼x11¾*
3780 A1657 A multi 1.75 .85

No. 3780 sold for 19k on day of issue.

Adolf Born (1930-2016), Illustrator A1658

2019, Jan. 20 Litho. *Perf. 11¾x11¼*
3781 A1658 A multi 1.75 .85
a. Booklet pane of 8 + 4 labels 14.00 —
Complete booklet, #3781a 14.00

Tradition of Czech stamp production. No. 3781 sold for 19k on day of issue.

Rudolf Tomás Jedlicka (1869-1926), Surgeon and Radiologist A1659

Perf. 11¾x11¼
2019, Feb. 14 Litho.
3782 A1659 19k multi 1.75 .85

Souvenir Sheet

Jirí Hanzelka (1920-2003) and Miroslav Zikmund, Travel Writers and Film Makers — A1660

No. 3783: a, Zikmund holding camera. b, Hanzelka.

Perf. 11¾x11½
2019, Feb. 14 Litho. & Engr.
3783 A1660 45k Sheet of 2, #a-b + 2 labels 8.00 4.00

100th birthday of Zikmund.

Process of Making Sugar Cubes by Jakub Krystof Rad, 175th Anniv. — A1661

2019, Mar. 6 Litho. *Perf. 11¼x11¾*
3784 A1661 19k multi 1.75 .85

Les Království Dam, Cent. — A1662

2019, Mar. 6 Litho. *Perf. 11¾x11¼*
3785 A1662 A multi 1.75 .85
a. Booklet pane of 8 + 4 labels 14.00 —
Complete booklet, #3785a 14.00

No. 3785 sold for 19k on day of issue.

Maltese Cross and Church of Our Lady Under the Chain, Prague, Headquarters of Grand Priory of Bohemia of the Sovereign Military Order of Malta — A1663

2019, Mar. 6 Litho. *Perf. 11¼x11¾*
3786 A1663 45k multi 4.00 2.00

Alois Rasin (1867-1923), Minister of Finance A1664

2019, Apr. 3 Litho. *Perf. 11¾x11¼*
3787 A1664 23k multi 2.00 1.00

Czechoslovakian currency, cent.

Alcedo Atthis — A1665

2019, Apr. 24 Litho. *Perf. 11*
3788 A1665 E multi 3.50 1.75

Europa. No. 3788 sold for 39k on day of issue.

Flowers Type of 2002

Design: E, Dandelion (pampeliska).

2019, May 22 Litho. *Perf. 11¾x11¼*
3789 A1215 E multi 3.50 1.75

No. 3789 sold for 39k on day of issue.

Art in Prague Castle Type of 2012

No. 3790 — Paintings by Adolf Absolon: a, Prague Castle in Summer. b, Prague Castle in Winter.

Litho. & Engr.
2019, May 22 *Perf. 11¾*
3790 A1457 Horiz. pair 7.00 3.50
a.-b. E Either single 3.50 1.75

Nos. 3790a-3790b each sold for 39k on day of issue.

Gelasius Dobner (1719-90), Historian A1666

2019, May 22 Litho. *Perf. 11¾x11¼*
3791 A1666 27k multi 2.40 1.25

A1667   Ctylistek Comic Strip, 50th Anniv. — A1668

Serpentine Die Cut 11 Syncopated
2019, May 22 Litho.
Booklet Stamps
Self-Adhesive
3792 A1667 A blue & multi 1.75 .85
3793 A1668 A red & multi 1.75 .85
a. Booklet pane of 10, 5 each #3792-3793 17.50

Nos. 3792-3793 each sold for 19k on day of issue.

Art Type of 1967 Inscribed "CESKA REPUBLIKA"

Designs: 27k, Line No. 56, by Zdenek Sykora (1920-2011). 45k, Poplars, by Václav Radimsky (1867-1946).

Litho. (27k), Engr. (45k)
2019, June 12 *Perf. 11¾*
3794-3795 A565 Set of 2 6.50 3.25

First Horse-drawn Tram in Brno, 150th Anniv. — A1669

Perf. 11¾x11¼
2019, June 26 Litho.
3796 A1669 A multi 1.75 .85

No. 3796 sold for 19k on day of issue.

Jan Palach (1948-1969) and Jan Zajic (1950-69), Student Protestors Who Set Themselves Afire — A1670

Perf. 11¾x11¼
2019, June 26 Litho.
3797 A1670 A multi 1.75 .85

No. 3797 sold for 19k on day of issue.

Mohandas K. Gandhi (1869-1948), Indian Nationalist Leader — A1671

Perf. 11¼x11¾
2019, June 26 Litho.
3798 A1671 Z multi 4.00 2.00

No. 3798 sold for 45k on day of issue.

Electra 10A in Flight A1672

Electra 10A at Airport A1673

Serpentine Die Cut 11½ Syncopated
2019, Sept. 4 Litho.
Booklet Stamps
Self-Adhesive
3799 A1672 E multi 3.50 1.75
3800 A1673 E multi 3.50 1.75
a. Booklet pane of 8, 4 each #3799-3800 28.00

Nos. 3799 and 3800 each sold for 39k on day of issue.

Clock and Horseman Lancing Dragon A1674

2019, Sept. 4 Litho. *Perf. 11¼x11¾*
3801 A1674 A multi + label 1.60 .80

No. 3801 was printed in sheets of 9 + 12 labels that could be personalized. On day of issue, No. 3801 had a franking value of 19k.

Miniature Sheet

Animals in Czech Republic Zoos A1675

No. 3802: a, 19k, Crocodylus mindorensis, Protivín Zoo (45x27mm). b, 23k, Ovis aries strepsiceros, Vyskov Zoopark (45x27mm). c, 27k, Platalea leucordia, Lutra lutra, Hluboká Zoo (45x54mm). e, 33k, Budorcas taxicolor bedfordi, Liberec Zoo (45x54mm).

Litho. & Engr.
2019, Sept. 4 *Perf. 11¾*
3802 A1675 Sheet of 4, #a-d, + 4 labels 8.75 4.50

Automobile Designed by Václav Král (1936-2005) A1676

2019, Oct. 2 Litho. *Perf. 11¾x11¼*
3803 A1676 A multi 1.75 .85
a. Booklet pane of 8 + 4 labels 14.00
Complete booklet, #3803a 14.00

No. 3803 sold for 19k on day of issue.

Souvenir Sheet

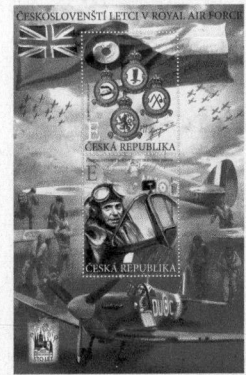

Service of Czechoslovakians in Royal Air Force in World War II — A1677

No. 3804: a, Flag of Czechoslovakia, Royal Air Force emblem and emblems of four Czechoslovak squadrons. b, Frantisek Perina (1911-2006), pilot.

2019, Oct. 2 Litho. *Perf. 11¾*
3804 A1677 E Sheet of 2, #a-b 7.00 3.50

Nos. 3804a-3804b each sold for 39k on day of issue.

Semafor Theater, Prague, 60th Anniv. — A1678

2019, Oct. 23 Litho. *Perf. 11¾x11¼*
3805 A1678 A gold & multi 1.75 .85

No. 3805 sold for 19k on day of issue.

Souvenir Sheet

Actors and Actresses — A1679

No. 3806: a, 23k, Dana Medrická (1920-83). b, 27k, Radovan Lukavsky (1918-2008).

2019, Oct. 23 Litho. Perf. 11¾
3806 A1679 Sheet of 2, #a-b 4.50 2.25

Ivan Blatny (1919-90), Poet — A1680

Perf. 11¼x11¾
2019, Nov. 13 Litho.
3807 A1680 A multi 1.75 .85
No. 3807 sold for 19k on day of issue.

Czechoslovakian Red Cross, Cent. — A1681

Perf. 11¾x11¼
2019, Nov. 13 Litho.
3808 A1681 19k multi 1.75 .85

Souvenir Sheet

Velvet Revolution, 30th Anniv. — A1682

Litho. & Engr.
2019, Nov. 13 Perf. 11¾
3809 A1682 44k multi 4.00 2.00
Joint Issue between Czech Republic and Slovakia.
See Slovakia No. 835.

Art Type of 1967 Inscribed "CESKA REPUBLIKA"

Designs: 39k, Touch of Fate II, sculpture by Ladislav Saloun. 45k, Flora, painting by Ota Janecek, horiz.

Litho. (39k), Litho. & Engr. (45k)
2019 Perf. 11¾
3810-3811 A565 Set of 2 7.25 7.25
Issued: 39k, 11/27; 45k, 11/13.

Bedrich Housa (1926-2020), Stamp Engraver A1683

2020, Jan. 20 Litho. Perf. 11¾x11¼
3812 A1683 A multi 1.75 .85
 a. Booklet pane of 8 + 4 labels 14.00 —
  Complete booklet, #3812a 14.00
No. 3812 sold for 19k on day of issue.

Minting of Thalers at Joachimstal Mint, 500th Anniv. — A1684

2020, Jan. 20 Litho. Perf. 11¾
3813 A1684 A multi 1.75 .85
No. 3813 sold for 19k on day of issue.

The Organ Grinder, by Josef Capek (1887-1945) A1685

Serpentine Die Cut 11½ Syncopated
2020, Jan. 20 Litho.
Booklet Stamp
Self-Adhesive
3814 A1685 Z multi 4.00 2.00
 a. Booklet pane of 6 24.00
No. 3814 sold for 45k on day of issue.

Favorit Bicycle — A1686

2020, Feb. 1 Litho. Perf. 11¾x11¼
3815 A1686 B multi 1.75 .85
No. 3815 sold for 19k on day of issue.

Post Rider — A1687

Serpentine Die Cut 11 Syncopated
2020, Feb. 1 Litho.
Booklet Stamp
Self-Adhesive
3816 A1687 B multi 1.75 .85
 a. Booklet pane of 10 17.50
No. 3816 sold for 19k on day of issue.

Pillars — A1688

Perf. 11¾x11¼
2020, Feb. 26 Litho.
3817 A1688 B multi 1.75 .85
Constitutional judiciary, cent. No. 3817 sold for 19k on day of issue.

Easter — A1689

Perf. 11¼x11¾
2020, Feb. 26 Litho.
3818 A1689 B multi 1.75 .85
No. 3818 sold for 19k on day of issue.

Temptation, by Vladimir Suchanek A1690

Perf. 11¼x11¾
2020, Feb. 26 Litho.
3819 A1690 B multi + label 1.75 .85
No. 3819 was printed in sheets of 9 + 12 labels that could be personalized. On day of issue, No. 3819 had a franking value of 19k.

Kasperk Castle — A1691

Perf. 11¾x11¼
2020, Mar. 11 Litho.
3820 A1691 27k multi 2.10 1.10

Carduelis Carduelis, Fringilla Coelebs, and Coccothraustes Coccothraustes A1692

Parus Palustris, Parus Cristatus, Parus Caeruleus, and Parus Major A1693

Perf. 11¼x11¾
2020, Mar. 11 Litho.
3821 A1692 B multi 1.50 .75
3822 A1693 B multi 1.50 .75
On day of issue, Nos. 3821-3822 each sold for 19k.

Souvenir Sheet

Modern Architecture of Hradec Kralove — A1694

No. 3823: a, J. K. Tyla Gymnasium, statue, Church of Prince Ambrose, designed by Josef Gocár (1880-1945). b, Gocár and map of Hradec Králové.

Perf. 11½x11¾
2020, Mar. 11 Litho.
3823 A1694 Sheet of 2 + label 5.25 2.75
 a. 23k multi 1.75 .90
 b. 45k multi 3.50 1.75

Apis Mellifica and Flowers — A1695

Serpentine Die Cut 11 Syncopated
2020, Mar. 25 Litho.
Self-Adhesive
3824 A1695 B multi 1.50 .75
No. 3824 sold for 19k on day of issue.

Post Wagon — A1696

2020, Apr. 22 Litho. Perf. 11
3825 A1696 E multi 3.25 1.60
Europa. No. 3825 sold for 39k on day of issue.

Amanita Muscaria A1697

Boletus Satanas A1698

Serpentine Die Cut 11 Syncopated
2020, Apr. 22 Litho.
Booklet Stamps
Self-Adhesive
3826 A1697 B multi 1.60 .80
3827 A1698 B multi 1.60 .80
 a. Booklet pane of 10, 5 each #3826-3827 16.00
On day of issue, Nos. 3826-3827 each sold for 19k.

Art Type of 1967 Inscribed "CESKA REPUBLIKA"

Designs: 30k, Portrait of Frantisek Ferdinand Khünburg, Archbishop of Prague, by Petr Brandl (1668-1735). 47k, Chiasmage Object, by Jirí Kolár (1914-2002), horiz.
No. 3830 — Paintings by Josef Liesler (1912-2005): a, How Do You Like it When I Grin?, 1985. b, Variations on an Old Master, Theme I, 1977. c, Variations on an Old Master, Theme II, 1978.

Litho., Litho. & Engr. (47k)
2020 Perf. 13½x14, 11¾ (47k)
3828 A565 30k multi 2.50 1.25
3829 A525 47k multi 4.00 2.00
Miniature Sheet
3830 Sheet of 4, #3830b, 3830c, 2 #3830a 10.50 5.25
 a. A565 B multi 1.60 .80
 b. A565 E multi 3.25 1.60
 c. A565 Z multi 3.75 1.90
Issued: Nos. 3828-3829, 5/13; No. 3830, 6/17. On day of issue, No. 3830a sold for 19k; No. 3830b, 39k; No. 3830c, 45k.

Václav Neumann (1920-95), Conductor A1699

2020, May 13 Litho. Perf. 14x13½
3831 A1699 19k multi 1.60 .80

Pica Pica, Garrulus Glandarius, and Corvus Corax A1700

Eritacus Rubecula, Phoenicurus Phoenicurus, and Turdus Pilaris A1701

Perf. 11¼x11¾

2020, June 17		Litho.
3832	A1700 B multi	1.60 .80
3833	A1701 B multi	1.60 .80

On day of issue, Nos. 3832-3833 each sold for 19k.

Protective Face Masks — A1702

No. 3834 — Various face masks with country name at: a, LL. b, UR.

Perf. 11¾x11¼

2020, June 24		Litho.
3834	A1702 B Pair, #a-b	3.25 1.60

Tribute to workers fighting the coronavirus pandemic. On day of issue, Nos. 3834a-3834b each sold for 19k.

Aero L-39 Albatros — A1703

Serpentine Die Cut 11 Syncopated
2020, Sept 9		Litho.
	Self-Adhesive	
3835	A1703 B multi	1.75 .85

No. 3835 sold for 19k on day of issue.

Jozin Eats Prazák from the Swamps, Painting by Ivan Mládek A1704

Serpentine Die Cut 11½ Syncopated
2020, Sept 9		Litho.
	Booklet Stamp	
	Self-Adhesive	
3836	A1704 B multi	1.75 .85
a.	Booklet pane of 8	14.00

Ivan Mládek's Banjo Band, 50th anniv. No. 3836 sold for 19k on day of issue.

Prague Castle Type of 2018
2020, Sept. 9	Litho.	Perf. 11¾x11¼
3837	A1616 B grn & brnsh blk + label	1.75 .85

No. 3837 was printed in sheets of 9 + 12 labels that could be personalized. On day of issue, No. 3837 had a franking value of 19k.

Birds A1705

No. 3838: a, Aegithalos caudatus, Passer montanus, Passer domesticus. b, Emberiza calandra, Emberiza schoeniclus, Emberiza citrinella, Emberiza hortulana.

2020, Sept. 9	Litho.	Perf. 11¼x11¾
3838	A1705 E Horiz. pair, #a-b	6.75 3.50

On day of issue, Nos. 3838a-3838b each sold for 39k.

Souvenir Sheet

Model of MB10 Space Base, by Ondrej Doule, Space Architect A1706

2020, Sept. 9	Litho.	Perf. 14x13½
3839	A1706 54k multi	4.75 2.40

Czechoslovakia No. J52a — A1707

Austria No. P4 — A1708

2020, Sept. 23	Litho.	Perf. 12
3840	A1707 B multi	1.75 .85
3841	A1708 E multi	3.50 1.75

On day of issue, No. 3840 sold for 19k, and No. 3841 sold for 39k.

Personalized Stamp — A1709

Serpentine Die Cut 11 Syncopated
2020, Sept. 23		Litho.
	Self-Adhesive	
3842	A1709 Z multi	4.00 2.00

No. 3842, a personalized stamp having a franking value of 45k on the day of issue, that has the generic image of Mauritius No. 1 shown, was printed in sheets of 25, of which 12 examples of No. 3842 alternated with 13 examples of No. 3540 showing an image of the not regularly issued 1919 4k Czechoslovakian semi-postal on granite paper.
Starting in 2021, stamps of the same size as No. 3842, bearing the letter "B" (having a franking value of 19k on the day of issue) instead of "Z," were printed in sheets of 25 on the apparatus that creates personalized stamps. The stamps on these sheets sold by the Czech Philatelic Bureau had 25 different vignettes that were chosen by them. Any stamp from these sheets, or any subsequent sheets of 25 different vignettes, bearing the letters "B," "E," or "Z," will be considered to be a variety of No. 3842 (stamps of this size bearing the letter "A" would be varieties of No. 3540).

Butterflies — A1711

Designs: 1k, Belásek (orange tip butterfly). 2k, Modrásek (common blue butterfly). 4k, Zluťásek (clouded yellow butterfly). 23k, Babocka (peacock butterfly).

2020-21		Litho.	Perf. 11¼x11¾
3844	A1711 1k multi	.25 .25
3845	A1711 2k multi	.25 .25
3846	A1711 4k multi	.35 .25
3847	A1711 23k multi	2.10 1.10
	Nos. 3844-3847 (4)	2.95 1.85

Issued: 2k, 4k, 10/7; 23k, 11/25; 1k, 2/15/21.

Souvenir Sheet

Actors A1712

No. 3848: a, 30k, Jiří Sovák (1920-2000). b, 34k, Vlastimil Brodský (1920-2002).

Litho. (30k), Litho. With Hologram Affixed (34k)
2020, Oct. 7		Perf. 13½x14
3848	A1712 Sheet of 2, #a-b	5.50 2.25

Aero 750 Sport Coupé — A1713

Serpentine Die Cut 11 Syncopated
2020, Oct. 21		Litho.
	Booklet Stamp	
	Self-Adhesive	
3849	A1713 B multi	1.75 .85
a.	Booklet pane of 10	17.50

No. 3849 sold for 19k on day of issue.

The Holy Night, by Josef Lada (1887-1957) — A1714

2020, Oct. 21	Litho.	Perf. 11¼x11¾
3850	A1714 B multi	1.75 .85

Christmas. No. 3850 sold for 19k on day of issue.

Art Type of 1967 Inscribed "CESKA REPUBLIKA"

Designs: 33k, Jump, painting by Grigorij A. Musatov (1889-1941). 40k, Groping, painting by Josef Vyletal (1940-89).

2020, Nov. 11	Litho.	Perf. 13½x14
3851-3852	A565 Set of 2	6.75 3.50

St. Norbert of Xanten (c. 1075-1134), Founder of Order of Prémontré A1715

2020, Nov. 25	Litho.	Perf. 12x11½
3853	A1715 B multi	1.75 .85

Order of Prémontré, 900th anniv. No. 3853 sold for 19k on day of issue.

Souvenir Sheet

Prague Castle as Seen From National Theater A1716

No. 3854 — Color of Prague Castle: a, E, Violet. b, Z, Light brown.

Litho. & Engr. (#3854a), Litho. (#3854b)
2020, Nov. 25		Perf. 11¾
3854	A1716 Sheet of 2, #a-b, + 2 labels	7.75 4.00

On day of issue, No. 3854a sold for 39k, and No. 3854b sold for 45k.

2021 Census — A1717

2021, Jan. 20	Litho.	Perf. 11¾x11¼
3855	A1717 B multi	1.75 .90

No. 3855 sold for 19k on day of issue.

Automobiles and Václav Zapadlík (1943-2018), Stamp Designer A1718

2021, Jan. 20	Litho.	Perf. 13½
3856	A1718 B multi	1.75 .90
a.	Booklet pane of 8 + 4 labels	14.00
	Complete booklet, #3856a	14.00 —

No. 3856 sold for 19k on day of issue.

Carnival Procession A1719

2021, Jan. 20	Litho.	Perf. 13½
3857	A1719 B multi	1.75 .90
a.	Booklet pane of 8 + 4 labels	14.00
	Complete booklet, #3857a	14.00 —

No. 3857 sold for 19k on day of issue.

Josef Masopust (1930-2015), Soccer Player and Coach — A1720

2021, Feb. 9	Litho.	Perf. 13½
3858	A1720 19k multi	1.75 .90

Milotice Chateau A1721

2021, Feb. 9	Litho.	Perf. 13½
3859	A1721 23k multi	2.25 1.10

Visegrád Group, 30th Anniv. — A1722

2021, Feb. 15	Litho.	Perf. 12
3860	A1722 39k multi	3.75 1.90

See Hungary No. 4582, Poland No. 4528, and Slovakia No. 870.

Negrelli Viaduct A1723

Perf. 11¾x11¼

2021, Mar. 24   Litho.
3861 A1723 B multi   1.75   .85
   a.   Booklet pane of 8 + 4 labels   14.00
      Complete booklet, #3861a   14.00

No. 3861 sold for 19k on day of issue.

Bohous, Sculpture by Bohumil Zemánek (1942-96) — A1724

2021, Mar. 24   Litho.   **Perf. 11¾**
3862 A1724 30k multi + label   2.75 1.40

First Soccer Match Between AC Sparta and SK Slavia, 125th Anniv. A1725

No. 3863 — Half of soccer ball and emblem of: a, AC Sparta (shield). b, SK Slavia (star).

Perf. 11¼x11¾

2021, Mar. 24   Litho.
3863 A1725 B Horiz. pair, #a-b   3.50 1.75

On day of issue, Nos. 3863a-3863b each sold for 19k.

Dancing House, Prague, Designed by Vlado Milunic and Frank Gehry A1726

Perf. 11¼x11¾

2021, Mar. 24   Litho.
3864 A1726 E multi + label   3.50 1.75

No. 3864 was printed in sheets of 7 + 14 labels that could be personalized and had a franking value of 39k on day of issue.

Mocked-up Hiking Map A1727

2021, Apr. 21   Litho.   **Perf. 11¼x11½**
3865 A1727 B multi + label   1.75   .90

No. 3865 was printed in sheets of 7 + 14 labels that could be personalized. On day of issue, No. 3865 had a franking value of 19k.

Rock Formation on Czech-Polish Border A1728

2021, Apr. 21   Litho.   **Perf. 11¾x11¼**
3866 A1728 23k multi   2.25 1.10

Felis Silvestris — A1729

2021, Apr. 21   Litho.   **Perf. 11**
3867 A1729 E multi   3.75 1.90

Europa. No. 3867 sold for 39k on day of issue.

Gustav Brom (1921-95), Jazz Musician and Band Leader A1730

2021, May 19   Litho.   **Perf. 11¾x11¼**
3868 A1730 27k multi   2.60 1.30

Black Stork in Wetlands A1731

2021, May 19   Litho.   **Perf. 11¾x11¼**
3869 A1731 Z multi   4.50 2.25

Ramsar Convention on Wetlands, 50th anniv. No. 3869 sold for 45k on day of issue.

Glass Sculpture From Prague Castle, by Borek Sípek (1949-2016) — A1732

2021, June 9   Litho.   **Perf. 14x13½**
3870 A1732 E multi   3.75 1.90

No. 3870 sold fior 39k on day of issue.

Souvenir Sheet

Krusnohorí Mining Region UNESCO World Heritage Site — A1733

No. 3871: a, Jezerí Castle. b, Wolf Pit tin mining area.

2021, June 9   Litho.   **Perf. 11½x11¾**
3871 A1733   Sheet of 2   5.00 2.50
  a.   26k multi   2.40 1.25
  b.   27k multi   2.50 1.25

Kyjov Folk Festival A1734

Perf. 11¾x11¼

2021, June 23   Litho.
3872 A1734 B multi   1.75   .90

No. 3872 sold for 19k on day of issue.

Souvenir Sheet

Mike the Tomcat, Children's Book by Josef Lada (1887-1957) — A1735

Litho. & Engr

2021, June 23   **Perf. 11¾**
3873 A1735 55k multi   5.25 2.60

Czech Mountain Dog Puppy A1736   Czech Mountain Dog Puppies A1737

Serpentine Die Cut 11¼ Syncopated
2021, Sept. 8   Litho.
Booklet Stamps
Self-Adhesive

3874 A1736 B multi   1.75   .85
3875 A1737 B multi   1.75   .85
  a.   Booklet pane of 10, 5 each
     #3874-3875   17.50

Nos. 3874-3875 each sold for 19k on day of issue.

Miniature Sheet

Flora and Fauna of Milovice Nature Reserve A1738

No. 3876: a, 23k, Phengaris alcon, Gentiana cruciata (27x45mm). b, 26k, Bison bonasus (54x45mm). c, 27k, Bos primigenius (54x45mm). d, 30k, Exmoor ponies (54x45mm).

Litho. & Engr.

2021, Sept. 8   **Perf. 11¾**
3876 A1738   Sheet of 4, #a-d, +
       2 labels   9.75 5.00

Miniature Sheet

Dante Alighieri (c. 1265-1321), Writer — A1739

No. 3877: a, B, Alighieri (45x27mm). b, E, Alighieri, diff. (45x54mm).

2021, Sept. 8   Litho.   **Perf. 13½x14**
3877 A1739   Sheet of 4, 2
      each #3877a-
      3877b, + label   11.00 5.50

On day of issue, Nos. 3877a-3877b sold for 19k and 39k, respectively.

Souvenir Sheet

Expo 2021, Dubai A1740

Litho. & Silk-Screened, Sheet Margin Litho. With Hologram Affixed

2021, Sept. 8   **Perf. 14x13½**
3878 A1740 Z multi   4.25 2.10

No. 3878 sold for 45k on day of issue.

Wikov 7/28 Roadster — A1741

Serpentine Die Cut 11¼ Syncopated
2021, Oct. 6   Litho.
Self-Adhesive

3879 A1741 B multi   1.75   .85

No. 3879 sold for 19k on day of issue.

Actors A1742

No. 3880: a, 27k, Bohumil Záhorsky (1906-80). b, 33k, Jirina Sejbalová (1905-81).

2021, Oct. 6   Litho.   **Perf. 14x13½**
3880 A1742   Vert. pair, #a-b   5.50 2.75

No. 3880 was printed in sheets containing two pairs + central label.

Art Type of 1967 Inscribed "CESKA REPUBLIKA"

Designs: 30k, Ecce Homo, by Theodor Pistek. 33k, Nude, by Frantizek Ronovsky (1929-2006), horiz. 34k, The Self-portrait by the Window, by Pistek.

Perf. 13½x14, 14x13½

2021, Oct. 20   Litho.
3881-3883 A565   Set of 3   8.75 4.50

Nos. 3881 and 3883 were printed in sheets containing two of each stamp + central label. No. 3882 was printed in sheets of 4 + central label.

Muriel, Comic Book Character Created by Kája Saudek (1935-2015) — A1743

Perf. 11¼x11¾

2021, Nov. 10   Litho.
3884 A1743 B multi   1.75   .85

No. 3884 sold for 19k on day of issue.

Karel Styblo (1921-98), Epidemiologist, and Tuberculosis Bacilli — A1744

Perf. 11¾x11¼
2021, Nov. 10   **Litho.**
3885 A1744 26k multi   2.40 1.25

Souvenir Sheet

Jan Kotera (1871-1923), Architect, and Charles University Law Faculty Building, Prague — A1745

Perf. 11½x11¾
2021, Nov. 10   **Litho.**
3886 A1745 52k multi + 2 labels   4.75 2.40

Souvenir Sheet

St. Ludmila (c. 860-921) A1746

Litho. & Engr.
2021, Nov. 10   **Perf. 11¾**
3887 A1746 60k multi   5.50 2.75

Christmas — A1747

Perf. 11¼x11¾
2021, Nov. 10   **Litho.**
3888 A1747 B multi   1.75 .85

No. 3888 sold for 19k on day of issue and is impregnated with a pine scent.

Infant Jesus of Prague Statue — A1748

Serpentine Die Cut 11¼ Syncopated
2021, Nov. 30   **Litho.**
Self-Adhesive
3889 A1748 E multi   3.50 1.75
No. 3889 sold for 39k on day of issue.

Pres. Tomás G. Masaryk (1850-1937), and Mosaic at Kfar Masaryk Kibbutz, Israel — A1749

2021, Nov. 30   **Litho.**   **Perf. 11¾**
3890 A1749 Z multi   4.00 2.00

No. 3890 sold for 45k on day of issue. See Israel No. 2299.

Waite & Saville Flat Plate Printing Press — A1750

2022, Jan. 20   **Engr.**   **Perf. 13½x14**
3891 A1750 B olive gray   1.75 .90
a.   Booklet pane of 8 + 2 labels   14.00
     Complete booklet, #3891a   14.00

No. 3891 sold for 19k on day of issue.

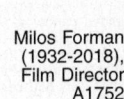

Molière (1622-73), Playwright and Actor — A1751

2022, Jan. 20   **Litho.**   **Perf. 11¾x11¼**
3892 A1751 23k multi   2.25 1.10

Milos Forman (1932-2018), Film Director — A1752

Perf. 11¾x11¼
2022, Feb. 16   **Litho.**
3893 A1752 19k multi   1.75 .85

Souvenir Sheet

Gothic Murals A1753

No. 3894: a, Crucifixion, attributed to Master of the Karlstejn Apocalypse, from Chapel of St. Catherine, Karlstejn Castle. b, Life of St. Margaret, from Velké Mezirící Castle.

2022, Feb. 16   **Litho.**   **Perf. 11¾**
3894 A1753   Sheet of 2   6.50 3.25
a.   34k multi   3.00 1.50
b.   40k multi   3.50 1.75

Fresco by Emil Filla (1882-1953) — A1754

The Girl with a Mandolin, Painting by Filla — A1755

2022, Mar. 8   **Litho.**   **Perf. 11¼x11¾**
3895 A1754   B multi + label   1.75 .85
Perf. 13½x14
3896 A1755 39k multi   3.50 1.75

No. 3895 was printed in sheets of 7 + 8 labels that could be personalized. On day of issue, No. 3895 had a franking value of 19k.

Souvenir Sheet

Kosice-Bohumín Railway, 150th Anniv. — A1756

Litho. & Engr.
2022, Mar. 18   **Perf. 11¾**
3897 A1756 58k multi + 2 labels   5.25 2.60

Joint issue between Czechoslovakia and Slovakia. See Slovakia No.

Schwarzenberg Canal — A1757

2022, Apr. 6   **Litho.**   **Perf. 11¾x11¼**
3898 A1757 B multi   1.75 .85
a.   Booklet pane of 8 + 4 labels   14.00
     Complete booklet, #3898a   14.00

No. 3898 sold for 19k on day of issue.

Legend of Libuse and Premysl — A1758

2022, Apr. 6   **Litho.**   **Perf. 11¼**
3899 A1758 E multi   3.50 1.75

Europa. No. 3899 sold for 39k on day of issue.

Actors A1759

No. 3900: a, 30k, Jan Werich (1905-80). b, 34k, Stella Zázvorková (1922-2005).

2022, Apr. 6   **Litho.**   **Perf. 14x13½**
3900 A1759   Vert. pair, #a-b   5.50 2.75

No. 3900 was printed in sheets containing two pairs + central label.

Philatelic Youth Olympiad, 50th Anniv. — A1760

2022, May 18   **Litho.**   **Perf. 11¼x11¾**
3901 A1760 B multi   1.75 .85
a.   Booklet pane of 8 + 4 labels   14.00
     Complete booklet, #3901a   14.00

No. 3901 sold for 19k on day of issue.

Czech Beekeepers Association, 150th Anniv. — A1761

Serpentine Die Cut 11 Syncopated
2022, May 18   **Litho.**
Self-Adhesive
3902 A1761 23k multi   2.00 1.00
No. 3903 was printed in sheets of 5.

Personalized Stamp — A1762

Serpentine Die Cut 11 Syncopated
2022, June 15   **Litho.**
Self-Adhesive
3903 A1762 B multi   1.60 .80

Nos. 3903 was printed in sheets of 5. Vignette of each stamp could be personalized. The generic vignette depicting a Brozík & Krizík tram car is shown. On day of issue, the franking value of No. 3903 was 19k.

Bengal Kitten A1763   Persian Kitten A1764

Serpentine Die Cut 11¼ Syncopated
2022, June 15   **Litho.**
Booklet Stamps
Self-Adhesive
3904 A1763 B multi   1.60 .80
3905 A1764 B multi   1.60 .80
a.   Booklet pane of 10, 5 each
     #3904-3905   16.00

On day of issue, Nos. 3904-3905 each sold for 19k.

2022 International Council of Museums General Conference, Prague — A1765

Perf. 11¼x11¾
2022, June 15   **Litho.**
3906 A1765 E multi   3.25 1.60

No. 3906 sold for 39k on day of issue.

Czech Presidency of the Council of the European Union — A1766

Perf. 11¾x11¼
2022, June 15   **Litho.**
3907 A1766 E multi   3.25 1.60

No. 3907 sold for 39k on day of issue.

Chudobín
Pine — A1767

2022, Sept. 7   **Litho.**   **Perf. 11¼**
3908   A1767   B multi   1.50   .75

No. 3908 sold for 19k on day of issue.

Road and
Roses on
Gate
A1768

2022, Sept. 7   **Litho.**   **Perf. 11¼x11¾**
3909   A1768   B multi + label   1.50   .75

No. 3909 was printed in sheets of 7 + 14 labels that could be personalized. On day of issue, No. 3909 had a franking value of 19k.

Jindrich Fügner
(1822-65), Co-
founder of
Sokol Sports
Organization
A1769

2022, Sept. 7   **Litho.**   **Perf. 11¾x11¼**
3910   A1769   27k blue & red   2.25   1.10

Souvenir Sheet

1952 Summer Olympic Gold
Medalists — A1770

No. 3911: a, Dana Zátopková (1922-2020), javelin gold medalist. b, Emil Zátopek (1922-2000), long-distance running gold medalist and husband of Zátopková.

2022, Sept. 7   **Litho.**   **Perf. 11¾**
3911   A1770   Sheet of 2   5.00   2.50
  a.   27k multi   2.25   1.10
  b.   33k multi   2.75   1.40

Miniature Sheet

Flora
and
Fauna of
Mácha
Lake
Region
A1771

No. 3912: a, 23k, Apatura iris, Lilium martagon (27x45mm). b, 26k, Cygnus olor, Trollius altissimus, Pinguicula bohemica (55x45mm). c, 27k, Grus grus, Ledum paluste, Dactylorhiza bohemica, Iris sibirica (55x45mm). d, 30k, Birds over Mácha Lake, sailboat and Bezdez Castle (55x45mm).

2022, Sept. 7   **Litho.**   **Perf. 14x13½**
3912   A1771   Sheet of 4, #a-d, +   8.50   4.25
         2 labels

Tiles From St. Wenceslas Rotunda,
Prague — A1772

No. 3913 — Tile depicting: a, Griffin. b, Lion.

2022, Sept. 21   **Litho.**   **Perf. 11¼**
3913   A1772   B Horiz. pair, #a-b   3.00   1.50

On day of issue, Nos. 3913a-3913b each sold for 19k.

2022
European
Stamp
Exhibition,
Liberec
A1773

No. 3914: a, Penguins carrying letters and stamps. b, Birds in birdhouses carrying stamps.

2022, Oct. 12   **Litho.**   **Perf. 11¼x11¾**
3914   A1773   E Horiz. pair, #a-b   6.50 3.25

On day of issue, Nos. 3914a-3914b each sold for 39k.

Miniature Sheet

Breeding and Training of Ceremonial
Carriage Horses at Kladruby and
Labem — A1774

No. 3915: a, 26k, Kladruber mare, foal and stud farm. b, 30k, Foal and stud farm. c, 34k, Coach and two horses. d, 40k, Two horses.

2022, Oct. 12   **Litho.**   **Perf. 14x13½**
3915   A1774   Sheet of 4, #a-d,   10.50 5.25
         + 2 labels

 Christmas — A1775

Serpentine Die Cut 11¼ Syncopated
2022, Oct. 26   **Litho.**
      Self-Adhesive
3916   A1775   B multi   1.60   .80

No. 3916 sold for 19k on day of issue.

Art Type of 1967 Inscribed "CESKA REPUBLIKA"

Designs: 39k, 45k, Plague, by Jaroslav Panuska (1872-1958).

2022, Nov. 9   **Engr.**   **Perf. 11¾**
3917   A565   39k black   3.25 1.60
            Litho.
3918   A565   45k multi   3.75 1.90

Printed in sheets of 4 containing two each of Nos. 3917 and 3918.

Vladimír
Suchánek
(1933-2021),
Stamp Designer
A1776

2023, Jan. 20   **Litho.**   **Perf. 11¾x11¼**
3919   A1776   B multi   1.90   .95

No. 3919 sold for 21k on day of issue.

SEMI-POSTAL STAMPS

Nos. B1-B123 were sold at 1½ times face value at the Philatelists' Window of the Prague P.O. for charity benefit. They were available for ordinary postage.

Almost all stamps between Nos. B1-B123 are known with misplaced or inverted overprints and/or in pairs with one stamp missing the overprint.

The overprints of Nos. B1-B123 have been well forged.

Austrian Stamps of
1916-18 Overprinted in
Black or Blue — a

Two sizes of type A40:
Type I: 25x30mm.
Type II: 26x29mm.

			1919		**Perf. 12½**
B1	A37	3h brt violet		.25	.25
B2	A37	5h lt green		.25	.25
B3	A37	6h dp orange (Bl)		.50	.70
B4	A37	6h dp orange (Bk)	3,250.	2,500.	
B5	A37	10h magenta		1.00	.85
B6	A37	12h lt blue		.70	.70
B7	A42	15h dull red		.35	.35
B8	A42	20h dark green		.35	.35
a.		20h green		55.00	40.00
B9	A42	25h blue		.30	.25
B10	A42	30h dull violet		.30	.25
B11	A39	40h olive grn		.35	.35
B12	A39	50h dk green		.35	.35
B13	A39	60h dp blue		.35	.35
B14	A39	80h orange brn		.35	.35
B15	A39	90h red violet		.70	.70
B16	A39	1k car, yel (Bl)		.50	.50
B17	A39	1k car, yel (Bk)		52.50	52.50
B18	A40	2k light blue (I)		3.00	3.00
a.		2k dark blue (II)	5,000.	3,500.	
B19	A40	3k car rose (I)		32.50	32.50
a.		3k claret (I)	3,750.	1,500.	
B20	A40	4k yellow grn (I)		27.50	21.00
a.		4k deep green (I)	55.00	45.00	
B21	A40	10k violet		300.00	160.00
a.		10k deep violet	375.00	275.00	
b.		10k black violet	450.00	350.00	

The used value of No. B18a is for a stamp that has only a Czechoslovakian cancellation. Some examples of Austria No. 160, which were officially overprinted with type "a" and sold by the post office, had previously been used and lightly canceled with Austrian cancellations. These canceled-before-overprinting stamps, which were postally valid, sell for about one-fourth as much.

Granite Paper

B22	A40	2k light blue	3.50 2.50
B23	A40	3k carmine rose	9.00 7.00

The 4k and 10k on granite paper with this overprint were not regularly issued. Excellent counterfeits of Nos. B1-B23 exist.

Austrian Newspaper
Stamps Overprinted — b

Imperf
On Stamp of 1908

B26	N8	10h carmine	3,500.	2,000.

On Stamps of 1916

B27	N9	2h brown	.25	.25
B28	N9	4h green	.35	.35
B29	N9	6h deep blue	.35	.35
B30	N9	10h orange	4.25	4.25
B31	N9	30h claret	1.40	1.40
		Nos. B27-B31 (5)	6.60	6.60

Austrian Special
Handling Stamps
Overprinted in
Blue or Black — c

Perf. 12½
Stamps of 1916 Overprinted

B32	SH1	2h claret, yel (Bl)	25.00	25.00
B33	SH1	5h dp grn, yel (Bk)	800.00	700.00

Stamps of 1917
Overprinted — d

B34	SH2	2h cl, yel (Bl)	.25	.35
a.		Vert. pair, imperf. btwn.	250.00	
B35	SH2	2h cl, yel (Bk)	35.00	32.50
B36	SH2	5h grn, yel (Bk)	.25	.25

Austrian Air Post Stamps, #C1-C3, Overprinted Type "c" Diagonally

B37	A40	1.50k on 2k lil	90.00	70.00
B38	A40	2.50k on 3k ocher	110.00	90.00
B39	A40	4k gray	800.00	650.00

1919
Austrian Postage Due Stamps of 1908-13 Overprinted Type "b"

B40	D3	2h carmine	4,500.	2,750.
B41	D3	4h carmine	17.50	17.50
B42	D3	6h carmine	10.50	9.00
B43	D3	14h carmine	35.00	32.50
B44	D3	25h carmine	30.00	30.00
B45	D3	30h carmine	325.00	250.00
B46	D3	50h carmine	650.00	650.00

Austria Nos. J49-J56 Overprinted Type "b"

B47	D4	5h rose red	.25	.30
B48	D4	10h rose red	.25	.30
B49	D4	15h rose red	.25	.30
B50	D4	20h rose red	1.75	1.75
B51	D4	25h rose red	1.75	1.75
B52	D4	30h rose red	.60	.60
B53	D4	40h rose red	1.75	1.75
B54	D4	50h rose red	300.00	250.00

Austria Nos. J57-J59 Overprinted Type "a"

B55	D5	1k ultra	10.50	9.00
B56	D5	5k ultra	21.00	21.00
B57	D5	10k ultra	225.00	200.00

Austria Nos. J47-J48, J60-J63 Overprinted Type "c" Diagonally

B58	A22	1h gray	20.00	16.00
B59	A23	15h on 2h vio	95.00	90.00
B60	A38	10h on 24h blue	80.00	70.00
B61	A38	15h on 36h vio	.35	.35
B62	A38	20h on 54h org	70.00	65.00
B63	A38	50h on 42h choc	.75	.75

Hungarian Stamps Ovptd. Type "b"

1919		**Wmk. 137**		**Perf. 15**

On Stamps of 1913-16

B64	A4	1f slate	2,200.	1,800.
B65	A4	2f yellow	5.25	4.50
B66	A4	3f orange	32.50	25.00
B67	A4	6f olive green	5.00	5.00
B68	A4	50f lake, bl	.90	.75
B69	A4	60f grn, sal	45.00	35.00
B70	A4	70f red brn, grn	2,250.	1,750.

On Stamps of 1916

B71	A8	10f rose	300.00	225.00
B72	A8	15f violet	150.00	100.00

On Stamps of 1916-18

B73	A9	2f brown orange	.25	.25
B74	A9	3f red lilac	.25	.25
B75	A9	5f green	.25	.25
B76	A9	6f grnsh blue	.50	.50
B77	A9	10f rose red	1.40	1.00
B78	A9	15f violet	.25	.25
B79	A9	20f gray brown	12.00	11.00
B80	A9	25f dull blue	.90	.70
B81	A9	35f brown	9.00	9.00
B82	A9	40f olive green	3.00	2.25

Overprinted Type "d"

B83	A10	50f red vio & lil	1.10	1.40
B84	A10	75f brt bl & pale bl	1.10	1.40
B85	A10	80f yel grn & pale grn	1.10	1.40
B86	A10	1k red brn & cl	2.10	2.00
B87	A10	2k ol brn & bis	9.00	9.00
B88	A10	3k dk vio & ind	37.50	35.00
B89	A10	5k dk brn & lt brn	90.00	60.00
B90	A10	10k vio brn & vio	1,300.	800.00

Overprinted Type "b"
On Stamps of 1918

B91	A11	10f scarlet	.25	.25
B92	A11	20f dark brown	.30	.30
B93	A11	25f deep blue	1.10	.75
B94	A12	40f olive grn	3.50	2.75
B95	A12	50f lilac	30.00	22.50

On Stamps of 1919

B96	A13	10f red	9.00	7.00
B97	A13	20f dk brn	6,500.	4,500.

Same Overprint On Hungarian Newspaper Stamp of 1914
Imperf

B98	N5	(2f) orange	.25	.25

Same Overprint On Hungarian Special Delivery Stamp
Perf. 15

B99	SD1	2f gray grn & red	.25	.25

Same Ovpt. On Hungarian Semi-Postal Stamps

B100	SP3	10f + 2f rose red	.70 .70
B101	SP4	15f + 2f violet	1.10 1.10
B102	SP5	40f + 2f brn car	3.50 3.50
	Nos. B98-B102 (5)		5.80 5.80

Hungarian Postage Due Stamps of 1903-18 Overprinted Type "b"

1919　　Wmk. 135　　Perf. 11½, 12

B103	D1	50f green & black	350.00 300.00

Wmk. Crown (136, 136a)
Perf. 11½x12, 15

B104	D1	1f green & black	1,200. 1,000.
B105	D1	2f green & black	750.00 650.00
B106	D1	5f green & black	4,250. 3,500.
B107	D1	50f green & black	275.00 150.

Wmk. Double Cross (137)
Perf. 15
On Stamps of 1914

B110	D1	1f green & black	1,250. 600.
B111	D1	2f green & black	700. 550.
B112	D1	5f green & black	1,325. 900.
B113	D1	20f green & black	5,250. 4,000.
B114	D1	50f green & black	275.00 150.

On Stamps of 1915-18

B115	D1	1f green & red	125.00 100.00
B116	D1	2f green & red	.75 .75
B117	D1	5f green & red	12.50 10.00
B118	D1	6f green & red	2.00 2.00
B119	D1	10f green & red	.50 .50
a.	Pair, one without overprint		
B120	D1	12f green & red	2.00 2.00
B121	D1	15f green & red	5.00 4.50
B122	D1	20f green & red	1.25 1.25
B123	D1	30f green & red	40.00 35.00
	Nos. B115-B123 (9)		189.00 156.00

Excellent counterfeits of Nos. B1-B123 exist.

Bohemian Lion Breaking its Chains SP1

Mother and Child SP2

Perf. 11½, 13¾ and Compound

1919　　Typo.　　Unwmk.
Pinkish Paper

B124	SP1	15h gray green	.25 .25
a.	15h light green		32.50 25.00
B125	SP1	25h dark brown	.25 .25
a.	25h light brown		5.00 4.00
B126	SP1	50h dark blue	.25 .25

Photo.
Yellowish Paper

B127	SP2	75h slate	.25 .25
B128	SP2	100h brn vio	.25 .25
B129	SP2	120h vio, yel	.25 .25
	Nos. B124-B129 (6)		1.50 1.50

Values are for perf 13¾. Other perfs are valued higher.
Nos. B124-B126 commemorate the 1st anniv. of Czechoslovak independence. Nos. B127-B129 were sold for the benefit of Legionnaires' orphans. Imperforates exist.
See No. 1581.

Regular Issues of Czechoslovakia Surcharged in Red

a　　　　b

1920　　　　　　Perf. 13¾

B130	A1(a)	40h + 20h bister	.75 1.00
B131	A2(a)	60h + 20h green	.75 1.00
B132	A4(b)	125h + 25h gray bl	3.25 2.75
	Nos. B130-B132 (3)		4.75 4.75
	Set, never hinged		12.00

President Masaryk — SP3

Wmk. Linden Leaves (107)

1923　　Engr.　　Perf. 13¾x14¾

B133	SP3	50h gray green	.60 .40
B134	SP3	100h carmine	1.10 .75
B135	SP3	200h blue	3.25 2.50
B136	SP3	300h dark brown	3.25 3.50
	Nos. B133-B136 (4)		8.20 7.15
	Set, never hinged		15.00

5th anniv. of the Republic.
The gum was applied through a screen and shows the monogram "ČSP" (Ceskoslovenska Posta). These stamps were sold at double their face values, the excess being given to the Red Cross and other charitable organizations.

International Olympic Congress Issue

Semi-Postal Stamps of 1923 Overprinted in Blue or Red

1925

B137	SP3	50h gray green	5.50 7.50
B138	SP3	100h carmine	7.00 12.00
B139	SP3	200h blue (R)	35.00 45.00
	Nos. B137-B139 (3)		47.50 64.50
	Set, never hinged		120.00

These stamps were sold at double their face values, the excess being divided between a fund for post office clerks and the Olympic Games Committee.

Sokol Issue

Semi-Postal Stamps of 1923 Overprinted in Blue or Red

1926

B140	SP3	50h gray green	1.60 4.00
B141	SP3	100h carmine	3.25 4.00
B142	SP3	200h blue (R)	10.00 11.00
a.	Double overprint		
B143	SP3	300h dk brn (R)	20.00 15.00
	Nos. B140-B143 (4)		34.85 34.00
	Set, never hinged		100.00

These stamps were sold at double their face values, the excess being given to the Congress of Sokols, June, 1926.

> **Catalogue values for unused stamps in this section, from this point to the end of the section, are for Never Hinged items.**

Midwife Presenting Newborn Child to its Father; after a Painting by Josef Manes
SP4　　　　SP5

1936　　Unwmk.　Engr.　Perf. 12½

B144	SP4	50h + 50h green	.50 .35
B145	SP5	1k + 50h claret	1.00 .60
B146	SP4	2k + 50h blue	2.50 1.25
	Nos. B144-B146 (3)		4.00 2.20

Nos. B144-B146 were each issued in sheets of 100 with 12 labels. Value, set $40.

SP6

"Lullaby" by Stanislav Sucharda — SP7

1937　　　　　　Perf. 12½

B147	SP6	50h + 50h dull green	.50 .25
B148	SP6	1k + 50h rose lake	1.00 .60
B149	SP7	2k + 1k dull blue	2.50 1.25
	Nos. B147-B149 (3)		4.00 2.10

Nos. B147-B149 were each issued in sheets of 100 with 12 labels. Value, set of singles with attached labels hinged mint $5; used $5.

President Masaryk and Little Girl in Native Costume — SP8

1938　　　　　　Perf. 12½

B150	SP8	50h + 50h deep green	.75 .50
B151	SP8	1k + 50h rose lake	.70 .55

Souvenir Sheet
Imperf

B152	SP8	2k + 3k black	4.25 5.00

88th anniv. of the birth of Masaryk (1850-1937).
Nos. B150-B151 were each issued in sheets of 100 stamps and 12 blank labels. Value, set of singles with attached labels: mint $4; used $3.

Allegory of the Republic Type
Souvenir Sheet

1938　　　　　　Perf. 12½

B153	A89	2k (+ 8k) dark blue	3.00 3.50

The surtax was devoted to national relief for refugees.

"Republic" and Congress Emblem — SP10

1945　　　　　　Engr.

B154	SP10	1.50k + 1.50k car rose	.25 .25
B155	SP10	2.50k + 2.50k blue	.25 .25

Students' World Cong., Prague, 11/17/45.

St. George Slaying the Dragon — SP11

1946

B156	SP11	2.40k + 2.60k car rose	.25 .25
B157	SP11	4k + 6k blue	.25 .25

Souvenir Sheet
Imperf

B158	SP11	4k + 6k blue	1.50 1.50

1st anniv. of Czechoslovakia's liberation. The surtax aided WW II orphans.
Nos. B156-B157 were each issued in sheets of 100 stamps and 12 inscribed labels. Value for set of singles with attached labels, mint or used $3.50.

Old Town Hall Type of 1946
Souvenir Sheet

1946, Aug. 3　　　　Imperf.

B159	A114	2.40k rose brown	1.10 .75

Brno Natl. Stamp Exhib., Aug., 1946. The sheet was sold for 10k.

"You Went Away" — SP14　　"You Remained Ours" — SP15

"You Came Back" — SP16

1946, Oct. 28　Photo.　Perf. 14

B160	SP14	1.60k + 1.40k red brn	.35 .35
B161	SP15	2.40k + 2.60k scarlet	.35 .35
B162	SP16	4k + 4k deep blue	.70 .70
	Nos. B160-B162 (3)		1.40 1.40

The surtax was for repatriated Slovaks.

Barefoot Boy — SP17

2k+1k, Mother and child. 3k+1k, Little girl.

1948, Dec. 18　Unwmk.　Engr.

B163	SP17	1.50k + 1k rose lilac	.45 .25
B164	SP17	2k + 1k dp blue	.25 .25
B165	SP17	3k + 1k rose car	.35 .25
	Nos. B163-B165 (3)		1.05 .75

The surtax was for child welfare.
Nos. B163-B165 were each issued in sheets of 100 stamps and 12 inscribed labels. Value for set of singles with attached labels: mint $3; used $2.

Woman and Child — SP18

Design: 3k+1k, Man lifting child.

1949, Dec. 18　　　Perf. 12½

B166	SP18	1.50k + 50h gray	4.75 1.90
B167	SP18	3k + 1k claret	7.00 2.75

The surtax was for child welfare.

SP19

Dove Carrying Olive Branch — SP20

1949, Dec. 18

B168	SP19	1.50k + 50h claret	4.50 1.50
B169	SP20	3k + 1k rose red	4.50 1.50

The surtax was for the Red Cross.

AIR POST STAMPS

Nos. 9, 39-40, 20, and Types of 1919 Srchd. in Red, Blue or Green

1920　　Unwmk.　　Imperf.

C1	A1	14k on 200h (R)	15.00 12.00
a.	Inverted surcharge		125.00
C2	A2	24k on 500h (Bl)	40.00 25.00
a.	Inverted surcharge		225.00
C3	A2	28k on 1000h (G)	25.00 20.00
a.	Inverted surcharge		150.00
b.	Double surcharge		200.00
	Nos. C1-C3 (3)		80.00 57.00

Perf. 13¾

C4	A1	14k on 200h (R)	22.50 *22.50*
a.	Perf. 13¾x13½		150.00 95.00

C5	A2	24k on 500h (Bl)	45.00	*70.00*
a.	Perf. 13¾x13½		150.00	*75.00*

Perf. 13¾x13½

C6	A2	28k on 1000h (G)	20.00	*17.50*
a.	Inverted surcharge		400.00	—
b.	Perf. 13¾		475.00	*475.00*
c.	As "b", invtd. surcharge		350.00	—
	Nos. C4-C6 (3)		87.50	*110.00*
	Nos. C1-C6 (6)		167.50	*167.00*

Excellent counterfeits of the overprint are known.

Stamps of 1920 Srchd. in Black or Violet

1922, June 15   **Perf. 13¾**

C7	A8	50h on 100h dl grn	1.75	1.50
a.	Inverted surcharge		150.00	
b.	Double surcharge		160.00	
C8	A8	100h on 200h vio	3.50	2.25
a.	Inverted surcharge		150.00	
C9	A8	250h on 400h brn (V)	5.00	3.50
a.	Inverted surcharge		275.00	
	Nos. C7-C9 (3)		10.25	7.25
	Set, never hinged		20.00	

Fokker Monoplane AP3   Smolik S 19 AP4

Smolik S 19 — AP5   Fokker over Prague — AP6

1930, Dec. 16   Engr.   Perf. 13½

C10	AP3	50h deep green	.25	.25
C11	AP3	1k deep red	.25	*.45*
C12	AP4	2k dark green	.40	*.90*
C13	AP4	3k red violet	.85	1.10
C14	AP5	4k indigo	.75	1.10
C15	AP5	5k red brown	1.75	*3.50*
C16	AP6	10k vio blue	3.00	3.50
a.	10k ultra		8.50	10.00
C17	AP6	20k gray violet	3.00	4.50
	Nos. C10-C17 (8)		10.25	15.30
	Set, never hinged		17.50	

Two types exist of the 50h, 1k and 2k, and three types of the 3k, differing chiefly in the size of the printed area. A "no hill at left" variety of the 3k exists.
Imperf. examples of Nos. C10-C17 are proofs.
See Bohemia and Moravia No. C1.

Perf. 12

C10a	AP3	50h deep green	2.50	*4.50*
C11a	AP3	1k deep red	13.00	*22.50*
C12a	AP4	2k dark green	13.00	*22.50*
C14a	AP5	4k indigo	2.00	*3.50*
C17a	AP6	20k gray violet	9.00	*7.00*

Perf. 12x13½, 13½x12

C11b	AP3	1k deep red	3.50	*6.50*
C12b	AP4	2k dark green	10.00	*15.00*

Perf. 13¾x12¼

C17b	AP6	20k gray violet	*1,750.*	

Perf. 12½

C15a	AP5	5k red brown	*2,000.*	

> **Catalogue values for unused stamps in this section, from this point to the end of the section, are for Never Hinged items.**

Capt. Frantisek Novak AP7   Plane over Bratislava Castle AP8

Plane over Charles Bridge, Prague — AP9

1946-47   **Perf. 12½**

C19	AP7	1.50k rose red	.25	.25
C20	AP7	5.50k dk gray bl	.50	.25
C21	AP7	9k sepia ('47)	.85	.25
C22	AP8	10k dl grn	.85	.35
C23	AP7	16k violet	1.50	.60
C24	AP8	20k light blue	1.60	1.10
C25	AP9	24k dk bl, *cr*	1.00	.65
C26	AP9	24k rose lake	1.75	1.00
C27	AP9	50k dk gray bl	3.25	2.60
	Nos. C19-C27 (9)		11.55	7.05

No. C25 was issued June 12, 1946, for use on the first Prague-New York flight. Nos. C22, C24-C27 were each issued in sheets of 100 stamps and 12 labels depicting airplane over globe. Values for singles with attached labels (mint/used): C22, $2/$1.50; C24, $4/$3; C25, $7.50/$4; C26, $5.50/$4.50; C27, $9/$7.50.

Nos. C19-C24, C26-C27 Surcharged with New Value and Bars in Various Colors

1949, Sept. 1   **Perf. 12½**

C28	AP7	1k on 1.50k (Bl)	.25	.25
C29	AP7	3k on 5.50k (C)	.35	.25
C30	AP7	6k on 9k (Br)	.55	.25
C31	AP7	7.50k on 16k (G)	.75	.25
C32	AP8	8k on 10k (R)	.75	.75
C33	AP8	12.50k on 20k (Bl)	1.10	.55
C34	AP9	15k on 24k rose lake (Bl)	2.75	1.00
C35	AP9	30k on 50k (Bl)	2.00	.90
	Nos. C28-C35 (8)		8.50	4.20

Karlovy Vary (Karlsbad) — AP10

1951, Apr. 2   Engr.   Perf. 13½

C36	AP10	6k shown	3.50	1.75
C37	AP10	10k Piestany	3.50	1.75
C38	AP10	15k Marienbad	6.00	1.75
C39	AP10	20k Silac	9.50	4.50
	Nos. C36-C39 (4)		22.50	9.75

Nos. C36-C39 were each issued in a sheet of 10 stamps. Value, set *$950.*

View of Cesky Krumlov AP11

Views: 1.55k, Olomouc. 2.35k, Banska Bystrica. 2.75k, Bratislava. 10k, Prague.

1955   Cream Paper   Perf. 11½

C40	AP11	80h olive green	1.00	.25
C41	AP11	1.55k violet brn	1.40	.45
C42	AP11	2.35k violet blue	1.90	.45
C43	AP11	2.75k rose brown	2.75	.45
C44	AP11	10k indigo	5.50	2.75
	Nos. C40-C44 (5)		12.55	4.15

Issue dates: 10k, Feb. 20. Others, Mar. 28.

Airline: Moscow-Prague-Paris — AP12

2.35k, Airline: Prague-Cairo-Beirut-Damascus.

Engraved and Photogravure
1957, Oct. 15   Unwmk.   Perf. 11½

C45	AP12	75h ultra & rose	1.00	.25
C46	AP12	2.35k ultra & org yel	1.00	.30

Planes at First Czech Aviation School, Pardubice AP13

Design: 1.80k, Jan Kaspar and flight of first Czech plane, 1909.

1959, Oct. 15

C47	AP13	1k gray & yel	.25	.25
C48	AP13	1.80k blk & pale bl	.75	.25

50th anniv. of Jan Kaspar's 1st flight Aug. 25, 1909, at Pardubice.

Mail Coach, Plane and Arms of Bratislava AP14

Design: 2.80k, Helicopter over Bratislava.

1960, Sept. 24   Unwmk.   Perf. 11½

C49	AP14	1.60k dk bl & gray	1.50	.75
C50	AP14	2.80k grn & buff	1.75	1.10

Issued to publicize the National Stamp Exhibition, Bratislava, Sept. 24-Oct. 9.

AP15

Designs: 60h, Prague hails Gagarin. 1.80k, Gagarin, rocket and dove.

1961, June 22

C51	AP15	60h gray & car	.30	.25
C52	AP15	1.80k gray & blue	.45	.25

No. C51 commemorates Maj. Gagarin's visit to Prague, Apr. 28-29; No. C52 commemorates the first man in space, Yuri A. Gagarin, Apr. 12, 1961.

AP16

"PRAGA" emblem and: 80h, Dove & Nest of Eggs. 1.40k, Dove. 2.80k, Symbolic flower with five petals. 4.20k, Five leaves.

1962, May 14   Engr.   Perf. 14

C53	AP16	80h multicolored	.75	.35
C54	AP16	1.40k blk, dk red & bl	1.50	1.50
C55	AP16	2.80k multicolored	1.50	1.50
C56	AP16	4.20k multicolored	1.50	1.50
	Nos. C53-C56 (4)		5.25	4.85

PRAGA 1962 World Exhibition of Postage Stamps, Aug. 18-Sept. 2, 1962.
Nos. C53-C56 were each issued in sheets of 10. Value, set $85.

Vostok 5 and Lt. Col. Valeri Bykovski AP17

2.80k, Vostok VI & Lt. Valentina Tereshkova.

1963, June 26

C57	AP17	80h slate bl & pink	1.00	.35
C58	AP17	2.80k dl red brn & lt bl	1.75	.35

Space flights of Valeri Bykovski, June 14-19, and Valentina Tereshkova, June 16-19, 1963.

PRAGA 1962 Emblem, View of Prague and Plane — AP18

Designs: 60h, Istanbul '63 (Hagia Sophia). 1k, Philatec Paris 1964 (Ile de la Cité). 1.40k, WIPA 1965 (Belvedere Palace, Vienna). 1.60k, SIPEX 1966 (Capitol, Washington). 2k, Amphilex '67 (harbor and old town, Amsterdam). 5k, PRAGA 1968 (View of Prague).

Engraved and Photogravure
1967, Oct. 30   Perf. 11½
Size: 30x50mm

C59	AP18	30h choc, yel & rose	.25	.25
C60	AP18	60h dk grn, yel & lil	.25	.25
C61	AP18	1k blk, brick red & lt bl	.35	.25
C62	AP18	1.40k vio, yel & dp org	.45	.25
C63	AP18	1.60k ind, tan & lil	.45	.25
C64	AP18	2k dk grn, org & red	.45	.25

Size: 40x50mm

C65	AP18	5k multi	2.50	1.60
	Nos. C59-C65 (7)		4.70	3.10

PRAGA 1968 World Stamp Exhibition, Prague, June 22-July 7, 1968. No. C59-C64 issued in sheets of 15 stamps and 15 bilingual labels. Values, set of singles with attached labels: mint $6.50; used $4.50. No. C65 issued in sheets of 4 stamps and one center label. Value $15.

Glider L-13 — AP19

Airplanes: 60h, Sports plane L-40. 80h, Aero taxi L-200. 1k, Crop-spraying plane Z-37. 1.60k, Aerobatics trainer Z-526. 2k, Jet trainer L-29.

1967, Dec. 11

C66	AP19	30h multi	.25	.25
C67	AP19	60h multi	.25	.25
C68	AP19	80h multi	.25	.25
C69	AP19	1k multi	.30	.25
C70	AP19	1.60k multi	.50	.25
C71	AP19	2k multi	1.60	.90
	Nos. C66-C71 (6)		3.15	2.15

Charles Bridge, Prague, and Balloon — AP20

Designs: 1k, Belvedere, fountain and early plane. 2k, Hradcany, Prague, and airship.

1968, Feb. 5   Unwmk.   Perf. 11½

C72	AP20	60h multicolored	.30	.25
C73	AP20	1k multicolored	.45	.30
C74	AP20	2k multicolored	.75	.30
	Nos. C72-C74 (3)		1.50	.85

PRAGA 1968 World Stamp Exhibition, Prague, June 22-July 7, 1968.
Nos. C72-C74 were each issued in a sheet of 10 stamps, Value, set $24.

Astronaut, Moon and Manhattan — AP21

Design: 3k, Lunar landing module and J. F. Kennedy Airport, New York.

1969, July 21
C75	AP21	60h blk, vio, yel & sil	.40	.25
C76	AP21	3k blk, bl, ocher & sil	1.60	.25

Man's 1st landing on the moon, July 20, 1969, US astronauts Neil A. Armstrong and Col. Edwin E. Aldrin, Jr., with Lieut. Col. Michael Collins piloting Apollo 11.
Nos. C75-C76 printed with label inscribed with names of astronauts and European date of moon landing. Values for pair of singles with attached labels: mint $3; used $1.

TU-104A over Bitov Castle — AP22

Designs: 60h, IL-62 over Bezdez Castle. 1.40k, TU-13A over Orava Castle. 1.90k, IL-18 over Veveri Castle. 2.40k, IL-14 over Pernstejn Castle. 3.60k, TU-154 over Trencin Castle.

1973, Oct. 24   **Engr.**   **Perf. 11½**
C77	AP22	30h multi	.25	.25
C78	AP22	60h multi	.25	.25
C79	AP22	1.40k multi	.25	.25
C80	AP22	1.90k multi	.40	.25
C81	AP22	2.40k multi	1.50	.75
C82	AP22	3.60k multi	.70	.25
		Nos. C77-C82 (6)	3.35	2.00

50 years of Czechoslovakian aviation. Nos. C77-C82 were each printed in sheets of 10. Values, set: mint $50; used $25.

Old Water Tower and Manes Hall AP23

Designs (Praga 1978 Emblem, Plane Silhouette and): 1.60k, Congress Hall. 2k, Powder Tower, vert. 2.40k, Charles Bridge and Old Bridge Tower. 4k, Old Town Hall on Old Town Square, vert. 6k, Prague Castle and St. Vitus' Cathedral, vert.

Engraved and Photogravure
1976, June 23   **Perf. 11½**
C83	AP23	60h ind & multi	.25	.25
C84	AP23	1.60k ind & multi	.25	.25
C85	AP23	2k ind & multi	.35	.25
C86	AP23	2.40k ind & multi	.40	.25
C87	AP23	4k ind & multi	.80	.30
C88	AP23	6k ind & multi	2.00	.80
		Nos. C83-C88 (6)	4.05	2.10

PRAGA 1978 International Philatelic Exhibition, Prague, Sept. 8-17, 1978.

Zeppelin, 1909 and 1928 — AP24

PRAGA '78 Emblem and: 1k, Ader, 1890, L'Eole & Dunn, 1914. 1.60k, Jeffries-Blanchard balloon, 1785. 2k, Otto Lilienthal's glider, 1896. 4.40k, Jan Kaspar's plane, Pardubice, 1911.

1977, Sept. 15   **Perf. 11½**
C89	AP24	60h multi	.25	.25
C90	AP24	1k multi	.30	.25
C91	AP24	1.60k multi	.35	.25
C92	AP24	2k multi	.45	.25
C93	AP24	4.40k multi	2.25	.50
		Nos. C89-C93 (5)	3.60	1.50

History of aviation.
Nos. C89-C93 were each issued in sheets of 30 stamps, 15 labels depicting the exhibition emblem, and 5 blank labels. Values for set of singles with attached inscribed labels: mint $5; used $2.50.

SPECIAL DELIVERY STAMPS

Doves — SD1

1919-20   **Unwmk.**   **Typo.**   *Imperf.*
E1	SD1	2h red vio, *yel*	.25	.25
E2	SD1	5h yel grn, *yel*	.25	.25
E3	SD1	10h red brn, *yel* ('20)	.75	.75
		Nos. E1-E3 (3)	1.25	1.25

For overprints and surcharge see Nos. P11-P13, Eastern Silesia E1-E2.

1921   **White Paper**
E1a	SD1	2h red violet	9.00
E2a	SD1	5h yellow green	6.00
E3a	SD1	10h red brown	140.00
		Nos. E1a-E3a (3)	155.00

It is doubted that Nos. E1a-E3a were regularly issued.

PERSONAL DELIVERY STAMPS

Catalogue values for unused stamps in this section are for Never Hinged items.

PD1

Design: No. EX2, "D" in each corner.

1937   **Unwmk.**   **Photo.**   **Perf. 13½**
EX1	PD1	50h blue	.25	*.25*
EX2	PD1	50h carmine	.25	*.25*

PD3

1946   **Perf. 13½**
EX3	PD3	2k deep blue	.50	*.75*

POSTAGE DUE STAMPS

D1

1918-20   **Unwmk.**   **Typo.**   *Imperf.*
J1	D1	5h deep bister	.25	.25
J2	D1	10h deep bister	.25	.25
J3	D1	15h deep bister	.25	.25
J4	D1	20h deep bister	.30	.25
J5	D1	25h deep bister	.45	.25
J6	D1	30h deep bister	.45	.25
J7	D1	40h deep bister	.60	.25
J8	D1	50h deep bister	.75	.25
J9	D1	100h blk brn	1.50	.25
J10	D1	250h orange	11.00	1.40
J11	D1	400h scarlet	15.00	1.40
J12	D1	500h gray grn	7.50	.25
J13	D1	1000h purple	7.50	.25
J14	D1	2000h dark brn	22.50	.60
		Nos. J1-J14 (14)	68.30	6.15

For surcharges and overprints see Nos. J32-J41, J57, Eastern Silesia J1-J11.

Nos. 1, 33-34, 10 Surcharged in Blue

1922
J15	A1	20h on 3h red vio	.30	.25
J16	A2	50h on 75h slate	1.50	.25
J17	A2	60h on 80h olive grn	.80	.25
J18	A2	100h on 80h olive grn	3.00	.25
J19	A1	200h on 400h purple	4.00	.25
		Nos. J15-J19 (5)	9.60	1.25

Same Surcharge on Nos. 1, 10, 30-31, 33-34, 36, 40 in Violet

1923-26
J20	A1	10h on 3h red vio	.25	.25
J21	A1	20h on 3h red vio	.30	.25
J22	A1	30h on 3h red vio	.25	.25
J23	A1	40h on 3h red vio	.25	.25
J24	A2	50h on 75h slate	1.25	.25
J25	A2	60h on 50h dk vio ('26)	4.00	1.25
J26	A2	60h on 50h dk bl ('26)	4.00	1.50
J27	A2	60h on 75h slate	.50	.25
J28	A2	100h on 80h ol grn	27.50	.25
J29	A2	100h on 120h gray blk	1.00	.25
J30	A1	100h on 400h pur ('26)	1.00	.25
J31	A2	100h on 1000h dp vio ('26)	1.60	.25
		Nos. J20-J31 (12)	41.90	5.25

Postage Due Stamp of 1918-20 Surcharged in Violet

1924
J32	D1	50h on 400h scar	.90	.25
J33	D1	60h on 400h scar	3.25	.60
J34	D1	100h on 400h scar	2.00	.25
		Nos. J32-J34 (3)	6.15	1.10

Postage Due Stamps of 1918-20 Surcharged with New Values in Violet as in 1924

1925
J35	D1	10h on 5h bister	.25	.25
J36	D1	20h on 5h bister	.25	.25
J37	D1	30h on 15h bister	.25	.25
J38	D1	40h on 15h bister	.25	.25
J39	D1	50h on 250h org	1.10	.25
J40	D1	60h on 250h org	1.50	.60
J41	D1	100h on 250h org	2.25	.25
		Nos. J35-J41 (7)	5.85	2.10

Stamps of 1918-19 Surcharged with New Values in Violet as in 1922

1926   **Perf. 14, 11½**
J42	A2	30h on 15h red	.50	.25
J43	A2	40h on 15h red	.50	.30

Surcharged in Violet

1926   **Perf. 14**
J44	A8	30h on 100h dk grn	.25	.25
J45	A8	40h on 200h violet	.25	.25
J46	A8	40h on 300h ver	.95	.25
a.		Perf. 14x13½		60.00
J47	A8	50h on 500h dp grn	.50	.25
a.		Perf. 14x13½	2.75	
J48	A8	60h on 400h brown	2.50	.35
J49	A8	100h on 600h dp vio	2.50	.35
a.		Perf. 14x13½	30.00	1.25
		Nos. J44-J49 (6)	5.45	1.60

Surcharged in Violet

1927
J50	A6	100h dark brown	.55	.25
a.		Perf. 13½	200.00	10.00

Surcharged in Violet

Surcharged in Violet

J51	A6	40h on 185h org	.25	.25
J52	A6	50h on 20h car	.25	.25
a.		50h on 50h carmine (error)		55,000.

J53	A6	50h on 150h rose	.25	.25
a.		Perf. 13½	12.50	2.00
J54	A6	60h on 25h brown	.25	.25
J55	A6	60h on 185h orange	.55	.25
J56	A6	100h on 25h brown	.55	.25
		Nos. J50-J56 (7)	2.65	1.75

No. J52a is known only used.

No. J12 Surcharged in Deep Violet

1927   *Imperf.*
J57	D1	200h on 500h gray grn	8.00	2.50

Catalogue values for unused stamps in this section, from this point to the end of the section, are for Never Hinged items.

D5

1928   **Perf. 14x13½**
J58	D5	5h dark red	.25	.25
J59	D5	10h dark red	.25	.25
J60	D5	20h dark red	.25	.25
J61	D5	30h dark red	.25	.25
J62	D5	40h dark red	.25	.25
J63	D5	50h dark red	.25	.25
J64	D5	60h dark red	.25	.25
J65	D5	1k ultra	.25	.25
J66	D5	2k ultra	.50	.25
J67	D5	5k ultra	.75	.25
J68	D5	10k ultra	1.90	.25
J69	D5	20k ultra	3.75	.30
		Nos. J58-J69 (12)	8.90	3.05

D6

1946-48   **Photo.**   **Perf. 14**
J70	D6	10h dark blue	.25	.25
J71	D6	20h dark blue	.25	.25
J72	D6	50h dark blue	.25	.25
J73	D6	1k carmine rose	.25	.25
J74	D6	1.20k carmine rose	.25	.25
J75	D6	1.50k carmine rose ('48)	.25	.25
J76	D6	1.60k carmine rose ('48)	.25	.25
J77	D6	2k carmine rose	.25	.25
J78	D6	2.40k carmine rose	.25	.25
J79	D6	3k carmine rose	.25	.25
J80	D6	5k carmine rose	.25	.25
J81	D6	6k carmine rose ('48)	.25	.25
		Nos. J70-J81 (12)	3.00	3.00

D7   D8

1954-55   **Engr.**   **Perf. 12½, 11½**
J82	D7	5h gray green ('55)	.25	.25
J83	D7	10h gray green ('55)	.25	.25
J84	D7	30h gray green	.25	.25
J85	D7	50h gray green ('55)	.25	.25
J86	D7	60h gray green ('55)	.25	.25
J87	D7	95h gray green	.35	.25
J88	D8	1k violet	.35	.25
J89	D8	1.20k violet ('55)	.35	.25
J90	D8	1.50k violet	.70	.25
J91	D8	1.60k violet ('55)	.45	.25
J92	D8	2k violet	.85	.25
J93	D8	3k violet	1.10	
J94	D8	5k violet ('55)	1.40	.25
		Nos. J82-J94 (13)	6.80	3.25

Perf. 11½ stamps are from a 1963 printing which lacks the 95h, 1.60k, and 2k.

Stylized Flower — D9

Designs: Various stylized flowers.

Engraved and Photogravure

1971-72				Perf. 11½	
J95	D9	10h	vio bl & pink	.25	.25
J96	D9	20h	vio & lt bl	.25	.25
J97	D9	30h	emer & lil rose	.25	.25
J98	D9	60h	pur & emer	.25	.25
J99	D9	80h	org & vio bl	.25	.25
J100	D9	1k	dk red & emer	.25	.25
J101	D9	1.20k	grn & org	.25	.25
J102	D9	2k	blue & red	.25	.25
J103	D9	3k	blk & yel	.30	.25
J104	D9	4k	brn & ultra	.45	.25
J105	D9	5.40k	red & lilac	.60	.25
J106	D9	6k	brick red & org	.75	.25

Nos. J95-J106 (12)   4.10 3.00

All except 5.40k issued in 1972.

OFFICIAL STAMPS

Coat of Arms — O1

1945	Unwmk.	Litho.	Perf. 10½x10	
O1	O1	50h dp slate grn	.25	.25
O2	O1	1k dp bl vio	.25	.25
O3	O1	1.20k plum	.25	.25
O4	O1	1.50k crimson rose	.25	.25
O5	O1	2.50k bright ultra	.25	.25
O6	O1	5k dk vio brn	.30	.25
O7	O1	8k rose pink	.30	.30

Nos. O1-O7 (7)   1.85 1.80

Redrawn

1947		Photo.	Perf. 14	
O8	O1	60h red	.25	.25
O9	O1	80h dk olive grn	.25	.25
O10	O1	1k dk lilac gray	.25	.25
O11	O1	1.20k dp plum	.25	.25
O12	O1	2.40k dk car rose	.25	.25
O13	O1	4k brt ultra	.25	.25
O14	O1	5k dk vio brn	.25	.25
O15	O1	7.40k purple	.25	.25

Nos. O8-O15 (8)   2.00 2.00

There are many minor changes in design, size of numerals, etc., of the redrawn stamps.

NEWSPAPER STAMPS

Windhover — N1

1918-20	Unwmk.	Typo.	Imperf.	
P1	N1	2h gray green	.25	.25
P2	N1	5h green ('20)	.25	.25
a.		5h dark green	.40	.25
P3	N1	6h red	.30	.25
P4	N1	10h dull violet	.25	.25
P5	N1	20h blue	.25	.25
P6	N1	30h gray brown	.25	.25
P7	N1	50h orange ('20)	.30	.25
P8	N1	100h red brown ('20)	.40	.25

Nos. P1-P8 (8)   2.25 2.00

Nos. P1-P8 exist privately perforated. For surcharges and overprints see Nos. P9-P10, P14-P16, Eastern Silesia P1-P5.

Stamps of 1918-20 Surcharged in Violet

1925-26				
P9	N1	5h on 2h gray green	.50	.40
P10	N1	5h on 6h red ('26)	.25	.40

Special Delivery Stamps of 1918-20 Overprinted in Violet

1926					
P11	SD1	5h apple grn, yel		.25	.25
a.		5h dull green, yellow		.50	.40
P12	SD1	10h red brn, yel		.25	.25

With Additional Surcharge of New Value

P13	SD1	5h on 2h red vio, yel	.35	.35

Nos. P11-P13 (3)   .85 .85

Newspaper Stamps of 1918-20 Overprinted in Violet

1934				
P14	N1	10h dull violet	.25	.25
P15	N1	20h blue	.25	.25
P16	N1	30h gray brown	.25	.25

Nos. P14-P16 (3)   .75 .75

Overprinted for use by commercial firms only.

Carrier Pigeon — N2

1937			Imperf.	
P17	N2	2h bister brown	.25	.25
P18	N2	5h dull blue	.25	.25
P19	N2	7h red orange	.25	.25
P20	N2	9h emerald	.25	.25
P21	N2	10h henna brown	.25	.25
P22	N2	12h ultra	.25	.25
P23	N2	20h dark green	.25	.25
P24	N2	50h dark brown	.25	.25
P25	N2	1k olive gray	.25	.25

Nos. P17-P25 (9)   2.25 2.25

For overprint see Slovakia Nos. P1-P9.

Bratislava Philatelic Exhibition Issue
Souvenir Sheet

1937			Imperf.	
P26	N2	10h henna brn, sheet of 25	4.00	4.00

Newspaper Delivery Boy — N4

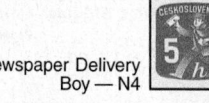

1945	Unwmk.	Typo.	Imperf.	
P27	N4	5h dull blue	.25	.25
P28	N4	10h red	.25	.25
P29	N4	15h emerald	.25	.25
P30	N4	20h dark slate green	.25	.25
P31	N4	25h bright red vio	.25	.25
P32	N4	30h ocher	.25	.25
P33	N4	40h red orange	.25	.25
P34	N4	50h brown red	.25	.25
P35	N4	1k slate gray	.25	.25
P36	N4	5k deep vio blue	.25	.25

Nos. P27-P36 (10)   2.50 2.50

CZECHOSLOVAK LEGION POST

The Czechoslovak Legion in Siberia issued these stamps for use on its mail and that of local residents. Forgeries exist.

For more detailed listings of Czechoslovak Legion Post issues, see the *Classic Specialized Catalogue of Stamps and Covers.*

Russia No. 79 Overprinted

1918		Typo.	Perf. 14x14½	
A1	A15	10k dark blue	2,500.	

No. A1 was sold for a few days in Chelyabinsk. It was withdrawn because of a spelling error ("CZESZKJA," instead of "CZESZKAJA").

This overprint was also applied to Russia Nos. 73-78, 80-81, 83-85, 119-121, 123 and 130-131. These were trial printings, never sold to the public, although favor-cancelled covers exist.

Urn and Cathedral at Irkutsk — A1

Armored Railroad Car — A2

Sentinel — A3

1919-20			Litho.	Imperf.	
1	A1	25k carmine		10.50	—
a.		Perf 11½ ('20)		15.00	—
2	A2	50k yellow green		10.50	—
a.		Perf 11½ ('20)		15.00	—
3	A3	1r red brown		19.00	—
a.		Perf 11½ ('20)		22.50	—

Originals of Nos. 1-3 and 1a-3a have a crackled yellow gum. Ungummed remainders, which were given a white gum, exist imperforate and perforated 11½ and 13¼. Value per set, $3.

Lion of Bohemia — A4

Two types: 1 — 6 points on star-like mace head at right of goblet; large saber handle; measures 20x25¼mm. 2 — 5 points on mace head; small saber handle; measures 19½x25mm.

Perce en Arc in Blue

1920			Embossed	
4	A4	(25k) blue & rose	3.00	—

No. 4 Overprinted

1920				
5	A4	(25k) bl & rose	10.00	—

Both types of No. 4 received overprint.

No. 5 Surcharged with New Values in Green

6	A4	2k bl & rose	35.00	—
7	A4	3k bl & rose	35.00	—
8	A4	5k bl & rose	35.00	—
9	A4	10k bl & rose	35.00	—
10	A4	15k bl & rose	35.00	—
11	A4	25k bl & rose	35.00	—
12	A4	35k bl & rose	35.00	—
13	A4	50k bl & rose	35.00	—
14	A4	1r bl & rose	35.00	—

Nos. 6-14 (9)   315.00

BOHEMIA AND MORAVIA

Masaryk Type of Czechoslovakia with hyphen in "Cesko-Slovensko" — A60

1939, Apr. 23				
1A	A60	1k rose lake	.25	.25

Prepared by Czechoslovakia prior to the German occupation March 15, 1939. Subsequently issued for use in Bohemia and Moravia.
See No. C1.

German Protectorate

Stamps of Czechoslovakia, 1928-39, Overprinted in Black

Perf. 10, 12½, 12x12½

1939, July 15				Unwmk.	
1	A29	5h dk ultra		.25	1.25
2	A29	10h brown		.25	1.25
3	A29	20h red		.25	1.25
4	A29	25h green		.25	1.25
5	A29	30h red vio		.25	1.25
6	A61a	40h dk bl		2.50	5.00
7	A85	50h dp grn		.25	1.25
8	A63	60h dl vio		2.50	5.00
9	A60	1k rose lake (#212)		.75	1.75
10	A60	1k rose lake		.30	1.25
11	A64	1.20k rose lilac		3.00	5.00
12	A65	1.50k carmine		3.00	5.75
13	A79	1.60k olive grn		5.00	5.75
a.		"Mähnen"		32.50	75.00
14	A66	2k dk bl grn		1.10	4.00
15	A67	2.50k dk bl		3.00	5.00
16	A68	3k brown		3.00	5.75
17	A70	4k dk vio		9.50	6.50
18	A71	5k green		5.50	10.00
19	A72	10k blue		5.50	15.00

Nos. 1-19 (19)   46.15 83.25
Set, never hinged   60.00

The size of the overprint varies, Nos. 1-10 measure 17½x15½mm, Nos. 11-16 19x18mm, Nos. 17 and 19 28x17½mm and No. 18 23½x23mm.

Nos. 11-13 exist with the period missing after the contraction "u.".

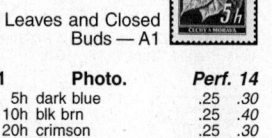

Linden Leaves and Closed Buds — A1

1939-41		Photo.		Perf. 14	
20	A1	5h dark blue		.25	.30
21	A1	10h blk brn		.25	.40
22	A1	20h crimson		.25	.30
23	A1	25h dk bl grn		.25	.30
24	A1	30h dp plum		.25	.30
24A	A1	30h golden brn ('41)		.25	.30
25	A1	40h orange ('40)		.25	.25
26	A1	50h slate grn ('40)		.25	.25

Nos. 20-26 (8)   2.00 2.40

See Nos. 49-51.

Castle at
Zvikov
A2

St.
Barbara's
Church,
Kutna Hora
A4

Brno
Cathedral
A6

1939 **Engr.** *Perf. 12½*

27	A2	40h dark blue	.25	.30
28	A3	50h dk bl grn	.25	.30
29	A4	60h dl vio	.25	.30
30	A5	1k dp rose	.25	.30
31	A6	1.20k rose lilac	.25	.50
32	A6	1.50k rose car	.25	.50
33	A7	2k dk bl grn	.25	.45
34	A7	2.50k dark blue	.25	.30
		Nos. 27-34 (8)	2.00	2.75

No. 31 measures 23½x29½mm, No. 42 measures 18½x23mm.
See #52-53, 53B. For overprints see #60-61.

Zlin — A8

Iron Works at
Moravská
Ostrava — A9

Prague — A10

1939-40

35	A8	3k dl rose vio	.25	.30
36	A9	4k slate ('40)	.25	.40
37	A10	5k green	.45	.65
38	A10	10k lt ultra	.35	.75
39	A10	20k yel brn	1.00	1.50
		Nos. 35-39 (5)	2.30	3.60

Types of 1939 and

Neuhaus
A11

Pernstein
Castle
A12

Pardubice
Castle
A13

Lainsitz Bridge
near Bechyne
A14

Samson
Fountain,
Budweis — A15

Kromeriz — A16

Wallenstein Palace,
Prague — A17

1940 **Engr.** *Perf. 12½*

40	A11	50h dk bl grn	.25	.25
41	A12	80h dp bl	.25	.30
42	A6	1.20k vio brn	.30	.25
43	A13	2k gray grn	.25	.25
44	A14	5k dk bl grn	.25	.25
45	A15	6k brn vio	.25	.50
46	A16	8k slate grn	.25	.30
47	A17	10k blue	.45	.30
48	A10	20k sepia	.75	2.00
		Nos. 40-48 (9)	3.00	4.40

No. 42 measures 18½x23mm; No. 31, 23½x29½mm.

Types of 1939-40

1941

49	A1	60h violet	.25	.25
50	A1	80h red org	.25	.25
51	A1	1k brown	.25	.25
52	A5	1.20k rose red	.25	.25
53	A4	1.50k lil rose	.25	.25
53A	A13	2k light blue	.25	.25
53B	A6	2.50k ultra	.25	.25
53C	A12	3k olive	.25	.25
		Nos. 49-53C (8)	2.00	2.00

Nos. 49-51 show buds open. Nos. 52 and 53B measure 18¾x23½mm and have no inscriptions below design.
For overprints see Nos. 60-61.

Antonin Dvorák — A18

1941, Aug. 25 **Engr.** *Perf. 12½*

54	A18	60h dull lilac	.40	.50
55	A18	1.20k sepia	.40	.50

Antonin Dvorák (1841-1904), composer.
Nos. 54-55 were issued in sheets of 50 stamps and 50 alternating inscribed labels. Value for set of singles with attached labels, unused or used, $1.25.

Farming
Scene
A19

Factories
A20

1941, Sept. 7 **Photo.** *Perf. 13½*

56	A19	30h dk red brn	.25	.30
57	A19	60h dark green	.25	.30
58	A20	1.20k dk plum	.25	.30
59	A20	2.50k sapphire	.25	1.50
		Nos. 56-59 (4)	1.00	2.40

Issued to publicize the Prague Fair.

Nos. 52 and 53B
Overprinted in Blue or
Red

1942, Mar. 15 *Perf. 12½*

60	A5	1.20k rose red (Bl)	.70	1.00
61	A6	2.50k ultra (R)	.70	1.00

3rd anniv. of the Protectorate of Bohemia and Moravia.

Adolf Hitler — A21

1942 **Photo.** *Perf. 14*
Size: 17½x21½mm

62	A21	10(h) gray blk	.25	.25
63	A21	30(h) bister brn	.25	.25
64	A21	40(h) slate blue	.25	.25
65	A21	50(h) slate grn	.25	.25
66	A21	60(h) purple	.25	.25
67	A21	80(h) org ver	.25	.25

Perf. 12½
Engr.
Size: 18x21mm

68	A21	1k dl brn	.25	.25
69	A21	1.20(k) carmine	.25	.30
70	A21	1.50(k) claret	.25	.30
71	A21	1.60(k) Prus grn	.25	.30
72	A21	2k light blue	.25	.30
73	A21	2.40(k) fawn	.25	.30

Size: 18½x24mm

74	A21	2.50(k) ultra	.25	.30
75	A21	3k olive grn	.25	.30
76	A21	4k brt red vio	.25	.30
77	A21	5k myrtle grn	.25	.30
78	A21	6k claret brn	.25	.40
79	A21	8k indigo	.25	.40

Size: 23½x29¾mm

80	A21	10k dk gray grn	.25	.75
81	A21	20k gray vio	.50	.90
82	A21	30k red	.75	1.50
83	A21	50k deep blue	1.50	2.50
		Nos. 62-83 (22)	7.50	10.90

17th Century
Messenger — A22

1943, Jan. 10 **Photo.** *Perf. 13½*

84	A22	60h dark rose violet	.40	.40

Stamp Day.

Scene from
"Die
Meistersinger"
A23

Richard
Wagner
A24

Scene from
"Siegfried" — A25

1943, May 22

85	A23	60h violet	.25	.25
86	A24	1.20k carmine rose	.25	.25
87	A25	2.50k deep ultra	.25	.25
		Nos. 85-87 (3)	.75	.75

Richard Wagner (1813-83).

St. Vitus' Cathedral,
Prague — A26

1944, Nov. 21 **Engr.** *Perf. 12½*

88	A26	1.50k dull rose brn	.25	.25
89	A26	2.50k dull lilac blue	.25	.35

Adolf Hitler — A27

1944

90	A27	4.20k green	.50	.50

SEMI-POSTAL STAMPS

Nurse and Wounded
Soldier — SP1

Perf. 13½
1940, June 29 **Photo.** *Unwmk.*

B1	SP1	60h + 40h indigo	.35	.75
B2	SP1	1.20k + 80h deep plum	.35	.75

Surtax for German Red Cross.
Nos. B1-B2 were issued in sheets of 50 stamps and 50 alternating inscribed labels. Value for set of singles with attached labels: unused $4.50; used $4.

Red Cross Nurse and
Patient — SP2

1941, Apr. 20

B3	SP2	60h + 40h indigo	.40	.75
B4	SP2	1.20k + 80h dp plum	.40	.75

Surtax for German Red Cross.
Nos. B3-B4 were issued in sheets of 50 stamps and 50 alternating inscribed labels. Value for set of singles with attached labels: unused $3.50; used $4.50.

Old Theater,
Prague
SP3

Mozart
SP4

1941, Oct. 26

B5	SP3	30h + 30h brown	.25	.25
B6	SP3	60h + 60h Prus grn	.25	.25
B7	SP4	1.20k + 1.20k scar	.25	.25
B8	SP4	2.50k + 2.50k dk bl	.45	.45
		Nos. B5-B8 (4)	1.20	1.20

150th anniversary of Mozart's death. Labels alternate with stamps in sheets of Nos. B5-B8. The labels with Nos. B5-B6 show two bars of Mozart's opera "Don Giovanni." Those with Nos. B7-B8 show Mozart's piano. Value for set of singles with attached labels: unused $2.50; used $3.50.

Adolf Hitler — SP5

1942, Apr. 20 **Engr.** *Perf. 12½*

B9	SP5	30h + 20h dl brn vio	.25	.25
B10	SP5	60h + 40h dl grn	.25	.25
B11	SP5	1.20k + 80h dp claret	.25	.35
B12	SP5	2.50k + 1.50k dl bl	.40	.75
		Nos. B9-B12 (4)	1.15	1.60

Hitler's 53rd birthday.
Nos. B9-B12 were issued in sheets of 100 stamps and 12 blank labels. Value for set of singles with attached labels: unused $3; used $2.25.

Nurse and
Soldier — SP6

1942, Sept. 4 *Perf. 13½*

B13	SP6	60h + 40h deep blue	.25	.25
B14	SP6	1.20(k) + 80(h) dp plum	.25	.25

The surtax aided the German Red Cross.

Emperor
Charles IV
SP7

Peter Parler
SP8

John the Blind, King of
Bohemia — SP9

1943, Jan. 29

B15	SP7	60h + 40h violet	.25	.25
B16	SP8	1.20k + 80h carmine	.25	.25
B17	SP9	2.50k + 1.50k vio bl	.25	.25
		Nos. B15-B17 (3)	.75	.75

The surtax was for the benefit of the German wartime winter relief.

Adolf Hitler — SP10

1943, Apr. 20　Engr.　*Perf. 12½*

| B18 | SP10 | 60h + 1.40k dl vio | .25 | .45 |
| B19 | SP10 | 1.20k + 3.80k carmine | .25 | .45 |

Hitler's 54th birthday.

Nos. B18-B19 were issued in sheets of 100 stamps and 12 blank labels. Value for set of singles with attached labels: unused $1.10; used $1.

Deathmask of Reinhard
Heydrich — SP11

1943, May 28　Photo.　*Perf. 13½*

| B20 | SP11 | 60h + 4.40k black | .75 | 1.50 |

No. B20 exists in a souvenir sheet containing a single stamp. It was given to high Nazi officials attending a ceremony one year after Heydrich's assassination. Value $15,000.

Eagle and Red
Cross — SP12

1943, Sept. 16　　　　*Perf. 13*

| B21 | SP12 | 1.20k + 8.80k blk & car | .60 | .35 |

The surtax aided the German Red Cross.

Native
Costumes
SP13

Nazi
Emblem,
Arms of
Bohemia,
Moravia
SP14

1944, Mar. 15　　　　*Perf. 13½*

B22	SP13	1.20(k) + 3.80(k) rose lake	.25	.25
B23	SP14	4.20(k) + 10.80(k) golden brn	.25	.25
B24	SP13	10k + 20k saph	.25	.25
		Nos. B22-B24 (3)	.75	.75

Fifth anniversary of protectorate.

Adolf Hitler — SP15

1944, Apr. 20

| B25 | SP15 | 60h + 1.40k olive blk | .30 | .25 |
| B26 | SP15 | 1.20k + 3.80k slate grn | .30 | .25 |

Bedrich
Smetana — SP16

1944, May 12　Engr.　*Perf. 12½*

| B27 | SP16 | 60h + 1.40k dk gray grn | .25 | .25 |
| B28 | SP16 | 1.20k + 3.80k brn car | .25 | .25 |

Bedrich Smetana (1824-84), Czech composer and pianist.

AIR POST STAMP

Catalogue values for unused stamps in this section are for never hinged items.

Type of Czechoslovakia 1930 with hyphen in "Cesko-Slovensko"

Fokker Monoplane — AP3

1939, Apr. 22　　　　*Perf. 13½*

| C1 | AP3 | 30h rose lilac | 1.60 | .25 |

Prepared by Czechoslovakia prior to the German occupation March 15, 1939. Subsequently issued for use in Bohemia and Moravia. See No. 1A.

PERSONAL DELIVERY STAMPS

PD1

1939-40　Unwmk. Photo.　*Perf. 13½*

EX1	PD1	50h indigo & blue ('40)	1.00	2.50
		Never hinged	2.25	
EX2	PD1	50h carmine & rose	.60	3.00
		Never hinged	1.60	

POSTAGE DUE STAMPS

Catalogue values for unused stamps in this section are for never hinged items.

D1

1939-40　Unwmk. Typo.　*Perf. 14*

J1	D1	5h dark carmine	.25	.30
J2	D1	10h dark carmine	.25	.30
J3	D1	20h dark carmine	.25	.30
J4	D1	30h dark carmine	.25	.30
J5	D1	40h dark carmine	.25	.30
J6	D1	50h dark carmine	.25	.30
J7	D1	60h dark carmine	.25	.30
J8	D1	80h dark carmine	.25	.30
J9	D1	1k bright ultra	.25	.35
J10	D1	1.20k brt ultra ('40)	.30	.35
J11	D1	2k bright ultra	.80	1.00
J12	D1	5k bright ultra	1.00	1.40
J13	D1	10k bright ultra	1.75	1.75
J14	D1	20k bright ultra	3.50	3.50
		Nos. J1-J14 (14)	9.60	10.75

OFFICIAL STAMPS

Catalogue values for unused stamps in this section are for never hinged items.

Numeral — O1

Unwmk.

1941, Jan. 1　Typo.　*Perf. 14*

O1	O1	30h ocher	.25	.25
O2	O1	40h indigo	.25	.25
O3	O1	50h emerald	.25	.25
O4	O1	60h slate grn	.25	.25
O5	O1	80h org red	.65	.25
O6	O1	1k red brn	.35	.25
O7	O1	1.20k carmine	.35	.25
O8	O1	1.50k dp plum	.50	.25
O9	O1	2k brt bl	.50	.25
O10	O1	3k olive	.50	.25
O11	O1	4k red vio	.70	.40
O12	O1	5k org yel	1.60	.90
		Nos. O1-O12 (12)	6.15	3.80

Eagle — O2

1943, Feb. 15

O13	O2	30(h) bister	.25	.30
O14	O2	40(h) indigo	.25	.30
O15	O2	50(h) yel grn	.25	.30
O16	O2	60(h) dp vio	.25	.30
O17	O2	80(h) org red	.25	.30
O18	O2	1k chocolate	.25	.30
O19	O2	1.20(k) carmine	.25	.30
O20	O2	1.50(k) brn red	.25	.30
O21	O2	2k lt bl	.25	.30
O22	O2	3k olive	.25	.30
O23	O2	4k red vio	.25	.40
O24	O2	5k dk grn	.25	.40
		Nos. O13-O24 (12)	3.00	3.80

NEWSPAPER STAMPS

Catalogue values for unused stamps in this section are for never hinged items.

Carrier Pigeon — N1

1939　Unwmk. Typo.　*Imperf.*

P1	N1	2h ocher	.25	.30
P2	N1	5h ultra	.25	.30
P3	N1	7h red orange	.25	.30
P4	N1	9h emerald	.25	.30
P5	N1	10h henna brown	.25	.30
P6	N1	12h dark ultra	.25	.30
P7	N1	20h dark green	.25	.30
P8	N1	50h red brown	.25	.35
P9	N1	1k greenish gray	.25	.80
		Nos. P1-P9 (9)	2.25	3.25

No. P5 Overprinted in Black

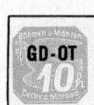

1940

| P10 | N1 | 10h henna brown | .45 | .65 |

Overprinted for use by commercial firms.

N2

1943, Feb. 15

P11	N2	2(h) ocher	.25	.25
P12	N2	5(h) light blue	.25	.25
P13	N2	7(h) red orange	.25	.25
P14	N2	9(h) emerald	.25	.25
P15	N2	10(h) henna brown	.25	.25
P16	N2	12(h) dark ultra	.25	.25
P17	N2	20(h) dark green	.25	.25
P18	N2	50(h) red brown	.25	.25
P19	N2	1k slate green	.25	.25
		Nos. P11-P19 (9)	2.25	2.25

DAHOMEY

də-'hō-mē

LOCATION — West coast of Africa
AREA — 43,483 sq. mi.
POP. — 3,030,000 (est. 1974)
CAPITAL — Porto-Novo

Formerly a native kingdom including Benin, Dahomey was annexed by France in 1894. It became part of the colonial administrative unit of French West Africa in 1895. Stamps of French West Africa superseded those of Dahomey in 1945. The Republic of Dahomey was proclaimed Dec. 4, 1958.

The republic changed its name to the People's Republic of Benin on Nov. 30, 1975. See Benin for stamps issued after that date.

100 Centimes = 1 Franc

Catalog values for unused stamps in this country are for Never Hinged items, beginning with Scott 137 in the regular postage section, Scott B15 in the semi-postal section, Scott C14 in the airpost section, Scott CQ1 in the airpost parcel post section, Scott J29 in the postage due section, and Scott Q1 in the parcel post section.

See French West Africa No. 71 for stamp inscribed "Dahomey" and "Afrique Occidentale Francaise."

Navigation and Commerce — A1

Perf. 14x13½

1899-1905 Typo. Unwmk.
Name of Colony in Blue or Carmine

1	A1	1c black, lil bl ('01)	1.60	.80
2	A1	2c brown, buff ('04)	1.60	.80
3	A1	4c claret, lav ('04)	2.40	2.40
4	A1	5c yellow grn ('04)	6.50	4.00
5	A1	10c red ('01)	8.00	4.00
6	A1	15c gray ('01)	4.00	4.00
7	A1	20c red, grn ('04)	20.00	16.00
8	A1	25c black, rose ('99)	24.00	24.00
9	A1	25c blue ('01)	20.00	16.00
10	A1	30c brown, bis ('04)	24.00	12.00
11	A1	40c red, straw ('04)	24.00	16.00
12	A1	50c brn, az (name in red) ('01)	40.00	24.00
12A	A1	50c brn, az (name in bl) ('05)	32.50	24.00
13	A1	75c dp vio, org ('04)	85.00	55.00
14	A1	1fr brnz grn, straw ('04)	40.00	32.50
15	A1	2fr violet, rose ('04)	110.00	72.50
16	A1	5fr red lilac, lav ('04)	135.00	105.00
		Nos. 1-16 (17)	578.60	413.00

Perf. 13½x14 stamps are counterfeits.
For surcharges see Nos. 32-41.

Gen. Louis Faidherbe — A2

Dr. Noel Eugène Ballay — A4

Oil Palm — A3

1906-07 Perf. 13½x14
Name of Colony in Red or Blue

17	A2	1c slate	1.60	.80
18	A2	2c chocolate	2.40	2.40
19	A2	4c choc, gray bl	4.00	3.25
20	A2	5c green	8.00	3.25

21	A2	10c carmine (B)	24.00	4.00
22	A3	20c black & red, azure	16.00	12.00
23	A3	25c blue, pnksh	16.00	12.00
24	A3	30c choc, pnksh	16.00	16.00
25	A3	35c black, yellow	87.50	12.00
26	A3	45c choc, grnsh ('07)	24.00	16.00
27	A3	50c deep violet	20.00	20.00
28	A3	75c blue, orange	24.00	24.00
29	A4	1fr black, azure	32.00	24.00
30	A4	2fr blue, pink	110.00	110.00
31	A4	5fr car, straw (B)	95.00	110.00
		Nos. 17-31 (15)	480.50	368.10

Nos. 2-3, 6-7, 9-13 Surcharged in Black or Carmine

Spacing between figures of surcharge 1.5mm (5c), 2mm (10c)

1912 Perf. 14x13½

32		5c on 2c brn, buff	2.00	2.40
33		5c on 4c claret, lav	1.60	2.00
a.		Double surcharge	275.00	
34		5c on 15c gray (C)	2.00	2.40
35		5c on 20c red, grn	2.00	2.40
36		5c on 25c blue (C)	2.00	2.40
a.		Inverted surcharge	240.00	
37		5c on 30c brown, bis (C)	2.00	2.40
38		5c on 40c red, straw	2.00	2.40
a.		Inverted surcharge	325.00	
39		10c on 50c brn, az, name in bl (C)	2.40	2.75
40		10c on 50c brn, az, name in red (C)	1,125.	1,300.
41		10c on 75c violet, org	8.00	8.00
a.		Double surcharge	5,500.	
		Nos. 32-39,41 (9)	24.00	27.15

Two spacings between the surcharged numerals are found on Nos. 32 to 41. For detailed listings, see the *Scott Classic Specialized Catalogue of Stamps and Covers.*

Man Climbing Oil Palm — A5

1913-39 Perf. 13½x14

42	A5	1c violet & blk	.40	.30
43	A5	2c choc & rose	.40	.40
44	A5	4c black & brn	.40	.40
45	A5	5c yel grn & bl grn	1.20	.55
46	A5	5c vio brn & vio ('22)	.40	.80
47	A5	10c org red & rose	1.60	.80
a.		Half used as 5c on wrapper or printed matter	—	
48	A5	10c yel grn & bl grn ('22)	.80	.80
49	A5	10c red & ol ('25)	.40	.40
50	A5	15c brn org & dk vio ('17)	.80	.80
51	A5	20c gray & red brown	.80	.75
52	A5	20c bluish grn & brn ('26)	.40	.40
53	A5	20c mag & blk ('27)	.40	.40
54	A5	25c ultra & dp blue	2.00	1.60
55	A5	25c vio brn & org ('22)	1.20	.80
56	A5	30c choc & vio	2.75	2.40
57	A5	30c red org & rose ('22)	3.25	3.25
58	A5	30c yellow & vio ('25)	.40	.40
59	A5	30c dl grn & grn ('27)	.40	.40
60	A5	35c brown & blk	.80	.80
61	A5	35c bl grn & grn ('38)	.40	.30
62	A5	40c black & red org	.80	.80
63	A5	45c gray & ultra	.80	.80
64	A5	50c chocolate & brn	6.50	6.00
a.		Half used as 25c on cover		500.00
65	A5	50c ultra & bl ('22)	1.60	1.60
66	A5	50c brn red & bl ('26)	1.20	1.20
67	A5	55c gray grn & choc ('38)	.80	.55
68	A5	60c vio, pnksh ('25)	.40	.40
69	A5	65c yel brn & ol grn ('26)	1.20	1.20

70	A5	75c blue & violet	1.20	1.20
71	A5	80c henna brn & ultra ('38)	.40	.40
72	A5	85c dk bl & ver ('26)	1.60	1.60
73	A5	90c rose & brn red ('30)	.80	.80
74	A5	90c yel bis & red org ('39)	1.20	.80
75	A5	1fr blue grn & blk	1.20	1.20
76	A5	1fr dk bl & ultra ('26)	1.60	1.60
77	A5	1fr yel brn & lt red ('28)	1.20	1.20
78	A5	1fr dk red & red org ('38)	1.05	.95
79	A5	1.10fr vio & bis ('28)	5.50	6.00
80	A5	1.25fr dp bl & dk brn ('33)	17.50	7.25
81	A5	1.50fr dk bl & lt bl ('30)	1.60	.80
82	A5	1.75fr dk brn & dp buff ('33)	4.00	2.00
83	A5	1.75fr ind & ultra ('38)	1.60	.95
84	A5	2fr yel org & choc	1.20	1.60
85	A5	3fr red violet ('30)	2.40	1.75
86	A5	5fr violet & dp bl ('33)	2.40	2.75
		Nos. 42-86 (45)	79.35	62.15

The 1c gray and yellow green and 5c dull red and black are Togo Nos. 193a, 196a.

Nos. 47a and 64a were authorized for use in Paouignan during the last part of November 1921. Other values exist as bisects but were not authorized.

For surcharges see Nos. 87-96, B1, B8-B11.

Type of 1913 Surcharged

1922-25

87	A5	60c on 75c vio, pnksh	1.20	1.20
a.		Double surcharge	200.00	
88	A5	65c on 15c brn org & dk vio ('25)	2.00	2.00
89	A5	85c on 15c brn org & dk vio ('25)	2.00	2.00
		Nos. 87-89 (3)	5.20	5.20

Stamps and Type of 1913-39 Surcharged with New Value and Bars

1924-27

90	A5	25c on 2fr org & choc	1.20	1.20
91	A5	90c on 75c cer & brn red ('27)	2.00	2.00
92	A5	1.25fr on 1fr dk bl & ultra (R) ('26)	1.60	1.60
93	A5	1.50fr on 1fr dk bl & grnsh bl ('27)	2.75	2.75
94	A5	3fr on 5fr olvn & dp org ('27)	10.50	10.50
95	A5	10fr on 5fr bl vio & red brn ('27)	8.00	8.00
96	A5	20fr on 5fr ver & dl grn ('27)	8.75	8.75
		Nos. 90-96 (7)	34.80	34.80

Common Design Types pictured following the introduction.

Colonial Exposition Issue
Common Design Types

1931 Engr. Perf. 12½
Name of Country in Black

97	CD70	40c deep green	6.50	6.50
98	CD71	50c violet	6.50	6.50
99	CD72	90c red orange	6.50	6.50
100	CD73	1.50fr dull blue	6.50	6.50
		Nos. 97-100 (4)	26.00	26.00

Paris International Exposition Issue
Common Design Types

1937 Engr. Perf. 13

101	CD74	20c deep violet	2.00	2.00
102	CD75	30c dark green	2.00	2.00
103	CD76	40c car rose	2.00	2.00
104	CD77	50c dark brown	1.60	1.60
105	CD78	90c red	1.60	1.60
106	CD79	1.50fr ultra	2.40	2.40
		Nos. 101-106 (6)	11.60	11.60

Souvenir Sheet
Imperf

107	CD77	3fr dp blue & blk	12.00	16.00
a.		Inscription inverted	1,600.	1,600.

Caillié Issue
Common Design Type

1939, Apr. 5 Engr. Perf. 12½x12

108	CD81	90c org brn & org	.40	1.20
109	CD81	2fr brt violet	.40	1.20
110	CD81	2.25fr ultra & dk blue	.40	1.20
		Nos. 108-110 (3)	1.20	3.60

New York World's Fair Issue
Common Design Type

1939 Engr.

111	CD82	1.25fr car lake	.80	1.60
112	CD82	2.25fr ultra	.80	1.60

Man Poling a Canoe — A7

Pile House — A8

Sailboat on Lake Nokoué A9

Dahomey Warrior A10

1941 Perf. 13

113	A7	2c scarlet	.25	.25
114	A7	3c deep blue	.25	.25
115	A7	5c brown violet	.70	.70
116	A7	10c green	.30	.30
117	A7	15c black	.25	.25
118	A8	20c violet brown	.30	.30
119	A8	30c dk violet	.30	.30
120	A8	40c scarlet	.70	.70
121	A8	50c slate green	.95	.95
122	A8	60c black	.30	.30
123	A8	70c brt red violet	1.20	1.20
124	A9	80c brown black	1.20	1.20
125	A9	1fr violet	1.20	1.20
126	A9	1.30fr brown violet	1.20	1.20
127	A9	1.40fr green	1.20	1.20
128	A9	1.50fr brt rose	1.20	1.20
129	A9	2fr brown orange	1.20	1.20
130	A10	2.50fr dark blue	1.20	1.20
131	A10	3fr scarlet	1.20	1.20
132	A10	5fr slate green	1.20	1.20
133	A10	10fr violet brown	2.00	2.00
134	A10	20fr black	2.40	2.40
		Nos. 113-134 (22)	20.70	20.70

Nos. 121, 122 without "RF," see Nos. 136A-136B.

Pile House and Marshal Pétain — A11

1941 Perf. 12½x12

135	A11	1fr green	.80	—
136	A11	2.50fr blue	.80	—

For surcharges see Nos. B14A-B14B.

Type of 1941 without "RF"

1944 Perf. 13

136A	A8	50c slate green	1.20	
136B	A8	60c black	1.20	

Nos. 136A-136B were issued by the Vichy government in France, but were not placed on sale in Dahomey.

Catalogue values for unused stamps in this section, from this point to the end of the section, are for Never Hinged items.

Republic

Village
Ganvié
A12

Unwmk.
1960, Mar. 1   Engr.   Perf. 12
137 A12 25fr dk blue, brn & red   .65 .25

For overprint see No. 152.

Imperforates

Most Dahomey stamps from 1960 onward exist imperforate in issued and trial colors, and also in small presentation sheets in issued colors.

C.C.T.A. Issue
Common Design Type
1960, May 16
138 CD106 5fr rose lilac & ultra   .50 .25

Emblem of the
Entente — A13

Council of the Entente Issue
1960, May 29 Photo.   Perf. 13x13½
139 A13 25fr multicolored   .65 .40

1st anniv. of the Council of the Entente (Dahomey, Ivory Coast, Niger and Upper Volta).

Prime Minister Hubert
Maga — A14

1960, Aug.   Engr.   Perf. 13
140 A14 85fr deep claret & blk   1.60 .90

Issued on the occasion of Dahomey's proclamation of independence, Aug. 1, 1960. For surcharge see No. 149.

Weaver — A15

2fr, 10fr, Wood sculptor. 3fr, 15fr, Fisherman and net, horiz. 4fr, 20fr, Potter, horiz.

1961, Feb. 17   Engr.   Perf. 13
141 A15 1fr red, org & carmine   .25 .25
142 A15 2fr bister brn & choc   .25 .25
143 A15 3fr green & orange   .25 .25
144 A15 4fr olive bis & dp clar   .25 .25
145 A15 6fr rose, lt vio & ver   .40 .25
146 A15 10fr blue & green   .55 .40
147 A15 15fr red lilac & violet   .75 .40
148 A15 20fr bluish vio & Prus bl   .90 .55
    Nos. 141-148 (8)   3.60 2.60

For surcharges see Benin No. 1374, Dahomey #Q1-Q7.

No. 140 Surcharged in
Black

1961, Aug. 1
149 A14 100fr on 85fr dp cl & blk 3.25 3.25

First anniversary of Independence.

Doves, UN Building and
Emblem — A16

1961, Sept. 20   Unwmk.   Perf. 13
150 A16 5fr multicolored   .35 .25
151 A16 60fr multicolored   1.20 .90

1st anniv. of Dahomey's admission to the UN. See No. C16 and souvenir sheet No. C16a.

No. 137 Overprinted in Black

1961, Dec. 24
152 A12 25fr dk blue, brn & red   .65 .40

Abidjan Games, Dec 24-31.

Interior of Burned-out
Fort Ouidah and
Wrecked Car — A17

1962, July 31   Photo.   Perf. 12½
153 A17 30fr multicolored   .45 .45
154 A17 60fr multicolored   .75 .60

Evacuation of Fort Ouidah by the Portuguese, and its occupation by Dahomey. 1st anniv.

African and Malgache Union Issue
Common Design Type
1962, Sept. 8   Perf. 12½x12
155 CD110 30fr red lil, bluish grn, red & gold   1.25 .90

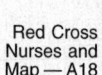

Red Cross
Nurses and
Map — A18

1962, Oct. 5   Engr.   Perf. 13
156 A18 5fr blue, choc & red   .30 .25
157 A18 20fr blue, dk grn & red   .60 .45
158 A18 25fr blue, brown & red   .65 .45
159 A18 30fr blue, black & red   .85 .70
    Nos. 156-159 (4)   2.40 1.85

Ganvié
Woman in
Canoe
A19

Peuhl Herdsman
and Cattle
A20

Designs: 3fr, 65fr, Bariba chief of Nikki. 15fr, 50fr, Ouidah witch doctor, rock python. 20fr, 30fr, Nessoukoué women carrying vases on heads, Abomey. 25fr, 40fr, Dahomey girl. 60fr, Peuhl herdsman and cattle. 85fr, Ganvié woman in canoe.

1963, Feb. 18   Unwmk.   Perf. 13
160 A19 2fr grnsh blue & vio   .25 .25
161 A19 3fr blue & black   .25 .25
162 A20 5fr brown, blk & grn   .35 .25
163 A19 15fr brn, bl grn & red brn   .35 .25
164 A19 20fr green, blk & car   .30 .25
165 A20 25fr dk brn, bl & bl grn   .40 .25
166 A19 30fr brn org, choc & mag   .60 .40
167 A20 40fr choc, grn & brt bl   1.00 .40
168 A19 50fr blk, grn, brn & red brn   1.60 .55
169 A20 60fr choc, org red & ol   3.50 1.00

---

170 A19 65fr orange brn & choc   1.75 .65
171 A19 85fr brt blue & choc   2.50 1.00
    Nos. 160-171 (12)   12.85 5.50

For surcharges see Nos. 211, 232-233, Benin 655A, 690F, 700, 722, 1375, 1417.

Boxers — A21

Designs: 1fr, 20fr, Soccer goalkeeper, horiz. 2fr, 5fr, Runners.

1963, Apr. 11   Engr.
172 A21 50c green & black   .25 .25
173 A21 1fr olive, blk & brn   .25 .25
174 A21 2fr olive, blue & brn   .25 .25
175 A21 5fr brown, crim & blk   .25 .25
176 A21 15fr dk violet & brn   .35 .25
177 A21 20fr multicolored   .55 .55
    Nos. 172-177 (6)   1.90 1.80

Friendship Games, Dakar, Apr. 11-21. For surcharges & overprint see Benin Nos. 697, 704, 716, 1372, 1382, 1384.

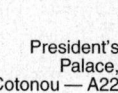

President's
Palace,
Cotonou — A22

1963, Aug. 1   Photo.   Perf. 12½x12
178 A22 25fr multicolored   .45 .25

Third anniversary of independence.

Gen. Toussaint
L'Ouverture — A23

1963, Nov. 18   Unwmk.   Perf. 12x13
179 A23 25fr multicolored   .55 .25
180 A23 30fr multicolored   .70 .25
181 A23 100fr ultra, brn & red   1.60 .80
    Nos. 179-181 (3)   2.85 1.30

Pierre Dominique Toussaint L'Ouverture (1743-1803), Haitian gen., statesman and descendant of the kings of Allada (Dahomey). For overprint, see Benin No. 1367. For surcharge, see Benin No. 1466.

UN Emblem, Flame,
"15" — A24

1963, Dec. 10   Perf. 12
182 A24 4fr multicolored   .25 .25
183 A24 6fr multicolored   .25 .25
184 A24 25fr multicolored   .45 .25
    Nos. 182-184 (3)   .95 .75

15th anniversary of the Universal Declaration of Human Rights. For surcharge, see Benin No. 1377.

Somba Dance — A25

Regional Dances: 3fr, Nago dance, Pobe-Ketou, horiz. 10fr, Dance of the baton. 15fr, Nago dance, Ouidah, horiz. 25fr, Dance of the Sakpatassi. 30fr, Dance of the Nes-souhouessi, horiz.

1964, Aug. 8   Engr.   Perf. 13
185 A25 2fr red, emerald & blk   .25 .25
186 A25 3fr dull red, blue & grn   .25 .25
187 A25 10fr purple, blk & red   .45 .25
188 A25 15fr magenta, blk & grn   .45 .25
189 A25 25fr Prus blue, brn & org   .90 .30
190 A25 30fr dk red, choc & org   1.15 .40
    Nos. 185-190 (6)   3.45 1.70

Runner
A26

1964, Oct. 20   Photo.   Perf. 11
191 A26 60fr shown   1.60 1.00
192 A26 85fr Bicyclist   2.75 1.40

18th Olympic Games, Tokyo, Oct. 10-25.

Cooperation Issue
Common Design Type
1964, Nov. 7   Engr.   Perf. 13
193 CD119 25fr org, vio & dk brn   .80 .35

UNICEF Emblem,
Mother and Child — A27

25fr, Mother holding child in her arms.

1964, Dec. 11   Unwmk.   Perf. 13
194 A27 20fr yel grn, dk red & blk   .40 .25
195 A27 25fr blue, dk red & blk   .60 .45

18th anniv. of UNICEF. For overprints, see Benin Nos. 691A, and 1368.

IQSY Emblem and
Apollo — A28

100fr, IQSY emblem, Nimbus weather satellite.

1964, Dec. 22 Photo.   Perf. 13x12½
196 A28 25fr green & lt yellow   .55 .25
197 A28 100fr deep plum & yellow 2.00 .95

International Quiet Sun Year, 1964-65.

Abomey
Tapestry — A29

Designs (Abomey tapestries): 25fr, Warrior and fight scenes. 50fr, Birds and warriors, horiz. 85fr, Animals, ship and plants, horiz.

1965, Apr. 12   Photo.   Perf. 12½
198 A29 20fr multicolored   .80 .25
199 A29 25fr multicolored   .95 .40
200 A29 50fr multicolored   1.50 .80
201 A29 85fr multicolored   3.25 1.10
    a. Min. sheet of 4, #198-201   8.00 8.00
    Nos. 198-201 (4)   6.50 2.55

Issued to publicize the local rug weaving industry.

Baudot Telegraph Distributor and Ader Telephone — A30

1965, May 17   Engr.   Perf. 13
202 A30 100fr lilac, org & blk   1.75 1.60
Cent. of the ITU.

Cotonou Harbor — A31

100fr, Cotonou Harbor, denomination at left.

1965, Aug. 1   Photo.   Perf. 12½
203   25fr multicolored   1.10 .25
204   100fr multicolored   2.50 1.10
a.   A31 Pair, #203-204   4.50 1.10
The opening of Cotonou Harbor. No. 204a has a continuous design.
For surcharges see Nos. 219-220.

Cybium Tritor — A32

Fish: 25fr, Dentex filosus. 30fr, Atlantic sailfish. 50fr, Blackish tripletail.

1965, Sept. 20   Engr.   Perf. 13
205 A32 10fr black & brt blue   .75 .25
206 A32 25fr brt blue, org & blk   1.00 .55
207 A32 30fr violet bl & grnsh bl   1.75 .80
208 A32 50fr black, gray bl & org   2.75 1.00
     Nos. 205-208 (4)   6.25 2.60

For surcharge see Benin No. 911.

Independence Monument — A33

1965, Oct. 28   Photo.   Perf. 12x12½
209 A33 25fr gray, black & red   .40 .25
210 A33 30fr lt ultra, black & red   .65 .25
October 28 Revolution, 2nd anniv. For surcharge, see Benin No. 1385.

No. 165 Surcharged

1965, Nov.   Engr.   Perf. 13
211 A20 1fr on 25fr   .30 .25

Porto Novo Cathedral — A34

Designs: 50fr, Ouidah Pro-Cathedral, vert. 70fr, Cotonou Cathedral.

1966, Mar. 21   Engr.   Perf. 13
212 A34 30fr Prus bl, vio brn & grn   .55 .25
213 A34 50fr vio brn, Prus bl & brn   .70 .50
214 A34 70fr grn, Prus bl & vio brn   1.25 .75
     Nos. 212-214 (3)   2.50 1.50

Jewelry — A35

Designs: 30fr, Architecture. 50fr, Musician. 70fr, Crucifixion, sculpture.

1966, Apr. 4   Engr.   Perf. 13
215 A35 15fr dull red brn & blk   .45 .25
216 A35 30fr dk brn, ultra & brn red   .70 .25
217 A35 50fr brt blue & dk brn   1.20 .55
218 A35 70fr red brown & blk   2.50 .85
     Nos. 215-218 (4)   4.85 2.10
International Negro Arts Festival, Dakar, Senegal, Apr. 1-24.

Nos. 203-204 Surcharged

1966, Apr. 24   Photo.   Perf. 12½
219 A31 15fr on 25fr multi   .55 .35
220 A31 15fr on 100fr multi   .55 .35
a.   Pair, #219-220   1.50 1.10
Fifth anniversary of the Cooperation Agreement between France and Dahomey.

WHO Headquarters from the East — A36

1966, May 3   Perf. 12½x13
Size: 35x22½mm
221 A36 30fr multicolored   .75 .25
Inauguration of the WHO Headquarters, Geneva. See No. C32.
For surcharge see Benin No. 717.

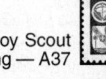

Boy Scout Signaling — A37

Designs: 10fr, Patrol standard with pennant, vert. 30fr, Campfire and map of Dahomey, vert. 50fr, Scouts building foot bridge.

1966, Oct. 17   Engr.   Perf. 13
222 A37 5fr dk brn, ocher & red   .30 .25
223 A37 10fr black, grn & rose cl   .30 .25
224 A37 30fr org, red brn & pur   .70 .35
225 A37 50fr vio bl, grn & dk brn   1.20 .45
a.   Min. sheet of 4, #222-225   3.00 3.00
     Nos. 222-225 (4)   2.50 1.30

Clappertonia Ficifolia — A38

Flowers: 3fr, Hewittia sublobata. 5fr, Butterfly pea. 10fr, Water lily. 15fr, Commelina forskalaei. 30fr, Eremomastax speciosa.

1967, Feb. 20   Photo.   Perf. 12x12½
226 A38 1fr multicolored   .25 .25
227 A38 3fr multicolored   .35 .25
228 A38 5fr multicolored   .55 .25
229 A38 10fr multicolored   .90 .35
230 A38 15fr multicolored   1.10 .55
231 A38 30fr multicolored   2.10 .90
     Nos. 226-231 (6)   5.25 2.55

For surcharges see Benin Nos. 707, 715, 1376, 1390, 1402.

Nos. 170-171 Surcharged

1967, Mar. 1   Engr.   Perf. 13
232 A19 30fr on 65fr   .85 .60
a.   Double surcharge   36.00

233 A19 30fr on 85fr   .85 .60
a.   Double surcharge   60.00
b.   Inverted surcharge   60.00

Lions Emblem, Dancing Children, Bird — A39

1967, Mar. 20
234 A39 100fr dl vio, dp bl & grn   1.50 1.10
50th anniversary of Lions International.

"Man in the City" Pavilion — A40

"The New Africa" Exhibit — A40a

1967, June 12   Engr.   Perf. 13
235 A40 30fr green & choc   .70 .25
236 A40a 70fr green & brn red   1.50 .65
EXPO '67, International Exhibition, Montreal, Apr. 28-Oct. 27, 1967. See No. C57 and miniature sheet No. C57a.
For overprint, see Benin No. 897.

Europafrica Issue

Trade (Blood) Circulation, Map of Europe and Africa — A41

1967, July 20   Photo.   Perf. 12x12½
237 A41 30fr multicolored   .70 .25
238 A41 45fr multicolored   1.10 .45
For surcharge, see Benin No. 1386.

Scouts Climbing Mountain, Jamboree Emblem — A42

70fr, Jamboree emblem, Scouts launching canoe.

1967, Aug. 7   Engr.   Perf. 13
239 A42 30fr brt bl, red brn & sl   .80 .25
240 A42 70fr brt bl, sl grn & dk brn   1.60 .65
12th Boy Scout World Jamboree, Farragut State Park, Idaho, Aug. 1-9. For souvenir sheet see No. C59a.
For surcharges see Benin Nos. 902, 912, 1391.

Rhone River and Olympic Emblems — A43

Designs (Olympic Emblems and): 45fr, View of Grenoble, vert. 100fr, Rhone Bridge, Grenoble, and Pierre de Coubertin.

1967, Sept. 2   Engr.   Perf. 13
241 A43 30fr bis, dp bl & grn   .70 .40
242 A43 45fr ultra, grn & brn   .90 .55
243 A43 100fr choc, grn & brt bl   2.25 1.00
a.   Min. sheet of 3, #241-243   4.50 4.50
     Nos. 241-243 (3)   3.85 1.95
10th Winter Olympic Games, Grenoble, Feb. 6-18, 1968.
For surcharges, see Benin Nos. 903, 1054E, 1054F, 1392.

Monetary Union Issue
Common Design Type

1967, Nov. 4   Engr.   Perf. 13
244 CD125 30fr grn, dk car & dk brn   .65 .65

Animals from the Pendjari Reservation A45

Designs: 15fr, Cape Buffalo. 30fr, Lion. 45fr, Buffon's kob. 70fr, African slender-snouted crocodile. 100fr, Hippopotamus.

1968, Mar. 18   Photo.   Perf. 12½x13
245 A45 15fr multicolored   .55 .25
246 A45 30fr purple & multi   .65 .50
247 A45 45fr blue & multi   1.25 .60
248 A45 70fr multicolored   2.25 .75
249 A45 100fr multicolored   4.00 2.25
     Nos. 245-249 (5)   8.70 4.35
See Nos. 252-256.
For surcharges see No. 310, Benin Nos. 655E, 725, 1415, 1420, 1421.

WHO Emblem — A46

1968, Apr. 22   Engr.   Perf. 13
250 A46 30fr multicolored   .60 .25
251 A46 70fr multicolored   1.40 .70
20th anniv. of WHO. For surcharges, see Benin Nos. 1012, 1387, 1465.

Animals from the Pendjari Reservation A47

Animals: 5fr, Warthog. 30fr, Leopard. 60fr, Spotted hyena. 75fr, Anubius baboon. 90fr, Hartebeest.

1969, Feb. 10   Photo.   Perf. 12½x12
252 A47 5fr dark brown & multi   .25 .25
253 A47 30fr deep ultra & multi   .70 .50
254 A47 60fr dark green & multi   1.25 .70
255 A47 75fr dark blue & multi   3.00 1.00
256 A47 90fr dark green & multi   4.00 2.25
     Nos. 252-256 (5)   9.20 4.70

For surcharges, see Benin Nos. 708, 1438.

Heads, Symbols of Agriculture and Science, and Globe — A48

1969, Mar. 10   Engr.   Perf. 13
257 A48 30fr orange & multi   .50 .25
258 A48 70fr maroon & multi   1.50 .70
50th anniv. of the ILO.
For surcharges see Benin Nos. 904, 913.

Arms of Dahomey A49

1969, June 30   Litho.   Perf. 13½x13
259 A49 5fr yellow & multi   .35 .30
260 A49 30fr orange red & multi   1.50 .45
See No. C101.

Development Bank Issue

Cornucopia and Bank Emblem — A50

1969, Sept. 10   Photo.   Perf. 13
261 A50 30fr black, grn & ocher   .75 .55

African Development Bank, 5th anniv. For surcharge see Benin No. 905.

Europafrica Issue

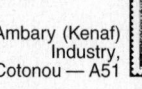

Ambary (Kenaf) Industry, Cotonou — A51

Design: 45fr, Cotton industry, Parakou.

1969, Sept. 22   Litho.   Perf. 14
262 A51 30fr multicolored   1.00 .50
263 A51 45fr multicolored   1.25 .75

See Nos. C105-C105a. For overprints and surcharges see Benin No. 1054A.

Sakpata Dance and Tourist Year Emblem — A52

Dances and Tourist Year Emblem: 30fr, Guelede dance. 45fr, Sato dance.

1969, Dec. 15   Litho.   Perf. 14
264 A52 10fr multicolored   .75 .30
265 A52 30fr multicolored   1.45 .45
266 A52 45fr multicolored   2.00 .50
Nos. 264-266 (3)   4.20 1.30

See No. C108. For surcharges see Benin Nos. 690J, 1054B, 1388, 1433.

UN Emblem, Garden and Wall — A53

1970, Apr. 6   Engr.   Perf. 13
267 A53 30fr ultra, red org & slate   .70 .25
268 A53 40fr ultra, brn & sl grn   1.25 .50

25th anniversary of the United Nations. For surcharge see No. 294. For overprint see Benin 647B.

ASECNA Issue
Common Design Type
1970, June 1   Engr.   Perf. 13
269 CD132 40fr red & purple   .90 .55

For surcharges, see Benin Nos. 906, 1396.

Mt. Fuji, EXPO '70 Emblem, Monorail Train — A54

1970, June 15   Litho.   Perf. 13½x14
270 A54 5fr green, red & vio bl   .40 .25

EXPO '70 International Exhibition, Osaka, Japan, 3/15-9/13/70. See Nos. C124-C125.

Alkemy, King of Ardres — A55

40fr, Sailing ships "La Justice" & "La Concorde," Ardres, 1670. 50fr, Matheo Lopes, ambassador of the King of Ardres & his coat of arms. 200fr, Louis XIV & fleur-de-lis.

1970, July 6   Engr.   Perf. 13
271 A55 40fr brt grn, ultra & brn   .75 .25
272 A55 50fr dk car, choc & emer   1.05 .40
273 A55 70fr gray, lemon & choc   1.60 .65
274 A55 200fr Prus bl, dk car & choc   4.00 1.25
Nos. 271-274 (4)   7.40 2.55

300th anniv. of the mission from the King of Ardres to the King of France, and of the audience with Louis XIV on Dec. 19, 1670. For surcharges see Benin Nos. 721, 724, 914.

Star of the Order of Independence — A56

1970, Aug. 1   Photo.   Perf. 12
275 A56 30fr multicolored   .40 .25
276 A56 40fr multicolored   .60 .25

10th anniversary of independence. For surcharge see Benin Nos. 720, 1464.

Bariba Warrior — A57

Designs: 2fr, 50fr, Two horsemen. 10fr, 70fr, Horseman facing left.

1970, Aug. 24   Perf. 12½x13
277 A57 1fr yellow & multi   .30 .25
278 A57 2fr gray grn & multi   .45 .25
279 A57 10fr blue & multi   .60 .25
280 A57 40fr yellow grn & multi   1.90 .35
281 A57 50fr gold & multi   2.40 .50
282 A57 70fr lilac rose & multi   3.00 .80
Nos. 277-282 (6)   8.65 2.40

For surcharges see Benin Nos. 350-351, 613, 703, 1373, 1401.

Globe and Heart — A58

Design: 40fr, Hands holding heart, vert.

1971, June 7   Engr.   Perf. 13
283 A58 40fr red, green & dk brn   2.00 .50
284 A58 100fr green, red & blue   4.00 1.25

For surcharges see Benin Nos. 617, 647A, 712, 907, 1429.

Intl. year against racial discrimination.

Ancestral Figures and Lottery Ticket — A59

1971, June 24   Litho.   Perf. 14
285 A59 35fr multicolored   .80 .25
286 A59 40fr multicolored   1.25 .35

4th anniv. of the National Lottery.

For overprint and surcharge, see Benin Nos. 710, 1430.

King Behanzin's Emblem (1889-1894) — A60

Emblems of the Kings of Abomey: 25fr, Agoliagbo (1894-1900). 35fr, Ganyehoussou (1620-45), bird and cup, horiz. 100fr, Guezo (1818-58), bull, tree and birds. 135fr, Ouegbadja (1645-85), horiz. 140fr, Glèle (1858-89), lion and sword, horiz.

Photo.; Litho. (25fr, 135fr)
1971-72   Perf. 12½
287 A60 25fr multicolored   .55 .25
288 A60 35fr green & multi   .90 .25
289 A60 40fr green & multi   1.25 .55
290 A60 100fr red & multi   2.25 .90
291 A60 135fr multicolored   3.25 1.40
292 A60 140fr brown & multi   3.75 1.90
Nos. 287-292 (6)   11.95 5.25

Issued: 25fr, 135fr, 7/17/72; others, 8/3/71. For surcharges and overprint, see Benin Nos. 614, 634B, 708A, 726, 791, 1054D, 1369, 1422, 1431, 1467, 1470.

Kabuki Actor, Long-distance Skiing — A61

1972, Feb.   Engr.   Perf. 13
293 A61 35fr dk car, brn & bl grn 2.50 .75

11th Winter Olympic Games, Sapporo, Japan, Feb. 3-13. See No. C153.

No. 268 Surcharged

1972
294 A53 35fr on 40fr multi   .90 .35

Brahms and "Soir d'été" — A62

Design: 65fr, Brahms, woman at piano & music, horiz.

1972, June 29   Engr.   Perf. 13
295 A62 30fr red brn, blk & lilac   4.00 .80
296 A62 65fr red brn, blk & lilac   6.75 1.50

75th anniversary of the death of Johannes Brahms (1833-1897), German composer. For surcharges see Benin Nos. 654B, 718, 1389.

The Hare and The Tortoise, by La Fontaine — A63

Fables: 35fr, The Fox and The Stork, vert. 40fr, The Cat, The Weasel and Rabbit.

1972, Aug. 28   Engr.   Perf. 13
297 A63 10fr multicolored   2.25 .75
298 A63 35fr dark red & multi   4.25 1.25
299 A63 40fr ultra & multi   5.50 1.75
Nos. 297-299 (3)   12.00 3.75

Jean de La Fontaine (1621-1695), French fabulist. For surcharges, see Benin Nos. 1380, 1393, 1397.

West African Monetary Union Issue
Common Design Type
1972, Nov. 2   Engr.   Perf. 13
300 CD136 40fr choc, ocher & gray   .65 .25

Dr. Armauer Hansen, Microscope, Bacilli — A65

Design: 85fr, Portrait of Dr. Hansen.

1973, May 14   Engr.   Perf. 13
301 A65 35fr ultra, vio brn & brn   .50 .35
302 A65 85fr yel grn, bis & ver   1.25 .75

Centenary of the discovery by Dr. Armauer G. Hansen of the Hansen bacillus, the cause of leprosy. For surcharges see Benin Nos. 655G, 1084, 1437.

Arms of Dahomey — A66

1973, June 25   Photo.   Perf. 13
303 A66 5fr ultra & multi   .25 .25
304 A66 35fr ocher & multi   .40 .25
305 A66 40fr red orange & multi   .60 .25
Nos. 303-305 (3)   1.25 .75

For overprint and surcharge see Benin Nos. 690A, 1403.

INTERPOL Emblem and Spiderweb — A67

Design: 50fr, INTERPOL emblem and communications symbols, vert.

1973, July   Engr.
306 A67 35fr ver, grn & brn   .60 .30
307 A67 50fr green, brn & red   .85 .45

50th anniversary of International Criminal Police Organization (INTERPOL). For overprints and surcharges, see Benin Nos. 634A, 810, 1011, 1434, 1471.

Education in Hygiene and Nutrition — A68

WHO, 25th Anniv.: 100fr, Prenatal examination and care, WHO emblem.

1973, Aug. 2   Photo.   Perf. 12½x13
308 A68 35fr multicolored   .50 .30
309 A68 100fr multicolored   1.50 .65

For surcharges, see Benin Nos. 655B, 1439.

No. 248 Srchd. and Ovptd. in Red

1973, Aug. 16
310 A45 100fr on 70fr multi   2.50 1.00

African solidarity in drought emergency.

African Postal Union Issue
Common Design Type

1973, Sept. 12   Engr.   *Perf. 13*
311 CD137 100fr red, purple &
     blk   1.25   .55

For surcharges, see Benin Nos. 690l, 1440.

Epinephelus
Aeneus
A69

Fish: 15fr, Drepane africana. 35fr, Pragus
ehrenbergi.

1973, Sept. 18
312 A69   5fr slate blue & indigo   1.00   .30
313 A69   15fr black & brt blue   1.50   .35
314 A69   35fr emerald, ocher &
     sep   4.00   .60
   Nos. 312-314 (3)   6.50   1.25

For surcharges, see Benin No. 698, 1378,
1383, 1394.

Chameleon
A70

40fr, Emblem over map of Dahomey, vert.

1973, Nov. 30   Photo.   *Perf. 13*
315 A70 35fr olive & multi   .55   .30
316 A70 40fr multicolored   1.25   .35

1st anniv. of the Oct. 26 revolution.

The
Chameleon
in the
Tree — A71

Designs: 5fr, The elephant, the hen and the
dog, vert. 10fr, The sparrowhawk and the dog,
vert. 25fr, The chameleon in the tree. 40fr, The
eagle, the viper and the hen.

1974, Feb. 14   Photo.   *Perf. 13*
317 A71   5fr emerald & multi   .75   .25
318 A71   10fr slate blue & multi   .90   .25
319 A71   25fr slate blue & multi   1.75   .30
320 A71   40fr light blue & multi   2.50   .45
   Nos. 317-320 (4)   5.90   1.25

Folktales of Dahomey.
For surcharges and overprint see Benin
Nos. 699, 709, 908, 1363, 1370, 1379, 1381,
1432.

German
Shepherd
A72

1974, Apr. 25   Photo.   *Perf. 13*
321 A72   40fr shown   1.50   .35
322 A72   50fr Boxer   1.75   .35
323 A72   100fr Saluki   3.50   .80
   Nos. 321-323 (3)   6.75   1.50

For surcharges, see Benin No. 1398, 1435,
1441.

Council Issue

Map and Flags of
Members — A73

1974, May 29   Photo.   *Perf. 13x12½*
324 A73 40fr blue & multi   .80   .25

15th anniversary of the Council of Accord.

Locomotive
232,
1911 — A74

Designs: Locomotives.

1974, Sept. 2   Photo.   *Perf. 13x12½*
325 A74   35fr shown   1.00   .30
326 A74   40fr Freight, 1877   2.00   .30
327 A74   100fr Crampton, 1849   3.00   1.00
328 A74   200fr Stephenson,
     1846   6.00   1.60
   Nos. 325-328 (4)   12.00   3.20

For overprints and surcharges see Benin
Nos. 654E, 690D, 690K, 727, 909, 1395,
1399, 1442, 1444.

Globe, Money,
People in
Bank — A75

1974, Oct. 31   Engr.   *Perf. 13*
329 A75 35fr multicolored   .50   .35

World Savings Day. For surcharge, see
Benin No. 1468.

Dompago Dance,
Hissi Tribe — A76

Folk Dances: 25fr, Fetish Dance, Vaudou-
Tchinan. 40fr, Bamboo Dance, Agbehoun.
100fr, Somba Dance, Sandoua, horiz.

1975, Aug. 4   Litho.   *Perf. 12*
330 A76   10fr yellow & multi   .65   .25
331 A76   25fr dk green & multi   1.25   .25
332 A76   40fr red & multi   1.60   .50
333 A76   100fr multicolored   3.00   .60
   Nos. 330-333 (4)   6.50   1.60

For surcharges and overprints see Benin
Nos. 655D, 690C, 713, 1371,1404, 1414,
1443.

Flags of Dahomey
and Nigeria over
Africa — A77

Design: 100fr, Arrows connecting maps of
Dahomey and Nigeria, horiz.

1975, Aug. 11   Photo.   *Perf. 12½x13*
334 A77   65fr multicolored   .75   .25
335 A77   100fr green & multi   1.00   .45

Year of intensified cooperation between
Dahomey and Nigeria.
For surcharges & overprint see Benin Nos.
690H, 701, 899, 901, 1419, 1423.

Map,
Pylons,
Emblem
A78

Benin Electric
Community Emblem
and Pylon — A79

1975, Aug. 18
336 A78 40fr multicolored   .75   .35
337 A79 150fr multicolored   2.00   1.00

Benin Electric Community and Ghana-Togo-
Dahomey cooperation.
For surcharges see Benin Nos. 601, 900,
910, 1400, 1405, Q12A, Q12B.

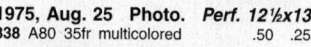

Map of Dahomey,
Rising Sun — A80

1975, Aug. 25   Photo.   *Perf. 12½x13*
338 A80 35fr multicolored   .50   .25

Cooperation Year for the creation of a new
Dahoman society.
For overprint see Benin No. 690E. For
surcharge, see Benin No. 1362.

Albert Schweitzer,
Nurse, Patient — A81

1975, Sept. 22   Engr.   *Perf. 13*
339 A81 200fr olive, grn & red
     brn   6.25   1.50

Birth centenary of Albert Schweitzer (1875-
1965), medical missionary and musician.
For surcharges, see Benin Nos. 655F, 1445.

Woman Speaking on
Telephone, IWY
Emblem — A82

150fr, IWY emblem and linked rings.

1975, Oct. 20   Engr.   *Perf. 12½x13*
340 A82   50fr Prus blue & lilac   .75   .35
341 A82   150fr emerald, brn & org   2.00   .80

International Women's Year 1975.
For surcharges, see Benin Nos. 655C,
1054C, 1436, 1469.

SEMI-POSTAL STAMPS

Regular Issue of 1913
Surcharged in Red

1915   Unwmk.   *Perf. 14x13½*
B1   A5   10c + 5c orange
     red & rose   1.60   1.60

Curie Issue
Common Design Type

1938   *Perf. 13*
B2   CD80 1.75fr + 50c brt
     ultra   9.50   9.50

French Revolution Issue
Common Design Type

1939   Photo.
Name and Value Typo. in Black
B3 CD83   45c + 25c green   9.50   9.50
B4 CD83   70c + 30c brown   9.50   9.50
B5 CD83   90c + 35c red org   9.50   9.50
B6 CD83   1.25fr + 1fr rose pink   9.50   9.50
B7 CD83   2.25fr + 2fr blue   9.50   9.50
   Nos. B3-B7 (5)   47.50   47.50

Postage Stamps of 1913-
38 Surcharged in Black

1941   *Perf. 13½x14*
B8   A5   50c + 1fr brn red &
     bl   3.25   3.25
B9   A5   80c + 2fr hn brn &
     ultra   7.25   7.25
B10 A5   1.50fr + 2fr dk bl & lt bl   7.25   7.25
B11 A5   2fr + 3fr yel org &
     choc   7.25   7.25
   Nos. B8-B11 (4)   25.00   25.00

Common Design Type and

Radio   Senegalese
Operator   Artillerymen
SP1   SP2

1941   Photo.   *Perf. 13½*
B12 SP1   1fr + 1fr red   1.20
B13 CD86   1.50fr + 3fr claret
B14 SP2   2.50fr + 1fr blue   1.20
   Nos. B12-B14 (3)   3.60

Surtax for the defense of the colonies.
Nos. B12-B14 were issued by the Vichy
government in France, but were not placed on
sale in Dahomey.

Nos. 135-136
Srchd. in Black or
Red

1944   Engr.   *Perf. 12½x12*
B14A   50c + 1.50fr on 2.50fr deep
     blue (R)   .80
B14B   + 2.50fr on 1fr green   .80

Colonial Development Fund.
Nos. B14A-B14B were issued by the Vichy
government in France, but were not placed on
sale in Dahomey.

> **Catalogue values for unused
> stamps in this section, from this
> point to the end of the section, are
> for Never Hinged items.**

Republic
Anti-Malaria Issue
Common Design Type

1962, Apr. 7   Engr.   *Perf. 12½x12*
B15 CD108 25fr + 5fr orange brn   .75   .75

Freedom from Hunger Issue
Common Design Type

1963, Mar. 21   Unwmk.   *Perf. 13*
B16 CD112 25fr + 5fr ol, brn red
     & brn   .80   .80

AIR POST STAMPS

Common Design Type

1940   Unwmk.   Engr.   *Perf. 12½*
C1 CD85 1.90fr ultra   .40   .40
C2 CD85 2.90fr dk red   .40   .40
C3 CD85 4.50fr dk gray grn   .80   .80

C4	CD85	4.90fr yel bister	.80	.80
C5	CD85	6.90fr deep org	1.60	1.60
		Nos. C1-C5 (5)	4.00	4.00

Common Design Types

1942

C6	CD88	50c car & bl	.30
C7	CD88	1fr brn & blk	.30
C8	CD88	2fr dk grn & red brn	.50
C9	CD88	3fr dk bl & scar	.95
C10	CD88	5fr vio & brn red	1.05

Frame Engr., Center Typo.

C11	CD89	10fr ultra, ind & org	1.05
C12	CD89	20fr rose car, mag & gray blk	1.10
C13	CD89	50fr yel grn, dl grn & dp bl	1.90 3.25
a.		50fr yellow green, dull green & pale blue	2.75 3.75
		Nos. C6-C13 (8)	7.15

Nos. C6-C12 were issued by the Vichy government in France, but were not placed on sale in Dahomey.

> **Catalogue values for unused stamps in this section, from this point to the end of the section, are for Never Hinged items.**

Republic

Somba House
AP4

Design: 500fr, Royal Court of Abomey.

Unwmk.

1960, Apr. 1		**Engr.**		***Perf. 13***
C14	AP4	100fr multi	3.25	.80
C15	AP4	500fr multi	13.50	4.00

For overprint see Benin Nos. C419, C541. For surcharges, see No. CQ5, Benin No. C609.

Type of Regular Issue, 1961

1961, Sept. 20				
C16	A16	200fr multi	3.50	2.25
a.		Souv. sheet of 3, #150-151, C16	7.00	7.00

Air Afrique Issue
Common Design Type

1962, Feb. 17				***Perf. 13***
C17	CD107	25fr ultra, blk & org brn	.80	.40

Palace of the African and Malgache Union, Cotonou
AP5

1963, July 27		**Photo.**		***Perf. 13x12***
C18	AP5	250fr multi	5.00	2.75

Assembly of chiefs of state of the African and Malgache Union held at Cotonou in July.

African Postal Union Issue
Common Design Type

1963, Sept. 8		**Unwmk.**		***Perf. 12½***
C19	CD114	25fr brt bl, ocher & red	.75	.25

See note after Cameroun No. C47.

Boeing 707 — AP6

Boeing 707: 200fr, On the ground. 300fr, Over Cotonou airport. 500fr, In the air.

1963, Oct. 25		**Engr.**		***Perf. 13***
C20	AP6	100fr multi	2.00	.60
C21	AP6	200fr multi	3.00	2.00
C22	AP6	300fr multi	5.00	2.00
C23	AP6	500fr multi	10.00	2.50
		Nos. C20-C23 (4)	20.00	7.10

For surcharges see Nos. CQ1-CQ5, Benin No. C610.

Priests Carrying Funerary Boat, Isis Temple, Philae
AP7

1964, Mar. 9		**Unwmk.**		***Perf. 13***
C24	AP7	25fr vio bl & brn	2.00	.95

UNESCO world campaign to save historic monuments in Nubia.

Weather Map and Symbols
AP8

1965, Mar. 23		**Photo.**		***Perf. 12½***
C25	AP8	50fr multi		.80 .55

Fifth World Meteorological Day.

ICY Emblem and Men of Various Races
AP9

1965, June 26		**Engr.**		***Perf. 13***
C26	AP9	25fr dl pur, mar & grn	.65	.25
C27	AP9	85fr dp bl, mar & sl grn	1.25	.80

International Cooperation Year, 1965

Winston Churchill — AP10

1965, June 15		**Photo.**		***Perf. 12½***
C28	AP10	100fr multi	2.25	1.75

For surcharges, see Benin Nos. C519, C611.

Abraham Lincoln
AP11

1965, July 15				***Perf. 13***
C29	AP11	100fr multi	2.00	1.00

Centenary of death of Lincoln
For surcharge see No. C55.

John F. Kennedy and Arms of Dahomey
AP12

1965, Nov. 22		**Photo.**		***Perf. 12½***
C30	AP12	100fr dp grn & blk	2.75	1.10

President John F. Kennedy (1917-63).
For surcharge see No. C56.

Dr. Albert Schweitzer and Patients
AP13

1966, Jan. 17		**Photo.**		***Perf. 12½***
C31	AP13	100fr multi	3.00	1.25

Dr. Albert Schweitzer (1875-1965), medical missionary, theologian and musician.
For surcharge see Benin No. C435.

WHO Type of Regular Issue
Design: WHO Headquarters from the West.

1966, May 3		**Unwmk.**		***Perf. 13***
		Size: 47x28mm		
C32	A36	100fr ultra, yel & blk	1.75	1.50

Pygmy Goose
AP14

Broad-billed Rollers
AP15

Birds: 100fr, Fiery-breasted bush-shrike. 250fr, Emerald cuckoos. 500fr, Emerald starling.

1966-67				***Perf. 12½***
C33	AP14	50fr multi	2.00	.55
C34	AP14	100fr multi	3.00	.85
C35	AP15	200fr multi	10.00	2.25
C36	AP15	250fr multi	10.00	3.00
C37	AP14	500fr multi	15.00	6.00
		Nos. C33-C37 (5)	40.00	12.65

Issued: 50fr, 100fr, 500fr, 6/13/66; others, 1/20/67.
For overprints and surcharges see No. C107, Benin Nos. 1472, C353-C355, C357, C368, C426, C436, C511, C550, C590.

Industrial Symbols — AP16

1966, July 21		**Photo.**		***Perf. 12x13***
C38	AP16	100fr multi	1.75	.80

Agreement between European Economic Community & the African & Malgache Union, 3rd anniv.

Pope Paul VI and St. Peter's, Rome
AP17

Pope Paul VI and UN General Assembly
AP18

70fr, Pope Paul VI and view of NYC.

1966, Aug. 22		**Engr.**		***Perf. 13***
C39	AP17	50fr multi	.75	.45
C40	AP17	70fr multi	.95	.55
C41	AP18	100fr multi	1.75	1.00
a.		Min. sheet of 3, #C39-C41	4.50	4.50
		Nos. C39-C41 (3)	3.45	2.00

Pope Paul's appeal for peace before the UN General Assembly, Oct. 4, 1965.

Air Afrique Issue, 1966
Common Design Type

1966, Aug. 31		**Photo.**		***Perf. 12½***
C42	CD123	30fr dk vio, blk & gray	.75	.25

"Science"
AP20

Designs: 45fr, "Art" (carved female statue), vert. 100fr, "Education" (book and letters).

1966, Nov. 4		**Engr.**		***Perf. 13***
C43	AP20	30fr mag, ultra & vio brn	.45	.25
C44	AP20	45fr mar & grn	.80	.55
C45	AP20	100fr blk, mar & brt bl	1.90	1.00
a.		Min. sheet of 3, #C43-C45	3.25	3.25
		Nos. C43-C45 (3)	3.15	1.80

20th anniversary of UNESCO.

Madonna by Alessio Baldovinetti
AP21

Christmas: 50fr, Nativity after 15th century Beaune tapestry. 100fr, Adoration of the Shepherds, by José Ribera.

1966, Dec. 25		**Photo.**		***Perf. 12½x12***
C46	AP21	50fr multi	3.25	2.25
C47	AP21	100fr multi	4.50	3.25
C48	AP21	200fr multi	9.00	5.00
		Nos. C46-C48 (3)	16.75	10.50

See Nos. C95-C96, C109-C115. For surcharges, see No. C60, Benin Nos. C427, C520. For overprint, see Benin No. C544.

1967, Apr. 10				***Perf. 12½x12***

Paintings by Ingres: No. C49, Self-portrait, 1804. No. C50, Œdipus and the Sphinx.

C49	AP21	100fr multi	3.25	1.75
C50	AP21	100fr multi	3.25	1.75

Jean Auguste Dominique Ingres (1780-1867), French painter.

Three-master Suzanne — AP22

Windjammers: 45fr, Three-master Esmeralda, vert. 80fr, Schooner Marie Alice, vert. 100fr, Four-master Antonin.

1967, May 8				***Perf. 13***
C51	AP22	30fr multi	1.00	.50
C52	AP22	45fr multi	1.25	.75
C53	AP22	80fr multi	2.50	1.25
C54	AP22	100fr multi	3.25	1.50
		Nos. C51-C54 (4)	8.00	4.00

For overprint and surcharges see Benin Nos. C369, C420, C606, C612.

Nos. C29-C30 Surcharged

1967, May 29		**Photo.**		***Perf. 13, 12½***
C55	AP11	125fr on 100fr	2.75	1.25
C56	AP12	125fr on 100fr	2.75	1.25

50th anniv. of the birth of Pres. John F. Kennedy.

EXPO '67 "Man In Space" Pavilion — AP23

1967, June 12   Engr.   Perf. 13
C57 AP23 100fr dl red & Prus bl   2.00   .75
   a. Min. sheet of 3, #235-236, C57 4.00   4.00

EXPO '67, International Exhibition, Montreal, Apr. 28-Oct. 27, 1967.

Europafrica Issue

Konrad Adenauer, by Oscar Kokoschká
AP24

1967, July 19   Photo.   Perf. 12½x12
C58 AP24 70fr multi   2.00   1.25
   a. Souv. sheet of 4   8.50   8.50

Konrad Adenauer (1876-1967), chancellor of West Germany (1949-1963). For surcharges, see Benin Nos. C428, C572, C602.

Jamboree Emblem, Ropes and World Map — AP25

1967, Aug. 7   Engr.   Perf. 13
C59 AP25 100fr lil, sl grn & dp bl 1.60   .75
   a. Souv. sheet of 3, #239-240,
     C59   3.50   3.50

12th Boy Scout World Jamboree, Farragut State Park, Idaho, Aug. 1-9.

No. C48 Srchd. in Red

1967, Aug. 12   Photo.   Perf. 12½x12
C60 AP21 150fr on 200fr   3.50   2.75
   a. "150F" omitted   300.00 300.00

Riccione, Italy Stamp Exhibition.

African Postal Union Issue, 1967
Common Design Type

1967, Sept. 9   Engr.   Perf. 13
C61 CD124 100fr red, brt lil &
     emer   1.75   .95

For surcharge see Benin No. C471.

Charles de Gaulle — AP26

1967, Nov. 21   Photo.   Perf. 12½x13
C62 AP26 100fr multi   3.75   2.50
   a.   16.00 16.00

Pres. Charles de Gaulle of France on the occasion of Pres. Christophe Soglo's state visit to Paris, Nov. 1967.

Madonna, by Matthias Grunewald
AP27

Paintings: 50fr, Holy Family by the Master of St. Sebastian, horiz. 100fr, Adoration of the Magi by Ulrich Apt the Elder. 200fr, Annunciation, by Matthias Grunewald.

1967, Dec. 11   Photo.   Perf. 12½
C63 AP27 30fr multi   .55   .45
C64 AP27 50fr multi   1.10   .60
C65 AP27 100fr multi   2.00   1.25
C66 AP27 200fr multi   5.00   2.00
    Nos. C63-C66 (4)   8.65   4.30

Christmas 1967.

Venus de Milo and Mariner 5 — AP28

#C68, Venus de Milo and Venera 4 rocket.

1968, Feb. 17   Photo.   Perf. 13
C67 AP28 70fr grnsh bl & multi 1.75   .75
C68 AP28 70fr dp bl & multi   1.75   .75
   a. Souv. sheet of 2, #C67-C68 4.00 4.00

Explorations of the planet Venus, Oct. 18-19, 1967.
For surcharges see Nos. C103-C104, Benin Nos. C573, C587.

Gutenberg Monument, Strasbourg Cathedral — AP29

Design: 100fr, Gutenberg Monument, Mainz, and Gutenberg press.

1968, May 20   Litho.   Perf. 14x13½
C69 AP29 45fr grn & org   1.00   .40
C70 AP29 100fr dk & lt bl   2.00   1.00
   a. Souv. sheet of 2, #C69-C70 3.75 3.75

500th anniv. of the death of Johann Gutenberg, inventor of printing from movable type.
For surcharges see Benin Nos. C512, C516.

Martin Luther King, Jr. — AP30

Designs: 30fr, "We must meet hate with creative love" in French, English and German. 100fr, Full-face portrait.

Perf. 12½, 13½x13
1968, June 17   Photo.
Size: 26x46mm
C71 AP30 30fr red brn, yel &
     blk   .60   .35
Size: 26x37mm
C72 AP30 55fr multi   1.00   .45
C73 AP30 100fr multi   1.50   .90
   a. Min. sheet of 3, #C71-C73 4.00 4.40
    Nos. C71-C73 (3)   3.10   1.70

Martin Luther King, Jr. (1929-68), American civil rights leader.
For surcharges, see Benin Nos. C517, C561, C613.

Robert Schuman
AP31

45fr, Alcide de Gasperi. 70fr, Konrad Adenauer.

1968, July 20   Photo.   Perf. 13
C74 AP31 30fr dp yel, blk & grn .40   .40
C75 AP31 45fr org, dk brn & ol   .85   .50
C76 AP31 70fr multi   1.40   .50
    Nos. C74-C76 (3)   2.65   1.40

5th anniversary of the economic agreement between the European Economic Community and the African and Malgache Union.
For surcharges, see Benin Nos. C462, C562, C603.

Battle of Montebello, by Henri Philippoteaux — AP32

Paintings: 45fr, 2nd Zouave Regiment at Magenta, by Riballier. 70fr, Battle of Magenta, by Louis Eugène Charpentier. 100fr, Battle of Solferino, by Charpentier.

1968, Aug. 12   Perf. 12½x12
C77 AP32 30fr multi   1.15   .50
C78 AP32 45fr multi   1.60   .65
C79 AP32 70fr multi   3.25   1.25
C80 AP32 100fr multi   4.00   1.00
    Nos. C77-C80 (4)   10.00 3.40

Issued for the Red Cross. For surcharges, see Benin Nos. C574, C594, C614.

Mail Truck in Village
AP33

Designs: 45fr, Mail truck stopping at rural post office. 55fr, Mail truck at river bank. 70fr, Mail truck and train.

1968, Oct. 7   Photo.   Perf. 13x12½
C81 AP33 30fr multi   .90   .50
C82 AP33 45fr multi   1.10   .55
C83 AP33 55fr multi   1.75   .55
C84 AP33 70fr multi   4.25   1.00
    Nos. C81-C84 (4)   8.00   2.60

For surcharges see Benin Nos. C352, C357A, C584.

Aztec Stadium, Mexico City — AP34

45fr, Ball player, Mayan sculpture, vert. 70fr, Wrestler, sculpture from Uxpanapan, vert. 150fr, Olympic Stadium, Mexico City.

1968, Nov. 20   Engr.   Perf. 13
C85 AP34 30fr dp cl & sl grn   .80   .30
C86 AP34 45fr ultra & dk rose
     brn   1.50   .60
C87 AP34 70fr sl grn & dk brn   2.10   .65
C88 AP34 150fr dk car & dk brn 3.00   1.25
   a. Min. sheet of 4, #C85-C88 7.50 7.50
    Nos. C85-C88 (4)   7.40   2.80

19th Olympic Games, Mexico City, Oct. 12-27. No. C88a is folded down the vertical gutter separating Nos. C85-C86 se-tenant at left and Nos. C87-C88 se-tenant at right.
For overprint and surcharges see Benin Nos. C457, C461, C513.

The Annunciation, by Foujita — AP35

Paintings by Foujita: 30fr, Nativity, horiz. 100fr, The Virgin and Child. 200fr, The Baptism of Christ.

Perf. 12x12½, 12½x12
1968, Nov. 25   Photo.
C89 AP35 30fr multi   .80   .55
C90 AP35 70fr multi   1.60   .80
C91 AP35 100fr multi   1.75   1.25
C92 AP35 200fr multi   4.00   2.75
    Nos. C89-C92 (4)   8.15   5.35

Christmas 1968. For surcharges see Benin Nos. C531, C563, C575, C615, C648.

PHILEXAFRIQUE Issue

Painting: Diderot, by Louis Michel Vanloo.

1968, Dec. 16   Perf. 12½x12
C93 AP35 100fr multi   3.75   3.75

PHILEXAFRIQUE, Philatelic Exhibition in Abidjan, Feb. 14-23. Printed with alternating label.
For surcharges, see Benin Nos. C522, C629.

2nd PHILEXAFRIQUE Issue
Common Design Type

50fr, Dahomey #119 and aerial view of Cotonou.

1969, Feb. 14   Engr.   Perf. 13
C94 CD128 50fr bl, brn & pur   2.25   2.25

For surcharge see Benin Nos. C467, C651.

Christmas Painting Type

Paintings: No. C95, Virgin of the Rocks, by Leonardo da Vinci. No. C96, Virgin with the Scales, by Cesare da Sesto.

1969, Mar. 17   Photo.   Perf. 12½x12
C95 AP21 100fr vio & multi   2.00   1.00
C96 AP21 100fr grn & multi   2.00   1.00

Leonardo da Vinci (1452-1519).
For surcharge see Benin No. C651B.

General Bonaparte, by Jacques Louis David — AP36

Paintings: 60fr, Napoleon I in 1809, by Robert J. Lefevre. 75fr, Napoleon on the Battlefield of Eylau, by Antoine Jean Gros, horiz. 200fr, Gen. Bonaparte at Arcole, by Gros.

1969, Apr. 14   Photo.   Perf. 12½x12
C97 AP36 30fr multi   1.50   1.25
C98 AP36 60fr multi   2.75   1.75
C99 AP36 75fr multi   3.25   2.50
C100 AP36 200fr multi   7.50   5.50
    Nos. C97-C100 (4)   15.00 11.00

Bicentenary of the birth of Napoleon I. For surcharges, see Benin Nos. C599, C605.

Arms Type of Regular Issue, 1969

1969, June 30   Litho.   Perf. 13½x13
C101 A49 50fr multi   .75   .30

For overprint and surcharge see Benin Nos. C417, C596.

Apollo 8 Trip Around the Moon
AP37

Embossed on Gold Foil

1969, July   *Die-cut Perf. 10½*
C102 AP37 1000fr gold   20.00 20.00

US Apollo 8 mission, which put the 1st men into orbit around the moon, Dec. 21-27, 1968.

Nos. C67-C68
Surcharged

1969, Aug. 1   **Photo.**   *Perf. 13*
C103 AP28 125fr on 70fr, #C67   2.50 1.75
C104 AP28 125fr on 70fr, #C68   2.50 1.75

Man's 1st landing on the moon, July 20, 1969; US astronauts Neil A. Armstrong, Col. Edwin E. Aldrin, Jr., with Lieut. Col. Michael Collins piloting Apollo 11.

Europafrica Issue
Type of Regular Issue, 1969

Design: 100fr, Oil palm industry, Cotonou.

1969, Sept. 22   **Litho.**   *Perf. 14*
C105 A51 100fr multi   2.25 .35
   a.   Souv. sheet of 3, #262-263, C105   4.25 4.25

For surcharge see Benin No. C523.

Dahomey Rotary
Emblem — AP38

1969, Sept. 25   *Perf. 14x13½*
C106 AP38 50fr multi   1.00 .75

For surcharge see Benin No. C468.

No. C33 Surcharged

1969, Nov. 15   **Photo.**   *Perf. 12½*
C107 AP14 10fr on 50fr multi   .45 .25

Dance Type of Regular Issue

Design: Teke dance and Tourist Year emblem.

1969, Dec. 15   **Litho.**   *Perf. 14*
C108 A52 70fr multi   2.50 1.50

For surcharge see Benin No. C398.

Painting Type of 1966

Christmas: 30fr, Annunciation, by Vrancke van der Stockt. 45fr, Nativity, Swabian School, horiz. 110fr, Madonna and Child, by the Master of the Gold Brocade. 200fr, Adoration of the Kings, Antwerp School.

1969, Dec. 20   *Perf. 12½x12, 12x12½*
C109 AP21 30fr multi   .50 .40
C110 AP21 45fr red & multi   .85 .65
C111 AP21 110fr multi   2.10 1.25
C112 AP21 200fr multi   3.75 2.25
   Nos. C109-C112 (4)   7.20 4.55

For surcharges see Benin #C425, C463, C475, C532, C595.

1969, Dec. 27   *Perf. 12½x12*

Paintings: No. C113, The Artist's Studio (detail), by Gustave Courbet. No. C114, Self-portrait with Gold Chain, by Rembrandt. 150fr, Hendrickje Stoffels, by Rembrandt.

C113 AP21 100fr red & multi   2.25 1.25
C114 AP21 100fr grn & multi   2.25 1.25
C115 AP21 150fr multi   3.75 1.75
   Nos. C113-C115 (3)   8.25 4.25

For overprints and surcharges see Benin Nos. C458, C472, C524.

Franklin D.
Roosevelt — AP39

1970, Feb.   **Photo.**   *Perf. 12½*
C116 AP39 100fr ultra, yel grn & blk   1.75 .80

25th anniversary of the death of Pres. Franklin Delano Roosevelt (1882-1945). For surcharges see Benin Nos. C525, C637.

Astronauts, Rocket, US
Flag — AP40

Astronauts: 50fr, Riding rocket through space. 70fr, In landing module approaching moon. 110fr, Planting US flag on moon.

1970, Mar. 9   **Photo.**   *Perf. 12½*
C117 AP40 30fr multi   .65 .25

Souvenir Sheet

C118   Sheet of 4   8.00 8.00
   a.   AP40 50fr violet blue & multi   .75 .75
   b.   AP40 70fr violet blue & multi   1.00 1.00
   c.   AP40 110fr violet blue & multi   1.25 1.25

See note after No. C104. No. C118 contains Nos. C117, C118a, C118b and C118c. For surcharge see No. C120.

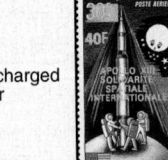

Walt
Whitman
and
Dahoman
Huts
AP41

1970, Apr. 30   **Engr.**   *Perf. 13*
C119 AP41 100fr Prus bl, brn & emer   1.40 .80

Walt Whitman (1818-92), American poet. For surcharge, see Benin No. C510.

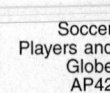

No. C117 Surcharged
in Silver

1970, May 15   **Photo.**   *Perf. 12½*
C120 AP40 40fr on 30fr multi   1.20 .75

The flight of Apollo 13.
For surcharge see Benin No. C464.

Soccer
Players and
Globe
AP42

Designs: 50fr, Goalkeeper catching ball. 200fr, Players kicking ball.

1970, May 19
C121 AP42 40fr multi   .75 .40
C122 AP42 50fr multi   .95 .50
C123 AP42 200fr multi   3.50 1.25
   Nos. C121-C123 (3)   5.20 2.15

9th World Soccer Championships for the Jules Rimet Cup, Mexico City, May 30-June 21, 1970.
For surcharges, see No. C126, Benin Nos. C502, C504.

EXPO '70 Type of Regular Issue

EXPO '70 Emblems and: 70fr, Dahomey pavilion. 120fr, Mt. Fuji, temple and torii.

1970, June 15   **Litho.**   *Perf. 13½x14*
C124 A54 70fr yel, red & dk vio   1.25 .60
C125 A54 120fr yel, red & grn   2.25 1.00

For surcharges see Benin Nos. C470, C477.

No. C123 Surcharged and Overprinted

1970, July 13   **Photo.**   *Perf. 12½*
C126 AP42 100fr on 200fr multi   2.10 1.00

Brazil's victory in the 9th World Soccer Championships, Mexico City.
For surcharge see Benin No. C515.

Mercury, Map of Africa
and Europe — AP43

Europafrica Issue, 1970

1970, July 20   **Photo.**   *Perf. 12x13*
C127 AP43 40fr multi   .90 .40
C128 AP43 70fr multi   1.50 .60

For surcharges see Benin Nos. C429, C488, C566.

Ludwig van
Beethoven — AP44

1970, Sept. 21   **Litho.**   *Perf. 14x13½*
C129 AP44 90fr brt bl & vio blk   1.40 .45
C130 AP44 110fr yel grn & dk brn   1.75 .65

Bicentenary of the birth of Ludwig van Beethoven (1770-1827), composer.
For surcharges, see Benin Nos. C476, C608.

Symbols of
Learning — AP45

1970, Nov. 6   **Photo.**   *Perf. 12½*
C131 AP45 100fr multi   1.40 .75

Laying of the foundation stone for the University at Calavi.
For overprint and surcharges see Benin Nos. C356, C399, C616.

Annunciation,
Rhenish School,
c.1340 — AP46

Paintings of Rhenish School, circa 1340: 70fr, Nativity. 110fr, Adoration of the Kings. 200fr, Presentation at the Temple.

1970, Nov. 9   *Perf. 12½x12*
C132 AP46 40fr gold & multi   .55 .40
C133 AP46 70fr gold & multi   1.00 .55
C134 AP46 110fr gold & multi   2.40 1.25
C135 AP46 200fr gold & multi   4.00 2.00
   Nos. C132-C135 (4)   7.95 4.20

Christmas 1970.
For surcharges see Benin Nos. C479, C518, C527.

Charles de Gaulle, Arc
de Triomphe and
Flag — AP47

Design: 500fr, de Gaulle as old man and Notre Dame Cathedral, Paris.

1971, Mar. 15   **Photo.**   *Perf. 12½*
C136 AP47 40fr multi   .80 .45
C137 AP47 500fr multi   6.50 3.25

Gen. Charles de Gaulle (1890-1970), President of France.
For surcharges see Benin Nos. C465, C567.

L'Indifférent, by
Watteau — AP48

Painting: No. C139, Woman playing stringed instrument, by Watteau.

1971, May 3   **Photo.**   *Perf. 13*
C138 AP48 100fr red brn & multi   3.25 1.75
C139 AP48 100fr red brn & multi   3.25 1.75

See Nos. C151-C152. For overprints and surcharges, see Benin Nos. C357D, C372, C456, C526, C617, C638.

1971, May 29   **Photo.**   *Perf. 13*

Dürer Paintings: 100fr, Self-portrait, 1498. 200fr, Self-portrait, 1500.

C140 AP48 100fr bl grn & multi   2.25 1.25
C141 AP48 200fr dk grn & multi   4.50 2.25

Albrecht Dürer (1471-1528), German painter and engraver. See Nos. C151-C152, C174-C175. For surcharges and overprints see Benin Nos. C357B, C381, C533, C545, C618.

Johannes
Kepler and
Diagram
AP49

200fr, Kepler, trajectories, satellite and rocket.

1971, July 12   **Engr.**   *Perf. 13*
C142 AP49 40fr brt rose lil, blk & vio bl   .90 .55
C143 AP49 200fr red, blk & dk bl   3.25 1.75

Kepler (1571-1630), German astronomer. For overprint and surcharges see Benin Nos. C342, C348, C466, C480, C568.

Europafrica Issue

Jet Plane, Maps of Europe and Africa AP50

100fr, Ocean liner, maps of Europe and Africa.

1971, July 19 Photo. Perf. 12½x12
C144 AP50 50fr blk, lt bl & org 1.60 .60
C145 AP50 100fr multi 2.50 1.00

For surcharges see Benin Nos. C374, C404, C421, C585, C630.

African Postal Union Issue, 1971
Common Design Type

Design: 100fr, Dahomey coat of arms and UAMPT building, Brazzaville, Congo.

1971, Nov. 13 Perf. 13x13½
C146 CD135 100fr bl & multi 1.75 .80

For overprint and surcharge see Benin Nos. C357E, C619.

Flight into Egypt, by Van Dyck AP51

Paintings: 40fr, Adoration of the Shepherds, by the Master of the Hausbuch, c. 1500, vert. 70fr, Adoration of the Kings, by Holbein the Elder, vert. 200fr, The Birth of Christ, by Dürer.

1971, Nov. 22 Perf. 13
C147 AP51 40fr gold & multi .85 .45
C148 AP51 70fr gold & multi 1.40 .55
C149 AP51 100fr gold & multi 2.10 .80
C150 AP51 200fr gold & multi 5.00 1.75
Nos. C147-C150 (4) 9.35 3.55

Christmas 1971
For overprint and surcharges see Benin Nos. C394, C394A, C397, C403, C403A, C405, C481, C503, C546, C581, C604, C631.

Painting Type of 1971 Inscribed: "25e ANNIVERSAIRE DE L'UNICEF"

Paintings: 40fr, Prince Balthazar, by Velasquez. 100fr, Infanta Margarita Maria, by Velázquez.

1971, Dec. 11
C151 AP48 40fr gold & multi 1.75 .55
C152 AP48 100fr gold & multi 3.00 .85

25th anniv. of UNICEF.
For surcharges see Benin Nos. C366, C418, C437, C592, C639.

Olympic Games Type

Design: 150fr, Sapporo '72 emblem, ski jump and stork flying.

1972, Feb. Engr. Perf. 13
C153 A61 150fr brn, dp rose lil & bl 3.50 1.25

11th Winter Olympic Games, Sapporo, Japan, Feb. 3-13.
For overprint and surcharge see Benin Nos. C347, C433, C645.

Boy Scout and Scout Flag — AP52

Designs: 40fr, Scout playing marimba. 100fr, Scouts doing farm work.

1972, Mar. 19 Photo. Perf. 13
Size: 26x35mm
C154 AP52 35fr multi .50 .25
C155 AP52 40fr multi .85 .40

Size: 26x46mm
C156 AP52 100fr yel & multi 1.75 .85
  a. Souvenir sheet of 3, #C154-
  C156, perf. 12½ 4.25 4.25
  Nos. C154-C156 (3) 3.10 1.50

World Boy Scout Seminar, Cotonou, Mar. 1972.
For overprint and surcharges see Benin Nos. C373, C414, C569.

Workers Training Institute and Friedrich Naumann AP53

Design: 250fr, Workers Training Institute and Pres. Theodor Heuss of Germany.

1972, Mar. 29 Photo. Perf. 13x12
C157 AP53 100fr brt rose, blk & vio 1.50 .65
C158 AP53 250fr blk & vio 3.50 1.40

Laying of foundation stone for National Workers Training Institute.
For surcharges see Benin Nos. C380, C473, C640, C649, Q25A.

Mosaic Floor, St. Mark's, Venice AP54

12th Century Mosaics from St. Mark's Basilica: 40fr, Roosters carrying fox on a pole. 65fr, Noah sending out dove.

1972, Apr. 10 Perf. 13
C159 AP54 35fr gold & multi 1.35 .75
C160 AP54 40fr gold & multi 1.50 .90
C161 AP54 65fr gold & multi 3.00 1.50
Nos. C159-C161 (3) 5.85 3.15

UNESCO campaign to save Venice.
For surcharges see Benin Nos. 690G, C600.

Neapolitan and Dahoman Dancers AP55

1972, May 3 Perf. 13½x13
C162 AP55 100fr multi 1.50 .65

12th Philatelic Exhibition, Naples.
For overprint and surcharge, see Benin Nos. C395, C620.

Running, German Eagle, Olympic Rings — AP56

85fr, High jump and Glyptothek, Munich. 150fr, Shot put and Propylaeum, Munich.

1972, June 12 Engr. Perf. 13
C163 AP56 20fr ultra, grn & brn .40 .25
C164 AP56 85fr brn, grn & ultra .95 .60
C165 AP56 65fr grn, brn & ultra 2.00 1.00
  a. Min. sheet of 3, #C163-C165 4.00 4.00
  Nos. C163-C165 (3) 3.35 1.85

20th Olympic Games, Munich, 8/26-9/10.
For overprints and surcharges see Nos. C170-C172, Benin C343, C346, C370, C404A, C559, C577, C651A.

Louis Blériot and his Plane AP57

1972, June 26
C166 AP57 100fr vio, cl & brt bl 4.00 1.75

Birth centenary of Louis Blériot (1872-1936), French aviation pioneer.
For surcharges see Benin Nos. C386, C621.

Adam, by Lucas Cranach — AP58

Design: 200fr, Eve, by Lucas Cranach.

1972, Oct. 24 Photo.
C167 AP58 150fr multi 2.75 1.25
C168 AP58 200fr multi 4.50 1.75

Cranach (1472-1553), German painter.
For surcharges see Benin Nos. C402, C434A, C537, C643.

Pauline Borghese, by Canova — AP59

1972, Nov. 8
C169 AP59 250fr multi 7.00 1.75

Antonio Canova (1757-1822), Italian sculptor.
For surcharge, see Benin No. 1366.

Nos. C163-C165 Overprinted

a   b

c

1972, Nov. 13 Engr. Perf. 13
C170 AP56(a) 20fr multi .45 .25
C171 AP56(b) 85fr multi 1.25 .60
C172 AP56(c) 150fr multi 2.25 1.25
  a. Miniature sheet of 3 5.25 5.25
  Nos. C170-C172 (3) 3.95 2.10

Gold medal winners in 20th Olympic Games: Lasse Viren, Finland, 5,000m. and 10,000m. races (20fr); Ulrike Meyfarth, Germany, women's high jump (85fr); Wladyslaw Komar, Poland, shot put (150fr).
For surcharges, see Benin Nos. C343A, C371, C538, C607.

Louis Pasteur — AP60

1972, Nov. 30
C173 AP60 100fr brt grn, lil & brn 2.50 1.00

Pasteur (1822-95), chemist and bacteriologist.
For surcharges see Benin Nos. C344, C622.

Painting Type of 1971

Paintings by Georges de La Tour (1593-1652), French painter: 35fr, Vielle player. 150fr, The Newborn, horiz.

1972, Dec. 11 Photo.
C174 AP48 35fr multi .80 .40
C175 AP48 150fr multi 2.25 1.25

For surcharges see Benin Nos. C364, C490, C578.

Annunciation, School of Agnolo Gaddi — AP61

Paintings: 125fr, Nativity, by Simone dei Crocifissi. 140fr, Adoration of the Shepherds, by Giovanni di Pietro. 250fr, Adoration of the Kings, by Giotto.

1972, Dec. 15
C176 AP61 35fr gold & multi .75 .25
C177 AP61 125fr gold & multi 2.00 .65
C178 AP61 140fr gold & multi 2.75 1.00
C179 AP61 250fr gold & multi 4.50 1.50
Nos. C176-C179 (4) 10.00 3.40

Christmas 1972. See Nos. C195-C198, C234, C251, C253-C254. For overprint and surcharges see Benin Nos. C383A, C384, C392, C401, C444, C528, C628, C652.

Statue of St. Teresa, Basilica of Lisieux AP62

100fr, St. Teresa, roses, and globe, vert.

1973, May 14 Photo. Perf. 13
C180 AP62 40fr blk, gold & lt ultra .75 .45
C181 AP62 100fr gold & multi 2.50 1.00

St. Teresa of Lisieux (Therese Martin, 1873-97), Carmelite nun.
For surcharges see Benin Nos. C390, C570, C623.

Scouts, African Scout Emblem AP63

Designs (African Scout Emblem and): 20fr, Lord Baden-Powell, vert. 40fr, Scouts building bridge.

1973, July 2 Engr. Perf. 13
C182 AP63 15fr bl, grn & choc .45 .25
C183 AP63 20fr ol & Prus bl .75 .25
C184 AP63 40fr grn, Prus bl & brn .90 .35
  a. Souvenir sheet of 3 3.00 3.00
  Nos. C182-C184 (3) 2.10 .85

24th Boy Scout World Conference, Nairobi, Kenya, July 16-21. No. C184a contains 3 stamps similar to Nos. C182-C184 in changed colors (15fr in ultramarine, slate green and chocolate; 20fr in chocolate, ultramarine and indigo; 40fr in slate green, indigo and chocolate).

For surcharges see Nos. C217-C218, Benin C365, C409, C558, C560, C571.

Copernicus, Venera and Mariner Satellites AP64

125fr, Copernicus, sun, earth & moon, vert.

1973, Aug. 20　　Engr.　　Perf. 13
C185 AP64 65fr blk, dk brn & org　　　　　　　1.50 .55
C186 AP64 125fr bl, slate grn & pur　　　　　　2.75 1.00

For surcharges and overprints see Benin Nos. C345, C349A, C375, C601, C642.

Head and City Hall, Brussels — AP64a

1973, Sept. 17　　Engr.　　Perf. 13
C187 AP64a 100fr blk, Prus bl & dk grn　　　　1.10 .60

African Weeks, Brussels, Sept. 15-30, 1973.
For surcharge see Benin No. C400.

WMO Emblem, World Weather Map AP65

1973, Sept. 25
C188 AP65 100fr ol grn & lt brn　1.40 .75

Cent. of intl. meteorological cooperation.
For surcharges and overprint see Nos. C199, Benin Nos. C382, C624.

Europafrica Issue

AP66

Design: 40fr, similar to 35fr.

1973, Oct. 1　　Engr.　　Perf. 13
C189 AP66 35fr multi　　　　　　.55 .35
C190 AP66 40fr bl, sepia & ultra　.70 .40

For overprint and surcharges, see Benin Nos. C411, C564, C593.

John F. Kennedy — AP67

1973, Oct. 18
C191 AP67 200fr bl grn, vio & sl grn　　　　　2.75 2.75

Souvenir Sheet
C191A AP67 200fr bl, rd brn, brn　5.00 5.00

For surcharge and overprint, see Benin Nos. C377, C441, C547.

Soccer AP68

40fr, 2 soccer players. 100fr, 3 soccer players.

1973, Nov. 19　　Engr.　　Perf. 13
C192 AP68 35fr multi　　　　　.55 .25
C193 AP68 40fr multi　　　　　.65 .25
C194 AP68 100fr multi　　　　1.25 .65
　Nos. C192-C194 (3)　　　2.45 1.15

World Soccer Cup, Munich 1974.
For surcharges and overprint see Nos. C219-C220, Benin Nos. C396, C591, C644.

Painting Type of 1972

Christmas: 35fr, Annunciation, by Dirk Bouts. 100fr, Nativity, by Giotto. 150fr, Adoration of the Kings, by Botticelli. 200fr, Adoration of the Shepherds, by Jacopo Bassano, horiz.

1973, Dec. 20　　　　　　Perf. 13
C195 AP61 35fr gold & multi　　　.80 .40
C196 AP61 100fr gold & multi　　1.50 .65
C197 AP61 150fr gold & multi　　3.00 1.10
C198 AP61 200fr gold & multi　　3.25 1.75
　Nos. C195-C198 (4)　　　　8.55 3.90

For overprints and surcharges see Benin Nos. C378, C388, C410, C434, C438, C442, C487, C565, C646.

No C188 Surcharged in Violet

1974, Feb. 4　　Engr.　　Perf. 13
C199 AP65 200fr on 100fr multi　2.25 1.25

Skylab US space missions, 1973-74.

Skiers, Snowflake, Olympic Rings AP69

1974, Feb. 25　　Engr.　　Perf. 13
C200 AP69 100fr vio bl, brn & brt bl　　　　　1.75 1.10

50th anniversary of first Winter Olympic Games, Chamonix, France. For surcharges, see Benin Nos. C389, C625.

Marie Curie — AP70

1974, June 7　　Engr.　　Perf. 13
C201 AP70 50fr Lenin　　　　　1.75 .65
C202 AP70 125fr shown　　　　2.25 .90
C203 AP70 150fr Churchill　　　2.50 1.40
　Nos. C201-C203 (3)　　　6.50 2.95

50th anniv. of the death of Lenin; 40th anniv. of the death of Marie Sklodowska Curie; cent. of the birth of Winston Churchill.
For overprints and surcharges see Benin Nos. C387A, C391A, C489, C529, C597, C632, C634.

Bishop, Persian, 18th Century — AP71

200fr, Queen, Siamese chess piece, 19th cent.

1974, June 14　　Photo.　　Perf. 12½x13
C204 AP71 50fr org & multi　　　2.50 1.00
C205 AP71 200fr brt grn & multi　6.00 2.50

21st Chess Olympiad, Nice, 6/6-30/74.
For surcharges and overprint see Benin Nos. C469, C482, C598, C627, Q11.

Frederic Chopin — AP72

Design: No. C207, Ludwig van Beethoven.

1974, June 24　　Engr.　　Perf. 13
C206 AP72 150fr blk & copper red　　　　　　4.50 1.40
C207 AP72 150fr blk & copper red　　　　　　4.50 1.40

Famous musicians: Frederic Chopin and Ludwig van Beethoven.
For overprints and surcharges see Benin Nos. C376, C452, C459, C539, C579, C647, C655.

Astronaut on Moon, and Earth — AP73

1974, July 10　　Engr.　　Perf. 13
C208 AP73 150fr multi　　　　　2.75 1.50

5th anniversary of the first moon walk.
For surcharges and overprint see Benin Nos. C391, C460, C635.

Litho. & Embossed 'Gold Foil' Stamps
These stamps generally are of a different design format than the rest of the issue. Since there is a commemorative inscription tying them to the issue a separate illustration is not being shown.

World Cup Soccer Championships, Munich — AP74

World Cup trophy and players and flags of: 35fr, West Germany, Chile, Australia, DDR. 40fr, Zaire, Scotland, Brazil, Yugoslavia. 100fr, Sweden, Bulgaria, Uruguay, Netherlands. 200fr, Italy, Haiti, Poland, Argentina. 300fr, Stadium. 500fr, Trophy and flags.

Perf. 14x13, 13x14
1974, July 16　　　　　　Litho.
C209 AP74 35fr multicolored　　.40 .25
C210 AP74 40fr multicolored　　.55 .25
C211 AP74 100fr multicolored　1.10 .70
C212 AP74 200fr multicolored　2.50 1.25
C213 AP74 300fr multi, horiz.　2.50 1.50

Souvenir Sheet
C215 AP74 500fr multi, horiz.　7.25 7.25

It is uncertain if this issue was valid for postage or recognized by the Dahomey government.

Nos. C182-C183 Srchd. and Ovptd. in Black or Red

1974, July 19
C217 AP63 100fr on 15fr multi　　1.25 .60
C218 AP63 140fr on 20fr multi (R)　1.75 .90

11th Pan-Arab Jamboree, Batrun, Lebanon, Aug. 1974. Overprint includes 2 bars over old denomination; 2-line overprint on No. C217, 3 lines on No. C218.

Nos. C193-C194 Overprinted and Surcharged

1974, July 26　　Engr.　　Perf. 13
C219 AP68 100fr on 40fr　　　1.10 .65
C220 AP68 150fr on 100fr　　1.60 1.00

World Cup Soccer Championship, 1974, victory of German Federal Republic.

Earth and UPU Emblem AP75

Designs (UPU Emblem and): 65fr, Concorde in flight. 125fr, French railroad car, c. 1860. 200fr, African drummer and Renault mail truck, pre-1939.

1974, Aug. 5　　Engr.　　Perf. 13
C221 AP75 35fr rose cl & vio　　.75 .40
C222 AP75 65fr Prus grn & cl　1.50 .95
C223 AP75 125fr multi　　　　3.50 1.50
C224 AP75 200fr multi　　　　3.50 2.00
　Nos. C221-C224 (4)　　　9.25 4.85

Centenary of Universal Postal Union.
For surcharges, see Benin Nos. C422, C530, C540, C586, C653, C657, Q13B, Q17B.

UPU, Cent. AP76

Communications and transportation: 50fr, Rocket, Indian shooting arrow. 100fr, Airplane, dog sled, vert. 125fr, Rocket launch, balloon. 150fr, Rocket re-entry into Earth's atmosphere, drum. 200fr, Locomotive, Pony Express rider. 500fr, UPU headquarters. No. C230, Train, 1829. No. C232, Astronaut canceling envelope on moon.

1974　　Litho.　　Perf. 13x14, 14x13
C225 AP76 50fr multicolored　　.50 .30
C226 AP76 100fr multicolored　.75 .60
C227 AP76 125fr multicolored　1.00 .85
C228 AP76 150fr multicolored　1.75 1.00
C229 AP76 200fr multicolored　2.50 1.25

Litho. & Embossed
Perf. 13½
Size: 48x60mm
C230 AP76 1000fr gold & multi　12.00 12.00

Souvenir Sheets
Litho.
Perf. 13x14
C231 AP76 500fr multicolored　4.50 4.50

Litho. & Embossed
Perf. 13½

C232 AP76 1000fr gold & multi　7.25 7.25
Issued: #C230, C232, Oct. 9; others, Aug. 5.

It is uncertain if this issue was valid for postage or recognized by the Dahomey government.

Lion of Belfort by Frederic A. Bartholdi AP77

1974, Aug. 20   Engr.   Perf. 13
C233 AP77 100fr rose brn   2.50 1.00

For surcharges see Benin Nos. C387, C626.

Paintins Type of 1972

1974, Aug. 20   Engr.   Perf. 13
Painting: 250fr, Girl with Falcon, by Philippe de Champaigne.
C234 AP61 250fr multi   4.00 2.40

For surcharges see Benin Nos. C363, C445, C551.

Prehistoric Animals AP78

1974, Sept. 23   Photo.
C235 AP78 35fr Rhamphorhynchus   1.50 .80
C236 AP78 150fr Stegosaurus   5.00 2.25
C237 AP78 200fr Tyrannosaurus   7.00 2.75
    Nos. C235-C237 (3)   13.50 5.80

For surcharges and overprint, see Benin Nos. C349, C350, C440, C443, C548, C636.

Conquest of Space — AP79

Various spacecraft and: 50fr, Mercury. 100fr, Venus. 150fr, Mars. 200fr, Jupiter. 400fr, Sun.

1974, Oct. 31   Litho.   Perf. 13x14
C238 AP79 50fr multicolored   .40 .30
C239 AP79 100fr multicolored   1.00 .50
C240 AP79 150fr multicolored   1.75 .90
C241 AP79 200fr multicolored   2.25 1.25
    Nos. C238-C241 (4)   5.40 2.95

Souvenir Sheet
C242 AP79 400fr multicolored   5.25 5.25

It is uncertain if this issue was valid for postage or recognized by the Dahomey government.

West Germany, World Cup Soccer Champions — AP80

Designs: 100fr, Team. 125fr, Paul Breitner. 150fr, Gerd Muller. 300fr, Presentation of trophy. 500fr, German team positioned on field.

1974, Nov.   Litho.   Perf. 13x14
C243 AP80 100fr multicolored   .75 .50
C244 AP80 125fr multicolored   1.00 .75
C245 AP80 150fr multicolored   1.50 1.00
C246 AP80 300fr multicolored   3.25 2.00
    Nos. C243-C246 (4)   6.50 4.25

Souvenir Sheet
C248 AP80 500fr multicolored   5.25 5.25

It is uncertain if this issue was valid for postage or recognized by the Dahomey government.

Europafrica Issue

Globe, Cogwheel, Emblem AP81

1974, Dec. 20   Typo.   Perf. 13
C250 AP81 250fr red & multi   3.25 2.75

Printed tête bêche in sheets of 10.
For surcharges see Benin Nos. C430, C509, C650.

Christmas Type of 1972 and

Nativity, by Martin Schongauer AP82

Paintings: 35fr, Annunciation, by Schongauer. 100fr, Virgin in Rose Arbor, by Schongauer. 250fr, Virgin and Child, with St. John the Baptist, by Botticelli.

1974, Dec. 23   Photo.   Perf. 13
C251 AP61 35fr gold & multi   .60 .30
C252 AP82 40fr gold & multi   .60 .40
C253 AP61 100fr gold & multi   1.60 .55
C254 AP61 250fr gold & multi   4.25 1.75
    Nos. C251-C254 (4)   7.05 3.00

For overprints and surcharges, see Benin Nos. C413, C431, C439, C446, C552, C641.

Apollo and Soyuz Spacecraft AP83

200fr, American and Russian flags, rocket take-off. 500fr, Apollo-Soyuz link-up.

1975, July 16   Litho.   Perf. 12½
C255 AP83 35fr multi   .50 .30
C256 AP83 200fr vio bl, red & bl 2.40 1.25
C257 AP83 500fr vio bl, ind &
           red   5.50 3.00
    Nos. C255-C257 (3)   8.40 4.55

Apollo Soyuz space test project (Russo-American cooperation); launching July 15; link-up, July 17.
For surcharges and overprints, see Benin Nos. C406, C415-C416, C451, C542-C543, C549, C580.

Nos. C255-C256 Surcharged

No. C258

No. C259

1975, July 17   Litho.   Perf. 12½
C258 AP83 100fr on 35fr (S)   1.25 .60
C259 AP83 300fr on 200fr   3.25 1.40

Apollo-Soyuz link-up in space, July 17, 1975.

ARPHILA Emblem, "Stamps" and Head of Ceres AP84

1975, Aug. 22   Engr.   Perf. 13
C260 AP84 100fr blk, bl & lilac 1.50 .75

ARPHILA 75, International Philatelic Exhibition, Paris, June 6-16.
For overprint and surcharge, see Benin Nos. C383, C474.

Europafrica Issue

Holy Family, by Michelangelo — AP85

1975, Sept. 29   Litho.   Perf. 12
C261 AP85 300fr gold & multi   4.50 1.50

For overprints, see Benin Nos. C447, C554.

Infantry and Stars — AP86

American bicentennial (Stars and): 135fr, Drummers and fifer. 300fr, Artillery with cannon. 500fr, Cavalry.

1975, Nov. 18   Engr.   Perf. 13
C262 AP86 75fr grn car & pur   1.00 .45
C263 AP86 135fr bl, mag & sep   1.75 .90
C264 AP86 300fr vio bl, ver &
           choc   3.25 1.75
C265 AP86 500fr ver, dk grn &
           brn   5.75 2.50
    Nos. C262-C265 (4)   11.75 5.60

For overprints and surcharges see Benin Nos. C247-C249, C385, C412, C429A, C453, C478, C534, C555, C557, C576, C588.

Diving and Olympic Rings — AP87

Design: 250fr, Soccer and Olympic rings.

1975, Nov. 24
C266 AP87 40fr vio, grnsh bl &
           ol brn   .55 .25
C267 AP87 250fr red, emer &
           brn   2.40 1.25

Pre-Olympic Year 1975.
For surcharges see Benin Nos. C341, C393, C553, C582.

AIR POST SEMI-POSTAL STAMPS

Maternity Hospital, Dakar SPAP1

Dispensary, Mopti SPAP2

Nurse Weighing Baby SPAP3

Perf. 13½x12½, 13 (#CB3)
Photo, Engr. (#CB3)
1942, June 22
CB1 SPAP1 1.50fr + 3.50fr
           green   .80 5.50
CB2 SPAP2 2fr + 6fr brown   .80 5.50
CB3 SPAP3 3fr + 9fr car red   .80 5.50
    Nos. CB1-CB3 (3)   2.40 16.50

Native children's welfare fund.

Colonial Education Fund
Common Design Type
Perf. 12½x13½
1942, June 22   Engr.
CB4 CD86a 1.20fr + 1.80fr blue
           & red   .80 5.50

AIR POST PARCEL POST STAMPS

Catalogue values for unused stamps in this section are for Never Hinged items.

Nos. C20-C23, C14 Surcharged in Black or Red

No. CQ2

No. CQ5

1967-69   Engr.   Perf. 13
CQ1 AP6 200fr on 200fr   2.10 2.10
CQ2 AP6 300fr on 100fr   2.40 2.40
CQ3 AP6 500fr on 300fr   4.50 4.50
CQ4 AP6 1000fr on 500fr   9.50 9.50
CQ5 AP4 5000fr on 100fr
        (R) ('69)   35.00 35.00
    Nos. CQ1-CQ5 (5)   53.50 53.50

On No. CQ5, "Colis Postaux" is at top, bar at right.

POSTAGE DUE STAMPS

Dahomey Natives — D1

1906   Unwmk.   Typo.   Perf. 14x13½
J1 D1 5c grn, grnsh   4.00 4.00
J2 D1 10c red brn   4.00 4.00
J3 D1 15c dark blue   8.00 8.00
J4 D1 20c blk, yellow   8.00 8.00
J5 D1 30c red, straw   12.00 12.00
J6 D1 50c violet   24.00 24.00
J7 D1 60c blk, buff   16.00 16.00
J8 D1 1fr blk, pinkish   52.50 40.00
    Nos. J1-J8 (8)   128.50 116.00

D2

1914

J9	D2	5c green	.25	.25
J10	D2	10c rose	.55	.55
J11	D2	15c gray	.55	.55
J12	D2	20c brown	1.10	1.10
J13	D2	30c blue	1.40	1.40
J14	D2	50c black	1.60	1.60
J15	D2	60c orange	2.00	2.00
J16	D2	1fr violet	2.10	2.10
		Nos. J9-J16 (8)	9.55	9.55

Type of 1914 Issue
Surcharged

1927

J17	D2	2fr on 1fr lilac rose	5.50	5.50
J18	D2	3fr on 1fr org brn	5.50	5.50

Carved Mask — D3

1941   Engr.   Perf. 14x13

J19	D3	5c black	.25	.25
J20	D3	10c lilac rose	.25	.25
J21	D3	15c dark blue	.25	.25
J22	D3	20c bright yel green	.30	.30
J23	D3	30c orange	.50	.50
J24	D3	50c violet brown	.70	.70
J25	D3	60c slate green	1.10	1.10
J26	D3	1fr rose red	1.40	1.40
J27	D3	2fr yellow	1.50	1.50
J28	D3	3fr dark purple	1.90	1.90
		Nos. J19-J28 (10)	8.15	8.15

Type D3 without "RF"

1944

J28A	D3	10c lilac rose	.50
J28B	D3	15c dark blue	.55
J28C	D3	20c bright yel green	.55
		Nos. J28A-J28C (3)	1.60

Nos. J28A-J28C were issued by the Vichy government in France, but were not placed on sale in Dahomey.

Catalogue values for unused stamps in this section, from this point to the end of the section, are for Never Hinged items.

Republic

Panther and Man — D4

Perf. 14x13½

1963, July 22   Typo.   Unwmk.

J29	D4	1fr green & rose	.25	.25
J30	D4	2fr brn & emerald	.30	.30
J31	D4	5fr org & vio bl	.30	.30
J32	D4	10fr magenta & blk	.65	.65
J33	D4	20fr vio bl & org	1.10	1.10
		Nos. J29-J33 (5)	2.60	2.60

Heliograph — D5

No. J35, Mail boat. No. J36, Morse receiver. No. J37, Mailman on bicycle. No. J38, Early telephone. No. J39, Autorail. No. J40, Mail truck. No. J41, Radio tower. No. J42, DC-8F jet plane. No. J43, Early Bird communications satellite.

1967, Oct. 24   Engr.   Perf. 11

J34	D5	1fr brn, dl pur & bl	.25	.25
J35	D5	1fr dl pur, brn & bl	.25	.25
a.		Pair, #J34-J35	.25	
J36	D5	3fr dk brn, dk grn & org	.25	.25
J37	D5	3fr dk grn, dk brn & org	.25	.25
a.		Pair, #J36-J37	.25	
J38	D5	5fr ol bis, lil & bl	.35	.35
J39	D5	5fr lil, ol bis & bl	.35	.35
a.		Pair, #J38-J39	.75	
J40	D5	10fr brn org, vio & grn	.50	.50
J41	D5	10fr vio, brn org & grn	.50	.50
a.		Pair, #J40-J41	1.10	

J42	D5	30fr Prus bl, mar & vio	1.00	1.00
J43	D5	30fr vio, Prus bl & mar	1.00	1.00
a.		Pair, #J42-J43	2.25	
		Nos. J34-J43 (10)	4.70	4.70

Pairs printed tete beche, se-tenant at the base.

PARCEL POST STAMPS

Catalogue values for unused stamps in this section are for Never Hinged items.

Nos. 141-146 and 148 Surcharged

1967, Jan. Unwmk. Engr. Perf. 13

Q1	A15	5fr on 1fr multi	.25	.25
Q2	A15	10fr on 2fr multi	.35	.35
Q3	A15	20fr on 6fr multi	.60	.60
Q4	A15	25fr on 3fr multi	.90	.90
Q5	A15	30fr on 4fr multi	1.00	1.00
Q6	A15	50fr on 10fr multi	1.40	1.40
a.		"20" instead of "50"	100.00	
Q7	A15	100fr on 20fr multi	2.50	2.50
		Nos. Q1-Q7 (7)	7.00	7.00

The surcharge is arranged to fit the shape of the stamp.
No. Q6a occurred once on the sheet.

DALMATIA

dal-'mă-shē-ə

LOCATION — A promontory in the northwestern part of the Balkan Peninsula, together with several small islands in the Adriatic Sea.
GOVT. — Part of the former Austro-Hungarian crownland of the same name.
AREA — 113 sq. mi.
POP. — 18,719 (1921)
CAPITAL — Zara.

Stamps were issued during Italian occupation. This territory was subsequently annexed by Italy.

100 Centesimi = 1 Corona = 1 Lira

Used values are for postally used stamps.

Issued under Italian Occupation

Italy No. 87 Surcharged

1919, May 1   Wmk. 140   Perf. 14

1	A46	1cor on 1 l brn & grn	3.00	12.00
a.		Pair, one without surcharge	1,050.	1,050.

Italian Stamps of 1906-08 Surcharged — a

1921-22

2	A48	5c on 5c green	4.00	8.00
3	A48	10c on 10c claret	4.00	8.00
a.		Pair, one without surcharge	775.00	
4	A49	25c on 25c blue ('22)	6.00	11.25
5	A49	50c on 50c vio ('22)	6.00	11.00
a.		Double surcharge		300.00
b.		Pair, one without surcharge	1,000.	

Italian Stamps of 1901-10 Surcharged — b

6	A46	1cor on 1 l brn & grn ('22)	10.00	24.00
7	A46	5cor on 5 l bl & rose ('22)	40.00	110.00
8	A51	10cor on 10 l gray grn & red ('22)	40.00	110.00
		Nos. 2-8 (7)	110.00	282.25

Surcharges similar to these but differing in style or arrangement of type were used in Austria under Italian occupation.

SPECIAL DELIVERY STAMPS

Italian Special Delivery No. E1 Srchd. Type "a"

1921   Wmk. 140   Perf. 14

E1	SD1	25c on 25c rose red	3.00	12.00
a.		Double surcharge	290.00	500.00

Italian Special Delivery Stamp Surcharged

1922

E2	SD2	1.20 l on 1.20 l	195.00

No. E2 was not placed in use.

POSTAGE DUE STAMPS

Italian Postage Due Stamps and Type Surcharged types "a" or "b"

1922   Wmk. 140   Perf. 14

J1	D3 (a)	50c on 50c buff & mag	4.00	9.00
J2	D3 (b)	1cor on 1 l bl & red	9.00	32.50
J3	D3 (b)	2cor on 2 l bl & red	55.00	135.00
J4	D3 (b)	5cor on 5 l bl & red	55.00	135.00
		Nos. J1-J4 (4)	123.00	311.50

DANISH WEST INDIES

'dā-nish 'west 'in-dēs

LOCATION — Group of islands in the West Indies, lying east of Puerto Rico
GOVT. — Danish colony
AREA — 132 sq. mi.
POP. — 27,086 (1911)
CAPITAL — Charlotte Amalie

The US bought these islands in 1917 and they became the US Virgin Islands, using US stamps and currency.

100 Cents = 1 Dollar
100 Bit = 1 Franc (1905)

Wmk. 111 — Small Crown

Wmk. 112 — Crown

Wmk. 113 — Crown

Wmk. 114 — Multiple Crosses

Coat of Arms — A1

Yellowish Paper
Yellow Wavy-line Burelage, UL to LR

1856   Typo.   Wmk. 111   Imperf.

1	A1	3c dark carmine, brown gum	210.	235.
a.		3c dark carmine, yellow gum	350.	375.
b.		3c carmine, white gum	3,750.	3,750.

The brown and yellow gums were applied locally.
Reprint: 1981, carmine, back-printed across two stamps ("Reprint by Dansk Post og Telegrafmuseum 1978"), value, pair, $10.

White Paper

1866
Yellow Wavy-line Burelage UR to LL

2	A1	3c rose	42.50	50.

No. 2 reprints, unwatermarked: 1930, carmine, value $100. 1942, rose carmine, back-printed across each row ("Nytryk 1942 G. A. Hagemann Danmark og Dansk Vestindiens Frimaerker Bind 2"), value $50.

1872   Perf. 12½

3	A1	3c rose	130.	320.

1873   Without Burelage

4	A1	4c dull blue	325.	700.
a.		Imperf., pair	775.	
b.		Horiz. pair, imperf. vert.	575.	

The 1930 reprint of No. 4 is ultramarine, unwatermarked and imperf., value $100.
The 1942 4c reprint is blue, unwatermarked, imperf. and has printing on back (see note below No. 2), value $60.

A2

Normal Frame

Inverted Frame

The arabesques in the corners have a main stem and a branch. When the frame is in normal position, in the upper left corner the branch leaves the main stem half way between two little leaflets. In the lower right corner the branch starts at the foot of the second leaflet. When the frame is inverted the corner designs are, of course, transposed.
Values for inverted frames, covers and blocks are for the cheapest variety.

White Wove Paper
Varying from Thin to Thick

1874-79   Wmk. 112   Perf. 14x13½

5	A2	1c green & brown red	35.00	32.50
a.		1c green & rose lilac, thin paper	160.00	190.00
b.		1c green & red violet, medium paper	50.00	65.00
c.		1c green & claret, thick paper	32.50	26.00
e.		As "c," inverted frame	40.00	26.00
f.		As "a," inverted frame	900.00	1,900.

No. 5 exists with a surcharge similar to the surcharge on No. 15, with 10 CENTS value and 1895 date. This stamp is an essay.

6	A2	3c blue & carmine	35.00	18.00
a.		3c light blue & rose carmine, thin paper	45.00	35.00
b.		3c deep blue & dark carmine, medium paper	45.00	25.00
c.		3c greenish blue & lake, thick paper	29.00	18.00

d.	Imperf., pair	325.00	—
e.	Inverted frame, thick paper	45.00	35.00
f.	As "a," inverted frame	800.00	1,200.
7	A2 4c brown & dull blue	23.00	22.50
b.	4c brown & ultramarine, thin paper	290.00	250.00
c.	Diagonal half used as 2c on cover		165.00
d.	As "b," inverted frame	1,450.	2,400.
8	A2 5c grn & gray ('76)	45.00	29.00
a.	5c yellow green & dark gray, thin paper	85.00	45.00
b.	Inverted frame, thick paper	37.50	26.00
9	A2 7c lilac & orange	40.00	135.00
a.	7c lilac & yellow	120.00	130.00
b.	Inverted frame	65.00	220.00
10	A2 10c blue & brn ('76)	57.50	34.00
a.	10c dark blue & black brown, thin paper	85.00	47.50
b.	Period between "t" & "s" of "cents"	72.50	47.50
c.	Inverted frame	26.00	27.50
11	A2 12c red lil & yel grn ('77)	60.00	170.00
a.	12c lilac & deep green	230.00	240.00
12	A2 14c lilac & green	1,050.	1,750.
a.	Inverted frame	4,000.	4,800.
13	A2 50c vio, thin paper ('79)	260.00	390.00
a.	50c gray violet, thick paper	310.00	525.00
	Nos. 5-13 (9)	1,606.	2,581.

The central element in the fan-shaped scrollwork at the outside of the lower left corner of Nos. 5a and 7b looks like an elongated diamond.

See Nos. 16-20. For surcharges see Nos. 14-15, 23-28, 40.

No. 9 Surcharged in Black

a

1887

14	A2 (a) 1c on 7c lilac & orange	140.00	275.00
b.	1c on 7c lilac & yellow	190.00	300.00
d.	Inverted frame	175.00	525.00

No. 13 Surcharged in Black

b

1895

15	A2 (b) 10c on 50c violet, thin paper	45.00	72.50

The "b" surcharge also exists on No. 5, with "10" found in two sizes. These are essays.

Type of 1874-79

1896-1901   *Perf. 13*

16	A2 1c grn & red vio, inverted frame ('98)	26.00	36.50
a.	Normal frame	590.00	735.00
17	A2 3c blue & lake, inverted frame ('98)	15.50	17.00
a.	Normal frame	400.00	600.00
18	A2 4c bister & dull blue ('01)	21.50	13.50
a.	Diagonal half used as 2c on cover		67.50
b.	Inverted frame	85.00	110.00
c.	As "b," diagonal half used as 2c on cover		425.00
19	A2 5c green & gray, inverted frame	47.50	42.50
a.	Normal frame	1,375.	1,700.
20	A2 10c blue & brn ('01)	110.00	145.00
a.	Inverted frame	1,550.	2,925.
b.	Period between "t" and "s" of "cents"	155.00	180.00
	Nos. 16-20 (5)	220.50	254.50

Arms — A5

1900

21	A5 1c light green	2.60	2.25
22	A5 5c light blue	17.00	25.00

See Nos. 29-30. For surcharges see Nos. 41-42.

Nos. 6, 17, 20 Surcharged

c

Surcharge "c" in Black

1902   *Perf. 14x13½*

23	A2 2c on 3c blue & carmine, inverted frame	1,075.	1,450.
a.	"2" in date with straight tail	1,200.	1,600.
b.	Normal frame		—

Perf. 13

24	A2 2c on 3c blue & lake, inverted frame	11.50	32.00
a.	"2" in date with straight tail	30.00	50.00
b.	Dated "1901"	1,000.	1,000.
c.	Normal frame	320.00	825.00
d.	Dark green surcharge	3,000.	
e.	As "d" & "a"		—
f.	As "d" & "c"		—

The overprint on No. 24b exists in two types: with "1901" measuring 2.5 mm or 2.2 mm high.

Only one example of No. 24f can exist.

25	A2 8c on 10c blue & brown	26.00	55.00
a.	"2" with straight tail	35.00	65.00
b.	On No. 20b	55.00	85.00
c.	Inverted frame	300.00	675.00

d

Surcharge "d" in Black

1902   *Perf. 13*

27	A2 2c on 3c blue & lake, inverted frame	15.75	63.00
a.	Normal frame	415.00	720.00
28	A2 8c on 10c blue & brown	14.00	15.00
a.	On No. 20b	26.00	32.00
b.	Inverted frame	415.00	675.00
	Nos. 23-28 (5)	1,142.	1,615.

1903   *Wmk. 113*

29	A5 2c carmine	9.50	25.00
30	A5 8c brown	36.00	62.00

King Christian IX — A8

St. Thomas Harbor — A9

1905   Typo.   *Perf. 13*

31	A8 5b green	4.75	3.00
32	A8 10b red	4.75	3.00
33	A8 20b green & blue	9.50	8.00
34	A8 25b ultramarine	9.50	8.00
35	A8 40b red & gray	9.50	7.00
36	A8 50b yellow & gray	14.00	11.00

Perf. 12
Wmk. Two Crowns (113)
Frame Typographed, Center Engraved

37	A9 1fr green & blue	17.50	50.00
38	A9 2fr orange red & brown	32.50	67.50
39	A9 5fr yellow & brown	85.00	315.00
	Nos. 31-39 (9)	187.00	472.50

Favor cancels exist on Nos. 37-39. Value 25% less.

Nos. 18, 22 and 30 Surcharged in Black

1905   *Wmk. 112*

40	A2 5b on 4c bister & dull blue	17.50	70.00
a.	Inverted frame	110.00	190.00
41	A5 5b on 5c light blue	13.00	64.00

Wmk. 113

42	A5 5b on 8c brown	13.00	75.00
	Nos. 40-42 (3)	43.50	209.00

Favor cancels exist on Nos. 40-42. Value 25% less.

Frederik VIII — A10

Frame Typographed, Center Engraved

1908

43	A10 5b green	2.75	1.90
44	A10 10b red	2.75	1.90
45	A10 15b violet & brown	5.00	5.75
46	A10 20b green & blue	32.50	27.50
47	A10 25b blue & dark blue	2.25	2.50
48	A10 30b claret & slate	67.50	60.00
49	A10 40b vermilion & gray	8.00	11.50
50	A10 50b yellow & brown	8.50	10.00
	Nos. 43-50 (8)	129.25	121.05

Christian X — A11

1915   *Wmk. 114*   *Perf. 14x14½*

51	A11 5b yellow green	5.25	6.25
52	A11 10b red	5.25	110.00
53	A11 15b lilac & red brown	5.25	110.00
54	A11 20b green & blue	5.25	110.00
55	A11 25b blue & dark blue	5.25	16.00
56	A11 30b claret & black	5.25	200.00
57	A11 40b orange & black	5.25	200.00
58	A11 50b yellow & brown	5.25	200.00
	Nos. 51-58 (8)	42.00	952.25

Forged and favor cancellations exist.

POSTAGE DUE STAMPS

Royal Cipher,
"Christian 9 Rex" — D1

1902   Litho.   Unwmk.   *Perf. 11½*

J1	D1 1c dark blue	8.25	45.00
J2	D1 4c dark blue	20.00	45.00
J3	D1 6c dark blue	40.00	87.50
J4	D1 10c dark blue	40.00	87.50
	Nos. J1-J4 (4)	108.25	265.00

There are five types of each value. On the 4c they may be distinguished by differences in the figure "4"; on the other values differences are minute.

Used values of Nos. J1-J8 are for canceled stamps. Uncanceled stamps without gum have probably been used. Value 60% of unused.

Excellent counterfeits of Nos. J1-J4 exist.

Numeral of value — D2

1905-13   *Perf. 13*

J5	D2 5b red & gray	6.50	8.00
J6	D2 20b red & gray	11.50	14.50
J7	D2 30b red & gray	9.50	14.50
J8	D2 50b red & gray	9.00	36.00
a.	Perf. 14x14½ ('13)	75.00	290.00
b.	Perf. 11½	475.00	
	Nos. J5-J8 (4)	36.50	73.00

All values of this issue are known imperforate, but were not regularly issued.

Used values of Nos. J5-J8 are for canceled stamps. Uncanceled examples without gum have probably been used. Value 60% of unused.

No. J8b is valued in the grade of fine.

Counterfeits of Nos. J5-J8 exist.

Danish West Indies stamps were replaced by those of the U.S. in 1917, after the U.S. bought the islands.

DANZIG

'dan̪t̪s-sig

LOCATION — In northern Europe bordering on the Baltic Sea
AREA — 754 sq. mi.
POP. — 407,000 (approx. 1939)
CAPITAL — Danzig

Established as a "Free City and State" under the protection of the League of Nations in 1920, Danzig was seized by Germany in 1939. It became a Polish province in 1945.

100 Pfennig = 1 Gulden (1923)
100 Pfennig = 1 Mark

Watermarks

Wmk. 108 — Honeycomb

Wmk. 109 — Webbing

Wmk. 110 — Octagons

Wmk. 125 — Lozenges

Wmk. 237 — Swastikas

Used Values of 1920-23 are for favor-canceled stamps unless otherwise noted. Postally used examples bring much higher prices.

For additional varieties, see the *Scott Classic Catalogue*.

German Stamps of 1906-20 Overprinted in Black

Perf. 14, 14½, 15x14½

			1920		Wmk. 125
1	A16	5pf green		.30	.50
a.		Pair, one without overprint	100.00		
b.		Double overprint	—		
2	A16	10pf car rose		.30	.30
3	A22	15pf violet brown		.30	.30
4	A16	20pf blue violet		.30	1.10
5	A16	30pf org & blk, *buff*		.30	.30
a.		Pair, one without overprint	—		—
6	A16	40pf car rose		.30	.30
7	A16	50pf pur & blk, *buff*		.50	.30
a.		Pair, one without overprint	175.00		
8	A17	1m red		.50	.60
a.		Pair, one without overprint	100.00		
9	A17	1.25m green		.50	.60
10	A17	1.50m yellow brn		.90	1.60
11	A21	2m blue		3.25	7.25
a.		Double overprint	375.00		
12	A21	2.50m lilac rose		3.00	4.50
c.		Double overprint	1,000.		
13	A19	3m black violet		7.50	10.50
a.		3m blackish slate-violet	67.50		135.00
b.		Double overprint	—		
14	A16	4m black & rose		4.75	6.00

15	A20	5m slate & car (25x17 holes)		2.50	3.75
a.		Center & "Danzig" invtd.	15,000.		
b.		Inverted overprint			20,000.
		Nos. 1-15 (15)		25.20	37.90
		Set, never hinged	122.50		

The 5pf brown, 10pf orange and 40pf lake and black with this overprint were not regularly issued. Value for trio, $450.
For surcharges see Nos. 19-23, C1-C3.
Issued: 40pf, 9/13; 1.50m, 3m 7/20; 4m, 12/21; others 6/14.

Nos. 5, 4 Surcharged in Various Sizes

1920

19	A16	5pf on 30pf (V)	.25	.25
20	A16	10pf on 20pf (R)	.25	.25
a.		Double surcharge	110.00	
21	A16	25pf on 30pf (G)	.25	.25
a.		Inverted surcharge	85.00	275.00
22	A16	60pf on 30pf (Br)	.70	1.00
a.		Double surcharge	85.00	290.00
b.		Pair, one without surcharge	75.00	
23	A16	80pf on 30pf (V)	.70	1.00

Issued: No. 21, 8/10. No. 20, 8/17. Nos. 19, 22-23, 11/1.

German Stamps Surcharged in Various Styles

No. 25   No. 27

No. 30

Burelage With Points Up

Gray Burelage with Points Up

25	A16	1m on 30pf org & blk, *buff* (Bk)	.85	1.50
a.		Pair, one without surcharge		
26	A16	1¼m on 3pf brn (R)	1.00	1.50
27	A22	2m on 35pf red brn (Bl)	1.50	1.50
d.		Surcharge omitted	70.00	—
28	A22	3m on 7½pf org (G)	1.00	1.50
29	A22	5m on 2pf gray (R)	1.00	2.00
30	A22	10m on 7½pf org (Bk)	3.00	7.00
		Nos. 19-30 (11)	10.50	17.75
		Set, never hinged	64.00	

Gray Burelage with Points Down

26a	A16	1¼m on 3pf brown	36.00	42.50
27a	A22	2m on 35pf red brn	400.00	325.00
28a	A22	3m on 7½pf orange	25.00	17.00
29a	A22	5m on 2pf gray	25.00	30.00
30a	A22	10m on 7½pf orange	5.75	11.00
		Nos. 26a-30a (5)	491.75	425.50
		Set, never hinged	2,100.	

Violet Burelage with Points Up

25b	A16	1m on 30pf org & blk, *buff*	85.00	30.00
26b	A16	1¼m on 3pf brown	4.50	6.50
27b	A22	2m on 35pf red brn	11.50	37.50
28b	A22	3m on 7½pf orange	2.50	2.50
29b	A22	5m on 2pf gray	1.25	2.50
30b	A22	10m on 7½pf orange	1.25	2.50
h.		Double overprint	70.00	
		Nos. 25b-30b (6)	106.00	81.50
		Set, never hinged	430.00	

Burelage with Points Down

Violet Burelage with Points Down

25c	A16	1m on 30pf org & blk, *buff*	1.25	2.50
26c	A16	1¼m on 3pf brown	6.50	11.00
e.		Double overprint	450.00	
27c	A22	2m on 35pf red brn	30.00	50.00
28c	A22	3m on 7½pf orange	40.00	85.00
29c	A22	5m on 2pf gray	6.50	8.50
30c	A22	10m on 7½pf orange	13.50	29.00
		Nos. 25c-30c (6)	97.75	186.00
		Set, never hinged	380.00	

Excellent counterfeits of the surcharges are known.

German Stamps of 1906-20 Overprinted in Blue

1920

31	A22	2pf gray	110.00	200.00
32	A22	2½pf gray	150.00	300.00
33	A16	3pf brown	11.00	17.00
a.		Double overprint	75.00	
34	A16	5pf green	.60	.70
a.		Double overprint	85.00	
35	A22	7½pf orange	40.00	57.50
36	A16	10pf carmine	3.75	7.00
b.		Double overprint	75.00	
37	A22	15pf dk violet	.60	.70
b.		Double overprint	85.00	
38	A16	20pf blue violet	.60	.70

Overprinted in Carmine or Blue

39	A16	25pf org & blk, *yel*	.60	.70
40	A16	30pf org & blk, *buff*	50.00	92.50
42	A16	40pf lake & blk	2.25	2.50
a.		Inverted overprint	210.00	
b.		Double overprint	425.00	
43	A16	50pf pur & blk, *buff*	175.00	300.00
44	A16	60pf mag (Bl)	1,250.	2,100.
45	A16	75pf green & blk	.60	.70
a.		Double overprint	450.00	
46	A16	80pf lake & blk, *rose*	2.40	4.25
47	A17	1m carmine	1,200.	2,100.
a.		Double overprint	4,250.	

Overprinted in Carmine

48	A21	2m gray blue	1,200.	2,100.

Counterfeit overprints of Nos. 31-48 exist.
Nos. 44, 47 and 48 were issued in small quantities and usually affixed directly to the mail by the postal clerk.
For surcharge see No. 62.

A8

Hanseatic Trading Ship — A9

Serrate Roulette 13½

1921, Jan. 31   Typo.   Wmk. 108

49	A8	5pf brown & violet	.25	.25
50	A8	10pf orange & dk vio	.25	.25
51	A8	25pf green & car rose	.50	.65
52	A8	40pf carmine rose	3.75	3.25
53	A8	80pf ultra	.50	.50
54	A9	1m car rose & blk	1.60	2.00
55	A9	2m dk blue & dk grn	5.00	5.00
56	A9	3m blk & grnsh bl	2.00	2.00
57	A9	5m indigo & rose red	2.00	2.00
58	A9	10m dk grn & brn org	2.50	4.00
		Nos. 49-58 (10)	18.35	20.40
		Set, never hinged	82.50	

Issued in honor of the Constitution.
Nos. 49 and 50 with center in red instead of violet and Nos. 49-51, 54-58 with center inverted are probably proofs. All values of this issue exist imperforate but are not known to have been regularly issued in that condition.

1921, Mar. 11   Perf. 14

59	A8	25pf green & car rose	.50	.85
60	A8	40pf carmine rose	.50	.85
61	A8	80pf ultra	5.50	10.00
		Nos. 59-61 (3)	6.50	11.70
		Set, never hinged	34.00	

No. 45 Surcharged in Black

1921, May 6   Wmk. 125

62	A16	60pf on 75pf	.95	.90
		Never hinged	5.50	
a.		Double surcharge	100.00	110.00

Surcharge on No. 62 normally appears at top of design.

Arms A11

Coat of Arms A12

Wmk. 108 (Upright or Sideways)

1921-22   Perf. 14

63	A11	5(pf) orange	.25	.25
64	A11	10(pf) dark brown	.25	.25
65	A11	15(pf) green	.25	.25
66	A11	20(pf) slate	.25	.25
67	A11	25(pf) dark green	.25	.25
68	A11	30(pf) blue & car	.25	.25
a.		Center inverted	75.00	150.00
69	A11	40(pf) green & car	.25	.25
a.		Center inverted	75.00	150.00
70	A11	50(pf) dk grn & car	.25	.25
71	A11	60(pf) carmine	.45	.45
72	A11	80(pf) black & car	.35	.45

Paper With Faint Gray Network

73	A11	1m org & car	.50	.40
a.		Center inverted	75.00	150.00
74	A11	1.20m blue violet	1.25	1.25
75	A11	2m gray & car	3.25	4.25
76	A11	3m violet & car	9.00	10.00

Serrate Roulette 13½
Wmk. 108 Upright

77	A12	5m grn, red & blk	1.25	3.00
78	A12	9m rose, red & org ('22)	3.00	8.50
79	A12	10m ultra, red & blk	1.25	3.00
80	A12	20m red & black	1.25	3.00
		Nos. 63-80 (18)	23.55	36.30
		Set, never hinged	85.00	

In this and succeeding issues the mark values usually have the face of the paper covered with a gray network. This network is often very faint and occasionally is omitted.
Nos. 64-76 exist imperf. Value, each $16-$50 unused, $50-$150 never hinged.
See Nos. 81-93, 99-105. For surcharges and overprints see Nos. 96-98, O1-O33.

Type of 1921 and

A13

Coat of Arms — A13a

1922   Wmk. 108 Upright   Perf. 14

81	A11	75(pf) deep vio	.25	.25
82	A11	80(pf) green	.25	.25
83	A11	1.25m vio & car	.25	.25
84	A11	1.50m slate gray	.25	.40
85	A11	2m car rose	.25	.25
86	A11	2.40m dk brn & car	1.15	2.00
87	A11	3m car lake	.25	.40
88	A11	4m dark blue	1.15	2.00
89	A11	5m deep grn	.25	.35
90	A11	6m car lake	.25	.35
a.		6m car rose, wmk. 109 sideways	1,800.	
91	A11	8m light blue	.45	1.60
92	A11	10m orange	.25	.35
93	A11	20m org brn	.25	.35
94	A13	50m gold & car	2.00	6.50
95	A13a	100m metallic grn & red	3.25	6.00
		Nos. 81-95 (15)	10.50	21.30
		Set, never hinged	42.50	

No. 95 has buff instead of gray network.
Nos. 81-83, 85-86, 88 exist imperf. Value, each $12.50.
Nos. 94-95 exist imperf. Value, each $50

Nos. 87, 88 and 91 Surcharged in Black or Carmine

1922

96	A11	6m on 3m car lake	.35	.60
a.		Double surcharge		
97	A11	8m on 4m dk blue	.35	.85
a.		Double surcharge	70.00	145.00
b.		Pair, one without surcharge	150.00	
98	A11	20m on 8m lt bl (C)	.35	.60
		Nos. 96-98 (3)	1.05	2.05
		Set, never hinged	4.00	

Wmk. 109 Sideways

1922-23   **Perf. 14**

99	A11	4m dark blue	.25	.40
100	A11	5m dark green	.25	.40
102	A11	10m orange	.25	.40
103	A11	20m orange brn	.25	.40

Paper Without Network
Wmk. 109 Upright

104	A11	40m pale blue	.25	.60
105	A11	80m red	.25	.60
		Nos. 99-105 (6)	1.50	2.80
		Set, never hinged	5.40	

Nos. 100, 102 and 103 also exist with watermark vertical. Values slightly higher.

Nos. 104-105 exist imperf. Value, each $12.50 unused, $32.50 never hinged.

A15   A15a

Coat of Arms — A16

1922-23   **Wmk. 109 Upright**   **Perf. 14**
Paper With Gray Network

106	A15	50m pale bl & red	.25	.40
107	A15a	100m dk grn & red	.25	.40
108	A15a	150m violet & red	.25	.40
109	A16	250m violet & red	.40	.40
110	A16	500m gray blk & red	.40	.40
111	A16	1000m brn & red	.40	.40
112	A16	5000m silver & red	1.50	6.00

Paper Without Network

113	A15	50m pale blue	.40	.60
114	A15a	100m deep green	.40	.60
115	A15	200m orange	.40	.60
		Nos. 106-115 (10)	4.65	10.20
		Set, never hinged	19.00	

Nos. 108-112 exist imperf. Value, each $50 unused, $125 never hinged.
Nos. 113-115 exist imperf. Value, each $35 unused, $92.50 never hinged.
See Nos. 123-125. For surcharges and overprints see Nos. 126, 137-140, 143, 156-167, O35-O38.

A17

1923   **Perf. 14**
Paper With Gray Network

117	A17	250m violet & red	.25	.55
118	A17	300m bl grn & red	.25	.55
119	A17	500m gray & red	.25	.55
120	A17	1000m brown & red	.25	.55
121	A17	3000m violet & red	.25	.55

123	A16	10,000m orange & red	.60	.60
124	A16	20,000m pale bl & red	.60	1.00
125	A16	50,000m green & red	.60	1.00
		Nos. 117-125 (8)	3.05	5.35
		Set, never hinged	12.50	

Nos. 117, 119-121 exist imperf. Value, each $19 unused, $45 never hinged; Nos. 123-125 also exist imperf. Values each, $25 unused, $85 never hinged.
See Nos. 127-135. For surcharges & overprints see Nos. 141-142, 144-155, O39-O41.

No. 124 Surcharged in Red

1923, Aug. 14

126	A16	100,000m on #124	1.00	6.00
		Never hinged	4.50	

No. 126 exists imperf. Value $50 unused, $125 never hinged.

1923   **Perf. 14**
Paper Without Network

127	A17	1000m brown	.25	.40
129	A17	5000m rose	.25	.40
131	A17	20,000m pale blue	.25	.40
132	A17	50,000m green	.25	.40

Paper With Gray Network

133	A17	100,000m deep blue	.25	.40
b.		Double impression	80.00	
134	A17	250,000m violet	.25	.40
135	A17	500,000m slate	.25	.40
		Nos. 127-135 (7)	1.75	2.80
		Set, never hinged	5.00	

Abbreviations:
th=(tausend) thousand
mil=million

Nos. 115, 114, 132, and Type of 1923 Surcharged

No. 137-139

No. 140

No. 141   No. 142

1923   **Perf. 14**
Paper Without Network

137	A15	40th m on 200m	.85	2.00
a.		Double surcharge	85.00	
138	A15	100th m on 200m	.85	2.00
139	A15	250th m on 200m	6.25	13.00
140	A15a	400th m on 100m	.60	.60
141	A17	500th m on #132	.40	.60

On 10,000m

142	A17	1mil m org	3.75	6.25

The surcharges on Nos. 140-142 differ in details from those on Nos. 137-139.

Type of 1923 Surcharged

Paper With Gray Network
On 1,000,000m

143	A16	10mil m org	.40	1.25
		Nos. 137-143 (7)	13.10	25.70
		Set, never hinged	60.00	

Nos. 142-143 exist imperf. Values: No. 142 unused $50, never hinged $125; No. 143 unused $25, never hinged $85.

Type of 1923 Surcharged

Wmk. 109 Upright
Perf. 14
10,000m rose on paper without Network

144	A17	1mil m on 10,000m	.25	.60
145	A17	2mil m on 10,000m	.25	.60
146	A17	3mil m on 10,000m	.25	.60
147	A17	5mil m on 10,000m	.35	.60
b.		Double surcharge	85.00	

10,000m gray lilac on paper without Network

148	A17	10mil m on 10,000m	.40	.75
149	A17	20mil m on 10,000m	.40	.75
150	A17	25mil m on 10,000m	.25	.75
151	A17	40mil m on 10,000m	.25	.75
a.		Double surcharge	52.50	
152	A17	50mil m on 10,000m	.25	.75

Type of 1923 Surcharged in Red

10,000m gray lilac on paper without Network

153	A17	100mil m on 10,000m	.25	.75
154	A17	300mil m on 10,000m	.25	.75
155	A17	500mil m on 10,000m	.25	.75
		Nos. 144-155 (12)	3.40	8.40
		Set, never hinged	15.00	

Nos. 144-147 exist imperf. Value, each $25 unused, $85 never hinged. Nos. 148-155 exist imperf. Value, each $32.50 unused, $85 never hinged.

Types of 1923 Surcharged

1923, Oct. 31   **Wmk. 110**   **Perf. 14**

156	A15	5pf on 50m	.45	.40
157	A15	10pf on 50m	.45	.40
158	A15a	20pf on 100m	.45	.40
159	A15	25pf on 50m	3.50	9.00
160	A15	30pf on 50m	3.50	2.00
161	A15a	40pf on 100m	2.25	2.00
162	A15a	50pf on 100m	2.25	3.00
163	A15a	75pf on 100m	8.00	16.00

Type of 1923 Surcharged

1923, Nov. 5

164	A16	1g on 1mil m rose	4.50	6.25
165	A16	2g on 1mil m rose	12.00	17.50
166	A16	3g on 1mil m rose	22.00	62.50
167	A16	5g on 1mil m rose	25.00	67.50
		Nos. 156-167 (12)	84.35	186.95
		Set, never hinged	400.00	

Coat of Arms — A19

1924-37   **Wmk. 109**   **Perf. 14**

168	A19	3pf brn, yelsh ('35)	1.25	1.50
a.		3pf dp brn, white ('27)	2.10	1.90
170	A19	5pf org, yelsh	3.25	.55
a.		White paper	8.50	2.00
c.		Tête bêche pair	375.00	
d.		Syncopated perf., #170	10.50	9.25
e.		Syncopated perf., #170a	25.00	22.50
171	A19	7pf yel grn ('33)	1.60	3.00
172	A19	8pf yel grn ('37)	1.60	6.00
173	A19	10pf grn, yelsh	5.50	.50
a.		White paper	11.50	2.50
c.		10pf blue grn, yellowish	7.75	1.10
d.		Tête bêche pair	325.00	
e.		Syncopated perf., #173	18.00	11.00
f.		Syncopated perf., #173a	27.50	13.00
g.		Syncopated perf., #173c	11.00	14.50
175	A19	15pf gray	3.75	.65
176	A19	15pf red, yelsh ('35)	2.10	1.10
a.		White paper ('25)	4.50	1.10
177	A19	20pf carmine & red	15.00	.65
178	A19	20pf gray ('35)	2.25	2.50
179	A19	25pf slate & red	27.00	3.75
180	A19	25pf carmine ('35)	16.00	1.60
181	A19	30pf green & red	14.00	.85
182	A19	30pf dk violet ('35)	2.25	4.25
183	A19	35pf ultra	4.50	1.50
184	A19	40pf dk blue & blue	12.00	1.00
185	A19	40pf yel brn & red	6.50	12.50
186	A19	40pf dk blue ('35)	2.25	3.75
a.		Imperf.	60.00	
187	A19	50pf blue & red	16.00	7.50
a.		Yellowish paper	17.50	32.50
188	A19	55pf plum & scar	5.00	14.50
189	A19	60pf dk grn & red	6.25	17.50
190	A19	70pf yel grn & red ('35)	2.25	7.50
191	A19	75pf violet & red, yellowish	7.50	29.00
a.		White paper	10.00	8.50
192	A19	80pf dk org brn & red ('35)	2.25	7.50
		Nos. 168-192 (23)	160.05	129.15
		Set, never hinged	675.00	

The 5pf and 10pf with syncopated perforations (Netherlands type C) are coils.
See Nos. 225-232. For overprints and surcharges see Nos. 200-209, 211-215, 241-252, B9-B11, O42-O52.

Oliva Castle and   St. Mary's
Cathedral   Church
A20   A23

Council Chamber on the
Langenmarkt — A24

2g, Mottlau River & Krantor. 3g, View of Zoppot.

1924-32   **Engr.**   **Wmk. 125**

193	A20	1g yel grn & blk	21.00	45.00
		Parcel post cancel		20.00
194	A20	1g org & gray blk ('32)	17.00	3.75
		Parcel post cancel		1.00
a.		1g red orange & blk	17.00	11.00
		Parcel post cancel		1.00
195	A20	2g red vio & blk	45.00	110.00
		Parcel post cancel		40.00
196	A20	2g rose & blk	3.75	8.00
		Parcel post cancel		1.75
197	A20	3g dk blue & blk	4.75	5.00
		Parcel post cancel		2.25
198	A23	5g brn red & blk	4.75	8.50
		Parcel post cancel		1.90
199	A24	10g dk brn & blk	21.00	110.00
		Parcel post cancel		18.00
		Nos. 193-199 (7)	117.25	290.25
		Set, never hinged	600.00	

See No. 233. For overprints and surcharges see Nos. 210, 253-254, C31-C35.

Stamps of 1924-25
Overprinted in Black,
Violet or Red

1930, Nov. 15   **Typo.**   **Wmk. 109**

200	A19	5pf orange	2.50	3.50
201	A19	10pf yellow grn (V)	3.50	4.25
202	A19	15pf red	6.00	10.00
203	A19	20pf carmine & red	3.00	5.50
204	A19	25pf slate & red	4.25	10.00
205	A19	30pf green & red	8.50	22.50
206	A19	35pf ultra (R)	32.50	90.00
207	A19	40pf dk bl & bl (R)	11.50	35.00
208	A19	50pf dp blue & red	32.50	75.00
209	A19	75pf violet & red	32.50	82.50

                Engr.   **Wmk. (125)**

210	A20	1g orange & blk (R)	32.50	75.00
		Nos. 200-210 (11)	169.25	413.25
		Set, never hinged	675.00	

10th anniv. of the Free State. Counterfeits exist.

Nos. 171 and 183 Surcharged in Red, Blue or Green

Nos. 211,   No. 212
213-214

No. 215

1934-36

211	A19	6pf on 7pf (R)	1.00	1.50
212	A19	8pf on 7pf (Bl)	2.00	2.25
213	A19	8pf on 7pf (Bl)	1.15	2.40
214	A19	8pf on 7pf (G)	.75	2.40
215	A19	30pf on 35pf (Bl)	11.00	24.50
	Nos. 211-215 (5)		15.90	33.05
	Set, never hinged		60.00	

Bathing Beach, Brösen — A25

View of Brösen Beach A26

War Memorial at Brösen A27

1936, June 23   Typo.   Wmk. 109

216	A25	10pf deep green	.70	.70
217	A26	25pf rose red	1.25	2.40
218	A27	40pf bright blue	2.25	4.50
	Nos. 216-218 (3)		4.20	7.60
	Set, never hinged		15.00	

Village of Brösen, 125th anniversary.
Exist imperf. Value each, $40 unused, $110 never hinged.

Skyline of Danzig — A28

1937, Mar. 27

219	A28	10pf dark blue	.50	1.40
220	A28	15pf violet brown	1.60	2.00
	Set, never hinged		11.25	
	Set of 2, #219-220 on one			
	1st day cover		20.00	

Air Defense League.

Danzig Philatelic Exhibition Issue
Souvenir Sheet

St. Mary's Church A29

1937, June 6   Wmk. 109   Perf. 14

221	A29	50pf dark opal green	4.00	20.00
	Never hinged		11.00	

Danzig Philatelic Exhib., June 6-8, 1937.

Arthur Schopenhauer
A30   A31

Design: 40pf, Full-face portrait, white hair.

Unwmk.
1938, Feb. 22   Photo.   Perf. 14

222	A30	15pf dull blue	1.35	2.40
223	A31	25pf sepia	3.25	8.00
224	A31	40pf orange ver	1.35	3.25
	Nos. 222-224 (3)		5.95	13.65
	Set, never hinged		20.00	
	Set of 3, #222-224 on one			
	1st day cover		37.50	

150th anniv. of the birth of Schopenhauer.

Type of 1924-35
1938-39   Typo.   Wmk. 237   Perf. 14

225	A19	3pf brown	.90	7.25
226	A19	5pf orange	.90	2.00
b.	Syncopated perf.		1.40	7.50
227	A19	8pf yellow grn	4.00	32.50
228	A19	10pf blue green	.90	2.00
b.	Syncopated perf.		3.00	10.00
229	A19	15pf scarlet	1.60	10.00
230	A19	25pf carmine	2.10	7.50
231	A19	40pf dark blue	2.10	27.50
232	A19	50pf brt bl & red	2.10	130.00

Engr.

233	A20	1g red org & blk	6.75	110.00
	Nos. 225-233 (9)		21.35	328.75
	Set, never hinged		90.00	

Sizes: No. 233, 32½x21¼mm; No. 194, 31x21mm.
Nos. 226b and 228b are coils with Netherlands type C perforation.

Knights in Tournament, 1500 — A33

French Leaving Danzig, 1814 — A35

Stamp Day: 10pf, Signing of Danzig-Sweden neutrality treaty, 1630. 25pf, Battle of Weichselmünde, 1577.

Unwmk.
1939, Jan. 7   Photo.   Perf. 14

234	A33	5pf dark green	.40	2.00
235	A33	10pf copper brown	.85	2.75
236	A35	15pf slate black	1.25	2.75
237	A35	25pf brown violet	1.60	3.75
	Nos. 234-237 (4)		4.10	10.75
	Set, never hinged		14.00	
	Set of 4, #234-237 on one			
	1st day cover		30.00	

Gregor Mendel — A37

15pf, Dr. Robert Koch. 25pf, Wilhelm Roentgen.

1939, Apr. 29   Photo.   Perf. 13x14

238	A37	10pf copper brown	.65	.85
239	A37	15pf indigo	.65	4.00
240	A37	25pf dark olive green	1.25	2.75
	Nos. 238-240 (3)		2.55	5.60
	Set, never hinged		7.25	

Issued in honor of the achievements of Mendel, Koch and Roentgen.

Issued under German Administration
Stamps of Danzig, 1925-39, Surcharged in Black

a   b

c

1939   Wmk. 109   Perf. 14

241	A19(b)	4rpf on 35pf ultra	.75	2.25
242	A19(b)	12rpf on 7pf yel grn	1.50	2.25
243	A19(a)	20rpf gray	3.00	8.50

Wmk. 237

244	A19(a)	3rpf brown	.75	2.40
245	A19(a)	5rpf orange	.65	3.00
246	A19(a)	8rpf yellow grn	1.10	4.25
247	A19(a)	10rpf blue grn	2.25	4.25
248	A19(a)	15rpf scarlet	6.00	11.00
249	A19(a)	25rpf carmine	4.50	10.00
250	A19(a)	30rpf dk violet	2.00	4.50

251	A19(a)	40rpf dk blue	2.75	6.00
252	A19(a)	50rpf brt bl & red	4.00	7.00

Thick Paper

253	A20(c)	1rm on 1g red org & blk	14.00	57.50

Wmk. 125
Thin White Paper

254	A20(c)	2rm on 2g rose & blk	20.00	62.50
	Nos. 241-254 (14)		63.25	185.40
	Set, never hinged		190.00	

Nos. 241-254 were valid throughout Germany.

SEMI-POSTAL STAMPS

St. George and Dragon — SP1

Wmk. 108
1921, Oct. 16   Typo.   Perf. 14
Size: 19x22mm

B1	SP1	30pf + 30pf grn & org	.45	.95
B2	SP1	60pf + 60pf rose & org	1.25	1.60

Size: 25x30mm
Serrate Roulette 13½

B3	SP1	1.20m + 1.20m dk bl & org	2.00	2.25
	Nos. B1-B3 (3)		3.70	4.80
	Set, never hinged		16.00	

Nos. B1-B3 exist imperf. Value each, $45 unused, $125 never hinged.

Aged Pensioner SP2

1923, Mar.   Wmk. 109   Perf. 14
Paper With Gray Network

B4	SP2	50m + 20m lake	.25	.60
B5	SP2	100m + 30m red vio	.25	.60
	Set, never hinged		2.50	

Nos. B4-B5 exist imperf. Value each, $50 unused, $30 used, $210 never hinged.

Philatelic Exhibition Issue

Neptune Fountain — SP3

Various Frames.

1929, July 7   Engr.   Unwmk.

B6	SP3	10pf yel grn & gray	2.40	1.60
B7	SP3	15pf car & gray	2.40	1.60
B8	SP3	25pf ultra & gray	8.50	13.00
a.	25pf violet blue & black		25.00	80.00
	Nos. B6-B8 (3)		13.30	16.20
	Set, never hinged		45.00	
	Set of 3, #B6-B8 on one 1st day cover		200.00	

These stamps were sold exclusively at the Danzig Philatelic Exhibition, June 7-14, 1929, at double their face values, the excess being for the aid of the exhibition.

Regular Issue of 1924-25
Surcharged in Black

1934, Jan. 15   Wmk. 109

B9	A19	5pf + 5pf orange	9.50	19.00
B10	A19	10pf + 5pf yel grn	22.50	45.00
B11	A19	15pf + 5pf carmine	13.50	35.00
	Nos. B9-B11 (3)		45.50	99.00
	Set, never hinged		220.00	

Surtax for winter welfare. Counterfeits exist.

Stock Tower SP4

George Hall SP6

City Gate, 16th Century — SP5

1935, Dec. 16   Typo.   Perf. 14

B12	SP4	5pf + 5pf orange	.65	1.50
B13	SP5	10pf + 5pf green	1.10	2.25
B14	SP6	15pf + 10pf scarlet	2.75	3.50
	Nos. B12-B14 (3)		4.50	7.25
	Set, never hinged		16.00	
	Set of 3, #B12-B14 on one			
	1st day cover		40.00	

Surtax for winter welfare.

Milk Can Tower SP7

Frauentor SP8

Krantor SP9

Langgarter Gate SP10

High Gate — SP11

1936, Nov. 25

B15	SP7	10pf + 5pf dk bl	1.60	4.50
a.	Imperf.		75.00	
B16	SP8	15pf + 5pf dull grn	1.60	5.75
B17	SP9	25pf + 10pf red brn	2.25	9.00
B18	SP10	40pf + 20pf brn & red brn	3.00	10.00
B19	SP11	50pf + 20pf bl & dk bl	5.25	15.00
	Nos. B15-B19 (5)		13.70	44.25
	Set, never hinged		80.00	

Surtax for winter welfare.

SP12   SP13

1937, Oct. 30   Wmk. 109 Sideways

B20	SP12	25pf + 25pf dk car	2.75	5.25

Wmk. 109 Upright

B21	SP13	40pf + 40pf blue & red	2.75	5.25
a.		Souvenir sheet of 2, #B20a-B21	60.00	110.00
		Set, never hinged	27.50	

Founding of Danzig community at Magdeburg. No. B21a exists imperf. Value, $1,600 unnused, $3,250 never hinged.

Madonna SP14

Mercury SP15

Weather Vane, Town Hall SP16

Neptune Fountain SP17

St. George and Dragon — SP18

1937, Dec. 13

B23	SP14	5pf + 5pf brt violet	2.50	7.50
B24	SP15	10pf + 10pf dk brn	2.50	5.75
B25	SP16	15pf + 5pf bl & yel	2.50	8.25
B26	SP17	25pf + 10pf bl grn & grn	3.25	11.00
B27	SP18	40pf + 25pf brt car & bl	5.75	15.00
		Nos. B23-B27 (5)	16.50	47.50
		Set, never hinged	65.00	
		Set of 5, #B23-B27 on one 1st day cover		100.00

Surtax for winter welfare. Designs are from frieze of the Artushof.

"Peter von Danzig" Yacht Race — SP19

Ships: 10pf+5pf, Dredger Fu Shing. 15pf+10pf, S. S. Columbus. 25pf+10pf, S. S. City of Danzig. 40pf+15pf, Peter von Danzig, 1472.

1938, Nov. 28 Photo. Unwmk.

B28	SP19	5pf + 5pf dk bl grn	1.40	1.50
B29	SP19	10pf + 5pf gldn brn	1.40	3.00
B30	SP19	15pf + 10pf ol grn	1.60	3.00
B31	SP19	25pf + 10pf indigo	2.50	4.00
B32	SP19	40pf + 15pf vio brn	3.00	6.75
		Nos. B28-B32 (5)	9.90	18.25
		Set, never hinged	50.00	
		Set of 5, #B28-B32 on one 1st day cover		60.00

Surtax for winter welfare.

AIR POST STAMPS

No. 6 Surcharged in Blue or Carmine

1920, Sept. 29 Wmk. 125 Perf. 14

C1	A16	40pf on 40pf	1.25	2.60
a.		Double surcharge	160.00	250.00
C2	A16	60pf on 40pf (C)	1.25	2.60
a.		Double surcharge	125.00	250.00
C3	A16	1m on 40pf	1.25	2.60
a.		Double surcharge	125.00	250.00
		Nos. C1-C3 (3)	3.75	7.80
		Set, never hinged	13.50	

Plane faces left on No. C2.

AP3

Plane over Danzig — AP4

Wmk. (108) Upright
1921-22 Typo. Perf. 14

C4	AP3	40(pf) blue green	.25	.45
C5	AP3	60(pf) dk violet	.25	.45
C6	AP3	1m carmine	.25	.45
C7	AP3	2m org brn	.25	.45

Serrate Roulette 13½
Size: 34½x23mm

C8	AP4	5m violet blue	1.25	2.25
C9	AP4	10m dp grn	2.00	4.25
		Nos. C4-C9 (6)	4.25	8.30
		Set, never hinged	18.00	

Nos. C4-C9 exist imperf. Value, each $32.50 unused, $125 never hinged.

1923 Wmk. (109) Upright Perf. 14

C10	AP3	40(pf) blue green	.55	1.90
C11	AP3	60(pf) dk violet	.55	1.90
a.		Double impression	—	
C12	AP3	1m carmine	.55	1.90
C13	AP3	2m org brown	.55	1.90
C14	AP3	25m pale blue	.40	.70

Serrate Roulette 13½
Size: 34½x23mm

C15	AP4	5m violet blue	.55	1.00
C16	AP4	10m deep green	.55	1.00

Paper With Gray Network

C17	AP4	20m org brn	.55	1.00

Size: 40x23mm

C18	AP4	50m orange	.40	.70
C19	AP4	100m red	.40	.70
C20	AP4	250m dark brown	.60	.70
C21	AP4	500m car rose	.60	.70
		Nos. C10-C21 (12)	6.25	14.10
		Set, never hinged	30.00	

Nos. C11, C12, C14-C21 exist imperf. Value, Nos. C11, C12, C15-C17, each $8.50 unused, $32.50 never hinged. Value, No. C14, C18-C21, each $40 never hinged.
Nos. C18, C19 and C21 exist with wmk. sideways, both perf and imperf. Value each, $60 unused, $160 never hinged.

Post Horn and Airplanes — AP5

1923, Oct. 18 Perf. 14
Paper Without Network

C22	AP5	250,000m scarlet	.35	1.25
C23	AP5	500,000m scarlet	.35	1.25
		Set, never hinged	2.50	

Exist imperf. Value, each: $50 unused; $125 never hinged.

Surcharged

On 100,000m

C24	AP5	2mil m scarlet	.35	1.25

On 50,000m

C25	AP5	5mil m scarlet	.35	1.25
b.		Cliché of 10,000m in sheet of 50,000m	32.50	160.00

Exist imperf. Value, each $125 unused, $290 never hinged.

Nos. C24 and C25 were not regularly issued without surcharge, although examples have been passed through the post. Values: C24 unused $8.50, never hinged $32.50; C25 unused $12, never hinged $21.

AP6

Plane over Danzig — AP7

1924

C26	AP6	10(pf) vermilion	21.00	3.50
C27	AP6	20(pf) carmine rose	2.10	1.50
C28	AP6	40(pf) olive brown	3.00	1.75
C29	AP6	1g deep green	3.00	3.00
C30	AP7	2½g violet brown	17.50	32.50
		Nos. C26-C30 (5)	46.60	42.25
		Set, never hinged	175.00	

Exist imperf. Value Nos. C26, C30, $85 unused; $200 never hinged; others, each $40 unused, $110 never hinged.

Nos. 193, 195, 197-199 Srchd. in Various Colors

1932 Wmk. 125

C31	A20	10pf on 1g (G)	9.00	21.00
C32	A20	15pf on 2g (V)	9.00	21.00
C33	A20	20pf on 3g (Bl)	9.00	21.00
C34	A23	25pf on 5g (R)	9.00	21.00
C35	A24	30pf on 10g (Br)	9.00	21.00
		Nos. C31-C35 (5)	45.00	105.00
		Set, never hinged	200.00	

Intl. Air Post Exhib. of 1932. The surcharges were variously arranged to suit the shapes and designs of the stamps. The stamps were sold at double their surcharged values, the excess being donated to the exhibition funds. No. C31 exists with inverted surcharge and with double surcharge. Value each, $85 unused; $210 never hinged.

Airplane
AP8   AP9

1935, Oct. 24 Wmk. 109

C36	AP8	10pf scarlet	1.75	.85
C37	AP8	15pf yellow	1.75	1.25
C38	AP8	25pf dark green	1.75	1.50
C39	AP8	50pf gray blue	9.00	9.25
C40	AP9	1g magenta	3.50	13.00
		Nos. C36-C40 (5)	17.75	25.85
		Set, never hinged	65.00	

Nos. C36 and C40 exist imperf. C36 unused $20, never hinged $62.50; C40 unused $29, never hinged $85.
See Nos. C42-C45.

Souvenir Sheet

St. Mary's Church AP10

1937, June 6 Perf. 14

C41	AP10	50pf dark grayish blue	3.75	16.00

Danzig Phil. Exhib., June 6-8, 1937.

Type of 1935
1938-39 Wmk. 237

C42	AP8	10pf scarlet	1.25	3.75
C43	AP8	15pf yellow ('39)	2.00	12.00
C44	AP8	25pf dark green	1.60	6.50
C45	AP8	50pf gray blue ('39)	4.00	57.50
		Nos. C42-C45 (4)	8.85	79.75
		Set, never hinged	42.50	

POSTAGE DUE STAMPS

Danzig Coat of Arms — D1

1921-22 Typo. Wmk. (108) Perf. 14
Paper Without Network

J1	D1	10(pf) deep violet	.35	.45
J2	D1	20(pf) deep violet	.35	.45
J3	D1	40(pf) deep violet	.35	.45
J4	D1	60(pf) deep violet	.35	.45
J5	D1	75(pf) dp violet ('22)	.35	.45
J6	D1	80(pf) deep violet	.35	.45
J7	D1	120(pf) deep violet	.35	.45
J8	D1	200(pf) dp violet ('22)	.95	1.00
J9	D1	240(pf) deep violet	.35	1.00
J10	D1	300(pf) dp violet ('22)	.95	1.00
J11	D1	400(pf) deep violet	.95	1.00
J12	D1	500(pf) deep violet	.95	1.00
J13	D1	800(pf) deep violet ('22)	.95	1.00
J14	D1	20m deep violet ('22)	.95	1.00
		Nos. J1-J14 (14)	8.50	10.15
		Set, never hinged	27.50	

Nos. J1-J14 exist imperf. Value, each $30 unused, $75 never hinged.

1923 Wmk. 109 Sideways

J15	D1	100(pf) deep violet	.60	.60
J16	D1	200(pf) deep violet	2.50	3.75
J17	D1	300(pf) deep violet	.60	.75
J18	D1	400(pf) deep violet	.60	.75
J19	D1	500(pf) deep violet	.60	.75
J20	D1	800(pf) deep violet	1.25	3.75
J21	D1	10m deep violet	.60	1.00
J22	D1	20m deep violet	.60	.75
J23	D1	50m deep violet	.60	.75

Paper With Gray Network

J24	D1	100m deep violet	.60	1.00
J25	D1	500m deep violet	.60	1.00
		Nos. J15-J25 (11)	9.15	15.00
		Set, never hinged	25.00	

Nos. J15, J17, J22-J25 exist imperf. Value each, $12.50 unused, $40 never hinged.

Nos. J22-J23 and Type of 1923 Surcharged

1923, Oct. 1
Paper without Network

J26	D1	5000m on 50m	.40	.75
J27	D1	10,000m on 20m	.40	.75
J28	D1	50,000m on 500m	.40	.75
J29	D1	100,000m on 20m	.85	1.25
		Nos. J26-J29 (4)	2.05	3.50
		Set, never hinged	8.00	

On No. J26 the numerals of the surcharge are all of the larger size.
A 1000(m) on 100m deep violet was prepared but not issued. Value, $145, never hinged $350.
Nos. J26-J28 exist imperf. Value each, $18 unused, $45 never hinged.

Danzig Coat of Arms — D2

1923-28 Wmk. 110

J30	D2	5(pf) blue & blk	.85	.75
J31	D2	10(pf) blue & blk	.40	.75
J32	D2	15(pf) blue & blk	1.25	1.10
J33	D2	20(pf) blue & blk	1.25	2.00
J34	D2	30(pf) blue & blk	9.00	2.00
J35	D2	40(pf) blue & blk	2.10	3.00
J36	D2	50(pf) blue & blk	2.10	2.25

J37	D2	60(pf)	blue & blk	13.00	18.00
J38	D2	100(pf)	blue & blk	17.50	9.75
J39	D2	3g	blue & car	10.00	40.00
a.		"Guldeu" instead of "Gulden"		325.00	1,050.
		Nos. J30-J39 (10)		57.45	79.60
		Set, never hinged		225.00	

Used values of Nos. J30-J39 are for postally used stamps.

See Nos. J43-J47.

Postage Due Stamps of 1923 Issue Surcharged in Red

1932, Dec. 20

J40	D2	5pf on 40(pf)		4.25	7.50
J41	D2	10pf on 60(pf)		32.50	9.00
J42	D2	20pf on 90(pf)		2.75	7.50
		Nos. J40-J42 (3)		39.50	24.00
		Set, never hinged		160.00	

Type of 1923

1938-39   Wmk. 237   Perf. 14

J43	D2	10(pf)	bl & blk ('39)	1.25	62.50
J44	D2	30(pf)	bl & blk	2.25	50.00
J45	D2	40(pf)	bl & blk ('39)	6.75	100.00
J46	D2	60(pf)	bl & blk ('39)	6.75	100.00
J47	D2	100(pf)	bl & blk	11.00	72.50
		Nos. J43-J47 (5)		28.00	385.00
		Set, never hinged		125.00	

OFFICIAL STAMPS

Regular Issues of 1921-22 Overprinted — a

1921-22   Wmk. 108   Perf. 14x14½

O1	A11	5(pf)	orange	.25	.25
O2	A11	10(pf)	dark brown	.25	.25
a.		Inverted overprint		60.00	
O3	A11	15(pf)	green	.25	.25
O4	A11	20(pf)	slate	.25	.25
O5	A11	25(pf)	dark green	.25	.25
a.		Pair, one without overprint		170.00	
O6	A11	30(pf)	blue & car	.60	.60
O7	A11	40(pf)	grn & car	.25	.25
O8	A11	50(pf)	dk grn & car	.25	.25
O9	A11	60(pf)	carmine	.25	.25
O10	A11	75(pf)	dp vio	.25	.40
O11	A11	80(pf)	black & car	.85	.85
O12	A11	80(pf)	green	.25	2.40

Paper With Faint Gray Network

O14	A11	1m	org & car	.25	.25
O15	A11	1.20m	blue violet	1.25	1.25
O16	A11	1.25m	vio & car	.25	.40
O17	A11	1.50m	slate gray	.25	.40
O18	A11	2m	gray & car	16.00	12.00
a.		Inverted overprint		110.00	
O19	A11	2m	car rose	.25	.40
O20	A11	2.40m	dk brn & car	1.25	2.40
O21	A11	3m	violet & car	8.50	10.00
O22	A11	3m	car lake	.25	.40
O23	A11	4m	dk blue	1.25	.85
O24	A11	5m	dp grn	.25	.40
O25	A11	6m	car lake	.25	.40
O26	A11	10m	orange	.25	.40
O27	A11	20m	org brn	.25	.40
		Nos. O1-O27 (26)		34.45	36.20
		Set, never hinged		175.00	

Double overprints exist on Nos. O1-O2, O5-O7, O10 and O12.

Same Overprint on No. 96

O28	A11	6m on 3m		.35	.75
		Never hinged		1.00	
a.		Inverted overprint		30.00	
		Never hinged		85.00	

No. 77 Overprinted

Serrate Roulette 13½

1922   Wmk. 108 Sideways

O29	A12	5m grn, red & blk		3.75	6.00
		Never hinged		18.00	

Nos. 99-103, 106-107 Overprinted Type "a"

1922-23   Wmk. 109   Perf. 14

O30	A11	4m	dark blue	.25	.60
O31	A11	5m	dark green	.25	.60
O32	A11	10m	orange	.25	.60
O33	A11	20m	orange brn	.25	.60
O34	A15	50m	pale blue & red	.25	.60
O35	A15a	100m	dk grn & red	.25	.60

Nos. 113-115, 118-120 Overprinted Type "a"

O36	A15	50m	pale blue	.25	.75
a.		Inverted overprint		25.00	
O37	A15a	100m	dark green	.25	.75
O38	A15	200m	orange	.25	.75
a.		Inverted overprint		25.00	

Paper With Gray Network

O39	A17	300m	bl grn & red	.25	.60
O40	A17	500m	gray & red	.25	.75
O41	A17	1000m	brn & red	.25	.75
		Nos. O30-O41 (12)		3.00	7.95
		Set, never hinged		16.80	

Regular Issue of 1924-25 Overprinted

1924-25   Perf. 14x14½

O42	A19	5pf	red orange	2.10	3.25
O43	A19	10pf	green	2.10	9.00
O44	A19	15pf	gray	2.10	3.25
O45	A19	15pf	red	19.00	10.00
O46	A19	20pf	car & red	2.10	2.10
O47	A19	25pf	slate & red	19.00	27.50
O48	A19	30pf	green & red	3.00	3.75
O49	A19	35pf	ultra	60.00	50.00
O50	A19	40pf	dk bl & dull bl	7.00	8.50
O51	A19	50pf	dp blue & red	21.00	42.50
O52	A19	75pf	violet & red	42.50	120.00
		Nos. O42-O52 (11)		179.90	279.85
		Set, never hinged		640.00	

Double overprints exist on Nos. O42-O44, O47, O50-O52.

DENMARK

'den-,märk

LOCATION — Northern part of a peninsula which separates the North and Baltic Seas, and includes the surrounding islands
GOVT. — Kingdom
AREA — 16,631 sq. mi.
POP. — 5,294,860 (1/1/1999)
CAPITAL — Copenhagen

96 Skilling = 1 Rigsbank Daler
100 Ore = 1 Krone (1875)

> Catalogue values for unused stamps in this country are for Never Hinged items, beginning with Scott 297 in the regular postage section, Scott B15 in the semipostal section, and Scott Q28 in the parcel post section.

Values for unused stamps are for examples with original gum as defined in the catalogue introduction. Very fine examples of Nos. 9-37 and O1-O9 will have perforations clear of the frame-lines but with the design noticeably off center. Well centered stamps are quite scarce and will command substantial premiums.

Watermarks

Wmk. 111 — Small Crown   Wmk. 112 — Crown

Wmk. 113 — Crown   Wmk. 114 — Multiple Crosses

Royal Emblems — A2   A1

1851   Typo.   Wmk. 111   Imperf.
With Yellow Brown Burelage

1	A1	2rs	blue	3,500.	1,000.
a.		First printing		8,250.	2,400.
2	A2	4rs	brown	600.00	40.00
a.		First printing		600.00	40.00
b.		4rs yellow brown		875.00	55.00

The first printing of Nos. 1 and 2 had the burelage printed from a copper plate, giving a clear impression with the lines in slight relief. The subsequent impressions had the burelage typographed, with the lines fainter and not rising above the surface of the paper.

Nos. 1-2 were reprinted in 1885 and 1901 on heavy yellowish paper, unwatermarked and imperforate, with a brown burelage. No. 1 was also reprinted without burelage, on both yellowish and white paper. Value for least costly reprint of No. 1, $50.

No. 2 was reprinted in 1951 in 10 shades with "Colour Specimen 1951" printed on the back. It was also reprinted in 1961 in 2 shades without burelage and with "Farve Nytryk 1961" printed on the back. Value for least costly reprint of No. 2, $8.50.

Dotting in Spandrels — A3

1854-57

3	A3	2s blue ('55)		75.00	60.00
4	A3	4s brown		325.00	15.00
a.		4s brown		350.00	15.00
5	A3	8s green ('57)		300.00	67.50
a.		8s yellow green		300.00	80.00
6	A3	16s gray lilac ('57)		525.00	190.00
		Nos. 3-6 (4)		1,225.	332.50

See No. 10. For denominations in cents see Danish West Indies Nos. 1-4.

Wavy Lines in Spandrels — A4

1858-62

7	A4	4s yellow brown		65.00	8.50
a.		4s brown		67.50	8.00
b.		Wmk. 112 ('62)		62.50	9.00
8	A4	8s green		800.00	82.50

Nos. 2 to 8 inclusive are known with unofficial perforation 12 or 13, and Nos. 4, 5, 7 and 8 with unofficial roulette 9½.

Nos. 3, 6-8 were reprinted in 1885 on heavy yellowish paper, unwatermarked, imperforate and without burelage. Nos. 4-5 were reprinted in 1924 on white paper, unwatermarked, imperforate, gummed and without burelage. Value for No. 3, $15; Nos. 4-5, each $110; No. 6, $20; Nos. 7-8, each $15.

1863   Wmk. 112   Rouletted 11

9	A4	4s brown		100.00	15.00
a.		4s deep brown		100.00	15.00
10	A3	16s violet		1,400.	650.00

Royal Emblems — A5

1864-68   Perf. 13

11	A5	2s blue ('65)		65.00	35.00
12	A5	3s red vio ('65)		80.00	75.00
13	A5	4s red		40.00	8.00
14	A5	8s bister ('68)		275.00	95.00
15	A5	16s olive green		475.00	175.00
		Nos. 11-15 (5)		935.00	388.00

Nos. 11-15 were reprinted in 1886 on heavy yellowish paper, unwatermarked, imperforate and without gum. The reprints of all values except the 4s were printed in two vertical rows of six, inverted with respect to each other, so that horizontal pairs are always tête bêche. Value $12 each.

Nos. 13 and 15 were reprinted in 1942 with printing on the back across each horizontal row: "Nytryk 1942. G. A. Hagemann: Danmarks og Vestindiens Frimaerker, Bind 2." Value, $70 each.

Imperf, single

11a	A5	2s blue	95.00	95.00
12a	A5	3s red violet	140.00	
13a	A5	4s red	77.50	90.00
14a	A5	8s bister	375.00	
15a	A5	16s olive green	450.00	

1870   Perf. 12½

11b	A5	2s blue	275.00	350.00
12b	A5	3s red violet	475.00	650.00
14b	A5	8s bister	475.00	475.00
15b	A5	16s olive green	725.00	1,450.
		Nos. 11b-15b (4)	1,950.	2,925.

A6

Normal Frame   Inverted Frame

The arabesques in the corners have a main stem and a branch. When the frame is in normal position, in the upper left corner the branch leaves the main stem half way between two little leaflets. In the lower right corner the branch starts at the foot of the second leaflet. When the frame is inverted the corner designs are, of course, transposed.

1870-71   Wmk. 112   Perf. 14x13½
Paper Varying from Thin to Thick

16	A6	2s gray & ultra ('71)		70.00	27.50
a.		2s gray & blue		70.00	27.50
17	A6	3s gray & brt lil ('71)		100.00	110.00
18	A6	4s gray & car		40.00	10.00
19	A6	8s gray & brn ('71)		200.00	75.00
20	A6	16s gray & grn ('71)		275.00	175.00

Perf. 12½

21	A6	2s gray & bl ('71)		2,000.	3,250.
22	A6	4s gray & car		150.00	125.00
24	A6	48s brn & blue		450.00	275.00

Nos. 16-20, 24 were reprinted in 1886 on thin white paper, unwatermarked, imperforate and without gum. These were printed in sheets of 10 in which 1 stamp has the normal frame (value $32.50 each) and 9 the inverted (value $11 each).

Imperf, single

16b	A6	2s	250.	
17a	A6	3s	240.	
18a	A6	4s	200.	
19a	A6	8s	250.	
20a	A6	16s	400.	
24a	A6	48s	425.	—

Inverted Frame

16c	A6	2s	1,000.	775.
17b	A6	3s	2,500.	2,000.
18b	A6	4s	775.	87.50
19b	A6	8s	1,750.	900.
20b	A6	16s	2,000.	1,750.
24b	A6	48s	2,750.	1,900.

1875-79   Perf. 14x13½

25	A6	3o	gray blue & gray	18.00	15.00
a.		1st "A" of "DANMARK" missing		60.00	150.00
b.		Imperf		750.00	
c.		Inverted frame		18.00	190.00
26	A6	4o	slate & blue	25.00	.50
a.		4o gray & blue		25.00	1.10
b.		4o slate & ultra		90.00	17.00
c.		4o gray & ultra		75.00	16.00
d.		Imperf		75.00	
e.		As #26, inverted frame		25.00	.50
27	A6	5o	rose & blue ('79)	30.00	72.50
a.		Ball of lower curve of large "5" missing		125.00	300.00
b.		Inverted frame		1,000.	2,250.
28	A6	8o	slate & car	22.50	.50
a.		8o gray & carmine		75.00	5.00
b.		Imperf		150.00	
c.		Inverted frame		22.50	.50
29	A6	12o	sl & dull lake	10.00	4.00
a.		12o gray & bright lilac		65.00	80.00
b.		12o gray & dull magenta		72.50	10.00
c.		Inverted frame		14.00	1.00

30	A6	16o slate & brn		77.50	6.50
a.		16o light gray & brown		77.50	17.00
b.		Inverted frame		52.50	4.50
31	A6	20o rose & gray		90.00	32.50
a.		20o carmine & gray		90.00	32.50
b.		Inverted frame		90.00	32.50
32	A6	25o gray & green		65.00	40.00
a.		Inverted frame		77.50	62.50
33	A6	50o brown & vio		70.00	37.50
a.		50o brown & blue violet		400.00	175.00
b.		Inverted frame		70.00	32.50
34	A6	100o gray & org ('77)		110.00	60.00
a.		Imperf, single		375.00	
b.		Inverted frame		150.00	60.00
		Nos. 25-34 (10)		518.00	269.00
		Set, never hinged		1,625.	

The stamps of this issue on thin semi-transparent paper are far scarcer than those on thicker paper.

See Nos. 41-42, 44, 46-47, 50-52. For surcharges see Nos. 55, 79-80, 136.

Arms — A7

Two types of numerals in corners

Small Numerals

Large Numerals

1882   Small Corner Numerals

35	A7	5o green		240.00	100.00
		Never hinged		725.00	
37	A7	20o blue		190.00	70.00
		Never hinged		650.00	

1884-88   Larger Corner Numerals

38	A7	5o green		15.00	3.50
a.		Imperf		—	
39	A7	10o carmine ('85)		16.00	2.50
a.		Small numerals in corners ('88)		550.00	725.00
b.		Imperf, single		175.00	
c.		Pair, Nos. 39, 39a		600.00	875.00
40	A7	20o blue		30.00	5.00
a.		Pair, Nos. 37, 40		400.00	875.00
b.		Imperf		—	
		Nos. 38-40 (3)		61.00	11.00
		Set, never hinged		285.00	

Stamps with large corner numerals have white line around crown and lower oval touches frame.

The plate for No. 39, was damaged and 3 clichés in the bottom row were replaced by clichés for post cards, which had small numerals in the corners.

Two clichés with small numerals were inserted in the plate of No. 40.

See Nos. 43, 45, 48-49, 53-54. For surcharge see No. 56.

1895-1901   Wmk. 112   *Perf. 13*

41	A6	3o blue & gray		10.00	7.25
42	A6	4o slate & bl ('96)		4.50	.40
43	A7	5o green		12.00	.75
44	A7	8o slate & red		4.50	.45
45	A7	10o rose car		24.00	.65
46	A6	12o sl & dull lake		7.00	4.00
47	A6	16o slate & brown		19.00	4.50
48	A7	20o blue		30.00	2.40
49	A7	24o brown ('01)		7.00	6.00
50	A6	25o gray & grn ('98)		110.00	19.50
51	A6	50o brown & vio ('97)		60.00	24.00
52	A6	100o slate & org		90.00	35.00
		Nos. 41-52 (12)		378.00	104.90
		Set, never hinged		875.00	

Inverted Frame

41b	A6	3o		12.00	7.00
42a	A6	4o		4.50	.45
44a	A6	8o		4.50	.50
46a	A6	12o		14.00	4.50
47a	A6	16o		30.00	5.00
50a	A6	25o		60.00	27.50
51a	A6	50o		95.00	32.50
52a	A6	100o		90.00	57.50
		Nos. 41b-52a (8)		310.00	134.95
		Set, never hinged		635.00	

1902-04   Wmk. 113

41c	A6	3o blue & gray		2.75	3.00
42b	A7	4o slate & blue		17.00	20.00
43a	A7	5o green		2.00	.25
44d	A6	8o slate & red		525.00	425.00
45a	A7	10o rose carmine		20.00	4.75
48a	A7	20o blue		20.00	4.75
50b	A6	25o gray & green		10.50	4.50
51b	A6	50o brown & violet		27.50	20.00
52b	A6	100o slate & orange		30.00	15.00
		Nos. 41c-52b (9)		637.75	492.75
		Set, never hinged		1,325.	

Inverted Frame

41d	A6	3o		75.00	130.00
42c	A6	4o		140.00	130.00
50c	A6	25o		210.00	60.00
51c	A6	50o		260.00	240.00
52c	A6	100o		225.00	240.00
		Nos. 41d-52c (5)		910.00	800.00
		Set, never hinged		2,500.	

1902   Wmk. 113

53	A7	1o orange		.75	.65
a.		Imperf		—	
54	A7	15o lilac		11.00	.75
a.		Imperf, single		4,250.	

Nos. 44d, 44, 49 Surcharged

a

b

1904-12   Wmk. 113

55	A6(a)	4o on 8o sl & red		3.50	4.00
a.		Wmk. 112 ('12)		21.00	60.00
		Never hinged		42.50	
b.		As "a," inverted frame		—	6,000.

Wmk. 112

56	A7(b)	15o on 24o brown		5.75	17.50
a.		Short "15" at right		27.50	105.00
		Never hinged		60.00	
		Set, never hinged		16.00	

A10

1905-17   Wmk. 113   *Perf. 13*

57	A10	1o orange ('06)		2.25	.75
58	A10	2o carmine		4.75	.40
a.		Perf. 14x14½ ('17)		3.75	19.00
59	A10	3o gray		9.75	.65
60	A10	4o dull blue		7.00	.60
a.		Perf. 14x14½ ('17)		11.00	37.50
61	A10	5o dp green ('12)		5.25	.35
62	A10	10o rose ('12)		6.75	.35
63	A10	15o lilac		25.00	2.25
64	A10	20o dk blue ('12)		35.00	.90
		Nos. 57-64 (8)		95.75	6.25
		Set, never hinged		310.00	

The three wavy lines in design A10 are symbolical of the three waters which separate the principal Danish islands.

See Nos. 85-96, 1338-1342A, 1468-1473. For surcharges and overprints see Nos. 163, 181, J1, J38, Q1-Q2.

King Christian IX — A11

1904-05   Engr.

65	A11	10o scarlet		4.00	.65
66	A11	20o blue		22.50	3.00
67	A11	25o brown ('05)		27.50	8.00
68	A11	50o dull vio ('05)		110.00	120.00
69	A11	100o ocher ('05)		13.00	60.00
		Nos. 65-69 (5)		177.00	191.65
		Set, never hinged		565.00	

1905-06   Re-engraved

70	A11	5o green		4.50	.35
71	A11	10o scarlet ('06)		21.00	.60
		Set, never hinged		56.00	

The re-engraved stamps are much clearer than the originals, and the decoration on the king's left breast has been removed.

King Frederik VIII — A12

1907-12

72	A12	5o green		1.75	.40
a.		Imperf.		—	
73	A12	10o red		4.25	.40
a.		Imperf.		—	
74	A12	20o indigo		19.00	.65
a.		20o bright blue ('11)		40.00	2.75
75	A12	25o olive brn		35.00	1.25
76	A12	35o dp org ('12)		6.00	10.00
77	A12	50o claret		35.00	7.00
78	A12	100o bister brn		100.00	5.00
		Nos. 72-78 (7)		201.00	24.70
		Set, never hinged		525.00	

Nos. 47, 31 and O9 Surcharged

c   d

Dark Blue Surcharge

1912   Wmk. 112   *Perf. 13*

79	A6(c)	35o on 16o		17.00	50.00
a.		Inverted frame		325.00	625.00

Perf. 14x13½

80	A6(c)	35o on 20o		30.00	85.00
a.		Inverted frame		130.00	325.00

Black Surcharge

81	O1(d)	35o on 32o		42.50	120.00
		Nos. 79-81 (3)		89.50	255.00
		Set, never hinged		185.00	

General Post Office, Copenhagen
A15

1912   Engr.   Wmk. 113   *Perf. 13*

82	A15	5k dark red		500.00	200.00
		Never hinged		1,500.	

See Nos. 135, 843.

Perf. 14x14½

1913-30   Typo.   Wmk. 114

85	A10	1o dp orange ('14)		.40	.45
a.		Bklt. pane, 2 ea #85, 91 + 2 labels		20.00	
86	A10	2o car ('13)		3.75	.35
a.		Imperf		150.00	300.00
b.		Booklet pane, 4 + 2 labels		27.50	
87	A10	3o gray ('13)		6.75	.40
88	A10	4o blue ('13)		8.00	.45
a.		Half used as 2o on cover			1,250.
89	A10	5o dk brown ('21)		.75	.35
a.		Imperf		190.00	
b.		Booklet pane, 4 + 2 labels		14.00	
90	A10	5o lt green ('30)		1.50	.40
a.		Booklet pane, 4 + 2 labels		16.00	
b.		Booklet pane of 50			
91	A10	7o apple grn ('26)		5.75	7.25
a.		Booklet pane, 4 + 2 labels		20.00	
92	A10	7o dk violet ('30)		16.00	6.50
93	A10	8o gray ('21)		7.00	3.25
94	A10	10o green ('21)		.85	.35
a.		Imperf		225.00	
b.		Booklet pane, 4 + 2 labels		37.50	
95	A10	10o bister brn ('30)		2.25	.35
a.		Booklet pane, 4 + 2 labels		16.00	
b.		Booklet pane of 50			
96	A10	12o violet ('26)		25.00	9.75
		Nos. 85-96 (12)		78.00	29.85
		Set, never hinged		200.00	

No. 88a was used with No. 97 in Faroe Islands, Jan. 3-23, 1919.

See surcharge and overprint note following No. 64.

King Christian X — A16

1913-28   Typo.   *Perf. 14x14½*

97	A16	5o green		1.40	.35
a.		Bklt. pane of 4, with P#		400.00	
98	A16	7o orange ('18)		2.25	2.75
99	A16	8o dk gray ('20)		14.00	6.50
100	A16	10o red		2.40	.40
a.		Imperf		300.00	
b.		Bklt. pane of 4, with P#		500.00	
101	A16	12o gray grn ('18)		7.50	10.00
102	A16	15o violet		3.25	.40
103	A16	20o dp blue		13.00	.35
104	A16	20o brown ('21)		1.25	.40
105	A16	20o red ('26)		1.50	.40
106	A16	25o dk brown		13.50	.50
107	A16	25o brn & blk ('20)		85.00	8.75
108	A16	25o red ('22)		4.25	.95
109	A16	25o yel grn ('25)		3.00	.50
110	A16	27o ver & blk ('18)		30.00	50.00
111	A16	30o green & blk ('18)		35.00	3.25
112	A16	30o orange ('21)		3.00	2.00
113	A16	30o dk blue ('25)		1.75	.40
114	A16	35o orange		29.00	7.50
115	A16	35o yel & blk ('19)		9.00	6.50
116	A16	40o vio & blk ('18)		18.00	4.00
117	A16	40o gray bl & blk ('20)		37.50	7.50
118	A16	40o dk blue ('22)		6.00	1.60
119	A16	40o orange ('25)		1.50	1.50
120	A16	50o claret		37.50	5.75
121	A16	50o claret & blk ('19)		75.00	2.50
122	A16	50o lt gray ('22)		9.25	.40
a.		50o olive gray ('21)		75.00	8.00
				210.00	
123	A16	60o brn & bl ('19)		60.00	3.75
a.		60o brown & ultra ('19)		225.00	12.50
		Never hinged		750.00	
124	A16	60o grn bl ('21)		9.00	.75
125	A16	70o brn & grn ('20)		26.00	2.25
126	A16	80o bl grn ('15)		50.00	22.50
127	A16	90o brn & red ('20)		18.00	3.25
128	A16	1k brn & bl ('22)		75.00	3.00
129	A16	2k gray & cl ('25)		67.50	15.00
130	A16	5k vio & brn ('27)		7.00	5.75
131	A16	10k ver & yel grn ('28)		325.00	65.00
		Nos. 97-131 (35)		1,082.	247.00
		Set, never hinged		3,085.	

No. 97 surcharged "2 ORE" is Faroe Islands No. 1. Two of the 14 printings of No. 97a have no P# in the selvage. These sell for more.

Nos. 87 and 98, 89 and 94, 89 and 104, 90 and 95, 97 and 103, 100 and 102 exist se-tenant in coils for use in vending machines.

For surcharges and overprints see Nos. 161-162, 176-177, 182-184, J2-J8, Q3-Q10.

King Christian X — A17

1913-20   Engr.

132	A17	1k yellow brown		95.00	1.25
133	A17	2k gray		150.00	7.00
134	A17	5k purple ('20)		15.00	10.00
		Nos. 132-134 (3)		260.00	18.25
		Set, never hinged		940.00	

For overprint see No. Q11.

King Christian X — A16

G.P.O. Type of 1912
Perf. 14x14½

1915 **Wmk. 114** **Engr.**
135 A15 5k dark red ('15)   500.00   175.00
    Never hinged   1,500.

Nos. 46 and O10 Surcharged in Black type "c" and

e

1915 **Wmk. 112** **Typo.** **Perf. 13**
136 A6 (c) 80o on 12o   40.00   100.00
  a.   Inverted frame   600.00   1,100.
    Never hinged   825.00
137 O1 (e) 80o on 8o   47.50   140.00
  a.   "POSTERIM"   95.00   325.00
    Never hinged   140.00
    Set, never hinged   155.00

Newspaper Stamps Surcharged

On Issue of 1907

1918 **Wmk. 113** **Perf. 13**
138 N1 27o on 1o olive   105.00   325.00
139 N1 27o on 5o blue   105.00   325.00
140 N1 27o on 7o car   105.00   325.00
141 N1 27o on 10o dp lil   105.00   325.00
142 N1 27o on 68o yel brn   7.50   37.50
143 N1 27o on 5k rose & yel grn   6.75   26.00
144 N1 27o on 10k bis & bl   7.50   35.00
    Nos. 138-144 (7)   441.75   1,399.
    Set, never hinged   940.00

On Issue of 1914-15
Wmk. Multiple Crosses (114)
Perf. 14x14½

145 N1 27o on 1o ol gray   5.00   15.50
146 N1 27o on 5o blue   7.50   30.00
147 N1 27o on 7o rose   5.00   12.50
148 N1 27o on 8o green   7.50   16.00
149 N1 27o on 10o dp lil   3.25   17.00
150 N1 27o on 20o green   8.00   16.50
151 N1 27o on 29o org yel   3.25   14.50
152 N1 27o on 38o orange   32.50   110.00
153 N1 27o on 41o yel brn   7.50   45.00
154 N1 27o on 1k bl grn & mar   5.00   14.50
    Nos. 145-154 (10)   84.50   291.50
    Set, never hinged   150.00

Kronborg Castle A20   Sonderborg Castle A21

Roskilde Cathedral — A22

Perf. 14½x14, 14x14½

1920, Oct. 5 **Typo.**
156 A20 10o red   7.00   .50
157 A21 20o slate   5.00   .50
158 A22 40o dark brown   17.00   4.50
    Nos. 156-158 (3)   29.00   5.50
    Set, never hinged   52.00

Reunion of Northern Schleswig with Denmark.
See Nos. 159-160. For surcharges see Nos. B1-B2.

1921
159 A20 10o green   9.00   .55
160 A22 40o dark blue   67.50   11.50
    Set, never hinged   174.00

Stamps of 1918 Surcharged in Blue

1921-22
161 A16 8o on 7o org ('22)   2.25   5.00
162 A16 8o on 12o gray grn   2.25   15.00
    Set, never hinged   15.75

No. 87 Surcharged

1921
163 A10 8o on 3o gray   3.75   5.25
    Never hinged   8.25

Christian X A23

Christian IV A24

A25   A26

1924, Dec. 1 **Perf. 14x14½**
164 A23 10o green   7.50   7.00
165 A24 10o green   7.50   7.00
166 A25 10o green   7.50   7.00
167 A26 10o green   7.50   7.00
  a.   Block of 4, #164-167   37.50   50.00
168 A23 15o violet   7.50   7.00
169 A24 15o violet   7.50   7.00
170 A25 15o violet   7.50   7.00
171 A26 15o violet   7.50   7.00
  a.   Block of 4, #168-171   37.50   50.00
172 A23 20o dark brown   7.50   7.00
173 A24 20o dark brown   7.50   7.00
174 A25 20o dark brown   7.50   7.00
175 A26 20o dark brown   7.50   7.00
  a.   Block of 4, #172-175   37.50   50.00
    Nos. 164-175 (12)   90.00   84.00
    Set, never hinged   180.00
#167a, 171a, 175a, never hinged   225.00

300th anniv. of the Danish postal service.

Stamps of 1921-22 Surcharged

k   l

1926
176 A16 (k) 20o on 30o org   6.75   15.00
177 A16 (l) 20o on 40o dk bl   9.00   18.00
    Set, never hinged   31.00

A27   A28

1926, Mar. 11 **Perf. 14x14½**
178 A27 10o dull green   1.50   .45
179 A28 20o dark red   2.00   .45
180 A28 30o dark blue   8.50   1.50
    Nos. 178-180 (3)   12.00   2.40
    Set, never hinged   24.50

75th anniv. of the introduction of postage stamps in Denmark.

Stamps of 1913-26 Surcharged in Blue or Black

No. 181   Nos. 182-184

1926-27 **Perf. 14x14½**
181 A10 7o on 8o gray (Bl)   1.50   4.75
182 A16 7o on 27o ver & blk   4.50   17.00
183 A16 7o on 20o red ('27)   .75   2.50
184 A16 12o on 15o violet   2.25   6.00

Surcharged on Official Stamps of 1914-23
185 O1 (e) 7o on 1o red   4.00   16.00
186 O1 (e) 7o on 3o gray   7.50   32.50
187 O1 (e) 7o on 4o blue   3.75   7.75
188 O1 (e) 7o on 5o grn   52.50   150.00
189 O1 (e) 7o on 10o grn   4.50   15.50

190 O1 (e) 7o on 15o vio   4.50   15.50
191 O1 (e) 7o on 20o ind   19.00   77.50
  a.   Double surcharge   750.00   975.00
    Nos. 181-191 (11)   104.75   345.00
    Set, never hinged   155.00

Caravel — A30

1927 **Typo.** **Perf. 14x14½**
192 A30 15o red   6.00   .40
193 A30 20o gray   11.00   2.40
194 A30 25o light blue   1.25   .40
195 A30 30o ocher   1.25   .40
196 A30 35o red brown   25.00   1.50
197 A30 40o yel green   25.00   .40
    Nos. 192-197 (6)   69.50   5.50
    Set, never hinged   200.00

See Nos. 232-238J. For surcharges & overprints see Nos. 244-245, 269-272, Q12-Q14, Q19-Q25.

Christian X — A31

1930, Sept. 26
210 A31 5o apple grn   2.50   .35
  a.   Booklet pane, 4 + 2 labels   18.00
211 A31 7o violet   6.75   3.00
212 A31 8o dk gray   22.50   32.50
213 A31 10o yel brn   5.00   .35
  a.   Booklet pane, 4 + 2 labels   29.00
214 A31 15o red   10.00   .35
215 A31 20o lt gray   25.00   9.75
216 A31 25o lt blue   8.50   1.25
217 A31 30o yel buff   9.00   1.75
218 A31 35o red brown   12.00   4.50
219 A31 40o dp green   10.00   1.25
    Nos. 210-219 (10)   111.25   55.05
    Set, never hinged   295.00

60th birthday of King Christian X.

Wavy Lines and Numeral of Value — A32

Type A10 Redrawn

1933-40 **Unwmk.** **Engr.** **Perf. 13**
220 A32 1o gray blk   .60   .30
  a.   Fluorescent paper ('69)   .50   .25
221 A32 2o scarlet   .35   .30
222 A32 4o blue   .40   .35
223 A32 5o yel grn   1.00   .35
  a.   5o gray green   37.50   60.00
  b.   Tête bêche gutter pair   8.00   15.50
  c.   Booklet pane of 4   11.00
  d.   Bkt. pane, 1 #223a, 3 #B6   37.50   70.00
    Never hinged   60.00
  e.   As "b," without gutter   17.50   27.50
224 A32 5o rose lake ('38)   .30   .30
  a.   Booklet pane of 4   1.20
  b.   Booklet pane of 10   12.00
  d.   Fluorescent paper ('80)   .50   .25
224C A32 6o orange ('40)   .30   .30
225 A32 7o violet   2.00   .35
226 A32 7o yel grn ('38)   1.10   .45
226A A32 7o lt brown ('40)   .35   .35
227 A32 8o gray   .45   .50
227A A32 8o yellow grn ('40)   .30   .35
228 A32 10o yellow org   12.50   .35
  a.   Tête bêche gutter pair   50.00   55.00
  b.   Booklet pane of 4   110.00
  c.   As "a," without gutter   60.00   70.00
    Never hinged   100.00
229 A32 10o lt brown ('37)   9.50   .35
  a.   Booklet pane of 4   100.00
  b.   Booklet pane of 4, 1 #229, 3 #B7   32.50   45.00
230 A32 10o violet ('38)   .75   .35
  a.   Booklet pane of 4   2.75
  b.   Bkt. pane, 2 #230, 2 #B10   2.50   7.00
    Never hinged   6.00
    Nos. 220-230 (14)   29.90   4.95
    Set, never hinged   75.00

Design A10 was typographed. They had a solid background with groups of small hearts below the heraldic lions in the upper corners and below "DA" and "RK" of "DANMARK." The numerals of value were enclosed in single-lined ovals.

Design A32 is line-engraved and has a background of crossed lines. The hearts have been removed and the numerals of value are now in double-lined ovals. Two types exist of some values.

No. 230 with wide margins is from booklet pane No. 230b.

Surcharges of 20, 50 & 60öre on #220, 224 and 224C are listed as Faroe Islands #2-3, 5-6.

See Nos. 318, 333, 382, 416, 437-437A, 493-498, 629, 631, 688-695, 793-795, 883-886, 1111-1113, 1116. For overprints and surcharges see Nos. 257, 263, 267-268, 355-356, Q15-Q17, Q31, Q43.

Certain tête-bêche pairs of 1938-55 issues which reached the market in 1971, and were not regularly issued, are not listed. This group comprises 24 different major-number vertical pairs of types A32, A47, A61 and SP3 (13 with gutters, 11 without), and pairs of some minor numbers and shades. They were removed from booklet pane sheets.

A32a

Type I

Type II

Type I — Two columns of squares between sail and left frame line.

Type I

1933-34 **Engr.** **Perf. 13**
232 A32a 20o gray   15.00   .35
233 A32a 25o blue   85.00   30.00
234 A32a 25o brown ('34)   30.00   .35
235 A32a 30o orange yel   1.50   1.40
236 A32a 30o blue ('34)   1.50   .40
237 A32a 35o violet   .60   .35
238 A32a 40o yellow grn   6.25   .35
    Nos. 232-238 (7)   139.85   33.20
    Set, never hinged   325.00

A32b

Type II — One column of squares between sail and left frame line.

1933-40 **Type II**
238A A32b 15o deep red   3.00   .35
  k.   Booklet pane of 4   26.00
  l.   Bkt. pane, 1 #238A, 3 #B8   45.00
    Never hinged   115.00
238B A32b 15o yel grn ('40)   9.00   .40
238C A32b 20o gray blk ('39)   4.50   .70
238D A32b 20o red ('40)   .90   .35
238E A32b 25o dp brown ('39)   .90   .35
238F A32b 30o blue ('39)   2.25   .70
238G A32b 30o orange ('40)   .75   .35
238H A32b 35o violet ('40)   1.00   .35
238I A32b 40o yel grn ('39)   15.00   .35
238J A32b 40o blue ('40)   1.40   .35
    Nos. 238A-238J (10)   38.70   4.25
    Set, never hinged   95.00

Nos. 232-238J, engraved, have crosshatched background. Nos. 192-197, typographed, have solid background.

For No. 238A surcharged 20 ore see Denmark No. 271, Faroe Islands No. 4.

See note on surcharges and overprints following No. 197.

King Christian X — A33

1934-41 **Perf. 13**
239 A33 50o gray   1.20   .30
240 A33 60o blue grn   2.40   .35
240A A33 75o dk blue ('41)   .45   .35
241 A33 1k lt brown   3.75   .35

242 A33 2k dull red   6.00 1.00
243 A33 5k violet   9.00 3.50
     Nos. 239-243 (6)   22.80 5.85
     Set, never hinged   75.00

For overprints see Nos. Q26-Q27.

Nos. 233, 235 Surcharged
in Black

1934, June 9
244 A30 4o on 25o blue   .50   .50
245 A30 10o on 30o org yel   2.40 3.25
     Set, never hinged   7.50

"The Ugly
Duckling"
A34

Andersen
A35

"The Little Mermaid" — A36

1935, Oct. 1   *Perf. 13*
246 A34 5o lt green   3.00   .30
   a. Tête bêche gutter pair   15.00 22.50
   b. Booklet pane of 4   40.00
   c. As "a," without gutter   17.00 21.00
       Never hinged   45.00
247 A35 7o dull vio   2.50 2.50
248 A36 10o orange   4.50   .30
   a. Tête bêche gutter pair   18.00 32.50
   b. Booklet pane of 4   65.00
   c. As "a," without gutter   20.00 40.00
       Never hinged   65.00
249 A35 15o red   11.00   .30
   a. Tête bêche gutter pair   45.00 52.50
   b. Booklet pane of 4   160.00
   c. As "a," without gutter   42.50 75.00
       Never hinged   110.00
250 A35 20o gray   9.50 1.25
251 A35 30o dl bl   3.00   .35
     Nos. 246-251 (6)   33.50 5.00
     Set, never hinged   87.50

Centenary of the publication of the earliest
installment of Hans Christian Andersen's
"Fairy Tales."

Nikolai
Church
A37

Hans
Tausen
A38

Ribe Cathedral — A39

1936   *Perf. 13*
252 A37 5o green   1.40   .40
   a. Booklet pane of 4   21.00
253 A37 7o violet   2.00 4.50
254 A38 10o lt brown   2.00   .40
   a. Booklet pane of 4   25.00
255 A38 15o dull rose   3.00   .30
256 A39 30o blue   16.00 1.40
     Nos. 252-256 (5)   24.40 7.00
     Set, never hinged   62.50

Church Reformation in Denmark, 400th
anniv.

No. 229 Overprinted in
Blue

1937, Sept. 17
257 A32 10o lt brown   1.50 1.60
     Never hinged   2.00

Jubilee Exhib. held by the Copenhagen Phil.
Club on their 50th anniv. The stamps were on
sale at the Exhib. only, each holder of a ticket
of admission (1k) being entitled to purchase
20 stamps at face value; of a season ticket
(5k), 100 stamps.

Yacht and
Summer
Palace,
Marselisborg
A40

Christian X
in Streets
of
Copenhagen
A41

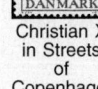

Equestrian Statue of
Frederik V and
Amalienborg
Palace — A42

1937, May 15   *Perf. 13*
258 A40 5o green   1.40   .30
   a. Booklet pane of 4   15.00
259 A41 10o brown   1.40   .30
   a. Booklet pane of 4   15.00
260 A42 15o scarlet   1.40   .30
   a. Booklet pane of 4   17.00
261 A41 30o blue   15.00 2.40
     Nos. 258-261 (4)   19.20 3.30
     Set, never hinged   42.50

25th anniv. of the accession to the throne of
King Christian X.

Emancipation Column,
Copenhagen — A43

1938, June 20   *Perf. 13*
262 A43 15o scarlet   .60   .30
     Never hinged   1.40

Abolition of serfdom in Denmark, 150th
anniv.

**No. 223 Overprinted in Red on
Alternate Stamps**

1938, Sept. 2
263 A32 5o yellow grn, pair   3.25 7.00
     Never hinged   4.50

10th Danish Philatelic Exhibition.

Bertel
Thorvaldsen
A44

Statue of
Jason
A45

1938, Nov. 17   *Engr.*   *Perf. 13*
264 A44 5o rose lake   .45   .30
265 A45 10o purple   .45   .30
266 A44 30o dark blue   1.50   .60
     Nos. 264-266 (3)   2.40 1.20
     Set, never hinged   5.25

The return to Denmark in 1838 of Bertel
Thorvaldsen, Danish sculptor.

**Stamps of 1933-39 Surcharged with
New Values in Black**

a

b

c

1940
267 A32 (a) 6o on 7o yel grn   .30   .35
268 A32 (a) 6o on 8o gray   .45   .35
269 A30 (b) 15o on 40o #238   .90 6.00
270 A30 (b) 15o on 40o #238l   .75   .95
271 A30 (c) 20o on 15o dp red   1.10   .30
272 A30 (b) 40o on 30o #238F   1.00   .35
     Nos. 267-272 (6)   4.50 8.30
     Set, never hinged   9.25

Stamps previously listed as Denmark No.
273-276 are listed as Faroe Islands Nos. 2-6 .

Bering's Ship — A46

1941, Nov. 27   *Engr.*   *Perf. 13*
277 A46 10o dk violet   .35   .30
278 A46 20o red brown   .60   .30
279 A46 40o dk blue   .40   .35
     Nos. 277-279 (3)   1.35   .95
     Set, never hinged   3.00

Death of Vitus Bering, explorer, 200th anniv.

King Christian X — A47

1942-46   *Unwmk.*   *Perf. 13*
280 A47 10o violet   .30   .35
281 A47 15o yel grn   .35   .35
282 A47 20o red   .40   .35
283 A47 25o brown ('43)   .50   .45
284 A47 30o orange ('43)   .45   .35
285 A47 35o brt red vio ('44)   .40   .35
286 A47 40o blue ('43)   .40   .35
286A A47 45o ol brn ('46)   .35   .35
286B A47 50o gray ('45)   .60   .35
287 A47 60o bluish grn ('44)   .55   .35
287A A47 75o dk blue ('46)   .55   .35
     Nos. 280-287A (11)   4.85 3.95
     Set, never hinged   8.00

For overprints see Nos. Q28-Q30.

Round Tower — A48

1942, Nov. 27
288 A48 10o violet   .35   .30

300th anniv. of the Round Tower,
Copenhagen.
For surcharge see No. B14.

Condor Plane — A49

1943, Oct. 29
289 A49 20o red   .25   .25
     Never hinged   .35

25th anniv. of the Danish Aviation Company
(Det Danske Luftfartsselskab).

Ejby Church — A50

15ö, Oesterlars Church. 20ö, Hvidbjerg
Church.

1944   *Engr.*   *Perf. 13*
290 A50 10o violet   .30   .25
291 A50 15o yellow grn   .30   .25
292 A50 20o red   .30   .25
     Nos. 290-292 (3)   .90   .75
     Set, never hinged   1.75

Ole Roemer — A53

1944, Sept. 25
293 A53 20o henna brown   .35   .30
     Never hinged   .65

Birth of Ole Roemer, astronomer, 300th
anniv.

Christian X — A54

1945, Sept. 26
294 A54 10o lilac   .25   .25
295 A54 20o red   .25   .25
296 A54 40o deep blue   .25   .25
     Nos. 294-296 (3)   .75   .75
     Set, never hinged   1.75

75th birthday of King Christian X.

**Catalogue values for unused
stamps in this section, from this
point to the end of the section, are
for Never Hinged items.**

Small State Seal — A55

1946-47   *Unwmk.*   *Perf. 13*
297 A55 1k brown   1.00   .25
   a. Fluorescent paper ('68)   .80   .25
298 A55 2k red ('47)   2.00   .25
   a. Fluorescent paper ('69)   .50   .25
299 A55 5k dull blue   6.00   .25
   a. Fluorescent paper ('68)   1.25   .25
     Nos. 297-299 (3)   9.00   .75

See Nos. 395-400, 441A-444D, 499-506,
643-650, 716-720A, 804-815, 909, 1134-
1138, 1304-1313, 1474-1478, 1508. For overprints see Nos. Q35, Q40, Q46-Q48.

Tycho Brahe — A56

1946, Dec. 14   *Engr.*
300 A56 20o dark red   .30   .25

Birth of Tycho Brahe, astronomer, 400th
anniv.

First Danish
Locomotive
A57

Modern
Steam
Locomotive
A58

Diesel
Locomotive — A59

1947, June 27
301 A57 15o steel blue   .60   .35
302 A58 20o red   1.10   .35
303 A59 40o deep blue   3.50 2.25
     Nos. 301-303 (3)   5.20 2.95

Inauguration of the Danish State Railways,
cent.

Jacobsen — A60

1947, Nov. 10   *Perf. 13*
304 A60 20o dark red   .30 .25

60th anniv. of the death of Jacob Christian Jacobsen, founder of the Glyptothek Art Museum, Copenhagen.

Frederik IX — A61

Three types among 15ö, 20ö, 30ö:
I — Background of horizontal lines. No outline at left for cheek and ear. King's uniform textured in strong lines.
II — Background of vertical and horizontal lines. Contour of cheek and ear at left. Uniform same.
III — Background and facial contour lines as in II. Uniform lines double and thinner.

1948-50   **Unwmk.**   *Perf. 13*
306 A61 15(o) green (II)   2.50 .30
   a.   Type III ('49)   1.60 .50
307 A61 20(o) dk red (I)   1.10 .25
   a.   Type III ('49)   1.40 .40
308 A61 25(o) lt brown   1.40 .25
309 A61 30(o) org (II)   13.00 .50
   a.   Type III ('50)   21.00 .50
310 A61 40(o) dl blue ('49)   4.75 1.00
311 A61 45(o) olive ('50)   2.10 .35
312 A61 50(o) gray ('49)   1.75 .30
313 A61 60(o) grnsh bl ('50)   2.50 .30
314 A61 75(o) lil rose ('50)   2.00 .30
   Nos. 306-314 (9)   31.10 3.55

See Nos. 319-326, 334-341, 354, For surcharges see Nos. 357-358, 370, B20, B24-B25, Q32-Q34, Q36-Q39.

Legislative Assembly, 1849 — A62

1949, June 5
315 A62 20o red brown   .35 .25

Adoption of the Danish constitution, cent.

Symbol of UPU — A63

1949, Oct. 9
316 A63 40o dull blue   .65 .35

75th anniv. of the UPU.

Kalundborg Radio Station and Masts — A64

1950, Apr. 1   **Engr.**   *Perf. 13*
317 A64 20o brown red   .50 .25

Radio broadcasting in Denmark, 25th anniv.

Types of 1933-50
1950-51   **Unwmk.**   *Perf. 13*
318 A32 10o green   .30 .25
   a.   Fluorescent paper   .25 .25
319 A61 15(o) lilac   1.00 .30
   b.   15(o) gray lilac   4.00 .25
320 A61 20(o) lt brown   1.10 .25
321 A61 25(o) dark red   3.50 .25
322 A61 35(o) gray grn ('51)   .95 .25
323 A61 40(o) gray   .95 .25
324 A61 50(o) dark blue   3.25 .25
325 A61 55(o) brown ('51)   32.50 2.75
326 A61 70(o) deep green   3.00 .30
   Nos. 318-326 (9)   46.55 4.90

Warship of 1701 — A65

1951, Feb. 26   **Engr.**   *Perf. 13*
327 A65 25o dark red   .50 .30
328 A65 50o deep blue   4.00 .80

250th anniv. of the foundation of the Naval Officers' College.

Oersted — A66

1951, Mar. 9   **Unwmk.**
329 A66 50o blue   1.40 .60

Cent. of the death of Hans Christian Oersted, physicist.

Post Chaise ("Ball Post") — A67

1951, Apr. 1   *Perf. 13*
330 A67 15o purple   .65 .25
331 A67 25o henna brown   .65 .25

Cent. of Denmark's 1st postage stamp.

Marine Rescue — A68

1952, Mar. 26
332 A68 25o red brown   .45 .35

Cent. of the foundation of the Danish Lifesaving Service.

Types of 1933-50
1952-53   *Perf. 13*
333 A32 12o lt yel grn   .30 .25
   a.   Fluorescent paper ('62)   2.50 3.50
334 A61 25(o) lt blue   1.10 .30
335 A61 30(o) brown red   1.00 .35
336 A61 50(o) aqua ('53)   1.00 .30
337 A61 60(o) dp blue ('53)   1.10 .35
338 A61 65(o) gray ('53)   1.10 .35
339 A61 80(o) orange ('53)   1.10 .35
340 A61 90(o) olive ('53)   3.00 .30
341 A61 95(o) red org ('53)   1.10 .25
   Nos. 333-341 (9)   10.80 2.80

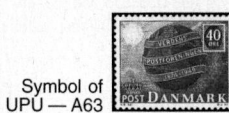

Jelling Runic Stone — A69

Designs: 15o, Vikings' camp, Trelleborg. 20o, Church of Kalundborg. 30o, Nyborg castle. 60o, Goose tower, Vordinborg.

1953-56   *Perf. 13*
342 A69 10o dp green   .30 .25
343 A69 15o lt rose vio   .30 .25
344 A69 20o brown   .30 .25
345 A69 30o red ('54)   .30 .25
346 A69 60o dp blue ('54)   .35 .25

Designs: 10o, Manor house, Spottrup. 15o, Hammershus castle ruins. 20o, Copenhagen stock exchange. 30o, Statue of Frederik V, Amalienborg. 60o, Soldier statue at Fredericia.

347 A69 10o green ('54)   .30 .25
348 A69 15o lilac ('55)   .30 .25
349 A69 20o brown ('55)   .30 .25
350 A69 30o red ('55)   .30 .25
351 A69 60o deep blue ('56)   .60 .25
   Nos. 342-351 (10)   3.35 2.50

1000th anniv. of the Kingdom of Denmark. Each stamp represents a different century.

Telegraph Equipment of 1854 — A70

1954, Feb. 2   *Perf. 13*
352 A70 30o red brown   .40 .25

Cent. of the telegraph in Denmark.

Frederik V — A71

1954, Mar. 31
353 A71 30o dark red   .55 .35

200th anniv. of the founding of the Royal Academy of Fine Arts.

Type of 1948-50
1955, Apr. 27
354 A61 25o lilac   1.00 .30

Nos. 224C and 226A Surcharged with New Value in Black. Nos. 307 and 321 Surcharged with New Value and 4 Bars
1955-56
355 A32 5o on 6o org   .30 .25
356 A32 5o on 7o lt brn   .30 .25
357 A61 30(o) on 20(o) dk red (I)   .80 .30
   a.   Type III   1.40 .35
   b.   Double surcharge   1,150. 1,150.
   c.   Inverted surcharge   650.00
358 A61 30(o) on 25(o) dk red ('56)   .60 .25
   a.   Double surcharge   —
   Nos. 355-358 (4)   2.00 1.05

A72

1955, Nov. 11   **Unwmk.**
359 A72 30o dark red   .50 .25

100th anniv. of the death of Sören Kierkegaard, philosopher and theologian.

A73

1956, Sept. 12   **Engr.**
360 A73 30o Ellehammer's plane   .50 .25

50th anniv. of the 1st flight made by Jacob Christian Hansen Ellehammer in a heavier-than-air craft.

Northern Countries Issue

Whooper Swans — A74

1956, Oct. 30   *Perf. 13*
361 A74 30o rose red   1.75 .25
362 A74 60o ultramarine   1.60 .80

Issued to emphasize the close bonds among the northern countries: Denmark, Finland, Iceland, Norway and Sweden.

Prince's Palace — A75

Design: 60ö, Sun God's Chariot.

1957, May 15   **Unwmk.**
363 A75 30o dull red   .90 .25
364 A75 60o dark blue   .90 .75

150th anniv. of the National Museum.

Harvester — A76

1958, Sept. 4   **Engr.**   *Perf. 13*
365 A76 30o fawn   .30 .25

Centenary of the Royal Veterinary and Agricultural College.

Frederik IX — A77

1959, Mar. 11
366 A77 30o rose red   .40 .25
367 A77 35o rose lilac   .50 .25
368 A77 60o ultra   .50 .25
   Nos. 366-368 (3)   1.40 .75

King Frederik's 60th birthday.

Ballet Dancer — A78

1959, May 16
369 A78 35o rose lilac   .30 .25

Danish Ballet and Music Festival, May 17-31. See Nos. 401, 422.

No. 319 Surcharged

1960, Apr. 7
370 A61 30o on 15o lilac   .30 .25

World Refugee Year, 7/1/59-6/30/60.

Seeder and Farm — A79

30ö, Harvester combine. 60ö, Plow.

1960, Apr. 28   **Engr.**   *Perf. 13*
371 A79 12o green   .25 .25
372 A79 30o dull red   .30 .25
373 A79 60o dk blue   .65 .50
   Nos. 371-373 (3)   1.20 1.00

King Frederik IX and Queen Ingrid — A80

1960, May 24   **Unwmk.**
374 A80 30o dull red   .45 .25
375 A80 60o blue   .65 .60

25th anniversary of the marriage of King Frederik IX and Queen Ingrid.

Bascule Light — A81

1960, June 8   **Engr.**
376 A81 30o dull red   .30 .25

400th anniv. of the Lighthouse Service.

Finsen — A82

1960, Aug. 1   *Perf. 13*
377 A82 30o dark red   .30   .25
Centenary of the birth of Dr. Niels R. Finsen, physician and scientist.

Nursing Mother — A83

1960, Aug. 16   *Unwmk.*
378 A83 60o ultra   .55   .50
10th meeting of the regional committee for Europe of WHO, Copenhagen, Aug. 16-20.

Europa Issue, 1960
Common Design Type
1960, Sept. 19   *Perf. 13*
Size: 28x21mm
379 CD3 60o ultra   .55   .50

DC-8 Airliner — A84

1961, Feb. 24
380 A84 60o ultra   .75   .50
   a.   Fluorescent paper   15.00   8.00
10th anniv. of the Scandinavian Airlines System, SAS.

Landscape — A85

1961, Apr. 21   *Perf. 13*
381 A85 30o copper brown   .30   .25
Denmark's Soc. of Nature Lovers, 50th anniv.

Fluorescent Paper
   as well as ordinary paper, was used in printing many definitive and commemorative stamps, starting in 1962. These include No. 220, 224; the 15, 20, 25, 30, 35 (Nos. 386 and 387), 50 and 60ö, 1.50k and 25k definitives of following set, and Nos. 297-299, 318, 333, 380, 401-427, 429-435, 438-439, 543, B30.
   Only fluorescent paper was used for Nos. 436-437, 437A and 440 onward; in semipostals from B31 onward.

Frederik IX — A86

1961-63	Engr.	Perf. 13
382 A32 15o green ('63)	.50	.35
a. Fluorescent paper	.70	.45
383 A86 20o brown	.45	.35
a. Fluorescent paper ('62)	3.50	4.00
384 A86 25o brown ('63)	.30	.35
a. Fluorescent paper	.30	.35
385 A86 30o rose red	.65	.35
a. Fluorescent paper ('62)	1.25	.35
386 A86 35o olive grn	.85	.75
a. Fluorescent paper ('62)	3.25	3.25
387 A86 35o rose red ('63)	.30	.35
a. Fluorescent paper	.35	.40
388 A86 40o gray	1.20	.35
389 A86 50o aqua	.55	.30
a. Fluorescent paper	1.00	.50
390 A86 60o ultra	1.10	.35
a. Fluorescent paper	1.50	1.00
391 A86 70o green	1.60	.35
392 A86 80o red orange	1.60	.35

393 A86 90o olive bister	4.25	.35
394 A86 95o claret ('63)	1.00	.90
Nos. 382-394 (13)	14.35	5.45

See Nos. 417-419, 438-441. For overprints see Nos. Q41-Q42, Q44-Q45.

State Seal Type of 1946-47
1962-70
395 A55 1.10k lilac ('65)	5.25	2.00
396 A55 1.20k gray	3.00	.35
397 A55 1.25k orange	3.00	.35
398 A55 1.30k green ('65)	5.50	1.75
399 A55 1.50k red lilac	2.75	.35
a. Fluorescent paper ('70)	1.60	.35
400 A55 25k yellow grn	35.00	2.00
a. Fluorescent paper ('69)	7.00	.35
Nos. 395-400 (6)	54.50	6.80

Dancer Type of 1959 Inscribed "15-31 MAJ"
1962, Apr. 26
401 A78 60o ultra   .30   .25
   a. Fluorescent paper ('70)   1.20   1.00
Issued to publicize the Danish Ballet and Music Festival, May 15-31.

Old Mill — A87

1962, May 10   *Unwmk.*   *Perf. 13*
402 A87 10o red brown   .30   .25
   a. Fluorescent paper   .30   .30
Cent. of the abolition of mill monopolies.

M.S. Selandia — A88

1962, June 14   *Engr.*
403 A88 60o dark blue   1.60   1.50
   a. Fluorescent paper   7.50   7.50
M.S. Selandia, the 1st Diesel ship, 50th anniv.

Violin Scroll, Leaves, Lights and Balloon — A89

1962, Aug. 31
404 A89 35o rose violet   .35   .25
   a. Fluorescent paper   .45   .30
150th anniv. of the birth of Georg Carstensen, founder of Tivoli amusement park, Copenhagen.

Cliffs on Moen Island — A90

1962, Nov. 22
405 A90 20o pale brown   .30   .25
   a. Fluorescent paper   .65   .40
Issued to publicize preservation of natural treasures and landmarks.

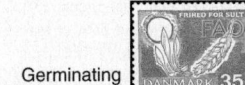

Germinating Wheat — A91

1963, Mar. 21   *Engr.*
406 A91 35o fawn   .35   .25
   a. Fluorescent paper   .45   .30
FAO "Freedom from Hunger" campaign.

Railroad Wheel, Tire Tracks, Waves and Swallow — A92

1963, May 14   *Unwmk.*   *Perf. 13*
407 A92 15o green   .60   .40
   a.   .60   .50
Inauguration of the "Bird Flight Line" railroad link between Denmark and Germany.

Sailing Vessel, Coach, Postilions and Globe — A93

1963, May 27
408 A93 60o dark blue   .40   .40
   a.   1.25   1.25
Cent. of the 1st Intl. Postal Conf., Paris, 1863.

Niels Bohr and Atom Diagram — A94

1963, Nov. 21   *Engr.*
409 A94 35o red brown   .40   .35
   a.   .40   .35
410 A94 60o dark blue   .65   .25
   a. Fluorescent paper   .95   .95
50th anniv. of Prof. Niels Bohr's (1885-1962) atom theory.
See Greeland Nos. 66-67.

Early Public School Drawn on Slate — A95

1964, June 19   *Unwmk.*   *Perf. 13*
411 A95 35o red brown   .60   .25
   a.   .75   .30
150th anniversary of the royal decrees for the public school system.

Fish and Chart — A96

1964, Sept. 7   *Engr.*
412 A96 60o violet blue   .35   .40
   a. Fluorescent paper   1.00   1.00
Conference of the International Council for the Exploration of the Sea, Copenhagen.

Danish Watermarks and Perforations — A97

1964, Oct. 10   *Perf. 13*
413 A97 35o pink   .30   .25
   a. Fluorescent paper   .45   .45
25th anniv. of Stamp Day and to publicize the Odense Stamp Exhibition, Oct. 10-11.

Landscape — A98

1964, Nov. 12   *Engr.*
414 A98 25o brown   .30   .25
   a. Fluorescent paper   .30   .30
Issued to publicize preservation of natural treasures and landmarks.

Calculator, Ledger and Inkwell — A99

1965, Mar. 8   *Unwmk.*
415 A99 15o light olive green   .30   .25
   a. Fluorescent paper   .30   .30
First Business School in Denmark, cent.

Types of 1933 and 1961
1965, May 15	Engr.	Perf. 13
416 A32 25o apple green	1.00	.35
a. Fluorescent paper	.55	.50
417 A86 40o brown	.45	.35
a. Fluorescent paper	.45	.35
418 A86 50o rose red	.90	.35
a. Fluorescent paper	.75	.65
419 A86 80o ultra	2.10	.35
a. Fluorescent paper	.75	.65
Nos. 416-419 (4)	4.45	1.40

For overprints see Nos. Q41-Q42.

ITU Emblem, Telegraph Key, Teletype Paper — A100

1965, May 17
420 A100 80o dark blue   .35   .25
   a. Fluorescent paper   .60   .60
Cent. of the ITU.

Carl Nielsen (1865-1931), Composer — A101

1965, June 9   *Engr.*
421 A101 50o brown red   .40   .25
   a. Fluorescent paper   .45   .45

Dancer Type of 1959 Inscribed "15-31 MAJ"
1965, Sept. 23
422 A78 50o rose red   .30   .25
   a. Fluorescent paper   .45   .45
Issued to publicize the Danish Ballet and Music Festival, May 15-31.

Bogo Windmill — A102

1965, Nov. 10   *Engr.*   *Perf. 13*
423 A102 40o brown   .30   .25
   a. Fluorescent paper   .45   .45
Issued to publicize the preservation of natural treasures and landmarks.

Mylius Dalgas Surveying Wasteland — A103

1966, Feb. 24
424 A103 25o olive green   .80   .25
   a. Fluorescent paper   .50   .30
Cent. of the Danish Heath Soc. (reclamation of wastelands), founded by Enrico Mylius Dalgas.

Christen Kold (1816-70), Educator — A104

1966, Mar. 29   *Perf. 13*
425 A104 50o dull red   .80   .25
   a. Fluorescent paper   .50   .45

Poorhouse, Copenhagen A105   Holte Allée, Bregentved A106

Dolmen (Grave) in
Jutland — A107

1966   **Unwmk.**
426 A105 50o dull red   .80   .25
  a.   Fluorescent paper   .55   .45
427 A106 80o dk blue   1.00   .40
  a.   Fluorescent paper   1.20   1.00
428 A107 1.50k dk slate grn   1.40   .25
      Nos. 426-428 (3)   3.20   .90
   Publicizing preservation of national
treasures and ancient monuments. Issued:
50o, May 12; 80o, June 16; 1.50k, Nov. 24.

George Jensen by Ejnar
Nielsen — A108

1966, Aug. 31   **Engr.**   *Perf. 13*
429 A108 80o dark blue   1.00   .40
  a.   Fluorescent paper   1.00   1.00
   George Jensen, silversmith, birth cent.

Music Bar and
Instruments — A109

1967, Jan. 9
430 A109 50o dark red   .70   .25
  a.   Fluorescent paper   .80   .45
   Royal Danish Academy of Music, cent.

Cogwheels, and
Broken Customs Duty
Ribbon — A110

1967, Mar. 2
431 A110 80o dark blue   .70   .25
  a.   Fluorescent paper   .90   .90
   European Free Trade Association. Industrial
tariffs were abolished Dec. 31, 1966, among
EFTA members: Austria, Denmark, Finland,
Great Britain, Norway, Portugal, Sweden and
Switzerland.

Windmill and Medieval
Fortress — A111

   Designs: 40ö, Ship's rigging and baroque
house front. 50ö, Old Town Hall. 80ö, New
building construction.

1967   **Engr.**   *Perf. 13*
432 A111 25o green   .70   .25
  a.   Fluorescent paper   .60   .60
433 A111 40o sepia   .35   .25
  a.   Fluorescent paper   .45   .45
434 A111 50o red brown   .35   .40
  a.   Fluorescent paper   .45   .45
435 A111 80o dk blue   .85   .80
  a.   Fluorescent paper   1.25   1.25
      Nos. 432-435 (4)   2.25   1.70
   The 800th anniversary of Copenhagen.
Issued: Nos. 432-433, 4/6; Nos. 434-435,
5/11.

Princess Margrethe
and Prince
Henri — A112

1967, June 10
436 A112 50o red   .30   .25
   Marriage of Crown Princess Margrethe and
Prince Henri de Monpezat.

Types of 1933-1961

1967-71   **Engr.**   *Perf. 13*
437 A32 30o dk green   .70   .35
437A A32 40o orange ('71)   .80   .35
438 A86 50o brown   1.25   .35
  a.   Fluorescent paper   .85   .35
      Complete booklet, 4 #318, 2
      each #437, 438   20.00

---

439 A86 60o rose red   1.25 .35
  a. Fluorescent paper   1.25 .35
440 A86 80o green   .85 .35
441 A86 90o ultra   .90 .35
441A A55 1.20o Prus grn ('71) 2.00 .45
442 A55 2.20k orange   3.50 .35
443 A55 2.80k gray   3.00 .35
444 A55 2.90k rose vio   5.25 .35
444A A55 3k dk sl grn ('69) 1.00 .35
444B A55 3.10k plum ('70)   8.50 .35
444C A55 4k gray ('69)   1.40 .35
444D A55 4.10k olive ('70) 8.50 .35
      Nos. 437-444D (14)   38.90 5.00
   Issued: Nos. 437-441, 6/30/67; Nos. 442-
443, 7/8/67; No. 444, 4/29/68; Nos. 444A,
444C, 8/28/69; Nos. 444B, 444D, 8/27/70;
Nos. 437A, 441A, 6/24/71.
   For overprints see Nos. Q44-Q45.

Sonne — A113

1967, Sept. 21
445 A113 60o red   .30   .25
   150th anniv. of the birth of Hans Christian
Sonne, pioneer of the cooperative movement
in Denmark.

Cross-anchor and
Porpoise — A114

1967, Nov. 9   **Engr.**   *Perf. 13*
446 A114 90o dk blue   .35   .25
   Centenary of the Danish Seamen's Church
in Foreign Ports.

Esbjerg
Harbor — A115

1968, Apr. 24
447 A115 30o dk yellow grn   .30   .25
   Centenary of Esbjerg Harbor.

Koldinghus — A116

1968, June 13
448 A116 60o copper red   .65   .25
   700th anniversary of Koldinghus Castle.

Shipbuilding
Industry — A117

   Designs: 50o, Chemical industry. 60o, Electric power. 90o, Engineering.

1968, Oct. 24   **Engr.**   *Perf. 13*
449 A117 30o green   .25   .25
450 A117 50o brown   .25   .25
451 A117 60o red brown   .25   .25
452 A117 90o dark blue   1.00   1.00
      Nos. 449-452 (4)   1.75   1.75
   Issued to publicize Danish industries.

Sower — A118

1969, Jan. 29
453 A118 30o gray green   .30   .25
   Royal Agricultural Soc. of Denmark, 200th
anniv.

Five Ancient
Ships — A119

Nordic Cooperation Issue

1969, Feb. 28   **Engr.**   *Perf. 13*
454 A119 60o brown red   .80   .25
455 A119 90o blue   1.60   1.60
   50th anniv. of the Nordic Soc. and cent. of
postal cooperation among the northern countries. The design is taken from a coin found at
the site of Birka, an ancient Swedish town.
See also Finland No. 481, Iceland Nos. 404-
405, Norway Nos. 523-524 and Sweden Nos.
808-810.

Frederik IX — A120

1969, Mar. 11
456 A120 50o sepia   .30   .25
457 A120 60o dull red   .30   .25
   70th birthday of King Frederik IX.

Common Design Types
pictured following the introduction.

Europa Issue, 1969
Common Design Type
1969, Apr. 28
      Size: 28x20mm
458 CD12 90o chalky blue   .75   .75

Kronborg
Castle — A121

1969, May 22   **Engr.**   *Perf. 13*
459 A121 50o brown   .30   .25
   Association of Danes living abroad, 50th
anniv.

Danish Flag — A122

1969, June 12
460 A122 60o bluish blk, red &
             gray   .30   .25
   750th anniversary of the fall of the Dannebrog (Danish flag) from heaven.

Nexø — A123

1969, Aug. 28
461 A123 80o deep green   .30   .25
   Centenary of the birth of Martin Andersen
Nexø (1869-1954), novelist.

Stensen — A124

1969, Sept. 25
462 A124 1k deep brown   .35   .25
   300th anniv. of the publication of Niels Stensen's geological work "On Solid Bodies."

Abstract Design — A125

1969, Nov. 10   **Engr.**   *Perf. 13*
463 A125 60o rose, red & ultra   .30   .25

Symbolic
Design — A126

1969, Nov. 20
464 A126 30o olive green   .30   .25
   Valdemar Poulsen (1869-1942), electrical
engineer and inventor.

Post Office
Bank — A127

1970, Jan. 15   **Engr.**   *Perf. 13*
465 A127 60o dk red & org   .30   .25
   50th anniv. of post office banking service.

School Safety
Patrol — A128

1970, Feb. 19
466 A128 50o brown   .30   .25
   Issued to publicize road safety.

Candle in Window — A129

1970, May 4   **Engr.**   *Perf. 13*
467 A129 50o slate, dull bl & yel .30   .25
   25th anniv. of liberation from the Germans.

Deer — A130

1970, May 28
468 A130 60o yel grn, red & brn   .30   .25
   Tercentenary of Jaegersborg Deer Park.

Elephant Figurehead,
1741 — A131

1970, June 15   *Perf. 11½*
469 A131 30o multicolored   .30   .25
   Royal Naval Museum, tercentenary.

"The Homecoming" by
Povl Christensen — A132

1970, June 15   *Perf. 13*
470 A132 60o org, dl vio & ol grn .30   .25
   Union of North Schleswig and Denmark,
50th anniv.

Electromagnet
A133

1970, Aug. 13   **Engr.**
471 A133 80o gray green   .30 .25
150th anniversary of Hans Christian Oersted's discovery of electromagnetism.

Bronze Age Ship — A134

Ships: 50o, Viking shipbuilding, from Bayeux tapestry. 60o, Thuroe schooner with topgallant. 90o, Tanker.

1970, Sept. 24
472 A134 30o ocher & brown .25 .25
473 A134 50o brn red & rose brn .25 .25
474 A134 60o gray ol & red brn .35 .25
475 A134 90o blue grn & ultra 1.25 1.25
   Nos. 472-475 (4) 2.10 2.00

UN Emblem — A135

1970, Oct. 22   **Engr.**   **Perf. 13**
476 A135 90o blue, grn & red 1.00 1.00
25th anniversary of the United Nations.

Bertel Thorvaldsen — A136

1970, Nov. 19
477 A136 2k slate blue .60 .50
Bicentenary of the birth of Bertel Thorvaldsen (1768-1844), sculptor.

Mathide Fibiger — A137

1971, Feb. 25
478 A137 80o olive green .30 .25
Danish Women's Association centenary.

Refugees — A138

1971, Mar. 26   **Engr.**   **Perf. 13**
479 A138 50o brown .25 .25
480 A138 60o brown red .35 .25
Joint northern campaign for the benefit of refugees.

Hans Egede — A139

1971, May 27
481 A139 1k brown .35 .25
250th anniversary of arrival of Hans Egede in Greenland and beginning of its colonization.

A140

1971, Oct. 14
482 A140 30o Swimming .25 .25
483 A140 50o Hurdlers .50 .25
484 A140 60o Soccer .75 .25
485 A140 90o Sailing .75 .25
   Nos. 482-485 (4) 2.25 1.50

A141

1971, Nov. 11   **Engr.**   **Perf. 13**
486 A141 90o dark blue .35 .35
Centenary of first lectures given by Georg Brandes (1842-1927), writer and literary critic.

A142

1972, Jan. 27
487 A142 80o slate green .35 .25
Centenary of Danish sugar production.

A143

1972, Mar. 11   **Engr.**   **Perf. 13**
488 A143 60o red brown .30 .25
Frederik IX (1899-1972).

Abstract Design — A144

1972, Mar. 11
489 A144 1.20k brt rose lil, bl gray & brn .65 .65
Danish Meteorological Institute, cent.

Nikolai F. S. Grundtvig — A145

1972, May 4   **Engr.**   **Perf. 13**
490 A145 1k sepia .50 .50
Nikolai Frederik Severin Grundtvig (1783-1872), theologian and poet.

Locomotive, 1847, Ferry, Travelers — A146

1972, June 26
491 A146 70o rose red .30 .25
125th anniversary of Danish State Railways.

Rebild Hills — A147

1972, June 26
492 A147 1k bl, sl grn & mar .35 .25

Types of 1933-46
1972-78   **Engr.**   **Perf. 13**
493 A32 20o slate bl ('74) .35 .35
494 A32 50o sepia ('74) .30 .30
   a. Bklt. pane of 12 (4 #318, 4 #493, 4 #494) 15.00
495 A32 60o apple grn ('76) 1.75 .90
496 A32 60o gray ('78) .70 .70
497 A32 70o red 1.00 .35
498 A32 70o apple grn ('77) 1.10 .35
499 A55 2.50k orange 1.75 .35
500 A55 2.80k olive ('75) 1.25 .65
501 A55 3.50k lilac 2.00 .35
502 A55 4.50k olive 5.50 .35

503 A55 6k vio blk ('76) 2.00 .35
504 A55 7k red lilac ('78) 2.10 .35
505 A55 9k brown ol ('77) 3.00 .35
With Vertical and Horizontal Engraving Lines
506 A55 10k lemon ('76) 3.00 .35
   Nos. 493-506 (14) 25.80 6.05
See footnote after No. 1313.

"Tinker Turned Politician" — A148

1972, Sept. 14
507 A148 70o dark red .30 .25
250th anniv. of the comedies of Ludvig Holberg (1684-1754) on the Danish stage.

WHO Building, Copenhagen A149

1972, Sept. 14
508 A149 2k bl, blk & lt red brn .60 .60
Opening of WHO Building, Copenhagen.

Bridge Across Little Belt — A150

Highway engineering (Diagrams): 60o, Hanstholm Harbor. 70o, Lim Fjord Tunnel. 90o, Knudshoved Harbor.

1972, Oct. 19   **Engr.**   **Perf. 13**
509 A150 40o dk green .25 .25
510 A150 60o dk brown .35 .25
511 A150 70o dk red .35 .25
512 A150 90o dk blue grn 1.40 .50
   Nos. 509-512 (4) 2.35 1.25

Aeroskobing House c. 1740 — A151

Danish Architecture: 60o, East Bornholm farmhouse, 17th century, horiz. 70o, House, Christianshavn, c. 1710. 1.20k, Hvide Sande Farmhouse, c. 1810, horiz.

1972, Nov. 23
Size: 20x28mm, 27x20mm
513 A151 40o red, brn & blk .35 .25
514 A151 60o blk, vio bl & grn .35 .25
Size: 18x37mm, 36x20mm
515 A151 70o red, dk red & blk .45 .30
516 A151 1.20k dk brn, red & grn 1.40 1.00
   Nos. 513-516 (4) 2.55 1.80

Jensen — A152

1973, Feb. 22   **Engr.**   **Perf. 13**
517 A152 90o green .35 .25
Centenary of the birth of Johannes Vilhelm Jensen (1873-1950), lyric poet and novelist.

Guard Rails, Cogwheels — A153

1973, Mar. 22
518 A153 50o sepia .55 .25
Centenary of first Danish Factory Act for labor protection.

Abildgaard — A154

1973, Mar. 22
519 A154 1k dull blue .70 .35
Bicentenary of Royal Veterinary College, Christianshaven, founded by Prof. P. C. Abildgaard.

Rhododendron — A155

Design: 70o, Dronningen of Denmark rose.

1973, Apr. 26
520 A155 60o brn, grn & vio .50 .25
521 A155 70o dk red, rose & grn .50 .25
Centenary of the founding of the Horticultural Society of Denmark.

Nordic Cooperation Issue

Nordic House, Reykjavik — A156

1973, June 26   **Engr.**   **Perf. 13**
522 A156 70o multicolored .50 .25
523 A156 1k multicolored 1.50 1.25
A century of postal cooperation among Denmark, Finland, Iceland, Norway and Sweden, and in connection with the Nordic Postal Conference, Reykjavik.

Sextant, Stella Nova, Cassiopeia — A157

1973, Oct. 18   **Engr.**   **Perf. 13**
524 A157 2k dark blue 1.75 .30
400th anniversary of the publication of "De Nova Stella," by Tycho Brahe.

St. Mark, from 11th Cent. Book of Dalby — A158

1973, Oct. 18   **Photo.**   **Perf. 14x14½**
525 A158 1200o buff & multi 1.10 .65
300th anniversary of Royal Library.

Devil and Gossips, Fanefjord Church, 1480 — A159

Frescoes: No. 527, Queen Esther and King Ahasuerus, Tirsted Church, c.1400. No. 528, Miraculous Harvest, Jetsmark Church, c.1474. No. 529, Jesus carrying cross, and wearing crown of thorns, Biersted Church, c.1400. No. 530, Creation of Eve, Fanefjord Church, c.1480.

1973, Nov. 28   **Engr.**   **Perf. 13**
Cream Paper
526 A159 70o dk red, yel & grn 1.40 .30
527 A159 70o dk red, yel & grn 1.40 .30
528 A159 70o dk red, yel & grn 1.40 .30
529 A159 70o dk red, yel & grn 1.40 .30
530 A159 70o dk red, yel & grn 1.40 .30
   a. Bklt. pane, 2 each #526-530 35.00
   b. Strip of 5, #526-530 6.75

Blood Donors — A160

1974, Jan. 24
531 A160 90o purple & red   1.10 .25
"Blood Saves Lives."

Queen Margrethe — A161

1974-81   **Engr.**   **Perf. 13**
532 A161 60o brown   1.00 .50
533 A161 60o orange   .60 .45
534 A161 70o red   1.00 .25
535 A161 70o dk brown   .80 .25
536 A161 80o green   .80 .25
537 A161 80o dp brn ('76)   1.10 .25
538 A161 90o red lilac   1.10 .25
539 A161 90o dull red   1.40 .30
540 A161 90o slate grn ('76)   1.10 .30
541 A161 100o dp ultra   1.10 .25
542 A161 100o gray ('75)   1.10 .25
543 A161 100o red ('76)   1.10 .35
   a.   Ordinary paper   1.10 .25
544 A161 100o brown ('77)   1.00 .25
   a.   Bkt. pane of 5 (#544, #494, 2
     #493, #318)   2.50
     Complete booklet, #544a   2.50
545 A161 110o orange ('78)   1.20 .25
546 A161 120o slate   1.00 .50
547 A161 120o red ('77)   1.10 .25
   Complete booklet, 4 each
     #318, 493, 544, 547   13.50
548 A161 130o ultra ('75)   1.60 1.40
549 A161 150o vio bl ('78)   1.40 .85
550 A161 180o slate grn ('77)   1.40 .40
551 A161 200o blue ('81)   1.40 1.00
   Nos. 532-551 (20)   22.60 8.55

See Nos. 630, 632-642. For overprint see No. Q49.

Pantomime Theater — A162

1974, May 16
552 A162 100o indigo   .40 .30
Cent. of the Pantomime Theater, Tivoli.

Hverringe — A163

Views: 60o, Norre Lyndelse, Carl Nielsen's childhood home. 70o, Odense, Hans Chr. Andersen's childhood home. 90o, Hesselagergaard, vert. 120o, Hindsholm.

1974, June 20   **Engr.**   **Perf. 13**
553 A163 50o brown & multi   .50 .50
554 A163 60o sl grn & multi   .65 .65
555 A163 70o red brn & multi   .50 .50
556 A163 90o dk green & mar   .55 .25
557 A163 120o red org & dk grn   .70 .50
   Nos. 553-557 (5)   2.90 2.40

Emblem, Runner with Map — A164

1974, Aug. 22   **Engr.**   **Perf. 13**
558 A164 70o brown   .70 .70
559 A164 80o Compass   .25 .25
World Orienteering Championships 1974.

Iris — A165

1974, Sept. 19
560 A165 90o shown   .50 .25
561 A165 120o Purple orchid   .75 .75
Copenhagen Botanical Garden centenary.

Mailman, 1624, and Postilion, 1780 A166

Carrier Pigeon A167

Design: 90o, Balloon and sailing ships.

1974, Oct. 9   **Engr.**   **Perf. 13**
562 A166 70o lemon & dk brn   .40 .25
563 A166 90o dull grn & sepia   .40 .25
564 A167 120o dark blue   .65 .65
   Nos. 562-564 (3)   1.45 1.15
350th anniv. of Danish PO (70o, 90o) and cent. of UPU (120o).

Souvenir Sheet

Ferslew's Essays, 1849 and 1852 A168

Engraved and Photogravure
1975, Feb. 27   **Perf. 13**
565 A168   Sheet of 4   7.50 8.50
   a.   70o Coat of arms   1.75 2.00
   b.   80o King Frederik VII   1.75 2.00
   c.   90o King Frederik VII   1.75 2.00
   d.   100o Mercury   1.75 2.00
HAFNIA 76 Intl. Stamp Exhib., Copenhagen, Aug. 20-29, 1976. Sold for 5k. See No. 585.

Early Radio Equipment — A169

1975, Mar. 20   **Engr.**   **Perf. 13**
566 A169 90o dull red   .35 .30
Danish broadcasting, 50th anniversary.

Flora Danica Plate — A170

Danish China: 90o, Flora Danica tureen. 130o, Vase and tea caddy, blue fluted china.

1975, May 22
567 A170 50o slate grn   .30 .25
568 A170 90o brown red   .65 .65
569 A170 130o violet bl   1.10 1.10
   Nos. 567-569 (3)   2.05 2.00

Church of Moravian Brethren, Christiansfeld — A171

120o, Kongsgaard farmhouse, Lejre. 150o, Anna Queenstraede, Helsingor, vert.

1975, June 19
570 A171 70o sepia   .65 .65
571 A171 120o olive green   .80 .80
572 A171 150o violet black   .65 .25
   Nos. 570-572 (3)   2.10 1.70
European Architectural Heritage Year 1975.

Andersen — A172

Designs: 70o, Numbskull Jack, drawing by Vilh. Pedersen. 130o, The Marshking's Daughter, drawing by L. Frohlich.

1975, Aug. 28   **Engr.**   **Perf. 13**
573 A172 70o brown & blk   .60 .60
574 A172 90o brn red & dk brn   .75 .30
575 A172 130o blue blk & sepia   1.75 1.75
   Nos. 573-575 (3)   3.10 2.65
Hans Christian Andersen (1805-75), writer.

Watchman's Square, Abenra — A173

Designs: 90o, Haderslev Cathedral, vert. 100o, Mögeltönder Polder. 120o, Mouth of Vidaaen at Höjer Floodgates.

1975, Sept. 25
576 A173 70o multicolored   .45 .45
577 A173 90o multicolored   .40 .25
578 A173 100o multicolored   .50 .25
579 A173 120o multicolored   .55 .50
   Nos. 576-579 (4)   1.90 1.45

European Kingfisher — A174

1975, Oct. 23   **Engr.**   **Perf. 13**
580 A174 50o shown   .45 .45
581 A174 70o Hedgehog   .45 .45
582 A174 90o Cats   .45 .45
583 A174 130o Avocets   1.25 1.25
584 A174 200o Otter   .65 .25
   Nos. 580-584 (5)   3.25 2.85
Protected animals, and for the centenary of the Danish Society for the Prevention of Cruelty to Animals (90o).

HAFNIA Type of 1974
Souvenir Sheet

1975, Nov. 20   **Engr. & Photo.**
585 A168   Sheet of 4   4.50 6.75
   a.   50o buff & brown, No. 2   1.10 1.60
   b.   70o buff, brown & blue, No. 1   1.10 1.60
   c.   90o buff, blue & brown, No. 11   1.10 1.60
   d.   130o olive, brown & buff, No. 19   1.10 1.60
HAFNIA 76 Intl. Stamp Exhib., Copenhagen, Aug. 20-29, 1976. Sold for 5k.

Copenhagen, Center A175

View from Round Tower A176

Copenhagen, Views: 100o, Central Station, interior. 130o, Harbor.

1976, Mar. 25   **Engr.**   **Perf. 12½**
586 A175 60o multicolored   .45 .45
587 A175 80o multicolored   .45 .45
588 A176 100o multicolored   .45 .25
589 A175 130o multicolored   1.50 1.50
   Nos. 586-589 (4)   2.85 2.65

Postilion, by Otto Bache — A177

1976, June 17   **Engr.**   **Perf. 12½**
590 A177 130o multicolored   1.00 1.25
Souvenir Sheet
591 A177 130o multicolored   10.00 16.00
HAFNIA 76 Intl. Stamp Exhib., Copenhagen, Aug. 20-29. No. 591 contains one stamp similar to No. 590 with design continuous into sheet margin. Sheet shows painting "A String of Horses Outside an Inn" of which No. 590 shows a detail. Sheet sold for 15k including exhibition ticket.

Emil Chr. Hansen, Physiologist, in Laboratory — A178

1976, Sept. 23   **Engr.**   **Perf. 13**
592 A178 100o orange red   .40 .30
Carlsberg Foundation (art and science), centenary.

Glass Blower Molding Glass — A179

Danish Glass Production: 80o, Finished glass removed from pipe. 130o, Glass cut off from foot. 150o, Glass blown up in mold.

1976, Nov. 18   **Engr.**   **Perf. 13**
593 A179 60o slate   .50 .50
594 A179 80o dk brown   .50 .25
595 A179 130o dk blue   1.00 1.00
596 A179 150o red brown   .60 .25
   Nos. 593-596 (4)   2.60 2.00

Five Water Lilies — A180

Photogravure and Engraved
1977, Feb. 2   **Perf. 12½**
597 A180 100o brt green & multi   .50 .35
598 A180 130o ultra & multi   2.00 2.00

Nordic countries cooperation for protection of the environment and 25th Session of Nordic Council, Helsinki, Feb. 19.

Road Accident — A181

1977, Mar. 24   **Engr.**   **Perf. 12½**
599 A181 100o brown red   .40 .30
Road Safety Traffic Act, May 1, 1977.

Europa — A182

1977, May 2   **Engr.**   **Perf. 12½**
600 A182 1k Allinge   .60 .30
601 A182 1.30k View, Ringsted   3.00 3.00

Kongeaen — A183

Landscapes, Southern Jutland: 90o, Skallingen. 150o, Torskind. 200o, Jelling.

1977, June 30   **Engr.**   **Perf. 12½**
602 A183 60o multicolored   1.25 1.25
603 A183 90o multicolored   .65 .65
604 A183 150o multicolored   .60 .50
605 A183 200o multicolored   .75 .50
   Nos. 602-605 (4)   3.25 2.90
See Nos. 616-619, 655-658, 666-669.

Hammers and Horseshoes — A184

Designs: 1k, Chisel, square and plane. 1.30k, Trowel, ceiling brush and folding ruler.

1977, Sept. 22   **Engr.**   **Perf. 12½**
606	A184	80o dk brown	.30	.25
607	A184	1k red	.40	.25
608	A184	1.30k violet bl	.75	.60
	Nos. 606-608 (3)		1.45	1.10

Danish crafts.

Globe Flower — A185

Endangered Flora: 1.50k, Cnidium dubium.

1977, Nov. 17   **Engr.**   **Perf. 12½**
609	A185	1k multicolored	.40	.25
610	A185	1.50k multicolored	1.25	1.25

Handball — A186

1978, Jan. 19   **Perf. 12½**
611	A186	1.20k red	.40	.30

Men's World Handball Championships.

Christian IV, Frederiksborg Castle A187

Frederiksborg Museum A188

1978, Mar. 16
612	A187	1.20k brown red	.50	.50
613	A188	1.80k black	.60	.30

Frederiksborg Museum, centenary.

Europa Issue

Jens Bang's House, Aalborg A189

Frederiksborg Castle, Ground Plan and Elevation A190

1978, May 11   **Engr.**   **Perf. 12½**
614	A189	1.20k red	.30	.25
615	A190	1.50k dk bl & vio bl	1.25	1.25

Landscape Type of 1977

Landscapes, Central Jutland: 70o, Kongenshus Memorial Park. 120o, Post Office, Old Town in Aarhus. 150o, Lignite fields, Soby. 180o, Church wall, Stadil Church.

1978, June 15   **Engr.**   **Perf. 12½**
616	A183	70o multicolored	.50	.50
617	A183	120o multicolored	.55	.25
	Complete booklet, 10 #617		9.00	
618	A183	150o multicolored	.80	.80
619	A183	180o multicolored	.60	.60
	Nos. 616-619 (4)		2.45	2.15

Boats in Harbor — A191

Danish fishing industry: 1k, Eel traps. 1.80k, Boats in berth. 2.50k, Drying nets.

1978, Sept. 7   **Engr.**   **Perf. 12½**
620	A191	70o olive gray	.50	.50
621	A191	1k redsh brown	.50	.25
622	A191	1.80k slate	.60	.50
623	A191	2.50k sepia	.85	.60
	Nos. 620-623 (4)		2.45	1.85

Edible Morel — A192

Design: 1.20k, Satan's mushroom.

1978, Nov. 16   **Engr.**   **Perf. 12½**
624	A192	1k sepia	.65	.55
625	A192	1.20k dull red	.65	.55

Telephones — A193

1979, Jan. 25   **Engr.**   **Perf. 12½**
626	A193	1.20k dull red	.40	.30

Centenary of Danish telephone.

University Seal A194

Pentagram: University Faculties A195

1979, Apr. 5   **Engr.**   **Perf. 12½**
627	A194	1.30k vermilion	.40	.25
628	A195	1.60k dk vio blue	.55	.55

University of Copenhagen, 500th anniv.

Types of 1933-1974

1979-82   **Engr.**   **Perf. 13**
629	A32	80o green	.35	.40
630	A32	90o slate	3.00	3.25
631	A32	100o dp green ('81)	.50	.40
632	A161	110o brown	.65	.40
a.	Bklt. pane, #493-494, 632, 2 #318 ('79)		1.50	
	complete booklet, #632a		1.50	
633	A161	130o red	.65	.40
a.	Bklt. pane, 2 ea #494, 629, 632, 4 #633 ('79)		7.50	
	Complete booklet, #633a		8.00	
634	A161	130o brown ('81)	.65	.60
635	A161	140o red org ('80)	2.00	2.50
636	A161	150o red org ('81)	.65	.80
637	A161	160o ultra	1.25	1.25
638	A161	160o red ('81)	.65	.40
a.	Bklt. pane, 2 ea #318, 634, 638, 8 #494)		12.00	
	Complete booklet, #638a		12.00	
639	A161	180o ultra ('80)	1.40	1.40
640	A161	210o gray ('80)	2.00	2.50
641	A161	230o ol grn ('81)	1.00	.65
642	A161	250o blue grn ('81)	1.40	1.00
643	A55	2.80k dull grn	1.40	1.10
644	A55	3.30k brn red ('81)	1.40	.80
645	A55	3.50k grnsh bl ('82)	2.50	3.00
646	A55	4.30k brn red ('80)	4.00	5.25
647	A55	4.70k rose lil ('81)	3.50	5.25
648	A55	8k orange	2.75	.40
649	A55	12k red ('81)	5.00	.15
650	A55	14k dk red brn ('82)	5.75	.80
	Nos. 629-650 (22)		42.45	33.20

A196

Europa: 1.30k, Mail cart, 1785. 1.60k, Morse key and amplifier.

1979, May 10   **Perf. 12½**
651	A196	1.30k red	1.00	.25
652	A196	1.60k dark blue	3.00	1.10

A197

Viking Art: 1.10k, Gripping beast pendant. 2k, Key with gripping beast design.

1979, June 14   **Engr.**   **Perf. 13**
653	A197	1.10k sepia	.40	.40
654	A197	2k grnsh gray	.50	.40

Landscape Type of 1977

Landscapes, Northern Jutland: 80o, Mols Bjerge. 90o, Orslev Kloster. 200o, Trans. 280o, Bovbjerg.

1979, Sept. 6   **Engr.**   **Perf. 12½**
655	A183	80o multicolored	.50	.50
656	A183	90o multicolored	1.60	1.60
657	A183	200o multicolored	.90	.35
658	A183	280o multicolored	1.10	1.10
	Nos. 655-658 (4)		4.10	3.55

Adam Oehlenschläger (1799-1850), Poet and Dramatist — A198

1979, Oct. 4   **Engr.**   **Perf. 13**
659	A198	1.30k dk carmine	.40	.30

Score, Violin, Dancing Couple A199

Ballerina A200

1979, Nov. 8   **Engr.**   **Perf. 13x12½**
660	A199	1.10k brown	.40	.30
661	A200	1.60k ultra	.60	.65

Jacob Gade (1879-63), composer; August Bournonville (1805-79), ballet master.

Royal Mail Guards' Office, Copenhagen, 1779 — A201

1980, Feb. 14   **Engr.**   **Perf. 13**
662	A201	1.30k brown red	.50	.35

National Postal Service, 200th anniversary.

Symbols of Occupation, Health and Education — A202

1980, May 5   **Engr.**   **Perf. 13**
663	A202	1.60k dark blue	.65	.50

World Conference of the UN Decade for Women, Copenhagen, July 14-30.

Karen Blixen (1885-1962), Writer (Pen Name Isak Dinesen) — A203

Europa: 1.60k, August Krogh (1874-1949), physiologist.

1980, May 5
664	A203	1.30k red	.65	.25
665	A203	1.60k blue	1.40	1.40

Landscape Type of 1977

Northern Jutland: 80o, Viking ship burial grounds, Lindholm Hoje. 110o, Lighthouse, Skagen, vert. 200o, Boreglum Monastery. 280o, Fishing boats, Vorupor Beach.

1980, June 19   **Engr.**   **Perf. 13**
666	A183	80o multicolored	.50	.50
667	A183	110o multicolored	.50	.50
668	A183	200o multicolored	.70	.30
669	A183	280o multicolored	2.00	2.00
	Nos. 666-669 (4)		3.70	3.30

Nordic Cooperation Issue

Silver Tankard, by Borchardt Rollufse, 1641 — A204

1.80K, Bishop's bowl, Copenhagen faience, 18th cent.

1980, Sept. 9   **Engr.**   **Perf. 13**
670	A204	1.30k shown	.50	.35
671	A204	1.80k multicolored	1.40	1.40

Frisian Sceat Facsimile, Obverse and Reverse, 9th Century — A205

Coins: 1.40k, Silver coin of Valdemar the Great and Absalom, 1157-1182. 1.80k, Gold 12-mark coin of Christian VII, 1781.

1980, Oct. 9   **Engr.**   **Perf. 13**
672	A205	1.30k red & redsh brn	.50	.45
673	A205	1.40k ol gray & sl grn	1.60	1.40
674	A205	1.80k dk bl & sl bl	1.25	1.25
	Nos. 672-674 (3)		3.35	3.10

Tonder Lace Pattern, North Schleswig — A206

Designs: Tonder lace patterns.

1980, Nov. 13   **Engr.**   **Perf. 13**
675	A206	1.10k brown	.65	.65
676	A206	1.30k brown red	.50	.30
677	A206	2k olive gray	.70	.30
	Nos. 675-677 (3)		1.85	1.25

Nyboder Development, Copenhagen, 350th Anniversary — A207

Design: 1.30k, View of Nyboder, diff.

1981, Mar. 19
678	A207	1.30k dp org & ocher	.90	.90
679	A207	1.60k dp org & ocher	.55	.30

Tilting at a Barrel on Shrovetide — A208

Design: 2k, Midsummer's Eve bonfire.

1981, May 4   **Engr.**   **Perf. 13**
680	A208	1.60k brown red	.40	.25
	Complete booklet, 10 #680		4.00	
681	A208	2k dk blue	1.25	.75

Soro Lake and Academy, Zealand — A209

Designs: Views of Zealand: 150o, Poet N.F.S. Grundtvig's home, Udby. 160o, Kaj Munk's home, Opager. 200o, Gronsund. 230o, Bornholm Island.

1981, June 18   **Engr.**   **Perf. 13**
682	A209	100o shown	.50	.50
683	A209	150o multicolored	.65	.65
684	A209	160o multicolored	.65	.30
685	A209	200o multicolored	.80	.80
686	A209	230o multicolored	1.10	.85
	Nos. 682-686 (5)		3.70	3.10

European Urban Renaissance Year — A210

1981, Sept. 10   **Engr.**   **Perf. 12½x13**
687	A210	1.60k dull red	.65	.35

Type of 1933

				Perf. 13
1981-85		**Engr.**		
688	A32	30o orange	.60	.40
a.	Bklt. pane 10 (2 #318, 2 #688, 6 #494)('84)		30.00	
	Complete booklet, #688a, 6 #708		30.00	
689	A32	40o purple	.50	.40
a.	Bklt. pane of 10 (4 #318, 2 #689, 4 #494) ('89)		4.50	
690	A32	80o ol bis ('85)	1.00	.80
691	A32	100o blue ('83)	.85	.40
b.	Bklt. pane of 8 (2 #494, 4 #691, 2 #706) ('83)		21.00	
	Complete booklet, #691b		21.00	
692	A32	150o dk green ('82)	.85	.40
693	A32	200o green ('83)	1.00	.90
694	A32	230o brt yel grn ('84)	1.50	.60
695	A32	250o brt yel grn ('85)	1.50	.60
	Nos. 688-695 (8)		7.80	4.50

Ellehammer's 18-horsepower Biplane, 1906 — A211

1.30k, R-1 Fokker CV reconnaissance plane, 1926. 1.60k, Bellanca J-300, 1931. 2.30k, DC-7C, 1957.

				Perf. 13
1981, Oct. 8		**Engr.**		
696	A211	1k black & bluish green	.65	.65
697	A211	1.30k brown & lt brown	1.10	1.10
698	A211	1.60k red & orange	.65	.30
699	A211	2.30k dark blue & pale blue	.90	.70
	Nos. 696-699 (4)		3.30	2.75

Arms Type of 1946 and

Queen Margrethe II, 10th Anniv. of Accession — A212

				Perf. 13
1982-85		**Engr.**		
700	A212	1.60k dull red	.65	.40
701	A212	1.60k dk ol grn	2.50	3.00
702	A212	1.80k sepia	.85	.70
703	A212	2k dull red	.90	.30
b.	Bklt. pane, 4 #494, 2 ea #493, 702, 703		20.00	
704	A212	2.20k ol grn ('83)	1.50	2.75
705	A212	2.30k violet ('83)	1.00	1.20
706	A212	2.50k org red ('83)	.85	.30
707	A212	2.70k dk blue	1.20	.80
708	A212	2.70k cop red ('84)	1.25	.40
c.	Booklet pane, 3 #688, 2 #494, 3 #708 ('84)		13.00	
709	A212	2.80k cop red ('85)	1.00	.50
	Complete booklet, #494a, 6 #709		13.50	
b.	Booklet pane, 3 #493, 2 #494, 3 #709 ('85)		6.75	
	Complete booklet, #709b		7.00	
710	A212	3k violet ('83)	1.20	.50
711	A212	3.30k bluish blk ('84)	1.75	1.00
712	A212	3.50k blue ('83)	1.50	.65
713	A212	3.50k dk vio ('85)	1.50	.80
714	A212	3.70k dp blue ('84)	1.75	.80
715	A212	3.80k dk blue ('85)	1.40	.60
716	A55	4.30k dk ol grn ('84)	4.50	4.75
717	A55	5.50k dk bl grn ('84)	2.75	1.25
718	A55	16k cop red ('83)	6.00	.90
719	A55	17k cop red ('84)	7.75	1.25
720	A55	18k brn vio ('85)	8.50	1.25
720A	A55	50k dk red ('85)	17.00	3.25
	Nos. 700-720A (22)		67.30	27.35

See Nos. 796-803, 887, 889, 896, 899.

World Figure Skating Championships A213

1982, Feb. 25			
721	A213	2k dark blue	.80 .50

Revenue Schooner Argus — A214

				Perf. 12½
1982, Feb. 25		**Engr.**		
722	A214	1.60k carmine red	.65	.35

Customs Service centenary

Europa — A215

2k, Abolition of adscription, 1788. 2.70k, Women's voting right, 1915.

				Perf. 12½
1982, May 3		**Engr.**		
723	A215	2k brown lake	.75	.25
	Complete booklet, 10 #723		7.50	
724	A215	2.70k deep blue	1.75	1.00

Butter Churn, Barn, Hjedding — A216

				Perf. 13
1982, June 10		**Engr.**		
725	A216	1.80k brown	.80	.65

Cooperative dairy farming centenary.

Records Office, 400th Anniv. — A217

1982, June 10			
726	A217	2.70k green	1.20 .50

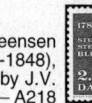

Steen Steensen Blicher (1782-1848), Poet, by J.V. Gertner — A218

				Perf. 13
1982, Aug. 26		**Engr.**		
727	A218	2k brown red	.35	.30

Robert Storm Petersen (1882-1949), Cartoonist — A219

Characters: 1.50k, Three little men and the number man. 2k, Peter and Ping the penguin, horiz.

				Perf. 12½
1982, Sept. 23		**Engr.**		
728	A219	1.50k dk bl & red	.70	.50
729	A219	2k red & ol grn	1.10	.40

Printing in Denmark, 500th Anniv. — A220

1982, Sept. 23			
730	A220	1.80k Press, text, ink balls	.80 .85

A221

1982, Nov. 4			
731	A221	2.70k Library seal	1.20 .50

500th anniv. of University Library.

World Communications Year — A222

				Perf. 13
1983, Jan. 27		**Engr.**		
732	A222	2k multicolored	.80	.35

Amusement Park, 400th Anniv. — A223

1983, Feb. 24			
733	A223	2k multicolored	.80 .35

Badminton Championship — A224

1983, Feb. 24			
734	A224	2.70k multicolored	1.20 .50

Nordic Cooperation Issue — A225

1983, Mar. 24			
735	A225	2.50k Egeskov Castle	.90 .40
736	A225	3.50k Troll Church, North Jutland	1.40 .75

50th Anniv. of Steel Plate Printed Stamps — A226

				Perf. 13
1983, Mar. 24		**Engr.**		
737	A226	2.50k car rose	1.00	.35

Europa 1983 — A227

2.50k, Kildekovshallen Recreation Center, Copenhagen. 3.50k, Salling Sound Bridge.

				Perf. 13
1983, May 5		**Engr.**		
738	A227	2.50k multicolored	1.10	.25
739	A227	3.50k multicolored	2.00	1.00

Weights and Measures Ordinance, 300th Anniv. — A228

1983, June 16			
740	A228	2.50k red	1.00 .35

Christian V Danish Law, 300th Anniv. — A229

				Engr.
1983, Sept. 8				
741	A229	5k Codex titlepage	2.00	1.00

A230

1k, Car crash, police. 2.50k, Fire, ambulance service. 3.50k, Sea rescue.

				Perf. 13
1983, Oct. 6				
742	A230	1k brown	.50	.50
743	A230	2.50k red	1.00	.35
744	A230	3.50k blue	1.25	.85
	Nos. 742-744 (3)		2.75	1.70

Life saving and salvage services.

Elderly in Society — A231

1983, Oct. 6			
745	A231	2k Stages of life	.80 .80
746	A231	2.50k Train passengers	1.00 .30

N.F.S. Grundtvig (1783-1872), Poet A232

Street Scene, by C.W. Eckersberg (1783-1853) A233

				Engr.
1983, Nov. 3				
747	A232	2.50k brown red	1.20	.50
748	A233	2.50k brown red	1.00	.35

Tree Planting Campaign — A234

				Litho. & Engr.
1984, Jan. 26				
749	A234	2.70k Shovel, sapling	1.20	.35

A235

				Engr.
1984, Jan. 26				
750	A235	3.70k Game	1.75	.50

1984 Billiards World Championships, Copenhagen, May 10-13.

Hydrographic Dept. Bicentenary A236

Pilotage Service, 300th Anniv. A237

				Perf. 13
1984, Mar. 22		**Engr.**		
751	A236	2.30k Compass	1.25	.90
752	A237	2.70k Boat	1.25	.50

2nd European Parliament Elections A238

Scouts Around Campfire, Emblems A239

				Litho. & Engr.
				Perf. 13
1984, Apr. 12				
753	A238	2.70k org & dk bl	1.75	.35
754	A239	2.70k multi	1.20	.35

Europa (1959-84) — A240

				Perf. 12½
1984, May 3		**Engr.**		
755	A240	2.70k red	1.75	.25
756	A240	3.70k blue	2.25	1.60

Prince
Henrik,
50th
Birthday
A241

D Day,
40th Anniv.
A242

1984, June 6   **Engr.**
757 A241 2.70k brown red   1.20 .35
758 A242 2.70k War Memorial,
     Copenhagen   1.20 .35
    See Greenland No. 160.

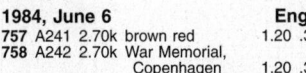

17th Cent.
Inn — A243

1984, June 6   **Engr.**
759 A243 3k multicolored   1.50 1.40

Fishing and
Shipping — A244

1984, Sept. 6   **Engr.**
760 A244 2.30k Research (Her-
     ring)   1.60 1.75
761 A244 2.70k Sea transport   1.10 .60
762 A244 3.30k Deep-sea fishing   1.60 1.75
763 A244 3.70k Deep-sea, diff.   1.60 1.75
    Nos. 760-763 (4)   5.90 5.85

A245

1984, Oct. 5   **Litho. & Engr.**
764 A245 1k Post bird   .35 .35

A246

Holberg Meets with an Officer, by Wilhelm
Marstrand (1810-73).

1984, Oct. 5
765 A246 2.70k multicolored   1.20 .35
    Ludvig Holberg (1684-1754), writer.

Jewish Community in
Copenhagen, 300th
Anniv. — A247

3.70k, Woman blessing Sabbath candles.

1984, Oct. 5
766 A247 3.70k multicolored   1.75 1.40

Carnival in
Rome, by
Christoffer
W.
Eckersberg
(1783-1853)
A248

Paintings: 10k, Ymer and Odhumble (Nordic
mythology figures), by Nicolai A. Abildgaard
(1743-1809), vert.

     Perf. 12½x13, 13x12½
1984, Nov. 22   **Litho. & Engr.**
767 A248 5k multicolored   3.25 3.25
768 A248 10k multicolored   5.75 5.75

German and French
Reform Church, 300th
Anniv. — A249

1985, Jan. 24   **Engr.**   ***Perf. 13***
769 A249 2.80k magenta   1.75 .35

Bonn-Copenhagen Declaration, 30th
Anniv. — A250

1985, Feb. 21   **Litho.**   ***Perf. 14***
770 A250 2.80k Map, flags   1.90 .65

Intl. Youth
Year — A251

1985, Mar. 14   ***Perf. 13***
771 A251 3.80k multicolored   1.75 .90

Souvenir Sheet

HAFNIA '87 Philatelic
Exhibition — A252

Early Postal Ordinances — 1k, Christian
IV's Ordinance on Postmen, 1624. 2.50k,
Plague Mandate, 1711. 2.80k, Ordinance on
Prohibition of Mail by Means other than the
Post, 1775. 3.80k, Act on Postal Articles,
1831.

1985, Mar. 14   **Litho. & Engr.**
772   Sheet of 4   5.50 *6.50*
  a.   A252 1k multi   1.25 *1.60*
  b.   A252 2.50k multi   1.25 *1.60*
  c.   A252 2.80k multi   1.25 *1.60*
  d.   A252 3.80k multi   1.25 *1.60*
     Sold for 15k.

Europa 1985 — A253

1985, May 2
773 A253 2.80k Musical staff   *1.50 .50*
774 A253 3.80k Musical staff,
     diff.   *1.90 1.25*

Arrival of Queen
Ingrid in Denmark,
50th Anniv. — A254

2.80k, Queen Mother, chrysanthemums.

1985, May 21
775 A254 2.80k multicolored   1.20 .35
    See Greenland No. 163.

Opening of the Faro
Bridges — A255

1985, May 21   **Litho.**   ***Perf. 13***
776 A255 2.80k Faro-Falster
     Bridge   1.20 .35

St. Cnut's Land Grant
to Lund Cathedral,
900th Anniv. — A256

Seal of King Cnut and: 2.80k, Lund Cathedral. 3k, City of Helsingdorg, Sweden.

1985, May 21   **Engr.**
777 A256 2.80k multi   1.10 .45
778 A256 3k multi   2.00 2.00
    See Sweden Nos. 1538-1539.

UN Decade for
Women — A257

1985, June 27   **Litho. & Engr.**
779 A257 3.80k Cyclist   1.75 1.00

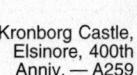

Sports — A258

1985, June 27
780 A258 2.80k Women's floor
     exercise   1.25 .30
781 A258 3.80k Canoe & kayak   1.75 .95
782 A258 6k Cycling   2.90 1.75
    Nos. 780-782 (3)   5.90 3.00

Kronborg Castle,
Elsinore, 400th
Anniv. — A259

1985, Sept. 5
783 A259 2.80k multi   1.75 .35

UN 40th Anniv. — A260

1985, Sept. 5
784 A260 3.80k Dove, emblem   1.75 1.20

Niels Bohr
(1885-1962),
Physicist
A261

1985, Oct. 3   ***Perf. 13x12½***
785 A261 2.80k With wife Mar-
     grethe   1.75 1.40
Winner of 1922 Nobel Prize in Physics for
theory of atomic structure.

Hand Signing "D" — A262

1985, Nov. 7   **Engr.**   ***Perf. 13***
786 A262 2.80k multicolored   1.40 .35
    Danish Assoc. for the Deaf, 50th anniv.

Boat, by Helge
Refn — A263

1985, Nov. 7   **Litho.**
787 A263 2.80k multicolored   1.40 .35

Abstract Iron
Sculpture by
Robert
Jacobsen
A264

Lithographed and Engraved
1985, Nov. 7   ***Perf. 13x12½***
788 A264 3.80k multicolored   3.50 3.75

Painting by
Bjorn Wiinblad
A265

1986, Jan. 23   **Litho.**   ***Perf. 13x12½***
789 A265 2.80k multicolored   1.75 1.40

Amnesty Intl.,
25th
Anniv. — A266

Lithographed and Engraved
1986, Jan. 23   ***Perf. 13***
790 A266 2.80k multicolored   1.20 .35

Miniature Sheet

HAFNIA '87 — A267

1986, Feb. 20
791 A267 Sheet of 4   7.50 11.00
  a.   100o Holstein carriage, c.
      1840   1.75 2.50
  b.   250o Iceboat, c. 1880   1.75 2.50
  c.   280o 1st mail van, 1908   1.75 2.50
  d.   380o Airmail service 1919   1.75 2.50
     Sold for 15k.

Changing of the
Guard — A268

1986, Mar. 20   ***Perf. 13***
792 A268 2.80k multicolored   1.20 .35
Royal Danish Life Guards barracks and
Rosenborg Drilling Ground, bicent.

     Types of 1933-85
1986-90   **Engr.**   ***Perf. 13***
793 A32 5o brn org ('89)   .35 .40
794 A32 270o brt yel grn   1.90 1.75
  b.   Bklt. pane, 6 #318, 2 #691, 2
      #794   18.00

795	A32	300o brt yel grn	1.75 .40
		Complete booklet, #794b, 4 #795	22.50
796	A212	3k cop red	1.20 .60
		Complete booklet, #691, #794, 3 #318, 2 #796	6.00
797	A212	3.20k deep vio	1.00 .80
798	A212	3.20k carmine	1.25 .40
c.		Bklt. pane, 2 #693, 4 #798	9.00
		Complete booklet, #689a, #798c	15.00
		Complete booklet, #693, 2 #798, 2 #318, #689, 2 #494	15.50
799	A212	3.40k dk grn	2.25 3.00
800	A212	3.80k dark vio	1.20 2.90
801	A212	4.10k dark blue	1.40 .60
802	A212	4.20k dk pur	3.50 3.00
803	A212	4.40k dp bl	2.50 .60
804	A55	4.60k gray	5.00 5.50
805	A55	6.50k dp grn	2.50 5.00
806	A55	6.60k green	5.00 5.50
807	A55	7.10k brn vio	3.50 3.50
808	A55	7.30k green	4.75 5.50
809	A55	7.70k dk brn vio	4.50 2.10
810	A55	11k brown	5.50 5.25
811	A55	20k dp ultra	6.75 .80
812	A55	22k henna brn	7.25 2.25
813	A55	23k dark vio grn	10.50 2.25
814	A55	24k dark olive grn	10.50 2.00
815	A55	26k dark olive grn	12.50 2.25
		Nos. 793-815 (23)	96.55 52.35

Issued: 6.50k, 20k, 1/9/86; 22k, 1/3/87; 270o, 3k, No. 797, 3.80k, 4.10k, 4.60k, 6.60k, 7.10k, 24k, 1/7/88; No. 794b, 1/28/88; 300o, No. 798, 3.40k, 4.20k, 4.40k, 7.30k, 7.70k, 11k, 26k, 1/26/89; 5o, 1989; 23k, 1/11/90.

No. 793 issued for use in lieu of currency of the same face value.

Soro Academy, 400th Anniv. — A269

1986, Apr. 28   **Litho. & Engr.**
816 A269 2.80k multi   1.40 .50

Intl. Peace Year — A270

1986, Apr. 28
817 A270 3.80k multi   1.60 1.10

A271

1986, May 26   **Litho.**
818 A271 2.80k multi   1.75 .50

Crown Prince Frederik, 18th birthday.

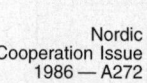

Nordic Cooperation Issue 1986 — A272

Sister towns.

1986, May 27   **Engr.**
819 A272 2.80k Aalborg Harbor   1.40 .35
820 A272 3.80k Thisted Church and Town Hall   1.60 1.25

Hoje Tastrup Train Station Opening, May 31 — A273

1986, May 27   **Litho.**
821 A273 2.80k multi   1.20 .35

Mailbox, Telegraph Lines, Telephone — A274

1986, June 19   **Litho.**   **Perf. 13**
822 A274 2.80k multi   1.00 .35

19th European Intl. PTT Congress, Copenhagen, Aug. 12-16.

Natl. Bird Candidates — A275

Finalists: a, Corvus corax. b, Sturnus vulgaris. c, Cygnus olor (winner). d, Vanellus vanellus. e, Alauda arvensis.

1986, June 19   **Litho. & Engr.**
823   Strip of 5   10.50 24.00
a.-e. A275 2.80k any single   2.00 1.00
   Complete booklet, 2 #823   21.00

A276

1986, June 19
824 A276 2.80k multi   1.20 .35

Danish Rifle, Gymnastics and Sports Club, 125th anniv.

Souvenir Sheet

HAFNIA '87 — A277

1986, Sept. 4
825   Sheet of 4   10.00 12.50
a. A277 100o Mailcoach, c. 1841   2.25 3.00
b. A277 250o Postmaster, c. 1840   2.25 3.00
c. A277 280o Postman, c. 1851   2.25 3.00
d. A277 380o Rural postman, c. 1893   2.25 3.00

Sold for 15k.

Europa 1986 — A278

1986, Sept. 4   **Engr.**
826 A278 2.80k Street sweeper   *2.50 .25*
827 A278 3.80k Garbage truck   *3.50 1.50*

Cupid — A279

1986, Oct. 9   **Litho.**
828 A279 3.80k multi   1.50 1.00

Premiere of The Whims of Cupid and the Ballet Master, by Vincenzo Galeotti, bicent.

Refugee — A280

1986, Oct. 9   **Litho. & Engr.**
829 A280 2.80k multi   1.20 .35

Danish Refugee Council Relief Campaign.

A281

Protestant Reformation in Denmark, 450th Anniv.: Sermon, altarpiece detail, 1561, Thorslunde Church, Copenhagen.

1986, Oct. 9   **Litho.**   **Perf. 13**
830 A281 6.50k multi   2.50 1.75

A282

1986, Nov. 6   **Litho. & Engr.**
831 A282 3.80k multi   3.00 3.00

Organization for Economic Cooperation and Development, 25th anniv.

Abstract by Lin Utzon — A283

1987, Jan. 22   **Litho.**   **Perf. 13**
832 A283 2.80k multi   1.00 .35
   Complete booklet, 10 #832   11.00

Art appreciation.

A284

1987, Feb. 26   **Engr.**   **Perf. 13**
833 A284 2.80k lake & black   1.00 .35

Danish Consumer Council, 40th anniv.

A285

Religious art (details) from Ribe Cathedral.

1987, Apr. 9   **Litho.**   **Perf. 13**
834 A285 3k Fresco   1.40 .60
835 A285 3.80k Stained-glass window   2.10 2.10
   Complete booklet, 10 #835   21.00
836 A285 6.50k Mosaic   3.50 3.50
   Nos. 834-836 (3)   7.00 6.20

Ribe Cathedral redecoration, 1982-1987, by Carl-Henning Pedersen.

A286

Europa (Modern architecture): 2.80k, Central Library, Gentofte, 1985. 3.80k, Hoje Tastrup High School, 1985, horiz.

1987, May 4   **Engr.**   **Perf. 13**
837 A286 2.80k rose claret   *2.50 .35*
838 A286 3.80k bright ultra   *3.50 2.25*

A287

1987, May 4
839 A287 2.50k dk red & bl blk   2.00 2.00

Danish Academy of Technical Sciences (ATV), 50th anniv.

8th Gymnaestrada, Herning, July 7-11 — A288

1987, June 18   **Litho. & Engr.**
840 A288 2.80k multi   1.00 .35
   Complete booklet, 10 #840   10.00

A289

1987, June 18
841 A289 3.80k multi   1.60 1.40

Danish Cooperative Bacon Factories, cent.

A290

1987, Aug. 27   **Litho.**
842 A290 3.80k Single-sculler   1.60 1.20

World Rowing Championships, Aug. 23-30.

HAFNIA '87, Bella Center, Copenhagen, Oct. 16-25 — A291

No. 843, Type A15, mail train c. 1912.

1987, Aug. 27   **Litho. & Engr.**   **Perf. 13x12½**
843 A291 280o multi   1.90 1.50
   Souvenir Sheet
843A A291 280o like No. 843   20.00 26.00

Purchase of No. 843A included admission to the exhibition. Sold for 45k.

Due to a color shift, some examples of No. 843A have a green lawn and locomotive.

Abstact by Ejler Bille — A292

1987, Sept. 24   **Litho.**   **Perf. 13**
844 A292 2.80k multi   1.00 .35
   Complete booklet, 10 #844   10.00

Rasmus Rask (1787-1832), Linguist — A293

1987, Oct. 15   **Engr.**   **Perf. 13x12½**
845 A293 2.80k dk hen brn   1.00 .45

A294

Emblem: Miraculous Catch (Luke 5:4-7), New Testament.

1987, Oct. 15   **Perf. 13**
846 A294 3k carmine lake   1.25 .50

Clerical Assoc. for the Home Mission in Denmark, 125th anniv.

A295

Designs: 3k, Two lions from the gate of Rosenburg Castle around the monogram of Christian IV. 4.10k, Portrait of the monarch painted by P. Isaacsz, vert.

Photo. & Engr., Litho. (4.10k)

1988, Feb. 18   *Perf. 13*

847	A295	3k blue gray & gold	1.25 .30
		Complete booklet, 10 #847	12.50
848	A295	4.10k multi	1.60 .75

Accession of Christian IV (1577-1648), King of Denmark and Norway (1588-1648), 400th anniv.

Ole Worm (1588-1654), Archaeologist, and Runic Artifacts — A296

1988, Feb. 18   **Engr.**

849	A296	7.10k chocolate	2.75 2.75

Odense, 1000th Anniv. — A297

Design: St. Cnut's Church and statue of Hans Christian Andersen, Odense.

1988, Mar. 10   **Engr.**

850	A297	3k multi	1.00 .35
		Complete booklet, 10 #850	10.00

 A298

1988, Apr. 7   **Litho.**

851	A298	2.70k multi	1.25 1.25

Danish Civil Defense and Emergency Planning Agency, 50th Anniv.

WHO, 40th Anniv. — A299

1988, Apr. 7   **Litho. & Engr.**

852	A299	4.10k multi	1.75 1.00

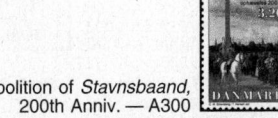

Abolition of *Stavnsbaand*, 200th Anniv. — A300

Painting: King Christian VII riding past the Liberty Memorial, Copenhagen, by C.W. Eckersberg (1783-1853).

1988, May 5   **Litho.**

853	A300	3.20k multi	1.40 1.00

Stavnsbaand (adscription) provided that all Danish farmers' sons from age 4 to 40 would be bound as villeins to the estates on which they were born, thus providing landowners with free labor.

 A301

Europa: Transport and communication — 3k, Postwoman on bicycle. 4.10k, Mobile telephone.

1988, May 5

854	A301	3k multicolored	1.75 .25
855	A301	4.10k multicolored	2.50 1.00

 A302

1988, June 16

856	A302	4.10k multi	1.60 .75

1988 Individual Speedway World Motorcycle Championships, Denmark, Sept. 3.

Federation of Danish Industries, 150th Anniv. — A303

Painting (detail): *The Industrialists*, by P.S. Kroyer.

1988, June 16   *Perf. 13½x13*

857	A303	3k multi	1.00 .50

Danish Metalworkers' Union, Cent. — A304

3k, Glass mosaic by Niels Winkel.

1988, Aug. 18   **Litho.**   *Perf. 13*

858	A304	3k multicolored	1.00 .50

Tonder Teachers' Training College, 200th Anniv. — A305

1988, Aug. 18   **Engr.**   *Perf. 13x12½*

859	A305	3k lake	1.00 .50

Homage to Leon Degand, Sculpture by Robert Jacobsen — A306

1988, Sept. 22   *Perf. 11½x13*

860	A306	4.10k blk, lake & gray	3.75 5.00

Danish-French cultural exchange program, 10th anniv. See France No. 2130.

Preservation of Historic Sites — A307

3k, Lumby Windmill, 1818. 7.10k, Vejstrup Water Mill, 1837.

1988, Oct. 13   **Engr.**   *Perf. 13x12½*

861	A307	3k red & org	1.60 .50
		Complete booklet, 10 #861	16.00
862	A307	7.10k dp blue & blu-ish grn	4.00 2.75

Paintings in the State Museum of Art, Copenhagen A308

4.10k, *Bathing Boys*, 1902, by Peter Hansen (1868-1928). 10k, *The Hill at Overkaerby*, 1917, by Fritz Syberg (1862-1939).

Litho. & Engr.

1988, Nov. 3   *Perf. 13*

863	A308	4.10k multi	3.25 4.50
864	A308	10k multi	6.50 8.00

See Nos. 881-882, 951-952, 972-973, 1018-1019.

The Little Mermaid, Sculpture by Edvard Eriksen — A309

1989, Feb. 16   **Engr.**

865	A309	3.20k dark green	1.75 .50
		Complete booklet, 10 #865	17.50

Tourism industry, cent.

Danish Soccer Assoc., Cent. — A310

1989, Mar. 16   **Litho.**

866	A310	3.20k multi	1.60 .50
		Complete booklet, 10 #866	16.00

NATO Membership, 40th Anniv. — A311

1989, Mar. 16

867	A311	4.40k dk blue, gold & lt blue	2.00 1.25

Nordic Cooperation Issue — A312

Folk costumes.

1989, Apr. 20   **Litho. & Engr.**

868	A312	3.20k Woman from Valby	1.40 .40
869	A312	4.40k Pork butcher	2.10 1.60

European Parliament 3rd Elections — A313

1989, May 11   **Litho.**

870	A313	3k blue & yellow	1.60 1.50

Europa 1989 — A314

Children's toys.

1989, May 11   **Litho. & Engr.**

871	A314	3.20k Lego blocks	1.90 .25
872	A314	4.40k Wooden soldiers, by Kay Bojesen	3.00 .90

Agricultural Museum, Cent. — A315

1989, June 15   **Engr.**   *Perf. 13*

873	A315	3.20k Tractor, 1889	1.25 .50

Interparliamentary Union, Cent. — A316

1989, June 15   **Litho. & Engr.**

874	A316	3.40k Folketing Chamber layout	3.50 4.00

Danish Fishery and Marine Research Institute, Cent. — A317

1989, Aug. 24   **Litho. & Engr.**

875	A317	3.20k multi	1.25 .50

Bernhard Severin Ingemann (1789-1862), Poet and Novelist — A318

1989, Aug. 24   **Engr.**

876	A318	7.70k dark green	3.00 1.90

 A319

Danish Film Office, 50th Anniv.: 3k, Scene from the short feature film *They Reached the Ferry*, 1948. 3.20k, Bodil Ipsen (d. 1964), actress. 4.40k, Carl Th. Dreyer (1889-1968), screenwriter and director.

1989, Sept. 28   **Litho.**

877	A319	3k multi	1.40 1.40
878	A319	3.20k multi	1.25 .50
879	A319	4.40k multi	1.75 1.00
		Nos. 877-879 (3)	4.40 2.90

Stamp Day, 50th Anniv. — A320

1989, Nov. 10   **Litho. & Engr.**

880	A320	3.20k multi	1.25 .50

Art Type of 1988

Paintings: 4.40k, *Part of the Northern Gate of the Citadel Bridge*, c. 1837, by Christen Kobke (1810-1848). 10k, *A Little Girl, Elise Kobke, With a Cup in Front of Her*, c. 1850, by Constantin Hansen (1804-1880).

1989, Nov. 10   *Perf. 12½x13*

881	A308	4.40k multi	3.00 4.00
882	A308	10k multi	6.25 8.50

Types of 1933-82 and

A321   A321a

Queen Margrethe II

1990-98		**Engr.**	*Perf. 12¾*
883	A32	25o bluish black	.55 .40
a.		Bklt. pane, 4 #691, 2 #883	4.75
884	A32	125o carmine lake	.95 .40
885	A32	325o lt yel grn	2.10 1.75
886	A32	350o yellow green	2.00 .95
887	A212	3.50k dark red	1.25 .40
a.		Bklt. pane, 2 each #691, 885, 887	8.00
		Complete booklet, #883, #885, #887, 3 #691	16.00
		Complete booklet, #883a, #887a	13.50
888	A321	3.50k henna brown	1.40 .40
b.		Bklt. pane, 4 each #883, #884, #888 ('91)	20.00
		Complete booklet, #888b	20.00
		Complete booklet, 2 each #883, #884, #888	16.00
889	A212	3.75k dark green	2.25 2.40
890	A321	3.75k green	4.00 3.75

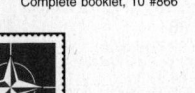

891	A321	3.75k red	3.00	.40
a.		Bklt. pane, 4 each #884, #891	17.50	
		Complete booklet, #891a	17.50	
b.		Booklet pane, 2 each #691, 883, 891	8.75	
		Complete booklet, #891b	8.75	
892	A321a	3.75k red	2.25	.50
a.		Booklet pane, 2 each #691, 883, 892	14.50	
		Complete booklet, #892a	14.50	
b.		Booklet pane, 2 #883, 4 #494, 2 #892	12.00	
		Complete booklet, #892b	12.00	
893	A321	4k brown	2.50	1.20
894	A321a	4k deep bl grn	2.25	.80
895	A321a	4.25k olive brown	2.90	1.90
896	A212	4.50k brown violet	2.75	3.25
897	A321a	4.50k violet	2.50	2.40
898	A321a	4.50k deep bl blk	2.60	2.40
899	A212	4.75k dark blue	1.90	.40
900	A321a	4.75k blue	2.50	.40
901	A321	4.75k violet	3.50	2.00
902	A321a	4.75k brown	3.50	2.10
903	A321a	5k violet	2.50	1.75
904	A321	5k blue	3.50	.40
905	A321	5.25k black	3.50	1.75
906	A321a	5.25k deep blue	3.25	.80
907	A321	5.50k green	3.25	3.75
908	A321a	5.50k henna brown	3.50	2.75
909	A55	7.50k dark bl grn	3.00	2.75
		Nos. 883-909 (27)	69.15	42.15

Queen Margrethe II's 50th birthday (No. 888).

Issued: No. 888, 4/5; Nos. 890, 897, 900, 1990; No. 888a, 2/14/91; Nos. 886, 891, 891a, 901, 904, 6/10/92; 5.50k, 1/13/94; 4k, 5.25k, 6/27/96; Nos. 892, 892a, 1/14/97; Nos. 894, 902, 903, 906, 8/28/97; Nos. 895, 898, 908, 909, 3/26/98; others, 1/11/90.

See Nos. 1114, 1125, 1130.

Museum of Decorative Art, Cent. — A322

Design: Silver coffee pot designed by Axel Johannes Kroyer, Copenhagen, 1726.

1990, Feb. 15   **Engr.**   ***Perf. 13***
911	A322	3.50k dark blue & blk	1.20	.80
		Complete booklet, 10 #911	12.00	

A323

Steam engine, 200th anniv.: Steam engine built by Andrew Mitchell, 1790.

1990, Feb. 15
912	A323	8.25k dull red brown	2.75	1.75

Nyholm, 300th Anniv. — A324

1990, Apr. 5   **Engr.**
913	A324	4.75k black	1.75	.90

Europa 1990 — A325

3.50k, Royal Monogram, Haderslev P.O. 4.75k, Odense P.O.

1990, Apr. 5   **Litho.**
914	A325	3.50k multi	1.10	.25
915	A325	4.75k multi	1.75	.60

A326

Pieces from the Flora Danica Banquet Service produced for King Christian VII: No. 916, Bell-shaped lid, dish. No. 917, Gravy boat, dish. No. 918, Ice pot, casserole, lid. No. 919, Serving dish.

1990, May 3   **Litho.**
916	A326	3.50k multicolored	1.25	1.90
917	A326	3.50k multicolored	1.25	1.90
918	A326	3.50k multicolored	1.25	1.90
919	A326	3.50k multicolored	1.25	1.90
a.		Strip of 4, #916-919	5.00	8.50

Flora Danica porcelain, 200th anniv.

A327

Endangered plant species.

1990, June 14
920	A327	3.25k Marshmallow	1.25	1.25
921	A327	3.50k Red helleborine	2.25	.35
		Complete booklet, 10 #921	30.00	
922	A327	3.75k Purple orchis	1.50	1.50
923	A327	4.75k Lady's slipper	1.90	.65
		Nos. 920-923 (4)	6.90	3.75

Village Churches, Jutland — A328

Perf. 13x12½, 12½x13

1990, Aug. 30   **Engr.**
924	A328	3.50k Gjellerup	1.20	.35
		Complete booklet, 10 #924	12.00	
925	A328	4.75k Veng	1.60	.75
926	A328	8.25k Bredsten, vert.	3.00	2.00
		Nos. 924-926 (3)	5.80	3.10

Fredericia, "The Town for Everybody" A329

Engr. & Embossed

1990, Oct. 5   ***Perf. 13***
927	A329	3.50k black & red	1.20	.90

Tordenskiold (Peter Wessel, 1690-1720), Admiral — A330

1990, Oct. 5   **Litho.**   ***Perf. 13½x13***
928	A330	3.50k multicolored	1.20	.60
		Complete booklet, 10 #928	12.00	

Prevent Bicycle Thefts — A331

Design: 3.50k, Stop drunk driving.

1990, Nov. 8   **Litho.**   ***Perf. 13x12½***
930	A331	3.25k shown	1.10	1.10
931	A331	3.50k Automobile, wine glass	1.10	.30

Locomotives A332

1991, Mar. 14   **Engr.**   ***Perf. 13***
932	A332	3.25k IC3 1990	1.40	1.50
933	A332	3.50k Class A 1882	1.10	.35
		Complete booklet, 10 #933	11.00	
934	A332	3.75k Class MY 1954	1.75	1.75
935	A332	4.75k Class P 1907	1.50	1.50
		Nos. 932-935 (4)	5.25	5.10

Europa — A333

Satellite photographs showing temperatures of Danish: 3.50k, Waters. 4.75k, Land.

1991, May 2   **Litho.**   ***Perf. 13***
936	A333	3.50k multicolored	1.75	.25
937	A333	4.75k multicolored	2.10	1.00

Jutland Law, 750th Anniv. — A334

1991, May 2
938	A334	8.25k multicolored	3.00	2.75

Danish Islands — A335

1991, June 6
939	A335	3.50k Fano	1.40	.30
		Complete booklet, 10 #939	18.00	
940	A335	4.75k Christianso	1.60	.90

Decorative Art — A336

Designs: 3.25k, Earthenware bowl and jars by Christian Poulsen. 3.50k, Chair by Hans Wegner, vert. 4.75k, Silver cutlery by Kay Bojesen, vert. 8k, Lamp by Poul Henningsen.

1991, Aug. 22   **Litho.**   ***Perf. 13***
941	A336	3.25k multicolored	1.10	1.50
942	A336	3.50k multicolored	1.00	.35
		Complete booklet, 10 #942	10.00	
943	A336	4.75k multicolored	1.25	1.75
944	A336	8.25k multicolored	3.00	4.50
		Nos. 941-944 (4)	6.35	8.10

Keep Denmark Clean — A337

Designs: 3.50k, Cleaning up after dog. 4.75k, Picking up litter.

1991, Sept. 19   **Engr.**   ***Perf. 13***
945	A337	3.50k red	2.00	.30
		Complete booklet, 10 #945	20.00	
946	A337	4.75k blue	2.00	1.00

Posters from Danish Museum of Decorative Arts — A338

Posters for: 3.50k, Nordic Advertising Congress, by Arne Ungermann (1902-1981). 4.50k, Poster Exhibition at Copenhagen Zoo (baboon), by Valdemar Andersen (1875-1928). 4.75k, Danish Air Lines, by Ib Andersen (1907-1969). 12k, The Sinner, by Sven Brasch (1886-1970).

1991, Sept. 19   **Litho.**
947	A338	3.50k multicolored	1.00	.30
948	A338	4.50k multicolored	1.75	2.50
949	A338	4.75k multicolored	1.25	1.50
950	A338	12k multicolored	4.00	3.50
		Nos. 947-950 (4)	8.00	7.80

Art Type of 1988

Designs: 4.75k, Lady at her Toilet by Harald Giersing (1881-1927), vert. 14k, Road through a Wood by Edvard Weie (1879-1943), vert.

Litho. & Engr.

1991, Nov. 7   ***Perf. 13x12½***
951	A308	4.75k multicolored	1.75	1.75
952	A308	14k multicolored	4.50	4.00

A339

Treasures of Natl. Museum: 3.50k, Earthenware bowl, Skarpsalling. 4.50k, Bronze dancer, Grevensvaenge. 4.75k, Bottom plate of silver cauldron, Gundestrup. 8.25k, Flint knife, Hindsgavl.

1992, Feb. 13   **Engr.**   ***Perf. 13***
953	A339	3.50k dk vio & brown	1.10	.30
		Complete booklet, 10 #953	11.00	
954	A339	4.50k dk bl & dk ol green	2.40	2.40
955	A339	4.75k brown & black	1.25	1.10
956	A339	8.25k dk ol grn & vio brown	2.75	2.75
		Nos. 953-956 (4)	7.50	6.55

A340

1992, Mar. 12   ***Perf. 13½x13***
957	A340	3.50k rose carmine	1.25	.65

Danish Society of Chemical, Civil, Electrical, and Mechanical Engineers, cent.

Souvenir Sheet

Queen Margaret I (1353-1412) — A341

Litho. & Engr.

1992, Mar. 12   ***Perf. 12½***
958	A341	Sheet of 2	6.25	7.25
a.		3.50k Fresco	3.00	3.50
b.		4.75k Alabaster bust	3.00	3.50

Nordia '94, Scandinavian Philatelic Exhibition. No. 958 sold for 12k to benefit the exhibition.

Discovery of America, 500th Anniv. — A342

1992, May 7   **Engr.**   ***Perf. 12½***
959	A342	3.50k Potato plant	2.25	.40
		Complete booklet, 10 #959	22.50	
960	A342	4.75k Ear of corn	4.25	1.75

Europa.

Protect the Environment A343

3.75k, Hare beside road. 5k, Fish, water pollution. 8.75k, Cut trees, vert.

Litho. & Engr.

1992, June 10   ***Perf. 13***
961	A343	3.75k multi	1.25	.30
		Complete booklet, 10 #961	12.50	
962	A343	5k multi	1.75	.70
963	A343	8.75k multi	3.50	2.00
		Nos. 961-963 (3)	6.50	3.00

Queen Margrethe II and Prince Henrik, 25th Wedding Anniv. A344

1992, June 10 Litho. Perf. 12½x13
964 A344 3.75k multicolored .90 1.60
See Greenland No. 253.

A345

1992, July 16 Perf. 13
965 A345 3.75k multicolored 1.75 .75
Denmark, European soccer champions.

Danish Pavilion, Expo '92, Seville — A346

1992, Aug. 27 Engr. Perf. 13
966 A346 3.75k blue 1.50 .75

Single European Market — A347

1992, Oct. 8 Litho. & Engr. Perf. 13
967 A347 3.75k blue & org 1.50 .75

A348

Cartoon characters: 3.50k, A Hug, by Ivar Gjorup. 3.75k, Love Letter, by Phillip Stein Jonsson. 4.75k, Domestic Triangle, by Nikoline Werdelin. 5k, Poet and His Little Wife, by Jorgen Mogensen.

Litho. & Engr.
1992, Oct. 8 Perf. 12½
968 A348 3.50k multicolored 1.75 1.00
Engr.
969 A348 3.75k red & purple 1.40 .30
970 A348 4.75k blk & red brn 2.50 2.50
971 A348 5k blue & red brn 1.75 .70
Nos. 968-971 (4) 7.40 4.50

Art Type of 1988
5k, Landscape from Vejby, 1843, by John Thomas Lundbye. 10k, Motif from Halleby Brook, 1847, by Peter Christian Skovgaard.

Litho. & Engr.
1992, Nov. 12 Perf. 12½x13
972 A308 5k multicolored 2.10 2.00
973 A308 10k multicolored 4.00 3.25

Publication of New Danish Bible — A349

3.75k, Jacob's fight with angel.

1992, Nov. 12 Perf. 13
974 A349 3.75k multi 1.75 1.20

A350

Archaeological Treasures. Anthropomorphic gold foil figures found in: 3.75k, Lundeborg, horiz. 5k, Bornholm.

Litho. & Engr.
1993, Feb. 4 Perf. 13
975 A350 3.75k multicolored 1.40 .30
976 A350 5k multicolored 1.90 .70

Butterflies — A351

3.75k, Small tortoiseshell. 5k, Large blue. 8.75k, Marsh fritillary. 12k, Red admiral.

1993, Mar. 11 Litho.
977 A351 3.75k multi 1.75 .40
  Complete booklet, 10 #977 17.50
978 A351 5k multi 2.50 .80
979 A351 8.75k multi 5.25 3.50
980 A351 12k multi 5.25 3.50
  Nos. 977-980 (4) 14.75 8.20

Tivoli Gardens, 150th Anniv. — A352

Posters: 3.75k, Pierrot, by Thor Bogelund, 1947, horiz. 5k, Balloons, by Wilhelm Freddie, 1987.

1993, May 6 Litho. Perf. 12½
981 A352 3.75k multicolored 1.75 1.00
  Complete booklet, 10 #981 17.50
982 A352 5k multicolored 1.75 .90

A353

Europa (Contemporary paintings by): 3.75k, Troels Worsel, horiz. 5k, Stig Brogger.

1993, May 6 Perf. 13
983 A353 3.75k multicolored 1.40 1.10
984 A353 5k multicolored 1.90 .90

A354

1993, June 17 Engr. Perf. 13
985 A354 5k dark blue green 4.00 1.00
Danish-Russian relations, 500th anniv. See Russia No. 6154.

Training Ships
A355 A356
Perf. 13, 13½x13 (#987)
1993, June 17 Litho. & Engr.
986 A355 3.75k Danmark 2.00 .30
987 A356 4.75k Jens Krogh 4.00 4.50
988 A355 5k Georg Stage, horiz. 3.00 1.75

Size: 39x28mm
Perf. 13x13½
989 A356 9.50k Marilyn Anne, horiz. 5.50 5.25
  Nos. 986-989 (4) 14.50 11.80

Child's Drawing of Viking Ships A357

Letter Writing Campaign A358

1993, Aug. 19 Litho. Perf. 13
990 A357 3.75k multicolored 2.25 .65
991 A358 5k lt & dk bl & blk 2.50 1.40

Ethnic Jewelry — A359

1993, Sept. 16 Litho. Perf. 13
992 A359 3.50k Falster 1.75 1.25
993 A359 3.75k Amager 1.75 .30
  Complete booklet, 10 #993 17.50
994 A359 5k Laeso 2.00 .90
995 A359 8.75k Romo 4.50 3.00
  Nos. 992-995 (4) 10.00 5.45

Cubist Paintings A360

5k, Assemblage, by Vilhelm Lundstrom, 1929. 15k, Composition, by Franciska Clausen, 1929.

Litho. & Engr.
1993, Nov. 11 Perf. 12½
996 A360 5k multicolored 2.75 2.25
997 A360 15k multicolored 6.75 5.00
See Nos. 1033-1034, 1080-1081.

Conservation — A361

1994, Jan. 27 Litho. Perf. 13
998 A361 3.75k Save water 3.50 .30
999 A361 5k CO2 4.50 1.10

Castles — A362

Castles: 3.50k, Marselisborg, Aarhus. 3.75k, Amalienborg, Copenhagen. 5k, Fredensborg, North Zealand. 8.75k, Graasten, South Jutland.

Litho. & Engr.
1994, Mar. 17 Perf. 13x12½
1000 A362 3.50k multicolored 1.50 .70
1001 A362 3.75k multicolored 1.75 .30
  Complete booklet, 10 #1001 17.50
1002 A362 5k multicolored 2.25 .30
1003 A362 8.75k multicolored 3.75 3.50
  a. Bklt. pane, #1000-1003 30.00 30.00
No. 1003a printed with 2 different labels. One shows a marching band, the other shows a ship.

Danmark Expedition, 1906-08 — A363

Europa: 3.75k, Expedition ship, Danmark, Alfred Wegener's weather balloon. 5k, Theodolite, Johan Peter Koch, cartographer.

1994, May 5 Engr. Perf. 13
1004 A363 3.75k deep brn vio 1.90 .25
1005 A363 5k dp slate grn 2.60 1.25
  Complete booklet, 10 #1005 35.00

Trams — A364

Designs: 3.75k, Copenhagen tram (Engelhardt). 4.75k, Aarhus car. 5k, Odense tram, vert. 12k, Horse-drawn tram.

Litho. & Engr.
1994, June 9 Perf. 13
1006 A364 3.75k multicolored 1.25 .30
1007 A364 4.75k multicolored 2.25 2.75
1008 A364 5k multicolored 1.75 1.40
Size: 38x21mm
1009 A364 12k multicolored 5.25 5.25
  Nos. 1006-1009 (4) 10.50 9.70

Children's Stamp Competition — A365

1994, Aug. 25 Litho. Perf. 12½
1010 A365 3.75k multicolored 1.50 .70

ILO, 75th Anniv. — A366

1994, Aug. 25 Perf. 13
1011 A366 5k multicolored 2.00 1.00

Wild Animals — A367

Litho. & Engr.
1994, Oct. 20 Perf. 12½
1012 A367 3.75k House sparrows 2.00 .35
1013 A367 4.75k Badger 3.00 2.25
1014 A367 5k Squirrel, vert. 2.60 1.00
1015 A367 9.50k Black grouse 5.00 4.50
Size: 36x26mm
Perf. 13
1016 A367 12k Grass snake 6.00 5.25
  Nos. 1012-1016 (5) 18.60 13.35

A368

1994, Nov. 10 Litho. Perf. 13
1017 A368 3.75k multicolored 1.75 .70
Folk High Schools, 150th anniv.

Painting Type of 1988
Designs: 5k, Study of Italian Woman and Sleeping Child, by Wilhelm Marstrand. 15k, Interior from Amaliegade with the Artist's Brothers, by Wilhelm Bendz.

Litho. & Engr.
1994, Nov. 10 Perf. 12½x13
1018 A308 5k multicolored 2.00 1.40
1019 A308 15k multicolored 6.00 3.25

Aarhus Cathedral School, 800th Anniv. — A369

Litho. & Engr.

1995, Jan. 26			**Perf. 13**	
1020	A369	3.75k multicolored	1.75	.70

UN, 50th Anniv. — A370

Litho. & Engr.

1995, Jan. 26			**Perf. 13**	
1021	A370	5k multicolored	2.50	1.20
	Complete booklet, 10 #1021		35.00	

Danish Islands — A371

1995, Mar. 16		**Engr.**	**Perf. 13**	
1022	A371	3.75k Avernako	2.25	.30
	Complete booklet, 10 #1022		22.50	
1023	A371	4.75k Fejo	2.75	2.50
1024	A371	5k Fur	.90	.90
1025	A371	9.50k Endelave	4.50	4.50
a.	Booklet pane, #1022-1025 + 2 labels		15.00	
	Complete booklet, 2 #1025a		32.50	
	Nos. 1022-1025 (4)		13.00	8.20

No. 1025a printed with four different large labels. Labels with one pane are MF Faaborg II and MF Endelave. The other pane has MF Bukken-bruse and MF Fursund.

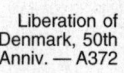

Liberation of Denmark, 50th Anniv. — A372

Designs: 3.75k, Gen. Montgomery, Town Hall Square, vert. 5k, White busses returning from concentration camps. 8.75k, Airplane dropping supplies to resistance. 12k, Jews escape across the Sound to Sweden.

1995, May 4		**Litho.**	**Perf. 13**	
1026	A372	3.75k multicolored	2.10	.30
	Complete booklet, 10 #1026		21.00	
1027	A372	5k multicolored	2.75	1.00
1028	A372	8.75k multicolored	4.25	4.00
1029	A372	12k multicolored	6.00	6.00
	Nos. 1026-1029 (4)		15.10	11.30

Europa (Nos. 1026-1027).

A373

1995, June 8		**Litho.**	**Perf. 13**	
1030	A373	3.50k multicolored	1.50	.70

Danish Rhymed Chronicle, 500th anniv.

A374

3.75k, Roskilde Festival. 5k, Tonder Festival.

1995, June 8				
1031	A374	3.75k multi, horiz.	1.60	.30
	Complete booklet, 10 #1031		16.00	
1032	A374	5k multi	2.25	1.00

No. 1031 Roskilde Festival, 25th anniv., No. 1032 Tonder Festival, 21st anniv.
No. 1031 is 28x21mm.

Paintings A375

Designs: 10k, "Sct. Hans Aften, 1955," by Jens Sondergaard. 15k, "Landskab-Gudhjem, 1939," by Niels Lergaard.

Litho. & Engr.

1995, Aug. 24			**Perf. 13x12½**	
1033	A375	10k multicolored	5.00	5.75
1034	A375	15k multicolored	7.50	7.50

Tycho Brahe (1546-1601), Astronomer — A376

3.75k, Uranienborg Observatory. 5.50k, Sextant.

Litho. & Engr.

1995, Oct. 27			**Perf. 13**	
1035	A376	3.75k multicolored	2.00	.65
1036	A376	5.50k multicolored	2.75	2.75

See Sweden Nos. 2149-2150.

Toys — A377

Designs: 3.75k, Tekno cars. 5k, Dolls, teddy bear. 8.75k, Model trains. 12k, Glud & Marstrand tin horse-drawn carriage & fire pumper.

1995, Nov. 9			**Perf. 13x12½**	
1037	A377	3.75k multicolored	1.60	.30
	Complete booklet, 10 #1037		16.00	
1038	A377	5k multicolored	2.10	1.00
1039	A377	8.75k multicolored	3.25	3.25
1040	A377	12k multicolored	4.25	4.25
	Nos. 1037-1040 (4)		11.20	8.80

A378

Cartoonlike views of Copenhagen: 3.75k, Round Tower as music box. 5k, Christiansborg Castle. 8.75k, Marble Church as top of balloon. 12k, The Little Mermaid statue on stage.

1996, Jan. 25			**Perf. 13**	
1041	A378	3.75k multicolored	1.25	.30
	Complete booklet, 10 #1041		13.00	
1042	A378	5k multicolored	1.75	.70
1043	A378	8.75k multicolored	3.00	3.00
1044	A378	12k multicolored	4.00	4.50
	Nos. 1041-1044 (4)		10.00	8.50

Copenhagen, 1996 cultural capital of Europe.

A379

1996, Mar. 21		**Litho.**	**Perf. 13**	
1045	A379	3.75k Sports for disabled	1.25	.30
	Complete booklet, 10 #1045		13.00	
1046	A379	4.75k Swimming	1.60	1.60
1047	A379	5k Sailing	1.75	.50
1048	A379	9.50k Cycling	3.25	3.25
a.	Bklt. pane of 4, #1045-1048 + 2 labels		14.00	
	Complete booklet, 2 #1048a		28.00	

No. 1048a printed with two different large labels. One shows hands and soccer ball, second shows tennis racket and tennis balls.
Danish Federation for Sports for the Disabled (No. 1045). Modern Olympic Games, cent., Sports Confederation of Denmark, cent.,

---

1996 Summer Olympics, Atlanta (Nos. 1046-1048).

A380

1996, May 9		**Litho.**	**Perf. 13**	
1049	A380	3.75k multicolored	1.50	1.00

Danish Employers' Confederation, cent.

A381

Famous Danish Women (Europa): 3.75k, Karen Blixen (1885-1962), writer. 5k, Asta Nielsen (1881-1972), silent screen actress.

1996, May 9				
1050	A381	3.75k lt brn & dk brn	1.50	.50
1051	A381	5k gray & dk blue	2.00	.75
	Complete booklet, 10 #1051		20.00	

A382

Wooden Dinghies: 3.50k, Roskilde Fjord sail boat. 3.75k, Limfjorden skiff. 12.25k, Two-masted smack, South Funen Archipelago.

Perf. 13, 12½ (#1053)

1996, June 13			**Engr.**	
1052	A382	3.50k multicolored	1.25	1.00
1053	A382	3.75k multicolored	1.50	.50
	Complete booklet, 10 #1053		16.00	
1054	A382	12.25k multicolored	4.50	5.25
	Nos. 1052-1054 (3)		7.25	6.75

No. 1053 is 20x39mm.

Lighthouses — A383

Litho. & Engr.

1996, Sept. 12			**Perf. 13x12½**	
1055	A383	3.75k Fornaes	1.50	.30
	Complete booklet, 10 #1055		16.00	
1056	A383	5k Blavandshuk	1.75	.50
a.	Bklt. pane, 8 #1055, 2 #1056		22.00	
	Complete booklet, #1056a		22.00	
1057	A383	5.25k Bovbjerg	2.00	2.00
1058	A383	8.75k Mon	3.00	3.00
	Nos. 1055-1058 (4)		8.25	5.80

Art Works of Thorvald Bindesboll (1846-1908) — A384

Litho. & Engr.

1996, Oct. 10			**Perf. 13**	
1059	A384	3.75k Pitcher	1.50	.30
	Complete booklet, 10 #1059		16.00	

Litho.

1060	A384	4k Portfolio cover	1.60	1.10

Paintings A385

Designs: 10k, "At Lunch," by P.S. Kroyer, 1893. 15k, "The Girl with Sunflowers," by Michael Ancher, 1889.

Litho. & Engr.

1996, Nov. 7			**Perf. 13x12½**	
1061	A385	10k multicolored	4.00	4.00
1062	A385	15k multicolored	5.25	5.25

A386

Queen Margrethe II: 3.50k, With Prince Henrik. 3.75k, With Crown Prince Frederik. 4k, Delivering New Year speech. 5.25k, Waving to crowd.

1997, Jan. 14		**Litho.**	**Perf. 13**	
1063	A386	3.50k multicolored	1.25	1.25
1064	A386	3.75k multicolored	1.50	.30
	Complete booklet, 10 #1064		16.00	
1065	A386	4k multicolored	1.40	.70
1066	A386	5.25k multicolored	2.00	1.50
a.	Sheet of 4, #1063-1066 + 2 labels		6.50	6.50
	Nos. 1063-1066 (4)		6.15	3.75

Queen Margrethe II, 25th anniv. of coronation.

A387

Open Air Museum, Copenhagen, Cent.: 3.50k, Kalstrup post mill. 3.75k, Ellested water mill. 5k, Fjellerup manor barn. 8.75k, Romo farm.

1997, Mar. 13		**Engr.**	**Perf. 13**	
1067	A387	3.50k multicolored	1.25	1.00
1068	A387	3.75k multicolored	1.25	.30
	Complete booklet, 10 #1068		12.50	
1069	A387	5k multicolored	1.75	.75
	Complete booklet, 10 #1069		17.50	
1070	A387	8.75k multicolored	3.00	2.50
a.	Booklet pane, #1067-1070 + label		14.00	
	Complete booklet, 2 #1070a		7.25	4.55
	Nos. 1067-1070 (4)			

No. 1070a printed with two different large labels. One shows a view of Ellested water mill, the other shows a farm in Ejersted.

Great Belt Railway Link — A388

1997, May 15		**Litho.**	**Perf. 13**	
1071	A388	3.75k East Tunnel	1.50	.50
	Complete booklet, 10 #1071		15.00	
1072	A388	4.75k West Bridge	1.75	1.75

A389

Kalmar Union, 600th Anniv.: No. 1073, Margrete I and Eric of Pomerania. No. 1074, The Three Graces symbolizing Denmark, Norway and Sweden.

1997, June 12		**Litho.**	**Perf. 13**	
1073		4k multicolored	2.60	2.75
1074		4k multicolored	2.60	2.75
a.	A389 Pair, #1073-1074		5.25	6.50

No. 1074a is a continuous design.

Copenhagen-Roskilde Railway, 150th Anniv. — A390

Designs: 3.75k, Two modern trains under Carlsberg Bridge. 8.75k, Early steam train going under Carlsberg Bridge.

Litho. & Engr.

1997, June 12			**Perf. 13**	
1075	A390	3.75k multicolored	2.75	.30
		Complete booklet, 10 #1075	27.50	
1076	A390	8.75k multicolored	5.00	2.50

End of Railway Mail Service — A391

1997, June 12			Litho.	
1077	A391	5k multicolored	1.75	.70

Stories and Legends — A392

Europa: 3.75k, Large cat on top of treasure chest, from "The Tinder Box." 5.25k, Butterfly, pond, frog, from "Thumbelina."

1997, Aug. 28			Engr.	**Perf. 13**	
1078	A392	3.75k multicolored		*1.40*	*.40*
1079	A392	5.25k multicolored		*1.75*	*1.50*

Painting Type of 1993

Designs: 9.75k, "Dust Dancing in the Sun," by Vilhelm Hammershoi (1864-1916). 13k, "Woman Mountaineer," by J.F. Willumsen (1863-1958).

Litho. & Engr.

1997, Sept. 18			**Perf. 13x12½**	
1080	A360	9.75k multicolored	4.75	5.50
1081	A360	13k multicolored	6.25	7.00

A393

Danish Design: 3.75k, Faaborg chair, vert. 4k, Margrethe bowl, vert. 5k, The Ant (chair). 12.25k, Georg Jensen silver bowl, vert.

1997, Nov. 6			Litho.	**Perf. 13**	
1082	A393	3.75k multicolored		1.25	.30
		Complete booklet, 10 #1082		12.50	
1083	A393	4k multicolored		1.25	.75
1084	A393	5k multicolored		2.00	.45
1085	A393	12.25k multicolored		4.50	5.25
		Nos. 1082-1085 (4)		*9.00*	*6.75*

Danish Confederation of Trade Unions, Cent. — A394

3.50k, General Workers Union in Denmark (SiD). 3.75k, Danish Confederation of Trade Unions (LO). 4.75k, Danish Nurse's Organization. 5k, Union of Commercial and Clerical Employees in Denmark (HK).

1998, Jan. 22			Litho.	**Perf. 13**	
1086	A394	3.50k multicolored		1.10	.90
1087	A394	3.75k multicolored		1.25	.30
		Complete booklet, 10 #1087		12.50	
1088	A394	4.75k multicolored		1.90	2.50
1089	A394	5k multicolored		2.00	.65
		Complete booklet, 10 #1089		20.00	
		Nos. 1086-1089 (4)		*6.25*	*4.35*

City of Roskilde, 1000th Anniv. — A395

Litho. & Engr.

1998, Mar. 26			**Perf. 13**	
1090	A395	3.75k multicolored	1.50	.90
		Complete booklet, 10 #1090	15.00	

A396

1998, Mar. 26		Litho.	**Perf. 13**	
1091	A396	5k Ladybug	1.75	.50

Reduce poison.

A397

New Post & Tele Museum, Copenhagen: 3.75k, Postman, 1922. 4.50k, Morse code operator, c. 1910. 5.50k, Telephone operator, 1910. 8.75k, Modern postman.

1998, May 28			Litho.	**Perf. 13**	
1092	A397	3.75k multicolored		1.25	.30
		Complete booklet, 10 #1092		12.50	
a.		Booklet pane, 2 each #1087,			
		1089, 3 ea. 1090, 1092		30.00	
		Complete booklet #1092a		30.00	
1093	A397	4.50k multicolored		1.50	1.50
1094	A397	5.50k multicolored		2.00	2.00
1095	A397	8.75k multicolored		2.75	2.75
a.		Booklet pane, #1092-1095		14.00	
		Complete booklet, 2 #1095a		28.00	
		Nos. 1092-1095 (4)		*7.50*	*6.55*

No. 1095a is printed with two backgrounds. One shows part of King Christian IV's "Order Concerning Postmen," 1624. The other shows part of Copenhagen c. 1923. Complete booklets contain panes with each background.

Bridges over Great Belt — A398

No. 1096, West Bridge. No. 1097, East Bridge (suspension).

1998, May 28			Engr.	**Perf. 13**	
1096	A398	5k shown		2.75	.75
1097	A398	5k multi		2.75	.75
a.		Pair, #1096-1097 + label		6.00	1.50

Nordic Stamps — A399

Shipping: No. 1098, Signal flags, harbor master with binoculars. No. 1099, Radar image of entrance to Copenhagen harbor, sextant.

1998, May 28			Litho.	**Perf. 13**	
1098	A399	6.50k multicolored		3.50	3.50
1099	A399	6.50k multicolored		3.50	3.50
a.		Pair, #1098-1099		7.25	7.25
b.		Souvenir sheet, #1099a		8.00	10.00

National Festivals — A400

Europa: 3.75k, Horse at Danish agricultural show. 4.50k, Theater, tents at Arhus Festival Week, Arhus.

Litho. & Engr.

1998, Sept. 3			**Perf. 13**	
1100	A400	3.75k multicolored	1.50	.60
		Complete booklet, 10 #1100	15.00	
1101	A400	4.50k multicolored	1.75	1.00

Contemporary Art — A401

Paintings: 3.75k, Danish Autumn, by Per Kirkeby. 5k, Alpha, by Mogens Andersen, vert. 8.75k, Imagery, by Ejler Bille, vert. 19k, Celestial Horse, by Carl-Henning Pedersen.

Perf. 12½x13, 13x12½

1998, Oct. 15			Litho. & Engr.		
1102	A401	3.75k multicolored		1.25	1.25

Litho.

1103	A401	5k multicolored		2.00	1.50
1104	A401	8.75k multicolored		3.25	3.25
1105	A401	19k multicolored		6.50	7.75
		Nos. 1102-1105 (4)		*13.00*	*13.75*

See Nos. 1160-1161, 1190-1191, 1204-1205, 1235-1236, 1255-1256, 1282-1283, 1333-1336.

A402

Fossil, name of Danish geologist: 3.75k, Ammonite, Ole Worm (1588-1654). 4.50k, Shark's teeth, Niels Stensen (1638-86). 5.50k, Sea Urchin, Soren Abildgaard (1718-91). 15k, Slit-shell snail, Erich Pontoppidan (1698-1764).

1998, Nov. 5			Engr.	**Perf. 13**	
1106	A402	3.75k multicolored		1.25	.30
		Complete booklet, 10 #1106		12.50	
1107	A402	4.50k multicolored		1.75	1.75
1108	A402	5.50k multicolored		1.75	1.75
1109	A402	15k multicolored		5.00	4.50
a.		Souvenir sheet, #1106-1109		12.00	12.50

Wavy Lines and Queen Types of 1933, 1997 and

Queen Margrethe II — A402a

1999-2004			Engr.	**Perf. 12¾**	
1111	A32	150o purple		.60	.25
1112	A32	375o green		2.60	.70
1113	A32	400o green		1.75	.65
1114	A321a	4k red		2.60	.50
a.		Booklet pane, 4 #883, 2			
		#494, 2 #1114		6.75	
		Complete booklet,			
		#1114a		7.00	
1115	A402a	4k red		1.75	.50
b.		Booklet pane, 4 #883, 2			
		#494, 2 #1115		5.00	
		Booklet, #1115b		5.00	
c.		Sheet of 8 + label		16.00	
1116	A32	425o green		2.75	.65
1117	A402a	4.25k blue		2.60	1.00
1118	A402a	4.25k red		1.75	.70
b.		Booklet pane, 6 #883, 2			
		#1118		5.00	
c.		Sheet of 8 + central label		36.00	—
1119	A402a	4.50k orange		2.00	1.50
a.		Vert. strip of 10 + 10 eti-			
		quettes		24.00	
1120	A402a	4.50k red		2.90	1.10
a.		Booklet pane, 2 #494, 2			
		#1120		6.00	—
		Complete booklet,			
		#1120a		6.00	
b.		Sheet of 8 + central label		26.00	—
1121	A402a	4.75k sepia		3.25	1.75
1122	A402a	5k dk green		2.00	1.00
a.		Sheet of 8 + 8 etiquettes		65.00	—
1123	A402a	5.25k ultra		2.10	1.00
1124	A402a	5.50k violet		2.50	.90
a.		Sheet of 8 + label		24.00	
b.		Sheet of 8 + 8 etiquettes		30.00	
1125	A321a	5.75k blue		2.25	1.25
1126	A402a	5.75k emerald		2.50	1.25
1127	A402a	6k bister		2.50	.75
a.		Sheet of 10 + 10 eti-			
		quettes		45.00	—

1128	A402a	6.25k green	4.00	2.00
1129	A402a	6.50k slate grn	2.50	.90
a.		Sheet of 8 + 8 etiquettes	32.00	
b.		Sheet of 8 + central label	42.00	—
1130	A321a	6.75k slate green	4.25	2.75
1131	A402a	6.75k henna brn	3.25	2.50
1132	A402a	7k rose lilac	3.00	2.50
1133	A402a	8.50k bright blue	*3.00*	3.00
1134	A55	10.50k dk bl gray	*4.00*	2.50
1135	A55	11.50k dk bl gray	5.75	4.00

With Diagonal Engraving Lines

1136	A55	12.50k gray	6.00	4.50
1137	A55	13k orange	5.50	4.50
1138	A55	15k blue	6.50	5.25
		Nos. 1111-1138 (28)	*86.15*	*49.85*

Issued: 375o, Nos. 1114, 1118, 1130, 1/13/99; No. 1125, 1/3/00; Nos. 1115, 1119, 1119a, 4.25k, 4.50k, 5k, 5.25k, 5.50k, Nos. 1126, 1131, 4/12/00; No. 1119b, 6k, 7k, 5/9/01; Nos. 1119c, 1121a, 1124a, 4/17/01; 150o, 4.75k, 6.50k, 10.50k, 1/2/02. 400o, No. 1120, 6.25k, 8.50k, 11.50k, 1/2/03. No. 1120b, 3/12. Nos. 1124b, 1129a, 3/12/03. Nos. 1128b, 1/2/03; No. 1122a, 4/2/02; 425o, No. 1120, 12.50k, 13k, 15k, 1/2/04. Nos. 1120b, 1127a, 1/2/04.

Type A55 stamps with diagonal engraving lines have engraver's name of Mörck at lower right. Earlier stamps of type A55 have vertical and horizontal engraving lines. The lettering was also changed slightly in the Mörck engraving.

See Nos. 1295, 1296-1303.

A403

1999, Jan. 13			Litho.	**Perf. 13**	
1143	A403	4k Oersted Satellite		1.40	.90

Deciduous Trees — A404

4k, Fagus sylvatica. 5k, Fraxinus excelsior, vert. 5.25k, Tilia cordata, vert. 9.25k, Quercus robur.

1999, Jan. 13			Litho. & Engr.		
1144	A404	4k multicolored		1.25	.30
		Complete booklet, 10 #1144		12.50	
1145	A404	5k multicolored		1.75	1.00
1146	A404	5.25k multicolored		1.75	.65
1147	A404	9.25k multicolored		3.00	3.00
		Nos. 1144-1147 (4)		*7.75*	*4.95*

50th Anniversaries A405

Litho. & Engr.

1999, Feb. 24			**Perf. 13**	
1148	A405	3.75k Home Guard	1.40	.90
1149	A405	4.25k NATO	2.00	1.00

Harbingers of Spring — A406

1999, Feb. 24			Litho.	
1150	A406	4k Lapwing in flight	1.60	.30
		Complete booklet, 10 #1150	16.00	
1151	A406	5.25k Geese	1.75	.90
a.		Souvenir sheet, #1150-1151	6.50	5.00

Nature Reserves — A407

Litho. & Engr.

1999, Apr. 28			**Perf. 13**
1152	A407	4.50k Vejlerne	1.75 1.00
1153	A407	5.50k Langli	2.00 1.25

Europa.

Council of Europe, 50th Anniv. — A408

1999, Apr. 28 — **Engr.**

1154	A408	9.75k blue	3.00 3.00

Danish Constitution, 150th Anniv. — A409

1999, June 2			**Litho.**	**Perf. 13**
1155	A409	4k red & black		1.40 .70

Danish Revue, 150th Anniv. — A410

Performers: 4k, Kjeld Petersen and Dirch Passer, comedians. 4.50k, Osvald Helmuth, singer. 5.25k, Preben Kaas and Jorgen Ryg, comedians, singers. 6.75k, Liva Weel, singer.

1999, June 2 — **Litho.** — **Perf. 13**

1156	A410	4k deep red	1.60 .50
	Complete booklet, 10 #1156		16.00
1157	A410	4.50k slate	1.75 1.40
1158	A410	5.25k deep blue	1.75 .85
	Complete booklet, 10 #1158		17.50
1159	A410	6.75k deep claret	2.25 1.60
a.	Bklt. pane, #1156-1159 + 2 labels		14.00 15.00
	Complete booklet, 2 #1159a		28.00
	Nos. 1156-1159 (4)		7.35 4.35

No. 1159a printed with two different pairs of labels. One version has showgirl label at left, the second version has showgirl label at right. Complete booklets contain one of each pane.

Contemporary Paintings Type

9.25k, Fire Farver, by Thomas Kluge. 16k, Dreng, by Lise Malinovsky.

1999, Aug. 25 — **Litho.** — **Perf. 12¾**

1160	A401	9.25k multi, vert.	3.25 4.00
1161	A401	16k multi, vert.	5.25 5.25

Opening of New Extension of the Royal Library, "The Black Diamond" — A411

1999, Aug. 25 — **Engr.** — **Perf. 13¾**

1162	A411	8.75k black	4.00 3.00

Migratory Birds — A412

Litho. & Engr.

1999, Sept. 29 — **Perf. 12¾**

1163	A412	4k Swallows	1.60 .30
	Complete booklet, 10 #1163		16.00
1164	A412	5.25k Gray-lag geese	1.75 1.00
a.	Souvenir sheet, #1163-1164		5.25 6.50
1165	A412	5.50k Common eider	1.75 .90
1166	A412	12.25k Arctic tern	4.50 5.25
a.	Souvenir sheet, #1165-1166		9.00 10.00
	Nos. 1163-1166 (4)		9.60 7.45

Stamps from Nos. 1164a and 1166a lack white border found on Nos. 1163-1166.

New Year 2000 — A413

1999, Nov. 10			**Litho.**	**Perf. 13¼**
1167	A413	4k Hearts		1.40 .50
1168	A413	4k Wavy lines		1.40 .50
a.	Bklt. pane, 5 ea #1167-1168			35.00
	Complete booklet, #1168a			35.00

The 20th Century — A414

4k, Prof. J.H. Deuntzer on front page of newspaper, 1901. 4.50k, Newspaper illustration, 1903. 5.25k, Asta Nielsen and Poul Reumert in the film "The Abyss," 1910. 5.75k, Advertising sticker showing woman on telephone, 1914.
See sheet of 16, #1184a.

2000, Jan. 12 — **Litho. & Engr.**

1169	A414	4k buff & blk	1.40 .50
	Complete booklet, 10 #1169		14.00
1170	A414	4.50k multicolored	1.75 1.00
1171	A414	5.25k multicolored	1.75 1.00
	Complete booklet, 10 #1171		17.50
1172	A414	5.75k multicolored	1.75 1.25
	Nos. 1169-1172 (4)		6.65 3.75

2000, May 9

4k, Allegory of women suffrage on front page of newspaper, 1915. 5k, Newspaper caricature of the Kanslergade Agreement, 1933. 5.50k, Film "Long and Short," 1927. 6.75k, Front page of Radio Weekly Review, 1925.

1173	A414	4k multi	1.40 .55
	Booklet, 10 #1173		14.00
1174	A414	5k multi	1.75 1.00
1175	A414	5.50k multi	2.00 1.60
1176	A414	6.75k multi	2.25 2.50
	Nos. 1173-1176 (4)		7.40 5.65

2000, Aug. 23

4k, Liberation of Denmark on front page of newspaper, 1945. 5.75k, Newspaper caricature of new constitution, 1953. 6.75k, Poster for film "Café Paradise," 1950. 12.25k, Advertisement for Arena television, 1957.

1177	A414	4k multi	1.40 .90
	Booklet, 10 #1177		14.00
1178	A414	5.75k multi	2.00 1.60
1179	A414	6.75k multi	2.25 2.50
1180	A414	12.25k multi	4.00 4.25
	Nos. 1177-1180 (4)		9.65 9.25

2000, Nov. 8

4k, Entry of Denmark into European Community on front page of newspaper, 1972. 4.50k, Newspaper caricature of youth revolt, 1969. 5.25k, Poster for film "The Ölsen Gang," 1968. 5.50k, Denmark Post website on Internet, 1999.

1181	A414	4k multi	1.40 .90
	Booklet, 10 #1181		14.00
1182	A414	4.50k multi	1.60 1.60
1183	A414	5.25k multi	1.75 1.00
	Booklet, 10 #1183		17.50
a.	Booklet pane, #1171, 1175, 1179, 1183 + label		8.00
	Booklet, 2 #1183a		16.00
1184	A414	5.50k multi	2.00 1.25
a.	Sheet of 16, #1169-1184		47.50 42.50
	Nos. 1181-1184 (4)		6.75 4.75

No. 1183a comes with two different labels. Booklet contains one of each.

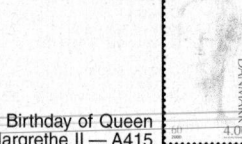

60th Birthday of Queen Margrethe II — A415

2000, Apr. 12		**Litho.**	**Perf. 12¾**
1185	A415	4k gray & car	1.60 .60
	Complete booklet, 10 #1185		16.00
1186	A415	5.25k gray & blue	1.75 .90
a.	Souvenir sheet, #1185-1186		4.00 4.25

Oresund Bridge, Sweden-Denmark — A416

Litho. & Engr.

2000, May 9			**Perf. 12¾**
1187	A416	4.50k shown	2.00 1.90

Litho.

1188	A416	4.50k Map	2.00 1.90
a.	Pair, #1187-1188		4.25 3.75

See Sweden Nos. 2391-2393.

Europa, 2000
Common Design Type

2000, May 9		**Litho.**	**Perf. 13**
1189	CD17	9.75k multi	3.50 2.25

Contemporary Art Type of 1998

Designs: 4k, Pegasus, by Kurt Trampedach. 5.25k, Landscape, by Nina Sten-Knudsen.

2000, Sept. 27			**Perf. 12¾**
1190	A401	4k multi	1.50 1.50
1191	A401	5.25k multi	1.50 1.50

Royal Danish Air Force, 50th Anniv. — A417

2000, Sept. 27 — **Engr.**

1192	A417	9.75k black & red	3.00 2.50
a.	Souvenir sheet of 1		3.00 3.50

Botanical Gardens, Copenhagen — A418

Litho. & Engr.

2001, Jan. 24			**Perf. 12¾**
1193	A418	4k Palm House	1.40 .60
	Booklet, 10 #1193		14.00

Size: 28x21mm

1194	A418	6k Lake	2.00 .85
1195	A418	12.25k Water lilies	4.00 4.50
	Nos. 1193-1195 (3)		7.40 5.95

"Use the Language" — A419

2001, Mar. 28		**Litho.**	**Perf. 13**
1196	A419	4k "A," text	1.40 .55
	Booklet, 10 #1196		14.00
1197	A419	7k "Z," text	2.75 .90

Danish Postage Stamps, 150th Anniv. — A420

Portion of #2 and: 4k, Engraver Martinus Willam Ferslew. 5.50k, Printer Andreas Thiele. 6k, Head Copenhagen postmaster Frantz Christopher von Jessen. 10.25k, Postmaster General Magrius Otto Spohus Count Danneskjold-Samsoe.

Litho. & Engr.

2001, Apr. 1			**Perf. 13¼x13**
1198	A420	4k multi	1.50 1.00
1199	A420	5.50k multi	1.90 1.25
	Booklet, 10 #1199		19.00
1200	A420	6k multi	2.00 1.25
1201	A420	10.25k multi	2.50 2.50
a.	Booklet pane, #1198-1201 + label		20.00 21.00
	Booklet, 2 #1201a		40.00
	Nos. 1198-1201 (4)		9.40 6.00

No. 1201a printed with two different labels. One version has proof of stamp design, sketch of proposed design and Ferslew's letter to

Danneskjold-Samsoe, and other shows two essays and letter from M. T. C. Bartholdy.

Europa — A421

Designs: 4.50k, Hands in water. 9.75k, Woman's head, water.

2001, May 9		**Litho.**	**Perf. 13¼x13**
1202	A421	4.50k multi	1.25 .90
a.	Booklet pane of 5 + 5 etiquettes		7.50
	Booklet, 2 #1202a		15.00
1203	A421	9.75k multi	3.00 3.50

Contemporary Paintings Type of 1998

Designs: 18k, Missus, by Jorn Larsen, horiz. 22k, Postbillede, by Henning Damgaard-Sorensen.

Perf. 13x12½, 12½x13

2001, Aug. 22			**Litho.**
1204	A401	18k multi	6.00 6.50
1205	A401	22k multi	7.25 7.75

Youth Culture — A422

Designs: 4k, Skateboarding. 5.50k, Kissing. 6k, Creating music. 10.25k, Tongue piercing.

2001, Aug. 22			**Perf. 13**
1206	A422	4k multi	1.60 .60
	Booklet, 10 #1206		16.00
1207	A422	5.50k multi	1.75 1.10
	Booklet, 10 #1207		17.50
1208	A422	6k multi	1.90 1.90
1209	A422	10.25k multi	4.00 4.00
a.	Souvenir sheet, #1206-1209		9.00 9.75
	Nos. 1206-1209 (4)		9.25 7.60

Hafnia 01 Philatelic Exhibition, Copenhagen — A423

Monarch and stamps: 4k, Queen Margrethe II, #757, 1000. 4.50k, King Frederik IX, #775, 1003. 5.50k, King Christian X, #1001, B10. 7k, King Christian IX, #1002, 66.

Litho. & Engr.

2001, Oct. 16			**Perf. 13x13¼**
1210	A423	4k multi	1.60 .75
1211	A423	4.50k multi	1.75 1.75
1212	A423	5.50k multi	1.75 1.75
1213	A423	7k multi	2.50 2.75
a.	Souvenir sheet, #1210-1213		6.50 7.50
	Strip, #1210-1213 + central label		10.00 11.50
	Nos. 1210-1213 (4)		7.60 7.00

Island Ferries — A424

Designs: 3.75k, Bukken-Bruse. 4k, Ouro. 4.25k, Hjarno. 6k, Barsofaergen.

2001, Nov. 7			**Perf. 12¾**
1214	A424	3.75k multi	1.25 1.60
1215	A424	4k multi	1.60 .60
	Booklet, 10 #1215		16.00
1216	A424	4.25k multi	1.60 1.60
1217	A424	6k multi	2.00 2.25
	Nos. 1214-1217 (4)		6.45 6.05

Comics and Cartoons — A425

Designs: 4k, Rasmus Klump, by Vilhelm Hansen. 5.50k, Valhalla, by Peter Madsen.

6.50k, Jungledyret Hugo, by Flemming Quist Moller. 10.50k, Cirkeline, by Hanne Hastrup.

2002, Jan. 16	Litho.		
1218	A425	4k multi	1.50 .55
	Booklet, 10 #1218		15.00
a.	Sheet of 8 + label		50.00
1219	A425	5.50k multi	1.75 1.00
	Booklet, 10 #1219		17.50
a.	Sheet of 8 + label		27.50
1220	A425	6.50k multi	2.10 1.75
1221	A425	10.50k multi	4.00 4.50
a.	Souvenir sheet, #1218-1221		8.00 9.00
	Nos. 1218-1221 (4)		9.35 7.80

The Girls in the Airport, Sculpture by Hanne Varming — A426

Designs: 4k, Rear view. 5k, Front view.

	Photo. & Engr.		
2002, Mar. 13			Perf. 12¾
1222	A426	4k multi, cream	1.60 .55
	Booklet, 10 #1222		16.00
1223	A426	5k multi, cream	1.75 1.60

Europa — A427

Winning drawings in children's stamp design contest: 4k, Clown, by Luna Ostergard. 5k, Clown, by Camille Wagner Larsen.

2002, May 15	Litho.		Perf. 13
1224	A427	4k multi	1.50 .90
	Booklet, 10 #1224		15.00
1225	A427	5k multi	1.75 1.75
a.	Booklet pane of 5 + 5 etiquettes		8.75
	Booklet, 2 #1225a		17.50

Landscapes — A428

2002, May 15			Engr.
1226	A428	4k Bornholm	1.60 .90
1227	A428	6k West Jutland	1.90 1.90
1228	A428	6.50k Langeland	1.75 2.25
1229	A428	12.50k Thy	4.50 4.50
	Nos. 1226-1229 (4)		9.75 9.55

Historic Postal Vehicles — A429

Designs: 4k, 1953 Nimbus motorcycle. 5.50k, 1962 Bedford van. 10k, 1984 Renault 4 van. 19k, 1998 Volvo FH12 tractor trailer.

	Litho. & Engr.		
2002, Aug. 21			Perf. 13x13¼
1230	A429	4k multi	1.60 .65
	Booklet, 10 #1230		16.00
a.	Sheet of 8 + central label		36.00
1231	A429	5.50k multi	1.90 1.50
	Booklet, 10 #1231		19.00
1232	A429	10k multi	4.00 4.00
1233	A429	19k multi	7.00 7.00
a.	Booklet pane of 4, #1230-1233		20.00
	Booklet, 2 #1233a		40.00
	Nos. 1230-1233 (4)		14.50 13.15

No. 1233a is printed with two different labels. One shows a 1908 Berliet van and the other a 2002 Peugeot Partner. Both are included in the booklet.

Opening of Copenhagen Metro — A430

2002, Sept. 25		Engr.	Perf. 12¾
1234	A430	5.50k multi, tan	1.50 1.40

Contemporary Paintngs Type of 1998

Designs: 5k, Children's Corner, by Jens Birkemose, vert. 6.50k, Maleren og Modellen, by Frans Kannik, vert.

2002, Sept. 25			Perf. 13x12½
1235	A401	5k red & blue	1.75 1.75
1236	A401	6.50k multi	2.25 2.25

Intl. Council for the Exploration of the Sea, Cent. — A431

Atlantic cod and: 4k, Exploration ship Dana. 10.50k, Hirtshals lighthouse.

	Litho. & Engr.		
2002, Sept. 25			Perf. 13¼x13
1237	A431	4k multi	1.60 .65
1238	A431	10.50k multi	4.00 4.00
a.	Souvenir sheet, #1237-1238		4.50 5.00

See Faroe Islands No. 426, Greenland Nos. 401-402.

Danish House Architecture A432

Designs: 4k, Dianas Have, Horsholm, by Vandkusten Design Studio, 1992. 4.25k, Blangstedgard, Odense, by Poul Ingemann, 1988. 5.50k, Dansk Folkeferie, Karrebaeksminde, by Stephan Kappel, 1979. 6.50k, Fredensborg Terraces, Fredensborg, by Jorn Utzon, 1963. 9k, Soholm, Klampenborg, by Arne Jacobsen, 1950.

	Litho. & Engr.		
2002, Nov. 8			Perf. 12¾
1239	A432	4k multi	1.60 1.00
	Booklet, 10 #1239		16.00
1240	A432	4.25k multi	1.60 .70
1241	A432	5.50k multi	1.90 1.50
1242	A432	6.50k multi	2.25 1.75
1243	A432	9k multi	3.00 3.00
	Nos. 1239-1243 (5)		10.35 7.95

See Nos. 1257-1261, 1267-1271, 1317-1321.

Youth Sports — A433

2003, Jan. 15	Litho.		Perf. 12¾
1244	A433	4.25k Soccer	1.50 .70
	Booklet, 10 #1244		16.00
a.	Sheet of 8 + central label		13.00 13.00
1245	A433	5.50k Swimming	1.75 1.50
	Booklet, 10 #1245		17.50
1246	A433	8.50k Gymnastics	3.25 3.25
1247	A433	11.50k Handball	4.00 4.25
	Nos. 1244-1247 (4)		10.50 9.70

Danish Literary Greenland Expedition, Cent. — A434

Designs: 4.25k, Expedition members Harald Moltke, Knud Rasmussen, Jorgen Bronlund, Ludvig Mylius-Erichsen and Gabriel Olsen. 7k, Campsite.

2003, Mar. 12		Engr.	Perf. 12¾
1248	A434	4.25k blue gray	1.25 .70

Size: 61x22mm

1249	A434	7k multi	2.25 2.25
a.	Souvenir sheet, #1248-1249 + label		5.00 5.00

See Greenland Nos. 407-408.

Europa — A435

Poster art: 4.25k, Poster for Copenhagen International Theater Festival, by Ole Fick, 1985. 5.50k, Poster for Bertel Thorvaldsen Museum, by Ole Woldbye, 1970.

2003, May 14	Litho.		Perf. 12¾
1250	A435	4.25k multi	1.50 .60
	Booklet, 10 #1250		15.00

	Engr.		
1251	A435	5.50k black	1.75 1.40
	Booklet, 10 #1251		17.50
a.	Sheet of 8 + central label		40.00

Insects — A436

Designs: 4.25k, Ephemera danica. 6.50k, Dytiscus latissimus. 12k, Cordulegaster boltoni, vert.

2003, May 14	Litho. & Engr.		
1252	A436	4.25k multi	1.50 .50
a.	Sheet of 8 + central label		25.00
1253	A436	6.50k multi	2.00 2.00
a.	Sheet of 8 + central label		50.00

Size: 21x39mm

1254	A436	12k multi	3.75 3.75
a.	Souvenir sheet, #1252-1254		7.00 7.50
	Nos. 1252-1254 (3)		7.25 6.25

Contemporary Art Type of 1998

Designs: 5.50k, Baering, by Sys Hindsbo. 19k, Det Forjaettede Land, by Poul Anker Bech.

2003, Aug. 27	Litho. & Engr.		
1255	A401	5.50k multi	1.75 1.75

	Litho.		
1256	A401	19k multi	6.50 6.50

Danish House Architecture Type of 2002

Designs: 4k, Bellahoj Apartment Complex, Copenhagen, by Tage Nielsen and Mogens Irming, 1944-58. 4.25k, Anchersvej, Klampenborg, by Mogens Lassen, 1935. 5.25k, Gerthasminde, Odense, by Anton Rosen, 1912-35. 9k, Solvang, Vallekilde College, by Andreas Bentsen and Martin Nyrop, 1889. 15k, Stenbrogard, Brorup, by Peter Holdensen, 1868.

	Litho. & Engr.		
2003, Aug. 27			Perf. 12¾
1257	A432	4k multi	1.60 1.60
1258	A432	4.25k multi	1.60 .90
	Complete booklet, 10 #1258		16.00
1259	A432	5.25k multi	1.75 1.75
1260	A432	9k multi	3.25 3.25
1261	A432	15k multi	4.50 4.50
	Nos. 1257-1261 (5)		12.70 12.00

A437

2003, Nov. 7		Engr.	Perf. 12¾
1262	A437	6.50k gray blue	2.00 1.75

Awarding of first Nobel Prize to a Dane (Niels Finsen for Physiology and Medicine), cent.

A438

Artifacts from Royal Jelling World Heritage Site: 4.25k, Queen Thyra's stone. 5.50k, King Gorm's cup. 8.50k, King Harald's stone. 11.50k, Wall paintings, Jelling Church.

2003, Nov. 7		Litho. & Engr.	
1263	A438	4.25k multi	1.50 1.25
	Booklet, 10 #1263		17.50
1264	A438	5.50k multi	1.75 1.50
	Booklet, 10 #1264		22.50
1265	A438	8.50k multi	2.75 2.75
1266	A438	11.50k multi	3.75 3.75
	Nos. 1263-1266 (4)		9.75 9.25

A spiral-bound booklet, enclosed in a slipcase, with four booklet panes containing single stamps of Nos. 1263-1266, and a booklet pane containing a strip of Nos. 1263-1266, sold for 99k. Value, $35.

Danish House Architecture Type of 2002

Designs: 4.50k, Spurveskjul, Virum, by Nicolai Abildgaard, 1805. 6k, Liselund, Mon, by Andreas Kirkerup, 1792. 7k, Kampmann's Yard, Varde, by Hans Wolff Ollgaard, Hack Kampmann and Mikkel Stobberup, 1781. 12.50k, Harsdorff's House, Copenhagen, by Caspar Frederik Harsdorff, 1780. 15k, Nyso Manor, Praesto, by Jens Lauridsen.

	Litho. & Engr.		
2004, Jan.14			Perf. 12¾
1267	A432	4.50k multi	1.60 1.00
	Booklet, 10 #1267		16.00
1268	A432	6k multi	2.40 1.60
1269	A432	7k multi	2.50 2.50
1270	A432	12.50k multi	4.00 4.00
1271	A432	15k multi	5.25 5.25
	Nos. 1267-1271 (5)		15.75 14.35

Academy of Fine Arts, Copenhagen, 250th Anniv. — A439

	Litho. & Engr.		
2004, Mar. 26			Perf. 13¼x13
1272	A439	5.50k multi	2.10 1.25
	Booklet, 10 #1272		21.00

Norse Gods — A440

Designs: 4.50k, Heimdal guarding Bifrost bridge. 6k, Gefion plowing Sjaelland out of Sweden.

2004, Mar. 26			
1273	A440	4.50k multi	1.75 .85
a.	Sheet of 8 + central label		35.00 35.00
1274	A440	6k multi	2.40 1.10
a.	Souvenir sheet, #1273-1274		8.00 8.00
b.	Sheet of 8 + central label		55.00 55.00

Wedding of Crown Prince Frederik and Mary Donaldson — A441

No. 1275: a, Couple facing right. b, Couple facing left.

	Litho. & Photo.		
2004, May 14			Perf. 13x13¼
1275	A441	Horiz. pair	3.50 3.50
	Booklet, 5 #1275		20.00
a.-b.	4.50k Either single, denomination 8½ mm wide		1.75 1.25
c.-d.	4.50k Either single, denomination 7½ mm wide		1.75 1.25
e.	Souvenir sheet, #1275c-1275d + central label		4.00 4.00

See Faroe Islands No. 444 and Greenland Nos. 429-430.

Frederiksberg Palace, 300th Anniv. — A442

Designs: 4.25k, Doorway overlooking Sondermarken Park. 4.50k, Gatehouse archway, castle yard. 6.50k, Aerial view.

	Litho. & Engr.		
2004, May 14			Perf. 13
1276	A442	4.25k multi	1.60 1.60
1277	A442	4.50k multi	1.75 1.00

Size: 55x32mm

1278	A442	6.50k multi	2.50 2.00
a.	Souvenir sheet, #1276-1278		6.00 7.00
	Nos. 1276-1278 (3)		5.85 4.60

Prince Henrik, 70th Birthday — A443

2004, June 9   Litho.   **Perf. 12¾**

1279	A443	4.50k multi	1.60	1.00

Europa — A444

2004, June 9   **Perf. 13**

1280	A444	6k Cyclists	2.50	1.60
1281	A444	9k Sailboats	3.50	3.00

Contemporary Paintings Type of 1998

Designs: 13k, Senses the Body Landscape, by Lars Ravn, vert. 21k, The Dog Bites, by Lars Norgard, vert.

Litho. & Engr.   **2004, Aug. 25**   **Perf. 13x12½**

1282	A401	13k multi	5.00	5.00

Litho.

1283	A401	21k multi	7.50	7.50

Viking Ship Museum, Roskilde — A445

Designs: 4.50k, Skuldelev 1 on Roskilde Fjord. 5.50k, Reconstruction of Skuldelev 2. 6.50k, Cross-section of ship. 12.50k, Excavation of archaeological site where ships were found.

Litho. & Engr.

2004, Aug. 25   **Perf. 13x13¼**

1284	A445	4.50k multi	1.60	1.00
		Complete booklet, 10 #1284	16.00	
1285	A445	5.50k multi	2.00	1.60
		Complete booklet, 10 #1285	20.00	
1286	A445	6.50k multi	2.40	2.00
1287	A445	12.50k multi	4.50	4.50
		Nos. 1284-1287 (4)	10.50	9.10

A spiral-bound booklet, enclosed in a slipcase, with four booklet panes containing single stamps of Nos. 1284-1287 and a booklet pane containing a strip of Nos. 1284-1287, sold for 99k. Value, $40.

Birds of Prey — A446

Designs: 4.50k, Falco tinnunculus. 5.50k, Accipiter nisus. 6k, Buteo buteo. 7k, Circus aeruginosus.

Litho. & Engr.

2004, Nov. 5   **Perf. 13**

1288	A446	4.50k multi	1.75	.90
		Complete booklet, 10 #1288	17.50	
a.		Sheet of 8 + central label	17.50	17.50
1289	A446	5.50k multi	2.10	1.00
a.		Sheet of 8 + central label	22.50	22.50
1290	A446	6k multi	2.40	2.00
1291	A446	7k multi	2.75	2.25
		Nos. 1288-1291 (4)	9.00	6.15

Queen and Small State Seal Types of 1946-2000

2005-09   Engr.   **Perf. 12¾**

1295	A402a	4.75k red	1.90	1.00
a.		Sheet of 8 + central label	17.00	
1296	A402a	5.50k red	2.25	.50
b.		Sheet of 8 #1296 + central label	20.00	—
1296A	A402a	6.50k blue	2.75	.50
1297	A402a	7.25k blk vio	3.00	.50
1298	A402a	7.50k blue	3.25	2.50
1299	A402a	7.75k vio blk	3.50	.90
1300	A402a	8k indigo	4.00	2.50
1301	A402a	8.25k Prus blue	2.50	2.50
1302	A402a	8.75k Prus blue	3.75	1.00
1303	A402a	9k blue	3.25	3.25

With Diagonal Engraving Lines

1304	A55	10k olive yellow	3.50	1.25
1304A	A55	10.50k car rose	4.00	3.25
1305	A55	13.50k green	5.00	4.25
1308	A55	16k Prus grn	7.25	1.25
1309	A55	16.50k red brn	6.00	5.25
1310	A55	17k sl grn	6.25	5.25
1311	A55	17.50k purple	6.25	5.25
1312	A55	20k blue	8.25	1.75
1312A	A55	20.50k purple	9.25	1.75
1313	A55	22k brn vio	8.25	6.00
		Nos. 1295-1313 (20)	94.15	52.40

Issued: 7.50k, 16.50k, 22k, 1/3. 4.75k, 8k, 11/11. 4.75k, 10k, 17k, 1/2/06. 7.25k, 8.25k, 11/10/06. 13.50k, 17.50k, 1/2/07. 20k, 11/8/07. 5.50k, 6.50k, 7.75k, 8.75k, 1/2/08. Nos. 1296b, 1308, 1312, 3/27/08. Nos. 1303, 1304A, 1/2/09. Type A55 stamps with diagonal engraving lines have engraver's name of Mörck at lower right. Earlier stamps of type A55 have vertical and horizontal engraving lines. The lettering was also changed slightly in the Mörck engraving.

Danish House Architecture Type of 2002

Designs: 4.25k, Hjarup Manse, Vamdrup, c. 1665. 4.50k, Ejdersted Farm, Southwest Schleswig, 1653. 7.50k, Provstegade, Randers, c. 1650. 9.50k, Smith's Yard, Koge, c. 1550. 16.50k, Carmelite Monastery, Elsinore, c. 1500.

Litho. & Engr.

2005, Jan. 12   **Perf. 12¾**

1317	A432	4.25k multi	1.75	1.75
1318	A432	4.50k multi	1.75	.65
		Complete booklet, 10 #1318	17.50	
a.		Booklet pane, 4 #691, 8 #1318	17.00	—
		Complete booklet, #1318a	17.00	
1319	A432	7.50k multi	2.90	2.90
1320	A432	9.50k multi	3.50	3.50
1321	A432	16.50k multi	7.25	7.25
		Nos. 1317-1321 (5)	17.15	16.05

Bonn-Copenhagen Declaration, 50th Anniv. — A447

2005, Mar. 2   **Litho.**

1322	A447	6.50k multi	2.50	2.00

See Germany No. 2330.

Hans Christian Andersen (1805-75), Author A448

Paper Cutting by Andersen, Scissors A449

Designs: 6.50k, Pen, inkwell, illustration of duckling, manuscript handwritten by Andersen. 7.50k, Andersen's drawing of Casino dell'Orlogio, Rome, and boots.

2005, Mar. 2   **Engr.**

1323	A448	4.50k black	1.60	1.60
a.		Sheet of 8 + central label	20.00	20.00

Litho. & Engr.

1324	A449	5.50k multi	2.00	2.00
		Complete booklet, 10 #1324	20.00	
a.		Sheet of 8 + central label	25.00	25.00
1325	A449	6.50k multi	2.25	2.00
1326	A449	7.50k multi	3.00	2.50
		Nos. 1323-1326 (4)	8.85	8.10

A spiral-bound booklet, enclosed in a slipcase, with four booklet panes containing single stamps of Nos. 1323-1326, and a booklet pane containing a strip of Nos. 1323-1326, sold for 99k. Value, $40.

See Malta Nos. 1196-1199.

August Bournonville (1805-79), Choreographer A450

Bournonville and: 4.50k, Dancer. 5.50k, Dancers.

Litho. & Engr.

2005, May 4   **Perf. 13¼x13**

1327	A450	4.50k multi	1.75	1.75
		Complete booklet, 10 #1327	17.50	
a.		Sheet of 8 + central label	19.00	
1328	A450	5.50k multi	2.00	2.00
a.		Sheet of 8 + central label	17.50	
b.		Souvenir sheet, #1327-1328	4.00	4.00

Sailors in World War II — A451

Designs: 4.50k, Ship convoy. 7.50k, Unloading of ship's cargo.

2005, May 4   Litho.   **Perf. 13**

1329	A451	4.50k multi	1.60	1.60
1330	A451	7.50k multi	2.75	2.75

Europa — A452

2005, May 4   **Perf. 12¾**

1331	A452	6.50k Hot dog	3.00	1.90
1332	A452	9.50k Fish	4.50	3.75

Contemporary Art Type of 1998

Designs: 5.50k, Telepathy, by Anna Fro Vodder, vert. 6.50k, Home Again, by Kaspar Bonnén, vert. 7.50k, Unrest, by John Korner, vert. 12.50k, Palace in the Morning, by Tal Rosenzweig.

Perf. 13x12½, 12½x13

2005, Aug. 24   **Litho.**

1333	A401	5.50k multi	2.40	2.40
1334	A401	6.50k multi	2.75	2.75
1335	A401	7.50k multi	3.00	3.00
1336	A401	12.50k multi	6.00	6.00
		Nos. 1333-1336 (4)	14.15	14.15

INDEX:2005 Intl. Design Exhibition, Copenhagen — A453

2005, Aug. 24   Engr.   **Perf. 13¼**

1337	A453	4.50k black	1.75	1.25
		Complete booklet, 10 #1337	17.50	

Wavy Lines Type of 1905-17

2005-08   Engr.   **Perf. 12¾**

1338	A10	25o indigo	.25	.25
a.		Booklet pane, 2 each #1295, 1338 ('06)	4.00	
		Complete booklet, #1338a	4.00	
1339	A10	50o brown	.25	.25
1340	A10	100o bright blue	.35	.25
1341	A10	200o dark green	.70	.25
1342	A10	450o green	1.60	.65
1342A	A10	500o brt yel grn	2.25	.65
		Nos. 1338-1342A (6)	5.40	2.30

Wavy Line stamps, cent.
Issued: Nos. 1338-1342, 10/28/05. No. 1338a, 1/2/06. No. 1342A, 3/27/08.

Seals — A454

Designs: 4.50k, Phoca vitulina. 5.50k, Halichoerus grypus.

2005, Nov. 11   Engr.   **Perf. 13x13¼**

1343	A454	4.50k multi	1.75	1.25
		Complete booklet, 10 #1343	17.50	
1344	A454	5.50k indigo	2.00	1.50
a.		Souvenir sheet, #1343-1344	4.00	4.00

Flowers — A455

Designs: 4.75k, Calanthus nivalis. 5.50k, Eranthis hyemalis. 7k, Crocus vernus hybrid. 8k, Anemone nemorosa.

2006, Jan. 11   Engr.   **Perf. 12¾**

1345	A455	4.75k multi	1.60	.90
		Complete booklet, 10 #1345	16.00	
a.		Sheet of 8 + central label	15.00	
1346	A455	5.50k multi	1.75	1.75
		Complete booklet, 10 #1346	17.50	
a.		Sheet of 8 + central label	17.00	—
1347	A455	7k multi	2.25	2.25
1348	A455	8k multi	2.50	2.50
		Nos. 1345-1348 (4)	8.10	7.40

Creatures in Norse Mythology — A456

Designs: 4.75k, Elf king and elf girls. 7k, Incubi, werewolves, hel-horse, gnome and troll.

Litho. & Engr.

2006, Mar. 29   **Perf. 13¼x13**

1349	A456	4.75k multi	1.60	1.60
1350	A456	7k multi	2.40	2.40
a.		Souvenir sheet, #1349-1350	4.50	4.50

Rosenborg Castle, 400th Anniv. — A457

Designs: 4.75k, Castle exterior. 5.50k, Silver lion, thrones of king and queen. 13k, Royal coat of arms ceiling decoration.

2006, Mar. 29

1351	A457	4.75k multi	1.60	1.60
		Complete booklet, 10 #1351	16.00	
1352	A457	5.50k multi	2.00	2.00
1353	A457	13k multi	4.50	4.50
		Nos. 1351-1353 (3)	8.10	8.10

A spiral-bound booklet, enclosed in a slipcase, with four booklet panes containing single stamps of Nos. 1351-1353 and a booklet pane containing a strip of Nos. 1351-1353, sold for 99k. Value, $35.

New Carlsberg Glyptotek, Cent. — A458

Designs: 4.75k, Marble relief from Athenian graveyard. 5.50k, Conservatory dome. 8k, Dancer Looking at the Sole of Her Right Foot, sculpture by Edgar Degas.

2006, June 7

1354	A458	4.75k multi	1.60	1.60
		Complete booklet, 10 #1354	16.00	
1355	A458	5.50k multi	2.00	2.00
1356	A458	8k multi	2.75	2.75
a.		Souvenir sheet, #1354-1356	6.50	6.50
		Nos. 1354-1356 (3)	6.35	6.35

Race Cars — A459

Designs: 4.75k, 1958 Alfa Dana Midget, Swebe Jap. 5.50k, 1965 Austin Mini Cooper S, 1965 Ford Cortina GT, 1965 Alfa Romeo 1600 GTA. 10k, 1963 Jaguar E Type, 1967 Volvo P 1800. 17k, 1965 Lotus Elan, Renault Alpine A 110.

2006, June 7   **Perf. 13x13¼**
1357	A459 4.75k multi	1.75	1.75
	Complete booklet, 10 #1357	17.50	
1358	A459 5.50k multi	2.00	2.00
	Complete booklet, 10 #1358	20.00	
1359	A459 10k multi	3.75	3.75
1360	A459 17k multi	6.00	6.00
	Nos. 1357-1360 (4)	13.50	13.50

Europa — A460

Winning designs in children's stamp design contest: 4.75k, Smiling children, by Rikke Veber Rasmussen. 7k, Two smiling children, by Anette Bertram Nielsen.

2006, Aug. 23   **Litho.**   **Perf. 13¼x13**
1361	A460 4.75k multi	1.90	.90
	Booklet, 10 #1361	19.00	
1362	A460 7k blk & dull grn	2.75	1.25

Airplanes — A461

Designs: 4.50k, J. C. H. Ellehammer's 1906 biplane. 4.75k, KZ II, 1946. 5.50k, KZ IV, 1944. 13k, KZ VII, 1947.

Litho. & Engr.
2006, Aug. 23   **Perf. 12¾**
1363	A461 4.50k multi	1.75	1.75
1364	A461 4.75k multi	1.75	1.75
a.	Miniature sheet of 8 + central label	14.00	14.00
1365	A461 5.50k multi	2.00	2.00
a.	Miniature sheet of 8 + central label	16.00	16.00
1366	A461 13k multi	4.50	4.50
	Nos. 1363-1366 (4)	10.00	10.00

Paintings by COBRA Group Artists — A462

Designs: 4.75k, Untitled, by Asger Jorn. 5.50k, Landscape of the Night, by Else Alfelt, vert. 7k, New Skin, by Pierre Alechinsky. 8k, The Olive Eater, by Egill Jacobsen, vert.

     Perf. 13x13¼, 13¼x13
2006, Nov. 10   **Litho.**
1367	A462 4.75k multi	1.75	1.75
	Booklet, 10 #1367	17.50	
1368	A462 5.50k multi	2.00	2.00
1369	A462 7k multi	2.75	2.75
1370	A462 8k multi	3.00	3.00
	Nos. 1367-1370 (4)	9.50	9.50

See Belgium Nos. 2168-2169.

Danish Soldiers in United Nations Peace-keeping Forces, 50th Anniv. — A463

Litho. & Engr.
2007, Jan. 10   **Perf. 13**
1371	A463 4.75k multi	1.75	1.75

Intl. Polar Year — A464

Designs: 7.25k, Wooden and walrus tusk carvings of Norse, Late Dorset and Thule cultures of Greenland. 13.50k, Research airplane used for measuring thickness of polar ice.

2007, Jan. 10   **Perf. 13¼**
1372	A464 7.25k multi	2.50	2.50
1373	A464 13.50k multi	4.75	4.75
a.	Souvenir sheet, #1372-1373	5.00	5.00

Windmills — A465

Designs: 4.50k, Askov Mill, 1891. 4.75k, Gedser Mil, 1957. 6k, Bogo Mill, 1989. 8.25k, Middelgrunden, 2000.

2007, Jan. 10   **Engr.**
1374	A465 4.50k brown	1.75	1.75
1375	A465 4.75k red	1.75	1.75
	Complete booklet, 10 #1375	17.50	
a.	Sheet of 8 + central label	15.00	15.00
1376	A465 6k green	2.00	2.00
	Complete booklet, 10 #1376	20.00	
a.	Sheet of 8 + central label	19.00	19.00
1377	A465 8.25k blue	3.00	3.00
	Nos. 1374-1377 (4)	8.50	8.50

Galathea 3 Scientific Expedition — A466

Satellite, ship and: 4.75k, Marine life. 7.25k, Globe showing route of expedition.

Litho. & Engr.
2007, Mar. 28   **Perf. 12¾**
1378	A466 4.75k multi	1.75	1.75
1379	A466 7.25k multi	2.50	2.50
a.	Souvenir sheet, #1378-1379	4.50	4.50

National Museum, Bicent. — A467

Designs: 4.75k, Ceremonial axes. 6k, Funen aquaemanale. 8.25k, Armillary sphere. 10.25k, Wooden mask, Borneo.

2007, Mar. 28   **Perf. 13¼**
1380	A467 4.75k Prus bl & blk	1.75	1.75
	Complete booklet, 10 #1380	17.50	
1381	A467 6k brn lake & blk	2.00	2.00
1382	A467 8.25k orange & blk	3.00	3.00
1383	A467 10.25k bl gray, blk & org	3.75	3.75
	Nos. 1380-1383 (4)	10.50	10.50

A spiral-bound booklet, enclosed in a slip-case, with four booklet panes containing single stamps of Nos. 1380-1383 and a booklet pane containing a strip of Nos. 1380-1383, sold for 109k. Value, $40.

Europa — A468

Scouts: 4.75k, On hike. 7.25k, Around campfire.

2007, June 6   **Perf. 13x13¼**
1384	A468 4.75k multi	1.75	1.75
	Complete booklet, 10 #1384	17.50	
1385	A468 7.25k multi	2.75	2.75

Scouting, cent.

Modern Art — A469

Designs: 4.75k, The Traveler, by Arne Haugen Sorensen. 8.25k, Trionfale, by Seppo Mattinen.

2007, June 6   **Litho.**   **Perf. 13x12½**
1386	A469 4.75k multi	1.75	1.60
a.	Miniature sheet of 8 + central label	15.00	15.00
1387	A469 8.25k multi	3.00	2.50

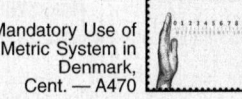

Mandatory Use of Metric System in Denmark, Cent. — A470

Litho. & Engr.
2007, Aug. 22   **Perf. 12¾**
1388	A470 4.75k black & red	1.90	.85

Nature of Denmark — A471

Flora and fauna of Rabjerg Dune: 4.75k, Niobe fritillary butterfly (klitperlemorsommerfugl). 6k, Northern dune tiger beetle (sandspringer). 7.25k, Sand lizard (markfirben). 13.50k, Seaside pansy (klitstedmoderblomst).

2007, Aug. 22
1389	A471 4.75k multi	1.75	.70
	Complete booklet, 10 #1389	17.50	
1390	A471 6k multi	2.25	.90
	Complete booklet, 10 #1390	22.50	
1391	A471 7.25k multi	2.75	1.00
1392	A471 13.50k multi	5.00	1.75
a.	Souvenir sheet, #1389-1392	12.50	12.50
	Nos. 1389-1392 (4)	11.75	4.35

Famous Men — A472

Designs: 4.75k, Poul Henningsen (1894-1967), designer, and Artichoke lamp. 6k, Victor Borge (1909-2000), comedian, and piano keys. 7.25k, Arne Jacobsen (1902-71), architect, and Egg chair. 8.25k, Piet Hein (1905-96), inventor, and superellipse.

2007, Nov. 8   **Engr.**   **Perf. 12¾**
1393	A472 4.75k multi	1.75	.85
	Complete booklet, 10 #1393	17.50	
1394	A472 6k blk & blue	2.00	1.00
1395	A472 7.25k multi	2.75	1.25
1396	A472 8.25k blk & purple	3.00	1.60
	Nos. 1393-1396 (4)	9.50	4.70

See Nos. 1412-1415, 1502-1505.

Danish National Theater — A473

Designs: 5.50k, Old Stage. 6.50k, Playhouse. 7.75k, Copenhagen Opera House.

Litho. & Engr.
2008, Jan. 9   **Perf. 13x13¼**
1397	A473 5.50k multi	2.25	1.10
	Complete booklet, 10 #1397	22.50	
a.	Sheet of 8 + central label	19.00	—
1398	A473 6.50k multi	2.60	1.25
	Complete booklet, 10 #1398	26.00	
1399	A473 7.75k multi	3.25	1.60
	Nos. 1397-1399 (3)	8.10	3.95

Royal Life Guards, 350th Anniv. — A474

Guards in: 5.50k, Red dress uniforms. 10k, Camouflage uniforms.

Litho. & Engr.
2008, Mar. 27   **Perf. 13¼x13**
1400	A474 5.50k multi	2.50	1.25
	Complete booklet, 10 #1400	25.00	
1401	A474 10k multi	4.50	2.10
a.	Souvenir sheet, #1400-1401	7.00	7.00

Nordic Mythology — A475

Places associated with mythology: 5.50k, Lindholm Hoje burial grounds. 7.75k, Feggeklit.

2008, Mar. 27   **Litho.**
1402	A475 5.50k black	2.40	1.25
1403	A475 7.75k black	3.25	1.60
a.	Souvenir sheet, #1402-1403	6.00	6.00

Europa — A476

Designs: 5.50k, Boy writing letter. 7.75k, Girl reading letter.

2008, June 4   **Litho.**   **Perf. 13**
1404	A476 5.50k multi	2.40	1.25
	Complete booklet, 10 #1404	24.00	
1405	A476 7.75k multi	3.25	1.60

Allotment Gardens — A477

Designs: 5.50k, Man tending Hjelm Allotment Association garden. 6.50k, Men sitting in Vennelyst Allotment Association garden.

Litho. & Engr.
2008, June 4   **Perf. 13x13¼**
1406	A477 5.50k multi	2.40	1.25
	Complete booklet, 10 #1406	24.00	
a.	Miniature sheet of 8 + central label	20.00	
1407	A477 6.50k multi	2.75	1.40
a.	Miniature sheet of 8 + central label	23.00	

Louisiana Museum of Art, Humlebaek, 50th Anniv. — A478

Designs: 5.50k, Original Museum building, Figures in Landscape, by Roy Lichtenstein, I Am in You, by Doug Aitken. 7.75k, I Am in You, glass corridor, A Closer Grand Canyon, by David Hockney. 8.75k, Reclining Figure No. 5, by Henry Moore, Walking Man, by Albert Giacometti, Big Head, by Giacometti, Slender Ribs, by Alexander Calder. 16k, Slender Ribs, people in concert hall, Untitled, by Sam Francis, seat designed by Poul Kjaerholm.

2008, June 4
1408	A478 5.50k multi	2.40	1.25
1409	A478 7.75k multi	3.25	1.60
a.	Booklet pane, #1408-1409	8.00	—
1410	A478 8.75k multi	3.75	1.90
1411	A478 16k multi	6.75	3.50
a.	Booklet pane, #1410-1411	14.50	—
b.	Booklet pane, #1408-1411	22.00	—
c.	Horiz. strip of 4, #1408-1411	19.00	19.00
	Complete booklet, #1409a, 1411a, 1411b	50.00	
	Nos. 1408-1411 (4)	16.15	8.25

Complete booklet sold for 102.40k.

Famous Men Type of 2007

Designs: 5k, Halfdan Rasmussen (1915-2002), poet, and line from poem. 5.50k, Erik Balling (1924-2005), film and television director, and actors in movie. 6.50k, Bodil Kjer (1917-2003), actress. 10k, Niels-Henning Orsted Pedersen (1946-2005), jazz musician, and bass.

2008, Aug. 27   **Engr.**   **Perf. 12¾**
1412	A472 5k blk & claret	2.40	.90
1413	A472 5.50k multi	2.75	1.10
	Complete booklet, 10 #1413	27.50	
1414	A472 6.50k multi	3.25	1.10
	Complete booklet, 10 #1414	32.50	
1415	A472 10k multi	4.50	1.75
	Nos. 1412-1415 (4)	12.90	4.85

Art Photography
A479

Designs: 5.50k, Trappe, by Viggo Rivad. 7.75k, Berlin, by Krass Clement, horiz.

2008, Aug. 27   Litho.   Perf. 13x12¾
1416 A479 5.50k black   2.50 2.00

Perf. 12¾x13
1417 A479 7.75k black   3.25 2.50

Winter Berries and
Flowers — A480

Designs: 5.50k, Ilex aquifolium berries. 6.50k, Helleborus niger flower. 7.75k, Taxus baccata berries. 8.75k, Symphoricarpos rivularis berries.

Litho. & Engr.
2008, Nov. 7   Perf. 13
1418 A480 5.50k multi   1.90 .95
  Complete booklet, 10 #1418   19.00
  a. Booklet pane of 4   7.75 —
1419 A480 6.50k multi   2.25 1.10
1420 A480 7.75k multi   2.75 1.40
1421 A480 8.75k multi   3.00 1.50
  a. Souvenir sheet, #1418-1421 10.00 5.00
  b. Booklet pane of 4, #1418-
    1421   10.00 —
  Complete booklet, #1418a,
    1421b   18.00
  Nos. 1418-1421 (4)   9.90 4.95

No. 1421b is No. 1421a sewn into the booklet.

COP15 Climate
Change
Conference,
Copenhagen
A481

Designs: 5.50k, Bioenergy. 9k, Low-energy building.

2009, Jan. 7   Engr.   Perf. 13x13¼
1422 A481 5.50k dark blue   2.00 1.00
1423 A481   9k dark blue   3.25 1.75

Old Town Open-
Air Museum,
Aarhus,
Cent. — A482

Designs: 5.50k, Mintmaster's Mansion, drummer. 6.50k, Mayor's House, woman in period costume. 8k, Museum of Clocks and Watches and Danish Poster Museum, painter. 10.50k, Steps to Kerteminde School, farm hand.

Litho. & Engr.
2009, Jan. 7   Perf. 13x13¼
1424 A482 5.50k multi   2.00 1.00
  Complete booklet, 10 #1424 20.00
1425 A482 6.50k multi   2.40 1.25
  Complete booklet, 10 #1425 24.00
1426 A482   8k multi   3.00 1.50
1427 A482 10.50k multi   3.75 1.90
  a. Souvenir sheet, #1424-1427 11.00 11.00
  Nos. 1424-1427 (4)   11.15 5.65

Europa — A483

Designs: 5.50k, Round Tower, Copenhagen. 8k, Tycho Brahe Planetarium.

2009, Mar. 25   Litho.   Perf. 13¼
1428 A483 5.50k multi   2.00 .95
  Complete booklet, 10 #1428 20.00
1429 A483   8k multi   3.25 1.40

Flora and Fauna — A484

Designs: 5k, Anacamptus pyramidalis. 5.50k, Falco peregrinus. 8k, Zygaena purpuralis. 17k, Tooth of Mosasaurus lemonnieri.

2009, Mar. 25   Litho.   Perf. 12¾
1430 A484   5k multi   1.90 .85
1431 A484 5.50k multi   2.40 .95
  Complete booklet, 10 #1431 24.00
  a. Miniature sheet of 8 + cen-
    tral label   17.00 17.00
1432 A484   8k multi   3.00 1.40
1433 A484 17k multi   6.75 3.00
  a. Souvenir sheet, #1430-1433 13.50 13.50
  Nos. 1430-1433 (4)   14.05 6.20

Copenhagen Zoo,
150th Anniv. — A485

Designs: 5.50k, Zoo Tower, rhinoceros. 6.50k, Elephants. 8k, Red-eyed tree frog, flamingos. 9k, Tiger python, golden lion tamarin.

2009, June 10   Litho.   Perf. 13¼x13
1434 A485 5.50k multi   2.10 1.10
  Complete booklet, 10 #1434 21.00
  a. Miniature sheet of 8 + cen-
    tral label   17.00 17.00
1435 A485 6.50k multi   2.50 1.25
  a. Miniature sheet of 8 + cen-
    tral label   20.00 20.00
  b. Booklet pane of 2, #1434-
    1435   8.00 —
1436 A485   8k multi   3.00 1.50
1437 A485   9k multi   3.50 1.75
  a. Booklet pane of 2, #1436-
    1437   12.00 —
  b. Booklet pane of 4, #1434-
    1437   20.00 —
  Complete booklet, #1435b,
    1437a, 1437b   40.00
  Nos. 1434-1437 (4)   11.10 5.60

Complete booklet containing Nos. 1435b, 1437a, 1437b sold for 109k.

Historic
Maps — A486

Maps of Denmark by: 5.50k, Royal Danish Academy of Sciences and Letters, 1841. 6.50k, Johannes Mejer, 1650. 12k, Marcus Jordan, 1585. 18k, Abraham Ortelius, 1570.

2009, July 15   Litho.   Perf. 12½
1438 A486 5.50k multi   2.10 1.10

Size: 41x24mm
Perf. 12¾
1439 A486 6.50k multi   2.50 1.25
1440 A486 12k multi   4.75 2.40
1441 A486 18k multi   7.00 3.50
  Nos. 1438-1441 (4)   16.35 8.25

Intl. Conference on the History of Cartography, Copenhagen.

Metropolitanskolen, 800th
Anniv. — A487

Designs: 5.50k, Author Hans Scherfig as boy and Metropolitanskolen building, Copenhagen. 6.50k, Two students and current school building, Norrebro.

2009, Sept. 9   Engr.   Perf. 13x13¼
1442 A487 5.50k red & black   2.25 1.10
1443 A487 6.50k black & grn   2.60 1.40

COP15, United
Nations Climate
Conference,
Copenhagen
A488

Designs: 5.50k, Fuel cell technology. 8k, Wind turbine.

2009, Sept. 9
1444 A488 5.50k dark blue   2.25 1.10
  Complete booklet, 10 #1444 22.50
1445 A488   8k dark blue   3.25 1.60

Modern
Art — A489

Designs: 5.50k, Houses in Motion, by Jes Fomsgaard. 12k, Garlic, by Karin Birgitte Lund, vert.

2009   Litho.   Perf. 12¾x13
1446 A489 5.50k multi   2.25 1.10
  a. Sheet of 8 + central label 18.00 18.00

Perf. 12½x12¾
1447 A489 12k multi   5.00 2.40
  Issued: 5.50k, 9/9; 12k, 10/27.

Children
Playing
in Snow
A490

Designs: 5.50k, Child rolling snow into large ball, snowman. 6.50k, Child in snow, child sledding. 8k, Child throwing snowball at two children. 9k, Two children making snow angels.

2009, Oct. 27   Litho.   Perf. 12½x12¾
1448 A490   Sheet of 4   12.50 12.50
  a. 5.50k multi   2.25 1.10
  b. 6.50k multi   2.60 1.40
  c. 8k multi   3.25 1.60
  d. 9k multi   3.75 1.90

Self-Adhesive
Die Cut Perf. 13x13½
1449 A490 5.50k multi   2.40 1.10
  a. Booklet pane of 12   29.00
1450 A490 6.50k multi   2.75 1.40
  a. Booklet pane of 12   33.00
1451 A490   8k multi   3.25 1.60
1452 A490   9k multi   3.75 1.90
  a. Sheet of 8, 2 each #1449-
    1452   25.00
  Nos. 1449-1452 (4)   12.15 6.00

Nos. 1449a and 1450a each exist with six different booklet covers.

Flora and Fauna — A491

Designs: 8.50k, Bufo calamita. 9.50k, Lycaena phlaeas. 12.50k, Alauda arvensis. 18.50k, Astragalus danicus.

2010, Jan. 2   Litho.   Perf. 12¼
1453   Souvenir sheet of 4   19.00 19.00
  a. A491 8.50k multi   3.25 1.60
  b. A491 9.50k multi   3.50 1.75
  c. A491 12.50k multi   4.75 2.40
  d. A491 18.50k multi   7.00 3.50

Self-Adhesive
Die Cut Perf. 13x13½
1454 A491 8.50k multi   3.25 1.60
1455 A491 9.50k multi   3.50 1.75
1456 A491 12.50k multi   5.00 2.40
1457 A491 18.50k multi   7.00 3.50
  Nos. 1454-1457 (4)   18.75 9.25

Queen Margrethe
II — A492

Die Cut Perf. 13
2010, Feb. 10   Litho. & Engr.
Self-Adhesive
Panel Color
1458 A492 5.50k red   2.25 1.00
1459 A492 6.50k Prus blue   2.60 1.25
  a. Booklet pane of 10   26.00
1460 A492 8.50k yel green   3.25 1.60
1461 A492 9.50k dark blue   3.75 1.75
  a. Miniature sheet of 8, 2 each
    #1458-1461   25.00
  Nos. 1458-1461 (4)   11.85 5.60

No. 1458 was issued in coils as well as sheets. Every fifth coil stamp has a control number printed on the backing paper.

No. 1461a sold for 99k. See Nos. 1516-1519, 1574-1575, 1619-1620, 1635, 1665-1666, 1697-1700.

Issued: No. 1459a, 1/2/14.

Queen Margrethe
II and
Family — A493

Die Cut Perf. 13¼
2010, Mar. 24   Litho. & Engr.
Self-Adhesive
1462 A493 5.50k multi   2.25 2.00
  a. Booklet pane of 12   27.00

Queen Margrethe II, 70th birthday.

Ribe, 1300th
Anniv. — A494

Designs: 5.50k, Ribe Cathedral. 6.50k, Statue of Queen Dagmar.

2010, Mar. 24   Engr.
1463 A494 5.50k black   2.25 1.00
1464 A494 6.50k black   2.40 1.25
  a. Booklet pane of 12   29.00
  b. Miniature sheet of 6, 3 each
    #1463-1464   16.00

Nordic
Coastlines — A495

Designs: 5.50k, Ship at Lindo Shipyard. 8.50k, Crane, Port of Aarhus.

Perf. 12¼x12½
2010, Mar. 24   Litho.
1465   Sheet of 2   5.50 6.00
  a. A495 5.50k multi   2.00 1.00
  b. A495 8.50k multi   3.25 1.60

Self-Adhesive
Die Cut Perf. 13¼
1466 A495 5.50k multi   2.00 1.00
1467 A495 8.50k multi   3.25 1.60

**Wavy Lines Type of 1905 and Small
State Seal Type of 1946**

2010   Engr.   Die Cut Perf. 13
Self-Adhesive
1468 A10   50o brown   .25 .25
1469 A10 100o blue   .40 .25
1470 A10 200o dark green   .75 .25
1471 A10 300o orange   1.20 .25
1472 A10 400o purple   1.60 .35
1473 A10 500o green   1.90 .45
1474 A55   10k lemon   3.75 .80
1475 A55   15k lilac   5.50 1.25
1476 A55   20k dark blue   7.50 1.60
1477 A55   30k red brown   11.50 2.75
1478 A55   50k red   18.00 4.00
  Nos. 1468-1478 (11)   52.35 12.20

Issued: 50o, 100o, 200o, 500o, 4/28; 300o, 400o, 30k, 3/24; 10k, 15k, 20k, 50k, 6/1.
Nos. 1474, 1476, 1478 were reissued in slightly different shades Mar. 10, 2014. No. 1476 was reissued Dec. 17, 2015. No. 1478 was reissued Oct. 1, 2016 in a pinker shade.

Album Cover for Gasolin' 3, by Gasolin' — A496

Die Cut Perf. 13½x13¼
2010, Apr. 28   **Litho.**
Self-Adhesive
1479	A496 5.50k multi		2.25	1.50
a.	Booklet pane of 12		27.00	
b.	Sheet of 4		19.00	15.00

Klampenborg Racetrack, Cent. — A497

Designs: 5.50k, Horses at finish line. 24k, Spectators watching race.

2010, June 1   **Self-Adhesive**
1480	A497 5.50k multi		2.25	1.10
1481	A497 24k multi		9.25	4.50

Europa — A498

Children's book characters: 5.50k, Sporge-Jorgen. 8.50k, Orla Fro-Snapper, horiz.

Die Cut Perf. 13¼x13½
2010, June 1
Self-Adhesive
1482	A498 5.50k multi		2.10	1.00
a.	Sheet of 8		18.00	

Die Cut Perf. 13½x13¼
1483	A498 8.50k multi		3.25	2.00

Booklet Stamp
Serpentine Die Cut 13½
1484	A498 5.50k multi		8.00	3.50
a.	Booklet pane of 12		96.00	
b.	Serpentine Die Cut 10		8.00	3.50
c.	Booklet pane of 12 #1484b		96.00	

Royal Danish Navy, 500th Anniv. — A499

Designs: 5.50k, Frigate Iver Huitfeldt. 6.50k, Artillery ship Niels Iuel. 8.50k, Ironclad warship Todenskjold. 9.50k, Screw frigate Jylland. 16k, Caravel Maria.

Die Cut Perf. 13¼x13
2010, June 1   **Litho. & Engr.**
Self-Adhesive (#1485-1489, 1491-1495)
1485	A499 5.50k red & black		2.00	.90
1486	A499 6.50k red & black		2.50	1.10
a.	Booklet pane of 12		25.00	
1487	A499 8.50k red & black		3.25	1.40
1488	A499 9.50k red & black		4.00	1.60
1489	A499 16k red & black		6.25	2.60
	Nos. 1485-1489 (5)		18.00	7.60

Booklet Stamps
Perf. 12¼x12½
1490	Booklet pane of 5		30.00	
a.	A499 5.50k red & black		3.00	2.60
b.	A499 6.50k red & black		3.75	3.00
c.	A499 8.50k red & black		5.25	4.25
d.	A499 9.50k red & black		5.75	4.75
e.	A499 16k red & black		9.50	7.75

Booklet Panes of 1
Serpentine Die Cut 13¼x13½
1491	A499 5.50k red & black		3.25	2.75
1492	A499 6.50k red & black		4.00	3.50
1493	A499 8.50k red & black		5.50	4.75
1494	A499 9.50k red & black		6.25	5.00
1495	A499 16k red & black		10.00	8.00
	Complete booklet, #1490-1495		60.00	
	Nos. 1491-1495 (5)		29.00	23.75

Complete booklet sold for 139k.

Greetings A500

Die Cut Perf. 13x13¼
2010, June 1   **Litho.**
Self-Adhesive
1496	A500 5.50k Heart		2.25	.90
1497	A500 5.50k Danish Flag		2.25	.90
1498	A500 5.50k "Tillykke"		2.25	.90
1499	A500 5.50k Gift		2.25	.90
1500	A500 5.50k Flower		2.25	.90
a.	Sheet of 10, 2 each #1496-1500		22.50	
	Nos. 1496-1500 (5)		11.25	4.50

The right third of Nos. 1496-1500 has straight-edged die cutting. See Nos. 1552-1556.

A501

A502

A503

A504

A505

A506

A507

A508

A509

Post Danmark Rundt Bicycle Race A510

2010, Aug. 4   Die Cut Perf. 13x13¼
1501	Sheet of 10		65.00	
a.	A501 5.50k multi		6.50	3.25
b.	A502 5.50k multi		6.50	3.25
c.	A503 5.50k multi		6.50	3.25
d.	A504 5.50k multi		6.50	3.25
e.	A505 5.50k multi		6.50	3.25
f.	A506 5.50k multi		6.50	3.25
g.	A507 5.50k multi		6.50	3.25
h.	A508 5.50k multi		6.50	3.25
i.	A509 5.50k multi		6.50	3.25
j.	A510 5.50k multi		6.50	3.25

The right third of Nos. 1501a-1501j has straight-edged die cutting.

Famous Men Type of 2007

Designs: 5.50k, Dan Turèll (1946-93), writer, and lines from poem. 6.50k, Tove Ditlevsen (1917-76), poet, and her childhood home. 9.50k, Henry Heerup (1907-93), and "Love in the Coffee Pot." 12.50k, Dea Trier Morch (1941-2001), writer and artist, and illustation from her novel, *Winter's Child.*

Die Cut Perf. 13½x12¾
2010, Aug. 25   **Litho. & Engr.**
Self-Adhesive
1502	A472 5.50k multi		2.25	.80
a.	Souvenir sheet of 8		17.50	
b.	Booklet pane of 12		27.50	
1503	A472 6.50k multi		2.50	1.10
1504	A472 9.50k multi		3.50	1.60
1505	A472 12.50k multi		5.00	3.25
	Nos. 1502-1505 (4)		13.25	6.75

Art — A511

Designs: 5.50k, Two Roses, by Inge Ellegaard. 18.50k, Night Flower, by Kirstine Roepstorff, vert.

Die Cut Perf. 13¼x13½
2010, Aug. 25   **Litho.**
Self-Adhesive
1506	A511 5.50k multi		2.25	1.50

Die Cut Perf. 13½x13¼
1507	A511 18.50k multi		7.25	5.00

Small State Seal Type of 1946
Die Cut Perf. 13
2010, Oct. 26   **Engr.**
With Diagonal Engraving Lines
1508	A55 25k green		9.50	4.75

"Winter Tales" — A512

Designs: 5.50k, Woman on park bench, ducks. 6.50k, Woman on park bench hugging snowman. 8.50k, Woman kissing snowman. 12.50k, Snowman coming to life, dog.

2010, Oct. 26   Litho.   Perf. 12¼x13
1509	Sheet of 4		13.00	6.50
a.	A512 5.50k multi		2.10	1.10
b.	A512 6.50k multi		2.50	1.25
c.	A512 8.50k multi		3.25	1.60
d.	A512 12.50k multi		4.75	2.40

Self-Adhesive
Die Cut Perf. 13¼
1510	A512 5.50k multi		2.10	1.10
1511	A512 6.50k multi		2.50	1.25
1512	A512 8.50k multi		3.25	1.60
1513	A512 12.50k multi		4.75	2.40
a,	Sheet of 8, #1511-1513, 5 #1510		21.00	
	Nos. 1510-1513 (4)		12.60	6.35

Booklet Stamps
Serpentine Die Cut 13½
1514	A512 5.50k multi		5.00	5.00
a.	Booklet pane of 12		60.00	
1515	A512 6.50k multi		5.00	5.00
a.	Booklet pane of 12		60.00	

Queen Margrethe II Type of 2010
Die Cut Perf. 13
2011, Mar. 9   **Litho. & Engr.**
Self-Adhesive
Panel Color
1516	A492 6k Prus blue		2.50	1.10
1517	A492 8k red		3.25	1.50
a.	With "Postnord" printer inscription at LL		—	
1518	A492 9k yel green		3.75	1.75
1519	A492 11k dark blue		4.50	2.10
	Nos. 1516-1519 (4)		14.00	6.45

Issued: No. 1517a, 12/1/15. Nos. 1516 and 1517 were issued in coils as well as sheets. Every fifth coil stamp has a control number printed on the backing paper.

Art — A513

Designs: 8k, Untitled (for Karl Pichert), by Claus Carstensen. 13k, Det Her Sted (This Place), by Lise Harlev.

Die Cut Perf. 13½x13¼
2011, Mar. 23   **Litho. & Engr.**
Self-Adhesive
1520	A513 8k sil & black		3.25	1.60

Litho.
1521	A513 13k multi		5.00	2.50

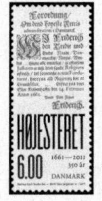

Supreme Court, 350th Anniv. — A514

Designs: 6k, Supreme Court decree of King Frederik III, 1661. 8k, Court and judges.

Litho. & Engr.
2011, Mar. 23   **Perf. 13x12½**
1522	Sheet of 2		5.75	6.25
a.	A514 6k multi		2.40	2.40
b.	A514 8k multi		3.25	1.60

Self-Adhesive
Die Cut Perf. 13x13½
1523	A514 6k multi		2.40	1.25
1524	A514 8k multi		3.25	1.60

Camping — A515

Designs: 6k, Man wearing t-shirt and shorts in front of trailer. 8k, Garden gnome in front of trailer.

Die Cut Perf. 13x13¼
2011, Mar. 23   **Litho.**
Self-Adhesive
1525	A515 6k multi		2.50	1.25
1526	A515 8k multi		3.25	1.60

Serpentine Die Cut 13½
1527	A515 6k multi		2.50	1.25
a.	Booklet pane of 12		30.00	
1528	A515 8k multi		3.25	1.60
a.	Booklet pane of 12		39.00	
b.	Pair, #1527-1528		5.75	
	Nos. 1525-1528 (4)		11.50	5.70

Nos. 1527-1528 were printed in sheets of 8 containing four of each stamp. Sheet sold for 56k.

Europa — A516

Designs: 8k, Caterpillar on branch in spring. 11k, Squirrel, tree in autumn.

Die Cut Perf. 13x13¼
2011, May 4
Self-Adhesive
1529	A516 8k multi		3.25	1.60
1530	A516 11k multi		4.25	2.10

Booklet Stamp
Serpentine Die Cut 13½
1531	A516 8k multi		3.25	3.00
a.	Booklet pane of 12		39.00	

Intl. Year of Forests.

Manor
Houses — A517

Designs: No. 1532, Norre Vosborg, near
Holstebro. No. 1533, Voergaard Castle, Vend-
syssel. No. 1534, Englesholm Castle, near
Vejle. No. 1535, Gammel Estrup, near
Randers.

Die Cut Perf. 13¼x13
2011, May 4   **Litho. & Engr.**
Self-Adhesive

1532	A517	6k multi	2.40	1.25
1533	A517	6k multi	2.40	1.25
1534	A517	8k multi	3.25	1.60
1535	A517	8k multi	3.25	1.60
	Nos. 1532-1535 (4)		11.30	5.70

Arabian Expedition of
Carsten Niebuhr, 250th
Anniv. — A518

Compass rose and: 8k, Niebuhr (1733-
1815), explorer. 13k, Horse-drawn grain mill
from Egypt.

2011, May 4   **Die Cut Perf. 13x13¼**
Self-Adhesive

1536	A518	8k multi	3.50	1.60
1537	A518	13k multi	5.25	2.50
a.	Souvenir sheet of 2, #1536-1537, + label		8.75	

Booklet Stamp
Serpentine Die Cut 13½

| 1538 | A518 | 8k multi | 3.25 | 1.60 |
| a. | Booklet pane of 12 | | 39.00 | |

Paddle Steamer
SS Hjejlen, 150th
Anniv. — A519

2011, June 8   **Die Cut Perf. 13**
Self-Adhesive

| 1539 | A519 | 8k multi | 3.50 | 1.60 |
| a. | Miniature sheet of 6 | | 21.00 | |

Children's
Television
Characters
A520

Designs: 6k, Bruno the Bear and French
fries. 8k, Bamse the Bear and balloons.

Die Cut Perf. 13¼x13
2011, June 8   **Litho.**
Self-Adhesive

1540	A520	6k multi	2.50	1.25
a.	Miniature sheet of 6		15.00	
1541	A520	8k multi	3.50	1.60
a.	Miniature sheet of 6		21.00	

Booklet Stamps
Serpentine Die Cut 13½

1542	A520	6k multi	2.50	2.00
a.	Booklet pane of 10 + 10 etiquettes		25.00	
1543	A520	8k multi	3.50	3.00
a.	Booklet pane of 12		35.00	

Summer Flowers — A521

Designs: 2k, Papaver rhoeas. 6k, Geranium.
8k, Astrantia major. 10k, Papaver nudicaule.

2011, June 8   **Perf. 12x12¾**
1544	Miniature sheet of 4	11.00	11.00
a.	A521 2k multi	.80	.40
b.	A521 6k multi	2.40	1.25
c.	A521 8k multi	3.25	1.60

| d. | A521 10k multi | 4.00 | 2.00 |

Self-Adhesive
Die Cut Perf. 13x13¼

1545	A521	2k multi	.80	.40
1546	A521	6k multi	2.40	1.25
1547	A521	8k multi	3.25	1.60
1548	A521	10k multi	4.00	2.00
	Nos. 1545-1548 (4)		10.45	5.25

Booklet Stamp
Serpentine Die Cut 13½

| 1549 | A521 | 6k multi | 2.50 | 2.25 |
| a. | Booklet pane of 10 + 10 etiquettes | | 25.00 | |

Sketch of
Woman's
Clothing
Designed by
Malene
Birger — A522

Fashion
Accessories
Designed by
Silas
Adler — A523

Die Cut Perf. 13x13¼
2011, Aug. 4   **Litho. & Engr.**
Self-Adhesive

1550	A522	6k black	2.40	1.25
1551	A523	8k multi	3.25	1.60
a.	Souvenir sheet of 2, #1550-1551		5.75	

Greetings Type of 2010
Die Cut Perf. 13x13¼
2011, Aug. 4   **Litho.**
Self-Adhesive

1552	A500	8k Heart	3.25	1.60
1553	A500	8k Danish Flag	3.25	1.60
1554	A500	8k "Tillykke"	3.25	1.60
1555	A500	8k Open envelope	3.25	1.60
1556	A500	8k Flower	3.25	1.60
a.	Sheet of 10, 2 each #1552-1556		32.50	
	Nos. 1552-1556 (5)		16.25	8.00

The right third of Nos. 1552-1556 has
straight-edged die cutting.

International Cycling
Union Road World
Championships,
Denmark — A524

2011, Aug. 4   **Die Cut Perf. 13x13¼**
Self-Adhesive

| 1557 | A524 | 8k multi | 3.25 | 1.60 |
| a. | Souvenir sheet of 6 | | 19.50 | |

Copenhagen
Central Railway
Station,
Cent. — A525

People and: 6k, Station's front. 8k, Clock.
9k, Arches. 16k, Train at platform.

Litho. & Engr.
2011, Sept. 10   **Perf. 13x12¼**
Booklet Stamps (#1558-1561, 1566)

1558	A525	6k multi	6.00	6.00
1559	A525	8k multi	6.00	6.00
a.	Booklet pane of 2, #1558-1559		12.00	—
1560	A525	9k multi	9.00	9.00
1561	A525	16k multi	9.00	9.00
a.	Booklet pane of 4, #1558-1561		30.00	—
b.	Booklet pane of 2, #1560-1561		18.00	—
	Complete booklet, #1559a, 1561a, 1561b		60.00	
	Nos. 1558-1561 (4)		30.00	30.00

Self-Adhesive
Die Cut Perf. 13¼x13

1562	A525	6k multi	2.25	1.25
1563	A525	8k multi	3.00	1.75
1564	A525	9k multi	3.50	2.00
1565	A525	16k multi	6.00	3.00
	Nos. 1562-1565 (4)		14.75	8.00

Serpentine Die Cut 13½
| 1566 | A525 | 8k multi | 3.25 | 3.00 |
| a. | Booklet pane of 12 | | 39.00 | |

The complete booklet sold for 139k.

People in
Winter — A526

Designs: 6k, Bathing Viking. 8k, Woman
feeding duck. 11k, Man walking dog. 13k, Ice
fisherman.

2011, Oct. 25   **Litho.**   **Perf. 12¼**
1567	Sheet of 4	15.00	7.50
a.	A526 6k multi	2.40	1.25
b.	A526 8k multi	3.00	1.75
c.	A526 11k multi	4.25	2.90
d.	A526 13k multi	5.00	3.25

Self-Adhesive
Die Cut Perf. 13x13¼

1568	A526	6k multi	2.40	1.25
1569	A526	8k multi	3.00	1.75
1570	A526	11k multi	4.25	2.90
1571	A526	13k multi	5.00	3.25
	Nos. 1568-1571 (4)		14.65	9.15

Booklet Stamps
Serpentine Die Cut 13½

1572	A526	6k multi	2.50	2.25
a.	Booklet pane of 10 + 10 etiquettes		25.00	
1573	A526	8k multi	3.50	3.25
a.	Booklet pane of 12		42.50	

Queen Margrethe II Type of 2010
Die Cut Perf. 13
2012, Jan. 2   **Litho. & Engr.**
Self-Adhesive
Panel Color

| 1574 | A492 | 12k purple | 4.50 | 3.75 |
| 1575 | A492 | 14k black | 5.25 | 2.90 |

Armillary
Spheres — A527

Designs: No. 1576, Equatorial armillary
sphere built by Tycho Brahe, 1595. No. 1577,
Simplified armillary sphere built by Guo Shouj-
ing, 1276.

Die Cut Perf. 13¾
2012, Jan. 4   **Litho. & Engr.**
Self-Adhesive

| 1576 | A527 | 6k multi | 2.50 | 1.50 |
| 1577 | A527 | 6k multi | 2.50 | 1.50 |

See People's Republic of China Nos. 3980-
3981.

Reign of Queen
Margrethe II,
40th
Anniv. — A528

2012, Jan. 4   **Perf. 13½**
Souvenir Sheet
| 1578 | A528 | 8k multi | 3.00 | 3.00 |

Self-Adhesive
Die Cut Perf. 13¼x13½
| 1579 | A528 | 8k multi | 3.00 | 3.00 |

Bridges — A529

Designs: 6k, Queen Alexandrine Bridge. 8k,
Faro Bridge.

2012, Jan. 4   **Litho.**   **Perf. 13¼**
Souvenir Sheet
1580	Sheet of 2	8.25	8.25
a.	A529 6k multi	3.00	2.00
b.	A529 8k multi	5.00	3.00

Self-Adhesive
Die Cut Perf. 13¼
| 1581 | A529 | 6k multi | 2.10 | 1.40 |
| 1582 | A529 | 8k multi | 3.25 | 2.00 |

Booklet Stamps
Serpentine Die Cut 13½
1583	A529	6k multi	2.10	1.40
a.	Booklet pane of 10 + 10 etiquettes		21.00	
1584	A529	8k multi	3.25	2.00
a.	Booklet pane of 10 + 10 etiquettes		32.50	

Nordia 2012 Stamp Exhibition, Roskilde.

Europa
A530

2012, Mar. 21   **Perf. 14**
Souvenir Sheet
| 1585 | A530 | 12k multi | 4.50 | 4.50 |

Self-Adhesive
Die Cut Perf. 14
| 1586 | A530 | 12k multi | 4.50 | 2.75 |

No. 1586 was printed in sheets of 30.

Sea
Rescue
A531

Designs: 6k, Helicopter and rescue boat.
11k, Helicopter over Copenhagen University
Hospital helipad.

2012, Mar. 21   **Perf. 13½x13¼**
Souvenir Sheet
1587	A531	Sheet of 2	6.50	6.50
a.	6k multi	2.40	1.60
b.	11k multi	4.00	2.40

Self-Adhesive
Die Cut Perf. 13½x13¼
| 1588 | A531 | 6k multi | 2.40 | 1.60 |
| 1589 | A531 | 11k multi | 4.00 | 2.40 |

Scenes From
Tales by Hans
Christian
Andersen — A532

Designs: 2k, The Shepherdess and the
Chimney Sweep. 3k, The Nightingale. 6k, The
Wild Swans. 8k, What the Old Man Does Is
Always Right.

Die Cut Perf. 13½x13¼
2012, June 1   **Litho. & Engr.**
Self-Adhesive

1590	A532	2k multi	1.10	.70
1591	A532	3k multi	1.00	1.00
1592	A532	6k multi	2.10	1.40
1593	A532	8k multi	2.75	1.75
	Nos. 1590-1593 (4)		6.95	4.85

Booklet Stamps
Serpentine Die Cut 13½x13¼

1594	A532	6k multi	2.25	1.50
a.	Booklet pane of 10 + 10 etiquettes		22.50	
1595	A532	8k multi	3.00	1.75
a.	Booklet pane of 10 + sticker		30.00	

Sandwiches
A533   A534

Designs: Nos. 1596, 1600, 1604, Egg and shrimp sandwich. Nos. 1597, 1601, 1605, Rolled sausage sandwich. 8k, Potato sandwich. 16k, Roast beef sandwich.

2012, June 1   Litho.   Perf. 13x13¼

1596	A533	6k multi	4.00	4.00
a.		Booklet pane of 1	4.00	—
1597	A534	6k multi	4.00	4.00
a.		Booklet pane of 1	4.00	—
1598	A534	8k multi	5.25	5.25
a.		Booklet pane of 1	5.25	—
1599	A534	16k multi	10.50	10.50
a.		Booklet pane of 1	10.50	—
b.		Booklet pane of 4, #1596-1599	24.00	—
		Complete booklet, #1596a, 1597a, 1598a, 1599a, 1599b	48.00	
		Nos. 1596-1599 (4)	23.75	23.75

Self-Adhesive
Die Cut Perf. 13x13¼

1600	A533	6k multi	2.00	1.00
1601	A534	6k multi	2.00	1.00
1602	A534	8k multi	2.75	1.40
1603	A534	16k multi	5.50	2.75
		Nos. 1600-1603 (4)	12.25	6.15

Serpentine Die Cut 13½

1604	A533	6k multi	2.10	1.10
1605	A534	6k multi	2.10	1.10
a.		Booklet pane of 10, 5 each #1604-1605 + 10 etiquettes	20.00	
1606	A534	8k multi	2.90	1.75
a.		Booklet pane of 10	27.50	
		Nos. 1604-1606 (3)	7.10	3.95

Complete booklet sold for 139k. Nos. 1604-1606 weree printed in a sheet of 8 containing 3 each nos. 1604-1605 and 2 No. 1606.

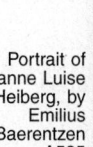

Portrait of Johanne Luise Heiberg, by Emilius Baerentzen
A535

Die Cut Perf. 14x13¾
2012, Sept. 5   Litho. & Engr.
Self-Adhesive

1607	A535	8k multi	3.00	1.75

Heiberg (1812-90), theater actress and director.

Flowers — A536

Designs: 8k, Saponaria officinalis. 12k, Centaurea scabiosa. 14k, Leontodon autumnalis.

Die Cut Perf. 13x13½
2012, Sept. 5   Litho.
Self-Adhesive

1608	A536	8k multi	3.00	1.75
1609	A536	12k multi	4.50	2.40
1610	A536	14k multi	5.25	3.75
		Nos. 1608-1610 (3)	12.75	7.90

Booklet Stamp
Serpentine Die Cut 13½

1611	A536	8k multi	3.00	2.50
a.		Booklet pane of 10	30.00	

Copenhagen Central Post Office, Cent. — A537

2012, Sept. 12   Engr.   Perf. 13x13¼

1612	A537	8k dark red	3.00	3.00

Post Scriptum, by Christian Vind — A538

Die Cut Perf. 14x13¾
2012, Nov. 2   Litho. & Engr.
Self-Adhesive

1613	A538	16k blk & yel org	5.75	4.00

Tree in Winter — A539

Tree and: 6k, Bird and musical notes. 8k, Birdhouse, bird. 12k, Moon, bird on branch of bush.

Die Cut Perf. 13x13¼
2012, Nov. 2   Litho.   Self-Adhesive

1614	A539	6k blue	2.10	1.10
1615	A539	8k dull blue	2.90	1.75
1616	A539	12k blue	4.25	3.50
		Nos. 1614-1616 (3)	9.25	6.35

Booklet Stamps
Serpentine Die Cut 13½

1617	A539	6k blue	2.10	1.10
a.		Booklet pane of 10 + 10 etiquettes	21.00	
1618	A539	8k dull blue	2.90	1.75
a.		Booklet pane of 10	29.00	

Queen Margrethe II Type of 2010
Self-Adhesive
Die Cut Perf. 13
Litho. & Engr.
2013, Jan. 2   Panel Color

1619	A492	12.50k purple	4.75	2.75
1620	A492	14.50k dark gray	5.25	2.75

Kaj and Andrea   Mr. Beard
A540   A541

Die Cut Perf. 13½x13¼
2013, Jan. 7   Self-Adhesive   Litho.

1621	A540	8k multi	3.00	2.50
a.		Sheet of 6	18.00	15.00

Die Cut Perf. 13¼x13½

1622	A541	8k multi	3.00	2.50

Booklet Stamps
Serpentine Die Cut 13½

1623	A540	8k multi	3.00	2.50
1624	A541	8k multi	3.00	2.50
a.		Booklet pane of 10, 5 each #1623-1624	30.00	

Characters on children's television programs.

Fish — A542

Designs: 6k, Clupea harengus. 8k, Gadus morhua. 12.50k, Platichthys flesus. 14.50k, Anguilla anguilla.

Booklet Stamps (#1625-1628, 1633-1634)
2013, Jan. 7   Litho.   Perf. 13

1625	A542	6k multi	3.50	3.50
a.		Booklet pane of 1	3.50	
1626	A542	8k multi	5.00	5.00
a.		Booklet pane of 1	5.00	
1627	A542	12.50k multi	7.50	7.50
a.		Booklet pane of 1	7.50	
1628	A542	14.50k multi	9.00	9.00
a.		Booklet pane of 1	9.00	
b.		Booklet pane of 4, #1625-1628	25.00	
		Complete booklet, #1625a, 1626a, 1627a, 1628a, 1628b	50.00	
		Nos. 1625-1628 (4)	25.00	25.00

Self-Adhesive
Die Cut Perf. 13

1629	A542	6k multi	2.25	1.20
1630	A542	8k multi	3.00	1.75
1631	A542	12.50k multi	4.50	3.75
1632	A542	14.50k multi	5.25	3.75
		Nos. 1629-1632 (4)	15.00	10.45

Serpentine Die Cut 13½

1633	A542	6k multi	2.25	1.20
a.		Booklet pane of 10 + 10 etiquettes	22.50	
1634	A542	8k multi	3.00	1.75
a.		Booklet pane of 10	30.00	

Complete booklet sold for 139k.

Queen Margrethe II Type of 2010
Die Cut Perf. 13
2013, Mar. 4   Litho. & Engr.
Self-Adhesive
Panel Color

1635	A492	16k orange	6.00	5.00
a.		With "Postnord" printer inscription at LL ('16)	—	—

Soren Kierkegaard (1813-55), Philosopher — A543

2013, Mar. 4   Die Cut Perf. 13¼x13

1636	A543	8k multi	3.00	2.50

Electric Postal Bicycle, Europa — A544

2013, Mar. 4   Perf. 13½x13
Souvenir Sheet

1637	A544	12.50k multi	4.75	3.00

Self-Adhesive
Die Cut Perf. 13¼x13

1638	A544	12.50k multi	4.75	2.25

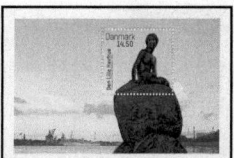

Manor Houses — A545

Designs: Nos. 1639, 1641, Egeskov Castle. Nos. 1640, 1642, Valdemar's Castle.

2013, Mar. 4   Die Cut Perf. 13¼x13
Self-Adhesive

1639	A545	8k multi	3.00	2.50
1640	A545	8k multi	3.00	2.50

Booklet Stamps
Serpentine Die Cut 13½

1641	A545	8k multi	3.00	2.50
1642	A545	8k multi	3.00	2.50
a.		Booklet pane of 10, 5 each #1641-1642	30.00	

The Little Mermaid Statue, Copenhagen, Cent. — A546

Litho. & Engr.
2013, May 27   Perf. 13½x13
Souvenir Sheet

1643	A546	14.50k multi	5.25	5.25

Self-Adhesive
Die Cut Perf. 13¼x13

1644	A546	14.50k multi	5.25	4.50

Danish Rock Music — A547

Designs: Nos. 1645, 1647, Crowd at rock concert. Nos. 1646, 1648, Electric guitar of Kasper Eistrup.

Die Cut Perf. 13¼x13
2013, May 27   Litho.
Self-Adhesive

1645	A547	8k multi	3.00	1.75
1646	A547	8k multi	3.00	1.75

Serpentine Die Cut 13½

1647	A547	8k multi	3.00	1.75
1648	A547	8k multi	3.00	1.75
a.		Booklet pane of 10, 5 each #1647-1648	30.00	
		Nos. 1645-1648 (4)	12.00	7.00

Nos. 1647-1648 were printed in sheets containing 3 of each stamp.

Culture Yard, Elsinore A548

Designs: 8k, Wing of building and reflecting pond. 12.50k, Building entrance and reflecting pond.

2013, Aug. 29   Litho.   Perf. 13x13¼
Souvenir Sheet

1649	A548	Sheet of 2	7.50	4.50
a.		8k multi	3.00	1.75
b.		12.50k multi	4.50	2.75

Self-Adhesive
Die Cut Perf. 13x13¼

1650	A548	8k multi	3.00	1.75
1651	A548	12.50k multi	4.50	2.75

Fifth INDEX: Intl. Design award ceremonies, Elsinore.

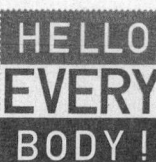

Best Wishes, by Jytte Hoy — A549

Die Cut Perf. 13¼x13½
2013, Sept. 2   Litho. & Engr.
Self-Adhesive

1652	A549	8k multi	3.00	1.75

Scenes from Stories by Hans Christian Andersen — A550

Scenes from: 6k, The Tinderbox. 8k, The Flying Trunk. 12.50k, The Sweethearts (The Top and the Ball). 14.50k, The Little Match Girl.

Die Cut Perf. 13¼x13
2013, Sept. 2   Litho. & Engr.
Self-Adhesive

1653	A550	6k multi	2.25	1.50
a.		Booklet pane of 10 + 10 etiquettes	22.50	
1654	A550	8k multi	3.00	1.75
a.		Booklet pane of 10	30.00	
1655	A550	12.50k multi	4.50	3.00
1656	A550	14.50k multi	5.25	3.75
		Nos. 1653-1656 (4)	15.00	10.00

Christmas — A551

Designs: 6k, Christmas rose. 8k, Skating girl. 12.50k, Robins.

2013, Oct. 29   **Litho.**   **Perf. 13x12¾**
Souvenir Sheet
1657	Sheet of 3	9.75	9.75
a.	A551 6k multi	2.25	1.75
b.	A551 8k multi	3.00	1.75
c.	A551 12.50k multi	4.50	3.75

Self-Adhesive
Die Cut Perf. 13x13¼
1658	A551 6k multi	2.25	1.20
1659	A551 8k multi	3.00	1.75
1660	A551 12.50k multi	4.50	3.00
	Nos. 1658-1660 (3)	9.75	5.95

Booklet Stamps
Serpentine Die Cut 13½
1661	A551 6k multi	2.25	1.20
a.	Booklet pane of 10 + 10 etiquettes	22.50	
1662	A551 8k multi	3.00	1.75
a.	Booklet pane of 10	30.00	

Trade Treaty Between Denmark and France, 350th Anniv. — A552

Map and compass rose with ship at: 8k, Right. 12.50k, Left.

Die Cut Perf. 13½x13¼
2013, Nov. 7   **Litho. & Engr.**
Self-Adhesive
1663	A552 8k rose & blue	3.00	1.75
1664	A552 12.50k blue & rose	4.50	2.75

See France Nos. 4526-4527.

Queen Margrethe II Type of 2010
Die Cut Perf. 13
2014, Jan. 2   **Litho. & Engr.**
Self-Adhesive
Panel Color
1665	A492 9k red	3.75	2.50
a.	Booklet pane of 10	37.50	
1666	A492 18k blue	7.50	4.50
a.	Booklet pane of 10	75.00	

Nordic Cuisine — A553

Aebleflaesk: 6.50k, Raw ingredients (Pig and apples). 14k, Finished dish.

Die Cut Perf. 13½x13
2014, Jan. 2   **Litho.**
Self-Adhesive
1667	A553 6.50k multi	2.50	1.50
a.	Booklet pane of 10	25.00	
1668	A553 14k multi	5.25	2.60

Flowers — A554

Designs: No. 1669, Fritillaria meleagris. No. 1670, Muscari botryoides.

Die Cut Perf. 13¾
2014, Jan. 2   **Litho.**
Self-Adhesive
1669	A554 9k multi	3.50	1.75
1670	A554 9k multi	3.50	1.75
a.	Horiz. pair, #1669-1670 on backing paper without printing	7.00	
b.	Booklet pane of 10, 5 each #1669-1670	35.00	

Nos. 1669 and 1670 were printed in sheets of 6 containing 3 of each stamp.

PH Grand Piano — A555

Die Cut Perf. 13½x13
2014, Mar. 15   **Litho. & Engr.**
Self-Adhesive
1671	A555 14k multi	5.25	3.75

Europa.

General Peter du Plat (1809-64) — A556

Prussian Soldiers at Battle of Dybbol A557

Litho. & Engr.   **Perf. 13x12¾**
2014, Mar. 15
Souvenir Sheet
1672	Sheet of 2 + label	10.50	10.50
a.	A556 9k multi	3.50	1.75
b.	A557 18k multi	6.75	3.50

Self-Adhesive
Die Cut Perf. 13½
1673	A556 9k multi	3.50	1.75
a.	Booklet pane of 10	35.00	

Die Cut Perf. 13x13½
1674	A557 18k multi	6.75	3.50

Battle of Dybbol, 150th anniv,

Chairs — A558

Designs: 6.50k, Three-legged shell chair, designed by Hans J. Wegner (1914-2007). 16k, Spanish chair, designed by Borge Mogensen (1914-72).

Die Cut Perf. 13½x13
2014, Mar. 15   **Litho. & Engr.**
Self-Adhesive
1675	A558 6.50k org & gray	2.40	1.50
a.	Booklet pane of 10	24.00	
1676	A558 16k brn & lt brn	6.00	3.00
a.	Booklet pane of 5	30.00	

A booklet containing perf. 13½x13 stamps with water-activated gum having designs identical to Nos. 1675 and 1676 sold for 139k. The booklet contained a pane containing one example of the 6.50k, another containing one example of the 16k, and another containing one example each of the 6.50k and 16k.

Sailboats — A559

Designs: 6.50k, Laser Radial dinghy. 14k, Hanse 430e yacht.

Perf. 12½x12¾
2014, Mar. 17   **Litho.**
Souvenir Sheet
1677	Sheet of 2	7.75	7.75
a.	A559 6.50k multi	2.40	1.50
b.	A559 14k multi	5.25	2.75

Self-Adhesive
Die Cut Perf. 13x13½
1678	A559 6.50k multi	2.40	1.50
a.	Booklet pane of 10	24.00	
1679	A559 14k multi	5.25	2.60

Princess Benedikte and Scouts — A560

Die Cut Perf. 13x13½
2014, Apr. 29   **Litho.**
Self-Adhesive
1680	A560 9k multi + label	3.50	3.50
a.	Booklet pane of 5 + 5 labels	17.50	

Princess Benedikte, 70th birthday.

Danish School System, 200th Anniv. — A561

Die Cut Perf. 13½
2014, June 11   **Litho.**
Self-Adhesive
1681	A561 6.50k multi	2.40	1.50
a.	Booklet pane of 10	24.00	

Prince Henrik, 80th Birthday — A562

Die Cut Perf. 13½
2014, June 11   **Litho.**
Self-Adhesive
1682	A562 9k multi	3.50	1.75
a.	Booklet pane of 4	14.00	

Den Frie Center of Contemporary Art, Cent. — A563

Die Cut Perf. 13½
2014, June 11   **Litho. & Engr.**
Self-Adhesive
1683	A563 9k multi	3.50	1.75
a.	Booklet pane of 2	7.00	

Manor Houses — A564

Designs: 6.50k, Knuthenborg. 9k, Ledreborg Palace.

Die Cut Perf. 13x13½
2014, June 11   **Litho. & Engr.**
Self-Adhesive
1684	A564 6.50k multi	2.40	1.25
a.	Booklet pane of 10	24.00	
1685	A564 9k multi	3.50	1.75
a.	Booklet pane of 10	35.00	

Guard Hussar Regiment, 400th Anniv. — A565

Die Cut Perf. 13½
2014, Aug. 30   **Litho. & Engr.**
Self-Adhesive
1686	A565 6.50k multi	2.40	1.25
a.	Booklet pane of 10	24.00	

Blank Space for Greetings, by Olafur Eliasson A566

Serpentine Die Cut 10¼
2014, Aug. 30   **Litho. & Engr.**
Self-Adhesive
1687	A566 9k blk & olive	3.25	1.60
a.	Booklet pane of 4	13.00	

The central portion of the stamp is die cut.

Characters from Stories by Hans Christian Andersen — A567

Designs: 6.50k, Klods-Hans (Clumsy Hans) and dead crow. 9k, Tommelise (Thumbelina) and toad.

Perf. 12¾x13¼
2014, Aug. 30   **Litho. & Engr.**
Souvenir Sheet
1688	Sheet of 2	5.75	3.00
a.	A567 6.50k multi	2.40	1.25
b.	A567 9k multi	3.25	1.60

Self-Adhesive
Die Cut Perf. 13½x13
1689	A567 6.50k multi	2.40	1.25
a.	Booklet pane of 10	24.00	
1690	A567 9k multi	3.25	1.60
a.	Booklet pane of 10	32.50	

Manuscripts A568

Designs: 9k, Valdemar's Law of Zealand, 13th cent. 14k, Njáls Saga, c. 1350.

Litho. & Engr.
2014, Aug. 30   **Perf. 13x12¾**
Souvenir Sheet
1691	Sheet of 2	8.25	4.25
a.	A568 9k multi	3.25	1.60
b.	A568 14k multi	5.00	2.50

Self-Adhesive
Die Cut Perf. 13½
1692	A568 9k multi	3.25	1.60
a.	Booklet pane of 10	32.50	
1693	A568 14k multi	5.00	2.50
a.	Booklet pane of 5	25.00	

See Iceland Nos. 1350-1352.

Berries — A569

Designs: 6.50k, Snowberries. 9k, Lingonberries. 14k, Firethorn.

Die Cut Perf. 13½x13¼
2014, Oct. 18   Litho.
Self-Adhesive

1694	A569 6.50k multi	2.25	1.10
a.	Booklet pane of 10	22.50	
1695	A569 9k multi	3.00	1.50
a.	Booklet pane of 10	30.00	
1696	A569 14k multi	4.75	2.40
a.	Booklet pane of 5	24.00	
	Nos. 1694-1696 (3)	10.00	5.00

Queen Margrethe II Type of 2010
Die Cut Perf. 13
2014, Nov. 17   Litho. & Engr.
Self-Adhesive
Panel Color

1697	A492 7k Prus blue	2.40	1.25
a.	Booklet pane of 10	24.00	
1698	A492 10k red	3.50	1.75
a.	Booklet pane of 10	35.00	
1699	A492 16.50k orange	5.50	2.75
a.	Booklet pane of 10	55.00	
1700	A492 19k blue	6.50	3.25
a.	Booklet pane of 10	65.00	
	Nos. 1697-1700 (4)	17.90	9.00

Children's Poems by Halfdan Rasmussen (1915-2002) — A570

Poems from *Halfdans ABC*: No. 1701, Bennys Bukser Braendte (Benn's Trouser's Burned). No. 1702, Kanonkongen Knold (Cannon King Knold).

Die Cut Perf. 13¾x13½
2015, Jan. 2   Litho. & Engr.
Self-Adhesive

1701	A570 7k blue & multi	2.25	1.10
1702	A570 7k dl grn & multi	2.25	1.10
a.	Booklet pane of 10, 6 #1701, 4 #1702	22.50	

Lego Blocks — A571

Blocks of various colors and: 10k, Boy. 14.50k, Girl.

Die Cut Perf. 13½x13
2015, Jan. 2   Self-Adhesive   Litho.

1703	A571 10k multi	3.25	1.60
a.	Booklet pane of 10	32.50	
b.	Sheet of 6 + 20 stickers	22.50	
1704	A571 14.50k multi	4.75	2.40
a.	Booklet pane of 10	4.75	2.40

No. 1703b sold for 70k.

Animals in Wadden Sea National Park — A572

Designs: Nos. 1705a, 1706, Texel sheep. Nos. 1705b, 1707, Black-tailed godwit, vert. Nos. 1705c, 1708, Harbor seals.

Litho. & Engr.
2015, Jan. 2   Perf. 13

1705	Souvenir sheet of 3	9.75	5.00
a.-c.	A572 10k Any single	3.25	1.60

Self-Adhesive
Die Cut Perf. 13¼x13½, 13½x13¼

1706	A572 10k multi	3.25	1.60
1707	A572 10k multi	3.25	1.60
1708	A572 10k multi	3.25	1.60
a.	Booklet pane of 10, 4 #1706, 6 #1708	32.50	
	Nos. 1706-1708 (3)	9.75	4.80

Herlufsholm, 450th Anniv. — A573

Die Cut Perf. 13½x13
2015, Mar. 14   Litho.
Self-Adhesive

1709	A573 10k multi	3.00	1.50
a.	Booklet pane of 10	30.00	—

Inventions — A574

Inventions: Nos. 1710a, 1711, Dry cell battery, by Wilhelm Hellesen, 1887. Nos. 1710b, 1712, Ready-mix concrete truck, by Kristian Hindhede, 1929, horiz. Nos. 1710c, 1713, Long John delivery bicycle, by Morten Rasmussen Mortensen, 1929, horiz. Nos. 1710d, 1714, Writing ball, by Rasmus Mallin-Hansen, 1867.

2015, Mar. 14   Litho.   Perf. 13
Souvenir Sheet

1710	Sheet of 4	12.00	6.00
a.-d.	A574 10k Any single	3.00	1.50

Booklet Stamps
Self-Adhesive
Litho. & Engr.
Die Cut Perf. 13½x13, 13x13½

1711	A574 10k multi	3.00	1.50
1712	A574 10k multi	3.00	1.50
1713	A574 10k multi	3.00	1.50
a.	Booklet pane of 10, 6 #1713, 4 #1712	30.00	
1714	A574 10k multi	3.00	1.50
a.	Booklet pane of 10, 6 #1711, 4 #1714	30.00	
	Nos. 1711-1714 (4)	12.00	6.00

Medal of Merit A575   Order of the Elephant A576

Order of Dannebrog — A577

Die Cut Perf. 13½x13
2015, Mar. 14   Litho. & Engr.
Self-Adhesive

1715	A575 7k multi	2.10	1.10

Booklet Stamps

1716	A576 7k multi	2.10	1.10
1717	A577 7k multi	2.10	1.10
a.	Booklet pane of 10, 6 #1716, 4 #1717	21.00	
	Nos. 1715-1717 (3)	6.30	3.30

A booklet containing perforated examples of Nos. 1715-1717 (three booklet panes containing one of each stamp and one booklet pane containing all three stamps) sold for 199k.

Woman Suffrage, Cent. — A578

Die Cut Perf. 13¼
2015, June 13   Litho.
Self-Adhesive

1718	A578 10k multi	3.00	1.50

Samosvej 8, 2300 Kobenhaven S, Danmark, by Jesper Christiansen A579

Die Cut Perf. 13¼
2015, June 13   Litho. & Engr.
Self-Adhesive

1719	A579 10k multi	3.00	1.50

Copenhagen Carpenters' Guild, 500th Anniv. — A580

Die Cut Perf. 13½x13
2015, June 13   Litho. & Engr.
Self-Adhesive

1720	A580 10k multi	3.00	1.50
a.	Booklet pane of 10	30.00	

Ships A581

Designs: Nos. 1721a, 1723, Georg Stage. Nos. 1721b, 1722, Danmark. Nos. 1721c, 1724, Kobenhavn. Nos. 1721d, 1725, Fulton.

2015, June 13   Litho.   Perf. 13x12¾

1721	A581 Sheet of 4	8.50	8.50
a.-d.	7k Any single	2.10	1.10

Self-Adhesive
Die Cut Perf. 13x13½

1722	A581 7k multi	2.10	1.10
1723	A581 7k multi	2.10	1.10
a.	Vert. pair, #1722-1723, on backing paper without printing	4.25	
1724	A581 7k multi	2.10	1.10
1725	A581 7k multi	2.10	1.10
a.	Vert. pair, #1724-1725, on backing paper without printing	4.25	
b.	Booklet pane of 10, 2 each #1723-1725, 4 #1722	21.00	
	Nos. 1722-1725 (4)	8.40	4.40

Miniature Sheet

25th Post Danmark Rundt Bicycle Race A582

No. 1726: a, Moreno Argentin. b, Jakob Fuglsang. c, Cyclists in Randers. d, Matti Breschel. e, Cyclists on Kiddesvej climb, Velje. f, Fabian Cancellara. g, Cyclists on Storebaelts Bridge. h, Cyclist on Frederiksberg Allé, Copenhagen. i, Mark Cavendish. j, Michael Valgren.

Die Cut Perf. 13x13¼ on 3 Sides
2015, June 27   Litho.
Self-Adhesive

1726	A582 Sheet of 10	25.50	
a.-e.	7k Any single	2.10	1.10
f.-j.	10k Any single	3.00	1.50

Christmas — A583

Honey cakes shaped as: Nos. 1727a, 1728, Man. Nos. 1727b, 1729, Woman. Nos. 1727c, 1730, Heart.

2015, Oct. 17   Litho.   Perf. 12¾x13¼
Souvenir Sheet

1727	Sheet of 3	7.25	3.75
a.-b.	A583 7k Either single	2.10	1.10
c.	A583 10k multi	3.00	1.50

Self-Adhesive
Die Cut Perf. 13½x13

1728	A583 7k multi	2.10	1.10
1729	A583 7k multi	2.10	1.10
a.	Booklet pane of 10, 6 #1728, 4 #1729	21.00	

Size:22x32mm
Die Cut Perf. 12¼x13 Syncopated

1730	A583 10k multi	3.00	1.50
	Nos. 1728-1730 (3)	7.20	3.70

Maribo Cathedral, 600th Anniv. — A584

Litho. & Engr.
2016, Jan. 4   Perf. 13½x13
Self-Adhesive

1731	A584 19k multi	5.50	2.75
a.	Booklet pane of 10	55.00	

Nordic Food Culture
A585   A586

2016, Jan. 4   Litho.   Perf. 13
Souvenir Sheet

1732	Sheet of 2	4.80	2.50
a.	A585 8k multi	2.40	1.25
b.	A586 8k multi	2.40	1.25

Self-Adhesive
Die Cut Perf. 13 Syncopated

1733	A585 8k multi	2.40	1.25
a.	Booklet pane of 5	12.00	
1734	A586 8k multi	2.40	1.25
a.	Booklet pane of 5	12.00	

Souvenir Sheet

Europa A587

No. 1735: a, Hands holding Earth wrapped in leaves. b, Bicylcist, wind generators, paint roller.

2016, Mar. 31   Litho.   Perf. 13

1735	A587 Sheet of 2	15.50	15.50
a.-b.	25k Either single	7.75	3.75

Think Green Issue.

Sports — A588

Designs: No. 1736, Runner in Lillebaelt Half Marathon. No. 1737, Cyclists in Fyen Rundt Bicycle Race. No. 1738, Cyclist in Haervejslobet Mountain Bike Race. No. 1739, Swimmer in Christiansborg Rundt Swimming Race. No. 1740, Bicycle helmet, running shoes, swimming goggles.

Die Cut Perf. 13¼ Syncopated
2016, Mar. 31   Litho.
Booklet Stamps
Self-Adhesive

1736	A588 8k multi	2.50	1.25
1737	A588 8k multi	2.50	1.25
1738	A588 8k multi	2.50	1.25
1739	A588 8k multi	2.50	1.25
1740	A588 8k multi	2.50	1.25
a.	Booklet pane of 10, 2 each #1736-1740	25.00	
	Nos. 1736-1740 (5)	12.50	6.25

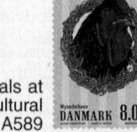

Prize-Winning Animals at Agricultural Shows — A589

Designs: No. 1741, Wyandotte cockerel. No. 1742, Danish Red Holstein cow. No. 1743, Oldenburg stallion. No. 1744, Shropshire ram. No. 1745, Satin rabbit.

Die Cut Perf. 13¼ Syncopated
2016, Mar. 31   Litho.
Booklet Stamps
Self-Adhesive

1741	A589	8k multi	2.50	1.25
1742	A589	8k multi	2.50	1.25
1743	A589	8k multi	2.50	1.25
1744	A589	8k multi	2.50	1.25
1745	A589	8k multi	2.50	1.25
a.	Booklet pane of 10, 2 each #1741-1745		25.00	
	Nos. 1741-1745 (5)		12.50	6.25

Famous Men — A590

Designs: No. 1746, Maersk Mc-Kinney Moller (1913-2012), shipping magnate, and M/S Emma Maersk. No. 1747, Jorn Utzon (1918-2008), architect, and Sydney Opera House.

Die Cut Perf. 13¼ Syncopated
2016, Mar. 31   Litho. & Engr.
Booklet Stamps
Self-Adhesive

1746	A590	19k multi	6.00	3.00
1747	A590	19k multi	6.00	3.00
a.	Booklet pane of 10, 6 #1746, 4 #1747		60.00	

Souvenir Sheet

Art by Trine Sondergaard — A591

No. 1748: a, Interior #12. b, Guldnakke #16.

2016, June 23   Litho.   Perf. 12½
1748	A591	Sheet of 2	15.00	15.00
a.-b.	25k Either single		7.50	3.75

Children's Songs — A592

Illustrations by Bitte Böcher from children's songbook De Sma Synger. Nos. 1749a, 1751, Den Lille Ole Med Paraplyen. Nos. 1749b, 1750, Der Sad to Katte pa et Bord. Nos. 1749c, 1753, Bro, Bro, Brille. Nos. 1749d, 1752, Mors Lille Ole.

2016, June 23   Litho.   Perf. 12¾x13
1749		Sheet of 4	9.75	9.75
a.-d.	A592 8k Any single		2.40	1.25

Booklet Stamps
Litho. & Engr.
Die Cut Perf. 13¼ Syncopated

1750	A592	8k blk & brt grn	2.40	1.25
1751	A592	8k blk & brt org	2.40	1.25
1752	A592	8k blk & brt grn	2.40	1.25
1753	A592	8k blk & brt org	2.40	1.25
a.	Booklet pane of 10, 2 each #1751-1753, 4 #1750		24.00	
	Nos. 1750-1753 (4)		9.60	5.00

Danish Porcelain Designs — A593

Designs: No. 1754, Magestellet (Seagull), 1892. No. 1755, Flora Danica, 1790. No. 1756, Bla Blomst Svejfet (Blue Flower Curved), 1779. No. 1757, Sort Mega Riflet (Black Fluted Mega), 2006. No. 1758, Musselmalet Halvblonde (Blue Fluted Half Lace), 1888.

Die Cut Perf. 13¼ Syncopated
2016, June 23   Litho.
Booklet Stamps
Self-Adhesive

1754	A593	8k multi	2.40	1.25
1755	A593	8k multi	2.40	1.25
1756	A593	8k multi	2.40	1.25
1757	A593	8k multi	2.40	1.25
1758	A593	8k multi	2.40	1.25
a.	Booklet pane of 10, 2 each #1754-1758		24.00	
	Nos. 1754-1758 (5)		12.00	6.25

A booklet containing 11 perf. 12¾x13¼ stamps with the designs of Nos. 1754-1758 and four perforated progressive proofs of the Flora Danica design sold for 199k.

Illustrations of Pixies by Peter Moller (1838-1910) A594

Designs: No. 1759, Pixie carrying baskets of toys and balloon. No. 1760, Pixie dancing with cat. No. 1761, Dog biting pixie's cap. No. 1762, Pixies dancing and playing concertina. No. 1763, Five pixie musicians.

Die Cut Perf. 13¼ Syncopated
2016, Sept. 29   Litho.
Booklet Stamps
Self-Adhesive

1759	A594	8k multi	2.40	1.25
1760	A594	8k multi	2.40	1.25
1761	A594	8k multi	2.40	1.25
1762	A594	8k multi	2.40	1.25
1763	A594	8k multi	2.40	1.25
a.	Booklet pane of 5, #1759-1763		12.00	
	Nos. 1759-1763 (5)		12.00	6.25

Christmas.

Souvenir Sheet

Frederksborg Castle, Hillerod — A595

No. 1764 — Aerial views of: a, Baroque Gardens. b, Castle.

2017, Jan. 2   Litho.   Perf. 13
1764	A595	Sheet of 2	14.00	7.00
a.-b.	25k Either single		7.00	3.50

Shellfish — A596

Designs: No. 1765, Taskekrabbe (crab). No. 1766, Jomfruhummer (lobster). No. 1767, Nordsoreje (shrimp). No. 1768, Blamusling (mussel). No. 1769, Limfjordsosters (oyster).

Die Cut Perf. 13¾ Syncopated
2017, Jan. 2   Litho.
Booklet Stamps
Self-Adhesive

1765	A596	8k multi	2.25	1.10
1766	A596	8k multi	2.25	1.10
1767	A596	8k multi	2.25	1.10
1768	A596	8k multi	2.25	1.10
1769	A596	8k multi	2.25	1.10
a.	Booklet pane of 10, 2 each #1765-1769		22.50	
	Nos. 1765-1769 (5)		11.25	5.50

Heart With Gay Pride Flag Stripes — A597

Heart at: No. 1770, Top. No. 1771, Bottom.

Die Cut Perf. 13¼ Syncopated
2017, Mar. 30   Litho.
Booklet Stamps
Self-Adhesive

1770	A597	8k multi	2.40	2.40
1771	A597	8k multi	2.40	2.40
a.	Booklet pane of 10, 6 #1770, 4 #1771		24.00	

Aarhus, 2017 European Capital of Culture — A598

Buildings in Aarhus: No. 1772, ARoS Art Museum. No. 1773, Moesgaard Museum. No. 1774, DOKK1 Culture Center. No. 1775, The Iceberg Apartment Complex. No. 1776, City Hall.

Die Cut Perf. 13¼ Syncopated
2017, Mar. 30   Litho.
Booklet Stamps
Self-Adhesive

1772	A598	25k multi	7.25	7.25
1773	A598	25k multi	7.25	7.25
1774	A598	25k multi	7.25	7.25
1775	A598	25k multi	7.25	7.25
1776	A598	25k multi	7.25	7.25
a.	Booklet pane of 10, 2 each #1772-1776		72.50	
	Nos. 1772-1776 (5)		36.25	36.25

Souvenir Sheet

Queen Margrethe II and Prince Henrik, 50th Wedding Anniversary — A599

2017, May 15	Litho.		Perf. 13½	
1777	A599	50k gold & multi	15.00	15.00

See Faroe Islands No. 686, Greenland No. 754.

A600   A601

A602   A603

Summer Houses — A604

Die Cut Perf. 13¼ Syncopated
2017, June 15   Litho.
Booklet Stamps
Self-Adhesive

1778	A600	8k multi	2.50	2.50
1779	A601	8k multi	2.50	2.50
1780	A602	8k multi	2.50	2.50
1781	A603	8k multi	2.50	2.50
1782	A604	8k multi	2.50	2.50
a.	Booklet pane of 10, 2 each #1778-1782		25.00	
	Nos. 1778-1782 (5)		12.50	12.50

Automobiles — A605

No. 1783: a, 1960 BMW Isetta 300. b, 1959 Volkswagen 1200 De Luxe. c, 1973 Citroen DS21 Pallas.

2017, June 15   Litho.   Perf. 13x13¼
1783	A605	Sheet of 3	23.50	23.50
a.-c.	25k Any single		7.75	7.75
d.	Booklet pane of 1 #1783a		15.00	—
e.	Booklet pane of 1 #1783b		15.00	—
f.	Booklet pane of 1 #1783c		15.00	—
g.	Booklet pane of 1 #1783c + 4 invalid for postage progressive proofs of #1783		15.00	—
	Complete booklet, #1783d, 1783e, 1783f, 1783g		60.00	
h.	As #1783, with Nordia 2017 emblem and text in sheet margin		23.50	23.50

Complete booklet sold for 199k.
Issued: No. 1783h, 10/27.

A606   A607

A608   A609

A610

Flowers — A610

Die Cut Perf. 13¼ Syncopated
2017, Sept. 28   Litho.
Booklet Stamps
Self-Adhesive

1784	A606	8k multi	2.60	2.60
1785	A607	8k multi	2.60	2.60
1786	A608	8k multi	2.60	2.60
1787	A609	8k multi	2.60	2.60
1788	A610	8k multi	2.60	2.60
a.	Booklet pane of 10, 2 each #1784-1788		26.00	
	Nos. 1784-1788 (5)		13.00	13.00

A611   A612

A613   A614

Art by Bjorn Wiinblad (1918-2006) — A615

Die Cut Perf. 13¼ Syncopated
2018, Jan. 2   Litho.
Booklet Stamps
Self-Adhesive

1789	A611	9k multi	3.00	3.00
1790	A612	9k multi	3.00	3.00
1791	A613	9k multi	3.00	3.00
1792	A614	9k multi	3.00	3.00
1793	A615	9k multi	3.00	3.00
a.	Booklet pane of 10, 2 each #1789-1793		30.00	
	Nos. 1789-1793 (5)		15.00	15.00

A booklet, issued on Sept. 6, 2018, containing 11 perf. 14¼ water-activated gum examples of Nos. 1789-1793 and four progressive proofs of No. 1790, sold for 199k.

Rose Varieties — A616

Designs: No. 1794, Jubilee Celebration. No. 1795, Rhapsody in Blue. No. 1796, Sekel. No. 1797, Ingrid Bergman. No. 1798, Crocus Rose.

Die Cut Perf. 13¾ Syncopated
2018, Jan. 2   **Litho.**
Booklet Stamps
Self-Adhesive
1794	A616	27k multi	8.75	8.75
1795	A616	27k multi	8.75	8.75
1796	A616	27k multi	8.75	8.75
1797	A616	27k multi	8.75	8.75
1798	A616	27k multi	8.75	8.75
a.		Booklet pane of 10, 2 each #1794-1798	87.50	
		Nos. 1794-1798 (5)	43.75	43.75

Souvenir Sheet

A617

No. 1799 — Stamps designed by Yoko Ono: a, Moon and "Dream." b, Sun and "Smile."

2018, Jan. 2   Litho.   Perf. 13¼x13¾
1799	A617	Sheet of 2	17.50	17.50
a.-b.		27k Either single	8.75	8.75

Souvenir Sheet

Great Belt Bridge A618

No. 1800: a, Bridge towers. b, Bridge approach.

2018, May 17   Litho.   Perf. 13¼
1800	A618	Sheet of 2	17.00	17.00
a.-b.		27k Either single	8.50	4.25

Europa.

Souvenir Sheet

Fish A619

No. 1801: a, Esox lucius (75x36mm). b, Perca fluviatilis (25x36mm).

2018, May 17   Litho.   Perf. 13½x13¼
1801	A619	Sheet of 2	17.00	17.00
a.-b.		27k Either single	8.50	4.25

Europa.

Wild Food — A620

Designs: No. 1802, Braende naelde (stinging nettles). No. 1803, Karljohan svamp (Karl Johan mushroom). No. 1804, Japansk pileurt (Japanese knotweed). No. 1805, Skvalder kal (ground elder). No. 1806, Hyben rose (rosehips).

Die Cut Perf. 13¼ Syncopated
2018, Sept. 6   **Litho.**
Booklet Stamps
Self-Adhesive
1802	A620	9k multi	3.00	3.00
1803	A620	9k multi	3.00	3.00
1804	A620	9k multi	3.00	3.00
1805	A620	9k multi	3.00	3.00
1806	A620	9k multi	3.00	3.00
a.		Booklet pane of 10, 2 each #1802-1806	30.00	

Lines and Hearts — A621

2019, Jan. 2 Litho. Die Cut Perf. 13
Booklet Stamp
Self-Adhesive
1807	A621	1k dark blue	.30	.30
a.		Booklet pane of 10	3.00	

Thor's Hammer with Runic Inscriptions A622

Necklace of Glass Beads A623

Buckle in Shape of Ship A624

Valkyrie Figurine A625

Decorative Clip — A626

Die Cut Perf. 13¼x13½ Syncopated
2019, Jan. 2   **Litho.**
Booklet Stamps
Self-Adhesive
1808	A622	30k multi	9.25	9.25
1809	A623	30k multi	9.25	9.25
1810	A624	30k multi	9.25	9.25
1811	A625	30k multi	9.25	9.25
1812	A626	30k multi	9.25	9.25
a.		Booklet pane of 10, 2 each #1808-1812	92.50	
		Nos. 1808-1812 (5)	46.25	46.25

Viking era artifacts.

Danish Flag, 800th Anniv. — A627

Flags and: Nos. 1813, 1818, Christianborg Palace Tower. Nos. 1814, 1819, Birthday cake, horiz. Nos. 1815, 1820, Soccer ball and net. Nos. 1816, 1821, Royal Yacht Dannebrog, horiz. Nos. 1817, 1822, Houses.

2019   **Litho.**   **Perf. 13¼**
Booklet Stamps
1813	A627	10k multi	5.50	5.50
1814	A627	10k multi	5.50	5.50
a.		Booklet pane of 1 + 4 perforated progressive proofs	5.50	—
1815	A627	10k multi	5.50	5.50
1816	A627	10k multi	5.50	5.50
a.		Booklet pane of 2, #1814, 1816	11.00	—
1817	A627	10k multi	5.50	5.50
a.		Booklet pane of 5, #1813-1817	27.50	—
b.		Booklet pane of 3, #1813, 1815, 1817	16.50	—
		Complete booklet, #1814a, 1816a, 1817a. 1817b	61.00	
		Nos. 1813-1817 (5)	27.50	27.50

Self-Adhesive
Die Cut Perf. 13¼ Syncopated
1818	A627	10k multi	3.00	3.00
a.		Coil single on translucent paper	3.00	
1819	A627	10k multi	3.00	3.00
1820	A627	10k multi	3.00	3.00
1821	A627	10k multi	3.00	3.00
1822	A627	10k multi	3.00	3.00
a.		Booklet pane of 10, 2 each #1818-1822	30.00	
		Nos. 1818-1822 (5)	15.00	15.00

Issued: Nos. 1813-1817, 5/16; Nos. 1818-1822, 1/2. Complete booklet sold for 199k.

Lighthouses — A628

Designs: No. 1823, Hammeren Lighthouse. No. 1824, Lyngvig Lighthouse. No. 1825, Hirtshals Lighthouse. No. 1826, Taksensand Lighthouse. No. 1827, Omo Lighthouse.

Die Cut Perf. 13¼x13 Syncopated
2019, May 16   **Litho.**
Booklet Stamps
Self-Adhesive
1823	A628	10k multi	3.00	3.00
1824	A628	10k multi	3.00	3.00
1825	A628	10k multi	3.00	3.00
1826	A628	10k multi	3.00	3.00
1827	A628	10k multi	3.00	3.00
a.		Booklet pane of 10, 2 each #1823-1827	30.00	
		Nos. 1823-1827 (5)	15.00	15.00

Souvenir Sheet

Europa A629

No. 1828: a, Mute swans and chicks (60x40mm). b, Mute swan and chick (30x40mm).

2019, May 16   Litho.   Perf. 13¼x13
1828	A629	Sheet of 2	18.00	18.00
a.-b.		30k Either single	9.00	9.00

Dogs — A630

Designs: No. 1829, Labrador retriever named Audi. No. 1830, Golden retriever named Chivas. No. 1831, Smooth fox terrier named Mille. No. 1832, Icelandic sheepdogs named Píla, Gaia and Blidha. No. 1833, German shepherd named Theo.

Die Cut Perf. 13x13½ Syncopated
2019, Sept. 19   **Litho.**
Booklet Stamps
Self-Adhesive
1829	A630	10k multi	3.00	3.00
1830	A630	10k multi	3.00	3.00
1831	A630	10k multi	3.00	3.00
1832	A630	10k multi	3.00	3.00
1833	A630	10k multi	3.00	3.00
a.		Booklet pane of 10, 2 each #1829-1833	30.00	
		Nos. 1829-1833 (5)	15.00	15.00

Miniature Sheet

Trying to Touch the Sun, by Morten Schelde A631

No. 1834 — Hand with country name and denomination at: a, LR. b, LL, country name on two lines. c, LL, country name on one line, palm visible. d, UL, country name on two lines. e, Left. f, LL, country name on one line, palm not visible.

2019, Sept. 19   Litho.   Perf. 13½
1834	A631	Sheet of 6	18.00	18.00
a.-f.		10k Any single	3.00	3.00

Mammals — A632

Designs: No. 1835, Capreolus capreolus. No. 1836, Erinaceus europaeus. No. 1837, Sciurus vulgaris. No. 1838, Muscardinus avellanarius. No. 1839, Mustela erminea.

Die Cut Perf. 13¼x13½ Syncopated
2020, Jan. 2   **Litho.**
Booklet Stamps
Self-Adhesive
1835	A632	10k multi	3.00	3.00
1836	A632	10k multi	3.00	3.00
1837	A632	10k multi	3.00	3.00
1838	A632	10k multi	3.00	3.00
1839	A632	10k multi	3.00	3.00
a.		Booklet pane of 10, 2 each #1835-1839	30.00	
		Nos. 1835-1839 (5)	15.00	15.00

UNESCO World Heritage Sites in Denmark — A633

Designs: No. 1840, Par Force Hunting Landscapes in North Zealand. No. 1841, Kronborg Castle. No. 1842, Stevns Klint. No. 1843, Jelling Mounds. No. 1844, Christiansfeld.

Die Cut Perf. 13¼ Syncopated
2020, Jan. 2   **Litho.**
Booklet Stamps
Self-Adhesive
1840	A633	30k multi	9.00	9.00
1841	A633	30k multi	9.00	9.00
1842	A633	30k multi	9.00	9.00
1843	A633	30k multi	9.00	9.00
1844	A633	30k multi	9.00	9.00
a.		Booklet pane of 10, 2 each #1840-1844	90.00	
		Nos. 1840-1844 (5)	45.00	45.00

See Nos. 1846-1850.

Miniature Sheet

Queen Margrethe II, 80th Birthday — A634

No. 1845: a, King Frederik IX and Princesses Margrethe, Benedikte and Anne-Marie (21x28mm). b, Princess Margrethe and Prince Consort Henrik on wedding day (21x28mm). c, Princess Margrethe and infant son, Frederik (21x28mm). d, Queen Margrethe II wearing tiara (21x28mm). e, Queen Margrethe II (42x56mm).

2020, Jan. 2   Litho.   Perf. 13x13½
1845	A634	Sheet of 5	21.00	21.00
a.-d.		10k Any single	3.00	3.00
e.		30k multi	9.00	9.00

UNESCO World Heritage Type of 2020

Designs: No. 1846, Par Force Hunting Landscapes in North Zealand. No. 1847, Kronborg Castle. No. 1848, Stevns Klint. No. 1849, Jelling Mounds. No. 1850, Christiansfeld.

2020, May 11   Litho.   Perf. 13¼
Booklet Stamps
1846	A633	30k multi	12.00	12.00
1847	A633	30k multi	12.00	12.00
a.		Booklet pane of 2, #1846-1847	24.00	—
1848	A633	30k multi	12.00	12.00
a.		Booklet pane of 1 + 4 progressive proofs	12.00	
1849	A633	30k multi	12.00	12.00
1850	A633	30k multi	12.00	12.00
a.		Booklet pane of 2, #1848-1850	24.00	—
		Complete booklet, #1847a, 1848a, 1850a	60.00	
		Nos. 1846-1850 (5)	60.00	60.00

Complete booklet sold for 199k.

Souvenir Sheet

Europa A635

No. 1851: a, Post rider. b, Copenhagen and two ships. c, Lutheran Church, Altona Borough of Hamburg, Germany, and ship on Elbe River.

2020, May 11   Litho.   Perf. 13
1851	A635	Sheet of 3	21.00	21.00
a.		10k multi	3.00	3.00
b.-c.		30k Either single	9.00	9.00

Ancient Postal Routes.

Souvenir Sheet

Reunification of Denmark and Part of
Schleswig, Cent. — A636

No. 1852: a, Residents of Aabenraa, 1918.
b, King Christian X on horseback, 1920.

2020, May 11   Litho.   Perf. 13
1852	A636	Sheet of 2	18.00	18.00
a.-b.		30k Either single	9.00	9.00

"What You
Write Is
Yourself"
A637

"Wait to
Send"
A638

"Spread a
Little Joy"
A639

"Who Do
You
Choose?"
A640

"Control Yourself,
Troll" — A641

Die Cut Perf. 13¾x13 Syncopated
2020, Sept. 16   Litho.
Booklet Stamps
Self-Adhesive
1853	A637	10k multi	3.25	3.25
1854	A638	10k multi	3.25	3.25
1855	A639	10k multi	3.25	3.25
1856	A640	10k multi	3.25	3.25
1857	A641	10k multi	3.25	3.25
a.		Booklet pane of 10, 2 each #1853-1857	32.50	
		Nos. 1853-1857 (5)	16.25	16.25

Campaign for courteous writing.

Desserts — A642

Designs: No. 1858, Citrus cake with vanilla
(citruskage med vanilje). No. 1859, Raspberry
pie with pistachios (hindbaertaert). No. 1860,
Chocolate cake with lime (chokoladekage med
lime). No. 1861, Meringue cakes with apricot
and licorice (marengskager med abrikos &
lakrids). No. 1862, Summer layer cake with
rhubarb and strawberries (sommerlagkage).

Die Cut Perf. 13½x13 Syncopated
2021, Jan. 4   Litho.
Booklet Stamps
Self-Adhesive
1858	A642	11k multi	3.75	3.75
1859	A642	11k multi	3.75	3.75
1860	A642	11k multi	3.75	3.75
1861	A642	11k multi	3.75	3.75

1862	A642	11k multi	3.75	3.75
a.		Booklet pane of 10, 2 each #1858-1862	37.50	
		Nos. 1858-1862 (5)	18.75	18.75

See Nos. 1873-1877.

Denmark's Golden
Age — A643

Designs: No. 1863, Ballet dancer from *La
Sylphide*, by August Bournonville (1805-79).
No. 1864, Odin steam locomotive. No. 1865,
Statue of Adam Oehlenschläger in
Sondermarken Park. No. 1866, Acoustic pat-
tern on vibrating plate studied by Hans Chris-
tian Oersted (1777-1851). No. 1867, Thorvald-
sen Museum, Copenhagen.

Die Cut Perf. 13½x13 Syncopated
2021, Jan. 4   Litho.
Booklet Stamp
Self-Adhesive
1863	A643	33k multi	11.00	11.00
1864	A643	33k multi	11.00	11.00
1865	A643	33k multi	11.00	11.00
1866	A643	33k multi	11.00	11.00
1867	A643	33k multi	11.00	11.00
a.		Booklet pane of 10, 2 each #1863-1867	110.00	
		Nos. 1863-1867 (5)	55.00	55.00

Endangered
Butterflies — A644

Designs: No. 1868, Boloria euphrosyne. No.
1869, Carterocephalus silvicola. No. 1870,
Pengaris alcon. No. 1871, Papilio machaon.
No. 1872, Lycaena hippothoe.

Die Cut Perf. 13¼x13½ Syncopated
2021, May 20   Litho.
Booklet Stamps
Self-Adhesive
1868	A644	11k multi	3.75	3.75
1869	A644	11k multi	3.75	3.75
1870	A644	11k multi	3.75	3.75
1871	A644	11k multi	3.75	3.75
1872	A644	11k multi	3.75	3.75
a.		Booklet pane of 10, 2 each #1868-1872	37.50	
		Nos. 1868-1872 (5)	18.75	18.75

Europa (Nos. 1868-1869).

Desserts Type of 2021

Designs: No. 1873, Summer layer cake with
rhubarb and strawberries (sommerlagkage).
No. 1874, Meringue cakes with apricot and
licorice (marengskager med abrikos & lakrids).
No. 1875, Raspberry pie with pistachios
(hindbaertaert). No. 1876, Chocolate cake
with lime (chokoladekage med lime). No.
1877, Citrus cake with vanilla (citruskage med
vanilje).

2021, May 20   Litho.   Perf. 13¼
Booklet Stamps
1873	A642	11k multi	6.50	6.50
a.		Booklet pane of 1 + 4 pro-gressive proofs	6.50	
1874	A642	11k multi	6.50	6.50
1875	A642	11k multi	6.50	6.50
a.		Booklet pane of 2, #1874-1875	13.00	
1876	A642	11k multi	6.50	6.50
1877	A642	11k multi	6.50	6.50
a.		Booklet pane of 2, #1876-1877	13.00	
b.		Booklet pane of 5, #1873-1877	32.50	
		Complete booklet, #1873a, 1875a, 1877a, 1877b	65.00	
		Nos. 1873-1877 (5)	32.50	32.50

Complete booklet sold for 199k.

Miniature Sheet

The Olsen Gang in Jutland, 50th
Anniv. of Movie's Premiere
A645

No. 1878: a, Egon Olsen carrying shovels
(24x30mm). b, Egon, Benny Fransen and Kjell
Jensen drinking beer (48x30mm). c, Benny,
Egon and Kjell on beach (48x30mm). d, Kjell
and Benny with shovels (24x30mm).

2021, May 20   Litho.   Perf. 13¼
1878	A645	Sheet of 4	14.50	14.50
a.-d.		11k Any single	3.50	3.50

Souvenir Sheet

Czesław Slania (1921-2005), Engraver
of Postage Stamps — A646

No. 1879 — Color of portrait: a, Deep blue
green. b, Dark blue.

Perf. 13¾x13¼
2021, Aug. 12   Litho. & Engr.
1879	A646	Sheet of 2	21.00	21.00
a.-b.		33k Either single	10.50	10.50

See Faroe Islands No. 788, Greenland No.

Everyday
Heroes — A647

Designs: No. 1880, Mikkel Madsen, boy
who raised funds for children affected by
COVID-19 with can and bottle deposit money.
No. 1881, Nancy Maati, community volunteer
organizer for Christmas projects. No. 1882,
Leif Framke, rescuer of drowning child. No.
1883, Luni Smil, hospital clown. No. 1884,
Villy Ronn, volunteer for local organizations.

Die Cut Perf. 13¼ Syncopated
2021, Sept. 16   Litho.
Booklet Stamps
Self-Adhesive
1880	A647	11k multi	3.50	3.50
1881	A647	11k multi	3.50	3.50
1882	A647	11k multi	3.50	3.50
1883	A647	11k multi	3.50	3.50
1884	A647	11k multi	3.50	3.50
a.		Booklet pane of 10, 2 each #1880-1884	35.00	
		Nos. 1880-1884 (5)	17.50	17.50

Souvenir Sheet

Reign of Queen Margrethe II, 50th
Anniv. — A648

No. 1885: a, Queen Margrethe II (facing
right) in 1972. b, Royal coat of arms. c, Queen
Margrethe II (facing left) in 2022.

2022, Jan. 3   Litho.   Perf. 14
1885	A648	Sheet of 3	11.50	11.50
a.-c.		12k Any single	3.75	3.75

"Every Bird
Sings With
Its Beak"
A649

"Many Small
Streams
Make a Big
One"
A650

"First Come
First
Served"
A651

"When the
Cat is Out,
the Mice
Play on the
Table"
A652

"Once Bitten, Twice
Shy" — A653

Die Cut Perf. 13¾x13 Syncopated
2022, Jan. 3   Litho.
Booklet Stamps
Self-Adhesive
1886	A649	12k multi	3.75	3.75
1887	A650	12k multi	3.75	3.75
1888	A651	12k multi	3.75	3.75
1889	A652	12k multi	3.75	3.75
1890	A653	12k multi	3.75	3.75
a.		Booklet pane of 10, 2 each #1886-1890	37.50	
		Nos. 1886-1890 (5)	18.75	18.75

Danish proverbs.

Danish Astronomical and
Space
Achievements — A654

Designs: No. 1891, Supernova of 1572 seen
by Tycho Brahe (1546-1601). No. 1892, 1676
observations of eclipses of Jupiter's moon Io
and first determination of the speed of light, by
Ole Romer (1644-1710). c, Brorfelde Astronomical Observatory. d, Andreas Mogensen,
first Danish astronaut, 2015. e, Mars 2020
Mission.

Die Cut Perf. 13¼x13¾ Syncopated
2022, Jan. 3   Litho.
Booklet Stamps
Self-Adhesive
1891	A654	36k sil & multi	11.00	11.00
1892	A654	36k sil & multi	11.00	11.00
1893	A654	36k sil & multi	11.00	11.00
1894	A654	36k sil & multi	11.00	11.00
1895	A654	36k sil & multi	11.00	11.00
a.		Booklet pane of 10, 2 each #1891-1895	110.00	
		Nos. 1891-1895 (5)	55.00	55.00

Souvenir Sheet

Legend of Bonavedde and the
Subterraneans — A655

No. 1896: a, Mermaid with Bonavedde in
womb (24x30mm). b, Ellestingeren, King of
the Subterraneans on horse (24x30mm). c,
Mound of the Subterraneans (48x30mm).

2022, May 19   Litho.   Perf. 13¼x13
1896	A655	Sheet of 3	17.50	17.50
a.-b.		12k Either single	3.50	3.50
c.		36k multi	10.50	10.50

Europa (No. 1896c).

Famous Women — A656

Designs: No. 1897, Nielsine Nielsen (1850-
1916), physician. No. 1898, Anne Marie Carl
Nielsen (1863-1945), sculptor. No. 1899,
Karen Volf (1864-1946), commercial baker.
No. 1900, Nina Bang (1866-1928), education
minister. No. 1901, Inge Lehmann (1888-

1993), seismologist. No. 1902, Bodil Begtrup (1903-87), diplomat. No. 1903, Lis Hartel (1921-2009), Olympic silver medalist in dressage. No. 1904, Inger Christensen (1935-2009), writer. No. 1905, Tine Bryld (1939-2011), writer and radio personality. No. 1906, Natasja Saad (1974-2007), musician.

Die Cut Perf. 13½x13 Syncopated
2022, May 19   **Litho.**

Booklet Stamps
Self-Adhesive

1897	A656	12k multi	3.50	3.50
1898	A656	12k multi	3.50	3.50
1899	A656	12k multi	3.50	3.50
1900	A656	12k multi	3.50	3.50
1901	A656	12k multi	3.50	3.50
1902	A656	12k multi	3.50	3.50
1903	A656	12k multi	3.50	3.50
1904	A656	12k multi	3.50	3.50
1905	A656	12k multi	3.50	3.50
1906	A656	12k multi	3.50	3.50
a.	Booklet pane of 10, #1897-1906		35.00	
	Nos. 1897-1906 (10)		35.00	35.00

Miniature Sheet

Danish Theater, 300th Anniv. A657

No. 1907: a, Theater exterior, seats, stage, curtain, pianist, emblem for rock band Gasolin. b, Stage, drawn curtain, actors, and male dancer. c, Male and female dancers, 1722 poster for a performance, theater exterior. d, Actor in *Jeppe paa Bjerget (Jeppe on the Hill)*, dancer wearing neck ruff, and theater backdrop.

Perf. 13¼x13¾
2022, Sept. 21   **Litho.**

1907	A657	Sheet of 4	13.00	13.00
a.-d.	12k Any single		3.25	3.25

Worldwide Fund for Nature (WWF) — A658

Endangered species: No. 1908, Kongeorn (Golden eagles). No. 1909, Snaebel (Houting). No. 1910, Isfugl (Kingfisher). No. 1911, Eremit (Hermit beetle). No. 1912, Marsvin (Porpoise).

Die Cut Perf. 13¼ Syncopated
2022, Sept. 21   **Litho.**

Booklet Stamps
Self-Adhesive

1908	A658	12k multi	3.25	3.25
1909	A658	12k multi	3.25	3.25
1910	A658	12k multi	3.25	3.25
1911	A658	12k multi	3.25	3.25
1912	A658	12k multi	3.25	3.25
a.	Booklet pane of 10, 2 each #1908-1912		32.50	
	Nos. 1908-1912 (5)		16.25	16.25

SEMI-POSTAL STAMPS

Nos. 159, 157 Surcharged in Red

Wmk. Multiple Crosses (114)
1921, June 17   **Perf. 14½x14**

B1	A20	10o + 5o green	27.50	60.00
B2	A21	20o + 10o slate	30.00	77.50
	Set, never hinged		167.50	

Crown and Staff of Aesculapius — SP1

1929, Aug. 1   **Engr.**

B3	SP1	10o yellow green	4.50	7.00
a.	Booklet pane of 2		27.50	

B4	SP1	15o brick red	9.00	12.00
a.	Booklet pane of 2		32.50	
B5	SP1	25o deep blue	25.00	40.00
a.	Booklet pane of 4		135.00	
	Nos. B3-B5 (3)		38.50	59.00
	Set, never hinged		100.00	

These stamps were sold at a premium of 5 öre each for benefit of the Danish Cancer Committee.

Dybbol Mill — SP2

1937, Jan. 20   **Unwmk.**   **Perf. 13**

B6	SP2	5o + 5o green	.60	1.40
B7	SP2	10o + 5o lt brown	2.25	9.00
B8	SP2	15o + 5o carmine	3.25	9.00
	Nos. B6-B8 (3)		6.10	19.40
	Set, never hinged		13.00	

The surtax was for a fund in memory of H. P. Hanssen, statesman.

Nos. 223a and B6, Nos. 229 and B7, Nos. 238A and B8 are found se-tenant in booklets. For booklet panes, see Nos. 223d, 229b and 238AI.

Queen Alexandrine — SP3

1939-40   **Perf. 13**

B9	SP3	5o + 3o rose lake & red ('40)	.25	.35
a.	Booklet pane of 4		2.00	2.00
B10	SP3	10o + 5o dk violet & red	.35	.25
B11	SP3	15o + 5o scarlet & red	.30	.50
	Nos. B9-B11 (3)		.90	1.10
	Set, never hinged		1.35	

The surtax was for the Danish Red Cross. Nos. 230 and B10 have been issued se-tenant in booklets. See No. 230b. In this pane No. 230 measures 23½x31mm from perf. to perf.

Crown Princess Ingrid and Princess Margrethe — SP4

1941-43

B12	SP4	10o + 5o dk violet	.25	.25
a.	Booklet pane of 10		32.50	
B13	SP4	20o + 5o red ('43)	.25	.25
	Set, never hinged		.60	

Surtax for the Children's Charity Fund.

No. 288 Surcharged in Red

1944, May 11

B14	A48	10o + 5o violet	.25	.25
	Never hinged		.30	
a.	Booklet pane of 10		27.50	

The surtax was for the Danish Red Cross.

> **Catalogue values for unused stamps in this section, from this point to the end of the section, are for Never Hinged items.**

Symbols of Freedom SP5

Explosions at Rail Junction SP6

Danish Flag — SP7

1947, May 4   **Engr.**   **Perf. 13**

B15	SP5	15o + 5o green	.35	.35
B16	SP6	20o + 5o dark red	.35	.35
B17	SP7	40o + 5o deep blue	.85	.85
	Nos. B15-B17 (3)		1.55	1.55

Issued in memory of the Danish struggle for liberty and the liberation of Denmark. The surtax was for the Liberty Fund. For surcharges see Nos. B22-B23.

Princess Anne-Marie — SP8

1950, Oct. 19   **Unwmk.**

B18	SP8	25o + 5o rose brown	.55	.50

The surtax was for the National Children's Welfare Association.

S. S. Jutlandia — SP9

1951, Sept. 13   **Perf. 13**

B19	SP9	25o + 5o red	.65	.60

The surtax was for the Red Cross.

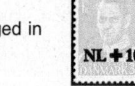

No. 335 Surcharged in Black

1953, Feb. 13

B20	A61	30o + 10o brown red	1.50	1.50

The surtax was for flood relief in the Netherlands.

Stone Memorial — SP10

1953, Mar. 26   **Perf. 13**

B21	SP10	30o + 5o dark red	1.40	1.25

The surtax was for cultural work of the Danish Border Union.

Nos. B15 and B16 Surcharged in Black

1955, Feb. 17

B22	SP5	20o + 5o on No. B15	1.00	.85
B23	SP6	30o + 5o on No. B16	1.00	.85

The surtax was for the Liberty Fund.

No. 341 Surcharged

1957, Mar. 25

B24	A61	30o + 5o on 95o red org	.65	.65

The surtax went to the Danish Red Cross for aid to Hungary.

No. 335 Surcharged in Black

1959, Feb. 23

B25	A61	30o + 10o brown red	.80	.90

The surtax was for the Greenland Fund.

Globe Encircled by Red Cross Flags — SP11

1959, June 24   **Engr.**   **Perf. 13**

B26	SP11	30o + 5o rose red	.50	.50
B27	SP11	60o + 5o lt ultra & car	.75	.75

Centenary of the Intl. Red Cross idea. The surtax was for the Red Cross. Crosses photogravure on No. B27.

Queen Ingrid — SP12

1960, Oct. 25   **Unwmk.**

B28	SP12	30o + 10o dark red	1.00	1.00

Queen Ingrid's 25th anniv. as a Girl Scout. The surtax was for the Scouts' fund for needy and sick children.

African Mother, Child — SP13

1962, May 24

B29	SP13	30o + 10o dark red	.75	1.00

Issued to aid underdeveloped countries.

Healthy and Crippled Hands — SP14

1963, June 24   **Perf. 13**

B30	SP14	35o + 10o dark red	1.10	1.10
a.	Fluorescent paper		1.10	1.10

The surtax was for the benefit of the Cripples' Foundation.

Old Bridge at Danish-German Border — SP15

1964, May 28   **Engr.**

B31	SP15	35o + 10o henna brn	.85	.90

Surtax for the Danish Border Union.

Princesses Margrethe, Benedikte, Anne-Marie — SP16

1964, Aug. 24

B32	SP16	35o + 10o dull red	.85	.75
B33	SP16	60o + 10o dk bl & red	1.10	.95

The surtax was for the Red Cross.

Happy Child — SP17

1965, Oct. 21   Engr.   _Perf. 13_
B34 SP17 50o + 10o brick red   .65   .65

The surtax was for the National Children's Welfare Association.

"Red Cross" in 32 Languages and Red Cross, Red Lion and Sun, and Red Crescent Emblems — SP18

1966, Jan. 20   Engr.   _Perf. 13_
B35 SP18 50o + 10o red   .65   .65
Engraved and Photogravure
B36 SP18 80o + 10o dk bl & red   .80   .80

The surtax was for the Red Cross.

"Refugees 66" — SP19

1966, Oct. 24   Engr.   _Perf. 13_
B37 SP19 40o + 10o sepia   .80   .80
B38 SP19 50o + 10o rose red   .80   .80
B39 SP19 80o + 10o blue   1.60   1.60
     Nos. B37-B39 (3)   3.20   3.20

The surtax was for aid to refugees.

Symbolic Rose — SP20

1967, Oct. 12
B40 SP20 60o + 10o brown red   .50   .55
The surcharge was for the Salvation Army.

Two Greenland Boys in Round Tower — SP21

1968, Sept. 12   Engr.   _Perf. 13_
B41 SP21 60o + 10o dark red   .65   .65

The surtax was for child welfare work in Greenland.

Princess Margrethe and Prince Henrik with Prince Frederik — SP22

1969, Dec. 11
B42 SP22 50o + 10o brn & red   .65   .65
B43 SP22 60o + 10o brn red & red   .65   .65

The surtax was for the Danish Red Cross.

Child Seeking Help — SP23

1970, Mar. 13
B44 SP23 60o + 10o brown red   .65   .65
Surtax for "Save the Children Fund."

Child — SP24

1971, Apr. 29   Engr.   _Perf. 13_
B45 SP24 60o + 10o copper red   .65   .65

Surtax was for the National Children's Welfare Association.

Marsh Marigold — SP25

1972, Aug. 17
B46 SP25 70o + 10o green & yel   .50   .55
Soc. and Home for the Disabled, cent.

Heimaey Town and Volcano — SP26

1973, Oct. 17   Engr.   _Perf. 13_
B47 SP26 70o + 20o vio blue & red   1.00   1.00

The surtax was for the victims of the eruption of Heimaey Volcano, Jan. 23, 1973.

Queen Margrethe, IWY Emblem — SP27

1975, Mar. 20   Engr.   _Perf. 13_
B48 SP27 90o + 20o red & cream   .95   .80

International Women's Year 1975. Surtax was for a foundation to benefit women primarily in Greenland and Faroe Islands.

Skuldelev I SP28

Ships: 90o+20o, Thingvalla, emigrant steamer. 100o+20o, Liner Frederick VIII, c. 1930. 130o+20o, Three-master Danmark.

1976, Jan. 22   Engr.   _Perf. 13_
B49 SP28 70 + 20o olive brown   .75   .85
B50 SP28 90 + 20o brick red   .75   .85
B51 SP28 100 + 20o olive green   .85   1.10
B52 SP28 130 + 20o violet blue   .90   1.60
     Nos. B49-B52 (4)   3.25   4.40

American Declaration of Independence, 200th anniv.

People and Red Cross — SP29

1976, Feb. 26   Engr.   _Perf. 13_
B53 SP29 100o + 20o red & black   .65   .65
B54 SP29 130o + 20o bl, red & blk   .80   .80

Centenary of Danish Red Cross.

Invalid in Wheelchair — SP30

1976, May 6   Engr.   _Perf. 13_
B55 SP30 100o + 20o ver & blk   .65   .65

The surtax was for the Foundation to Aid the Disabled.

Mother and Child — SP31

1977, Mar. 24   Engr.   _Perf. 12½_
B56 SP31 1k + 20o multicolored   .80   .80

Danish Society for the Mentally Handicapped, 25th anniv. Surtax was for the Society.

Anti-Cancer Campaign — SP32

1978, Oct. 12   Engr.   _Perf. 13_
B57 SP32 120o + 20o red   .65   .65

Danish Anti-Cancer Campaign, 50th anniversary. Surtax was for campaign.

Child and IYC Emblem — SP33

1979, Jan. 25   Engr.   _Perf. 12½_
B58 SP33 1.20k + 20o red & brown   .65   .65

International Year of the Child.

Foundation for the Disabled, 25th Anniversary — SP34

1980, Apr. 10   Engr.   _Perf. 13_
B59 SP34 130o + 20o brown red   .65   .70

Children Playing Ball — SP35

1981, Feb. 5   Engr.   _Perf. 12½x13_
B60 SP35 1.60k + 20o brown red   .70   .90

Surtax was for child welfare.

Intl. Year of the Disabled — SP36

1981, Sept. 10   Engr.   _Perf. 12½x13_
B61 SP36 2k + 20o dark blue   1.00   1.10

Stem and Broken Line — SP37

1982, May 3   Engr.   _Perf. 13_
B62 SP37 2k + 40o dull red   1.10   1.20

Surtax was for Danish Multiple Sclerosis Society.

Nurse with Patient — SP38

1983, Jan. 27   Engr.
B63 SP38 2k + 40o multicolored   1.40   1.40

1984 Olympic Games — SP39

1984, Feb. 23   Litho. & Engr.
B64 SP39 2.70k + 40o multi   1.75   1.40

Electrocardiogram Reading, Heart — SP40

1984, Sept. 6   Engr.   _Perf. 12½_
B65 SP40 2.70k + 40o red   1.75   2.00

Surtax was for Heart Foundation.

SP41

1985, May 2   Litho.   _Perf. 13_
B66 SP41 2.80k + 50o multi   1.40   2.25

Liberation from German Occupation, 40th Anniv. Surtax for benefit of World War II veterans.

SP42

Design: Tapestry detail, by Caroline Ebbeson (1852-1936), former patient, St. Hans Hospital, Roskilade.

1985, Oct. 3   Litho. & Engr.
B67 SP42 2.80k + 40o multi   1.40   1.90

Natl. Soc. for the Welfare of the Mentally Ill, 25th Anniv. Surtax benefited the mentally ill.

Danish Arthritis Assoc., 50th Anniv. — SP43

1986, Mar. 20   Litho.   _Perf. 13_
B68 SP43 2.80k + 50o multi   2.25   2.25

Surtax for the Arthritis Assoc.

Poul Reichhart (1913-1985), as Papageno in The Magic Flute — SP44

1986, Feb. 6   Litho.   _Perf. 13_
B69 SP44 2.80k + 50o multi   2.25   2.25

Surtax for the physically handicapped.

Danish Society for the Blind, 75th Anniv. — SP45

Litho. & Engr.
1986, Feb. 20   _Perf. 13_
B70 SP45 2.80k + 50o blk, vio brn & dk red   2.25   2.75

Danish Assoc. of Epileptics, 25th Anniv. — SP46

1987, Sept. 24   Engr.   _Perf. 13_
B71 SP46 2.80k + 50o dk red, brt ultra & dk grn   2.40   3.00

Folkekirkens Nodhjaelp Relief Organization — SP47

1988, Mar. 10 **Engr.**
B72 SP47 3k +50o multicolored 2.25 2.75
Surtax for the relief organization.

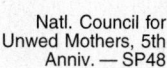

Natl. Council for Unwed Mothers, 5th Anniv. — SP48

1988, Sept. 22 **Photo.**
B73 SP48 3k +50o dk rose brn 2.50 3.25

Salvation Army — SP49

1989, Feb. 16 **Litho.**
B74 SP49 3.20k +50o multi 2.50 3.00

Insulin Crystal — SP50

1990, Aug. 30 **Litho.** **Perf. 13**
B75 SP50 3.50k +50o multi 3.25 4.50
Danish Diabetes Assoc., 50th anniv.

Children's Telephone — SP51

1991, June 6 **Engr.** **Perf. 13**
B76 SP51 3.50k +50o dark blue 2.40 2.75
Surtax benefits Borns Vilkar, children's welfare organization.

Danish Dyslexia Assoc., 50th Anniv. — SP52

Litho. & Engr.
1992, Aug. 27 **Perf. 13**
B77 SP52 3.75k +50o multi 3.75 5.00

YMCA Social Work, 75th Anniv. — SP53

1993, Aug. 19 **Litho.** **Perf. 13**
B78 SP53 3.75k +50o multi 2.75 3.25

Prince Henrik, 60th Birthday — SP54

Litho. & Engr.
1994, June 9 **Perf. 13**
B79 SP54 3.75k +50o multi 2.10 3.00
Surtax for Danish Red Cross.

Natl. Society of Polio and Accident Victims, 50th Anniv. — SP55

1995, June 8 **Litho.**
B80 SP55 3.75k +50o red 1.90 2.75

The AIDS Foundation — SP56

1996, Oct. 10 **Litho.** **Perf. 13**
B81 SP56 3.75k +50o red & black 3.50 2.25

Asthma-Allergy Assoc. — SP57

1997, May 15 **Litho.** **Perf. 13**
B82 SP57 3.75k +50o multi 2.50 2.75

Danish Cancer Society — SP58

1998, Sept. 3 **Litho.** **Perf. 13**
B83 SP58 3.75k +50o multi 2.25 2.50

SP59

1999, Aug. 25 **Litho.** **Perf. 13**
B84 SP59 4k +50o blue & red 2.00 2.25
For the Alzheimer's Association.

SP60

2000, Sept. 27 **Engr.** **Perf. 13**
B85 SP60 4k +50o red & blue 1.60 2.00
For the Cerebral Palsy Association.

Amnesty International — SP61

2001, Jan. 24 **Engr.** **Perf. 12¾**
B86 SP61 4k +50o blk & red 2.25 2.25

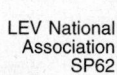

LEV National Association — SP62

2002, Mar. 13 **Engr.** **Perf. 12¾**
B87 SP62 4k + 50o multi, greenish 2.25 2.25

Doctors Without Borders — SP63

2003, Mar. 12 **Litho.** **Perf. 12¾**
B88 SP63 4.25k +50o multi 1.60 1.25
  Booklet, 10 #B88 16.00

Children's Aid Day — SP64

2004, Jan. 14 **Litho.** **Perf. 12¾**
B89 SP64 4.50k +50o multi 1.75 2.10
  Booklet, 10 #B89 17.50

SOS Children's Villages — SP65

2005, Jan. 12 **Litho.** **Perf. 12¾**
B90 SP65 4.50k +50o multi 2.40 2.75
  Complete booklet, 10 #B90 24.00
Surtax was originally intended for an SOS Children's Village in Burundi, but surtax went to the relief fund for Dec. 26, 2004 tsunami victims. A sticker noting this change was to be applied to the front covers of the booklets.

Danish Refugee Council, 50th Anniv. — SP66

2006, Jan. 11 **Engr.** **Perf. 12¾**
B91 SP66 4.75k +50o blk & red, tan 2.75 2.75
  Complete booklet, 10 #B91 27.50

Crown Prince Frederik, Crown Princess Mary, and Prince Christian — SP67

2007, Jan. 10 **Engr.** **Perf. 13x13¼**
B92 SP67 4.75k +50o multi 2.75 2.40
  Complete booklet, 10 #B92 27.50
Surtax for Crown Prince Frederik and Crown Princess Mary's Fund for Charitable and Humanitarian Purposes.

Danish Cancer Society, 80th Anniv. — SP68

2008, Jan. 9 **Engr.** **Perf. 12¾**
B93 SP68 5.50k +50o blk & red 2.50 2.40
  Complete booklet, 10 #B93 25.00

SP69

Design: Prince Henrik, Farm Field, Viet Nam, Emblem of Worldwide Fund for Nature (WWF).

2009, Jan. 7 **Litho.** **Perf. 13x13¼**
B94 SP69 5.50k + 50o multi 2.75 3.25
  Complete booklet, 10 #B94 27.50
Surtax for Worldwide Fund for Nature.

Danish Children's Cancer Foundation — SP70

Die Cut Perf. 13¼x13½
2010, Jan. 6 **Litho.**
Self-Adhesive
B95 SP70 5.50k +50o multi 2.40 2.50
  a. Souvenir sheet of 4 9.75

Booklet Stamp
Serpentine Die Cut 10
B96 SP70 5.50k +50o multi 2.40 2.50
  a. Booklet pane of 12 29.00
  Issued: No. B95a, 8/4.

Eight People — SP71

2011 **Litho.** *Die Cut Perf. 13½x13*
Self-Adhesive
B97 SP71 5.50k+50o blk & red 2.50 2.50
B98 SP71 8k+50o blk & red 3.50 3.50

Booklet Stamps
Serpentine Die Cut 13½
B99 SP71 5.50k+50o blk & red 2.50 2.50
  a. Booklet pane of 10 25.00
B100 SP71 8k+50o blk & red 3.50 3.50
  a. Booklet pane of 10 35.00
  b. Sheet of 6 + 7 labels 21.00 21.00
Surtax for Danish Rheumatism Association.
Issued: Nos. B97, B99, 1/6; Nos. B98, B100, 3/9. No. B100b, 8/4.

Crown Princess Mary — SP72

2012, June 10 *Die Cut Perf. 13x13½*
Self-Adhesive
B101 SP72 8k+50o multi 3.00 3.00
Booklet Stamp
Serpentine Die Cut 13½
B102 SP72 8k+50o multi 3.00 3.00
  a. Booklet pane of 10 + sticker 30.00
Surtax for Danish Heart Foundation.

Crown Princess Mary Type of 2012
Serpentine Die Cut 13½
2012, June 10
Self-Adhesive
Stochastic Litho. Printing
B103 SP72 8k+50o multi 3.50 3.50
The black dots that make up the design on No. B102 are arranged in lines, but are randomly placed on No. B103. No. B103 was printed in sheets of 6.

Girl's Head — SP73

Die Cut Perf. 13x13¼
2013-14 **Litho.**
B104 SP73 8k+1k multi 3.25 3.25
Booklet Stamp
Serpentine Die Cut 13½
B105 SP73 8k+1k multi 3.25 3.25
  a. Booklet pane of 10 32.50
Self-Adhesive
Die Cut Perf. 13½x13
B106 SP73 9k+1k multi 3.75 3.75
  a. Booklet pane of 10 37.50
Surtax for Save the Children charity.
Issued: Nos. B104-B105, 5/27; No. B106, 1/2/14.
No. B106 was printed in sheets of 6. Surtax was for Save the Children charity.

Red Cross, 150th Anniv. — SP74

2014-15   Litho.   Die Cut Perf. 13½
Self-Adhesive

B107	SP74	9k+1k gray & red	3.75	3.75
a.		Booklet pane of 10	37.50	
B108	SP74	10k+1k gray & red	3.50	3.50
a.		Booklet pane of 10	35.00	

Surtax for Red Cross. Issued: No. B107, 6/3; No. B108, 1/2/15.

Worldwide Fund for Nature (WWF) — SP75

Sun, bird and: No. B109. Deer. No. B110, Farmhouse and wind generator.

Die Cut Perf. 13¼ Syncopated
2015, May 7   Litho.
Self-Adhesive

B109	SP75	10k+1k multi	3.25	3.25
a.		Booklet pane of 10, 6 #B109, 4 #B110	32.50	
B110	SP75	10k+1k multi	3.25	3.25

Surtax for Worldwide Fund for Nature. See Sweden No. B63.

WWF Type of 2015

Designs: No. B111, Like #B109. No. B112, Like #B110.

Die Cut Perf. 13½ Syncopated
2016, Jan. 4   Litho.
Self-Adhesive

B111	SP75	8k+1k multi	2.60	2.60
B112	SP75	8k+1k multi	2.60	2.60
a.		Booklet pane of 5, 3 #B111, 2 #B112	13.00	

AIR POST STAMPS

Airplane and Plowman — AP1

Wmk. Multiple Crosses (114)
1925-29   Typo.   Perf. 12x12½

C1	AP1	10o yellow green	27.50	50.00
C2	AP1	15o violet ('26)	70.00	110.00
C3	AP1	25o scarlet	45.00	72.50
C4	AP1	50o lt gray ('29)	130.00	315.00
C5	AP1	1k choc ('29)	105.00	300.00
		Nos. C1-C5 (5)	377.50	847.50
		Set, never hinged	975.00	

Towers of Copenhagen — AP2

Unwmk.
1934, June 9   Engr.   Perf. 13

C6	AP2	10o orange	.75	1.10
C7	AP2	15o red	2.60	5.50
C8	AP2	20o Prus blue	2.60	5.50
C9	AP2	50o olive black	2.60	5.50
C10	AP2	1k brown	10.50	19.00
		Nos. C6-C10 (5)	19.05	36.60
		Set, never hinged	40.00	

LATE FEE STAMPS

LF1

Perf. 14x14½
1923   Typo.   Wmk. 114

I1	LF1	10o green	17.00	5.25
		Never hinged	50.00	
a.		Double overprint	3,000.	

No. I1 was, at first, not a postage stamp but represented a tax for the services of the post office clerks in filling out postal forms and writing addresses. In 1923 it was put into use as a Late Fee stamp.

Coat of Arms — LF2

1926-31

I2	LF2	10o green	13.50	1.00
I3	LF2	10o brown ('31)	9.00	.70
		Set, never hinged	60.00	

1934   Unwmk.   Engr.   Perf. 13

I4	LF2	5o green	.35	.30
I5	LF2	10o orange	.35	.30
		Set, never hinged	1.30	

POSTAGE DUE STAMPS

Regular Issues of 1913-20 Overprinted

Perf. 14x14½
1921, May 1   Wmk. 114

J1	A10	1o deep orange	2.50	7.00
J2	A16	5o green	7.00	7.00
J3	A16	7o orange	4.50	8.50
J4	A16	10o red	30.00	17.00
J5	A16	20o deep blue	22.50	14.00
J6	A16	25o brown & blk	30.00	10.00
J7	A16	50o claret & blk	13.50	8.50
		Nos. J1-J7 (7)	110.00	72.00
		Set, never hinged	300.00	

Same Overprint in Dark Blue On Military Stamp of 1917
1921, Nov. 23

J8	A16	10o red	15.00	20.00
		Never hinged	37.50	
a.		"S" inverted	175.00	240.00
		Never hinged	350.00	

Numeral of Value — D1

Typographed (Solid Panel)
1921-30   Perf. 14x14½

J9	D1	1o orange ('22)	2.00	2.50
J10	D1	4o blue ('25)	3.75	3.25
J11	D1	5o brown ('22)	3.25	2.50
J12	D1	5o lt green ('30)	3.75	2.50
J13	D1	7o apple grn ('27)	18.00	24.00
J14	D1	7o dk violet ('30)	50.00	40.00
J15	D1	10o yellow grn ('22)	4.50	2.25
J16	D1	10o lt brown ('30)	4.50	2.25
J17	D1	20o grnsh blue ('21)	3.50	3.25
a.		Double impression	2,700.	
J18	D1	20o gray ('30)	4.75	5.00
J19	D1	25o scarlet ('23)	4.50	6.00
J20	D1	25o violet ('26)	3.75	7.75
J21	D1	25o lt blue ('30)	7.25	10.75
J22	D1	1k dk blue ('21)	90.00	20.00
J23	D1	1k brn & dk bl ('25)	10.00	18.00
J24	D1	5k purple ('25)	22.50	18.00
		Nos. J9-J24 (16)	236.00	168.00
		Set, never hinged	615.00	

Engraved (Lined Panel)
1934-55   Unwmk.   Perf. 13

J25	D1	1o slate	.30	.30
J26	D1	2o carmine	.35	.30
J27	D1	5o yellow green	.45	.30
J28	D1	6o dk olive ('41)	.45	.30
J29	D1	8o magenta ('50)	2.00	4.00
J30	D1	10o orange	.35	.30
J31	D1	12o dp ultra ('55)	.55	1.50
J32	D1	15o lt violet ('54)	.85	.30
J33	D1	20o gray	.65	.30
J34	D1	25o blue	.75	.30
J35	D1	30o green ('53)	.50	.30
J36	D1	40o claret ('49)	.60	.25
J37	D1	1k brown	.25	.30
		Nos. J25-J37 (13)	8.60	8.75
		Set, never hinged	14.50	

No. 96 Surcharged in Black

1934   Wmk. 114   Perf. 14x14½

J38	A10	15o on 12o violet	6.00	4.50
		Never hinged	18.00	

MILITARY STAMPS

Nos. 97 and 100 Overprinted in Blue

1917   Wmk. 114   Perf. 14x14½

M1	A16	5o green	19.00	40.00
a.		"S" inverted	300.00	375.00
M2	A16	10o red	16.00	27.00
a.		"S" inverted	225.00	375.00
		Set, never hinged	70.00	
		#M1a, M2a, never hinged	975.00	

The letters "S F" are the initials of "Soldater Frimaerke" (Soldier's Stamp). For overprint see No. J8.

OFFICIAL STAMPS

Small State Seal — O1

Wmk. Crown (112)
1871   Typo.   Perf. 14x13½

O1	O1	2s blue	275.00	200.00
a.		2s ultra	275.00	200.00
b.		Imperf	450.00	
O2	O1	4s carmine	77.50	40.00
a.		Imperf	450.00	
O3	O1	16s green	450.00	350.00
a.		Imperf	450.00	

Perf. 12½

O4	O1	4s carmine	6,500.	650.00
O5	O1	16s green	450.00	600.00
		#O1-O3, O5, never hinged	3,575.	

Nos. O4-O5 values are for stamps with defective perfs.

Nos. O1-O3 were reprinted in 1886 upon white wove paper, unwatermarked and imperforate. Value $10 each.

1875   Perf. 14x13½

O6	O1	3o violet	15.00	55.00
O7	O1	4o grnsh blue	18.00	6.25
O8	O1	8o carmine	15.00	2.00
a.		Imperf	—	
O9	O1	32o green	32.50	30.00
		Nos. O6-O9 (4)	80.50	93.25
		Set, never hinged	245.00	

For surcharge see No. 81.

1899-02   Perf. 13

O9A	O1	3o red lilac ('02)	4.50	15.00
c.		Imperf	400.00	
		As "c," pair	1,100.	
O9B	O1	4o blue	3.75	4.50
O10	O1	8o carmine	20.00	26.00
		Nos. O9A-O10 (3)	28.25	45.50
		Set, never hinged	85.00	

For surcharge see No. 137.

1902-06   Wmk. 113

O11	O1	1o orange	2.25	3.25
O12	O1	3o red lilac ('06)	1.50	1.90
O13	O1	4o blue ('03)	3.00	4.50
O14	O1	5o green	3.00	.85
O15	O1	10o carmine	4.50	3.50
		Nos. O11-O15 (5)	14.25	14.00
		Set, never hinged	36.00	

1914-23   Wmk. 114   Perf. 14x14½

O16	O1	1o orange	1.25	2.75
O17	O1	3o gray ('18)	4.50	17.00
O18	O1	4o blue ('16)	30.00	60.00
O19	O1	5o green ('15)	3.00	2.25
O20	O1	5o choc ('23)	7.50	30.00
O21	O1	10o red ('17)	15.00	8.00
O22	O1	10o green ('21)	5.25	6.00

O23	O1	15o violet ('19)	20.00	37.50
O24	O1	20o indigo ('20)	22.50	20.00
		Nos. O16-O24 (9)	109.00	183.50
		Set, never hinged	250.00	

For surcharges see Nos. 185-191.
No. O20 is valued CTO.
Official stamps were discontinued Apr. 1, 1924.

NEWSPAPER STAMPS

Numeral of Value — N1

1907   Typo.   Wmk. 113   Perf. 13

P1	N1	1o olive	20.00	3.00
P2	N1	5o blue	30.00	15.00
P3	N1	7o carmine	18.00	1.25
P4	N1	10o deep lilac	57.50	5.00
P5	N1	20o green	45.00	1.50
P6	N1	38o orange	62.50	2.50
P7	N1	68o yellow brown	150.00	27.50
P8	N1	1k bl grn & claret	37.50	6.00
P9	N1	5k rose & yel grn	225.00	45.00
P10	N1	10k bister & blue	225.00	45.00
		Nos. P1-P10 (10)	870.50	151.75
		Set, never hinged	3,050.	

For surcharges see Nos. 138-144.

1914-15   Wmk. 114   Perf. 14x14½

P11	N1	1o olive gray	18.00	10.00
P12	N1	5o blue	45.00	12.50
P13	N1	7o rose	45.00	3.00
P14	N1	8o green ('15)	45.00	7.00
P15	N1	10o deep lilac	75.00	3.00
P16	N1	20o green	300.00	3.25
a.		Imperf., pair	1,200.	
P17	N1	29o orange yel ('15)	75.00	8.00
P18	N1	38o orange	2,000.	190.00
P19	N1	41o yellow brn ('15)	95.00	5.75
P20	N1	1k blue grn & mar	125.00	3.25
		Nos. P11-P17,P19-P20 (9)	823.00	47.75
		Set, never hinged	3,200.	

For surcharges see Nos. 145-154.

PARCEL POST STAMPS

These stamps were for use on postal packets sent by the Esbjerg-Fano Ferry Service.

Regular Issues of 1913-30 Overprinted

1919-41   Wmk. 114   Perf. 14x14½

Q1	A10	10o green ('22)	20.00	20.00
Q2	A10	10o bister brn ('30)	15.00	8.50
Q3	A16	10o red	45.00	90.00
a.		"POSFFAERGE"	200.00	500.00
Q4	A16	15o violet	20.00	35.00
a.		"POSFFAERGE"	250.00	525.00
Q5	A16	30o orange ('22)	22.50	47.50
Q6	A16	30o dk blue ('26)	4.50	8.00
Q7	A16	50o cl & blk	300.00	350.00
Q8	A16	50o lt gray ('22)	30.00	30.00
a.		50o olive gray ('22)	225.00	450.00
Q9	A16	1k brn & bl ('24)	60.00	30.00
Q9A	A16	5k vio & brn ('41)	3.75	3.25
Q10	A16	10k ver & grn ('30)	80.00	150.00

Engr.

Q11	A17	1k yellow brn	120.00	225.00
a.		"POSFFAERGE"	1,500.	2,600.
		Nos. Q1-Q11 (12)	720.75	997.25
		Set, never hinged	1,750.	

1927-30

Q12	A30	15o red ('27)	27.00	15.00
Q13	A30	30o ocher ('27)	18.00	20.00
Q14	A30	40o yel grn ('30)	27.00	17.00
		Nos. Q12-Q14 (3)	72.00	52.00
		Set, never hinged	180.00	

Overprinted on Regular Issues of 1933-40

		1936-42	Unwmk.	Perf. 13	
Q15	A32	5o rose lake ('42)		.35	.35
Q16	A32	10o yellow org		35.00	35.00
Q17	A32	10o lt brown ('38)		1.50	2.75
Q18	A32	10o purple ('39)		.35	.35
Q19	A30	15o deep red		1.50	2.00
Q20	A30	30o blue, I		4.50	7.50
Q21	A30	30o blue, II ('40)		15.00	32.50
Q22	A30	30o org, II ('42)		.60	1.25
Q23	A30	40o yel grn, I		4.50	7.00
Q24	A30	40o yel grn, II ('40)		15.00	32.50
Q25	A30	40o blue, II ('42)		.60	1.10
Q26	A33	50o gray		1.20	2.40
Q27	A33	1k lt brown		1.40	1.40
		Nos. Q15-Q27 (13)		81.50	126.10
		Set, never hinged		160.00	

Catalogue values for unused stamps in this section, from this point to the end of the section, are for Never Hinged items.

Overprinted on Nos. 284, 286, 286B

		1945			
Q28	A47	30o orange		4.00	2.40
Q29	A47	40o blue		1.90	1.90
Q30	A47	50o gray		2.00	2.00
		Nos. Q28-Q30 (3)		7.90	6.30

Ovptd. on #318, 309, 310, 312, 297

		1949-53			
Q31	A32	10o green ('53)		.65	.50
Q32	A61	30o orange		5.50	2.25
Q33	A61	40o dull blue		4.50	2.25
Q34	A61	50o gray ('50)		24.00	1.25
Q35	A55	1k brown ('50)		2.40	1.50
		Nos. Q31-Q35 (5)		37.05	7.75

Ovptd. on #335, 323, 336, 326, 397

		1955-65			
Q36	A61	30o brown red		2.25	2.25
Q37	A61	40o gray		2.25	2.25
Q38	A61	50o aqua		2.25	2.25
Q39	A61	70o deep green		2.25	2.25
Q40	A55	1.25k orange ('65)		10.00	12.00
		Nos. Q36-Q40 (5)		19.00	21.00

Overprinted on Nos. 417 and 419

		1967	Engr.	Perf. 13	
Q41	A86	40o brown		.65	1.25
Q42	A86	80o ultra		.65	1.25

Nos. 224, 438, 441, 297-299 Overprinted

		1967-74	Engr.	Perf. 13	
Q43	A32	5o rose lake		.60	.50
Q44	A86	50o brown ('74)		.65	.90
Q45	A86	90o ultra ('70)		1.10	1.60
Q46	A55	1k brown		2.50	2.75
Q47	A55	2k red ('72)		2.90	4.25
Q48	A55	5k dull bl ('72)		3.50	4.50
		Nos. Q43-Q48 (6)		11.25	14.50

Nos. Q44-Q45, Q47-Q48 are on fluorescent paper.

Overprinted on No. 541

		1975, Feb. 27			
Q49	A161	100o deep ultra		1.60	2.40

DIEGO-SUAREZ

dē-ˌā-gō ˈswär-əs

LOCATION — A town at the northern end of Madagascar
GOVT. — French colony
POP. — 12,237

From 1885 to 1896 Diego-Suarez, (Antsirane), a French naval base, was a separate colony and issued its own stamps. These were succeeded by stamps of Madagascar.

100 Centimes = 1 Franc

Values for unused stamps are for examples with original gum as defined in the catalogue introduction except for Nos. 6-10 and J1-J2 which are valued without gum.

Stamps of French Colonies Handstamp Surcharged in Violet

		1890	Unwmk.	Perf. 14x13½	
1	A9	15c on 1c blk, *bl*		300.00	100.00
2	A9	15c on 5c grn, *grnsh*		650.00	100.00
3	A9	15c on 10c blk, *lav*		300.00	92.50
4	A9	15c on 20c red, *grn*		650.00	80.00
5	A9	15c on 25c blk, *rose*		130.00	52.50

This surcharge is found inverted, double, etc. See the *Scott Classic Catalogue*. Counterfeits exist.

Ship Flying French Flag
A2

France
A5

Symbolical of Union of France and Madagascar
A3   A4

		1890	Litho.	Imperf.	
6	A2	1c black		1,150.	240.00
7	A3	5c black		1,100.	200.00
8	A4	15c black		210.00	95.00
9	A5	25c black		225.00	110.00

Counterfeits exist of Nos. 6-9.

A6

		1891			
10	A6	5c black		350.00	100.00

Excellent counterfeits exist of No. 10.

Stamps of French Colonies Surcharged in Red or Black

No. 11   No. 12

		1892		Perf. 14x13½	
11	A9	5c on 10c blk, *lav* (R)		210.00	105.00
a.		Inverted surcharge		475.00	400.00
12	A9	5c on 20c red, *grn*		190.00	72.50
a.		Inverted surcharge		450.00	400.00

Stamps of French Colonies Overprinted in Black or Red

		1892			
13	A9	1c blk, *lilac blue* (R)		32.50	20.00
14	A9	2c brown, *buff*		32.50	20.00
15	A9	4c claret, *lav*		55.00	45.00
16	A9	5c green, *grnsh*		120.00	80.00
17	A9	10c black, *lavender*		40.00	32.50
b.		Double overprint		240.00	180.00
18	A9	15c blue, *pale blue*		32.50	20.00
19	A9	20c red, *grn*		40.00	32.50
20	A9	25c black, *rose*		36.00	20.00
21	A9	30c brown, *bis* (R)		1,300.	925.00
22	A9	35c black, *yellow*		1,300.	925.00
23	A9	75c carmine, *rose*		72.50	52.50
a.		Double overprint		400.00	
24	A9	1fr brnz grn, *straw* (R)		80.00	52.50
a.		Double overprint		240.00	210.00

Inverted Overprint

13a	A9	1c		225.00	190.00
14a	A9	2c		225.00	190.00
15a	A9	4c			325.00
16a	A9	5c		240.00	200.00
17a	A9	10c		240.00	200.00
20a	A9	25c		240.00	200.00
21a	A9	30c			1,700.
22a	A9	35c			1,700.

Navigation and Commerce
A10   A11

	1892	Typo.		Perf. 14x13½	

Name of Colony in Blue or Carmine

25	A10	1c black, *blue*		2.00	2.00
26	A10	2c brown, *buff*		2.75	2.75
27	A10	4c claret, *lav*		3.25	3.25
28	A10	5c green, *grnsh*		6.50	6.50
29	A10	10c black, *lavender*		8.75	7.25
30	A10	15c bl, quadrille paper		16.50	11.00
31	A10	20c red, *green*		22.50	16.00
32	A10	25c black, *rose*		17.50	14.50
33	A10	30c brown, *bister*		22.50	16.00
34	A10	40c red, *straw*		27.50	21.00
35	A10	50c carmine, *rose*		45.00	35.00
36	A10	75c violet, *org*		52.50	45.00
37	A10	1fr brnz grn, *straw*		75.00	60.00
		Nos. 25-37 (13)		302.25	240.25

Perf. 13½x14 stamps are counterfeits.

		1894		Perf. 14x13½	
38	A11	1c black, *blue*		2.00	2.00
39	A11	2c brown, *buff*		2.75	2.40
40	A11	4c claret, *lav*		3.25	2.75
41	A11	5c green, *grnsh*		5.50	4.75
42	A11	10c black, *lavender*		7.25	7.25
43	A11	15c blue, quadrille paper		12.00	6.50
44	A11	20c red, *grn*		20.00	13.50
45	A11	25c black, *rose*		12.00	9.50
46	A11	30c brown, *bister*		13.50	6.50
47	A11	40c red, *straw*		13.50	6.50
48	A11	50c carmine, *rose*		20.00	13.50
49	A11	75c violet, *org*		12.00	8.75
50	A11	1fr brnz grn, *straw*		27.50	24.00
		Nos. 38-50 (13)		151.25	107.90

Bisected stamps of type A11 are mentioned in note after Madagascar No. 62.
For surcharges see Madagascar Nos. 56-57, 61-62.
Perf. 13½x14 stamps are counterfeits.

POSTAGE DUE STAMPS

D1   D2

		1891	Unwmk.	Litho.	Imperf.
J1	D1	5c violet		240.00	120.00
J2	D2	50c black		260.00	140.00

Excellent counterfeits exist of Nos. J1-J2.

Postage Due Stamps of French Colonies Ovptd. Like Nos. 13-24

		1892			
J3	D1	1c black		130.00	72.50
J4	D1	2c black		130.00	65.00
a.		Inverted overprint		450.00	300.00

J5	D1	3c black		130.00	65.00
J6	D1	4c black		130.00	60.00
J7	D1	5c black		130.00	72.50
J8	D1	10c black		40.00	32.50
a.		Inverted overprint		460.00	450.00
J9	D1	15c black		36.00	32.50
a.		Double overprint		575.00	500.00
J10	D1	20c black		200.00	135.00
a.		Double overprint		600.00	450.00
J11	D1	30c black		120.00	60.00
a.		Inverted overprint		450.00	300.00
J12	D1	60c black		1,200.	775.00
J13	D1	1fr brown		2,800.	1,500.

DJIBOUTI

jə-'bü-tē

LOCATION — East Africa
GOVT. — Republic
AREA — 8,958 sq. mi.
POP. — 447,439 (1999 est.)
CAPITAL — Djibouti

Djibouti franc (1977)

The French territory of Afars and Issas became the Republic of Djibouti June 27, 1977. For 1894-1902 issues with "Djibouti" or "DJ," see Somali Coast.

> Catalogue values for all unused stamps in this country are for Never Hinged items.

Afars and Issas Issues of 1972-1977 Ovptd. and Srchd. in Black, Dark Green, Blue or Brown

No. 439

No. 440

No. 441

Nos. 442, 447

Nos. 443, 445

Nos. 444, 451

No. 446

Nos. 448, 453

No. 449

No. 450   No. 452

No. 454

No. 455   No. 456

Printing and Perforations as Before

1977				
439	A63	1fr on 4fr (#358;B)	2.50	.25
440	A81	2fr on 5fr (#433;B)	2.50	.25
441	A75	5fr on 20fr (#421;B)	.40	.25
442	A70	8fr (#380;B)	.40	.25
443	A71	20fr (#387;DG)	3.75	1.00
444	A81	30fr (#434;B)	4.00	.80
445	A71	40fr (#388;DG)	5.50	1.25
446	A71	45fr (#389;Bl)	5.50	5.50
447	A78	45fr (#428;B)	8.00	5.00
448	A72	50fr (#394;B)	9.00	2.50
449	A71	60fr (#391;Br)	7.50	2.50
450	A79	70fr (#430;B)	8.50	2.50
451	A81	70fr (#435;B)	6.50	3.00
452	A74	100fr (#418;B)	12.00	4.00
453	A72	150fr (#399;B)	12.00	5.00
454	A76	200fr (#422;B)	6.00	4.50
455	A80	200fr (#432;B)	10.00	10.00
456	A74	300fr (#419;B)	10.00	10.00
		Nos. 439-456,C106-C108 (21)	140.05	77.80

Map and Flag of Djibouti — A83

Design: 65fr, Map and flag of Djibouti, map of Africa, horiz.

1977, June 27   **Litho.**   *Perf. 12½*
457	A83	45fr multicolored	1.50	.85
458	A83	65fr multicolored	2.25	.85

Independence, June 27.

A84

1977, July 4
459	A84	10fr Headrest, horiz.	.35	.25
460	A84	20fr Water cask	.70	.25
461	A84	25fr Pitcher	1.00	.45
		Nos. 459-461 (3)	2.05	.95

Ostrich — A85

1977, Aug. 11   **Litho.**   *Perf. 12½*
462	A85	90fr shown	3.00	.80
463	A85	100fr Weaver	4.50	1.25

Snail — A86

Designs: 15fr, Fiddler crab. 50fr, Klipspringers. 70fr, Green turtle. 80fr, Priacanthus hamrur (fish). 150fr, Dolphinfish.

1977   **Litho.**   *Perf. 12½*
464	A86	15fr multicolored	.65	.25
465	A86	45fr multicolored	1.25	.60
466	A86	50fr multicolored	1.75	.50
467	A86	70fr multicolored	1.75	.60
468	A86	80fr multicolored	2.25	.85
469	A86	150fr multicolored	4.50	1.75
		Nos. 464-469 (6)	12.15	4.55

Issued: 45fr, 70fr, 80fr, 9/14; others, 12/5.

Pres. Hassan Gouled Aptidon and Djibouti Flag — A87

1978, Feb. 12   **Litho.**   *Perf. 13*
470	A87	65fr multicolored	1.50	.50

Charaxes Hansali — A88

Butterflies: 20fr, Colias electo. 25fr, Acraea chilo. 150fr, Junonia hierta.

1978, Mar. 13   **Litho.**   *Perf. 12½x13*
471	A88	5fr multicolored	.50	.25
472	A88	20fr multicolored	.85	.25
473	A88	25fr multicolored	1.25	.75
474	A88	150fr multicolored	5.50	2.50
		Nos. 471-474 (4)	8.10	3.75

Necklace — A89

Design: 55fr, Necklace, diff.

1978, May 29   **Litho.**   *Perf. 12½x13*
475	A89	45fr pink & multi	1.25	.35
476	A89	55fr blue & multi	1.25	.45

Bougainvillea — A90

Flowers: 35fr, Hibiscus schizopetalus. 250fr, Caesalpinia pulcherrima.

1978, July 10   **Photo.**   *Perf. 12½x13*
477	A90	15fr multicolored	.50	.25
478	A90	35fr multicolored	.85	.25
479	A90	250fr multicolored	6.00	.90
		Nos. 477-479 (3)	7.35	1.40

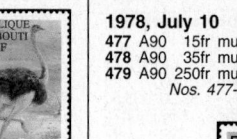
Charonia Nodifera A91

Sea Shell: 80fr, Charonia variegata.

1978, Oct. 9   **Litho.**   *Perf. 13*
480	A91	10fr multicolored	1.10	.25
481	A91	80fr multicolored	4.25	.95

Chaetodon — A92

30fr, Yellow surgeonfish. 40fr, Harlequinfish.

1978, Nov. 20   **Litho.**   *Perf. 13x12½*
482	A92	8fr multicolored	.55	.25
483	A92	30fr multicolored	1.10	.25
484	A92	40fr multicolored	2.75	.75
		Nos. 482-484 (3)	4.40	1.25

Alsthom BB 1201 at Dock — A93

55fr, Steam locomotive 231. 60fr, Steam locomotive 130 and map of route. 75fr, Diesel.

1979, Jan. 29   **Litho.**   *Perf. 13*
485	A93	40fr multicolored	1.25	.25
486	A93	55fr multicolored	1.40	.30
487	A93	60fr multicolored	1.75	.30
488	A93	75fr multicolored	2.25	.40
		Nos. 485-488 (4)	6.65	1.25

Djibouti-Addis Ababa railroad.

Children and IYC Emblem A94

Design: 200fr, Mother, child, IYC emblem.

1979, Feb. 26   **Litho.**   *Perf. 13*
489	A94	20fr multicolored	.50	.25
490	A94	200fr multicolored	4.00	1.10

International Year of the Child.
Nos. 489-490 exist in souvenir sheets of one. Value, set, $20.

Plane over Ardoukoba Volcano A95

30fr, Helicopter over Ardoukoba Volcano.

1979, Mar. 19
491	A95	30fr multi, vert.	1.00	.35
492	A95	90fr multi	3.00	.65

Rowland Hill, Postal Clerks, No. C109 A96

100fr, Somali Coast #22, Djibouti #457, letters, Rowland Hill. 150fr, Letters hoisted onto ship, smoke signals, Rowland Hill.

1979, Apr. 17   Litho.   Perf. 13x12½
493	A96	25fr multicolored	.40	.25
494	A96	100fr multicolored	2.00	.45
495	A96	150fr multicolored	3.00	.70
		Nos. 493-495 (3)	5.40	1.40

Sir Rowland Hill (1795-1879), originator of penny postage.
Nos. 493-495 exist in souvenir sheets of one. Value, set, $50.

View of Djibouti, Bird and Local Woman — A97

Design: 80fr, Map and flag of Djibouti, UPU emblem, Boeing 747, train and mail runner.

1979, June 8   Litho.   Perf. 13x12½
496	A97	55fr multicolored	4.00	.85
497	A97	80fr multicolored	4.75	1.10

Philexafrique II, Libreville, Gabon, June 8-17. Nos. 496, 497 each printed in sheets of 10 with 5 labels showing exhibition emblem.

Solanacea — A98

Flowers: 2fr, Opuntia, vert. 15fr, Trichodesma. 45fr, Acacia etbaica. 50fr, Thunbergia alata, vert.

Perf. 13x13½, 13½x13
1979, June 18
498	A98	2fr multicolored	.25	.25
499	A98	8fr multicolored	.25	.25
500	A98	15fr multicolored	.50	.25
501	A98	45fr multicolored	1.00	.25
502	A98	50fr multicolored	1.25	.25
		Nos. 498-502 (5)	3.25	1.25

Running — A99

Olympic Emblem and: 70fr, Basketball, vert. 200fr, Soccer.

Perf. 12½x13, 13x12½
1979, Oct. 22   Litho.
503	A99	70fr multicolored	1.50	.25
504	A99	120fr multicolored	2.25	.50
505	A99	200fr multicolored	3.75	.75
		Nos. 503-505 (3)	7.50	1.50

Pre-Olympic Year.

Cypraecassis Rufa — A100

Shells: 40fr, Lambis chiragra arthritica. 300fr, Harpa connaidalis.

1979, Dec. 22   Litho.   Perf. 13
506	A100	10fr multicolored	.25	.25
507	A100	40fr multicolored	1.00	.25
508	A100	300fr multicolored	6.50	1.50
		Nos. 506-508 (3)	7.75	2.00

Rotary International, 75th Anniversary — A101

1980, Feb. 19   Litho.   Perf. 13x12½
509	A101	90fr multicolored	2.25	.75
a.		Souvenir sheet of 1 #509	15.00	15.00

Lions Club of Djibouti — A102

1980, Feb. 19
510	A102	100fr multicolored	2.25	.75

Colotis Danae — A103

1980, Mar. 17   Perf. 13x13½
511	A103	5fr shown	.90	.50
512	A103	55fr Danaus chrysippus	3.75	1.50

Chess Players, Knight — A104

Chess Federation Creation: 75fr, Chess Game, Florence, 1493.

1980, June 9   Litho.   Perf. 13
513	A104	20fr multicolored	1.25	.25
514	A104	75fr multicolored	3.25	.35

Cribraria — A105

1980, Aug. 12   Litho.   Perf. 13
515	A105	15fr shown	.75	.25
516	A105	85fr Nautilius pompilius	2.75	.50

Alexander Fleming, Discoverer of Penicillin — A106

Design: 130fr, Jules Verne, French science fiction writer; earth, moon and spacecraft.

1980, Sept. 1
517	A106	20fr multicolored	1.00	.35
518	A106	130fr multicolored	3.00	.60

Capt. Cook and Endeavor — A107

Capt. James Cook Death Bicentenary: 90fr, Ships and Maps of voyages.

1980, Nov. 20   Litho.   Perf. 13
519	A107	55fr multicolored	1.40	.65
520	A107	90fr multicolored	2.25	.90

Souvenir sheets of 1 exist, perf. 12½x12. Value, each $10.

Angel Fish — A108

1981, Apr. 13   Litho.   Perf. 12½
521	A108	25fr shown	1.75	.25
522	A108	55fr Moorish idol	3.25	.50
523	A108	70fr Scad	3.75	1.50
		Nos. 521-523 (3)	8.75	2.25

13th World Telecommunications Day — A109

1981, May 17   Litho.   Perf. 13
524	A109	140fr multicolored	2.75	.70

Type 231 Steam Locomotive, Germany, 1958 and Amtrak, US, 1980 — A110

Locomotives: 55fr, Stephenson and his Rocket, Djibouti Railways 230 engine. 65fr, Type TGV, France, Type 962, Japan.

1981, June 9   Litho.   Perf. 13
525	A110	40fr multicolored	1.50	.30
526	A110	55fr multicolored	2.00	.35
527	A110	65fr multicolored	2.50	.40
		Nos. 525-527 (3)	6.00	1.05

Radio Amateurs Club — A111

1981, June 25
528	A111	250fr multicolored	5.00	1.00

Prince Charles and Lady Diana — A112

1981, June 29
529	A112	180fr shown	2.50	.75
530	A112	200fr Couple, diff.	3.00	1.00

Royal Wedding.
Nos. 529-530 exist in souvenir sheets of one. Value, set, $30.

Lord Nelson and Victory — A113

1981, July 6   Litho.   Perf. 13x12½
531	A113	100fr multicolored	1.90	.45
532	A113	175fr multicolored	3.25	.90

Lord Horatio Nelson (1758-1805).

Scout Tending Campfire — A114

Design: 105fr, Scout giving sign.

1981, July 16   Litho.   Perf. 13
533	A114	60fr shown	3.00	.70
534	A114	105fr multicolored	3.75	.80

28th World Scouting Conference, Dakar, Aug. (60fr); 4th Pan-African Scouting Conference, Abidjan, Aug. (105fr).

Pawn and Queen, Swedish Bone Chess Pieces, 13th Cent. — A115

130fr, Pawn, knight, Chinese, 19th cent., vert.

1981, Oct. 15   Litho.   Perf. 13
535	A115	50fr shown	1.50	.35
536	A115	130fr multicolored	3.00	.85

For overprints see Nos. 542-543.

Sheraton Hotel Opening — A116

1981, Nov. 15   Litho.   Perf. 13x12½
537	A116	75fr multicolored	1.50	.45

For surcharge see No. 623.

Acacia Mellifera — A117

Designs: 10fr, Clitoria ternatea, vert. 35fr, Punica granatum. 45fr, Malvaceous plant, vert.

1981, Dec. 21   Perf. 13
538	A117	10fr multicolored	.40	.25
539	A117	30fr shown	.80	.25
540	A117	35fr multicolored	1.15	.25
541	A117	45fr multicolored	1.40	.30
		Nos. 538-541 (4)	3.75	1.05

See Nos. 558-560.

Nos. 535-536 Overprinted

1981, Dec.   Litho.   Perf. 13
542	A115	50fr multicolored	2.00	.50
543	A115	130fr multicolored	4.00	1.00

World Chess Championship.

TB Bacillus Centenary — A117a

Design: Koch, slide, microscope.

1982, Mar. 24   Litho.   Perf. 13
544	A117a	305fr multicolored	7.00	1.50

A117b

Designs: 125fr, Ivory bishop. 175fr, Queen, pawn, 19th cent.

1982, Apr. 8   **Litho.**   **Perf. 13**
545 A117b 125fr multi   3.50 .75
546 A117b 175fr multi   4.25 1.25
1982 World Chess Championship.

A118

1982, May 17
547 A118 150fr multicolored   3.00 .85
14th World Telecommunications Day.
For surcharge see No. 647.

Bus and Jeep
A119

1982, July 27   **Litho.**   **Perf. 13**
548 A119 20fr shown   .55 .25
549 A119 25fr Dhow, ferry   .70 .25
550 A119 55fr Train, jet   1.50 .45
    Nos. 548-550 (3)   2.75 .95
Nos. 548-550 exist in souvenir sheets of one. Value, set, $25.

Shells from the Red Sea — A120

10fr, Cypraea erythraeensis. 15fr, Conus sumatrensis. 25fr, Cypraea pulchra. 30fr, Conus inscriptus. 70fr, Casmaria ponderosa. 150fr, Cypraea exusta.

1982, Nov. 20   **Litho.**   **Perf. 12½**
551 A120 10fr multicolored   .45 .25
552 A120 15fr multicolored   .75 .30
553 A120 25fr multicolored   .90 .35
554 A120 30fr multicolored   1.10 .40
555 A120 70fr multicolored   2.25 .50
556 A120 150fr multicolored   4.50 1.50
   a.   Strip of 6, #551-556   9.95 3.30
    Nos. 551-556 (6)   9.95 3.30
See Nos. 563-567.

Intl. Palestinian Solidarity Day — A121

1982, Nov. 29   **Litho.**   **Perf. 13**
557 A121 40fr multicolored   1.00 .25

Local Flowers type of 1981
Various flowers. 5fr, 55fr, vert.

1983, Apr. 14   **Litho.**   **Perf. 13**
558 A117 5fr multicolored   .25 .25
559 A117 55fr multicolored   1.25 .40
560 A117 55fr multicolored   1.40 .40
    Nos. 558-560 (3)   2.90 1.05

World Communications Year — A123

1983, June 20   **Litho.**   **Perf. 13**
561 A123 500fr multicolored   9.00 2.25

Conference of Donors, Nov. 21-23
A124

1983, Nov. 21   **Litho.**   **Perf. 13x12½**
562 A124 75fr multicolored   1.50 .40

Shell Type of 1982
15fr, Marginella obtusa. 30fr, Conus jickelli. 55fr, Cypraea macandrewi. 80fr, Conus cuvieri. 100fr, Turbo petholatus.

1983, Dec. 20   **Litho.**   **Perf. 12½**
563 A120 15fr multicolored   .50 .25
564 A120 30fr multicolored   1.00 .25
565 A120 55fr multicolored   1.60 .40
566 A120 80fr multicolored   2.25 .50
567 A120 100fr multicolored   2.50 .65
    Nos. 563-567 (5)   7.85 2.05

Local Butterflies — A125

5fr, Colotis chrysonome. 20fr, Colias erate. 30fr, Junonia orithyia. 75fr, Acraea doubledayi. 110fr, Byblia ilithya.

1984, Jan. 24   **Litho.**   **Perf. 13½x13**
568 A125 5fr multicolored   .50 .25
569 A125 20fr multicolored   1.00 .25
570 A125 30fr multicolored   1.50 .35
571 A125 75fr multicolored   4.25 1.00
572 A125 110fr multicolored   5.50 1.50
    Nos. 568-572 (5)   12.75 3.35

Landscapes and Animals
A126

2fr, Randa Klipspringer. 8fr, Ali Sabieh, gazelles. 10fr, Lake Assal, oryx. 15fr, Tadjoura, gazelle. 40fr, Alaila Dada, jackal, vert. 45fr, Lake Abbe, warthog. 55fr, Obock, seagull. 125fr, Presidential Palace, bird.

1984, Apr. 29   **Litho.**   **Perf. 13**
573 A126 2fr multicolored   .25 .25
574 A126 8fr multicolored   .25 .25
575 A126 10fr multicolored   .25 .25
576 A126 15fr multicolored   .25 .25
577 A126 40fr multicolored   .75 .25
578 A126 45fr multicolored   .75 .30
579 A126 55fr multicolored   1.90 .75
580 A126 125fr multicolored   3.75 1.25
    Nos. 573-580 (8)   8.15 3.55
For surcharges see Nos. 646, 657-658, 660.

Fire Prevention
A127

1984, Sept. 9   **Litho.**   **Perf. 13**
581 A127 25fr Fire truck   1.00 .25
582 A127 95fr Hook & ladder   3.25 .50
583 A127 100fr Fire plane   3.25 1.00
    Nos. 581-583 (3)   7.50 1.75

International Olympic Committee Membership — A128

1984, July 22   **Litho.**   **Perf. 13**
584 A128 45fr Runners   .90 .35

Motor Carriage, 1886 — A128a

1984, Nov. 11   **Litho.**   **Perf. 12½**
585 A128a 35fr shown   .80 .30
586 A128a 65fr Cabriolet, 1896   1.60 .65
587 A128a 90fr Phoenix, 1900   2.25 .95
    Nos. 585-587 (3)   4.65 1.90
Gottlieb Daimler (1834-1900), pioneer automobile manufacturer.

Marie and Pierre Curie — A129

1984, Dec. 3   **Litho.**   **Perf. 12½**
588 A129 150fr Pierre Curie   3.25 1.10
589 A129 150fr Marie Curie   3.25 1.10
Nos. 588-589 exist in souvenir sheet of two. Value, set, $30.

A130

Audubon Bicentenary — A130a

5fr, Merops albicollis. 15fr, Pterocles exustus. 20fr, Trachyphonus margaritatus somalicus. 25fr, Coracias garrulus. 200fr, Pandion haliaetus, vert.

1985, Jan. 27   **Litho.**   **Perf. 13**
590 A130 5fr multi   .75 .35
591 A130 15fr multi   3.25 .85
592 A130 20fr multi   3.75 1.00
593 A130 25fr multi   4.50 1.10
    Nos. 590-593 (4)   12.25 3.30

Souvenir Sheet
Self-Adhesive
Perf. 12½
593A A130a 200fr multi   27.50 27.50
No. 593A is airmail and printed on wood.

Intl. Youth Year — A131

1985, Mar. 26   **Litho.**   **Perf. 13**
594 A131 10fr multicolored   .30 .25
595 A131 30fr multicolored   .65 .30
596 A131 40fr multicolored   .90 .40
    Nos. 594-596 (3)   1.85 .95

German Railways, 150th Anniv.
A132

Designs: 55fr, Engine No. 29, Addis Ababa-Djibouti Railways. 75fr, Adler, museum facsimile of the first German locomotive.

1985, Apr. 22   **Litho.**   **Perf. 13**
597 A132 55fr multicolored   2.25 .65
598 A132 75fr multicolored   3.25 .90

Scouting — A133

35fr, Planting saplings. 65fr, Hygiene, family health care.

1985, May 23
599 A133 35fr multicolored   1.00 .45
600 A133 65fr multicolored   1.75 .75

A134

80fr, Victor Hugo (1802-1885), Novelist. 100fr, Arthur Rimbaud (1854-1891), poet.

1985, June 24   **Litho.**
601 A134 80fr brt blue & slate   1.60 .80
602 A134 100fr multicolored   2.00 1.00

Sea Shells — A135

Designs: 10fr, Cypraea nebrites. 15fr, Cypraea turdus. 30fr, Conus acuminatus. 40fr, Cypraea camelopardalis. 55fr, Conus terebra.

1985, July 15   **Litho.**   **Perf. 12½**
603 A135 10fr multicolored   .40 .25
604 A135 15fr multicolored   .60 .25
605 A135 30fr multicolored   1.50 .30
606 A135 40fr multicolored   1.75 .55
607 A135 55fr multicolored   2.75 .70
    Nos. 603-607 (5)   7.00 2.05

1st World Cup Marathon '85, Hiroshima
A136

Designs: 75fr, Winners. 100fr, Approaching finish.

1985, Sept. 2   **Perf. 12½x13**
608 A136 75fr multicolored   1.25 .75
609 A136 100fr multicolored   2.00 1.00

Halley's Comet
A137

Designs: 85fr, Bayeux Tapestry, Comet and Halley. 90fr, Vega I, Giotto space probes, map of planets, comet trajectory.

1986, Jan. 27   Litho.   Perf. 13
610 A137 85fr multicolored   1.50 .50
611 A137 90fr multicolored   1.75 .85

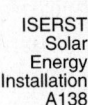

ISERST Solar Energy Installation A138

Designs: 50fr, Runners on beach. 150fr, Windmill, headquarters, power control station.

1986, Mar. 20
612 A138 50fr multicolored   .95 .40
613 A138 150fr multicolored   2.75 1.25

Ships from Columbus's Fleet, 1492 A139

1986, Apr. 14
614 A139 60fr Santa Maria   1.90 .55
615 A139 90fr Nina, Pinta   3.25 .95

Fish, Red Sea — A140

Designs: 20fr, Elagatis bipinnulatus. 25fr, Valamugil seheli. 55fr, Lutjanus rivulatus.

1986, June 16   Litho.   Perf. 13½x13
616 A140 20fr multicolored   .65 .30
617 A140 25fr multicolored   .75 .45
618 A140 55fr multicolored   2.00 .75
      Nos. 616-618 (3)   3.40 1.50

Public Buildings A141

105fr, People's Palace. 115fr, Ministry of the Interior, Posts & Telecommunications.

1986, July 21   Litho.   Perf. 13
619 A141 105fr multicolored   1.75 .90
620 A141 115fr multicolored   2.10 1.00

Sea-Me-We Building, Keyboard A142

1986, Sept. 8   Litho.   Perf. 13
621 A142 100fr multicolored   2.00 .70
Souvenir Sheet
Perf. 12½
622 A142 250fr multicolored   13.50 13.50

Southeast Asia, Middle East, Western Europe Submarine Cable System inauguration.

No. 537 Surcharged

1986, Nov. 15   Perf. 13x12½
623 A116 55fr on 75fr multi   1.40 .50

Pasteur Institute, Cent. A143

1987, Feb. 19   Litho.   Perf. 13
624 A143 220fr multicolored   5.00 1.60

Natl. Vaccination Campaign.

Edible Mushrooms — A144

35fr, Macrolepiota imbricata. 50fr, Lentinus squarrosulus. 95fr, Terfezia boudieri.

1987, Apr. 16   Litho.   Perf. 13x12½
625 A144 35fr multicolored   1.50 .65
626 A144 50fr multicolored   2.25 .85
627 A144 95fr multicolored   3.00 1.50
      Nos. 625-627 (3)   6.75 3.00

Wildlife — A145

1987, May 14   Perf. 12½x13
628 A145   5fr Hare   .50 .25
629 A145 30fr Dromedary   1.25 .30
630 A145 140fr Cheetah   5.00 1.00
      Nos. 628-630 (3)   6.75 1.55

1988 Olympics, Seoul and Calgary A146

85fr, Pierre de Coubertin (1863-1937), founder of the modern Olympics, & lighting of the flame. 135fr, Ski jumping. 140fr, Running.

1987, July 16   Perf. 13
631 A146 85fr multicolored   1.60 .55
632 A146 135fr multicolored   2.75 .95
633 A146 140fr multicolored   3.00 1.00
      Nos. 631-633 (3)   7.35 2.50

Traditional Art — A147

1988, Jan. 20   Litho.   Perf. 13
634 A147 30fr Nomad's comb   .60 .30
635 A147 70fr Wash jug   1.25 .60

UN Universal Immunization by 1990 Campaign — A148

1988, Apr. 10   Perf. 12½
636 A148 125fr multicolored   2.50 1.00

16th Africa Cup Soccer Championships, Morocco — A149

Design: Athletes, view of Rabat.

1988, Mar. 13   Perf. 13
637 A149 55fr multicolored   1.20 .50

1988 Winter Olympics, Calgary — A150

1988, May 7   Litho.   Perf. 13
638 A150 45fr Ski jump   1.00 .40

Campaign Against Thirst — A151

1988, Sept. 10 Litho.   Perf. 12½x13
639 A151 50fr multicolored   1.25 .45

Intl. Fund for Agricultural Development, 10th Anniv. — A152

1988, Nov. 14   Perf. 13
640 A152 135fr multicolored   2.50 1.00

Michel Lafoux Air Club, 40th Anniv. A153

Design: 145fr, 1948 Tiger Moth, 1988 Tobago-10.

1988, Dec. 6
641 A153 145fr multi   2.75 1.00

Marine Life — A154

Designs: 90fr, Lobophyllia costata. 160fr, Lambis truncata.

1989, Jan. 20 Litho.   Perf. 12½
642 A154 90fr multicolored   2.25 .30
643 A154 160fr multicolored   4.25 1.40

Colotis protomedia A155

1989, Feb. 15
644 A155 70fr multicolored   5.00 2.10

Nos. 573 and 547 Surcharged

1989
646 A126 70fr on 2fr No. 573   2.25 .50
647 A118 70fr on 150fr No. 547   2.25 .50
      Issued: 646, 12/20; 647, 12/29.

Folk Dances — A157

1989, Mar. 20
648 A157 30fr shown   .50 .25
649 A157 70fr multicolored, diff.   1.40 .50

Francolin of Djibouti — A159

1989, Apr. 10   Litho.   Perf. 12½
651 A159 35fr multicolored   2.50 .75

Rare Flora — A160

1989, June 12
652 A160 25fr Calotropis procera   .90 .25

A161

1989, Aug. 10   Litho.   Perf. 13
653 A161 70fr multicolored   1.60 .75

Interparliamentary Union, cent.

Intl. Literacy Year — A162

1989, Oct. 1
654 A162 145fr multicolored   2.75 1.10

Petroglyph A163

1989, Nov. 18   Litho.   Perf. 13
655 A163 5fr multicolored   1.00 .40

Girl — A164

1989, Dec. 6
656 A164 55fr multicolored 1.60 .65

Nos. 574, 576-577 Surcharged

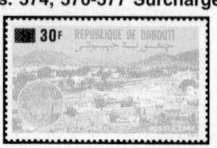

1989-1990   Litho.   Perf. 13
657 A126 30fr on 8fr multi .50 .30
658 A126 50fr on 40fr multi 2.00 .55
660 A126 120fr on 15fr multi 2.25 1.00
    Nos. 657-660 (3) 4.75 1.85
Issue dates: 30fr, 12/20/89; 50fr, 7/3/90;
120fr, 3/17/90.

Water
Conservation
A165

1990, May 5   Litho.   Perf. 11½
665 A165 120fr multicolored 2.25 .90

Traditional
Jewelry — A166

1990, Mar. 10
666 A166 70fr multicolored 1.75 .45

Commiphora
A167

1990, Feb. 20   Perf. 12
667 A167 30fr multicolored 1.50 .35

Baskets
A168

1990, July 3
668 A168 30fr multicolored .70 .40

A169

1990, June 12   Perf. 11½
669 A169 100fr multicolored 2.00 .80
World Cup Soccer Championships, Italy.

A170

1990, Apr. 16   Perf. 11½
670 A170 55fr shown 1.50 .45
20 kilometer race of Djibouti.

Vaccination
Campaign — A171

1990, Aug. 22   Litho.   Perf. 11½
Granite Paper
671 A171 300fr multicolored 4.75 2.00

Charles de
Gaulle — A172

1990, Sept. 16   Granite Paper
672 A172 200fr multicolored 4.00 1.25

African Tourism
Year — A173

1991, Jan. 23   Litho.   Perf. 13
673 A173 115fr multicolored 2.25 .80

Corals — A174

1991, Jan. 28   Perf. 12½
674 A174 40fr Acropora .90 .50
675 A174 45fr Seriatopora hytrise 1.25 .50

Aquatic Birds — A175

10fr, Pelecanus rufescens. 15fr, Egretta
gularis. 20fr, Ardea goliath, horiz. 25fr,
Platalea leucorodia, horiz.

1991, Feb. 12
676 A175 10fr multicolored .70 .25
677 A175 15fr multicolored 1.50 .25
678 A175 20fr multicolored 1.75 .30
679 A175 25fr multicolored 1.90 .35
    Nos. 676-679 (4) 5.85 1.15

UNO Development
Conference — A176

1990, Oct. 9   Litho.   Perf. 11½x12
Granite Paper
680 A176 45fr multicolored 1.10 .45

Fossils — A177

1990, Nov. 1   Granite Paper
681 A177 90fr pur, org & blk 5.25 1.75

Papio
Hamadryas — A178

1990, Dec. 6   Granite Paper
682 A178 50fr multicolored 1.75 .55

Pandion
Haliaetus — A179

1991, Mar. 20   Litho.   Perf. 12x11½
683 A179 200fr multicolored 5.00 1.60

Traditional
Game — A180

1991, Apr. 4
684 A180 250fr multicolored 5.25 3.25
    See No. 696.

Djibouti-Ethiopia
Railroad — A181

1991, May 25   Litho.   Perf. 11½
685 A181 85fr multicolored 4.00 2.25

World Environment
Day — A182

1991, June 10
686 A182 110fr multicolored 2.75 .65

Philexafrique
A183

1991, Jul. 16   Litho.   Perf. 11½
687 A183 120fr Islands 3.25 1.75

Pre-Olympic
Year — A184

1991, Sept. 25
688 A184 175fr Handball 4.50 3.00

World Food
Day — A185

1991, Oct. 16   Litho.   Perf. 11½x12
689 A185 105fr multicolored 2.50 1.10

Underwater
Cable
Network — A186

1991, Nov. 28   Perf. 12x11½
690 A186 130fr multicolored 3.00 1.00

Discovery of
America, 500th
Anniv. — A187

1991, Dec. 19   Litho.   Perf. 11½
691 A187 145fr multicolored 3.25 1.60

Arthur Rimbaud
(1854-1891) Poet
and
Merchant — A188

1991-92   Perf. 11½
692 A188 90fr Young man, ship 2.75 .90
693 A188 150fr Old man, camels 3.00 .90
Issued: 90fr, 2/5/92; 150fr, 12/23/91.

Djibouti-Ethiopia
Railroad — A189

Design: 250fr, Locomotive, map.

1992   Litho.   Perf. 12x11½
694 A189 70fr multicolored 2.75 1.10
Souvenir Sheet
Perf. 13x12½
695 A189 250fr multicolored 5.25 5.25
Issue dates: 70fr, Feb. 2; 250fr, Jan. 30.

Traditional Game Type of 1991
1992, Feb. 10   Perf. 11½
696 A180 100fr Boys playing Go 2.10 .85

A190

1992, June 9   Litho.   Perf. 14
697 A190 80fr multicolored 2.10 1.25
1992 Summer Olympics, Barcelona.

A191

Traditional food preparation — 30fr, Pounding grain. 45fr, Preparing mofo. 70fr, Winnowing grain. 75fr, Cooking mofo.

1992   Litho.   Perf. 14x13½
698   A191   30fr multi   1.25   .50
698A A191   45fr multi   90.00   —
699   A191   70fr multi   1.25   .65
699A A191   75fr multi   90.00   —

Issued: Nos. 698, 699, 4/20; No. 698A, 12/6.

Discovery of America, 500th Anniv. — A192

1992, May 16   Litho.   Perf. 11½
700   A192 125fr multicolored   3.25   .95

African Soccer Championships A193

1992, July 22   Perf. 14
701   A193   15fr multicolored   .75   .25

Intl. Space Year — A194

Designs: 120fr, Rocket, satellite. 135fr, Astronaut, satellite, horiz.

Perf. 14x13½, 13½x14
1992, Sept. 28
702   A194 120fr multi   2.75   .85
703   A194 135fr multi   2.75   .95

Wildlife—A195

1992, Nov. 11   Perf. 14
704   A195   5fr Dik-dik   1.25   .25
705   A195 200fr Caretta caretta 5.00 1.60

Taeniura Lymma — A195a

Perf. 11½x11¾
1990, Mar. 24   Litho.
Panel Color
705A A195a   30fr pink   —   —
705B A195a   70fr yellow   —   —
705C A195a 100fr green   —   —
705D A195a 120fr lilac   —   —

Nomad Girls in Traditional Costumes — A196

1993, Jan. 26   Litho.   Perf. 13
706   A196   70fr Girl beside hut 1.75   .45
707   A196 120fr shown   2.75   .75

White-eyed Seagull — A197

1993, Feb. 28   Litho.   Perf. 12½
708   A197 300fr multicolored   5.75 1.75

Amin Salman Mosque A198

1993, Feb. 17   Litho.   Perf. 13¾x14
709   A198 500fr multicolored   52.50 5.50

Handcrafts A199

1993, Apr. 23   Litho.   Perf. 13¾x14
710   A199 100fr Neck rest   100.00 15.00
711   A199 125fr Sword   100.00 15.00

Cercopithecus Aethiops — A200

1993, May 29   Litho.   Perf. 14¼x13½
712   A200 150fr multi   80.00 5.00

Organization of African Unity, 30th Anniv. — A201

Perf. 14¼x13½
1993, June 20   Litho.
713   A201 200fr multi   100.00 2.25

Water Carriers — A202

1993, July 6   Litho.   Perf. 14x13¾
714   A202   30fr Woman   100.00
715   A202   50fr Man   100.00

Conquest of Space — A203

1993, Sept. 30   Litho.   Perf. 14x13¾
716   A203   90fr multicolored   —   —

A204

Traditional utensils.

1993, Sept. 30   Litho.   Perf. 13½
717   A204   15fr Weyso   .45   .25
718   A204   20fr Hangol   .90   .25
719   A204   25fr Saqaf   1.00   .25
720   A204   30fr Subrar   1.40   .45
      Nos. 717-720 (4)   3.75 1.20

A205

Traditional musical instruments.

1993, Nov. 10   Litho.   Perf. 14
721   A205   5fr Flute   1.00 1.00
722   A205 10fr Drum   1.00 1.00

Souvenir Sheet

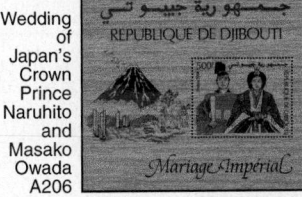

Wedding of Japan's Crown Prince Naruhito and Masako Owada A206

1994, Jan. 10   Litho.   Perf. 13x12½
Self-Adhesive
723   A206 500fr multicolored   22.50 22.50
No. 723 printed on wood.

20 Kilometer Race of Djibouti — A207

1994   Litho.   Perf. 11½
724   A207   50fr multicolored   2.50 1.00

Promotion of Breastfeeding — A208

1994
725   A208   40fr shown   1.90   .40
726   A208   45fr Mother, infant 2.10   .40

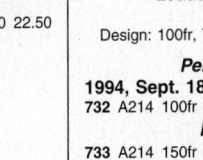

Hassan Gouled Aptidon Stadium — A209

1994
727   A209   70fr multicolored   2.50 1.10

Stenella Longirostris A210

1994, May 1   Litho.   Perf. 11¾x11½
728   A210 120fr multicolored   —

World Housing Day — A211

1994, May 9   Litho.   Perf. 11½x11¾
729   A211   30fr multi   100.00

Eupodotis Senegalensis A212

Perf. 11¾x11½
1994, June 16   Litho.
730   A212   10fr multicolored   180.00

1994 World Cup Soccer Tournament A213

1994, Sept. 7
731   A213 200fr multicolored   150.00

Dress of a Village Leader — A214

Design: 100fr, Traditional nomad costume.

Perf. 11½x11¾
1994, Sept. 18   Litho.
732   A214 100fr multicolored   100.00

Perf. 11¾
733   A214 150fr multicolored   10.00   —

Canis Aureus — A215

Perf. 11¾x11½
1994, Sept. 28   Litho.
734   A215 400fr multi   135.00   —

World Walking Day — A216

1994, Oct. 19   Litho.   Perf. 11¾x11½
735   A216   75fr multicolored   150.00

A217

1994, Nov. 26   Litho.   Perf. 11¾
736 A217 55fr Book stand   75.00

A218

1994, Dec. 6   Litho.   Perf. 11½x11¾
737 A218 35fr Traditional
           dance   60.00 12.00

Souvenir Sheet

Sea-Me-We 2 Submarine Cable —
A218a

1994   Perf. 12½
737A A218a 350fr multi   175.00 —

Volleyball,
Cent. — A219

1995, Feb. 25   Litho.   Perf. 11¾
738 A219 70fr multicolored   —   —

United Nations, 50th
Anniv. — A220

1995, Feb. 25
739 A220 120fr multicolored   —   —

Fight Against
Thirst — A221

Perf. 11¾x11½
1995, Mar. 29   Litho.
740 A221 100fr multicolored

Threskiornis
Aethiopica — A222

Design: 30fr, Phoenicopterus ruber

1995, Apr. 5   Litho.   Perf. 11¾
741 A222 30fr multicolored   —   —
742 A222 50fr multicolored   —   —

World Telecommunications
Day — A223

Perf. 11¾x11½
1995, June 10   Litho.
743 A223 125fr multicolored   70.00 1.25

Crocuta
Crocuta — A224

1995, June 12   Litho.   Perf. 11¾
744 A224 200fr multi   105.00

People Meeting
Under
Tree — A225

1995, July 3   Litho.   Perf. 11¾x11½
745 A225 150fr multi   65.00

Nomads Around
Fire — A226

1995, Aug. 9   Perf. 11¾
746 A226 45fr multi   60.00 12.00

FAO, 50th
Anniv. — A227

1995, Sept. 27   Perf. 11½x11¾
747 A227 250fr multi   70.00 12.00

Traditional
Costume — A228

1995, Dec. 6   Perf. 11¾
748 A228 90fr multicolored   —   12.00

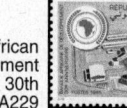

African
Development
Bank, 30th
Anniv. — A229

1995, Dec. 18   Perf. 11¾x11½
749 A229 300fr multi   60.00 12.00

African Soccer
Cup — A230

1996, Feb. 28
750 A230 70fr multicolored   180.00   —

Ostrich — A231

1996, Apr. 23
751 A231 120fr multi   100.00   —

Leopard — A232

1996, May 6
752 A232 70fr multi   105.00   —

Amber
Necklace — A233

1996, June 13   Litho.
753 A233 30fr multi   100.00

1996 Summer Olympic
Games,
Atlanta — A234

Perf. 11½x11¾
1996, Sept. 21   Litho.
754 A234 105fr multicolored 125.00 12.00

Commicarpus
Grandiflorus — A236

1996, Oct. 6   Litho.   Perf. 11½x11¾
756 A236 350fr multi   60.00 12.00

Djibouti
Folklore — A237

1996, Nov. 28   Litho.   Perf. 11¾
757 A237 95fr multi   60.00

Legend of the
Lion and Three
Bulls — A238

1996, Nov. 28   Litho.   Perf. 11¾
758 A238 95fr multi   80.00 12.00

Children's
Day — A239

1996, Dec. 17   Perf. 11¾x11½
759 A239 130fr multi   60.00 12.00

A240

Legend of the Tortoise and the Fox: No.
760, Tortoise and fox at starting line. No. 761,
Fox leaves tortoise behind. No. 762, Tortoise
passes sleeping fox.

1997, Jan. 17   Perf. 11¾
760 A240 60fr multi   —   —
761 A240 60fr multi   —   —
762 A240 60fr multi   —   —
  a.   Horiz. strip, #760-762   135.00

UNICEF, 50th
Anniv. — A241

1997, Feb. 9   Litho.   Perf. 11¾
763 A241 80fr Mother, child   50.00 10.00
764 A241 90fr Hands around
            globe   100.00 12.00

Dancers — A242

1997, May 14   Litho.   Perf. 11¾
765 A242 70fr multi   70.00 12.00

Fortune
Teller — A243

Designs: 200fr, Fortune teller and woman.
300fr, Fortune teller, camel.

1997, May 29   Litho.   Perf. 11¾
766 A243 200fr multi   60.00 12.00
767 A243 300fr multi   60.00 12.00

Woman's Day — A244

1997, May 30   Litho.   Perf. 11¾
768 A244 250fr multi   160.00 12.00

Traditional
Objects — A245

Design: 30fr, Writing board, horiz. 400fr,
Bowl and spoon.

1997, June 5   Litho.   Perf. 11¾
769 A245 30fr multi   45.00 10.00
770 A245 400fr multi   45.00 10.00

Telecommunications
A246

Designs: 30fr, Arta post office. 100fr, Map, building with antenna and satellite dishes. 120fr, Ships, map showing submarine cable route, horiz.

1997, June 27 Litho. **Perf. 11¾**
771 A246 30fr multi — 12.00
772 A246 100fr multi — 12.00
773 A246 120fr multi — 12.00

Goats in Tree — A247

1997, July 26 Litho. **Perf. 11¾**
774 A247 120fr multi 50.00 15.00

A248

Portrait of Diana: a, 125fr. b, 130fr. c, 150fr.

1998, Mar. 25 Litho. **Perf. 13½**
775 A248 Strip of 3, #a.-c. 5.00 5.00

Diana, Princess of Wales (1961-97). No. 775 was isssued in sheets of 6 stamps.

Mother Teresa (1910-97) — A249

1998 Litho. **Perf. 13½**
776 A249 130fr multicolored 2.75 1.40

No. 776 was issued in sheets of 4.

Intl. Year of the Ocean — A250

a, Tangara chilensis. b, Agalychnis callidryas. c, Delphinus delphis, megaptera novaeangliae. d, Cercopithecus aethiops (h). e, Laticaudia colubrina (i), sphyrna mokarran. f, Lactoria cornuta, delphinus delphis (g). g, Delphinus delphis (k). h, Aspidontus taeniatus, lo vulpinus. i, Sepioteuthis lessoniana. j, Prionace glauca (i), chaetodon ornatissimus. k, Eupagurus bernherdus. l, Octopus vulgaris (k).

1998, Apr. 20 Litho. **Perf. 13½**
777 A250 75fr Sheet of 12, #a.-l. 16.00 16.00

Mahatma Gandhi (1869-1948) — A251

1998, Apr. 20 Litho. **Perf. 11¾**
778 A251 250fr multi 80.00 12.00

Traditional Art — A252

1998, Apr. 25 Litho. **Perf. 11½x11¾**
779 A252 30fr multicolored 120.00 12.00

Women's Rights and International Peace — A253

1998, May 3 **Perf. 11¾x11½**
780 A253 70fr multicolored 60.00 12.00

World Water Day — A254

1998, May 10 Litho. **Perf. 11¾**
781 A254 45fr multi 60.00 12.00

1998 World Cup Soccer Championships, France — A255

1998, June 10 Litho. **Perf. 11¾**
782 A255 200fr multi 145.00 —

Marine Life — A256

Perf. 11½x11¾, 11¾x11½
1998, July 2 Litho.
783 A256 20fr Octopus 135.00 —
784 A256 25fr Shark, horiz. 135.00 —

Cats and Bush — A257

1998, Aug. 30 **Perf. 11½x11¾**
785 A257 120fr multi 135.00 —

World Telecommunications Day — A258

1996, Sept. 27 Litho. **Perf. 11¾**
786 A258 150fr multi 100.00 —

National Bank — A259

1998, Sept. 30 Litho. **Perf. 11¾**
787 A259 100fr multi 135.00 12.00

Flags and IGAD Emblem — A260

Perf. 11½x11¾
1998, Sept. 30 Litho.
788 A260 85fr multi 75.00 —

Traditional Game Goos — A261

1998, Oct. 1 **Perf. 11¾x11½**
789 A261 110fr multi 60.00 —

Fishing Port — A262

1998
790 A262 100fr multi 115.00 —

Maskali Island — A263

1998
791 A263 500fr multi 140.00 —

Fish — A264

1999 Litho. **Perf. 13¼x13½**
792 A264 70fr multi 100.00 —

Antelope — A264a

Perf. 13¼x13½
1999, Mar. 16 Litho.
792A A264a 120fr multi 90.00 —

Djibouti Franc, 50th Anniv. — A265

1999
793 A265 100fr multi 60.00 —

World Telecommunications Day — A266

1999
794 A266 125fr multi 55.00 —

Worldwide Fund for Nature (WWF) — A267

Phacochoerus africanus aeliani: a, Adult and young. b, Adult standing. c, Head. d, Adult walking.

2000, Apr. 13 Litho. **Perf. 14**
795 A267 100fr Block of 4, #a-d 9.00 9.00

Wild Animals A268

No. 796: a, Flamingo. b, Ostrich. c, Sifaka. d, Yellow-billed stork. e, Scarlet macaw. f, Dwarf puff adder. g, Toucan. h, Whooping crane.

2000, Apr. 13
796 A268 100fr Sheet of 8, #a-h 22.50 22.50

Butterflies — A269

No. 797: a, Doxocopa cherubina. b, Heliconius charitonius. c, Cantonephele numili. d, Danaus gilippus. e, Morpho peleides. f, Heliconius doris.
No. 798, 250fr, Agraulis vanillae. No. 799, 250fr, Strymon melinus.

2000, Apr. 13
797 A269 100fr Sheet of 6, #a-f 12.00 12.00

Souvenir Sheets
798-799 A269 Set of 2 11.00 11.00

No. 797 contains six 28x42mm stamps.

Water Resources — A270

2000, Apr. 13
800 A270 500fr multi 8.00 8.00

Trains and Landmarks — A271

No. 801: a, 5fr, Class OJ 2-10-2, China. b, 25fr, Eurostar, France-England. c, 15fr, Glacier Express, Switzerland. d, 40fr, Unidentified train. e, 35fr, Class WP 4-6-2, India.
No. 802, 110fr: a, Nord Chapelon Pacific, France. b, Class 23 2-6-2, Germany. c, Class GS-4 4-8-4, US. d, Class A4 4-6-2, Great Britain. e, Pacific 4-6-2, South Africa. f, Class HP, India.
No. 803, 120fr: a, VT601, Germany. b, ICIII Bo-Bo EMU, Netherlands. c, TGV, France. d, ETR 450, Italy. e, AVE, Spain. f, Bullet Train, Japan.
No. 804, 250fr, GM War Bonnet, US. No. 805, 250fr, Class 8 Pacific, Great Britain.

2000, Apr. 28
801 A271 Horiz. strip of 5, #a-e 3.00 3.00
Sheets of 6, #a-f
802-803 A271 Set of 2 15.00 15.00
Souvenir Sheets
804-805 A271 Set of 2 6.00 6.00

Dancers — A272

2000, Apr. 28
806 A272 75fr multi   4.00 1.50

Blacksmith
A273

2000, May 14
807 A273 100fr multi   6.00 2.50

Marine
Life
A274

No. 808, vert.: a, Dendrochirus biocellatus. b, Hippocampus. c, Amphiprion ocellaris, Amphiprion percula. d, Periclimenes imperator. e, Pomacnetridae. f, Octopus vulgaris.
No. 809, 50fr: a, Cephalopholis miniata. b, Ptereleotris hanae. c, Sphyraena genie. d, Tripterygion segmentatum. e, Odontaspididae. f, Cirrhitidae. g, Amphiprion. h, Capros aper. i, Balistidae. j, Trygonorhina fasciata. k, Cephalopholis. l, Corythoichthys ocellatus.
No. 810, 60fr: a, Lutjanus kasmira. b, Chaetodon fasciatus. c, Epinephelinae. d, Hypoplectrus gutavarius. e, Loligo opalescens. f, Diodontinae. g, Coelenterata. h, Sargocentron xantherythrum. i, Thalassoma lunare. j, Hemichromis bimaculatus. k, Dasyatis. l, Fromia monilis.
No. 811, 250fr, Eschrichtis robustus. No. 812, 250fr, Cheloniidae.

2000, May 14
808 A274 55fr Sheet of 6, #a-f   8.00 8.00
Sheets of 12, #a-l
809-810 A274   Set of 2   30.00 30.00
Souvenir Sheets
811-812 A274   Set of 2   8.00 8.00

Camels and
Tender — A275

2000, June 26
813 A275 35fr multi   4.75 .90

Ships — A276

Designs: 10fr, Thomas W. Lawson, 1902. 15fr, BT Global Challenge, 2000. 20fr, Reliance and Shamrock III, 1903. 25fr, Archibald Russell, 1905. 50fr, Greek merchantman, 8th cent. B.C.
No. 819, 130fr: a, Norman warship, 1066. b, Hanseatic cog, c. 1300. c, Santa Maria, 1492. d, Mary Rose, 1510. e, Golden Hind, 1577. f, Sovereign of the Seas, 1637.
No. 820:, 135fr: a, HMS Endeavour, 1768. b, USS Constitution, 1797. c, Chasse-Maree, 1800. d, Baltimore clipper, 1812. e, Lightning, 1853. f, Bluenose, 1921.
No. 821, 250fr, HM Yacht Britannia, 1893. No. 822, 250fr, Herzogin Cecilie, 1902.

2000, June 26
814-818 A276   Set of 5   2.00 2.00

Sheets of 6, #a-f
819-820 A276   Set of 2   25.00 25.00
Souvenir Sheets
821-822 A276   Set of 2   8.00 8.00

Millennium
A277

2000, July 18
823 A277 125fr multi   2.75 2.75

Birds — A278

2000, Aug. 23
824   Horiz. strip of 5   2.75 2.75
a. A278 5fr Lanius excubitor   .35 .35
b. A278 10fr Phoenicopterus minor   .35 .35
c. A278 15fr Eupodatis senegalensis   .35 .35
d. A278 40fr Noephron perchopterus   .60 .60
e. A278 50fr Pterocles lichtensteinii   .75 .75

Space Exploration — A279

No. 825, 100fr, vert.: a, John Glenn and Mercury capsule, 1962. b, Soyuz capsule, Apollo-Soyuz mission, 1975. c, Hubble Telescope, 1990. d, Apollo capsule, Apollo-Soyuz mission. e, Glenn at speaker's stand, 1974. f, Space Shuttle Columbia, 1981.
No. 826, 100fr, vert.: a, Apollo 11 service module, 1969. b, Telstar, 1962. c, Ariane 4, 1988. d, Apollo 11 lunar module. e, Neil Armstrong, 1969. f, Splashdown of Apollo 11, 1969.
No. 827, 200fr, Astronaut on moon saluting. No. 828, 250fr, Astronauts conducting experiments on moon. No. 829, 250fr, Space Shuttle Challenger.

2000, Aug. 23   Sheets of 6, #a-f
825-826 A279   Set of 2   20.00 20.00
Souvenir Sheets
827-829 A279   Set of 3   12.00 12.00

2000 Summer
Olympics,
Sydney — A280

Olympic flame, flag and: 80fr, Runner. 90fr, Tennis player.

2000   Perf. 14
830-831 A280   Set of 2   4.00 4.00

Unknown Soldier
Monument—A280a

2004, Apr. 18   Litho.   Perf. 13x12¾
832 A280a 175fr multi   50.00 20.00

Independence, 27th Anniv. — A281

2004, June 27   Litho.   Perf. 13
833 A281 45fr multi

Dragon Tree
A282

Pregnant
Woman at
Hospital
A283

Camel Caravan
A284

Natl. Union of
Djibouti
Women
A285

National
Arms — A286

Perf. 12¾x13, 13x12¾
2004, Dec. 18   Litho.
834 A282 15fr multi   37.50 20.00
835 A283 25fr multi   37.50 20.00
836 A284 45fr multi   37.50 20.00
837 A285 70fr multi   37.50 20.00
838 A286 100fr multi   25.00 20.00
   Nos. 834-838 (5)   175.00 100.00

Friendship
Between Djibouti
and People's
Republic of
China, 25th
Anniv.

Designs: 5fr, Djibouti Electricity Building. 10fr, Hassan Gouled Stadium. 15fr, Djibouti Central Bank. 30fr, People's Palace. 45fr, Ministry of Foreign Affairs Building.

2004, Dec. 27   Perf. 12
839-843 A286a   Set of 5   115.00 115.00

Items commemorating the death of Pope John Paul II were declared as "fraudulent" by Djibouti Post.

2006 World Cup Soccer
Championships, Germany — A287

2005, June 8   Litho.   Perf. 13
844 A287 100fr multi   95.00 —

Tanker in
Port of
Doraleh
A288

2006, Nov. 6   Litho.   Perf. 13
845 A288 120fr multi   50.00 —
Printed in sheets of 4.

Common
Market for
Eastern and
Southern
Africa
Summit,
Djibouti
A289

2006, Nov. 6   Litho.   Perf. 13¼x13
846 A289 150fr multi   50.00 —

Djibouti Chamber of
Commerce,
Cent. — A290

2007   Litho.   Perf. 12¾
847 A290 50fr multi   12.00 —
a.   Souvenir sheet of 2   52.50 —

Independence,
30th
Anniv. — A291

2007, June 27   Litho.   Perf. 13
848 A291 75fr multi   25.00 —
a.   Souvenir sheet of 2   50.00 —

Mahamoud Harbi
(1921-60),
Politician — A292

2007, Aug. 17   Litho.   Perf. 13x12¾
849 A292 165fr multi   30.00 5.00

Indo-Suez Red Sea Bank — A293

2008, Oct. 19   Litho.   Perf. 13x13½
850 A293 220fr multi   25.00 6.00
a.   Souvenir sheet of 2   50.00

2010 World Cup Soccer
Championships, South Africa — A295

2010, May   Litho.   Perf. 13
852 A295 105fr multi   25.00 —
a.   Souvenir sheet of 1   27.50

Djibouti postal authorities have declared "illegal" the following items:
Sheets of 8 stamps of various values: Mushrooms
Sheets of 6 stamps of various values: Fire trucks and Scouts (3 different)
Sheets of 6 700f stamps: Butterflies and Orchids, Butterflies and Scouts, Trains
Sheets of 6 300f stamps: Birds
Sheets of 6 800f stamps: Bonsai
Sheets of 4 700f stamps: Dogs (4 different), Cats (4 different), Babe Ruth and Tiger Woods, Dinosaurs
Sheets of 2 stamps of various values: Fire trucks (2 different).

2014 Africa Internet Summit, Djibouti
A296

2014	Litho.	Perf. 13	
853	A296 170fr multi	15.00	—
a.	Souvenir sheet of 1	50.00	—

A297

A298

A299

Personalized Stamps — A300

2016, Jan. 25	Litho.	Perf. 13¼x13	
854	A297 250fr multi	3.00	3.00
855	A298 250fr multi	3.00	3.00
856	A299 250fr multi	3.00	3.00
857	A300 250fr multi	3.00	3.00
	Nos. 854-857 (4)	12.00	12.00

Nos. 854-857 were each printed in sheets of 16 that could be personalized. A generic image showing Santa Claus with the inscription "Bonne Année 2016!" was made available. Values are for stamps with or without any printed vignette.

Fauna
A301

No. 858, 260fr — Primates: a, Lemur catta. b, Leontopithecus rosalia. c, Macaca fuscata. d, Mandrillus sphinx.
No. 859, 260fr — Bats: a, Plecotus auritus. b, Erophylla sezekorni. c, Sturnira lilium. d, Desmodus rotundus.
No. 860, 260fr — Wild cats: a, Panthera tigris. b, Panthera pardus melas. c, Panthera onca. d, Panthera leo.
No. 861, 260fr — Lions: a, Panthera leo nubica. b, Panthera leo bleyenberghi. c, Panthera leo leo. d, Panthera leo azandica.
No. 862, 260fr — Dugong dugon: a, One dugong surfacing, fish at LR. b, Two dugongs, and calf. c, Dugong swimming, surrounded by fish. d, One dugong on sea floor, two fish at UL.
No. 863, 260fr — Dolphins: a, Delphinus capensis. b, Lagenorhynchus obscurus. c, Stenella frontalis. d, Delphinus delphis.
No. 864, 260fr — Whales: a, Delphinapterus leucas. b, Megaptera novaeangliae. c, Eubalaena australis. d, Physeter macrocephalus.
No. 865, 260fr — Eagles: a, Lophaetus occipitalis. b, Geranoaetus melanoleucus. c, Haliaeetus leucogaster. d, Aquila heliaca.
No. 866, 260fr — Parrots: a, Eclectus roratus. b, Anodorhynchus hyacinthinus. c, Conuropsis carolinensis. d, Trichoglossus moluccanus.
No. 867, 260fr — Owls: a, Megascops asio. b, Pulsatrix perspicillata. c, Bubo sumatranus. d, Ptilopsis leucotis.
No. 868, 260fr — Starlings: a, Sturnus vulgaris. b, Spreo fischeri. c, Sturnia sinensis. d, Mino dumontii.
No. 869, 260fr — Sunbirds: a, Leptocoma minima. b, Nectarinia famosa. c, Leptocoma sperata and Aetopyga siparaja. d, Anthreptes malacensis and Nectarinia tacazze.
No. 870, 260fr — Warblers: a, Lioparus chrysotis. b, Psittiparus gularis. c, Sylvia rueppelli. d, Parophasma galinieri.
No. 871, 260fr — Butterflies: a, Limenitis archippus. b, Apatura iris. c, Teinopalpus imperialis. d, Iphiclides podalirius.
No. 872, 260fr — Turtles: a, Terrapene carolina bauri. b, Chelonoidis nigra. c, Testudo graeca. d, Stigmochelys pardalis.
No. 873, 260fr — Snakes: a, Bitis arietans. b, Dispholidus typus. c, Echis pyramidum. d, Atractaspis fallax.
No. 874, 260fr — Crocodiles: a, Crocodylus siamensis. b, Crocodylus porosus. c, Crocodylus rhombifer. d, Crocodylus acutus.
No. 875, 260fr — Chameleons: a, Chamaeleo calyptratus. b, Chameleon hoehnelii. c, Chamaeleo chamaeleon. d, Furcifer pardalis.
No. 876, 260fr — Scorpions: a, Centruroides margaritatus. b, Parabuthus liosoma. c, Androctonus crassicauda, Blaptica dubia. d, Babycurus jacksoni.
No. 877, 960fr, Cebus capucinus. No. 878, 960fr, Acerodon jubatus. No. 879, 960fr, Puma concolor. No. 880, 960fr, Panthera leo senegalensis. No. 881, 960fr, Two dugong dugon. No. 882, 960fr, Stenella coeruleoalba. No. 883, 960fr, Physeter macrocephalus, diff. No. 884, 960fr, Aquila rapax. No. 885, 960fr, Psittacus erithacus. No. 886, 960fr, Strix nebulosa. No. 887, 960fr, Lamprotornis hildebrandti. No. 888, 960fr, Cinnyris chalybeus. No. 889, 960fr, Myzornis pyrrhoura. No. 890, 960fr, Lasiommata megera. No. 891, 960fr, Aldabrachelys gigantea. No. 892, 960fr, Naja pallida. No. 893, 960fr, Crocodylus acutus, diff. No. 894, 960fr, Kinyongia fischeri. No. 895, 960fr, Hottentotta tamulus.

2016, Jan. 25	Litho.	Perf. 13¼	
Sheets of 4, #a-d			
858-876	A301	Set of 19	225.00 225.00
Souvenir Sheets			
877-895	A301	Set of 19	205.00 205.00

Artisans de paix et humanistes
NELSON MANDELA
A302

No. 896, 260fr — Nelson Mandela (1918-2013), President of South Africa, and: a, Three doves. b, Prison cell. c, Amethyst crystal. d, Dove and flag of South Africa.
No. 897, 270fr — Mahatma Gandhi (1869-1948), Indian nationalist leader: a, Sitting at

small table. b, With spinning wheel, automobile. c, Seated, pulling thread. d, Seated in chair.
No. 898, 270fr — St. John Paul II (1920-2005): a, With two doves. b, With Nelson Mandela. c, With Mother Teresa. d, Holding crucifix.
No. 899, 270fr — Queen Elizabeth II, longest-reigning British monarch, wearing: a, Crown and blue sash. b, Pink hat. c, Green hat. d, Tiara and orange sash.
No. 900, 270fr — Princess Diana (1961-97), with: a, Princes William and Harry. b, Mother Teresa. c, Child and Red Cross flag. d, Princes Charles and William.
No. 901, 270fr — Lord Robert Baden-Powell (1857-1941), founder of Scouting movement, Scouting emblem: a, Wearing military uniform. b, Wearing Indian headdress. c, Holding animal horn, British flag in background. d, With Scout bugler.
No. 902, 270fr — Nobel laureates: a, Ei-ichi Negishi, 2010 Chemistry laureate. b, Malala Yousafzai, 2014 Peace laureate. c, James D. Watson, 1962 Physiology or Medicine laureate. d, Doris Lessing, 2007 Literature laureate.
No. 903, 270fr — Soccer players and stadiums for 2016 European Soccer Championships, France: a, Stade Pierre Mauroy, Lille. b, Stade Vélodrome, Marseille. c, Stade de Lyon, Lyon. d, Stade de Bordeaux, Bordeaux.
No. 904, 270fr — Sports of the 2016 Summer Olympics, Rio de Janeiro: a, Artistic gymnastics. b, Kayak slalom. c, Women's beach volleyball. d, Rugby.
No. 905, 270fr — Attack on Pearl Harbor, 75th anniv.: a, USS Arizona. b, U.S. P-40B airplane. c, Japanese Mitsubishi A6M Zero airplane. d, USS Missouri.
No. 906, 270fr — Walt Disney (1901-66), animated filmmaker, and: a, Bavarian Castle. b, Awards. c, Film camera. d, Drawing board and sketches.
No. 907, 270fr — Marilyn Monroe (1926-62), actress, wearing: a, Necklace. b, Black bathing suit. c, Blue bathing suit. d, White dress and gloves.
No. 908, 270fr — Elvis Presley (1935-77): a, Playing guitar. b, Holding microphone. c, Wearing striped shirt. d, With Hollywood Walk of Fame star.
No. 909, 270fr — Wolfgang Amadeus Mozart (1756-91), composer, and: a, His father, Johann Georg Leopold Mozart (1719-87). b, His mother, Anna Maria Pertl Mozart (1720-78). c, His wife, Maria Constanze Mozart (1762-1842). d, Young Mozart blindfolded behind piano.
No. 910, 270fr — Georg Alfred Schumann (1866-1952), composer: a, Violin, score, hands of conductor. b, Wearing black suit. c, At piano. d, Conducting musicians.
No. 911, 270fr — Paintings by Vincent van Gogh (1853-90): a, Self-portrait, 1889. b, Vase with Twelve Sunflowers, 1889. c, Portrait of Doctor Gachet, 1890. d, Starry Night Over the Rhône, 1888.
No. 912, 270fr — Paintings by Claude Monet (1840-1926): a, Flowering Garden in Saint-Adresse, 1866. b, Les Meules à Giverny, 1884. c, The Bridge at Argenteuil, 1874. d, The Bridge Over the Water Lily Pond, 1905.
No. 913, 270fr — Paintings by Pablo Picasso (1881-1973): a, Self-portrait, 1907. b, Boy with a Pipe, 1905. c, The Old Guitarist, 1903. d, Portrait of Daniel-Henry Kahnweiler, 1910.
No. 914, 270fr — Christmas: a, Ded Moroz and Snegurochka. b, Santa Claus and reindeer. c, Saint Nicholas on horse. d, Joulupukki.
No. 915, 270fr — New Year 2016 (Year of the Monkey): a, Monkey on branch. b, Monkey with open mouth. c, Head of monkey. d, Adult and juvenile monkey.
No. 916, 960fr, Mandela, diff. No. 917, 960fr, Gandhi and tiger. No. 918, 960fr, St. John Paul II and 14th Dalai Lama. No. 919, 960fr, Queen Elizabeth II and Prince Philip. No. 920, 960fr, Princess Diana and Queen Elizabeth II. No. 921, 960fr, Baden-Powell, Boy Scout and Scouting emblem. No. 922, 960fr, 14th Dalai Lama receiving 1989 Nobel Peace Prize. No. 923, 960fr, Soccer player, Stade de France, Saint-Denis. No. 924, 960fr, Women's 100-meter sprint, boxers. No. 925, 960fr, Explosion on USS Shaw, Herbert C. Jones, Medal of Honor. No. 926, 960fr, Disney, diff. No. 927, 960fr, Monroe, diff. No. 928, 960fr, Presley playing guitar, diff. No. 929, 960fr, Mozart, Masonic compass and square. No. 930, 960fr, Schumann conducting musicians, diff. No. 931, 960fr, Self-portrait with Bandaged Ear and Pipe, by van Gogh, 1889. No. 932, 960fr, Woman with a Parasol, by Monet, 1875. No. 933, 960fr, Seated Woman, by Picasso, 1937. No. 934, 960fr, Saint Nicholas waving. No. 935, 960fr, Adult and juvenile monkeys, diff.

2016, Mar. 15	Litho.	Perf. 13¼	
Sheets of 4, #a-d			
896-915	A302	Set of 20	245.00 245.00
Souvenir Sheets			
916-935	A302	Set of 20	220.00 220.00

Inscriptions on Nos. 911b and 932 are incorrect.

LA LUTTE CONTRE LE PALUDISME
A303

No. 936, 280fr — Campaign against malaria: a, Two adults watching sleeping child. b, Mosquito, person tending to patient. c, Mother watching sleeping child. d, Child behind mosquito netting.
No. 937, 280fr — Rugby players: a, Player kicking ball. b, Two players with red shirts attempting tackle. c, Player running with ball and opponent. d, Player with black shirt tackling ball carrier.
No. 938, 280fr — Table tennis players: a, Fan Zhendong. b, Liu Shiwen. c, Kasumi Ishikawa. d, Xu Xin.
No. 939, 280fr — Chess players: a, Magnus Carlsen. b, Sergey Karjakin. c, Viswanathan Anand. d, Judit Polgár.
No. 940, 280fr — Pilgrimage to Mecca: a, Pilgrims circling Ka'aba. b, Stoning of the devil. c, Great Mosque of Mecca, Koran. d, Shaving of heads.
No. 941, 280fr — Lighthouses: a, Les Eclaireurs Lighthouse, Argentina. b, Jeddah Lighthouse, Saudi Arabia. c, Lindau Lighthouse, Germany. d, New London Ledge Lighthouse, U.S.
No. 942, 280fr — Ships: a, Kruzenshtern. b, Flying Dutchman and Phocéa. c, Götheborg. d, Europa.
No. 943, 280fr — Steam locomotives: a, Class C38, Australia. b, Class 19D, South Africa. c, DRB Class 52, Germany. d, Class P36, Russia.
No. 944, 280fr — High-speed trains: a, CRH380A, People's Republic of China. b, Shinkansen Series E6, E621-1, Japan. c, Shinkansen Series N700A, Japan. d, Shinkansen Series H5, H523-1, Japan.
No. 945, 280fr — Race cars: a, Aston Martin DBRS 9. b, Ferrari F150 Italia. c, Ford Fiesta RS WRC. d, Maserati MC12 GT1.
No. 946, 280fr — Fire trucks: a, 1964 Bedford. b, 1962 Chevrolet Apache. c, 1959 Ford Galaxie. d, 1937 Chevrolet.
No. 947, 280fr — First commercial flight of the Concorde, 40th anniv.: a, Concorde in flight, passenger cabin. b, Concorde in flight, nose of Concorde. c, Concorde taking off. d, Under wing view of Concorde.
No. 948, 280fr — Scenes from Apollo space missions: a, Apollo 11. b, Apollo 16. c, Apollo 15. d, Apollo 17.
No. 949, 280fr — Sled dogs: a, Samoyeds. b, Siberian huskies and Alaskan malamutes. c, Alaskan malamutes. d, Man carrying Siberian husky.
No. 950, 280fr — Raptors: a, Melierax poliopterus. b, Torgos tracheliotus. c, Glaucidium passerinum. d, Terathopius ecaudatus.
No. 951, 280fr — Butterflies: a, Boloria aquilonaris. b, Pontia protodice. c, Strymon melinus. d, Aricia agestis.
No. 952, 280fr — Dinosaurs: a, Tyrannosaurus rex. b, Microraptor zhaoianus. c, Dakotaraptor steini. d, Chasmosaurus.
No. 953, 280fr — Orchids: a, Caucaea mimetica. b, Diuris magnifica. c, Thelymitra pulcherrima. d, Thelymitra campanulata.
No. 954, 280fr — Mushrooms: a, Craterellus tubaeformis. b, Tricholoma matsutake. c, Cantharellus cibarius. d, Stropharia rugoso.
No. 955, 280fr — Minerals: a, Sulfur. b, Chalcanthite. c, Colemanite. d, Legrandite.
No. 956, 960fr, Malaria-carrying mosquito, horiz. No. 957, 960fr, Rugby players, horiz. No. 958, 960fr, Ma Long playing table tennis, horiz. No. 959, 960fr, Chess players Anatoly Karpov and Garry Kasparov, horiz. No. 960, 960fr, Pilgrims on Mount Arafat, horiz. No. 961, 960fr, Cape Hatteras Lighthouse, U.S., Onychoprion fuscatus, horiz. No. 962, 960fr, El Galeón, horiz. No. 963, 960fr, Erie Berkshire locomotive, horiz. No. 964, 960fr, Frecciarossa 1000 train, Italy, horiz. No. 965, 960fr, Aston Martin DBR9, horiz. No. 966, 960fr, 1927 Ahrens-Fox fire truck, horiz. No. 967, 960fr, Concorde in flight and cockpit, horiz. No. 968, 960fr, Apollo 16 astronaut John Young on Moon, horiz. No. 969, 960fr, Dogs pulling sled, horiz. No. 970, 960fr, Aquila pomarina, horiz. No. 971, 960fr, Colotis danae, horiz. No. 972, 960fr, Deinocheirus mirificus, horiz. No. 973, 960fr, Cattleya schroederae, horiz. No. 974, 960fr, Boletus edulis, horiz. No. 975, 960fr, Galèna and fluorite, horiz.

2016, May 5　Litho.　Perf. 13¼
Sheets of 4, #a-d
936-955 A303　Set of 20　255.00　255.00
Souvenir Sheets
956-975 A303　Set of 20　220.00　220.00

No. 940a inscription is missing "c" of circumambulation. Nos. 956-975 each contain one 66x42mm stamp.

Investiture of Pres. Ismail Omar Guelleh A304

2016, May 8　Litho.　Perf. 13¼
976 A304　1000fr bister & multi　11.50　11.50
Litho. With Foil Application
Souvenir Sheet
977 A304　5000fr gold & multi　57.50　57.50

No. 976 was printed in sheets of 4. No. 977 contains one 51x51mm stamp.

A305

Independence, 39th Anniv. — A306

2016, June 27　Litho.　Perf. 13½x13
978 A305　250fr multi　3.00　3.00
Souvenir Sheet
Perf. 13¼
979 A306　500fr multi　5.75　5.75

Souvenir Sheet

Hassan Gouled Aptidon (1916-2006), First President of Djibouti — A307

2016, June 27　Litho.　Perf. 13¼
980 A307　500fr multi　5.75　5.75

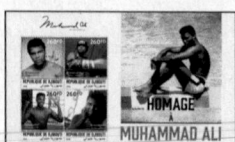

Muhammad Ali (1942-2016), Boxer — A308

No. 981 — Ali: a, With sign taped to wall. b, Wearing boxing gloves and headgear. c, In boxing ring. d, With hand touching face. 960fr, Ali running.

2016, July 28　Litho.　Perf. 13¼
981 A308　260fr Sheet of 4, #a-d　12.00　12.00
Souvenir Sheet
982 A308　960fr multi　11.00　11.00

No. 982 contains one 38x54mm stamp.

A309

No. 983, 260fr — Steve Jobs (1955-2011), co-founder and chief executive officer of Apple Inc., and: a, Steve Wozniak, co-founder of Apple. b, Three computers. c, Apple 1 computer. d, Computer and apple.

No. 984, 260fr — Pope Francis: a, With Patriarch Cyril of Moscow. b, With child and dove. c, With statue and rosary beads. d, Washing feet of refugees.

No. 985, 260fr — Paintings by Pierre-Auguste Renoir (1841-1919): a, Young Woman Sewing, 1879. b, Luncheon of the Boating Party, 1880-81. c, Two Girls at the Piano, 1892. d, The Bridge at Chatou, 1875.

No. 986, 260fr — Paintings by Francisco de Goya (1746-1828): a, The Umbrella, 1777. b, Clothed Maja, 1800. c, Saturn Devouring His Son, 1819-23. d, Charles IV of Spain and His Family, 1800.

No. 987, 260fr — Paintings by Berthe Morisot (1841-95): a, The Garden at Bougival, 1884. b, Hide-and-Seek, 1873. c, Lucie Leon at the Piano, 1892. d, Dahlias, 1876.

No. 988, 260fr — Paintings by Paul Cézanne (1839-1906): a, Kitchen Table, 1888-90. b, The Bridge at Maincy, 1879. c, Still Life with Apples and Oranges, 1895. d, Mont Sainte-Victoire with Large Pine, 1887.

No. 989, 260fr — Museum visitors looking at paintings in the Musée d'Orsay: a, Yellow Haystacks, by Paul Gauguin, 1889. b, Luncheon on the Grass, by Edouard Manet, 1862-63. c, The Floor Scrapers, by Gustave Caillebotte, 1875. d, Self-portrait, by Vincent van Gogh, 1889.

No. 990, 260fr — Items from ancient Egypt: a, Bust of Nefertiti. b, Gayer-Anderson Cat. c, Horus and Temple of Amun, Luxor. d, Funerary mask of Tutankhamun and Giza Pyramids.

No. 991, 260fr — Royal Mail, 500th anniv.: a, Postman emptying pillar box, Morris J Type mail van. b, Horse-drawn mail wagon. c, Postal worker rowing to SS Mona's Queen. d, Postmen on bicycles.

No. 992, 260fr — Battle of Moscow, 75th anniv.: a, German soldier and battlefield map. b, T-34 tank. c, Telegrapher and telegraph key. d, German General Erich Hoepner (1886-1944) and Sturmgeschütz III.

No. 993, 260fr — First flight of LZ-129 (Hindenburg), 80th anniv.: a, Pianist and singer on Hindenburg. b, Workers under docked Hindenburg. c, Hindenburg and hangar. d, Hindenburg, tables and chairs.

No. 994, 260fr — Yuri Gagarin (1934-68), 55th anniv. of first spaceflight, and: a, Launch of rocket. b, Vostok 1 in space. c, Gagarin seated in spacesuit. d, Monument to Gagarin, Moscow.

No. 995, 260fr — Intl. Year of Pulses: a, Woman, child and legumes. b, Hands holding seedling. c, Farm machinery, sprout. d, Poicephalus senegalus, legume.

No. 996, 260fr — Gold medalists at 2014 Winter Olympics, Sochi, Russia: a, Alexander Tretyakov, skeleton. b, Matthias Mayer, downhill skiing. c, Darya Domracheva, mass start, pursuit and individual biathlon. d, Michel Mulder, speed skating.

No. 997, 260fr — Host cities for 2018 World Cup soccer championships, Russia: a, Yekaterinburg. b, St. Petersburg. c, Kazan. d, Volgograd.

No. 998, 260fr — Cat breeds: a, Ragdoll, standing. b, Siamese. c, Ragdoll, prone. d, Australian Mist.

No. 999, 260fr — Dolphins: a, Stenella longirostris. b, Tursiops truncatus with open mouth, beak of Stenella longirostris. c, Stenella coeruleoalba. d, Two Tursiops truncatus.

No. 1000, 260fr — Owls: a, Asio stygius. b, Strix leptogrammica. c, Surnia ulula. d, Tyto alba.

No. 1001, 260fr — Turtles: a, Cuora flavomarginata. b, Terrapene carolina carolina. c, Terrapene carolina carolina, Geochelone elegans. c, Trachemys scripta elegans. d, Terrapene ornata ornata, Stigmochelys pardalis.

No. 1002, 260fr — Jobs, computer and iPhone. No. 1003, 960fr, Pope Francis and dove. No. 1004, 960fr, Portrait of Marie-Thérèse Durand Ruel, by Renoir, 1882. No. 1005, 960fr, Witches' Sabbath, by Goya, 1789. No. 1006, 960fr, On the Balcony of Eugene Manet's room at Bougival, by Morisot, 1881. No. 1007, 960fr, A Modern Olympia, by Cézanne, 1870. No. 1008, 960fr, Visitor looking at Portrait of Doctor Paul Gachet , 1890 at Musée d'Orsay. No. 1009, 960fr, Painting from Tomb of Userhat. No. 1010, 960fr, British postman, pillar box, Titan Airways Boeing 737. No. 1011, 960fr, Soviet General Georgy Zhukov (1896-1974), anti-aircraft fire of Battle of Moscow. No. 1012, 960fr, Mooring of the Hindenburg at Lakehurst, New Jersey. No. 1013, 960fr, Gagarin, Vostok 1, flag of Soviet Union. No. 1014, 960fr, Hands holding legumes. No. 1015, 960fr, Sage Kotsenburg, 2014 Winter Olympics snowboarding gold medalist. No. 1016, 960fr, Moscow, host city for 2018 World Cup. No. 1017, 960fr, Burmese cat. No. 1018, 960fr, Inia geoffrensis. No. 1019, 960fr, Bubo scandiacus. No. 1020, 960fr, Centrochelys sulcata.

2016, July 28　Litho.　Perf. 13¼
Sheets of 4, #a-d
983-1001 A309　Set of 19　225.00　225.00
Souvenir Sheets
1002-1020 A309　Set of 19　205.00　205.00

A310

No. 1021, 260fr — Ursus maritimus: a, Head of bear with open mouth. b, Looking at water. c, Two adults and cub. d, Bear walking.

No. 1022, 260fr — Hippopotamus amphibius: a, One animal with head near ground. b, One animal with open mouth, Latin name on two lines. c, Adult and juvenile. d, One adult with open mouth, Latin name on one line.

No. 1023, 260fr — Pandas: a, Ailuropoda melanoleuca eating. b, Ailurus fulgens, feet on mound. c, Ailurus fulgens, prone. d, Adult and juvenile Ailuropoda melanoleuca.

No. 1024, 260fr — Tigers: a, Head of Panthera tigris altaica. b, Panthera tigris tigris with open mouth. c, Panthera tigris tigris with closed mouth. d, Panthera tigris altaica walking.

No. 1025, 260fr — Dog breeds: a, Brussels griffon. b, Neapolitan mastiff. c, Canary Island hound. d, Kerry Blue terrier.

No. 1026, 260fr — Elephants: a, Loxodonta africana and tree. b, Two Loxodonta africana. c, Loxodonta africana and man. d, Loxodonta cyclotis.

No. 1027, 260fr — Water birds: a, Morus bassanus. b, Tadorna ferruginea. c, Dendrocygna bicolor. d, Cygnus atratus.

No. 1028, 260fr — Kingfishers: a, Corythornis cristatus, Halcyon smyrnensis. b, Alcedo atthis. c, Corythornis cristatus. d, Ceyx erithaca, Halcyon smyrnensis.

No. 1029, 260fr — Pigeons: a, Columba palumbus. b, Gymnophaps albertisii. c, Columba livia. d, Patagioenas leucocephala.

No. 1030, 260fr — Falcons: a, Falco vespertinus. b, Falco fasciinucha. c, Falco amurensis. d, Falco sparverius.

No. 1031, 260fr — Bees: a, Xylocopa micans. b, Euglossa dilemma. c, Anthidium manicatum. d, Augochlorella aurata.

No. 1032, 260fr — Butterflies: a, Cupidopsis cissus. b, Graphium porthaon. c, Myrina silenus. d, Tarucus sybaris.

No. 1033, 260fr — Fish: a, Acanthurus leucosternon, Acanthurus triostegus. b, Pterois volitans. c, Pygoplites diacanthus. d, Manta alfredi.

No. 1034, 260fr — Shells: a, Cypraecassis rufa. b, Charonia tritonis. c, Trochus nodulosus. d, Conus mustelinus.

No. 1035, 260fr — Extinct animals: a, Mammuthus columbi. b, Moropus elatus. c, Elasmotherium sibiricum. d, Smilodon populator.

No. 1036, 260fr — Prehistoric aquatic animals: a, Enchodus. b, Mosasaurus hoffmannii. c, Ammonoidea. d, Helicoprion bessonovi.

No. 1037, 260fr — Mushrooms: a, Rhodotus palmatus. b, Phallus indusiatus. c, Lactarius deliciosus. d, Leccinum scabrum.

No. 1038, 260fr — Minerals: a, Chalcanthite. b, Legrandite. c, Gadolinite. d, Fluorite.

No. 1039, 260fr — Cartoon characters on stamps: a, U.S. Nos. 4399-4402 (Characters from *The Simpsons*). b, U.S. No. 4470, Switzerland Nos. 1536-1537 (Characters from *Garfield*). c, U.S. Zazzle personalized stamps depicting *SpongeBob SquarePants*. d, Switzerland No. 1497, Belgium Nos. 2320-2321 (Characters from *The Smurfs*).

No. 1040, 960fr, Ursus maritimus adult and cub. No. 1041, 960fr, Hippopotamus amphibius adult and juvenile, diff. No. 1042, 960fr, Two Ailuropoda melanoleuca. No. 1043, 960fr, Two Panthera tigris altaica. No. 1044, 960fr, Akita. No. 1045, 960fr, Elephas maximus. No. 1046, 960fr, Gavia immer. No. 1047, 960fr, Alcedo atthis, diff. No. 1048, 960fr, Goura scheepmakeri. No. 1049, 960fr, Falco peregrinus. No. 1050, 960fr, Andrena cineraria. No. 1051, 960fr, Myrina silenus ficedula. No. 1052, 960fr, Plectorhinchus vittatus, Heniochus pleurotaenia. No. 1053, 960fr, Lambis lambis. No. 1054, 960fr, Glyptodon clavipes. No. 1055, 960fr, Dinichthys terrelli. No. 1056, 960fr, Morchella esculenta. No. 1057, 960fr, Cassiterite. No. 1058, 960fr, Netherlands No.1080a, U.S. Zazzle srtamps depicting *Tom and Jerry*.

2016, Sept. 26　Litho.　Perf. 13¼
Sheets of 4, #a-d
1021-1039 A310　Set of 19　225.00　225.00
Souvenir Sheets
1040-1058 A310　Set of 19　210.00　210.00

Worldwide Fund for Nature (WWF) — A311

No. 1059 — Torgos tracheliotos: a, Bird on branch. b, Two birds. c, Two birds and carrion. d, Bird and animal bones.
960fr, Torgos tracheliotos in flight.

2016, Sept. 26　Litho.　Perf. 13¼
1059 A311　260fr Sheet of 4, #a-d　12.00　12.00
Souvenir Sheet
1060 A311　960fr multi　11.00　11.00

No. 1060 lacks the WWF emblem on the stamp and sheet margin. For surcharges, see Nos. 1814-1821.

Miniature Sheet

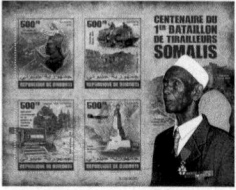

First Batallion of Somali Snipers, Cent. A312

No. 1061: a, Medal, Battle of Douaumont. b, Tank and Malmaison, 1917. c, Monument. d, Airplane over Pointe de Grave and Cordouan Lighthouse, France, 1945.

2016, Oct. 24　Litho.　Perf. 13¼
1061 A312　500fr Sheet of 4, #a-d　22.50　22.50

A313

No. 1062, 280fr — Rotary International in Djibouti: a, Boy holding stick and water bottle. b, Woman and children at well. c, Woman holding child to receive vaccination. d, Children.

No. 1063, 280fr — Red Cross-Red Crescent in Djibouti: a, Red Crescent, map of Africa, Red Crescent workers carrying litter. b, Red Crescent worker assisting woman. c, Red

Crescent worker looking at notebook. d, Red Crescent worker holding water bucket.

No. 1064, 280fr — Canonization of Mother Teresa (1910-97): a, Mother Teresa and building. b, Mother Teresa, dove, Pres. Ronald Reagan and wife, Nancy. c, Mother Teresa holding child. d, Mother Teresa and flag of India.

No. 1065, 280fr — Extraordinary Jubilee of Mercy: a, Pope Francis in Kenya. b, Pope Francis opening holy doors. c, Pope Benedict XVI. d, Dove and Popes Francis, Benedict XVI.

No. 1066, 280fr — British royal family: a, Queen Elizabeth II. b, Duke and Duchess of Cambridge. c, Prince George and Princess Charlotte. d, Duke and Duchess of Cambridge, Prince George and Princess Charlotte.

No. 1067, 280fr — Publication of Albert Einstein's Theory of General Relativity, cent.: a, Einstein, globes, equation, model of atom. b, Einstein and equation. c, Hand holding orb depicting Einstein. d, Einstein and light bulb.

No. 1068, 280fr — Battle of the Somme, cent.: a, Mark I tank. b, British Gen. Ivor Maxse (1862-1958) and soldiers. c, French soldiers at munitions wagon. d, German soldier on horse.

No. 1069, 280fr — Navy ships: a, San Marco, Italy. b, Zubr Class hovercraft, Russia, and tank. c, USS Coronado, United States. d, BSF Azov 151, BF Minsk 127, Russia.

No. 1070, 280fr — Submarines: a, Type 035, People's Republic of China. b, Typhoon Class Project 941, Russia. c, A26 submarine. d, HMS Triumph, Great Britain.

No. 1071, 280fr — High-speed trains.: a, ETR 500 Frecciarossa, Italy. b, SNCF TGV Duplex, France. c, AVE Class 103, Spain. d, Eurostar e320, Great Britain.

No. 1072, 280fr — Motorcycles: a, BMW K1600GTL. b, Suzuki TU250X. c, MV Agusta F3 800. d, Yamaha Star VMAX.

No. 1073, 280fr — Russian military aircraft: a, Sukhoi Su-35. b, Mil Mi-28 helicopter. c, Kamov KA-50 helicopter. d, Mikoyan MiG-41.

No. 1074, 280fr — Space exploration: a, Mars Rover Spirit, 2004. b, Neil Armstrong (1930-2012) on ladder of Lunar Module, 1969. c, Yuri Gagarin (1934-68), and Vostok 1, 1961. d, Final mission of Space Shuttle Atlantis, 2011.

No. 1075, 280fr — 2016 Ice Hockey World Championships, Russia: a, Players fighting for puck near goaltender. b, U.S. player and Russian goaltender. c, Canadian and Russian players. d, Finnish player and Canadian goaltender.

No. 1076, 280fr — Chess players: a, Magnus Carlsen. b, Anatoly Karpov. c, Bobby Fischer. d, Mariya Muzychuk.

No. 1077, 280fr — Islamic art: a, Battle scene from the Shahnameh. b, Interior of Cathedral-Mosque of Córdoba, Spain. c, Jameh Mosque, Isfahan, Iran. d, Pyxis of al-Mughira.

No. 1078, 280fr — Lighthouses: a, Petit Minou Lighthouse, France. b, Hornby Lighthouse, Australia. c, Store Faerder Lighthouse, Norway. d, Point Betsie Lighthouse, Michigan.

No. 1079, 280fr — Orchids: a, Cattleya labiata. b, Cypripedium kentuckiense. c, Vanda denisoniana. d, Orchis purpurea.

No. 1080, 280fr — New Year 2017 (Year of the Rooster): a, Rooster with leg raised and wings extended. b, Rooster facing right, pagoda in background. c, Rooster facing right, torii in background. d, Rooster in air, flapping wings.

No. 1081, 960fr, Child and containers, Rotary International emblem. No. 1082, 960fr, Red Crescent worker with water bottle tending to injured person. No. 1083, 960fr, Mother Teresa and child, diff. No. 1084, 960fr, Pope Francis holding creche figure of infant Jesus. No. 1085, 960fr, Queen Elizabeth II, diff. No. 1086, 960fr, Einstein at blackboard. No. 1087, 960fr, German soldier at Battle of the Somme. No. 1088, 960fr, USS Essex and CH-53E helicopters. No. 1089, 960fr, USS Scorpion. No. 1090, 960fr, IC3 3 train, Germany. No. 1091, 960fr, Beta 450 RR motorcycle. No. 1092, 960fr, Mikoyan MiG-35. No. 1093, 960fr, Sputnik 1, 1957. No. 1094, 960fr, Russian ice hockey player sprawled on ice. No. 1095, 960fr, Sergey Karjakin, chess pieces. No. 1096, 960fr, Qutub Minar and Alai Darwaza, India. No. 1097, 960fr, La Vieille Lighthouse, France. No. 1098, 960fr, Vanda coerulea. No. 1099, 960fr, Rooster and Great Wall of China.

2016, Nov. 25   Litho.   Perf. 13¼
Sheets of 4, #a-d
1062-1080 A313 Set of 19   240.00 240.00
Souvenir Sheets
1081-1099 A313 Set of 19   205.00 205.00

Election of Donald Trump as U.S.
President — A314

No. 1100: a, Trump and stars. b, Trump and Republican Party emblem. c, Trump with wife, Melania, and son, Barron. d, Trump and running mate, Mike Pence.
960fr, Trump, diff.

2016, Nov. 25   Litho.   Perf. 13¼
1100 A314 280fr Sheet of 4,
    #a-d   12.50 12.50
Souvenir Sheet
1101 A314 960fr multi   11.00 11.00
No. 1101 contains one 51x90mm stamp.

A315

No. 1102, 280fr — St. John Paul II (1920-2005), with: a, Boy and girl. b, Crowd worshiping. c, Candles. d, Religious sculpture.

No. 1103, 280fr — Michèle Morgan (1920-2016), actress, with: a, Unidentified actor. b, Hand on head. c, Clapboard and film reel. d, Gérard Philipe (1922-59), actor.

No. 1104, 280fr — John Glenn, Jr. (1921-2016), astronaut: a, U.S. flag, Mercury capsule, launch of Atlas 8 rocket. b, Glenn and Space Shuttle Discovery. c, Glenn, military airplane and Pres. John F. Kennedy (1917-63). d, Glenn, U.S. flag and rocket launch.

No. 1105, 280fr — Rotary International emblem and: a, Paul P. Harris (1868-1947), founder of Rotary International, holding book. b, Rotary volunteer giving vaccine to child. c, Children reading. d, Harris with reversed Paul Harris Fellow pin.

No. 1106, 280fr — Scouting, 110th anniv.: a, Scouts in canoe, Nettapus auritus. b, Scout with binoculars, Circaetus cinereus. c, Scouts with Scouting flag. d, Scout and Lentinus squarrosolus.

No. 1107, 280fr — Paintings by Ivan Aivazovsky (1817-1900): a, Portrait of Loris-Melikov, 1888. b, Battle of Cesme at Night, 1848. c, Boat Ride by Kumpaki in Constantinople, 1846. d, Odessa, 1840.

No. 1108, 280fr — Paintings by Edgar Degas (1834-1917): a, In a Cafe, 1875-76. b, Emma Dobigny, 1869. c, A Cotton Office in New Orleans, 1873. d, Ballet Rehearsal on Stage, 1874.

No. 1109, 280fr — Paintings by Frida Kahlo (1907-54): a, Tree of Hope, Keep Firm, 1946. b, Still Life with Parrot, 1951. c, The Wounded Deer, 1946. d, Portrait of Lucha Maria, a Girl from Tehuacan, 1942.

No. 1110, 280fr — Sculptures by Auguste Rodin (1840-1917): a, The Thinker, 1903. b, Lady Sackville-West, 1913. c, Young Woman with Flowered Hat, 1870-75. d, The Clenched Hand, 1885, The Gates of Hell, 1880-90.

No. 1111, 280fr — Primates: a, Pongo pygmaeus. b, Indri indri. c, Loris tardigradus. d, Papio hamadryas.

No. 1112, 280fr — Wild cats: a, Panthera tigris altaica. b, Panthera neofelis nebulosa. c, Puma concolor. d, Panthera pardus kotiya.

No. 1113, 280fr — Dolphins: a, Stenella longirostris. b, Grampus griseus. c, Lagenorhynchus obscurus. d, Tursiops truncatus.

No. 1114, 280fr — Whales: a, Balaena mysticetus. b, Delphinapterus leucas. c, Physeter macrocephalus. d, Balaenoptera musculus.

No. 1115, 280fr — Owls: a, Aegolius harrisii, Aegolius acadicus. b, Athene noctua. c, Bubo virginianus. d, Glaucidium passerinum.

No. 1116, 280fr — Birds of prey: a, Caracara plancus. b, Aegolicus acadicus. c, Coragyps atratus. d, Gymnogyps californianus.

No. 1117, 280fr — Water birds: a, Rynchops niger. b, Eudocimus ruber. c, Gavia immer. d, Mycteria leucocephala.

No. 1118, 280fr — Butterflies: a, Perrhybris pamela. b, Junonia lemonias lemonias. c, Ixias pyrene. d, Colotis euippe.

No. 1119, 280fr — Fish: a, Acanthurus leucosternon. b, Ostracion cubicus. c, Antennarius coccineus. d, Scarus coelestinus.

No. 1120, 280fr — Turtles: a, Batagur trivittata. b, Chelus fimbriatus. c, Lepidochelys kempii. d, Lepidochelys olivacea.

No. 1121, 280fr — Snakes: a, Pituophis catenifer. b, Diadophis punctatus. c, Oxyrhopus trigeminus. d, Natrix natrix.

No. 1122, 280fr — Dinosaurs: a, Iguanodon. b, Spinops sternbergorum. c, Cryolophosaurus. d, Spinosaurus.

No. 1123, 280fr — Endangered animals: a, Campephilus principalis. b, Panthera pardus orientalis. c, Helarctos malayanus. d, Lepilemur septentrionalis.

No. 1124, 280fr — Mushrooms: a, Cantharellus cibarius. b, Gyromitra esculenta. c, Ramaria formosa. d, Tylopilus felleus.

No. 1125, 280fr — Orchids: a, Vanda coerulea. b, Cattleya. c, White Phalaenopsis. d, Zygopetalum.

No. 1126, 280fr — Minerals: a, Amazonite. b, Wulfenite. c, Rhodochrosite. d, Aquamarine.

No. 1127, 960fr, St. John Paul II and crosses. No. 1128, 960fr, Morgan with strings of pearls. No. 1129, 960fr, Glenn receiving Presidential Medal of Freedom from Pres. Barack Obama. No. 1130, 960fr, Rotary International emblem and bust of Harris. No. 1131, 960fr, Scout blowing horn, Colotis danae. No. 1132, 960fr, The Roads at Kronstadt, by Aivazovsky, 1840. No. 1133, 960fr, The Dance Class, by Degas, 1874. No. 1134, 960fr, Portrait of My Father, by Kahlo, 1951. No. 1135, 960fr, The Burghers of Calais, by Rodin, 1884-89. No. 1136, 960fr, Leontopithecus rosalia. No. 1137, 960fr, Lynx pardinus. No. 1138, 960fr, Cephalorhynchus heavisidii. No. 1139, 960fr, Megaptera novaeangliae. No. 1140, 960fr, Asio capensis. No. 1141, 960fr, Buteo lagopus. No. 1142, 960fr, Anas rhynchotis. No. 1143, 960fr, Delias eucharis. No. 1144, 960fr, Sparisoma cretense. No. 1145, 960fr, Geochelone elephantopus. No. 1146, 960fr, Naja sumatrana. No. 1147, 960fr, Parasaurolophus. No. 1148, 960fr, Gyps indicus. No. 1149, 960fr, Clitocybe phyllophila. No. 1150, 960fr, Black Phalaenopsis orchid. No. 1151, 960fr, Pyromorphite.

2017, Jan. 20   Litho.   Perf. 13¼
Sheets of 4, #a-d
1102-1126 A315 Set of 25   310.00 310.00
Souvenir Sheets
1127-1151 A315 Set of 25   265.00 265.00

Varanus Komodoensis — A316

No. 1152 — Komodo dragon: a, With head down, tongue out. b, With head raised, tongue not visible. c, Climbing rock. d, With head raised, tongue out.
950fr, Komodo dragon, tongue touching ground.

2017, Mar. 15   Litho.   Perf. 13¼
1152 A316 240fr Sheet of 4,
    #a-d   11.00 11.00
Souvenir Sheet
1153 A316 950fr multi   10.50 10.50
Bandung 2017 World Stamp Exhibition. No. 1153 contains one 48x48mm stamp.

A317

No. 1154 — 240fr — Wilbur Wright (1867-1912), aviation pioneer: a, Wright, with brother, Orville (1871-1948) and Wright Flyer. b, Wind testing of Wright Flyer, 1901. c, Wilbur and Wright Flyer in flight. d, Wilbur at controls of airplane.

No. 1155, 240fr — Concorde: a, British Airways Concorde over Paris. b, British Airways Concorde over Nice, France. c, Air France Concorde over London. d, British Airways Concorde over Mecca, Saudi Arabia.

No. 1156, 240fr — Military aircraft: a, Mikoyan-Gurevich MiG-29. b, A-10 Thunderbolt II. c, Junkers Ju 52. d, Boeing-Bell V-22 Osprey.

No. 1157, 240fr — Disappearance of Amelia Earhart (1897-1937), pilot: a, Earhart and her airplane. b, Earhart, airplane and hangar. c, Earhart and husband, George P. Putnam (1887-1950). d, Electra 10E in flight.

No. 1158, 240fr — Ferdinand von Zeppelin (1838-1917), airship manufacturer: a, Zeppelin, passengers boarding Graf Zeppelin. b, Zeppelin LZ-1. c, Zeppelin LZ-4. d, Zeppelin and schematic drawings of airship.

No. 1159, 240fr — 80th birthday of Valentina Tereshkova, first woman in space: a, In car with Russia Premier Nikita Khrushchev (1894-1971). b, With Yuri Gagarin (1934-68), first man in space. c, With obverse and reverse of 1983 1-ruble Russian coin depicting her. d, With Vostok 6.

No. 1160, 240fr — Steam trains: a, Pennsylvania Railroad 1223. b, London and North Eastern Railway Class A4 Mallard 4468. c, Great Western Railway 4-4-0 City of Truro 3717. d, Deutsche Reichsbahn 18 201.

No. 1161, 240fr — High-speed trains: a, Talgo 350. b, NTV Alstom AGV 575. c, Shinkansen Series 500. d, Renfe Series S-103.

No. 1162, 240fr — Sinking of the Titanic, 105th anniv.: a, Titanic and map of voyage. b, Titanic sinking and overturned lifeboat. c, Titanic and iceberg. d, Titanic and Thomas Andrews (1873-1912), designer of Titanic.

No. 1163, 240fr — Submarines: a, HMAS Collins, Australia. b, SSK Kilo Class Type 636 and Icebreaker Ivan Kruzenshtern, Russia. c, HMS Ambush, Great Britain. d, Terrible, France.

No. 1164, 240fr — Donald Campbell (1921-67), land and water speed record holder: a, Wearing helmet. b, In Bluebird K7, waving. c, Sitting. d, With wife, Tonia Bern-Campbell.

No. 1165, 240fr — Special transportation: a, Telescope transporter. b, Victoria, Australia police vehicle. c, Euclid dump truck. d, Snowcat.

No. 1166, 240fr — Fire-fighting vehicles: a, Caterpillar CT660 fire truck, United States. b, Foremost Nodwell 240, Canada. c, Delta 2 wheeled carrier, Canada. d, Hopedale, Massachusets Tanker 1, United States.

No. 1167, 240fr — 1947 Ferrari 125 S, 70th anniv., with background design of: a, Trees. b, Ferrari emblem. c, Steering wheel and dashboard. d, Clouds.

No. 1168, 240fr — Motorcycles: a, 1912 Henderson 4-cylinder. b, 1923 BMW R32. c, 1962-63 BSA Rocket Gold Star A10. d, 1974 Hercules-Wankel 2000.

No. 1169, 240fr — Transportation for Pres. Donald Trump: a, Sikorsky S-76 helicopter. b, 2015 Mercedes-Benz Class S600. c, 1997 Lamborghini Diablo. d, Boeing 757.

No. 1170, 240fr — Sled dogs: a, Five sled dogs and two drivers. b, Two Seppala Siberian sled dogs. c, Husky and Malamutes. d, Sled dogs resting with driver.

No. 1171, 240fr — Jacques Cousteau (1910-97), conservationist and filmmaker: a, Calypso and hot air balloon in Antarctica. b, Cousteau and SP-350 Denise. c, Cousteau holding cup. d, Cousteau and Calypso.

No. 1172, 240fr — Charles Darwin (1809-82), naturalist: a, Portrait of Darwin and his wife, Emma, by George Richmond. b, HMS Beagle and map of its voyage, Conolophus subcristatus. c, Darwin, primate and skulls of Homo neanderthalensis and Homo sapiens. d, Darwin and specimens of Pseudoscarus lepidus, Eleginops maclovinus, and Ceroglossus darwinii.

No. 1173, 240fr — Russian October Revolution, cent.: a, Barricades at St. Isaac Cathedral, St. Petersburg. b, Soldiers at Hermitage and Winter Palace, St. Petersburg. c, Demonstrators in St. Petersburg. d, Lenin (1870-1924), and Cruiser Aurora.

No. 1174, 240fr — Battle of Stalingrad, 75th anniv.: a, Aug. 23, 1942 air raid. b, Soviet Gen. Georgi Zhukov (1896-1974). c, German Gen. Friedrich Paulus (1890-1957). d, Soviet troops, Feb. 1943.

No. 1175, 240fr — Lighthouses: a, Punta Palascia Lighthouse, Italy. b, Lindesnes Lighthouse, Norway. c, Pointe aux Barques Lighthouse, Michigan. d, North Head Lighthouse, Washington.

No. 1176, 240fr — Windmills and tulips: a, Kinderdijk, Netherlands windmills, red and white tulips. b, Kuremaa, Estonia windmill, yellow tulips. c, Sonderho, Denmark windmill, orange tulips. d, Halanker, Great Britain windmill, red tulips.

No. 1177, 240fr — Endangered animals: a, Anolis gorgonae. b, Anolis proboscis. c, Neurergus kaiseri. d, Tokay gecko.

No. 1178, 950fr, Orville Wright on bicycle, Wright Flyer in flight. No. 1179, 950fr, British Airways Concorde over New York City. No. 1180, 950fr, F-16 Fighting Falcon. No. 1181, 950fr, Earhart holding propeller. No. 1182, 950fr, Zeppelin and his signature. No. 1183, 950fr, Tereshkova and stylized rocket. No. 1184, 950fr, St. Louis-San Francisco train. No. 1185, 950fr, Shinkansen Series E6. No. 1186, 950fr, Titanic and its captain, Edward Smith (1850-1912). No. 1187, 950fr, Victoria Class submarine, Canada. No. 1188, 950fr, Campbell in Bluebird K7. No. 1189, 950fr, Lockheed Martin hybrid dirigibles. No. 1190, 950fr, San José, California fire truck. No. 1191, 950fr, Enzo Ferrari (1898-1988), automobile manufacturer in 1947 Ferrari 125 S. No. 1192, 950fr, 2006 Royal Enfield Bullet motorcycle. No. 1193, 950fr, Gold Trump sledge. No. 1194, 950fr, Siberian husky sled dogs. No. 1195, 950fr, Cousteau holding walkie-talkie. No. 1196, 950fr, Darwin, Geospiza fortis, heads of Galapagos finches. No. 1197, 950fr, Lenin and Cruiser Aurora, diff. No. 1198, 950fr, Vasily Zaytsev (1915-91), Soviet sniper at Battle of Stalingrad. No. 1199, 950fr, Petit Minou Lighthouse, France. No. 1200, 950fr, Mostert, South Africa windmill, red and yellow tulips. No. 1201, 950fr, Neurergus kaiseri, diff.

2017, Mar. 15   Litho.   Perf. 13¼
Sheet of 4, #a-d
1154-1177 A317 Set of 24 260.00 260.00
Souvenir Sheets
1178-1201 A317 Set of 24 255.00 255.00

Miniature Sheets

Opening of Djibouti-Ethiopia Electric Rail Line — A318

Nos. 1202 and 1203: a, Tracks and catenary network. b, Electric train. c, Holl Holl Bridge. d, Nagad Station.

2017, Apr. 25 Litho.   Perf. 12¾x13¼
1202 A318 200fr Sheet of 4,
         #a-d   9.00 9.00
1203 A318 250fr Sheet of 4,
         #a-d   11.00 11.00

A319

No. 1204, 240fr — Ailuropoda melanoleuca (Giant panda): a, On branch. b, Adult and cub. c, On back. d, Facing left.
No. 1205, 240fr — Dogs: a, Papillons. b, French bulldog. c, English cocker spaniel. d, Basset hounds.
No. 1206, 240fr — Dolphins: a, Lagenorhynchus obscurus. b, Tursiops truncatus. c, Cephalorhynchus commersonii. d, Stenella frontalis.
No. 1207, 240fr — Owls: a, Tyto alba. b, Bubo cinerascens. c, Bubo lacteus. d, Glaucidium perlatum.
No. 1208, 240fr — Bees and orchids: a, Euglossa imperialis, Cattleya aclandiae. b, Exaerete frontalis, Cymbidium madidum. c, Euglossa tridentata, Maxillaria tenuifolia. d, Euglossa dilemma, Cattleya lueddemanniana.
No. 1209, 240fr — Butterflies: a, Batesia hypochlora. b, Papilio demoleus. c, Melitaea didyma. d, Phengaris arion.
No. 1210, 240fr — Turtles: a, Graptemys pseudogeographica kohni. b, Rhinoclemmys pulcherrima. c, Trachemys scripta scripta. d, Trachemys scripta elegans.
No. 1211, 240fr — Extinct animals: a, Mammuthus meridionalis. b, Raphus cucullatus. c, Megacerops coloradensis. d, Thalassocnus antiquus.
No. 1212, 240fr — Mahatma Gandhi (1869-1948), Indian nationalist: a, With spinning wheel. b, Walking, holding walking stick. c, With building. d, With decorated cow.
No. 1213, 240fr — Princess Diana (1961-97): a, With Prince Charles and coat of arms.

b, Wearing white blouse. c, Wearing white blouse, with sunglasses in hair. d, Holding Prince Harry.
No. 1214, 950fr, Ailuropoda melanoleuca adult and cub, diff. No. 1215, 950fr, Rottweilers. No. 1216, 950fr, Sotalia fluviatilis. No. 1217, 950fr, Otus senegalensis. No. 1218, 950fr, Euglossa imperialis, Laelia anceps. No. 1219, 950fr, Colotis ione. No. 1220, 950fr, Apalone mutica. No. 1221, 950fr, Glyptodon clavipes. No. 1222, 950fr, Gandhi and Taj Mahal. No. 1223, 950fr, Princess Diana, Duke and Duchess of Cambrige, Prince Harry.

2017, July 5   Litho.   Perf. 13¼
Sheets of 4, #a-d
1204-1213 A319 Set of 10 110.00 110.00
Souvenir Sheets
1214-1223 A319 Set of 10 105.00 105.00

International Day of Girls in Information and Communications Technology — A319a

2017, July 13   Litho.   Perf. 13¼
1223A A319a 100fr multi   1.10 1.10
Souvenir Sheet
1223B A319a 200fr multi   2.25 2.25

"Eid Mubarak" — A319b

Designs: 150fr, Lantern at right, Arabic text at left.
300fr, Lantern and star at left, Arabic text at right.

2017, July 20   Litho.   Perf. 13x13¼
1223C A319b 150fr multi   1.75 1.75
Souvenir Sheet
Perf. 13½x13¼
1223D A319b 300fr multi   3.50 3.50

A319c

Independence, 40th Anniv. — A319d

No. 1223E — Flag of Djibouti and: g, "Unité" at LL. h, Arabic inscription at LL. i, "Inkitino" at LL. j, "Midnimo" at LL.

2017, July 20   Litho.   Perf. 13¼
1223E A319c 150fr Sheet of 4,
         #g-j   6.75 6.75

Souvenir Sheet
Litho. With Foil Application
1223F A319d 500fr sil & multi 5.75 5.75

A320

No. 1224, 240fr — Formula I race cars: a, Blue and yellow cars. b, Orange car. c, Bright red car. d, Red and orange cars.
No. 1225, 240fr — Ice hockey: a, Norwegian player in dark blue jersey, player in white and blue jersey. b, Henrik Lundqvist, goaltender for New York Rangers. c, Referee and Washington Capitals player with stick raised. d, Boston Bruins player in black and yellow jersey, player in red and white jersey.
No. 1226, 240fr — Cricket players: a, Batsman swinging and falling fielder. b, Shikhar Dhawan. c, Josh Hazlewood. d, Batsman holding bat behind back, celebrating player.
No. 1227, 240fr — Tennis players: a, Rafael Nadal. b, Stan Wawrinka. c, Angelique Kerber. d, Serena Williams.
No. 1228, 240fr — Table tennis players: a, Zhang Jike. b, Liu Shiwen. c, Ding Ning. d, Liu Guoliang.
No. 1229, 240fr — Golfers: a, Dustin Johnson. b, So-yeon Ryu. c, Lydia Ko. d, Rory McIlroy.
No. 1230, 240fr — Pierre de Coubertin (1863-1937), President of International Olympic Committee: a, Coubertin, wrestlers in background. b, Statue of Coubertin, Beijing. c, Coubertin facing right. d, Coubertin, ancient Greek soldiers in background.
No. 1231, 240fr — Chess pieces: a, Black knight, queen in silhouette. b, White queen, hand moving black piece. c, White queen and king, black king. d, Carved piece depicting elephant carrying howdah, queen in background.
No. 1232, 240fr — Metropolitan Museum of Art, 145th anniv.: a, Fragment of bust of Roman Emperor Caracalla. b, Charles Engelhard Court. c, Bust of Young Girl Identified as Anne Audéoud of Geneva, by Jean Antoine Houdon. d, Silver Buffalo Figure from Benin, 19th cent.
No. 1233, 240fr — Red Cross-Red Crescent Campaign Against Malaria: a, Man spraying insecticide in village. b, Woman and mosquito netting. c, Medical worker examining child. d, Medical worker taking blood sample from child.
No. 1234, 240fr — Pres. John F. Kennedy (1917-63), and: a, U.S. flag. b, Wife, Jacqueline. c, Daughter, Caroline. d, Wife, daughter, and son, John, Jr.
No. 1235, 240fr — 35th birthday of Prince William of Cambridge: a, In helicopter. b, With wife and children. c, As child, with parents and brother. d, Playing polo with brother, Prince Harry.
No. 1236, 240fr — Tall ships: a, Royal Clipper, Sweden. b, Belem, France. c, Palinuro, Italy. d, Juan Sebastián de Elcano, Spain.
No. 1237, 240fr — Naval vessels: a, Gloire, France, 1859. b, USS Texas, 1912. c, Yamato, Japan, 1940. d, La Fayette, France, 1996.
No. 1238, 240fr — European high-speed trains: a, TGV Thalys PBKA, France. b, TGV Lyria, France and Switzerland. c, ICE 3, Germany. d, TCDD HT80000, Turkey.
No. 1239, 240fr — Fire trucks: a, Citroen 46 CDU. b, Rosenbauer Panther. c, MAZ7310 Airfield Crash Tender. d, Ladder truck with tank treads.
No. 1240, 240fr — Opel automobiles: a, Opel Ascona A. b, Opel Kapitän. c, Opel Mokka. d, Opel Tigra.
No. 1241, 240fr — Supersonic aircraft: a, Aerion SBJ. b, North American XB-70 Valkyrie. c, Tupolev Tu-22M. d, Lockheed SR-71 Blackbird.
No. 1242, 240fr — Sergei Korolev (1907-66), spacecraft designer: a, Luna 3, Sputnik 1. b, Korolev and Luna 8K72. c, Korolev and R-7 Semyorka missile. d, Yuri Gagarin (1934-68), cosmonaut, and Vostok 1.
No. 1243, 240fr — Birds of Djibouti: a, Dendropicos namaquus. b, Phoeniculus somaliensis. c, Caprimulgus stellatus. d, Trachyphonus darnaudii.
No. 1244, 950fr, Nico Rosberg, 2016 Formula 1 racing champion and car. No. 1245, 950fr, Ice hockey player taking shot. No. 1246, 950fr, Cricket batsman and wicket-keeper. No. 1247, 950fr, Tennis player Andy Murray. No. 1248, 950fr, Table tennis player Ma Long. No. 1249, 950fr, Golfer Jason Day. No. 1250, 950fr, Coubertin and hurdlers. No. 1251, 950fr, King and queen chess pieces. No. 1252, 950fr, Statue of William Shakespeare, by John Quincy Adams Ward. No. 1253, 950fr,

Woman carrying child, Anopheles maculipennis. No. 1254, 950fr, Pres. Kennedy and U.S. flag, diff. No. 1255, 950fr, Wedding of Prince William of Cambridge and Catherine Middleton. No. 1256, 950fr, Tovarishch, Russia. No. 1257, 950fr, Gloire, France, 1935. No. 1258, 950fr, Renfe Series S-114, Spain. No. 1259, 950fr, Bulldog 4x4 fire truck. No. 1260, 950fr, Opel Astra J. No. 1261, 950fr, Panavia Tornado IDS. No. 1262, 950fr, Korolev and Vostok 1. No. 1263, 950fr, Tricholaema melanocephala.

2017, July 28   Litho.   Perf. 13¼
Sheets of 4, #a-d
1224-1243 A320 Set of 20 215.00 215.00
Souvenir Sheets
1244-1263 A320 Set of 20 215.00 215.00

Birdpex 8 Philatelic Exhibition, Mondorf-les-Bains, Luxembourg (Nos. 1243, 1263).

A321

No. 1264, 240fr — Marilyn Monroe (1926-62), actress: a, Wearing white fur coat. b, With signature. c, With star from Hollywood Walk of Fame. d, Wearing black sweater.
No. 1265, 240fr — Paul McCartney, rock musician, and: a, Emblem of the Beatles. b, Wife, Linda. c, Beatle bandmates, John Lennon, Ringo Starr and George Harrison. d, Musical score and curved piano keyboard.
No. 1266, 240fr — Charlie Chaplin (1889-1977), film actor, and: a, Actor Ben Turpin. b, Signature. c, Woman holding flower. d, Child actor.
No. 1267, 240fr — Marie Curie (1867-1934), chemist and physicist, and: a, Pitchblende, husband, Pierre (1859-1906). b, Nobel medals and Daughter, Irène Joliot-Curie (1897-1956). c, Curie Pavilion of Institut du Radium. d, World War I mobile radiological unit.
No. 1268, 240fr — Nelson Mandela (1918-2013), President of South Africa: a, With F. W. de Klerk, Pres. of South Africa, and Nobel medals and diplomas. b, With fist raised. c, Holding dove. d, With trophy and South African rugby player.
No. 1269, 240fr — Pres. Franklin D. Roosevelt (1882-1945): a, Signing declaration of war against Germany. b, Wearing top hat. c, With wife, Eleanor (1884-1962). d, Signing Social Security legislation.
No. 1270, 240fr — Battle of Dunkirk: a, British Admiral Bertram Home Ramsay (1883-1945). b, Airplane flying over battle. c, Battle aftermath. d, Troops in water.
No. 1271, 240fr — Pompidou Center, Paris, 40th anniv.: a, La Roue Rouge, by Fernand Léger. b, Quatre Passagers Roses de Face, by Jean Dubuffet. c, Blue in Violet, by Wassily Kandinsky. d, Vieilles Maisons, Saint-Ilpize en Haute Loire.
No. 1272, 240fr — Alexander Pushkin (1799-1837), poet: a, Portrait. b, Dueling pistols. c, Pushkin sitting on railing, signature. d, Sculpture and drawing of Pushkin.
No. 1273, 240fr — Tigers: a, Panthera tigris altaica. b, Panthera tigris tigris cub. c, Two Panthera tigris tigris. d, Panthera tigris tigris with white fur.
No. 1274, 240fr — Shells: a, Lunella smaragdus. b, Nautilus macromphalus. c, Cymbiola innexa. d, Bolinus brandaris.
No. 1275, 240fr — Mushrooms: a, Suillus luteus. b, Macrolepiota rhacodes. c, Boletus edulis. d, Tricholoma portentosum.
No. 1276, 240fr — Windmills and birds: a, Oud-Zuilen, Netherlands windmill and Alopochen aegyptiaca. b, East Hampton, New York windmill and Tyrannus tyrannus. c, Ramsey, United Kingdom windmill and Carduelis carduelis. d, Lautrec, France windmill and Cyanistes caeruleus.
No. 1277, 240fr — Lighthouses: a, Lorain Lighthouse, Ohio. b, Big Sable Point Lighthouse, Michigan. c, Cape Lookout Lighthouse, North Carolina. d, Block Island Southeast Lighthouse, Rhode Island.
No. 1278, 240fr — Japanese high-speed trains: a, Shinkansen Series E3. b, Shinkansen Series E4. c, Shinkansen Series 800. d, Shinkansen Series E5.
No. 1279, 240fr — Louis Renault (1877-1944), automobile manufacturer, and: a, Renault Dauphinoise Juvaquatre fire vehicle.

b, Renault FT-17 tank. c, Renault Type B. d, Renault Reinastella, Arc de Triomphe.

No. 1280, 240fr — Louis Blériot (1872-1936), aviation pioneer: a, Blériot XI airplane on ground. b, Blériot and Eiffel Tower. c, Blériot and mountains. d, Blériot XI in flight.

No. 1281, 240fr — Outer Space Treaty, 50th anniv.: a, World Map. b, Moon, planets, balance. c, Earth, satellites in orbit, gavel. d, Satellite and nuclear missile.

No. 1282, 240fr — Christmas: a, Children placing ornaments on Christmas tree. b, Carolers and violinist near Christmas tree. c, Santa Claus and child. d, Child pulling sled carrying Christmas tree.

No. 1283, 240fr — New Year 2018 (Year of the Dog): a, Pekingese dog facing right. b, Pekingese dog facing forward, Chinese characters at top left. c, Pekingese dog facing forward, Chinese characters at top right. d, Pekingese dog facing left.

No. 1284, 950fr, Monroe in automobile. No. 1285, 950fr, McCartney playing guitar. No. 1286, 950fr, Chaplin dancing. No. 1287, 950fr, Marie Curie and model of atom. No. 1288, 950fr, Mandela with fist raised, diff. No. 1289, 950fr, Roosevelt at desk. No. 1290, 950fr, Map of Battle of Dunkirk, troops boarding ship. No. 1291, 950fr, Rythmes, by Robert Delaunay. No. 1292, 950fr, Pushkin holding quill pen. No. 1293, 950fr, Two Panthera tigris altaica. No. 1294, 950fr, Ceratosoma amoenum, Cypraea aurantia. No. 1295, 950fr, Lycoperdon perlatum. No. 1296, 950fr, Kuremaa, Estonia windmill and Ciconia ciconia. No. 1297, 950fr, Greens Ledge Lighthouse, Connecticut. No. 1298, 950fr, Shinkansen Series 500 Type EVA. No. 1299, 950fr, Renault and Renault 4CV. No. 1300, 950fr, Blériot and Eiffel Tower, diff. No. 1301, 950fr, Sputnik 1. No. 1302, 950fr, Santa Claus and reindeer. No. 1303, 950fr, Pekingese dog, diff.

2017, Sept. 29   Litho.   Perf. 13¼
Sheets of 4, #a-d

1264-1283	A321	Set of 20	215.00	215.00

Souvenir Sheets

1284-1303	A321	Set of 20	215.00	215.00

Television Broadcasting in Djibouti, 50th Anniv. — A321a

2017, Nov. 9   Litho.   Perf. 13¼x13

1303A	A321a	50fr multi	.60	.60

Miniature Sheet

Landscapes — A321b

No. 1303B: c, Grand Bara. d, Port of Obock (land at top). e, Sable Blanc. f, Ras Bir. g, Port of Obock (no land at top). h, Dikhil Region. i, Village of Assamo ("humilité, jaillir, slalomer" inscription). j, Tewo Daba. k, Village of Assamo ("apurer, adepte, décuivrer" inscription). l, Djibouti City.

2017, Nov. 9   Litho.   Perf. 13¼

1303B	A321b	300fr Sheet of 10, #c-l	34.00	34.00

A322   A323

A324   Polar Bear — A325

Design: 950fr, Polar bear, diff.

Perf. 12¾x13¼
2017, Dec. 11   Litho.

1304	A322	240fr multi	2.75	2.75
1305	A323	240fr multi	2.75	2.75
1306	A324	240fr multi	2.75	2.75
1307	A325	240fr multi	2.75	2.75
Nos. 1304-1307 (4)			11.00	11.00

Souvenir Sheet
Perf. 13¼

1308	A325	950fr multi	11.00	11.00

Nos. 1304-1307 were each printed in sheets of 16 + 4 labels. No. 1308 contains one 45x38mm stamp.

A326

No. 1309, 240fr — Ursus maritimus: a, One polar bear, tree at left. b, Polar bear with head at right. c, Adult and two cubs. d, Polar bear with head at left, mouth open.

No. 1310, 240fr — Cat breeds: a, Korat. b, Toyger. c, Selkirk Rex. d, Chantilly.

No. 1311, 240fr — Wild dogs: a, Cuon alpinus. b, One Canis lupus dingo. c, Lycaon pictus. d, Two Canis lupus dingo.

No. 1312, 240fr — Loxodonta africana: a, One elephant facing right. b, One elephant facing left. c, Two elephants with trunks touching. d, Two elephants walking.

No. 1313, 240fr — Dolphins: a, Inia geoffrensis. b, Stenella coeruleoalba. c, Cephalorhynchus commersonii. d, Grampus griseus.

No. 1314, 240fr — Parrots: a, One Ara ararauna in flight. b, Psittacula krameri. c, Two Ara ararauna. d, Eolophus roseicapilla.

No. 1315, 240fr — Pigeon breeds: a, African Owl. b, Bouclier de Saxe (Saxon Shield). c, American Domestic Show Flight. d, Barbe Anglais (English Barb).

No. 1316, 240fr — Bee-eaters: a, Merops apiaster. b, Merops variegatus. c, Merops malimbicus. d, Merops breweri.

No. 1317, 240fr — Owls: a, Bubo scandiacus. b, Bubo lacteus. c, Bubo bubo. d, Strix seloputo.

No. 1318, 240fr — Butterflies: a, Apatura iris. b, Papilio glaucus. c, Battus philenor. d, Callophrys rubi.

No. 1319, 240fr — Turtles: a, Aldabrachelys gigantea. b, Malaclemys terrapin. c, Trachemys scripta elegans. d, Chelonia mydas.

No. 1320, 240fr — Dinosaurs: a, Lambeosaurus lambei. b, Oviraptor philoceratops. c, Archaeopteryx siemensii. d, Stegosaurus ungulatus.

No. 1321, 240fr — Prehistoric marine animals: a, Pteraspis stensioei, Prognathodon solvayi. b, Dearcmhara shawcrossi. c, Parapuzosia seppenradensis. d, Shastasaurus pacificus.

No. 1322, 240fr — Global warming: a, Giraffa camelopardalis tippelskirchi and text. b, Ursus maritimus and text. c, Cervus elaphus and text. d, Turbinaria reniformis and text.

No. 1323, 240fr — Orchids: a, Odontoglossum crispum. b, Cattleya "Blc. Greenwich". c, Vanda coerulea. d, Miltonia regnellii.

No. 1324, 240fr — Minerals: a, Brookite, quartz. b, Uvarovite. c, Andradite. d, Willemite.

No. 1325, 240fr — Fire trucks: a, 2010 Oshkosh Striker 3000. b, 2012 Iveco Trakker. c, 2011 DAF LF. d, 2011 Scania P.

No. 1326, 240fr — Protestant Reformation, 500th anniv.: a, Martin Luther (1483-1546). b, Martin Bucer (1491-1551). c, Ulrich Zwingli (1484-1531). d, John Calvin (1509-64).

No. 1327, 240fr — 2017 Nobel Laureates: a, Michael Rosbach (Physiology or Medicine). b, Joachim Frank (Chemistry). c, Beatrice Fihn, director of International Campaign to Abolish Nuclear Weapons (Peace). d, Kazuo Ishiguro (Literature).

No. 1328, 950fr, Ursus maritiumus, diff. No. 1329, 950fr, Abyssinian cat. No. 1330, 950fr, Cuon alpinus, diff. No. 1331, 950fr, Loxodonta africana, diff. No. 1332, 950fr, Lagenorhynchus acutus. No. 1333, 950fr, Guaruba guarouba. No. 1334, 950fr, Belgian Ringbeater pigeon. No. 1335, 950fr, Merops nubicoides. No. 1336, 950fr, Megascops kennicottii. No. 1337, 950fr, Papilio troilus. No. 1338, 950fr, Graptemys geographica. No. 1339, 950fr, Pterodactylus antiquus. No. 1340, 950fr, Dunkleosteus terrelli. No. 1341, 950fr, Aptenodytes forsteri. No. 1342, 950fr, Beallara marfitch "Howard's Dream." No. 1343, 950fr, Brazilianite. No. 1344, 950fr, 1984 Oshkosh P19 fire truck. No. 1345, 950fr, Luther, diff.

No. 1346, 950fr, Richard H. Thaler, 2017 Nobel Laureate in Economics, Nobel medal, Robert Fludd (1574-1637), mathematician.

2017, Dec. 11   Litho.   Perf. 13¼
Sheets of 4, #a-d

1309-1327	A326	Set of 19	200.00	200.00

Souvenir Sheets

1328-1346	A326	Set of 19	200.00	200.00

Souvenir Sheet

Djibouti Chamber of Commerce, 110th Anniv. — A326a

Perf. 13¼x13½
2017, Dec. 21   Litho.

1346A	A326a	110fr multi	1.25	1.25

Souvenir Sheet

Emblem of Djibouti International Fair — A326b

Perf. 13¼x13½
2017, Dec. 21   Litho.

1346B	A326b	110fr multi	1.25	1.25

A327

No. 1347, 240fr — Bobby Fischer (1943-2008), World Chess Champion: a, Scratching face and holding clock. b, Playing against Mikhail Tal (1936-92). c, Without hands visible. d, With hand on forehead.

No. 1348, 240fr — Garry Kasparov, World Chess Champion: a, With hands covering ears. b, Holding chess piece. c, Scratching head. d, Looking down at chess board, two chess pieces.

No. 1349, 240fr — Golf: a, Player wearing green shirt addressing ball, player in red shirt carrying golf bag and club. b, Golf bag and player in red shirt swinging. c, Golf ball and player finishing swing. d, Player carrying golf bag.

No. 1350, 240fr — Ice hockey players: a, Nikita Gusev. b, Nathan MacKinnon. c, Nikita Kucherov. d, Bogdan Kiselevich.

No. 1351, 240fr — Formula I race cars of team: a, Mercedes-AMG Petronas. b, Renault Sport. c, Sauber. d, McLaren.

No. 1352, 240fr — Ferrari automobiles: a, Ferrari Enzo. b, Ferrari F12 Berlinetta. c, Ferrari Pininfarina Sergio Concept, Ferrari F40. d, Ferrari 125 S.

No. 1353, 240fr — Special transportation: a, B-377-SG/SGT Super Guppy airplane. b, GAZ 47 all-terrain vehicle. c, ZIL-4906 Blue Bird all-terrain vehicle. d, Mil V-12 Homer helicopter.

No. 1354, 240fr — Wright Flyer and Orville Wright (1871-1948): a, Wright Flyer. b, Wright and Wright Flyer. c, Wright Flyer, Orville and Wilbur Wright. d, Wright Flyer, Orville and Wilbur Wright, American flag.

No. 1355, 240fr — Concorde: a, British Airways airplane, nose at LL. b, British Airways airplane, nose at LL. c, Air France airplane, nose at UR. d, Air France airplane, nose at UL.

No. 1356, 240fr — Sailing ships: a, Palinuro, Italy. b, ARC Gloria, Colombia. c, Coast Guard Cutter Eagle, United States. d, STS Sedov, Russia.

No. 1357, 240fr — Submarines: a, Victoria Class submarine. b, HMAS Collins. c, K-535 Yury Dolgorukiy. d, USS Virginia.

No. 1358, 240fr — Steam trains: a, Jacobite, flag of Great Britain. b, Class 520 Sir Malcolm Barclay Harvey, flag of Australia. c, North and Western Class J611, flag of Great Britain. d, Class 26 4-8-4 Red Devil, flag of South Africa.

No. 1359, 240fr — High-speed trains: a, 0 series Shinkansen, flag of Japan. b, NTV ETR575, flag of Italy. c, TGV Lyria, flag of Switzerland. d, CRH, flag of People's Republic of China.

No. 1360, 240fr — Launch of Vostok 6, 55th anniv.: a, Earth, arrow and rocket. b, Statue of

---

Valentina Tereshkova, Moscow, and medal. c, Tereshkova and Vostok 6. d, Vostok 6 and red star.

No. 1361, 240fr — End of World War I, cent.: a, 155-mm cannon of Saint Chamond tank. b, Signing of armistice, 1918. c, Marshal Ferdinand Foch (1851-1929). d, Two soldiers.

No. 1362, 240fr — 50th birthday of King Felipe VI of Spain: a, With Prince William. b, With Queen Elizabeth II. c, With Pope Francis. d, With father, King Juan Carlos I.

No. 1363, 240fr — Dogs: a, Bedlington terrier. b, Chihuahua. c, Lancashire heeler. d, Pomeranian.

No. 1364, 240fr — Butterflies: a, Euphaedra themis. b, Bebearia tentyris. c, Cymothoe egesta. d, Junonia sophia.

No. 1365, 240fr — Marine life: a, Eretmochelys imbricata. b, Octopus vulgaris. c, Amphiprion ocellaris. d, Paguristes cadenati.

No. 1366, 950fr, Fischer, diff. No. 1367, 950fr, Kasparov, diff. No. 1368, 950fr, Golfer placing ball on ground. No. 1369, 950fr, Artemi Panarin. No. 1370, 950fr, Red Bull Racing Team Formula I car. No. 1371, 950fr, Ferrari 250. No. 1372, 950fr, Mil Mi-6 Hook helicopter. No. 1373, 950fr, Orville Wright, wearing hat and aviation headgear. No. 1374, 950fr, British Airways Concorde, diff. No. 1375, 950fr, Royal Clipper, Sweden. No. 1376, 950fr, Seawolf Class submarine. No. 1377, 950fr, Japan Railways C11-171 SL Hakodate Onuma Go, flag of Japan. No. 1378, 950fr, N700 Series Shinkansen, flag of Japan. No. 1379, 950fr, Launch of Vostok 6, red star and dove. No. 1380, 950fr, Foch and soldiers, diff. No. 1381, 950fr, King Felipe VI of Spain. No. 1382, 950fr, Swedish vallhund. No. 1383, 950fr, Rhetus periander. No. 1384, 950fr, Synchiropus splendidus.

2018, Feb. 19   Litho.   Perf. 13¼
Sheets of 4, #a-d

1347-1365	A327	Set of 19	205.00	205.00

Souvenir Sheets

1366-1384	A327	Set of 19	205.00	205.00

See Nos. 1387-1388.

2018 Winter Olympics, PyeongChang, South Korea — A328

No. 1385 — Venues of 2014 and 2018 Winter Olympics: a, Fisht Olympic Stadium, Sochi, Russia. b, PyeongChang Olympic Stadium. c, Sochi Olympic Complex. d, Speed skating venue, PyeongChang.

950fr, Yin yang with Russian and South Korean flags.

2018, Feb. 19   Litho.   Perf. 13¼

1385	A328	240fr Sheet of 4, #a-d, + central label	11.00	11.00

Souvenir Sheet

1386	A328	950fr multi	11.00	11.00

No. 1386 contains one 72x72mm diamond-shaped stamp.

Type of 2018

No. 1387 — Fire trucks: a, Robur LO 2002A. b, Barkas B 1000 KLF. c, Ural-43206. d, 1960 Ford Thames 800.

950fr, American-La France Type 0-11A.

2018, Mar. 15   Litho.   Perf. 13¼

1387	A327	240fr Sheet of 4, #a-d	11.00	11.00

Souvenir Sheet

1388	A327	950fr multi	11.00	11.00

February 6, 2018 SpaceX Flight A329

No. 1389: a, Launch of Falcon Heavy rocket. b, Tesla Roadster in opened rocket hatch. c, Recovery of two launched rocket stages. d, Tesla Roadster in space.

950fr, View from front seat of Tesla Roadster in space.

2018, Mar. 15   Litho.   Perf. 13¼
1389 A329 240fr Sheet of 4,
    #a-d   11.00 11.00
Souvenir Sheet
1390 A329 950fr multi   11.00 11.00

A330

No. 1391, 240fr — Ursus maritimus: a, Leaping. b, Two adult bears on ice. c, Two cubs in ice den. d, Swimming underwater.

No. 1392, 240fr — Ailuropoda melanoleuca: a, Eating in bamboo forest. b, Walking. c, Rolling on back. d, Eating on hillside.

No. 1393, 240fr — Wild cats: a, Felis chaus. b, Puma concolor. c, Catopuma temminckii. d, Caracal caracal.

No. 1394, 240fr — Whales: a, Kogia breviceps. b, Mesoplodon mirus. c, Eubalaena glacialis. d, Balaenoptera brydei.

No. 1395, 240fr — Owls: a, Tyto alba. b, Bubo bubo sibiricus. c, Glaucidium passerinum. d, Bubo scandiacus.

No. 1396, 240fr — Birds of prey: a, Terathopius ecaudatus. b, Pandion haliaetus. c, Aquila nipalensis. d, Lophaetus occipitalis.

No. 1397, 240fr — Turtles: a, Malaclemys terrapin. b, Emydoidea blandingii. c, Graptemys pseudogeographica. d, Stigmochelys pardalis.

No. 1398, 240fr — Extinct animals a, Diprotodon optatum. b, Coelodonta antiquitatis. c, Megatherium americanum. d, Incilius periglenes (incorrect Latin name).

No. 1399, 240fr — Mushrooms: a, Cantharellus cibarius, Parnassius mnemosyne. b, Entoloma hochstetteri, Vespa mandarinia. c, Laccaria amethystina, Chrysodeixis chalcites. d, Boletus edulis.

No. 1400, 240fr — Bird illustrations of Alexander Wilson (1766-1813), ornithologist: a, Portrait of Wilson and Bonasa umbellus. b, Anas strepera, Somateria mollissima, Mergellus albellus, Oxyura jamaicensis. c, Charadrius wilsonia, Fulica atra, Porphyrio martinicus, Phalaropus fulicarius. d, Tympanuchus cupido.

No. 1401, 240fr — Paintings by Edouard Manet (1832-83): a, The Railway, 1873. b, The Execution of Emperor Maximilian, 1867. c, Music in the Tuileries Gardens, 1862. d, At Father Lathuille, 1879.

No. 1402, 240fr — Paintings by Paul Gauguin (1848-1903): a, Winter at Pont-Aven, and Small Breton Shepherd, 1888. b, The Siesta, c. 1892-94. c, Pastorales Tahitiennes, 1892. d, Sacred Spring, Sweet Dreams (Nave Nave Moe), 1894.

No. 1403, 240fr — Paintings by Vincent van Gogh (1853-90) and various self-portraits: a, A Pair of Shoes, 1887. b, The Old Mill, 1888. c, Prisoners Exercising, 1890. d, Old Man in Sorrow, 1890.

No. 1404, 240fr — Paintings by Pablo Picasso (1881-1973): a, Cat Devouring a Bird, 1939. b, Au Lapin Agile, 1905. c, Mother and Child, 1921. d, Portrait of Dora Maar, 1937.

No. 1405, 240fr — Paintings in the Louvre Museum: a, Mona Lisa, by Leonardo da Vinci (1452-1519). b, An Old Man and His Grandson, by Domenico Ghirlandaio (1448-94). c, The Veiled Woman, by Raphael (1483-1520). d, Portrait of Daniele Barbaro, by Paolo Veronese (1528-88).

No. 1406, 240fr — Famous people associated with the International Red Cross: a, Agatha Christie (1890-1976), writer. b, Jackie Chan, actor. c, LL Cool J, actor. d, Marie Curie (1867-1934), physicist and chemist.

No. 1407, 240fr — Paul P. Harris (1868-1947), founder of Rotary International: a, Three people near modern bookmobile sponsored by Rotary International. b, Harris, his wife, Jean (1881-1963), Sarcochilus falcatus. c, Harris, Rotary International emblem, Cymbidium sanderae. d, Two children near old bookmobile sponsored by Rotary International.

No. 1408, 240fr — Princess Diana (1961-97): a, Skiing with young sons, Princes William and Harry. b, With small boy. c, With small girl. d, With sons, as adults.

No. 1409, 950fr, Ursus maritimus, diff. No. 1410, 950fr, Ailuropoda melanoleuca, diff. No. 1411, 950fr, Felis margarita. No. 1412, 950fr, Delphinapterus leucas. No. 1413, 950fr, Aegolius funereus. No. 1414, 950fr, Falco hypoleucos. No. 1415, 950fr, Chelonia mydas. No. 1416, 950fr, Incilius periglenes (frog). No. 1417, 950fr, Russula emetica and Rana sylvatica. No. 1418, 950fr, Haliaeetus leucocephala illustration by Wilson. No. 1419, 950fr, A Studio at Batignolles, by Henri Fantin-Latour (1836-1904). No. 1420, 950fr, Self-portrait with Portrait of Emile Bernard (Les Misérables), by Gauguin. No. 1421, 950fr, Self-portraits by van Gogh. No. 1422, 950fr, Acrobat's Family with a Monkey, by Picasso. No. 1423, 950fr, Portrait of a Man, by Antonello da Messina (c. 1430-79). No. 1424, 950fr, Walt Disney (1901-66), movie producer, Ford Model T Red Cross vehicle. No. 1425, 950fr, Harris and Rotary International emblem. No. 1426, 950fr, Princess Diana and Queen Elizabeth II.

2018, Mar. 15   Litho.   Perf. 13¼
Sheets of 4, #a-d
1391-1408 A330 Set of 18 195.00 195.00
Souvenir Sheets
1409-1426 A330 Set of 18 195.00 195.00

A331

No. 1427, 240fr — Marilyn Monroe (1926-62), actress: a, Brushing hair. b, Sitting on staircase. c, Sitting near plants. d, Near movie camera.

No. 1428, 240fr — Pres. John F. Kennedy (1917-63): a, And Frank Sinatra (1915-98), singer. b, Wearing naval uniform, sitting behind desk. c, And wife, Jacqueline (1929-94). d, With U.S. flag.

No. 1429, 240fr — Nelson Mandela (1918-2013), President of South Africa, and minerals: a, Phosphophyllite. b, Spessartine. c, Anglesite. d, Red beryl.

No. 1430, 240fr — Fifth birthday of Prince George of Cambridge: a, With mother, Catherine, Duchess of Cambridge. b, With sister, Princess Charlotte. c, Sitting alone. d, With father, Prince William.

No. 1431, 240fr — Wedding of Prince Harry and Meghan Markle: a, Couple, flags of Great Britain and United States. b, Couple and foliage. c, Couple kissing in background. d, Couple and castle in background.

No. 1432, 240fr — Ferdinand von Zeppelin (1838-1917), airship builder: a, Zeppelin wearing helmet and Hindenburg (LZ129). b, Zeppelin LZ4. c, Medal depicting Zeppelin and Graf Zeppelin (LZ127). d, Zeppelin wearing red tie.

No. 1433, 240fr — Motorcycle racers in Isle of Man TT races: a, Morgan Govignon, 2016. b, Bruce Anstey, 2007. c, Gary Johnson, 2016. d, James Hillier, 2011.

No. 1434, 240fr — Lamborghini automobiles, 55th anniv.: a, Lamborghini Centenario. b, Lamborghini Gallardo. c, Lamborghini Aventador. d, Lamborghini Diablo.

No. 1435, 240fr — Fire trucks: a, GPM-54. b, CCFM. c, Mercedes-Benz Zetros. d, OES Type III.

No. 1436, 240fr — European high-speed trains: a, Eurostar, France. b, ICE 3, Germany. c, Bombardier Zefiro V300, Italy. d, RENFE Series S-130, Spain.

No. 1437, 240fr — 1958 Munich airplane crash, 60th anniv.: a, Airplane and Manchester United soccer team. b, Refueling of Airspeed Ambassador airplane. c, Rescuers at crash site. d, Nose of crashed airplane.

No. 1438, 240fr — Yuri Gagarin (1934-68), first man in space: a, Gagarin waving. b, Vostok-K rocket, statue of Gagarin, Moscow. c, Gagarin and dove. d, Gagarin in spacesuit.

No. 1439, 240fr — Lighthouses: a, Vlaming Head Lighthouse, Australia. b, Esopus Meadows Lighthouse, New York. c, Cabo de la Huerta Lighthouse, Spain. d, Eckmühl Lighthouse, France.

No. 1440, 240fr — Scouts: a, Two Boy Scouts and campfire. b, Four Girl Scouts and leader. c, Two Boy Scouts saluting. d, Boy Scout and Scoutmaster.

No. 1441, 240fr — Organization of African Unity (African Union), 55th anniv.: a, Pan-African Parliament. b, Roger Nkodo Dang, Parliamentary President. c, African Union building, Addis Ababa, Ethiopia. d, Amara Essy, 2001-02 Secretary-General of OAU.

No. 1442, 240fr — Dolphins: a, Two Tursiops truncatus, one facing right. b, Stenella longirostris. c, Two Tursiops truncatus facing left. d, Orcinus orca.

No. 1443, 240fr — Butterflies: a, Papilio machaon. b, Melanargia galathea. c, Parnassius apollo. d, Morpho helenor.

No. 1444, 240fr — Dinosaurs: a, Velociraptor mongoliensis. b, Triceratops horridus. c, Tyrannosaurus rex. d, Parasaurolophus walkeri.

No. 1445, 240fr — Orchids: a, Laeliocattleya. b, Ophrys apifera. c, Vanda coerulea. d, Anacamptis papilionacea.

No. 1446, 240fr — Minerals: a, Kunzite, California. b, Red beryl, New Mexico. c, Anglesite, Morocco. d, Celestine, Madagascar.

No. 1447, 950fr, Monroe, diff. No. 1448, 950fr, Pres. Kennedy, diff. No. 1449, 950fr, Mandela and Brookite. No. 1450, 950fr, Prince George of Cambridge. No. 1451, 950fr, Prince Harry and Meghan Markle, diff. No. 1452, 950fr, Graf Zeppelin (LZ127) and LZ4. No. 1453, 950fr, Motorcycle racer Ryan Farquhar, 2015. No. 1454, 950fr, Ferruccio Lamborghini (1916-93), industrialist, and Lamborghini Urraco. No. 1455, 950fr, Russian fire truck. No. 1456, 950fr, RABDe 500, Switzerland. No. 1457, 950fr, Harry Gregg, goaltender for Manchester United soccer team who survived plane crash. No. 1458, 950fr, Gagarin in spacesuit, diff. No. 1459, 950fr, St. Nicholas Church Lighthouse, Ukraine. No. 1460, 950fr, Two Boy Scouts following map. No. 1461, 950fr, Gamal Abdel Nasser (1918-70), 1964-65 Chairman of Organization of African Unity. No. 1462, 950fr, One Tursiops truncatus. No. 1463, 950fr, Ypthima baldus. No. 1464, 950fr, Compsognathus longipes. No. 1465, 950fr, Phalaenopsis lueddemanniana. No. 1466, 950fr, Brookite, Pakistan.

2018, June 12   Litho.   Perf. 13¼
Sheets of 4, #a-d
1427-1446 A331 Set of 20 215.00 215.00
Souvenir Sheets
1447-1466 A331 Set of 20 215.00 215.00

Medals — A332

DesignsL Nos. 1467, 1470a, 200fr, Star of Devotion Military Order. Nos. 1468, 1470b, 300fr, Order of June 27. Nos. 1469, 1470c, 400fr, Order of the Grand Star of Djibouti.

2018, June 27   Litho.   Perf. 13¼x13
1467-1469 A332 Set of 3 10.00 10.00
Souvenir Sheet
Perf. 13¼
1470 A332   Sheet of 3, #a-c 10.00 10.00
No. 1470 contains three 30x51mm stamps.

Armed Forces   Police
Emblem   Emblem
A333   A334

Republican   Gendarmerie
Guard   Emblem
Emblem   A336
A335

Coast Guard
Emblem — A337

2018, June 27   Litho.   Perf. 13¼x13
1471 A333 400fr multi   4.50 4.50
1472 A334 400fr multi   4.50 4.50
1473 A335 400fr multi   4.50 4.50
1474 A336 400fr multi   4.50 4.50
1475 A337 400fr multi   4.50 4.50
  Nos. 1471-1475 (5)   22.50 22.50

Souvenir Sheets
Stamps With Colored Frames
Perf. 13¼
1476 A333 500fr multi   5.75 5.75
1477 A334 500fr multi   5.75 5.75
1478 A335 500fr multi   5.75 5.75
1479 A336 500fr multi   5.75 5.75
1480 A337 500fr multi   5.75 5.75
  Nos. 1476-1480 (5)   28.75 28.75

Nos. 1476-1480 each contain one 39x51mm stamp.

Homage to Army
Martyrs — A338

2018, June 27   Litho.   Perf. 13x13¼
1481 A338 400fr multi   4.50 4.50
Souvenir Sheet
Stamp With Colored Frame
Perf. 13¼
1482 A338 500fr multi   5.75 5.75
No. 1482 contains one 51x39mm stamp.

Soldiers of African
Union Mission in
Somalia — A339

2018, June 27   Litho.   Perf. 13¼x13
1483 A339 400fr multi   4.50 4.50
Souvenir Sheet
Stamp With Colored Frame
Perf. 13¼
1484 A339 500fr multi   5.75 5.75
No. 1484 contains one 39x51mm stamp.

Firefighters — A340

2018, June 27   Litho.   Perf. 13¼x13
1485 A340 400fr multi   4.50 4.50
Souvenir Sheet
Stamp With Colored Frame
Perf. 13¼
1486 A340 500fr multi   5.75 5.75
No. 1486 contains one 33x51mm stamp.

Souvenir Sheets

Flags
A341

Flag of: No. 1487, 500fr, United States. No. 1488, 500fr, People's Republic of China. No. 1489, 500fr, France. No. 1490, 500fr, Germany. No. 1491, 500fr, Italy. No. 1492, 500fr, Japan. No. 1493, 500fr, Spain.

2018, June 27   Litho.   Perf. 13¼
1487-1493 A341 Set of 7 40.00 40.00

Souvenir Sheet

Imploration, by Rifki Abdoulkader Bamakhrama — A342

2018, June 27   Litho.   Perf. 13¼
1494 A342 3000fr multi   34.00 34.00
Aid for orphans.

Flag of Djibouti and Barkat Gourad Hamadou (1930-2001), Prime Minister — A343

2018, June 27   Litho.   Perf. 13¼x13
1495 A343 500fr multi   5.75 5.75
a.   Souvenir sheet of 1   5.75 5.75

Isao Takahata (1935-2018), Film Director — A344

No. 1496 — Takahata and: a, Hayao Miyazaki, film director. b, Firefly. c, Japanese raccoon dog. d, Princess Kaguya. 950fr, Takahata and Miyazaki, diff.

2018, July 27   Litho.   Perf. 13¼
1496 A344 240fr Sheet of 4,
      #a-d   11.00 11.00

Souvenir Sheet
1497 A344 950fr multi   11.00 11.00

A345

No. 1498, 240fr — Milos Forman (1932-2018), film director, and: a, Scene from *Amadeus*. b, Clapboard and signature. c, Poster for *One Flew Over the Cuckoo's Nest*. d, Poster for *Loves of a Blonde*.
No. 1499, 240fr — Frank Sinatra (1915-98), singer and actor, and: a, Microphone. b, Luciano Pavarotti (1935-2007), opera singer. c, Kim Novak, actress. d, Academy Award.
No. 1500, 240fr — Film actors who have portrayed James Bond: a, Daniel Craig. b, Timothy Dalton. c, Roger Moore (1927-2017). d, Pierce Brosnan.
No. 1501, 240fr — Composers: a, Ludwig van Beethoven (1770-1827). b, Johann Sebastian Bach (1685-1750). c, Franz Schubert (1797-1828). d, Joseph Haydn (1732-1809).
No. 1502, 240fr — David Livingstone (1813-73), African explorer and missionary, and: a, David Livingstone Memorial Church, Blantyre, Scotland. b, Henry Morton Stanley (1841-1904), journalist and explorer. c, Livingstone Monument, Zambia. d, African people.
No. 1503, 240fr — Mahatma Gandhi (1869-1948), Indian nationalist: a, Gandhi Assassination Memorial, Delhi. b, Gandhi and *Mountain Landscape with Indians*, by John Mix

Stanley. c, Gandhi, dove, flag of India. d, Birthplace of Gandhi, Porbandar, India.
No. 1504, 240fr — Queen Elizabeth II, 65th anniv. of coronation: a, With coat of arms. b, With husband, Prince Philip. c, Riding in coach. d, At coronation.
No. 1505, 240fr — Dr. Martin Luther King, Jr. (1929-68), civil rights activist, and: a, Malcolm X (1925-65), civil rights activist. b, Iwo Jima Memorial. c, Pres. John F. Kennedy (1917-63). d, Bald eagle.
No. 1506, 240fr — Ships and airplanes used by Roald Amundsen (1872-1928), polar explorer: a, Gjoa. b, Dornier Wal N25. c, Maud. d, Latham 47.
No. 1507, 240fr — André Citroen (1878-1935), automobile manufacturer: a, Citroen GT. b, Citroen ZX Rallye-Raid. c, Citroen and Citroen Traction Avant. d, Citroen and Citroen Mehari.
No. 1508, 240fr — Motorcycles from Isle of Man Tourist Trophy Races: a, Suzuki GSX-R1000. b, BMW S1000RR. c, Yamaha YZF R1. d, Honda CBR1000RR.
No. 1509, 240fr — Japanese high-speed trains: a, Shinkansen Series E5. b, Shinkansen Series E3. c, SC Maglev L0. d, Shinkansen Series E6.
No. 1510, 240fr — Naval vessels: a, USS Coronado. b, HMS Gloucester. c, HMAS Anzac. d, USS San Antonio.
No. 1511, 240fr — World War II watercraft and tanks: a, Type VII U-boat. b, Tiger II tank. c, Churchill tank. d, USS Missouri.
No. 1512, 240fr — Sled dogs: a, Greenland dogs. b, Siberian huskies. c, Chinooks. d, Samoyeds.
No. 1513, 240fr — Henry Dunant (1828-1910), founder of Red Cross: a, On horse carrying flag, nurse caring for patient. b, With Nobel medal, 1864 Geneva Convention. c, With Red Cross flag, medic treating injured soldier. d, With nurses and Red Crescent flags.
No. 1514, 240fr — Launch of Apollo 8, 50th anniv.: a, Frank Borman, mission commander and rocket launch. b, Apollo 8 crew members, Jim Lovell, William Anders and Borman. c, Lovell and Apollo 8 capsule in ocean. d, Anders and Apollo 8 in space.
No. 1515, 240fr — Rugby players: a, Player wearing No. 6 at left. b, Player with green shirt at left. c, Player with white and red shirt at left. d, Female rugby players.
No. 1516, 240fr — Chess: a, Chess Players, by Ernest Meissonier. b, 12th century chess pieces. c, Chess clock, pieces on chess board. d, Game of Chess, by Benjamin Eugène Fichel.
No. 1517, 950fr, Forman and Jim Carrey, actor. No. 1518, 950fr, Sinatra shooting revolver. No. 1519, 950fr, Sean Connery, actor, and diamonds. No. 1520, 950fr, Wolfgang Amadeus Mozart (1756-91), composer. No. 1521, 950fr, Livingstone and Victoria Falls. No. 1522, 950fr, Gandhi, dove and flag of India, diff. No. 1523, 950fr, Queen Elizabeth II at coronation, diff. No. 1524, 950fr, Dr. King, White House. No. 1525, 950fr, Amundsen and airship Norge. No. 1526, 950fr, Citroen and Citroen DS21. No. 1527, 950fr, Yamaha YZR-M1, Tower of Refuge. No. 1528, 950fr, Shinkansen Series E7. No. 1529, 950fr, USS Oakland. No. 1530, 950fr, Lockheed P-38 Lightning. No. 1531, 950fr, Alaskan malamutes. No. 1532, 950fr, Dunant, Red Cross flag, Red Cross workers carrying corpse. No. 1533, 950fr, Moon and Apollo 8 crew members. No. 1534, 950fr, American football players. No. 1535, 950fr, Magnus Carlsen, chess player, chess board and pieces.

2018, July 27   Litho.   Perf. 13¼
      Sheets of 4, #a-d
1498-1516 A345 Set of 19 205.00 205.00
      Souvenir Sheets
1517-1535 A345 Set of 19 205.00 205.00

Beagle
A346

2018, Aug. 27   Litho.   Perf. 13¼
1536 A346 240fr multi   2.75 2.75
      Souvenir Sheet
1537 A346 950fr multi   11.00 11.00
No. 1536 was printed in sheets of 4.

Les lions
A347

No. 1538, 240fr — Panthera leo: a, Male lion roaring. b, Female lion and cubs. c, Male lion standing on rock. d, Female lion roaring.
No. 1539, 240fr — Panthera tigris: a, Tiger with mouth open. b, Tiger and trees. c, Streak of tigers. d, Tiger in snow.
No. 1540, 240fr — Cats: a, American bobtail. b, Canadian Sphynx. c, Mekong bobtail. d, Abyssinian.
No. 1541, 240fr — Elephants: a, Two Elephas maximus. b, Loxodonta africana and zebras. c, Loxodonta africana with trunk raised. d, One Elephas maximus calf.
No. 1542, 240fr — Primates: a, Rhinopithecus roxellana. b, Hylobates lar. c, Nasalis larvatus. d, Colobus guereza.
No. 1543, 240fr — Water birds: a, Anas platyrhynchos. b, Chauna torquata. c, Bucephala albeola. d, Cygnus olor.
No. 1544, 240fr — Owls: a, Tyto alba. b, Bubo bubo. c, Strix nebulosa. d, Strix aluco.
No. 1545, 240fr — Pigeons: a, Phaps chalcoptera. b, Columbina inca. c, Zenaida graysoni. d, Columba guinea.
No. 1546, 240fr — Kingfishers: a, Tanysiptera sylvia. b, Megaceryle maxima. c, Ceryle rudis. d, Syma torotoro.
No. 1547, 240fr — Apis mellifera: a, Bee on flower, facing right. b, Swarm of bees. c, Line of bees. d, Bee on flower facing left.
No. 1548, 240fr — Butterflies: a, Papilio glaucus. b, Vanessa virginiensis. c, Pochliopta aristolochiae. d, Aglais io.
No. 1549, 240fr — Turtles: a, Aldebrachelys gigantea. b, Chelodina longicollis. c, Chelydra serpentina. d, Eretmochelys imbricata.
No. 1550, 240fr — Snakes: a, Lampropeltis getula. b, Lampropeltis zonata. c, Morelia viridis. d, Trimeresurus albolabris.
No. 1551, 240fr — Prehistoric marine creatures: a, Drepanaspis gemuendenensis. b, Eurhinosaurus longirostris. c, Plesiosaurus dolichodeirus. d, Dinichthys terrelli.
No. 1552, 240fr — Orchids: a, Paphiopedilum hennisianum. b, Paphiopedilum callosum. c, Oncidium incurvum. d, Anguloa superba.
No. 1553, 240fr — Mushrooms: a, Mycena polygramma. b, Cantharellus cibarius. c, Lactarius deliciosus. d, Macrolepiota procera.
No. 1554, 240fr — High-speed Japanese trains: a, Train with two blue stripes on side and orange lights. b, Train with hot pink stripe on front in foreground. c, Train with one blue and two brown stripes. d, Train with two blue stripes, no lights.
No. 1555, 950fr, Panthera leo, diff. No. 1556, 950fr, Panthera tigris, diff. No. 1557, 950fr, American curl cat. No. 1558, 950fr, Loxodonta africana, diff. No. 1559, 950fr, Mandrillus sphinx. No. 1560, 950fr, Chen caerulescens. No. 1561, 950fr, Bubo scandiacus. No. 1562, 950fr, Spilopelia chinensis. No. 1563, 950fr, Ceyx erithaca. No. 1564, 950fr, Apis mellifera on flower, diff. No. 1565, 950fr, Troides helena. No. 1566, 950fr, Chelonia mydas. No. 1567, 950fr, Elaphe obsoleta lindheimeri. No. 1568, 950fr, Carcharocles megalodon. No. 1569, 950fr, Miltonia vexillaria. No. 1570, 950fr, Handkea utriformis. No. 1571, 950fr, JR700 Japanese bullet train on bridge.

2018, Aug. 27   Litho.   Perf. 13¼
      Sheets of 4, #a-d
1538-1554 A347 Set of 17 185.00 185.00
      Souvenir Sheets
1555-1571 A347 Set of 17 185.00 185.00

New Year 2019 (Year of the Pig) A348

No. 1572 — Pig: a, Facing right. b, Facing forward. c, Sleeping. d, Facing left. 950fr, Pig wearing santa hat.

2018, Aug. 27   Litho.   Perf. 13¼
1572 A348 240fr Sheet of 4,
      #a-d   11.00 11.00
Souvenir Sheet
1573 A348 950fr multi   11.00 11.00

Miniature Sheets

Chinese Zodiac Animals A349

Nos. 1574 and 1575: a, Rat. b, Ox (buffle). c, Tiger (tigre). d, Rabbit (lapin). e, Dragon. f, Snake (serpent). g, Horse (cheval). h, Goat (chèvre). i, Monkey (singe). j, Rooster (coq). k, Dog (chien). l, Pig (cochon).

2018, Aug. 27   Litho.   Perf. 13¼x13
1574 A349 300fr Sheet of 12,
      #a-l   40.00 40.00
m.   Souvenir sheet of 1, #1574a   3.25 3.25
n.   Souvenir sheet of 1, #1574b   3.25 3.25
o.   Souvenir sheet of 1, #1574c   3.25 3.25
p.   Souvenir sheet of 1, #1574d   3.25 3.25
q.   Souvenir sheet of 1, #1574e   3.25 3.25
r.   Souvenir sheet of 1, #1574f   3.25 3.25
s.   Souvenir sheet of 1, #1574g   3.25 3.25
t.   Souvenir sheet of 1, #1574h   3.25 3.25
u.   Souvenir sheet of 1, #1574i   3.25 3.25
v.   Souvenir sheet of 1, #1574j   3.25 3.25
w.   Souvenir sheet of 1, #1574k   3.25 3.25
x.   Souvenir sheet of 1, #1574l   3.25 3.25

Printed on Wood Veneer Self-Adhesive
1575 A349 300fr Sheet of 12,
      #a-l   40.00 40.00
See Central Africa No. , Guinea No. , Sierra Leone No.

Diplomatic Relations Between Djibouti and Japan, 40th Anniv. — A349a

2018, Dec. 1   Litho.   Perf. 13¼x13
1575M A349a 400fr multi   4.50 4.50

Labor Inspection Laws — A349b

2018, Dec. 1   Litho.   Perf. 13¼
1575N A349b 5000fr multi   57.50 57.50

Nelson Mandela (1918-2013), President of South Africa — A350

2018, Dec. 13   Litho.   Perf. 13¼
1576 A350 210fr multi   2.40 2.40

Souvenir Sheet
1577 A350 500fr multi   5.75 5.75

A351

No. 1578, 240fr — Michael Jackson (1958-2009), singer: a, With hand over groin at right. b, With heart in background at right. c, As child at right. d, With both arms extended to side at right.

No. 1579, 240fr — 2018 Chess Olympics gold medalists: a, Ju Wenjun, flag of People's Republic of China. b, Ding Liren, flag of People's Republic of China. c, Nguyen Ngoc Truong Son, flag of Viet Nam. d, Mariya Muzychuk, flag of Ukraine.

No. 1580, 240fr — 2018 Nobel laureates: a, Nadia Murad, Peace. b, George P. Smith, Chemistry. c, Gregory P. Winter, Chemistry. d, Denis Mukwege, Peace.

No. 1581, 240fr — Scouts: a, Three Scouts lighting campfire. b, Queen Elizabeth II greeting Scout leaders. c, Girl Scouts raising U.S. flag. d, Scouts and Lord Robert Baden-Powell (1857-1941), founder of Scouting movement.

No. 1582, 240fr — Russian trains: a, Sinara GT1s at Balashikha Station. b, ER-200 at Riga Station, Moscow. c, L-3653 locomotive at Kazan Station. d, Novocherkassk VL85 at Velsk Station.

No. 1583, 240fr — Japanese Shinkansen high-speed trains: a, Series 500. b, Series N700. c, Series E2. d, Series 700.

No. 1584, 240fr — Voyage of USS Nautilus under North Pole, 60th anniv.: a, USS Nautilus under water, emblem. b, USS Nautilus, Commander William R. Anderson (1921-2007), Legion of Merit medal. c, USS Nautilus, Admiral Hyman G. Rickover (1900-86). d, USS Nautilus, map of Arctic, Presidential Unit Citation and National Defense Service Medal.

No. 1585, 240fr — Streamliner motorcycles that broke motorcycle speed records: a, Harley-Davidson, 1970. b, BUB Seven, 2009. c, Yamaha Silver Bird, 1975. d, Ack Attack, 2010.

No. 1586, 240fr — Fire engines: a, FAUN TLF 20 Crashtender. b, Oshkosh MB1. c, Oshkosh P-23 ARFF. d, MAZ-543.

No. 1587, 240fr — Airplanes: a, Antonov An-225 Mriya carrying Buran space shuttle. b, Airbus A300-600ST Beluga. c, Lockheed C-5 Galaxy and F-15s. d, N911NA shuttle carrier with Space Shuttle Endeavour.

No. 1588, 240fr — Space exploration: a, TESS. b, InSight on Mars. c, OSIRIS-REx. d, Falcon Heavy.

No. 1589, 240fr — Minerals: a, Disthene (kyanite). b, Anatase. c, Andradite. d, Cassiterite.

No. 1590, 240fr — Dolphins: a, Lagenorhynchus obscurus. b, Delphinus delphis. c, Stenella frontalis. d, Tursiops truncatus.

No. 1591, 240fr — Fish: a, Acanthurus xanthopterus. b, Zebrasoma xanthurum. c, Carangoides bajad. d, Acanthurus leucopareius.

No. 1592, 240fr — Shells and lighthouses: a, Cypraea mappa and La Vieille Lighthouse, France. b, Cypraecassis rufa and Ile Verte Lighthouse, Canada. c, Cassis cornuta and Cape Meares Lighthouse, Oregon. d, Cymbiola imperialis and Point Loma Lighthouse, California.

No. 1593, 240fr — Dinosaurs: a, Dilophosaurus wetherilli. b, Brontosaurus excelsus. c, Stegosaurus stenops. d, Therizinosaurus cheloniformis.

No. 1594, 240fr — Endangered species: a, Elephas maximus. b, Panthera tigris. c, Aloeides nubilus. d, Equus grevyi.

No. 1595, 240fr — Animals threatened by climate change: a, Pygoscelis antarcticus. b, Ursus maritimus. c, Bombus pascuorum. d, Phascolarctos cinereus.

No. 1596, 240fr — Animals on stamps: a, Panthera tigris on Russia #6181. b, Coracias garrulus on Lithuania #877. c, Lutra lutra on German Democratic Republic #2620. d, Vulpes corsac on Kyrgyzstan #384a.

No. 1597, 950fr, Jackson, diff. No. 1598, 950fr, Jorge Cori, chess gold medalist, flag of Peru. No. 1599, 950fr, Arthur Ashkin 2018

Nobel Physics laureate. No. 1600, 950fr, Two scouts practicing first aid. No. 1601, 950fr, ER-9 train at Yalutorovsk Station, Russia. No. 1602, 950fr, Shinkansen Series 200. No. 1603, 950fr, USS Nautilus under water. No. 1604, 950fr, Gyronaut X-1, 1966. No. 1605, 950fr, Dennis Mk9 fire truck. No. 1606, 950fr, Antonov An-124 and MiG-29. No. 1607, 950fr, Hayabusa 2. No. 1608, 950fr, Red beryl. No. 1609, 950fr, Platanista gangetica. No. 1610, 950fr, Balistapus undulatus. No. 1611, 950fr, Pinctada margaritifera and Point Reyes Lighthouse, California. No. 1612, 950fr, Giganotosaurus carolinii. No. 1613, 950fr, Ailurus fulgens. No. 1614, 950fr, Two Ursus maritimus. No. 1615, 950fr, Castor fiber on Belarus #119.

2018, Dec. 13   Litho.   Perf. 13¼
Sheets of 4, #a-d
1578-1596 A351 Set of 19   205.00 205.00

Souvenir Sheets
1597-1615 A351 Set of 19   205.00 205.00

Mohandas K. Gandhi (1869-1948), Indian Nationalist Leader — A352

2019, Feb. 27   Litho.   Perf. 13¼x13
1616 A352 100fr multi   1.10 1.10

Fauna and Mushrooms — A353

No. 1617, 240fr — Ailuropoda melanoleuca: a, Eating. b, Sitting. c, Climbing on tree. d, Walking.

No. 1618, 240fr — Bats: a, Rhinolophus hipposideros. b, Pteropus lylei. c, Micropteropus pussilus. d, Pteropus poliocephalus.

No. 1619, 240fr — Dogs: a, Airedale terrier. b, Akitai. c, American pit bull terrier. d, Boston terrier.

No. 1620, 240fr — Orcinus orca: a, Head above water, fins at right. b, Pair leaping out of water to right. c, Head above water, fins at left. d, Pair leaping out of water to left.

No. 1621, 240fr — Owls: a, Athene brama. b, Aegolius acadicus. c, Bubo virginianus. d, Bubo scandiacus.

No. 1622, 240fr — Bee-eaters: a, Nyctiornis amictus. b, Merops viridis. c, Merops orientalis. d, Merops nubicoides.

No. 1623, 240fr — Butterflies: a, Papilio glaucus. b, Limenitis arthemis. c, Pachliopta hector. d, Papilio dardanus.

No. 1624, 240fr — Turtles: a, Caretta caretta. b, Emys orbicularis. c, Carettochelys insculpta. d, Pangshura smithii.

No. 1625, 240fr — Spiders: a, Latrodectus mactans. b, Hogna radians. c, Verrucosa arenata. d, Aranea pilipes.

No. 1626, 240fr — Mushrooms: a, Macrolepiota procera. b, Leccinum aurantiacum. c, Boletus edulis. d, Lactaris deterrimus.

No. 1627, 950fr, Ailuropoda melanoleuca, diff. No. 1628, 950fr, Eptesicus fuscus. No. 1629, 950fr, Dalmatian. No. 1630, 950fr, Orcinus orca, diff. No. 1631, 950fr, Athene noctua. No. 1632, 950fr, Merops leschenaulti. No. 1633, 950fr, Battus philenor. No. 1634, 950fr, Geoclemys hamiltonii. No. 1635, 950fr, Araneus diadematus. No. 1636, 950fr, Leccinum versipelle.

2019, Feb. 27   Litho.   Perf. 13¼
Sheets of 4, #a-d
1617-1626 A353 Set of 10   110.00 110.00

Souvenir Sheets
1627-1636 A353 Set of 10   110.00 110.00

Nos. 1627-1636 each contain one 45x60mm stamp.

A354

No. 1637, 240fr — Princess Diana (1961-97): a, With British flags in background. b, Holding infant. c, Touching face of young boy. d, With building and statue in background.

No. 1638, 240fr — Princess Grace of Monaco (1929-82): a, In automobile with Frank Sinatra (1915-98). b, With two children. c, With royal monogram. d, With her coat of arms.

No. 1639, 240fr — Yuri Gagarin (1934-68), first man in space: a, Standing beside automobile. b, Wearing spacesuit, with Vostok 1. c, Wearing military uniform. d, With wife, Valentina and infant daughter.

No. 1640, 240fr — Niki Lauda (1949-2019), race car driver: a, Lauda and McLaren MP4/1. b, Ferrari 312 T2. c, March 721 G. d, Brabham BT48 and Brabham BT46.

No. 1641, 240fr — European high-speed trains: a, Frecciarossa 1000, flag of Italy. b, TGV Réseau, flag of France. c, ICE 4, flag of Germany. d, Eurostar e320, flag of Great Britain.

No. 1642, 240fr — Submarines: a, USS Los Angeles. b, Akula II class SSN Project 971U, Russia. c, USS Skate. d, Alfa class Project 705 Lyra, Russia.

No. 1643, 240fr — Red Cross campaign against malaria: a, Insect exterminator and Anopheles gambiae. b, Medical staffer, Plasmodium malariae and chemical structure of Primaquine. c, Doctor inoculating child. d, Malaria patient and hand holding hypodermic needle.

No. 1644, 240fr — Ice hockey players: a, Sidney Crosby, Canada. b, Alexander Ovechkin, Russia. c, Patrick Kane, U.S. d, Erik Karlsson, Sweden.

No. 1645, 950fr, Princess Diana and Prince Charles on wedding day. No. 1646, 950fr, Princess Grace and Academy Award. No. 1647, 950fr, Gagarin and technician. No. 1648, 950fr, Lauda and Ferrari 312 B3 cars. No. 1649, 950fr, Eurostar e320, flag of Great Britain. No. 1650, 950fr, USS Triton. No. 1651, 950fr, Hands of malaria patient and medical staffer, mosquito and giraffe. No. 1652, 950fr, Evgeni Malkin, Russia.

2019, Feb. 27   Litho.   Perf. 13¼
Sheets of 4, #a-d
1637-1644 A354 Set of 8   87.50 87.50

Souvenir Sheets
1645-1652 A354 Set of 8   87.50 87.50

First Man on the Moon, 50th Anniv. A355

No. 1653: a, Apollo 11 astronaut Neil Armstrong (1930-2012), patch of Gemini 8. b, Apollo 11 astronaut Edwin E. "Buzz" Aldrin, Jr. patch of Gemini 12. c, Apollo 11 astronaut Michael Collins, patch of Gemini 10. c, Aldrin, Armstrong, Collins and patch of Apollo 11. 950fr, Aldrin on moon, Pres. John F. Kennedy (1917-63).

2019, Feb. 27   Litho.   Perf. 13¼
1653 A355 240fr Sheet of 4,
             #a-d   11.00 11.00

Souvenir Sheet
1654 A355 950fr multi   11.00 11.00

No. 1654 contains one 45x51mm stamp.

Paintings by Pablo Picasso (1881-1973) — A356

No. 1655: a, Mother and Child, 1902. b, Le Pigeon aux Petits Pois, 1911. c, Vase of Flowers on a Table, 1969. d, The Card Player, 1913-14. 1000fr, Portrait of Woman with an Ermine Collar (Olga), 1923.

2019, Mar. 14   Litho.   Perf. 13¼x13
1655 A356 250fr Sheet of 4,
             #a-d   11.50 11.50

Souvenir Sheet
1656 A356 1000fr multi   11.50 11.50

A357

No. 1657, 250fr — Napoleon Bonaparte (1769-1821), Emperor of France, with denomination in: a, Gray lilac (66x40mm triangular stamp). b, Rose (30x42mm). c, Dull violet blue (30x42mm). d, Bright green (30x42mm).

No. 1658, 250fr — Composers: a, Ludwig van Beethoven (1770-1827) (66x40mm triangular stamp). b, Franz Schubert (1797-1828) (30x42mm). c, Johann Sebastian Bach (1685-1750) (30x42mm). d, Joseph Haydn (1732-1809) (30x42mm).

No. 1659, 250fr — Tennis players: a, Novak Djokovic (66x40mm triangular stamp). b, Rafael Nadal (30x42mm). c, Petra Kvitova (30x42mm). d, Alexander Zverev (30x42mm).

No. 1660, 250fr — Chess players: a, Bobby Fischer (1943-2008) (66x40mm triangular stamp). b, Ding Liren (30x42mm). c, Judit Polgár (30x42mm). d, Magnus Carlsen (30x42mm).

No. 1661, 250fr — Scouts: a, Scout examining rocks (66x40mm triangular stamp). b, Scout cooking (30x42mm). c, Scout holding laptop computer (30x42mm). d, Scout writing in notebook (30x42mm).

No. 1662, 250fr — Trains of India: a, Jabalpur Express (66x40mm triangular stamp). b, WAG 9 electric locomotive (30x42mm). c, Maharajas' Express car interior (30x42mm). d, DEMU (30x42mm).

No. 1663, 250fr — Fire engines: a, Ford C series (66x40mm triangular stamp). b, ZIL-157 (30x42mm). c, GAZ-51 (30x42mm). d, IFA W 50 (30x42mm).

No. 1664, 250fr — Concorde, 50th anniv., with denomination in: a, Gray violet (66x40mm triangular stamp). b, Rose (30x42mm). c, Dull violet blue (30x42mm). d, Bright green (30x42mm).

No. 1665, 250fr — Prehistoric aquatic animals: a, Nothosaurus mirabilis (66x40mm triangular stamp). b, Carcharocles megalodon (30x42mm). c, Mosasaurus hoffmanni (30x42mm). d, Plesiosaurus dolichodeirus (30x42mm).

No. 1666, 1000fr, Bonaparte, diff. No. 1667, 1000fr, Wolfgang Amadeus Mozart (1756-91), composer. No. 1668, 1000fr, Tennis player Naomi Osaka. No. 1669, 1000fr, Chess player Garry Kasparov. No. 1670, Lord Robert Baden-Powell (1857-1941), founder of Scouting movement. No. 1671, 1000fr, WCP1 Diesel locomotive. No. 1672, 1000fr, Dennis F2 fire engine. No. 1673, 1000fr, Concorde, diff. No. 1674, 1000fr, Geosaurus giganteus.

2019, Mar. 14   Litho.   Perf. 13¼
Sheets of 4, #a-d
1657-1665 A357 Set of 9   100.00 100.00
Souvenir Sheets
1666-1674 A357 Set of 9   100.00 100.00
Nos. 1666-1674 each contain one 66x40mm triangular stamp.

A358

No. 1675, 250fr — Primates: a, Leontopithecus rosalia (40mm diameter). b, Pan paniscus (40mm diameter). c, Saimiri sciureus (50x30mm). d, Macaca sinica (50x30mm).
No. 1676, 250fr — Cats: a, Korat (40mm diameter). b, Selkirk Rex (40mm diameter). c, Turkish Angora (50x30mm). d, American Shorthair (50x30mm).
No. 1677, 250fr — Sharks: a, Sphyrna lewini (40mm diameter). b, Triaenodon obesus (40mm diameter). c, Prionace glauca (50x30mm). d, Rhincodon typus (50x30mm).
No. 1678, 250fr — Kingfishers: a, Alcedo azurea (40mm diameter). b, Alcedo atthis (40mm diameter). c, Ceyx erithaca (50x30mm). d, Pelargopsis capensis (50x30mm).
No. 1679, 250fr — Bees: a, Bombus sylvarum (40mm diameter). b, Megachile lagopoda (40mm diameter). c, Apis mellifera facing right (50x30mm). d, Apis mellifera facing left (50x30mm).
No. 1680, 250fr — Orchids: a, Paphiopedilum hirsutissimum (40mm diameter). b, Brassovola nodosa (40mm diameter). c, Phalaenopsis hybrid (50x30mm). d, Dendrobium kingianum (50x30mm).
No. 1681, 250fr — Minerals: a, Apophyllite (40mm diameter). b, Amethyst (40mm diameter). c, Grossular (50x30mm). d, Apatite (50x30mm).
No. 1682, 250fr — Lighthouses and various unnamed shells: a, Marblehead Light, Ohio (40mm diameter). b, Tawas Point Light, Michigan (40mm diameter). c, Castle Hill Lighthouse, Rhode Island (50x30mm). d, West Point Light, Washington (50x30mm).
No. 1683, 1000fr, Pongo abelii. No. 1684, 1000fr, Ocicat. No. 1685, 1000fr, Carcharodon carcharias. No. 1686, 1000fr, Dacelo leachii. No. 1687, 1000fr, Bombus ruderarius. No. 1688, 1000fr, Phalaenopsis Sogo Yukidian. No. 1689, 1000fr, Emerald. No. 1690, 1000fr, Fastnet Lighthouse, Ireland, shell and starfish.

2019, Mar. 14   Litho.   Perf. 13¼
Sheets of 4, #a-d
1675-1682 A358 Set of 8   90.00 90.00
Souvenir Sheets
Perf.
1683-1690 A358 Set of 8   90.00 90.00
Nos. 1683-1690 each conatin one 40mm diameter stamp.

Souvenir Sheets

Nobel Laureates — A359

Designs: No. 1691, 1000fr, Dr. Martin Luther King, Jr. (1929-68), 1964 Peace laureate. No. 1692, 1000fr, Pablo Neruda (1904-73), 1971 Literature laureate. No. 1693, 1000fr, Mikhail Gorbachev, 1990 Peace laureate. No. 1694, 1000fr, Tu Youyou, 2015 Physiology or Medicine laureate.

2019, Mar. 14   Litho.   Perf.
1691-1694 A359 Set of 4   45.00 45.00

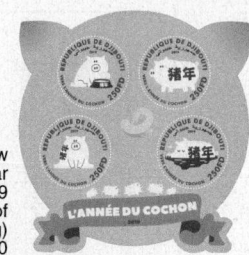

New Year 2019 (Year of the Pig) A360

No. 1695: a, Pig and bowl. b, Pig facing left. c, Pig sitting. d, Pig in mud. 1000fr, Pig snout.

Litho. With Foil Application
2019, Mar. 14   Perf.
1695 A360 250fr Sheet of 4, #a-d   11.50 11.50
Souvenir Sheet
1696 A360 1000fr multi   11.50 11.50

Naval Vessels of the People's Republic of China — A361

Flag of the Navy of People's Republic of China and: No. 1697, 200fr, Type 001A aircraft carrier. No. 1698, 200fr, Type 075 amphibious assault ship.
No. 1699, 500fr, Like #1697. No. 1700, 500fr, Like #1698.

2019, May 27   Litho.   Perf. 13
1697-1698 A361 Set of 2   4.50 4.50
Souvenir Sheets
1699-1700 A361 Set of 2   11.50 11.50

Eid ul-Fitr Activities — A362

Emblem and: 1000fr, People making art for disabled children. 3000fr, People in march for equality, horiz.

Litho. & Embossed
2019, May 27   Perf. 13
1701-1702 A362 Set of 2   45.00 45.00

A363

No. 1703, 250fr — 50th birthday of Vassily Ivantchuk, chess player: a, Touching chess piece at bottom. b, With chin resting on hands at bottom. c, Writing. d, With hands on forehead at left.
No. 1704, 250fr — Richard F. Gordon, Jr. (1929-2017), astronaut: a, Apollo 12 service and command modules, mission patch. b, Wearing spacesuit without helmet. c, Wearing spacesuit and helmet. d, With astronaut Pete Conrad (1930-99).
No. 1705, 250fr — Ernest H. Shackleton (1874-1922), Antarctic explorer: a, Standing with penguins. b, Marine chronometer. c, Sled dog. d, His ship, Endurance.
No. 1706, 250fr — Birth of Archie Harrison Mountbatten-Windsor, son of the Duke and Duchess of Sussex: a, With parents. b, With mother. c, Duke of Sussex. d, Duke of Sussex as child, with his mother, Princess Diana.
No. 1707, 250fr — Paintings by Pierre-Auguste Renoir (1841-1919): a, Children at the Seashore, Guernsey, 1883. b, The Swing,

1876. c, Riding in the Bois du Boulogne, 1873. d, Woman Sitting by the sea, 1883.
No. 1708, 250fr — Japanese high-speed trains: a, Shinkansen Series E6. b, Shinkansen Series 500, blue black trim. c, Shinkansen Series E7. d, Shinkansen Series 500, blue trim.
No. 1709, 250fr — Fire trucks: a, Isuzu Elf. b, Opel Blitz 1.75t. c, Opel Blitz LF8 TS. d, Ford Transit MK1.
No. 1710, 250fr — Motorcycles: a, Moto Guzzi V85TT. b, 2019 BMW R 1250 GS. c, Suzuki GSX1100S Katana. d, Kawasaki Z125.
No. 1711, 250fr — Dinosaurs: a, Beipiaosaurus inexpectus. b, Caudipteryx dongi. c, Archaeoceratops oshimai. d, Rubeosaurus ovatus.
No. 1712, 1000fr, Ivanchuk and Magnus Carlsen playing chess, horiz. No. 1713, 1000fr, Gordon and Apollo 12 mission patch. horiz. No. 1714, 1000fr, Shackleton and foundering ship, horiz. No. 1715, 1000fr, Feet of Mountbatten-Windsor, horiz. No. 1716, 1000fr, Odalisque, by Renoir, horiz. No. 1717, 1000fr, Shinkansen Series E5, horiz. No. 1718, 1000fr, IFA W50 La fire truck, horiz. No. 1719, 1000fr, Yamaha YZF-R125 motorcycle, horiz. No. 1720, 1000fr, Brachylophosaurus canadensis, horiz.

Perf. 13¼x12¾
2019, June 12   Litho.
Sheets of 4, #a-d
1703-1711 A363 Set of 9   100.00 100.00
Souvenir Sheets
Perf. 12¾x13¼
1712-1720 A363 Set of 9   100.00 100.00

Animals A364

No. 1721, 250fr — Hippopotamus amphibius: a, Adult and calf. b, Bird sitting on adult. c, Adult. d, Adult underwater.
No. 1722, 250fr — Wild cats: a, Panthera tigris tigris. b, Panthera uncia. c, Puma concolor. d, Panthera pardus orientalis.
No. 1723, 250fr — Sled dogs: a, Siberian huskies. b, Sakhalin husky. c, Alaskan malamute. d, Greenland dogs.
No. 1724, 250fr — Dolphins: a, Lagenorhynchus obscurus. b, Delphinus capensis. c, Tursiops truncatus. d, Stenella frontalis.
No. 1725, 250fr — Birds of prey: a, Aquila rapax. b, Pandion haliaetus. c, Milvus migrans. d, Aquila clanga.
No. 1726, 250fr — Hummingbirds: a, Chlorostilbon lucidus. b, Mellisuga helenae. c, Calypte anna. d, Archilochus colubris.
No. 1727, 250fr — Hornbills: a, Rhyticeros cassidix. b, Buceros bicornis. c, Tockus erythrorhynchus. d, Anthracoceros albirostris.
No. 1728, 250fr — Fish and coral: a, Paracanthurus hepatus, Acabaria splendens. b, Pomacanthus xanthometopon, Zoanthus gigantus. c, Pomacanthus imperator, Discosoma nummiforme. d, Balistoides conspicillum, Ricordea florida.
No. 1729, 250fr — Snakes: a, Trimeresurus insularis. b, Natrix natrix. c, Morelia viridis. d, Atheris ceratophora.
No. 1730, 250fr — Extinct animals: a, Ara gossei. b, Numenius borealis. c, Macropus greyi. d, Pyrenean ibex.
No. 1731, 1000fr, Choeropsis liberiensis. No. 1732, 1000fr, Panthera onca. No. 1733, 1000fr, Alaskan malamute, diff. No. 1734, 1000fr, Stenella coeruleoalba. No. 1735, 1000fr, Aquila heliaca. No. 1736, 1000fr, Calypte anna, diff. No. 1737, 1000fr, Tockus leucomelas. No. 1738, 1000fr, Zebrasoma desjardinii, Annella mollis. No. 1739, 1000fr, Drepanoides anomalus and Heliconia rostrata. No. 1740, 1000fr, Ectopistes migratorius.

Perf. 13¼x12¾
2019, June 12   Litho.
Sheets of 4, #a-d
1721-1730 A364 Set of 10   115.00 115.00
Souvenir Sheets
1731-1740 A364 Set of 10   115.00 115.00

Chinese Bridges — A365

Various unnamed Chinese bridges numbered: 100fr, (15-01). 125fr, (15-02). 150fr, (15-03). 175fr, (15-04). 200fr, (15-05). 225fr, (15-06). 250fr, (15-07). 275fr, (15-08). 300fr, (15-09). 325fr, (15-10). 350fr, (15-11). 375fr, (15-12). 400fr, (15-13). 425fr, (15-14). 450fr, (15-15).

2019, June 12   Litho.   Perf. 13x13¼
1741-1755 A365 Set of 15   46.50 46.50
Diplomatic relations between Djibouti and People's Republic of China, 40th anniv. Nos. 1741-1755 were each printed in sheets of 15 + label.

Chinese Buildings — A366

Various unnamed Chinese buildings numbered: 100fr, (15-01). 125fr, (15-02). 150fr, (15-03). 175fr, (15-04). 200fr, (15-05). 225fr, (15-06). 250fr, (15-07). 275fr, (15-08). 300fr, (15-09). 325fr, (15-10). 350fr, (15-11). 375fr, (15-12). 400fr, (15-13). 425fr, (15-14). 450fr, (15-15).

2019, June 12   Litho.   Perf. 13x13¼
1756-1770 A366 Set of 15   46.50 46.50
Diplomatic relations between Djibouti and People's Republic of China, 40th anniv. Nos. 1756-1770 were each printed in sheets of 15 + label.

Stamps With Emblem of Worldwide Fund for Nature (WWF) — A367

No. 1771: a, Dominica #827. b, Domincan Republic #1158c. c, Djibouti #795b. d, Dominica #2520b.
No. 1772, 300fr, Dominica #829. No. 1773, 300fr, Dominican Republic #1158b. No. 1774, 300fr, Djibouti #795a. No. 1775, 300fr, Dominica #2520a.

2019, July 27   Litho.   Perf. 13x13¼
1771 A367 200fr Sheet of 4, #a-d   9.00 9.00
Souvenir Sheets
1772-1775 A367 Set of 4   13.50 13.50
Nos. 1772-1775 each contain one 50x39mm stamp.

A368

No. 1776, 250fr — Mohandas K. Gandhi (1869-1948), Indian nationalist leader: a, With spinning wheel. b, Holding walking stick. c, Facing right, flag of India and Taj Mahal in background. d, Facing left with hands together, flags of India and Taj Mahal in background.
No. 1777, 250fr — 50th birthday of Michael Schumacher, race car driver: a, With race car in background. b, With Eddie Irvine and Jean Todt. c, In race car. d, With arms raised.

No. 1778, 250fr — Golfers: a, Phil Mickelson. b, Tiger Woods. c, Rory McIlroy. d, Brooks Koepka.

No. 1779, 250fr — 2018 Nobel laureates: a, Peace laureates Nadia Murad and Denis Mukwege. b, Physiology or Medicine laureates Tasuku Honjo and James P. Allison. c, Economics laureates Paul Romer and William Nordhaus. d, Chemistry laureates George Smith, Gregory Winter and Frances Arnold.

No. 1780, 250fr — Paintings by Vincent van Gogh (1853-90): a, The Drinkers, 1890. b, The Langlois Bridge at Arles with Women Washing, 1888. c, Boats on the Banks of the Oise at Auvers, 1890. d, Two Peasants Digging (After Millet), 1889.

No. 1781, 250fr — World War II tanks: a, TKS, Poland. b, 7TP, Poland. c, Panzer IV, Germany. d, Panzer I, Germany.

No. 1782, 250fr — Spaceflight of Apollo 11, 50th anniv.: a, Launch. b, Lunar Module landing on Moon. c, Command and Service Modules above Moon. d, Capsule returning to Earth.

No. 1783, 1000fr, Gandhi and crowd holding flags of India. No. 1784, 1000fr, Schumacher and race car, diff. No. 1785, 1000fr, Woods, diff. No. 1786, 1000fr, 2018 Nobel laureates in Physics, Donna Strickland, Arthur Ashkin, and Gérard Mourou. No. 1787, 1000fr, Self-portrait with Straw Hat, by van Gogh. No. 1788, 1000fr, Panzer III tank, Germany. No. 1789, 1000fr, Astronaut Neil Armstrong on Moon, holding U.S. flag, Apollo 11 mission patch.

2019, July 27 Litho. *Perf. 13¼x12¾*
Sheets of 4, #a-d
1776-1782 A368 Set of 7   80.00 80.00
Souvenir Sheets
1783-1789 A368 Set of 7   80.00 80.00

A369

No. 1790, 250fr — Panthera tigris tigris: a, Two tigers. b, One tiger facing forward with front legs apart. c, One tiger, standing in water. d, Tiger, reclining, with cub.

No. 1791, 250fr — Elephants: a, Three Loxodonta africana. b, Loxodonta cyclotis looking forward. c, Loxodonta cyclotis walking to right. d, Two Loxodonta africana.

No. 1792, 250fr — Whales: a, Megaptera novaeangliae, head at right. b, Megaptera novaeangliae, head at left. c, Two Megaptera novaeangliae. d, Physeter macrocephalus.

No. 1793, 250fr — Pigeons: a, Streptopelia turtur. b, Streptopelia decaocto. c, Ocyphaps lophotes. d, Goura victoria.

No. 1794, 250fr — Owls: a, Glaucidium californicum. b, Bubo africanus. c, Megascops asio. d, Bubo sumatranus.

No. 1795, 250fr — Parrots: a, Ara ararauna. b, Anodorhynchus hyacinthinus. c, Psittacus erithacus. d, Nymphicus hollandicus.

No. 1796, 250fr — Butterflies: a, Danaus eresimus. b, Gonepteryx cleopatra. c, Graphium sarpedon. d, Caligo eurilochus.

No. 1797, 250fr — Turtles: a, Clemmys guttata. b, Apalone spinifera. c, Trachemys scripta. d, Chelydra serpentina.

No. 1798, 250fr — Endangered animals: a, Canis lupus baileyi. b, Grus americana. c, Lynx pardinus. d, Gorilla beringei.

No. 1799, 250fr — Mushrooms: a, Tricholoma equestre. b, Gyroporus cyanescens. c, Boletus betulicola. d, Boletus aereus.

No. 1800, 250fr — Volcanoes: a, Volcán de Fuego, Guatemala. b, Piton de la Fournaise, Reunion Island. c, Parinacota, Bolivia, and Vicugna pacos. d, Sakurajima, Japan.

No. 1801, 250fr — Ships: a, HMS Diadem. b, Lai Fong. c, HMS Prince Royal. d, HMS Bounty.

No. 1802, 1000fr, Panthera tigris tigris, diff. No. 1803, 1000fr, Loxodonta cyclotis adult and calf. No. 1804, 1000fr, Megaptera novaeangliae, diff. No. 1805, 1000fr, Columba livia domestica. No. 1806, 1000fr, Aegolius funereus. No. 1807, 1000fr, Psittacula krameri. No. 1808, 1000fr, Agalis io. No. 1809, 1000fr, Pseudemys nelsoni. No. 1810, 1000fr, Crocodylus siamensis. No. 1811, 1000fr, Hydnum repandum. No. 1812, 1000fr, Popocatepetl, Mexico. No. 1813, 1000fr, USS Providence.

2019, July 27 Litho. *Perf. 13¼x12¾*
Sheets of 4, #a-d
1790-1801 A369 Set of 12   135.00 135.00
Souvenir Sheets
1802-1813 A369 Set of 12   135.00 135.00

Nos. 1059a-1059d Surcharged in Gold or Metallic Red

Methods and Perfs. As Before
2019, Aug. 27
1814 A311 590fr on 260fr
             #1059a (G)   6.75 6.75
1815 A311 590fr on 260fr
             #1059a
             (MR)   6.75 6.75
1816 A311 590fr on 260fr
             #1059b   6.75 6.75
1817 A311 590fr on 260fr
             #1059b
             (MR)   6.75 6.75
1818 A311 590fr on 260fr
             #1059c (G)   6.75 6.75
1819 A311 590fr on 260fr
             #1059c
             (MR)   6.75 6.75
1820 A311 590fr on 260fr
             #1059d (G)   6.75 6.75
1821 A311 590fr on 260fr
             #1059d
             (MR)   6.75 6.75
   Nos. 1814-1821 (8)   54.00 54.00

A370

No. 1822, 250fr — Cats: a, Balinese. b, American Shorthair. c, Russian Blue. d, Japanese bobtail.

No. 1823, 250fr — Horses: a, Paint horse. b, Lusitano. c, Knabstruper. d, Holsteiner.

No. 1824, 250fr — Bee-eaters: a, Merops albicollis. b, Merops apiaster. c, Merops leschenaulti. d, Merops bulocki.

No. 1825, 250fr, vert. — Sunbirds: a, Hedydipna collaris. b, Aethopyga gouldiae. c, Aethopyga siparaja. d, Aethopyga nipalensis.

No. 1826, 250fr, vert. — Ducks: a, Netta rufina. b, Aythya fuligula. c, Bucephala clangula. d, Tadorna tadorna.

No. 1827, 250fr, vert. — Bees: a, Bombus pascuorum. b, Xylocopa virginica. c, Apis cerana. d, Bombus terrestris.

No. 1828, 250fr, vert. — Orchids: a, Prosthechea brassavolae. b, Phalaenopsis mariae. c, Zygopetalum crinitum. d, Ondidium flexuosum.

No. 1829, 250fr, vert. — Minerals: a, Azurite. b, Pyrite. c, Celestine. d, Demantoid.

No. 1830, 1000fr, Abyssinian cats. No. 1831, 1000fr, Shire horses. No. 1832, 1000fr, Merops nubicus, vert. No. 1833, 1000fr, Arachnothera magna, vert. No. 1834, 1000fr, Marmaronetta angustirostris, vert. No. 1835, 1000fr, Apis mellifera, vert. No. 1836, 1000fr, Catasetum fimbriatum, vert. No. 1837, 1000fr, Heliodor.

Perf. 13x13¼, 13¼x13
2019, Aug. 27   Litho.
Sheets of 4, #a-d
1822-1829 A370 Set of 8   90.00 90.00
Souvenir Sheets
1830-1837 A370 Set of 8   90.00 90.00

MARILYN MONROE

A371

No. 1838, 250fr — Marilyn Monroe (1926-62), actress: a, Holding dogs. b, Wearing blue dress at right. c, Wearing red dress at right. d, Seated in chair.

No. 1839, 250fr — Charlie Chaplin (1889-1977), actor, in scene from 1914 film: a, *Charlot garde-malade* (His New Profession). b, *Charlot est content de lui* (Kid Auto Races at Venice). c, *Charlot et le Mannequin* (Mabel's Married Life). d, *Charlot artiste peintre* (The Face on the Bar Room Floor).

No. 1840, 250fr — Tigran Petrosian (1929-84), chess player, wearing: a, Gray pinstripe suit. b, Brown suit. c, White shirt and tie. d, White and green plaid shirt.

No. 1841, 250fr — Rotary International emblem and: a, Paul P. Harris (1868-1947), founder, world map and doves. b, Child at water spigot. c, Doctor examining child. d, Children carrying blackboard.

No. 1842, 250fr — Duke and Duchess of Sussex: a, Duke and Duchess with son Archie carried by Duke. b, Duke of Sussex holding baby clothes. c, Archie Mountbatten-Windsor. d, Duke and Duchess with son carried by Duchess.

No. 1843, 250fr — Robert Stephenson (1803-59), civil engineer: a, With flag of Great Britain. b, Signature of Stephenson and Rocket locomotive. c, Standing on Planet locomotive. d, With his yacht, Titania.

No. 1844, 250fr — Scout: a, Fishing. b, At campfire. c, Birdwatching. d, Playing guitar.

No. 1845, 250fr — Japanese Shinkansen high-speed trains: a, Series 400. b, Series N700. c, Series 700. d, Series E3-1000.

No. 1846, 250fr — Operation Market Garden, 75th anniv.: a, DeHavilland DH.98 Mosquitos. b, Douglas C-47 Skytrains. c, Airspeed AS.51 Horsa gliders and Short Stirling Mark IV airplanes. d, Spitfire F Mk II and Messerschmitt Bf 109 airplanes.

No. 1847, 250fr — Flying dinosaurs: a, Eudimorphodon ranzii. b, Caviramus schesaplanensis. c, Caulkicephalus trimicrodon. d, Pterosaur.

No. 1848, 1000fr, Monroe, diff. No. 1849, 1000fr, Chaplin in *Making a Living.* No. 1850, 1000fr, Petrosian, diff. No. 1851, 1000fr, Harris and Rotary International emblem, diff. No. 1852, 1000fr, Archie Mountabtten-Windsor, diff. No. 1853, 1000fr, Britannia Bridge, built by Stephenson. No. 1854, 1000fr, Scout, badge and canoe. No. 1855, 1000fr, Shinkansen Series 500. No. 1856, 1000fr, Hawker Tempest and Junkers Ju88 airplanes. No. 1857, 1000fr, Harpactognathus gentryii.

2019, Aug. 27   *Perf. 13¼x13*
1838-1847 A371 Set of 10   115.00 115.00
Souvenir Sheets
1848-1857 A371 Set of 10   115.00 115.00

VERS L'ANNÉE DU RAT

New Year 2020 (Year of the Rat) — A372

No. 1858 — Rat and: a, "2020." b, Fireworks. c, Lantern. d, Fireworks and "2020." 1000fr, Rat with gift.

Litho. With Foil Application
2019, Aug. 27   *Perf. 13¼x13*
1858 A372 250fr Sheet of 4,
             #a-d   11.50 11.50
Souvenir Sheet
1859 A372 1000fr multi   11.50 11.50

Navires militaires norvégiens

Norwegian Navy Ships — A373

No. 1860 — Norwegian state flag and: a, HNoMS Trygvason. b, NoCGV Svalbard. c, KNM Storm. d, Rauma. 1000fr, KNM Fridtjof Nansen.

2019, Dec. 12 Litho. *Perf. 13x13¼*
1860 A373 250fr Sheet of 4,
             #a-d   11.50 11.50
Souvenir Sheet
1861 A373 1000fr multi   11.50 11.50

A374

No. 1862, 250fr — Paul Morphy (1837-84), chess champion, and: a, Queen. b, Bishop. c, Rook. d, Knight.

No. 1863, 250fr — Formula 1 race cars and drivers: a, Ferrari SF90 and Charles Leclerc. b, Ferrari SF90 and Sebastian Vettel. c, Mercedes AMG F1 W10 and Lewis Hamilton. d, Mercedes AMG F1 W10 and Valteri Bottas.

No. 1864, 250fr — Bentley automobiles, cent.: a, Bentley MH7580. b, Bentley EXP 10 Speed 6. c, Bentley Mark VI Drophead Coupe. d, Bentley Benayga.

No. 1865, 250fr — Fire trucks: a, Mercedes-Benz Zetros. b, Pierce. c, Seagrave Marauder II. d, Kenworth T800.

No. 1866, 250fr — Early locomotives: a, Locomotion No. 1, 1825. b, Salamanca, 1812. c, Atlantic, 1832. d, Cherepanov steam locomotive, 1833.

No. 1867, 250fr — African trains: a, South African Class SE1 Series 5. b, South African Gautrain. c, EMD G22C Series. d, South African Class 33-400.

No. 1868, 250fr — Start of World War I, 105th anniv.: a, Mark V tank, Great Britain. b, French soldier. c, A7V tank, Germany. d, British soldier.

No. 1869, 250fr — Dinosaurs: a, Triceratops horridus. b, Gallimimus bullatus. c, Ankylosaurus magniventris. d, Tyrannosaurus rex.

No. 1870, 1000fr, Morphy and king. No. 1871, 1000fr, Red Bull RB15 and Max Verstappen. No. 1872, 1000fr, Bentley Flying Spur. No. 1873, 1000fr, E-One fire truck. No. 1874, 1000fr, Catch Me Who Can (M'attrape qui peut) locomotive, 1808. No. 1875, 1000fr, South African Class 19D4-8-2. No. 1876, 1000fr, Fokker Dr. I airplane, Germany. No. 1877, 1000fr, Parasaurolophus walkeri.

2019, Dec. 12 Litho. *Perf. 13¼*
Sheets of 4, #a-d
1862-1869 A374 Set of 8   90.00 90.00
Souvenir Sheets
1870-1877 A374 Set of 8   90.00 90.00

LES CHIENS

A375

No. 1878, 250fr — Dogs: a, Shetland sheepdog. b, Papillon. c, English bulldog. d, English cocker spaniel.

No. 1879, 250fr — Dolphins: a, Tursiops aduncus. b, Stenella longirostris, Stenella coeruleoalba. c, Tursiops truncatus. d, Lagenorhynchus obliquidens, Cephalorhynchus hectori.

No. 1880, 250fr — Kingfishers: a, Ceyx erithaca. b, Halcyon pileata. c, Ceryle rudis. d, Megaceryle alcyon.

No. 1881, 250fr — Birds of prey: a, Accipiter gentilis. b, Gyps fulvus. c, Haliaeetus leucocephalus. d, Otus scops.

No. 1882, 250fr — Aquatic birds: a, Anas platyrhynchos. b, Ardea alba modesta. c, Alcedo atthis. d, Fratercula arctica.

No. 1883, 250fr — Butterflies: a, Tithorea harmonia. b, Ornithoptera euphorion. c, Papilio rutulus. d, Myscelia cyaniris.

No. 1884, 250fr — Fish: a, Apistogramma cacatuoides. b, Pomacanthus imperator. c, Paracanthurus hepatus. d, Chelmon rostratus.

No. 1885, 250fr — Antarctic animals: a, Leptonychotes weddellii. b, Leucocarbo bransfieldensis. c, Lobodon carcinophaga. d, Pygoscelis antarctica.

No. 1886, 250fr — Mushrooms: a, Leccinum versipelle. b, Hypsizygus tessellatus. c, Leccinum scabrum. d, Morchella esculenta.

No. 1887, 250fr — Lighthouses: a, Bodie Island Lighthouse, North Carolina. b, Split Rock Lighthouse, Minnesota. c, Punta Carena Lighthouse, Italy. d, Tower of Hercules Lighthouse, Spain.

No. 1888, 1000fr, Mastiff. No. 1889, 1000fr, Inia geoffrensis. No. 1890, 1000fr, Dacelo novaeguineae. No. 1891, 1000fr, Sarcoramphus papa. No. 1892, 1000fr, Recurvirostra avosetta. No. 1893, 1000fr, Parnassius tianschanicus. No. 1894, 1000fr, Pterois antennata. No. 1895, 1000fr, Megaptera novaeangliae. No. 1896, 1000fr, Boletus edulis. No. 1897, 1000fr, Point Cabrillo Lighthouse, California.

2019, Dec. 12   Litho.   Perf. 13¼
Sheets of 4, #a-d

1878-1887	A375	Set of 10	115.00	115.00

Souvenir Sheets

1888-1897	A375	Set of 10	115.00	115.00

A376

A377

A378

A379

A380

A381

A382

A383

A384

A385

A386

A387

A388

A389

A390

Chinese Paintings — A391

2019, Dec. 12   Litho.   Perf. 13¼

1898	A376	250fr multi	3.00	3.00
1899	A377	250fr multi	3.00	3.00
1900	A378	250fr multi	3.00	3.00
1901	A379	250fr multi	3.00	3.00
1902	A380	250fr multi	3.00	3.00
1903	A381	250fr multi	3.00	3.00
1904	A382	250fr multi	3.00	3.00
1905	A383	250fr multi	3.00	3.00
1906	A384	250fr multi	3.00	3.00
1907	A385	250fr multi	3.00	3.00
1908	A386	250fr multi	3.00	3.00
1909	A387	250fr multi	3.00	3.00
1910	A388	250fr multi	3.00	3.00
1911	A389	250fr multi	3.00	3.00
1912	A390	250fr multi	3.00	3.00
1913	A391	250fr multi	3.00	3.00
a.		Sheet of 16, #1898-1913	48.00	48.00
	Nos. 1898-1913 (16)		48.00	48.00

Global Compact on Migration — A392

2019   Litho.   Perf. 13¼x12¾

1914	A392	100fr multi	1.25	1.25

Djibouti's Candidacy for 2021-22 United Nations Security Council Seat — A393

2019   Litho.   Perf. 13¼x13

1915	A393	100fr multi + label	1.25	1.25

Kiwis A394

No. 1916: a, Apteryx mantelli. b, Apteryx australis. c, Apteryx owenii. d, Apteryx rowi. 1000fr, Apteryx mantelli, diff.

Litho., Sheet Margin Litho With Foil Application
2020, Feb. 27   Perf. 13¼

1916	A394	250fr Sheet of 4, #a-d	11.50	11.50

Litho. With Foil Application
Souvenir Sheet

1917	A394	1000fr multi	11.50	11.50

New Zealand 2020 International Stamp Exhibition, Auckland. No. 1917 contains one 52x52mm stamp.

Famous Men — A395

Designs: No. 1918, 250fr, St. John Paul II (1920-2005). No. 1919, 250fr, Nelson Mandela (1918-2013), President of South Africa. No. 1920, 250fr, Mohandas K. Gandhi (1869-1948), Indian nationalist leader.

Perf. 13¼x12¾

2020, Feb. 27   Litho.

1918-1920	A395	Set of 3	8.50	8.50
1920a		Souvenir sheet of 6, 2 each #1918-1920	17.00	17.00

Nos. 1918-1920 were each printed in sheets of 8 + central label.

A396

Butterflies: No. 1921, 250fr, Ornithoptera euphorion. No. 1922, 250fr, Vanessa cardui. No. 1923, 250fr, Idea malabarica. No. 1924, 250fr, Euploea core.

No. 1925, 1000fr, Heliconius ismenius, horiz.

Orchids: No. 1926, 250fr, Vanda coerulea. No. 1927, 250fr, Cattleya harrisoniana. No. 1928, 250fr, Platanthera chlorantha. No. 1929, 250fr, Neottia nidus-avis.

No. 1930, 1000fr, Cattleya Nancy Off "Linwood," horiz.

Mushrooms: No. 1931, 250fr, Cantharellus cibarius. No. 1932, 250fr, Rhodotus palmatus. No. 1933, 250fr, Morchella esculenta. No. 1934, 250fr, Boletus edulis.

No. 1935, 1000fr, Amanita muscaria, horiz.

Perf. 13¼x12¾, 12¾x13¼ (horiz. stamps)

2020, Feb. 27   Litho.

Butterflies

1921-1924	A396	Set of 4	11.50	11.50
a.		Souvenir sheet of 4, #1921-1924	11.50	11.50

Souvenir Sheet

1925	A396	1000fr multi	11.50	11.50

Orchids

1926-1929	A396	Set of 4	11.50	11.50
a.		Souvenir sheet of 4, #1926-1929	11.50	11.50

Souvenir Sheet

1930	A396	1000fr multi	11.50	11.50

Mushrooms

1931-1934	A396	Set of 4	11.50	11.50
a.		Souvenir sheet of 4, #1931-1934	11.50	11.50

Souvenir Sheet

1935	A396	1000fr multi	11.50	11.50

A397

Alain Prost, Formula 1 race car driver: No. 1936, 250fr, Close-up of Prost, Prost driving race car. No. 1937, 250fr, Prost driving race car, flag of France. No. 1938, 250fr, Prost driving race car. No. 1939, 250fr, Close-up of Prost in race car.

No. 1940, 1000fr, Prost and Ayrton Senna (1960-94) Formula 1 race car driver.

Senna: No. 1941, 250fr, Signature of Senna, Senna driving Lotus 97T. No. 1942, 250fr, Close-up of Senna, crowd watching race. No. 1943, 250fr, Senna driving McLaren MP4/4. No. 1944, 250fr, Senna driving Lotus 99T.

No. 1945, 1000fr, Senna as child, seated in toy Jeep.

Elvis Presley (1935-77), with: No. 1946, 250fr, Guitar in background. No. 1947, 250fr, Guitar and crown. No. 1948, 250fr, Guitar and star. No. 1949, 250fr, Bill Haley (1925-81), rock musician.

No. 1950, 250fr, Presley holding microphone.

St. John Paul II (1920-2005): No. 1951, 250fr, And St. Peter's Basilica. No. 1952, 250fr, Kissing baby. No. 1953, 250fr, With St. Teresa of Calcutta (1910-97). No. 1954, 250fr, And his coat of arms.

No. 1955, 1000fr, Wearing miter, St. Peter's Basilica in background.

Rotary International, 115th anniv.: No. 1956, 250fr, Child writing at desk. No. 1957, 250fr, Paul P. Harris (1868-1947), founder, microscope and medical supplies. No. 1958, 250fr, Seedling, hands holding Earth. No. 1959, 250fr, Child drinking water from spigot.

No. 1960, 1000fr, Harris and stack of books.

Discovery of Antarctica, 200th anniv.: No. 1961, 250fr, Edward Bransfield (1785-1852), sailor on Antarctic expeditions, and penguins. No. 1962, 250fr, Map of Antarctica, medal commemorating 1819 Bellingshausen expedition. No. 1963, 250fr, Bird, seal and ship. No. 1964, 250fr, Nathaniel Palmer (1799-1877), Antarctic explorer, and sculpture.

No. 1965, 1000fr, Fabian Gottlieb von Bellingshausen (1778-1852), Antarctic explorer.

Battle of Iwo Jima, 75th anniv.: No. 1966, 250fr, LVT(A)-1 tank. No. 1967, 250fr, Lockheed P-38 Lightning and A6M5. No. 1968, 250fr, F4U Corsair and A6M5. No. 1969, 250fr, Soldier and M4A2 Sherman tank.

No. 1970, 1000fr, Jeep and tank.

MiG-17 prototype jet, 70th anniv.: No. 1971, 250fr, Three silver jets flying to right. No. 1972, 250fr, Two green jets flying to left, mechanical drawing. No. 1973, 250fr, Red jet flying to right. No. 1974, 250fr, Silver jet taking off.

No. 1975, 1000fr, Silver jet and Artem Mikoyan (1905-70), aircraft designer.

Treaty of Versailles, cent.: No. 1976, 250fr, Soldier and David Lloyd George (1863-1945), British Prime Minister. No. 1977, 250fr, Woodrow Wilson (1856-1924), U.S. President, and people at peace conference. No. 1978, 250fr, Dirigibles over battlefield and Milenko Vesnic (1863-1921), Serbian representative at Paris Peace Conference. No. 1979, 250fr, Airplane, tank and Vittorio Emanuele Orlando (1860-1952), Italian representative at Paris Peace Conference.

No. 1980, 1000fr, People at peace conference and Georges Clemenceau (1841-1929), French Prime Minister.

Yalta Conference, 75th anniv: No. 1981, 250fr, Winston Churchill (1874-1965), British Prime Minister, Franklin D. Roosevelt (1882-1945), U.S. President, and Joseph Stalin (1878-1953), General Secretary of the Soviet Union. No. 1982, 250fr, Churchill and British flag. No. 1983, 250fr, Roosevelt and U.S. flag. No. 1984, 250fr, Stalin and flag of Soviet Union.

No. 1985, 1000fr, Roosevelt and U.S flag, diff.

90th birthday of Edwin E. "Buzz" Aldrin, Jr., astronaut: No. 1986, 250fr, Gemini 12 mission patch and Titan II rocket on launch pad. No. 1987, 250fr, Apollo 11 mission patch, command and service modules. No. 1988, 250fr, Gemini 12 capsuel in space. No. 1989, 250fr, Aldrin in spacesuit.

No. 1990, 1000fr, Gemini 12 mission patch and capsule, and its crew members, Aldrin and James A. Lovell, Jr.

Launch of Osumi, first Japanese satellite: No. 1991, 250fr, Osumi satellite and Japanese flag. No. 1992, 250fr, Osumi in space, antennae at bottom. No. 1993, 250fr, Osumi in space, antennae at top. No. 1994, 250fr, Uchinoura launch pad and rocket.

No. 1995, 1000fr, Drawing of Osumi satellite and Hideo Itokawa (1912-99), rocketry pioneer.

Sir Alexander Fleming (1881-1955), discoverer of penicillin: No. 1996, 250fr, Fleming, molecular diagram of benzylpenicillin, Morchella rufobrunnea. No. 1997, 250fr, Passer domesticus, Amanita phalloides and chemistry apparatus. No. 1998, 250fr, Microscope, Amanita muscaria. No. 1999, 250fr, Fleming, Chrysuronia oenone, Cantharellus cibarius.

No. 2000, 1000fr, Fleming and Penecillium chrysogenum.

COVID-19 pandemic: No. 2001, 250fr, Diamond Princess, quarantined cruise ship on which many passengers contracted COVID-19. No. 2002, 250fr, COVID-19 virus, map of People's Republic of China. No. 2003, 250fr, Li Wenliang (1985-2020), ophthalmologist who noted early COVID-19 cases in Wuhan. No. 2004, 250fr, Foton G9 ambulance, flag of People's Republic of China, Red Cross/Red Crescent emblem.

No. 2005, 1000fr, Li Wenliang and COVID-19 virus.

Dinosaurs: No. 2006, 250fr, Tyrannosaurus rex. No. 2007, 250fr, Spinosaurus aegyptiacus. No. 2008, 250fr, Velociraptor mongoliensis. No. 2009, 250fr, Tarbosaurus bataar.

No. 2010, 1000fr, Triceratops horridus.

Perf. 12¾x13¼
2020, Feb. 27   **Litho.**

Alain Prost
1936-1939	A397	Set of 4	11.50	11.50
a.		Souvenir sheet of 4, #1936-1939	11.50	11.50

Souvenir Sheet
1940	A397	1000fr multi	11.50	11.50

Ayrton Senna
1941-1944	A397	Set of 4	11.50	11.50
a.		Souvenir sheet of 4, #1941-1944	11.50	11.50

Souvenir Sheet
1945	A397	1000fr multi	11.50	11.50

Elvis Presley
1946-1949	A397	Set of 4	11.50	11.50
a.		Souvenir sheet of 4, #1946-1949	11.50	11.50

Souvenir Sheet
1950	A397	1000fr multi	11.50	11.50

St. John Paul II
1951-1954	A397	Set of 4	11.50	11.50
a.		Souvenir sheet of 4, #1951-1954	11.50	11.50

Souvenir Sheet
1955	A397	1000fr multi	11.50	11.50

Rotary International
1956-1959	A397	Set of 4	11.50	11.50
a.		Souvenir sheet of 4, #1956-1959	11.50	11.50

Souvenir Sheet
1960	A397	1000fr multi	11.50	11.50

Discovery of Antarctica
1961-1964	A397	Set of 4	11.50	11.50
a.		Souvenir sheet of 4, #1961-1964	11.50	11.50

Souvenir Sheet
1965	A397	1000fr multi	11.50	11.50

Battle of Iwo Jima
1966-1969	A397	Set of 4	11.50	11.50
a.		Souvenir sheet of 4, #1966-1969	11.50	11.50

Souvenir Sheet
1970	A397	1000fr multi	11.50	11.50

MiG-17
1971-1974	A397	Set of 4	11.50	11.50
a.		Souvenir sheet of 4, #1971-1974	11.50	11.50

Souvenir Sheet
1975	A397	1000fr multi	11.50	11.50

Treaty of Versailles
1976-1979	A397	Set of 4	11.50	11.50
a.		Souvenir sheet of 4, #1976-1979	11.50	11.50

Souvenir Sheet
1980	A397	1000fr multi	11.50	11.50

Yalta Conference
1981-1984	A397	Set of 4	11.50	11.50
a.		Souvenir sheet of 4, #1981-1984	11.50	11.50

Souvenir Sheet
1985	A397	1000fr multi	11.50	11.50

Edwin E. "Buzz" Aldrin, Jr.
1986-1989	A397	Set of 4	11.50	11.50
a.		Souvenir sheet of 4, #1986-1989	11.50	11.50

Souvenir Sheet
1990	A397	1000fr multi	11.50	11.50

Osumi Satellite
1991-1994	A397	Set of 4	11.50	11.50
a.		Souvenir sheet of 4, #1991-1994	11.50	11.50

Souvenir Sheet
1995	A397	1000fr multi	11.50	11.50

Sir Alexander Fleming
1996-1999	A397	Set of 4	11.50	11.50
a.		Souvenir sheet of 4, #1996-1999	11.50	11.50

Souvenir Sheet
2000	A397	1000fr multi	11.50	11.50

COVID-19 Pandemic
2001-2004	A397	Set of 4	11.50	11.50
a.		Souvenir sheet of 4, #2001-2004	11.50	11.50

Souvenir Sheet
2005	A397	1000fr multi	11.50	11.50

Dinosaurs
2006-2009	A397	Set of 4	11.50	11.50
a.		Souvenir sheet of 4, #2006-2009	11.50	11.50

Souvenir Sheet
2010	A397	1000fr multi	11.50	11.50

 A398

Albert Einstein (1879-1955), physicist, and: No. 2011, 250fr, Chalkboard with model of atom and mass-energy equation. No. 2012, 250fr, Sun, Moon, and mathematical calculations. No. 2013, 250fr, Diagram of curvature of space-time and Nobel medal. No. 2014, 250fr, Gravitational lens.

No. 2015, 1000fr, Einstein and diagram of theory of special relativity.

Dr. Albert Schweitzer (1875-1965), 1952 Nobel peace laureate: No. 2016, 250fr, Holding child. No. 2017, 250fr, Playing pipe organ. No. 2018, 250fr, With Nobel medal. No. 2019, 250fr, Examining child.

No. 2020, 1000fr, Schweitzer and Nobel medal, diff.

Eva Gabor (1919-95), actress: No. 2021, 250fr, With Liberace (1919-87), pianist. No. 2022, 250fr, Wearing green hat. No. 2023, 250fr, With Louis Jourdan (1921-2015), in movie, Gigi. No. 2024, 250fr, With suitcases.

No. 2025, 1000fr, Gabor dancing with Jourdan in Gigi.

Johann Sebastian Bach (1685-1750), composer: No. 2026, 250fr, Portrait of Bach. No. 2027, 250fr, Nativity scene and statue of Bach. No. 2028, 250fr, Felix Mendelssohn (1809-47), composer. No. 2029, 250fr, Violin and sheet music.

No. 2030, 1000fr, Portrait of Bach, diff.

Illustrations by Alphonse Mucha (1860-1939): No. 2031, 250fr, The Arts: Dance, 1898. No. 2032, 250fr, Poster for Job Cigarette Paper, 1896. No. 2033, 250fr, The Arts: Poetry, 1898. No. 2034, 250fr, Princess Hyacinth, 1911.

No. 2035, 1000fr, Woman with a Daisy, by Mucha, 1900.

Paintings by Vincent van Gogh (1853-90): No. 2036, 250fr, The Church at Auvers, 1890. No. 2037, 250fr, The Shepherdess (After Millet), 1889. No. 2038, 250fr, Portrait of Doctor Gachet, 1890. No. 2039, 250fr, Wheat Field Behind Saint-Paul Hospital, 1889.

No. 2040, 1000fr, Wheat Fields with Reaper at Sunrise, by van Gogh, 1889.

Penny Black stamp (Great Britain #1), 180th anniv.: No. 2041, 250fr, Gibraltar 50p coin depicting Penny Black No. 2042, 250fr, Penny Black held by stamp tongs. No. 2043, 250fr, Penny Black under magnifying glass. No. 2044, 250fr, Sir Rowland Hill (1795-1879), postal reformer.

No. 2045, 1000fr, Hill and Penny Black.

Charles de Gaulle (1890-1970), President of France: No. 2046, 250fr, With British Prime Minister Winston Churchill (1874-1965). No. 2047, 250fr, With flag of France. No. 2048, 250fr, With flag of France, saluting. No. 2049, 250fr, Behind microphones, with arms raised.

No. 2050, 1000fr, Behind microphone, holding script for speech.

Battle of France, 80th anniv.: No. 2051, 250fr, German soldiers and Sd Kfz 231 armored car. No. 2052, 250fr, German Panzer IV tank. No. 2053, 250fr, French soldier, T13 tank destroyer. No. 2054, 250fr, French SOMUA S35 tank.

No. 2055, 1000fr, German Panzer IV tank, diff.

Battle of Okinawa, 75th anniv: No. 2056, 250fr, Mitsubishi Ki-67, Japan. No. 2057, 250fr, USS Chilton, United States. No. 2058, 250fr, Yamato-class battleship, Japan. No. 2059, 250fr, Lockheed P-38 Lightning, United States.

No. 2060, 1000fr, Mitsubishi A6M Zero and USS Idaho.

Minerals: No. 2061, 250fr, Fluorine. No. 2062, 250fr, Quartz. No. 2063, 250fr, Magnesite. No. 2064, 250fr, Azurite.

No. 2065, 1000fr, Amazonite.

Volcanoes: No. 2066, 250fr, Mount Etna, Italy. No. 2067, 250fr, Mount Aso, Japan. No. 2068, 250fr, Sakurajima, Japan. No. 2069, 250fr, Arenal Volcano, Costa Rica.

No. 2070, 1000fr, Mount Fuji, Japan.

Jacques-Yves Cousteau (1910-97), marine conservationist: No. 2071, 250fr, With Katsuwonus pelamis. No. 2072, 250fr, SP-350 Denise submarine and Albula vulpes. No. 2073, 250fr, Cousteau's ship, Calypso, and Plectropomus pessuliferus. No. 2074, 250fr, Cousteau and Esox sphyraena.

No. 2075, 1000fr, Cousteau and Manta alfredi.

Spaceflight of Apollo 13, 50th anniv.: No. 2076, 250fr, Service module explosion. No. 2077, 250fr, Crew members James A. Lovell, Jr., Fred W. Haise, Jr., and Jack Swigert, Jr. (1931-82), and mission patch. No. 2078, 250fr, Separation and transposition of Apollo 13 modules and Lovell at rest. No. 2079, 250fr, Recovery of Apollo 13 capsule.

No. 2080, 1000fr, Launch of Apollo 13, mission patch separation and transposition of modules.

Launch of Hubble Space Telescope, 30th anniv.: No. 2081, 250fr, Telescope in space, aperture at UR. No. 2082, 250fr, Space Shuttle Discovery deploying telescope, and commemorative medal. No. 2083, 250fr, Space Shuttle Discovery deploying teleescope, STS-31 mission patch. No. 2084, 250fr, Telescope in space, aperture at LL.

No. 2085, 1000fr, Launch of Space Shuttle Discovery mission STS-31.

Cats: No. 2086, 250fr, Himalayan cat. No. 2087, 250fr, Singapura cat. No. 2088, 250fr, Bombay cat. No. 2089, 250fr, Bengal cat. No. 2090, 1000fr, Manx cat.

Dolphins: No. 2091, 250fr, Delphinus delphis. No. 2092, 250fr, Stenella attenuata. No. 2093, 250fr, Cephalorhynchus commersonii. No. 2094, 250fr, Stenella frontalis.

No. 2095, 1000fr, Inia geoffrensis.

Bees: No. 2096, 250fr, Osmia cornuta. No. 2097, 250fr, Eucera longicornis. No. 2098, 250fr, Nomada subcornuta. No. 2099, 250fr, Xylocopa violacea.

No. 2100, 1000fr, Bombus magnus.

Perf. 13¼x12¾
2020, Mar. 13   **Litho.**

Albert Einstein
2011-2014	A398	Set of 4	11.50	11.50
a.		Souvenir sheet of 4, #2011-2014	11.50	11.50

Souvenir Sheet
2015	A398	1000fr multi	11.50	11.50

Dr. Albert Schweitzer
2016-2019	A398	Set of 4	11.50	11.50
a.		Souvenir sheet of 4, #2016-2019	11.50	11.50

Souvenir Sheet
2020	A398	1000fr multi	11.50	11.50

Eva Gabor
2021-2024	A398	Set of 4	11.50	11.50
a.		Souvenir sheet of 4, #2021-2024	11.50	11.50

Souvenir Sheet
2025	A398	1000fr multi	11.50	11.50

Johann Sebastian Bach
2026-2029	A398	Set of 4	11.50	11.50
a.		Souvenir sheet of 4, #2026-2029	11.50	11.50

Souvenir Sheet
2030	A398	1000fr multi	11.50	11.50

Alphonse Mucha Illustrations
2031-2034	A398	Set of 4	11.50	11.50
a.		Souvenir sheet of 4, #2031-2034	11.50	11.50

Souvenir Sheet
2035	A398	1000fr multi	11.50	11.50

Vincent van Gogh Paintings
2036-2039	A398	Set of 4	11.50	11.50
a.		Souvenir sheet of 4, #2036-2039	11.50	11.50

Souvenir Sheet
2040	A398	1000fr multi	11.50	11.50

Penny Black
2041-2044	A398	Set of 4	11.50	11.50
a.		Souvenir sheet of 4, #2041-2044	11.50	11.50

Souvenir Sheet
2045	A398	1000fr multi	11.50	11.50

Charles de Gaulle
2046-2049	A398	Set of 4	11.50	11.50
a.		Souvenir sheet of 4, #2046-2049	11.50	11.50

Souvenir Sheet
2050	A398	1000fr multi	11.50	11.50

Battle of France
2051-2054	A398	Set of 4	11.50	11.50
a.		Souvenir sheet of 4, #2051-2054	11.50	11.50

Souvenir Sheet
2055	A398	1000fr multi	11.50	11.50

Battle of Okinawa
2056-2059	A398	Set of 4	11.50	11.50
a.		Souvenir sheet of 4, #2056-2059	11.50	11.50

Souvenir Sheet
2060	A398	1000fr multi	11.50	11.50

Minerals
2061-2064	A398	Set of 4	11.50	11.50
a.		Souvenir sheet of 4, #2061-2064	11.50	11.50

Souvenir Sheet
2065	A398	1000fr multi	11.50	11.50

Volcanoes
2066-2069	A398	Set of 4	11.50	11.50
a.		Souvenir sheet of 4, #2066-2069	11.50	11.50

Souvenir Sheet
2070	A398	1000fr multi	11.50	11.50

Jacques-Yves Cousteau
2071-2074	A398	Set of 4	11.50	11.50
a.		Souvenir sheet of 4, #2071-2074	11.50	11.50

Souvenir Sheet
2075	A398	1000fr multi	11.50	11.50

Apollo 13
2076-2079	A398	Set of 4	11.50	11.50
a.		Souvenir sheet of 4, #2076-2079	11.50	11.50

Souvenir Sheet
2080	A398	1000fr multi	11.50	11.50

Hubble Space Telescope
2081-2084	A398	Set of 4	11.50	11.50
a.		Souvenir sheet of 4, #2081-2084	11.50	11.50

Souvenir Sheet
2085	A398	1000fr multi	11.50	11.50

Cats
2086-2089	A398	Set of 4	11.50	11.50
a.		Souvenir sheet of 4, #2086-2089	11.50	11.50

Souvenir Sheet
2090	A398	1000fr multi	11.50	11.50

Dolphins
2091-2094	A398	Set of 4	11.50	11.50
a.		Souvenir sheet of 4, #2091-2094	11.50	11.50

Souvenir Sheet
2095	A398	1000fr multi	11.50	11.50

Bees
2096-2099	A398	Set of 4	11.50	11.50
a.		Souvenir sheet of 4, #2096-2099	11.50	11.50

Souvenir Sheet
2100	A398	1000fr multi	11.50	11.50

Nos. 2015, 2020, 2025, 2030, 2035, 2040, 2045, 2050, 2055, 2060, 2065, 2070, 2075, 2080, 2085, 2090, 2095, and 2100 each contain one 40x60mm stamp.

Souvenir Sheets

Pandas
A399

Horses
A400

2020, Mar. 13   **Litho.**   **Perf. 13¼**
Self-Adhesive
On Textured Paper Simulating Wood Veneer
2101	A399	4000fr multi	45.00	45.00
2102	A400	4000fr multi	45.00	45.00

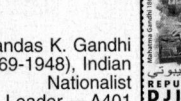

Mohandas K. Gandhi (1869-1948), Indian Nationalist Leader — A401

2020, Mar. 13   **Litho.**   **Perf. 13¼x13**
2103	A401	60fr multi	.70	.70

No. 2103 was printed in sheets of 10 + 2 central labels.

Worldwide Fund for Nature Stamps of Various Countries — A402

No. 2104, 200fr: a, Laos #519. b, Liberia #1009. c, Lesotho #512. d, Libya #1326. e, Liechtenstein #907. f, Laos #1174. g, Latvia #381. h, Lithuania #529. i, Libya #1594a.

No. 2105, 200fr: a, Lesotho #1091c. b, Liberia #1321b. c, Lesotho, #1336a. d, Laos #1625b. e, Liberia #2370c. f, Laos, #1719. g, Latvia #703. h, Libya #1718. i, Lithuania #876.
No. 2106, 300fr, Laos #520, vert. No. 2107, 300fr, Laos #1177. No. 2108, 300fr, Laos #1625c. No. 2109, 300fr, Laos #1722. No. 2110. 300fr, Latvia #384. No. 2111, 300fr, Latvia #706, vert. No. 2112, 300fr, Lesotho #515, vert. No. 2113, 300fr, Lesotho #1091a. No. 2114, 300fr, Lesotho #1336c. No. 2115, 300fr, Liberia #1010. No. 2116, 300fr, Liberia #1321d. No. 2117, 300fr, Liberia #2370a. No. 2118, 300fr, Libya #1594d. No. 2120, 300fr, Libya #1717. No. 2121, 300fr, Liechtenstein #908, vert. No. 2122, 300fr, Lithuania #530. No. 2123, 300fr, Lithuania #877.

2020, June 12 Litho. Perf. 13x13¼
Sheets of 9 #a-i
2104-2105 A402 Set of 2 41.00 41.00
Souvenir Sheets
Perf. 13¼x13, 13x13¼
2106-2123 A402 Set of 18 61.00 61.00
Nos. 2106-2123 each contain one 39x50mm vertical stamp or one 50x39mm horizontal stamp.

A403

No. 2124, 250fr — Scouts: a, Reading and starting fire. b, Carrying backpack and reading compass. c, Standing near campfire. d, Cooking on campfire and saluting.
No. 2125, 250fr — International Year of Plant Health: a, Scientist using microscope. b, Scientist examining Petri dish, parrot in flight. c, Hands holding seedling. d, Scientist using eyedropper.
No. 2126, 250fr — Paintings by Caravaggio (1571-1610): a, Saint Jerome Writing, 1605-06. b, Cardsharps, c. 1595. c, Supper at Emmaus, 1601-02. d, Fortune Teller, 1598-99.
No. 2127, 250fr — Owls: a, Tyto alba. b, Bubo virginianus. c, Strix varia. d, Strix aluco.
No. 2128, 250fr — Shells: a, Gyrineum perca. b, Cymbiola nobilis. c, Nerita lineata. d, Strombus sinuatus.
No. 2129, 1000fr, Scouts near campfire, diff. No. 2130, 1000fr, Hands touching over flowers. No. 2131, 1000fr, Still Life with Flowers and Fruit, c. 1590, by Caravaggio. No. 2132, 1000fr, Bubo scandiacus. No. 2133, 1000fr, Cymatium femorale.

2020, June 12 Litho. Perf. 13x13¼
Sheets of 4, #a-d
2124-2128 A403 Set of 5 57.00 57.00
Souvenir Sheets
2129-2133 A403 Set of 5 57.00 57.00

Dorje Chang Buddha III, Religious Leader — A404

2020, June 12 Litho. Perf. 13¼x13
2134 A404 250fr multi 3.00 3.00

A405

A406

St. John Paul II (1920-2005) — A408

2020, June 12 Litho. Perf. 13
2135 A405 100fr multi 1.25 1.25
  a. Souvenir sheet of 6 + 6 labels 7.50 7.50
2136 A406 100fr multi 1.25 1.25
  a. Souvenir sheet of 5 + 7 labels 6.25 6.25
2137 A407 100fr multi 1.25 1.25
  a. Souvenir sheet of 5 + 7 labels 6.25 6.25
2138 A408 100fr multi 1.25 1.25
  a. Souvenir sheet of 5 + 7 labels 6.25 6.25
  Nos. 2135-2138 (4) 5.00 5.00

A409

Ingrid Bergman (1915-82), Actress — A410

Designs: 1000fr, Bergman, diff.
No. 2142: a, Like #2139. b, Like #2140.

2020, June 12 Litho. Perf. 13¼x13
2139 A409 200fr multi 2.25 2.25
2140 A410 200fr multi 2.25 2.25
  a. Souvenir sheet of 2, #2139-2140 4.50 4.50
Souvenir Sheets
2141 A410 1000fr multi 11.50 11.50
Perf. 13¼
2142 400fr Sheet of 2, #a-b 9.00 9.00
Nos. 2139-2140 were each printed in sheets of 8 + central label. No. 2142 contains two 51x71mm stamps.

A411

Greta Garbo (1905-90), Actress — A412

Designs: 1000fr, Garbo, diff.
No. 2146: a, Like #2143. b, Like #2144.

2020, June 12 Litho. Perf. 13¼x13
2143 A411 200fr multi 2.25 2.25
2144 A412 200fr multi 2.25 2.25
  a. Souvenir sheet of 2, #2143-2144 4.50 4.50
Souvenir Sheets
2145 A412 1000fr multi 11.50 11.50
Perf. 13¼
2146 400fr Sheet of 2, #a-b 9.00 9.00
Nos. 2143-2144 were each printed in sheets of 8 + central label. No. 2146 contains two 51x71mm stamps.

A413

Rock Band Queen, 50th Anniv. — A414

Designs: 1000fr, Band members.
No. 2150: a, Like #2147. b, Like #2148.

2020, June 12 Litho. Perf. 13¼x13
2147 A413 200fr multi 2.25 2.25
2148 A414 200fr multi 2.25 2.25
  a. Souvenir sheet of 2, #2147-2148 4.50 4.50
Souvenir Sheets
2149 A414 1000fr multi 11.50 11.50
Perf. 13¼
2150 400fr Sheet of 2, #a-b 9.00 9.00
Nos. 2147-2148 were each printed in sheets of 8 + central label. No. 2150 contains two 51x71mm stamps.

Magnus Carlsen, Chess Player, 30th Birthday A415

Carlsen and Garry Kasparov A416

Designs: 1000fr, Carlsen, Norwegian flag.
No. 2154: a, Like #2151. b, Like #2152.

2020, June 12 Litho. Perf. 13¼x13
2151 A415 200fr multi 2.25 2.25
2152 A416 200fr multi 2.25 2.25
  a. Souvenir sheet of 2, #2151-2152 4.50 4.50
Souvenir Sheets
2153 A416 1000fr multi 11.50 11.50
Perf. 13¼
2154 400fr Sheet of 2, #a-b 9.00 9.00
Nos. 2151-2152 were each printed in sheets of 8 + central label. No. 2154 contains two 51x71mm stamps.

Salvation Army Worker Writing Letter for World War II Soldier A417

Salvation Army Worker Giving Doughnuts to World War I Soldier A418

Designs: 1000fr, William Booth (1829-1912), founder of Salvation Army.
No. 2158: a, Like #2155. b, Like #2156.

2020, June 12 Litho. Perf. 13¼x13
2155 A417 200fr multi 2.25 2.25
2156 A418 200fr multi 2.25 2.25
  a. Souvenir sheet of 2, #2155-2156 4.50 4.50
Souvenir Sheets
2157 A418 1000fr multi 11.50 11.50
Perf. 13¼
2158 400fr Sheet of 2, #a-b 9.00 9.00
Salvation Army, 155th anniv. Nos. 2155-2156 were each printed in sheets of 8 + central label. No. 2158 contains two 51x71mm stamps.

Messerschmitt Bf 110C Over Parliament Building, London A419

Hurricane Mk I and Hugh Dowding (1882-1970), British Air Chief Marshal A420

Designs: 1000fr, Hurricane Mk i over St. Paul's Cathedral, London.
No. 2162: a, Like #2159. b, Like #2160.

2020, June 12 Litho. Perf. 13¼x13
2159 A419 200fr multi 2.25 2.25
2160 A420 200fr multi 2.25 2.25
  a. Souvenir sheet of 2, #2159-2160 4.50 4.50
Souvenir Sheets
2161 A420 1000fr multi 11.50 11.50
Perf. 13¼
2162 400fr Sheet of 2, #a-b 9.00 9.00
Battle of Britain, 80th anniv. Nos. 2159-2160 were each printed in sheets of 8 + central label. No. 2162 contains two 51x71mm stamps.

Mil Mi-8 Helicopter A421

DAF YA-328 Military Truck A422

Designs: 1000fr, FV-107 Scimitar tank.
No. 2166: a, Like #2163. b, Like #2164.

2020, June 12 Litho. Perf. 13¼x13
2163 A421 200fr multi 2.25 2.25
2164 A422 200fr multi 2.25 2.25
  a. Souvenir sheet of 2, #2163-2164 4.50 4.50
Souvenir Sheets
2165 A422 1000fr multi 11.50 11.50
Perf. 13¼
2166 400fr Sheet of 2, #a-b 9.00 9.00
United Nations, 75th anniv. Nos. 2163-2164 were each printed in sheets of 8 + central label. No. 2166 contains two 51x71mm stamps.

International Loadstar 1700 Fire Truck — A423

Kenworth T300 Fire Truck — A424

Designs: 1000fr, Ford L9000 fire truck.
No. 2170: a, Like #2167. b, Like #2168.

2020, June 12 Litho. Perf. 13¼x13
2167 A423 200fr multi 2.25 2.25
2168 A424 200fr multi 2.25 2.25
  a. Souvenir sheet of 2, #2167-2168 4.50 4.50
Souvenir Sheets
2169 A424 1000fr multi 11.50 11.50
Perf. 13¼
2170 400fr Sheet of 2, #a-b 9.00 9.00
Nos. 2167-2168 were each printed in sheets of 8 + central label. No. 2170 contains two 51x71mm stamps.

Zeppelin LZ
1 — A425

Zeppelin LZ
4 — A426

A431

Designs: 1000fr, LZ 129 Hindenburg and
Ferdinand von Zeppelin (1838-1917), airship
manufacturer.
No. 2174: a, Like #2171. b, Like #2172.

2020, June 12 Litho. Perf. 13¼x13
2171 A425 200fr multi 2.25 2.25
2172 A426 200fr multi 2.25 2.25
a. Souvenir sheet of 2, #2171-2172 4.50 4.50

Souvenir Sheets
2173 A426 1000fr multi 11.50 11.50
Perf. 13¼
2174 400fr Sheet of 2, #a-b 9.00 9.00

First Zeppelin flight, 120th anniv. Nos. 2171-2172 were each printed in sheets of 8 + central label. No. 2174 contains two 51x71mm stamps.

Saturn V
Rocket and
Neil
Armstrong
(1930-2012),
First Man on
Moon — A427

Armstrong
and Apollo 11
Crewmate,
Edwin E.
"Buzz" Aldrin,
Jr. — A428

Designs: 1000fr, Armstrong and Lunar Module on Moon.
No. 2178: a, Like #2175. b, Like #2176.

2020, June 12 Litho. Perf. 13¼x13
2175 A427 200fr multi 2.25 2.25
2176 A428 200fr multi 2.25 2.25
a. Souvenir sheet of 2, #2175-2176 4.50 4.50

Souvenir Sheets
2177 A428 1000fr multi 11.50 11.50
Perf. 13¼
2178 400fr Sheet of 2, #a-b 9.00 9.00

Nos. 2175-2176 were each printed in sheets of 8 + central label. No. 2178 contains two 51x71mm stamps.

Lunokhod I on
Moon — A429

Lunokhod I
and Luna
17 — A430

Designs: 1000fr, Lunokhod I on Moon, diff.
No. 2182: a, Like #2179. b, Like #2180.

2020, June 12 Litho. Perf. 13¼x13
2179 A429 200fr multi 2.25 2.25
2180 A430 200fr multi 2.25 2.25
a. Souvenir sheet of 2, #2179-2180 4.50 4.50

Souvenir Sheets
2181 A430 1000fr multi 11.50 11.50
Perf. 13¼
2182 400fr Sheet of 2, #a-b 9.00 9.00

Lunokhod I on Moon, 50th anniv. Nos. 2179-2180 were each printed in sheets of 8 + central label. No. 2182 contains two 51x71mm stamps.

Prehistoric Painters of
Lascaux Cave
Paintings — A432

Designs: 1000fr, Prehistoric painters, diff.
No. 2186: a, Like #2183. b, Like #2184.

2020, June 12 Litho. Perf. 13¼x13
2183 A431 200fr multi 2.25 2.25
2184 A432 200fr multi 2.25 2.25
a. Souvenir sheet of 2, #2183-2184 4.50 4.50

Souvenir Sheets
2185 A432 1000fr multi 11.50 11.50
Perf. 13¼
2186 400fr Sheet of 2, #a-b 9.00 9.00

Discovery of Lascaux Cave Paintings, 80th anniv. Nos. 2183-2184 were each printed in sheets of 8 + central label. No. 2186 contains two 51x71mm stamps.

Italian Soldier
Looking for
COVID-19 Curfew
Breakers — A433

Stylized Globe
and COVID-19
Health
Workers — A434

Vaccine
Researcher
A435

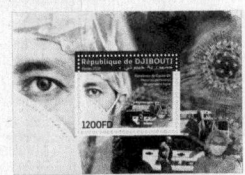

Ambulance and COVID-19 Health
Workers — A436

Stadium, Soccer Balls and COVID-19
Virus — A437

Perf. 12¾x13¼
2020, June 12 Litho.
2187 Horiz. strip of 3 10.50 10.50
a. A433 300fr multi 3.50 3.50
b. A434 300fr multi 3.50 3.50
c. A435 300fr multi 3.50 3.50

Souvenir Sheets
Perf. 13x13¼
2188 A436 1200fr multi 13.50 13.50
Perf. 13¼
2189 A437 2000fr multi 22.50 22.50

Stylized Depictions of COVID-19
Viruses — A438

No. 2190 — Various depictions, as shown. 1000fr, Depiction of virus, diff.

2020, June 12 Litho. Perf.
2190 A438 250fr Sheet of 4, #a-d 11.50 11.50

Souvenir Sheet
2191 A438 1000fr multi 11.50 11.50

Miniature Sheet

Queen Victoria on Great Britain #1
Wearing Protective Face
Masks — A439

No. 2192: a, White mask. b, Black and red mask. c, Blue mask. d, Blue and white plaid mask. e, Brown patterned mask. f, Gray, white and blue mask.

Perf. 13¼x12¾
2020, June 12 Litho.
2192 A439 160fr Sheet of 6, #a-f 11.00 11.00

Ludwig van
Beethoven 91770-1827),
Composer — A440

2020, July 27 Litho. Perf. 12¾x13¼
2193 A440 250fr multi + label 3.00 3.00

Presentation of Medal to Chinese
Medical Team — A441

Nos. 2194 and 2195: a, Doctors, patient and child. b, Medals.

2020, July 27 Litho. Perf. 13¼
2194 A441 300fr Horiz. pair, #a-b 6.75 6.75

Souvenir Sheet
Self-Adhesive
2195 A441 2000fr Sheet of 2, #a-b 45.00 45.00

No. 2195 was printed on silk.

A442

No. 2196, 250fr — Concorde and: a, British flag, London Eye, Big Ben. b, French flag, Arc de Triomphe. c, French flag, Eiffel Tower. d, British flag, silhouettes of London Eye, Houses of Parliament, Tower Bridge.
No. 2197, 250fr — Steam trains: a, New York Central Hudson. b, E 3/3 No. 456. c, British Rail Class 5. d, Pennsylvania Railroad Class T1.
No. 2198, 250fr — High-speed trains: a, CRH2C. b, EVS1/EVS2 Sapsan. c, SBB ETR 610. d, British Rail Class 370.
No. 2199, 250fr — The Titanic: a, RMS Titanic. b, Edward Smith (1850-1912), captain of the Titanic. c, Thomas Andrews (1873-1912), builder of the Titanic. d, RMS Titanic and newspaper front page announcing the ship's sinking.
No. 2200, 250fr — Submarines: a, Akula-class submarine, flag of Russia. b, Vanguard-class submarine, flag of Great Britain. c, Ohio-class submarine, flag of United States. d, Typhoon-class submarine, flag of Russia.
No. 2201, 250fr — Flying dinosaurs: a, Anhanguera blittersdorffi. b, Peteinosaurus zambelli. c, Quetzalcoatlus northropi. d, Pteranodon longiceps.
No. 2202, 1000fr, Concorde, flag of France, silhouettes of Eiffel Tower, Arc de Triomphe, Brandenburg Gate and buildings. No. 2203, 1000fr, LMS Stanier Class 5 4-6-0 No. 44871. No. 2204, 1000fr, Amtrak Acela Express. No. 2205, 1000fr, RMS Titanic, diff. No. 2206, 1000fr, Triomphant-class submarine, flag of France. No. 2207, 1000fr, Ornithocephalus banthensis.

2020, July 27 Litho. Perf. 12¾x13¼
Sheets of 4, #a-d
2196-2201 A442 Set of 6 67.50 67.50
Souvenir Sheets
2202-2207 A442 Set of 6 67.50 67.50

A443

No. 2208, 250fr — Dogs: a, Poodle (caniche). b, Rhodesian ridgeback (chien de Rhodésie à crête dorsale). c, Soft-coated Irish terrier (terrier irlandaise à poil doux). d, Labrador retriever.
No. 2209, 250fr — Warblers: a, Phylloscopus sibilatrix. b, Setophaga petechia. c, Acrocephalus arundinaceus. d, Iduna caligata.
No. 2210, 250fr — Bee-eaters: a, Merops philippinus. b, Merops orientalis. c, Merops bulocki. d, Merops nubicoides.
No. 2211, 250fr — Birds of prey: a, Aquila rapax. b, Buteo rufofuscus. c, Circus aeruginosus. d, Melierax canorus.
No. 2212, 250fr — Butterflies: a, Pieris rapae. b, Agraulis vanillae. c, Kallima inachus. d, Melanargia galathea.
No. 2213, 250fr — Fish: a, Coryphaena hippurus. b, Oncorhynchus mykiss. c, Esox lucius. d, Silurus glanis.
No. 2214, 250fr — Turtles: a, Podocnemis expansa. b, Malaclemys terrapin. c, Kinosternon leucostomum. d, Clemmys insculpta.
No. 2215, 250fr — Fossils: a, Tooth of Carcharocles megalodon. b, Triceratops horridus and Ammonite. c, Ammonite. d, Trilobite.
No. 2216, 250fr — Orchids: a, Brassavola nodosa. b, Ophrys apifera. c, Anacamptis coriophora. d, Cattleya walkeriana.
No. 2217, 250fr — Mushrooms: a, Pleurotus eryngii. b, Craterellus cornucopioides. c, Russula decolorans. d, Geastrum triplex.
No. 2218, 250fr — Lighthouses: a, Skongenes Lighthouse, Norway. b, Tyrhaug Lighthouse, Norway. c, Portland Head Lighthouse, Maine. d, Utsira Lighthouse, Norway.
No. 2219, 1000fr, Hungarian viszla (braque hongrois à poil court). No. 2220, 1000fr, Sylvia

atricapilla. No. 2221, 1000fr, Merops ornatus. No. 2222, 1000fr, Milvus milvus. No. 2223, 1000fr, Vanessa atalanta. No. 2224, 1000fr, Betta splendens. No. 2225, 1000fr, Deirochelys reticularia. No. 2226, 1000fr, Seymouria fossil. No. 2227, 1000fr, Vanda coerulea. No. 2228, 1000fr, Coprinus comatus. No. 2229, 1000fr, Montauk Lighthouse, New York.

2020, July 27 Litho. Perf. 13¼x12¾
Sheets of 4, #a-d
2208-2218 A443 Set of 11 125.00 125.00

Souvenir Sheets
2219-2229 A443 Set of 11 125.00 125.00

Miniature Sheet

Zoonotic Viruses A444

No. 2230 — Virus and vector animal: a, Hantavirus (rodent). b, West Nile virus (mosquito). c, Influenza A virus subtype H1N1 (pig). d, Dengue virus (Aedes mosquito). e, Rabies virus (dog). f, Tick-borne meningoencephalitis (tick). g, Ebolavirus (fruit bat). h, Zika virus (Aedes mosquito). i, SARS-CoV-2 (bats).

2020, July 27 Litho. Perf. 13x13¼
2230 A444 120fr Sheet of 9,
#a-i 12.50 12.50

Miniature Sheet

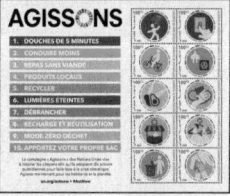

Act Now Climate Action Campaign — A445

No. 2231: a, Man in shower. b, Hand on light switch. c, Bicyclist. d, Electric plug and socket. e, Knife, fork, vegetables. f, Hand, container, and recycling arrow. g, Produce stand. h, Clothing on clothes hanger. i, Man placing bottle in recycling bin. j, Man carrying reusable shopping bag.

2020, July 27 Litho. Perf. 13x13¼
2231 A445 100fr Sheet of 10,
#a-j 11.50 11.50

Campaign Against COVID-19 — A446

No. 2232 — Red Cross and Red Crescent emblem, COVID-19 virus and: a, Two medical workers. b, Medical worker using microscope. c, Medical worker examining x-ray image. d, Medical worker with arms raised.
1000fr, Medical workers with clipboard and vial of blood.

Perf. 13¼x12¾
2020, Nov. 25 Litho.
2232 A446 250fr Sheet of 4,
#a-d 11.50 11.50
Souvenir Sheet
2233 A446 1000fr multi 11.50 11.50

A447

No. 2234, 250fr — Loxodonta africana: a, Adult and juvenile. b, Adult facing forward. c, Adult walking to right. d, Adult near water puddle.
No. 2235, 250fr — Pandas: a, Ailuropoda melanoleuca standing on tree branch. b, Ailurus fulgens standing on log. c, Ailurus fulgens on log, tail at front. d, Ailuropoda melanoleuca laying on tree branch.
No. 2236, 250fr — Lions: a, Panthera leo bleyenberghi. b, Panthera leo nubica. c, Panthera leo krugeri. d, Panthera leo persica.
No. 2237, 250fr — Whales: a, Balaena mysticetus. b, Eubalaena australis. c, Megaptera novaeangliae. d, Balaenoptera musculus.
No. 2238, 250fr — Water birds: a, Actophilornis africanus. b, Plegadis falcinellus. c, Phalacrocorax carbo. d, Platalea leucorodia.
No. 2239, 250fr — Kingfishers: a, Megaceryle alcyon. b, Chloroceryle americana. c, Alcedo meninting. d, Corythornis cristatus.
No. 2240, 250fr — Endangered animals: a, Panthera pardus orientalis. b, Elephas maximus. c, Pongo abelii. d, Lycaon pictus.
No. 2241, 250fr — Minerals: a, Apatite. b, Amethyst. c, Carnelian (cornaline). d, Calcite.
No. 2242, 250fr — Museums and their works: a, Louvre Museum, Paris, France, Psyche Revived by Cupid's Kiss, sculpture by Antonio Canova (1757-1822). b, Rijksmuseum, Amsterdam, Netherlands, The Night Watch, painting by Rembrandt van Rijn (1606-69). c, State Hermitage Museum, St. Petersburg, Russia, Combat of a Tiger and a Buffalo, painting by Henri Rousseau (1844-1910). d, Uffizi Gallery, Florence, Italy, Leonardo da Vinci, sculpture by Luigi Pampaloni (1791-1847).
No. 2243, 1000fr, Loxodonta cyclotis. No. 2244, 1000fr, Ailuropoda melanoleuca on ground. No. 2245, 1000fr, Panthera leo krugeri, diff. No. 2246, 1000fr, Physeter macrocephalus. No. 2247, 1000fr, Xenus cinereus. No. 2248, 1000fr, Todiramphus chloris. No. 2249, 1000fr, Gorilla gorilla gorilla. No. 2250, 1000fr, Tricolor calcite. No. 2251, 1000fr, Musée d'Orsay, Paris, France, The Floor Scrapers, painting by Gustave Caillebotte (1848-94).

Perf. 12¾x13¼
2020, Nov. 25 Litho.
Sheets of 4, #a-d
2234-2242 A447 Set of 9 100.00 100.00
Souvenir Sheets
2243-2251 A447 Set of 9 100.00 100.00

A448

Grace Kelly (1929-82), actress and Princess of Monaco: No. 2252, 250fr, And her signature. No. 2253, 250fr, Touching railing, and her royal monogram. No. 2254, 250fr, With Bing Crosby (1903-77), in movie, *High Society*. No. 2255, 250fr, Wearing striped blouse, and her royal monogram.
No. 2256, 1000fr, Kelly and her husband Prince Rainier III of Monaco (1923-2005), flag of Monaco.
Marilyn Monroe (1926-62), actress, and movie poster for: No. 2257, 250fr, *How to Marry a Millionaire*. No. 2258, 250fr, *Niagara*. No. 2259, 250fr, *The Asphalt Jungle*. No. 2260, 250fr, *Gentlemen Prefer Blondes*.
No. 2261, 1000fr, *Some Like it Hot*.
Masonic emblem and: No. 2262, 250fr, Shaquille O'Neal, basketball player. No. 2263, 250fr, Sir Winston Churchill (1874-1965), Prime Minister of Great Britain. No. 2264, 250fr, Edwin E. "Buzz" Aldrin, astronaut. No. 2265, 250fr, Leonardo DiCaprio, actor.
No. 2266, 1000fr, Sir Alexander Fleming (1881-1955), discoverer of penicillin.
Red Cross/Red Crescent emblem and: No. 2267, 250fr, Map of Djibouti, mother and child at water spigot. No. 2268, 250fr, Volunteers unloading medical supplies from truck. No. 2269, 250fr, Flag of Djibouti, man spraying

chemical, child with protective mask having his temperature taken. No. 2270, 250fr, Volunteer assisting flood victims.
No. 2271, 1000fr, Cardiopulmonary resuscitation lesson with dummy.
Ships: No. 2272, 250fr, Bluenose II, Canada. No. 2273, 250fr, STV Black Jack, Canada. No. 2274, 250fr, Kaljaasi Ansio, Finland. No. 2275, 250fr, Alexander von Humboldt II, Germany.
No. 2276, 1000fr, Europa, Netherlands.
African trains: No. 2277, 250fr, SDJ6 DMU train, flag of Nigeria. No. 2278, 250fr, HXD1C train, flags of Djibouti and Ethiopia. No. 2279, 250fr, Gautrain, flag of South Africa. No. 2280, 250fr, DF8B train, flag of Kenya.
No. 2281, 1000fr, DF11GN train, flag of Kenya.
Fire trucks: No. 2282, 250fr, Mercedes Atego fire truck. No. 2283, 250fr, Pierce Quantum fire truck. No. 2284, 250fr, Crimson GMC Midi fire pumper. No. 2285, 250fr, Deep South International fire truck.
No. 2286, 1000fr, HME 4x4 pumper truck.
Extinct animals: No. 2287, 250fr, Thylacinus cynocephalus. No. 2288, 250fr, Conuropsis carolinensis. No. 2289, 250fr, Bolyeria multocarinata. No. 2290, 250fr, Panthera pardus adersi.
No. 2291, 1000fr, Raphus cucullatus.

Perf. 13¼x12¾
2020, Nov. 25 Litho.
Grace Kelly

2252-2255	A448 Set of 4	11.50	11.50
2253a	Souvenir sheet of 4, 2 each #2252-2253, + 2 central labels	11.50	11.50
2255a	Souvenir sheet of 4, 2 each #2254-2255, + 2 central labels	11.50	11.50

Souvenir Sheet
2256	A448 1000fr multi	11.50	11.50

Marilyn Monroe
2257-2260	A448 Set of 4	11.50	11.50
2258a	Souvenir sheet of 4, 2 each #2257-2258, + 2 central labels	11.50	11.50
2260a	Souvenir sheet of 4, 2 each #2259-2260, + 2 central labels	11.50	11.50

Souvenir Sheet
2261	A448 1000fr multi	11.50	11.50

Famous Masons
2262-2265	A448 Set of 4	11.50	11.50
2263a	Souvenir sheet of 4, 2 each #2262-2263, + 2 central labels	11.50	11.50
2265a	Souvenir sheet of 4, 2 each #2264-2265, + 2 central labels	11.50	11.50

Souvenir Sheet
2266	A448 1000fr multi	11.50	11.50

Red Cross/Red Crescent
2267-2270	A448 Set of 4	11.50	11.50
2268a	Souvenir sheet of 4, 2 each #2267-2268, + 2 central labels	11.50	11.50
2270a	Souvenir sheet of 4, 2 each #2269-2270, + 2 central labels	11.50	11.50

Souvenir Sheet
2271	A448 1000fr multi	11.50	11.50

Tall Ships
2272-2275	A448 Set of 4	11.50	11.50
2273a	Souvenir sheet of 4, 2 each #2272-2273, + 2 central labels	11.50	11.50
2275a	Souvenir sheet of 4, 2 each #2274-2275, + 2 central labels	11.50	11.50

Souvenir Sheet
2276	A448 1000fr multi	11.50	11.50

African Trains
2277-2280	A448 Set of 4	11.50	11.50
2278a	Souvenir sheet of 4, 2 each #2277-2278, + 2 central labels	11.50	11.50
2280a	Souvenir sheet of 4, 2 each #2279-2280, + 2 central labels	11.50	11.50

Souvenir Sheet
2281	A448 1000fr multi	11.50	11.50

Fire Trucks
2282-2285	A448 Set of 4	11.50	11.50
2283a	Souvenir sheet of 4, 2 each #2282-2283, + 2 central labels	11.50	11.50
2285a	Souvenir sheet of 4, 2 each #2284-2285, + 2 central labels	11.50	11.50

Souvenir Sheet
2286	A448 1000fr multi	11.50	11.50

Extinct Animals
2287-2290	A448 Set of 4	11.50	11.50
2288a	Souvenir sheet of 4, 2 each #2287-2288, + 2 central labels	11.50	11.50
2290a	Souvenir sheet of 4, 2 each #2289-2290, + 2 central labels	11.50	11.50

Souvenir Sheet
2291	A448 1000fr multi	11.50	11.50

A449

A450

A451

A452

A453

A454

A455

A456

A457

A458

A459

A460

A461

A462

A463

A464

A465

A466

A467

Chinese
Opera — A468

2020, Nov. 25 Litho. Perf. 13¼x13

2292	Sheet of 20	48.00	48.00
a.	A449 210fr multi	2.40	2.40
b.	A450 210fr multi	2.40	2.40
c.	A451 210fr multi	2.40	2.40
d.	A452 210fr multi	2.40	2.40
e.	A453 210fr multi	2.40	2.40
f.	A454 210fr multi	2.40	2.40
g.	A455 210fr multi	2.40	2.40
h.	A456 210fr multi	2.40	2.40
i.	A457 210fr multi	2.40	2.40
j.	A458 210fr multi	2.40	2.40
k.	A459 210fr multi	2.40	2.40
l.	A460 210fr multi	2.40	2.40
m.	A461 210fr multi	2.40	2.40
n.	A462 210fr multi	2.40	2.40
o.	A463 210fr multi	2.40	2.40
p.	A464 210fr multi	2.40	2.40
q.	A465 210fr multi	2.40	2.40
r.	A466 210fr multi	2.40	2.40
s.	A467 210fr multi	2.40	2.40
t.	A468 210fr multi	2.40	2.40

A469   A470

A471   A472

A473   A474

A475   A476

A477   A478

A479   A480

A481   A482

A483   A484

A485   A486

A487   A488

A489   A490

A491   A492

A493   A494

A495   A496

A497   A498

A499   A500

A501   A502

A503   A504

A505   A506

A507   A508

A509   A510

A511   A512

A513   A514

Paintings Depicting
Mao Zedong
(1893-1976),
Chairman of the
Communist Party
of the People's
Republic of
China — A515

Perf. 12¾x13¼

2020, Nov. 25   **Litho.**

2293	Sheet of 16	40.00	40.00
a.	A469 225fr multi	2.50	2.50
b.	A470 225fr multi	2.50	2.50
c.	A471 225fr multi	2.50	2.50
d.	A472 225fr multi	2.50	2.50
e.	A473 225fr multi	2.50	2.50
f.	A474 225fr multi	2.50	2.50
g.	A475 225fr multi	2.50	2.50
h.	A476 225fr multi	2.50	2.50
i.	A477 225fr multi	2.50	2.50
j.	A478 225fr multi	2.50	2.50
k.	A479 225fr multi	2.50	2.50
l.	A480 225fr multi	2.50	2.50
m.	A481 225fr multi	2.50	2.50
n.	A482 225fr multi	2.50	2.50
o.	A483 225fr multi	2.50	2.50
p.	A484 225fr multi	2.50	2.50
2294	Sheet of 16	40.00	40.00
a.	A485 225fr multi	2.50	2.50
b.	A486 225fr multi	2.50	2.50
c.	A487 225fr multi	2.50	2.50
d.	A488 225fr multi	2.50	2.50
e.	A489 225fr multi	2.50	2.50

f.	A490 225fr multi	2.50	2.50
g.	A491 225fr multi	2.50	2.50
h.	A492 225fr multi	2.50	2.50
i.	A493 225fr multi	2.50	2.50
j.	A494 225fr multi	2.50	2.50
k.	A495 225fr multi	2.50	2.50
l.	A496 225fr multi	2.50	2.50
m.	A497 225fr multi	2.50	2.50
n.	A498 225fr multi	2.50	2.50
o.	A499 225fr multi	2.50	2.50
p.	A500 225fr multi	2.50	2.50
2295	Sheet of 15	42.00	42.00
a.	A501 240fr multi	2.75	2.75
b.	A502 240fr multi	2.75	2.75
c.	A503 240fr multi	2.75	2.75
d.	A504 240fr multi	2.75	2.75
e.	A505 240fr multi	2.75	2.75
f.	A506 240fr multi	2.75	2.75
g.	A507 240fr multi	2.75	2.75
h.	A508 240fr multi	2.75	2.75
i.	A509 240fr multi	2.75	2.75
j.	A510 240fr multi	2.75	2.75
k.	A511 240fr multi	2.75	2.75
l.	A512 240fr multi	2.75	2.75
m.	A513 240fr multi	2.75	2.75
n.	A514 240fr multi	2.75	2.75
o.	A515 240fr multi	2.75	2.75
	Nos. 2293-2295 (3)	122.00	122.00

Communist Party of China, cent.

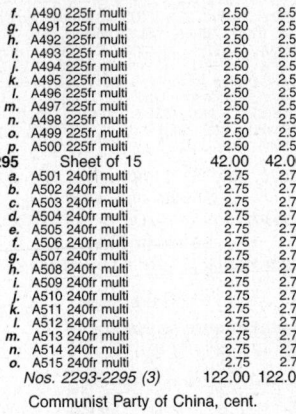

New Year 2021
(Year of the
Ox) — A516

Various depictions of an ox: 250fr, 550fr.

2020, Nov. 25   **Litho.**   **Perf. 13¼**
2296-2297 A516   Set of 2   9.00   9.00

A517   A518

A519   A520

A521   A522

A523   A524

A525   A526

A527   A528

A529   A530

A531   A532

A533   A534

A535   A536

A537   A538

A539   Chinese Paintings
Depicting
Oxen — A540

Perf. 12¾x13¼

2020, Nov. 25   Litho.
2298   Sheet of 24   42.00 42.00
a. A517 150fr multi   1.75   1.75
b. A518 150fr multi   1.75   1.75
c. A519 150fr multi   1.75   1.75
d. A520 150fr multi   1.75   1.75
e. A521 150fr multi   1.75   1.75
f. A522 150fr multi   1.75   1.75
g. A523 150fr multi   1.75   1.75
h. A524 150fr multi   1.75   1.75
i. A525 150fr multi   1.75   1.75
j. A526 150fr multi   1.75   1.75
k. A527 150fr multi   1.75   1.75
l. A528 150fr multi   1.75   1.75
m. A529 150fr multi   1.75   1.75
n. A530 150fr multi   1.75   1.75
o. A531 150fr multi   1.75   1.75
p. A532 150fr multi   1.75   1.75
q. A533 150fr multi   1.75   1.75
r. A534 150fr multi   1.75   1.75
s. A535 150fr multi   1.75   1.75
t. A536 150fr multi   1.75   1.75
u. A537 150fr multi   1.75   1.75
v. A538 150fr multi   1.75   1.75
w. A539 150fr multi   1.75   1.75
x. A540 150fr multi   1.75   1.75

New Year 2021 (Year of the Ox).

A541

Mohandas K. Gandhi
(1869-1948), Indian
Nationalist
Leader — A542

Perf. 12¾x13¼

2020, Dec. 30   Litho.
2299 A541 100fr multi   1.10   1.10

Perf. 13¼x13

2300 A542 100fr multi   1.10   1.10

Souvenir Sheet

2301 A542 1000fr multi   11.50 11.50

A543

Giraffes: No. 2302, 250fr, Giraffa camelo-pardalis facing right, No. 2303, 250fr, Giraffa camelopardalis facing left. No. 2304, 250fr, Two Giraffa camelopardalis. No. 2305, 250fr, Giraffa camelopardalis on ground.
Wild cats: No. 2306, 250fr, Panthera leo. No. 2307, 250fr, Panthera tigris. No. 2308, 250fr, Acinonyx jubatus. No. 2309, 250fr, Lynx lynx.
Owls: No. 2310, 250fr, Tyto alba. No. 2311, 250fr, Strix nebulosa. No. 2312, 250fr, Bubo scandiacus. No. 2313, 250fr, Glaucidium brasilianum.
Butterflies: No. 2314, 250fr, Chetone phyleis. No. 2315, 250fr, Heliconius wallacei. No. 2316, 250fr, Chetone angulosa. No. 2317, 250fr, Ituna phenarete.
Dinosaurs: No. 2318, 250fr, Vulcanodon karibaensis. No. 2319, 250fr, Proceratosaurus bradleyi. No. 2320, 250fr, Melanorosaurus readi. No. 2321, 250fr, Xiaosaurus dashanpensis.
Mushrooms: No. 2322, 250fr, Cantharellus cibarius. No. 2323, 250fr, Armillaria mellea. No. 2324, 250fr, Boletus edulis. No. 2325, 250fr, Amanita muscaria.
Meteorites: No. 2326, 250fr, Diablo Canyon meteorite. No. 2327, 250fr, Campo del Cielo meteorite. No. 2328, 250fr, Chelyabinsk meteorite. No. 2329, 250fr, Sikhote-Aline meteorite.
Lighthouses: No. 2330, 250fr, San Giorgio Maggiore Lighthouse, Italy. No. 2331, 250fr, Saint-Tropez Lighthouse, France. No. 2332, 250fr, Peggys Cove Lighthouse, Nova Scotia, Canada. No. 2333, 250fr, Aniva Lighthouse, Russia.
Scouts: No. 2334, 250fr, Two Scouts, one holding bugle. No. 2335, 250fr, Two Scouts, one holding guitar. No. 2336, 250fr, Two Scouts, one holding pennant on pole. No. 2337, 250fr, Two Scouts, tent and mountain in background.

2020, Dec. 30   Litho.   **Perf. 13¼**
Giraffes
2302-2305 A543 Set of 4   11.50 11.50
2303a   Souvenir sheet of 2,
         #2302-2303, + central label   5.75   5.75
2305a   Souvenir sheet of 2,
         #2304-2305, + central label   5.75   5.75
Wild Cats
2306-2309 A543 Set of 4   11.50 11.50
2307a   Souvenir sheet of 2,
         #2306-2307, + central label   5.75   5.75
2309a   Souvenir sheet of 2,
         #2308-2309, + central label   5.75   5.75
Owls
2310-2313 A543 Set of 4   11.50 11.50
2311a   Souvenir sheet of 2,
         #2310-2311, + central label   5.75   5.75
2313a   Souvenir sheet of 2,
         #2312-2313, + central label   5.75   5.75
Butterflies
2314-2317 A543 Set of 4   11.50 11.50
2315a   Souvenir sheet of 2,
         #2314-2315, + central label   5.75   5.75
2317a   Souvenir sheet of 2,
         #2316-2317, + central label   5.75   5.75
Dinosaurs
2318-2321 A543 Set of 4   11.50 11.50
2319a   Souvenir sheet of 2,
         #2318-2319, + central label   5.75   5.75
2321a   Souvenir sheet of 2,
         #2320-2321, + central label   5.75   5.75
Mushrooms
2322-2325 A543 Set of 4   11.50 11.50
2323a   Souvenir sheet of 2,
         #2322-2323, + central label   5.75   5.75
2325a   Souvenir sheet of 2,
         #2324-2325, + central label   5.75   5.75
Meteorites
2326-2329 A543 Set of 4   11.50 11.50
2327a   Souvenir sheet of 2,
         #2326-2327, + central label   5.75   5.75
2329a   Souvenir sheet of 2,
         #2328-2329, + central label   5.75   5.75
Lighthouses
2330-2333 A543 Set of 4   11.50 11.50
2331a   Souvenir sheet of 2,
         #2330-2331, + central label   5.75   5.75
2333a   Souvenir sheet of 2,
         #2332-2333, + central label   5.75   5.75
Scouts
2334-2337 A543 Set of 4   11.50 11.50
2335a   Souvenir sheet of 2,
         #2334-2335, + central label   5.75   5.75
2337a   Souvenir sheet of 2,
         #2336-2337, + central label   5.75   5.75

Orchids of Venezuela — A544

No. 2338, 330fr: a, Catasetum pileatum. b, Schomburgkia undulata. c, Oncidium cebolleta.
No. 2339, 330fr, horiz.: a, Sobralia violacea. b, Cattleya mossiae. c, Telipogon latifolius.
No. 2340, 1000fr, Bletia purpurea. No. 2341, 1000fr, Catasetum barbatum. No. 2342, 1000fr, Catasetum callosum, horiz.

Perf. 13x13¼, 13¼x13 (#2339)
2020, Dec. 30   Litho.
Sheets of 3, #a-c
2338-2339 A544 Set of 2   22.50 22.50
Souvenir Sheets
Perf. 13¼
2340-2342 A544 Set of 3   34.00 34.00
No. 2340 contains one 51x64mm stamp; No. 2341, one 51x83mm stamp; No. 2342, one 67x51mm stamp.

A545

No. 2343, 250fr — Joseph R. Biden, Jr., 46th President of the United States, with: a, Blue, red and white tie, Presidential seal, U.S. flag. b, Vice-President Kamala Harris. c, Wife, Jill, and White House. d, Red and white tie, Presidential seal, U.S. flag.
No. 2344, 250fr — Mohandas K. Gandhi (1869-1948), Indian nationalist leader, with: a, Spinning wheel, flag of India, Nelumbo nucifera. b, Asoka pillar, flag of Incia. c, Taj Mahal, Dandi March sculpture. d, Taj Mahal, Nelumbo nucifera sculpture of Gandhi.
No. 2345, 250fr — Princess Diana (1961-97), with: a, Nelson Mandela (1918-2013), President of South Africa. b, Castle and gates. c, Houses of Parliament. d, Queen Elizabeth II, flag of Great Britain.
No. 2346, 250fr — Diego Maradona (1960-2020), soccer player: a, In stadium. b, Shaking hands with Brazilian player. c, With flag of Argentina and Italian player. d, Wearing Barcelona team uniform.
No. 2347, 250fr — 2020 Nobel laurates: a, Physics laureates Reinhard Genzel, Andrea M. Ghez, and Roger Penrose. b, Literature laureate Louise Glück. c, Economics laureates Paul Milgrom and Robert B. Wilson. d, Chemistry laureates Emmanuelle Charpentier and Jennifer Doudna.
No. 2348, 250fr — Norwegian trains: a, NSB BM70. b, NSB BM75. c, NSB EL 18. d, NSB BM73.

No. 2349, 250fr — Japanese high-speed trains: a, Shinkansen Series 200. b, Shinkansen Series E4. c, ALFA-X. d, Shinkansen Series E6.
No. 2350, 250fr — Motorcycles: a, Indian Scout. b, Ducati 848. c, Suzuki DR 650. d, Harley-Davidson FXDF Dyna Fat Bob.
No. 2351, 250fr — Special transport: a, Aérospatiale HH-65 Dolphin helicopter. b, MAN KAT.1 16.422 Buffalo truck. c, Lenco BearCat armored vehicle. d, BMW R1200RT motorcycle.
No. 2352, 1000fr, Biden, his signature, and U.S. flag. No. 2353, 1000fr, Gandhi and sculpture of Gandhi. No. 2354, 1000fr, Princess Diana and Prince William. No. 2355, 1000fr, Maradona holding World Cup trophy. No. 2356, 1000fr, 2020 Nobel laureates in Physiology or Medicine Michael Houghton, Harvey J. Alter, and Charles M. Rice. No. 2357, 1000fr, NSB BM72. No. 2358, 1000fr, Shinkansen Series 500. No. 2359, 1000fr, Honda CBR1000RR motorcycle. No. 2360, 1000fr, Lamborghini Gallardo LP560-4.

2020, Dec. 30 Litho. **Perf. 13¼**
Sheets of 4, #a-d
2343-2351 A545 Set of 9 100.00 100.00
Souvenir Sheets
2352-2360 A545 Set of 9 100.00 100.00

Chinese Zodiac
Animals — A546

Designs: No. 2361, 100fr, Rat. No. 2362, 100fr, Ox. No. 2363, 100fr, Tiger. No. 2364, 100fr, Rabbit. No. 2365, 100fr, Dragon. No. 2366, 100fr, Snake. No. 2367, 100fr, Horse. No. 2368, 100fr, Ram. No. 2369, 100fr, Monkey. No. 2370, 100fr, Rooster. No. 2371, 100fr, Dog. No. 2372, 100fr, Pig.

2020, Dec. 30 Litho. **Perf. 13¼x13**
2361-2372 A546 Set of 12   13.50 13.50
2372a   Souvenir sheet of 12,
         #2361-2372   13.50 13.50

Participants in 2020 Education Relief
Foundation Forum, Djibouti — A547

2021, Mar. 1 Litho. **Perf. 13¼x13**
2373 A547 250fr multi   3.00   3.00
Two stamps from some sheets of No. 2373 are inscribed "000FDJ" instead of denomination.

First
Djibouti
Satellite
A548

2021, Mar. 1 Litho. **Perf. 13¼x13**
2374 A548 100fr multi   1.10   1.10
Souvenir Sheet
2375 A548 250fr multi   3.00   3.00
Two stamps from some sheets of No. 2374 are inscribed "000FDJ" instead of denomination.

Reversals of Policies of U. S. Pres.
Donald Trump by Pres. Joseph R.
Biden, Jr. — A549

No. 2376: a, Biden and Eiffel Tower
(rejoining of Paris Accord on Climate Change).
b, Biden, U.S. flag, World Health Organization
emblem (rejoining of World Health Organization). c, United States-Mexico border wall
(cessation of wall construction). d, Biden signing documents.
1000fr, Biden, syringe and vials of COVID-
19 vaccine (accelerated vaccine availability).

2021, Mar. 1   Litho.   Perf. 12¾x13¼
2376 A549 250fr Sheet of 4,
              #a-d   11.50 11.50
          Souvenir Sheet
2377 A549 1000fr multi   11.50 11.50

Paintings by Pierre-Auguste Renoir
(1841-1919) — A550

No. 2378: a, Woman with a Cat, c. 1875. b,
The Lovers, 1875. c, Madame Camille Monet
Reading, 1872. d, Algerian Woman, 1881.
1000fr, By the Seashore, 1883.

2021, Mar. 1   Litho.   Perf. 13¼x12¾
2378 A550 250fr Sheet of 4,
              #a-d   11.50 11.50
          Souvenir Sheet
          Perf. 13x13¼
2379 A550 1000fr multi   11.50 11.50
No. 2379 contains one 40x60mm stamp.

Flora and
Fauna — A551

Cats: No. 2380, 250fr, Black and white Brit-
ish Shorthair cats. No. 2381, 250fr, Tortoise-
shell Persian cats. No. 2382, 250fr, Abyssinian
and Indian cats. No. 2383, Gray and white
Persian cats.
No. 2384, 1000fr, Manx and Siamese cats.
Dogs: No. 2385, 250fr, Airedale terrier and
Bedlington terrier. No. 2386, 250fr, Three
Great Danes (dogue allemand). No. 2387,
250fr, English pointer. No. 2388, 250fr,
English foxhound and American foxhound.
No. 2389, 1000fr, Three greyhounds.
Horses: No. 2390, 250fr, Hackney horse.
No. 2391, 250fr, Polo ponies. No. 2392, 250fr,
Thoroughbred horse and colt (Pur-sang). No.
2393, Standardbred pony (Etalon).
No. 2394, 1000fr, Thoroughbred horse.
Birds of prey: No. 2395, 250fr, Circus
pygargus, vert. No. 2396, 250fr, Circaetus gal-
licus, vert. No. 2397, 250fr, Milvus milvus, vert.
No. 2398, 250fr, Buteo lagopus, vert.
No. 2399, 1000fr, Circus hudsonius, vert.
Parrots: No. 2400, 250fr, Lorius domicella,
vert. No. 2401, 250fr, Agapornis canus, vert.
No. 2402, 250fr, Agapornis roseicollis, vert.
No. 2403, 250fr, Cacatua alba, vert.
No. 2404, 1000fr, Eolophus roseicapilla,
vert.
Fish: No. 2405, 250fr, Scorpaenodes
guamensis. No. 2406, 250fr, Pterois radiata.
No. 2407, 250fr, Centropyge bispinosa. No.
2408, 250fr, Acanthurus lineatus.
No. 2409, 1000fr, Heniochus acuminatus,
vert.

Shells: No. 2410, 250fr, Bulinus wrighti. No.
2411, 250fr, Turcica monilifera. No. 2412,
250fr, Kelletia kelletii. No. 2413, 250fr, Naque-
tia barclayi.
No. 2414, 1000fr, Neptunea heros.
Turtles: No. 2415, 250fr, Caretta caretta.
No. 2416, 250fr, Hydromedusa maximiliani.
No. 2417, 250fr, Testudo graeca. No. 2418,
250fr, Eretmochelys imbricata.
No. 2419, 1000fr, Lissemys punctata.
Orchids: No. 2420, 250fr, Cattleya mossiae,
vert. No. 2421, 250fr, Cattleya skinneri alba,
vert. No. 2422, 250fr, Cattleya aliciae, vert.
No. 2423, 250fr, Cattleya skinneri, vert.
No. 2424, 1000fr, Cattleya trianae, vert.

2021, Mar. 1   Litho.   Perf. 13¼
                    Cats
2380-2383 A551   Set of 4   11.50 11.50
2383a   Souvenir sheet of 4,
           #2380-2383   11.50 11.50
          Souvenir Sheet
2384 A551 1000fr multi   11.50 11.50
                    Dogs
2385-2388 A551   Set of 4   11.50 11.50
2388a   Souvenir sheet of 4,
           #2385-2388   11.50 11.50
          Souvenir Sheet
2389 A551 1000fr multi   11.50 11.50
                   Horses
2390-2393 A551   Set of 4   11.50 11.50
2393a   Souvenir sheet of 4,
           #2390-2393   11.50 11.50
          Souvenir Sheet
2394 A551 1000fr multi   11.50 11.50
                Birds of Prey
2395-2398 A551   Set of 4   11.50 11.50
2398a   Souvenir sheet of 4,
           #2395-2398   11.50 11.50
          Souvenir Sheet
2399 A551 1000fr multi   11.50 11.50
                   Parrots
2400-2403 A551   Set of 4   11.50 11.50
2403a   Souvenir sheet of 4,
           #2400-2403   11.50 11.50
          Souvenir Sheet
2404 A551 1000fr multi   11.50 11.50
                    Fish
2405-2408 A551   Set of 4   11.50 11.50
2408a   Souvenir sheet of 4,
           #2405-2408   11.50 11.50
          Souvenir Sheet
2409 A551 1000fr multi   11.50 11.50
                   Shells
2410-2413 A551   Set of 4   11.50 11.50
2413a   Souvenir sheet of 4,
           #2410-2413   11.50 11.50
          Souvenir Sheet
2414 A551 1000fr multi   11.50 11.50
                   Turtles
2415-2418 A551   Set of 4   11.50 11.50
2418a   Souvenir sheet of 4,
           #2415-2418   11.50 11.50
          Souvenir Sheet
2419 A551 1000fr multi   11.50 11.50
                   Orchids
2420-2423 A551   Set of 4   11.50 11.50
2423a   Souvenir sheet of 4,
           #2420-2423   11.50 11.50
          Souvenir Sheet
2424 A551 1000fr multi   11.50 11.50

A552

No. 2425, 250fr — Emanuel Lasker (1868-
1941), chess player: a, As young man, with
glasses, and older man, chess pieces. b, As
young man, chess board and knight. c, As
young man, chess pieces and knight. d, As
older man, chess board and king.
No. 2426, 250fr — Wolfgang Amadeus
Mozart (1756-91), composer: a, Portraits in
purple and blue, musical notes and clefs. b,
Portraits in orange and green, curved keyboard. c, Portrait, G clef, sheet music and
bass. d, Portrait as child, at harpsichord.
No. 2427, 250fr — Sir Alexander Fleming
(1881-1955), discoverer of penicillin: a, Fleming examining Petri dish, mold sample. b,
Sculpture and photograph of Fleming,
medicine bottle and Cantharellus cibarius. c,

Fleming examining Petri dish, Clitocybe nuda.
d, Two photographs of Fleming.
No. 2428, 250fr — Vostok I flight of Yuri
Gagarin (1934-68), 60th anniv.: a, Gagarin
wearing military uniform and Vostok 3KA. b,
Gagarin in spacesuit, red star, and Vostok
rocket. c, Gagarin in space suit, cutaway view
of Vostok 3KA. d, Gagarin wearing headgear,
and Vostok rocket launch.
No. 2429, 250fr — Marilyn Monroe (1926-
62), actress: a, Holding glass. b, With star. c,
With husband, Joe DiMaggio (1914-99). d,
With Pres. John F. Kennedy (1917-63).
No. 2430, 250fr — Queen Elizabeth II, 95th
birthday: a, With husband, Prince Philip (1921-
2021). b, Two photographs as young woman.
c, Holding purse. d, As young woman, wearing
military uniform.
No. 2431, 250fr — High-speed trains: a,
ETR 610, flag of Italy. b, Sapsan, flag of Russia. c, BM 71, flag of Norway. d, TGV Duplex,
flag of France.
No. 2432, 250fr — Concorde passenger
service, 45th anniv.: a, Concorde, Arc de Triomphe, flag of France. b, Concorde, Tower
Bridge, flag of Great Britain. c, Concorde, Eiffel Tower, flag of France. d, Concorde, St.
Paul's Cathedral, flag of Great Britain.
No. 2433, 1000fr, Lasker as young man,
chess pieces. No. 2434, 1000fr, Portrait and
sculpture of Mozart, keyboard. No. 2435,
1000fr, Fleming and Boletus edulis. No. 2436,
1000fr, Gagarin and monument to Gagarin,
Moscow. No. 2437, 1000fr, Two photographs
of Monroe. No. 2438, 1000fr, Queen Elizabeth
II and Prince Philip, diff. No. 2439, 1000fr,
Shinkansen Seried E3-700, flag of Japan. No.
2440, 1000fr, Concorde and Eiffel Tower.

2021, Mar. 1   Litho.   Perf. 13¼
          Sheets of 4, #a-d
2425-2432 A552 Set of 8   90.00 90.00
          Souvenir Sheets
2433-2440 A552 Set of 8   90.00 90.00

          Miniature Sheet

Minerals From Bou-Azzer,
Morocco — A553

No. 2441: a, Erythrite. b, Gersdorffite. c,
Imiterite. d, Talmessite. e, Spherocobaltite. f,
Xanthoconite. g, Karibibite. h, Roselite.

2021, Mar. 1   Litho.   Perf. 12¾x13¼
2441 A553 270fr Sheet of 8,
              #a-h   24.50 24.50

          Miniature Sheet

International Sporting Events Affected
by the COVID-19 Pandemic — A554

No. 2442: a, 2020 Summer Olympics, Tokyo
(postponed to 2021). b, 44th International
Chess Olympiad, Moscow (postponed to
2022). c, 2020 Wimbledon Tennis Championships (canceled). d, 2020 Arctic Winter Games
(canceled). e, 2020 African Cup of Nations
Soccer Championships (postponed to 2022). f,
2020 Archery World Cup (canceled).

2021, May 20   Litho.   Perf. 13x13¼
2442 A554 200fr Sheet of 6,
              #a-f   13.50 13.50

Paintings by Pablo Picasso (1881-
1973) — A555

No. 2443: a, Girl Before a Mirror, 1932. b,
Head of a Woman, 1960. c, Woman in a Che-
mise in an Armchair, 1914. d, Harlequin, 1901.
1000fr, The Weeping Woman, 1937.

2021, May 20   Litho.   Perf. 13¼x13
2443 A555 250fr Sheet of 4,
              #a-d   11.50 11.50
          Souvenir Sheet
          Perf. 13¼
2444 A555 1000fr Sheet of 4,
              #a-d   11.50 11.50
No. 2444 contains one 39x50mm stamp.

A556

No. 2445, 250fr — Wild cats: a, Panthera
leo. b, Felis lynx. c, Panthera tigris. d,
Panthera onca.
No. 2446, 250fr — Dolphins: a, Tursiops
truncatus, white denomination. b, Tursiops
truncatus, black denomination. c, Stenella
frontalis. d, Stenella coeruleoalba.
No. 2447, 250fr — Bee-eaters: a, Nycty-
ornis amictus. b, Merops nubicoides. c, Merops ornatus. d, Merops leschenaulti.
No. 2448, 250fr — Pigeons: a, Columba
livia. b, Columba livia domestica. c,
Patagioenas fasciata. d, Columba palumbus.
No. 2449, 250fr — Butterflies: a, Graphium
tyndereus. b, Papilio glaucus. c, Papilio polyx-
enes. d, Papilio bianor.
No. 2450, 250fr — Flying dinosaurs: a,
Rhamphorhynchus muensteri. b, Dsun-
garipterus weii. c, Ornithodesmus latidens. d,
Pterodactylus simus.
No. 2451, 250fr — Mushrooms: a, Russula
emetica. b, Amanita vaginata, Trichodes
alvearius. c, Amanita muscaria, Rosalia
batesi. d, Armillaria mellea.
No. 2452, 250fr — Volcanoes: a, Rishiri-to,
Japan. b, Mount Usu, Japan. c, Mount Asama,
Japan. d, Mount Kaimon, Japan.
No. 2453, 250fr — Lighthouses and birds: a,
Fastnet Lighthouse, Ireland, Larus smithsoni-
anus. b, Pontusval Lighthouse, France, Larus
pacificus. c, Dyrhólaey Lighthouse, Iceland,
Creagrus furcatus. d, Skudenes Lighthouse,
Norway, Larus delawarensis.
No. 2454, 1000fr, Felis lynx, diff. No. 2455,
1000fr, Tursiops truncatus, diff. No. 2456,
1000fr, Merops persicus. No. 2457, 1000fr,
Columba arquatrix. No. 2458, 1000fr, Euploea
mulciber. No. 2459, 1000fr, Pterodactylus antiquus. No. 2460, 1000fr, Leccinum aurantiacum, Chrysomela populi. No. 2461, 1000fr,
Mount Daisen, Japan. No. 2462, 1000fr, La
Madonetta Lighthouse, France, Larus
smithsonianus.

2021, May 20 Litho. Perf. 12¾x13¼
          Sheets of 4, #a-d
2445-2453 A556 Set of 9   100.00 100.00
          Souvenir Sheets
2454-2462 A556 Set of 9   100.00 100.00

A557

No. 2463, 250fr — Antonio Vivaldi (1678-1741) composer: a, With musical score and violin. b, With his signature, musical score and violin. c, With his signature and small cup. d, Holding violin, musical score.

No. 2464, 250fr — Napoleon Bonaparte (1769-1821), Emperor of France: a, With flag of France, wearing hat. b, Napoleon in Egypt, painting by Edouard Detaille (1848-1912). c, With hand in vest. d, With eagle.

No. 2465, 250fr — Wedding of Prince Charles and Lady Diana Spencer, 40th anniv.: a, Couple, Prince Charles in military uniform, castle. b, Couple on wedding day. c, Couple, flag of Great Britain, Diana. d, Prince Charles, Obverse of 1981 Australian 50-cent coin commemorating the wedding.

No. 2466, 250fr — William Speirs Bruce (1867-1921), Antarctic explorer: a, Playing bagpipes, with penguin. b, Penguins and map of Antarctica. c, With ship. d, With sled dog.

No. 2467, 250fr — Steam trains: a, DR 18 201, buildings in Dresden, Germany. b, DRG Class 05, buildings in Berlin, Germany. c, Great Western Railway Class 3440 City of Truro, Conwy Castle, Wales. d, Nilgiri Mountain Railway Class X, buildings in Udaipur, India.

No. 2468, 250fr — Bugatti automobiles: a, Bugatti Type 35 and Ettore Bugatti (1881-1947), automobile manufacturer. b, Bugatti 16C Galibier c, Bugatti Type 57. d, Bugatti and Bugatti Type 57 Stelvio.

No. 2469, 250fr — Fire engines: a, KamAZ-53213. b, Bedford RL. c, Mercedes-Benz Atego 1325F. d, Merceedes-Benz 614D.

No. 2470, 250fr — First flight of LZ 129 Hindenburg airship, 85th anniv.: a, Airship and its pilot, Max Pruss (1891-1960). b, Airship in flight, and nameplate. c, Globe, airship over New York City. d, Airship and Paul von Hindenburg (1847-1934), President of Germany.

No. 2471, 250fr — Operation Barbarossa (German invasion of the Soviet Union), 80th anniv.: a, T-26 tank and Soviet soldiers. b, PzKpfW IV tank and German soldier. c, Junkers Ju87 divebomber, tank and soldier. d, MiG-3 fighter plane and Soviet soldiers.

No. 2472, 250fr — Landing of Perseverance rover on Mars: a, Perseverance on Mars. b, Descent stage lowering Perseverance to Mars. c, Atlas V 541 rocket and Launchpad 41, Cape Canaveral, Florida. d, Perseverance and emblem.

No. 2473, 1000fr, Vivaldi and musical score. No. 2474, 1000fr, Portrait and medal depicting Napoleon Bonaparte. No. 2475, 1000fr, Prince Charles and Princess Diana, diff. No. 2476, 1000fr, Bruce, ship and bird in flight. No. 2477, 1000fr, London and North Eastern Railway Class A4 No. 4468 Mallard, and Big Ben, London. No. 2478, 1000fr, Bugatti and Bugatti Type 57 Ventoux. No. 2479, 1000fr, Scania P360 fire truck. No. 2480, 1000fr, LZ 129 Hindenburg over New York City. No. 2481, 1000fr, KV-1 tanks, barbed wire, and battle map. No. 2482, 1000fr, Perseverence rover on Mars, diff.

2021, May 20 Litho. *Perf. 13¼x12¾*
Sheets of 4, #a-d
2463-2472 A557 Set of 10 115.00 115.00
Souvenir Sheets
2473-2482 A557 Set of 10 115.00 115.00

Paintings by Paul Cézanne (1839-1906) — A558

No. 2483: a, Self-portrait in a White Cap, 1882. b, Still Life with Fruit and a Pot of Ginger, c. 1895. c, Bibemus Quarry, c. 1898. d, Boy with a Red Vest, c. 1890.
1000fr, Madame Cézanne in a Red Armchair, 1878.

2021, Aug. 9 Litho. *Perf. 13¼x13*
2483 A558 250fr Sheet of 4,
      #a-d   11.50 11.50
Souvenir Sheet
Perf. 13¼
2484 A558 1000fr multi   11.50 11.50
No. 2484 contains one 40x60mm stamp.

A559

No. 2485, 330fr — Mikhail Lomonosov (1711-65), scientist: a, Lomonosov, Lomonosovite, Lomonosov State University of Moscow. b, Lomonosov Shows Catherine the Great Her Own Mosaic Works in Her Office, painting by Alexey D. Kivshenko (1851-95). c, Lomonosov and telescope.

No. 2486, 330fr — Anatoly Karpov, chess player, and: a, Salvador Dalí (1904-89), painter. b, Boris Spassky, chess player. c, Garry Kasparov, chess player and Russia #5291.

No. 2487, 330fr — First flight of Virgin Galactic commercial spacecraft: a, Virgin Galactic spacecraft facing right. b, Richard Branson, founder of Virgin Galactic, Space Ship Two and White Knight Two. c, Virgin Galactic spacecraft facing left.

No. 2488, 330fr — Flag of People's Republic of China and high-speed Chinese trains: a, Shanghai Transrapid. b, CRH380A. c, CRH6.

No. 2489, 330fr — Fire trucks: a, 1911 Christie. b, 1941 Ford. c, 1925 Ahrens Fox NS4.

No. 2490, 1000fr, Lomonosov. No. 2491, 1000fr, Karpov playing chess. No. 2492, 1000fr, Virgin Galactic Space Ship Two and White Knight Two. No. 2493, 1000fr, DJJ2 China Star train. No. 2494, 1000fr, 1926 American LaFrance fire truck.

2021, Aug. 9   Litho.   *Perf.*
Sheets of 3, #a-c
2485-2489 A559 Set of 5 56.00 56.00
Souvenir Sheets
2490-2494 A559 Set of 5 57.50 57.50

A560

No. 2495, 330fr — Cats: a, Aphrodite's giant cat. b, Somali cat. c, Bengal cat.

No. 2496, 330fr — Dogs: a, German shorthaired pointer, flag of Germany. b, Estonian hound, Lithuanian hound, flags of Estonia and Lithuania. c, English cocker spaniel, flag of United Kingdom.

No. 2497, 330fr — Birds of prey: a, Aquila adelberti. b, Buteo rufinus. c, Necrosyrtes monachus.

No. 2498, 330fr — Bees: a, Coelioxys argenteus. b, Andrena nubecula. c, Andrena gravida.

No. 2499, 330fr — Greta oto: a, On yellow flower at left. b, On lilac flower. c, On yellow flower at right.

No. 2500, 330fr — Fish: a, Pterophyllum scalare. b, Paracanthurus hepatus. c, Amphiprion ocellaris.

No. 2501, 330fr — Shells: a, Doxander vittatus. b, Pleuroploca trapezium paeteli. c, Sinistrofulgur perversum.

No. 2502, 330fr — Turtles: a, Pseudemys rubriventris. b, Aldabrachelys gigantea. c, Trachemys scripta elegans.

No. 2503, 330fr — Extinct animals: a, Viverra leakeyi. b, Iniopteryx. c, Arctodus simus.

No. 2504, 330fr — Orchids: a, Laelia x Cattleya hybrid. b, Paphiopedilum "Rosy Dawn." c, Cattleya bicolor brasiliensis.

No. 2505, 330fr — Mushrooms: a, Cortinarius archeri. b, Amanita phalloides. c, Galerina marginata.

No. 2506, 330fr — Lighthouses: a, Anorisaki Lighthouse, Japan, and Lsarus heermanni. b, Landsort Lighthouse, Sweden. c, Erie Harbor

North Pier Lighthouse, Pennsylvalnia, and Creagrus furcatus.

No. 2507, 1000fr, Scottish Fold cat. No. 2508, 1000fr, Irish setter, flag of Ireland. No. 2509, 1000fr, Neophron percnopterus. No. 2510, 1000fr, Osmia cornuta. No. 2511, 1000fr, Greta oto on white and yellow fllower. No. 2512, 1000fr, Scarus frenatus. No. 2513, 1000fr, Liguus virgineus. No. 2514, 1000fr, Chelydra serpentina. No. 2515, 1000fr, Pachycrocuta brevirostris. No. 2516, 1000fr, Epicattleya Kyoguchi. No. 2517, 1000fr, Cortinarius caperatus. No. 2518, 1000fr, Kyogamisaki Lighthouse, Japan.

2021, Aug. 9   Litho.   *Perf.*
Sheets of 3, #a-c
2495-2506 A560 Set of 12 135.00 135.00
Souvenir Sheets
2507-2518 A560 Set of 12 135.00 135.00

COVID-19 Delta Variant — A561

No. 2519 — Map of India and: a, Vial of vaccine, man wearing protective face mask, health care worker vaccinating patient. b, Health care worker with large vaccine vial and hypodermic needle, COVID-19 virus. c, Vial of vaccine, health care workers administering vaccine.

2021, Aug. 9 Litho. *Perf. 12¾x13¼*
2519 A561 330fr Sheet of 3,
      #a-c   11.50 11.50

Souvenir Sheets

27th Universal Postal Union Congress, Abidjan, Ivory Coast — A562

Denominations: 500fr, 1000fr.

2021, Aug. 9 Litho. *Perf. 12¾x13¼*
2520-2521 A562 Set of 2 17.00 17.00

Souvenir Sheet

Chinese Communist Party, Cent. — A563

No. 2522: a, "1921." b, "2021."

2021, Aug. 9   Litho.   *Perf.*
2522 A563 500fr Sheet of 2,
      #a-b   11.50 11.50

Paintings by Henri de Toulouse-Lautrec (1864-1901) — A564

No, 2523: a, In the Salon of the Rue des Moulins, 1894. b, Monsieur Boileau, 1893. c, Woman with Gloves, 1891. d, At the Moulin-Rouge, 1890.
1000fr, Marcelle Lender Dancing the Bolero in Chilpéric, 1895-96.

2021, Aug. 30 Litho. *Perf. 13¼x13*
2523 A564 250fr Sheet of 4,
      #a-d   11.50 11.50
Souvenir Sheet
Perf. 13¼
2524 A564 1000fr multi   11.50 11.50
No. 2524 contains one 40x60mm stamp.

Miniature Sheet

Mohandas K. Gandhi (1869-1948), Indian Nationalist Leader — A565

No. 2525 — Portrait of Gandhi in: a, 250fr, Green (30x40mm). b, 250fr, Purple (30x40mm). c, 250fr, Red (30x40mm). d, 250fr, Violet (30x40mm). e, 1000fr, Maroon (60x80mm).

2021, Aug. 30 Litho. *Perf. 13x13¼*
Self-Adhesive
On Wood Veneer
2525 A565 Sheet of 5, #a-e 22.50 22.50

Souvenir Sheet

Chinese Vaccine Against COVID-19 in Africa — A566

No. 2526: a, 250fr, Flag of People's Republic of China at left, map of Africa, COVID-19 virus and hypodermic needles (50x39mm). b, 250fr, Flag of People's Republic of China at rigth, map of Africa, COVID-19 virus and hypodermic needles (50x39). c, 500fr, Map of Africa and emblem of Sinopharm (40mm diameter).

Perf. 13x13¼ (#2526a, 2526b), Perf.
(#2526c)
2021, Aug. 30   Litho.
2526 A566 Sheet of 3, #a-c 11.50 11.50

Souvenir Sheet

Fabergé
Egg
A567

Perf. 13¼, 9½ on Diagonal Perfs.
2021, Aug. 30   **Litho.**
2527 A567 1000fr multi   11.50 11.50

A568

No. 2528, 330fr — Scouts with: a, Tent in background. b, Campfire. c, Folding chair and backpack in background.
No. 2529, 330fr — Large cats: a, Panthera tigris. b, Panthera leo leo. c, Panthera tigris with its kill.
No. 2530, 330fr — Whales: a, Globicephala sp. b, Physeter macrocephalus. c, Balaena mysticetus.
No. 2531, 330fr — Owls: a, Glaucidium passerinumi. b, Strix nebulosa. c, Athene noctua.
No. 2532, 330fr — Kingfishers: a, Halcyon coromanda. b, Halcyon albiventris. c, Todiramphus sanctus.
No. 2533, 330fr — Butterflies: a, Morpho adonis. b, Meandrusa sciron. c, Dasyophthalma creusa.
No. 2534, 330fr — Dinosaurs: a, Euplocephalus tutus. b, Tyrannosaurus rex. c, Alioramus remotus.
No. 2535, 330fr — Fruits and vegetables: a, Citrus sinensis. b, Raphanus raphanistrum subsp. sativus. c, Prunus domestica.
No. 2536, 330fr — Fossils: a, Cyclurus minor. b, Sphyraenodus priscus. c, Vomer longispinus.
No. 2537, 330fr — Prehistoric humans: a, Australopithecus afarensis. b, Cro-Magnon woman and child. c, Homo neanderthalensis.
No. 2538, 330fr — Minerals: a, Tanzanite. b, Malachite. c, Aragonite.
No. 2539, 1000fr, Scouts, chopped log and recreational vehicle. No. 2540, 1000fr, Panthera leo. No. 2541, 1000fr, Delphinapterus leucas. No. 2542, 1000fr, Otus scops. No. 2543, 1000fr, Ceryle rudis. No. 2544, 1000fr, Parnassius phoebus. No. 2545, 1000fr, Alectrosaurus olseni. No. 2546, 1000fr, Allium cepa. No. 2547, 1000fr, Fossil of Anguilla pachyura. No. 2548, 1000fr, Homo neanderthalensis, diff. No. 2549, 1000fr, Halite.

Perf. 12¾x13¼
2021, Aug. 30   **Litho.**
Sheets of 3, #a-c
2528-2538 A568 Set of 11 122.50 122.50
Souvenir Sheets
2539-2549 A568 Set of 11 125.00 125.00

A569

No. 2550, 330fr — Michael Collins (1930-2021), Apollo 11 Command Module pilot, and : a, Apollo 11 Command Module. b, Astronaut

and Lunar Module on Moon. c, Earth in background.
No. 2551, 330fr — Sergei Korolev (1907-66), rocket engineer: a, Sputnik 1. b, Korolev and medal. c, Vostok 1.
No. 2552, 330fr — Circumnavigation of the Earth by crew of Ferdiand Magellan (1480-1521), 500th anniv.: a, 2021 Nicaraguan gold coin depicting Magellan and his ship. b, Magellan, compass and ship. c, Monument to Magellan in Punta Arenas, Chile, and Spheniscus magellanicus.
No. 2553, 330fr — The Titanic: a, Titanic at sea. b, Titanic and iceberg. c, Titanic, iceberg and flag of United Kingdom.
No. 2554, 330fr — African trains and animals: a, SNCFT Hyundai Rotem EMU, Macaca sylvanus. b, Madaraka Express, Xerus inauris. c, Blue Train, Oreotrgus.
No. 2555, 330fr — Mikhail Botvinnik 1911-95), chess player, and chess players: a, Mikhail Tal (1936-92). b, José Raúl Capablanca (1888-1942). c, Tigran Petrossian (1929-84).
No. 2556, 1000fr, Collins and Saturn V rocket. No. 2557, 1000fr, Korolev and Yuri Gagarin (1934-68), first man in space. No. 2558, 1000fr, Magellan and ships. No. 2559, 1000fr, Titanic at sea, flag of United Kingdom. No. 2560, 1000fr, South African class train No. E1114, Lucaon pictus. No. 2561, 1000fr, Botvinnik.

Perf. 12¾x13¼
2021, Aug. 30   **Litho.**
Sheets of 3, #a-c
2550-2555 A569 Set of 6   67.00 67.00
2556-2561 A569 Set of 6   67.50 67.50

Paintings and Drawings by Vincent van Gogh (1853-90) — A570

No. 2562: a, The Church at Auvers, 1890. b, Young Man with a Pipe, 1884. c, Head of a Woman, 1885. d, Willows at Sunset, 1888. 1000fr, Self-portrait, 1888.

2021, Nov. 1 Litho. Perf. 13¼x12¾
2562 A570 250fr Sheet of 4,
                        #a-d   11.50 11.50

Souvenir Sheet
Perf. 13¼
2563 A570 1000fr multi   11.50 11.50

No. 2563 contains one 40x80mm stamp.

Miniature Sheet

COVID-19 Variants — A571

No. 2564: a, Alpha, flag of Great Britain. b, Beta, flag of South Africa. c, Gamma, flag of Brazil. d, Delta, flag of India.

2021, Nov. 1 Litho. Perf. 13x13¼
2564 A571 250fr Sheet of 4,
                        #a-d   11.50 11.50

Doves, Flag of the Palestinian Authority, and Dome of the Rock, Jerusalem A572

2021, Nov. 1 Litho. Perf. 13x13¼
2565 A572 250fr multi   3.00 3.00

2566 A572 400fr multi   4.75 4.75
Souvenir Sheets
Perf. 13¼x13
2567 A572 1000fr multi   11.50 11.50
Litho. With Foil Application
2568 A572 1000fr gold & multi 11.50 11.50

Nos. 2567 and 2568 each contain one 80x40mm stamp.

Les oiseaux de Djibouti

A573

No. 2569, 250fr — Birds of Djibouti: a, Melierax poliopterus. b, Phoenicopterus roseus. c, Sula dactylatra. d, Centropus superciliosus. e, Circaetus gallicus. f, Himantopus himantopus.
No. 2570, 250fr — Butterflies: a, Melanitis leda. b, Acraea cabira. c, Acraea horta. d, Papilio dardanus. e, Graphium antheus. f, Papilio demoducus.
No. 2571, 250fr — Sharks: a, Rhincodon typus, country name in red. b, Notorhynchus cepedianus. c, Isurus oxyrinchus. d, Carcharodon carcharias. e, Ginglymostoma cirratum. f, Galeocerdo cuvier.
No. 2572, 250fr — Fauna of Djibouti: a, Orycteropus afer. b, Papio hamadryas. c, Orcinus orca with tail underwater. d, Buteo buteo vulpinus. e, Rhinolophus hipposideros. f, Gazella dorcas.
No. 2573, 250fr — Marine biodiversity: a, Orcinus orca with tail above water. b, Octopus vulgaris. c, Taseniura lymma. d, Chelonia mydas. e, Chrysaora melanaster. f, Rhincodon typus, country name in blue.
No. 2574, 250fr — Prehistoric aquatic animals: a, Otodus megalodon. b, Archelon ischyros. c, Dunkleosteus terrelli. d, Ichthyosaurus communis. e, Utatsusaurus hataii. f, Helicoprion bessonowi.
No. 2575, 250fr — Cacti: a, Mammillaria elongata "Cristata." b, Opuntia basilaris. c, Mammillaria bocasana. d, Astrophytum coahuilense. e, Echinocactus grusonii. f, Mammillaria haageana.
No. 2576, 250fr — Minerals: a, Tetrahedrite. b, Rhodonite. c, Fuchsite. d, Okenite. e, Prehnite. f, Strontianite.
No. 2577, 250fr — Art by Albrecht Dürer: a, Portrait of Barbara Dürer, 1490. b, Lamentation for Christ, 1500. c, Virgin and Child with a Pear, 1512. d, Young Hare, 1502. e, Portrait of Dürer's Father at 70, 1497. f, Great Piece of Turf, 1503.
No. 2578, 1000fr, Terathopius ecaudatus. No. 2579, 1000fr, Danaus chrysippus. No. 2580, 1000fr, Shyrna mokarran. No. 2581, 1000fr, Panthera pardus pardus. No. 2582, 1000fr, Dugong dugon. No. 2583, 1000fr, Mosasaurus hoffmannii. No. 2584, 1000fr, Jasminocereus thouarsii. No. 2585, 1000fr, Apophyllite. No. 2586, 1000fr, St. Jerome, by Dürer, 1521.

2021, Nov. 1 Litho. Perf. 13¼x13
Sheets of 6, #a-f
2569-2577 A573 Set of 9 150.00 150.00
Souvenir Sheets
Perf. 13¼x12¾
2578-2586 A573 Set of 9 100.00 100.00
Nos. 2578-2586 each contain one 40x50mm stamp.

Grand maître d'échecs Nona Gaprindashvili

A574

No. 2587, 330fr — Nona Gaprindashvili, chess player: a, Playing chess on blue table. b, Scene from movie Glory to the Queen. c, With male chess player in background.
No. 2588, 330fr — Elvis Presley (1935-77): a, Dancing with Ann-Margret. b, Dancing and wearing horizontally striped shirt. c, Wearing vertically striped shirt.

No. 2589, 330fr — Marilyn Monroe (1926-62), actress: a, With her husband, Joe DiMaggio (1914-99). b, Holding fur stole. c, Wearing black strapless dress.
No. 2590, 330fr — Princess Diana (1961-97), with: a, Flowers. b, Big Ben and flag of Great Britain. c, Queen Elizabeth II.
No. 2591, 330fr — Red Cross: a, Worker distributing sacks of food. b, People waiting near Red Cross building. c, Worker monitoring flood waters.
No. 2592, 330fr — Steam trains: a, Fairy Queen, flag of India. b, London and North Eastern Railway A3 60103 Flying Scotsman, flag of Great Britain. c, Union Pacific 4014 Big Boy, flag of United States.
No. 2593, 330fr — Indian trains: a, WAP-4, Buceros bicornis. b, WDM-3D, Panthera tigris tigris. c, WDG-4, Panthera uncia.
No. 2594, 330fr — Space flight of Shenzhou-12: a, Mission emblem and lauch of Shenzhou-12. b, Shenzhou-12 docking in space. c, Crew members Tang Hongbo, Nie Haisheng and Liu Boming, capsule returning to Earth.
No. 2595, 330fr — Space flight of Inspiration4: a, Lauch of Inspiration4. b, Crew members Christopher Sembroski and Sian Proctor. c, Crew members Jared Isaacman and Hayley Arceneaux.
No. 2596, 1000fr, Gaprindashvili and Garry Kasparov playing chess. No. 2597, 1000fr, Presley playing guitar. No. 2598, 1000fr, Monroe and poster for her movie, Niagara. No. 2599, 1000fr, Princess Diana and Nelson Mandela (1918-2013), president of South Africa. No. 2600, 1000fr, Red Cross water distribution project site. No. 2601, 1000fr, Japanese National Railways Class C55 locomotive, flag of Japan. No. 2602, 1000fr, WAG-9H locomotive, buildings of Mumbai, India. No. 2603, 1000fr, Shenzhou-12 above Earth. No. 2604, 1000fr, Inspiration4 and flag of United States.

2021, Nov. 1 Litho. Perf. 13¼x13
Sheets of 3, #a-c, + 3 labels
2587-2595 A574 Set of 9 100.00 100.00
Souvenir Sheets
Perf. 13¼x12¾
2596-2604 A574 Set of 9 100.00 100.00
Nos. 2596-2604 each contain one 40x50mm stamp.

A575   New Year 2022 (Year of the Tiger) — A576

2021, Nov. 1 Litho. Perf. 13¼
2605 A575 250fr multi   3.00 3.00
2606 A576 550fr multi   6.25 6.25
  a. Souvenir sheet of 2, #2605-
        2606   9.25 9.25
Souvenir Sheets
2607 A575 1000fr multi   11.50 11.50
2608 A576 1000fr multi   11.50 11.50

No. 2606a was printed with two different sheet margins, one with a blue green background and the other with a maroon background. Value is for either sheet.

Miniature Sheet

COVID-19 Revaccination — A577

No. 2609: a, Male health care worker vaccinating woman wearing yellow blouse. b, Female health care worker vaccinating man wearing red shirt. c, Female health care worker vaccinating man wearing green shirt. d, Male health care worker vaccinating woman wearing red blouse. e, Vials of vaccine.

2021, Dec. 20 Litho. Perf. 13¼x13
2609 A577 200fr Sheet of 5,
#a-e, + 4 la-
bels 11.50 11.50

Miniature Sheet

Rotary International COVID-19
Pandemic Relief Efforts — A578

No. 2610: a, Truck, vaccine vials, COVID-19
virus (delivery of vaccines). b, Vaccine vials
and arrows (equal distribution of vaccines). c,
Worker carrying box, coin, protective glove
and mask (purchase of medical supplies). d,
Teacher, hypodermic needle, COVID 19 virus
and pill bottle vaccination education). e,
COVID-19 virus, antiseptic spray and hands
under faucet (promotion of hygiene). f, People,
loudspeaker and Earth (diffusion of precise
information). g, Man wearing protective mask
(promotion of mask wearing). h, Hands,
money, box of groceries (promotion of
donations).

Perf. 12¾x13¼
2021, Dec. 20 Litho.
2610 A578 200fr Sheet of 8,
#a-h, + cen-
tral label 18.00 18.00

A579

No. 2611, 250fr — Concorde: a, Over street
view of European city. b, Over skyscrapers. c,
Over Eiffel Tower. d, Over Arc de Triomphe,
Paris.
No. 2612, 250fr — Flying Hospitals: a,
McDonnell Douglas DC-10, attendant laying
out medical tools. b, Lockheed L-1011-100
Tristar, medical workers, patient on gurney. c,
McDonnell Douglas DC-10 and schematic dia-
gram of Flying Hospital. d, Lockheed L-1011-
100 Tristar, gurney, chair and medical
equipment.
No. 2613, 250fr — Fire trucks: a, Interna-
tional B180. b, International KB-7. c, Commer.
d, Mack B85FSW.
No. 2614, 250fr — Japanese high-speed
trains: a, Hikari, Kyoto skyline. b, Shinkansen
Series N700S, Himeji Castle. c, Shinkansen
Series 0, Osaka skyline. d, Shinkansen Series
E3, aerial view of Asahikawa.
No. 2615, 250fr — German trains: a, MVG
Class, Siegestor, Munich. b, Munich-Nurem-
berg Express Class 101, Marienplatz, Munich.
c, ICE3, Berlin Konzerthaus. d, Bombardier
Talent 2, Cologne skyline.
No. 2616, 250fr — Space flight of William
Shatner: a, Shatner and launch of Blue Origin
rocket. b, New Shepard-18 over Earth. c, New
Shepard-18 and diagram of its flight. d,
Shatner with members of flight crew, Audrey
Powers, Chris Boshuizen, and Glen de Vries.
No. 2617, 250fr — Space flight of
Shenzhou-13: a, Launch of Long March 2F
rocket. b, Crew members Zhai Zhigang, Wang
Yaping, and Ye Guangfu. c, Chinese Space
Station over Earth. d, Docking of Shenzhou-13
and Chinese Space Station.
No. 2618, 250fr — Creation of first film in
space on Soyuz MS-19 flight: a, Soyuz MS-19
at International Space Station, and crew members. b, Soyuz MS-19, map of Russia. c,
Launch of Soyuz-19, Yulia Peresild, crew
member and actress. d, Peresild and mission
emblem.
No. 2619, 250fr — Russian lighthouses: a,
Anapa Lighthouse, Phoebastria immutabilis.
b, Tolbukhin Lighthouse. c, Tokarevsky Lighthouse. d, Basargin Lighthouse, Rissa
brevirostris.
No. 2620, 250fr — Scouts: a, At campfire
near tent. b, With medical bag. c, With knapsack, bow and arrow. d, With musical instruments, firewood and tent.

No. 2621, 250fr — Hornbills: a, Rhinoplax
vigil. b, Buceros rhinoceros. c, Anthracoceros
albirostris. d, Anorrhinus galeritus.
No. 2622, 250fr — Butterflies: a, Hebomoia
leucippe. b, Idea idea. c, Consul fabius,
Cyrestis cocles. d, Papilio ulysses.
No. 2623, 250fr — Dinosaurs: a, Bac-
trosaurus johnsoni. b, Massospondylus
carinatus. c, Alectrosaurus olseni. d, Haplo-
canthosaurus priscus.
No. 2624, 250fr — African mammals: a,
Panthera pardus. b, Equus zebra. c, Giraffa
camelopardalis. d, Panthera leo leo.
No. 2625, 250fr — Orchids: a, Paphiopedilum bellatulum. b, Odontoglossum hallii.
c, Anguloa clowesii. d, Vanda coerulea alba.
No. 2626, 250fr — Mushrooms: a, Ramaria
flava. b, Lactarius deliciosus. c, Cortinarius
violaceus. d, Lactarius piperatus.
No. 2627, 250fr — 2021 Nobel laureates: a,
Peace laureate Dmitri Muratov, Spassky
Tower, Moscow, and Anna Politkovskaya
(1958-2006), murdered Russian journalist. b,
Peace laureate Maria Ressa, dove and flag of
Philippines. c, Physiology or Medicine laure-
ates Ardem Patapoutian and David Julius. d,
Chemistry laureates David MacMillan and
Benjamin List, amethyst crystal.
No. 2628, 250fr — Paintings by Jan Brue-
ghel the Younger (1601-78): a, A Basket of
Flowers, c. 1620. b, A Village Street, 1630. c,
Farmyard, 1650. d, Paradise, c. 1620.
No. 2629, 1000fr, Concorde flying over the
Beatles on rooftop. No. 2630, 1000fr, McDon-
nell Douglas DC-10 Flying Hospital, gurneys,
chair and medical equipment. No. 2631,
1000fr, International Loadstar 1700 fire truck
and fire plane. No. 2632, 1000fr, Shinkansen
Series 6 train and Tokyo skyline. No. 2633,
1000fr, DB Class 103 Blauer Enzian train,
Neuschwanstein Castle. No. 2634, 1000fr,
Shatner and New Shepard-18 rocket. No.
2835, 1000fr, Shenzhou-13 and its crew, flag
of People's Republic of China. No. 2636,
1000fr, Peresild and Soyuz MS-19 mission
emblem, diff. No. 2637, 1000fr, Gelendzhik
Lighthouse, Russia, Haliaeetus pelagicus. No.
2638, 1000fr, Scouts with ax and lantern. No.
2639, 1000fr, Rhyticeros undulatus. No. 2640,
1000fr, Cepora judith, Appias libythea. No.
2641, 1000fr, Tyrannosaurus rex. No. 2642,
1000fr, Loxodonta africana. No. 2643, 1000fr,
Cattleya candida. No. 2644, 1000fr, Helvella
crispa, Clitocybe laccata. No. 2645, 1000fr,
Giorgio Parisi, 2021 Nobel laureate in Physics,
Space X Dragon. No. 2646, 1000fr, Allegory of
the Tulipomania, c. 1640, by Brueghel the
Younger.

Perf. 13¼x12¾
2021, Dec. 20 Litho.
Sheets of 4, #a-d, + 2 labels
2611-2628 A579 Set of 18 205.00 205.00
Souvenir Sheets
2629-2646 A579 Set of 18 205.00 205.00

AIR POST STAMPS

**Afars and Issas Nos. C104-C105,
C103 Overprinted in Brown or Black**

Nos. C106,
C107

No. C108

1977 Engr. Perf. 13
C106 AP37 55fr multi (Br) 2.00 1.75
C107 AP37 75fr multi 9.00 4.00
Litho. Perf. 12
C108 AP36 500fr multi 15.00 13.50
Nos. C106-C108 (3) 26.00 19.25

Map of
Djibouti,
Dove, UN
Emblem
AP38

1977, Oct. 19 Photo. Perf. 13
C109 AP38 300fr multi 6.50 4.25
Djibouti's admission to the United Nations.

Marcel
Brochet MB
101, 1955
AP39

Djibouti Aero Club: 85fr, Tiger Moth, 1960.
200fr, Rallye-Commodore, 1973.

1978, Feb. 27 Litho. Perf. 13
C110 AP39 60fr multi 1.10 .40
C111 AP39 85fr multi 2.00 .65
C112 AP39 200fr multi 4.00 1.10
Nos. C110-C112 (3) 6.70 2.15

Old Man, by
Rubens — AP40

500fr, Hippopotamus Hunt, by Rubens.

1978, Apr. 24 Photo. Perf. 13
C113 AP40 50fr multi 1.50 .50
C114 AP40 500fr multi, horiz. 11.00 5.00
Peter Paul Rubens (1577-1640).

Player Holding Soccer
Cup — AP41

Design: 300fr, Soccer player, map of South
America with Argentina, Cup and emblem.

1978, June 20 Litho. Perf. 13
C115 AP41 100fr multi 1.75 .50
C116 AP41 300fr multi 5.50 1.25
11th World Cup Soccer Championship,
Argentina, June 1-25.
For overprints see Nos. C117-C118.

Nos. C115-C116 Overprinted

a b

1978, Aug. 20 Litho. Perf. 13
C117 AP41 (a) 100fr multi 1.60 .75
C118 AP41 (b) 300fr multi 5.50 2.00
Argentina's victory in 1978 Soccer
Championship.

Tahitian
Women, by
Gauguin
AP42

Young Hare, by
Dürer — AP43

Perf. 13x12½, 12½x13
1978, Sept. 25 Litho.
C119 AP42 100fr multi 2.75 .40
C120 AP43 250fr multi 5.50 2.50
Paul Gauguin (1848-1903) and Albrecht
Dürer (1471-1528), painters.

Common Design Types
pictured following the introduction.

Philexafrique II-Essen Issue
Common Design Types

Designs: No. C121, Lynx and Djibouti No.
456. No. C122, Jay and Brunswick No. 3.

1978, Dec. 13 Litho. Perf. 13x12½
C121 CD138 90fr multi 3.00 1.50
C122 CD139 90fr multi 3.00 1.50
a. Pair, Nos. C121-C122 + label 6.50 6.50

UPU Emblem, Map of
Djibouti, Dove — AP44

1978, Dec. 18 Engr. Perf. 13
C123 AP44 200fr multi 3.25 1.10
Centenary of Congress of Paris.

Junkers JU-
52 and
Dewoitine D-
338
AP45

Powered Flight, 75th Anniversary: 250fr,
Potez P63-11, 1941 and Supermarine Spitfire
HF-VII, 1942. 500fr, Concorde, 1969 and
Sikorsky S-40 "American Clipper," 1931.

1979, May 21 Litho. Perf. 13x12½
C124 AP45 140fr multi 3.00 .60
C125 AP45 250fr multi 4.50 1.00
C126 AP45 500fr multi 9.00 1.75
Nos. C124-C126 (3) 16.50 3.35

The Laundress,
by Honore
Daumier — AP46

1979, July 10 Litho. Perf. 12½x13
C127 AP46 500fr multi 12.00 3.00

Olympic
Emblem,
Skis, Sleds
AP47

1980, Jan. 21 Litho. Perf. 13
C128 AP47 150fr multi 3.00 .60
13th Winter Olympic Games, Lake Placid,
N.Y., Feb. 12-24.
For surcharges see Nos. C133-C134.

Cathedral of the
Archangel, Basketball,
Moscow '80
Emblem — AP48

Page 194

120fr, Lomonossov Univ., Moscow, soccer.
250fr, Cathedral of the Annunciation, running.

1980, Apr. 10   Litho.   Perf. 13
C129 AP48 60fr multi .... 1.05 .25
C130 AP48 120fr multi .... 2.10 .40
C131 AP48 250fr multi 4.25 1.00
 Nos. C129-C131 (3) 7.40 1.65

22nd Summer Olympic Games, Moscow,
July 18-Aug. 3.

Air Djibouti,
1st
Anniversary
AP49

1980, Mar. 29   Litho.   Perf. 13x12½
C132 AP49 400fr multi 9.00 2.50

**No. C128 Surcharged in Black and
Blue or Purple**

1980, Apr. 5   Litho.   Perf. 13
C133 AP47 80fr on 150fr ...... 1.75 .50
C134 AP47 200fr on 150fr (P) . 4.00 1.50

Apollo 11
Moon
Landing,
10th
Anniversary
AP50

Space Conquests: 300fr, Apollo-Soyuz
space project, 5th anniversary.

1980, May 8
C135 AP50 200fr multi .... 4.00 .75
C136 AP50 300fr multi 6.50 1.25

Nos. C135-C136 exist in souvenir sheets of
one. Value, set, $22.50.

Satellite
Earth
Station
Inauguration
AP51

1980, July 3   Litho.   Perf. 13
C137 AP51 500fr multi 9.50 1.75

Graf
Zeppelin
AP52

1980, Oct. 2   Litho.   Perf. 13
C138 AP52 100fr shown .... 2.25 .40
C139 AP52 150fr Ferdinand von
        Zeppelin, blimp 3.25 .60

Zeppelin flight, 80th anniversary.

Voyager
Passing
Saturn
AP53

1980, Dec. 21   Litho.   Perf. 13
C140 AP53 250fr multi 5.50 1.00

AP54

World Cup Soccer Preliminary Games:
200fr, Players, diff.

1981, Jan. 14
C141 AP54 80fr multi .... 1.75 .30
C142 AP54 200fr multi .... 4.25 .65

AP55

1981, Feb. 10   Litho.   Perf. 13
C143 AP55 100fr multi .... 3.50 .50

European-African Economic Convention.

5th
Anniversary
of Viking I
Take-off to
Mars
AP56

20th Anniversary of Various Space Flights:
75fr, Vostok I, Yuri Gagarin, vert. 150fr, Freedom 7, Alan B. Shepard, vert.

1981, Mar. 9   Litho.   Perf. 13
C144 AP56 75fr multi .... 1.75 .35
C145 AP56 120fr multi .... 2.25 .45
C146 AP56 150fr multi .... 3.00 .65
 Nos. C144-C146 (3) 7.00 1.45

Football
Players, by
Picasso
(1881-1973)
AP57

Design: 400fr Man Wearing a Turban, by
Rembrandt (1606-1669), vert.

Perf. 13x12½, 12½x13
1981, Aug. 3   Litho.
C147 AP57 300fr multi 7.00 1.40
C148 AP57 400fr multi 7.50 1.75

Columbia
Space
Shuttle
AP58

90fr, Shuttle launching.

1981, Sept. 24   Litho.   Perf. 13
C149 AP58 90fr multicolored .. 1.75 .40
C150 AP58 120fr shown .... 2.50 .60

Nos. C149-C150 exist in souvenir sheets of
one. Value, set, $22.50.

**Nos. C149-C150 Overprinted in
Brown**

No. C151

No. C152

1981, Nov. 12   Litho.   Perf. 13
C151 AP58 90fr multi .... 1.75 .50
C152 AP58 120fr multi .... 2.50 .75

1982 World
Cup Soccer
AP59

Designs: Various soccer players.

1982, Jan. 20
C153 AP59 110fr multi .... 2.10 .60
C154 AP59 220fr multi 4.75 1.25

For overprints see Nos. C166-C167.

Space Anniversaries — AP60

Designs: 40fr, Luna 9 moon landing, 15th,
vert. 60fr, John Glenn's flight, 20th, vert.
180fr, Viking I Mars landing, 5th.

1982, Feb. 15
C155 AP60 40fr multi .... .70 .25
C156 AP60 60fr multi .... 1.10 .30
C157 AP60 180fr multi 3.00 1.00
 Nos. C155-C157 (3) 4.80 1.55

21st Birthday of
Princess Diana of
Wales — AP61

1982, Apr. 29   Litho.   Perf. 12½x13
C158 AP61 120fr Portrait ..... 2.25 .75
C159 AP61 180fr Portrait, diff. 3.50 1.00

For overprints see Nos. C168-C169.

No. 489,
Boy
Examining
Collection
AP62

1982, May 10   Perf. 13x12½
C160 AP62 80fr shown .... 2.50 .75
C161 AP62 140fr No. 495 ..... 3.75 1.00
 a. Pair, Nos. C160-C161 + label 6.50 6.50

PHILEXFRANCE '82 Stamp Exhibition,
Paris, June 11-21.

1350th Anniv. of
Mohammed's Death at
Medina — AP63

1982, June 8   Litho.   Perf. 13
C162 AP63 500fr Medina
        Mosque 9.00 2.00

Scouting
Year
AP64

1982, June 28
C163 AP64 95fr Baden-Powell . 1.75 .50
C164 AP64 200fr Camp, scouts 4.00 1.25

AP65

Design: 2nd UN conference on peaceful
uses of outer space, Vienna, Aug. 9-21.

1982, Aug. 19
C165 AP65 350fr multi 6.75 3.00

Nos. C153-C154 Overprinted

1982, July 21   Litho.   Perf. 13
C166 AP59 110fr multi .... 2.00 .60
C167 AP59 220fr multi 4.00 1.10

Italy's victory in 1982 World Cup.

**Nos. C158-C159 Overprinted in Blue
or Red**

No. C168

No. C169

1982, Aug. 9   Perf. 12½x13
C168 AP61 120fr multi .... 2.50 .75
C169 AP61 180fr multi (R) 3.50 1.00

Birth of Prince William of Wales, June 21.

Franklin D. Roosevelt
(1882-1945) — AP66

1982, Oct. 7   Litho.   Perf. 13
C170 AP66 115fr shown   2.00 .50
C171 AP66 250fr George Wash-
                      ington   5.25 1.00

Manned Flight
Bicentenary — AP67

35fr, Montgolfiere, 1783. 45fr, Giffard, Paris
Exposition, 1878. 120fr, Double Eagle II, 1978.

1983, Jan. 20   Litho.
C172 AP67 35fr multi   .80 .25
C173 AP67 45fr multi   1.35 .30
C174 AP67 120fr multi   3.50 .80
      Nos. C172-C174 (3)   5.65 1.35

Pre-olympic
Year — AP68

1983, Feb. 15
C175 AP68 75fr Volleyball   1.50 .55
C176 AP68 125fr Wind surfing 2.75 .85

Nos. C175-C176 exist in souvenir sheets of
one. Value, set, $25.

50th Anniv.
of Air
France
AP69

1983, Mar. 20   Litho.   Perf. 13
C177 AP69 25fr Bloch 220   .50 .25
C178 AP69 100fr DC-4   1.75 .70
C179 AP69 175fr Boeing 747   3.50 1.10
      Nos. C177-C179 (3)   5.75 2.05

AP70

180fr, Martin Luther King, Jr. (1929-68), civil
rights leader. 250fr, Alfred Nobel (1833-96)

1983, May 18   Litho.   Perf. 13
C180 AP70 180fr multi   3.50 1.25
C181 AP70 250fr multi   4.50 2.00

AP71

Service Clubs: 90fr, Rotary Club Intl., Sailing Show, Toronto, June 5-9. 150fr, Lions
Club Intl., Honolulu Meeting, June 22-24, Djibouti lighthouse.

1983, July 18   Litho.   Perf. 13
C182 AP71 90fr multi   3.00 1.50
C183 AP71 150fr multi   3.00 1.00
  a.   Pair, Nos. C182-C183 + label 5.50 5.50

Vintage
Motor Cars
AP72

Designs: 60fr, Renault, 1904. 80fr, Mercedes, 1910, vert. 110fr, Lorraine-Dietrich, 1912.

1983, Sep. 20   Litho.   Perf. 13x12½
C184 AP72 60fr multi   1.90 .50
C185 AP72 80fr multi   2.50 .65
C186 AP72 110fr multi   3.00 .85
      Nos. C184-C186 (3)   7.40 2.00

Souvenir Sheet

Air
France,
50th
Anniv.
AP73

1983, Oct. 7   Litho.   Perf. 12½
           Self-Adhesive
C187 AP73 250fr multicolored 25.00 25.00
           Printed on wood.

Vostok VI — AP74

1983, Oct. 20   Litho.   Perf. 12
C188 AP74 120fr shown   2.25 .80
C189 AP74 200fr Explorer I   3.75 1.10

1984 Winter
Olympics
AP75

1984, Feb. 14   Litho.   Perf. 13
C190 AP75 70fr Speed skating 1.50 .55
C191 AP75 130fr Figure skating 2.50 1.10

For overprints see Nos. C196-C197.

Souvenir Sheet

Ship — AP76

1984, Feb. 14   Litho.   Perf. 12½
C192 AP76 250fr multi   11.00 11.00

Sea-Me-We (South-east Asia-Middle East-
Western Europe) submarine cable construc-
tion agreement.
  No. C192 exists in a souvenir sheet of one.
Value, $12.50.

Motorized
Hang
Gliders
AP77

Various hang gliders.

1984, Mar. 12   Perf. 13x12½
C193 AP77 65fr multi   1.25 .50
C194 AP77 85fr multi   1.60 .60
C195 AP77 100fr multi   2.10 .75
      Nos. C193-C195 (3)   4.95 1.85

**Nos. C190-C191 Overprinted with
Winners' Names and Country**

1984, Mar. 28   Perf. 13
C196 AP75 70fr multi   1.50 .50
C197 AP75 130fr multi   2.75 1.00

Portrait of
Marguerite
Matisse, 1910, by
Henri
Matisse — AP78

Design: 200fr, Portrait of Mario Varvogli, by
Amedeo Modigliani.

1984, Apr. 15   Litho.   Perf. 12½x13
C198 AP78 150fr multi   3.75 1.00
C199 AP78 200fr multi   4.75 1.40

1984
Summer
Olympics
AP79

1984, May 24   Perf. 13
C200 AP79 50fr Running   1.00 .40
C201 AP79 60fr High jump   1.25 .40
C202 AP79 80fr Swimming   1.50 .60
      Nos. C200-C202 (3)   3.75 1.40

Nos. C200-C202 exist in a souvenir sheet of
3. Value, $32.50.

Battle
Scene
AP80

1984, June 16 Litho. Perf. 13x12½
C203 AP80 300fr multi   6.00 2.75

125th anniv. of Battle of Solferino and 120th
anniv. of Red Cross.

Bleriot's
Flight over
English
Channel,
75th Anniv.
AP81

Designs: 40fr, 14-Bis plans. 75fr, Britten-
Norman Islander. 90fr, Air Djibouti jet.

1984, July 8
C204 AP81 40fr multi   .90 .40
C205 AP81 75fr multi   1.40 .75
C206 AP81 90fr multi   1.50 1.00
      Nos. C204-C206 (3)   3.80 2.15

375th Anniv., Galileo's
Telescope — AP82

120fr, Telescopes, spacecraft. 180fr,
Galileo, telescopes.

1984, Oct. 7   Litho.   Perf. 13
C207 AP82 120fr multicolored 2.50 .80
C208 AP82 180fr multicolored 3.50 1.10

1984
Soccer
Events
AP83

Designs: No. C209, Euro Cup. No. C210,
Los Angeles Olympics.

1984, Oct. 20   Litho.   Perf. 13
C209 AP83 80fr multi   2.50 .60
C210 AP83 80fr multi   2.50 .60
  a.   Pair, Nos. C209-C210 + label 4.50 4.00

Service Clubs — AP84

50fr, Lions, World Leprosy Day. 60fr,
Rotary, chess board, pieces.

1985, Feb. 23   Litho.   Perf. 13
C211 AP84 50fr multicolored   1.40 .50
C212 AP84 60fr multicolored   1.60 .55

Nos. C211-C212 exist in souvenir sheets of
1.

Telecommunications
Technology — AP85

No. C213, Technician, researchist, operator.
No. C214, Offshore oil rig, transmission tower,
government building.

1985, July 2   Perf. 13x12½
C213 AP85 80fr multi   2.50 .55
C214 AP85 80fr multi   2.50 .55
  a.   Pair, Nos. C213-C214 + label 6.25 1.25

PHILEXAFRICA '85, Lome.

Telecommunications
Development — AP86

50fr, Intl. transmission center. 90fr, Ariane
rocket, vert. 120fr, ARABSAT satellite.

1985, Oct. 2   **Perf. 13**
C215 AP86 50fr multi   .90 .35
C216 AP86 90fr multi   1.60 .65
C217 AP86 120fr multi   2.00 .90
    Nos. C215-C217 (3)   4.50 1.90

Youths
Windsurfing,
Playing
Tennis
AP87

No. C219, Tadjoura Highway construction.

1985, Nov. 13   **Perf. 13x12½**
C218 AP87 100fr multi   2.50 1.00
C219 AP87 100fr multi   2.50 1.00
   a.   Pair, Nos. C218-C219 + label   6.00 5.00
PHILEXAFRICA '85, Lome, Togo, 11/16-24.

1986 World Cup Soccer
Championships, Mexico — AP88

Design: 100fr, Players, stadium.

1986, Feb. 24   **Perf. 13**
C220 AP88 75fr shown   1.50 .50
C221 AP88 100fr multi   2.00 .70
   For overprints see Nos. C223-C224.

Statue of
Liberty,
Cent.
AP89

1986, May 21
C222 AP89 250fr multi   4.50 1.75

**Nos. C220-C221 Ovptd. with
Winners**

1986, Sept. 15   **Litho.**   **Perf. 13**
C223 AP88 75fr "FRANCE -
           BELGIQUE / 4-
           2"   1.25 .65
C224 AP88 100fr "3-2 ARGEN-
           TINE-RFA"   1.75 .80

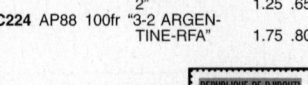

1986 World Chess
Championships, May
1-19 — AP89a

Malayan animal chess pieces: 80fr, Knight,
bishops. 120fr, Rook, king, pawn.

1986, Oct. 13   **Litho.**   **Perf. 13**
C225 AP89a 80fr multi   2.00 .60
C226 AP89a 120fr multi   3.25 .90

Yuri
Gagarin,
Vostok
Spacecraft
AP90

Design: 200fr, Space rendezvous, 1966.

1986, Nov. 27   **Litho.**   **Perf. 13**
C227 AP90 150fr shown   3.00 1.10
C228 AP90 200fr multi   4.25 1.25
   First man in space, 25th anniv.; Gemini 8-
Agena link-up, 20th anniv.

Historic
Flights
AP91

Designs: 55fr, Amiot 370. 80fr, Spirit of St.
Louis. 120fr, Voyager.

1987, Jan. 22   **Litho.**   **Perf. 13**
C229 AP91 55fr multi   1.25 .40
C230 AP91 80fr multi   1.75 .55
C231 AP91 120fr multi   2.50 .90
    Nos. C229-C231 (3)   5.50 1.85
   First flight from Istria to Djibouti, 1942;
Lindbergh's Transatlantic flight, 1927; nonstop
world circumnavigation without refueling.
   For surcharge see No. C240.

Souvenir Sheet

Fight
Against
Leprosy
AP91a

Design: Raoul Follereau (b. 1903), care
giver to lepers, Gerhard Hansen (1841-1912),
discoverer of bacillus of leprosy.

1987, Mar. 23   **Litho.**   **Perf. 13x12½**
            Self-Adhesive
C231A   AP91a 500fr multi   20.00 15.00
   No. C231A printed on wood.

Pres. Aptidon,
Natl. Crest and
Flag — AP92

1987, June 27   **Litho.**   **Perf. 12½x13**
C232 AP92 250fr multi   4.50 1.50
   Natl. independence, 10th anniv.

Telstar, 25th
Anniv.
AP93

Design: 250fr, Samuel Morse, telegraph
key.

1987, Oct. 1   **Perf. 13**
C233 AP93 190fr shown   3.50 1.25
   a.   Souvenir sheet 1 #C233   14.00 —
C234 AP93 250fr multi   4.50 1.50
   a.   Souvenir sheet 1 #C234   14.00 —
   Invention of the telegraph, 150th anniv.
(250fr).
   Nos. C233a and C234a also exist imperf.
Value, set of 2, $40.

City of
Djibouti,
Cent.
AP94

100fr, Djibouti Creek & quay, 1887. 150fr,
Aerial view of city, 1987. 250fr, Somali Coast
#6, 20, postmarks of 1898 & 1903.

1987, Nov. 15   **Litho.**   **Perf. 13x12½**
C235 AP94 100fr blk & buff   2.00 1.10
C236 AP94 150fr multi   3.00 1.60
   a.   Pair, Nos. C235-C236 + label   6.00 2.75
           Souvenir Sheet
C237 AP94 250fr multi   6.00 5.50
   No. C237 has decorative margin like design
of 100fr.

Intl. Red Cross and
Red Crescent
Organizations, 125th
Anniv. — AP95

1988, Feb. 17   **Litho.**   **Perf. 13**
C238 AP95 300fr multi   6.00 3.25

1988
Summer
Olympics,
Seoul
AP96

1988, June 15   **Litho.**   **Perf. 13**
C239 AP96 105fr multi   3.00 1.00
   For overprint see No. C242.
   No. C239 exists in a souvenir sheet of one.
Value, $25.

No. C229 Surcharged in Black

1988, June 28
C240 AP91 70fr on 55fr multi   3.00 1.50
   Air race in memory of the Paris-Djibouti-St.
Denis flight of French aviator Roland Garros
(1888-1913).

World Post
Day
AP97

1988, Oct. 9   **Litho.**   **Perf. 13**
C241 AP97 1000fr multi   18.00 10.00

No. C239 Overprinted

1988, Dec. 15   **Litho.**   **Perf. 13**
C242 AP96 105fr multi   2.25 1.50

World Telecommunications
Day — AP98

1989, May 17   **Litho.**   **Perf. 12½**
C243 AP98 150fr multi   2.75 1.50

PHILEXFRANCE
'89, Declaration of
Human Rights
and Citizenship
Bicent. — AP99

1989, July 14   **Litho.**   **Perf. 12½x13**
C244 AP99 120fr multi   2.75 1.25

Salt, Lake
Assal
AP100

1989, Sept. 15   **Litho.**   **Perf. 13**
C245 AP100 300fr multicolored   6.75 3.50

POSTAGE DUE STAMP

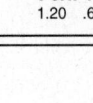

Urn for Milking
Camel — D1

1988, Jan. 20   **Litho.**   **Perf. 13**
J1 D1 60fr multicolored   1.20 .65

DOMINICA

,dä-mə-'nē-kə

LOCATION — The largest island of the Windward group in the West Indies. Southeast of Puerto Rico.
GOVT. — Republic in British Commonwealth
AREA — 290 sq. mi.
POP. — 64,881 (1999 est.)
CAPITAL — Roseau

Formerly a Presidency of the Leeward Islands, Dominica became a separate colony under the governor of the Windward Islands on January 1, 1940. Dominica joined the West Indies federation April 22, 1958. In 1968, Dominica became an associate state of Britain; in 1978, an independent nation.

12 Pence = 1 Shilling
20 Shillings = 1 Pound
100 Cents = 1 Dollar (1949)

> **Catalogue values for unused stamps in this country are for Never Hinged items, beginning with Scott 112.**

Watermark

Wmk. 334 — Rectangles

Queen Victoria — A1

Perf. 12½

		1874, May 4	Typo.	Wmk. 1	
1	A1	1p violet		170.00	55.00
a.		Vertical half used as ½p on cover			9,000.
2	A1	6p green		625.00	115.00
3	A1	1sh deep lilac rose		375.00	80.00
		Nos. 1-3 (3)		1,170.	250.00

During 1875-87 some issues were manuscript dated with village names. These are considered postally used. Stamps with entire village names sell for much more, starting at $100.

		1877-79		**Perf. 14**	
4	A1	½p bister ('79)		20.00	62.50
5	A1	1p violet		24.00	3.75
a.		Diagonal or vertical half used as ½p on cover			2,600.
6	A1	2½p red brown ('79)		275.00	45.00
7	A1	4p blue ('79)		130.00	3.75
8	A1	6p green		170.00	22.50
9	A1	1sh dp lilac rose		140.00	57.50
		Nos. 4-9 (6)		759.00	195.00

For surcharges see Nos. 10-15.

No. 5 Bisected and Surcharged in Black or Red

a   b   c

1882
10	A1(a)	½p on half of 1p		240.00	57.50
a.		Inverted surcharge		1,150.	900.00
b.		Surcharge tete beche pair		2,600.	2,000.
11	A1(b)	½p on half of 1p		72.50	42.50
a.		Surch. reading downward		72.50	42.50
b.		Double surcharge		900.00	

12	A1(c)	½p on half of 1p (R)		40.00	20.00
a.		Inverted surcharge		1,150.	550.00
b.		Double surcharge		1,850.	750.00
		Nos. 10-12 (3)		352.50	120.00

The existence of genuine examples of No. 10b has been questioned.

Nos. 8 and 9 Surcharged in Black

Half Penny

1886
13	A1	½p on 6p green		13.00	15.00
14	A1	1p on 6p green		45,000.	12,500.
15	A1	1p on 1sh		24.00	22.00
a.		Double surcharge		11,500.	4,250.

All examples of No. 14 may have small pin marks which may have been part of the surcharging process.

		1883-89		**Wmk. 2**	
16	A1	½p bister ('83)		7.50	11.50
17	A1	½p green ('86)		6.00	5.75
18	A1	1p violet ('86)		60.00	16.00
a.		Half used as ½p on cover			2,350.
19	A1	1p dp carmine ('89)		5.75	15.00
a.		1p rose ('87)		19.00	28.00
b.		Vert. half used as ½p on cover			2,100.
20	A1	2½p red brn ('84)		160.00	5.00
21	A1	2½p ultra ('88)		4.25	9.00
22	A1	4p gray ('86)		9.00	7.75
23	A1	6p orange ('88)		23.00	92.50
24	A1	1sh dp lil rose ('88)		200.00	500.00
		Nos. 16-24 (9)		475.50	662.50

Roseau, Capital of Dominica — A6

King Edward VII — A7

		1903	Wmk. 1	**Perf. 14**	
25	A6	½p gray green		5.25	4.75
26	A6	1p car & black		17.50	.80
27	A6	2p brn & gray grn		6.00	8.00
28	A6	2½p ultra & blk		13.00	5.25
29	A6	3p black & vio		11.50	4.50
30	A6	6p org brn & blk		15.00	22.50
31	A6	1sh gray grn & red vio		42.50	52.50
32	A6	2sh red vio & blk		40.00	35.00
33	A6	2sh6p ocher & gray grn		23.00	92.50
34	A7	5sh brown & blk		125.00	175.00
		Nos. 25-34 (10)		298.75	400.80

Nos. 25 to 29 and 31 are on both ordinary and chalky paper. For detailed listings, see the *Scott Classic Specialized Catalogue of Stamps & Covers*.

		1907-20	**Chalky Paper**	**Wmk. 3**	
35	A6	½p gray green		15.00	11.00
36	A6	1p car & black		2.50	.55
37	A6	2p brn & gray grn		16.00	24.00
38	A6	2½p ultra & black		5.50	27.50
39	A6	3p black & vio		5.00	20.00
40	A6	3p vio, yel, chalky paper ('09)		3.75	5.25
41	A6	6p org brn & blk ('08)		65.00	100.00
42	A6	6p vio & dl vio, chalky paper ('09)		12.50	19.00
43	A6	1sh gray grn & red vio		4.75	67.50
44	A6	1sh blk, green, chalky paper ('10)		3.75	5.00
45	A6	2sh red vio & blk ('08)		30.00	40.00
46	A6	2sh ultra & vio, bl ('19)		32.50	110.00
47	A6	2sh6p ocher & gray grn ('08)		27.50	75.00
48	A6	2sh6p red & blk, bl ('20)		32.50	125.00
49	A7	5sh brn & blk ('08)		75.00	75.00
		Nos. 35-49 (15)		331.25	704.80

Nos. 40, 42 and 44 are on both ordinary and chalky paper. For detailed listings, see the

---

Scott Classic Specialized Catalogue of Stamps & Covers.
For type surcharged see No. 55.

		1908-09		**Ordinary Paper**	
50	A6	½p green		9.50	6.25
51	A6	1p scarlet		2.00	.75
a.		1p carmine		4.50	.45
52	A6	2p gray ('09)		5.00	17.50
53	A6	2½p ultramarine		9.50	9.75
a.		2½p bright blue ('09)		5.75	10.50
		Nos. 50-53 (4)		26.00	34.25

King George V — A8

		1914	**Chalky Paper**	**Perf. 14**	
54	A8	5sh grn & scar, yel		70.00	100.00

Type of 1903 Surcharged

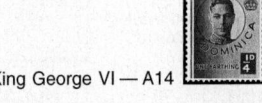

1920
55	A6	1½p on 2½p orange		8.25	4.75

		1921	**Ordinary Paper**	**Wmk. 4**	
56	A6	½p green		3.50	25.00
57	A6	1p rose red		3.00	4.00
58	A6	1½p orange		4.75	21.00
59	A6	2p gray		4.25	4.00
60	A6	2½p ultra		3.25	17.50
61	A6	6p vio & dl vio		5.00	50.00
62	A6	2sh ultra & vio, bl		50.00	145.00
63	A6	2sh6p red & blk, bl		45.00	165.00
		Nos. 56-63 (8)		118.75	431.50

No. 61 is on chalky paper.

Seal of Colony and George V — A9

		1923-33	**Chalky Paper**	**Wmk. 4**	
65	A9	½p green & blk		2.50	.85
66	A9	1p violet & blk		7.50	2.25
67	A9	1p scar & black		18.00	1.40
68	A9	1½p car & black		6.75	.90
69	A9	1½p dp brn & blk		15.50	.95
70	A9	2p gray & black		4.50	.65
71	A9	2½p org & black		4.50	10.00
72	A9	2½p ultra & black		7.75	2.25
73	A9	3p ultra & black		4.50	19.00
74	A9	3p red & blk, yel		4.75	1.40
75	A9	4p brown & blk		5.25	7.25
76	A9	6p red vio & blk		5.50	9.00
77	A9	1sh blk, emerald		3.50	4.25
78	A9	2sh ultra & blk, bl		26.00	40.00
79	A9	2sh6p red & blk, bl		27.50	40.00
80	A9	3sh vio & blk, yel		4.50	15.00
81	A9	4sh red & blk, emer		23.00	40.00
82	A9	5sh grn & blk, yel		42.50	62.50
		Nos. 65-82 (18)		214.00	257.65

Issue years: Nos. 80, 82, 1927; Nos. 72, 74, 1928; Nos. 67, 69, 1933; others, 1923.

Many values of this set are known with a forged G.P.O. cancellation dated "MY 19 27".

		1923		**Wmk. 3**	
83	A9	3sh vio & blk, yel		5.75	72.50
84	A9	5sh grn & blk, yel		10.00	65.00
85	A9	£1 vio & blk, red		240.00	375.00
		Nos. 83-85 (3)		255.75	512.50

Common Design Types
pictured following the introduction.

Silver Jubilee Issue
Common Design Type
Perf. 13½x14

		1935, May 6	**Wmk. 4**		**Engr.**
90	CD301	1p car & blue		1.60	.35
91	CD301	1½p gray blk & ultra		5.75	3.25
92	CD301	2½p blue & brn		5.75	4.75
93	CD301	1sh brt vio & ind		5.75	11.50
		Nos. 90-93 (4)		18.85	19.85
		Set, never hinged		27.50	

Coronation Issue
Common Design Type

		1937, May 12		**Perf. 11x11½**	
94	CD302	1p dark carmine		.25	.25
95	CD302	1½p brown		.25	.25
96	CD302	2½p deep ultra		.35	1.90
		Nos. 94-96 (3)		.85	2.40
		Set, never hinged		1.50	

Fresh-Water Lake — A10

Layou River — A11

Picking Limes — A12

Boiling Lake — A13

		1938-47		**Wmk. 4**	**Perf. 12½**
97	A10	½p grn & red brn		.25	.25
98	A11	1p car & gray		.25	.25
99	A12	1½p rose vio & grn		.25	.75
100	A13	2p brn blk & dp rose		.35	2.25
101	A12	2½p ultra & rose vio		2.25	2.25
a.		2½p bl & rose vio		2.75	1.90
102	A11	3p red brn & ol		.25	.60
103	A12	3½p red vio & brt ultra		1.00	2.10
104	A10	6p vio & yel grn		.50	1.60
105	A11	7p org brn & grn		1.00	1.60
106	A13	1sh olive & vio		2.50	1.60
107	A11	2sh red vio & blk		4.50	12.50
108	A10	2sh6p scar ver & blk		10.00	5.75
109	A11	5sh dk brn & bl		8.00	12.00
110	A13	10sh dl org & blk		10.00	22.50
		Nos. 97-110 (14)		39.10	66.00
		Set, never hinged		80.00	

Issued: No. 101, 8/42; 3½p, 7p, 2sh, 10sh, 10/15/47; others, 8/15/38.

King George VI — A14

		1940, Apr. 15	**Photo.**	**Perf. 14½x14**	
111	A14	¼p brown violet		1.00	.25
a.		Ordinary paper ('42)		.25	1.50

No. 111 is on chalky paper.

> **Catalogue values for unused stamps in this section, from this point to the end of the section, are for Never Hinged items.**

Peace Issue
Common Design Type

		1946, Oct. 14	**Engr.**	**Perf. 13½x14**	
112	CD303	1p carmine		.25	.25
113	CD303	3½p deep blue		.25	.25

Silver Wedding Issue
Common Design Types

		1948, Dec. 1	**Photo.**	**Perf. 14x14½**	
114	CD304	1p scarlet		.25	.25

Engraved; Name Typographed
Perf. 11½x11

115	CD305	10sh orange brn		25.00	32.50

UPU Issue
Common Design Types

Engr.: Name Typo. on 6c and 12c

		1949, Oct. 10		**Perf. 13½, 11x11½**	
116	CD306	5c blue		1.25	
117	CD307	6c chocolate		1.25	3.00
118	CD308	12c rose violet		.50	2.10
119	CD309	24c olive		.30	.30
		Nos. 116-119 (4)		2.30	5.65

University Issue
Common Design Types

		1951, Feb. 16	**Engr.**	**Perf. 14x14½**	
120	CD310	3c purple & green		.60	1.25
121	CD311	12c dp car & dk bl grn		.80	.50

George VI
A15

Drying Cocoa
A16

Picking Oranges — A17

Designs: 2c and 60c, Carib Baskets. 3c and 48c, Lime Plantation. 4c, Picking Oranges. 5c, Bananas. 6c, Botanical Gardens. 8c, Drying Vanilla Beans. 12c and $1.20, Fresh Water Lake. 14c, Layou River. 24c, Boiling Lake.

Perf. 14½x14

1951, July 1	**Photo.**	**Wmk. 4**	
122	A15	½c brown	.25	.25

Perf. 13x13½
Engr.

123	A16	1c red org & blk	.25	.30
124	A16	2c dp grn & red brn	.25	.25
125	A16	3c red vio & bl grn	.25	3.50
126	A16	4c dk brn & brn org	.75	3.75
127	A16	5c rose red & blk	.85	.30
128	A16	6c org brn & ol grn	1.00	.30
129	A16	8c dp bl & dp grn	3.00	1.75
130	A16	12c emer & gray	.75	1.25
131	A16	14c pur & blue	1.25	3.50
132	A16	24c rose car & red vio	1.00	.40
133	A16	48c red org & bl grn	5.00	13.50
134	A16	60c gray & car	4.00	9.25
135	A16	$1.20 gray & emer	8.25	7.25

Perf. 13½x13

136	A17	$2.40 gray & org	30.00	52.50
		Nos. 122-136 (15)	56.85	98.05

Nos. 125, 127, 129 and 131 Overprinted in Black or Carmine

1951, Oct. 15			**Perf. 13x13½**	
137	A16	3c red vio & bl green	.25	.60
138	A16	5c rose red & black	.25	1.75
139	A16	8c dp blue & dp grn (C)	.30	.30
140	A16	14c purple & blue (C)	1.75	.30
		Nos. 137-140 (4)	2.55	2.90

Adoption of a new constitution for the Windward Islands, 1951.

Coronation Issue
Common Design Type

1953, June 2	**Engr.**	**Perf. 13½x13**		
141	CD312	2c dk green & black	.40	.40

Types of 1951 with Portrait of Queen Elizabeth II

1954, Oct. 1	**Photo.**	**Perf. 14½x14**		
142	A15	½c brown	.25	1.25

Perf. 13x13½
Engr.

143	A16	1c red org & blk	.25	.30
144	A16	2c dp grn & red brn	1.10	2.00
145	A16	3c red vio & bl grn	1.50	.40
146	A16	4c dk brn & brn org	.25	.30
147	A16	5c rose red & blk	2.75	1.00
148	A16	6c org brn & ol	.55	.30
149	A16	8c dp bl & dp grn	1.50	.30
150	A16	12c emer & gray	.60	.25
151	A16	14c pur & bl	.45	.25
152	A16	24c rose car & red vio	.55	.30
153	A16	48c red org & bl grn	2.75	11.00
154	A16	60c gray & car	3.50	1.50
155	A16	$1.20 gray & emer	22.50	7.00

Perf. 13½x13

156	A17	$2.40 gray & org	22.50	14.00
		Nos. 142-156 (15)	61.00	40.15

Mat Making — A18

5c, Canoe making. 10c, Bananas.

1957, Oct. 15	**Wmk. 4**	**Perf. 13x13½**		
157	A18	3c car rose & black	4.00	2.50
158	A18	5c brown & blue	12.00	1.10
159	A18	10c redsh brn & brt grn	6.00	3.25
160	A18	48c violet & brown	3.25	2.75
		Nos. 157-160 (4)	25.25	9.60

West Indies Federation
Common Design Type

		Perf. 11½x11		
1958, Apr. 22		**Wmk. 314**		
161	CD313	3c green	.50	.35
162	CD313	6c blue	.60	1.10
163	CD313	12c car rose	.85	.40
		Nos. 161-163 (3)	1.95	1.85

Sailing Canoe
A19

Traditional Costume
A20

Type I

Type II

Two types of 14c:
I — Mountain light violet. Girl's eyes look straight out.
II — Mountain blue. Eyes look sideways.
Designs: 1c, Seashore, Rosalie. 2c, 5c, Queen Elizabeth II by Annigoni. 4c, Sulphur Springs. 6c, Road making. 8c, Dugout canoe. 10c, Frog (mountain chicken). 12c, Boats and Scotts Head. 15c, Bananas. 24c, Imperial parrot. 48c, View of Goodwill. 60c, Cacao tree. $1.20, Coat of Arms. $2.40, Trafalgar Falls. $4.80, Coconut palm.

Perf. 14½x14, 14x14½

1963, May 16	**Photo.**	**Wmk. 314**		
164	A19	1c bl, brn & grn	.25	.90
165	A20	2c ultramarine	.30	.25
166	A19	3c lt ultra & blk	1.50	1.10
167	A19	4c sl, grn & brn	.25	.25
168	A20	5c magenta	.30	.25
169	A19	6c lt grn, vio & buff	.25	.50
170	A19	8c tan, blk & lt grn	.30	.25
171	A19	10c pink & brn	.25	.25
172	A19	12c bl, blk, grn & brn	.90	.25
173	A20	14c multi (II)	2.50	2.50
a.		Type I	.90	.30
174	A19	15c grn, yel & brn	1.25	.25
175	A20	24c multicolored	8.50	.25
176	A19	48c bl, blk & grn	.90	.90
177	A19	60c blk, grn, org & brn	1.00	.75
178	A19	$1.20 multicolored	6.25	1.60
179	A20	$2.40 grn, bl, brn & blk	4.75	4.00
180	A20	$4.80 blk, grn & blk	20.00	30.00
		Nos. 164-180 (17)	49.45	44.25

For overprints see Nos. 211-232.

1966-67		**Wmk. 314 Sideways**		
167a	A19	4c ('67)	1.25	.90
169a	A19	6c	.25	.80
170a	A19	8c	.45	.90
171a	A19	10c ('67)	.70	.95
174a	A19	15c ('67)	.85	1.50
		Nos. 167a-174a (5)	3.50	5.05

Freedom from Hunger Issue
Common Design Type

1963, June 4		**Perf. 14x14½**		
181	CD314	15c lilac	.30	.30

Red Cross Centenary Issue
Common Design Type
Wmk. 314

1963, Sept. 2	**Litho.**	**Perf. 13**		
182	CD315	5c black & red	.25	.25
183	CD315	15c ultra & red	.45	.80

Shakespeare Issue
Common Design Type

1964, Apr. 23	**Photo.**	**Perf. 14x14½**		
184	CD316	15c lilac rose	.35	.35

ITU Issue
Common Design Type

1965, May 17	**Photo.**	**Perf. 11x11½**		
185	CD317	2c emerald & blue	.25	.25
186	CD317	48c grnsh blue & slate	.30	.30

Intl. Cooperation Year Issue
Common Design Type

1965, Oct. 25		**Perf. 14½**		
187	CD318	1c blue grn & claret	.25	.25
188	CD318	15c lt violet & grn	.30	.30

Churchill Memorial Issue
Common Design Type

1966, Jan. 24	**Photo.**	**Perf. 14**		

Design in Black, Gold and Carmine Rose

189	CD319	1c bright blue	.25	.25
a.		Gold omitted	2,000.	
190	CD319	5c green	.25	.25
191	CD319	15c brown	.30	.30
192	CD319	24c violet	.35	.35
		Nos. 189-192 (4)	1.15	1.15

Royal Visit Issue
Common Design Type

1966, Feb. 4	**Litho.**	**Perf. 11x12**		
193	CD320	5c violet blue	.75	.25
194	CD320	15c dk car rose	2.25	.35

World Cup Soccer Issue
Common Design Type

1966, July 1	**Litho.**	**Perf. 14**		
195	CD321	5c multicolored	.35	.25
196	CD321	24c multicolored	.85	.50

WHO Headquarters Issue
Common Design Type

1966, Sept. 20	**Litho.**	**Perf. 14**		
197	CD322	5c multicolored	.25	.25
198	CD322	24c multicolored	.50	.50

UNESCO Anniversary Issue
Common Design Type

1966, Dec. 1	**Litho.**	**Perf. 14**		
199	CD323	5c "Education"	.35	.25
200	CD323	15c "Science"	.45	.25
201	CD323	24c "Culture"	.80	.25
		Nos. 199-201 (3)	1.60	.75

Carib, Negro and Caucasian Children — A21

10c, Columbus' ship Santa Maria & banderol. 15c, Hands with banderol. 24c, Belaire dancers.

Perf. 14½x14

1967, Nov. 3	**Photo.**	**Wmk. 314**		
202	A21	5c multicolored	.25	.25
203	A21	10c multicolored	.25	.25
204	A21	15c multicolored	.25	.25
205	A21	24c multicolored	.25	.25
		Nos. 202-205 (4)	1.00	1.00

Issued for National Day, Nov. 3.

John F. Kennedy and Human Rights Flame — A22

Human Rights Flame and: 10c, Cecil E. A. Rawle (1891-1938), Dominican crusader for human rights. 12c, Pope John XXIII. 48c, Florence Nightingale. 60c, Dr. Albert Schweitzer.

Wmk. 314 Sideways

1968, Apr. 20	**Litho.**	**Perf. 14**		
206	A22	1c multicolored	.25	.25
207	A22	10c multicolored	.25	.25
208	A22	12c multicolored	.25	.25

209	A22	48c multicolored	.25	.25
210	A22	60c multicolored	.25	.25
		Nos. 206-210 (5)	1.25	1.25

International Human Rights Year.

Stamps and Types of 1963-67 Overprinted in Silver or Black: "ASSOCIATED / STATEHOOD"
Perf. 14½x14, 14x14½

1968, July 8	**Photo.**	**Wmk. 314**		
211	A19	1c multi	.25	.25
212	A20	2c ultra	.25	.25
213	A19	3c lt ultra & blk	.25	.25
214	A19	4c multi	.25	.25
215	A20	5c magenta	.25	.25
216	A19	6c multi (B)	.25	.25
217	A19	8c multi (B)	.25	.25
218	A19	10c pink & brn	.55	.25
219	A19	12c multi	.25	.50
a.		Watermark upright	.25	.25
220	A20	14c multi (II)	.25	.25
221	A19	15c multi	.25	.25
222	A20	24c multi	4.00	.25
223	A19	48c multi	.55	2.25
a.		Watermark upright	.50	1.00
224	A19	60c multi (B)	.90	.75
225	A19	$1.20 multi (B)	1.00	3.00
226	A20	$2.40 multi	1.00	2.25
227	A20	$4.80 multi	1.00	2.25
		Nos. 211-227 (17)	11.75	19.50

In this set, overprint was applied to 2c, 3c, 12c, 14c, 24c, 48c, 60c, $1.20, $2.40 and $4.80 with watermark upright. A reprinting of the 1c, 4c, 6c, 8c, 10c, 12c, No. 219, 15c and 48c, No. 223 on paper with watermark sideways was made. Same value.

Nos. 164-166, 173 and 178 Overprinted: "NATIONAL DAY / 3 NOVEMBER 1968"
Perf. 14½x14, 14x14½

1968, Nov. 3	**Photo.**	**Wmk. 314**		
228	A19	1c blue, brn & grn	.25	.25
229	A20	2c ultra	.25	.25
230	A19	3c lt ultra & blk	.25	.25
231	A20	14c multi (I)	.25	.25
232	A19	$1.20 multicolored	.55	.55
		Nos. 228-232 (5)	1.55	1.55

A23

No. 233: a, 3 soccer players; b, Soccer player, goalie. No. 234: a, Swimmers at start; b, Divers. No. 235: a, Javelin thrower, hurdlers; b, Hurdlers. No. 236: a, Basketball; b, 3 basketball players.

Perf. 11½

1968, Nov. 23	**Unwmk.**	**Litho.**		
233	A23	1c Pair, #a-b	.25	.25
234	A23	5c Pair, #a-b	.25	.25
235	A23	48c Pair, #a-b	.50	.50
236	A23	60c Pair, #a-b	1.40	1.40
		Nos. 233-236 (4)	2.40	2.40

19th Olympic Games, Mexico City, 10/12-27.

The Small Cowper Madonna, by Raphael — A24

Perf. 12½x12

1968, Dec. 23	**Photo.**	**Unwmk.**		
241	A24	5c multicolored	.30	.30

Christmas. No. 241 printed in sheets of 20. Sheets of 6 (3x2) exist containing two each of 12c, 24c, and $1.20 stamps, each picturing a different madonna painting. Value $6.

Venus and Adonis, by Rubens — A25

Paintings: 15c, The Death of Socrates, by Louis Jacques David. 24c, Christ at Emmaus, by Velazquez. 50c, Pilate Washing his Hands, by Rembrandt.

Perf. 14½x15

1969, Jan. 30   Litho.   Wmk. 314

242	A25	5c lilac & multi	.25	.25
243	A25	15c emerald & multi	.25	.25
244	A25	24c red & multi	.25	.25
245	A25	50c crimson & multi	.45	.45
		Nos. 242-245 (4)	1.20	1.20

20th anniv. (in 1968) of the WHO.

Citrus Fruit Picker — A26

No. 247, Woman and child. No. 248, Hotel. No. 249, Red-necked parrots. No. 250, Calypso band. No. 251, Women dancers. No. 252, Tropical fish and coelenterates. No. 253, Diver and turtle.

1969, Mar. 10   Perf. 14½

246	A26	10c multicolored	.25	.25
247	A26	10c multicolored	.25	.25
a.		Pair, #246-247	.25	.25
248	A26	12c multicolored	.25	.25
249	A26	12c multicolored	.25	.25
a.		Pair, #248-249	.25	.25
250	A26	24c multicolored	.25	.25
251	A26	24c multicolored	.25	.25
a.		Pair, #250-251	.50	.50
252	A26	48c multicolored	.65	.65
253	A26	48c multicolored	.65	.65
a.		Pair, #252-253	1.30	1.30
		Nos. 246-253 (8)	2.80	2.80

Tourist publicity.

Spinning, by Millet, Flags and ILO Emblem — A27

50th anniv. of the ILO (Etchings by Jean F. Millet, Flags and ILO Emblem): 30c, Threshing. 30c, Flax pulling.

1969, July   Unwmk.   Perf. 13½

254	A27	15c multicolored	.25	.25
255	A27	30c multicolored	.30	.30
256	A27	38c multicolored	.30	.30
		Nos. 254-256 (3)	.85	.85

"Strength in Unity," Bananas and Cacao — A28

"Strength in Unity" Emblem and: 8c, Map of Dominica and Hawker Siddeley 748. 12c, Map of Caribbean. 24c, Ships in harbor.

1969, July   Litho.

257	A28	5c orange & multi	.30	.30
258	A28	8c gray & multi	.30	.30
259	A28	12c lilac & multi	.30	.30
260	A28	24c lt blue & multi	.30	.30
		Nos. 257-260 (4)	1.20	1.20

Caribbean Free Trade Area (CARIFTA).

Gandhi at Spinning Wheel and Big Ben, London — A29

38c, Gandhi, Nehru and Fatehpur Sikri Mausoleum. $1.20, Gandhi & Taj Mahal.

1969, Oct.   Litho.   Perf. 14½

261	A29	6c multicolored	.55	.25
262	A29	38c multicolored	.75	.25
263	A29	$1.20 multicolored	.85	.85
		Nos. 261-263 (3)	2.15	1.35

Mohandas K. Gandhi (1869-1948), leader in India's fight for independence. "Gandhi" is misspelled "Ghandi" on Nos. 261-263.

St. Joseph — A30

Stained Glass Windows, from 17th Century French Churches: 8c, St. John. 12c, St. Peter. 60c, St. Paul.

1969, Nov. 10   Litho.   Perf. 14

264	A30	6c black & multi	.25	.25
265	A30	8c black & multi	.25	.25
266	A30	12c black & multi	.25	.25
267	A30	60c black & multi	.40	.40
		Nos. 264-267 (4)	1.15	1.15

National Day, Nov. 3. Issued in sheets of 16 (4x4) with control numbers and 4 tabs with a patriotic poem by W. O. M. Pond.

Queen Elizabeth II A31

Purplethroated Carib (Hummingbird) A32

2c, Poinsettia. 3c, Red-necked pigeon. 4c, Imperial parrot. 5c, Swallowtail butterfly. 6c, Brown Julia butterfly. 8c, Banana shipment. 10c, Portsmouth Harbor. 12c, Copra processing plant. 15c, Women with straw work. 25c, Timber plant. 30c, Mining pumice. 38c, Cricket, Grammar School. 50c, Roman Catholic Cathedral. 60c, Government headquarters. $1.20, Melville Hall Airport. $2.40, Coat of Arms. $4.80, Queen Elizabeth II.

Perf. 13½

1969, Nov. 26   Unwmk.   Photo.

Chalky Paper

268	A31	½c silver & multi	.25	1.50
269	A32	1c yellow & multi	.75	2.00
270	A32	2c yellow & multi	.25	.25
271	A32	3c yellow & multi	2.50	2.50
272	A32	4c yellow & multi	2.50	2.50
273	A32	5c yellow & multi	2.50	2.50
274	A32	6c brown & multi	2.00	3.50
275	A32	8c brown & multi	.25	.25
276	A32	10c yellow & multi	.25	.25
277	A32	12c citron & multi	.25	.25
278	A32	15c blue & multi	.25	.25
279	A32	25c pink & multi	.25	.25
280	A32	30c olive & multi	1.50	.25
281	A32	38c multicolored	8.50	1.75
282	A32	50c brown & multi	.65	.65

Wmk. Rectangles (334)

Perf. 14

Size: 38x26mm, 26x38mm

283	A32	60c yel & multi	1.00	1.50
284	A32	$1.20 yel & multi	2.00	2.00
285	A32	$2.40 gold & multi	1.50	4.00
286	A31	$4.80 gold & multi	3.00	7.50
		Nos. 268-286 (19)	30.30	33.65

1972   On glazed Paper

268a	A31	½c silver & multi	.30	2.00
269a	A32	1c yellow & multi	1.40	1.50
270a	A32	2c yellow & multi	.50	.50
271a	A32	3c yellow & multi	3.00	1.50
272a	A32	4c yellow & multi	3.00	1.50
273a	A32	5c yellow & multi	2.75	1.25
274a	A32	6c brown & multi	2.75	2.75
275a	A32	8c brown & multi	.45	.60
276a	A32	10c yellow & multi	.35	.25
277a	A32	12c citron & multi	.35	.25
278a	A32	15c blue & multi	.35	.30
279a	A32	25c pink & multi	.30	.25
280a	A32	30c olive & multi	1.50	.65
281a	A32	38c multicolored	8.00	14.00
282a	A32	50c brown & multi	.85	1.25
		Nos. 268a-282a (15)	25.85	28.55

Madonna and Child, by Filippino Lippi — A33

Paintings: 10c, Holy Family with Lamb, by Raphael. 15c, Virgin and Child, by Perugino. $1.20, Madonna of the Rose Hedge, by Botticelli.

Perf. 14½

1969, Dec.   Unwmk.   Litho.

287	A33	6c lt blue & multi	.25	.25
288	A33	10c multicolored	.25	.25
289	A33	15c lilac & multi	.25	.25
290	A33	$1.20 lt grn & multi	.25	.25
a.		Souvenir sheet of 2	1.25	1.25
		Nos. 287-290 (4)	1.00	1.00

Christmas. 290a contains 2 imperf. stamps with simulated perforations similar to Nos. 289-290.

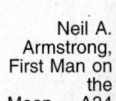

Neil A. Armstrong, First Man on the Moon — A34

Designs: 5c, American flag and astronauts on moon. 8c, Astronauts collecting moon rocks. 30c, Landing module, moon and earth. 50c, Memorial tablet left on moon. 60c, Astronauts Armstrong, Aldrin and Collins.

1970, Feb. 2   Litho.   Perf. 12½

291	A34	½c lilac & multi	.25	.25
292	A34	5c lt blue & multi	.25	.25
293	A34	8c orange & multi	.25	.25
294	A34	30c blue & multi	.25	.25
295	A34	50c red brn & multi	.40	.30
296	A34	60c rose & multi	.50	.45
a.		Souvenir sheet of 4	2.60	2.60
		Nos. 291-296 (6)	1.90	1.75

See note after US No. C76. No. 296a contains 4 stamps similar to Nos. 293-296, but imperf. with simulated perforations.

Giant Green Turtle — A35

Designs: 24c, Flying fish. 38c, Anthurium lily. 60c, Imperial and red-necked parrots.

1970, Sept. 6   Litho.   Perf. 13½x13

297	A35	6c lt green & multi	.50	.50
298	A35	24c multicolored	.65	.65
299	A35	38c green & multi	.75	.75
300	A35	60c yellow & multi	3.50	3.50
a.		Souvenir sheet of 4, #297-300	8.50	8.50
		Nos. 297-300 (4)	5.40	5.40

Women in 18th Century Dress — A36

Natl. Day: 8c, Carib mace & wife leader, 18th cent. $1, Map & flag of Dominica.

1970, Nov. 3   Litho.   Perf. 14

301	A36	5c yellow & multi	.25	.25
302	A36	8c green & multi	.25	.25
303	A36	$1 lt blue & multi	.40	.40
a.		Souv. sheet of 3, #301-303 + 3 labels	1.25	1.50
		Nos. 301-303 (3)	.90	.90

Marley's Ghost — A37

Designs (from A Christmas Carol, by Dickens): 15c, Fezziwig's Ball. 24c, Scrooge and his Nephew's Christmas Party. $1.20, The Ghost of Christmas Present.

1970, Nov. 23   Litho.   Perf. 14x14½

304	A37	2c blue & multi	.25	.25
305	A37	15c multicolored	.25	.25
306	A37	24c red & multi	.25	.25
307	A37	$1.20 multicolored	.75	.75
a.		Souvenir sheet of 4, #304-307	2.75	2.75
		Nos. 304-307 (4)	1.50	1.50

Christmas; Charles Dickens (1812-1970).

Hands and Red Cross — A38

Designs: 8c, The Doctor, by Sir Luke Fildes. 15c, Dominica flag and Red Cross. 50c, The Sick Child, by Edvard Munch.

1970, Dec. 28   Perf. 14½x14

308	A38	8c multicolored	.25	.25
309	A38	10c multicolored	.25	.25
310	A38	15c multicolored	.25	.25
311	A38	50c multicolored	.50	.50
a.		Souvenir sheet of 4, #308-311	2.00	2.00
		Nos. 308-311 (4)	1.25	1.25

Centenary of the British Red Cross Society.

Marigot Primary School — A39

Education Year Emblem and: 8c, Goodwill Junior High School. 14c, University of the West Indies. $1, Trinity College, Cambridge, England.

1971, Mar. 1   Litho.   Perf. 13½

312	A39	5c multicolored	.25	.25
313	A39	8c multicolored	.25	.25
314	A39	14c multicolored	.25	.25
315	A39	$1 multicolored	.45	.45
a.		Souvenir sheet of 2, #314-315	1.50	1.50
		Nos. 312-315 (4)	1.20	1.20

International Education Year.

Waterfall and Bird-of-Paradise Flower — A40

Tourist Publicity: 10c, Boat building. 30c, Sailboat along North Coast. 50c, Speed boat and steamer.

1971, Mar. 22   Perf. 13½x14

316	A40	5c multicolored	.25	.25
317	A40	10c multicolored	.25	.25
318	A40	30c multicolored	.25	.25
319	A40	50c multicolored	.35	.35
a.		Souvenir sheet of 4, #316-319	1.10	1.10
		Nos. 316-319 (4)	1.10	1.10

UNICEF Emblem, Letter "D" — A41

1971, June 14   Litho.   Perf. 14

320	A41	5c multicolored	.25	.25
321	A41	10c multicolored	.25	.25
322	A41	38c multicolored	.25	.25
323	A41	$1.20 multicolored	.25	.25
a.		Souvenir sheet of 2, #321, 323	.85	.85
		Nos. 320-323 (4)	1.00	1.00

25th anniv. of UNICEF.

Boy Scout, Jamboree Emblem, Torii, Camp and Mt. Fuji — A42

24c, British Scout, flag. 30c, Japanese Scout, flag. $1, Dominican Scout, flag.

1971, Oct. 18   Unwmk.   Perf. 11

324	A42	20c bister & multi	.25	.25
325	A42	24c green & multi	.30	.30
326	A42	30c red lilac & multi	.40	.40

327	A42	$1 blue & multi	.80	.80
a.		Souvenir sheet of 2, #326-327	1.75	1.75
		Nos. 324-327 (4)	1.75	1.75

13th Boy Scout World Jamboree, Asagiri Plain, Japan, Aug. 2-10.

Boats at
Portsmouth
A43

15c, Carnival street scene. 20c, $1.20, Anthea Mondesire, Carifta Queen. 50c, Rock of Atkinson.

Perf. 13½x14, 14x13½

1971, Nov. 15			Litho.
328	A43	8c multi	.25 .25
329	A43	15c multi	.25 .25
330	A43	20c multi, vert.	.25 .25
331	A43	50c multi, vert.	.25 .25
		Nos. 328-331 (4)	1.00 1.00

Souvenir Sheet
Perf. 15

332	A43	$1.20 multi, vert.	.85	.85

National Day.

First Dominica
Coin, 8 Reals,
1761 — A44

Early Dominica Coins: 30c, Eleven and 3-bit pieces, 1798. 35c, Two-real coin, 1770, vert. 50c, Three "mocos" and piece of 8, 1798.

1972, Feb. 7			Litho.	Perf. 14
333	A44	10c violet, silver & blk	.25	.25
334	A44	30c green, silver & blk	.25	.25
335	A44	35c ultra, silver & blk	.25	.25
336	A44	50c red, silver & blk	.25	.25
a.		Souvenir sheet of 2, #335-336	1.00	1.00
		Nos. 333-336 (4)	1.00	1.00

Margin of No. 336a inscribed "Christmas 1971."

Common
Opossum,
Environment
Emblem — A45

Environment Emblem and: 35c, Agouti. 60c, Oncidium papillo (orchid). $1.20, Hibiscus.

1972, June 5				
337	A45	½c yel grn & multi	.25	.25
338	A45	35c org brn & multi	.30	.30
339	A45	60c lt blue & multi	2.25	2.25
340	A45	$1.20 yellow & multi	1.75	1.75
a.		Souvenir sheet of 4, #337-340	6.75	6.75
		Nos. 337-340 (4)	4.55	4.55

UN Conf. on Human Environment, Stockholm, June 5-16.

100-meter
Sprint, Olympic
Rings — A46

Olympic Rings and: 35m, 400-meter hurdles. 58c, Hammer throw, vert. 72c, Broad jump, vert.

1972, Oct. 9			Litho.	Perf. 14
341	A46	30c dp org & multi	.25	.25
342	A46	35c blue & multi	.25	.25
343	A46	58c lilac rose & multi	.30	.30
344	A46	72c yel green & multi	.40	.40
a.		Souv. sheet of 4, #341-344, perf. 15	1.25	1.25
		Nos. 341-344 (4)	1.20	1.20

20th Olympic Games, Munich, Aug. 26-Sept. 11.

General Post
Office — A47

1972, Nov. 1			Perf. 13½
345	A47	10c shown	.25 .25
346	A47	20c Morne Diablotin Mountain	.25 .25
347	A47	30c Rodney's Rock	.25 .25
a.		Souv. sheet of #346-347, perf. 15	.60 .60
		Nos. 345-347 (3)	.75 .75

National Day.

Adoration of the
Shepherds, by
Caravaggio — A48

Paintings: 14c, Madonna and Child, by Rubens. 30c, Madonna and Child, with St. Anne by Orazio Gentileschi. $1, Adoration of the Kings, by Jan Mostaert. (On 8c, painting is mistakenly attributed to Boccaccino, according to Fine Arts Philatelist.)

1972, Dec. 4.				
348	A48	8c gold & multi	.25	.25
349	A48	14c gold & multi	.25	.25
350	A48	30c gold & multi	.25	.25
351	A48	$1 gold & multi	.35	.35
a.		Souvenir sheet of 2	1.10	1.10
		Nos. 348-351 (4)	1.10	1.10

Christmas. No. 351a contains one each of Nos. 350-351 with simulated perforations.

Silver Wedding Issue, 1972
Common Design Type

Design: Queen Elizabeth II, Prince Philip, bananas, sisseron parrot.

Perf. 14x14½

1972, Nov. 13		Photo.	Wmk. 314
352	CD324	5c olive & multi	.25 .25
353	CD324	$1 multicolored	.40 .40

See note after Antigua No. 296.

Launching of Tiros
Weather
Satellite — A49

1c, Nimbus satellite. 2c, Radiosonde balloon & equipment. 30c, Radarscope. 35c, General circulation of atmosphere. 50c, Picture of hurricane transmitted by satellite. $1, Computer weather map. 30c, 35c, 50c, $1, horiz.

Perf. 14½

1973, July 16		Unwmk.	Litho.
354	A49	½c black & multi	.25 .25
355	A49	1c black & multi	.25 .25
356	A49	2c black & multi	.25 .25
357	A49	30c black & multi	.25 .25
358	A49	35c black & multi	.25 .25
359	A49	50c black & multi	.30 .30
360	A49	$1 black & multi	.55 .55
a.		Souvenir sheet of 2, #359-360	1.40 1.40
		Nos. 354-360 (7)	2.10 2.10

Intl. meteorological cooperation, cent.

Going to the
Hospital — A50

WHO Emblem and: 1c, Maternity and infant care. 2c, Inoculation against smallpox. 30c, Emergency service. 35c, Waiting patients. 50c, Examination. $1, Traveling physician.

1973, Aug. 20		Unwmk.	Perf. 14½
361	A50	½c lt blue & multi	.25 .25
362	A50	1c gray grn & multi	.25 .25
363	A50	2c yellow & multi	.25 .25
364	A50	30c lt vio & multi	.25 .25
365	A50	35c yel grn & multi	.30 .30
366	A50	50c multicolored	.30 .30
367	A50	$1 bister & multi	.45 .45
a.		Souvenir sheet of 2, #366-367, perf. 14x14½	1.25 1.25
		Nos. 361-367 (7)	2.05 2.05

WHO, 25th anniv. No. 367a exists perf. 14½.

Cyrique Crab — A51

1973, Oct.				
368	A51	½c shown	.25	.25
369	A51	22c Blue land crab	.35	.35
370	A51	25c Breadfruit	.45	.45
371	A51	$1.20 Sunflower	1.00	1.00
a.		Souvenir sheet of 4, #368-371	2.75	2.75
		Nos. 368-371 (4)	2.05	2.05

Princess
Anne and
Mark
Phillips — A52

1973, Nov. 14			Perf. 13½
372	A52	25c salmon & multi	.25 .25
373	A52	$2 blue & multi	.60 .60
a.		Souv. sheet of 2 (75c, $1.20)	.60 .60

Wedding of Princess Anne and Capt. Mark Phillips.

Nos. 372-373 were issued in sheets of 5 + label. No. 373a contains 2 stamps of type A52: 75c in colors of the 25c, and $1.20 in colors of the $2.

Nativity, by
Brueghel — A53

Paintings of the Nativity by: 1c, Botticelli. 2c, Dürer. 12c, Botticelli. 22c, Rubens. 35c, Dürer. $1, Giorgione (inscribed "Giorgeone").

1973		Unwmk.	Perf. 14½x15
374	A53	½c gray & multi	.25 .25
375	A53	1c gray & multi	.25 .25
376	A53	2c gray & multi	.25 .25
377	A53	12c gray & multi	.25 .25
378	A53	22c gray & multi	.25 .25
379	A53	35c gray & multi	.25 .25
380	A53	$1 gray & multi	.60 .60
a.		Souvenir sheet of 2	1.30 1.30
		Nos. 374-380 (7)	2.10 2.10

Christmas. No. 380a contains one each of Nos. 379-380 in changed colors.

Carib Basket
Weaving
A54

Designs: 10c, Staircase of the Snake. 50c, Miss Caribbean Queen, Kathleen Telemacque, vert. 60c, Miss Carifta Queen, Esther Fadelle, vert. $1, La Jeune Etoile Dancers.

1973, Dec. 17		Perf. 13½x14, 14x13½		
381	A54	5c buff & multi	.25	.25
382	A54	10c multicolored	.25	.25
383	A54	50c multicolored	.25	.25
384	A54	60c multicolored	.25	.25
385	A54	$1 multicolored	.25	.25
a.		Souv. sheet of 3, #381-382, 385	.75	.75
		Nos. 381-385 (5)	1.25	1.25

National Day.

U.W.I. Center,
Dominica
A55

30c, Graduation. $1, University coat of arms.

1974, Jan. 21		Litho.	Perf. 13½x14
386	A55	12c dp orange & multi	.25 .25
387	A55	30c violet & multi	.25 .25
388	A55	$1 multicolored	.35 .35
a.		Souvenir sheet of 3, #386-388	.50 .50
		Nos. 386-388 (3)	.85 .85

University of the West Indies, 25th anniv.

Dominica No. 1
and Map of
Island — A56

Designs: 1c, 50c, No. 8 and post horn. 2c, $1.20, No. 9 and coat of arms. 10c, Like ½c.

1974, May 4			Litho.	Perf. 14½
389	A56	½c brt pur & multi	.25	.25
390	A56	1c salmon & multi	.25	.25
391	A56	2c ultra & multi	.25	.25
392	A56	10c violet & multi	.25	.25
393	A56	50c yel grn & multi	.40	.40
394	A56	$1.20 rose & multi	.65	.65
a.		Souv. sheet of #392-394, perf. 15	1.60	1.60
		Nos. 389-394 (6)	2.05	2.05

Centenary of Dominican postage stamps.

Soccer Player and Cup,
Brazilian Flag — A57

Soccer cup, various players and flags: 1c, Germany, Fed. Rep. 2c, Italy. 30c, Scotland. 40c, Sweden. 50c, Netherlands. $1, Yugoslavia.

1974, July			Litho.	Perf. 14½
395	A57	½c shown	.25	.25
396	A57	1c multicolored	.25	.25
397	A57	2c multicolored	.25	.25
398	A57	30c multicolored	.25	.25
399	A57	40c multicolored	.30	.30
400	A57	50c multicolored	.75	.75
401	A57	$1 multicolored	1.10	1.10
a.		Souvenir sheet of 2, #400-401, perf. 13½	1.25	1.25
		Nos. 395-401 (7)	3.15	3.15

World Cup Soccer Championship, Munich, June 13-July 7.

Indian
Hole — A58

40c, Teachers' Training College. $1, Petite Savane Co-operative Bay Oil Distillery.

1974, Nov. 1		Litho.	Perf. 13½x14
402	A58	10c multicolored	.25 .25
403	A58	40c multicolored	.25 .25
404	A58	$1 multicolored	.50 .50
a.		Souvenir sheet of 3, #402-404	.80 .80
		Nos. 402-404 (3)	1.00 1.00

Churchill at Race
Track — A59

Sir Winston Churchill (1874-1965): 1c, with Gen. Eisenhower. 2c, with Franklin D. Roosevelt. 20c, as First Lord of the Admiralty. 45c, painting outdoors. $2, giving "V" sign.

1974, Nov. 25		Litho.	Perf. 14½
405	A59	½c multicolored	.25 .25
406	A59	1c multicolored	.25 .25
407	A59	2c multicolored	.25 .25
408	A59	20c multicolored	.25 .25
409	A59	45c multicolored	.25 .25
410	A59	$2 multicolored	.50 .50
a.		Souvenir sheet of 2, #409-410, perf. 13½	1.25 1.25
		Nos. 405-410 (6)	1.75 1.75

Virgin and Child, by
Oronzo Tiso — A60

Paintings (Virgin and Child): 1c, by Lorenzo Costa. 2c, by unknown Master. 10c, by G. F. Romanelli. 25c, Holy Family, by G. S. da Sermoneta. 45c, Adoration of the Shepherds, by Guido Reni. $1, Adoration of the Kings, by Cristoforo Caselli.

1974, Dec. 16   Litho.   Perf. 14

411	A60	½c multicolored	.25	.25
412	A60	1c multicolored	.25	.25
413	A60	2c multicolored	.25	.25
414	A60	10c multicolored	.25	.25
415	A60	25c multicolored	.25	.25
416	A60	45c multicolored	.35	.25
417	A60	$1 multicolored	.65	.50
a.		Souvenir sheet of 2, #416-417	1.10	1.10
		Nos. 411-417 (7)	2.25	2.00

Christmas.

Seamail, "Orinoco," 1851, and "Geesthaven," 1966 — A61

Cent. of UPU: $2, $2.40, Airmail, De Havilland 4, 1918, and Boeing 747, 1974.

1974, Dec. 4   Litho.   Perf. 13½

418	A61	10c multicolored	.25	.25
419	A61	$2 multicolored	1.25	1.25

Souvenir Sheet

419A		Sheet of 2	1.50	1.50
b.	A61	$1.20 multicolored	.45	.45
c.	A61	$2.40 multicolored	.90	.90

Nos. 418-419 were each printed in sheets of 50 and 5 + label.

Oldwife — A62

1c, Ocyurus chrysurus. 2c, Blue marlin. 3c, Swordfish. 20c, Great barracuda. $2, Grouper.

1975, June 2   Litho.   Perf. 14½

421	A62	½c shown	.25	.25
422	A62	1c multicolored	.25	.25
423	A62	2c multicolored	.25	.25
424	A62	3c multicolored	.25	.25
425	A62	20c multicolored	.90	.90
426	A62	$2 multicolored	2.75	2.75
a.		Souvenir sheet, perf. 13½	4.00	4.00
		Nos. 421-426 (6)	4.65	4.65

Myscelia Antholia — A63

Butterflies: 1c, Lycorea ceres. 2c, Siderone nemesis. 6c, Battus polydamas. 30c, Anartia lytrea. 40c, Morpho peleides. $2, Dryas Julia.

1975, July 28   Litho.   Perf. 14½

427	A63	½c shown	.25	.25
428	A63	1c multicolored	.25	.25
429	A63	2c multicolored	.25	.25
430	A63	6c multicolored	.75	.75
431	A63	30c multicolored	1.50	1.00
432	A63	40c multicolored	1.50	1.00
433	A63	$2 multicolored	2.25	6.75
a.		Souvenir sheet, perf. 13½	4.00	4.00
		Nos. 427-433 (7)	6.75	10.25

Royal Mail Ship Yare — A64

Ships Tied in with Dominican History: 1c, Royal mail ship Thames. 2c, Canadian National S.S. Lady Nelson. 20c, C.N. S.S. Lady Rodney. 45c, Harrison Line M.V. Statesman. 50c, Geest Line M.V. Geestcape. $2, Geest Line M.V. Geeststar.

1975, Sept. 1   Perf. 14

434	A64	½c black & multi	.40	.35
435	A64	1c black & multi	.40	.35
436	A64	2c black & multi	.45	.40
437	A64	20c black & multi	1.25	.60
438	A64	45c black & multi	1.50	.80
439	A64	50c black & multi	1.50	1.00
440	A64	$2 black & multi	2.50	4.50
a.		Souvenir sheet of 2, #439-440	4.00	4.00
		Nos. 434-440 (7)	8.00	8.00

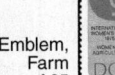

IWY Emblem, Farm Women — A65

$2, IWY emblem, dressmaker & saleswoman.

1975, Oct. 30   Litho.   Perf. 14

441	A65	10c pink & multi	.25	.25
442	A65	$2 yellow & multi	.65	.65

International Women's Year.

Public Library — A66

5c, Miss Caribbean Queen 1975. 30c, Citrus factory. $1, National Day Cup.

1975, Nov. 6

443	A66	5c multi, vert.	.25	.25
444	A66	10c multi	.25	.25
445	A66	30c multi	.25	.25
446	A66	$1 multi, vert.	.40	.40
a.		Souvenir sheet of 3	.90	.90
		Nos. 443-446 (4)	1.15	1.15

National Day. No. 446a contains 3 stamps similar to Nos. 444-446 with simulated perforations.

Virgin and Child, by Mantegna — A67

Christmas: Paintings of the Virgin and Child.

1975, Nov. 24

447	A67	½c shown	.25	.25
448	A67	1c Fra Filippo Lippi	.25	.25
449	A67	2c Bellini	.25	.25
450	A67	10c Botticelli	.25	.25
451	A67	25c Bellini	.25	.25
452	A67	45c Correggio	.25	.25
453	A67	$1 Durer	.50	.50
a.		Souvenir sheet of 2, #452-453	1.25	1.25
		Nos. 447-453 (7)	2.00	2.00

Hibiscus — A68   Queen Elizabeth II — A69

Designs: 1c, African tulip. 2c, Castor oil tree. 3c, White cedar flower. 4c, Eggplant. 5c, Garfish. 6c, Okra. 8c, Zenaida doves. 10c, Screw pine. 20c, Mangoes. 25c, Crayfish. 30c, Manicou. 40c, Bay leaf groves. 50c, Tomatoes. $1, Lime factory. $2, Rum distillery. $5, Bay oil distillery.

1975, Dec. 8   Litho.   Perf. 14½

454	A68	½c ultra & multi	.25	.80
455	A68	1c lilac & multi	.25	.80
456	A68	2c orange & multi	.25	.80
457	A68	3c multicolored	.25	.80
458	A68	4c pink & multi	.25	.80
459	A68	5c multicolored	.25	.80
460	A68	6c gray & multi	.25	1.00
461	A68	8c multicolored	3.25	1.10
462	A68	10c violet & multi	.25	.25
a.		Perf. 13½	30.00	—
463	A68	20c yellow & multi	.35	.25
464	A68	25c lemon & multi	.40	.25
465	A68	30c salmon & multi	.85	.80
466	A68	40c multicolored	.85	.80
467	A68	50c red & multi	.50	.50
468	A68	$1 citron & multi	.75	.25
469	A68	$2 multicolored	1.30	3.25
470	A68	$5 multicolored	1.60	5.00

Perf. 14

471	A69	$10 blue & multi	2.25	14.50
		Nos. 454-471 (18)	14.10	33.15

Nos. 454-465 measure 38½mm x 25mm; nos. 466-470 measure 44½mm x 28mm. For overprints see Nos. 584-601, 640-643. All except 3c and 25c exist imperf.

American Infantry — A70

Designs: 1c, English three-decker, 1782. 2c, George Washington. 45c, English sailors. 75c, English ensign with regimental flag. $2, Admiral Hood. All designs have old maps in background.

1976, Apr. 12   Litho.   Perf. 14½

472	A70	½c green & multi	.25	.25
473	A70	1c purple & multi	.25	.25
474	A70	2c orange & multi	.25	.25
475	A70	45c brown & multi	.45	.25
476	A70	75c ultra & multi	.75	.75
477	A70	$2 red & multi	.90	1.50
a.		Souvenir sheet of 2	2.75	2.75
		Nos. 472-477 (6)	2.85	3.25

American Bicentennial. No. 477a contains 2 stamps similar to Nos. 476-477, perf. 13.

Rowing — A71

1c, Shot put. 2c, Swimming. 40c, Relay race. 45c, Gymnastics. 60c, Sailing. $2, Archery.

1976, May 24   Litho.   Perf. 14½

478	A71	½c ocher & multi	.25	.25
479	A71	1c ocher & multi	.25	.25
480	A71	2c ocher & multi	.25	.25
481	A71	40c ocher & multi	.25	.25
482	A71	45c ocher & multi	.25	.25
483	A71	60c ocher & multi	.25	.25
484	A71	$2 ocher & multi	.65	.65
a.		Souv. sheet of 2, #483-484, perf 13	1.75	1.75
		Nos. 478-484 (7)	2.15	2.15

21st Olympic Games, Montreal, Canada, July 17-Aug. 1.

Ringed Kingfisher — A72

Birds: 1c, Mourning dove. 2c, Green heron. 15c, Broad-winged hawk. 30c, Blue-headed hummingbird. 45c, Banana-quit. $2, Imperial parrot. 15c, 30c, 45c, $2, vert.

1976, June 28

485	A72	½c multicolored	.25	.25
486	A72	1c multicolored	.25	.25
487	A72	2c multicolored	.25	.25
488	A72	15c multicolored	.90	.90
489	A72	30c multicolored	1.25	1.25
490	A72	45c multicolored	1.50	1.50
491	A72	$2 multicolored	3.00	3.00
a.		Souv. sheet of 3, #489-491, perf. 13	7.00	7.00
		Nos. 485-491 (7)	7.40	7.40

Map of West Indies, Bats, Wicket and Ball — A72a

Prudential Cup — A72b

1976, July 26   Litho.   Perf. 14

492	A72a	15c lt blue & multi	.45	.45
493	A72b	25c lilac rose & black	.85	.85

World Cricket Cup, won by West Indies Team, 1975.

Viking Spacecraft — A73

1c, Titan launch center, horiz. 2c, Titan 3-D & Centaur D-IT. 3c, Orbiter & landing capsule. 45c, Capsule with closed parachute. 75c, Capsule with open parachute. $1, Landing capsule descending on Mars, horiz. $2, Viking on Mars, horiz.

1976, Sept. 20   Litho.   Perf. 15

494	A73	½c multicolored	.25	.25
495	A73	1c multicolored	.25	.25
496	A73	2c multicolored	.25	.25
497	A73	3c multicolored	.25	.25
498	A73	45c multicolored	.25	.25
499	A73	75c multicolored	.30	.30
500	A73	$1 multicolored	.35	.35
501	A73	$2 multicolored	.60	.60
a.		Souvenir sheet of 2, #500, 501, perf. 13½	1.75	1.75
		Nos. 494-501 (8)	2.50	2.50

Viking mission to Mars.

Virgin and Child, by Giorgione — A74

Virgin and Child by: 1c, Bellini. 2c, Mantegna. 6c, Mantegna. 25c, Memling. 45c, 50c, Correggio. $1, $3, Raphael.

1976, Nov. 1   Litho.   Perf. 14

502	A74	½c multicolored	.25	.25
503	A74	1c multicolored	.25	.25
504	A74	2c multicolored	.25	.25
505	A74	6c multicolored	.25	.25
506	A74	25c multicolored	.25	.25
507	A74	45c multicolored	.25	.25
508	A74	$3 multicolored	.60	.60
		Nos. 502-508 (7)	2.10	2.10

Souvenir Sheet

509		Sheet of 2	1.10	1.10
a.	A74	50c multicolored	.35	.35
b.	A74	$1 multicolored	.75	.75

Christmas.

Island Craft Co-operative A75

National Day: 50c, Banana harvest, Castle Bruce Co-operative. $1, Banana shipping plant, Bourne Farmers' Co-operative.

1976, Nov. 22   Litho.   Perf. 13½x14

510	A75	10c multicolored	.25	.25
511	A75	50c multicolored	.25	.25
512	A75	$1 multicolored	.30	.30
a.		Souvenir sheet of 3, #510-512	.75	.75
		Nos. 510-512 (3)	.80	.80

Common Sundial — A76

Sea Shells: 1c, Flame helmet. 2c, Mouse cone. 20c, Caribbean vase. 40c, West Indian fighting conch. 50c, Short coral shell. $2, Long-spined star shell. $3, Apple murex.

1976, Dec. 20   Litho.   Perf. 14

513	A76	½c black & multi	.25	.25
514	A76	1c black & multi	.25	.25
515	A76	2c black & multi	.25	.25

516	A76	20c black & multi	.30	.25
517	A76	40c black & multi	.55	.45
518	A76	50c black & multi	.60	.50
519	A76	$3 black & multi	2.25	2.25

Nos. 513-519 (7)   4.45 4.20

Souvenir Sheet

520 A76 $2 black & multi   2.00 2.00

Queen Enthroned A77

Designs: 1c, Imperial crown. 45c, Elizabeth II and Princess Anne. $2, Coronation ring. $2.50, Ampulla and spoon. $5, Royal visit to Dominica.

1977, Feb. 7   Perf. 14

521	A77	½c multicolored	.25	.25
522	A77	1c multicolored	.25	.25
523	A77	45c multicolored	.25	.25
524	A77	$2 multicolored	.35	.35
525	A77	$2.50 multicolored	.50	.50

Nos. 521-525 (5)   1.60 1.60

Souvenir Sheet

526 A77 $5 multicolored   1.40 1.40

25th anniv. of the reign of Elizabeth II. Nos. 521-525 were printed in sheets of 40 (4x10), perf. 14, and sheets of 5 plus label, perf. 12, in changed colors.
For overprints see Nos. 549-554.

Joseph Haydn — A78

Designs: 1c, Fidelio, act I, scene IV. 2c, Dancer Maria Casentini. 15c, Beethoven working on Pastoral Symphony. 30c, "Wellington's Victory." 40c, Soprano Henriette Sontag. $2, Young Beethoven.

1977, Apr. 25   Litho.   Perf. 14

527	A78	½c multicolored	.25	.25
528	A78	1c multicolored	.25	.25
529	A78	2c multicolored	.25	.25
530	A78	15c multicolored	.50	.50
531	A78	30c multicolored	.50	.50
532	A78	40c multicolored	.50	.50
533	A78	$2 multicolored	1.60	1.60
a.	Souvenir sheet of 3, #531-533		2.60	2.60

Nos. 527-533 (7)   3.85 3.85

Ludwig van Beethoven (1770-1827), composer.

Boy Scouts on Hike — A79

Saluting Boy Scout and: 1c, First aid. 2c, Scouts setting up camp. 45c, Rock climbing. 50c, Kayaking. 75c, Map reading. $2, Campfire. $3, Sailing.

1977, Aug. 8   Litho.   Perf. 14

534	A79	½c multicolored	.25	.25
535	A79	1c multicolored	.25	.25
536	A79	2c multicolored	.25	.25
537	A79	45c multicolored	.35	.35
538	A79	50c multicolored	.50	.50
539	A79	$3 multicolored	2.00	2.00

Nos. 534-539 (6)   3.60 3.60

Souvenir Sheet

540		Sheet of 2	1.90	1.90
a.	A79	75c multicolored	.55	.55
b.	A79	$2 multicolored	1.35	1.35

6th Caribbean Jamboree, Kingston, Jamaica, Aug. 5-14.

Nativity — A80

Christmas: 1c, Annunciation to the Shepherds. 2c, 45c, Presentation at the Temple (different). 6c, $2, $3, Flight into Egypt (different). 15c, Adoration of the Kings. 50c, Virgin

and Child with Angels. ½c to 45c are illustrations from De Lisle Psalter, 14th century. 50c, $2, $3 are from other Psalters.

1977, Nov. 14   Litho.   Perf. 14

541	A80	½c multicolored	.25	.25
542	A80	1c multicolored	.25	.25
543	A80	2c multicolored	.25	.25
544	A80	6c multicolored	.25	.25
545	A80	15c multicolored	.25	.25
546	A80	45c multicolored	.35	.35
547	A80	$3 multicolored	.85	.85

Nos. 541-547 (7)   2.45 2.45

Souvenir Sheet

548		Sheet of 2	1.35	1.35
a.	A80	50c multicolored	.25	.25
b.	A80	$2 multicolored	1.10	1.10

Nos. 521-526 Overprinted

1977, Nov. 24   Litho.   Perf. 12, 14

549	A77	½c multicolored	.25	.25
550	A77	1c multicolored	.25	.25
551	A77	45c multicolored	.25	.25
552	A77	$2 multicolored	.40	.40
553	A77	$2.50 multicolored	.45	.45

Nos. 549-553 (5)   1.60 1.60

Souvenir Sheet
Perf. 14

554 A77 $5 multicolored   1.10 1.10

Caribbean visit of Queen Elizabeth II. Nos. 549-550 are perf. 12, others perf. 12 and 14.
Two types of No. 554: I. Overprinted only on stamp. II. Overprinted "W.I. 1977" on stamp and "Royal Visit W.I. 1977" on margin.

Masqueraders A81

Designs: 1c, Sensay costume. 2c, Street musicians. 45c, Douiette band. 50c, Pappy Show wedding. $2, $2.50, Masquerade band.

1978, Jan. 9   Perf. 14

555	A81	½c multicolored	.25	.25
556	A81	1c multicolored	.25	.25
557	A81	2c multicolored	.25	.25
558	A81	45c multicolored	.25	.25
559	A81	50c multicolored	.30	.30
560	A81	$2 multicolored	.50	.50

Nos. 555-560 (6)   1.80 1.80

Souvenir Sheet

561 A81 $2.50 multicolored   1.50 1.50

History of Carnival.

Lindbergh and Spirit of St. Louis — A82

Designs: 10c, Spirit of St. Louis take-off, Long Island, May 20, 1927. 15c, Lindbergh and map of route New York to Paris. 20c, Lindbergh and plane in Paris. 40c, 1st Zeppelin, trial over Lake Constance. 50c, Spirit of St. Louis. 60c, Count Zeppelin and Zeppelin LZ-2, 1906. $2, Graf Zeppelin, 1928. $3, LZ-127, 1928.

1978, Mar. 13   Litho.   Perf. 14½

562	A82	6c multicolored	.25	.25
563	A82	10c multicolored	.25	.25
564	A82	15c multicolored	.30	.30
565	A82	20c multicolored	.40	.40
566	A82	40c multicolored	.60	.60
567	A82	60c multicolored	.85	.85
568	A82	$3 multicolored	2.25	2.25

Nos. 562-568 (7)   4.90 4.90

Souvenir Sheet

569		Sheet of 2	2.00	2.00
a.	A82	60c multicolored	.40	.40
b.	A82	$2 multicolored	1.60	1.60

Charles A. Lindbergh's solo transatlantic flight from New York to Paris, 50th anniv., and flights of Graf Zeppelin.

Royal Family on Balcony — A83

Designs: 45c, Coronation. $2.50, Elizabeth II and Prince Philip. $5, Elizabeth II.

1978, June 2   Litho.   Perf. 14

570	A83	45c multicolored	.25	.25
571	A83	$2 multicolored	.45	.45
572	A83	$2.50 multicolored	.55	.55

Nos. 570-572 (3)   1.25 1.25

Souvenir Sheet

573 A83 $5 multicolored   1.00 1.00

Coronation of Queen Elizabeth II, 25th anniv. Nos. 570-572 were issued in sheets of 50, and in sheets of 3 stamps and label, in changed colors, perf. 12.

Wright Plane Coming out of Hangar — A84

Designs: 40c, 1908 plane. 60c, Flyer I gliding. $2, Flyer I taking off. $3, Wilbur and Orville Wright and Flyer I.

1978, July 10   Litho.   Perf. 14½

574	A84	30c multicolored	.25	.25
575	A84	40c multicolored	.25	.25
576	A84	60c multicolored	.30	.30
577	A84	$2 multicolored	1.25	1.25

Nos. 574-577 (4)   2.05 2.05

Souvenir Sheet

578 A84 $3 multicolored   1.75 1.75

75th anniv. of first powered flight.
A set of 30 stamps embossed on gold foil exists. Value, $400.

Two Apostles, by Rubens — A85

Rubens Paintings: 45c, Descent from the Cross. 50c, St. Ildefonso Receiving Chasuble. $2, Holy Family. $3, Assumption of the Virgin.

1978, Oct. 16   Litho.   Perf. 14

579	A85	20c multicolored	.25	.25
580	A85	45c multicolored	.25	.25
581	A85	50c multicolored	.25	.25
582	A85	$3 multicolored	.90	.90

Nos. 579-582 (4)   1.65 1.65

Souvenir Sheet

583 A85 $2 multicolored   1.00 1.00

Christmas.

Nos. 454-471 Overprinted

1978 Nov. 1   Litho.   Perf. 14½

584	A68	½c ultra & multi	.25	.25
585	A68	1c lilac & multi	.25	.25
586	A68	2c orange & multi	.30	.25
587	A68	3c multicolored	.30	.25
588	A68	4c pink & multi	.30	.25
589	A68	5c multicolored	.30	.25
590	A68	6c gray & multi	.35	
591	A68	8c multicolored	3.00	.25
592	A68	10c violet & multi	1.00	.25
a.	Perf. 13½ ('79)		.50	.25
593	A68	20c yellow & multi	.60	.25
594	A68	25c lemon & multi	.65	.25
595	A68	30c salmon & multi	.70	.30
596	A68	40c multicolored	.70	.55
597	A68	50c red & multi	.75	.75
598	A68	$1 citron & multi	.80	1.40
599	A68	$2 multicolored	1.50	2.75
600	A68	$5 multicolored	2.00	5.50

Perf. 14

601	A69	$10 blue & multi	3.00	12.50

Nos. 584-601 (18)   16.75 26.50

Map of Dominica with Parishes — A86

25c, Sabinea carinalis, natl. flower, & map. 45c, New flag & map. 50c, Coat of arms & map. $2, Prime Minister Patrick John.

1978, Nov. 1   Perf. 14

602	A86	10c multicolored	.75	.40
603	A86	25c multicolored	.55	.25
604	A86	45c multicolored	1.50	.35
605	A86	50c multicolored	.65	.35
606	A86	$2 multicolored	1.50	2.75

Nos. 602-606 (5)   4.95 4.10

Souvenir Sheet

607 A86 $2.50 multicolored   2.60 2.60

Dominican independence.

Rowland Hill — A87

45c, Great Britain #2. 50c, Dominica #1. $2, Maltese Cross handstamps. $5, Penny Black.

1979, Mar. 19

608	A87	25c multicolored	.25	.25
609	A87	45c multicolored	.25	.25
610	A87	50c multicolored	.25	.25
611	A87	$2 multicolored	.35	.35

Nos. 608-611 (4)   1.10 1.10

Souvenir Sheet

612 A87 $5 multicolored   1.40 1.40

Sir Rowland Hill (1795-1879), originator of penny postage.
Nos. 608-611 printed in sheets of 5 plus label, perf. 12x12½, in changed colors.
For overprints see Nos. 663A-663D.

Boys and Dugout Canoe — A88

IYC Emblem and: 40c, Children carrying bananas. 50c, Boys playing cricket. $3, Child feeding rabbits. $5, Boy showing catch of fish.

1979, Apr. 23   Litho.   Perf. 14

613	A88	30c multicolored	.30	.30
614	A88	40c multicolored	.45	.45
615	A88	50c multicolored	.50	.50
616	A88	$3 multicolored	2.00	2.00

Nos. 613-616 (4)   3.25 3.25

Souvenir Sheet

617 A88 $5 multicolored   2.00 2.00

Grouper — A89

30c, Striped dolphin. 50c, White-tailed tropic birds. 60c, Brown pelicans. $1, Pilot whale. $2, Brown booby. $3, Elkhorn coral.

1979, May 21   Litho.   Perf. 14

618	A89	10c multicolored	.50	.25
619	A89	30c multicolored	1.00	.50
620	A89	50c multicolored	1.75	.75
621	A89	60c multicolored	2.00	2.00
622	A89	$1 multicolored	2.50	2.50
623	A89	$2 multicolored	4.25	4.25

Nos. 618-623 (6)   12.00 10.25

Souvenir Sheet

624 A89 $3 multicolored   2.75 2.75

Wildlife protection.

Capt. Cook, Bark
Endeavour
A90

Capt. Cook and: 50c, Resolution, map of
2nd voyage. 60c, Discovery, map of 3rd voyage. $2, Cook's map of New Zealand, 1770.
$5, Portrait.

1979, July 16   Litho.   *Perf. 14*
625 A90 10c multicolored .60 .40
626 A90 50c multicolored 1.00 1.00
627 A90 60c multicolored 1.25 1.25
628 A90 $2 multicolored 1.50 *2.50*
   Nos. 625-628 (4) 4.35 5.15
Souvenir Sheet
629 A90 $5 multicolored 2.00 2.00
200th death anniv. of Capt. James Cook
(1728-1779).

Girl Guides
Cooking — A91

Girl Guides: 20c, Setting up emergency rain
tent. 50c, Raising flag of independent Dominica. $2.50, Playing accordion and singing. $3,
Leader and Guides of different ages.

1979, July 30
630 A91 10c multicolored .25 .25
631 A91 20c multicolored .25 .25
632 A91 50c multicolored .30 .30
633 A91 $2.50 multicolored 1.25 1.25
   Nos. 630-633 (4) 2.05 2.05
Souvenir Sheet
634 A91 $3 multicolored 1.50 1.50
50th anniv. of Dominican Girl Guides.

Colvillea — A92

Flowering Trees: 40c, Lignum vitae. 60c,
Dwarf poinciana. $2, Fern tree. $3, Perfume
tree.

1979, Sept. 3   Litho.   *Perf. 14*
635 A92 20c multicolored .25 .25
636 A92 40c multicolored .25 .25
637 A92 60c multicolored .35 .35
638 A92 $2 multicolored .90 .90
   Nos. 635-638 (4) 1.75 1.75
Souvenir Sheet
639 A92 $3 multicolored 1.75 1.75

Nos. 459, 466, 470-471 Overprinted

No. 640   No. 643

Perf. 14½, 13½, 13½x14, 14
1979, Oct. 29   Litho.
640 A68 5c multicolored .25 .25
641 A68 40c multicolored .30 .30
642 A68 $5 multicolored 2.00 2.00
643 A69 $10 multicolored 3.50 3.50
   Nos. 640-643 (4) 6.05 6.05
Hurricane devastation, Aug. 29. Vertical
overprint on No. 643, others horizontal.

Music
Scenes — A92a

½c, Mickey Mouse. 1c, Goofy playing guitar.
2c, Mickey Mouse and Goofy. 3c, Donald
Duck. 4c, Minnie Mouse. 5c, Goofy playing
accordion. 10c, Horace Horsecollar and Dale.
$2, Huey, Dewey, Louie. $2.50, Donald and
Huey.
$3, Mickey Mouse playing piano.

1979, Nov. 2   Litho.   *Perf. 11*
644 A92a ½c multicolored .25 .25
645 A92a 1c multicolored .25 .25
646 A92a 2c multicolored .25 .25
647 A92a 3c multicolored .25 .25
648 A92a 4c multicolored .25 .25
649 A92a 5c multicolored .25 .25
650 A92a 10c multicolored .25 .25
651 A92a $2 multicolored 1.50 1.50
652 A92a $2.50 multicolored 1.50 1.50
   Nos. 644-652 (9) 4.75 4.75
Souvenir Sheet
Perf. 13
653 A92a $3 multicolored 3.25 3.25

Cathedral of the
Assumption
A93

Cathedrals: 40c, St. Patrick's, New York.
45c, St. Paul's, London, vert. 60c, St. Peter's,
Rome. $2, Cologne Cathedral. $3, Notre
Dame, Paris, vert.

1979, Nov. 26   Litho.   *Perf. 14*
654 A93 6c multicolored .25 .25
655 A93 45c multicolored .25 .25
656 A93 60c multicolored .25 .25
657 A93 $3 multicolored .90 .90
   Nos. 654-657 (4) 1.65 1.65
Souvenir Sheet
658   Sheet of 2 .80 .80
a.   A93 40c multicolored .25 .25
b.   A93 $2 multicolored .55 .55
Christmas.

Nurse and
Patients, Rotary
Emblem — A94

20c, Electrocardiogram machine. 40c,
Mental hospital. $2.50, Paul Harris, founder.
$3, Map of Africa and Europe.

1980, Mar. 31   Litho.   *Perf. 14*
659 A94 10c shown .25 .25
660 A94 20c multicolored .25 .25
661 A94 40c multicolored .25 .25
662 A94 $2.50 multicolored .75 .75
   Nos. 659-662 (4) 1.50 1.50
Souvenir Sheet
663 A94 $3 multicolored 1.25 1.25
Rotary International, 75th anniv. Nos. 659-
662 each contain quadrant of Rotary emblem.

Nos. 608-611
Overprinted in Black

1980, May 6   Litho.   *Perf. 12*
663A A87 25c multicolored .35 .35
663B A87 45c multicolored .55 .55
663C A87 50c multicolored .60 .60
663D A87 $2 multicolored 1.50 1.50
   Nos. 663A-663D (4) 3.00 3.00
London 80 Intl. Stamp Exhib., May 6-14.

Shot Put,
Moscow '80
Emblem — A95

1980, May 27   Litho.   *Perf. 14*
664 A95 30c shown .25 .25
665 A95 40c Basketball .60 .30
666 A95 60c Swimming .40 .40
667 A95 $2 Gymnast .70 .70
   Nos. 664-667 (4) 1.95 1.65
Souvenir Sheet
668 A95 $3 Running 1.25 1.25
22nd Summer Olympic Games, Moscow,
July 19-Aug. 3.

Embarkation
for Cythera,
by Watteau
A96

Paintings: 20c, Supper at Emmaus, by
Caravaggio. 25c, Charles I Hunting, by Van
Dyck, vert. 30c, The Maids of Honor, by Velaz-
quez, vert. 45c, Rape of the Sabine Women,
by Poussin. $1, Embarkation for Cythera, by
Watteau. $3, Holy Family, by Rembrandt. $5,
Girl before a Mirror, by Picasso, vert.

Perf. 14x13½, 13½x14
1980, July 22   Litho.
669 A96 20c multicolored .25 .25
670 A96 25c multicolored .25 .25
671 A96 30c multicolored .25 .25
672 A96 45c multicolored .25 .25
673 A96 $1 multicolored .40 .40
674 A96 $5 multicolored 1.50 1.50
   Nos. 669-674 (6) 2.90 2.90
Souvenir Sheet
675 A96 $3 multicolored 1.10 1.10

Queen Mother
Elizabeth, 80th
Birthday — A97

1980, Aug. 4   *Perf. 12, 14*
676 A97 40c multicolored .25 .25
677 A97 $2.50 multicolored .50 .50
Souvenir Sheet
678 A97 $3 multicolored .75 .75

Tinkerbell
A98

Designs: Scenes from Disney's Peter Pan.

1980, Oct. 1   Litho.   *Perf. 11*
679 A98 ½c multicolored .25 .25
680 A98 1c multicolored .25 .25
681 A98 2c multicolored .25 .25
682 A98 3c multicolored .25 .25
683 A98 4c multicolored .25 .25
684 A98 5c multicolored .25 .25
685 A98 10c multicolored .25 .25
686 A98 $2 multicolored 2.25 1.60
687 A98 $2.50 multicolored 2.25 1.75
   Nos. 679-687 (9) 6.25 5.10
Souvenir Sheet
688 A98 $4 multicolored 5.00 5.00
Christmas.

Douglas
Bay — A99

30c, Valley of Desolation. 40c, Emerald
Pool, vert. $3, Indian River, vert.
$4, Trafalgar Falls.

1981, Feb. 12   Litho.   *Perf. 14*
689 A99 20c shown .25 .25
690 A99 30c multicolored .25 .25
691 A99 40c multicolored .25 .25
692 A99 $2 multicolored .70 .70
   Nos. 689-692 (4) 1.45 1.45
Souvenir Sheet
693 A99 $4 multicolored 1.40 1.40

Pluto and
Fifi — A100

$4, Pluto in Blue Note (1947 cartoon).

1981, Apr. 30   Litho.   *Perf. 13½x14*
694 A100 $2 multicolored 1.75 1.75
Souvenir Sheet
695 A100 $4 multicolored 2.75 2.75
50th anniversary of Walt Disney's Pluto.

Forest
Thrush — A101

30c, Stolid flycatcher. 40c, Blue-hooded
euphonia. $5, Lesser antillean peewee.
$3, Sisserou parrot.

1981, Apr. 30   *Perf. 14*
696 A101 20c shown .60 .25
697 A101 30c multicolored .70 .35
698 A101 40c multicolored .80 .45
699 A101 $5 multicolored 4.75 4.75
   Nos. 696-699 (4) 6.85 5.80
Souvenir Sheet
700 A101 $3 multicolored 3.75 3.75

Royal Wedding Issue
Common Design Type

45c, Couple. 60c, Windsor Castle. $4,
Charles.
$5, Helicopter.

1981, June 16   Litho.   *Perf. 14*
701 CD331a 45c multi .25 .25
702 CD331a 60c multi .25 .25
703 CD331a $4 multi .60 .60
   Nos. 701-703 (3) 1.10 1.10
Souvenir Sheet
704 CD331 $5 multi 1.25 1.25
Booklet
705 CD331   multi 6.00
a.   Pane of 6 (3x25c, Lady Di-
     ana, 3x$2, Charles) 2.25 *4.50*
b.   Pane of 1, $5, Couple 3.00 *3.50*
No. 705 contains imperf., self-adhesive
stamps.
Nos. 701-703 also printed in sheets of 5
plus label, perf. 12, in changed colors. Value,
set of three sheets $10.

Elves
Repairing
Santa's
Sleigh
A102

Christmas: Scenes from Walt Disney's
Santa's Workshop.

1981, Nov. 2   Litho.   *Perf. 14*
706 A102 ½c multicolored .25 .25
707 A102 1c multicolored .25 .25
708 A102 2c multicolored .25 .25
709 A102 3c multicolored .25 .25
710 A102 4c multicolored .25 .25
711 A102 5c multicolored .25 .25
712 A102 10c multicolored .25 .25
713 A102 45c multicolored 2.00 .40
714 A102 $5 multicolored 4.00 *5.50*
   Nos. 706-714 (9) 7.75 7.65
Souvenir Sheet
715 A102 $4 multicolored 5.75 5.75

Ixora — A103

2c, Flamboyant. 4c, Poinsettia. 5c, Sabinea carinalis. 8c, Annatto roucou. 10c, Passion fruit. 15c, Breadfruit. 20c, Allamanda buttercup. 25c, Cashew. 35c, Soursop. 40c, Bougainvillea. 45c, Anthurium. 60c, Cacao. 90c, Pawpaw tree. $1, Coconut palm. $2, Coffee tree. $5, Lobster claw. $10, Banana fig.

1981, Dec. 1   Litho.   Perf. 14

716	A103	1c shown	.25	.90
717	A103	2c multicolored	.25	.90
718	A103	4c multicolored	.25	.60
719	A103	5c multicolored	.25	.90
720	A103	8c multicolored	.25	.90
721	A103	10c multicolored	.30	.25
722	A103	15c multicolored	.50	.50
723	A103	20c multicolored	.35	.25
724	A103	25c multicolored	.40	.25
725	A103	35c multicolored	.45	.40
726	A103	40c multicolored	.45	.65
727	A103	45c multicolored	.50	.70
728	A103	60c multicolored	1.00	.95
729	A103	90c multicolored	.75	1.40
730	A103	$1 multicolored	2.00	1.50
731	A103	$2 multicolored	1.50	3.00
732	A103	$5 multicolored	2.00	7.00
c.		Perf. 12½x12 ('85)	3.25	5.00
733	A103	$10 multicolored	3.50	13.00
		Nos. 716-733 (18)	14.95	34.05

For overprints see Nos. 852-853.

1984   Inscribed "1984"   Perf. 12

721a	A103	10c	1.75	.40
730a	A103	$1	2.50	3.00
732a	A103	$5	3.25	5.00
733a	A103	$10	5.25	10.00
		Nos. 721a-733a (4)	12.75	18.40

1985   Inscribed "1985"   Perf. 14

721b	A103	10c	1.00	.65
722b	A103	15c Breadfruit	4.00	2.00
728b	A103	60c Cacao	5.00	3.50
732b	A103	$5 Lobster claw	3.25	5.00
		Nos. 721b-732b (4)	13.25	11.15

Intl. Year of the Disabled — A104

45c, Ramp curb. 60c, Bus steps. 75c, Hand-operated car. $4, Bus lift. $5, Elevator buttons.

1981, Dec. 22   Litho.   Perf. 14

734	A104	45c multicolored	.45	.30
735	A104	60c multicolored	.55	.40
736	A104	75c multicolored	.65	.50
737	A104	$4 multicolored	2.00	2.40
		Nos. 734-737 (4)	3.65	3.60

Souvenir Sheet

738	A104	$5 multicolored	5.00	5.00

Bathers, by Picasso — A105

45c, Olga in Armchair. 75c, Woman in Spanish Costume. $4, Dog and Cock. $5, Sleeping Peasants.

1981, Dec. 30   Perf. 14½

739	A105	45c multicolored	.30	.30
740	A105	60c shown	.40	.40
741	A105	75c multicolored	.50	.50
742	A105	$4 multicolored	2.25	2.25
		Nos. 739-742 (4)	3.45	3.45

Souvenir Sheet

743	A105	$5 multicolored	4.00	4.00

1982 World Cup Soccer A106

Various Disney characters playing soccer.

1982, Jan. 29   Perf. 14

744	A106	½c multicolored	.25	.25
745	A106	1c multicolored	.25	.25
746	A106	2c multicolored	.25	.25
747	A106	3c multicolored	.25	.25
748	A106	4c multicolored	.25	.25
749	A106	5c multicolored	.25	.25
750	A106	10c multicolored	.25	.25
751	A106	60c multicolored	1.25	1.25
752	A106	$5 multicolored	6.25	6.25
		Nos. 744-752 (9)	9.25	9.25

Souvenir Sheet

753	A106	$4 multicolored	5.75	5.75

Golden Days, by Norman Rockwell — A107

25c, The Morning News. 45c, The Marbles Champ. $1, Speeding Along.

1982, Mar. 10   Litho.   Perf. 14x13½

754	A107	10c shown	.25	.25
755	A107	25c multicolored	.25	.25
756	A107	45c multicolored	.30	.30
757	A107	$1 multicolored	.55	.55
		Nos. 754-757 (4)	1.35	1.35

Intl. Decade for Women (1975-85) A108

Famous Women: 10c, Elma Napier (1890-1973), first woman elected to Legislative Council in British West Indies, 1940. 45c, Margaret Mead (1901-1978), anthropologist. $1, Mabel Caudiron (1909-1968), musician and folk historian. $3, Florence Nightingale, founder of modern nursing. $4, Eleanor Roosevelt.

1982, Apr. 15   Litho.   Perf. 14

758	A108	10c multicolored	.25	.25
759	A108	45c multicolored	.35	.35
760	A108	$1 multicolored	.60	.60
761	A108	$4 multicolored	2.50	2.50
		Nos. 758-761 (4)	3.70	3.70

Souvenir Sheet

762	A108	$3 multicolored	3.00	3.00

A109

Washington or Roosevelt and: 45, George Washington and Independence Hall, Philadelphia. 60c, Capitol Building. 90c, The Surrender of Cornwallis, by John Trumbull. $2, Dam construction during New Deal (mural by William Gropper). $5, Washington, Roosevelt.

1982, May 1   Perf. 14½

763	A109	45c multicolored	.35	.35
764	A109	60c multicolored	.40	.40
765	A109	90c multicolored	.55	.55
766	A109	$2 multicolored	1.00	1.00
		Nos. 763-766 (4)	2.30	2.30

Souvenir Sheet

767	A109	$5 multicolored	3.00	3.00

George Washington's 250th birth anniv. and Franklin D. Roosevelt's birth cent.

Godman's Leaf Butterfly — A110

45c, Zebra. 60c, Mimic. $3, Red rim. $5, Southern dagger tail.

1982, June 1   Litho.   Perf. 14

768	A110	15c shown	1.75	1.75
769	A110	45c multicolored	2.75	2.75
770	A110	60c multicolored	3.00	3.00
771	A110	$3 multicolored	6.25	6.25
		Nos. 768-771 (4)	13.75	13.75

Souvenir Sheet

772	A110	$5 multicolored	7.00	7.00

Princess Diana Issue
Common Design Type

45c, Buckingham Palace. $2, Engagement portrait. $4, Diana in wedding dress. $5, Diana sitting in chair in white dress.

1982, July 1   Litho.   Perf. 14½x14

773	CD332	45c multicolored	.30	.30
774	CD332	$2 multicolored	1.00	1.00
775	CD332	$4 multicolored	2.25	2.25
		Nos. 773-775 (3)	3.55	3.55

Souvenir Sheet

776	CD332	$5 multicolored	3.50	3.50

Also issued in sheet of 5 plus label.
For overprints see Nos. 782-785.

Scouting Year — A111

45c, Cooking. 60c, Meteorological study. 75c, Sisserou parrot, cub scouts. $3, Canoeing, Indian River. $5, Flagbearer.

1982, July 1   Litho.   Perf. 14

777	A111	45c multicolored	1.25	1.25
778	A111	60c multicolored	1.75	1.75
779	A111	75c multicolored	2.25	2.25
780	A111	$3 multicolored	5.25	5.25
		Nos. 777-780 (4)	10.50	10.50

Souvenir Sheet

781	A111	$5 multicolored	3.50	3.50

Nos. 773-776 Overprinted

1982, Sept. 1   Litho.   Perf. 14½x14

782	CD332	45c multicolored	.30	.30
783	CD332	$2 multicolored	1.00	1.00
784	CD332	$4 multicolored	2.25	2.25
		Nos. 782-784 (3)	3.55	3.55

Souvenir Sheet

785	CD332	$5 multicolored	3.50	3.50

Birth of Prince William of Wales, June 21.
Also issued in sheet of 5 plus label.

Christmas — A112

Holy Family Paintings by Raphael.

1982, Oct. 18   Litho.   Perf. 14

786	A112	25c multicolored	.25	.25
787	A112	30c multicolored	.25	.25
788	A112	90c multicolored	.40	.40
789	A112	$4 multicolored	1.75	1.75
		Nos. 786-789 (4)	2.65	2.65

Souvenir Sheet

790	A112	$5 multicolored	3.50	3.50

Goosebeak Whale Eating Squid — A113

60c, Humpback whale. 75c, Great right whale. $3, Melonhead whale. $5, Pygmy sperm whale.

1983, Feb. 15   Litho.   Perf. 14

791	A113	45c shown	1.75	1.75
792	A113	60c multicolored	2.00	2.00
793	A113	75c multicolored	2.25	2.25
794	A113	$3 multicolored	7.50	7.50
		Nos. 791-794 (4)	13.50	13.50

Souvenir Sheet

795	A113	$5 multicolored	6.25	6.25

Commonwealth Day — A113a

25c, Banana industry. 30c, Road construction. 90c, Community nursing. $3, Basket weavers.

1983, Mar. 14

796	A113a	25c multicolored	.25	.25
797	A113a	30c multicolored	.25	.25
798	A113a	90c multicolored	.40	.40
799	A113a	$3 multicolored	1.25	1.25
		Nos. 796-799 (4)	2.15	2.15

World Communications Year — A114

45c, Hurricane pattern, map. 60c, Air-to-ship communication. 90c, Columbia shuttle, dish antenna. $2, Walkie-talkie. $5, Satellite.

1983, Apr. 18   Litho.   Perf. 14

800	A114	45c multicolored	.30	.30
801	A114	60c multicolored	.35	.35
802	A114	90c multicolored	.50	.50
803	A114	$2 multicolored	1.00	1.00
		Nos. 800-803 (4)	2.15	2.15

Souvenir Sheet

804	A114	$5 multicolored	2.50	2.50

Manned Flight Bicentenary A115

45c, Mayo Composite. 60c, Macchi M-39. 90c, Fairey Swordfish. $4, Zeppelin LZ-3. $5, Double Eagle II, vert.

1983, July 19   Litho.   Perf. 15

805	A115	45c multicolored	.50	.50
806	A115	60c multicolored	.60	.60
807	A115	90c multicolored	.85	.85
808	A115	$4 multicolored	3.00	3.00
		Nos. 805-808 (4)	4.95	4.95

Souvenir Sheet

809	A115	$5 multicolored	3.00	3.00

Duesenberg SJ, 1935 — A116

45c, Studebaker Avanti, 1962. 60c, Cord 812, 1936. 75c, MG-TC, 1945. 90c, Camaro 350-SS, 1967. $3, Porsche 356, 1948. $5, Ferrari 312-T, 1975.

1983, Sept. 1   Litho.   Perf. 14

810	A116	10c shown	.35	.35
811	A116	45c multicolored	.45	.45
812	A116	60c multicolored	.50	.50
813	A116	75c multicolored	.55	.55
814	A116	90c multicolored	.60	.60
815	A116	$3 multicolored	1.75	1.75
		Nos. 810-815 (6)	4.20	4.20

Souvenir Sheet

816	A116	$5 multicolored	3.00	3.00

Raphael Paintings.

Christmas
A117

1983, Oct. 4   Litho.   Perf. 13½
817 A117 45c multicolored   .30   .30
818 A117 60c multicolored   .35   .35
819 A117 90c multicolored   .50   .50
820 A117 $4 multicolored   2.00   2.00
Nos. 817-820 (4)   3.15   3.15

Souvenir Sheet
821 A117 $5 multicolored   3.00   3.00

23rd Olympic Games,
Los Angeles, July 28-
Aug. 12 — A118

30c, Gymnastics. 45c, Javelin. 60c, Diving.
$4, Fencing. $5, Equestrian.

1984, Mar.   Litho.   Perf. 14
822 A118 30c multicolored   .25   .25
823 A118 45c multicolored   .35   .35
824 A118 60c multicolored   .45   .45
825 A118 $4 multicolored   2.50   2.50
Nos. 822-825 (4)   3.55   3.55

Souvenir Sheet
826 A118 $5 multicolored   3.75   3.75

Local
Birds — A119

5c, Plumbeous warbler. 45c, Imperial parrot.
60c, Blue-headed hummingbird. 90c, Red-
necked parrot.
$5, Roseate flamingoes.

1984, May   Litho.
827 A119 5c multicolored   3.00   3.00
828 A119 45c multicolored   7.00   7.00
829 A119 60c multicolored   8.50   8.50
830 A119 90c multicolored   11.00   11.00
Nos. 827-830 (4)   29.50   29.50

Souvenir Sheet
831 A119 $5 multicolored   9.00   9.00

Easter — A120

Various Disney characters and Easter
bunnies.

1984, Apr. 15   Litho.   Perf. 11
832 A120 ½c multicolored   .25   .25
833 A120 1c multicolored   .25   .25
834 A120 2c multicolored   .25   .25
835 A120 3c multicolored   .25   .25
836 A120 4c multicolored   .25   .25
837 A120 5c multicolored   .25   .25
838 A120 10c multicolored   .25   .25
839 A120 $2 multicolored   3.00   3.00
840 A120 $4 multicolored   6.25   6.25
Nos. 832-840 (9)   11.00   11.00

Souvenir Sheet
Perf. 14
841 A120 $5 multicolored   5.75   5.75

Ships — A121

45c, Atlantic Star. 60c, Atlantic. 90c, Carib
fishing pirogue. $4, Norway.
$5, Santa Maria.

1984, June 14   Litho.   Perf. 14
842 A121 45c multicolored   1.75   1.75
843 A121 60c multicolored   2.00   2.00
844 A121 90c multicolored   2.50   2.50
845 A121 $4 multicolored   6.75   6.75
Nos. 842-845 (4)   13.00   13.00

Souvenir Sheet
846 A121 $5 multicolored   5.00   5.00

Local Plants — A122

45c, Guzmania lingulata. 60c, Pitcairnia
angustifolia. 75c, Tillandsia fasciculata. $3,
Aechmea smithiorum.
$5, Tillandsia utriculata.

1984, Aug. 13
847 A122 45c multicolored   .40   .40
848 A122 60c multicolored   .50   .50
849 A122 75c multicolored   .60   .60
850 A122 $3 multicolored   2.40   2.40
Nos. 847-850 (4)   3.90   3.90

Souvenir Sheet
851 A122 $5 multicolored   3.75   3.75

Ausipex Intl. Stamp Exhibition.

Nos. 721, 732 Overprinted

1984   Litho.   Perf. 14
852 A103 10c multicolored   .25   .25
853 A103 $5 multicolored   4.00   4.00

Correggio &
Degas — A122a

Correggio: 25c, Virgin and Child with Young
St. John. 60c, Christ Bids Farewell to the Virgin Mary. 90c, Do Not Touch Me. $4, The Mys-
tical Marriage of St. Catherine. No. 862, Adoration of the Magi.
Degas, horiz.: 30c, Before the Start. 45c,
On the Racecourse. $1, Jockeys at the Flag-
pole. $3, Racehorses at Longchamp. No. 863,
Self-portrait.

1984, Nov.   Litho.   Perf. 15
854 A122a 25c multicolored   .35   .35
855 A122a 30c multicolored   .40   .40
856 A122a 45c multicolored   .45   .45
857 A122a 60c multicolored   .50   .50
858 A122a 90c multicolored   .65   .65
859 A122a $1 multicolored   .75   .75
860 A122a $3 multicolored   1.75   1.75
861 A122a $4 multicolored   1.90   1.90
Nos. 854-861 (8)   6.75   6.75

Souvenir Sheets
862 A122a $5 multicolored   3.00   3.00
863 A122a $5 multicolored   3.00   3.00

A123

1984, Dec.   Perf. 14
864 A123 30c Avro 748   1.25   1.25
865 A123 60c Twin Otter   2.25   2.25
866 A123 $1 Islander   2.50   2.50
867 A123 $3 Casa   4.75   4.75
Nos. 864-867 (4)   10.75   10.75

Souvenir Sheet
868 A123 $5 Boeing 747   5.50   5.50

Intl. Civil Aviation Org., 40th anniv.

A124

Scenes from various Donald Duck movies.

1984, Nov.   Litho.
869 A124 45c multicolored   1.25   1.25
870 A124 60c multicolored   1.50   1.50
871 A124 90c multicolored   2.00   2.00
872 A124 $2 multicolored,
        perf. 12x12½   3.50   3.50
873 A124 $4 multicolored   5.75   5.75
Nos. 869-873 (5)   14.00   14.00

Souvenir Sheet
Perf. 13½x14
874 A124 $5 multicolored   5.50   5.50

Christmas and 50th anniv. of Donald Duck.

Cats — A125

10c, Tabby. 15c, Calico shorthair. 20c, Siamese. 25c, Manx. 45c, Abyssinian. 60c, Tortoise shell longhair. $1, Rex. $2, Persian. $3,
Himalayan. No. 884, $5, Burmese.
No. 885, $5, Gray Burmese, Persian, Ameri-
can shorthair.

1984, Nov. 12   Litho.   Perf. 15
875 A125 10c multicolored   .25   .25
876 A125 15c multicolored   .25   .25
877 A125 20c multicolored   .25   .25
878 A125 25c multicolored   .25   .25
879 A125 45c multicolored   .40   .40
880 A125 60c multicolored   .50   .50
881 A125 $1 multicolored   .75   .75
882 A125 $2 multicolored   1.00   1.00
883 A125 $3 multicolored   2.00   2.00
884 A125 $5 multicolored   3.50   3.50
Nos. 875-884 (10)   9.15   9.15

Souvenir Sheet
885 A125 $5 multicolored   5.50   5.50

Girl Guides, 75th
Anniv. — A126

35c, Lady Baden-Powell. 45c, Inspecting
Dominican troop. 60c, With Dominican troop
leaders. $3, Lord and Lady Baden-Powell,
vert.
$5, Flag ceremony.

1985, Feb. 18   Perf. 14
886 A126 35c multicolored   .60   .60
887 A126 45c multicolored   .70   .70
888 A126 60c multicolored   .90   .90
889 A126 $3 multicolored   3.50   3.50
Nos. 886-889 (4)   5.70   5.70

Souvenir Sheet
890 A126 $5 multicolored   5.50   5.50

John James
Audubon
A127

45c, King rails. $1, Black & white warbler,
vert. $2, Broad-winged hawks, vert. $3, Ring-
necked ducks.
$5, Reddish egrets, vert.

1985, Apr. 4
891 A127 45c multicolored   1.25   1.25
892 A127 $1 multicolored   2.00   2.00
893 A127 $2 multicolored   3.25   3.25
894 A127 $4 multicolored   4.25   4.25
Nos. 891-894 (4)   10.75   10.75

Souvenir Sheet
895 A127 $5 multicolored   5.50   5.50

Nos. 891-894 exist vertically se-tenant with
labels showing additional bird species.
See Nos. 965-969.

Duke of Edinburgh
Awards, 1984 — A128

45c, Woman at computer terminal. 60c,
Medical staff, patient. 90c, Runners. $4, Fam-
ily jogging.
$5, Duke of Edinburgh.

1985, Apr. 30
896 A128 45c multicolored   .50   .50
897 A128 60c multicolored   1.60   1.60
898 A128 90c multicolored   2.00   2.00
899 A128 $4 multicolored   3.25   3.25
Nos. 896-899 (4)   7.35   7.35

Souvenir Sheet
900 A128 $5 multicolored   4.00   4.00

Intl. Youth
Year — A129

45c, Cricket match. 60c, Environmental
study, parrot. $1, Stamp collecting. $3, Boating, leisure.
$5, Youths join hands.

1985, July 8   Litho.   Perf. 14
901 A129 45c multicolored   3.00   2.00
902 A129 60c multicolored   3.75   2.50
903 A129 $1 multicolored   4.00   3.50
904 A129 $3 multicolored   5.25   7.50
Nos. 901-904 (4)   16.00   15.50

Souvenir Sheet
905 A129 $5 multicolored   4.00   4.00

Queen Mother, 85th
Birthday — A130

60c, Visiting Sadlers Wells. $1, Fishing. $3,
At Clarence House, 1984.
$5, Attending Windsor Castle Garter
Ceremony.

1985, July 15
906 A130 60c multicolored   1.00   .75
907 A130 $1 multicolored   1.50   .75
908 A130 $3 multicolored   2.00   2.00
Nos. 906-908 (3)   4.50   3.50

Souvenir Sheet
909 A130 $5 multicolored   3.75   3.75

Johann Sebastian
Bach — A131

Portrait, signature, music from Explication
and: 45c, Cornett 60c, Coiled trumpet. $1, Pic-
colo. $3, Violoncello piccolo.

1985, Sept. 2

910	A131	45c multicolored	1.00	1.00
911	A131	60c multicolored	1.50	1.50
912	A131	$1 multicolored	2.00	2.00
913	A131	$4 multicolored	4.25	4.25
		Nos. 910-913 (4)	8.75	8.75

Souvenir Sheet

914	A131	$5 Portrait	4.00	4.00

State Visit of Elizabeth II, Oct. 25 A132

60c, Flags of UK, Dominica. $1, Elizabeth II, vert. $4, HMS Britannia. $5, Map.

1985, Oct. 25　　　　　**Perf. 14½**

915	A132	60c multicolored	.75	.75
916	A132	$1 multicolored	.75	.75
917	A132	$4 multicolored	3.50	3.50
		Nos. 915-917 (3)	5.00	5.00

Souvenir Sheet

918	A132	$5 multicolored	3.75	3.75

Mark Twain A133

Disney characters in Tom Sawyer.

1985, Nov. 11　**Litho.**　**Perf. 14**

919	A133	20c multicolored	.75	.35
920	A133	60c multicolored	1.50	.35
921	A133	$1 multicolored	2.00	2.00
922	A133	$1.50 multicolored	2.50	2.50
923	A133	$2 multicolored	3.00	3.00
		Nos. 919-923 (5)	9.75	8.20

Souvenir Sheet

924	A133	$5 multicolored	6.50	6.50

Christmas.

The Brothers Grimm A134

Disney characters in Little Red Cap (Little Red Riding Hood).

1985, Nov. 11

925	A134	10c multicolored	.40	.40
926	A134	45c multicolored	1.00	.50
927	A134	90c multicolored	2.00	2.00
928	A134	$1 multicolored	2.25	2.25
929	A134	$3 multicolored	4.25	4.25
		Nos. 925-929 (5)	9.90	9.40

Souvenir Sheet

930	A134	$5 multicolored	7.75	7.75

Christmas.

UN, 40th Anniv. — A135

Stamps of UN, famous men and events: 45c, No. 442 and Lord Baden-Powell. $2, No. 157 and Maimonides (1135-1204) Judaic scholar. $3, No. 278 and Sir Rowland Hill. $5, Apollo-Soyuz Mission, 10th anniv.

1985, Nov. 22　　　　**Perf. 14½**

931	A135	45c multicolored	.90	.90
932	A135	$2 multicolored	2.00	2.00
933	A135	$3 multicolored	2.00	2.00
		Nos. 931-933 (3)	4.90	4.90

Souvenir Sheet

934	A135	$5 multicolored	3.75	3.75

1986 World Cup Soccer Championships, Mexico — A136

Various soccer plays.

1986, Mar. 26　　　　**Perf. 14**

935	A136	45c multicolored	1.25	1.25
936	A136	60c multicolored	1.75	1.75
937	A136	$1 multicolored	2.25	2.25
938	A136	$3 multicolored	5.50	5.50
		Nos. 935-938 (4)	10.75	10.75

Souvenir Sheet

939	A136	$5 multicolored	8.50	8.50

For overprints see Nos. 974-978.

Statue of Liberty, Cent. — A137

Statue and: 15c, New York police pursuing river pirates, c. 1890. 25c, Police patrol boat. 45c, Hoboken Ferry Terminal, c. 1890. $4, Holland Tunnel. $5, Statue, vert.

1986, Mar. 26

940	A137	15c multicolored	1.50	.75
941	A137	25c multicolored	1.50	1.00
942	A137	45c multicolored	2.50	1.00
943	A137	$4 multicolored	5.00	5.00
		Nos. 940-943 (4)	10.50	7.75

Souvenir Sheet

944	A137	$5 multicolored	5.50	5.50

Halley's Comet — A138

5c, Jantal Mantar Observatory, Delhi, India, Nasir al Din al Tusi (1201-1274), astronomer. 10c, US Bell X-1 rocket plane breaking sound barrier. 45c, Astronomicum Caesareum, 1540, manuscript diagram of comet's trajectory, 1531. $4, Mark Twain, comet appeared at birth and death. $5, Comet.

1986, Apr. 17

945	A138	5c multicolored	.60	.60
946	A138	10c multicolored	.60	.60
947	A138	45c multicolored	1.25	1.25
948	A138	$4 multicolored	3.25	3.25
		Nos. 945-948 (4)	5.70	5.70

Souvenir Sheet

949	A138	$5 multicolored	3.75	3.75

For overprints see Nos. 984-988.

Queen Elizabeth II, 60th Birthday
Common Design Type

2c, Wedding, 1947. $1, With Pope John Paul II, 1982. $4, Royal visit, 1971. $5, Age 10.

1986, Apr. 21　**Litho.**　**Perf. 14**

950	CD339	2c multicolored	.25	.25
951	CD339	$1 multicolored	.75	.75
952	CD339	$4 multicolored	2.50	2.50
		Nos. 950-952 (3)	3.50	3.50

Souvenir Sheet

953	CD339	$5 multicolored	3.75	3.75

AMERIPEX '86 — A139

Walt Disney characters involved in stamp collecting: 25c, Mickey Mouse and Pluto. 45c, Donald Duck. 60c, Chip-n-Dale. $4, Donald, nephews. $5, Uncle Scrooge.

1986, May 22　　　　**Perf. 11**

954	A139	25c multicolored	.75	.75
955	A139	45c multicolored	.95	.95
956	A139	60c multicolored	1.25	1.25
957	A139	$4 multicolored	4.00	4.00
		Nos. 954-957 (4)	6.95	6.95

Souvenir Sheet
Perf. 14

958	A139	$5 multicolored	6.00	6.00

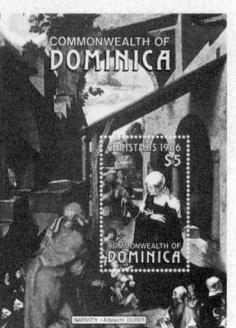

William I

British Monarchs — A140

1986, June 9　　　　**Perf. 14**

959	A140	10c William I	.40	.40
960	A140	40c Richard II	.75	.75
961	A140	50c Henry VIII	.90	.90
962	A140	$1 Charles II	1.00	1.00
963	A140	$2 Queen Anne	1.50	1.50
964	A140	$4 Queen Victoria	3.00	3.00
		Nos. 959-964 (6)	7.55	7.55

Audubon Type of 1985

25c, Black-throated diver. 60c, Great blue heron. 90c, Yellow-crowned night heron. $4, Shoveler duck. $5, Goose.

Perf. 12½x12, 12x12½

1986, June 18

965	A127	25c multicolored	1.25	.50
966	A127	60c multicolored	1.75	1.75
967	A127	90c multicolored	2.25	2.25
968	A127	$4 multicolored	4.50	4.50
		Nos. 965-968 (4)	9.75	9.00

Souvenir Sheet
Perf. 14

969	A127	$5 multicolored	10.00	10.00

Nos. 966-967 vert.

Royal Wedding Issue, 1986
Common Design Type

1986, July 23　　　　**Perf. 14**

970	CD340	45c Couple	.40	.40
971	CD340	60c Prince Andrew	.60	.60
972	CD340	$4 Prince, aircraft	2.50	2.50
		Nos. 970-972 (3)	3.50	3.50

Souvenir Sheet

973	CD340	$5 Couple, diff.	3.75	3.75
		Nos. 970-973 (4)	7.25	7.25

Nos. 935-939 Overprinted in Gold

1986, Sept. 15　**Litho.**　**Perf. 14**

974	A136	45c multicolored	1.25	.50
975	A136	60c multicolored	1.50	1.50
976	A136	$1 multicolored	2.00	2.00
977	A136	$3 multicolored	4.75	4.75
		Nos. 974-977 (4)	9.50	8.75

Souvenir Sheet

978	A136	$5 multicolored	8.75	8.75

Paintings by Albrecht Durer — A141

A142

45c, Virgin in Prayer. 60c, Madonna and Child. $1, Madonna and Child, diff. $3, Madonna and Child with St. Anne. $5, Nativity.

1986, Dec. 2　**Litho.**　**Perf. 14**

979	A141	45c multicolored	.85	.35
980	A141	60c multicolored	1.40	1.40
981	A141	$1 multicolored	2.00	2.00
982	A141	$3 multicolored	5.50	5.50
		Nos. 979-982 (4)	9.75	9.25

Souvenir Sheet

983	A142	$5 multicolored	8.75	8.75

Nos. 945-949 Printed with Halley's Comet Logo in Black or Silver

1986, Dec. 16

984	A138	5c multicolored	.25	.25
985	A138	10c multicolored	.25	.25
986	A138	45c multicolored	.50	.50
987	A138	$4 multicolored	3.75	3.75
		Nos. 984-987 (4)	4.75	4.75

Souvenir Sheet

988	A138	$5 multi (S)	4.50	4.50

Birds — A143

1c, Broad-winged hawk. 2c, Ruddy quail dove. 5c, Red-necked pigeon. 10c, Green heron. 15c, Common gallinule. 20c, Ringed kingfisher. 25c, Brown pelican. 35c, White-tailed tropicbird. 45c, Red-legged thrush. 60c, Purple throated carib. 90c, Magnificent frigatebird. $1, Trembler. $2, Black-capped petrel. $5, Barn owl. $10, Imperial parrot.

1987, Jan. 20　**Litho.**　**Perf. 15**

989	A143	1c multicolored	.25	.75
990	A143	2c multicolored	.25	.75
991	A143	5c multicolored	.30	.75
992	A143	10c multicolored	.30	.25
993	A143	15c multicolored	.40	.30
994	A143	20c multicolored	.40	.30
995	A143	25c multicolored	.40	.25
996	A143	35c multicolored	.40	.30
997	A143	45c multicolored	.50	.40
998	A143	60c multicolored	.60	.55
999	A143	90c multicolored	.70	.70
1000	A143	$1 multicolored	.80	.80
1001	A143	$2 multicolored	1.50	1.50
1002	A143	$5 multicolored	3.75	3.75
1003	A143	$10 multicolored	6.25	6.25
		Nos. 989-1003 (15)	16.80	17.60

Inscribed "1989" and "Questa"

1989, Aug. 31　**Litho.**　**Perf. 14**

990a	A143	2c	.35	.90
991a	A143	5c	.35	.80
992a	A143	10c	.40	.25
993a	A143	15c	.55	.30
994a	A143	20c	.65	.35
995a	A143	25c	.65	.35
996a	A143	35c	.85	.30
997a	A143	45c	1.00	.50
998a	A143	60c	1.50	.50
1000a	A143	$1	1.75	1.50
1001a	A143	$2	3.00	3.00
1002a	A143	$5	6.00	6.00
1003a	A143	$10	8.00	8.00
		Nos. 990a-1003a (13)	25.05	22.05

Inscribed "1989" and "Questa"

1990		Litho.	Perf. 12	
990b	A143	2c	.40	.95
991b	A143	5c	.40	.85
992b	A143	10c	.40	.35
993b	A143	15c	.45	.35
994b	A143	20c	.70	.40
995b	A143	25c	.70	.40
996b	A143	35c	.85	.35
997b	A143	45c	1.00	.35
998b	A143	60c	1.50	1.60
1000b	A143	$1	1.75	1.00
1001b	A143	$2	3.00	3.00
1002b	A143	$5	6.25	6.25
1003b	A143	$10	8.25	8.25
	Nos. 990b-1003b (13)		25.70	24.10

Inscribed "1989" and "Questa"

1991		Litho.	Perf. 13x11½	
990c	A143	2c	.50	1.10
991c	A143	5c	.50	.95
992c	A143	10c	.55	.40
993c	A143	15c	.55	.35
994c	A143	20c	.75	.35
995c	A143	25c	.75	.40
996c	A143	35c	.85	.40
997c	A143	45c	1.40	1.25
998c	A143	60c	2.00	1.40
1000c	A143	$1	2.00	1.50
1001c	A143	$2	3.50	3.50
1002c	A143	$5	7.00	7.00
1003c	A143	$10	10.00	10.00
	Nos. 990c-1003c (13)		30.35	28.60

Paintings by Marc Chagall (1887-1985) A144

Designs: 25c, Artist and His Model. 35c, Midsummer Night's Dream. 45c, Joseph the Shepherd. 60c, the Cellist. 90c, Woman with Pigs. $1, the Blue Circus. $3, For Vava. $4, the Rider. No. 1012, Purim. No. 1013, Firebird design for the curtain of the Stravinsky Ballet production.

1987, Mar. 2			Perf. 14	
1004	A144	25c multicolored	.50	.25
1005	A144	35c multicolored	.65	.30
1006	A144	45c multicolored	.85	.35
1007	A144	60c multicolored	1.00	.50
1008	A144	90c multicolored	1.10	.70
1009	A144	$1 multicolored	1.25	1.25
1010	A144	$3 multicolored	2.50	2.50
1011	A144	$4 multicolored	3.50	3.50

Size: 110x95mm
Imperf

1012	A144	$5 multicolored	4.00	4.00
1013	A144	$5 multicolored	4.00	4.00
	Nos. 1004-1013 (10)		19.35	17.35

A145

America's Cup — A146

45c, Reliance, 1903. 60c, Freedom, 1980. $1, Mischief, 1881. $3, Australia, 1977. $5, Courageous, Australia, 1977.

1987, Feb. 5			Perf. 15	
1014	A145	45c multicolored	.60	.45
1015	A145	60c multicolored	.70	.50
1016	A145	$1 multicolored	.90	1.00
1017	A145	$3 multicolored	2.75	2.00
	Nos. 1014-1017 (4)		4.95	3.95

Souvenir Sheet

1018	A146	$5 multicolored	3.75	3.75

Conch Shells — A147

Designs: 35c, Morch Poulsen's triton. 45c, Swainson globe purple sea snail. 60c, Banded tulip. No. 1022, Lamarck deltoid rock shell. No. 1023, Junoia volute.

1987, Apr. 13			Litho.	
1019	A147	35c multicolored	.35	.35
1020	A147	45c multicolored	.45	.45
1021	A147	60c multicolored	.55	.55
1022	A147	$5 multicolored	3.50	3.50
	Nos. 1019-1022 (4)		4.85	4.85

Souvenir Sheet

1023	A147	$5 multicolored	4.50	4.50

CAPEX '87 — A148

Mushrooms: 45c, Cantharellus cinnabarinus. 60c, Boletellus cubenis. $2, Eccilia cystiophorus. $3, Xerocomus guadelupae. $5, Gymnopilus chrysopellus.

1987, June 15			Perf. 14	
1024	A148	45c multicolored	1.50	.75
1025	A148	60c multicolored	2.00	2.00
1026	A148	$2 multicolored	3.75	3.75
1027	A148	$3 multicolored	4.50	4.50
	Nos. 1024-1027 (4)		11.75	11.00

Souvenir Sheet

1028	A148	$5 multicolored	10.00	10.00

A149

Discovery of America, 500th Anniv. (in 1992) — A150

Explorations of Christopher Columbus: 10c, Discovery of Dominica. 15c, Ships greeted by Carib Indians. 45c, Claiming New World for Spain. 60c, Wrecking of the Santa Maria. 90c, Fleet setting sail. $1, Sighting land. $3, Trading with the Indians. No. 1036, First settlement. No. 1037, Arrival of Second Fleet at Dominica, Nov. 3, 1493. No. 1038, Map of exploration of the Leeward Islands.

1987, July 27			Perf. 15	
1029	A149	10c multicolored	.40	.40
1030	A149	15c multicolored	.50	.50
1031	A149	45c multicolored	.75	.75
1032	A149	60c multicolored	.95	.95
1033	A149	90c multicolored	1.20	1.20
1034	A149	$1 multicolored	1.25	1.25
1035	A149	$3 multicolored	2.50	2.50
1036	A149	$5 multicolored	3.25	3.25
	Nos. 1029-1036 (8)		10.80	10.80

Souvenir Sheets

1037	A150	$5 multicolored	4.75	4.75
1038	A150	$5 multicolored	4.75	4.75

For overprints see Nos. 1083-1084.

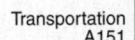

Transportation A151

10c, Warrior, 1st iron-clad warship. 15c, Maglev-MLU 001, fastest passenger train. 25c, Clipper Flying Cloud, fastest NYC-San Francisco voyage, 1852. 35c, 1st elevated railway, NYC. 45c, Tom Thumb, 1st US passenger train locomotive. 60c, Joshua Slocum, 1st solo circumnavigation of the world in a sloop.

90c, Se-Land Commerce, fastest Pacific crossing. $1, 1st cable car, San Francisco. $3, Orient Express. $4, The North River Steamboat of Clermont, invented by Robert Fulton, 1st successful commercial steamboat.

1987		Litho.	Perf. 14	
1039	A151	10c multicolored	.50	.50
1040	A151	15c multicolored	.75	.75
1041	A151	25c multi, vert.	.80	.80
1042	A151	35c multi, vert.	1.00	1.00
1043	A151	45c multi, vert.	1.10	1.10
1044	A151	60c multi, vert.	1.25	1.25
1045	A151	90c multi, vert.	1.40	1.40
1046	A151	$1 multicolored	1.50	1.50
1047	A151	$3 multicolored	3.75	3.75
1048	A151	$4 multicolored	4.00	4.00
	Nos. 1039-1048 (10)		16.05	16.05

Issued: 10c, 15c, 45c, 60c, $4, 9/28; others 8/1.
For overprints see Nos. 1081-1082.

Christmas — A152

Paintings (details): 20c, Virgin and Child with St. Anne, by Durer. 25c, The Virgin and Child, by Murillo. $2, Madonna and Child, by Vincenzo Foppa (c. 1427-1516). $4, Madonna and Child, by Paolo Veronese (1528-1588). $5, Angel of the Annunciation, anonymous.

1987, Nov. 16				
1049	A152	20c multicolored	.30	.30
1050	A152	25c multicolored	.30	.30
1051	A152	$2 multicolored	2.00	2.00
1052	A152	$4 multicolored	4.25	4.25
	Nos. 1049-1052 (4)		6.85	6.85

Souvenir Sheet

1053	A152	$5 multicolored	3.75	3.75

Mickey Mouse, 60th Anniv. — A153

Disney theme parks and trains: 20c, People Mover, Disney World. 25c, Horse-drawn Trolley, Disneyland. 45c, Roger E. Broggie, Disney World. 60c, Big Thunder Mountain, Disneyland. 90c, Walter E. Disney, Disneyland. $1, Monorail, Disney World. $3, Casey Jr. from Dumbo. $4, Lilly Belle, Disney World. No. 1062, Rainbow Caverns Mine Train, Disneyland, horiz. No. 1063, Toy train from movie Out of Scale, horiz.

1987, Dec. 7			Perf. 14	
1054	A153	20c multicolored	.55	.55
1055	A153	25c multicolored	.55	.55
1056	A153	45c multicolored	.90	.90
1057	A153	60c multicolored	1.00	1.00
1058	A153	90c multicolored	1.60	1.60
1059	A153	$1 multicolored	1.75	1.75
1060	A153	$3 multicolored	4.00	4.00
1061	A153	$4 multicolored	5.25	5.25
	Nos. 1054-1061 (8)		15.60	15.60

Souvenir Sheets

1062	A153	$5 multicolored	4.00	4.00
1063	A153	$5 multicolored	4.00	4.00

40th Wedding Anniv. of Queen Elizabeth II and Prince Philip — A154

45c, Couple, wedding party, 1947. 60c, Elizabeth, Charles, c. 1952. $1, Royal Family, c. 1952. $3, Queen with tiara, c. 1960. $5, Elizabeth, 1947.

1988, Feb. 15		Litho.	Perf. 14	
1064	A154	45c multicolored	.75	.75
1065	A154	60c multicolored	.80	.80
1066	A154	$1 multicolored	1.00	1.00
1067	A154	$3 multicolored	2.40	2.40
	Nos. 1064-1067 (4)		4.95	4.95

Souvenir Sheet

1068	A154	$5 multicolored	3.50	3.50

1988 Summer Olympics, Seoul — A155

1988, Mar. 15				
1069	A155	45c Kayaking	.85	.85
1070	A155	60c Tae kwon-do	1.25	1.25
1071	A155	$1 Diving	1.40	1.40
1072	A155	$3 Parallel bars	2.50	2.50
	Nos. 1069-1072 (4)		6.00	6.00

Souvenir Sheet

1073	A155	$5 Soccer	3.25	3.25

For overprints see Nos. 1151-1155.

Reunion '88 Tourism Campaign A156

10c, Carib Indian, vert. 25c, Mountainous interior. 35c, Indian River, vert. 60c, Belaire dancer. 90c, The Boiling Lake, vert. $3, Coral reef.
$5, Belaire dancer, diff., vert.

1988, Apr. 13		Litho.	Perf. 15	
1074	A156	10c multicolored	.25	.25
1075	A156	25c multicolored	.25	.25
1076	A156	35c multicolored	.25	.25
1077	A156	60c multicolored	.25	.25
1078	A156	90c multicolored	.30	.30
1079	A156	$3 multicolored	.90	.90
	Nos. 1074-1079 (6)		2.20	2.20

Souvenir Sheet

1080	A156	$5 multicolored	3.00	3.00

Independence, 10th anniv.

Nos. 1046-1047, 1037-1038 Ovptd. for Philatelic Exhibitions in Black

a

b

c

d

1988, June 1		Litho.	Perf. 14	
1081	A151(a)	$1 multi	1.00	1.00
1082	A151(b)	$3 multi	3.75	3.75

Souvenir Sheets
Perf. 15

1083	A150(c)	$5 multi	4.00	4.00
1084	A150(d)	$5 multi	4.00	4.00

Miniature Sheet

Rain Forest Flora and Fauna A157

Designs: a, White-tailed tropicbirds. b, Blue-throated euphonia. c, Smooth-billed ani. d, Scaly-breasted thrasher. e, Purple-throated carib. f, Southern daggertail and Clench's hairstreak. g, Trembler. h, Imperial parrot. i, Mangrove cuckoo. j, Hercules beetle. k, Orion. l, Red-necked parrot. m, Tillandsia. n, Polystacha luteola and bananaquit. o, False chameleon. p, Iguana. q, Hypolimnas. r, Greenthroated carib. s, Heliconia. t, Agouti.

1988, July 25   Perf. 14½

1085	A157	Sheet of 20	14.00	14.00
a.-t.		45c any single	.60	.60

Intl. Fund for Agricultural Development (IFAD), 10th Anniv. — A158

1988, Sept. 5   Litho.   Perf. 14

1086	A158	45c Hen house	.65	.65
1087	A158	60c Pig farm	.90	.90
1088	A158	90c Cattle	1.25	1.25
1089	A158	$3 Black-belly sheep	3.50	3.50
		Nos. 1086-1089 (4)	6.30	6.30

Souvenir Sheet

1090	A158	$5 Mixed crops, vert.	3.75	3.75

Entertainers — A159

10c, Gary Cooper. 35c, Josephine Baker. 45c, Maurice Chevalier. 60c, James Cagney. $1, Clark Gable. $2, Louis Armstrong. $3, Liberace. $4, Spencer Tracy. No. 1099, Elvis Presley. No. 1100, Humphrey Bogart.

1988, Sept. 8

1091	A159	10c multicolored	.40	.25
1092	A159	35c multicolored	.50	.25
1093	A159	45c multicolored	.55	.30
1094	A159	60c multicolored	.75	.30
1095	A159	$1 multicolored	1.00	.30
1096	A159	$2 multicolored	1.75	1.75
1097	A159	$3 multicolored	2.00	2.00
1098	A159	$4 multicolored	2.50	2.50
		Nos. 1091-1098 (8)	9.45	7.65

Souvenir Sheets

1099	A159	$5 multicolored	4.25	4.25
1100	A159	$5 multicolored	4.25	4.25

Flowering Trees and Shrubs — A160

1988, Sept. 29   Litho.   Perf. 14

1101	A160	15c Sapodilla	.25	.25
1102	A160	20c Tangerine	.25	.25
1103	A160	25c Avocado pear	.25	.25
1104	A160	45c Amherstia	.30	.30
1105	A160	90c Lipstick tree	.55	.55
1106	A160	$1 Cannonball tree	.60	.60
1107	A160	$3 Saman	1.50	1.50
1108	A160	$4 Pineapple	2.00	2.00
		Nos. 1101-1108 (8)	5.70	5.70

Souvenir Sheets

1109	A160	$5 Lignum vitae	3.75	3.75
1110	A160	$5 Sea grape	3.75	3.75

Paintings by Titian — A161

Designs: 25c, Jacopo Strada, c. 1567. 35c, Titian's Daughter Lavinia, c. 1565. 45c, Andrea Navagero, c. 1515. 60c, Judith with Head of Holoferenes, c. 1570. $1, Emilia di Spilimbergo, c. 1560. $2, Martyrdom of St. Lawrence, c. 1548. $3, Salome With the Head of St. John the Baptist, 1560. $4, St. John the Baptist, c. 1540. No. 1119, Self-portrait, c. 1555. No. 1120, Sisyphus, 1549.

1988, Oct. 10   Litho.   Perf. 13½x14

1111	A161	25c multicolored	.25	.25
1112	A161	35c multicolored	.25	.25
1113	A161	45c multicolored	.35	.35
1114	A161	60c multicolored	.45	.45
1115	A161	$1 multicolored	.90	.90
1116	A161	$2 multicolored	1.25	1.25
1117	A161	$3 multicolored	2.00	2.00
1118	A161	$4 multicolored	2.50	2.50
		Nos. 1111-1118 (8)	7.95	7.95

Souvenir Sheets

1119	A161	$5 multicolored	3.50	3.50
1120	A161	$5 multicolored	3.50	3.50

Independence, 10th Anniv. — A162

20c, Imperial parrot. 45c, No. 1, landscape. $2, No. 602, waterfall. $3, Carib wood. $5, Natl. band performing.

1988, Oct. 31   Litho.   Perf. 14

1121	A162	20c multicolored	1.75	.50
1122	A162	45c multicolored	1.00	.40
1123	A162	$2 multicolored	1.75	1.75
1124	A162	$3 multicolored	2.00	3.00
		Nos. 1121-1124 (4)	6.50	5.65

Souvenir Sheet

1125	A162	$5 multicolored	3.75	3.75

Nos. 1122-1123 horiz.

John F. Kennedy — A163

20c, With Jackie. 25c, Sailing Vicuna. $2, Walking in Hyannis Port. $4, Berlin Wall speech. $5, Portrait.

1988, Nov. 22

1126	A163	20c multicolored	.25	.25
1127	A163	25c multicolored	.25	.25
1128	A163	$2 multicolored	.95	.95
1129	A163	$4 multicolored	2.25	2.25
		Nos. 1126-1129 (4)	3.70	3.70

Souvenir Sheet

1130	A163	$5 multicolored	3.50	3.50

Nos. 1126-1128 horiz.

Miniature Sheet

Christmas, Mickey Mouse 60th Anniv. — A164

No. 1131: a, Huey, Dewey, Louie. b, Daisy Duck. c, Winnie-the-Pooh. d, Goofy. e, Donald Duck. f, Mickey Mouse. g, Minnie Mouse. h, Chip-n-Dale. No. 1132, Mickey, Morty and Ferdy. No. 1133, Characters visiting shopping mall Santa.

1988, Dec. 1   Perf. 13½x14

1131	A164	Sheet of 8	6.75	6.75
a.-h.		60c any single	.80	.80

Souvenir Sheets

1132	A164	$6 multi	5.00	5.00
1133	A164	$6 multi, horiz.	5.00	5.00

UN Declaration of Human Rights, 40th Anniv. — A165

Designs: $3, Flag of Sweden and Raoul Wallenberg, who helped save 100,000 Jews in Budapest from deportation to Nazi concentration camps. $5, Human Rights Flame.

1988, Dec. 12   Perf. 14

1134	A165	$3 multicolored	3.00	3.00

Souvenir Sheet

1135	A165	$5 multi, vert.	4.00	4.00

Coastal Game Fish — A166

10c, Greater amberjack. 15c, Blue marlin. 35c, Cobia. 45c, Dolphin. 60c, Cero. 90c, Mahogany snapper. $3, Yellowfin tuna. $4, Rainbow parrotfish. No. 1144, Manta ray. No. 1145, Tarpon.

1988, Dec. 22   Litho.   Perf. 14

1136	A166	10c multicolored	.25	.25
1137	A166	15c multicolored	.25	.25
1138	A166	35c multicolored	.40	.40
1139	A166	45c multicolored	.50	.50
1140	A166	60c multicolored	.75	.75
1141	A166	90c multicolored	1.00	1.00
1142	A166	$3 multicolored	2.50	2.50
1143	A166	$4 multicolored	3.50	3.50
		Nos. 1136-1143 (8)	9.15	9.15

Souvenir Sheets

1144	A166	$5 multicolored	5.00	5.00
1145	A166	$5 multicolored	5.00	5.00

Caribbean Insects and Reptiles — A167

10c, Leatherback turtle. 25c, Monarch butterfly. 60c, Green anole. $3, Praying mantis. $5, Hercules beetle.

1988, Dec. 29

1146	A167	10c multicolored	.60	.60
1147	A167	25c multicolored	1.75	1.75
1148	A167	60c multicolored	2.00	2.00
1149	A167	$4 multicolored	5.50	5.50
		Nos. 1146-1149 (4)	9.85	9.85

Souvenir Sheet

1150	A167	$5 multicolored	5.00	5.00

Nos. 1069-1073 Overprinted

a   b

c   d

e

1989, Mar. 20   Litho.   Perf. 14

1151	A155(a)	45c multi	.30	.30
1152	A155(b)	60c multi	.40	.40
1153	A155(c)	$1 multi	.75	.75
1154	A155(d)	$3 multi	1.90	1.90
		Nos. 1151-1154 (4)	3.35	3.35

Souvenir Sheet

1155	A155(e)	$5 multi	3.75	3.75

Pre-Columbian Societies and Their Customs — A168

UPAE and discovery of America anniv. emblems and: 20c, Carib Indians canoeing. 35c, Bow hunting. $1, Canoe making. $3, Shield wrestling. $6, Dancing.

1989, May 8   Litho.   Perf. 14

1156	A168	20c multicolored	.25	.25
1157	A168	35c multicolored	.35	.35
1158	A168	$1 multicolored	1.00	1.00
1159	A168	$3 multicolored	2.75	2.75
		Nos. 1156-1159 (4)	4.35	4.35

Souvenir Sheet

1160	A168	$6 multicolored	4.25	4.25

Discovery of America 500th anniv. (in 1992).

Paintings by Yokoyama Taikan (1868-1958) A169

Designs: 10c, Lao-tzu. 20c, Red Maple Leaves (panels 1-2). 45c, King Wen Learns a Lesson from His Cook. 60c, Red Maple Leaves (panels 3-4). $1, Wild Flowers. $2, Red Maple Leaves (panels 5-6). $3, Red Maple Leaves (panels 7-8). $4, The Indian Ceremony of Floating Lamps on the River. No. 1169, Innocence. No. 1170, Red Maple Leaves (4 panels).

1989, Aug. 8   Litho.   Perf. 13½x14

1161	A169	10c multicolored	.25	.25
1162	A169	20c multicolored	.25	.25
1163	A169	45c multicolored	.30	.30
1164	A169	60c multicolored	.40	.40
1165	A169	$1 multicolored	.65	.65
1166	A169	$2 multicolored	1.25	1.25
1167	A169	$3 multicolored	1.75	1.75
1168	A169	$4 multicolored	2.25	2.25
		Nos. 1161-1168 (8)	7.10	7.10

Souvenir Sheets

1169	A169	$5 multicolored	3.75	3.75
1170	A169	$5 multicolored	3.75	3.75

Hirohito (1901-89) and enthronement of Akihito as emperor of Japan.

PHILEXFRANCE '89, July 7-17, Paris — A170

Designs: 10c, Map of Dominica with French place names, 1766. 35c, French coin, 1688. $1, French ship, 1720. $4, Introduction of coffee to Dominica by the French, 1772. $5, Text.

1989, July 17   Litho.   Perf. 14
1171	A170	10c multi, vert.	1.00	1.00
1172	A170	35c shown	1.00	1.00
1173	A170	$1 multicolored	1.50	1.50
1174	A170	$4 multicolored	3.00	3.00
		Nos. 1171-1174 (4)	6.50	6.50

Souvenir Sheet
1175	A170	$5 multicolored	5.25	5.25

Butterflies
A171

Designs: 10c, Homerus swallowtail. 15c, *Morpho peleides.* 25c, Julia. 35c, Gundlach's swallowtail. 60c, Monarch. $1, Gulf fritillary. $3, Red-splashed sulphur. $5, *Papilio andraemon.* No. 1184, *Heliconius doris, Adelpha cytherea, Calliona argensiza, Eurema proterpia.* No. 1185, *Adelpha iphicla, Dismorphia spio, Lucinia sida.*

1989, Sept. 11   Litho.   Perf. 14
1176	A171	10c multicolored	.40	.40
1177	A171	15c multicolored	.40	.40
1178	A171	25c multicolored	.70	.70
1179	A171	35c multicolored	.80	.80
1180	A171	60c multicolored	1.10	1.10
1181	A171	$1 multicolored	1.50	1.50
1182	A171	$3 multicolored	3.50	3.50
1183	A171	$5 multicolored	6.00	6.00
		Nos. 1176-1183 (8)	14.40	14.40

Souvenir Sheets
1184	A171	$6 multicolored	6.50	6.50
1185	A171	$6 multicolored	6.50	6.50

Misspellings: No. 1181, "Frittillary"; No. 1182, "Sulper."

Orchids — A172

10c, Oncidium pusillum. 35c, Epidendrum cochleata. 45c, Epidendrum ciliare. 60c, Cyrtopodium andersonii. $1, Habenaria pauciflora. $2, Maxillaria alba. $3, Selenipedium palmifolium. $4, Brassavola cucullata.
No. 1194, Oncidium lanceanum. No. 1195, Comparettia falcata.

1989, Sept. 28
1186	A172	10c multicolored	.40	.40
1187	A172	35c multicolored	.75	.75
1188	A172	45c multicolored	.85	.85
1189	A172	60c multicolored	1.10	1.10
1190	A172	$1 multicolored	1.50	1.50
1191	A172	$2 multicolored	2.50	2.50
1192	A172	$3 multicolored	3.00	3.00
1193	A172	$4 multicolored	4.75	4.75
		Nos. 1186-1193 (8)	14.85	14.85

Souvenir Sheets
1194	A172	$5 multicolored	6.50	6.50
1195	A172	$5 multicolored	6.50	6.50

1st Moon Landing, 20th Anniv. — A173

10c, Columbia in lunar orbit. 60c, Aldrin descending ladder. $2, Aldrin, Sea of Tranquillity. $3, Flag raising. $6, Liftoff.

1989, Oct. 31   Litho.   Perf. 14
1196	A173	10c multicolored	.35	.35
1197	A173	60c multicolored	.80	.80
1198	A173	$2 multicolored	2.25	2.25
1199	A173	$3 multicolored	3.25	3.25
		Nos. 1196-1199 (4)	6.65	6.65

Souvenir Sheet
1200	A173	$6 multicolored	7.00	7.00

Souvenir Sheets

A174

1990 World Cup Soccer Championships, Italy — A175

Past championship match scenes, flags and soccer ball: a, Brazil vs. Italy, Mexico, 1970. b, England vs. West Germany, England, 1966. c, West Germany vs. Netherlands, West Germany, 1974. d, Italy vs. West Germany, Spain, 1982.

1989, Nov. 7   Perf. 14
1201	A174	Sheet of 4	8.75	8.75
a.-d.		$1 any single	2.00	2.00

Perf. 14
1202	A175	$6 shown	6.00	6.00

Souvenir Sheet

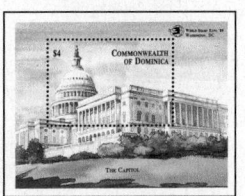

The Capitol, Washington, DC — A176

1989, Nov. 17   Litho.   Perf. 14
1203	A176	$4 multicolored	3.75	3.75

World Stamp Expo '89.

Miniature Sheets

American Presidency, 200th Anniv. — A177

US presidents, historic events and monuments.
No. 1204: a, Washington, 1st inauguration. b, John Adams, presidential mansion, 1800. c, Jefferson, Graff House in Philadelphia, excerpt from the 1st draft of the Declaration of Independence. d, Madison, USS *Constitution* at the defeat of HMS *Guerriere,* 1812. e, Monroe, freed slaves settle Liberia, 1822. f, John Quincy Adams, opening of the Erie Canal, 1825.
No. 1205: a, Fillmore, Commodore Perry laying groundwork for US trade agreement with Japan. b, Pierce, Jefferson Davis and San Xavier del Bac mission, Tucson, AZ, Gadsden Purchase, 1853. c, Buchanan, Pony Express stamp, Buffalo Bill Cody as express rider. d, Lincoln, UPU emblem, Intl. Postal Congress, Paris, 1863. e, Andrew Johnson, polar bear, purchase of Alaska from Russia, 1867. f, Grant, 1st transcontinental railway link, Promontory Point, Utah, 1869.
No. 1206: a, Theodore Roosevelt, construction of the Panama Canal, 1904. b, Taft, Adm. Peary becomes 1st man to reach the North Pole, 1909. c, Wilson, US #C3, cancel commemorating 1st scheduled airmail service, 1918. d, Harding, airship USS *Shenandoah* at Lakehurst, NJ. e, Coolidge, Lindbergh's solo transatlantic flight, 1927. f, Mt. Rushmore, by Gutzon Borglum, 1927.
No. 1207: a, Lyndon B. Johnson, space exploration. b, Nixon visiting PRChina, 1971. c, Ford, tall ship in NY Harbor for Operation Sail, 1976, US bicentennial celebrations. d,

Carter, Sadat of Egypt and Begin of Israel during the Camp David Accords, 1979. e, Reagan, European Space Agency emblem, flags and *Columbia* space shuttle. f, Bush, Grumman Avenger bomber he piloted during WWII.

1989, Nov. 17   Perf. 14
1204	A177	Sheet of 6	6.50	6.50
a.-f.		60c any single	1.00	1.00
1205	A177	Sheet of 6	6.50	6.50
a.-f.		60c any single	1.00	1.00
1206	A177	Sheet of 6	6.50	6.50
a.-f.		60c any single	1.00	1.00
1207	A177	Sheet of 6	6.50	6.50
a.-f.		60c any single	1.00	1.00

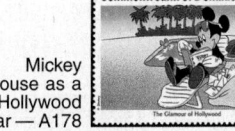

Mickey Mouse as a Hollywood Star — A178

Walt Disney characters: 20c, Reading script. 35c, Television interview. 45c, Named a star in tabloid headline. 60c, Signing autographs. $1, In dressing room, holding fans at bay. $2, Riding in limousine. $3, With Minnie in the limelight. $4, Accepting award. No. 1216, Giving interview during celebrity tennis tournament. No. 1217, Footprint impression in cement outside theater.

1989, Nov. 30   Litho.   Perf. 14x13½
1208	A178	20c multicolored	.50	.50
1209	A178	35c multicolored	.70	.70
1210	A178	45c multicolored	.80	.80
1211	A178	60c multicolored	.90	.90
1212	A178	$1 multicolored	1.25	1.25
1213	A178	$2 multicolored	2.25	2.25
1214	A178	$3 multicolored	3.00	3.00
1215	A178	$4 multicolored	4.00	4.00
		Nos. 1208-1215 (8)	13.40	13.40

Souvenir Sheets
1216	A178	$5 multicolored	5.50	5.50
1217	A178	$5 multicolored	5.50	5.50

Christmas — A179

Religious paintings by Botticelli: 20c, *Madonna in Glory with Seraphim.* 25c, *The Annunciation.* 35c, *Madonna of the Pomegranate.* 45c, *Madonna of the Rose Garden.* 60c, *Madonna of the Book.* $1, *Madonna and Child Under a Baldachin with Three Angels.* $4, *Madonna and Child with Angels.* No. 1225, *Bardi Madonna.* No. 1226, *The Mystic Nativity.* No. 1227, *The Adoration of the Magi.*

1989, Dec. 4   Perf. 14
1218	A179	20c multicolored	.45	.45
1219	A179	25c multicolored	.45	.45
1220	A179	35c multicolored	.60	.60
1221	A179	45c multicolored	.75	.75
1222	A179	60c multicolored	.90	.90
1223	A179	$1 multicolored	1.10	1.10
1224	A179	$4 multicolored	3.00	3.00
1225	A179	$5 multicolored	4.75	4.75
		Nos. 1218-1225 (8)	12.00	12.00

Souvenir Sheets
1226	A179	$5 multicolored	5.00	5.00
1227	A179	$5 multicolored	5.00	5.00

Nehru — A180

$5, Parliament House, New Delhi, horiz.

1989, Dec. 27   Litho.   Perf. 14
1228	A180	60c shown	2.00	2.00

Souvenir Sheet
1229	A180	$5 multicolored	6.00	6.00

Jawaharlal Nehru (1889-1964), 1st prime minister of independent India.

Girl Guides — A181

Guide movement in Dominica, 60th anniv.: 60c, Lady Baden-Powell and Agatha Robinson, former Guide leader on Dominica. $5, Dorris Stockmann, chairman of the world committee of the World Assoc. of Girl Guides and Girl Scouts, and Judith Pestaina, chief commissioner of the Dominica Girl Guides Assoc., horiz.

1989, Dec. 29
1230	A181	60c multicolored	1.25	1.25

Souvenir Sheet
1231	A181	$5 multi, horiz.	5.25	5.25

Miniature Sheet

Marine Life — A182

Designs: a, Cocoa damselfish. b, Stinging jellyfish. c, Dolphin. d, Queen angelfish. e, French angelfish. f, Blue striped grunt. g, Pork fish. h, Hammerhead shark. i, Spadefish. j, Great barracuda. k, Stingray. l, Black grunt. m, Two-spotted butterflyfish. n, Dog snapper. o, Southern puffer. p, Four-eyed butterflyfish. q, Lane snapper. r, Green moray.

1990   Litho.   Perf. 14
1232	A182	Sheet of 18	11.00	11.00
a.-r.		45c any single	.55	.55

Penny Black, 150th Anniv. — A183

Stamp World London '90: 50c, Post Office accelerator, 1830. 60c, $4, No. 1239, London skyline, St. Paul's Cathedral. 90c, Railway post car, 1838. $3, Center cycle, 1883. No. 1240, Mail truck, 1899.

1990, May 3   Litho.   Perf. 13½
1233	A183	45c green & black	.60	.60
1234	A183	50c blk & slate blue	.80	.80
1235	A183	60c dk blue & blk	.85	.85
1236	A183	90c black & green	1.50	1.50
1237	A183	$3 blk & dk bl vio	2.75	2.75
1238	A183	$4 dk bl vio & blk	3.75	3.75
		Nos. 1233-1238 (6)	10.25	10.25

Souvenir Sheet
1239	A183	$5 beige & black	4.50	4.50
1240	A183	$5 gray & red brn	4.50	4.50

A184

Birds: 10c, Blue-headed hummingbird. 20c, Black-capped petrel. 45c, Red-necked parrot. 60c, Black swift. $1, Troupial. $2, Brown noddy. $4, Lesser Antillean pewee. $5, Little blue heron. No. 1249, House wren. No. 1250, Imperial parrot.

1990, July 16   Litho.   Perf. 14
1241	A184	10c multicolored	.40	.40
1242	A184	20c multicolored	.55	.55
1243	A184	45c multicolored	.75	.75

1244	A184	60c multicolored	.95	.95
1245	A184	$1 multicolored	1.60	1.60
1246	A184	$2.25 multicolored	2.25	2.25
1247	A184	$4 multicolored	3.75	3.75
1248	A184	$5 multicolored	4.25	4.25
		Nos. 1241-1248 (8)	14.50	14.50

Souvenir Sheets

1249	A184	$6 multicolored	5.00	5.00
1250	A184	$6 multicolored	5.00	5.00

A185

Shells: 10c, Reticulated cowrie-helmet. 20c, West Indian chank. 35c, West Indian fighting conch. 60c, True tulip. $1, Sunrise tellin. $2, Crown cone. $3, Common dove shell. $4, Atlantic fig shell. No. 1259, Giant tun. No. 1260, King helmet.

1990, July 19

1251	A185	10c multicolored	.40	.40
1252	A185	20c multicolored	.55	.55
1253	A185	35c multicolored	.70	.70
1254	A185	60c multicolored	1.00	1.00
1255	A185	$1 multicolored	1.40	1.40
1256	A185	$2 multicolored	2.25	2.25
1257	A185	$3 multicolored	3.00	3.00
1258	A185	$4 multicolored	3.75	3.75
		Nos. 1251-1258 (8)	13.05	13.05

Souvenir Sheets

1259	A185	$5 multicolored	5.00	5.00
1260	A185	$5 multicolored	5.00	5.00

A186

Queen Mother, 90th Birthday: various photos.

1990, Sept. 10

1261	A186	20c multicolored	.25	.25
1262	A186	45c multicolored	.40	.40
1263	A186	60c multicolored	.60	.60
1264	A186	$3 multicolored	2.50	2.50
		Nos. 1261-1264 (4)	3.75	3.75

Souvenir Sheet

1265	A186	$5 multicolored	3.50	3.50

A187

45c, Men's singles, tennis. 60c, Men's foil fencing. $2, 100m freestyle swimming. $3, Star class yachting. $5, Coxless pairs, rowing.

1990, Nov. 5   Litho.   Perf. 14

1266	A187	45c multicolored	1.25	1.25
1267	A187	60c multicolored	1.40	1.40
1268	A187	$2 multicolored	2.25	2.25
1269	A187	$3 multicolored	3.25	3.25
		Nos. 1266-1269 (4)	8.15	8.15

Souvenir Sheet

1270	A187	$5 multicolored	6.75	6.75

1992 Summer Olympics, Barcelona.

Christmas — A188

Walt Disney characters on carousel animals: 10c, Mickey, frog. 15c, Huey, Dewey &

Louie, white elephant. 25c, Donald, polar bear. 45c, Goofy, goat. $1, Donald, giraffe. $2, Daisy, stork. $4, Goofy, lion. $5, Daisy, horse. No. 1279, Mickey, swan chariot, horiz. No. 1280, Mickey, Minnie & Goofy, griffin chariot.

1990, Dec. 13   Perf. 13½x14

1271	A188	10c multicolored	.40	.40
1272	A188	15c multicolored	.50	.50
1273	A188	25c multicolored	.60	.60
1274	A188	45c multicolored	.90	.90
1275	A188	$1 multicolored	1.25	1.25
1276	A188	$2 multicolored	2.00	2.00
1277	A188	$4 multicolored	4.00	4.00
1278	A188	$5 multicolored	5.00	5.00
		Nos. 1271-1278 (8)	14.65	14.65

Souvenir Sheets
Perf. 14x13½

1279	A188	$6 multicolored	7.00	7.00
1280	A188	$6 multicolored	7.00	7.00

World Cup Soccer Championships, Italy — A189

Players and coaches from participating countries.

1990, Dec. 28   Litho.   Perf. 14

1281	A189	15c England	.45	.45
1282	A189	45c Brazil	.75	.75
1283	A189	60c West Germany	1.00	1.00
1284	A189	$4 Austria	4.25	4.25
		Nos. 1281-1284 (4)	6.45	6.45

Souvenir Sheets

1285	A189	$6 Ireland, vert.	5.00	5.00
1286	A189	$6 USSR, vert.	5.00	5.00

Cog Trains of Switzerland A190

Designs: 10c, Glion-Roches de Naye, 1890. 35c, Electric cog rail car ascending Mt. Pilatus. 45c, Cog railway to Schynige Platte, view of Eiger, Monch and Jungfrau Mountains. 60c, Furka-Oberalp train on Bugnli Viaduct, vert. $1, 1910 Jungfraubahn Cog Railway, Jungfrau Mountain, 1910. $2, Testing Swiss rail cars built for Pike's Peak on Arth-Rigibahn, 1963. $4, Brienz-Rothorn Bahn, 1991. $5, Private 1870 Rigi-Scheideck Hotel post stamp, 1890 Arth-Rigi Railway Engine. No. 1295, Sherlock Holmes watching Brunigline train descending from Brunig Pass. No. 1296, Switzerland #738 and first passenger train to ascend Mt. Rigi, 1871.

1991, Mar. 26   Litho.   Perf. 14

1287	A190	10c multicolored	.60	.60
1288	A190	35c multicolored	1.00	1.00
1289	A190	45c multicolored	1.10	1.10
1290	A190	60c multicolored	1.25	1.25
1291	A190	$1 multicolored	1.40	1.40
1292	A190	$2 multicolored	2.00	2.00
1293	A190	$4 multicolored	3.00	3.00
1294	A190	$5 multicolored	3.50	3.50
		Nos. 1287-1294 (8)	13.85	13.85

Souvenir Sheets
Perf. 13½

1295	A190	$6 multicolored	6.00	6.00
1296	A190	$6 multicolored	6.00	6.00

Nos. 1295-1296 each contain one 50x37mm stamp.

Voyages of Discovery A191

Explorer's ships: 10c, Gil Eannes, 1433-1434. 25c, Alfonso Gonclaves Baldaya, 1436. 45c, Bartolomeu Dias, 1487. 60c, Vasco da Gama, 1497-1499. $1, Vallarte the Dane. $2, Aloisio Cadamosto, 1456-1458. $4, Diogo Gomes, 1455. $5, Diogo Cao, 1482-1485. No. 1305, Blue and yellow macaw. No. 1306, Red and yellow macaw.

1991, Apr. 8   Litho.   Perf. 14

1297	A191	10c multicolored	.45	.45
1298	A191	25c multicolored	.55	.55
1299	A191	45c multicolored	.65	.65
1300	A191	60c multicolored	.75	.75
1301	A191	$1 multicolored	1.10	1.10
1302	A191	$2 multicolored	1.60	1.60
1303	A191	$4 multicolored	2.75	2.75
1304	A191	$5 multicolored	3.25	3.25
		Nos. 1297-1304 (8)	11.10	11.10

Souvenir Sheets

1305	A191	$6 multicolored	4.75	4.75
1306	A191	$6 multicolored	4.75	4.75

Discovery of America, 500th anniv. (in 1992).

Japanese Costumes A192

Walt Disney characters wearing Japanese costumes: 10c, Donald as soldier. 15c, Mickey as Kabuki actor. 25c, Mickey, Minnie in traditional wedding clothes. 45c, Daisy as Geisha girl, vert. $1, Mickey in sokutai dress of high government official, vert. $2, Goofy as mino farmer, vert. $4, Pete as shogun, vert. $5, Donald as warlord. No. 1315, Mickey, as Noh player, vert. No. 1316, Goofy as Kabubei-Jishi street performer, vert.

1991, May 22   Litho.   Perf. 14

1307	A192	10c multicolored	.65	.65
1308	A192	15c multicolored	.75	.75
1309	A192	25c multicolored	.90	.90
1310	A192	45c multicolored	1.10	1.10
1311	A192	$1 multicolored	2.00	2.00
1312	A192	$2 multicolored	2.75	2.75
1313	A192	$4 multicolored	3.50	3.50
1314	A192	$5 multicolored	4.25	4.25
		Nos. 1307-1314 (8)	15.90	15.90

Souvenir Sheets

1315	A192	$6 multicolored	7.50	7.50
1316	A192	$6 multicolored	7.50	7.50

Phila Nippon '91.

Mushrooms — A193

10c, Horn of plenty. 15c, Shaggy mane. 45c, Yellow morel. 60c, Chanterelle. $1, Blewit. $2, Slippery jack. $4, Emetic russula. $5, Honey mushroom.
No. 1326, Beefsteak polypore. No. 1327, Voluminous-latex milky.

1991, June 3   Litho.   Perf. 14

1318	A193	10c multicolored	.25	.25
1319	A193	15c multicolored	.45	.45
1320	A193	45c multicolored	.55	.55
1321	A193	60c multicolored	.65	.65
1322	A193	$1 multicolored	1.00	1.00
1323	A193	$2 multicolored	1.75	1.75
1324	A193	$4 multicolored	3.00	3.00
1325	A193	$5 multicolored	4.00	4.00
		Nos. 1318-1325 (8)	11.65	11.65

Souvenir Sheets

1326	A193	$6 multicolored	5.00	5.00
1327	A193	$6 multicolored	5.00	5.00

Royal Family Birthday, Anniversary
Common Design Type

1991, June 17   Litho.   Perf. 14

1328	CD347	10c multicolored	.45	.45
1329	CD347	15c multicolored	.90	.90
1330	CD347	40c multicolored	1.00	1.00
1331	CD347	60c multicolored	1.10	1.10
1332	CD347	$1 multicolored	2.00	2.00
1333	CD347	$2 multicolored	2.75	2.75
1334	CD347	$4 multicolored	4.00	4.00
1335	CD347	$5 multicolored	4.50	4.50
		Nos. 1328-1335 (8)	16.70	16.70

Souvenir Sheets

1336	CD347	$5 Elizabeth, Philip	5.00	5.00
1337	CD347	$5 Charles, Diana, sons	8.50	8.50

10c, 60c, $2, $4, No. 1336, Queen Elizabeth II, 65th birthday. Others, Charles and Diana, 10th wedding anniversary.

Vincent Van Gogh (1853-1890), Painter A194

Paintings: 10c, Thatched Cottages. 25c, The House of Pere Eloi. 45c, The Midday Siesta. 60c, Portrait of a Young Peasant, vert. $1, Still Life: Vase with Irises Against a Yellow Background, vert. $2, Still Life Vase with Irises. $4, Blossoming Almond Tree. $5, Irises. No. 1346, A Meadow in the Mountains: Le Mas De Saint-Paul. No. 1347, Doctor Gachet's Garden in Auvers, vert.

1991, July 8   Litho.   Perf. 13½

1338	A194	10c multicolored	.65	.65
1339	A194	25c multicolored	.90	.90
1340	A194	45c multicolored	1.10	1.10
1341	A194	60c multicolored	1.40	1.40
1342	A194	$1 multicolored	2.00	2.00
1343	A194	$2 multicolored	2.50	2.50
1344	A194	$4 multicolored	3.75	3.75
1345	A194	$5 multicolored	4.00	4.00
		Nos. 1338-1345 (8)	16.30	16.30

Size: 101x75mm
Imperf

1346	A194	$6 multicolored	6.50	6.50
1347	A194	$6 multicolored	6.50	6.50

Intl. Literacy Year — A195

Scenes from Walt Disney's "The Little Mermaid": 10c, Ariel with Flounder and Sebastian. 25c, King Triton. 45c, Sebastian drums in "Kiss De Girl" concert. 60c, Flotsam and Jetsam taunt Ariel. $1, Scuttle, Flounder and Ariel. $2, Ariel and Flounder discover a book. $4, Prince Eric, dog Max, manservant Grimsby, and crew. $5, Ursula the sea witch. No. 1356, Ariel transformed into human being. No. 1357, Ariel and Prince Eric dancing in town, vert.

1991, Aug. 6   Perf. 14

1348	A195	10c multicolored	.35	.35
1349	A195	25c multicolored	.45	.45
1350	A195	45c multicolored	.65	.65
1351	A195	60c multicolored	.90	.90
1352	A195	$1 multicolored	1.50	1.50
1353	A195	$2 multicolored	2.75	2.75
1354	A195	$4 multicolored	4.50	4.50
1355	A195	$5 multicolored	5.50	5.50
		Nos. 1348-1355 (8)	16.60	16.60

Souvenir Sheets

1356	A195	$6 multicolored	6.50	6.50
1357	A195	$6 multicolored	6.50	6.50

World Landmarks A196

Designs: 10c, Empire State Building, US, vert. 25c, Kremlin, USSR. 45c, Buckingham Palace, United Kingdom. 60c, Eiffel Tower, France, vert. $1, Taj Mahal, India. $2, Sydney Opera House, Australia. $4, Colosseum, Italy. $5, Pyramids, Egypt. No. 1366, Galileo demonstrating laws of physics from Tower of Pisa, Italy. No. 1367, Great Wall of China and Emperor Shi Huang Ti.

1991, Aug. 12   Litho.   Perf. 14

1358	A196	10c multicolored	.45	.45
1359	A196	25c multicolored	.55	.55
1360	A196	45c multicolored	.90	.90
1361	A196	60c multicolored	1.10	1.10
1362	A196	$1 multicolored	2.00	2.00
1363	A196	$2 multicolored	3.00	3.00
1364	A196	$4 multicolored	4.75	4.75
1365	A196	$5 multicolored	5.50	5.50
		Nos. 1358-1365 (8)	18.25	18.25

Souvenir Sheets

1366	A196	$6 multicolored	8.00	8.00
1367	A196	$6 multicolored	8.00	8.00

Japanese Attack
on Pearl Harbor,
50th
Anniv. — A197

Designs: 10c, 6:00am, First wave of Japanese planes leave carrier Akagi. 15c, 6:40am, Destroyer Ward and PBY attack midget submarine. 45c, 7:00am, Second wave of Japanese planes leave carriers. 60c, 7:48am, Japanese Zeros attack on Kaneohe Air Station. $1, 8:30am, Destroyers Breeze, Medusa and Curtiss sink midget submarine. $2, 8:45am, Damaged battleship Nevada sorties. $4, 8:10am, Battleship Arizona explodes, killing 1,177 men. $5, 9:45am, Japanese attack ends. No. 1376, 8:00am, Japanese fighters and bombers attack Hickam Air Base. No. 1377, 7:55am, Pearl Harbor attack begins.

1991, Sept. 2

1368	A197	10c multicolored	.60	.60
1369	A197	15c multicolored	.70	.70
1370	A197	45c multicolored	1.10	1.10
1371	A197	60c multicolored	1.25	1.25
1372	A197	$1 multicolored	1.50	1.50
1373	A197	$2 multicolored	2.00	2.00
1374	A197	$4 multicolored	2.75	2.75
1375	A197	$5 multicolored	3.00	3.00
		Nos. 1368-1375 (8)	12.90	12.90

Souvenir Sheets

1376	A197	$6 multicolored	5.25	5.25
1377	A197	$6 multicolored	5.25	5.25

Butterflies — A198

1c, Little yellow. 2c, Gulf fritillary. 5c, Monarch. 10c, Red rim. 15c, Flambeau. 20c, Large orange sulphur. 25c, Caribbean buckeye. 35c, Polydamas swallowtail. 45c, Cassius blue. 55c, Great southern white. 60c, Godman's leaf. 65c, Hanno blue. 90c, Mimic. $1, Longtailed skipper. $1.20, Orion. $2, Cloudless sulphur. $5, Painted lady. $10, Southern daggertail. $20, White peacock.

Perf. 13½x13, 13½x14 (2c, 10c, 15c, 25c, 45c, 90c, $1, $20)

1991-93

1378	A198	1c multi	.35	.90
1379	A198	2c multi	.35	.90
1380	A198	5c multi	.65	.90
1381	A198	10c multi	.65	.25
1382	A198	15c multi	.75	.25
1383	A198	20c multi	.75	.25
1384	A198	25c multi	.75	.25
1385	A198	35c multi	.85	.35
1386	A198	45c multi	.85	.35
1386A	A198	55c multi	1.25	.60
1387	A198	60c multi	1.00	.40
1387A	A198	65c multi	1.25	.60
1388	A198	90c multi	1.40	.60
1389	A198	$1 multi	1.40	.75
1389A	A198	$1.20 multi	1.50	1.50
1390	A198	$2 multi	2.25	2.25
1391	A198	$5 multi	3.75	5.50
1391A	A198	$10 multi	9.00	11.00
1391B	A198	$20 multi	14.00	16.00
		Nos. 1378-1391B (19)	42.75	43.60

Issued: 55c, 65c, $1.20, 1/11/93; others, 10/14/91.

Charles de Gaulle,
Birth Cent. — A199

1991, Nov. 1

1392	A199	45c shown	2.25	2.25

Souvenir Sheet

1393	A199	$5 blk & bl, horiz.	6.00	6.00

Creole Week — A200

45c, Man in 18th cent. costume. 60c, Accordion player. $1, Dancers. $5, Stick fight c. 1785.

1991, Nov. 1   *Perf. 14*

1394	A200	45c multicolored	.60	.60
1395	A200	60c multicolored	.90	.90
1396	A200	$1 multicolored	1.50	1.50
		Nos. 1394-1396 (3)	3.00	3.00

Souvenir Sheet

1397	A200	$5 multicolored	6.50	6.50

Credit Union, 40th
Anniv. — A201

60c, Emblem, founder, horiz.

1991, Nov. 1

1398	A201	10c black	.55	.55
1399	A201	60c blk, red, org, yel	1.50	1.50

Year of the
Environment and
Shelter — A202

15c, Keep the beaches clean. 60c, No. 1402, Amazona imperalis. No. 1403, Lagoon outlet.

1991, Nov. 18

1400	A202	15c multicolored	.50	.50
1401	A202	60c multicolored	2.75	2.75

Souvenir Sheets

1402	A202	$5 multicolored	7.75	7.75
1403	A202	$5 multicolored	7.75	7.75

Christmas — A203

Paintings by Jan van Eyck: 10c, The Virgin Enthroned with Child (detail). 20c, The Madonna at the Fountain. 35c, The Virgin in a Church. 45c, The Madonna with Canon van der Paele. 60c, The Madonna with Canon van der Paele (detail). $1, The Madonna in an Interior. $3, The Annunciation. $5, The Annunciation, diff. No. 1412, The Madonna with Chancellor Rolin. No. 1413, Virgin and Child with Saints and Donor.

1991, Dec. 2   *Perf. 12*

1404	A203	10c multicolored	.55	.55
1405	A203	20c multicolored	.75	.75
1406	A203	35c multicolored	.90	.90
1407	A203	45c multicolored	1.00	1.00
1408	A203	60c multicolored	1.50	1.50
1409	A203	$1 multicolored	1.75	1.75
1410	A203	$3 multicolored	2.75	2.75
1411	A203	$5 multicolored	4.00	4.00
		Nos. 1404-1411 (8)	13.20	13.20

Souvenir Sheets
Perf. 14x14½

1412	A203	$6 multicolored	6.50	6.50
1413	A203	$6 multicolored	6.50	6.50

**Queen Elizabeth II's Accession to
the Throne, 40th Anniv.**
Common Design Type

1992, Feb. 6   Litho.   *Perf. 14*

1414	CD348	10c multicolored	.25	.25
1415	CD348	15c multicolored	.25	.25
1416	CD348	$1 multicolored	.75	.75
1417	CD348	$5 multicolored	3.75	3.75
		Nos. 1414-1417 (4)	5.00	5.00

Souvenir Sheets

1418	CD348	$6 River scene	3.75	3.75
1419	CD348	$6 Seaside village	3.75	3.75

Botanical Gardens,
Cent. — A204

Designs: 10c, Cricket match. 15c, Scenic entrance. 45c, Traveller's tree. 60c, Bamboo house. $1, Old pavilion. $2, Ficus benjamina. $4, Cricket ground. $5, Thirty-five steps. No. 1428, Fountain. No. 1429, Cricket masters.

1992, Mar. 30   Litho.   *Perf. 14*

1420	A204	10c multicolored	.40	.40
1421	A204	15c multicolored	.40	.40
1422	A204	45c multicolored	.40	.40
1423	A204	60c multicolored	.60	.60
1424	A204	$1 multicolored	1.00	1.00
1425	A204	$2 multicolored	1.75	1.75
1426	A204	$4 multicolored	4.25	4.25
1427	A204	$5 multicolored	4.50	4.50
		Nos. 1420-1427 (8)	13.30	13.30

Souvenir Sheets

1428	A204	$6 multicolored	5.00	5.00
1429	A204	$6 multicolored	5.00	5.00

Spanish
Art — A205

Paintings or details from paintings by Velazquez: 10c, Pope Innocent X. 45c, The Forge of Vulcan (different details). 60c, Queen Mariana of Austria. $1, Pablo de Valladolid. $2, Sebastian de Morra. $3, Felipe IV (detail). $4, Felipe IV. No. 1438, Surrender of Breda. No. 1439, The Drunkards.

1992, May 4   *Perf. 13*

1430	A205	10c multicolored	.25	.25
1431	A205	15c multicolored	.25	.25
1432	A205	45c multicolored	.45	.45
1433	A205	60c multicolored	.55	.55
1434	A205	$1 multicolored	.80	.80
1435	A205	$2 multicolored	1.50	1.50
1436	A205	$3 multicolored	2.25	2.25
1437	A205	$4 multicolored	2.75	2.75

Size: 120x95mm
Imperf

1438	A205	$6 multicolored	4.75	4.75
1439	A205	$6 multicolored	4.75	4.75
		Nos. 1430-1439 (10)	18.30	18.30

Granada '92.

Easter
A206

Paintings: 10c, The Supper at Emmaus, studio of Gerrit Van Honthorst. 15c, Christ before Caiaphas, by Van Honthorst, vert. 45c, The Taking of Christ, by Valentin de Boulogne. 60c, Pilate Washing his Hands, by Mattia Preti, vert. $1, The Last Supper (detail), by Master of the Reredos of The Chapel of the Church of S. Francisco D'Evora. $2, The Three Marys at the Tomb (detail), by Adolphe William Bouguereau, vert. $3, Denial of St. Peter, by Hendrik Terbrugghen. $5, Doubting Thomas, by Bernardo Strozzi, vert. No. 1448, The Crucifixion (detail), by Mathias Grunewald, vert. No. 1449, The Resurrection (detail), by Caravaggio, vert.

1992   *Perf. 14*

1440	A206	10c multicolored	.25	.25
1441	A206	15c multicolored	.25	.25
1442	A206	45c multicolored	.50	.50
1443	A206	60c multicolored	.75	.75
1444	A206	$1 multicolored	.90	.90
1445	A206	$2 multicolored	1.50	1.50
1446	A206	$3 multicolored	2.25	2.25
1447	A206	$5 multicolored	3.75	3.75
		Nos. 1440-1447 (8)	10.15	10.15

Souvenir Sheets

1448	A206	$6 multicolored	5.00	5.00
1449	A206	$6 multicolored	5.00	5.00

Columbus and New
World Flora and
Fauna — A207

10c, Hercules beetle. 25c, Crapaud frog. 75c, Parrot. $2, Anole. $4, Royal gramma. $5, Hibiscus.

No. 1456, Giant katydid. No. 1457, Columbus' fleet.

1992, May 18

1450	A207	10c multi	.50	.50
1451	A207	25c multi	1.00	1.00
1452	A207	75c multi	1.75	1.75
1453	A207	$2 multi	2.00	2.00
1454	A207	$4 multi	2.75	2.75
1455	A207	$5 multi	3.50	3.50
		Nos. 1450-1455 (6)	11.50	11.50

Souvenir Sheets

1456	A207	$6 multi	5.00	5.00
1457	A207	$6 multi	5.00	5.00

Nos. 1456-1457 are horiz.

Hummingbirds
A208

10c, Purple throated carib. 15c, Rufous breasted hermit. 45c, Puerto Rican emerald. 60c, Antillean mango. $1, Green throated carib. $2, Blue headed. $4, Eastern streamertail. $5, Antillean crested. No. 1466, Green mango. No. 1467, Vervain hummingbird.

1992, May 28

1458	A208	10c multicolored	.50	.50
1459	A208	15c multicolored	.50	.50
1460	A208	45c multicolored	.75	.75
1461	A208	60c multicolored	.90	.90
1462	A208	$1 multicolored	1.25	1.25
1463	A208	$2 multicolored	2.25	2.25
1464	A208	$4 multicolored	3.75	3.75
1465	A208	$5 multicolored	4.50	4.50
		Nos. 1458-1465 (8)	14.40	14.40

Souvenir Sheets

1466	A208	$6 multicolored	6.75	6.75
1467	A208	$6 multicolored	6.75	6.75

Genoa '92.

Dinosaurs
A209

10c, Camptosaurus. 15c, Edmontosaurus. 25c, Corythosaurus. 60c, Stegosaurus. $1, Torosaurus. $3, Euoplocephalus. $4, Tyrannosaurus. $5, Parasaurolophus.

1992, June 23   Litho.   *Perf. 14*

1468	A209	10c multi	.50	.50
1469	A209	15c multi	.60	.60
1470	A209	25c multi	.75	.75
1471	A209	60c multi	.85	.85
1472	A209	$1 multi	1.00	1.00
1473	A209	$3 multi	1.90	1.90
1474	A209	$4 multi	3.00	3.00
1475	A209	$5 multi	3.50	3.50
		Nos. 1468-1475 (8)	12.10	12.10

Souvenir Sheets

1476	A209	$6 like #1472	4.75	4.75
1477	A209	$6 like #1470	4.75	4.75

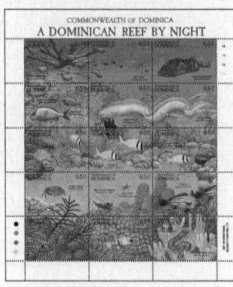

Marine Life — A210

No. 1478: a, Copper sweeper (b). b, Sea wasp (c). c, Nassau grouper. d, Glasseye snapper, margate. e, Green moray (f). f, Reef squid. g, Octopus. h, Porkfish (g, i). i, Reef squirrelfish (h). j, Coral crab, flower coral. k, Red coral shrimp, sea star, pillar coral (l, n). l, Cubbyu, brain coral (n, m, Basket starfish, thick finger coral. n, Belted cardinal fish, boulder coral (k, m). o, Fire worm, crenelated fire coral.

No. 1479: a, Trumpetfish, blue chromis. b, Queen triggerfish. c, Hawksbill turtle. d, Sergeant major, rock beauty. e, Sharksucker. f, Lemon shark. g, Spotted trunkfish, bluehead. h, Blue tang, yellowtail damselfish. i, Queen angelfish, banded butterflyfish. j, Spotted seahorse, flower coral. k, Stoplight parrotfish, pillar coral. l, Smallmouth grunt, brain coral. m, Flamingo tongue, thick finger coral. n, Arrow crab, boulder coral. o, Sharknose goby, crenelated fire coral.

No. 1480, Harlequin bass. No. 1481, Flamefish.

1992, July 20		Litho.	Perf. 14	
1478	A210	65c Sheet of 15, #a.-o.	7.75	7.75
1479	A210	65c Sheet of 15, #a.-o.	7.75	7.75

Souvenir Sheets

1480	A210	$6 multicolored	6.50	6.50
1481	A210	$6 multicolored	6.50	6.50

A211

10c, Archery. 15c, Two-man canoeing. 25c, 110-meter hurdles. 60c, Men's high jump. $1, Greco-Roman wrestling. $2, Men's rings. $4, Men's parallel bars. $5, Equestrian.
No. 1490, Field hockey. No. 1491, Women's platform diving.

1992, Aug. 10		Litho.	Perf. 14	
1482	A211	10c multi	.30	.30
1483	A211	15c multi	.35	.35
1484	A211	25c multi	.40	.40
1485	A211	60c multi	.65	.65
1486	A211	$1 multi	.90	.90
1487	A211	$2 multi	1.50	1.50
1488	A211	$4 multi	2.75	2.75
1489	A211	$5 multi	3.25	3.25
		Nos. 1482-1489 (8)	10.10	10.10

Souvenir Sheets

1490	A211	$6 multi	5.50	5.50
1491	A211	$6 multi	5.50	5.50

1992 Summer Olympics, Barcelona.

A212

1992		Litho.	Perf. 14½	
1492	A212	$1 Coming ashore	1.00	1.00
1493	A212	$2 Natives, ships	1.75	2.00

Discovery of America, 500th anniv. Organization of East Caribbean States.

Walt Disney's Goofy, 60th Anniv. A213

Scenes from Disney cartoon films: 10c, Two Weeks Vacation, 1952. 15c, Aquamania, 1961. 25c, Goofy Gymnastics, 1949. 45c, How to Ride a Horse, 1941. $1, Foul Hunting, 1947. $2, For Whom the Bulls Toil, 1953. $4, Tennis Racquet, 1949. $5, Double Dribble, 1946. No. 1502, Aquamania, 1961, vert. No. 1503, The Goofy Sports Story, 1956, vert.

1992, Nov. 11		Litho.	Perf. 14x13½	
1494	A213	10c multicolored	.45	.45
1495	A213	15c multicolored	.55	.55
1496	A213	25c multicolored	.80	.80
1497	A213	45c multicolored	.90	.90
1498	A213	$1 multicolored	1.50	1.50
1499	A213	$2 multicolored	2.75	2.75
1500	A213	$4 multicolored	4.75	4.75
1501	A213	$5 multicolored	5.25	5.25
		Nos. 1494-1501 (8)	16.95	16.95

Souvenir Sheets
Perf. 13½x14

1502	A213	$6 multicolored	7.75	7.75
1503	A213	$6 multicolored	7.75	7.75

Model Trains — A214

15c, Brass Reno 4-4-0, HO scale, c. 1963. 25c, Union Pacific Golden Classic, G gauge, 1992. 55c, LMS 3rd class brake coach, OO scale, 1970s. 65c, Brass Wabash 2-6-0, HO scale, c. 1958. 75c, Pennsylvania RR T-1 duplex, O gauge, 1991. $1, Streamline engine 2-6-0, O gauge, post World War II. $3, Japanese Natl. Railways class C62, HO scale, c. 1960. $5, Tinplate friction-drive floor trains, 1960s. No. 1512, 1st "toy" train in Japan, 1854. No. 1513, Stephenson's Rocket, 1:26 scale, c. 1972, vert.

1992, Nov. 11			Perf. 14	
1504	A214	15c multicolored	.45	.45
1505	A214	25c multicolored	.50	.55
1506	A214	55c multicolored	.75	.75
1507	A214	65c multicolored	.90	.90
1508	A214	75c multicolored	1.00	1.00
1509	A214	$1 multicolored	1.25	1.25
1510	A214	$3 multicolored	2.75	2.75
1511	A214	$5 multicolored	4.50	4.50
		Nos. 1504-1511 (8)	12.10	12.15

Souvenir Sheets
Perf. 13

1512	A214	$6 multicolored	5.50	5.50
1513	A214	$6 multicolored	5.50	5.50

No. 1512 contains one 52x40mm stamp, No. 1513 one 39x51mm stamp.

Hummel Figurines — A215

Angel: 20c, Playing violin. 25c, Playing horn. 55c, Playing mandolin. 65c, Seated, playing trumpet. 90c, On cloud with lantern. $1, Holding candle. $1.20, Flying. $6, On cloud with candle.

1992, Nov.			Perf. 14	
1514	A215	20c multicolored	.35	.35
1515	A215	25c multicolored	.35	.35
1516	A215	55c multicolored	.55	.55
1517	A215	65c multicolored	.70	.70
a.		Sheet of 4, #1514-1517	2.25	2.25
1518	A215	90c multicolored	1.00	1.00
1519	A215	$1 multicolored	1.25	1.25
1520	A215	$1.20 multicolored	1.50	1.50
1521	A215	$6 multicolored	3.25	3.25
a.		Sheet of 4, #1518-1521	8.00	8.00
		Nos. 1514-1521 (8)	8.95	8.95

Anniversaries and Events
A216   A217

Designs: 25c, Graf Zeppelin, 1929. No. 1523, Elderly man, plant. No. 1524, Elderly man on bicycle. No. 1525, Elderly man helping boy bait hook. No. 1526, Konrad Adenauer. No. 1527, Space shuttle. No. 1528, Wolfgang Amadeus Mozart. No. 1529, Snowy egret. No. 1530, Sir Thomas Lipton, Shamrock V, 1930. $2, Men pulling fishing net toward beach. $3, Helen Keller. No. 1533, Earth Resources Satellite. No. 1534, Map of Germany, 1949. No. 1535, Eland. $5, Count Ferdinand von Zeppelin. No. 1537, Cologne Cathedral, Germany. No. 1538, Scene from the Magic Flute. No. 1539, Mir Space Station. No. 1540, Engine of Graf Zeppelin. No. 1541, Rhinoceros hornbill.

1992		Litho.	Perf. 14	
1522	A216	25c multicolored	.60	.60
1523	A216	45c multicolored	.80	.80
1524	A216	45c multicolored	.80	.80
1525	A216	45c multicolored	.80	.80
1526	A216	90c multicolored	.90	.90
1527	A216	90c multicolored	.90	.90
1528	A217	$1.20 multicolored	2.00	2.00
1529	A216	$1.20 multicolored	1.50	1.50
1530	A216	$1.20 multicolored	1.75	1.75
1531	A216	$2 multicolored	1.75	1.75
1532	A216	$3 multicolored	3.00	3.00
1533	A216	$4 multicolored	3.00	3.00
1534	A216	$4 multicolored	4.25	4.25
1535	A216	$4 multicolored	4.25	4.25
1536	A216	$5 multicolored	5.00	5.00
		Nos. 1522-1536 (15)	31.30	31.30

Souvenir Sheets

1537	A216	$6 multicolored	6.25	6.25
1538	A217	$6 multicolored	6.75	6.75
1539	A216	$6 multicolored	6.25	6.25
1540	A216	$6 multicolored	6.25	6.25
1541	A216	$6 multicolored	5.75	5.75

Konrad Adenauer, 25th anniv. of death (Nos. 1526, 1534, 1537). Intl. Space Year (Nos. 1527, 1533, 1539). Mozart, 200th anniv. of death (in 1991) (Nos. 1528, 1538). Count Zeppelin, 75th anniv. of death (Nos. 1522, 1536, 1540). Intl. Day of the Elderly (Nos. 1523-1525). UN Earth Summit, Rio (Nos. 1529, 1535, 1541). America's Cup yacht race (No. 1530). WHO Intl. Conference on Nutrition, Rome (No. 1531). Lions Intl., 75th anniv. (No. 1532).
Issued: Nos. 1528, 1539, Oct.; Nos. 1523-1527, 1533-1534, 1537-1538, Nov.; Nos. 1522, 1529, 1535-1536, 1540-1541, Dec.

Miniature Sheet

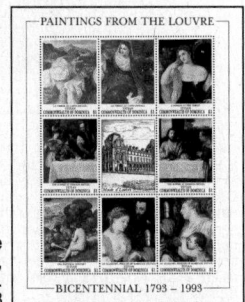

Louvre Museum, Bicent. A218

Details or entire paintings by Titian: a-b, Madonna and Child with St. Catherine and a Rabbit (diff. details). c, A Woman at Her Toilet. d-e, The Supper at Emmaus (diff. details). f, The Pastoral Concert. g-h, An Allegory, Perhaps of Marriage (diff. details).
Painting by Hieronymus Bosch: $6, The Ship of Fools.

1993, Mar. 24		Litho.	Perf. 12	
1542	A218	$1 Sheet of 8, #a.-h. + label	9.50	9.50

Souvenir Sheet
Perf. 14½

1543	A218	$6 multicolored	5.75	5.75

No. 1543 contains one 55x88mm stamp.

Elvis Presley, 15th Anniv. of Death (in 1992) — A219

a, Portrait. b, With guitar. c, Holding microphone.

1993, Feb.			Perf. 14	
1544	A219	$1 Strip of 3, #a.-c.	3.75	3.75

Miniature Sheet

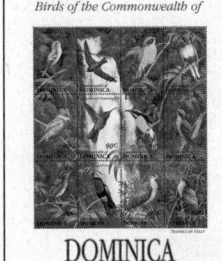

Birds of Dominica A220

a, Plumbeous warbler. b, Black swift. c, Blue-hooded euphonia. d, Rufous-throated solitaire. e, Ringed kingfisher. f, Blue-headed hummingbird. g, Bananaquit. h, Trembler. i, Forest thrush. j, Purple-throated carib. k, Ruddy quail dove. l, Least bittern.
No. 1546, Imperial parrot. No. 1547, Red-necked parrot (Amazona arausiaca).

1993, Apr. 30				
1545	A220	90c Sheet of 12, #a.-l.	18.00	18.00

Souvenir Sheets

1546	A220	$6 multicolored	6.50	6.50
1547	A220	$6 multicolored	6.50	6.50

Turtles — A221

25c, Leatherback laying eggs. 55c, Hawksbill. 65c, Atlantic Ridley. 90c, Green turtle laying eggs. $1, Green turtle at sea. $2, Hawksbill, diff. $4, Loggerhead. $5, Leatherback at sea. No. 1556, Green turtle hatchling. No. 1557, Head of hawksbill.

1993, May 26		Litho.	Perf. 14	
1548	A221	25c multicolored	.45	.45
1549	A221	55c multicolored	.55	.55
1550	A221	65c multicolored	.75	.75
1551	A221	90c multicolored	.95	.95
1552	A221	$1 multicolored	1.10	1.10
1553	A221	$2 multicolored	1.75	1.75
1554	A221	$4 multicolored	3.25	3.25
1555	A221	$5 multicolored	4.25	4.25
		Nos. 1548-1555 (8)	13.05	13.05

Souvenir Sheets

1556	A221	$6 multicolored	5.75	5.75
1557	A221	$6 multicolored	5.75	5.75

For overprints see Nos. 2103-2107.

Automobiles A222

Designs: 90c, 1928 Model A Ford. $1.20, Mercedes-Benz winning Swiss Grand Prix, 1936. $4, Mercedes-Benz winning German Grand Prix, 1935. $5, 1915 Model T Ford.
No. 1562: a, 1993 Mercedes-Benz coupe/roadster. b, 1893 Benz Viktoria. No. 1563, Ford GT-40.

1993, May		Litho.	Perf. 14	
1558	A222	90c multicolored	.80	.80
1559	A222	$1.20 multicolored	1.10	1.10
1560	A222	$4 multicolored	2.75	2.75
1561	A222	$5 multicolored	3.75	3.75
		Nos. 1558-1561 (4)	8.40	8.40

Souvenir Sheets

1562	A222	$3 Sheet of 2,		
		#a.-b.	5.00	5.00
1563	A222	$6 multicolored	5.00	5.00

No. 1563 contains one 57x42mm stamp. First Ford gasoline engine, cent. (Nos. 1558, 1561, 1563). Benz's first four-wheeled vehicle, cent. (Nos. 1559-1560, 1562).

Dominica Grammar School, Cent. — A223

Designs: 25c, School crest. 30c, V. A. A. Archer, first West Indian headmaster. 65c, Hubert A. Charles, first Dominican headmaster. 90c, Present school building.

1993, May

1564	A223	25c multicolored	.25	.25
1565	A223	30c multicolored	.30	.30
1566	A223	65c multicolored	.60	.60
1567	A223	90c multicolored	.85	.85
		Nos. 1564-1567 (4)	2.00	2.00

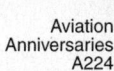

Aviation Anniversaries A224

Designs: 25c, New York ticker tape parade, 1928. 55c, BAC Lightning F2. 65c, Graf Zeppelin over Sphinx, pyramids, 1929. $1, Boeing 314 flying boat. $2, Astronaut stepping onto moon. $4, Viktoria Louise over Kiel harbor, 1912. $5, Supermarine Spitfire, vert. No. 1575, Royal Air Force Crest, vert. No. 1576, Hugo Eckener in airship cockpit, vert. No. 1577, Jean-Pierre Blanchard's hot air balloon, 1793, vert.

1993, May 28   **Litho.**   **Perf. 14**

1568	A224	25c multicolored	.90	.90
1569	A224	55c multicolored	1.10	1.10
1570	A224	65c multicolored	1.50	1.50
1571	A224	$1 multicolored	1.75	1.75
1572	A224	$2 multicolored	3.00	3.00
1573	A224	$4 multicolored	4.00	4.00
1574	A224	$5 multicolored	4.25	4.25
		Nos. 1568-1574 (7)	16.50	16.50

Souvenir Sheets

1575	A224	$6 multicolored	6.25	6.25
1576	A224	$6 multicolored	6.25	6.25
1577	A224	$6 multicolored	5.75	5.75

Zeppelin Capt. Hugo Eckener, 125th anniv. of birth (Nos. 1568, 1570, 1573, 1576). Royal Air Force, 75th anniv. (Nos. 1569, 1574-1575). Nos. 1575-1576 each contain one 42x57mm stamp.

Miniature Sheet

Coronation of Queen Elizabeth II, 40th Anniv. — A225

Designs: No. 1578a, 20c, Official coronation photograph. b, 25c, Ceremony. c, 65c, Gold State Coach. d, $5, Queen Elizabeth II, Queen Mother.
$6, Portrait, by Norman Hutchinson, 1969.

1993, June 2   **Litho.**   **Perf. 13½x14**

1578	A225	Sheet, 2 each		
		#a.-d.	13.00	13.00

Souvenir Sheet
Perf. 14

1579	A225	$6 multicolored	6.75	6.75

No. 1579 contains one 28x42mm stamp. For overprints see Nos. 1688-1689.

A226

Cameo photos of couple and: 90c, Crown Prince holding flowers. $5, Princess wearing full-length coat.
$6, Princess riding in limousine.

1993, June 14   **Litho.**   **Perf. 14**

1580	A226	90c multicolored	.75	.75
1581	A226	$5 multicolored	5.00	5.00

Souvenir Sheet

1582	A226	$6 multicolored	6.00	6.00

Wedding of Japan's Crown Prince Naruhito and Masako Owada.

Inauguration of Pres. William J. Clinton — A227

$5, Bill, Hillary Clinton. $6, Bill Clinton, vert.

1993, July 30   **Litho.**   **Perf. 14**

1583	A227	$5 multicolored	4.25	4.25

Souvenir Sheet

1584	A227	$6 multicolored	6.00	6.00

Willy Brandt (1913-92), German Chancellor A228

Brandt and: 65c, Pres. Eisenhower, 1959. $5, N.K. Winston, 1964. $6, Portrait.

1993, July 30

1585	A228	65c black & brown	.90	.90
1586	A228	$5 black & brown	4.75	4.75

Souvenir Sheet

1587	A228	$6 black & brown	6.00	6.00

Picasso (1881-1973) — A229

Paintings: 25c, Bather with Beach Ball, 1929. 90c, Portrait of Leo Stein, 1906. $5, Portrait of Wilhelm Unde, 1910. $6, Man with a Pipe, 1915.

1993, July 30

1588	A229	25c multicolored	.40	.40
1589	A229	90c multicolored	.85	.85
1590	A229	$5 multicolored	4.75	4.75
		Nos. 1588-1590 (3)	6.00	6.00

Souvenir Sheet

1591	A229	$6 multicolored	6.00	6.00

Polska '93 — A230

Paintings: 90c, Self-portrait, by Marian Szczyrbula, 1921. $3, Portrait of Bruno Jasienski, by Tytus Czyzewski, 1921. $6, Miser, by Tadeusz Makowski, 1973.

1993, July 30

1592	A230	90c multicolored	1.50	1.50
1593	A230	$3 multicolored	3.50	3.50

Souvenir Sheet

1594	A230	$6 multicolored	6.00	6.00

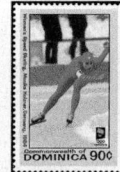

A231

90c, Monika Holzner, speedskating, 1984. $4, US hockey players, Ray Leblanc, Tim Sweeney, 1992. $6, Men's ski jump.

1993, July 30

1595	A231	90c multicolored	1.50	1.50
1596	A231	$4 multicolored	4.00	4.00

Souvenir Sheet

1597	A231	$6 multicolored	5.75	5.75

1994 Winter Olympics, Lillehammer, Norway.

Copernicus (1473-1543) — A232

Designs: $1.20, Astronomer using quadrant. $3, Observatory. $5, Copernicus.

1993, July 30

1598	A232	$1.20 multicolored	1.50	1.50
1599	A232	$3 multicolored	3.75	3.75

Souvenir Sheet

1600	A232	$5 multicolored	6.00	6.00

Opening of New General Post Office — A233

New General Post Office and: 25c, Prince Philip. 90c, Queen Elizabeth II.

1993, July 30

1601	A233	25c multicolored	.25	.25
1602	A233	90c multicolored	1.00	1.00

1994 World Cup Soccer Championships, US — A234

25c, Maradona, Buchwald. 55c, Gullit. 65c, Chavarria, Bliss. No. 1606, 90c, Maradona. No. 1607, 90c, Alvares. $1, Altobelli, Yonghwang. $2, Referee, Stopyra. $5, Renquin, Yaremtchuk.
No. 1611, Brehme. No. 1612, Fabbri.

1993, Sept. 8   **Litho.**   **Perf. 14**

1603	A234	25c multicolored	.65	.65
1604	A234	55c multicolored	.75	.75
1605	A234	65c multicolored	.85	.85
1606	A234	90c multicolored	1.00	1.00
1607	A234	90c multicolored	1.00	1.00
1608	A234	$1 multicolored	1.25	1.25
1609	A234	$2 multicolored	2.00	2.00
1610	A234	$5 multicolored	3.00	3.00
		Nos. 1603-1610 (8)	10.50	10.50

Souvenir Sheets

1611	A234	$6 multicolored	4.50	4.50
1612	A234	$6 multicolored	4.50	4.50

Taipei '93 — A235

25c, Tiger Balm Gardens. 65c, Building, Kenting Park. 90c, Tzu-en Tower. $5, Villa, Lan Tao Island.
No. 1617 — Chinese kites: a, Chang E Rising up to the Moon. b, Red Phoenix and Rising Sun. c, Heavenly Judge. d, Monkey King. e, Goddess of the Luo River. f, Heavenly Maiden Scatters Flowers.
$6, Jade Girl, Liao Dynasty.

1993, Oct. 4   **Litho.**   **Perf. 13½x14**

1613	A235	25c multi	.30	.30
1614	A235	65c multi	.55	.55
1615	A235	90c multi	1.00	1.00
1616	A235	$5 multi	4.25	4.25
		Nos. 1613-1616 (4)	6.10	6.10

Miniature Sheet

1617	A235	$1.65 Sheet of 6,	10.00	10.00

Souvenir Sheet

1618	A235	$6 multi	5.25	5.25

With Bangkok '93 Emblem

25c, Tugu Monument, Java. 55c, Candi Cangkuang, West Java. 90c, Pura Taman Ayun, Mengwi. $5, Stone mosaics, Ceto.
No. 1623 — Puppets: a, Thai, Rama and Sita. b, Burmese, Tha Khi Lek. c, Burmese, diff. d, Thai, Demons, Wat Phra Kaew. e, Thai, Hun Lek performing Khun Chang, Khun Phaen. f, Thai, Hun Lek performing Ramakien.
$6, Stone carving, Thailand.

1993

1619	A235	25c multi	.30	.30
1620	A235	55c multi	.55	.55
1621	A235	90c multi	1.00	1.00
1622	A235	$5 multi	4.00	4.00
		Nos. 1619-1622 (4)	5.85	5.85

Miniature Sheet

1623	A235	$1.65 Sheet of 6,		
		#a.-f.	10.00	10.00

Souvenir Sheet

1624	A235	$6 multi	5.25	5.25

With Indopex '93 Emblem

Designs: 25c, Ornate Chedi, Wat Phra Boromathat Chaiya. 55c, Preserved temple ruins, Sukhothai Historical Park. 90c, Prasat Hin Phimai, Thailand. $5, Main sanctuary, Prasat Phanom Rung, Thailand.
Indonesian puppets — No. 1629: a, Arjuna & Prabu Gilling Wesi. b, Loro Blonyo. c, Yogyanese puppets, Menak cycle. d, Wayang gedog, Ng Setro. e, Wayang golek, Kencana Wungu. f, Wayang gedog, Raden Damar Wulan.
$6, Sculpture of Majapahit noble, Pura Sada, Kapel.

1993, Oct. 4   **Litho.**   **Perf. 13½x14**

1625	A235	25c multicolored	.40	.40
1626	A235	55c multicolored	.60	.60
1627	A235	90c multicolored	1.25	1.25
1628	A235	$5 multicolored	4.00	4.00
		Nos. 1625-1628 (4)	6.25	6.25

Miniature Sheet

1629	A235	$1.65 Sheet of 6,		
		#a.-f.	10.00	10.00

Souvenir Sheet

1630	A235	$6 multicolored	5.25	5.25

Miniature Sheet

Willie the Operatic Whale — A236

Nos. 1631-1633, Characters and scenes from Disney's animated film Willie the Operatic Whale.

1993, Nov. 1   **Litho.**   **Perf. 14x13½**

1631	A236	$1 Sheet of 9, #a.-i.	14.00	14.00

Souvenir Sheets

1632	A236	$6 multicolored	5.00	5.00

Perf. 13½x14

1633	A236	$6 multi, vert.	5.00	5.00

Christmas A237

25c, 55c, 65c, 90c (No. 1637), Details or entire woodcut, The Adoration of the Magi, by Durer.
90c (No. 1638), $1, $3, $5, Details or entire painting, The Foligni Madonna, by Raphael.

Souvenir Sheets: No. 1642, $6, The Adoration of the Magi, by Durer. No. 1643, $6, The Foligni Madonna, by Raphael.

1993, Nov. 8   Litho.   Perf. 13
1634-1643 A237 Set of 10   20.00 20.00

A238

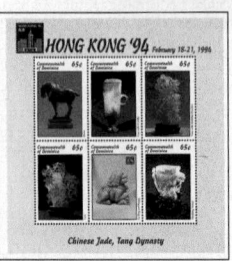

Hong Kong '94 — A239

Stamps, scene from Peak Tram: No. 1644, Hong Kong #527, city buildings, trees. No. 1645, Trees, tram, #1292.
Chinese jade: No. 1646a, Horse. b, Cup with handle. c, Vase with birthday peaches. d, Vase. e, Fu dog and puppy. f, Drinking vessel.

1994, Feb. 18   Litho.   Perf. 14
1644 A238 65c multicolored   .50 .50
1645 A238 65c multicolored   .50 .50
  a.   Pair, #1644-1645   1.10 1.10

Miniature Sheet
1646 A239 65c Sheet of 6, #a.-f.   5.75 5.75

Nos. 1644-1645 issued in sheets of 5 pairs. No. 1645a is a continuous design.
New Year 1994 (Year of the Dog) (No. 1646e).

Insects, Butterflies, & Birds — A240

Various Hercules beetles: 20c, 25c, 65c, Male. 90c, Female.
$1, Imperial parrot. $2, Southern dagger tail. $3, The mimic. $5, Purple-throated carib.
Each $6: No. 1655, Snout butterfly. No. 1656, Blue-headed hummingbird.

1994, Mar. 15   Litho.   Perf. 14
1647-1654 A240 Set of 8   11.00 11.00
  1650a   Min. sheet, 3 each #1647-1650   10.00 10.00

Souvenir Sheets
1655-1656 A240 Set of 2   12.00 12.00

World Wildlife Fund (Nos. 1647-1650).

Mushrooms — A241

Designs: 20c, Russula matoubenis. 25c, Leptonia caeruleocapita. 65c, Inocybe littoralis. 90c, Russula hygrophytica. $1, Pyrrhoglossum lilaceipes. $2, Hygrocybe konradii. $3, Inopilus magnificus. $5, Boletellus cubensis.
No. 1665, Gerronema citrinum. No. 1666, Lentinus strigosus.

1994, Apr. 18
1657 A241 20c multicolored   .45 .45
1658 A241 25c multicolored   .50 .50
1659 A241 65c multicolored   .65 .65
1660 A241 90c multicolored   .80 .80
1661 A241 $1 multicolored   .95 .95
1662 A241 $2 multicolored   1.50 1.50
1663 A241 $3 multicolored   2.00 2.00
1664 A241 $5 multicolored   3.00 3.00
  Nos. 1657-1664 (8)   9.85 9.85

Souvenir Sheets
1665 A241 $6 multicolored   4.75 4.75
1666 A241 $6 multicolored   4.75 4.75

Orchids — A242

Designs: 20c, Laeliocattleya. 25c, Sophrolaeliocattleya. 65c, Odontocidium. 90c, Laeliocattleya, diff. $1, Cattleya. $2, Odontocidium, diff. $3, Epiphronitis. $4, Oncidium.
Each $6: No. 1675, Schombocattleya. No. 1676, Cattleya, diff.

1994, May 3
1667-1674 A242 Set of 8   10.00 10.00

Souvenir Sheets
1675-1676 A242 Set of 2   10.00 10.00

New Year 1994 (Year of the Dog) — A243

Designs: 20c, Dachshund. 25c, Beagle. 55c, Greyhound. 90c, Jack Russell terrier. $1, Pekingese. $2, White fox terrier. $4, English toy spaniel. $5, Irish setter.
No. 1686, Welsh corgi. No. 1687, Labrador retriever.

1994, May 17
1678 A243 20c multicolored   .30 .30
1679 A243 25c multicolored   .35 .35
1680 A243 55c multicolored   .50 .50
1681 A243 90c multicolored   .80 .80
1682 A243 $1 multicolored   1.00 1.00
1683 A243 $2 multicolored   1.50 1.50
1684 A243 $4 multicolored   2.50 2.50
1685 A243 $5 multicolored   3.00 3.00
  Nos. 1678-1685 (8)   9.95 9.95

Souvenir Sheets
1686 A243 $6 multicolored   5.00 5.00
1687 A243 $6 multicolored   5.00 5.00

Nos. 1578-1579 Ovptd. in Black or Silver

1994, June 27   Litho.   Perf. 13½x14
1688 A225   Sheet, 2 ea #a-d   15.00 15.00

Souvenir Sheet
1689 A225 $6 multicolored (S)   7.25 7.25

Overprint on No. 1689 appears in sheet margin.

Miniature Sheet

1994 World Cup Soccer Championships, US — A244

No. 1690: a, Dos Armstrong, US. b, Dennis Bergkamp, Netherlands. c, Roberto Baggio, Italy. d, Rai, Brazil. e, Cafu, Brazil. f, Marco Van Basten, Netherlands.
Each $6: No. 1691, Roberto Mancini, Italy. No. 1692, Stanford Stadium, Palo Alto.

1994, July 5   Perf. 14
1690 A244 $1 Sheet of 6, #a.-f.   6.00 6.00

Souvenir Sheets
1691-1692 A244 Set of 2   10.00 10.00

Butterflies A245

20c, Florida white. 25c, Red rim. 55c, Barred sulphur. 65c, Mimic. $1, Large orange sulphur. $2, Southern dagger tail. $3, Dominican snout butterfly. $5, Caribbean buckeye.
No. 1700, Clench's hairstreak. No. 1701, Painted lady.

1994, May 3   Litho.   Perf. 14
1693 A245 20c multi   .40 .40
1694 A245 25c multi   .40 .40
1695 A245 55c multi   .75 .75
1696 A245 65c multi   .80 .80
1697 A245 $1 multi   1.00 1.00
1698 A245 $2 multi   1.50 1.50
1698A A245 $3 multi   2.00 2.00
1699 A245 $5 multi   3.50 3.50
  Nos. 1693-1699 (8)   10.35 10.35

Souvenir Sheets
1700 A245 $6 multi   5.50 5.50
1701 A245 $6 multi   5.50 5.50

10th Caribbean Scout Jamboree A246

Designs: 20c, Backpacking. 25c, Cooking over campfire. 55c, Making camp. 65c, Camping. $1, Scout drum unit. $2, Planting trees. $4, Sailing. $5, Scout salute.
Each $6: No. 1710, Early Scout troop. No. 1711, Pres. C.A. Sorhaindo, vert.

1994, July 18   Litho.   Perf. 14
1702-1709 A246 Set of 8   11.50 11.50

Souvenir Sheets
1710-1711 A246 Set of 2   11.50 11.50

For overprints see Nos. 1762-1766.

D-Day, 50th Anniv. — A247

Designs: 65c, US Waco glider brings reinforcements. $2, British Horsa gliders land more troops. $3, Glider troops take Pegasus Bridge.
$6, Hadrian glider.

1994, July 26
1712-1714 A247 Set of 3   5.00 5.00

Souvenir Sheet
1715 A247 $6 multicolored   4.75 4.75

A248

Intl. Olympic Committee, Cent. — A249

Designs: 55c, Ulrike Meyfarth, Germany, high jump, 1984. $1.45, Dieter Baumann, Germany, 5000-meter run, 1992.
$6, Ji Hoon Chae, South Korea, 500-meter short track speed skating, 1994.

1994, July 26
1716 A248 55c multicolored   .90 .90

1717 A248 $1.45 multicolored   2.00 2.00

Souvenir Sheet
1718 A249 $6 multicolored   5.75 5.75

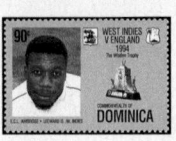

English Touring Cricket, Cent. — A250

Designs: 55c, D.I. Goweer Leics, England, vert. 90c, E.C.L. Ambrose, Leeward Islands. $1, G.A. Gooch, England, vert. $3, First English team, 1895.

1994, July 26
1719-1721 A250 Set of 3   4.00 4.00

Souvenir Sheet
1722 A250 $3 multicolored   5.75 5.75

Miniature Sheet of 6

First Manned Moon Landing, 25th Anniv. A251

No. 1723: a, Apollo 14 crew. b, Apollo 14 patch. c, Apollo 14 lunar module Antares at Fra Mauro Crater. d, Apollo 15 crew. e, Apollo 15 patch. f, Apollo 15 mission, Mount Hadley from rover.
$6, 25th anniv. emblem, lunar surface.

1994, July 26
1723 A251 $1 #a.-f.   7.75 7.75

Souvenir Sheet
1724 A251 $6 multicolored   6.50 6.50

A252

PHILAKOREA '94 — A253

Designs: 65c, P'alsang-jon Hall, Korea. 90c, Popchu-sa Temple. $2, Uhwajong Pavillion, Korea.
Screen, Late Choson Dynasty showing flowers and: No. 1728a, c, e, Birds. b, g, Butterfly. d, Roosters. f, Duck. h, Pheasant. i, Cranes. j, Deer.
$4, Stylized "spirit post" guardian.

1994, July 26   Perf. 14, 13 (#1728)
1725-1727 A252 Set of 3   3.50 3.50

Miniature Sheet of 10
1728 A253 55c #a.-j.   6.00 6.00

Souvenir Sheet
1729 A252 $4 multicolored   3.00 3.00

Mickey Mouse, 65th Birthday — A254

Disney characters: 20c, Dippy dawg. 25c, Clarabelle Cow. 55c, Horace Horsecollar. 65c, Mortimer Mouse. $1, Joe Piper. $3, Mr. Casey. $4, Chief O'Hara. $5, Mickey and the Blot.
Each $6: No. 1738, Minnie, Tanglefoot. No. 1739, Pluto, Minnie, horiz.

Perf. 13½x14, 14x13½ (#1739)

1994, Oct. 3

1730-1737 A254 Set of 8   14.00 14.00

Souvenir Sheets

1738-1739 A254 Set of 2   13.00 13.00

A255

Local Entertainers: 20c, Sonia Llyod, folk singer. 25c, Ophelia Marie, singer. 55c, Edney Francis, accordionist. 65c, Norman Letang, saxophonist. 90c, Edie Andre, steel drummer.

1994, Dec. 1   Litho.   Perf. 14

1740-1744 A255 Set of 5   3.25 3.25

Miniature Sheet

A256

Marilyn Monroe (1926-62), Actress: Nos. 1745a-1745i, Various portraits. No. 1746, $6, Hands above head. No. 1747, $6, Holding hat.

1994, Dec. 1

1745 A256 90c #a.-i.   11.50 11.50

Souvenir Sheets

1746-1747 A256 Set of 2   10.00 10.00

Christmas — A257

Details or entire Spanish paintings: 20c, Madonna and child, by Luis de Morales. 25c, Madonna and Child with Yarn Winder, by Morales. 55c, Our Lady of the Rosary, by Zurbaran. 65c, Dream of the Patrician, by Bartolome Murillo. 90c, Madonna of Charity, by El Greco. $1, The Annunciation, by Zurbaran. $2, Mystical Marriage of St. Catherine, by Jusepe de Ribera. $3, The Holy Family with St. Bruno and Other Saints, by Ribera.

Each $6: No. 1756, Vision of the Virgin to St. Bernard, by Murillo. No. 1757, Adoration of the Shepherds, by Murillo.

1994, Dec. 2   Perf. 13½x14

1748-1755 A257 Set of 8   7.00 7.00

Souvenir Sheets

1756-1757 A257 Set of 2   10.00 10.00

Order of the Caribbean Community A258

First award recipients: 25c, Sir Shridath Ramphal, statesman, Guyana. 55c, William Gilbert Demas, economist, Trinidad & Tobago. 90c, Derek Walcott, writer, St. Lucia.

1994, Dec. 16   Perf. 14

1758-1760 A258 Set of 3   2.00 2.00

Jeffrey Edmund, 1994 World Cup Soccer Player — A259

1994, Dec. 28

1761 A259 25c multicolored   .35 .35

Nos. 1705, 1708-1711 Ovptd.

1995, Mar. 21   Litho.   Perf. 14

1762-1764 A246 Set of 3   7.00 7.00

Souvenir Sheets

1765-1766 A246 Set of 2   10.00 10.00

Location of overprint varies.

New Year 1995 (Year of the Boar) — A260

Stylized boars: a, 25c, Facing right. b, 65c, Facing forward. c, $1, Facing left. $2, Two facing each other, horiz.

1995, Apr. 15   Litho.   Perf. 14½

1767 A260 Strip of 3, #a.-c.   1.60 1.60
    d.   Souv. sheet of 3, #1767a-1767c   1.60 1.60

Souvenir Sheet

1768 A260 $2 multicolored   1.50 1.50

No. 1767 was issued in sheets of 4 strips.

Birds — A261

Designs: 25c, Wood duck. 55c, Mallard. 65c, Blue-winged teal. $5, Blood eared parakeet.

No. 1773, vert.: a, Cattle egret. b, Snow goose (a, c). c, Peregrine falcon. d, Barn owl. e, Black-crowned night heron. f, Common grackle. g, Brown pelican. h, Great egret. i, Ruby-throated hummingbird. j, Laughing gull. k, Greater flamingo. l, Common moorhen.

No. 1774, Trumpeter swan, vert. No. 1775, White-eyed vireo.

1995, Apr. 15   Litho.   Perf. 14

1769-1772 A261 Set of 4   5.00 5.00

Miniature Sheet of 12

1773 A261 65c #a.-l.   16.00 16.00

Souvenir Sheets

1774 A261 $5 multicolored   5.00 5.00
1775 A261 $6 multicolored   6.00 6.00

Miniature Sheets

End of World War II, 50th Anniv. — A262

No. 1776: a, Mitsubishi A6M2 Zero. b, Aichi D3A1 Type 99 "Val." c, Nakajima 97-B5N "Kate." d, Zuikaku. e, Akagi. f, Ryuho.

No. 1777: a, German Panther tank, Ardennes. b, Allied fighter bomber. c, Patton's army crosses the Rhine. d, Rocket-powered ME 163. e, V-2 rocket on launcher. f, German U-boat surrenders in North Atlantic. g, Round the clock bombardment of Berlin. h, Soviet soldiers reach center of Berlin.

Each $6: No. 1778, Statue atop Dresden's town hall after Allied bombing. No. 1779, Japanese attack plane.

1995   Litho.   Perf. 14

1776 A262 $2 #a.-f. + label   9.00 9.00
1777 A262 $2 #a.-h. + label   13.00 13.00

Souvenir Sheets

1778-1779 A262 Set of 2   14.00 14.00

Issued: Nos. 1777-1778, 5/18; others, 7/21.

1996 Summer Olympics, Atlanta — A263

Designs: 15c, Mark Breland, boxing. 20c, Lou Banach, Joseph Atiyeh, freestyle wrestling. 25c, Judo. 55c, Fencing. 65c, Matt Biondi, swimming. $1, Gushiken on rings, vert. $2, Cycling, vert. $5, Volleyball.

Each $6: No. 1788, Joe Fargis on Touch of Class, equestrian. No. 1789, Soccer, vert.

1995, July 21

1780-1787 A263 Set of 8   9.50 9.50

Souvenir Sheets

1788-1789 A263 Set of 2   10.50 10.50

UN, 50th Anniv. — A264

No. 1790: a, 65c, Signatures on UN charter, attendee. b, $1, Attendee. $2, Attendees. $6, Winston Churchill.

1995, Aug. 16   Litho.   Perf. 14

1790 A264 Strip of 3, #a.-c.   2.75 2.75

Souvenir Sheet

1791 A264 $6 multicolored   5.00 5.00

No. 1790 is a continuous design.

Souvenir Sheets

FAO, 50th Anniv. — A265

Street market scene: a, 90c, Woman in red dress. b, $1, Woman seated. c, $2, Vendors, women.

$6, Woman in field, woman holding water cans, vert.

1995, Aug. 16

1792 A265 Sheet of 3, #a.-c.   2.50 2.50
1793 A265 $6 multicolored   4.50 4.50

No. 1792 is a continuous design.

1995, Aug. 16

Queen Mother, 95th Birthday — A266

No. 1794: a, Drawing. b, Wearing crown, green dress. c, Formal portrait. d, Blue dress. $6, Portrait as younger woman.

1995, Aug. 16   Perf. 13½x14

1794 A266 $1.65 Strip or block of 4, #a.-d.   5.50 5.50

Souvenir Sheet

1795 A266 $6 multicolored   5.50 5.50

No. 1794 was issued in sheets of 8 stamps. Sheet margins of Nos. 1794-1795 exist with black frame and text "In Memoriam — 1900-2002" overprinted in sheet margins.

Rotary, 90th Anniv. — A267

1995   Perf. 14

1796 A267 $1 Paul Harris, emblem   1.00 1.00

Souvenir Sheet

1797 A267 $6 Rotary emblems   4.75 4.75

Dinosaurs A268

20c, Monoclonius. 25c, Euoplocephalus. 55c, Coelophysis. 65c, Compsognathus.

No. 1802: a, Dimorphodon. b, Ramphorynchus. c, Giant alligator. d, Pentaceratops.

No. 1803, vert: a, Ceratosaurus. b, Comptosaurus (a). c, Stegosaur. d, Camarasaurs. e, Baronyx. f, Dilophosaurus. g, Dromaeosaurids (f). h, Deinonychus. i, Dinicthys. j, Carcharodon (k). k, Nautiloid. l, Trilobite.

$5, Sauropelta. $6, Triceratops, vert.

1995, Sept. 8

1798-1801 A268 Set of 4   1.75 1.75
1802 A268 90c Strip of 4, #a.-d.   3.00 3.00

Miniature Sheet of 12

1803 A268 90c #a.-l.   10.00 10.00

Souvenir Sheets

1804 A268 $5 multicolored   5.00 5.00
1805 A268 $6 multicolored   5.00 5.00

Singapore '95 (Nos. 1798-1801, 1803-1805).

Miniature Sheets of 6

Nobel Prize Fund Established, Cent. — A269

Recipients, each $2: No. 1806a, Oscar A. Sanchez, peace, 1987. b, Ernst B. Chain, medicine, 1945. c, Aage Bohr, physics, 1975. d, Jaroslav Seifert, literature, 1984. e, Joseph E. Murray, medicine, 1990. f, Jaroslav Heyrovsky, chemistry, 1959.

No. 1807, each $2: a, Adolf von Baeyer, chemistry, 1905. b, Edward Buchner, chemistry, 1907. c, Carl Bosch, chemistry, 1931. d, Otto Hahn, chemistry, 1944. e, Otto Paul Herman Diels, chemistry, 1950. f, Kurt Alder, chemistry, 1950.

No. 1808, Emil A. von Behring, medicine, 1901.

1995, Oct. 24   Litho.   Perf. 14

1806-1807 A269 Set of 2   19.00 19.00

Souvenir Sheet

1808 A269 $2 multicolored   1.75 1.75

Christmas — A270

Details or entire paintings: 20c, Madonna and Child, by Pontormo. 25c, The Immaculate Conception, by Murillo. 55c, The Adoration of the Magi, by Filippino Lippi. 65c, Rest on the Flight into Egypt, by Van Dyck. 90c, Sacred Family, by Van Dyck. $5, The Annunciation, by Van Eyck.

No. 1815, The Virgin and the Infant, by Van Eyck. No. 1816, The Holy Family, by Ribera.

1995, Nov. 30   Litho.   Perf. 13½x14

1809-1814 A270 Set of 6   6.00 6.00

Souvenir Sheets

1815 A270 $5 multicolored   3.75 3.75
1816 A270 $6 multicolored   4.75 4.75

Miniature Sheets

Sierra Club, Cent. — A271

Designs: No. 1817, each $1: a, Florida panther with mouth open. b, Florida panther looking right. c, Manatee. d, Two manatees. e, Three sockeye salmon. f, Group of sockeye salmon. g, Two southern sea otters. h, Southern sea otter. i, Southern sea otter showing both front paws.
No. 1818, vert, each $1: a, Florida panther. b, Manatee. c, Sockeye salmon. d, Key deer facing left. e, Key deer. f, Key deer with antlers, up close. g, Wallaby with young in pouch. h, Wallaby. i, Wallaby with young.

1995, Dec. 10		**Perf. 14**	
1817-1818 A271 Set of 2		13.00 13.00	

Chinese Paintings, A City of Cathay — A272

No. 1819, brown lettering, each 90c: a, Boats docked, people on shore. b, River, bridge. c, Two boats on river. d, River, pavilion along shore. e, Open sea, people in courtyard.
No. 1820, black lettering, each 90c: a, City scene. b, City scene, wall. c, Outside wall, river. d, Large boat on river. e, People crossing over bridge.
No. 1821, $2: a, Boat on river, city above. b, People walking across bridge.
No. 1822, $2: a, Lifting ramp to another boat, vert. b, Holding lines in water, tree, vert.

1995, Dec. 27	**Litho.**	**Perf. 14½**
Strips of 5		
1819-1820 A272 Set of 2		7.50 7.50
Souvenir Sheets of 2		
1821-1822 A272 Set of 2		6.00 6.00

Nos. 1819-1822 are each continuous designs.

Classic Western Art — A273

Paintings by Raphael: No. 1823, Agony in the Garden. No. 1824, Pope Leo X with Two Cardinals. No. 1825, Bindo Altoviti.
$6, Triumphant entry of Constantine into Rome, by Rubens.

1995, Dec. 27		**Perf. 14**
1823-1825 A273 $2 Set of 3		5.25 5.25
Souvenir Sheet		
1826 A273 $6 multicolored		5.25 5.25

New Year 1996 (Year of the Rat) — A274

Stylized rats, Chinese inscriptions: No. 1827a, 25c, purple & brown. b, 65c, orange & green. c, $1, red lilac & blue.
$2, Two rats, horiz.

1996, Jan. 16		**Perf. 14½**
1827 A274 Strip of 3, #a.-c.		1.90 1.90
Miniature Sheet		
1828 A274 Sheet of 1 #1827		1.60 1.60
Souvenir Sheet		
1829 A274 $2 multicolored		1.75 1.75

No. 1827 was issued in sheets of 12 stamps.

Miniature Sheet

Disney Lunar New Year — A275

Disney characters representing year of the: No. 1830a, Rat. b, Ox. c, Tiger. d, Hare. e, Dragon. f, Snake. g, Horse. h, Sheep. i, Monkey. j, Rooster. k, Dog. l, Pig.
$3, Rat character. $6, Pig, rat, ox characters on lunar calendar wheel.

1996, Jan. 16		**Perf. 14x13½**
1830 A275 55c Sheet of 12, #a.-l.		11.00 11.00
Souvenir Sheets		
1831 A275 $3 multicolored		4.00 4.00
1832 A275 $6 multicolored		8.00 8.00

Methods of Transportation A276

Designs: 65c, Donkey cart, 1965. 90c, 1910 Car. $2, 1950 Taxi. $3, 1955 Bus.

1996, Jan. 29	**Litho.**	**Perf. 14**
1833-1836 A276 Set of 4		8.00 8.00

Miniature Sheets

Locomotives — A277

No. 1837, each $2: a, "Dragon," Hawaii. b, "Regina," Italy. c, Calazo to Padua, Italy. d, "Mogul," Philippines. e, Nuremberg, Germany. f, "Stanislas," French Natl. Railway. g, "Black Five," Scotland. h, SNCF diesel electric, France. i, "Sir Nigel Gresley," England.
No. 1838, each $2: a, Hohi Line 9600 class, Japan. b, Peloponnese Express, Greece. c, Porter 2-4-0S, Hawaii. d, Norway-Swedish Jodemans Railway. e, 220 Diesel, Federal German Railway. f, 2-8-4T Indian Railways. g, East African Railways. h, Electrical trains, USSR. i, 0-8-0, Austria.
$5, "Duchess of Hamilton," England. $6, Diesel engine, China.

1996, Jan. 29		
1837-1838 A277 Set of 2		28.00 28.00
Souvenir Sheets		
1839 A277 $5 multicolored		4.75 4.75
1840 A277 $6 multicolored		5.25 5.25

No. 1837h has a face value of $1.

Giant Panda — A278

Designs: a, With right leg up on rock. b, Front legs up on rock. c, Seated. d, Holding head down.

1996, May 15	**Litho.**	**Perf. 13½x14**
1841 A278 55c Block of 4, #a.-d.		4.50 4.50

Souvenir Sheet
Perf. 14x13½

1842 A278 $3 Panda, horiz.		3.75 3.75

CHINA '96, 9th Asian Intl. Philatelic Exhibition. No. 1841 was issued in sheets of 8 stamps.
See No. 1911.

Queen Elizabeth II, 70th Birthday A279

No. 1843: a, Portrait. b, Wearing regalia of Order of the Garter. c, Wearing bright blue dress, pearls.
$6, In uniform.

1996, May 16	**Litho.**	**Perf. 13½x14**
1843 A279 $2 Strip of 3, #a.-c.		4.25 4.25
Souvenir Sheet		
1844 A279 $6 multicolored		4.25 4.25

No. 1843 was issued in sheets of 9 stamps.

Legendary Film Detectives — A280

Designs: a, Humphrey Bogart as Sam Spade. b, Sean Connery as James Bond. c, Warren Beatty as Dick Tracy. d, Basil Rathbone as Sherlock Holmes. e, William Powell as the Thin Man. f, Sidney Toler as Charlie Chan, g, Peter Sellers as Inspector Clouseau. h, Robert Mitchum as Philip Marlowe. i, Peter Ustinov as Inspector Poirot.
$6, Margaret Rutherford as Miss Marple.

1996, July		
1845 A280 $1 Sheet of 9, #a.-i.		13.00 13.00
Souvenir Sheet		
1846 A280 $6 multicolored		6.00 6.00

1996 Summer Olympics, Atlanta — A281

Designs: 20c, Olympic Stadium, Moscow, 1980. 25c, Hermine Joseph, vert. 55c, Women's field hockey, Zimbabwe, 1980. 90c, Jerome Romain, vert. $1, Polo, discontinued sport, vert. $2, Greg Louganis, diving.

1996		**Perf. 14**
1847-1852 A281 Set of 6		4.25 4.25

See Nos. 1897-1900.

Local Entertainers A282

Designs: 25c, Irene Peltier, national dress of Dominica. 55c, Rupert Bartley, street band player. 65c, Rosemary Cools-Lartigue, pianist. 90c, Celestine "Orion" Theophile, belle queen, Grand Bay. $1, Cecil Bellot, former government band master.

1996, July 31	**Litho.**	**Perf. 14**
1853-1857 A282 Set of 5		2.75 2.75

Jerusalem, 3000th Anniv. — A283

Designs: a, 90c, Shrine of the Book, Israel Museum. b, $1, Church of All Nations. c, $2, The Great Synagogue.
$5, Hebrew University, Mount Scopus.

1996, July 31		
1858 A283 Sheet of 3, #a.-c.		3.00 3.00
Souvenir Sheet		
1859 A283 $5 multicolored		4.50 4.50

Radio, Cent. — A284

Entertainers: 90c, Artie Shaw. $1, Benny Goodman. $2, Duke Ellington. $4, Harry James.
$6, Tommy Dorsey, Jimmy Dorsey, horiz.

1996, July 31		
1860-1863 A284 Set of 4		6.25 6.25
Souvenir Sheet		
1864 A284 $6 multicolored		5.00 5.00

UNICEF, 50th Anniv. — A285

20c, Girl looking at globe. 55c, Boy with stethoscope, syringe. $5, Doctor examining child.
No. 1868, Girl, vert.

1996, July 31		
1865-1867 A285 Set of 3		4.25 4.25
Souvenir Sheet		
1868 A285 $5 multicolored		4.50 4.50

World Post Day — A286

Scenes of 18th cent. life in Dominica: 10c, Captain of ship taking letters by hand. 25c, Anthony Trollope vists Dominica to organize postal service. 55c, Steam vessel "Yare" carries mail around island. 65c, Post offices and agencies. 90c, Country postman carrying mail around mountain tracks. $1, West Indies Federation stamp, first airmail sent on German "goose" seaplane. $2, #602, General Post Office, old and new.
$5, Captain of ship.

1996, Oct. 1	**Litho.**	**Perf. 14**
1869-1875 A286 Set of 7		6.25 6.25
Souvenir Sheet		
1876 A286 $5 multicolored		5.50 5.50

Fish — A287

Designs: 1c, Scrawled filefish. 2c, Lion fish. 5c, Porcupine fish. 10c, Powder blue surgeonfish. 15c, Red hind. 20c, Golden butterfly fish. 25c, Long-nosed butterfly fish. 35c, Pennant butterfly fish. 45c, Spotted drum. 55c, Blue-girdled angelfish. 60c, Scorpion fish. 65c, Harlequin sweetlips. 90c, Flame angelfish. $1, Queen trigger. $1.20, Stoplight parrot. $1.45,

Black durgon. $2, Glasseye snapper. $5, Balloon fish. $10, Creole wrasse. $20, Seabass.

1996, Oct. 1   Litho.   Perf. 14

1877	A287	1c multicolored	.30	.50
1878	A287	2c multicolored	.30	.50
1879	A287	5c multicolored	.35	.50
1880	A287	10c multicolored	.45	.45
1881	A287	15c multicolored	.50	.50
1882	A287	20c multicolored	.55	.55
1883	A287	25c multicolored	.55	.55
1884	A287	35c multicolored	.70	.70
1885	A287	45c multicolored	.90	.90
1886	A287	55c multicolored	1.00	1.00
1887	A287	60c multicolored	1.00	1.00
1888	A287	65c multicolored	1.00	1.00
1889	A287	90c multicolored	1.25	1.00
1890	A287	$1 multicolored	1.50	1.00
1891	A287	$1.20 multicolored	1.60	1.00
1892	A287	$1.45 multicolored	1.75	1.25
1893	A287	$2 multicolored	2.00	2.00
1894	A287	$5 multicolored	5.00	5.00
1895	A287	$10 multicolored	10.00	10.00
1896	A287	$20 multicolored	19.00	19.00
	Nos. 1877-1896 (20)		49.70	48.40

See Nos. 2024-2039B for size 20x18mm stamps.

1996 Summer Olympic Games Type

Past Olympic medalists, vert, each 90c: No. 1897a, Ulrike Meyfarth, high jump. b, Pat McCormick, diving. c, Takeichi Nishi, equestrian. d, Peter Farkas, Greco-Roman wrestling. e, Carl Lewis, track & field. f, Agnes Keleti, gymnastics. g, Yasuhiro Yamashita, judo. h, John Kelly, single sculls. i, Naim Suleymanoglu, weight lifting.

No. 1898, vert, each 90c: a, Sammy Lee, diving. b, Bruce Jenner, decathlon. c, Olga Korbut, gymnastics. d, Steffi Graf, tennis. e, Florence Griffith-Joyner, track and field. f, Mark Spitz, swimming. g, Li Ning, gymnastics. h, Erika Salumae, cycling. i, Abebe Bikila, marathon.

#1899, $5, Joan Benoit, 1st women's marathon, vert.

#1900, $5, Milt Campbell, discus.

1996, June 7   Litho.   Perf. 14
Sheets of 9

1897-1898	A281	Set of 2	15.00	15.00

Souvenir Sheets

1899-1900	A281	Set of 2	8.25	8.25

A288

Christmas (Details or entire paintings): 25c, Enthroned Madonna and Child, by Stefano Veneziano. 55c, Noli Me Tangere, by Beato Angelico. 65c, Madonna and Child, by Angelico. 90c, Madonna of Corneta Tarquinia, by Filippo Lippi. $2, Annunciation, by Angelico. $5, Madonna with Child, by Angelico, diff.

Each $6: No. 1907, Coronation of the Virgin, by Beato Angelico. No. 1908, Holy Family with St. Barbara, by Veronese, horiz.

1996, Nov. 25

1901-1906	A288	Set of 6	8.50	8.50

Souvenir Sheets

1907-1908	A288	Set of 2	10.00	10.00

A289

Paintings of "Herdboy and Buffalo," by Li Keran (1907-89): No. 1909: a, f, Herdboy Plays the Flute. b, g, Playing Cricket in the Autumn. c, h, Listen to the Summer Cicada. d, i, Grazing in the Spring.

$2, Return in Wind and Rain.

1997   Litho.   Perf. 14

1909	A289	90c Strip of 4, #a.-d.	3.25	3.25

Souvenir Sheets

1909E	A289	55c Sheet of 4, #f.-i.	2.00	2.00

Perf. 15x14½

1910	A289	$2 multicolored	2.00	2.00

New Year 1997 (Year of the Ox).
No. 1909 was printed in sheets of 8 stamps.
No. 1910 contains one 34x52mm stamp.

Souvenir Sheet

Huangshan Mountain, China — A290

1996, May 15   Litho.   Perf. 12

1911	A290	$2 multicolored	2.25	2.25

China '96. No. 1911 was not available until March 1997.

A291

Lee Lai-Shan, 1996 Olympic Gold Medalist in Wind Surfing — A291a

1997   Litho.   Perf. 15x14

1912	A291	$2 multicolored	1.75	1.75

Souvenir Sheet
Perf. 14

1913	A291	$5 multicolored	4.25	4.25

No. 1912 was issued in sheets of 3.
No. 1913 contains one 38x51mm stamp.

Litho. & Embossed
Perf. 9
Without Gum

1913A	A291a	$35 gold & multi, like #1913		

Butterflies
A292

No. 1914: a, Meticalla metis. b, Coeliades forestan. c, Papilio dardanus. d, Mylothris chloris. e, Poecilmitis thyshe. f, Myrina silenus. g, Bematistes aganice. h, Euphaedra neophron. i, Precis hierta.

No. 1915, vert: a, Striped policeman. b, Mountain sandman. c, Brown-veined white. d, Bowker's widow. e, Foxy charaxes. f, Pirate. g, African clouded yellow. h, Garden inspector.

Each $6: No. 1916, Acraea natalica. No. 1917, Eurytela dryope.

1997, Apr. 1   Litho.   Perf. 14

1914	A292	55c Sheet of 9, #a.-i.	4.75	4.75
1915	A292	90c Sheet of 8, #a.-h.	6.75	6.75

Souvenir Sheets

1916-1917	A292	Set of 2	12.00	12.00

UNESCO, 50th Anniv. — A293

55c, View from temple, China. 65c, Palace of Diocletian, Croatia. 90c, St. Mary's Cathedral, Hildesheim, Germany. $1, Monastery of Rossanou, Mount Athos, Greece. $2, Scandola Nature Reserve, France. $4, Church of San Antao, Portugal.

No. 1924: a, Ruins of Copan, Honduras. b, Cuzco Cathedral, Peru. c, Olinda, Brazil, d, Canaima Natl. Park, Venezuela. e, Galapagos Islands Natl. Park, Ecuador. f, Ruins of Church, Jesuit missions of Santisima, Paraguay. g, Fortress, San Lorenzo, Panama. h, Natl. Park, Fortress, Haiti.

Each $6: No. 1925, Chengde Lakes, China. No. 1926, Kyoto, Japan.

1997, Apr. 7   Perf. 13½x14

1918-1923	A293	Set of 6	8.75	8.75
1924	A293	$1 Sheet of 8, #a.-h. + label	7.75	7.75

Souvenir Sheets

1925-1926	A293	Set of 2	10.50	10.50

Disney Scenes "Sealed with a Kiss" — A294

Cartoon film, year released: 25c, Mickey's Horse, Tanglefoot, 1933. 35c, Shanghaied, 1935. 55c, Pluto's Judgment Day, 1935. 65c, Race for Riches, 1935. 90c, Elmer Elephant, 1936. $1, Brave Little Tailor, 1938. $2, Donald's Crime, 1945. $4, In Dutch, 1946.

Each $6: No. 1935, Nifty Nineties, 1941. No. 1936, Mickey's Surprise Party, 1939.

1997, Apr. 15   Perf. 13½x14

1927-1934	A294	Set of 8	11.00	11.00

Souvenir Sheets

1935-1936	A294	Set of 2	10.00	10.00

Cats — A295

25c, Cream Burmese. $1, Snowshoe. $2, Sorrell Abyssinian. $5, Torbie Persian.

No. 1941: a, British bicolor shorthair (d, e). b, Maine coon kitten, Somali kitten (c). c, Maine coon kitten, diff. d, Lynx point Siamese (e). e, Blue Burmese kitten, white Persian (odd-eyed) (f). f, Persian kitten.

No. 1942, Silver tabby.

1997, Apr. 24   Perf. 14

1937-1940	A295	Set of 4	7.00	7.00
1941	A295	$2 Sheet of 6, #a.-f.	10.50	10.50

Souvenir Sheet

1942	A295	$6 multicolored	5.50	5.50

Dogs — A296

Designs: 20c, Afghan hound. 55c, Cocker spaniel. 65c, Smooth fox terrier. 90c, West Highland white terrier.

No. 1947a, St. Bernard. b, Boy with grand basset. c, Rough collie. d, Golden retriever. e, Golden retriever, Tibetan spaniel, smooth fox terrier. f, Smooth fox terrier, diff.

$6, Shetland sheepdog.

1997, Apr. 24

1943-1946	A296	Set of 4	2.00	2.00
1947	A296	90c Sheet of 6, #a.-f.	5.25	5.25

Souvenir Sheet

1948	A296	$6 multicolored	5.50	5.50

A297

No. 1949: a, Queen Elizabeth II. b, Royal Arms. c, Prince, Queen walking among crowd. d, Queen, Prince in military attire. e, Buckingham Palace. f, Prince Philip.

$6, Portrait of Queen and Prince on balcony.

1997, May 29   Litho.   Perf. 14

1949	A297	$1 Sheet of 6, #a.-f.	5.50	5.50

Souvenir Sheet

1950	A297	$6 multicolored	5.00	5.00

Queen Elizabeth II and Prince Philip, 50th wedding anniv.

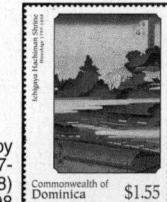

Paintings by Hiroshige (1797-1858) A298

No. 1951: a, Ichigaya Hachiman Shrine. b, Blossoms on the Tama River Embankment. c, Kumano Junisha Shrine, Tsunohazu ("Juniso"). d, Benkei Moat from Soto-Sakurada to Kojimachi. e, Kinokuni Hill & View of Akasak Tameike. f, Naito Shinjuku, Yotsuya.

Each $6: No. 1952, Kasumigaseki. No. 1952A, Sanno Festival Procession at Kojimachi I-chome.

1997, May 29

1951	A298	$1.55 Sheet of 6, #a.-f.	10.50	10.50

Souvenir Sheets

1952-1952A	A298	Set of 2	12.50	12.50

Orchids — A299

Designs, vert: 20c, Oncidium altissimum. 25c, Oncidium papilio. 55c, Epidendrum fragrans. 65c, Oncidium lanceanum. 90c, Campylocentrum micranthum. $4, Pogonia rosea.

No. 1959: a, Brassavola cucculata. b, Epidendrum ibaguense. c, Ionopsis utriculariodes. d, Rodriguezia lanceolata. e, Oncidium cebolleta. f, Epidendrum ciliare.

Each $5: No. 1960, Stanhopea grandiflora. No. 1961, Oncidium ampliatum.

1997, May 10   Litho.   Perf. 14

1953-1958	A299	Set of 6	8.00	8.00
1959	A299	$1 Sheet of 6, #a.-f.	7.00	7.00

Souvenir Sheets

1960-1961	A299	Set of 2	11.00	11.00

Paul P. Harris (1868-1947), Founder of Rotary, Intl. — A300

Portrait of Harris and: $2, Rotary Village Corps, irrigation project, Honduras. $6, Emblems, world community service.

1997, May 29

1962	A300	$2 multicolored	1.60	1.60

Souvenir Sheet

1963	A300	$6 multicolored	6.00	6.00

Heinrich von Stephan (1831-97) A301

Portraits of Von Stephan and: No. 1964 a, Kaiser Wilhelm II. b, UPU emblem. c, Postal messenger, ancient Japan.

$6, Von Stephan, Russian dog team carrying post, 1859.

1997, May 29
1964 A301 $2 Sheet of 3, #a.-c.   4.25 4.25

Souvenir Sheet
1965 A301 $6 multicolored   4.50 4.50

PACIFIC 97.

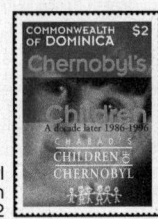

Chernobyl Disaster, 10th Anniv. — A302

Designs: No. 1966, Chabad's Children of Chernobyl. No. 1967, UNESCO.

1997, May 29   **Perf. 13½x14**
1966 A302 $2 multicolored   2.25 2.25
1967 A302 $2 multicolored   2.25 2.25

Grimm's Fairy Tales — A303

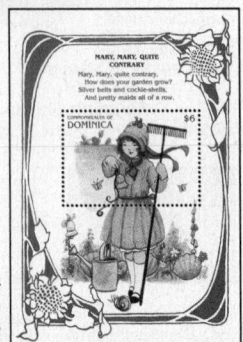

Mother Goose Rhymes A304

The Goose Girl: No. 1968: a, Girl with horse. b, Geese, pond, castle. c, Girl. No. 1969, Girl, horiz.
No. 1970: Mary, Mary, Quite Contrary.

1997, May 29   **Perf. 13½x14**
1968 A303 $2 Sheet of 3, #a.-c.   6.00 6.00

Souvenir Sheets
Perf. 14x13½
1969 A303 $6 multicolored   6.00 6.00
Perf. 14
1970 A304 $6 multicolored   5.00 5.00

Return of Hong Kong to China — A305

Designs: $1, View of Hong Kong at night. $1.45, View of Hong Kong in daytime. $2, View of Hong Kong at night, diff.
Hong Kong skyline at dusk: No. 1974: a, 65c. b, 90c. c, $1. d, $3.

1997, July 1   **Perf. 14**
1971-1973 A305 Set of 3   3.75 3.75
1974 A305 Sheet of 4, #a.-d.   5.00 5.00

Nos. 1971-1973 were issued in sheets of 4.

1998 Winter Olympics, Nagano — A306

Medal winners: 20c, Yukio Kasaya, 1972 ski jump. 25c, Jens Weissflog, 1994 ski jump. No. 1977, 55c, Anton Maier, 1968 men's speed skating. No. 1978, 55c, Ljubov Egorova, 1994 women's cross-country skiing. 65c, 1994 Ice hockey, Sweden. 90c, Bernhard Glass, 1980 men's luge. $4, Frank-Peter Roetsch, 1988 men's biathlon.
No. 1982: a, like #1975. b, like #1976. c, like #1977. d, Christa Rothenburger, 1988 women's speed skating.
Each $5: No. 1983, Jacob Tullin Thams, 1924 ski jumping. No. 1984, Charles Jewtraw, 1924 men's speed skating.

1997, July 15
1975-1981 A306 Set of 7   8.75 8.75
1982 A306 $1 Strip or block of 4, #a.-d.   5.00 5.00

Souvenir Sheets
1983-1984 A306 Set of 2   9.00 9.00

No. 1982 issued in sheets of 8 stamps.

1998 World Cup Soccer Championships, France — A307

Players, vert: 20c, Klinsmann, Germany. 55c, Bergkamp, Holland. 65c, Ravanelli, Italy. 90c, Kinkladze, Georgia. $2, Shearer, England. $4, Dani, Portugal.
Stadiums: No. 1991, each 65c: a, Wembley, England. b, Bernabeu, Spain. c, Maracana, Brazil. d, Torino, Italy. e, Centenary, Uruguay. f, Olympic, Germany. g, Rose Bowl, US. h, Azteca, Mexico.
Team Captains: No. 1992, each 65c: a, Meazza, Italy, 1934. b, Matthaus, Germany, 1990. c, Walter, W. Germany, 1954. d, Maradona, Argentina, 1986. e, Beckenbauer, Germany, 1974. f, Moore, England, 1966. g, Dunga, Brazil, 1994. h, Zoff, Italy, 1982.
$5, Mario Kempes, Argentina, vert. $6, Ally McCoist, Scotland, vert.

1997, July 21   **Litho.**   **Perf. 14**
1985-1990 A307 Set of 6   8.00 8.00
Sheets of 8 + Label
1991-1992 A307 Set of 2   9.00 9.00

Souvenir Sheets
1993 A307 $5 multicolored   4.50 4.50
1994 A307 $6 multicolored   5.50 5.50

Dominica Credit Union — A308

25c, Joffre Robinson, former Credit Union president. 55c, Sister Alicia, founder credit union movement in Dominica. 65c, Lorrel Bruce, 1st Cooperative Credit Union president. 90c, Roseau Credit Union Building.
$5, Bruce, Robinson, Sister Alicia.

1997, Aug. 15   **Litho.**   **Perf. 14x13½**
1995-1998 A308 Set of 4   2.25 2.25

Souvenir Sheet
Perf. 14
1999 A308 $5 multicolored   4.50 4.50

No. 1999 contains one 28x60mm stamp.

Medical Pioneers: 20c, Louis Pasteur, father of bacteriology. 25c, Christiaan Barnard, performed first heart transplant. 55c, Sir Alexander Fleming, developer of penicillin. 65c, Camillo Golgi, neurologist. 90c, Jonas Salk, developer of polio vaccine. $1, Har Ghobind Khorana, geneticist. $2, Elizabeth Blackwell, first woman physician. $3, Sir Frank Macfarlane Burnet, immunologist.
$5, Fleming, diff. $6, Pasteur, diff.

1997, Sept. 1   **Litho.**   **Perf. 14**
2000-2007 A309 Set of 8   10.00 10.00

Souvenir Sheets
2008 A309 $5 multicolored   5.25 5.25
2009 A309 $6 multicolored   6.25 6.25

A310

Diana, Princess of Wales (1961-97): Various portraits.

1997, Oct. 20   **Litho.**   **Perf. 14**
2010 A310 $2 Sheet of 4, #a.-d.   6.50 6.50

Souvenir Sheet
2011 A310 $5 multicolored   4.75 4.75

Christmas — A311

Entire paintings or details: 20c, Echo and Narcissus, by Poussin. 55c, Angel Departing from the Family of Tobias, by Rembrandt. 65c, Seated Nymphs with Flute, by Francois Boucher. 90c, Angel, by Rembrandt. $2, Dispute of the Holy Sacrament, by Raphael. $4, Garden of Love, by Rubens.
Each $6: No. 2018, Annunciation, by Botticelli. No. 2019, Christ on the Mount of Olives, by El Greco.

1997, Nov. 10   **Litho.**   **Perf. 14**
2012-2017 A311 Set of 6   7.00 7.00

Souvenir Sheets
2018-2019 A311 Set of 2   11.00 11.00

The $4 is incorrectly inscribed Holy Trinity, by Raphael. No. 2018 is incorrectly inscribed Study of a Muse, by Raphael.

A312

Paintings of tigers, by Ling-Nan School: No. 2020: a, 55c, Gao Qifeng. b, 65c, Zhao Shao'ang. c, 90c, Gao Jianfu. d, $1.20, Gao Jianfu, diff.
$3, Tiger running down mountain, by Gao Jianfu.

1998, Jan. 5   **Litho.**   **Perf. 14½**
2020 A312 Sheet of 4, #a.-d.   3.00 3.00

Souvenir Sheet
Perf. 14x14½
2021 A312 $3 multicolored   2.25 2.25

New Year 1998 (Year of the Tiger). No. 2021 contains one 44x36mm stamp.

Fish Type of 1996

5c, Porcupine fish. 10c, Powder-blue surgeonfish. 15c, Red hind. 20c, Golden butterflyfish. 25c, Long-nosed butterflyfish. 35c, Pennant butterflyfish. 45c, Spotted drum. 55c, Blue-girdled angelfish. 60c, Scorpion fish. 65c, Harlequin sweetlips. 90c, Flame angelfish. $1, Queen trigger. $1.20, Stoplight parrot. $1.45, Black durgon. $2, Glasseye snapper. $5, Balloon fish. $10, Creole wrasse. $20, Seabass.

1998   **Perf. 13x13½**
Size: 20x18mm

2024	A287	5c multi	.30	.50
2025	A287	10c multi	.30	.50
2026	A287	15c multi	.40	.50
2027	A287	20c multi	.40	.40
2028	A287	25c multi	.45	.45
2029	A287	35c multi	.50	.50
2030	A287	45c multi	.70	.70
2031	A287	55c multi	.80	.80
2032	A287	60c multi	.90	.90
2033	A287	65c multi	.90	.90
2034	A287	90c multi	1.00	.90
2035	A287	$1 multi	1.25	1.25
2036	A287	$1.20 multi	1.50	1.40
2037	A287	$1.45 multi	1.75	1.75
2038	A287	$2 multi	2.25	2.25
2039	A287	$5 multi	5.00	5.00
2039A	A287	$10 multi	9.50	9.50
2039B	A287	$20 multi	20.00	20.00
	Nos. 2024-2039B (18)		47.90	48.20

A313

Famous 20th cent. athletes — No. 2040: a, Jesse Owens. b, Owens jumping in 1936 Summer Olympic Games, Berlin. c, Isaac Berger lifting weights. d, Berger. e, Boris Becker. f, Becker playing tennis. g, Arthur Ashe playing tennis, holding Wimbledon trophy. h, Ashe.
No. 2041, Franz Beckenbauer, soccer player, horiz.

1998, Feb. 9   **Litho.**   **Perf. 14**
Sheet of 8
2040 A313 $1 #a.-h.   7.50 7.50

Souvenir Sheet
2041 A313 $6 multi   6.25 6.25

Nos. 2040b-2040c, 2040f-2040g are each 53x38mm.

A314

Japanese Cinema Stars — No. 2042: a, Akira Kurosawa. b, Kurosawa's 1950 film, "Rashomon." c, Toshiro Mifune in 1954 film, "Seven Samurai." d, Mifune. e, Yasujiro Ozu. f, Ozu's 1949 film, "Late Spring." g, Sessue Hayakawa in 1957 film, "Bridge on the River Kwai." h, Hayakawa.
No. 2043, Akira Kurosawa, director.

1998, Feb. 9   **Litho.**   **Perf. 14**
Sheet of 8
2042 A314 $1 #a.-h.   7.50 7.50

Souvenir Sheet
2043 A314 $6 multi   6.25 6.25

Nos. 2042b-2042c, 2042f-2042g are each 53x38mm.

A315

Mushrooms: 10c, Omphalotus illudens. 15c, Inocybe fastigiata. 20c, Marasmius plicatulus. 50c, Mycena lilacifolia. 55c, Armillaria straminea. 90c, Tricholomopsis rutilans.

No. 2050, each $1: a, Lepiota naucina. b, Cortinarius violaceus. c, Boletus aereus. d, Tricholoma aurantium. e, Lepiota procera. f, Clitocybe geotropa. g, Lepiota acutes-quamosa. h, Tricholoma saponaceum. i, Lycoperdon gemmatum.

No. 2051, each $1: a, Boletus ornatipes. b, Russula xerampelina. c, Cortinarius collinitus. d, Agaricus meleagris. e, Coprinus comatus. f, Amanita caesarea. g, Amanita brunnescens. h, Amanita muscaria. i, Morchella esculenta.

$6, Cortinarius violaceus.

1998, Mar. 2   Litho.   Perf. 14
2044-2049 A315   Set of 6   3.00 3.00
Sheets of 9
2050-2051 A315   Set of 2   17.50 17.50
Souvenir Sheet
2052 A315 $6 multicolored   5.25 5.25

Sailing Ships — A316

Designs: 65c, Greek bireme. 90c, Egyptian felucca. $1, Viking longboat. $2, Chinese junk.

No. 2057: a, Two-masted topsail schooner. b, The Golden Hinde. c, Roman merchant ship. d, Gazela Primeiro. e, Moshulu. f, Bluenose.

Each $5: No. 2058, Pinta. No. 2059, Chesapeake Bay skipjack.

1998, Mar. 16   Litho.   Perf. 14
2053-2056 A316   Set of 4   4.50 4.50
2057 A316 55c Block of 6, #a.-
           f.   3.25 3.25
Souvenir Sheets
2058-2059 A316   Set of 2   10.00 10.00

No. 2053 incorrectly inscribed "Egyptian felucca."

No. 2057 was issued in sheets of 12 stamps.

Mickey & Minnie Mouse's 70th Anniv. A317

25c, Steamboat Willie, 1928. 55c, The Brave Little Tailor, 1938. 65c, Nifty Nineties, 1941. 90c, Mickey Mouse Club, 1955. $1, Mickey, Minnie at the opening of Walt Disney World, 1971. $1.45, Mousercise Mickey & Minnie, 1980.

Each $5: No. 2061, Walt Disney, Mickey, Minnie. No. 2062, Surprise Party for Mickey & Minnie.

1998, June 16 Litho.   Perf. 14x13½
2060A A317   25c black   .30   .30
2060B A317   55c multi   .60   .60
2060C A317   65c multi   .75   .75
2060D A317   90c multi   1.00 1.00
2060E A317 $1 multi   1.10 1.10
2060F A317 $1.45 multi   1.60 1.60
  Nos. 2060A-2060F (6)   5.35 5.35
Souvenir Sheet of 7
2060G #2060A-2060F, 2060h 11.50 11.50
  h. $5 Runaway brain, perf 13½
      at left   3.50 3.50

Size: 130x104mm
Imperf
2061-2062 A317   Set of 2   10.00 10.00

Souvenir Sheet

Disney's The Lion King A318

1998, June 16 Litho.   Perf. 13½x14
2063 A318 $5 multicolored   7.00 7.00

Sea Birds — A319

25c, Erect crested penguin. 65c, Humboldt penguin. 90c, Red knot. $1, Audubon's shearwater.

No. 2068: a, Crested tern. b, Franklin's gull. c, Australian pelican. d, Fairy prion. e, Andean gull. f, Imperial shag. g, Red phalarope. h, Hooded grebe. i, Least auklet. j, Little grebe. k, Cape petrel. l, Horned grebe.

Each $5: No. 2069, Sula nebouxii. No. 2070, Fulmarus glacialis.

1998, Aug. 4   Perf. 14
2064-2067 A319   Set of 4   2.50 2.50
2068 A319 90c Sheet of 12,
           #a.-l.   10.00 10.00
Souvenir Sheets
2069-2070 A319   Set of 2   10.50 10.50

Airplanes A320

20c, Jetstar II. 25c, AN 225. 55c, Dash-8. 65c, Beech-99. 90c, American Eagle. $2, HFB 320 Itansa Jet.

No. 2077, each $1: a, SR 71 "Blackbird." b, Stealth bomber. c, Northrop YF23. d, F-14 A "Tomcat." e, F-15 "Eagle S." f, MiG 29 "Fulcrum." g, Europa X5. h, Camion.

No. 2078, each $1: a, E400. b, CL-215 C-GKDN Amphibian. c, Piper jet. d, Beech Hawker. e, Lockheed YF22. f, Piper Seneca V. g, CL-215 Amphibian. h, Vantase.

Each $6: No. 2079, F-1 Fighter. No. 2080, Sea Hopper.

1998, Aug. 17
2071-2076 A320   Set of 6   4.50 4.50
Sheets of 8
2077-2078 A320   Set of 2   17.00 17.00
Souvenir Sheets
2079-2080 A320   Set of 2   11.00 11.00

Intl. Year of the Ocean — A321

Marine life: 25c, Fridman fish. 55c, Hydrocoral. 65c, Feather star. 90c, Royal angelfish.

No. 2085, each $1: a, Monk seal. b, Galapagos penguin. c, Manta ray. d, Hawksbill turtle. e, Moorish idol. f, Nautilus. g, Giant clam. h, Tubeworms. i, Nudibranch.

No. 2086, each $1: a, Spotted dolphin. b, Atlantic sailfish. c, Sailfin flying fish. d, Fairy basslet. e, Atlantic spadefish. f, Leatherback turtle. g, Blue tang. h, Coral banded shrimp. i, Rock beauty.

No. 2087, Humpback whale. No. 2088, Leafy sea dragon.

1998, Sept. 7   Litho.   Perf. 14
2081-2084 A321   Set of 4   2.50 2.50
Sheets of 9
2085-2086 A321   Set of 2   19.00 19.00
Souvenir Sheets
2087 A321 $5 multicolored   4.75 4.75
2088 A321 $6 multicolored   5.50 5.50

Organization of American States, 50th Anniv. — A322

1998, Sept. 1   Litho.   Perf. 14
2089 A322 $1 multicolored   1.25 1.25

Ferrari Sports Cars — A323

55c, 365 GT 2+2. 90c, Boano/Ellena 250 GT. $1, 375 MM coupe. $5, 212.

1998, Sept. 1
2090-2092 A323   Set of 3   3.75 3.75
Souvenir Sheet
2093 A323 $5 multicolored   5.50 5.50

No. 2093 contains one 91x35mm stamp.

Gandhi — A324

1998, Sept. 1
2094 A324 90c shown   1.50 1.50
Souvenir Sheet
2095 A324 $6 Seated   5.25 5.25

No. 2094 was issued in sheets of 4.

Pablo Picasso — A325

Paintings: 90c, The Painter and His Model, 1926. $1, The Crucifixion, 1930. $2, Nude with Raised Arms, 1908, vert. $6, Cafe at Royan, 1940.

1998, Sept. 1   Perf. 14½
2096-2098 A325   Set of 3   4.50 4.50
Souvenir Sheet
2099 A325 $6 multicolored   5.75 5.75

Royal Air Force, 80th Anniv. — A326

No. 2100: a, Nimrod MR2P. b, C-130 Hercules Mk3. c, Panavia Tornado GR1. d, C-130 Hercules landing.

$5, Biplane, hawk. $6, Hawker Hart, jet.

1998, Sept. 1   Perf. 14
2100 A326 $2 Sheet of 4, #a.-d. 7.00 7.00
Souvenir Sheets
2101 A326 $5 multicolored   4.75 4.75
2102 A326 $6 multicolored   5.25 5.25

No. 2100d incorrectly inscribed Panavia Tornado GR1.

Nos. 1548-1549, 1551-1552, 1554 Ovptd.

1998, Sept. 14
2103-2107 A221   Set of 5   6.00 6.00

A327

1998 World Scouting Jamboree, Chile: 65c, Scout sign. $1, Scout handshake. $2, World Scout flag.

$5, Lord Baden-Powell.

1998
2108-2110 A327   Set of 3   3.25 3.25
Souvenir Sheet
2111 A327 $5 multicolored   5.25 5.25

A328

Birds: 25c, Northern cardinal. 55c, Eastern bluebird. 65c, Carolina wren. 90c, Blue jay. $1, Evening grosbeak. $2, Bohemian waxwing. $5, Northern parula. $6, Painted bunting.

1998, Dec. 1   Litho.   Perf. 14
2112-2117 A328   Set of 6   5.50 5.50
Souvenir Sheets
2118 A328 $5 multicolored   5.25 5.25
2119 A328 $6 multicolored   6.25 6.25

Christmas.

New Year 1999 (Year of the Rabbit) — A329

1999, Jan. 4   Litho.   Perf. 14
2120 A329 $1.50 multicolored   2.00 2.00

No. 2120 was issued in sheets of 4.

Orchids — A330

55c, Broughtonia sanguinea. 65c, Cattleyonia Keith Roth "Roma." 90c, Comparettia falcata. $2, Cochleanthes discolor.

No. 2125, each $1: a, Dracula erythiochaete. b, Lycaste aromatica. c, Masdevallia marguerile. d, Encyclia marfae. e, Laelia gouldiana. f, Huntleya meleagris. g, Galeandria baueri. h, Lycale deppei.

No. 2126, each $1: a, Anguloa clowesii. b, Lemboglossum cervantesii. c, Oncidium cebolleta. d, Millonia. e, Pescatorea lehmannll. f, Sophronitis coccinea. g, Pescatorea cerina. h, Encyclia vitellina.

Each $5: No. 2127, Lepanthes ovalis. No. 2128, Encyclia cochleata.

1999, Apr. 26   Litho.   Perf. 14
2121-2124 A330   Set of 4   4.50 4.50
Sheets of 8
2125-2126 A330   Set of 2   17.50 17.50
Souvenir Sheets
2127-2128 A330   Set of 2   10.00 10.00

Trains — A331

No. 2129, each $1: a, Class 103.1 Co-Co, Germany. b, Class .24, "Trans Pennine," UK. c, GG1 2-Co-Co-2, US. d, LRC Bo-Bo, Canada. e, Class EW, New Zealand. f, Class SS1 "Shao-Shani," China. g, Gulf, Mobile Ohio, US. h, Class 9100 2-Do-2, France.

No. 2130, each $1: a, County Donegal Petrol Rail Car No. 10, Ireland. b, RDC Single Rail Car, US. c, WDM Class Co-Co, India. d, Bipolar No. E-2, US. e, Class X Co-Co, Australia. f, Beijing Bo-Bo, China. g, Class E428 2-

Bo-Bo-2, Italy. h, Class 581 Twelve-Car Train, Japan.
$5, X-2000 Tilting Express Train, Sweden, vert. $6, Class 87 Bo-Bo, Great Britain, vert.

1999, May 10   Litho.   Perf. 14
Sheets of 8
2129-2130 A331   Set of 2   13.00 13.00
Souvenir Sheets
2131 A331 $5 multicolored   4.00 4.00
2132 A331 $6 multicolored   5.00 5.00
Australia '99, World Stamp Expo.

Prehistoric Animals — A332

25c, Tyrannosaurus, vert. 65c, Hypacrosaurus. 90c, Sauropelta. $2, Zalambdalestes.
No. 2137, each $1: a, Barosaurus. b, Rhamphorhynchus. c, Apatosaurus. d, Archaeopteryx. e, Diplodocus. f, Ceratosaurus. g, Stegosaurus. h, Elaphrosaurus. i, Vulcanodon.
No. 2138, each $1: a, Psittacosaurus. b, Pteranodon. c, Ichthyornis. d, Spinosaurus. e, Parasaurolophus. f, Ornithomimus. g, Anatosaurus. h, Triceratops. i, Baronyx.
$5, Yangchuanosaurus. $6, Brachiosaurus.

1999, June 1   Litho.   Perf. 14
2133-2136 A332   Set of 4   3.50 3.50
Sheets of 9
2137-2138 A332   Set of 2   18.00 18.00
Souvenir Sheets
2139 A332 $5 multicolored   4.50 4.50
2140 A332 $6 multicolored   5.50 5.50

Wedding of Prince Edward and Sophie Rhys-Jones — A333

No. 2141: a, Sophie. b, Sophie, Edward. c, Edward.
$6, like No. 2141b.

1999, June 19   Litho.   Perf. 13½
2141 A333 $3 Sheet of 3, #a.-c.   7.25 7.25
Souvenir Sheet
2142 A333 $6 multicolored   5.00 5.00

IBRA '99, World Philatelic Exhibition, Nuremberg — A334

Exhibition emblem, sailing ship Eendraght and: 65c, Cameroun #58, #56. 90c, Cameroun #11, #9.
Emblem, early German train and: $1, Cameroun #19. $2, Cameroun #6.
$6, Cover with Cameroun #19.

1999, June 22   Perf. 14
2143-2146 A334   Set of 4   4.00 4.00
Souvenir Sheet
2147 A334 $6 multicolored   6.25 6.25

Souvenir Sheets

PhilexFrance '99 — A335

Trains: $5, L'Aigle, 1855. $6, Mainline diesel locomotive, 1963.

1999, June 22   Perf. 13¾
2148 A335 $5 multicolored   4.50 4.50
2149 A335 $6 multicolored   5.50 5.50

Apollo 11 Moon Landing, 30th Anniv. — A336

No. 2150: a, Command Module separation b, Service Module separation. c, 3rd Stage Booster separation. d, Landing, Command Modules go to the moon. e, Apollo Ground Tracker. f, Goldstone Radio Telescope.
$6, Apollo 11 after splashdown.

1999, June 22   Perf. 14
2150 A336 $1.45 Sheet of 6, #a.-f.   9.00 9.00
Souvenir Sheet
2151 A336 $6 multicolored   6.00 6.00

Paintings by Hokusai (1760-1849) A337

Details or entire paintings — No. 2152:, each $2 a, Pilgrims at Kirifuri Waterfall. b, Kakura-Sato (rats looking at book, pulling on rope). c, Travelers on the Bridge by Ono Waterfall. d, Fast Cargo Boat Battling the Waves. e, Kakura-Sato (rats working with bales). f, Buufinfinh and Weeping cherry.
No. 2153, each $2: a, Cuckoo and Azalea. b, Soldiers (spear in left hand). c, Lover in the snow. d, Ghost of Koheiji. e, Soldiers (spear in right hand). f, Chinese Poet in Snow.
$5, Empress Jitó. $6, One Hundred Poems by One Hundred Poets.

Perf. 13½x13¾
1999, June 22   Litho.
Sheets of 6
2152-2153 A337   Set of 2   19.00 19.00
Souvenir Sheets
2154 A337 $5 multicolored   4.50 4.50
2155 A337 $6 multicolored   5.50 5.50

Johann Wolfgang von Goethe (1749-1832), Poet — A338

No. 2156: a, Faust perceives an astrological sign. b, Portrait of Goethe and Friedrich von Schiller (1759-1805). c, Faust tempted by Mephistopheles.
$6, Profile portrait of Goethe.

1999, June 22   Perf. 14
2156 A338 $2 Sheet of 3, #a.-c.   5.00 5.00
Souvenir Sheet
2157 A338 $6 multicolored   5.00 5.00

Rights of the Child — A339

No. 2158: a, Woman, child. b, Child in blue sweater. c, Two children.
$6, Dove, horiz.

1999, June 22   Litho.   Perf. 14
2158 A339 $3 Sheet of 3, #a.-c.   7.50 7.50
Souvenir Sheet
2159 A339 $6 multicolored   5.00 5.00

Queen Mother (b. 1900) — A340

A340a

Gold Frames
No. 2160: a, In 1939. b, In Australia, 1958. c, At Badminton, 1982. d, Hatless, in 1982. $6, In 1953.

1999, Aug. 4   Perf. 14
2160 A340 $2 Sheet of 4, #a.-d. + label   7.50 7.50
Souvenir Sheet
Perf. 13¾
2161 A340 $6 multicolored   5.00 5.00
No. 2161 contains one 38x51mm stamp.
Compare with Nos. 2345-2346. Backdrop of photo is more pink on No. 2161 than on No. 2346. No. 2161 has embossed arms in margin, while No. 2346 does not.

Litho. & Embossed
Die Cut Perf. 8¾
Without Gum
2161A A340a $20 gold & multi 20.00 20.00
See Nos. 2345-2346.

Flora & Fauna — A341

Designs: 25c, Heliconia lobster claw. 65c, Broad winged hawk. $1, Anthurium. $1.55, Blue-headed hummingbird. $2, Bananaquit. $4 Agouti.
No. 2168: a, White-throated sparrow. b, Blue-winged teal. c, Raccoon. d, Alfalf butterfly. e, Bridge. f, Whitetail deer. g, Gray squirrel. h, Banded purple butterfly. i, Snowdrop. j, Bullfrog. k, Mushrooms. l, Large-blotched ensatina.
$5, Eastern chipmunk. $6, Black-footed ferret.

1999
2162-2167 A341   Set of 6   9.00 9.00
Sheet of 12
2168 A341 90c #a.-l.   10.00 10.00
Souvenir Sheets
2169 A341 $5 multicolored   5.00 5.00
2170 A341 $6 multicolored   6.00 6.00

A342

Dominica Festival Commission: 25c, Domfesta. 55c, $5, Dominica's 21st anniv. as a republic. 65c, Carnival development committee. 90c, World Creole Music Festival.

1999   Perf. 12½
2171-2174 A342   Set of 4   2.00 2.00
Souvenir Sheet
Perf. 13¼
2175 A342 $5 multicolored   4.50 4.50
No. 2175 contains one 38x51mm stamp.

A343

Intl. Year of the Elderly: 25c, Family. 65c, Four people. 90c, Four people, one in chair.

1999, Aug. 4   Perf. 14
2176 A343 Sheet of 3, #a.-c.   1.50 1.50

A345

Christmas: 25c, Yellow-crowned parrot. 55c, Red bishop. 65c, Troupial. 90c, Puerto Rican woodpecker. $2, Mangrove cuckoo. $3, American robin.
$6, Mary with Child Beside the Wall, by Albrecht Dürer.

1999, Dec. 7   Litho.   Perf. 14
2178-2183 A345   Set of 6   6.75 6.75
Souvenir Sheet
2184 A345 $6 multi   5.25 5.25
Inscription on No. 2181 is misspelled.

A346

Millennium (Highlights of the early 13th Cent.) — No. 2185: a, Leonardo Fibonacci publishes "Liber Abaci," 1202. b, St. Francis of Assisi. c, Mongols conquer China. d, Children's Crusade begins, 1212. e, Magna Carta signed, 1215. f, Founding of Salamanca University, 1218. g, Snorri Sturluson writes "Prose Edda". h, Chinese painter Ma Yuan dies, 1225. i, Genghis Khan dies, 1227. j, Zen Buddhism in Japan. k, Sixth Crusade. l, Lubeck-Hamburg League. m, Inquisitions begin, 1231. n, Cordoba conquered by Castilians, 1236. o, Democracy in San Marino. p, Maimonides (60x40mm). q, Notre Dame Cathedral, Paris.
Highlights of the 1940s — No. 2186: a, Japan bombs Pearl Harbor. b, Churchill becomes Prime Minister of Great Britain. c, Regular television broadcasting begins in the US. d, Anne Frank hid in Amsterdam. e, D-Day Invasion. f, Yalta Conference. g, Establishment of the UN. h, Germany surrenders, concentration camps exposed. i, Russians hoist flag over gutted Reichstag building. j, Eniac computer. k, Independence for India. l, Bell Laboratories produce 1st transistor. m, Gandhi assassinated. n, Israel achieves statehood. o, Blockade of West Berlin, Berlin Airlift. p, Atomic bomb tested in New Mexico (60x40mm). q, Establishment of People's Republic of China.

Perf. 12¾x12½
1999, Dec. 31   Sheets of 17   Litho.
2185 A346 55c #a.-q. + label   8.50 8.50
2186 A346 55c #a.-q. + label   8.50 8.50
See Nos. 2249-2252.

New Year 2000 (Year of the Dragon) — A347

2000, Feb. 5   *Perf. 13¾*
2187 A347 $1.50 shown   1.25 1.25
Souvenir Sheet
2188 A347 $4 Dragon, horiz.   3.75 3.75
    No. 2187 printed in sheets of 4.

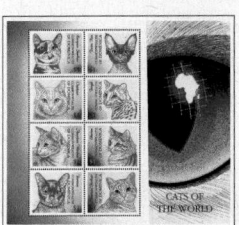

Cats
A348

No. 2189, each $1: a, European Shorthair.
b, Devon Rex. c, Chartreux. d, Bengal. e,
American Wirehair. f, Siberian. g, Burmese. h,
American Shorthair.
    No. 2190, each $1: a, Asian Longhair. b,
Burmilla. c, Snowshoe. d, Pekeface Persian. e,
Himalayan Persian. f, Japanese Bobtail. g,
Seychelles Longhair. h, Exotic Shorthair.
    Each $6: No. 2191, Awake cat. No. 2192,
Sleeping cat.

2000, Feb. 21   *Perf. 14¼*
Sheets of 8, #a.-h.
2189-2190 A348 Set of 2   16.00 16.00
Souvenir Sheets
2191-2192 A348 Set of 2   12.00 12.00

Puppies — A349

No. 2193: a, Jack Russell Terrier. b, Shar
Peis. c, Basset Hound. d, Boxers. e, Wire-
haired Terrier. f, Golden Retrievers.
    No. 2194, Beagle.

2000, Feb. 21   *Perf. 14½x14¼*
2193 A349 $1 Sheet of 6, #a.-f.   6.00 6.00
Souvenir Sheet
2194 A349 $6 multi   6.00 6.00

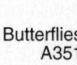

Flowers — A350

    Various flowers making up a photomosaic of
Princess Diana.

2000, Apr. 3   *Perf. 13¾*
2195 A350 $1 Sheet of 8, #a.-h.   7.50 7.50
      See No. 2225.

Butterflies
A351

No. 2196, each $1.50: a, Giant swallowtail.
b, Tiger pierid. c, Orange theope. d, White
peacock. e, Blue tharops. f, Mosaic.
    No. 2197, each $1.50: a, Banded king shoe-
maker. b, Figure-of-eight. c, Grecian shoemaker. d, Blue night. e, Monarch. f, Common
morpho.
    No. 2198, each $1.50: a, Orange-barred
sulphur. b, Clorinde. c, Small flambeau. d,
Small lace-wing. e, Polydamas swallowtail. f,
Atala.
    Each $6: No. 2199, Polydamas swallowtail,
vert. No. 2200, Sloane's urania, vert. No.
2201, Blue-green reflector, vert.

2000, Apr. 10   *Perf. 14*
Sheets of 6, #a.-f.
2196-2198 A351 Set of 3   24.00 24.00
Souvenir Sheets
2199-2201 A351 Set of 3   17.50 17.50

Flowers — A352

    Designs: 65c, Passion flower. 90c, Spray
orchid. $1, Peach angel's trumpet. $4,
Allamanda.
    No. 2206, each $1.65: a, Bird of paradise. b,
Lobster claw heliconia. c, Candle bush. d, Flor
de San Miguel. e, Hibiscus. f, Oleander.
    No. 2207, each $1.65: a, Anthurium. b, Fire
ginger. c, Shrimp plant. d, Sky vine
thunbergia. e, Ceriman. f, Morning glory.
    Each $6: No. 2208, Bird of paradise, diff.
No. 2109, Hibiscus, diff.

2000, Apr. 25   *Litho.*   *Perf. 14*
2202-2205 A352 Set of 4   6.00 6.00
Sheets of 6, #a-f
Perf. 13¾
2206-2207 A352 Set of 2   17.00 17.00
Souvenir Sheets
Perf. 13½x 13¾
2208-2209 A352 Set of 2   12.00 12.00
    Size of stamps: Nos. 2106-2107, 32x48mm;
Nos. 2108-2109, 38x51mm.

Paintings
of
Anthony
Van
Dyck
A353

No. 2210, each $1.65: a, Lady Jane Good-
win. b, Philip Herbert, 4th Earl of Pembroke. c,
Philip, Lord Wharton. d, Sir Thomas Hammer.
e, Olivia Porter, Wife of Enymion Porter. f, Sir
Thomas Chaloner.
    No. 2211, horiz, each $1.65: a, Ladies in
Waiting. b, Thomas Wentworth, Earl of Straf-
ford, with Sir Philip Mainwaring. c, Dorothy
Rivers Savage, Viscountess Andover and Her
Sister Lady Elizabeth Thimbleby. d, Mountjoy
Blount, Earl of Newport, and Lord George
Goring with a Page. e, Thomas Killigrew and
an Unidentified Man. f, Elizabeth Villiers, Lady
Dalkeith, and Cecilia Killigrew.
    No. 2212, horiz, each $1.65: a, The Ages of
Man. b, Portrait of a Girl as Erminia Accompa-
nied by Cupid. c, Cupid and Psyche. d, Ver-
tumnus and Pomona. e, The Continence of
Scipio. f, Diana and Endymion Surprised by a
Satyr.
    No. 2213, $5, Achilles and the Daughters of
Lycomedes. No. 2214, $5, Amaryllis and Mir-
tillo. No. 2215, $6, Thomas Howard, 2nd Earl
of Arundel, with Alathea, Countess of Arundel.

2000, May 29   *Perf. 13¾*
Sheets of 6, #a-f
2210-2212 A353 Set of 3   27.00 27.00
Souvenir Sheets
2213-2214 A353 Set of 2   9.00 9.00
2215 A353 $6 multi   5.50 5.50

First
Zeppelin
Flight,
Cent.
A354

No. 2216: a, Count Ferdinand von Zeppelin
(1838-1917). b, First takeoff of LZ-1. c, LZ-10
over field. d, LZ-6 and Deutschland in hangar.
e, Arrival of Z-4 at Luneville. f, Victoria Luise.
No. 2217, LZ-1, diff.

2000, June 21   *Litho.*   *Perf. 14*
2216 A354 $1.65 Sheet of 6, #a-f 9.00 9.00
Souvenir Sheet
2217 A354 $6 multi   5.50 5.50

Berlin
Film
Festival,
50th
Anniv.
A355

    No. 2218: a, Director Satyajit Ray. b,
Mahangar. c, Fanfan La Tulipe. d, Le Salaire
de la Peur. e, Les Cousins. f, Hon Dansede en
Sommar.
    No. 2219, Buffalo Bill and the Indians.

2000, June 21
2218 A355 $1.65 Sheet of 6, #a-f 9.00 9.00
Souvenir Sheet
2219 A355 $6 multi   5.50 5.50

100th Test Match at
Lord's Ground — A356

2000, June 21
2220 A356 $4 Norbert Phillip   3.50 3.50
Souvenir Sheet
2221 A356 $6 Lord's Ground   5.50 5.50

Souvenir Sheets

2000 Summer Olympics,
Sydney — A357

    a, Jesse Owens. b, Pole vault. c, Lenin Sta-
dium Moscow, Soviet Union flag. d, Ancient
Greek discus thrower.

2000, June 21
2222 A357 $2 Sheet of 4, #a-d   8.00 8.00

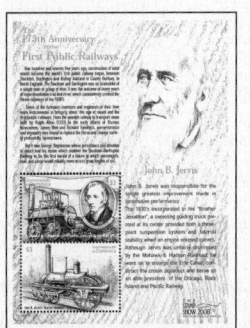

Public Railways, 175th Anniv. — A358

    No. 2223: a, Locomotion No. 1, George Ste-
phenson. b, Brother Jonathon.

2000, June 21
2223 A358 $3 Sheet of 2, #a-b   6.25 6.25
    The Stamp Show 2000, London.

Johann Sebastian Bach — A359

2000, June 21
2224 A359 $6 multi   5.50 5.50

Flower Type of 2000

    Various pictures of religious sites making up
a photomosaic of Pope John Paul II.

2000, June 21   *Litho.*   *Perf. 13¾*
2225 A350 $1 Sheet of 8, #a-h   8.00 8.00

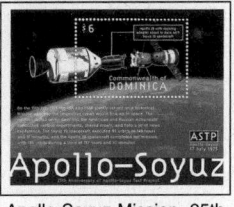

Apollo-Soyuz Mission, 25th
Anniv. — A360

    No. 2226, vert.: a, Saturn IB launch vehicle.
b, Apollo 18. c, Donald K. Slayton.
$6, Apollo and Soyuz docking.

2000, June 21   *Perf. 14*
2226 A360 $3 Sheet of 3, #a-c   9.50 9.50
Souvenir Sheet
2227 A360 $6 multi   6.00 6.00

Souvenir Sheet

Albert Einstein (1879-1955) — A361

2000, June 21   *Perf. 14¼*
2228 A361 $6 multi   5.50 5.50

Prince
William,
18th
Birthday
A362

    No. 2229: a, In ski gear. b, In jacket and red
sweater. c, In suit and tie. d, In plaid shirt.
$6, With Prince Harry.

2000, June 22   *Perf. 14*
2229 A362 $1.65 Sheet of 4,
       #a-d   6.25 6.25
Souvenir Sheet
Perf. 13¾
2230 A362 $6 multi   5.50 5.50
    No. 2229 contains four 28x42mm stamps.

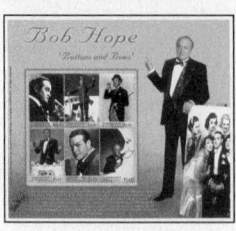

Bob Hope A363

No. 2231: a, Microphone at right. b, Entertaining troops. c, Wearing bowler. d, Standing in cake. e, Microphone at left. f, With moon.

2000, Aug. 7   **Perf. 14**
2231 A363 $1.65 Sheet of 6,
    #a-f   10.00 10.00

Monty Python and the Holy Grail, 25th Anniv. A364

No. 2232: a, Close-up of Eric Idle. b, Terry Jones, Graham Chapman and John Cleese as three-headed giant, horiz. c, Knights facing castle wall. d, Chapman as King Arthur, with helmeted knight. e, Beheaded knight. f, Armless and legless Black Knight and King Arthur.

2000, Aug. 7   **Perf. 13¾**
2232 A364 90c Sheet of 6, #a-f   5.25 5.25

Popes A365

No. 2233: a, Clement X, 1670-76. b, Innocent X, 1644-55. c, Nicholas V, 1447-55. d, Martin V, 1417-31. e, Julius III, 1550-55. f, Innocent XII, 1691-1700.
$6, Clement XIV, 1769-74.

2000, Sept. 5
2233 A365 $1.65 Sheet of 6,
    #a-f   10.00 10.00
Souvenir Sheet
2234 A365 $6 multi   5.50 5.50

Monarchs — A366

No. 2235: a, Edward IV of England, 1461-83. b, Peter the Great of Russia, 1682-1725. c, Henry VI of England, 1422-61. d, Henry III of England, 1216-72. e, Richard III of England, 1483-85. f, Edward I of England, 1272-1307.
$6, Henry VIII of England, 1509-47.

2000, Sept. 5
2235 A366 $1.65 Sheet of 6,
    #a-f   10.00 10.00
Souvenir Sheet
2236 A366 $6 multi   5.50 5.50

World Stamp Expo 2000, Anaheim A367

Spacecraft — No. 2237, $1.65: a, Explorer 14. b, Luna 16. c, Copernicus. d, Explorer 16. e, Luna 10. f, Arybhattan.
No. 2238, $1.65: a, ESSA 8. b, Echo 1. c, Topex Poseidon. d, Diademe. e, Early Bird. f, Molniya.
No. 2239, $6, Hipparcos. No. 2240, $6, Eole.

2000, June 21   Litho.   Perf. 14¼x14
Sheets of 6, #a-f
2237-2238 A367   Set of 2   20.00 20.00
Souvenir Sheets
2239-2240 A367   Set of 2   11.00 11.00

David Copperfield, Magician — A368

2000, Aug. 8   **Perf. 14**
2241 A368 $2 multi   1.75 1.75
Printed in sheets of 4.

Souvenir Sheet

Female Recording Groups of the 1960s — A369

No. 2242 — The Crystals, yellow spotlight covering: a, UR, LL and LR corners. b, UL and LL corners. c, UR and LR corners. d, UL, LL and LR corners.

2000, Aug. 8
2242 A369 90c Sheet of 4, #a-d   3.50 3.50

Christmas — A370

Angel: 25c, No. 2247a, Looking right, purple and yellow green background. 65c, No. 2247b, At left, looking left, purple background. 90c, No. 2247c, At right, purple and orange background. $5, No. 2247d, At center, blue and purple background.

2000, Dec. 4
2243-2246 A370   Set of 4   6.25 6.25
Sheet of 4
2247 A370 $1.90 #a-d   7.00 7.00
Souvenir Sheet
2248 A370 $6 Angel   5.50 5.50

Millennium Type of 1999

Chinese Art — No. 2249, 55c: a, Eight Prize Steeds, by Giuseppe Castiglione. b, Oleanders, by Wu Hsi Tsai. c, Mynah and Autumn Flowers, by Chang Hsiung. d, Hen and Chicks Beneath Chrysanthemums, by Chu Ch'ao. e, Long Living Pine and Crane, by Xugu. f, Flowers and Fruits, by Chu Lien. g, Lotus and Willow, by Pu Hua. h, Kuan-Yin, by Ch'ien Hui-An. i, Human Figures, by Jen hsun. j, Han-Shan and Shih-Te, by Ren Yii. k, Landscape and Human Figure, by Jen Yu. l, Poetic Thoughts While Walking With a Staff, by Wangchen. m, Peony, by Chen Heng-Ko. n, Plum and Orchids, by Wu Chang-Shih. o, Monkey, by Kao Chi-Feng. p, Grapes and Locust, by Ch'i Pai-Shih and Galloping Horse, by Xu Beihong (60x40mm). q, The Beauty, by Lin Fengmian.

History of Change — No. 2250, 55c: a, Star charts. b, Precision tools. c, Science of the stars. d, Investigation into healing a human

being. e, Sharing of medical information. f, Church. g, Water alarm clock. h, Weighted clock. i, Spring-loaded miniature clock. j, New technology of glass blowing. k, First screws. l, Wood lathe. m, New systems for assembly blocks for ships. n, Interchangeable parts for rifles. o, Study of movement. p, Efficiency and the Industrial Revolution (60x40mm). q, Concept of efficiency.

Highlights of the 1960s — No. 2251, 55c: a, First birth control pill developed. b, Yuri Gagarin becomes first man in space. c, The first hit for the Beatles in Britain. d, Assassination of John F. Kennedy. e, Dr. Martin Luther King's "I Have a Dream" speech. f, Betty Friedan writes "The Feminine Mystique." g, Kenya gains independence. h, U.S. Surgeon General warns about smoking-related health hazards. i, U.S. Congress passes Civil Rights Act. j, U.S. increases military presence in South Viet Nam. k, Ernesto "Che" Guevara. l, First heart transplant. m, Israel wins Six-day War. n, Ho Chi Minh dies. o, First man on the Moon. p, Communists build wall to divide East and West Berlin (60x40mm). q, Woodstock rock concert.

Highlights of the late 14th Century — No. 2252: a, Minnesingers. b, Acampitzin, King of the Aztecs. c, Black Death eases. d, Giotto's campanile built. e, First French franc. f, Ming Dynasty in China. g, Tamerlane begins conquest of Asia. h, Triumph of Death painted by Francesco Traini. i, Robin Hood. j, Geoffrey Chaucer writes "The Canterbury Tales." k, Succession dispute in Japan. l, Jewish exodus from France. m, Temple of the Golden Pavilion built . n, Strasbourg Cathedral built. o, Alhambra Palace (60x40mm). p, Ife bronzes in Nigeria.

2000, Dec. 31   **Perf. 12¾x12½**
Sheets of 17, #a-q
2249-2251 A346   Set of 3   26.00 26.00
2252 A347 65c Sheet of 17,
    #a-h, j-p, 2 #i   10.00 10.00

Hummingbirds — A371

No. 2253, $1.25: a, Green-throated carib. b, Bee, on branch. c, Bee, in flight. d, Bahama woodstar. e, Antillean mango. f, Blue-headed.
No. 2254, $1.65: a, Eastern streamertail. b, Purple-throated carib. c, Vervain. d, Bahama woodstar. e, Puerto Rican emerald. f, Antillean crested.
No. 2255, $5, Feeders. No. 2256, $6, Hispaniolan.

2000, Dec. 18   **Litho.**   **Perf. 14**
Sheets of 6, #a-f
2253-2254 A371   Set of 2   16.00 16.00
Souvenir Sheets
2255-2256 A371   Set of 2   10.00 10.00
Misspellings abound on Nos. 2253-2254.

New Year 2001 (Year of the Snake) — A372

2001, Jan. 2   **Perf. 12x12¼**
2257 A372 $1.20 multi   1.00 1.00
Printed in sheets of 4.

Fauna — A373

Designs: 15c, Puerto Rican crested toad. 20c, Axolotl. $1.90, Panamanian golden frog. $2.20, Manatee.

No. 2262, $1.45: a, St. Vincent parrot. b, Indigo macaw. c, Cock of the rock. d, Cuban solenodon. e, Cuban hutia. f, Chinchilla.
No. 2263, $1.45: a, South American flamingo. b, Golden conure. c, Ocelot. d, Giant armadillo. e, Margay. f, Maned wolf.
No. 2264, $6, Anteater. No. 2265, $6, Hawksbill turtle.

2000, Dec. 18   **Litho.**   **Perf. 14**
2258-2261 A373   Set of 4   4.75 4.75
Sheets of 6, #a-f
2262-2263 A373   Set of 2   17.00 17.00
Souvenir Sheets
2264-2265 A373   Set of 2   12.00 12.00

Pokémon A374

No. 2266, horiz.: a, Butterfree. b, Bulbasaur. c, Caterpie. d, Charmander. e, Squirtle. f, Pidgeotto.

2001, Feb.   **Perf. 13¾**
2266 A374 $1.65 Sheet of 6, #a-f 7.00 7.00
Souvenir Sheet
2267 A374 $6 Nidoking   4.25 4.25

A375

Marine Life — A376

Designs: No. 2268, 15c, Banded sea snake. 25c, Soldier fish. 55c, Banner fish. No. 2271, 90c, Crown of thorns starfish.
No. 2272, 15c, Fish. 65c, Ray. No. 2274, 90c, Octopus. $3, Fish, diff.
No. 2276, $1.65: a, White-tip reef shark, lionfish, sergeant major. b, Blue-striped snappers. c, Great hammerhead shark, stovepipe sponge, pink vase sponge. d, Hawaiian monk seal, blue tube coral. e, Seahorse, common clownfish, red feather star coral. f, Bat starfish, brown octopus.
No. 2277, $1.65: a, Red sponge, shoal of Anthias. b, Orange-striped triggerfish. c, Coral grouper, soft tree coral. d, Peacock fan worms, gorgonian sea fan. e, Sweetlips, sea fan. f, Giant clam, golden cup coral.
No. 2278: a, Shark. b, Starfish. c, Seahorse. d, Fish. e, Crab. f, Eel.
No. 2279, $5, Royal angelfish. No. 2280, $5, Pink anemone fish. No. 2281, Turtle.

2001, Feb. 27   **Perf. 14**
2268-2271 A375   Set of 4   2.00 2.00
2272-2275 A376   Set of 4   5.00 5.00
Sheets of 6, #a-f
2276-2277 A375   Set of 2   19.00 19.00
2278 A376 $2 Sheet of 6, #a-f 11.00 11.00
Souvenir Sheets
2279-2280 A375   Set of 2   10.00 10.00
2281 A376 $5 multi   5.00 5.00

Phila Nippon '01, Japan — A377

Art: 25c, Gathering of Chinese Women, by Tsuji Kako. 55c, Village by Bamboo Grove, by Takeuchi Seiho. 65c, Mountain Village in Spring, by Suzuki Hyakunen. 90c, Gentleman Amusing Himself, by Domoto Insho. $1, Calmness of Spring Light, by Seiho. $2, Su's Embankment on a Spring Morning, by Tomioka Tessai.

No. 2288, $1.65: a, Thatched Cottages in the Willows, by Kako. b, Joy in the Garden, by Kako. c, Azalea and butterfly, by Kikuchi Hobun. d, Pine Grove, by Kako. e, Woodcutters Talking in Autumn Valley, by Kubota Beisen.

No. 2289, $1.65: a, Waterfowl in Snow, by Kako. b, Heron and Willow, by Kako. c, Crow and Cherry Blossoms, by Hobun. d, Chrysanthemum Immortal, by Yamamoto Shunkyo. e, Cranes of Immortality, by Kako.

No. 2290, $6, Kamo Riverbank in the Misty Rain, by Kako. No. 2291, $6, Diamond Gate, by Kako. No. 2292, $6, Woman, by Suzuki Harunobu.

2001, May 15		**Litho.**	**Perf. 14**	
2282-2287	A377	Set of 6	5.25	5.25
		Sheets of 5, #a-e		
2288-2289	A377	Set of 2	15.00	15.00
		Souvenir Sheets		
		Perf. 13¾		
2290-2292	A377	Set of 3	12.00	12.00

Nos. 2290-2292 each contain one 38x51mm stamp.

Queen Victoria (1819-1901) — A378

No. 2293: a, Prince Albert in uniform. b, Victoria with silver crown. c, Victoria with gold crown. d, Albert in suit.
$6, Victoria as old woman.

2001, May 15			**Perf. 14**	
2293	A378	$2 Sheet of 4, #a-d	7.25	7.25
		Souvenir Sheet		
		Perf. 13¾		
2294	A378	$6 multi	5.50	5.50

No. 2294 contains one 38x51mm stamp.

Queen Elizabeth II, 75th Birthday A379

No. 2295: a, With crown. b, With white dress. c, Formal portrait by Pietro Annigoni. d, With orange coat. e, With child. f, With green dress.
$6, In uniform.

2001, May 15			**Perf. 14**	
2295	A379	$1.20 Sheet of 6, #a-f	6.25	6.25
		Souvenir Sheet		
2296	A379	$6 multi	5.50	5.50

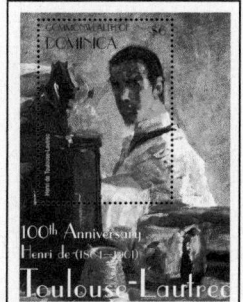

Toulouse-Lautrec Paintings — A380

No. 2297: a, Two Women Waltzing. b, The Medical Inspection. c, The Two Girlfriends. d, Woman Pulling Up Her Stocking.

2001, May 15		**Litho.**	**Perf. 13¾**	
2297	A380	$2 Sheet of 4, #a-d	7.25	7.25
		Souvenir Sheet		
2298	A380	$6 Self-portrait	5.50	5.50

Giuseppe Verdi (1813-1901), Opera Composer — A381

No. 2299: a, Verdi. b, Lady Macbeth. c, Orchestra. d, Score.

2001, May 15			**Perf. 14**	
2299	A381	$2 Sheet of 4, #a-d	7.25	7.25
		Souvenir Sheet		
2300	A381	$6 Verdi, score	5.50	5.50

Mushrooms — A382

Designs: 15c, Cantharellus cibarius. 25c, Hygrocybe pratensis. 55c, Leccinum aurantiacum. $3, Mycena haematopus.

No. 2305, 90c, horiz.: a, Caesar's amanita. b, Agaricus augustus. c, Clitocybe nuda. d, Hygrocybe plavescens. e, Stropharia kaufmanii. f, Hygrophorus speciosus.
No. 2306, $2: a, Marasmiellus candidus. b, Calostoma cinnabarina. c, Cantharellus infundibuliformis. d, Hygrocybe punicea. e, Basket stinkhorn. f, Agrocybe praecox.
No. 2307, $5, Fly agaric, horiz. No. 2308, $5, Gymnopilus spectabilis, horiz.

2001, June 18				
2301-2304	A382	Set of 4	4.50	4.50
		Sheets of 6, #a-f		
2305-2306	A382	Set of 2	18.00	18.00
		Souvenir Sheets		
2307-2308	A382	Set of 2	10.00	10.00

Mao Zedong (1893-1976) — A383

No. 2309 — Picture from: a, 1945. b, 1926. c, 1949. d, 1930.
$3, 1930.

2001, May 15		**Litho.**	**Perf. 14**	
2309	A383	$2 Sheet of 3, #a-c	5.25	5.25
		Souvenir Sheet		
2310	A383	$3 multi	2.75	2.75

Monet Paintings A384

No. 2311, horiz.: a, The Basin of Argenteuil. b, The Bridge at Argenteuil. c, The Railway Bridge, Argenteuil. d, The Seine Bridge at Argenteuil.
$6, Woman with a Parasol — Madame Monet and Her Son.

2001, May 15			**Perf. 13¾**	
2311	A384	$2 Sheet of 4, #a-d	7.25	7.25
		Souvenir Sheet		
2312	A384	$6 multi	5.25	5.25

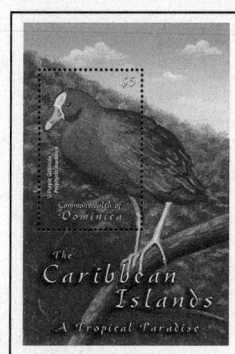

Fauna A385

No. 2313: a, St. Vincent parrot. b, Painted bunting. c, Jamaican giant anole. d, White-fronted capuchin. e, Strand racerunner. f, Agouti.
No. 2314: a, Cook's tree boa. b, Tamandua. c, Common iguana. d, Solenodon.
No. 2315, $5, Purple gallinule. No. 2316, $5, Rufous-tailed jacamar. No. 2317, $5, Ruby-throated hummingbird, horiz. No. 2318, $5, Bottlenose dolphins, horiz.

2001, Sept. 3			**Perf. 14**	
2313	A385	$1.45 Sheet of 6, #a-f	8.75	8.75
2314	A385	$2 Sheet of 4, #a-d	8.25	8.25
		Souvenir Sheets		
2315-2318	A385	Set of 4	19.00	19.00

Birds — A386

Designs: 5c, Yellow warbler. 10c, Palmchat. 15c, Snowy cotinga. 20c, Blue-gray gnatcatcher. 25c, Belted kingfisher. 55c, Red-legged thrush. 65c, Bananaquit. 90c, Yellow-bellied sapsucker. $1, White-tailed tropicbird. $1.45, Ruby-throated hummingbird. $1.90, Painted bunting. $2, Great frigatebird. $5, Brown trembler. $10, Red-footed booby. $20, Sooty tern.

2001, Sept. 3		**Litho.**	**Perf. 14¾x14**	
2319	A386	5c multi	.30	.80
2320	A386	10c multi	.30	.80
2321	A386	15c multi	.35	.35
2322	A386	20c multi	.35	.35
2323	A386	25c multi	.35	.35
2324	A386	55c multi	.65	.65
2325	A386	65c multi	.75	.75
2326	A386	90c multi	1.00	.80
2327	A386	$1 multi	1.25	1.25
2328	A386	$1.45 multi	1.60	1.60
2329	A386	$1.90 multi	2.00	2.00
2330	A386	$2 multi	2.50	2.50
2331	A386	$5 multi	5.00	5.00
2332	A386	$10 multi	8.50	8.50
2333	A386	$20 multi	17.50	17.50
Nos. 2319-2333 (15)			42.40	43.20

No. 2323 exists dated "2005."
See No. 2513.

Photomosaic of Queen Elizabeth II — A387

2001, Nov. 15			**Perf. 14**	
2334	A387	$1 multi	1.00	1.00

Issued in sheets of 8.

Christmas — A388

Paintings by Giovanni Bellini: 25c, Madonna and Child. 65c, Madonna and Child, diff. 90c, Baptism of Christ. $1.20, Madonna and Child, diff. $4, Madonna and Child, diff.
$6, Madonna and Child with Sts. Catherine and Mary Magdalene.

2001, Dec. 3				
2335-2339	A388	Set of 5	6.75	6.75
		Souvenir Sheet		
2340	A388	$6 multi	5.50	5.50

2002 World Cup Soccer Championships, Japan and Korea — A389

No. 2341, $2: a, US team, 1950. b, Poster, 1954. c, Poster, 1958. d, Zozimo, 1962. e, Gordon Banks, 1966. f, Pelé, 1970.
No. 2342, $2: a, Daniel Passarella, 1978. b, Paolo Rossi, 1982. c, Diego Maradona, 1986. d, Poster, 1990. e, Seo Jungulon, 1994. f, Jürgen Klinsmann, 1998.
No. 2343, $5, Face on World Cup, 1930. No. 2344, $5, Face and globe on Jules Rimet Trophy, 2002.

2001, Dec. 13			**Perf. 13¾x14¼**	
		Sheets of 6, #a-f		
2341-2342	A389	Set of 2	21.00	21.00
		Souvenir Sheets		
		Perf. 14¼		
2343-2344	A389	Set of 2	10.00	10.00

Queen Mother Type of 1999 Redrawn

No. 2345: a, In 1939. b, In Australia, 1958. c, At Badminton, 1982. d, Hatless, in 1982. $6, In 1953.

2001, Dec.   **Perf. 14**
Yellow Orange Frames
2345 A340 $2 Sheet of 4, #a-d, + label   7.00 7.00

Souvenir Sheet
Perf. 13¾

2346 A340 $6 multi   5.25 5.25

Queen Mother's 101st birthday. No. 2346 contains one 38x51mm stamp with a bluer backdrop than that found on No. 2161. Sheet margins of Nos. 2345-2346 lack embossing and gold arms and frames found on Nos. 2160-2161.

Souvenir Sheets

Betty Boop A390

Betty Boop: No. 2347, $5, In chair, pink rose background. No. 2348, $5, Wearing blue blouse, in jungle. No. 2349, $5, With heart and stars, cat with film reel. No. 2350, $5, Wearing nurse's cap.

2001, Oct. 1   **Litho.**   **Perf. 13¾**
2347-2350 A390   Set of 4   18.00 18.00

The Three Stooges A391

No. 2351: a, Man, Larry, Moe with sledgehammer, Joe Besser. b, Larry, woman, Joe Besser, Moe. c, Joe Besser, Larry and Moe on hands and knees. d, Larry grabbing throat of woman holding Joe Besser and Moe. e, Joe Besser drinking from baby bottle, pony, Moe and Larry. f, Military policeman, Joe Besser, Larry, woman. g, Larry. h, Joe Besser. i, Moe. No. 2352, $5, Moe and Larry, "On the air" sign. No. 2353, $5, Larry and pony.

2001, Oct. 1   **Litho.**   **Perf. 13¾**
2351 A391 $1 Sheet of 9, #a-i   8.00 8.00

Souvenir Sheets
2352-2353 A391   Set of 2   9.00 9.00

Souvenir Sheet

New Year 2002 (Year of the Horse) A392

No. 2354: a, Man with pole, horse. b, Horses grazing. c, Man currying horse. d, Horses with heads up.

2001, Dec. 17   **Perf. 14**
2354 A392 $1.65 Sheet of 4, #a-d   6.00 6.00

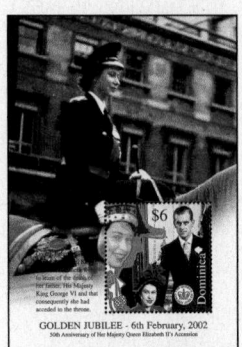

Reign of Queen Elizabeth II, 50th Anniv. A393

No. 2355: a, Wearing blue coat. b, With Prince Philip. c, Wearing tiara. d, Wearing flowered hat.
$6, With Prince Philip, diff.

2002, Feb. 6   **Perf. 14¼**
2355 A393 $2 Sheet of 4, #a-d   7.00 7.00

Souvenir Sheet
2356 A393 $6 multi   5.00 5.00

United We Stand — A394

2002, Feb.   **Perf. 13½x13¼**
2357 A394 $2 multi   1.50 1.50
Printed in sheets of 4.

Shirley Temple in "Just Around the Corner" A395

No. 2358, horiz.: a, Temple, woman with dogs. b, Temple, man and woman. c, Temple and man. d, Boy eating turkey leg, Temple carving turkey. e, Temple with old man. f, Temple with group of boys.
No. 2359: a, Boy, Temple with purse. b, Man and Temple using fingers as guns. c, Temple and man. d, Temple cutting boy's hair.
$6, Temple with black man on toadstool.

2002, Apr. 8   **Perf. 12¼**
2358 A395 $1.90 Sheet of 6, #a-f   10.00 10.00
2359 A395 $2 Sheet of 4, #a-d   7.25 7.25

Souvenir Sheet
2360 A395 $6 multi   5.25 5.25

Japanese Art — A396

No. 2361, $1.20: a, The Courtesan Tsuki-oka of the Teahouse Hyogo-Ya, by Eisui Ichirakutei. b, Woman and Servant in the Snow, by Choki Eishosai. c, The Courtesan Shiratsuyu of the Teahouse Wakana-Ya, by Eisho Chokosai. d, Ohisa of the Takashima-Ya, by Toyokuni Utagawa. e, Woman and a Cat, by Kunimasa Utagawa. f, One of "Genre Scenes of Beauties," by Eisen Keisai.
No. 2362, $1.65: a, Women Inside and Outside a Mosquito Net, by Harushige Suzuki. b, Komachi at Shimizu, by Harushige Suzuki. c, Women Viewing Plum Blossoms, by Harunobu Suzuki. d, Women Cooling Themselves at Shijogawara in Kyoto, by Toyohiro Utagawa. e, Woman Reading a Letter, by Utamaro Kitagawa. f, Women Dressed for the Kashima Dance at the Niwaka Festival, by Utamaro Kitagawa.
No. 2363, $1.90: a, Actor Kiyotaro Iwai, by Kunimasa Utagawa. b, Actors Hiriji Otani III and Ryuzo Arashi, by Sharaku Toshusai. c, Actor Komazo Ichikawa II, by Shunko Katsukawa. d, Actors Yaozo Ichikawa and Hangoro Sakata III, by Sharaku Toshusai. e, Actor Torazo Tanimura, by Sharaku Toshusai. f, Actor Kiyotaro Iwai as Oishi, by Toyokuni Utagawa.
No. 2464, $5, Actor Riko Nakamura, by Shunsho Katsukawa. No. 2365, $5, Actors Hanshiro Iwai IV and Sojuro Sawamura III, by Kiyonaga Torii, horiz. No. 2366, $6, Ofuji, Daughter of the Motoyanagi-Ya, by Harunobu Suzuki.

2002, June 17   **Perf. 14¼**
Sheets of 6, #a-f
2361-2363 A396   Set of 3   24.00 24.00
Souvenir Sheets
2364-2366 A396   Set of 3   12.00 12.00

Souvenir Sheet

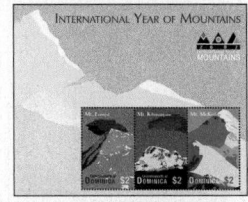

Intl. Year of Mountains — A397

No. 2367: a, Mt. Everest. b, Mt. Kilimanjaro. c, Mt. McKinley.

2002, July 15   **Perf. 14**
2367 A397 $2 Sheet of 3, #a-c   5.00 5.00

2002 Winter Olympics, Salt Lake City — A398

Designs: No. 2368, $2, Skiing. No. 2369, $2, Bobsled.

2002, July 15   **Perf. 13½**
2368-2369 A398   Set of 2   3.50 3.50
   a. Souvenir sheet, #2368-2369   3.50 3.50

First Solo Trans-Atlantic Flight, 75th Anniv. — A399

No. 2370: a, Charles Lindbergh and Spirit of St. Louis. b, Charles and Anne Morrow Lindbergh.
$6, Charles Lindbergh and Spirit of St. Louis, diff.

2002, July 15   **Perf. 14**
2370 A399 $3 Sheet of 2, #a-b   5.00 5.00
Souvenir Sheet
2371 A399 $6 multi   5.00 5.00

Popeye in New York A400

No. 2372, $1: a, Olive Oyl. b, Brutus. c, Sweet Pea. d, Wimpy. e, Jeep. f, Popeye.
No. 2373, $1.90: a, Popeye and Olive Oyl, giraffe at Bronx Zoo. b, Popeye and Olive Oyl, Statue of Liberty. c, Popeye, Olive Oyl, Empire State Building. d, Popeye skating at Rockefeller Center. e, Popeye at Yankee Stadium. f, Popeye helping firefighters.
No. 2374, $6, Popeye, Atlas Statue, Rockefeller Center. No. 2375, $6, Popeye, Olive Oyl and Radio City Music Hall Rockettes, horiz.

2002, July 22
Sheets of 6, #a-f
2372-2373 A400   Set of 2   15.00 15.00
Souvenir Sheets
2374-2375 A400   Set of 2   10.50 10.50

20th World Scout Jamboree, Thailand — A401

No. 2376: a, Lord Robert Baden-Powell (facing forward). b, Lady Olave Baden-Powell. c, Maceo Johnson.
$6, Lord Baden-Powell (profile).

2002, July 15   **Litho.**   **Perf. 14¼x14**
2376 A401 $3 Sheet of 3, #a-c   8.00 8.00
Souvenir Sheet
2377 A401 $6 multi   5.25 5.25

Birds, Insects, Moths and Whales A402

No. 2378, $1.50, vert. — Birds: a, Brown trembler. b, Snowy ctinga. c, Bananaquit. d, Painted bunting. e, Belted kingfisher. f, Ruby-throated hummingbird.
No. 2379, $1.50, vert. — Insects: a, Field cricket. b, Migratory grasshopper. c, Honey bee. d, Hercules beetle. e, Black ant. f, Cicada.
No. 2380, $1.50, vert. — Moths: a, Carolina sphinx. b, White-lined sphinx. c, Orizaba silkmoth. d, Hieroglyphic moth. e, Hickory tussock moth. f, Diva moth.
No. 2381, $1.50, vert. — Whales: a, Sei. b, Killer. c, Blue. d, White. e, Pygmy. f, Sperm.
No. 2382, $6, Yellow-bellied sapsucker. No. 2383, $6, Bumble bee. No. 2384, $6, Ornate moth. No. 2385, $6, Gray whale.

2002, July 29   **Perf. 14**
Sheets of 6, #a-f
2378-2381 A402   Set of 4   28.00 28.00
Souvenir Sheets
2382-2385 A402   Set of 4   22.00 22.00

A403

A404

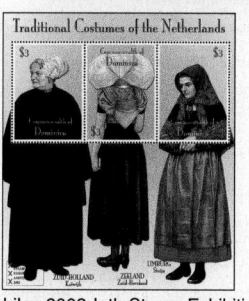

Amphilex 2002 Intl. Stamp Exhibition, Amsterdam — A405

No. 2386 — Dutch Nobel Prize winners: a, Willem Einthoven, Medicine, 1924. b, Nobel Economics medal. c, Peter J. W. Debye, Chemistry, 1936. d, Frits Zernike, Physics, 1953. e, Jan Tinbergen, Economics, 1969. f, Simon van der Meer, Physics, 1984.
No. 2387 — Dutch lighthouses: a, Marken. b, Harlingen. c, Den Oever. d, De Ven. e, Urk. f, Oosterleek.
No. 2388 — Traditional women's costumes: a, South Holland woman with small white head covering (facing forward). b, Zeeland woman with large white head covering (facing backwards). c, Limburg woman with black scarf.

2002, Aug. 30		**Perf. 13½x13¼**		
2386	A403	$1.50 Sheet of 6,		
		#a-f	8.00	8.00
2387	A404	$1.50 Sheet of 6,		
		#a-f	8.00	8.00
		Perf. 13½		
2388	A405	$3 Sheet of 3,		
		#a-c	8.00	8.00

Intl. Year of Ecotourism — A406

Island scenes and cartoon characters: 45c, Detective H2O. 50c, Factman. 55c, B.B. 60c, Stanley the Starfish. 90c, Toxi. $1.20, Adopt. $6, Litterbit.

2002, Oct. 16		**Perf. 14¼**		
2389-2394	A406	Set of 6	3.25	3.25
Souvenir Sheet				
2395	A406	$6 multi	5.00	5.00

Elvis Presley (1935-77) — A407

2002, Oct. 28		**Perf. 13¾**		
2396	A407	$1.50 multi	1.10	1.10

Printed in sheets of 6 stamps with slightly differing frames.

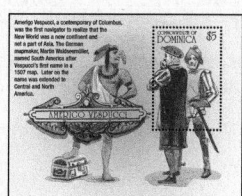

Amerigo Vespucci (1454-1512), Explorer — A408

No. 2397: a, Compass rose. b, Vespucci with map. c, Map scroll.
$5, Two men.

2002, Nov. 28		**Perf. 13¾**		
2397	A408	$3 Sheet of 3, #a-c	8.00	8.00
Souvenir Sheet				
Perf. 14				
2398	A408	$5 multi	4.50	4.50

No. 2397 contains three 50x38mm stamps.

Pres. John F. Kennedy (1917-63) — A409

No. 2399, $1.90: a, Wearing military uniform. b, With red denomination at UL. c, With blue denomination at UR. d, Wearing tan suit.
No. 2400, $1.90 (denominations at UL in blue): a, Wearing red tie. b, Wearing blue tie (profile). c, Wearing black tie. d, With hand on chin.

2002, Dec. 16		**Perf. 14**		
Sheets of 4, #a-d				
2399-2400	A409	Set of 2	13.50	13.50

Pres. Ronald Reagan A410

No. 2401, $1.90: a, Wearing cowboy hat. b, Wearing blue green sweater. c, Wearing red sweater. d, Wearing blue sweater.
No. 2402, $1.90, horiz.: a, Wearing blue shirt, and with wife, Nancy. b, Nancy and US flag. c, Ronald. d, Wearing pink shirt, and with wife.

2002, Dec. 16	**Litho.**	**Perf. 14**		
Sheets of 4, #a-d				
2401-2402	A410	Set of 2	13.50	13.50

Princess Diana (1961-97) — A411

No. 2403 — Various depictions of Princess Diana with background colors of: a, Tan. b, Pink. c, Light blue. d, Light green.

2002, Dec. 16				
2403	A411	$1.90 Sheet of 4,		
		#a-d	7.00	7.00
Souvenir Sheet				
2404	A411	$5 multi	4.50	4.50

Elizabeth "Ma Pampo" Israel, 128th Birthday — A412

2003, Jan. 27		**Perf. 13½x13¼**		
2405	A412	90c multi	.70	.70

New Year 2003 (Year of the Ram) — A413

2003, Feb. 10		**Perf. 13¾**		
2406	A413	$1.65 multi	1.25	1.25

Printed in sheets of 4.

Souvenir Sheets

Science Fiction A414

Designs: No. 2407, $6, Mayan calendar. No. 2408, $6, Atlas. No. 2409, $6, Confucius. No. 2410, $6, Nazca Lines. No. 2411, $6, Pres. Franklin D. Roosevelt and Pres. John F. Kennedy. No. 2412, $6, Zoroaster.

2003, Feb. 10		**Perf. 13¼**		
2407-2412	A414	Set of 6	27.50	27.50

A415

Coronation of Queen Elizabeth II, 50th Anniv. — A416

No. 2413: a, Wearing white dress, no crown. b, Wearing black robe. c, Wearing crown. $6, Wearing crown, diff. $20, Wearing red robe.

2003	**Litho.**	**Perf. 14**		
2413	A415	$3 Sheet of 3,		
		#a-c	6.25	6.25
Souvenir Sheet				
2414	A415	$6 multi	4.25	4.25
Miniature Sheet				
Litho. & Embossed				
Perf. 13¼x13				
2415	A416	$20 gold & multi	14.00	14.00

Issued: Nos. 2413-2414, 5/13; No. 2415, 2/24.

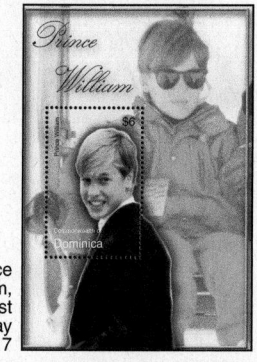

Prince William, 21st Birthday A417

No. 2416: a, Wearing dark blue shirt. b, Wearing blue suit, holding flowers. c, In polo uniform.
$6, Wearing black suit.

2003, June 21	**Litho.**	**Perf. 14**		
2416	A417	$3 Sheet of 3, #a-c	6.50	6.50
Souvenir Sheet				
2417	A417	$6 multi	4.50	4.50

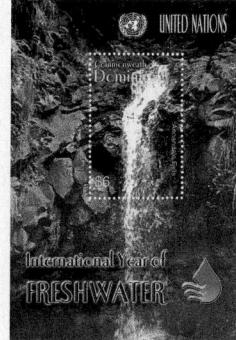

Intl. Year of Fresh Water A418

No. 2418: a, Trafalgar Falls. b, YS Falls. c, Dunn's River.
$6, Annandale Falls.

2003, June 21		**Perf. 13½**		
2418	A418	$3 Sheet of 3, #a-c	6.75	6.75
Souvenir Sheet				
2419	A418	$6 multi	4.50	4.50

Teddy Bears, Cent. A419

No. 2420 — Bear with: a, Purple shirt. b, Pink shirt and party favor. c, Green shirt and party favor. d, Black hat. e, Purple hat. f, Pink shirt and birthday cake.

No. 2421 — Bear with: a, Reindeer sweater, text at top. b, Santa Claus costume, text at top. c, Santa Claus costume, text at bottom. d, Reindeer sweater, text at bottom.

2003, June 21   **Perf. 13½**
2420 A419 $1.65 Sheet of 6, #a-f   7.50 7.50
2421 A419 $2 Sheet of 4, #a-d   6.00 6.00

No. 2421 contains four 37x51mm stamps.

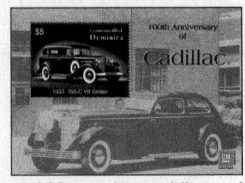

General Motors Automobiles — A420

No. 2422, $2 — Cadillacs: a, 1903 Model A Runabout. b, 1912 Model 30. c, 1918 Type 57 Victoria Coupe. d, 1927 Lasalle Convertible Coupe.
No. 2423, $2 — Corvettes: a, 1953. b, 1956. c, 1957. d, 1962.
No. 2424, $5, 1933 Cadillac 355-C V8 sedan. No. 2425, $5, 1959 Corvette.

2003, June 21   **Perf. 13¼**
Sheets of 4, #a-d
2422-2423 A420 Set of 2   12.00 12.00
Souvenir Sheets
2424-2425 A420 Set of 2   7.50 7.50

Tour de France Bicycle Race, Cent. A421

No. 2426 — Champions: a, Firmin Lambot, 1919. b, Phillippe Thys, 1920. c, Léon Scieur, 1921. d, Lambot, 1922.
$5, François Faber.

2003, June 21
2426 A421 $2 Sheet of 4, #a-d   6.00 6.00
Souvenir Sheet
2427 A421 $5 multi   3.75 3.75

History of Aviation A422

No. 2428: a, Sputnik, first orbiting satellite, 1957. b, Yuri Gagarin, first man in space, 1961. c, Neil Armstrong, first man on the Moon, 1969. d, Skylab 1, 1973.
$6, Flight over Mt. Everest, 1933.

2003, June 21   **Perf. 14**
2428 A422 $2 Sheet of 4, #a-d   6.50 6.50
Souvenir Sheet
2429 A422 $6 multi   5.00 5.00

Lewis & Clark Expedition A423

Designs: 20c, Dealing with the Chinook Indians. 50c, Compass used in expedition. 55c, Rocky Mountains. 65c, Medals presented to the Indians, vert. 90c, First encounter with grizzly bear. $1, Befriending Shoshone Indians. $2, Lewis after the expedition, vert. $4, Lewis & Clark, vert.
No. 2438, $5, Meriwether Lewis, vert. No. 2439, $5, William Clark, vert.

2003, June 21
2430-2437 A423 Set of 8   7.50 7.50
Souvenir Sheets
2438-2439 A423 Set of 2   7.00 7.00

2002 World Cup Soccer Championships, Japan and Korea — A424

No. 2440, $1.45: a, Danny Mills. b, Paul Scholes. c, Darius Vassell. d, Michael Owen. e, Emile Heskey. f, Rio Ferdinand.
No. 2441, $1.45: a, Bobby Moore. b, Roger Hunt. c, Gordon Banks. d, Bobby Charlton. e, Alan Ball. f, Geoff Hurst.
No. 2442, $3: a, Ashley Cole. b, David Seaman.
No. 2443, $3: a, Sven-Goran Eriksson. b, Nikki Butt.
No. 2444, $3: a, Robbie Fowler. b, Sol Campbell.
No. 2445, $3: a, Charlton, Ball and Hunt. b, Nobby Stiles.
No. 2446, $3: a, Franz Beckenbauer. b, Oliver Kahn.

2003, June 21   **Perf. 13¼**
Sheets of 6, #a-f
2440-2441 A424 Set of 2   11.00 11.00
Souvenir Sheets of 2, #a-b
2442-2446 A424 Set of 5   20.00 20.00

CARICOM, 30th Anniv. — A425

2003, July 25   **Perf. 13½**
2447 A425 $1 multi   .75 .75

Christmas — A426

Painting details: 50c, Madonna and Child with the Young St. John, by Correggio. 90c, Madonna in Glory with the Christ Child and Sts. Frances and Alvise with the Donor, by Titian. $1.45, Madonna and Child with Angels Playing Musical Instruments, by Correggio. $3, Madonna of the Cherries, by Titian.
$6, Holy Family with John the Baptist, by Andrea del Sarto.

2003, Nov. 17   **Litho.**   **Perf. 14¼**
2448-2451 A426 Set of 4   4.50 4.50
Souvenir Sheet
2452 A426 $6 multi   4.50 4.50

New Year 2004 (Year of the Monkey) A427

No. 2453: a, Orange monkey, hindquarters of brown monkey. b, Monkey with brown face. c, Brown monkey drinking water. d, Monkey with blue face.

2004, Jan. 5   **Litho.**   **Perf. 14**
2453 A427 $1.50 Sheet of 4, #a-d   4.50 4.50

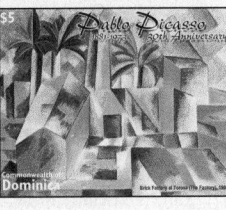

Paintings of Pablo Picasso A428

No. 2454, vert.: a, Portrait of Manuel Pallarés. b, Woman with Vase of Flowers. c, Woman with a Fan (Fernande). d, Portrait of Clovis Sagot.
$5, Brick Factory at Torosa (The Factory).

2004, Mar. 8   **Perf. 14¼**
2454 A428 $1 Sheet of 4, #a.-d.   3.00 3.00
Imperf
2455 A428 $5 multi   3.75 3.75

No. 2454 contains four 38x50mm stamps.

Paintings of Paul Gauguin A429

No. 2456: a, Village Tahitien avec la Femme en Marche. b, La Barriere. c, Bonjour, Monsieur Gauguin. d, Vegetation Tropicale.
$5, Petites Bretonnes Devant la Mer.

2004, Mar. 8   **Perf. 14¼**
2456 A429 $2 Sheet of 4, #a.-d.   6.00 6.00
Imperf
2457 A429 $5 multi   3.75 3.75

No. 2456 contains four 38x50mm stamps.

Paintings of Presidents by Norman Rockwell A430

No. 2458: a, Dwight D. Eisenhower. b, John F. Kennedy. c, Lyndon B. Johnson. d, Richard M. Nixon.
$5, Abraham Lincoln.

2004, Mar. 8   **Perf. 14¼**
2458 A430 $2 Sheet of 4, #a.-d.   6.00 6.00
Imperf
2459 A430 $5 multi   3.75 3.75

No. 2458 contains four 38x50mm stamps.

Paintings of James McNeill Whistler A431

Designs: 50c, Symphony in White No. 3. $1, The Artist's Studio, vert. $1.65, The Thames in Ice, vert. No. 2463, $2, Arrangement in Black: Portrait of F. R. Leyland, vert.
No. 2464, $2, vert.: a, Arrangement in Brown & Black: Portrait of Miss Rosa Corder. b, Harmony in Red: Lamplight. c, Symphony in Flesh Color & Pink: Portrait of Mrs. Frances Leyland. d, Arrangement in Yellow & Gray: Effie Deans.

$5, Harmony in Gray and Green: Miss Cicely Alexander, vert.

2004, Mar. 8   **Perf. 14¼**
2460-2463 A431 Set of 4   4.00 4.00
     Perf. 13½
2464 A431 $2 Sheet of 4, #a-d   6.00 6.00
Imperf
Size: 71x103mm
2465 A431 $5 multi   3.75 3.75

No. 2464 contains four 35x70mm stamps.

Fish — A432

Designs: 20c, Banded butterflyfish. 25c, Queen angelfish. 55c, Porkfish. No. 2469, $5, Redband parrotfish.
No. 2470: a, Beaugregory. b, Porkfish, diff. c, Bicolor cherubfish. d, Rock beauty. e, Blackfin snapper. f, Blue tang.
No. 2471, $5, Indigo hamlet.

2004, Mar. 8   **Perf. 14¼x13¾**
2466-2469 A432 Set of 4   4.50 4.50
2470 A432 $2 Sheet of 6, #a-f   9.00 9.00
Souvenir Sheet
2471 A432 $5 multi   3.75 3.75

Nos. 2470-2471 each contain 42x28mm stamps.

Shells A433

Designs: 20c, Siratus perelegans. 90c, Polystira albida. $1.45, Cypraea cervus. $2, Strombus gallus.
No. 2476: a, Strombus pugilis. b, Cittarium pica. c, Distorsio clathrata. d, Melongena morio. e, Prunum labiata. f, Chione paphia.
$5, Strombus alatus, vert.

2004, Mar. 8   **Perf. 14¼x13¾**
2472-2475 A433 Set of 4   3.50 3.50
     Perf. 14
2476 A433 $1.90 Sheet of 6, #a-f 8.50 8.50
Souvenir Sheet
2477 A433 $5 multi   3.75 3.75

No. 2476 contain six 42x28mm stamps; No. 2477 contains one 28x42mm stamp.

Orchids A434

Designs: 25c, Epidendrum pseudepidendrum. 55c, Aspasia epidendroides. $1.50, Cochleanthes discolor. $4, Brassavola nodosa.
No. 2482: a, Laelia anceps. b, Caularthron bicornutum. c, Cattleya velutina. d, Cattleya warneri. e, Oncidium splendidum. f, Psychlis atropurpurea.
$5, Maxillaria cuculata, vert.

2004, Mar. 8   **Perf. 14¼x13¾**
2478-2481 A434 Set of 4   4.75 4.75
     Perf. 14
2482 A434 $1.90 Sheet of 6, #a-f 8.50 8.50
Souvenir Sheet
2483 A434 $5 multi   3.75 3.75

No. 2482 contains six 42x28mm stamps; No. 2483 contains one 28x42mm stamp.

Butterflies A435

Designs: 50c, Small flambeau. 90c, Tiger pierid. $1, White peacock. No. 2469, $2, Cramer's mesene.

No. 2488, $2: a, Figure-of-eight. b, Orange theope. c, Clorinde. d, Grecian shoemaker. e, Orange-barred sulphur. f, Common morpho. $5, Giant swallowtail, vert.

2004, Mar. 8   **Perf. 14¼x14¾**
2484-2487 A435 Set of 4   3.00 3.00
    Perf. 14
2488 A435 $2 Sheet of 6, #a-f   8.00 8.00
    Souvenir Sheets
2489 A435 $5 multi   3.75 3.75

No. 2488 contains six 42x28mm stamps; No. 2489 contains one 28x42mm stamp.

Olympic Gold Medalists — A436

Designs: 20c, Elizabeth Robinson, Amsterdam, 1928. 25c, Károly Takács, London, 1948. 55c, Bob Beamon, Mexico City, 1968. 65c, Mildred Didrikson, Los Angeles, 1932. $1, Ville Ritola, Paris, 1924. $1.65, Alfred Hajós (Guttman), Athens, 1896. $2, Paavo Nurmi, Antwerp, 1920. $4, Nedo Nadi, Antwerp, 1920.

2004, Apr. 12   **Perf. 13¼**
2490-2497 A436 Set of 8   7.75 7.75

Election of Pope John Paul II, 25th Anniv. (in 2003) A437

No. 2498: a, Praying for peace in Falkland Islands, 1982. b, In Croatia, 1998. c, Seated, 1998. d, With Franciscan monks, 1999. e, Remembering the Holocaust, 2001.

2004, June 21   **Litho.**   **Perf. 14**
2498 A437 $2 Sheet of 5, #a-e   7.50 7.50

European Soccer Championships, Portugal — A438

No. 2499, vert.: a, Jose Luis Villalonga. b, Lev Yashin. c, Marcelino Martinez. d, Santiago Bernabeu Stadium. $6, 1964 Spain team.

2004, June 21   **Perf. 14**
2499 A438 $2 Sheet of 4, #a-d   6.00 6.00
    Souvenir Sheet
    Perf. 14¼
2500 A438 $6 multi   4.50 4.50
No. 2499 contains four 28x42mm stamps.

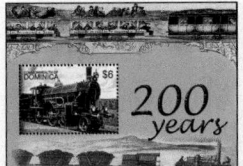

Trains A439

No. 2501, $1: a, Engine #22, V7 T4-4-0, V7T4-6-0. b, Don J12. c, Baldwin 2-D-D. d,

Southern Engine #20. e, 143-890 2DB class electric locomotive. f, Engine #1.

No. 2502, $1: a, Canadian Pacific freight train. b, Queensland Rail IM U railroad. c, Green and white Shinkansen locomotive. d, Amtrak locomotive. e, Shinkansen locomotive in station. f, YPDMU rail cars.

No. 2503, $1: a, Santa Fe Railroad locomotive. b, Via Rail train, Canada. c, Two Conrail road switchers. d, Strasburg Railroad #90. e, Deltic diesel-electric engine. f, Brighton Belle.

No. 2504, $6, Golsdorf two cylinder compound locomotive 4-4-0. No. 2505, $6, Southern Pacific 4449 4-8-4. No. 2506, $6, White, yellow and blue Shinkansen.

2004, July 12   **Perf. 13¼x13½**
    Sheets of 6, #a-f
2501-2503 A439 Set of 3   13.50 13.50
    Souvenir Sheets
2504-2506 A439 Set of 3   13.50 13.50

D-Day, 60th Anniv. — A440

Designs: $1, Eddie Hannath. $4, Pres. Franklin D. Roosevelt.

No. 2509: a, Rangers make their way towards the cliffs of Pointe du Hoc. b, Rangers begin scaling the cliffs of Pointe du Hoc. c, British troops advance on Sword Beach. d, An AVRE Petard heads inland off Sword Beach. $6, British troops landing on Sword Beach.

2004, July 22   **Perf. 14**
    Stamp + Label (#2507-2508)
2507-2508 A440 Set of 2   3.75 3.75
2509 A440 $2 Sheet of 4, #a-d   6.00 6.00
    Souvenir Sheet
2510 A440 $6 multi   4.50 4.50

George Herman "Babe" Ruth (1895-1948), Baseball Player — A441

No. 2511: a, Swinging bat. b, Swinging bat, looking up. c, Holding three bats. d, Hand on knee.

2004, Aug. 18   **Perf. 13½x13¼**
2511 A441 $2 Sheet of 4, #a-d   6.00 6.00

Marilyn Monroe (1926-62), Actress — A442

No. 2512: a, Wearing earrings and necklace. b, Wearing earrings. c, Wearing no earrings or necklace. d, Wearing necklace.

2004, Aug. 18
2512 A442 $2 Sheet of 4, #a-d   6.00 6.00

Bird Type of 2001
2004, Sept. 3   **Perf. 14¾x14**
2513 A386 50c Baltimore oriole   .45 .45
    Exists dated "2005."

Queen Juliana of the Netherlands (1909-2004) A443

2004, Sept. 21   **Perf. 13¼**
2514 A443 $2 multi   1.50 1.50
    Printed in sheets of 6.

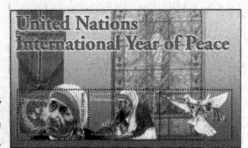

Intl. Year of Peace A444

No. 2515: a, Mother Teresa, UN emblem. b, Mother Teresa feeding poor. c, Dove.

2004, Sept. 21   **Perf. 14**
2515 A444 $2 Sheet of 3, #a-c   4.50 4.50
    Souvenir Sheet

Deng Xiaoping (1904-97) and Mao Zedong (1893-1976), Chinese Leaders — A445

2004, Sept. 21   **Perf. 14**
2516 A445 $6 multi   4.50 4.50

National Soccer Team A446

2004, Nov. 8   **Litho.**   **Perf. 12**
2517 A446 90c multi   .70 .70

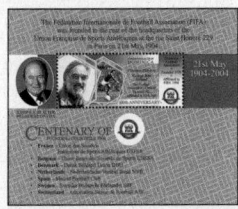

FIFA (Fédération Internationale de Football Association), Cent. — A447

No. 2518: a, Ferenc Puskas. b, Rivaldo. c, Carsten Jancker. d, Johan Cruyff. $6, George Best.

2004, Nov. 8   **Perf. 12¾x12½**
2518 A447 $2 Sheet of 4, #a-d   6.00 6.00
    Souvenir Sheet
2519 A447 $6 multi   4.50 4.50

Worldwide Fund for Nature (WWF) — A448

No. 2520: a, Green-throated Carib (denomination in blue). b, Purple-throated Carib (denomination in white). c, Green-throated Carib (denomination in white). d, Purple-throated Carib (denomination in red).

2005, Jan. 10   **Perf. 14**
2520 A448 $2 Block of 4, #a-d   5.50 5.50
   e.   Miniature sheet, 2 each #2520a-2520d   11.00 11.00

Prehistoric Animals — A449

No. 2521, $2: a, Tyrannosaurus rex. b, Velociraptor. c, Stegosaurus. d, Psittacosaurus.

No. 2522, $2: a, Mammuthus columbi. b, Spinosaurus. c, Ankylosaurus. d, Mammuthus primigenius.

No. 2523, $2: a, Pterodactylus. b, Pteranodon. c, Sordes. d, Caudiptheryx zoui. $3, Compsognathus. $5, Archaeopteryx. $6, Mammuthus primigenius, diff.

2005, Jan. 10   **Perf. 12¾**
    Sheets of 4, #a-d
2521-2523 A449 Set of 3   18.00 18.00
    Souvenir Sheets
2524-2526 A449 Set of 3   10.50 10.50

Birds — A450

Designs: 25c, Brown booby. 90c, Brown pelican. $1, Red-billed tropicbird. $4, Northern gannet.

No. 2531: a, Great egret. b, Black-necked grebe. c, Turkey vulture. d, Snail kite. $6, Red knot.

2005, Jan. 10   **Perf. 14**
2527-2530 A450 Set of 4   4.50 4.50
2531 A450 $2 Sheet of 4, #a-d   5.75 5.75
    Souvenir Sheet
2532 A450 $6 multi   4.00 4.00

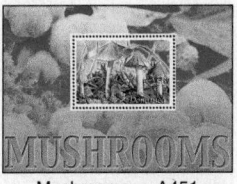

Mushrooms — A451

No. 2533: a, Cortinarius mucosus. b, Cortinarius splendens. c, Cortinarius rufoolivaceus. d, Inocybe erubescens. $6, Split fibercap.

2005, Jan. 10
2533 A451 $2 Sheet of 4, #a-d   6.00 6.00
    Souvenir Sheet
2534 A451 $6 multi   4.50 4.50

Miniature Sheet

Flowers — A452

No. 2535: a, Sweetshrub. b, Pink turtle-heads. c, Flowering quince. d, Water lily.
$6, Glory of the snow, vert.

2005, Jan. 10   Litho.   Perf. 14
2535 A452 $2 Sheet of 4, #a-d   6.00 6.00
Souvenir Sheet
2535E A452 $6 multi   4.50 4.50

New Year 2005 (Year
of the
Rooster) — A453

2005, Jan. 24   Perf. 12¾x12½
2536 A453 $1 shown   .75   .75
Souvenir Sheet
Perf. 12
2537 A453 $4 Roosters   3.00 3.00
No. 2537 contains one 56x36mm stamp.

A454

Elvis Presley (1935-77) — A455

Elvis Presley (1935-77) — A455a

No. 2538: a, Green background under coun-try name and near shirt collar. b, Guitar. c, Large red violet areas at side of head. d, Dark green background under country name, blue background near shirt collar. e, Purple back-ground near shirt collar. f, Small red violet areas at side of head.
No. 2539: a, Country name in white, blue background at UR. b, Country name in white, pink background at UR. c, Country name in white, orange background at UR. d, Country name in blue, green background at UR. e, Presley and guitar. f, Country name in blue, yellow background at UR. g, Country name in blue, blue background at UR.
No. 2539H illustration reduced.

2005, Apr. 5   Perf. 13½
2538 A454 $1 Sheet of 9, #a-
              c, 2 each #d-f   6.75 6.75
2539 A455 $1 Sheet of 9, #a,
              c, e-g, 2 each
              #b, d   6.75 6.75

Litho. & Embossed
Variable Serpentine Die Cut
Without Gum
2539H A455a $20 gold & multi   14.00 14.00
No. 2539H was not available in the market-place until 2006.

Miniature Sheet

Rotary International, Cent. — A456

No. 2540: a, Globe and Rotary emblem. b, Rotary emblem. c, Women and children.

2005, Sept. 7   Perf. 12½x12¾
2540 A456 $3 Sheet of 3, #a-c   6.75 6.75

Battle of
Trafalgar,
Bicent.
A457

Designs: 55c, Admiral Horatio Nelson explaining plan of attack before battle. 65c, Orient explodes during the Battle of the Nile, vert. $1, Nelson and his men board San Nico-las during the Battle of Cape St. Vincent, vert. $2, Ships Agamemnon and Ca Ira in battle.
$6, HMS Victory.

2005, Sept. 7   Perf. 13¼
2541-2544 A457 Set of 4   3.25 3.25
Souvenir Sheet
Perf. 12
2545 A457 $6 multi   4.50 4.50

Hans Christian Andersen (1805-75),
Author — A458

No. 2546: a, The Swineherd. b, The Nightin-gale. c, The Fir Tree.
$6, The Ugly Duckling.

2005, Sept. 7   Perf. 12¾
2546 A458 $2 Sheet of 3, #a-c   4.50 4.50
Souvenir Sheet
Perf. 12
2547 A458 $6 multi   4.50 4.50
No. 2546 contains three 42x28mm stamps.

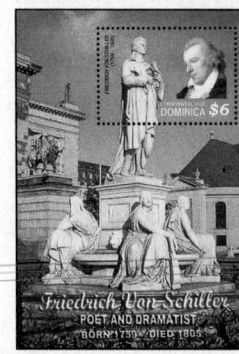

Friedrich von Schiller (1759-1805),
Writer — A459

No. 2548, vert. — Schiller and German Democratic Republic stamps: a, #241. b, #242. c, #243.
$6, Statue of Schiller.

2005, Sept. 7   Perf. 12¾
2548 A459 $3 Sheet of 3, #a-c   6.75 6.75
Souvenir Sheet
2549 A459 $6 multi   4.50 4.50

Jules Verne (1828-1905),
Writer — A460

No. 2550: a, Men, dog and rooster in space. b, Astronauts. c, Men looking at undersea creature. d, Submarine.
$6, Portrait of Verne.

2005, Sept. 7
2550 A460 $2 Sheet of 4, #a-d   6.00 6.00
Souvenir Sheet
2551 A460 $6 multi   4.50 4.50

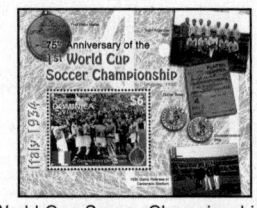

World Cup Soccer Championships,
75th Anniv. — A461

No. 2552: a, 1934 Italy team. b, Scene from 1934 Italy victory over Czechoslovakia. c, Flaminio Stadium. d, Angelos Schiavo.
$6, Italian team celebrating.

2005, Sept. 7   Perf. 12
2552 A461 $2 Sheet of 4, #a-d   6.00 6.00
Souvenir Sheet
2553 A461 $6 multi   4.50 4.50

Christmas — A462

Painting details: 25c, Madonna and Child with Two Angels, by Sandro Botticelli. 50c, Madonna and Child with Angels, by Botticelli. 65c, Madonna and Child, by Pietro Lorenzetti. 90c, Madonna del Roseto, by Botticelli. $1.20, Adoration of the Magi, by Lorenzetti. $3, Madonna in Glory with the Seraphim, by Botticelli.
$5, Madonna of Frari, by Titian, horiz.

2005, Nov. 15   Perf. 12¾
2554-2559 A462 Set of 6   5.00 5.00
Souvenir Sheet
2560 A462 $5 multi   3.75 3.75

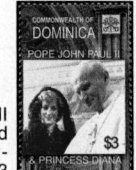

Pope John Paul II
(1920-2005) and
Princess Diana (1961-
97) — A463

2005   Perf. 13½x13¼
2561 A463 $3 multi   2.25 2.25

Pope Benedict
XVI — A464

2005   Litho.   Perf. 13½x13¼
2562 A464 $2 multi   1.50 1.50
Printed in sheets of 4.

Souvenir Sheet

New
Year
2006
(Year of
the Dog)
A465

No. 2563 — Dog figurines with background colors of: a, Pale green and green. b, Orange and pink. c, Rose pink and yellow.

2006, Jan. 3   Perf. 13¼x13½
2563 A465 $1 Sheet of 3, #a-c   2.25 2.25

Miniature Sheets

National Basketball Association
Players and Team Emblems — A466

No. 2564, 90c: a, Orlando Magic emblem. b, Hedo Turkoglu.
No. 2565, 90c: a, Denver Nuggets emblem. b, Kenyon Martin.
No. 2566, 90c: a, Miami Heat emblem. b, Antoine Walker.
No. 2567, 90c: a, Golden State Warriors emblem. b, Jason Richardson.
No. 2568, 90c: a, Phoenix Suns emblem. b, Amaré Stoudemire.
No. 2569, 90c: a, Los Angeles Clippers emblem. b, Elton Brand.

2006, Feb. 14   Perf. 14
Sheets of 12, 2 each #a, 10 each #b
2564-2569 A466 Set of 6   47.50 47.50

Léopold Sédar
Senghor (1906-2001),
First President of
Senegal — A467

2006, Mar. 20   Perf. 13¼
2570 A467 $2 multi   1.50 1.50

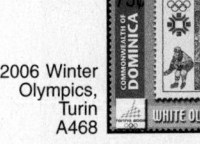

2006 Winter Olympics, Turin
A468

Designs: 75c, Yugoslavia #1670. 90c, 1984 Sarajevo Winter Olympics poster, vert. $2, Japan #2607g, vert. $3, 1998 Nagano Winter Olympics poster, vert.

2006, Mar. 29
2571-2574 A468 Set of 4 5.00 5.00
Each stamp printed in sheets of 4.

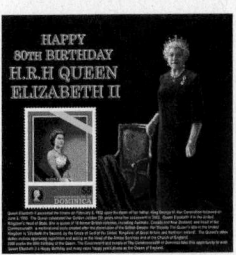

Queen Elizabeth II, 80th Birthday
A469

No. 2575: a, As infant, with mother. b, As young child. c, As baby, wearing bonnet. d, As young girl, wearing jacket.
$5, Wearing tiara and sash.

2006, Mar. 29
2575 A469 $2 Sheet of 4, #a-d 6.00 6.00
Souvenir Sheet
2576 A469 $5 multi 3.75 3.75

Marilyn Monroe (1926-62), Actress — A470

2006, Apr. 7
2577 A470 $3 multi 2.25 2.25
Printed in sheets of 4.

Space Achievements — A471

No. 2578 — Viking I: a, Trenches dug by Viking I. b, Sunset at Viking I landing site. c, Chryse Planitia looking northwest over Viking I. d, First panoramic image of Chryse Planitia, country name and denomination in white. e, As "d," country name in black, denomination in white. f, As "d", country name and denomination in black.
No. 2579, $3, vert. — Luna 9: a, Flight apparatus. b, Modified SS-6 Sapwood rocket. c, Luna 9 Soft Lander. d, Tyuratam.
No. 2580, $3, vert. — Giotto Comet Probe: a, Launch of Giotto. b, Giotto during solar simulation test. c, Halley's Comet develops seven tails. d, Giotto and Comet Grigg-Skjellerup approach trajectories.
No. 2581, $6, Intl. Space Station. No. 2582, $6, Mars Reconnaissance Orbiter. No. 2583, $6, Venus Express Orbiter.

2006, June 6 **Litho.** **Perf. 14**
2578 A471 $2 Sheet of 6, #a-f 9.00 9.00
Sheets of 4, #a-d
2579-2580 A471 Set of 2 18.00 18.00
Souvenir Sheets
2581-2583 A471 Set of 3 13.50 13.50

Miniature Sheet

Wolfgang Amadeus Mozart (1756-91), Composer — A472

No. 2584: a, Oval portrait. b, Playing harpsichord. c, Wearing red coat. d, Head of Mozart.

2006, Sept. 1 **Perf. 13¼**
2584 A472 $3 Sheet of 4, #a-d 9.00 9.00

Miniature Sheet

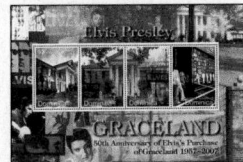

Purchase of Graceland by Elvis Presley, 50th Anniv. — A473

No. 2585: a, View of path leading to front door. b, Graceland, columns at right. c, Graceland, columns at left. d, Room with Presley's costumes.

2006, Sept. 1 **Perf. 13¼**
2585 A473 $3 Sheet of 4, #a-d 9.00 9.00

Miniature Sheets

Pres. John F. Kennedy (1917-63) — A474

No. 2586, $3: a, Supporters holding campaign sign. b, Kennedy campaigning. c, Kennedy waiting for concession. d, Kennedy addressing the nation.
No. 2587, $3: a, Kennedy on crutches from war injuries. b, Kennedy on stretcher. c, Dust jacket of Profiles in Courage. d, Kennedy as senator.

2006, Oct. 1 **Perf. 13¼**
Sheets of 4, #a-d
2586-2587 A474 Set of 2 18.00 18.00

Shells — A475

Designs: 5c, Turbinella angulata. 10c, Vasum muricatum. 15c, Fusinus closter. 20c, Crasispira gibbosa. 25c, Terebra strigata. 50c, Prunum carneum. 65c, Purpura patula. 90c, C. chrysostoma. $1, M. nodulosa. $2, Conus regius. $3.50, Conus hieroglyphus. $5, Anodontia alba, vert. $10, C. cassidiformis. $20, Strigilla carnaria, vert.

2006, Oct. 1 **Perf. 14x15, 15x14**
2588 A475 5c multi .30 .50
2589 A475 10c multi .30 .50
2590 A475 15c multi .40 .80
2591 A475 20c multi .40 .30
2592 A475 25c multi .40 .30
2593 A475 50c multi .55 .35
2594 A475 65c multi .75 .50
2595 A475 90c multi 1.00 .75
2596 A475 $1 multi 1.25 1.25
2597 A475 $2 multi 2.00 2.00
2598 A475 $3.50 multi 3.25 3.25
2599 A475 $5 multi 4.00 4.00
2600 A475 $10 multi 7.00 7.00
2601 A475 $20 multi 14.00 14.00
Nos. 2588-2601 (14) 35.60 35.50

Souvenir Sheet

Ludwig Durr (1878-1956), Engineer — A476

2006, Nov. 15 **Litho.** **Perf. 12¾**
2602 A476 $5 multi 3.75 3.75

Betty Boop
A477

No. 2603, vert.: a, Betty Boop with black background and leg raised. b, Lips. c, Betty Boop with black background. d, Dog on leash, star. e, Betty Boop, white background. f, Dog, two stars.
No. 2604 — Betty Boop with: a, Light blue panel at top. b, Light yellow panel at top.

2006, Nov. 15
2603 A477 $2 Sheet of 6, #a-f 9.00 9.00
Souvenir Sheet
2604 A477 $3.50 Sheet of 2, #a-b 5.25 5.25

Christmas — A478

Christmas stocking showing: No. 2605, 25c, No. 2609a, $2, Christmas tree. No. 2606, 50c, No. 2609b, $2, Bell. No. 2607, 90c, No. 2609c, $2, Candy canes. No. 2608, $1, No. 2609d, $2, Stars.

2006, Dec. 1 **Perf. 14¼**
2605-2608 A478 Set of 4 2.00 2.00
Souvenir Sheet
2609 A478 $2 Sheet of 4, #a-d 5.00 3.00

Souvenir Sheet

Christopher Columbus (1451-1506), Explorer — A479

2007, Jan. 10 **Perf. 12**
2610 A479 $5 brn & black 3.75 3.75

Scouting, Cent.
A480

2007, Jan. 10
2611 A480 $3.50 blue & multi 2.60 2.60
Souvenir Sheet
2612 A480 $5 org & multi 3.75 3.75
No. 2611 was printed in sheets of 3.

Concorde Prototype 001 F-WTSS — A481

No. 2613: a, $1, Airplane in hangar. b, $2, Airplane out of hangar.

2007, Jan. 23 **Perf. 13¼**
2613 A481 Pair, #a-b 2.25 2.25
Printed in sheets containing 3 of each stamp.

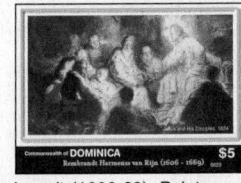

Rembrandt (1606-69), Painter — A482

No. 2614, vert. — Details from Christ Driving the Money Changers from the Temple: a, Christ. b, Man with moustache looking up. c, Man with striped headdress. d, Man protecting face with hands.
$5, Jesus and His Disciples.

2007, Jan. 23 **Perf. 13¼**
2614 A482 $2 Sheet of 4, #a-d 6.00 6.00
Imperf
2615 A482 $5 shown 3.75 3.75
No. 2614 contains four 38x50mm stamps.

Cricket World Cup — A483

Designs: 90c, Cricket bats, ball and wicket, map and flag of Dominica. $1, Umpire Billy Doctrove.
$5, Cricket bats, ball and wicket.

2007, Apr. 11 **Perf. 14**
2616-2617 A483 Set of 2 2.50 2.50
Souvenir Sheet
2618 A483 $5 multi 4.00 4.00

Birds — A484

Designs: 10c, Great frigatebird. 25c, Peruvian booby. 90c, Black stork, vert. No. 2622, $5, Lipkin, vert.
No. 2623: a, Antillean crested hummingbird. b, Rufous-breasted hermit. c, Cuban hummingbird. d, Blue-headed hummingbird.
No. 2624, $5, Red-capped manakin, vert.

2007, Apr. 11 **Perf. 12¾**
2619-2622 A484 Set of 4 5.25 5.25
2623 A484 $2 Sheet of 4, #a-d 7.50 7.50
Souvenir Sheet
2624 A484 $5 multi 5.25 5.25

Flowers — A485

Designs: 10c, Red jasmine. 25c, Bougainvillea. 90c, Portia tree. No. 2628, $5, Rose bay. No. 2629 — Orchids: a, $1, Tolumnia urophylla. b, $1, Brassavola cucullata. c, $2, Isochilus linearis. d, Spathoglottis plicata.
No. 2630, horiz.: a, Red ginger. b, Baobab. c, Purple wreath. d, Thunbergia.
No. 2631, $5, Flamboyant. No. 2632, $5, Oncidium altissimum.

2007, Apr. 11		Litho.	Perf. 12¾	
2625-2628	A485	Set of 4	4.75	4.75
2629	A485	Sheet of 4, #a-d	4.50	4.50
2630	A485	$2 Sheet of 4, #a-d	6.00	6.00

Souvenir Sheets

2631-2632	A485	Set of 2	7.50	7.50

Princess Diana (1961-97) — A486

No. 2633: a, Holding flowers, wearing purple hat. b, Without hat. c, Not holding flowers, wearing purple hat. d, Close-up of #2633a, lines on face. e, Close-up of #2633b, lines on face. f, Close-up of #2633c, lines on face. $5, Wearing purple sweater.

2007, June 11			Perf. 13½	
2633	A486	$1 Sheet of 6, #a-f	4.50	4.50

Souvenir Sheet

2634	A486	$5 multi	3.75	3.75

No. 2633 contains six 28x42mm stamps.

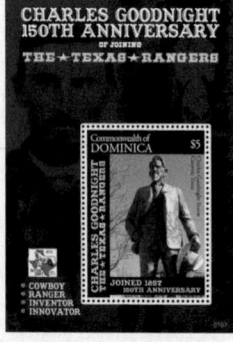
Texas Rangers A487

No. 2635, horiz.: a, Two Rangers on horses. b, Seven Rangers in front of building with pillars. c, Ten rangers showing rifles. d, Rangers on horses. e, Rangers around still. f, Three Rangers at Justice of the Peace office. g, Rangers and tents. h, Rangers and locomotive. i, Five Rangers on horses near house. $5, Statue of Charles Goodnight.

2007, June 15			Perf. 13½	
2635	A487	$1 Sheet of 9, #a-i	6.75	6.75

Souvenir Sheet

2636	A487	$5 multi	3.75	3.75

American Topical Association National Topical Stamp Show, Irving, TX.

Miniature Sheet

New Year 2007 (Year of the Pig) A488

No. 2637 — Text in: a, Red. b, Green. c, Blue green. d, Purple.

2007, July 2

2637	A488	$2 Sheet of 4, #a-d	6.00	6.00

A489

A490

A491

Christmas A492

2007, Nov. 19		Litho.	Perf. 14¾x14	
2638	A489	25c multi	.25	.25
2639	A490	50c multi	.40	.40
2640	A491	90c multi	.70	.70
2641	A492	$1 multi	.75	.75
	Nos. 2638-2641 (4)		2.10	2.10

New Year 2008 (Year of the Rat) — A493

2008, Feb. 28			Perf. 12	
2642	A493	$1 multi	.75	.75

Printed in sheets of 4.

University of the West Indies, 60th Anniv. — A494

University crest, Dr. Bernard A. Sorhaindo and denomination in: 50c, Red brown. 65c, Green. 90c, Brown.
No. 2646, $5, Crest, Sorhaindo, denomination in black. No. 2647, $5, Crest, Sorhaindo, denomination in blue. No. 2648, $5, Crest, diploma, 60th anniversary emblem.

2008, Apr. 8			Perf. 13¼	
2643-2645	A494	Set of 3	1.60	1.60

Souvenir Sheets

2646-2648	A494	Set of 3	11.50	11.50

Miniature Sheet

Miniature Sheet

Visit of Pope Benedict XVI to New York A496

No. 2650 — Pope and part of St. Patrick's Cathedral in background: a, Small circular window under spire. b, Large central circular window. c, Archway below spire. d, Archway above main door.

2008, June 16		Litho.	Perf. 13½	
2650	A496	$1.40 Sheet of 4, #a-d	4.25	4.25

Miniature Sheet

Wedding of Queen Elizabeth II and Prince Philip, 60th Anniv. A497

No. 2651: a, Couple, denomination in white. b, Queen, denomination in red violet. c, Couple, denomination in black. d, Queen, denomination in white. e, Couple, denomination in red violet. f, Queen, denomination in black.

2008, June 16

2651	A497	$1 Sheet of 6, #a-f	4.50	4.50

Miniature Sheet

Elvis Presley (1935-77) — A498

No. 2652 — Presley and: a, Black and red background, Prussian blue denomination. b, Gray and black background, purple denomination. c, Blue and black background, Prussian blue denomination. d, Purple and black background, purple denomination. e, Gray and black background, Prussian blue denomination. f, Brown and black background, purple denomination.

2008, June 16

2652	A498	$1.50 Sheet of 6 #a-f	6.75	6.75

A499

Miniature Sheet

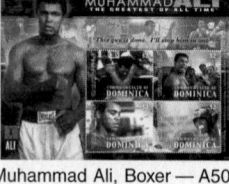
Muhammad Ali, Boxer — A500

No. 2653 — Ali: a, Sweating, denomination in white. b, Smiling, denomination in black. c, Wearing headgear. d, With arms raised.
No. 2654 — Ali: a, Seated in corner of boxing ring. b, Speaking to the press. c, Punching bag. d, Wearing headgear and mouth guard.

2008, July 7				
2653	A499	$2 Sheet of 4, #a-d	6.25	6.25
2654	A500	$2 Sheet of 4, #a-d	6.25	6.25

Convent High School, 150th Anniv. — A501

Panel color: 50c, Red violet. 65c, Yellow orange. 90c, Blue. $1, Red.
$5, Denomination in LR corner.

2008, Oct. 1			Perf. 12½	
2655-2658	A501	Set of 4	2.40	2.40

Souvenir Sheet

2659	A501	$5 multi	4.00	4.00

Dogs — A502

Designs: 25c, Dandie Dinmont terrier. 50c, Alaskan malamute. 90c, Welsh Springer spaniel. $1, Pug. $2, Norfolk terrier. $5, Vizsla.
No. 2666: a, Akita. b, Australian cattle dog. c, Border collie. d, Staffordshire bull terrier cross.

		Perf. 14¼x14¾		
2008, Dec. 11			Litho.	
2660-2665	A502	Set of 6	8.50	8.50
2666	A502	$2.50 Sheet of 4, #a-d	9.00	9.00

Miniature Sheet

Marilyn Monroe (1926-62), Actress — A503

No. 2667 — Monroe wearing: a, Purple sweater, hand on arm. b, Orange sweater, looking in mirror. c, Purple sweater, holding post. d, Orange sweater, holding wine glass.

2008, Dec. 11			Perf. 14	
2667	A503	$2 Sheet of 4, #a-d	6.00	6.00

Christmas A504

Designs: 25c, Santa Claus. 50c, Palm tree with Christmas ornaments. 90c, Christmas stocking. $1, Poinsettias.

2008, Dec. 15			Perf. 12	
2668-2671	A504	Set of 4	2.00	2.00

Miniature Sheet

2008 Summer Olympics, Beijing — A495

No. 2649: a, Archery. b, Men's gymnastics. c, Badminton. d, Boxing.

2008, Apr. 8			Perf. 13¼x13	
2649	A495	$1.40 Sheet of 4, #a-d	4.25	4.25

New Year 2009 (Year of the Ox) — A505

2009, Jan. 5   *Perf. 14¾x14¼*
2672 A505 $2 multi   1.50 1.50
Printed in sheets of 4.

Inauguration of Barack Obama as US President — A506

Pres. Obama: 65c, With raised hand. 90c, Hand not showing.
No. 2675: a, $2.25, Like 65c. b, $2.25, Looking over shoulder. c, $2.25, Like 90c. d, $2.50, Like 90c. e, $2.50, Looking over shoulder. f, $2.50, Like 65c.

2009, Jan. 20   *Perf. 11½*
2673-2674 A506 Set of 2   1.25 1.25
2675 A506 Sheet of 6, #a-f   11.00 11.00

A507

Denominations: 50c, 65c, 90c, $1.

2009, Mar. 23   *Perf. 14¾x14¼*
2676-2679 A507 Set of 4   2.40 2.40
Souvenir Sheet
2680 A507 $5 multi   3.75 3.75
Diplomatic relations between Dominica and People's Republic of China, 5th anniv.

Peony — A508

2009, Apr. 10   *Perf. 13¼*
2681 A508 75c shown   .55 .55
Souvenir Sheet
2682 A508 $5 Peonies   3.75 3.75
No. 2682 contains one 44x44mm stamp.

Miniature Sheet

Elvis Presley (1935-77) — A509

No. 2683 — Various photos of Presley with background colors of: a, Yellow orange. b, Gray and blue. c, Blue. d, Gray.

2009, May 23   *Perf. 13¼*
2683 A509 $2.50 Sheet of 4, #a-d   7.75 7.75

Miniature Sheet

Joseph Haydn (1732-1809), Composer — A510

No. 2684: a, Haydn. b, Haydn's birthplace, Rohrau, Austria. c, Wolfgang Amadeus Mozart. d, St. Stephen's Cathedral, Vienna. e, Nikolaus Esterházy, sponsor of Haydn. f, Esterházy Palace, Fertod, Hungary.

2009, June 10   *Perf. 11½*
2684 A510 $2.25 Sheet of 6, #a-f   10.00 10.00

Mushrooms — A511

Designs: 50c, Leucopaxillus gracillimus. 65c, Calvatia cyathiformis. 90c, Hygrocybe viridiphylla. $1, Boletellus coccineus.
No. 2689, $2: a, Hygrocybe acutoconica. b, Lepiota sulphureocyanescens. c, Lactarius rubrilacteus. d, Lactarius ferrugineus. e, Asterophera lycoperdoides. f, Amanita polypyramis.

2009, Sept. 8   **Litho.**   *Perf. 14x14¾*
2685-2688 A511 Set of 4   2.25 2.25
2689 A511 $2 Sheet of 6, #a-f   9.00 9.00

A512

Corals and Marine Life A513

Designs: 50c, Lobed star coral and shark. 65c, Orange cup coral and fish. 90c, Grooved brain coral and turtle. $1, Elkhorn coral and fish.
No. 2694, $2: a, Rough star coral and fish. b, Branched finger coral and fish. c, Wire coral and ray. d, Great star coral and fish. e, Pillar coral and fish. f, Rose lace coral and fish.

2009, Sept. 8   *Perf. 14¾x14*
2690-2693 A512 Set of 4   2.25 2.25
2694 A513 $2 Sheet of 6, #a-f   9.00 9.00

Butterflies A514

Designs: 90c, Banded orange heliconian. $1, Gulf fritillary. $2, Julia longwing. $5, Zebra longwing.
No. 2699: a, Cuban cattleheart. b, White peacock. c, Bahamian swallowtail. d, Tropical buckeye.
No. 2700, $6, Purple emperor. No. 2701, $6, Atala black.

2009, Sept. 8   *Perf. 14¾x14*
2695-2698 A514 Set of 4   6.75 6.75
2699 A514 $2.50 Sheet of 4, #a-d   7.50 7.50
Souvenir Sheets
Perf. 14¼
2700-2701 A514 Set of 2   9.00 9.00
Nos. 2700-2701 each contain one 50x38mm stamp.

Dolphins and Whales — A515

Designs: 50c, Irawaddy dolphin. 65c, Pantropical spotted dolphin. 90c, Atlantic humpback dolphin. $1, Indian humpback dolphin.
No. 2706: a, Melon-headed whale. b, Striped dolphin. c, Atlantic spotted dolphin. d, Clymene dolphin. e, Pantropical spotted dolphin (Stenella attenuata graffmani). f, Pantropical spotted dolphin (Stenella attenuata).

Shells — A516

2009, Sept. 8   **Litho.**   *Perf. 14¾x14*
2702-2705 A515 Set of 4   2.25 2.25
2706 A515 $2 Sheet of 6, #a-f   9.00 9.00
See No. 2732.

Designs: 50c, Oliva reticularis. 65c, Vasum muricatum. 90c, Olivella nivea. $1, Olivella mutica.
No. 2711: a, Hyalina avena. b, Persicula fluctuata. c, Agatrix agassizi. d, Trigonostoma rugosum. e, Olivella floralia. f, Marginella eburneola.

2009, Sept. 8
2707-2710 A516 Set of 4   2.25 2.25
2711 A516 $2 Sheet of 6, #a-f   9.00 9.00

Miniature Sheet

Expo 2010, Shanghai — A517

No. 2712: a, Bund. b, Shanghai Museum. c, Yangpu Bridge. d, Shanghai Theater.

2009, Oct. 16   *Perf. 13x12¾*
2712 A517 $1.50 Sheet of 4, #a-d   4.50 4.50

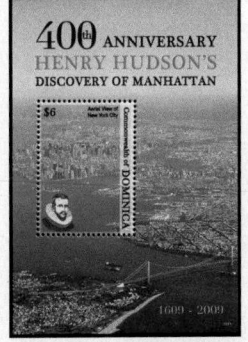

Discovery of Manhattan Island by Henry Hudson, 400th Anniv. — A518

No. 2713, horiz.: a, Panoramic view of New York City, 1913. b, Hudson, the Dreamer, by Jean L.G. Ferris. c, Henry Hudson. d, Hudson's ship, Half Moon. e, Map of Hudson River, c. 1600. f, Henry Hudson Memorial Column, Bronx, NY.
$6, Hudson, aerial view of New York City.

2009, Oct. 16   *Perf. 13x12¾*
2713 A518 $2.25 Sheet of 6, #a-f   10.00 10.00
Souvenir Sheet
Perf. 12¾x13
2714 A518 $6 multi   4.50 4.50

Miniature Sheet

Pres. John F. Kennedy (1917-63) — A519

No. 2715 — Pres. Kennedy: a, On telephone. b, With family. c, With Vice-president Lyndon B. Johnson. d, Pointing.

2009, Oct. 30   *Perf. 11½x12*
2715 A519 $2.50 Sheet of 4, #a-d   7.50 7.50

Miniature Sheet

First Man on the Moon, 40th Anniv. A520

No. 2716: a, Apollo 11 crew. b, Moon landing on television. c, Apollo 11 capsule with parachutes. d, Earth, Apollo 11 modules and patch. e, Command Module in Moon orbit. f, Project Orion.

2009, Nov. 2   *Perf. 11½*
2716 A520 $2 Sheet of 6, #a-f   9.00 9.00

Chinese Aviation, Cent. A521

No. 2717: a, H-5. b, H-6. c, H-6H. d, H-6L. $6, H-6U.

2009, Nov. 12   *Perf. 14*
2717 A521 $2 Sheet of 4, #a-d   6.50 6.50
Souvenir Sheet
Perf. 14¼
2718 A521 $6 multi   4.75 4.75
Aeropex 2009 Intl. Philatelic Exhibition, Beijing. No. 2717 contains four 42x28mm stamps.

Christmas — A522

Designs: 50c, Bell-shaped Christmas tree ornament. 65c, Candles and poinsettia. 90c, Gingerbread man. $1.10, Decorated palm tree. $2.25, Christmas tree ornaments. $2.75, Women dancers.

2009, Nov. 16   *Perf. 11½*
2719-2724 A522 Set of 6   6.25 6.25

Personalized Stamp — A523

2009, Dec. 18   **Perf. 14x14¾**
2725 A523 $3 gray   2.25 2.25
The vignette on the stamp shown is a generic image. Stamps without a vignette were also made available. Printed in sheets of 12.

Pope John Paul II (1920-2005) — A524

2010, Jan. 4   **Perf. 12x11½**
2726 A524 $2.75 multi   2.10 2.10
Printed in sheets of 4.

Miniature Sheet

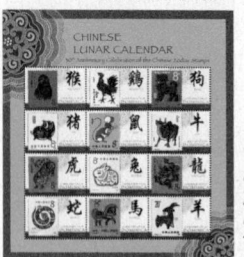

Chinese Zodiac Animals — A524a

No. 2726A — Various stamps of People's Republic of China depicting Zodiac animals: b, Monkey. c, Rooster. d, Dog. e, Pig. f, Rat. g, Ox. h, Tiger. i, Rabbit. j, Dragon. k, Snake. l, Horse. m, Ram.

2010, Jan. 4   Litho.   Perf. 12¾
2726A A524a 60c Sheet of 12,
          #b-m   6.00 6.00

Souvenir Sheet

New Year 2010 (Year of the Tiger) A525

2010, Jan. 4   **Perf. 12¾**
2727 A525 $5 multi   4.00 4.00

Miniature Sheet

Elvis Presley (1935-77) — A526

Various drawings of Presley.

2010, Jan. 8   **Perf. 11½**
2728 A526 $2.50 Sheet of 4, #a-
          d   7.75 7.75

Miniature Sheet

NASCAR Drivers and Their Cars A527

No. 2729: a, Denny Hamlin. b, Kyle Busch. c, Joey Logano. d, Hamlin's car (#11). e, Busch's car (#18). f, Logano's car (#20).

2010, Jan. 19   **Litho.**
2729 A527 $3.25 Sheet of 6,
          #a-f   15.00 15.00

Miniature Sheets

Dogs A528

No. 2730, $2.50 — Dalmatian and: a, Books. b, Stone wall. c, Swimming pool. d, Stack of logs.
No. 2731, $2.50 — Boxer and: a, Brick wall. b, Bush. c, Window. d, Fence.

2010, Jan. 19   **Perf. 11½x11¾**
          Sheets of 4, #a-d
2730-2731 A528 Set of 2   15.50 15.50

No. 2706 With "Haiti Earthquake Relief Fund" and Map of Haiti Added to Stamps and Sheet Margin
Miniature Sheet

Designs as before.

2010, Feb. 4   **Perf. 14¾x14**
2732 A515 $2 Sheet of 6, #a-f   9.25 9.25
Position of added text varies on each stamp.

Ferraris and Their Parts — A529

No. 2733, $1.25: a, Engine of 1982 208 GTB Turbo. b, 1982 208 GTB Turbo.
No. 2734, $1.25: a, Engine of 1983 126 C3. b, 1983 126 C3.
No. 2735, $1.25: a, Side panel and rear wheel of 1984 Testarossa. b, 1984 Testarossa.
No. 2736, $1.25: a, Suspension of 1987 408 4RM. b, 1987 408 4RM.

2010, Feb. 17   **Perf. 12**
          Vert. Pairs, #a-b
2733-2736 A529 Set of 4   8.00 8.00
Nos. 2733-2736 each were printed in sheets containing four pairs.

Miniature Sheet

Mother Teresa (1910-97), Humanitarian — A530

No. 2737 — Mother Teresa: a, Denomination in black. b, Holding rosary. c, Wearing white habit. d, Kissing hand of Pope John Paul II.

2010, Feb. 24   **Perf. 11¼x11½**
2737 A530 $2.50 Sheet of 4, #a-
          d   8.00 8.00

Boy Scouts of America, Cent. A531

No. 2738, $2.50: a, Outdoor skills. b, Campfire inspirations.
No. 2739, $2.50: a, Emergency one-man carry. b, Swimming fun with safety.

2010, Feb. 24   **Perf. 13¼**
          Pairs, #a-b
2738-2739 A531 Set of 2   8.00 8.00
Nos. 2738-2739 each were printed in sheets containing two pairs.

Miniature Sheet

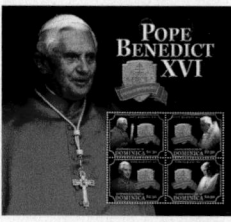

Pope Benedict XVI A532

No. 2740 — Pope Benedict XVI: a, Wearing red, holding candle. b, Wearing white, hands clasped. c, Wearing red, not holding candle. d, Wearing white, hands not clasped.

2010, Mar. 23   **Perf. 11½x12**
2740 A532 $2.50 Sheet of 4, #a-
          d   7.50 7.50

Caravaggio Paintings — A533

No. 2741, vert.: a, Mary Magdalene. b, Sick Bacchus. c, Bacchus. d, The Inspiration of Saint Matthew.
$6, Saint Gerolamo.

2010, Mar. 23   **Perf. 12x11½**
2741 A533 $2.50 Sheet of 4, #a-
          d   7.50 7.50
          Souvenir Sheet
          Perf. 11½
2742 A533 $6 multi   4.50 4.50

Miniature Sheet

Girl Guides, Cent. A534

No. 2743: a, Rainbows. b, Brownies. c, Guides. d, Senior Section. $6, Girl Guide, vert.

2010, Apr. 19   **Perf. 11½x12**
2743 A534 $2.75 Sheet of 4,
          #a-d   8.25 8.25
          Souvenir Sheet
          Perf. 11¼x11½
2743E A534 $6 multi   4.50 4.50

Souvenir Sheets

A535

A536

A537

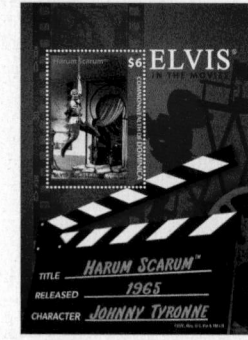

Elvis Presley (1935-77) — A538

2010, May 12   **Perf. 13½**
2744 A535 $6 multi   4.50 4.50
2745 A536 $6 multi   4.50 4.50
2746 A537 $6 multi   4.50 4.50
2747 A538 $6 multi   4.50 4.50
     Nos. 2744-2747 (4)   18.00 18.00

Miniature Sheets

Pres. Abraham Lincoln (1809-65) — A539

No. 2748, $2.50 — Photographs of Lincoln: a, Without beard. b, Without beard, arms crossed. c, Reading to son, Tad. d, With beard.
No. 2749, $2.50: a, Statue of Lincoln, Bascom Hill, University of Wisconsin. b, Aerial view of Lincoln Memorial. c, Statue of Lincoln in Lincoln Memorial. d, Sculpture of Lincoln, Mount Rushmore.

2010, June 22   Litho.   Perf. 11½
Sheets of 4, #a-d
2748-2749 A539 Set of 2   15.00 15.00

Whales A540

No. 2750: a, Sowerby's beaked whale. b, Blainville's beaked whale. c, Short-finned pilot whale. d, True's beaked whale. e, False killer whale. f, Dwarf sperm whale.
$6, Sperm whale.

2010, June 22 Litho.   Perf. 13x13½
2750 A540 $2 Sheet of 6, #a-f   9.00 9.00
Souvenir Sheet
2751 A540 $6 multi   4.50 4.50

Miniature Sheets

A541

Princess Diana (1961-97) — A542

No. 2752 — Princess Diana wearing: a, Plaid jacket. b, Wedding gown. c, Black jacket. d, Red and white dress.
No. 2753 — Princess Diana with: a, Prince Charles. b, Princes Charles, William and Harry. c, Crowd, holding flowers. d, Small child.

2010, May 12   Litho.   Perf. 13x13¼
2752 A541 $2.75 Sheet of 4, #a-d   8.25 8.25
2753 A542 $2.75 Sheet of 4, #a-d   8.25 8.25

Christmas — A543

Painting details: 90c, Geburt Christi (Birth of Christ), by Hans Baldung. $1.45, Thomas

Altar, by Meister Francke. $2, Nativity, by Baldung.

2010, Dec. 1   Perf. 13x13½
2754-2756 A543   Set of 3   3.25 3.25
Nos. 2754-2756 each were printed in sheets of 6.

Henri Dunant (1828-1910), Founder of Red Cross — A544

No. 2757 — Red Cross, nurses aiding wounded and portrait of Dunant in: a, Green. b, Brown. c, Purple. d, Blue.
$5, Red Cross, nurses, Dunant in purplish gray.

2010, Dec. 15   Perf. 12½x12
2757 A544 $3.50 Sheet of 4, #a-d   10.50 10.50
Souvenir Sheet
2758 A544 $5 multi   3.75 3.75

Tenth Cricket World Cup, India, Sri Lanka and Bangladesh A545

Designs: 90c, Chris Gayle. $2, Windsor Park Sports Stadium, Roseau, horiz. $5, Cricket World Cup.

2011, June 1   Litho.   Perf. 12½
2759-2760 A545 Set of 2   2.25 2.25
Souvenir Sheet
Perf. 12
2761 A545 $5 multi   3.75 3.75
No. 2761 contains one 30x40mm stamp.

National HIV and AIDS Response Program — A545a

2011, June 1   Litho.   Perf. 13½
2761A A545a 90c multi   — —

Lizards — A546

Designs: 5c, Golden skink. 10c, Dominican ground lizard. 15c, Crested anole. 20c, Dominican tree lizard. 25c, Pygmy skink. 50c, House gecko. 65c, Fantastic gecko. 90c, Iguana. $1, Vincent's least gecko. $2, Turnip-tailed gecko. $5, House gecko, diff. $10, Fantastic gecko, diff. $20, Vincent's least gecko, diff.

2011, Oct. 1   Perf. 14
2762 A546 5c multi   .25   .25
2763 A546 10c multi   .25   .25
2764 A546 15c multi   .25   .25
2765 A546 20c multi   .25   .25
2766 A546 25c multi   .25   .25
2767 A546 50c multi   .40   .40
2768 A546 65c multi   .50   .50
2769 A546 90c multi   .70   .70
2770 A546 $1 multi   .75   .75
2771 A546 $2 multi   1.50 1.50
2772 A546 $5 multi   3.75 3.75
2773 A546 $10 multi   7.50 7.50
2774 A546 $20 multi   15.00 15.00
Nos. 2762-2774 (13)   31.35 31.35

Christmas — A547

Paintings: 90c, The Annunciation, by Andrea del Sarto. $1.45, Madonna with Child, by Jacopo Bellini. $2, The Virgin, by Carlo Dolci.

2011, Nov. 1
2775-2777 A547   Set of 3   3.25 3.25

Christmas — A548

Paintings: 50c, Virgin in Adoration Before the Christ Child, by Peter Paul Rubens. 90c, Altarpiece of the Rose Garlands, by Albrecht Dürer. $3.50, Crowning of St. Catherine, by Rubens. $5, Adoration of the Magi, by Dürer.

2012, Nov. 19   Perf. 13¾
2778-2781 A548   Set of 4   7.50 7.50

New Year 2011 (Year of the Rabbit) — A549

2013, Aug. 29   Litho.   Perf. 12
2782 A549 $4 multi   3.00 3.00
No. 2782 was printed in sheets of 2.

Cats A550

No. 2783: a, Cat with brown-tipped tail, eyes not visible. b, Cat with black tail and four white paws. c, Head of cat and two front paws. d, Cat with black tail, paw touching "A" in "Cats." e, Cat with white tail, with one black paw visible. f, Cat with one black and three white paws.
$5, Cat, diff.

2013, Sept. 2   Litho.   Perf. 14
2783 A550 $1 Sheet of 6, #a-f   4.50 4.50
Souvenir Sheet
Perf. 12
2784 A550 $5 multi   3.75 3.75

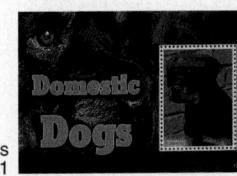

Dogs A551

No. 2785, $1.45: a, Airedale terrier. b, Bernese mountain dog. c, Pekingese. d, Samoyed.
No. 2786, $1.45, horiz.: a, Labrador retriever. b, Border collie. c, Cocker spaniel. d, Dalmatian.
No. 2787, $5, Rottweiler. No. 2788, $5, Great Dane.

2013, Sept. 2   Litho.   Perf. 12
Sheets of 4, #a-d
2785-2786 A551   Set of 2   8.75 8.75
Souvenir Sheets
2787-2788 A551   Set of 2   7.50 7.50

Bees and Wasps A552

No. 2789: a, Carpenter bee. b, Golden digger wasp. c, Bumblebee. d, Yellowjacket. $5, Golden paper wasp.

2013, Sept. 2   Litho.   Perf. 13¾
2789 A552 $2 Sheet of 4, #a-d   6.00 6.00
Souvenir Sheet
2790 A552 $5 multi   3.75 3.75

Corals A553

No. 2791 — Various unnamed corals with colors of; a, Pink (with anemone-like tips). b, Purple and pink (small bead-like appearance). c, Dark red. d, Blue (tubes). e, Purple and pink (with lines). f, Pink (with branches). g, Yellow green. h, Blue (with black curved lines).
$5, Nephthyigorgia sp.

2013, Sept. 2   Litho.   Perf. 14
2791 A553 90c Sheet of 8, #a-h   5.50 5.50
Souvenir Sheet
Perf. 12¾x12½
2792 A553 $5 multi   3.75 3.75
No. 2792 contains one 38x51mm stamp.

Election of Pope Francis A554

No. 2793 — Pope Francis: a, With top of head visible (40x60mm). b, Waving, without eyeglasses, horiz. (40x30mm). c, With top of head not visible, horiz. (40x30mm). d, Waving, wearing eyeglasses, horiz. (40x30mm).
$5, Pope Francis, horiz.

2013, Sept. 2   Litho.   Perf. 14
2793 A554 $3.50 Sheet of 4, #a-d   10.50 10.50
Souvenir Sheet
Perf. 12¾x12½
2794 A554 $5 multi   3.75 3.75
No. 2794 contains one 51x38mm stamp.

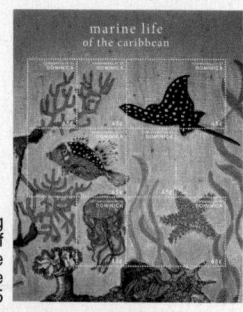

Painting of Marine Life
A555

Painting of Parrot
A556

No. 2795: a, Coral, denomination on coral (30x40mm). b, Coral, denomination on blue background (30x40mm). c, Ray (60x40mm). d, Fish and coral (60x40mm). e, Sea grass (30x40mm). f, Jellyfish (30x40mm). g, Sea grass and starfish (60x40mm).

2013, Sept. 2   Litho.   Perf. 14
2795 A555 65c Sheet of 7, #a-g   3.50 3.50
Souvenir Sheet
Perf. 12
2796 A556 $5 multi   3.75 3.75

Butterflies — A557

No. 2797, $2: a, Malachite. b, Silver-banded hairstreak.
No. 2798, $2: a, Gold rim swallowtail. b, Mangrove buckeye.

2013, Sept. 2   Litho.   Perf. 13¾
Pairs, #a-b
2797-2798 A557 Set of 2   6.00 6.00
Nos. 2797 and 2798 each were printed in sheets containing two pairs.

Birth of Prince George of Cambridge — A558

No. 2799: a, Duke and Duchess of Cambridge, Prince George. b, Duke of Cambridge holding Prince George. c, Duchess of Cambridge holding Prince George. d, Close-up of Prince George.
$6, Duke and Duchess of Cambridge, Prince George, diff.

2013   Litho.   Perf. 14
2799 A558 $2 Sheet of 4, #a-d   6.00 6.00
Souvenir Sheet
2800 A558 $6 multi   4.50 4.50

Nelson Mandela
In Memoriam
1918-2013
A559

Nelson Mandela (1918-2013), President of South Africa — A560

No. 2801 — Mandela: a, Holding loudspeaker. b, Wearing green and black shirt and jacket. c, With arms raised, color photograph. d, With arms raised, black-and-white photograph. e, Wearing black and gray shirt. f, Wearing black shirt.
$5, Mandela wearing gray shirt. $20, Mandela wearing shirt with leaf design.

2014, Jan. 6   Litho.   Perf. 13¾
2801 A559 $2.50 Sheet of 6, #a-f   11.00 11.00
Souvenir Sheets
2802 A559 $5 multi   3.75 3.75
Litho., Margin Embossed With Foil Application
Imperf
2803 A560 $20 multi   15.00 15.00

New Year 2014 (Year of the Horse) A561

No. 2804 — Various Chinese characters for "horse" and: a, Horse in red at left, red chop at right, orange background. b, Horse in yellow at left, yellow chop at left, red orange background. c, Horse in red at left, red chop at left, yellow orange background. d, Horse in yellow at right, red chop at left, brown background. e, Horse in red at right, red chop at left, yellow orange background. f, Horse in yellow at right, red chop at left, dull orange background.
No. 2805 — Chinese characters for "horse" and: a, Horse in red at right. b, Horse in yellow brown at right.

2014, Jan. 8   Litho.   Perf. 14
2804 A561 $2.50 Sheet of 6, #a-f   11.00 11.00
Souvenir Sheet
2805 A561 $5 Sheet of 2, #a-b   7.50 7.50

Sea Turtles
A562

No. 2806: a, Leatherback turtle. b, Green sea turtle. c, Hawksbill turtle.
$5, Green sea turtle, diff.

2014, May 1   Litho.   Perf. 11½x12
2806 A562 $3.50 Sheet of 3, #a-c   7.75 7.75
Souvenir Sheet
2807 A562 $5 multi   3.75 3.75

Morne Trois Pitons National Park UNESCO World Heritage Site, 70th Anniv. — A563

No. 2808: a, Fumarole, mountain in background. b, Fumarole, rocks in foreground. c, Lesser Antillean iguana. d, Smoke-enshrouded landscape. e, Smoke above waterfall. g, Waterfall.
$10, Waterfall, diff.

2015, Dec. 1   Litho.   Perf. 12
2808 A563 $3.50 Sheet of 6, #a-f   15.50 15.50
Souvenir Sheet
2809 A563 $10 multi   7.50 7.50

First Man on the Moon, 50th Anniv. (in 2019) A564

No. 2810: a, Michael Collins (1930-2021), Apollo 11 Command Module pilot. b, Neil Armstrong (1930-2012), Apollo 11 commander, and first man on the Moon. c, Edwin E. Aldrin, Jr., Apollo 11 Lunar Module pilot.
$5, Aldrin on Moon, vert.

2020, Nov. 3   Litho.   Perf. 14
2810 A564 $2.50 Sheet of 3, #a-c   5.75 5.75
Souvenir Sheet
Perf. 12
2811 A564 $5 multi   3.75 3.75
No. 2811 contains one 30x80mm stamp.

Miniature Sheet

Tribute to Workers in COVID-19 Pandemic — A565

No. 2812: a, Police officer wearing cap and protective mask and face shield. b, Health care worker wearing hair net, protective eyeglasses and face mask. c, Medical emblem. d, Vial of coronavirus vaccine.

2020, Nov. 3   Litho.   Perf. 14
2812 A565 $5 Sheet of 4, #a-d 15.00 15.00

Dorje Chang Buddha III, Religious Leader — A566

2020, Nov. 18   Litho.   Perf. 13¼
2813 A566 $5 multi   3.75 3.75
No. 2813 was printed in sheets of 5.

A567

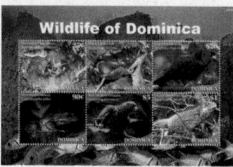

Wildlife of Dominica
A568

Nos. 2814, 2821a, 5c, Black land crab. Nos. 2815, 2821b, 25c, Dominica cloud boa. Nos. 2816, 2821c, 90c, Mountain chicken. Nos. 2817, 2821d, $1, Lesser Antillean iguana. Nos. 2818, 2821e, $5, Red-necked Amazon. Nos. 2819, 2821f, $20, Imperial Amazon. $250, Flag of Dominica.

Perf. 12½x13¼
2020, Nov. 18   Litho.
2814 A567   5c multi   .25   .25
2815 A567   25c multi   .25   .25
2816 A567   90c multi   .65   .65
2817 A567 $1 multi   .75   .75
2818 A567 $5 multi   3.75   3.75
2819 A567 $20 multi   15.00 15.00
2820 A567 $250 multi 185.00 185.00
  Nos. 2814-2819 (6)   20.65 20.65
Miniature Sheet
Perf. 14
2821 A568 Sheet of 6, #a-f   21.00 21.00

Paintings by Raphael (1483-1520) — A569

No. 2822: a, Portait of Elisabetta Gonzaga, 1505. b, Young Man with an Apple, 1505. c, Portrait of Guidobaldo da Montefeltro, 1506. d, Young Woman with Unicorn, 1506.
$5, Portrait of Maddalena Doni, 1506.

2020, Nov. 18   Litho.   Perf. 14
2822 A569 $2.50 Sheet of 4, #a-d   7.50 7.50
Souvenir Sheet
Perf. 12½
2823 A569 $5 multi   3.75 3.75
No. 2823 contains one 38x51mm stamp.

Forbidden City, Beijing, People's Republic of China, 600th Anniv. — A570

No. 2824: a, Yongzheng Emperor (1678-1735) holding off tiger with trident. b, Yongzheng Emperor in armor. c, Yongzheng Emperor in court dress. d, Yongzheng Emperor wearing robe.
$5, Yongzheng Emperor Offering Sacrifice at the Xiannong Altar, horiz.

2020, Nov. 18   Litho.   Perf. 12½
2824 A570 $2.50 Sheet of 4, #a-d   7.50 7.50
Souvenir Sheet
Perf. 12
2825 A570 $5 multi   3.75 3.75
No. 2825 contains one 50x30mm stamp.

Visit to United Kingdom of Pres. Donald Trump
A571

No. 2826: a, First Lady Melania Trump. b, Pres. Trump, with wife Melania in background. c, Pres. Trump. d, John Hall, Dean of Westminster.
$5, Pres. Trump and wife, Melania, diff.

2020, Nov. 18   Litho.   Perf. 14
2826 A571 $2.50 Sheet of 4, #a-d 7.50 7.50

Souvenir Sheet
Perf. 13¾
2827 A571 $5 multi 3.75 3.75
No. 2827 contains one 35x35mm stamp.

New Year 2020 (Year of the Rat) — A572

2020, Nov. 18   Litho.   Perf. 12½
2828 A572 $5 multi 3.75 3.75
No. 2828 was printed in sheets of 2.

WAR TAX STAMPS

No. 50 Surcharged in Red

1916   Wmk. 3   Perf. 14
MR1 A6 ½p on ½p green .... 3.50 .85

No. 50 Overprinted in Black

1918
MR2 A6 ½p green 7.50 6.25

Nos. 50, 40 in Black or Red

1918
MR3 A6 ½p green .... .25 .30
MR4 A6 3p violet, yel (R) 5.50 4.50

Type of 1908-09 Surcharged in Red

1919
MR5 A6 1½p on 2½p orange ...... .25 .60

DOMINICAN REPUBLIC

də-'mi-ni-kən ri-'pə-blik

LOCATION — Comprises about two-thirds of the island of Hispaniola in the West Indies
GOVT. — Republic
AREA — 18,700 sq. mi.
POP. — 8,129,734 (1999 est.)
CAPITAL — Santo Domingo

8 Reales = 1 Peso
100 Centavos = 1 Peso (1880)
100 Centimos = 1 Franco (1883)
100 Centavos = 1 Peso (1885)

Catalogue values for unused stamps in this country are for Never Hinged items, beginning with Scott 437 in the regular postage section, Scott B1 in the semipostal section, Scott C75 in the airpost section, Scott CB1 in the airpost semi-postal section, Scott E7 in the special delivery section, Scott G13 in the insured letter section, Scott J14 in the postage due section, Scott O26 in the officials section, and Scott RA20 in the postal tax section.

Watermarks

Wmk. 115
Diamonds

Wmk. 116
Crosses and Circles

Coat of Arms
A1   A2

1865   Unwmk.   Typo.   Imperf.
Wove Paper

| 1 | A1 | ½r black, *rose* | 700. | 650. |
| 2 | A1 | 1r black, *dp green* | 1,100. | 1,000. |

Twelve varieties of each.

Laid Paper

| 3 | A2 | ½r black, *pale green* | 550. | 475. |
| 4 | A2 | 1r black, *straw* | 1,800. | 1,200. |

Twelve varieties of the ½r, ten of the 1r.

A3   A4

1866   Laid Paper   Unwmk.

5	A3	½r black, *straw*	200.00	160.00
6	A3	1r black, *pale green*	2,500.	2,000.
7	A4	1r black, *pale green*	175.00	125.00

Nos. 5-8 have 21 varieties (sheets of 21).

Wmk. 115

| 8 | A3 | 1r blk, *pale grn* | 13,000. | 13,000. |
| a. | | "CORREOS" and "Un Real" doubled | 21,000. | |

The unique example of No. 8a is centered in the grade of fine, has a shallow thin spot and pinhole.

1866-67   Wove Paper   Unwmk.

9	A3	½r blk, *rose* ('67)	60.00	60.00
10	A3	1r blk, *pale green*	85.00	75.00
a.		Inscription dbl., top & bottom	400.00	400.00

11	A3	1r black, *blue* ('67)	60.00	37.50
a.		1r black, *light blue* ('67)	50.00	30.00
b.		No space btwn. "Un" and "real"	600.00	500.00
c.		Without inscription at top & bottom	1,500.	1,000.
d.		Inscription invtd., top & bottom	—	—
		Nos. 9-11 (3)	205.00	172.50

1867-71   Pelure Paper

13	A3	½r black, *rose*	150.00	75.00
15	A3	½r black, *lav* ('68)	250.00	210.00
a.		Without inscription at top and bottom		525.00
b.		Dbl. inscriptions, one invtd.		425.00
16	A3	½r black, *grnsh gray* ('68)	260.00	225.00
17	A3	½r black, *yel* ('68)	12,000.	
18	A3	½r blk, *ol* ('69)	3,000.	5,500.
22	A3	1r black, *blue*	4,000.	
23	A3	1r black, *lav*	225.00	200.00
24	A4	1r blk, *rose* ('68)	225.00	225.00
25	A4	1r blk, *mag* ('69)	2,250.	1,300.
26	A4	1r blk, *sal* ('71)	300.00	225.00

Value for No. 17 is for an example with very fine centering and small faults. Value for No. 22 is for a faulty example with very fine centering and appearance.

1870-73   Ordinary Paper

27	A3	½r blk, *mag*	2,500.	4,750.
28	A3	½r blue, *rose* (blk inscription) ('71)	50.00	42.50
a.		Blue inscription	500.00	500.00
b.		Without inscription at top and bottom		
29	A3	½r blk, *yel* ('73)	30.00	21.00
a.		Without inscription at top and bottom	700.00	700.00
30	A4	1r blk, *vio* ('73)	30.00	21.00
a.		Without inscription at top and bottom	700.00	700.00
31	A4	1r black, *dk grn*	60.00	50.00

Nos. 9-31 have 21 varieties (sheets of 21). Nos. 29 and 30 are known pin-perforated, unofficially.
Bisects are known of several of the early 1r stamps.

A5

1879   Perf. 12½x13

32	A5	½r violet	3.00	2.10
a.		Imperf., pair	9.00	9.00
b.		Horiz. pair, imperf. vert.	17.00	
33	A5	½r violet, *bluish*	2.50	1.80
a.		Imperf., pair	9.00	7.50
34	A5	1r carmine	4.50	2.10
a.		Imperf., pair	11.50	9.00
b.		Perf. 13	11.50	7.50
c.		Perf. 13x12½	11.50	7.50
35	A5	1r carmine, *sal*	2.50	1.50
a.		Imperf., pair	8.25	8.25
		Nos. 32-35 (4)	12.50	7.50

In 1891 15 stamps of 1879-83 were surcharged "U P U," new values and crossed diagonal lines.

A6

1880   Typo.   Rouletted in Color

36	A6	1c green	1.40	.90
b.		Laid paper	50.00	50.00
37	A6	2c red	1.00	.75
a.		Pelure paper	40.00	40.00
b.		Laid paper	40.00	40.00
38	A6	5c blue	1.50	.70
39	A6	10c rose	3.25	.90
40	A6	20c brown	2.00	.75
41	A6	25c lilac	2.25	1.25
42	A6	50c orange	3.00	1.75
43	A6	75c ultra	5.75	3.00
a.		Laid paper	40.00	40.00
44	A6	1p bister	7.50	4.50
a.		Laid paper	50.00	50.00
b.		Double impression	42.50	42.50
		Nos. 36-44 (9)	27.65	14.50

1881   Network Covering Stamp

45	A6	1c green	.90	.50
46	A6	2c red	.90	.50
47	A6	5c blue	1.25	.65
48	A6	10c rose	1.50	.65
49	A6	20c org brown	1.50	.90
50	A6	25c lilac	1.75	1.00

51	A6	50c orange	2.00	1.40
52	A6	75c ultra	6.00	4.50
53	A6	1p bister	8.00	7.00
		Nos. 45-53 (9)	23.80	16.95

Preceding Issues (Type A6) Srch. with Value in New Currency

5 céntimos	5 céntimos
a	b

50 céntimos.	1 franco.
c	d

1 Franco.	1 franco
e	f

1 franco, 25 céntimos	5 francos.
g	h

	5 francos
	i

1883   Without Network

54	(a)	5c on 1c green	1.50	1.60
b.		Inverted surcharge	21.00	21.00
c.		Surcharged "25 céntimos"	50.00	50.00
d.		Surcharged "10 céntimos"	27.50	27.50
55	(b)	5c on 1c green	25.00	9.00
b.		Double surcharge	100.00	
c.		Inverted surcharge	65.00	65.00
56	(c)	5c on 1c green	17.00	9.50
b.		Surcharged "10 céntimos"	35.00	35.00
c.		Inverted surcharge	37.50	37.50
57	(a)	10c on 2c red	5.00	3.00
a.		Inverted surcharge	27.50	27.50
d.		Surcharged "5 céntimos"	52.50	52.50
e.		Surcharged "25 céntimos"	75.00	75.00
58	(c)	10c on 2c red	4.50	3.50
a.		"Céntimso"		
b.		Inverted surcharge	37.50	37.50
c.		Surcharged "25 céntimos"	60.00	60.00
d.		"10" omitted	60.00	
59	(a)	25c on 5c blue	7.00	4.50
a.		Surcharged "5 céntimos"	52.50	
b.		Surcharged "10 céntimos"	52.50	52.50
c.		Surcharged "50 céntimos"	75.00	75.00
d.		Inverted surcharge	50.00	50.00
60	(c)	25c on 5c blue	7.50	3.50
a.		Inverted surcharge	45.00	37.50
b.		Surcharged "10 céntimos"	45.00	37.50
e.		"25" omitted	75.00	
f.		Surcharged on back		75.00
61	(a)	50c on 10c rose	27.50	12.50
a.		Inverted surcharge	70.00	60.00
62	(c)	50c on 10c rose	35.00	17.50
a.		Inverted surcharge	52.50	52.50
63	(d)	1fr on 20c brn	15.00	10.00
64	(e)	1fr on 20c brn	17.50	10.00
a.		Comma after "Franco,"	27.50	27.50
65	(f)	1fr on 20c brn	25.00	20.00
a.				75.00
66	(g)	1fr25c on 25c violet	21.00	15.00
a.		Inverted surcharge	65.00	65.00
67	(g)	2fr50c on 50c org	16.00	12.00
a.		Inverted surcharge	35.00	27.50
68	(g)	3fr75c on 75c ultra	30.00	25.00
b.		Inverted surcharge	60.00	60.00
c.		Laid paper	75.00	75.00
70	(i)	5fr on 1p gold	550.00	500.00
a.		"s" of "francos" inverted	700.00	700.00

With Network

71	(a)	5c on 1c green	3.00	2.50
b.		Inverted surcharge	22.50	22.50
c.		Double surcharge	22.50	22.50
d.		Surcharged "25 céntimos"	42.50	42.50
e.		"5" omitted	75.00	75.00
72	(b)	5c on 1c green	21.00	9.00
b.		Inverted surcharge	60.00	60.00
73	(c)	5c on 1c green	27.50	11.50
b.		Surcharged "10 céntimos"	50.00	42.50
c.		Surcharged "25 céntimos"	60.00	
74	(a)	10c on 2c red	3.75	2.25
b.		Surcharged "5 céntimos"	52.50	45.00
c.		Surcharged "25 céntimos"	67.50	67.50
d.		"10" omitted	60.00	
75	(c)	10c on 2c red	3.00	2.00
a.		Inverted surcharge	30.00	30.00
76	(a)	25c on 5c blue	7.50	3.50
a.		Inverted surcharge	75.00	
b.		Surcharged "5 céntimos"	60.00	
c.		Surcharged "25 céntimos"	67.50	
77	(c)	25c on 5c blue	60.00	30.00
a.		Inverted surcharge		
b.		Surcharged on back		

78	(a)	50c on 10c rose	25.00	7.50
a.		Inverted surcharge	50.00	30.00
b.		Surcharged "25 céntimos"	60.00	
79	(c)	50c on 10c rose	30.00	9.50
a.		Inverted surcharge	60.00	
80	(d)	1fr on 20c brn	12.00	10.00
81	(e)	1fr on 20c brn	14.50	12.50
a.		Comma after "Franco"	35.00	35.00
b.		Inverted surcharge	75.00	
82	(f)	1fr on 20c brown	25.00	20.00
83	(g)	1fr25c on 25c violet	45.00	30.00
a.		Inverted surcharge	75.00	
84	(g)	2fr50c on 50c org	19.00	12.50
a.		Inverted surcharge	35.00	27.50
85	(g)	3fr75c on 75c ultra	45.00	42.50
86	(h)	5fr on 1p gold	140.00	140.00
a.		Inverted surcharge		
87	(i)	5fr on 1p gold	190.00	190.00

Many minor varieties exist in Nos. 54-87: accent on "i" of "centimos"; "5" with straight top; "1" with straight serif.

A7   A7a

1885-91   Engr.   Perf. 12

88	A7	1c green	1.00	.50
89	A7	2c vermilion	1.00	.50
90	A7	5c blue	1.40	.50
91	A7a	10c orange	2.25	.65
92	A7a	20c dark brown	2.25	.80
93	A7a	50c violet ('91)	7.50	7.50
94	A7	1p carmine ('91)	20.00	20.00
95	A7	2p red brown ('91)	25.00	25.00
		Nos. 88-95 (8)	60.40	55.45

Nos. 93, 94, 95 were issued without gum.
Imperf. varieties exist.
For surcharges see Nos. 166-168.

In 1891 certain denominations of the 1879-83 issues were overprinted with a large "X" separating the stamp into four triangles. The top triangle has the letter "U," and the left and right triangles have the letter "P". The bottom triangle is surcharged with a new value. Although this issue was authorized by the president, the entire supply was given to a single French dealer. A few covers exist, most addressed to the dealer's wife in New York. Numerous forgeries exist.

Coat of Arms — A8

1895   Perf. 12½x14

96	A8	1c green	1.25	.50
97	A8	2c orange red	1.25	.50
98	A8	5c blue	1.40	.50
99	A8	10c orange	3.25	1.60
		Nos. 96-99 (4)	7.15	3.10

Exist imperforate but were proofs.

1897   Perf. 14

96a	A8	1c green	1.40	.50
97a	A8	2c orange red	8.00	.75
98a	A8	5c blue	1.40	.75
99a	A8	10c orange	2.75	1.50
		Nos. 96a-99a (4)	13.55	3.50

Voyage of Diego Méndez from Jamaica — A9

Enriquillo's Revolt — A10

Sarcophagus of Columbus A11

"Española" Guarding Remains of Columbus A12

Toscanelli
Replying to
Columbus
A13

Bartolomé de las
Casas Defending
Indians
A14

Columbus at
Salamanca
A15

Columbus'
Mausoleum
A16

1899, Feb. 27   Litho.   Perf. 11½

100	A9	1c brown violet	7.25	5.25
102	A10	2c rose red	1.75	.70
103	A11	5c blue	2.00	.70
104	A12	10c orange	5.00	1.60
a.		Tête bêche pair	42.50	42.50
105	A13	20c brown	10.00	8.25
106	A14	50c yellow green	11.50	9.75
a.		Tête bêche pair	60.00	60.00
107	A15	1p black, gray bl	27.00	22.00
108	A16	2p bister brown	45.00	47.50

1900, Jan.

109	A11	¼c black	.75	1.60
110	A15	½c black	.75	1.60
110A	A9	1c gray green	.75	.65
		Nos. 100-110A (11)	111.75	99.60

Nos. 100-110A were issued to raise funds for a Columbus mausoleum.

Imperf., Pairs

100a	A9	1c brown violet	16.50	16.50
102a	A10	2c rose red	5.00	
103a	A11	5c blue	5.75	
104b	A12	10c orange	8.75	
105a	A13	20c brown	15.00	
106b	A14	50c yellow green	17.50	
c.		As "b," tête bêche pair	125.00	
107a	A15	1p black, gray blue	42.50	
108a	A16	2p bister brown	70.00	
109a	A11	¼c black	3.75	4.25
110b	A15	½c black	3.75	4.25
110c	A9	1c gray green	3.50	

Map of
Hispaniola — A17

1900, Oct. 21   Unwmk.   Perf. 14

111	A17	¼c dark blue	.75	.40
112	A17	½c rose	.75	.40
113	A17	1c olive green	.75	.40
114	A17	2c deep green	.75	.40
115	A17	5c red brown	.75	.40
a.		Vertical pair, imperf. between	17.50	

Perf. 12

116	A17	10c orange	.75	.40
117	A17	20c lilac	3.00	2.50
a.		20c rose (error)	25.00	25.00
118	A17	50c black	2.75	2.50
119	A17	1p brown	3.00	2.50
		Nos. 111-119 (9)	13.25	9.90

Several varieties in design are known in this issue. They were deliberately made. Counterfeits of Nos. 111-119 abound.

A18

1901-06   Typo.   Perf. 14

120	A18	½c carmine & vio	.70	.40
121	A18	½c blk & org ('05)	1.80	.95
122	A18	½c grn & blk ('06)	.85	.30
123	A18	1c ol grn & vio	.70	.30
124	A18	1c blk & ultra ('05)	1.80	.85
125	A18	1c car & blk ('06)	1.00	.45
126	A18	2c dp grn & vio	.80	.30
127	A18	2c blk & vio ('05)	2.25	.70
128	A18	2c org brn & blk ('06)	1.40	.30
129	A18	5c org brn & vio	.80	.30
130	A18	5c blk & cl ('05)	2.50	1.25
131	A18	5c blue & blk ('06)	1.25	.30
132	A18	10c orange & vio	1.40	.45
133	A18	10c blk & grn ('05)	4.25	2.25
134	A18	10c red vio & blk ('06)	1.40	.40
135	A18	20c brn vio & vio	2.50	.95
136	A18	20c blk & ol ('05)	13.50	8.75
137	A18	20c ol grn & blk ('06)	7.25	3.25

138	A18	50c gray blk & vio	8.00	5.50
139	A18	50c blk & red brn ('05)	47.50	34.00
140	A18	50c brn & blk ('06)	8.75	7.75
141	A18	1p org brn & lil	18.00	10.00
142	A18	1p blk & gray ('05)	200.00	225.00
143	A18	1p vio & blk ('06)	21.00	13.50
		Nos. 120-143 (24)	349.40	318.20

Issued: 11/15/01; 5/11/05; 8/17/06.
See Nos. 172-176. For surcharges see Nos.151-156.

Francisco
Sánchez
A19

Juan Pablo
Duarte
A20

Ramón Mella
A21

Ft. Santo
Domingo
A22

1902, Feb. 25   Engr.   Perf. 12

144	A19	1c dk grn & blk	.35	.35
145	A20	2c scarlet & blk	.35	.35
146	A20	5c blue & blk	.35	.35
147	A19	10c orange & blk	.35	.35
148	A21	12c purple & blk	.35	.35
149	A21	20c rose & blk	.60	.60
150	A22	50c brown & blk	.90	.90
		Nos. 144-150 (7)	3.25	3.25

Center Inverted

144a	A19	1c	17.50	17.50
145a	A20	2c	17.50	17.50
146a	A20	5c	17.50	17.50
148a	A21	12c	17.50	17.50
149a	A21	20c	17.50	17.50
150a	A22	50c	17.50	17.50
		Nos. 144a-150a (6)	105.00	105.00

400th anniversary of Santo Domingo. Imperforate varieties of Nos. 144 to 150 were never sold to the public.

Nos. 138, 141 Surcharged in Black

1904, Aug.

151	A18	2c on 50c	9.25	7.25
152	A18	2c on 1p	13.50	9.25
b.		"2" omitted	50.00	50.00
153	A18	5c on 50c	4.25	2.25
154	A18	5c on 1p	5.25	4.00
155	A18	10c on 50c	8.25	6.75
156	A18	10c on 1p	8.75	6.75
		Nos. 151-156 (6)	49.25	36.25

Inverted Surcharge

151a	A18	2c on 50c	15.00	15.00
152a	A18	2c on 1p	15.00	15.00
c.		As "a," "2" omitted	85.00	85.00
153a	A18	5c on 50c	5.50	5.50
154a	A18	5c on 1p	7.00	6.50
155a	A18	10c on 50c	14.00	14.00
156a	A18	10c on 1p	10.00	10.00
		Nos. 151a-156a (6)	66.50	66.00

Official Stamps of
1902 Overprinted

1904, Aug. 16   Red Overprint

157	O1	5c dk blue & blk	5.75	3.00
a.		Inverted overprint	7.25	5.75

Black Overprint

158	O1	2c scarlet & blk	17.00	5.25
a.		Inverted overprint	20.00	6.50
159	O1	5c dk blue & blk	3,500.	3,500.
160	O1	10c yellow grn & blk	10.50	10.50
a.		Inverted overprint	15.00	15.00

Official Stamps of
1902 Surcharged

161	O1	1c on 20c yellow & blk	4.75	3.00
a.		Inverted surcharge	7.25	7.25

Nos. J1-J2 Surcharged
or Overprinted in Black

1904-05   Surcharged "CENTAVOS"

162	D1	1c on 2c olive gray	250.00	200.00
a.		"entavos"		—
b.		"Dominican"	350.00	300.00
c.		"Centavo"	350.00	300.00

Carmine Surcharge or Overprint

163	D1	1c on 2c olive gray	3.50	1.10
a.		Inverted surcharge	4.75	4.75
b.		"Dominicana"	15.00	15.00
c.		As "b," inverted	40.00	40.00
d.		"Dominican"	10.50	10.50
e.		"Centavos" omitted	30.00	30.00
g.		"entavos"	30.00	30.00
163F	D1	1c on 4c olive gray	35.00	7.00
164	D1	2c olive gray	.95	.60
a.		"Domihicana"	11.00	11.00
b.		Inverted overprint	2.00	2.00
c.		As "a," inverted	25.00	25.00
d.		"Dominican"	25.00	25.00
e.		"Centavo" omitted	12.50	10.00
f.		"entavos"	12.50	12.50
g.		As "f," inverted	40.00	40.00
h.		As "d," inverted		

Surcharged "CENTAVO"

165	D1	1c on 4c olive gray	.95	.70
a.		"Domihicana"	10.00	10.00
c.		Inverted surcharge	1.75	1.75
d.		"1" omitted	3.50	3.50
e.		As "a," inverted	32.50	32.50
f.		As "d," inverted	40.00	40.00
g.		Double surcharge	30.00	30.00

No. 92 Surcharged in Red

1905, Apr. 4

166	A7a	2c on 20c dk brown	8.75	7.25
a.		Inverted surcharge	15.00	15.00
167	A7a	5c on 20c dk brown	4.75	2.50
a.		Inverted surcharge	16.00	16.00
b.		Double surcharge	25.00	25.00
168	A7a	10c on 20c dk brown	8.75	7.25
		Nos. 166-168 (3)	22.25	17.00

Nos. 166-168 exist with inverted "A" for "V" in "CENTAVOS" in surcharge.

No. J2 Surcharged in
Red

1906, Jan. 16   Perf. 14

169	D1	1c on 4c olive gray	.95	.50
a.		Inverted surcharge	10.50	10.50
b.		Double surcharge	25.00	

Nos. J4, J3 Surcharged in Black

1906, May 1

170	D1	1c on 10c olive gray	1.10	.40
a.		Inverted surcharge	10.50	10.50
b.		Double surcharge	14.00	14.00
c.		"OMINICANA"	20.00	20.00
d.		As "c," inverted	150.00	
171	D1	2c on 5c olive gray	1.10	.40
a.		Inverted surcharge	10.50	10.50
b.		Double surcharge	35.00	

The varieties small "C" or small "A" in "REPUBLICA" are found on Nos.169, 170, 171.

Arms Type of 1901-06

1907-10   Wmk. 116

172	A18	½c grn & blk ('08)	.85	.25
173	A18	1c carmine & blk	.85	.25
174	A18	2c orange brn & blk	.85	.25
175	A18	5c blue & blk	.85	.25
176	A18	10c red vio & blk ('10)	8.00	1.00
		Nos. 172-176 (5)	11.40	2.00

No. O6 Overprinted in
Red

1911, July 11   Perf. 13½x14, 13½x13

177	O2	2c scarlet & brn blk	1.60	.60
a.		"HABILITAOO"	8.75	6.00
b.		Inverted overprint	21.00	
c.		Double overprint	21.00	

A23

1911-13   Center in Black   Perf. 14

178	A23	½c orange ('13)	.25	.25
179	A23	1c green	.25	.25
180	A23	2c carmine	.25	.25
181	A23	5c gray blue ('13)	.80	.25
182	A23	10c red violet	1.60	.45
183	A23	20c olive green	11.50	11.50
184	A23	50c yellow brn ('12)	3.75	3.75
185	A23	1p violet ('12)	5.75	4.25
		Nos. 178-185 (8)	24.15	20.95

See Nos. 230-232.

Juan Pablo
Duarte — A24

1914, Apr. 13   Perf. 13x14
Background Red, White and Blue

186	A24	½c orange & blk	.60	.30
187	A24	1c green & blk	.60	.30
188	A24	2c rose & blk	.60	.30
189	A24	5c slate & blk	.60	.40
190	A24	10c magenta & blk	1.40	.70
191	A24	20c olive grn & blk	2.50	1.90
192	A24	50c brown & blk	3.50	2.75
193	A24	1p dull lilac & blk	5.50	4.00
		Nos. 186-193 (8)	15.30	10.65

Cent. of the birth of Juan Pablo Duarte (1813-1876), patriot and revolutionary.

Official Stamps of 1909-12
Surcharged in Violet or Overprinted in Red

a   b

1915, Feb.   Perf. 13½x13, 13½x14

194	O2 (a)	½c on 1c brn org & blk	.50	.35
a.		Inverted surcharge	6.00	6.00
b.		Double surcharge	8.75	8.75
c.		"Habilitado" omitted	5.25	5.25
195	O2 (b)	1c blue grn & blk	.80	.25
a.		Inverted overprint	6.00	6.00
b.		Double overprint	7.00	
c.		Overprinted "1915" only	12.50	
196	O2 (b)	2c scarlet & blk	1.25	.25
a.		Inverted overprint	5.25	5.25
b.		Double overprint	7.75	7.75
c.		Overprinted "1915" only	8.75	
d.		"1915" double		
197	O2 (b)	5c dk blue & blk	1.00	.25
a.		Inverted overprint	7.00	7.00
b.		Double overprint	8.75	8.75
c.		Double ovpt., one invtd.	27.50	
d.		Overprinted "1915" only	8.75	
198	O2 (b)	10c yel grn & blk	2.75	2.50
a.		Inverted overprint	15.00	
199	O2 (b)	20c orange & blk	9.25	7.25
a.		"Habilitado" omitted		
		Nos. 194-199 (6)	15.55	10.85

Nos. 194, 196-198 are known with both perforations. Nos. 195, 199 are only perf. 13½x13.

The variety capital "I" for "1" in "Habilitado" occurs once in each sheet in all denominations.

Type of 1911-13 Redrawn

A25

SMALL LETTERS

LARGE LETTERS

TWO CENTAVOS:

Type I — "DOS" in small letters.
Type II — "DOS" in larger letters with white dot at each end of the word.

Overprinted "1915" in Red

1915		**Unwmk.**	**Litho.**	**Perf. 11½**
200	A25	½c violet & blk	.85	.25
a.		Imperf., pair	5.75	
201	A25	1c yel brn & blk	.85	.25
a.		Imperf., pair	6.50	
b.		Vert. pair, imperf. horiz.	10.50	
c.		Horiz. pair, imperf. vert.	10.50	
202	A25	2c ol grn & blk (I)	3.75	.25
a.		Imperf., pair	10.00	
203	A25	10c ol grn & blk (II)	6.00	.25
a.		Center omitted	87.50	
b.		Frame omitted	87.50	
c.		Imperf., pair	15.00	
d.		Horiz. pair, imperf. vert.	15.00	
204	A25	5c magenta & blk	3.75	.25
a.		Pair, one without overprint	65.00	
b.		Imperf., pair	6.50	
205	A25	10c gray blue & blk	3.75	.50
a.		Imperf., pair	10.00	
b.		Horiz. pair, imperf. vert.	35.00	
206	A25	20c rose red & blk	8.25	1.40
a.		Imperf., pair	12.50	
207	A25	50c green & blk	10.50	4.00
a.		Imperf., pair	25.00	
208	A25	1p orange & blk	21.00	7.00
a.		Imperf., pair	52.50	
		Nos. 200-208 (9)	58.70	14.15

Type of 1915 Overprinted "1916" in Red

1916				
209	A25	½c violet & blk	2.25	.25
a.		Imperf., pair	21.00	
210	A25	1c green & blk	3.25	.25
a.		Imperf., pair	21.00	

Type of 1915 Overprinted "1917" in Red

1917-19				
213	A25	½c red lilac & blk	3.50	.30
a.		Horiz. pair, imperf. btwn.	47.50	47.50
214	A25	1c yellow grn & blk	1.60	.25
a.		Vert. pair, imperf. btwn.	50.00	
215	A25	2c olive grn & blk	2.25	.25
a.		Imperf., pair	35.00	
216	A25	5c magenta & blk	23.00	.85
		Nos. 213-216 (4)	30.35	1.65

Type of 1915 Overprinted "1919" in Red

1919				
219	A25	2c olive grn & blk	17.00	.25

Type of 1915 Overprinted "1920" in Red

1920-27				
220	A25	½c lilac rose & blk	.60	.25
a.		Horiz. pair, imperf. btwn.	25.00	25.00
b.		Inverted overprint		
c.		Double overprint		
d.		Double overprint, one invtd.		
221	A25	1c yellow grn & blk	.75	.25
a.		Overprint omitted	70.00	
b.		Horiz. pair, imperf. btwn.	40.00	
222	A25	2c olive grn & blk	.75	.25
a.		Vertical pair, imperf. between	27.50	
223	A25	5c dp rose & blk	9.00	.50
224	A25	10c blue & black	5.75	.25
225	A25	20c rose red & blk ('27)	7.75	.50
226	A25	50c green & blk ('27)	65.00	21.00
		Nos. 220-226 (7)	89.60	23.00

Type of 1915 Overprinted "1921" in Red

1921				
227	A25	1c yellow grn & blk	5.25	.30
a.		Horiz. pair, imperf. btwn.	45.00	45.00
b.		Imperf., pair	45.00	45.00
228	A25	2c olive grn & blk	5.75	.40
a.		Vert. pair, imperf. btwn.	45.00	

Redrawn Design of 1915 without Overprint

1922				
230	A25	1c green	3.75	.30
231	A25	2c carmine (II)	3.75	.30
232	A25	5c blue	5.75	.30
		Nos. 230-232 (3)	13.25	.90

Nos. 230-232 exist imperf.

A26

Type I

Type II

TEN CENTAVOS:
Type I — Numerals 2mm high. "DIEZ" in thick letters with large white dot at each end.
Type II — Numerals 3mm high. "DIEZ" in thin letters with white dot with colored center at each end.

1924-27		**Second Redrawing**		
233	A26	1c green	1.60	.25
a.		Vert. pair, imperf. btwn.	35.00	35.00
234	A26	2c red	.85	.25
235	A26	5c blue	2.25	.25
236	A26	10c pale bl & blk (I) ('26)	12.00	3.00
236A	A26	10c pale bl & blk (II)	22.50	1.10
236B	A26	50c gray grn & blk ('26)	60.00	33.00
237	A26	1p org & blk ('27)	19.00	12.50
		Nos. 233-237 (7)	118.20	50.35

In the second redrawing the shield has a flat top and the design differs in many details from the stamps of 1911-13 and 1915-22.

A27

1927				
238	A27	½c lilac rose & blk	.30	.25

Exhibition Pavilion — A28

1927		**Unwmk.**	**Perf. 12**	
239	A28	2c carmine	1.10	.50
240	A28	5c ultra	2.10	.50

Natl. and West Indian Exhib. at Santiago de los Caballeros.

Ruins of Columbus' Fortress — A29

1928				
241	A29	½c lilac rose	.95	.35
242	A29	1c deep green	.70	.25
a.		Horiz. pair, imperf. btwn.	25.00	
243	A29	2c red	.95	.25
244	A29	5c dark blue	2.75	.35
245	A29	10c light blue	2.75	.30
246	A29	20c rose	4.75	.40
247	A29	50c yellow green	13.50	8.25
248	A29	1p orange yellow	35.00	27.00
		Nos. 241-248 (8)	61.35	37.15

Reprints exist of 1c, 2c and 10c.
Issued: 1c, 2c, 10c, Oct. 1; others, Dec.

Horacio Vasquez — A30

1929, May-June				
249	A30	½c dull rose	.60	.30
250	A30	1c gray green	.60	.25
251	A30	2c red	.70	.25
252	A30	5c dark ultra	1.40	.35
253	A30	10c pale blue	2.10	.50
		Nos. 249-253 (5)	5.40	1.65

Signing of the "Frontier" treaty with Haiti.
Issue dates: 2c, May; others, June.

Imperf., Pairs

249a	A30	½c	12.50
250a	A30	1c	12.50
251a	A30	2c	12.50
252a	A30	5c	14.00

Convent of San Ignacio de Loyola — A31

1930, May 1			**Perf. 11½**	
254	A31	½c red brown	.70	.45
a.		Imperf., pair	55.00	55.00
255	A31	1c deep green	.65	.25
a.		Imperf., pair	60.00	
256	A31	2c vermilion	.65	.25
257	A31	5c deep blue	2.10	.35
258	A31	10c light blue	4.25	1.25
		Nos. 254-258 (5)	8.35	2.55

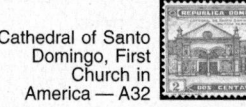

Cathedral of Santo Domingo, First Church in America — A32

1931			**Perf. 12**	
260	A32	1c deep green	.85	.25
a.		Imperf., pair	50.00	
261	A32	2c scarlet	.60	.25
a.		Imperf., pair	50.00	
262	A32	3c violet	.85	.25
263	A32	7c dark blue	2.50	.25
264	A32	8c bister	3.00	.85
265	A32	10c light blue	5.75	1.25
a.		Imperf., pair	35.00	
		Nos. 260-265 (6)	13.55	3.10

Issued: 3c-7c, Aug. 1; others, July 11.
For overprint see No. RAC8.

A33

Overprinted or Surcharged in Black

1932, Dec. 20			**Perf. 12**	
Cross in Red				
265B	A33	1c yellow green	.55	.50
265C	A33	3c on 2c violet	.80	.60
265D	A33	5c blue	4.50	4.75
265E	A33	7c on 10c pale bl	6.00	6.25
		Nos. 265B-265E (4)	11.85	12.10

Proceeds of sale given to Red Cross. Valid Dec. 20 to Jan. 5, 1933.
Inverted and pairs, one without surcharge or overprint, exist on Nos. 265B-265D, as well as missing letters.

Fernando Arturo de Merino (1833-1906) as President A35

Cathedral of Santo Domingo A36

Designs: ½c, 5c, 8c, Tomb of Merino. 1c, 3c, 10c, as Archbishop.

1933, Feb. 27		**Engr.**	**Perf. 14**	
266	A35	½c lt violet	.45	.35
267	A35	1c yellow green	.60	.25
268	A35	2c lt red	1.00	.75
269	A35	3c deep violet	.70	.30
270	A35	5c dark blue	.80	.35
271	A35	7c ultra	1.40	.50
272	A35	8c dark green	1.75	1.00
273	A35	10c orange yel	1.50	.60
274	A35	20c carmine rose	3.00	1.75
275	A36	50c lemon	11.25	7.75
276	A36	1p dark brown	26.00	19.00
		Nos. 266-276 (11)	48.45	32.60

For surcharges see Nos. G1-G7.

Tower of Homage, Ozama Fortress — A37

1932		**Litho.**	**Perf. 12**	
278	A37	1c green	1.75	.25
279	A37	3c violet	1.10	.25

Issue dates: 1c, July 2; 3c, June 22.

"CORREOS" added at left

1933, May 28				
283	A37	1c dark green	.50	.25

President Rafael L. Trujillo
A38   A39

1933, Aug. 16		**Engr.**	**Perf. 14**	
286	A38	1c yellow grn & blk	1.75	.35
287	A39	3c dp violet & blk	2.50	.35
288	A38	7c ultra & blk	5.75	.75
		Nos. 286-288 (3)	10.00	1.45

42nd birthday of President Rafael Leonidas Trujillo Molina.

San Rafael Bridge — A40

1934		**Litho.**	**Perf. 12**	
289	A40	½c redsh lil	.70	.40
290	A40	1c dp bl grn	1.00	.25
291	A40	3c violet	1.75	.25
		Nos. 289-291 (3)	3.45	.90

Opening of San Rafael Bridge.
Issue dates: ½c, 3c, Mar. 3; 1c, Feb. 17.

Trujillo Bridge — A41

1934				
292	A41	½c red brown	.70	.25
293	A41	1c dp grn	1.00	.25
294	A41	3c violet	1.40	.25
		Nos. 292-294 (3)	3.10	.75

Opening of the General Trujillo Bridge near Ciudad Trujillo.
Issue dates: 1c, Aug. 24. Others, Sept. 7.

Ramfis Bridge — A42

1935, Apr. 6				
295	A42	1c bl grn	.70	.25
296	A42	3c org brown	.70	.25
297	A42	5c dp redsh pur	2.10	1.00
298	A42	10c rose	4.25	1.40
		Nos. 295-298 (4)	7.75	2.90

Opening of the Ramfis Bridge over the Higuamo River.

President Trujillo A43

A44

A45

1935 **Perf. 11**
299 A43 3c yellow & brown .30 .25
300 A44 5c org red, bl, red & bis .40 .25
301 A45 7c ultra, bl, red & brn .60 .25
302 A44 10c red vio, bl, red & bis 1.00 1.00
Nos. 299-302 (4) 2.30 1.00

Ratification of a treaty setting the frontier between Dominican Republic and Haiti.
Issued: 3c, 10/29; 5c, 10c, 11/25; 7c, 11/8.

National Palace — A46

1935, Apr. 1 **Perf. 11½**
303 A46 25c yellow orange 3.75 .30

Obligatory for all mail addressed to the president and cabinet ministers.

Post Office, Santiago — A47

1936
304 A47 ½c bright violet .30 .35
305 A47 1c green .30 .25

Issue dates: ½c, Jan. 14; 1c, Jan. 4.

George Washington Ave., Ciudad Trujillo A48

1936, Feb. 22
306 A48 ½c brn & vio brn .40 .45
a. Imperf., pair 52.50
307 A48 2c carmine & brn .40 .30
308 A48 3c yel org & red brn .70 .25
309 A48 7c ultra, blue & brn 1.60 1.25
a. Imperf., pair 52.50
Nos. 306-309 (4) 3.10 2.25

Dedication of George Washington Avenue, Ciudad Trujillo.

José Nuñez de Cáceres A49

Felix M. del Monte A55

Proposed National Library — A56

1c, Gen. Gregorio Luperon. 2c, Emiliano Tejera. 3c, Pres. Trujillo. 5c, Jose Reyes. 7c,

---

Gen. Antonio Duverge. 25c, Francisco J. Peynado. 30c, Salome Urena. 50c, Gen. Jose M. Cabral. 1p, Manuel de Jesus Galvan. 2p, Gaston F. Deligne.

1936 Unwmk. Engr. **Perf. 13½, 14**
310 A49 ½c dull violet .40 .25
311 A49 1c dark green .30 .25
312 A49 2c carmine .30 .25
313 A49 3c violet .40 .25
314 A49 5c deep ultra .70 .30
315 A49 7c slate blue 1.25 .25
316 A55 10c orange 1.25 .30
317 A56 20c olive green 5.75 3.00
318 A55 25c gray violet 6.75 8.75
319 A55 30c scarlet 8.25 11.50
320 A55 50c black brown 9.75 6.25
321 A55 1p black 27.50 35.00
322 A55 2p yellow brown 80.00 90.00
Nos. 310-322 (13) 142.60 156.70

The funds derived from the sale of these stamps were returned to the National Treasury Fund for the erection of a building for the National Library and Archives.
Issued: 3c, 7c, Mar. 18; others, May 22.

President Trujillo and Obelisk — A62

1937, Jan. 11 **Litho.** **Perf. 11½**
323 A62 1c green .30 .25
324 A62 3c violet .40 .25
325 A62 7c blue & turq blue 1.10 1.10
Nos. 323-325 (3) 1.80 1.60

1st anniv. of naming Ciudad Trujillo.

Discus Thrower and Flag — A63

Flag in Red and Blue

1937, Aug. 14
326 A63 1c dark green 6.00 .75
327 A63 3c violet 9.00 .75
328 A63 7c dark blue 15.00 3.50
Nos. 326-328 (3) 30.00 5.00

1st Natl. Olympic Games, Aug. 16, 1937.

Symbolical of Peace, Labor and Progress — A64

1937, Sept. 18 **Perf. 12**
329 A64 3c purple .50 .25

"8th Year of the Benefactor."

Monument to Father Francisco Xavier Billini (1837-90) — A65

1937, Dec. 29
330 A65 ½c deep orange .25 .25
331 A65 5c purple .60 .25

Globe and Torch of Liberty — A66

1938, Feb. 22 **Perf. 11½**
332 A66 1c green .50 .25
333 A66 3c purple .70 .25
334 A66 10c orange 1.40 .25
Nos. 332-334 (3) 2.60 .75

150th anniv. of the Constitution of the US.

Pledge of Trinitarians, City Gate and National Flag — A67

1938, July 16 **Perf. 12**
335 A67 1c green, red & dk bl .50 .25
336 A67 3c purple, red & bl .60 .25
337 A67 10c orange, red & bl 1.25 .40
Nos. 335-337 (3) 2.35 .90

Trinitarians and patriots, Francisco Del Rosario Sanchez, Matías Ramón Mella and Juan Pablo Duarte, who helped free their country from foreign domination.

Seal of the University of Santo Domingo — A68

1938, Oct. 28
338 A68 ½c orange .40 .25
339 A68 1c dp green & lt green .40 .25
340 A68 3c purple & pale vio .40 .25
341 A68 7c dp blue & lt blue 1.00 .50
Nos. 338-341 (4) 2.30 1.25

Founding of the University of Santo Domingo, on Oct. 28, 1538.

A69

Design: Trylon and perisphere, flag and proposed Columbus lighthouse.

Flag in Blue and Red

1939, Apr. 30 **Litho.** **Perf. 12**
342 A69 ½c red org & org .35 .25
343 A69 1c green & lt green .40 .25
344 A69 3c purple & pale vio .40 .25
345 A69 10c orange & yellow 1.40 .65
Nos. 342-345,C33 (5) 4.55 2.25

New York World's Fair.

A70

1939, Sept. **Typo.**
346 A70 ½c black & pale gray .40 .25
347 A70 1c black & yel grn .50 .25
348 A70 3c black & yel brn .50 .25
349 A70 7c black & dp ultra 1.10 .90
350 A70 10c black & brt red vio 2.10 .40
Nos. 346-350 (5) 4.60 2.05

José Trujillo Valdez (1863-1935), father of President Trujillo Molina.

A71

Map of the Americas and flags of 21 American republics.

Flags in National Colors

1940, Apr. 14 **Litho.** **Perf. 11½**
351 A71 1c deep green .35 .25
352 A71 2c carmine .45 .25
353 A71 3c red violet .60 .25
354 A71 10c orange 1.25 .25
355 A71 1p chestnut 18.00 13.50
Nos. 351-355 (5) 20.65 14.50

Pan American Union, 50th anniv.

Sir Rowland Hill — A72

1940, May 6 **Perf. 12**
356 A72 3c dp mag & rose lil 3.25 .40
357 A72 7c dk blue & lt blue 6.75 1.75

Centenary of first postage stamp.

Julia Molina Trujillo — A73

1940, May 26
358 A73 1c grn, lt grn & dk grn .40 .25
359 A73 2c brt red, buff & dp rose .40 .25
360 A73 3c org, dl org & brn org .55 .25
361 A73 7c bl, pale bl & dk bl 1.10 .35
Nos. 358-361 (4) 2.45 1.10

Issued in commemoration of Mother's Day.

Map of Caribbean — A74

1940, June 6 **Perf. 11½**
362 A74 3c brt car & pale rose .50 .25
363 A74 7c dk blue & lt blue 1.00 .25
364 A74 1p yel grn & pale grn 10.00 9.00
Nos. 362-364 (3) 11.50 9.50

2nd Inter-American Caribbean Conf. held at Ciudad Trujillo, May 31 to June 6.

Marion Military Hospital — A75

1940, Dec. 24
365 A75 ½c chestnut & fawn .25 .25

Fortress, Ciudad Trujillo — A76

Statue of Columbus, Ciudad Trujillo — A77

1941
366 A76 1c dk green & lt green .25 .25
367 A77 2c brt red & rose .25 .25
368 A77 10c orange brn & buff .70 .25
Nos. 366-368 (3) 1.20 .75

Issue dates: 1c, Mar. 27; others, Apr. 7.

Sánchez, Duarte, Mella and Trujillo — A78

1941, May 16
369 A78 3c brt red lil & red vio .30 .25
370 A78 4c brt red, crim & pale rose .40 .25
371 A78 13c dk blue & lt blue .85 .35
372 A78 15c orange brn & buff 2.75 2.10
373 A78 17c lt bl, bl & pale bl 2.75 2.10
374 A78 1p org, yel brn & pale org 11.50 10.50

375 A78　2p lt gray & pale gray　25.00　10.50
　Nos. 369-375 (7)　43.55　26.05
Trujillo-Hull Treaty signed Sept. 24, 1940 and effective Apr. 1, 1941.

Bastion of February 27 — A79

1941, Oct. 20
376 A79　5c brt blue & lt blue　.50　.25

School, Torch of Knowledge, Pres. Trujillo — A80

1941
377 A80　½c chestnut & fawn　.25　.25
378 A80　1c dk green & lt green　.25　.25
　Education campaign.
　Issue dates: ½c, Dec. 12, 1c, Dec. 2.

Reserve Bank of Dominican Republic — A81

1942　　　　　　Unwmk.
379 A81　5c lt brown & buff　.50　.25
380 A81　17c dp blue & lt blue　1.00　.45
　Founding of the Reserve Bank, 10/24/41.

Representation of Transportation — A82

1942, Aug. 15
381 A82　3c dk brn, grn yel & lt bl　4.25　.50
382 A82　15c vio, grn, yel & lt bl　11.00　5.50
　Day of Posts and Telegraph, 8th anniv.

Virgin of Altagracia — A83

1942, Aug. 15
383 A83　½c gray & pale gray　1.00　.25
384 A83　1c dp grn & lt grn　2.10　.25
385 A83　3c brt red lil & lil　13.50　.25
386 A83　5c dk vio brn & vio brn　2.75　.25
387 A83　10c rose pink & pink　4.75　.25
388 A83　15c dp blue & lt blue　10.50　.30
　Nos. 383-388 (6)　34.60　1.55
　20th anniv. of the coronation of Our Lady of Altagracia.

Bananas A84　　　Cows A85

1942-43
389 A84　3c dk brn & grn ('43)　.60　.25
390 A84　4c vermilion & blk ('43)　.60　.40
391 A85　5c dp blue & cop brn　.60　.25
392 A85　15c dk pur & blue grn　1.00　.50
　Nos. 389-392 (4)　2.80　1.40
　Issue date: 5c, 15c, Aug. 18.

Emblems of Dominican and Trujillista Parties — A86

1943, Jan. 15
393 A86　3c orange　.50　.25
394 A86　4c dark red　.60　.25
395 A86　13c brt red lilac　1.40　.25
396 A86　1p lt blue　6.75　1.60
　Nos. 393-396 (4)　9.25　2.35
　Re-election of President Rafael Trujillo Molina, May 16, 1942.

Model Market, Ciudad Trujillo — A87

1944
397 A87　2c dk brown & buff　.25　.25

Bastion of Feb. 27 and National Flag — A88

1944, Feb. 27　　　　Unwmk.
Flag in Dark Blue and Carmine
398 A88　½c ocher　.25　.25
399 A88　1c yellow green　.25　.25
400 A88　2c scarlet　.25　.25
401 A88　3c brt red vio　.25　.25
402 A88　5c yellow orange　.25　.25
403 A88　7c brt blue　.25　.25
404 A88　10c orange brown　.40　.30
405 A88　20c olive green　.65　.60
406 A88　50c lt blue　1.90　1.75
　Nos. 398-406,C46-C48 (12)　7.25　6.15

Souvenir Sheet
Imperf
407 A88　Sheet of 12　110.00　110.00
　a.-l.　Single stamp　3.00　3.00
　Centenary of Independence.
No. 407 contains 1 each of Nos. 398-406 and C46-C48 with simulated perforations. Size: 141x205mm.

Battlefield and Nurse with Child — A90

1944, Aug. 1
408 A90　1c gray grn, buff & red　.25　.25
　a.　Vertical pair, imperf. btwn.　15.00
　b.　Horiz. pair, imperf. vert.　15.00
409 A90　2c dk brn, buff & red　.40　.25
410 A90　3c brt bl, buff & red　.40　.25
411 A90　10c rose car, buff & red　.80　.25
　Nos. 408-411 (4)　1.85　1.00
　80th anniv. of the Intl. Red Cross.

Municipal Building, San Cristóbal — A91

　　　　Unwmk.
1945, Jan. 10　Litho.　Perf. 12
412 A91　½c blue & lt blue　.25　.25
413 A91　1c dk green & green　.25　.25
414 A91　2c red org & org　.25　.25
415 A91　3c dk brown & brown　.25　.25
416 A91　10c ultra & gray blue　1.25　.25
　Nos. 412-416 (5)　2.25　1.25
　Centenary of the constitution.

Emblem of Communications A92

1945, Sept. 1
Center in Dark Blue and Carmine
417 A92　3c orange　.25　.25
418 A92　20c yellow green　.85　.25
419 A92　50c light blue　1.75　.70
　Nos. 417-419,C53-C56 (7)　5.00　2.20

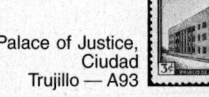

Palace of Justice, Ciudad Trujillo — A93

1946　　　　　　Perf. 11½
420 A93　3c dk red brown & buff　.25　.25

Map of Hispaniola A94

1946, Aug. 4　　　　Perf. 12
421 A94　10c multicolored　.75　.25
　Nos. 421,C62-C63 (3)　2.85　.75
　450th anniv. of the founding of Santo Domingo.

Waterfall of Jimenoa — A95

1946-47　　　Center Multicolored
422 A95　1c yellow grn ('47)　.25　.25
423 A95　2c carmine ('47)　.25　.25
424 A95　3c deep blue　.25　.25
425 A95　13c red violet ('47)　.45　.35
426 A95　20c chocolate ('47)　.80　.35
427 A95　50c orange ('47)　1.75　1.25
　Nos. 422-427,C64-C67 (10)　11.45　5.50
　Nos. 422-423, 425-427 issued Mar. 18.
For surcharge see No. 540.

Executive Palace — A96

1948, Feb. 27
428 A96　1c yellow green　.25　.25
429 A96　3c deep blue　.25　.25
　Nos. 428-429,C68-C69 (4)　8.35　3.60

Church of San Francisco Ruins — A97

1949, Apr. 13　　　Perf. 11½
430 A97　1c dk grn & pale grn　.25　.25
431 A97　3c dp bl & pale bl　.25　.25
　Nos. 430-431,C70-C73 (6)　4.30　1.90

Gen. Pedro Santana — A98

1949, Aug. 10
432 A98　3c deep blue & blue　.25　.25
　Battle of Las Carreras, cent. See No. C74.

Pigeon and Globe — A99

Center and Inscriptions in Brown
1950, Mar. 23
433 A99　1c green & pale green　.25　.25
434 A99　2c yel grn & yel　.25　.25
435 A99　5c blue & pale blue　.25　.25
436 A99　7c dk vio bl & pale bl　.40　.25
　Nos. 433-436 (4)　1.15　1.00
　75th anniv. of the UPU.

> **Catalogue values for unused stamps in this section, from this point to the end of the section, are for Never Hinged items.**

Hotel Jimani — A100

　Hotels: 1c, 2c, Hamaca. 5c, Montana. 15c, San Cristobal. 20c, Maguana.

1950-52
437 A100　½c org brn & buff　.25　.25
438 A100　1c dp grn & grn ('51)　.25　.25
439 A100　2c red org & sal ('52)　.25　.25
440 A100　5c blue & lt blue　.50　.25
441 A100　15c dp orange & yel　.75　.25
442 A100　20c lilac & rose lilac　1.40　.25
443 A100　1p brn & yel　5.75　1.90
　Nos. 437-443,C75-C76 (9)　12.90　6.15
　Issue dates: 1c, Dec. 1, 1951; 2c, Jan. 11, 1952; others, Sept. 8, 1950.
The ½c, 15c and 20c exist imperf.

Ruins of Church and Hospital of San Nicolas de Bari A101

School of Medicine A102

1950, Oct. 2
444 A101　2c dk green & rose brn　.55　.25
445 A102　5c vio blue & org brn　.70　.25
　Nos. 444-445,C77 (3)　2.25　.75
　13th Pan-American Health Conference. Nos. 444-445 and C77 exist imperf.

Queen Isabella I — A103

1951, Oct. 12
446 A103　5c dk blue & red brn　.95　.25
　500th anniversary of the birth of Queen Isabella I of Spain. Exists imperf.

Dr. Salvador B. Gautier Hospital — A104

1952, Aug.
447 A104　1c dark green　.35　.25
448 A104　2c red　.35　.25
449 A104　5c violet blue　.55　.25
　Nos. 447-449,C78-C79 (5)　5.70　4.20

Columbus Lighthouse and Flags of 21 Republics — A105

1953, Jan. 6   Engr.   Perf. 13
450	A105	2c dark green	.30	.25
451	A105	5c deep blue	.40	.25
452	A105	10c deep carmine	.70	.25

Nos. 450-452,C80-C86 (10)   6.75 4.80

Treasury Building, Ciudad Trujillo — A106

Sugar Industry, "Central Rio Haina" — A107

1953   Litho.   Perf. 11½
453	A106	½c brown	.45	.25
454	A106	2c dark blue	.45	.25
455	A107	5c blue & vio brn	.45	.25
456	A106	15c orange	1.40	.25

Nos. 453-456 (4)   2.75 1.00

For surcharge see No. 539.

José Marti — A108

1954   Perf. 12½
457	A108	10c dp blue & dk brown	.85	.25

Centenary of the birth of Jose Marti (1853-1895), Cuban patriot.

Monument to the Peace of Trujillo — A109

1954, May 25
458	A109	2c green	.50	.25
459	A109	7c blue	.50	.25
460	A109	20c orange	1.75	.25

Nos. 458-460 (3)   2.75 .75

See No. 493.

Rotary Emblem — A110

1955, Feb. 23   Perf. 12
461	A110	7c deep blue	1.00	.25

50th anniv., Rotary Intl. See No. C90.

Gen. Rafael L. Trujillo — A111

4c, Trujillo in civilian clothes. 7c, Trujillo statue. 10c, Symbols of culture & prosperity.

1955, May 16   Engr.   Perf. 13½x13
462	A111	2c red	.50	.25
463	A111	4c lt olive green	.50	.25
464	A111	7c dp blue	.65	.25
465	A111	10c brown	1.25	.25

Nos. 462-465,C91-C93 (7)   7.10 2.05

25th anniversary of the Trujillo era.

General Rafael L. Trujillo — A112

1955, Dec. 20   Unwmk.   Perf. 13
466	A112	7c deep claret	.60	.25
467	A112	10c dark blue	.80	.25

Nos. 466-467,C94 (3)   2.00 .75

Angelita Trujillo — A113

1955, Dec. 20   Litho.   Perf. 12½
468	A113	10c blue & ultra	.75	.25

Nos. 466-468 were issued to publicize the International Fair of Peace and Brotherhood in Ciudad Trujillo, Dec. 1955.

Airport — A114

1956, Apr. 6   Perf. 12½
469	A114	1c brown	.25	.25
470	A114	2c red orange	.25	.25

Nos. 469-470,C95 (3)   1.75 .75

3rd Caribbean conf. of the ICAO.

Cedar — A115

1956, Dec. 8   Perf. 11½x12
471	A115	5c car rose & grn	1.75	.25
472	A115	6c red vio & grn	2.00	.25

Nos. 471-472,C96 (3)   6.00 .75

Reforestation program.

Fair Emblem — A116

1957, Jan. 10   Perf. 12½
473	A116	7c blue, lt brn & ver	.40	.25

2nd International Livestock Show, Ciudad Trujillo, Jan. 10-20, 1957. Exists imperf.

Fanny Blankers-Koen, Netherlands — A117

Olympic Winners and Flags: 2c, Jesse Owens, US. 3c, Kee Chung Sohn, Japan. 5c, Lord Burghley, England. 7c, Bob Mathias, US.

Flags in National Colors
Engraved & Lithographed
1957, Jan. 24   Perf. 11½, Imperf.
474	A117	1c brn, lt bl, vio & mar	.30	.25
475	A117	2c dk brn, lt bl & vio	.30	.25
476	A117	3c red lilac & red	.30	.25
477	A117	5c red org & vio	.40	.25
478	A117	7c green & violet	.50	.25

Nos. 474-478,C97-C99 (8)   2.75 2.00

16th Olympic Games, Melbourne, Nov. 22-Dec. 8, 1956.
Miniature sheets of 5 exist, perf. and imperf., containing Nos. 474-478. Value, 2 sheets, perf. and imperf., $16.
For surcharges see Nos. B1-B5, B26-B30, CB1-CB3, CB16-CB18.

Lars Hall, Sweden, Pentathlon A118

Olympic Winners and Flags: 2c, Betty Cuthbert, Australia, 100 & 200 meter dash. 3c, Egil Danielsen, Norway, javelin. 5c, Alain Mimoun, France, marathon. 7c, Norman Read, New Zealand, 50 km. walk.

Perf. 13½, Imperf.
1957, July 18   Photo.   Unwmk.
Flags in National Colors
479	A118	1c brn & brt bl	.50	.25
480	A118	2c org ver & dk bl	.50	.25
481	A118	3c dark blue	.50	.25
482	A118	5c ol & dk bl	.50	.25
483	A118	7c rose brn & dk bl	.50	.30

Nos. 479-483,C100-C102 (8)   3.45 2.05

1956 Olympic winners.
Miniature sheets of 8 exist, perf. and imperf., containing Nos. 479-483 and C100-C102. The center label in these sheets is printed in two forms: Olympic gold medal or Olympic flag. Sheets measure 140x140mm. Value, 4 sheets, perf. and imperf., medal and flag, $20.
A third set of similar miniature sheets (perf. and imperf.) with center label showing an incorrect version of the Dominican Republic flag (colors transposed) was printed. These sheets are said to have been briefly sold on the first day, then withdrawn as the misprint was discovered. Value, 2 sheets, perf. & imperf., $150.
For surcharges see Nos. B6-B10, CB4-CB6.

Gerald Ouellette, Canada, Small Bore Rifle, Prone — A119

Ron Delaney, Ireland, 1,500 Meter Run A120

Olympic Winners and Flags: 3c, Tenley Albright, US, figure skating. 5c, Joaquin Capilla, Mexico, platform diving. 7c, Ercole Baldini, Italy, individual road race (cycling).

Engraved and Lithographed
1957, Nov. 12   Perf. 13½, Imperf.
Flags in National Colors
484	A119	1c red brown	.30	.25
485	A120	2c gray brown	.30	.25
486	A119	3c violet	.30	.25
487	A120	5c red orange	.30	.25
488	A119	7c Prus green	.30	.25

Nos. 484-488,C103-C105 (8)   2.55 2.00

1956 Olympic winners.
Miniature sheets of 5 exist, perf. and imperf., containing Nos. 484-488. Value, 2 sheets, perf. and imperf., $5.50.
For surcharges see Nos. B11-B20, CB7-CB12.

Mahogany Flower — A121

1957-58   Litho.   Perf. 12½
489	A121	2c bl grn & red brn	.30	.25

Perf. 12
490	A121	4c brt mauve & ver ('58)	.30	.25
491	A121	7c blue & gray grn	.40	.25
492	A121	25c brown & org ('58)	1.20	.35

Nos. 489-492 (4)   2.20 1.10

Sizes: No. 489, 25x29¼mm; Nos. 490-492, 24x28¾mm. In 1959, the 2c was reissued in size 24¼x28½mm with slightly different tones of green and maroon.
Issued: 2c, 10/24; 7c, 11/6; 4c, 25c, 4/7/58.
For surcharges see Nos. 537-538.

Type of 1954, Redrawn
Perf. 12x11½
1957, June 12   Unwmk.
493	A109	7c bright blue	.75	.25

On No. 493 the cent symbol is smaller, the shading of the sky and steps stronger and the letters in "Correos" shorter and bolder.

Cervantes, Globe, Book — A122

1958, Apr. 23   Litho.   Perf. 12½
494	A122	4c yellow green	.45	.25
495	A122	7c red lilac	.45	.25
496	A122	10c lt olive brown	.75	.25

Nos. 494-496 (3)   1.65 .75

4th Book Fair, Apr. 23-28. Exist imperf.

Gen. Rafael L. Trujillo — A123

1958, Aug. 16   Perf. 12
497	A123	2c red lilac & yel	.35	.25
498	A123	4c green & yel	.35	.25
499	A123	7c brown & yel	.35	.25
a.		Souv. sheet of 3, #497-499, imperf.	1.25	.80

Nos. 497-499 (3)   1.05 .75

25th anniv. of Gen. Trujillo's designation as "Benefactor of his country."

S. S. Rhadames — A124

1958, Oct. 27   Perf. 12½
500	A124	7c bright blue	1.50	.30

Day of the Dominican Merchant Marine. Exists imperf.

Shozo Sasahara, Japan, Featherweight Wrestling — A125

Olympic Winners and Flags: 1c, Gillian Sheen, England, fencing, vert. 2c, Milton Campbell, US, decathlon, vert. 5c, Madeleine Berthod, Switzerland, downhill skiing. 7c, Murray Rose, Australia, 400 & 1,500 meter freestyle.

Perf. 13½, Imperf.

1958, Oct. 30   Photo.

Flags in National Colors

501 A125	1c rose, ind & ultra	.40	.25
502 A125	2c brown & blue	.40	.25
503 A125	3c gray, vio, blk & buff	.40	.25
504 A125	5c rose, dk bl, brn & red	.40	.25
505 A125	7c lt brn, dk bl & red	.40	.25
Nos. 501-505,C106-C108 (8)		3.10	2.00

1956 Olympic winners.

Miniature sheets of 5 exist, perf. and imperf. containing Nos. 501-505. Value, 2 sheets, perf. and imperf., $5.

For surcharges see Nos. B21-B25, CB13-CB15.

Globe and Symbolic Fire — A126

1958, Nov. 3   Litho.   *Perf. 11½*

506 A126   7c blue & dp carmine   .50   .25

UNESCO Headquarters in Paris opening, Nov. 3.

Dominican Republic Pavilion, Brussels Fair — A127

1958, Dec. 9   Unwmk.   *Perf. 12½*

507 A127   7c blue green   .30   .25
    Nos. 507,C109-C110 (3)   1.45   .90

Universal & Intl. Exposition at Brussels.

Gen. Trujillo Placing Wreath on Altar of the Nation — A128

1959, July 10   *Perf. 12*

508 A128   9c brn, grn, red & gold   .45   .25
  a.   Souv. sheet of 1, imperf.   1.25   .75

29th anniversary of the Trujillo regime.

Lt. Leonidas Rhadames Trujillo, Team Captain A129   Jamaican Polo Team A130

Design: 10c, Lt. Trujillo on polo pony.

1959, May 15

509 A129	2c violet	.25	.25
510 A130	7c yellow brown	.50	.25
511 A130	10c green	.60	.25
Nos. 509-511,C111 (4)		1.75	1.05

Jamaica-Dominican Republic polo match at Ciudad Trujillo.

Symbolical of Census — A131

1959, Aug. 15   Litho.   *Perf. 12½*

Flag in Ultramarine and Red

512 A131	1c blue & black	.30	.25
513 A131	9c green & black	.50	.25
514 A131	13c orange & black	.60	.30
Nos. 512-514 (3)		1.40	.80

Issued to publicize the 1960 census.

Trujillo Stadium A132

1959, Aug. 27

515 A132   9c green & gray   .60   .25

Issued to publicize the 3rd Pan American Games, Chicago, Aug. 27-Sept. 7.

Charles V — A133

1959, Oct. 12   Unwmk.   *Perf. 12*

516 A133   5c bright pink   .40   .25
517 A133   9c violet blue   .60   .25

400th anniv. of the death of Charles V (1500-1558), Holy Roman Emperor.

Rhadames Bridge — A134

1c and No. 520, Different view of bridge.

1959-60   Litho.   *Perf. 12*

518 A134	1c green & gray ('60)	.40	.25
519 A134	2c ultra & gray	.40	.25
520 A134	2c red & gray ('60)	.40	.25
521 A134	5c brn & dull red brn	.40	.25
Nos. 518-521 (4)		1.60	1.00

Issued: No. 519, 10/22; 5c, 11/30; 1c, No. 520, 2/6.
For surcharge see No. 536.

Sosua Refugee Settlement and WRY Emblem — A135

1960, Apr. 7   *Perf. 12½*

Center in Gray

522 A135	5c red brn & yel grn	.25	.25
523 A135	9c carmine & lt blue	.25	.25
524 A135	13c orange & green	.50	.25
Nos. 522-524,C113-C114 (5)		2.55	1.35

World Refugee Year, 7/1/59-6/30/60.
For surcharges see Nos. B31-B33.

Sholam Takhti, Iran, Lightweight Wrestling A136

Olympic Winners: 2c, Masaru Furukawa, Japan, 200 meter breast stroke. 3c, Mildred McDaniel, US, high jump. 5c, Terence Spinks, England, featherweight boxing. 7c, Carlo Pavesi, Italy, fencing.

Perf. 13½, Imperf.

1960, Sept. 14   Photo.

Flags in National Colors

525 A136	1c red, yel grn & blk	.35	.25
526 A136	2c org, grnsh bl & brn	.35	.25
527 A136	3c henna brn & bl	.35	.25
528 A136	5c brown & ultra	.35	.25
529 A136	7c grn, bl & rose brn	.35	.25
Nos. 525-529,C115-C117 (8)		2.80	2.20

17th Olympic Games, Rome, 8/25-9/11.
Miniature sheets of 5 exist, perf. and imperf., containing Nos. 525-529. Value, 2 sheets, perf. & imperf., $5.
For surcharges see Nos. B34-B38, CB21-CB23.

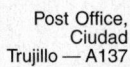
Post Office, Ciudad Trujillo — A137

1960, Aug. 26   Litho.   *Perf. 11½x12*

530 A137   2c ultra & gray   .30   .25

Exists imperf.

Cattle — A138

1960, Aug. 30

531 A138   9c carmine & gray   .30   .25

Issued to publicize the Agricultural and Industrial Fair, San Juan de la Maguana.

Nos. 518, 490-491, 453, 427 Surcharged in Red, Black or Blue

1960-61   *Perf. 12*

536 A134	2c on 1c grn & gray (R)	.30	.25
537 A121	9c on 4c lilac & rose (R)	.60	.25
a.	Inverted surcharge	21.00	
538 A121	9c on 7c ultra & gray grn (R)	.60	.25
539 A106	36c on ½c brown	1.90	1.75
a.	Inverted surcharge	18.00	
540 A95	1p on 50c multi (Bl)	4.25	3.25
Nos. 536-540 (5)		7.65	5.75

Issue dates: No. 536, Dec. 30, 1960; No. 537, Dec. 20, 1960; others, Feb. 4, 1961.

Trujillo Memorial — A139

1961   Unwmk.   *Perf. 11½*

548 A139	1c brown	.30	.25
549 A139	2c green	.30	.25
550 A139	4c rose lilac	.50	.30
551 A139	5c light blue	.60	.25
552 A139	9c red orange	.50	.25
Nos. 548-552 (5)		2.20	1.30

Gen. Rafael L. Trujillo (1891-1961).
Issued: 2c, 8/7; 4c, 10/24; others 8/30.

Coffee, Cacao — A140

1961, Dec. 30   Litho.   *Perf. 12½*

553 A140	1c blue green	.35	.25
554 A140	2c orange brown	.35	.25
555 A140	4c violet	.35	.25
556 A140	5c blue	.35	.25
557 A140	9c gray	.45	.25
Nos. 553-557,C118-C119 (7)		3.00	2.25

Nos. 553-557 exist imperf.

Dagger Pointing at Mosquito — A141

1962, Apr. 29   Photo.   *Perf. 12*

558 A141	10c brt pink & red lilac	.30	.25
559 A141	20c pale brn & brn	.60	.30
560 A141	25c pale grn & yel grn	.85	.40
Nos. 558-560,B39-B40,C120-C121 (9)		6.05	3.75

WHO drive to eradicate malaria.

Broken Fetters and Laurel A142   "Justice," Map of Dominican Republic A143

Design: 20c, Flag, torch and inscription.

1962, May 30   Litho.   *Perf. 12½*

561 A142	1c grn, yel, ultra & red	.25	.25
562 A143	9c bister ultra & red	.40	.25
563 A142	20c lt blue, ultra & red	.85	.25
a.	Souvenir sheet of 3, #561-563	1.90	1.90
564 A143	1p lilac, ultra & red	4.50	2.50
Nos. 561-564,C122-C123 (6)		7.80	4.55

1st anniv. of end of Trujillo era. Nos. 561-564 exist imperf.

Farm, Factory and Flag — A144

1962, May 22

565 A144	1c ultra, red & green	.30	.25
566 A144	2c ultra & red	.30	.25
567 A144	3c ultra, red & brown	.30	.25
568 A144	5c ultra, red & blue	.30	.25
569 A144	15c ultra, red & orange	.40	.30
Nos. 565-569 (5)		1.60	1.30

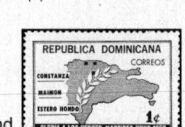
Map and Laurel — A145

1962, June 14   Litho.

570 A145   1c black   .45   .25

Honoring the martyrs of June 1959 revolution.

Western Hemisphere and Carrier Pigeon — A146

1962, Oct. 23   Unwmk.   *Perf. 12½*

571 A146	2c rose red	.30	.25
572 A146	9c orange	.30	.25
573 A146	14c blue green	.60	.25
Nos. 571-573,C124-C125 (5)		2.25	1.50

50th anniv. of the founding of the Postal Union of the Americas and Spain, UPAE.

Archbishop Adolfo Alejandro Nouel — A147

1962, Dec. 18

574 A147	2c bl grn & dull bl	.30	.25
575 A147	9c orange & red brn	.35	.25
576 A147	13c maroon & vio brn	.45	.25
Nos. 574-576,C126-C127 (5)		2.30	1.50

Cent. of the birth of Archbishop Adolfo Alejandro Nouel, President of Dominican Republic in 1911.

Globe, Banner and Emblems — A148

1963, Apr. 15   Unwmk.   Perf. 11½
Banner in Dark Blue & Red

577	A148	2c green	.30	.25
578	A148	5c brt rose lilac	.30	.25
579	A148	9c orange	.60	.25
		Nos. 577-579,B41-B43 (6)	2.25	1.50

FAO "Freedom from Hunger" campaign.

Juan Pablo
Duarte — A149

1963, July 7   Litho.   Perf. 12x11½

580	A149	2c shown	.30	.25
581	A149	7c Francisco Sanchez	.35	.25
582	A149	9c Ramon Mella	.45	.25
		Nos. 580-582 (3)	1.10	.75

120th anniv. of separation from Haiti. See No. C128.

Ulises F. Espaillat, Benigno F. de Rojas and Pedro F. Bono — A150

Designs: 4c, Generals Santiago Rodriguez, Jose Cabrera and Benito Moncion. 5c, Capotillo monument. 9c, Generals Gaspar Polanco, Gregorio Luperon and Jose A. Salcedo.

1963, Aug. 16   Unwmk.   Perf. 11½

583	A150	2c green	.30	.25
584	A150	4c red orange	.30	.25
585	A150	5c brown	.75	.25
586	A150	9c bright blue	.35	.25
a.		Souvenir sheet of 4	1.20	1.00
		Nos. 583-586 (4)	1.70	1.00

Cent. of the Restoration. No. 586a contains 4 imperf. stamps similar to Nos. 583-586.

Patient and
Nurse — A151

1963, Oct. 25   Unwmk.   Perf. 12½

587	A151	3c gray & carmine	.35	.25
588	A151	6c emerald & red	.35	.25
		Nos. 587-588,C129 (3)	1.15	.75

Centenary of International Red Cross. Nos. 587-588 exist imperf. Value, set of pairs $18. See No. C129.

Scales, Globe, UNESCO
Emblem — A152

1963, Dec. 10   Litho.

589	A152	6c pink & deep pink	.30	.25
590	A152	50c lt green & green	.85	.85
		Nos. 589-590,C130-C131 (4)	1.75	1.60

Universal Declaration of Human Rights, 15th anniv. Nos. 589-590 exist imperf.

Ramses II Battling the Hittites (from Abu Simbel) A153

Design: 6c, Two heads of Ramses II.

1964, Mar. 8   Unwmk.   Perf. 12½

591	A153	3c pale pink & ver	.30	.25
592	A153	6c pale blue & ultra	.30	.25
593	A153	9c pale rose & red brn	.30	.25
		Nos. 591-593,C132-C133 (5)	1.50	1.25

UNESCO world campaign to save historic monuments in Nubia.
For surcharges see Nos. B44-B46.

Maximo Gomez — A154

1964, Apr. 30   Litho.

594	A154	2c lt blue & blue	.30	.25
595	A154	6c dull pink & dull claret	.30	.25

Bicent. of the founding of the town of Bani.

Palm Chat — A155

Design: 6c, Hispaniolan parrot.

Size: 27x37½mm

1964, June 8   Unwmk.   Perf. 12½

596	A155	3c ultra, brn & yel	2.50	.25
597	A155	6c gray & multi	3.25	.25
		Nos. 596-597,C134 (3)	11.50	.75

See Nos. 602-604.

Rocket Leaving Earth — A156

Designs: 1c, Launching of rocket, vert. 3c, Space capsule orbiting earth. 6c, As 2c.

1964, July 28   Litho.

598	A156	1c sky blue	.30	.25
599	A156	2c emerald	.30	.25
600	A156	3c blue	.30	.25
601	A156	6c sky blue	.40	.25
		Nos. 598-601,C135-C136 (6)	2.00	1.55

Conquest of space.

Bird Type of 1964

Designs: 1c, Narrow-billed tody. 2c, Hispaniolan emerald hummingbird. 6c, Hispaniolan trogon.

1964, Nov. 7   Perf. 11½
Size: 26x37mm
Birds in Natural Colors

602	A155	1c bright pink	2.50	.25
603	A155	2c dark brown	2.50	.25
604	A155	6c blue	4.25	.25
		Nos. 602-604 (3)	9.25	.75

Universal Postal Union and United Nations Emblems A157

1964, Dec. 5   Litho.   Perf. 12½

605	A157	1c red	.35	.25
606	A157	4c green	.35	.25
607	A157	5c orange	.35	.25
		Nos. 605-607,C138 (4)	1.40	1.00

15th UPU Cong., Vienna, May-June 1964.

International Cooperation Year Emblem — A158

1965, Feb. 16   Unwmk.   Perf. 12½

608	A158	2c lt blue & ultra	.35	.25
609	A158	3c emerald & dk grn	.35	.25
610	A158	6c salmon pink & red	.35	.25
		Nos. 608-610,C139 (4)	1.50	1.05

UN Intl. Cooperation Year.

Virgin of Altagracia — A159

Design: 2c, Hands holding lily.

1965, Mar. 18   Unwmk.   Perf. 12½

611	A159	2c grn, emer & dp rose	.35	.25
612	A159	6c multicolored	.45	.25
		Nos. 611-612,C140 (3)	1.30	.75

4th Mariological Cong. and 11th Intl. Marian Cong. No. 612 exists imperf.

Flags of 21 American Nations — A160

1965, Apr. 14   Litho.   Perf. 11½

613	A160	2c brown, yel & multi	.30	.25
614	A160	6c red lilac & multi	.50	.25

Organization of American States.

Stamp of 1865 (No. 1) — A161

1965, Dec. 28   Litho.   Perf. 12½

615	A161	1c pink, buff & blk	.35	.25
616	A161	2c blue, buff & blk	.35	.25
617	A161	6c emerald, buff & blk	.35	.25
a.		Souvenir sheet of 2	1.20	1.10
		Nos. 615-617,C142-C143 (5)	1.85	1.30

Cent. of 1st Dominican postage stamps. No. 617a shows replicas of Nos. 1-2. Sold for 50c.

WHO Headquarters, Geneva — A162

1966, May 21   Litho.   Perf. 12½

618	A162	6c blue	.30	.25
619	A162	10c red lilac	.50	.25

New WHO Headquarters, Geneva.

Man Holding Map of Republic — A163

1966, May 23

620	A163	2c black & brt green	.30	.25
621	A163	6c black & dp orange	.50	.25

General elections, June 1, 1966.

Ascia Monuste — A164

1966   Litho.   Perf. 12½
Various Butterflies in Natural Colors
Size: 31x21mm

622	A164	1c blue & vio bl	1.50	.25
623	A164	2c lt grn & brt grn	1.50	.25
624	A164	3c lt gray & gray	2.00	.25
625	A164	6c pink & magenta	2.25	1.00
626	A164	8c buff & brown	4.00	1.40
		Nos. 622-626,C146-C148 (8)	41.50	7.90

Issued: 1c, 9/7; 3c, 9/11; others, 11/8.

For surcharges see Nos. B47-B51, CB28-CB30.

Natl. Altar — A165

1967, Jan. 18   Litho.   Perf. 11½

627	A165	1c bright blue	.30	.25
628	A165	2c carmine rose	.30	.25
629	A165	3c emerald	.30	.25
630	A165	4c gray	.30	.25
631	A165	5c orange yellow	.30	.25
632	A165	6c orange	.30	.25
		Nos. 627-632,C149-C151 (9)	2.95	2.30

Map of Republic and Emblem — A166

1967, Mar. 30   Litho.   Perf. 12½

633	A166	2c yellow, blue & blk	.30	.25
634	A166	6c orange, blue & blk	.30	.25
635	A166	10c emerald, blue & blk	.85	.45
		Nos. 633-635 (3)	1.45	.95

Development Year, 1967.

Rook and Knight — A167

1967, June 23   Litho.   Perf. 12½

636	A167	25c multicolored	3.00	.50

5th Central American Chess Championships, Santo Domingo. See Nos. C152-C152a.

Alliance for Progress — A168

1967, Sept. 16   Litho.   Perf. 12½

637	A168	1c bright green	.35	.25
		Nos. 637,C153-C154 (3)	1.45	.85

6th anniv. of the Alliance for Progress.

Institute Emblem — A169

1967, Oct. 7

638	A169	3c bright green	.35	.25
639	A169	6c salmon pink	.35	.25
		Nos. 638-639,C155 (3)	1.45	.80

25th anniversary of the Inter-American Agriculture Institute.

Globe and Satellite A170

1968, June 15   Typo.   Perf. 12

640	A170	6c black & multi	.35	.25
		Nos. 640,C156-C157 (3)	1.20	.80

World Meteorological Day, Mar. 23.

Boxers — A171

1968, June 29
641 A171 6c rose red & dp claret   .35   .25
    Nos. 641,C158-C159 (3)   1.70   .75

Fight between Carlos Ortiz, Puerto Rico, and Teo Cruz, Dominican Republic, for the World Lightweight Boxing Championship.

Lions Emblem — A172

1968, Aug. 9   Litho.   Perf. 11½
642 A172 6c brown & multi   .30   .25

Lions Intl., 50th anniv. (in 1967). See No. C160.

Wrestling and Olympic Emblem — A173

1968, Nov. 12   Litho.   Perf. 11½
643 A173 1c shown   .30   .25
644 A173 6c Running   .35   .25
645 A173 25c Boxing   1.25   .40
    Nos. 643-645,C161-C162 (5)   3.50   1.90

19th Olympic Games, Mexico City, 10/12-27.

Map of Americas and House — A174

1969, Jan. 25   Litho.   Perf. 12½
646 A174 6c brt bl, lt bl & grn   .35   .25

7th Inter-American Conference for Savings and Loans, Santo Domingo, Jan. 25-31. See No. C163.

Stool in Human Form — A175

Taino Art: 2c, Wood carved mother figure, vert. 3c, Face carved on 3-cornered stone. 4c, Stone hatchet, vert. 5c, Clay pot.

1969, Jan. 31   Litho.   Perf. 12½
647 A175 1c yellow, org & blk   .40   .25
648 A175 2c lt grn, grn & blk   .40   .25
649 A175 3c citron, ol & brt grn   .40   .25
650 A175 4c lt lil, lil & brt grn   .40   .25
651 A175 5c yellow, org & brn   .40   .25
    Nos. 647-651,C164-C166 (8)   3.50   2.05

Taino art flourished in the West Indies at the time of Columbus.

Community Day Emblem — A176

1969, Mar. 25   Litho.   Perf. 12½
652 A176 6c dull green & gold   .30   .25

Community Development Day, Mar. 22.

COTAL Emblem A177

Headquarters Building and COTAL Emblem A178

Design: 2c, Boy and COTAL emblem.

1969, May 25   Litho.   Perf. 12½
653 A177 1c lt & dk blue & red   .40   .25
654 A177 2c emerald & dk grn   .40   .25
655 A178 6c vermilion & pink   .40   .25
    Nos. 653-655,C167 (4)   1.60   1.00

12th Congress of the Confederation of Latin American Tourist Organizations (COTAL), Santo Domingo, May 25-29.

ILO Emblem — A179

1969, June 27   Litho.   Perf. 12½
656 A179 6c lt grnsh bl, grnsh bl
     & blk   .40   .25

50th anniv. of the ILO. See No. C168.

Sliding into Base — A180

Designs: 1c, Catching a fly ball. 2c, View of Cibao Stadium, horiz.

Size: 21x31mm (1c, 3c); 43x30mm (2c)

1969, Aug. 15   Litho.   Perf. 12½
657 A180 1c green & gray   .35   .25
658 A180 2c green & lt green   .35   .25
659 A180 3c purple & red brown   .35   .25
    Nos. 657-659,C169-C171 (6)   7.30   4.85

17th World Amateur Baseball Championships, Santo Domingo.

Las Damas Dam — A181

Tavera Dam — A182

Designs: 2c, Las Damas hydroelectric station, vert. 6c, Arroyo Hondo substation.

1969   Litho.   Perf. 12
660 A181 2c green & multi   .35   .25
661 A181 3c dk blue & multi   .35   .25
662 A181 6c brt rose lilac   .35   .25
663 A182 6c multicolored   .60   .25
    Nos. 660-663,C172-C173 (6)   2.70   1.50

National electrification plan.
Issued: Nos. 660-662, Sept. 15; No. 663, Oct. 15.

Juan Pablo Duarte — A183

1970, Jan. 26   Litho.   Perf. 12
664 A183 1c emerald & dk grn   .35   .25
665 A183 2c sal pink & dp car   .35   .25
666 A183 3c brt pink & plum   .35   .25
667 A183 6c blue & violet blue   .35   .25
    Nos. 664-667,C174 (5)   2.15   1.25

Issued for Duarte Day in memory of Juan Pablo Duarte (1813-1876), liberator.

Map of Republic, People, Census Emblem — A184

Design: 6c, Census emblem and inscription.

1970, Feb. 6   Perf. 11
668 A184 5c emerald & blk   .35   .25
669 A184 6c ultra & blue   .35   .25
    Nos. 668-669,C175 (3)   1.45   .75

Census of 1970.

Abelardo Rodriguez Urdaneta A185

"One of Many" A186

1970, Feb. 20   Litho.   Perf. 12½
670 A185 3c ultramarine   .35   .25
671 A186 6c green & yel grn   .35   .25
    Nos. 670-671,C176 (3)   1.25   .75

Issued to honor Abelardo Rodriguez Urdaneta, sculptor.

Masonic Symbols — A187

1970, Mar. 2
672 A187 6c green   .30   .25

8th Inter-American Masonic Conference, Santo Domingo, Mar. 1-7. See No. C177.

Communications Satellite — A188

1970, May 25   Litho.   Perf. 12½
673 A188 20c olive & gray   .80   .30

World Telecommunications Day. See No. C178.

UPU Headquarters, Bern — A189

1970, June 5   Perf. 11
674 A189 6c gray & brown   .40   .25

Inauguration of the new UPU headquarters in Bern. See No. C179.

Education Year Emblem — A190

1970, June 26   Litho.   Perf. 12½
675 A190 4c rose lilac   .40   .25

Issued for International Education Year, 1970. See No. C180.

Pedro Alejandrino Pina — A191

1970, Aug. 24   Litho.   Perf. 12½
676 A191 6c lt red brn & blk   .40   .25

Pedro Alejandrino Pina (1820-70), author.

Children Reading — A192

1970, Oct. 12   Litho.   Perf. 12½
677 A192 5c dull green   .40   .25
    Nos. 677,C181-C182 (3)   1.25   .75

1st World Exhibition of Books and Culture Festival, Santo Domingo, Oct. 11-Dec. 11.

Virgin of Altagracia — A193

1971, Jan. 20   Litho.   Perf. 12½
678 A193 3c multicolored   .45   .25

Inauguration of the Basilica of Our Lady of Altagracia. See No. C184.

Rodriguez Objio — A194

1971, June 18   Litho.   Perf. 11
679 A194 6c light blue   .45   .25

Manuel Rodriguez Objio (1838-1871), poet.

Boxing and Canoeing — A195

1971, Sept. 10   Litho.
680 A195 2c shown   .30   .25
681 A195 5c Basketball   .30   .25
    Nos. 680-681,C186 (3)   1.00   .75

2nd National Games.

Goat and Fruit — A196

Designs: 2c, Cow and goose. 3c, Cacao and horse. 6c, Bananas, coffee and pig.

1971, Sept. 29   **Perf. 12½**
682 A196 1c brown & multi .40 .25
683 A196 2c plum & multi .40 .25
684 A196 3c green & multi .40 .25
685 A196 6c blue & multi .40 .25
    Nos. 682-685,C187 (5) 3.60 1.35
6th Natl. agriculture and livestock census.

José Nuñez de Cáceres — A197

1971, Dec. 1   **Perf. 11**
686 A197 6c lt bl, lil & dk bl .45 .25
Sesquicentennial of first national independence. See No. C188.

Shepherds and Star — A198

1971, Dec. 10   **Perf. 12½**
687 A198 6c blue, brown & yel .45 .25
Christmas 1971. See No. C189.

UNICEF Emblem, Child on Beach — A199

1971, Dec. 14   **Litho.**   **Perf. 11**
688 A199 6c gray blue & multi .30 .25
UNICEF, 25th anniv. See No. C190.

Book Year Emblem — A200

1972, Jan. 25   **Perf. 12½**
689 A200 1c green, ultra & red .30 .25
690 A200 2c brown, ultra & red .30 .25
    Nos. 689-690,C191 (3) 1.35 .80
Intl. Book Year 1972.

Taino Mask — A201

4c, Ladle and amulet. 6c, Human figure.

1972, May 10   **Litho.**   **Perf. 11**
691 A201 2c pink & multi .50 .25
692 A201 4c black, bl & ocher .50 .25
693 A201 6c gray & multi .50 .25
    Nos. 691-693,C194-C196 (6) 4.20 1.70
Taino art. See note after No. 651.

Globe — A202

1972, May 17   **Perf. 12½**
694 A202 6c blue & multi .35 .25
4th World Telecommunications Day. See No. C197.

"1972," Stamps and Map of Dominican Republic — A203

1972, June 3
695 A203 2c green & multi .30 .25
First National Philatelic Exhibition, Santo Domingo, June 3-17. See No. C198.

Basketball — A204

1972, Aug. 25   **Litho.**   **Perf. 12½**
696 A204 2c blue & multi .30 .25
20th Olympic Games, Munich, Aug. 26-Sept. 11. See No. C199.

Club Emblem — A205

1972, Sept. 29   **Litho.**   **Perf. 10½**
697 A205 1c lt green & multi .30 .25
50th anniversary of the Club Activo 20-30 International. See No. C200.

Emilio A. Morel — A206

1972, Oct. 20   **Perf. 12½**
698 A206 6c brt pink & multi .30 .25
Emilio A. Morel (1884-1958), poet and journalist. See No. C201.

Central Bank Building A207

1972, Oct. 23
699 A207 1c shown .30 .25
700 A207 5c 1-peso note .30 .25
    Nos. 699-700,C202 (3) 1.85 1.05
25th anniv. of Central Bank.

Holy Family A208

Poinsettia A209

1972, Nov. 21
701 A208 2c rose lil, pur & gold .30 .25
702 A209 6c red & multi .30 .25
    Nos. 701-702,C203 (3) 1.55 .75
Christmas 1972.

Mail Box and Student — A210

1972, Dec. 15
703 A210 2c rose red .30 .25
704 A210 6c blue .30 .25
705 A210 10c emerald .50 .25
    Nos. 703-705 (3) 1.10 .75
Publicity for correspondence schools.

Tavera Dam — A211

1973, Feb. 26   **Litho.**   **Perf. 12½**
706 A211 10c multicolored .45 .25
Inauguration of the Tavera Dam.

Various Sports A212

Designs: a, UL. b, UR. c, LL. d, LR.

1973, Mar. 30   **Perf. 13½x13**
707 A212   Block of 4 1.00 1.00
  a.-d.   2c, any single .30 .25
708 A212   Block of 4 5.50 5.50
  a.-d.   25c, any single 1.00 .35
    Nos. 707-708,C204-C205 (4) 11.00 11.00
12th Central American and Caribbean Games, Santo Domingo, Summer 1974.

Christ Carrying the Cross — A213

6c, Belfry of Church of Our Lady of Carmen.

1973, Apr. 18   **Litho.**   **Perf. 10½**
709 A213 2c multicolored .30 .25
710 A213 6c multicolored, vert. .30 .25
    Nos. 709-710,C206 (3) 1.35 .75
Holy Week, 1973.

WMO Emblem, Weather Satellite, "Weather" — A214

1973, Aug. 10   **Litho.**   **Perf. 13½x13**
711 A214 6c magenta & multi .35 .25
Centenary of international meteorological cooperation. See No. C208.

Mask, Cibao — A215

1973, Oct. 12   **Litho.**   **Perf. 10½**
712 A215 1c Maguey drum, horiz .40 .25
713 A215 2c Carved amber, horiz .40 .25
714 A215 4c shown .40 .25
715 A215 6c Pottery .40 .25
    Nos. 712-715,C210-C211 (6) 3.35 1.50
Opening of Museum of Mankind in Santo Domingo.

Nativity — A216

Christmas: 6c, Stained glass window, vert.

Perf. 13½x13, 13x13½
1973, Nov. 26
716 A216 2c black, bl & yel .35 .25
717 A216 6c rose & multi .35 .25
    Nos. 716-717,C212 (3) 1.20 .75
No. 717 exists imperf.

Dominican Scout Emblem — A217

Design: 5c, Scouts and flag.

1973, Dec. 7   **Litho.**   **Perf. 12**
    Size: 35x35mm
718 A217 1c ultra & multi .35 .25
    Size: 26x36mm
719 A217 5c black & multi .35 .25
    Nos. 718-719,C213 (3) 1.95 1.25
Dominican Republic Boy Scouts, 50th anniv.

Sports Palace, Basketball Players — A218

Design: 6c, Bicyclist and race track.

1974, Feb. 25   **Litho.**   **Perf. 13½**
720 A218 2c red brown & multi .30 .25
721 A218 6c yellow & multi .30 .25
    Nos. 720-721,C214-C215 (4) 2.00 1.00
12th Central American and Caribbean Games, Santo Domingo, 1974.

Bell Tower, Cathedral of Santo Domingo A219

Mater Dolorosa A220

1974, June 27   **Litho.**   **Perf. 13½**
722 A219 2c multicolored .30 .25
723 A220 6c multicolored .40 .25
    Nos. 722-723,C216 (3) 1.35 .75
Holy Week 1974.

Francisco del Rosario Sanchez Bridge — A221

1974, July 12   **Perf. 12**
724 A221 6c multicolored .45 .25
See No. C217.

Map, Emblem and Patient A222

Design: 5c, Map of Dominican Republic, diabetics' emblem and pancreas.

1974, Aug. 22   Litho.   Perf. 13
725 A222 4c blue & multi   .30   .25
726 A222 5c yellow grn & multi   .30   .25
      Nos. 725-726,C218-C219 (4)   3.05   1.50
           Fight against diabetes.

Train and UPU
Emblem — A223

Design: 6c, Mail coach and UPU emblem.

1974, Oct. 9   Litho.   Perf. 13½
727 A223 2c blue & multi   .60   .60
728 A223 6c brown & multi   .45   .25
      Nos. 727-728,C220-C221 (4)   5.55   1.95
              Cent. of UPU.

Golfers — A224

Design: 2c, Championship emblem and
badge of Dominican Golf Association, horiz.

1974, Oct. 24   Perf. 13x13½, 13½x13
729 A224 2c yellow & blk   1.00   .25
730 A224 6c blue & multi   1.25   .25
      Nos. 729-730,C222-C223 (4)   3.55   1.15
      World Amateur Golf Championships.

Christmas   Virgin and
Decorations   Child
A225   A226

1974, Dec. 3   Litho.   Perf. 12
731 A225 2c multicolored   .30   .25
732 A226 6c multicolored   .40   .25
      Nos. 731-732,C224 (3)   1.20   .75
              Christmas 1974.

Tomatoes,
FAO Emblem
A227

1974, Dec. 5
733 A227 2c shown   1.00   .25
734 A227 3c Avocados   1.00   .25
735 A227 5c Coconuts   1.00   .25
      Nos. 733-735,C225 (4)   4.75   1.00
      World Food Program, 10th anniv.

Dr. Fernando A. Defillo
(1874-1949),
Physician — A228

1975, Feb. 14   Litho.   Perf. 13½x13
736 A228 1c dull brown   .40   .25
737 A228 6c dull green   .40   .25

Tower, Our Lady of the
Rosary Convent — A229

Design: 2c, Jesus saying "I am the Resurrection and the Life."

1975, Mar. 26   Litho.   Perf. 13½
738 A229 2c brown & multi   .30   .25
739 A229 6c multicolored   .30   .25
      Nos. 738-739,C226 (3)   1.25   .75
              Holy Week 1975.

Hands (Steel
Beams) with
Symbols of
Agriculture,
Industry — A230

1975, May 19   Litho.   Perf. 10½x10
740 A230 6c dull blue & multi   .35   .25
16th Assembly of the Governors of the International Development Bank, Santo Domingo,
May 1975. See No. C228.

Satellite Tracking
Station — A231

1975, June 21   Litho.   Perf. 13½
741 A231 5c multicolored   .30   .25
Opening of first earth satellite tracking station in Dominican Republic. See No. C229.

Apollo — A232

1975, July 24   Size: 35x25mm
742 A232 1c shown   .30   .25
743 A232 4c Soyuz   .30   .25
      Nos. 742-743,C230 (3)   6.60   4.50
Apollo Soyuz space test project (Russo-
American cooperation), launching July 15;
link-up, July 17.

Father Rafael C.
Castellanos — A233

1975, Aug. 6   Litho.   Perf. 12
744 A233 6c brown & buff   .45   .25
Castellanos (1875-1934), 1st Apostolic
Administrator in Dominican Republic.

Women and
Men Around
IWY Emblem
A234

1975, Aug. 6   Perf. 13
745 A234 3c orange & multi   .45   .25
      International Women's Year 1975.

Guacanagarix — A235

Indian Chiefs: 2c, Guarionex. 3c, Caonabo.
4c, Bohechio. 5c, Cayacoa. 6c, Anacona
(woman). 9c, Hatuey.

1975, Sept. 27   Litho.   Perf. 12
746 A235 1c yellow & multi   .60   .25
747 A235 2c salmon & multi   .60   .25
748 A235 3c violet bl & multi   .60   .25
749 A235 4c green & multi   .60   .25
750 A235 5c blue & multi   .60   .25
751 A235 6c violet & multi   .60   .25
752 A235 9c rose & multi   1.00   .25
      Nos. 746-752,C231-C233 (10)   7.10   2.60

Basketball — A236

Design: 6c, Baseball and Games' emblem.

1975, Oct. 24   Litho.   Perf. 12
753 A236 2c pink & multi   .50   .25
754 A236 6c orange & multi   .50   .25
      Nos. 753-754,C234-C235 (4)   3.00   1.05
7th Pan-American Games, Mexico City, Oct.
13-26.

Carolers
A237

6c, Dominican nativity with farmers &
shepherds.

1975, Dec. 12   Litho.   Perf. 13x13½
755 A237 2c yellow & multi   .40   .25
756 A237 6c blue & multi   .40   .25
      Nos. 755-756,C236 (3)   1.40   .75
              Christmas 1975.

Abudefdul
Marginatus
A238

1976, Jan. 23   Litho.   Perf. 13
757 A238 10c shown   .75   .25
758 A238 10c Doncella   .75   .25
759 A238 10c Carajuelo   .75   .25
760 A238 10c Reina de los
                  Angeles   .75   .25
761 A238 10c Pargo Colorado   .75   .25
  a.   Strip of 5, #757-761   11.00 11.00

Ascension, by J.
Priego — A239

2c, Mary Magdalene, by Enrique Godoy.

1976, Apr. 14   Litho.   Perf. 13½
762 A239 2c blue & multi   .40   .25
763 A239 6c yellow & multi   .40   .25
      Nos. 762-763,C238 (3)   1.55   .80
              Holy Week 1976.

"Separacion
Dominicana" and
Adm.
Cambiaso — A240

1976, Apr. 15   Perf. 13½x13
764 A240 20c multicolored   1.25   .45
      Naval Battle off Tortuga, Apr. 15, 1844.

Maps of US
and Dominican
Republic
A241

Design: 9c, Maps within cogwheels.

1976, May 29   Litho.   Perf. 13½
765 A241 6c violet bl & multi   .40   .25
766 A241 9c violet bl & multi   .40   .25
      Nos. 765-766,C239-C240 (4)   3.15   2.00
           American Bicentennial.

Flags of
Dominican
Republic and
Spain — A242

1976, May 31
767 A242 6c multicolored   .65   .25
Visit of King Juan Carlos I and Queen Sofia
of Spain. See No. C241.

Various
Telephones — A243

1976, July 15   Perf. 12x12½
768 A243 6c multicolored   .40   .25
Cent. of 1st telephone call by Alexander
Graham Bell, Mar. 10, 1876. See No. C242.

Vision of Duarte, by   Juan Pablo
Luis   Duarte, by
Desangles — A244   Rhadames
                            Mejia — A245

1976, July 20   Litho.   Perf. 13x13½
769 A244 2c multicolored   .30   .25
              Perf. 13½
770 A245 6c multicolored   .30   .25
      Nos. 769-770,C243-C244 (4)   3.25   1.85
Juan Pablo Duarte, liberation hero, death
centenary.

Fire Hydrant — A246

Design: 6c, Firemen's emblem.

1976, Sept. 13   Litho.   Perf. 12
771 A246 4c multicolored   .50   .25
772 A246 6c multicolored   .50   .25
      Nos. 771-772,C245 (3)   4.50   .80
Honoring firemen. Nos. 771-772 inscribed
"Corrreos."

Radio and Atom Symbols — A247

1976, Oct. 8   Litho.   Perf. 13½
773 A247 6c red & black   .40 .25
Dominican Radio Club, 50th anniv. See No. C246.

Spain, Central and South America, Galleon — A248

1976, Oct. 22   Litho.   Perf. 13½
774 A248 6c multicolored   .40 .25
Spanish heritage. See No. C247.

Boxing and Montreal Emblem — A249

Design: 3c, Weight lifting.

1976, Oct. 22   Perf. 12
775 A249 2c blue & multi   .40 .25
776 A249 3c multicolored   .40 .25
Nos. 775-776,C248-C249 (4)   2.90 1.50
21st Olympic Games, Montreal, Canada, July 17-Aug. 1.

Virgin and Child A250   Three Kings A251

1976, Dec. 8   Litho.   Perf. 13½
777 A250 2c multicolored   .40 .25
778 A251 6c multicolored   .40 .25
Nos. 777-778,C250 (3)   1.55 .80
Christmas 1976.

Cable Car and Beach Scenes A252

1977, Jan. 7
779 A252 6c multicolored   .40 .25
Nos. 779,C251-C253 (4)   2.35 1.20
Tourist publicity.

Championship Emblem — A253

1977, Mar. 4   Litho.   Perf. 13½
780 A253 3c rose & multi   .40 .25
781 A253 5c yellow & multi   .40 .25
Nos. 780-781,C254-C255 (4)   2.90 1.50
10th Central American and Caribbean Children's and Young People's Swimming Championships, Santo Domingo.

Christ Carrying Cross — A254

Design: 6c, Head with crown of thorns.

1977, Apr. 18   Litho.   Perf. 13½x13
782 A254 2c multicolored   .40 .25
783 A254 6c black & rose   .40 .25
Nos. 782-783,C256 (3)   1.55 .75
Holy Week 1977.

Doves, Lions Emblem — A255

1977, May 6   Perf. 13½x13
784 A255 2c lt blue & multi   .40 .25
785 A255 6c salmon & multi   .40 .25
Nos. 784-785,C257 (3)   1.40 .75
12th annual Dominican Republic Lions Convention.

Battle Scene — A256

1977, June 15   Litho.   Perf. 13x13½
786 A256 20c multicolored   1.20 .35
Dominican Navy.

Water Lily — A257

National Botanical Garden: 4c, "Flor de Mayo" (orchid). 6c, Sebesten.

1977, Aug. 19   Litho.   Perf. 12
787 A257 2c multicolored   .50 .25
788 A257 4c multicolored   .50 .25
789 A257 6c multicolored   .60 .25
Nos. 787-789,C259-C260 (5)   5.10 2.10

Chart and Computers A258

1977, Nov. 30   Litho.   Perf. 13
790 A258 6c multicolored   .40 .25
7th Interamerican Statistics Conf. See No. C261.

Solenodon Paradoxus A259

Design: 20c, Iguana and Congress emblem.

1977, Dec. 29   Litho.   Perf. 13
791 A259 6c multicolored   2.50 .25
792 A259 20c multicolored   4.25 .30
Nos. 791-792,C262-C263 (4)   14.75 1.35
8th Pan-American Veterinary and Zoo-technical Congress.

Main Gate, Casa del Cordon, 1503 — A260

1978, Jan. 19   Perf. 13x13½
Size: 26x36mm
793 A260 6c multicolored   .40 .25
Spanish heritage. See No. C264.

Crown of Thorns, Tools at the Cross — A261

6c, Head of Jesus with crown of thorns.

Size: 22x33mm
1978, Mar. 21   Perf. 12
794 A261 2c multicolored   .40 .25
795 A261 6c slate   .40 .25
Nos. 794-795,C265-C266 (4)   2.30 1.05
Holy Week 1978.

Cardinal Octavio A. Beras Rojas — A262

1978, May 5   Litho.   Perf. 13
796 A262 6c multicolored   .40 .25
First Cardinal from Dominican Republic, consecrated May 24, 1976. See No. C268.

Pres. Manuel de Troncoso — A263

1978, June 12   Litho.   Perf. 13½
797 A263 2c black, rose & brn   .40 .25
798 A263 6c black, gray & brn   .60 .25
Manuel de Jesus Troncoso de la Concha (1878-1955), pres. of Dominican Republic, 1940-42.

Father Juan N. Zegri y Moreno — A264

1978, July 11   Litho.   Perf. 13x13½
799 A264 6c multicolored   .40 .25
Congregation of the Merciful Sisters of Charity, centenary. See No. C273.

Boxing and Games' Emblem — A265

1978, July 21   Perf. 12
800 A265 2c shown   .50 .25
801 A265 6c Weight lifting   .75 .25
Nos. 800-801,C274-C275 (4)   3.75 1.00
13th Central American & Caribbean Games, Medellin, Colombia.

Sun over Landscape — A266

Design: 6c, Sun over beach and boat.

1978, Sept. 12   Litho.   Perf. 12
802 A266 2c multicolored   .40 .25
803 A266 6c multicolored   .40 .25
Nos. 802-803,C280-C281 (4)   2.35 1.00
Tourist publicity.

Ships of Columbus, Map of Dominican Republic — A267

1978, Oct. 12   Litho.   Perf. 13½
804 A267 2c multicolored   .40 .25
Spanish heritage. See No. C282.

Dove, Lamp, Poinsettia — A268

Design: 6c, Dominican family and star, vert.

1978, Dec. 5   Litho.   Perf. 12
805 A268 2c multicolored   .40 .25
806 A268 6c multicolored   .50 .25
Nos. 805-806,C284 (3)   1.65 .80
Christmas 1978.

Starving Child, IYC Emblem — A269

1979, Feb. 26   Litho.   Perf. 12
807 A269 2c orange & black   .40 .25
Nos. 807,C287-C289 (4)   3.15 1.85
Intl. Year of the Child.

Crucifixion — A270

Design: 3c, Jesus carrying cross, horiz.

1979, Apr. 9   Litho.   Perf. 13½
808 A270 2c multicolored   .40 .25
809 A270 3c multicolored   .60 .25
Nos. 808-809,C290 (3)   5.00 1.75
Holy Week.

Stigmaphyllon Periplocifolium A271

1979, May 17   Litho.   Perf. 12
810 A271 50c multicolored   2.00 .50
Nos. 810,C293-C295 (4)   7.00 1.80
Dr. Rafael M. Moscoso National Botanical Garden.

Heart, Diseased
Blood
Vessel — A272

Design: 1p, Cardiology Institute and heart.

1979, June 2   Litho.   Perf. 13½
811 A272 3c multicolored   .40   .25
812 A272 1p multicolored   2.75   .75
    Nos. 811-812,C296 (3)   3.90   1.40

Dominican Cardiology Institute.

Baseball, Games'
Emblem — A273

3c, Bicycling and Games' emblem, vert.

1979, June 20
813 A273 2c multicolored   .40   .25
814 A273 3c multicolored   .40   .25
    Nos. 813-814,C297 (3)   2.30   .80

8th Pan American Games, Puerto Rico,
June 30-July 15.

Soccer — A274

Design: 25c, Swimming, horiz.

1979, Aug. 9   Litho.   Perf. 12
815 A274 2c multicolored   .40   .25
816 A274 25c multicolored   .50   .25
    Nos. 815-816,C298 (3)   1.55   .80

Third National Games.

Thomas A.
Edison — A275

1979, Aug. 27   Perf. 13½
817 A275 25c multicolored   1.00   .45

Cent. of invention of electric light. See No.
C300.

Hand Holding
Electric
Plug — A276

Design: 6c, Filling automobile gas tank.

1979, Aug. 30
818 A276 2c multicolored   .40   .25
819 A276 6c multicolored   .50   .25

Energy conservation.

Parrot — A277

Birds: 6c, Temnotrogon roseigaster.

1979, Sept. 12   Litho.   Perf. 12
820 A277 2c multicolored   2.10   .25
821 A277 6c multicolored   2.10   .25
    Nos. 820-821,C301-C303 (5) 20.20   2.10

A278

Lions Emblem, Map of Dominican Republic.

1979, Nov. 13   Litho.   Perf. 12
822 A278 20c multicolored   .75   .40

Lions International Club of Dominican
Republic, 15th anniversary. See No. C304.

Christmas — A279

1979, Dec. 18   Litho.   Perf. 12
823 A279 2c Holy Family   .40   .25
    See No. C305.

Holy Week — A280

Design: Jesus Carrying Cross.

1980, Mar. 27   Litho.   Perf. 12
824 A280 3c multicolored   .40   .25
    Nos. 824,C306-C307 (3)   1.55   .80

A281

1980, May 15   Litho.   Perf. 13½
825 A281 1c shown   .60   .25
826 A281 2c Coffee   .60   .25
827 A281 3c Plantain   .60   .25
828 A281 4c Sugar cane   .60   .25
829 A281 5c Corn   .60   .25
    Nos. 825-829 (5)   3.00   1.25

Cacao Harvest (Agriculture Year)

Cotuf Gold Mine,
Pueblo Viejo,
Flag of Dominican
Republic — A282

1980, July 8   Litho.   Perf. 13½
830 A282 6c multicolored   .40   .25
    Nos. 830,C310-C311 (3)   2.40   1.15

Nationalization of gold mining.

Blind Man's
Buff — A283

1980, July 21   Perf. 12
831 A283 3c shown   .40   .25
832 A283 4c Marbles   .40   .25
833 A283 5c Drawing in sand   .50   .25
834 A283 6c Hopscotch   .50   .25
    Nos. 831-834 (4)   1.80   1.00

Iguana — A284

1980, Aug. 30   Litho.   Perf. 12
835 A284 20c multicolored   2.75   .45
    Nos. 835,C314-C317 (5)   16.15   2.80

Dance, by
Jaime Colson
A285

50c, Woman, by Gilberto Hernandez
Ortega, vert.

Perf. 13x13½, 13½x13
1980, Sept. 23   Litho.
836 A285 3c shown   .40   .25
837 A285 50c multicolored   1.50   .90
    Nos. 836-837,C318-C319 (4) 3.40   2.00

Three Kings — A286

1980, Dec. 5   Litho.   Perf. 13½
838 A286 3c shown   .40   .25
839 A286 6c Carolers   .40   .25
    Nos. 838-839,C327 (3)   1.45   .80

Christmas 1980.

Salcedo Province
Cent. — A287

1981, Jan. 14   Litho.   Perf. 13½
840 A287 6c multicolored   .40   .25
    See No. C328.

Juan Pablo Duarte,
Liberation Hero, 105th
Anniv. of
Death — A288

1981, Feb. 6   Litho.   Perf. 12
841 A288 2c sepia & deep bister .60   .25

Gymnast — A289

1981, Mar. 31   Litho.   Perf. 13½
842 A289 1c shown   .50   .25
843 A289 2c Running   .50   .25
844 A289 3c Pole vault   .50   .25
845 A289 6c Boxing   1.00   .25
    Nos. 842-845,C331 (5)   5.00   1.35

5th National Games.

Mother
Mazzarello — A290

1981, Apr. 14   Perf. 12
846 A290 6c multicolored   .45   .25

Mother Maria Mazzarello (1837-1881),
founder of Daughters of Mary.

A291

1981, May 18   Litho.   Perf. 13½
847 A291 6c gray vio & lt gray .45   .25

Pedro Henriquez Urena, Historian (1884-
1946)

Forest
Conservation — A292

1981, June 30   Litho.   Perf. 12
848 A292 2c shown   .45   .25
849 A292 6c River, forest   .45   .25

Family in House,
Census
Emblem — A293

1981, Aug. 14   Litho.   Perf. 12
850 A293 3c shown   .45   .25
851 A293 6c Farmer   .45   .25

1981 natl. population and housing census.

Christmas — A294

1981, Dec. 23   Litho.   Perf. 13½
852 A294 2c Bells   .45   .25
853 A294 3c Poinsettia   .45   .25
    Nos. 852-853,C353 (3)   1.80   .95

A295

1982, Jan. 29   Litho.   Perf. 13½
854 A295 2c Juan Pablo Duarte   .80   .25

National
Elections — A296

Designs: Voters casting votes. 3c, 6c vert.

1982, Mar. 30 Litho. Perf. 13½
855 A296 2c multicolored .40 .25
856 A296 3c multicolored .40 .25
857 A296 6c multicolored .50 .25
   Nos. 855-857 (3) 1.30 .75

A297

Energy Conservation: Various forms of energy.

1982, May 10 Litho. Perf. 12
858 A297 1c multicolored .40 .25
859 A297 2c multicolored .40 .25
860 A297 3c multicolored .40 .25
861 A297 4c multicolored .50 .25
862 A297 5c multicolored .50 .25
863 A297 6c multicolored .50 .25
   Nos. 858-863 (6) 2.70 1.50

A298

1982, Aug. 2 Perf. 12x12½
864 A298 6c multicolored .40 .25

Emilio Prud'Homme (1856-1932), composer.

Pres. Antonio Guzman Fernandez (1911-1982) — A299

1982, Aug. 4 Perf. 13x13½
865 A299 6c multicolored .40 .25

14th Central American and Caribbean Games — A300

1982, Aug. 13 Perf. 12, Imperf.
866 A300 3c Baseball 1.00 .25
   See Nos. C368-C370.

San Pedro de Macoris Province Centenary A301

Designs: 1c, Wagon. 2c, Stained-glass window. 5c, Views.

1982, Aug. 26 Perf. 13
867 A301 1c multicolored .40 .25
868 A301 2c multicolored .40 .25
869 A301 5c multicolored .50 .25
   Nos. 867-869,C375 (4) 2.05 1.05
   Size of 2c, 25x35mm.

St. Teresa of Jesus of Avila (1515-1582) — A302

1982, Nov. 17 Litho. Perf. 13½
870 A302 6c multicolored .60 .25

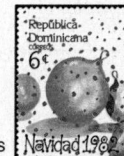

Christmas 1982 — A303

Various Christmas balls.

1982, Dec. 8
871 A303 6c multicolored 1.10 .25
   See No. C380.

Environmental Protection — A304

1982, Dec. 15 Perf. 12
872 A304 2c Bird .40 .25
873 A304 3c Water .40 .25
874 A304 6c Forest .40 .25
875 A304 20c Fish 1.25 .35
   Nos. 872-875 (4) 2.45 1.10

Natl. Literacy Campaign A305

Designs: 2c, Vowels on blackboard. 3c, Writing, reading. 6c, Children, pencil.

1983, Mar. 9 Litho. Perf. 13½
876 A305 2c multicolored .40 .25
877 A305 3c multicolored .40 .25
878 A305 6c multicolored .50 .25
   Nos. 876-878 (3) 1.30 .75

A306

5c, similar arms, incorporating stylized centenary monument.

1983, Apr. 4 Perf. 12
879 A306 1c multicolored .40 .25
880 A306 5c multicolored .50 .25
   Mao City centenary.

A307

Dominican Historians: 2c, Antonio del Monte y Tejada (1780-1861). 3c, Manuel Ubaldo Gomez (1857-1941). 5c, Emiliano Tejera (1841-1923). 6c, Bernardo Pichardo (1877-1924). 7c, Americo Lugo (1870-1952). 10c, José Gabriel Garcia (1834-1910). 7c, 10c airmail.

1983, Apr. 25 Litho. Perf. 12
881 A307 2c multicolored .40 .25
882 A307 3c multicolored .40 .25
883 A307 5c multicolored .40 .25
884 A307 6c multicolored .40 .25
885 A307 7c multicolored .50 .25
886 A307 10c multicolored .75 .30
   Nos. 881-886 (6) 2.85 1.55

National Anthem, 100th Anniv. — A308

Emilio Prud'Homme, & Jose Reyes, composer.

1983, Sept. 13 Litho. Perf. 13½
887 A308 6c copper red & blk .45 .25

Free Masons, 125th Anniv. — A309

1983, Oct. 24 Litho. Perf. 12
888 A309 4c Emblem .45 .25

Church of Our Lady of Regla, 300th Anniv. — A310

1983, Nov. 5 Perf. 13½
889 A310 3c Church .40 .25
890 A310 6c Statue .50 .25

450th Anniv. of Monte Cristi Province — A311

Designs: 1c, Tower. 2c, Arms. 5c, Cuban independence site, horiz. 7c, Workers, horiz.

1983, Nov. 25 Perf. 12
891 A311 1c dark grn & blk .45 .25
892 A311 2c multicolored .45 .25
893 A311 5c gray .45 .25
894 A311 7c gray & blue .45 .25
   Nos. 891-894 (4) 1.80 1.00

6th Natl. Games — A312

6c, Bicycling, boxing, baseball. 10c, Runner, weight lifting, swimming.

1983, Dec. 9
895 A312 6c multicolored .40 .25
896 A312 10c multicolored .65 .25
   10c airmail.

Restoration of the Republic, 120th Anniv. — A313

Design: 1c, Capotillo Heroes Monument.

1983, Dec. 30 Litho. Perf. 13½
897 A313 1c multicolored .45 .25

140th Anniv. of Independence A314

Designs: 6c, Matia Ramon Mella (Patriot), flag. 25c, Mella's Blunderbuss rifle, Gate of Deliverance (independence declaration site).

1984, Feb. 24 Litho. Perf. 13½
898 A314 6c multicolored .40 .25
899 A314 25c multicolored 1.00 .35

Heriberto Pieter (1884-1972), Physician, First Negro Graduate — A315

1984, Mar. 16
900 A315 3c multicolored .45 .25

Battle of Barranquita, 67th Anniv. — A316

1983, Dec. 30 Perf. 12
901 A316 5c multicolored .45 .25

Battle of Santiago, 140th Anniv. — A317

1984, Mar. 29 Perf. 13½
902 A317 7c multicolored .45 .25

Coast Guard Ship DC-1, 1934 — A318

1984, Apr. 13 Litho.
903 A318 10c multicolored .65 .25

Navy Day and 140th anniv. of Battle of Tortuguero.

Salome Urena — A319

Poem "Mi Pedro" — A319a

Designs: 22c, Pedro Henriquez Urena.

1984, June 29 Litho. Perf. 12
904 A319 7c pink & brown .45 .25
905 A319a 10c cream & chestnut .65 .25
906 A319 22c cream & brown .60 .25
   Nos. 904-906 (3) 1.70 .75

Birth centenary of Pedro Henriquez Urena.

Monument to
Heroes of June
1959 — A320

1984, June 20   *Perf. 13½*
907 A320 6c silver & blue   .60   .25

Costal towns of Constanza, Maimon and
Estero Hondo - sites of attempted overthrow of
Rafael Trujillo, 25th anniv.

1984 Summer
Olympics — A321

1984, Aug. 1
908 A321 1p Hurdles   2.50   1.90
909 A321 1p Weightlifting   2.50   1.90
910 A321 1p Boxing   2.50   1.90
911 A321 1p Baseball   2.50   1.90
  a.   Block of 4, #908-911   18.00   18.00
    Nos. 908-911 (4)   10.00   7.60

Protection of
Fauna — A322

1984, Oct. 3   **Litho.**   *Perf. 12*
912 A322 10c Owl   3.75   .25
913 A322 15c Flamingo   4.75   .35
914 A322 25c Wild Pig   6.50   .50
915 A322 35c Solenodon   7.50   .70
    Nos. 912-915 (4)   22.50   1.80

500th Anniv. of
Discovery of
America — A323

10c, Landing on Hispaniola. 35c, Destruction of Ft. Navidad. 65c, First Mass in
America. 1p, Battle of Santo Cerro.

1984, Oct. 10   **Litho.**   *Perf. 13½x13*
916 A323 10c multicolored   .45   .25
917 A323 35c multicolored   .80   .35
918 A323 65c multicolored   1.50   .80
919 A323 1p multicolored   2.50   1.10
    Nos. 916-919 (4)   5.25   2.50

Visit of Pope John
Paul II — A324

1984, Oct. 11   **Litho.**   *Perf. 13x13½*
920   Block of 4   9.00   9.00
  a.   A324 75c shown   1.90   1.90
  b.   A324 75c Pope, map of Carib-
     bean   1.90   1.90
  c.   A324 75c Pope, globe   1.90   1.90
  d.   A324 75c Bishop's crozier   1.90   1.90

150th Anniv. of
Birth of Maximo
Gomez
(1986) — A325

10c, Gomez on horseback. 20c, Maximo
Gomez.

1984, Dec. 6   **Litho.**   *Perf. 13½*
921 A325 10c multicolored   .45   .25
922 A325 20c multicolored   .55   .25

Christmas
1984 — A326

    Perf. 13½x13, 13x13½
1984, Dec. 14   **Litho.**
923 A326 5c multicolored   .40   .25
924 A326 10c multicolored, vert.   .50   .25

Sacrifice of the
Goat, by Eligio
Pichardo — A327

Paintings and sculpture: 10c, The Pumpkin
Sellers, by Gaspar Mario Cruz; 25c, The Mar-
ket, by Celeste Woss y Gil; 50c, Horses in the
Rain, by Dario Suro.

1984, Dec. 19   **Litho.**   *Perf. 13½*
925 A327 5c multi   .50   .25
926 A327 10c multi, vert.   .50   .25
927 A327 25c multi   .85   .45
928 A327 50c multi   1.50   .65
    Nos. 925-928 (4)   3.35   1.60

Day of Our Lady
of Altagracia
A328

5c, Old church at Higuey, 1572. 10c, Our
Lady of Altagracia 1514, vert. 25c, Basilica of
the Protector, Higuey 1971, vert.

1985, Jan. 21
929 A328 5c multicolored   .40   .25
930 A328 10c multicolored   .50   .25
931 A328 25c multicolored   .75   .35
    Nos. 929-931 (3)   1.65   .85

Independence,
141st
Anniv. — A329

Painting: The Fathers of Our Country
(Duarte, Sanchez and Mella).

1985, Mar. 8   *Perf. 12½*
932 A329 5c multicolored   .40   .25
933 A329 10c multicolored   .45   .25
934 A329 25c multicolored   .70   .25
    Nos. 932-934 (3)   1.55   .75

Battle of Azua,
141st
Anniv. — A330

10c, Gen. Antonio Duverge, Statue.

1985, Apr. 8   **Litho.**   *Perf. 13½*
935 A330 10c multicolored   .55   .25

Santo Domingo
Lighthouse,
1853 — A331

1985, Apr. 15   **Litho.**
936 A331 25c multicolored   .85   .25

Battle of Tortuguero, 141st anniv.

A332

1985, Apr. 15   **Litho.**   *Perf. 12*
937 A332 35c multicolored   1.10   .45

American Airforces Cooperation System,
25th anniv.

Espaillat Province
Cent. — A333

10c, Don Carlos M. Rojas, 1st governor.

1985, May 24   **Litho.**   *Perf. 13½*
938 A333 10c multicolored   .55   .30

A334

1985, July 5   **Litho.**   *Perf. 12*
939 A334 5c Table tennis   .40   .25
940 A334 10c Walking race   .50   .30

MOCA '85, 7th Natl. Games.

Intl. Youth
Year — A335

1985, July 29   *Perf. 13½*
941 A335 5c Youth   .35   .25
942 A335 25c The Haitises   1.10   .45
943 A335 35c Mt. Duarte summit   1.25   .50
944 A335 2p Mt. Duarte   7.25   2.75
    Nos. 941-944 (4)   9.95   3.95

Interamerican
Development
Bank, 25th
Anniv. — A336

10c, Haina Harbor. 25c, Map of development sites. 1p, Tavera-Bao-Lopez Hydroelectric Complex.

1985, Aug. 23
945 A336 10c multicolored   .40   .25
946 A336 25c multicolored   .85   .40
947 A336 1p multicolored   2.75   1.75
    Nos. 945-947 (3)   4.00   2.40

Intl. Decade for
Women — A337

Design: Evangelina Rodriguez (1879-1947),
first Dominican woman doctor.

1985, Sept. 26
948 A337 10c multicolored   .55   .25

15th Central American
and Caribbean Games,
Santiago — A338

1985, Oct. 9   *Perf. 12*
949 A338 5c multicolored   .50   .25
950 A338 25c multicolored   1.40   .45

4th Adm.
Christopher
Columbus
Regatta, Casa de
Espana — A339

Designs: 50c, Founding of Santo Domingo,
1496. 65c, Chapel of Our Lady of the Rosary,
1496, Santo Domingo. 1p, Columbus, American Indian and old Spanish coat of arms.

1985, Oct. 10   *Perf. 13½*
951 A339 35c multicolored   1.40   .85
952 A339 50c multicolored   1.80   1.20
953 A339 65c multicolored   2.50   1.50
954 A339 1p multicolored   4.50   2.40
    Nos. 951-954 (4)   10.20   5.95

Discovery of America, 500th anniv. (in 1992).

Cacique
Enriquillo — A340

Designs: 5c, Enriquillo in the Bahuroco
Mountains, mural detail.

1985, Oct. 31
955 A340 5c multicolored   .50   .25
956 A340 10c multicolored   .75   .25

Enriquillo (d. 1536), leader of revolution
against Spain. Size of No. 955: 47x33mm.

Archbishop Fernando
Arturo de
Merino — A341

1985, Dec. 3   *Perf. 12*
957 A341 25c multicolored   .75   .40

Cent. of holy orders granted to Merino
(1833-1906), pres. of the republic 1880-82.

Mirabal Sisters,
Political Martyrs
1960 — A342

1985, Dec. 18   *Perf. 13½*
958 A342 10c multicolored   .50   .25

Christmas
A343

1985, Dec. 18
959 A343 10c multicolored   .40   .25
960 A343 25c multicolored   .90   .35

Day of
Independence,
Feb. 27 — A344

Design: Mausoleum of founding fathers Duarte, Sanchez and Mella.

1986, Feb. 26   Litho.   Perf. 13½
961 A344 5c multicolored   .40 .25
962 A344 10c multicolored   .50 .25

Holy Week — A345

Colonial churches.

1986, Apr. 10
963 A345 5c San Miguel   .60 .25
964 A345 5c San Andres   .60 .25
965 A345 10c Santa Barbara   .65 .25
966 A345 10c San Lazaro   .65 .25
967 A345 10c San Carlos   .65 .25
    Nos. 963-967 (5)   3.15 1.25

Navy Day — A346

Design: Juan Bautista Cambiaso, Juan Bautista Maggiolo and Juan Alejandro Acosta, 1844 independence battle heroes.

1986, Apr. 15
968 A346 10c multicolored   .60 .25

Natl. Elections — A347

1986, Apr. 29
969 A347 5c Voters, map   .45 .25
970 A347 10c Ballot box   .55 .25

Natl. Postal Institute Inauguration — A348

1986, June 10
971 A348 10c gold, blue & red   .40 .25
972 A348 25c silver, blue & red   1.00 .30
973 A348 50c black, blue & red   1.75 .65
    Nos. 971-973 (3)   3.15 1.20

Central America and Caribbean Games, Santiago — A349

1986, July 17   Litho.   Perf. 13½
974 A349 10c Weight lifting   .40 .25
975 A349 25c Gymnastics   .85 .30
976 A349 35c Diving   1.25 .45
977 A349 50c Equestrian   1.50 .70
    Nos. 974-977 (4)   4.00 1.70

Historians A350

Designs: 5c, Ercilia Pepin (b. 1886), vert. 10c, Ramon Emilio Jimenez (b. 1886) and Victor Garrido (1886-1972).

1986, Aug. 1   Litho.   Perf. 13½
978 A350 5c silver & dull brn   .40 .25
979 A350 10c silver & dull brn   .55 .25

A351   A352

Discovery of America, 500th Anniv. (in 1992) — A353

Designs: 25c, Yachts racing, 5th Adm. Christopher Columbus Regatta, Casa de Espana. 50c, Columbus founding La Isabela City. 65c, Exploration of the hidalgos. 1p, Columbus returning to the Court of Ferdinand and Isabella. 1.50p, Emblems.

1986, Oct. 10   Litho.   Perf. 13½
980 A351 25c multicolored   .75 .35
981 A352 50c multicolored   1.50 .55
982 A352 65c multicolored   2.00 .95
983 A352 1p multicolored   3.50 1.30

**Textured Paper
Size: 86x58mm
Imperf**
984 A353 1.50p multicolored   6.25 6.00
    Nos. 980-984 (5)   14.00 9.15

1986 World Cup Soccer Championships, Mexico — A354

Various soccer plays.

1986, Oct. 21   Perf. 13½
985 A354 50c multicolored   1.40 .65
986 A354 75c multicolored   3.00 1.10

Medicinal Plants — A355

5c, Zea mays. 10c, Bixa orellana. 25c, Momordica charantia. 50c, Annona muricata.

1986, Dec. 5
987 A355 5c multicolored   .40 .25
988 A355 10c multicolored   .45 .25
989 A355 25c multicolored   .75 .25
990 A355 50c multicolored   1.60 .55
    Nos. 987-990 (4)   3.20 1.30

Second Caribbean Pharmacopeia Seminar.

Christmas A356

1986, Dec. 19
991 A356 5c Urban scene   .50 .25
992 A356 25c Rural scene   1.50 .35

A357

1986, Dec. 31   Litho.   Perf. 13½
993 A357 10c shown   .40 .25
994 A357 25c Portrait, c. 1900   1.00 .40

Maximo Gomez (1836-1905), revolutionary, statesman.

A358

1987, Mar. 30   Litho.   Perf. 13½
995 A358 50c brt blue, blk & red   1.40 .65

16th Pan American Ophthalmological Conf., Apr. 5-10.

A359

Stained-glass window, San Juan Bosco church, Santo Domingo: Ascension of Christ to Heaven.

1987, May 28
996 A359 35c multicolored   1.50 .50

Edible Plants — A360

5c, Sorghum bicolor. 25c, Martanta arundinacea. 65c, Calathaea allouia. 1p, Voandzeia subterranea.

1987, Aug. 21
997 A360 5c multicolored   .25 .25
998 A360 25c multicolored   1.00 .30
999 A360 65c multicolored   2.00 .95
1000 A360 1p multicolored   3.50 1.40
    Nos. 997-1000 (4)   6.75 2.90

Activo 20-30 Intl., 25th Anniv. — A361

1987, Aug. 26
1001 A361 35c multicolored   1.75 .50

Adm. Christopher Columbus Regatta — A362

A363

Columbus Memorial, Santo Domingo — A364

1p, Building Ft. Santiago. 1.50p, Columbus imprisoned by Bombadilla.

1987, Oct. 14
1002 A362 50c shown   1.50 .70
1003 A363 75c shown   2.25 1.00
1004 A363 1p multicolored   3.00 1.30
1005 A363 1.50p multicolored   4.50 2.00

**Size: 82x70mm
Imperf**
1006 A364 2.50p shown   10.00 6.50
    Nos. 1002-1006 (5)   21.25 11.50

Discovery of America, 500th anniv. in 1992.

A365

1987, Sept. 28
1007 A365 40c multicolored   1.20 .50

Junior Olympics, La Vega, 50th anniv.

A366

Historians and authors: 10c, Jose Antonio Hungria. 25c, Joaquin Sergio Inchaustegui.

1987, Nov. 10   Litho.   Perf. 13½
1008 A366 10c buff & brown   .35 .25
1009 A366 25c pale grn & grn   .90 .25

SAN CRISTOBAL '87, 8th Natl. Games — A367

1987, Nov. 19
1010 A367 5c Baseball   .90 .25
1011 A367 10c Boxing   1.00 .25
1012 A367 50c Judo   3.00 .70
    Nos. 1010-1012 (3)   4.90 1.20

Christmas 1987 — A368

1987, Dec. 9   Litho.   Perf. 13½
1013 A368 10c Roasting pig   .55 .25
1014 A368 50c Arriving at airport   1.75 .60

Fr. Xavier Billini (b. 1837) — A369

10c, Statue. 25c, Portrait. 75c, Ana Hernandez de Billini, his mother.

1987, Dec. 18   Litho.   Perf. 13½
1015 A369 10c blue gray & dark blue   .35 .25
1016 A369 25c cream & dark grn   .75 .35
1017 A369 75c pink & blkish pur   2.25 1.10
    Nos. 1015-1017 (3)   3.35 1.70

Frank Feliz, Sr., and Aircraft — A370

1987, Dec. 22
1018 A370 25c shown   .80 .25

Size: 86x106mm
Imperf
1019 A370 2p No. C30, map   12.50 6.50

Pan-American goodwill flight to South American countries by the planes Colon, Pinta, Nina and Santa Maria, 50th anniv.

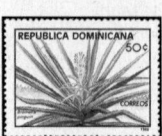

Flora — A371

No. 1020, Bromelia pinguin. No. 1021, Tillandsia fasciculata. No. 1022, Tillandsia hotteana, vert. No. 1023, Tillandsia compacta, vert.

1988, Feb. 3   Litho.   Perf. 13½
1020 A371 50c multi   2.10 .70
1021 A371 50c multi   2.10 .70
1022 A371 50c multi   2.10 .70
1023 A371 50c multi   2.10 .70
    Nos. 1020-1023 (4)   8.40 2.80

St. John Bosco (1815-1888) — A372

1988, Feb. 23   Litho.   Perf. 13½
1024 A372 10c shown   .45 .25
1025 A372 70c Stained-glass
        window   2.70 .95

Dominican Rehabilitation Assoc., 25th Anniv. — A373

1988, Mar. 1
1026 A373 20c multicolored   .75 .30

A374

1988, Apr. 6   Litho.   Perf. 13½
1027 A374 20c dk red brn & lt
        fawn   .75 .30

Dr. Manuel Emilio Perdomo (b.1886).

A375

1988, Apr. 29   Litho.   Perf. 13½
1028 A375 20c multicolored   .75 .30

Dominican College of Engineers, Architects and Surveyors (CODIA), 25th Anniv.

Independence Day, Mexico — A376

Flags and: No. 1029, Fr. Miguel Hidalgo y Costilla (1753-1811), Mexican revolutionary. No. 1030, Juan Pablo Duarte (1813-1876), father of Dominican independence.

1988, Sept. 12   Litho.   Perf. 13½
1029 A376 50c multicolored   1.40 .65
1030 A376 50c multicolored   1.40 .65

1988 Summer Olympics, Seoul — A377

50c, Running, vert. 70c, Table tennis, vert. 1p, Judo, vert. 1.50p, Mural by Tete Marella.

1988, Sept. 21   Litho.   Perf. 13½
1031 A377 50c multicolored   1.10 .50
1032 A377 70c multicolored   1.60 .75
1033 A377 1p multicolored   2.50 .95
1034 A377 1.50p multicolored   3.75 1.50
    Nos. 1031-1034 (4)   8.95 3.70

A378

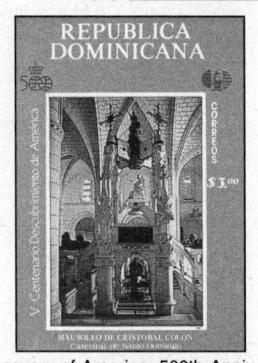

Discovery of America, 500th Anniv. (in 1992) — A379

Designs: 50c, 7th Adm. Christopher Columbus Regatta, Casa de Espana, 1988. 70c, La Concepcion Fortress, La Vega Real, 1494. 1.50p, Ft. Bonao. 2p, Nicolas de Ovando (c. 1451-1511), governor of Spanish possessions in America from 1502 to 1509. 3p, Mausoleum of Christopher Columbus, Santo Domingo Cathedral.

1988, Oct. 14   Perf. 13½
1035 A378 50c multicolored   1.10 .65
1036 A378 70c multicolored   1.75 .95
1037 A378 1.50p multicolored   3.50 1.90
1038 A378 2p multicolored   5.00 2.40

Size: 78x109mm
Imperf
1039 A379 3p multicolored   6.25 5.50
    Nos. 1035-1039 (5)   17.60 11.40

Discovery of America, 500th anniv. (in 1992). No. 1038 inscribed "1501-1509."

Duverge Parish, Cent. — A380

1988, July 13   Litho.   Perf. 13½
1040 A380 50c multicolored   1.25 .40

A381

Trinitarians, 150th Anniv. — A382

Designs: 10c, Freedom fighters. 1p, Trinitarian Plaza. 5p, Independence Plaza.

1989, May 15
1051 A389 10c multicolored   .30 .25
1052 A389 20c multicolored   .35 .25
1053 A389 50c multicolored   .65 .25

1988, Nov. 11
1041 A381 10c red, blue, gray   .45 .25
1042 A382 1p multicolored   2.00 .45
1043 A382 5p mutlicolored   13.00 4.75
    Nos. 1041-1043 (3)   15.45 5.45

See footnote after No. 337.

Pharmacology and Biochemistry — A383

1988, Nov. 28   Litho.   Perf. 13½
1044 A383 1p multicolored   2.00 1.40

13th Pan American and 16th Central American Congresses.

The Holy Family, 1504, by Miguel Angel — A384

Design: 20c, Stained-glass window.

1988, Dec. 12
1045 A384 10c shown   .45 .25
1046 A384 20c multicolored   .75 .30

    Christmas.

Municipal Technical Advisory Organization (LIGA), 50th Anniv. — A385

1988, Dec. 23
1047 A385 20c multicolored   .75 .35

Ana Teresa Paradas (1890-1960), 1st Female Lawyer of the Republic, 1913 — A386

1988, Dec. 26
1048 A386 20c deep claret   .75 .35

French Revolution Bicent. — A387

1989, Mar. 10   Litho.   Perf. 13½
1049 A387 3p red & violet blue   3.25 2.75

Battle of Tortuga, Apr. 15, 1844 — A388

1989, Apr. 14   Litho.   Perf. 13½
1050 A388 40c multicolored   1.10 .50

Natl. Anti-drug Campaign — A389

1054 A389 70c multicolored   .90 .30
1055 A389 1p multicolored   1.40 .45
1056 A389 1.50p multicolored   1.90 .50
1057 A389 2p multicolored   2.60 .70
1058 A389 5p multicolored   6.50 1.50
1059 A389 10p multicolored   12.50 3.75
    Nos. 1051-1059 (9)   27.10 7.95

Mother's Day — A390

1989, May 30   Litho.   Perf. 13½
1060 A390 20c multicolored   .70 .25

Eugenio Maria de Hostos (b. 1839) — A391

1989, Aug. 22   Litho.   Perf. 13½
1061 A391 20c multicolored   .70 .25

Gen. Gregorio Luperon (b. 1839) — A392

1989, Aug. 28
1062 A392 20c multicolored   .70 .25

Little League Baseball, 50th Anniv. — A393

1989, Sept. 29
1063 A393 1p multicolored   1.75 1.00

Diabetes '89, 7th Latin American Congress — A394

1989, Oct. 9   Litho.   Perf. 13½
1064 A394 1p multicolored   1.75 .60

America Issue — A395

UPAE emblem, pre-Columbian artifacts and customs: 20c, Cohoba silver statue and ritual dance. 1p, Taina mortar, pestle and family preparing cazabe.

1989, Oct. 12
1065 A395 20c multicolored   .75 .25
1066 A395 1p multicolored   3.75 2.10

8th Adm.
Christopher
Columbus
Regatta, Casa
de Espana
A396

European
Colonization of the
Americas
A397

Designs: 70c, Fr. Pedro de Cordoba converting the Indians to Catholicism. 1p, Christopher Columbus trading with the Indians. 3p, Sermon of Pedro de Cordoba.

1989, Oct. 13
1067	A396	50c shown	.65	.30
1068	A397	70c shown	.85	.55
1069	A397	1p multicolored	1.75	.75
1070	A397	3p multicolored	3.25	2.10
		Nos. 1067-1070 (4)	6.50	3.70

Discovery of America, 500th anniv. (in 1992).

Natl.
Afforestation — A398

Designs: 20c, Tree. 50c, Forest. 1p, Sapling, mature trees.

1989, Oct. 30   Litho.   Perf. 13½
1071	A398	10c shown	.30	.25
1072	A398	20c multicolored	.35	.25
1073	A398	50c multicolored	1.10	.55
1074	A398	1p multicolored	2.25	1.20
		Nos. 1071-1074 (4)	4.00	2.25

9th Natl. Games, La
Vega — A399

1990, Mar. 20   Litho.   Perf. 13½
1075	A399	10c Cycling	.30	.25
1076	A399	20c Running	.45	.30
1077	A399	50c Basketball	1.40	.75
		Nos. 1075-1077 (3)	2.15	1.30

Holy Week
(Easter) — A400

Design: 50c, Jesus carrying cross.

1990, Apr. 5
1078	A400	20c shown	.50	.30
1079	A400	50c multicolored	1.25	.75

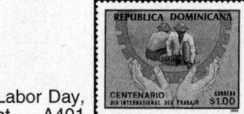

Labor Day,
Cent. — A401

1990, Apr. 30   Litho.   Perf. 13½
1080	A401	1p multicolored	1.60	.65

Urban
Renewal — A402

Designs: 20c, Highway underpass. 50c, Library. 1p, City street.

1990, May 10
1081	A402	10c shown	.30	.25
1082	A402	20c multi	.40	.25
1083	A402	50c multi	.85	.25
1084	A402	1p multi	2.00	.80
		Nos. 1081-1084 (4)	3.55	1.55

No. 1084 inscribed $100 instead of $1.00.

Penny Black, 150th
Anniv. — A403

Design: 3p, Sir Rowland Hill, Penny Black.

1990, May 29
1085	A403	1p multicolored	2.25	1.60

Size: 62x80mm
Imperf
1086	A403	3p multi	6.25	6.25

A404

1990, Oct. 5   Litho.   Perf. 13½
1087	A404	2p Flags	4.00	2.40

Organization of American States, Cent.

Children's
Drawings — A405

No. 1088, House of Tostado. No. 1089, Ruins of St. Nicolas of Bari.

1990, Aug. 7
1088	A405	50c multicolored	1.25	.75
1089	A405	50c multicolored	1.25	.75

Discovery of
America, 500th
Anniv. (in
1992) — A406

Designs: 1p, Fight at the Gulf of Arrows. 2p, Columbus talking with Guacanagari Indians. 5p, Columbus and Caonabo Indian prisoner.

1990, Oct. 12
1090	A406	1p multicolored	2.25	1.40
1091	A406	2p multicolored	4.50	3.00
1092	A406	5p multicolored	11.00	7.50
		Nos. 1090-1092 (3)	17.75	11.90

9th Adm. Christopher
Columbus
Regatta — A407

1990, Oct. 12
1093	A407	50c multicolored	1.50	.70

America
Issue — A408

UPAE emblem and: 50c, Men in canoe. 3p, Man on hammock.

1990, Nov. 7   Litho.   Perf. 13½
1094	A408	50c multicolored	1.90	.70
1095	A408	3p multicolored	8.00	4.75

A409

Discovery of Hispaniola: 50c, 1st official mass in Americas. 1p, Arms of 1st religious order in Americas. 3p, Map of island, horiz. 4p, Christopher Columbus, 1st viceroy and governor in Americas.

1991, July 17   Litho.   Perf. 13½
1096	A409	50c multicolored	.90	.55
1097	A409	1p multicolored	1.75	1.20
1098	A409	3p multicolored	4.75	2.75
1099	A409	4p multicolored	8.25	5.00
		Nos. 1096-1099 (4)	15.65	9.50

A410

1991
1100	A410	30c Boxing	.40	.25
1101	A410	50c Cycling	1.25	.50
1102	A410	1p Bowling	2.50	1.00
		Nos. 1100-1102 (3)	4.15	1.75

11th Pan American Games, Havana.

Dr. Tomas Eudoro
Perez Rancier, Birth
Cent. — A411

1991, July 3
1103	A411	2p yellow & black	7.50	1.90

10th Columbus
Regatta, Casa
de Espana
A412

Discovery of
America, 500th
Anniv. (in 1992)
A413

Designs: 50c, Encounter of three cultures. 3p, Columbus and Dr. Alvarez Chanca caring for sick. 4p, Rebellion of Enriquillo.

1991, Oct. 15   Litho.   Perf. 13½
1104	A412	30c multicolored	.65	.25
1105	A413	50c multicolored	.90	.50
1106	A413	3p multicolored	5.50	3.00
1107	A413	4p multicolored	7.50	4.00
		Nos. 1104-1107 (4)	14.55	7.75

See No. 1116.

A414

1991, Nov. 18
1108	A414	3p black & red	4.75	2.10

Cornea Bank.

America Issue — A415

Designs: 1p, Santa Maria. 3p, Christopher Columbus.

1991   Litho.   Perf. 13½
1109	A415	1p multi	3.00	.85
1110	A415	3p multi	7.00	3.50

33rd Meeting of
Inter-American
Development
Bank Governors,
Santo
Domingo — A416

1992   Litho.   Perf. 13½
1111	A416	1p multicolored	1.75	.85

A417

1992   Litho.   Perf. 13½
1112	A417	3p multicolored	5.25	2.75

Espanola '92 Philatelic Exposition.

A418

Valentin Salinero, Order of the Apostles founder.

1992   Litho.   Perf. 13½
1113	A418	1p blue & brown	1.75	.90

Order of the Apostles, cent.

Ruins of
Monastery of San
Francisco — A419

Designs: 3p, Ruins of San Nicolas hospital, first in the Americas.

1992, July 28
1114	A419	50c multicolored	.75	.50
1115	A419	3p multicolored	5.50	3.25

Type of 1991 and

A420

Designs: 50c, Racing yacht. 1p, Native women, Columbus. 2p, Natives offering Columbus tobacco. 3p, Native woman, Columbus, corn.

1992, Oct. 6   Litho.   Perf. 13½
1116	A412	50c multicolored	.70	.35
1117	A420	1p multicolored	1.60	.75
1118	A420	2p multicolored	4.50	2.75
1119	A420	3p multicolored	6.50	3.25
		Nos. 1116-1119 (4)	13.30	7.10

11th Columbus Regatta (No. 1116), Discovery of America, 500th anniv. (Nos. 1117-1119).

23rd Convention of the Alliance of Panamerican Round Tables, Santo Domingo — A421

1992, Oct. 14
1120　A421　1p multicolored　　1.75　.85

Visit by Pope John Paul II — A422

Cathedrals: 50c, Vega. 3p, Santo Domingo.

1992, Oct. 1　　　　Photo.
1121　A422　50c multicolored　1.40　.60
1122　A422　3p multicolored　4.75　2.25

Columbus Lighthouse A423

Design: 3p, Lighthouse at night.

1992, Oct. 12　　　　Litho.
1123　A423　30c multicolored　1.00　.45
1124　A423　1p multicolored　2.00　.70

Size: 70x133mm
Imperf
1125　A423　3p multicolored　10.00　10.00

America Issue — A424

Designs: 50c, First royal residence in America, Santo Domingo. 3p, First viceregal residence in America, Royal Palace, Colon.

1992, Nov. 13　　Litho.　Perf. 13½
1126　A424　50c multicolored　.75　.40
1127　A424　3p multicolored　4.00　2.50

A425

1992, Dec. 2　　Litho.　Perf. 13½
1128　A425　30c Torch bearer　.45　.25
1129　A425　1p Emblems　1.50　.80
1130　A425　4p Judo　7.00　3.50
　　　Nos. 1128-1130 (3)　8.95　4.55

1992 Natl. Sports Games, San Juan. Secretary of Sports, Education, Exercise and Recreation (No. 1129).

Natl. Census — A426

1992-93　　Litho.　Perf. 13½
1131　A426　50c black, buff & blue　.70　.25
1132　A426　1p blk, brn & blue　1.40　.75
1133　A426　3p blk, gray & bl　4.75　2.50
1134　A426　4p blk, yel grn & bl　6.00　3.00
　　　Nos. 1131-1134 (4)　12.85　6.50

　Issued: 50c, 1p, 5/12/92; 3p, 4p, 9/9/93.

A427

1993, May 30
1135　A427　30c multicolored　.50　.25
1136　A427　50c multicolored　.90　.30
1137　A427　1p multicolored　1.90　.80
　　　Nos. 1135-1137 (3)　3.30　1.35

　Ema Balaguer, humanitarian.

A428

1993, Oct. 7　　Litho.　Perf. 13½
1138　A428　30c shown　1.00　.45
1139　A428　1p Emblem, flags　2.75　1.00

　Rotary Club of Santo Domingo, 50th anniv.

17th Central American & Caribbean Games, Ponce — A429

1993, Dec. 21　　Litho.　Perf. 13½
1140　A429　50c Tennis　.65　.25
1141　A429　4p Swimming　7.00　2.00

Natl. Education Plan — A430

1993, Dec. 8
1142　A430　1.50p multicolored　2.40　.90

Spanish America — A431

Designs: 50c, First university lecturn. 3p, First city coat of arms.

1993, Dec. 28
1143　A431　50c multi　.75　.25
1144　A431　3p multi　5.25　1.50

America Issue — A432

Designs: 1p, Aratinga chloroptera. 3p, Cyclura cornuta.

1993, Dec. 30
1145　A432　1p multi　1.25　.50
1146　A432　3p multi　5.25　2.75

Opening of New Natl. Post Office — A433

1993, Nov. 12
Color of Inscription
1147　A433　1p olive　1.00　.55
1148　A433　3p red　3.00　1.60
1149　A433　4p blue　3.75　1.90
1150　A433　5p green　4.75　2.25
1151　A433　10p black　9.50　4.50

Size: 105x96mm
Imperf
1152　A433　5p black　12.50　12.50
　　　Nos. 1147-1152 (6)　34.50　23.30

First Mass in America, 500th Anniv. — A434

1994, Feb. 3　　Litho.　Perf. 13½
1153　A434　2p multicolored　3.00　1.25

5th Natl. Philatelic Exhibition — A435

1994, Feb. 25
1154　A435　3p multicolored　4.50　1.60

Natl. Independence, 150th Anniv. — A436

　No. 1155: a, Men with document, left side of table. b, Document on right side of table, men. c, Flag. d, Couple at window. e, Child holding material, mother making flag.
　No. 1156: a, Men looking upward, shooting muskets. b, Men with guns, swords looking backwards. c, Natl. coat of arms. d, Men with guns, swords, one pointing upward. e, Men with weapons, one with flag.
　10p, Three men, angel carrying musket, flag.

1994, Feb. 26　　　　Strips of 5
1155　A436　2p #a.-e.　8.25　4.00
1156　A436　3p #a.-e.　12.50　6.00

Size: 161x104mm
Imperf
1157　A436　10p multicolored　13.50　13.50
　　　Nos. 1155-1157 (3)　34.25　23.50

Nos. 1155a-1155b, 1155d-1155e, 1156a-1156b, 1156d-1156e have a continuous design.

Solenodon Paradoxus — A437

Designs: a, Crawling on rock. b, Walking in leaves. c, Looking up. d, With food in mouth.

1994, Mar. 15　　Litho.　Perf. 13½
1158　A437　1p Block of 4, #a.-d.　9.00　5.25

　World Wildlife Fund.

Battle of March 19, 150th Anniv. — A438

　No. 1160, Soldiers advancing uphill toward fort.

1994
1159　A438　2p multicolored　3.00　1.50
1160　A438　2p multicolored　3.00　1.50

　Issued: No. 1159, Mar. 18; No. 1160, Mar. 29.

Virgin of Amparo — A439

1994, Apr. 15　　Litho.　Perf. 13½
1161　A439　3p multicolored　4.50　1.75

　Battle of Puerto Tortuguero, 150th anniv.

Natl. Elections, May 16 — A440

1994, Apr. 4
1162　A440　2p multicolored　3.00　1.50

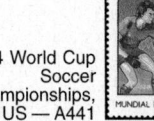

1994 World Cup Soccer Championships, US — A441

1994, June 24　　Litho.　Perf. 13½
1163　A441　4p multicolored　5.00　2.25
1164　A441　6p multicolored　7.00　3.25

Ema Balaguer City of Children — A442

1994, July 20　　Litho.　Perf. 13½
1165　A442　1p magenta & brown　2.75　.60

Stamp Day — A443

1994, Oct. 18　　Litho.　Perf. 13½
1166　A443　5p Type A3　7.75　3.00

America Issue — A444

1994, Oct. 28
1167　A444　2p Pony Express　3.00　1.50
1168　A444　6p Sailing ship　10.00　4.00

Province of LaVega, 500th Anniv. — A445

3p, Ruins of San Francisco Monastery.

1994, Nov. 24　　Litho.　Perf. 13½
1169　A445　3p multicolored　7.25　1.60

First Church the New World, 500th Anniv. A446

a, "La Isabela," cradle of evangelization. b, "Temple of the Americas," first mission.

1994, Dec. 5 *Perf. 11½*
1170 A446 3p Pair, #a.-b. 10.00 3.00

Constitution, 150th Anniv. — A447

1994, Nov. 6 *Perf. 13½*
1171 A447 3p multicolored 5.00 1.60

Christmas — A448

2p, Holy family's flight into Egypt. 3p, Modern family of three standing at river's edge.

1994, Nov. 18
1172 A448 2p multicolored 3.50 1.25
1173 A448 3p multicolored 4.75 1.60

Intl. Year of the Family.

Firsts in America — A449

1994, Dec. 21 Litho. *Perf. 13½*
1174 A449 2p Circulating coins 3.50 .75
1175 A449 5p Sermon for Justice 7.75 2.00

Snakes — A450

No. 1176, Hypsirhynchus ferox. No. 1177, Antillophis parvifrons. No. 1178, Uromacer catesbyi. No. 1179, Epicrates striatus.

1994, Dec. 26
1176 2p multicolored 3.00 1.00
1177 2p multicolored 3.00 1.00
a. A450 Pair, #1176-1177 6.00 5.50
1178 2p multicolored 3.00 1.00
1179 2p multicolored 3.00 1.00
a. A450 Pair, #1178-1179 6.00 5.50

Nos. 1177a, 1179a are continuous designs.

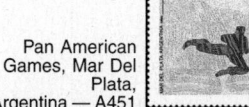

Pan American Games, Mar Del Plata, Argentina — A451

1995, Apr. 20 *Perf. 13½*
1180 A451 4p Tae kwon do 4.75 1.75
1181 A451 13p Tennis 14.50 5.00

FAO, 50th Anniv. A452

1995, Apr. 21 Litho. *Perf. 11½*
1182 A452 4p multicolored 4.50 2.25

A453

Designs: 2p, Jose Marti, Maximo Gomez. 3p, Marti. 4p, Marti seated at desk, Gomez.

1995, May 19 Litho. *Perf. 13½*
1183 A453 2p multicolored 1.90 .75
1184 A453 3p multicolored 2.50 1.40
1185 A453 4p multicolored 3.75 2.00
Nos. 1183-1185 (3) 8.15 4.15

Jose Marti (1853-95), Montecristi Manifesto, cent.

Basketball, Cent. — A454

1995, May 22
1186 A454 3p multicolored 3.00 .45

Medicinal Plants — A455

Designs: No. 1187, Pimenta ozua. No. 1188, Melocactus communis. No. 1189, Smilax. No. 1190, Zamia.

1995, May 26
1187 A455 2p multicolored 2.00 1.00
1188 A455 2p multicolored 2.00 1.00
1189 A455 3p multicolored 3.00 1.50
1190 A455 3p multicolored 3.00 1.50
Nos. 1187-1190 (4) 10.00 5.00

Tourism — A456

4p, San Souci Port. 5p, Barahona Airport. 6p, G. Luperon Airport. 13p, Airport of the Americas.

1995, June 21
1191 A456 4p multicolored 3.00 .50
1192 A456 5p multicolored 3.75 .75
1193 A456 6p multicolored 4.75 .85
1194 A456 13p multicolored 10.00 1.75
Nos. 1191-1194 (4) 21.50 3.85

Santiago de Los Caballeros, 500th Anniv. — A457

1995, July 29 Litho. *Perf. 13½*
1195 A457 3p Jacagua ruins 4.75 .90

Whales — A458

Designs: No. 1196, Physeter macrocephalus. No. 1197, Balaenoptera borealis. No. 1198, Ziphius cavirostris. No. 1199, Megaptera novaeangliae.

1995, Aug. 14
1196 A458 3p multicolored 3.00 .50
1197 A458 3p multicolored 3.00 .50
1198 A458 3p multicolored 3.00 .50
1199 A458 3p multicolored 3.00 .50
Nos. 1196-1199 (4) 12.00 2.00

Stamp Day — A459

1995, Oct. 18 Litho. *Perf. 13½*
1200 A459 4p No. 37 3.25 .50

Popular Singers — A460

1995, Oct. 8
1201 A460 2p Rafael Colon 1.75 .75
1202 A460 3p Casandra Damiron 2.25 1.10

Cathedral of Santiago, Cent. — A461

1995, Dec. 28 Litho. *Perf. 13½*
1203 A461 3p multicolored 2.50 1.10

4th World Conference of Women, Beijing — A462

1995, Nov. 23
1204 A462 2p multicolored 5.25 1.10

Volleyball, Cent. — A463

Norceca '95 — A464

1995, Oct. 19 *Imperf.*
1205 A463 5p multicolored 5.50 1.90
Perf. 13½
1206 A464 6p multicolored 6.50 4.25

Singers — A465

1995, Dec. 27 *Perf. 13½*
1207 A465 2p Antonio Mesa 1.75 .80
1208 A465 2p Julieta Otero 1.75 .80
1209 A465 2p Susano Polanco 1.75 .80
Nos. 1207-1209 (3) 5.25 2.40

Columbus Lighthouse — A466

1995, Dec. 5
1210 A466 10p dk bl, bl & gray 11.00 3.50

See Nos. 1241, 1265, 1299, 1337, 1371, 1375, 1382.

A467 UN, 50th Anniv. — A468

1995, Oct. 24
1211 A467 2p multicolored 1.75 .75
Perf. 11½
1212 A468 6p multicolored 5.00 1.00

Environmental Protection A469

America issue: 2p, Flamingos, sea gull. 6p, Manglar.

1995, Dec. 19 Litho. *Perf. 13½*
1213 A469 2p multicolored 1.75 .65
1214 A469 6p multicolored 5.00 1.00

Dominican Republic Air Force, 50th Anniv. — A470

Aircraft: a, O2U-35D Corsair. b, PT-17 Stearman. c, AT-6 Texan. d, PBY-5A Catalina. e, TF-10 Beaufighter. f, FB-6 Mosquito. g, P-38 Lightning. h, P-51D Mustang. i, B-17G Flying Fortress. j, P-47D Thunderbolt. k, FB-5 Vampire. l, C-46 Commander. m, B-26 Invader. n, C-47 Skytrain. o, T-28D Trojan. p, T-33A Silverstar. q, Cessna T-41D. r, T-34 Mentor. s, Cessna O-2A. t, A-37B Dragonfly.

1995, Dec. 30
1215 A470 2p Sheet of 20, #a-t 30.00 17.00

See No. 1228.

UNICEF, 50th
Anniv. — A471

1996, Feb. 23
1216 A471 2p shown   1.50   .45
1217 A471 4p Mirror image of
          #1216   3.00 1.40

Intl. Sailing
Competition
A472

1996, Mar. 8
1218 A472 5p multicolored   3.25 1.60

Eduardo Brito, Singer,
50th Death
Anniv. — A473

1996, Jan. 15
1219 A473 1p shown   .65   .30
1220 A473 2p With maracas   1.40   .75
1221 A473 3p Portrait   2.10 1.10
     Nos. 1219-1221 (3)   4.15 2.15

No. 1220 is 54x35mm.

Natl. Journalist
Day — A474

Design: Arturo J. Pellerano Alfau, Dr.
Freddy Gaton Arce, Rafael Herrera Cabral.

1996, Apr. 17   Litho.   Perf. 13½
1222 A474 5p multicolored   3.75 1.75

ESPAMER '96,
Seville — A475

1996, June 7   Litho.   Perf. 13½
1223 A475 15p multicolored   9.50 4.75

1996 Summer Olympic
Games,
Atlanta — A476

1996, July 5
1224 A476 5p Judo   4.00 1.40
1225 A476 15p Torch   10.00 4.25

Modern
Olympic
Games,
Cent. — A477

1996, July 5
1226 A477 6p Greece No. 118 3.75 1.90
1227 A477 15p No. 328   9.00 4.25

Dominican Republic Air Force, 50th
Anniv. Type of 1995

Helicoptors: a, Sikorsky S-55. b, Alouette II.
c, Alouette III. d, OH-6A Cayuse. e, Bell 205
A-1. f, Dauphin II SA.365C.

1996, July 31   Litho.   Perf. 13½
1228 A470 3p Sheet of 6, #a.-f.   8.00 8.00

World Day Against
Illegal Drugs — A478

1996, Sept. 23   Litho.   Perf. 13½
1229 A478 15p multicolored   9.75 4.25

Mail
Delivery — A479

No. 1230, World delivery, putting mail in letter box, mailman receiving mail on motorcycle.
No. 1231, Woman giving mail to man on
horseback, vert. No. 1232, Child holding letter
beside mailbox.

1996, July 17   Litho.   Perf. 13½
1230 A479 3p multicolored   2.50 1.25
1231 A479 3p multicolored   2.50 1.25
1232 A479 3p multicolored   2.50 1.25
     Nos. 1230-1232 (3)   7.50 3.75

America Issue — A480

1996, Oct. 15   Litho.   Perf. 13½
1233 A480 2p Men's costume   1.40   .65
1234 A480 6p Women's costume 3.75 1.75

Stamp
Day — A481

1996, Oct. 18
1235 A481 5p No. 142   3.25 1.40

26th Intl. Sunfish
Championships
A482

6p, Sun, natl. flag, sailboat, vert. 10p, Man
sailing boat.

1996, Oct. 16
1236 A482 6p multicolored   3.75 1.75
1237 A482 10p multicolored   6.25 3.25

A483

1996, Nov. 25   Litho.   Perf. 13½
1238 A483 5p green & multi   3.25 1.60
1239 A483 10p pink & multi   6.25 3.25

Intl. Day to End Violence Against Women.

Birds — A484

a, Buteo ridgwayi. b, Aratinga chloroptera. c,
Amazona ventralis. d, Hyetornis rufigularis. e,
Saurothera longirostris. f, Siphonorhis brew-
steri. g, Chlorostilbon swainsonii. h, Todus
angustirostris. i, Todus subulatus. j, Temnotrogon roseigaster. k, Nesoctites micromegas.
l, Melanerpes striatus. m, Turdus swalesi. n,
Carduelis dominicensis. o, Dulus dominicus.
p, Microligea palustris. q, Vireo nanus. r,
Xenoligea montanta. s, Turdus swalesi dodae.
t, Calyptophilus frugivorus tertius. u, Corvus
leucognaphalus. v, Calyptophilus frugivorus
neibae.

1996, Nov. 11
1240 A484 2p Sheet of 22, #a-
          v   45.00 30.00

Lighthouse Type of 1995
1996, Dec. 27   Litho.   Perf. 13½
1241 A466 10p grn, sil & gray 7.00 3.50

Turtles — A485

a, Dermochelys coriacea. b, Caretta caretta.
c, Chelonia mydas. d, Eretmochelys imbricata.

1996, Dec. 30
1242 A485 5p Block of 4, #a.-
          d.   12.00 10.00

Natl. Youth
Day — A486

1997, Jan. 31
1243 A486 3p multicolored   2.00 1.00

National
Anthem — A487

Designs: 2p, Lyrics, by Emilio Prudhome.
3p, Music, by Jose Reyes.

1997, Feb. 26
1244 A487 2p multicolored   1.50   .65
1245 A487 3p multicolored   2.00   .95

Salomé Urena (1850-
97), Poet — A488

1997, Mar. 6   Perf. 13½
1246 A488 3p multicolored   1.90   .95

Comet Hale-
Bopp — A489

1997, Apr. 1
1247 A489 5p multicolored   4.25 1.60
          Size: 72x47mm
          Imperf
1248 A489 10p multicolored   11.00 11.00

A490

11th Natl. Sports
Games, Mao
'97 — A491

2p, Mascot running with torch. 3p, Mascot in
batting stance, vert. 5p, Runner breaking finish line.

1997, Apr. 3
1249 A490 2p multicolored   1.75   .65
1250 A491 3p multicolored   2.75 1.00
1251 A491 5p multicolored   4.25 1.60
     Nos. 1249-1251 (3)   8.75 3.25

A492

Design: 10p, 5p, Heinrich von Stephan
(1831-97), founder of UPU.

1997, Apr. 8   Litho.   Perf. 13½
1252 A492 10p multicolored   6.25 3.25
          Souvenir Sheet
          Imperf
1253 A492 5p like #1252   3.25 2.75

No. 1253 has simulated perforations.

A493

1997, Apr. 29   Perf. 13½
1254 A493 10p multicolored   9.50 3.25

25th Intl. Congress of CLAHT (Caracas and
Latin American Group of Hemostasis and
Thrombosis).

Gregorio Luperón
(1839-1897),
Politician — A494

1997, May 21
1255 A494 3p multicolored   2.00 1.00

House of Spain, 80th Anniv. — A495

1997, July 4
1256 A495 5p multicolored   3.25 1.60

First Peso Coin, Cent. — A496

1997, Aug. 6   Litho.   Perf. 13½
1257 A496 2p multicolored   1.50 .65

A497

Coronation of the Image of Our Lady of Alta Gracia, 75th Anniv. — A498

1997, Aug. 12
1258 A497 3p multicolored   1.90 .85
1259 A498 5p multicolored   3.25 1.60

America Issue — A499

Life of a postman: 2p, Dog grabbing pants leg of postman on motorcycle. 6p, Dog tearing pants leg of postman with letter.

1997, Oct. 9   Litho.   Perf. 13½
1260 A499 2p multicolored   1.25 .65
    Size: 35½x35½mm
1261 A499 6p multicolored   3.25 1.60

Mother Teresa (1910-97) — A500

1997, Oct. 17
1262 A500 5p multicolored   3.00 1.60

Stamp Day — A501

1997, Oct. 18
1263 A501 5p Nos. 108, 322   2.75 1.60

Central Bank of the Dominican Republic, 50th Anniv. — A502

1997, Oct. 30   Perf. 11½
1264 A502 10p multicolored   5.50 3.25

Lighthouse Type of 1995
1997, Dec. 15   Litho.   Perf. 13½
1265 A466 10p bright rose & gray   7.50 3.25

Bats — A503

a, Erophylius bombifrons. b, Brachyphylla nana. c, Molossus molossus. d, Lasiurus borealis.

1997, Nov. 11
1266 A503 5p Block of 4, #a.-d.   11.00 11.00

Dominican Air Force, 50th Anniv. — A504

Insignias: a, Air Force, red, white, and blue target. b, Northern Air Command, "shark plane." c, Air Command, eagle's wings over target. d, Rescue Force, eagle. e, Maintenance Command. f, Combat Force, dragon, target.

1997, Dec. 19
1267 A504 3p Sheet of 6, #a.-f.   11.00 11.00

Construction of the National Palace, 50th Anniv. — A505

1997, Dec. 30   Litho.   Perf. 13½
1268 A505 10p multicolored   6.25 3.50

First Regional Symposium on Pre-Columbian Culture and Caribbean Contemporary Art — A506

1998, Jan. 28
1269 A506 6p multicolored   3.75 1.60

A507

1998, Apr. 2   Litho.   Perf. 13½
1270 A507 10p multicolored   6.25 3.25

American Chamber of Commerce of the Dominican Republic, 75th anniv.

A508

Book Fair: 3p, Natl. Book Fair, 25th anniv. 5p, Intl. Book Fair, Santo Domingo '98.

1998, Apr. 26
1271 A508 3p black, blue & red   1.90 .85
    Size: 35x33mm
1272 A508 5p black, blue & red   3.25 1.60

Organization of American States, 50th Anniv. — A509

1998, Apr. 30
1273 A509 5p blue & multi   3.25 1.60
1274 A509 5p pink & multi   3.25 1.60

Establishment of the State of Israel, 50th Anniv. — A510

1998, Apr. 30
1275 A510 10p multicolored   9.00 4.50

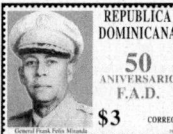

Dominican Air Force, 50th Anniv. — A511

a, Gen. Frank Felix Miranda, portrait at left. b, Early aircraft. c, Col. Ernesto Tejeda, portrait at right. d, As "c," portrait at left. e, As "a," portrait at right.

1998, June 26   Sheet of 6
1276 A511 3p Sheet of 6, #a, c-e, 2 #b   11.00 11.00

City of Santo Domingo, 500th Anniv. — A512

2p, Sun clock. 3p, St. Lazaro Church & Hospital. 4p, First Cathedral in America. 5p, Royal Palace. 6p, Tower of Honor. 10p, St. Nicolas of Bari Church & Hospital.

1998, Aug. 6   Litho.   Perf. 13½
1277 A512 2p multi, vert.   1.25 .65
1278 A512 3p multi   1.90 .90
1279 A512 4p multi   2.50 1.25
1280 A512 5p multi   3.25 1.60
1281 A512 6p multi   3.75 1.90
1282 A512 10p multi, vert.   6.25 3.25
    Nos. 1277-1282 (6)   18.90 9.55

National Theater, 25th Anniv. — A513

1998, Aug. 14   Perf. 13x13½
1283 A513 10p multicolored   6.25 3.00

Latin Union, 44th Anniv. — A514

1998, Aug. 26   Perf. 13½
1284 A514 10p multicolored   6.25 3.00

ICCO (Intl. Cocoa Organization of America & Europe), 25th Anniv. — A515

1998, Sept. 3
1285 A515 10p multicolored   7.75 3.50

Nino Ferrua (1909-79), Stamp Designer — A516

1998, Oct. 18   Litho.   Perf. 13½x13
1286 A516 5p multicolored   3.25 1.50
    Stamp Day.

Pontificate of John Paul II, 20th Anniv. — A517

1998, Oct. 22   Perf. 13½
1287 A517 5p shown   3.25 1.50
1288 A517 10p Portrait, diff.   6.75 2.10

Medicinal Plants — A518

a, Pimenta racemosa. b, Pimenta haitiensis. c, Cymbopogon citratus. d, Citrus aurantium.

1998, Nov. 2
1289 A518 3p Block of 4, #a.-d.   7.00 3.25

Famous Women — A519

America Issue: 2p, Juana Saltitopa standing with cannon. 6p, Anacaona, Indian maiden, group of Indians.

1998, Nov. 5
1290 A519 2p multicolored   2.00 .65
1291 A519 6p multicolored   4.50 2.00

Intl. Year of the Ocean — A520

1998, Nov. 20
1292 A520 5p multicolored   4.00 1.50

A521

1998, Nov. 23
1293 A521 5p multicolored   2.75 1.50

Expofila '98, Santo Domingo. Santo Domingo, 500th anniv.

National Military
Heroes — A522

Designs: a, Fernando Valerio. b, Benito Moncion. c, Jose Maria Cabral. d, Antonio Duverge. e, Gregorio Luperon. f, Jose A. Salcedo. g, Fco. A. Salcedo. h, Gaspar Polanco. i, Santiago Rodriguez. j, Juan Bta. Cambiaso. k, Jose J. Puello. l, Jose Ma. Imbert. m, Juan A. Acosta. n, Marcos Adon. o, Matias R. Mella. p, Francisco R. Sanchez. q, Juan Pablo Duarte. r, Olegario Tenares. s, Pedro Santana. t, Juan Sanchez Ramirez.

1998, Nov. 29
1294 A522 3p Sheet of 20,
    #a.-t.   27.50 24.50

1st Natl.
Paper
Money,
150th
Anniv.
A523

1998, Nov. 30   *Perf. 11½*
1295 A523 10p multicolored   4.75 2.10

Christmas
A524

1998, Dec. 7   *Perf. 13½*
1296 A524 2p Roasting hog   .90 .45
1297 A524 5p Magi   2.25 1.10

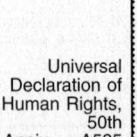

Universal
Declaration of
Human Rights,
50th
Anniv. — A525

1998, Dec. 10
1298 A525 10p multicolored   4.50 2.10

Columbus Lighthouse Type of 1995
1998, Dec. 11
1299 A466 10p orange & black   6.00 3.00

Shells — A526

Designs: a, Lyria vegai. b, Strombus gigas. c, Cittarium pica. d, Nerita peloronta.

1998, Dec. 16
1300 A526 5p Block of 4, #a.-d. 11.00 5.25

Gaspar
Hernández (1798-
1858),
Priest — A527

1998, Dec. 18
1301 A527 3p multicolored   1.40 .70

Dominican Society
of Endocrinology
and Nutrition, 25th
Anniv. — A528

1999, Feb. 24   **Litho.**   *Perf. 13¼*
1302 A528 10p multicolored   4.00 2.00

Office of
Comptroller
General
A529

1999, May 4   **Litho.**   *Perf. 13¼*
1303 A529 2p multicolored   1.00 .45

Export
Industries — A530

Perf. 13½x13¼, 13¼x13½
1999, Apr. 30   **Litho.**
1304 A530 6p Tobacco   2.25 1.10
1305 A530 10p Textiles, vert. 3.75 1.60

Pan American Games,
Winnipeg   A530a

1999, July 29 Litho. *Perf. 13¼x13½*
1306 A530a 5p Baseball   2.75 1.25
1307 A530a 6p Weight lifting 3.25 1.50

Native Plants — A531

Designs: a, Pseudophoenix ekmanii. b, Murtigia calabura. c, Pouteria dominguensis. d, Rubus dominguensis focke.

1999, July 13
1308 A531 5p Block of 4, #a.-d. 9.50 9.50

Presidents of the
Dominican
Republic — A532

Designs: a, Tomas Bobadilla y Briones. b, Pedro Santana. c, Manuel Jimenez. d, Buenaventura Baez. e, Manuel de Regla Mota. f, José Desiderio Valverde. g, José A. Salcedo. h, Gaspar Polanco.

1999, Aug. 31   *Perf. 13½x13¼*
1309 A532 3p Sheet of 8, #a.-
    h. + label   10.00 10.00

A533

Sovereign Military
Order of
Malta — A534

Perf. 13¼x13½
1999, Sept. 20   **Litho.**
1310 A533 2p multicolored   .85 .45
        Perf. 13½
1311 A534 10p multicolored   4.50 2.75

Paintings by
José Vela
Zanetti (1913-
99)
A535

Various paintings.

Perf. 13½x13¼, 13¼x 13½
1999, Sept. 8
1312 A535 2p multi, vert.   .70 .45
1313 A535 3p multi, vert.   1.25 .80
1314 A535 5p multi   1.90 1.10
1315 A535 6p multi, vert.   2.40 1.40
1316 A535 10p multi, vert. 3.75 2.10
  Nos. 1312-1316 (5)   10.00 5.85

Insects
A536

Designs: a, Strataegus quadrifoveatus. b, Anetia jaegeri. c, Polyancistroydes tettigonidae. d, Aploppus phasmidae.

1999, Sept. 10   *Perf. 13½x13¼*
1317 A536 5p Block of 4, #a.-d. 8.00 8.00

SOS Children's
Villages, 50th
Anniv. — A537

1999, Sept. 29   *Perf. 13¼x13½*
1318 A537 10p multicolored   4.00 2.10

Intl. Year of the
Elderly — A538

1999, Oct. 1
1319 A538 2p Man   .75 .25
1320 A538 5p Woman   2.00 1.00

World Education
Day — A539

1999, Oct. 5
1321 A539 5p multicolored   2.00 .90

A540

Designs: 2p, Skull and crossbones, land mines, shattered gun. 6p, Mushroom cloud.

1999, Oct. 18
1322 A540 2p multicolored   .80 .50
1323 A540 6p multicolored   2.60 1.25

America Issue, a new millennium without arms.

Stamp Day — A541

1999, Oct. 22
1324 A541 5p Luis F. Thomen 2.00 .90

Account of Gen.
Juan Pablo
Duarte — A542

1999, July 16   *Perf. 13½*
1325 A542 3p multicolored   1.25 .25

A543

Contemporary
Writers — A544

Perf. 13¼x13½, 13½x13¼
1999, June 23
1326 A543 2p multicolored   .75 .25
1327 A544 10p multicolored   4.75 2.25

Dermatological
Society, 50th
Anniv. — A545

1999, Sept. 15 Litho. *Perf. 13¼*
1328 A545 3p multi   1.75 .80

Millennium
A546

3p, Earth, trees. 5p, Scientific achievements.

Perf. 13¼x13½
1999, Nov. 10   **Litho.**
1329 A546 3p multi   1.25 .75
1330 A546 5p multi   2.25 1.10

2nd Summit of African, Caribbean and Pacific Heads of State — A547

Emblem and: 5p, Map of Caribbean area, whale. 6p, Map of Pacific area, Easter Island statues. 10p, Map of Africa, lion.

1999, Nov. 23
1331	A547	5p multi	2.00	1.00
1332	A547	6p multi	2.50	1.10
1333	A547	10p multi	4.00	2.00
	Nos. 1331-1333 (3)		8.50	4.10

UPU, 125th Anniv. — A548

6p, Globe, envelope, computer, electronic circuits. 10p, Envelope, electronic circuits.

1999, Nov. 29
1334	A548	6p multi	2.25	1.00

Size: 50x75mm
Imperf
1335	A548	10p multi	4.50	2.10

Union of Latin American Universities, 50th Anniv. — A549

1999, Dec. 3   *Perf. 13½x13¼*
1336	A549	6p multi	2.25	1.00

Lighthouse Type of 1995
1999, Dec. 14   *Perf. 13¼x13½*
1337	A466	10p brown & silver	4.50	2.10

Classical Musicians — A550

No. 1338, José de Jésus Ravelo (1876-1951), clarinet. No. 1339, Juan Francisco Garcia (1892-1974), cornet. No. 1340, Manuel Simo (1916-88), saxophone.

1999, Dec. 17
1338	A550	5p multi	2.00	1.00
1339	A550	5p multi	2.00	1.00
1340	A550	5p multi	2.00	1.00
	Nos. 1338-1340 (3)		6.00	3.00

Municipal Notes, Cent. — A551

Notes and background colors — No. 1341: a, Santo Domingo, San Pedro de Macorís, deep purple. b, Puerto Plata, Moca, purple.
No. 1342, vert.: a, Santiago, Cotui, blue green. b, San Francisco de Macorís, La Vega, golden brown. c, San Cristobal, Samana, peacock blue.
No. 1343: a, As No. 1342a, green background. b, As No. 1342b, brown background. c, As No. 1342c, Prussian blue background.

1999, Dec. 30   *Perf. 13¼*
1341	A551	2p Pair, #a.-b.	2.00	1.00
1342	A551	2p Strip of 3, #a.-c.	2.50	1.10

Souvenir Sheet
Imperf
1343	A551	2p Sheet of 5, Nos. 1341a-1341b, 1343a-1343c	4.50	2.25

Chamber of Spanish Commerce and Industry, 75th Anniv. — A552

1999, Dec. 30   *Perf. 13¼x13½*
1344	A552	10p multi	4.50	2.40

Fight Against Drugs — A553

2000, Feb. 17   Litho.   *Perf. 13½*
1345	A553	5p multi	2.25	1.10

Hogar Crea Dominicana Inc., 25th anniv.

Duarte Institute A554

2000, Feb. 25   *Perf. 13¼*
1346	A554	2p multi	1.00	.50

Prevention of Child Abuse — A555

2000, Mar. 31
1347	A555	2p multi	1.00	.45

National Police — A556

2000, Apr. 6   *Perf. 13½*
1348	A556	2p shown	1.50	.45

Size: 37x28mm
Perf. 13½x13¼
1349	A556	5p Crest	3.00	1.10

Dominican Institute of Industrial Technology, 25th Anniv. — A557

2000, Apr. 11   *Perf. 13½*
1350	A557	2p multi	1.00	.45

Independencia Province, 50th Anniv. — A558

2000, Apr. 15
1351	A558	3p multi	1.25	.65

A559

12th Natl. Games, La Romana — A560

2000, Apr. 27   *Perf. 13½x13¼*
1352	A559	2p Baseball	1.00	.45
1353	A559	3p Boxing	2.00	.80

Perf. 13½
1354	A560	5p Emblem	3.00	1.00
	Nos. 1352-1354 (3)		6.00	2.25

Paintings — A561

Designs: 5p, The Violinist, by Darío Suro. 10p, Self-portrait, by Théodore Chassériau.

2000, May 5   *Perf. 13¼*
1355	A561	5p multi	3.25	1.10
1356	A561	10p multi	5.50	2.50

Presidential Elections — A562

2000, May 12
1357	A562	2p multi	1.40	.45

Classical Musicians A563

No. 1358, Julio Alberto Hernandez Camejo (1900-99), pianist. No. 1359, Ramon Diaz (1901-76), bassoonist. No. 1360, Enrique de Marchena Dujarric (1908-88), pianist.

2000, May 31   *Perf. 13½*
1358	A563	5p multi	3.25	1.10
1359	A563	5p multi	3.25	1.10
1360	A563	5p multi	3.25	1.10
	Nos. 1358-1360 (3)		9.75	3.30

Expo 2000, Hanover — A564

2000, June 1
1361	A564	5p shown	2.25	1.10
1362	A564	10p Emblem, diff.	4.50	2.10

Art by Jaime Colson — A565

Designs: 2p, Woman on horseback. 3p, Abstract. 5p, Musicians and dancers, horiz. 6p, Nudes. 10p, Colson.

2000   Litho.   *Perf. 13¼*
1363-1367	A565	Set of 5	19.00	6.75

Holy Year 2000 — A566

Churches: 2p, Santo Cristo de los Milagros de Bayaguana Sanctuary. 5p, Santa María la Menor Cathedral, first in the Americas, vert. 10p, Nuestra Señora de la Altagracia Basilica, vert.

2000   *Perf. 13½x13¼, 13¼x13½*
1368-1370	A566	Set of 3	10.00	4.00

Lighthouse Type of 1995
2000   *Perf. 13¼x13½*
1371	A466	10p buff, brn & sil	7.25	3.50

Dominican Republic — Republic of China Diplomatic Relations — A566a

Flags of Dominican Republic and Republic of China and: 5p, Illustration of dragon. 10p, Carved dragon.

Serpentine Die Cut 11¼
2000, Dec. 15   Litho.
Self-Adhesive
1371A-1371B	A566a	Set of 2	12.00	3.50

America Issue — Campaign Against AIDS — A566b

Designs: 2p, Child. 6p, AIDS patient (38x38mm).

2000, Dec. 21   **Self-Adhesive**
1371C-1371D	A566b	Set of 2	4.00	2.00

UN High Commissioner for Refugees, 50th Anniv. — A566c

2000, Dec. 29   **Self-Adhesive**
1371E	A566c	10p multi	4.50	2.25

Environmental Protection — A567

Designs: 2p, Lizard on leaf, vert. $3, House. $5, River rapids, vert.

Serpentine Die Cut 11¼
2000   Litho.
Self-Adhesive
1372-1374	A567	Set of 3	6.50	2.50

Lighthouse Type of 1995

2001 Litho. Perf. 13¼x13½
1375 A466 15p lt bl, dk bl & sil ... 9.00 3.50

Concepcion Bona, Seamstress of First Dominican Republic Flag, Cent. of Death — A568

2001 Perf. 13½x13¼
1376 A568 10p multi ... 5.50 2.75

Stamp Day — A569

2001
1377 A569 5p multi ... 3.00 1.10

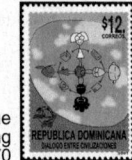

Year of Dialogue Among Civilizations — A570

2001 Perf. 13¼x13½
1378 A570 12p multi ... 5.50 2.50

America Issue — UNESCO World Heritage — A571

Designs: 4p, San Felipe Fort. 15p, Ruins of San Nicolas de Bari Hospital (27x37mm).

2001 Perf. 13½, 13¼x13½ (15p)
1379-1380 A571 Set of 2 ... 10.00 4.25

Lighthouse Type of 1995

2002, Oct. 17 Litho. Perf. 13½x13¾
1382 A466 15p yel & multi ... 5.00 2.00

Mushrooms — A572

No. 1383: a, Pycnoporus sanguineus. b, Morchella elata. c, Mycena epipterygia. d, Coriolopsis polyzona.

Perf. 13¼x13½
2001, Sept. 13 Litho.
1383 A572 6p Block of 4, #a-d ... 13.00 6.50

National Botanical Gardens, 25th Anniv. A573

No. 1384: a, Isidorea pungens. b, Pereskia quisqueyana. c, Goetzea ekmanii. d, Cubanola domingensis.

Perf. 13¼x13½
2001, Sept. 20 Litho.
1384 A573 4p Block of 4, #a-d ... 9.50 9.50

Presidents of the Dominican Republic — A574

No. 1385: a, Gen. José María Cabral. b, Gen. Gregório Luperón. c, Gen. Ignacio María González. d, Ulises Espaillat. e, Pedro A. Pimentel. f, Federico de Jesús García. g, Frenando Arturo de Mariño. h, Gen. Ulises Heureaux.

2001, Sept. 27 Litho. Perf. 13¼
1385 A574 6p Sheet of 8, #a-h, + label ... 27.50 15.00

Blessed Josemaría Escrivá de Balaguer (1902-75), Founder of Opus Dei — A575

2002, Aug. 29 Perf. 13½x13¼
1386 A575 10p multi ... 6.50 1.90

Loyola Polytechnic Institute, 50th Anniv. — A576

2002, Oct. 24 Perf. 13¼x13½
1387 A576 6p multi ... 2.25 1.40

12th Iberoamerican Heads of State Summit A577

Designs: 12p, Flags below map. 15p, Flags above map.

Perf. 13¾x13½
2002, Nov. 14 Litho.
1388-1389 A577 Set of 2 ... 12.00 4.75
Compare with Type A637a.

America Issue — Youth Education and Literacy — A578

Designs: 4p, Teacher helping child write. 15p, Child writing on blackboard.

2002, Dec. 20 Perf. 13¼x13½
1390-1391 A578 Set of 2 ... 8.50 3.00

Coccothrinax Spissa — A579

Perf. 13¼x13½
2002, Dec. 20 Litho.
1392 A579 10p multi ... 4.00 1.50

2003 Pan American Games, Santo Domingo — A580

Color of "2003" in design: 4p, Light green blue. 6p, Blue. 12p, Red.

2003, Feb. 25
1393-1395 A580 Set of 3 ... 6.50 3.00

Medicinal Plants — A581

No. 1396: a, Hymenaea courbaril. b, Spondias mombin. c, Genipa americana. d, Guazuma ulmifonia.

2003, June 17
1396 A581 5p Block of 4, #a-d ... 6.00 2.75

Dr. José Francisco Peña Gomez (1937-98), Politician — A582

Litho. & Engr.
2003, Dec. 17 Perf. 11½
1397 A582 10p multi ... 4.00 1.40

José Marti (1853-95), Cuban Patriot — A583

2003, Nov. 5 Litho. Perf. 13x13¼
1398 A583 15p multi ... 4.50 2.25

Pan American Health Organization, Cent. (in 2002) — A583a

Perf. 13½x13¼
2006, July. 12 Litho.
1398A A583a 20p multi ... 5.00 2.00

America Issue — Flora and Fauna A584

Designs: 5p, Aristelliger lar. 15p, Corpernicia berteroana, vert.

Perf. 13½x13¼, 13¼x13½
2004, Jan. 19 Set of 2 ... 8.50 3.00
1399-1400 A584
Nos. 1399-1400 are dated "2003."

Election of Pope John Paul II, 25th Anniv. — A585

Pope John Paul II: 10p, With hand touching face. 15p, Blessing crowd, horiz. 25p, Vignettes of 10p and 15p stamps.

Perf. 13¼x13½, 13½x13¼
2005, Nov. 26 Set of 2 ... 11.00 3.25
1401-1402 A585
Size: 57x85mm
Imperf
1403 A585 25p multi ... 12.00 3.50

National Council for Children — A586

2004, Mar. 10 Perf. 13½x13¼
1404 A586 7p multi ... 2.75 1.10

Exfilna National Philatelic Exhibition A587

2004, Dec. 8 Litho. Perf. 13½x13¼
1405 A587 7p multi ... 3.00 1.10

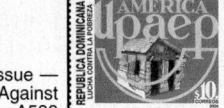

America Issue — Fight Against Poverty — A588

Design: 10p, Shack. 20p, Poor woman.

2004, Dec. 23
1406-1407 A588 Set of 2 ... 12.00 5.75

Dominican Republic - Canada Diplomatic Relations, 50th Anniv. — A589

2004, Dec. 31
1408 A589 20p multi ... 8.50 3.75

Interexpo '05 Intl.
Philatelic
Exhibition
A590

Designs: 7p, Dove and stamp. 20p, Map highlighting Dominican Republic, vert. 10p, Similar to 7p.

Perf. 13½x13¼, 13¼x13½

2005			**Litho.**
1409-1410	A590	Set of 2	11.00 4.75
Souvenir Sheet			
1410A	A590	10p multi	15.00 2.00

Dominican Republic Philatelic Society, 50th anniv.
Issued: 20p, 10/16; 7p, 10/17; 10p, 2005.

America Issue —
Environmental
Protection — A591

Prevention of: 10p, Water pollution. 20p, Air pollution.

2005			**Perf. 13¼x13½**
1411-1412	A591	Set of 2	11.00 4.75

Monte Plata
Maternity
Clinic — A592

Perf. 13½x13¼

2005, Nov. 14			**Litho.**
1413	A592	15p multi	6.25 2.50

Proclamation of
Sister City Status
of Santo Domingo
and La Guardia,
Spain — A593

2005, Nov. 11			
1414	A593	10p multi	3.50 1.50

Stamp
Day — A594

2005	**Litho.**		**Perf. 13½x13¼**
1415	A594	10p multi	3.50 1.50

Palace of Fine
Arts, 50th
Anniv.
A595

2006, Oct. 10	**Litho.**		**Perf. 13¾x13¼**
1416	A595	7p multi	3.00 1.10

Dominican
History
Academy,
75th Anniv.
A596

2006, Oct. 30			**Perf. 13¼**
1417	A596	10p multi	3.75 1.50

16th Intl. Boxing
Congress, Santo
Domingo — A597

2006, Nov. 2			**Perf. 13¼x13½**
1418	A597	20p multi	6.50 2.50

Pope John Paul II
(1920-2005) — A598

Pope and: 10p, Crucifix. 20p, Dove, horiz.

2006, Nov. 4			**Perf. 13½**
1419-1420	A598	Set of 2	11.50 4.50

Blessing of Natl.
Sacred Heart of
Jesus Sanctuary,
50th Anniv. — A599

2006, Nov. 24			**Perf. 13½x13¼**
1421	A599	10p multi	4.50 1.50

Ninth Latin American
Botanical
Congress — A600

2007, Feb/ 26			**Perf. 13¼x13½**
1422	A600	20p multi	7.00 3.00

America Issue,
Energy
Conservation
A601

Designs: 10p, Light bulb in hands. 20p, Transmission lines and tower.

2007, June 11			**Perf. 13x13¼**
1423-1424	A601	Set of 2	8.50 4.25

Pres. Joaquin
Balaguer (1906-
2002) — A602

Balaguer: 7p, Wearing bow tie. 10p, Holding book.

2006, Sept. 1			**Perf. 13¼x13½**
1425-1426	A602	Set of 2	7.00 2.75

Office of the First
Lady — A603

Emblem and: 10p, Tree. 25p, Computer and keyboard.

2007, Mar. 1			**Perf. 13½x13¼**
1427-1428	A603	Set of 2	11.00 4.75

Selection of Nicolás de
Jesus Cardinal López
Rodríguez as
Archbishop of Santo
Domingo, 25th
Anniv. — A604

López Rodríguez: 10p, Standing next to chair. 15p, With Pope John Paul II. 25p, Holding crucifix.

2007, May 25			**Perf. 13¼x13½**
1429-1431	A604	Set of 3	15.00 6.00

2007 Pan American
Games, Rio de
Janeiro — A605

Designs: 15p, High jump. 20p, Weight lifting.

2007, July 6			**Litho.**
1432-1433	A605	Set of 2	11.00 4.50

Podilymbus
Podiceps — A606

2007, Sept. 7	**Litho.**		**Perf. 13½x13¼**
1434	A606	20p multi	7.00 3.00

Dated 2006.

Stamp Day — A607

2007, Oct. 4			**Perf. 13¼x13½**
1435	A607	15p multi	5.00 2.00

America Issue,
Education For
All — A608

Top panel in: 10p, Red. 20p, Blue.

2007, Dec. 26			
1436-1437	A608	Set of 2	11.00 4.50

Treaty of
Friendship With
the Netherlands,
150th
Anniv. — A609

2007, Nov. 9			**Perf. 13½x13¼**
1438	A609	25p multi	7.00 3.00

Palace of
Columbus
A610

2008, Apr. 18			
1439	A610	10p multi	3.50 1.50

Barahona Province,
Cent. — A611

2007, Nov. 23			**Perf. 13¼x13**
1440	A611	10p multi	2.50 1.00

Salvaléon de
Higuey, 500th
Anniv. — A612

2008, Jan. 17			**Perf. 13½**
1441	A612	15p multi	4.00 1.50

Friendship and
Cooperation
Between
Dominican
Republic and
Republic of
China — A613

Designs: 10p, Prunus mume, Swietenia mahagonni. 15p, Urocissa caeruela, Dulus dominicus. 35p, Buildings from China and Dominican Republic.

2008, Feb. 6			
1442-1444	A613	Set of 3	13.00 5.50

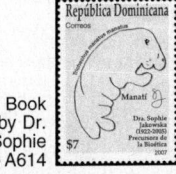

Children's Book
Illustrations by Dr.
Sophie
Jakowska — A614

Initials of Dr. Jakowska and: No. 1445, 7p, Trichechus manatus manatus. No. 1446, 7p, Eretmochelys imbricata, horiz. No. 1447, 10p, Photograph of Jakowska. No. 1448, 10p, Amazona ventralis. 15p, Crocodylus acutus, horiz.

2007, Dec. 7			**Perf. 13¼x13, 13x13¼**
1445-1449	A614	Set of 5	12.50 5.00

Scouting,
Cent. — A615

Designs: 10p, Dominican Republic Scouting emblem. 15p, Scouts, knotted rope.

2008, Jun. 5	**Litho.**			**Perf. 13½**
1450-1451	A615	Set of 2		6.50 2.50

Dominican
Diaspora — A616

2008, Apr. 5			**Perf. 13¼x13**
1452	A616	15p multi	3.50 1.50

Freemasonry in Dominican Republic, 150th Anniv. — A617

2008, Oct. 25   *Perf. 13¼x13½*
1453 A617 25p multi   6.50 2.50

Stamp Day — A618

2008, Oct. 2   *Perf. 13¼*
1454 A618 20p brown   5.25 2.00

2008 Summer Olympics, Beijing — A619

No. 1455: a, Taekwondo. b, Boxing. c, Table tennis. d, Judo.

2008, Aug. 15   *Perf. 13x13¼*
1455 A619 10p Block of 4, #a-d   10.00 4.00

Women Involved in Fight for Independence — A620

No. 1456: a, Juana de la Merced Trinidad (d. 1860). b, Joaquina Filomena Gomez de la Cova (1800-93). c, Maria Baltasara de los Reyes (1789-1867). d, Rosa Protomartir Duarte y Diaz (1820-88). e, Manuela Diaz y Jimenez (1786-1858). f, Petronila Abreu y Delgado (1815-1904). g, Micaela de Rivera de Santana (1785-1854). h, Froilana Febles de Santana (1814-88). i, Rosa Montas de Duvergé (1813-95). j, Josefa Antonia Perez de la Paz (1788-1855). k, Ana Valverde (1798-1864). l, Maria de la Concepción Bona y Hernandez (1824-1901). m, Maria de Jesus Pina y Benitez (1825-58). n, Maria Trinidad Sanchez y Ramona (1794-1845).

2008, Mar. 10   *Perf. 13¼x13½*
1456 A620   Sheet of 14 + 31 labels   32.50 16.00
   a.-n.   10p Any single   1.75 .90

Arms of Santiago, 500th Anniv. — A621

2008, Dec. 7   Litho.   *Perf. 13x13¼*
1457 A621 10p multi   1.50 .50

Discovery of Quisqueya (Hispaniola) by Christopher Columbus, 1492 — A622

2008, Dec. 17
1458 A622 10p multi   1.50 .50

General Timoteo Ogando Encarnación (1818-1908) — A623

2008   *Perf. 13¼x13*
1459 A623 10p multi   1.50 .50

Campaign Against Commercial Sexual Exploitation — A624

2008, Nov. 14
1460 A624 10p multi   1.50 .50

Intl. Swimming Federation, Cent. — A625

2009, Feb. 23   *Perf. 13½*
1461 A625 15p multi   1.50 .50

America Issue, National Festivals A626

No. 1462: a, 15p, Shot of Independence. b, 25p, Sword of the Restoration.

2008   *Perf. 13¼x13*
1462 A626   Horiz. pair, #a-b   6.50 2.50

Duarte y Díez Family Tree A627

No. 1463: a, Juan J. Duarte (1768-1843) and wife, Manuela Díez (1786-1858). b, Juan J. Duarte's sons, Juan Pablo (1813-76), Dominican independence leader, and Vicente (1802-65). c, Juan J. Duarte's son, Manuel (1826-90), and daughter, Rosa (1820-88). d, Juan J. Duarte's daughters, Francisca (1831-99), and Filomena (1818-65).

2009, Feb. 26   *Perf. 13½x13¼*
1463 A627 10p Block of 4, #a-d   6.50 2.50

Chinatown, Santo Domingo — A628

Designs: 15p, Confucius Plaza. 20p, Gateway.

2009, Apr. 17
1464-1465 A628   Set of 2   7.50 3.00

De La Salle Schools in Dominican Republic, 75th Anniv. A629

St. Jean Baptiste de la Salle (1651-1719) A630

2009, May 14   *Perf. 13½x13¼*
1466 A629 7p multi   1.50 .60
             Perf. 13¼x13½
1467 A630 10p multi   2.50 1.10

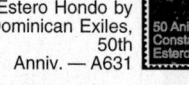

Invasion of Constanza, Maimón and Estero Hondo by Dominican Exiles, 50th Anniv. — A631

2009, June 17   *Perf. 13½*
1468 A631 10p multi   2.75 1.10

Pres. Juan Bosch (1909-2001) — A632

2009, Jun. 19   *Perf. 13¼x13*
1469 A632 20p multi   4.25 1.90

Crabs A633

No. 1470: a, Epilobocera haytensis. b, Gecarcinus ruricola. c, Coenobita clypeatus. d, Callinectes sapidus.

           Perf. 13½x13¼
2009, Sept. 17   Litho.
1470 A633 10p Block of 4, #a-d   4.50 2.25

Winning Designs in Children's Christmas Stamp Design Contest — A634

No. 1471: a, Dancers and musicians in front of house. b, Parade. c, Family and livestock. d, Villagers, manger and Christmas tree.

2009, Oct. 5   Litho.   *Perf. 13x13¼*
1471 A634 10p Block of 4, #a-d   6.00 2.25

Plazas A635

Designs: 15p, Galicia Plaza, Santo Domingo. 25p, Santo Domingo Plaza, La Guardia, Spain.

2009, Oct. 15   *Perf. 13¼*
1472-1473 A635   Set of 2   5.00 2.25

15th American Genealogical Reunion — A636

2009, Nov. 3   *Perf. 13x13¼*
1474 A636 75p multi   10.00 4.25

Natl. School of Judicature A637

2009, Nov. 4   *Perf. 13½*
1475 A637 7p multi   .85 .40

12th Iberoamerican Heads of State Summit — A637a

Designs: 12p, Ribbon of flags below map. 15p, Flags above and to sides of map.

2009   Litho.   *Perf. 13¾x13¼*
1475A-1475B A637a   Set of 2   7.00 —
Dated 2002. Compare with type A577.

America Issue, Toys and Games — A638

Designs: 10p, Fu-fu. 15p, Hopscotch, horiz. 20p, Pañuelo, horiz.

2009, Dec. 15   *Perf. 13x13, 13x13¼*
1476-1477 A638   Set of 2   5.00 1.75
           Imperf
           Size: 76x50mm
1478 A638 20p multi   4.50 1.75

Miniature Sheet

Dominican Republic Presidents — A639

No. 1479: a, Benigno Filomeno De Rojas. b, Jacinto B. De Castro. c, Maetos Cabral. d, Gen. Cesáreo Guillermo. e, Francisco G. Billini. f, Alejandro Woss y Gil. g, Carlos Felipe Morales Languasco. h, Ramón Cáceres.

2009   *Perf. 13¼*
1479 A639 7p Sheet of 8, #a-h, + central label   7.50 3.25

See Nos. 1531, 1585.

National Coat of Arms — A640

2010, Feb. 10   **Perf. 13¼x13½**
1480 A640 50p multi   5.00 2.75

14th Ibero-American Notaries Meeting — A641

2010, June 3 Litho.   **Perf. 13¼x13**
1481 A641 26p multi   3.25 1.40

Preservation of Polar Regions — A642

2010, July 7   **Perf. 13½x13¼**
1482 A642 20p multi   2.25 1.10

Solenodon Paradoxus A643

2010, July 28
1483 A643 25p multi   3.00 1.40
Biodiversity protection.

National Philatelic and Numismatic Museum, 25th Anniv. — A644

2010, Aug. 10   **Perf. 13¼x13**
1484 A644 33p ocher & black   4.00 1.90

Juan Pablo Duarte (1813-76), Independence Leader, and Birthplace, Santo Domingo — A645

2010, Aug. 30   **Perf. 11½x13¼**
1485 A645 25p multi   3.25 1.40

Delivery of the Flag A646   National Pantheon A647

2010, Oct. 12 Litho.   **Perf. 13½**
1486 A646 26p multi   3.25 1.40
     Perf. 13¼x13
1487 A647 33p multi   4.25 1.75
America Issue.

Stamp Day — A648

2010, Oct. 18   **Perf. 13x13¼**
1488 A648 15p multi   1.75 .80

Miniature Sheet

Tourism A649

No. 1489 — Tourist attractions: a, Los Tres Ojos. b, Juan Dolio Beach. c, Altos de Chavón. d, Bayahibe Beach. e, Bávaro Beach. f, Cayo Levantado. g, Las Terrenas Beach. h, Cabarete Beach. i, River rafters, Jarabacoa. j, Lake Enriquillo.

2010, Nov. 4
1489 A649 10p Sheet of 10, #a-j, + 2 labels   10.00 10.00

Veritas Odd Fellows Lodge, Santo Domingo — A650

2010, Nov. 26   **Perf. 13½x13¼**
1490 A650 60p multi   6.50 3.25

World AIDS Day — A651

Designs: 15p, Hands with AIDS ribbons on thumbs. 46p, Flower with AIDS ribbon petals.

2010, Dec. 1   **Perf. 13¼x13**
1491-1492 A651 Set of 2   6.50 3.25

Dominican Order in the Americas, 500th Anniv. — A652

Designs: 15p, Monastery. 26p, Dominican monk and native boy, vert.

2010, Dec. 7   **Perf. 13x13¼, 13¼x13**
1493-1494 A652 Set of 2   4.50 2.25

National Archives, 75th Anniv. — A653

2010, Dec. 14   **Perf. 13½x13¼**
1495 A653 20p multi   2.50 1.10

Santo Domingo, 2010 American Capital of Culture — A654

2010, Dec. 16   **Imperf.**
1496 A654 26p multi   3.00 3.00

Santo Domingo Gates A655

No. 1497: a, Puerta de la Misericordia, "Republica" at bottom. b, Puerta del Conde, "Republica" at left. c, Puerta del Conde, "Republica" at top. d, Puerta de la Misericordia, "Republica" at left.
20p, Puerta de la Misericordia, Puerta del Conde, arms of Dominican Republic.

2011, Feb. 21   **Perf. 13x13¼**
1497 A655 10p Block of 4, #a-d   4.50 4.50
     Size: 90x70mm
     Imperf
1498 A655 20p multi   2.25 2.25

Sur Futuro Foundation — A656

Designs: 15p, Tree and rainbow. 20p, Lake.

2011, Mar. 3   **Perf. 13¼x13½**
1499-1500 A656 Set of 2   4.00 1.90

Caves A657

No. 1501: a, Pomier Caves, San Cristobal. b, Fun Fun Cave, Hato Mayor del Rey. c, Guácara de Hernando Alonzo, La Mata, Sánchez Ramírez. d, Golondrinas Cave, Río San Juan.

2011, Mar. 15   **Perf. 13½x13¼**
1501 A657 10p Block of 4, #a-d   4.50 4.50
     Dated 2010.

Postal Union of the Americas, Spain and Portugal (UPAEP), Cent. — A658

Designs: 20p, "100" with map of Americas and Iberian peninsula in zeroes. 26p, Map of Americas and Iberian peninsula, doves with letters.

2011, Mar. 18   **Litho.**
1502-1503 A658 Set of 2   4.50 2.50

Flowers A659

No. 1504: a, Pereskia quisqueyana. b, Cereus hexagonus. c, Catalpa longissima. d, Tolumnia variegata.

2011, Mar. 31   **Perf. 13¼x13**
1504 A659 10p Block of 4, #a-d   4.50 4.50
     Dated 2010.

Colonel Rafael T. Fernandez Dominguez (1934-65) — A660

2011, May 19 Litho.   **Perf. 13¼x13**
1505 A660 15p multi   1.75 .80

Liberty Day, 50th Anniv. A661

2011, June 2   **Imperf.**
1506 A661 33p multi   4.00 4.00
Assassination of Pres. Rafael Trujillo, 50th anniv.

Aviation — A662

No. 1507: a, 20p, Airplane of Zoilo H. Garcia. b, 25p, Garcia (1849-1922), first Dominican pilot.

2011, June 16   **Perf. 13x13¼**
1507 A662 Vert. pair, #a-b   5.00 5.00

Places Associated With Independence Leader Juan Pablo Duarte — A663

Designs: 15p, Santa Barbara Church, Santo Domingo. 20p, Baptismal font.

2011, Aug. 30
1508-1509 A663 Set of 2   4.25 1.90

Worldwide Fund for Nature
(WWF) — A664

No. 1510 — Hypsiboas heilprini: a, Blue denomination at LR. b, Red denomination at LL. c, Red denomination at LR. d, Blue denomination at LL.

2011, Sept. 7
1510 A664 10p Block of 4, #a-d   5.00 5.00

Father of the Fatherland, by Martin de San Juan — A665

2011, Nov. 9   Litho.   Imperf.
1511 A665 20p multi   2.50 2.50

Execution of Francisco del Rosario Sánchez, 150th anniv.

Pastoral and Social Work in Dominican Republic of Bishop Francisco José Arnáiz, 50th Anniv. — A666

2011, Dec. 21
1512 A666 33p multi   3.00 1.75

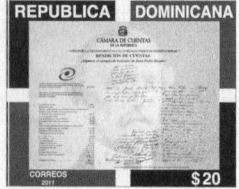

Juan Pablo Duarte and Camara de Cuentas (Governmental Accounting Office) Document — A667

2011
1513 A667 20p multi   2.50 1.10

Sermon Denouncing Mistreatment of Indians of Friar Antonio de Montesinos, 500th Anniv. (in 2011) — A668

2012, Jan. 5   Perf. 11½
1514 A668 60p multi   7.50 3.25

Dated 2011.

National Police, 75th Anniv. (in 2011) — A669

2012, Jan. 12   Perf. 13x13¼
1515 A669 20p multi   2.50 1.10

Dated 2011.

Order of the Pilgrims of the Way of St. James — A670

2012, Feb. 8   Perf. 13¼x13½
1516 A670 33p multi   3.50 1.75

Miniature Sheets

A671

A672

A673

A674

Carnival Masks and Painted Faces A675

No. 1517: a, Azua (white face with headband). b, Bani. c, Barahona (red and black face). d, Barahona (green, yellow and red face). e, Cotuí (black and red face). f, La Romana (red, white and blue face with hat). g, La Romana (red and blue face with flower). h,

Montecristi (yellow face with black and yellow hat). i, San Luis. j, Santo Domingo (red and yellow face with blue spots).
No. 1518: a, Cotuí (pink and red woman's face mask with blue eye lashes), horiz. b, Navarrette. c, Puerto Plata (white and brown mask). d, La Vega (mask with large pointed teeth), horiz. e, Rio San Juan (fish-head mask with large teeth), horiz. f, Samaná. g, San Juan de la Maguana. h, San Pedro de Macoris. i, Santo Domingo (green mask with horns). j, Villa Rivas.
No. 1519: a, Bonao (blue, green and red dragon's head mask). b, Cotuí (hat in flag colors with slits for eyes and mouth). c, La Vega (green and red dragon's head mask). d, Montecristi (red, gold, white, black and green mask). e, La Joya, Guerra, horiz. f, La Romana (yellow and blue bull's head mask with open mouth), horiz. g, Rio San Juan (blue, yellow, green and red demon-head mask with projections). h, Salcedo. i, Santiago (red, white and blue mask with spiked horns). j, Santo Domingo (mask with yellow beard).
No. 1520: a, Barahona (red, white and blue bull's head mask with horns), horiz. b, Bonao (mask with beard, moustache and gold hat). c, Constanza. d, Cabral, horiz. e, Elias Piña. f, La Vega (black, green and red cat's head mask). g, Valverde-Mao, horiz. h, Santiago (white, red and orange mask with spiked horns). i, Santo Domingo (red and yellow mask with horns). j, Puerto Plata (green, white and black pottery head mask), horiz.
No. 1521: a, Azua (red face with green hair). b, Barahona (blue, red, white and black face). c, Cotuí (black and white striped face with green hat). d, Cotuí (black face with flag hat). e, Cotuí (yellow, green, red and black face), horiz. f, Puerto Plata (brown and red mask, black, red and white face), horiz. g, Santo Domingo (yellow and black striped face). h, Santo Domingo (red, blue, white, green and black face). i, Rio San Juan (black face). j, Santiago (red, white and blue face).

Perf. 13¼x13 (vert. stamps), 13x13¼ (horiz. stamps)
2012, Feb. 27
1517 A671 20p Sheet of 10, #a-j, + 2 central labels   20.00 20.00
1518 A672 20p Sheet of 10, #a-j, + 2 central labels   20.00 20.00
1519 A673 20p Sheet of 10, #a-j, + 2 central labels   20.00 20.00
1520 A674 20p Sheet of 10, #a-j, + 2 central labels   20.00 20.00
1521 A675 20p Sheet of 10, #a-j, + 2 central labels   20.00 20.00
    Nos. 1517-1521 (5)   100.00 100.00

A676

2012, Mar. 1   Perf. 13½x13¼
1522 A676 20p multi   2.50 1.10

Dated 2011.
Diplomatic Relations Between Dominican Republic and Ecuador, 125th Anniv.

Pontifical Catholic University, Santo Domingo, 50th Anniv. — A677

2012, Apr. 17   Perf. 13¼x13
1523 A677 25p multi   4.50 1.40

Mailboxes — A678

Designs: 20p, Mailbox with legs. 25p, Mailbox without legs.

2012, May 8   Perf. 13¼x13½
1524-1525 A678   Set of 2   5.00 2.40

America Issue. Dated 2011.

Maria Montez (1912-51), Actress — A679

2012, June 2   Perf. 13¼x13
1526 A679 100p multi   10.00 5.25

Juan Pablo Duarte (1813-76), Patriot — A680

No. 1527: a, 15p, Photograph of Duarte in Hamburg. b, 25p, Oath of the Trinitaria.

2012, July 24   Perf. 13½x13¼
1527 A680   Pair, #a-b   4.50 2.10

Expo Cibao, 25th Anniv. — A681

2012, Sept. 5   Perf. 13¼x13
1528 A681 20p multi   2.00 1.10
  a.   Tete-beche pair   4.50 4.50

Miniature Sheet

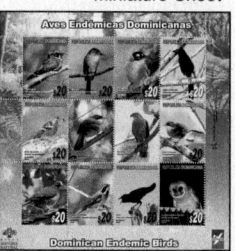
Birds A682

No. 1529: a, Caprimulgus eckmani. b, Contopus hispaniolensis. c, Phaenicophilus palmarum. d, Icterus dominicensis. e, Loxia megaplaga. f, Calyptophilus frugivorus. g, Geotrygon leucometopia. h, Spindalis dominicensis. i, Corvus palmarum. j, Tyto glaucops.

2012, Sept. 19
1529 A682 20p Sheet of 10, #a-j, + 2 central labels   25.00 25.00

No. 1529d in the sheet of 10 was inscribed "CIGUA AMARILLA" in the first part of the print run. The error was discovered and corrected to "CIGUA CANARIA" on the remainder of the printing.

Orchids A683

No. 1530: a, Sudamerylcaste peguerol. b, Tolumnia calochila. c, Quisqueya ekmanii. d, Tolumnia henekenii.

2012, Oct. 18
1530 A683 15p Block of 4, #a-d   6.50 6.50

Presidents Type of 2009
Miniature Sheet

No. 1531: a, Pedro Guillermo. b, Wenceslao Figuereo. c, Horacio Vásquez. d, Juan Isidro Jiménez. e, Eladio Victoria. f, Adolfo Alejandro Nouel. g, José Bordas Valdéz. h, Ramón Báez Machado.

2012   *Perf. 13¼*
1531 A639 15p Sheet of 8, #a-h, + central label   12.00 12.00

America Issue A684

No. 1532 — Legend of: a, El Caracaracol. b, La Ciguapa.

2012, Dec. 18   *Perf. 13¼x13*
1532 A684 20p Horiz. pair, #a-b   15.00 15.00

Miniature Sheet

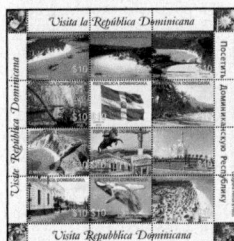

Tourism A685

No. 1533: a, Beach, Saona Island. b, Beach, Bahia de las Aguilas. c, San Rafael Beach. d, Gri-Gri Lagoon. e, Dominican Republic flag. f, Playa Dorada. g, El Morro Beach. h, Puerto Plata. i, Monument to the Heroes of the Restoration, Santiago. j, Historic center of Santiago. k, Jordobadas Whale Sanctuary. l, Beach, Punta Cana.

2013, May 23   *Perf. 13½x13¼*
1533 A685 10p Sheet of 12, #a-l   15.00 15.00

Arachnids — A686

No. 1534: a, Phrynus longipes. b, Mastigoproctus proscorpio. c, Phormictopus cancerides. d, Rhopalurus princeps.

2013, May 28
1534 A686 20p Block of 4, #a-d   10.00 10.00

Pedro Mir (1913-2000), Poet — A687

2013, June 24   *Perf. 13¼x13*
1535 A687 50p multi   3.00 2.40

La Trinitaria Secret Society, 175th Anniv. A688

2013, July 15   *Imperf.*
1536 A688 60p multi   3.75 3.75

María Ugarte (1914-2011), Investigative Reporter — A689

2013, July 31   Litho.   Perf. 13¼x13
1537 A689 33p multi   2.25 1.60

A690

General Gregoio Luperón (1839-97) — A691

Perf. 13½x13¼
2013, Aug. 12   *Litho.*
1538 A690 15p multi   1.10 .70

Imperf
1539 A691 33p multi   2.10 2.10

Dominican War of the Restoration, 150th anniv.

Dominican Rehabilitation Association, Inc., 50th Anniv. — A692

2013, Oct. 23   Litho.   Perf. 13½x13
1540 A692 15p red & blue   1.10 .70

Dominican Postal Institute (Inposdom), 50th Anniv. — A693

Designs: 15p, Emblem for InposPak service. 20p, Inposdom emblem, vert. 25p, Exhibit frames at stamp exhibition. 80p, Inposdom Headquarters.

2013, Nov. 28   Litho.   Perf. 13¼
1541 A693 15p multi   .70 .70
    Size: 30x40mm
    Perf. 13¼x13½
1542 A693 20p multi   .95 .95
    Size: 40x30mm
    Perf. 13½x13¼
1543 A693 25p multi   1.25 1.25
    Nos. 1541-1543 (3)   2.90 2.90
    Size: 80x50mm
    Imperf
1544 A693 80p multi   5.50 5.50

A694

Juan Pablo Duarte (1813-76), Leader of Independence Movement — A695

No. 1545: a, Atarazana School where Duarte taught fencing. b, House of Josefa Pérez de la Paz, birthplace of La Trinitaria Secret Society. c, Duarte directing "La Dramatica." d, 1844 return of Duarte from exile. e, Duarte and Dominican Republic Constitution and flag.

2013, Dec. 9   Litho.   Perf. 13
1545   Horiz. strip of 5   5.00 5.00
a.-e. A694 15p Any single   1.00 1.00
    Imperf
1546 A695 25p multi   1.90 1.90

Campaign Against Discrimination A696

Designs: 15p, Five children. 20p, Map of Dominican Republic, hands.

2014, Jan. 30   Litho.   Perf. 13x13¼
1547-1548 A696   Set of 2   2.75 1.75
    America issue. Dated 2013.

A697

Designs: 20p, Building. 25p, Buildings and university crest.

2014, Feb. 14   Litho.   Perf. 13x13¼
1549 A697 20p multi   1.40 .95
    Size: 89x60mm
    Imperf
1550 A697 25p multi   1.75 1.75
    Dated 2013.
    Founding of St. Thomas Aquinas University, Santo Domingo, 475th Anniv. (in 2013). Reopening of university as Autonomous University of Santo Domingo, cent.

Julia de Burgos (1914-53), Poet — A698

2014, Mar. 28   Litho.   Perf. 13¼x13
1551 A698 100p multi   6.75 4.75

Souvenir Sheets

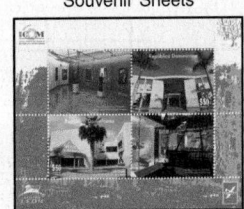

Centro León Museum — A699

National Botanical Gardens — A700

Bellapart Museum — A701

Numismatic and Philatelic Museum — A702

National Museum of Natural History — A703

Museum of Modern Art — A704

No. 1552: a, Entrance to Jimenes Cultural Center. b, Caribeño Patio of Eduardo León Jimenes Cultural Center.
No. 1553: a, Bridge in Japanese Garden. b, Path in Japanese Garden.
No. 1554: a, Permanent Gallery. b, Merengue, painting by Jaime Colson.
No. 1555: a, Exhibit of money with metal ingot. b, Display case in Numismatics Gallery.
No. 1556: a, Museum entrance. b, Skeleton of humpback whale.
No. 1557: a, Sculptures. b, Sculptures and paintings in Permanent Gallery.

2014, May 21   Litho.   Perf. 13½
1552 A699 50p Sheet of 2, #a-b, + 2 labels   6.50 6.50
1553 A700 50p Sheet of 2, #a-b, + 2 labels   6.50 6.50
1554 A701 50p Sheet of 2, #a-b, + 2 labels   6.50 6.50
1555 A702 50p Sheet of 2, #a-b, + 2 labels   6.50 6.50
1556 A703 50p Sheet of 2, #a-b, + 2 labels   6.50 6.50
1557 A704 50p Sheet of 2, #a-b, + 2 labels   6.50 6.50
    Nos. 1552-1557 (6)   39.00 39.00

World Museum Day.

Duarte Institute, 50th Anniv. — A705

2014, June 24   Litho.   Perf. 13½
1558 A705 50p multi   3.50 2.40

Flowers — A706

No. 1559: a, Salcedoa mirabaliarum. b, Ekmanianthe longiflora, vert. c, Coccothrinax jienezii, vert. d, Rhytidophyllum daisyanum.

2014, Aug. 27   Litho.   Perf. 13x13¼
1559 A706 20p Block of 4, #a-d   5.75 5.75

Dated 2013.

National Literacy Plan — A707

2014, Sept. 8   Litho.   Perf. 13½
1560 A707 15p multi   1.10 .70

Dated 2013.

Miniature Sheets

Heroes and Flags of Nations of North and South America — A708

No. 1561, 50p: a, José de San Martín, flag of Argentina. b, Joaquim José Da Silva Xavier (Tiradentes), flag of Brazil. c, Francisco de Paula Santander, flag of Colombia. d, Pedro Alvarado y Bonilla, flag of Costa Rica. e, José Martí, flag of Cuba. f, Juan Pablo Duarte (standing), flag of Dominican Republic. g, Quote by Duarte, flag of Dominican Republic. h, Bernardo O'Higgins Riquelme, flag of Chile. i, José Matías Delgado de León, flag of El Salvador. j, George Washington, flag of United States. k, Jean Jacques Dessalines, flag of Haiti. l, Francisco Morazán Quezada, flag of Honduras.

No. 1562, 50p: a, Simón Bolívar, flag of Bolivia. b, Georges-Etienne Cartier, flag of Canada. c, Máximo Gómez y Báez, flag of Cuba. d, Manuela Sáenz y Aizpuru, flag of Ecuador. e, Pedro Molina Mazariegos, flag of Guatemala. f, Miguel Hidalgo y Costilla, flag of Mexico. g, Head of Duarte, flag of Dominican Republic. h, Augusto César Sandino, flag of Nicaragua. i, Gaspar Rodríguez de Francia, flag of Paraguay. j, José Gabriel Condorcanqui (Túpac Amaru II), flag of Peru. k, José Gervado Artigas Arnal, flag of Uruguay. l, Bolívar, flag of Venezuela.

2014, Sept. 30   Litho.   Perf. 13¼x13
Sheets of 12, #a-l
1561-1562 A708   Set of 2   70.00 70.00

America issue.

World Food Day — A709

No. 1563: a, Boy holding apple. b, Boy eating broccoli, vert. c, Fruit picker on ladder. d, Girl eating cob of corn, vert.

2014, Oct. 15   Litho.   Perf. 13½
1563 A709 25p Block of 4, #a-d   7.00 7.00

Miniature Sheet

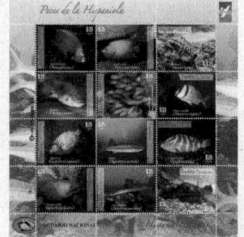

Wildlife A710

No. 1564, 25p — Fish: a, Pomacanthus paru. b, Holacanthus ciliaris. c, Serranus tigrinus. d, Nandopsis haitensis. e, Haemulon flavolineatum. f, Anisotremus virginicus. g, Cantherhines macrocerus. h, Agonostomus monticola. i, Epinephelus striatus. j, Gymnothorax funebris. k, Aulostomus maculatus. l, Dasyatis americana.
No. 1565, 25p — Butterflies: a, Anaea troglodyta. b, Anartia lytrea. c, Burca stillmani. d, Burca hispaniolae. e, Myscelia aracynthia. f, Archimestra teleboas. g, Atlante cryptadia. h, Greta diaphanus quisqueya. i, Heraclides machaonides. j, Choranthus haitensis. k, Memphis verticordia. l, Pyrisitia pyro.

Perf. 13½x13¼
2014, Nov. 20   Litho.
Sheets of 12, #a-l
1564-1565 A710   Set of 2   35.00 35.00

Miniature Sheet

Merengue Musicians and Instruments — A711

No. 1566: a, Nico Lora playing accordion. b, Accordion, horiz. c, Tatico Henriquez playing accordion, horiz. d, Güira. e, Tambora. f, Trio Reynosa performing, horiz. g, Marimba. g, Guandulito playing accordion, horiz.

Perf. 13¼x13½, 13½x13¼
2014, Nov. 26   Litho.
1566 A711 15p Sheet of 8, #a-h,
    + central label   7.50 7.50

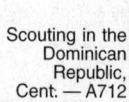

Scouting in the Dominican Republic, Cent. — A712

2014, Dec. 3   Litho.   Perf. 13½x13¼
1567 A712 20p multi   1.25 .90

ISA University, 50th Anniv. (in 2014) — A713

2015, Mar. 5   Litho.   Perf. 13½
1568 A713 200p multi   10.00 9.00

Bani, 250th Anniv. (in 2014) — A714

2015, Mar. 6   Litho.   Perf. 13¼
1569 A714 100p multi   5.50 4.50

Dated 2014.

Gustavo A. Moré González (1925-2002), President of Dominican Philatelic Society — A715

2015, Apr. 9   Litho.   Perf. 13½
1570 A715 75p multi   4.00 3.50

Stamp Day. Dated 2014.

Programs Run Through Office of the First Lady — A716

No. 1571: a, Newborn Screening Program. b, Comprehensive Care Center for Disability.

2015, Apr. 28   Litho.   Perf. 13¼x13
1571 A716 250p Horiz. pair,
    #a-b   25.00 25.00

Miniature Sheets

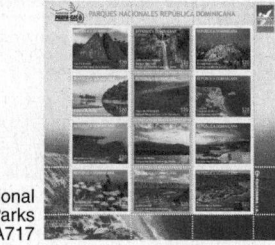

National Parks A717

No. 1572, 20p: a, Pyramids, Valle Nuevo National Park. b, Rio Grande Waterfall, Francisco Alberto Caamaño Deñó National Park. c, Coral reef and fish, Monte Cristi Underwater National Park. d, Hatillo Dam Reservoir with small islands at left, Aniana Vargas National Park. e, Hoyo de Pelempito, Sierra de Bahoruco National Park. f, Aerial view of El Morro Beach, El Morro National Park. g, Coastal hills, Los Haitises National Park. h, Sierra de Neiba, Sierra de Neiba National Park. i, Salado de Neiba, La Gran Sabana National Park. j, Haemulon spp., La Caleta Underwater National Park. k, Quita Coraza, Anacona National Park. l, La Isabela ruins, La Hispaniola National Park.

No. 1573, 20p: a, Baiguate Waterfall, Baiguate National Park. b, Punta Aguila Cliffs, Jaragua National Park. c, Waterfall, Saltos de la Jalda National Park, vert. d, Cliffs, Sierra Martin García National Park. e, Cyclura ricordii, Lago Enriquillo e Isla Cabritos National Park. f, Offshore rocks, Los Haitises National Park. g, Rock art, Aniana Vargas National Park, vert. h, Whales, Quita Cabrón National Park. i, Plagiodontia aedium, Sierra de Bahoruco National Park. j, Mountains, Nalga de Maco National Park. k, Sea level view of cliffs and El Morro Beach, El Morro National Park. l, Palm trees, Sierra Martin García National Park.

No. 1574, 20p: a, Tetero Valley, José del Carmen Ramírez National Park. b, Isla Saona, Este National Park. c, Fregata magnificens, Este National Park. d, Mountains, Armando Bermúdez National Park. e, Sun over water, Lago Enriquillo e Isla Cabritos National Park. f, Cabo Cabrón, Cabo Cabrón National Park. g, Epilobocera wetherbeei, Valle Nuevo National Park. h, Punta Espada, Punta Espada National Park. i, Río Amina, Manolo Tavárez Justo National Park. j, La Humeadora, La Humeadora National Park. k, Rivers, Humedales del Ozama National Park. l, Río Mana, Máximo Gómez National Park, vert.

No. 1575, 20p: a, Balsa Estuary, Mangiares de Estero Balsa National Park. b, Río Mao, Piky Lora National Park. c, Lakes, Humedales del Ozama National Park. d, Shoreline, Mangiares del Bajo Yuna National Park. e, Foggy landscape, Valle Nuevo National Park. f, Bahia de las Aguilas, Jaragua National Park. g, Siproeta stelenes, Máximo Gómez National Park, vert. h, Hatillo Dam Reservoir with rocks at LR, Aniana Vargas National Park. i, Phaenicophilus palmarum, Luis Quin National Park. j, Loma La Tachuela, Luis Quin National Park. k, Shoreline, Este National Park. l, Mountains, Manolo Tavárez Justo National Park.

2015, May 22   Litho.   Perf. 13½
Sheets of 12, #a-l
1572-1575 A717   Set of 4   55.00 55.00

Dominican Chapter of Lions International, 50th Anniv. — A718

2015, May 24   Litho.   Perf. 13¼
1576 A718 50p multi   2.75 2.25

Matías Ramón Mella Castillo (1816-64), Vice-President — A719

2015, June 10   Litho.   Imperf.
1577 A719 300p multi   16.00 16.00

Dated 2014.

Cooperation Between Brazilian and Dominican Republic Universities, 50th Anniv. — A720

2015, June 22   Litho.   Perf. 13½
1578 A720 50p multi   2.50 2.25

Santiago Chamber of Commerce, Cent. — A721

2015, July 9   Litho.   Perf. 13¼
1579 A721 50p multi   2.50 2.25

Oscar de la Renta (1932-2014), Fashion Designer — A722

2015, Oct. 13   Litho.   Perf. 13¼x13
1580 A722 250p multi   12.50 11.00

St. Teresa of Avila (1515-82) — A723

2015, Oct. 16   Litho.   Perf. 13¼x13½
1581 A723 45p multi   2.25 2.00

Rights for Disabled People A724

2015, Nov. 16   Litho.   Perf. 13¼
1582 A724 100p multi   5.00 4.50

Campaign to End Violence Against Women — A725

Perf. 13¼x13½

2015, Nov. 25   **Litho.**
1583 A725 35p multi   1.75 1.60

See Ecuador No. 2173, Guatemala No. 717, El Salvador No. 1747, and Venezuela No. 1731.

Religious Objects — A726

No. 1584: a, Pax, 17th cent. (portapaz). b, Processional cross, 18th cent. (cruz procesional). c, Monstrance, 19th cent. (custodia). d, Eucharistic ark, 16th cent. (arca eucaristica). e, Chalice, 16th cent. (cáliz).

2015, Dec. 1   **Litho.**   **Perf. 13¼x13½**
1584   Strip of 5   12.00 12.00
a.-e. A726 45p Any single   2.00 2.00

Presidents Type of 2009
Miniature Sheet

No. 1585: a, Francisco Henríquez y Carvajal. b, Juan Bautista Vicini Burgos. c, Rafael Estrella Ureña. d, Inscriptions "1930-1938" and "1942-1952" (rule of Rafael Trujillo). e, Inscription "1952-1960" (rule of Hector Trujillo). f, Jacinto Bienvenido Peynado. g, Manuel de Jesús Troncoso de la Concha. h, Joaquín Balaguer Ricardo.

2015, Dec. 18   **Litho.**   **Perf. 13¼**
1585 A639 20p Sheet of 8, #a-h,
    + central label   9.00 9.00

Dated 2014.

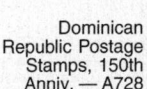

Campaign Against Human Trafficking — A727

No. 1586: a, People in suitcase. b, Chained hands holding Earth.

2015, Dec. 18   **Litho.**   **Perf. 13x13½**
1586 A727 50p Pair, #a-b   5.25 5.25

America Issue.

Dominican Republic Postage Stamps, 150th Anniv. — A728

Designs: 30p, Dominican Republic #1. 35p, Dominican Republic #2. 45p, Dominican Republic #3. 50p, Dominican Republic #4. 150p, Dominican Republic #1-4, cover bearing #1, printing press.

2015, Dec. 18   **Litho.**   **Perf. 13x13½**
1587-1590 A728   Set of 4   8.50 7.00
    Size: 140x100mm
    Imperf.
1591 A728 150p multi   7.50 7.50

Luis María "Billo" Frómeta (1915-88), Orchestra Conductor A729

2016, Mar. 30   **Litho.**   **Perf. 13½**
1592 A729 150p multi   8.50 6.75

Pedro Henriquez Ureña National University, 50th Anniv. — A730

2016, Apr. 20   **Litho.**   **Perf. 13½**
1593 A730 50p multi   2.50 2.25

Marine Mammals — A731

No. 1594: a, Tursiops truncatus. b, Trichechus manatus manatus. c, Megaptera novaeangliae. d, Globicephala.

Perf. 13½x13¼

2016, June 15   **Litho.**
1594 A731 50p Block of 4, #a-
    d   11.00 11.00

Anoles A732

No. 1595: a, Anolis divius. b, Anolis prasinorius. c, Anolis viridius. d, Anolis eladioi.

Perf. 13½x13¼

2016, June 15   **Litho.**
1595 A732 50p Block of 4, #a-
    d   11.00 11.00

Miniature Sheet

Dominican Scientists — A733

No. 1596: a, Dr. Pedro Troncoso Sánchez (1904-89), ambassador and historian. b, Dr. Henri Alain Liogier (1916-2009), botanist. c, Dr. Pablo Rafael Iñiguez Pérez (1925-2007), gastroenterologist. d, Dr. José Luís Alemán Dupuy (1928-2007), economist. e, Dr. Juan Manuel Taveras Rodríguez (1919-2002), neuroradiologist. f, Dr. José Altagracia Silié Gatón (1919-2014), judge. g, Dr. Hugo R. Mendoza Tapia (1930-2009), pediatrician. h, Dr. Francisco R. Guarocuya Batista del Villar (1934-2013), cardiologist.

2016, Aug. 10   **Litho.**   **Perf. 13½**
1596 A733 20p Sheet of 8, #a-
    h   11.00 11.00

Matías Ramón Mella Castillo (1816-64), National Hero — A734

2016, Sept. 29   **Litho.**   **Imperf.**
1597 A734 150p multi   9.50 9.50

A735

Designs: 35p, Florence Terry Griswold (1875-1941), Founder of Pan America Round Tables, and Hotel Menger, San Antonio, Texas.

2016, Oct. 12   **Litho.**   **Perf. 13x13¼**
1598 A735 35p multi   2.75 1.50

First Pan American Round Table, cent.

2016 Summer Olympics, Rio de Janeiro — A736

No. 1599: a, Track and field. b, Boxing. c, Weight lifting. d, Taekwondo.

2016, Oct. 18   **Litho.**   **Perf. 13½x13¼**
1599 A736 15p Block of 4, #a-d   4.75 4.75

America Issue.

Miniature Sheet

National Botanical Garden A737

No. 1600: a, Peltophorum berteroanum. b, Phyllostylon rhamnoides. c, Guarea guidonia. d, Haematoxylon campechianum. e, Magnolia pallescens. f, Capparis cynophollophora. g, Guaiacum officinale. h, Coccoloba pubescens. i, Calophyllum calaba. j, Krugiodendron ferreum. k, Ekmanianthe longiflora. l, Juniperus gracilior.

2016, Oct. 27   **Litho.**   **Perf. 13x13¼**
1600 A737 10p Sheet of 12, #a-l   9.50 9.50

No. 1600h "pubescens" is spelled wrong on stamp.

Dr. Román Bautista Brache (1905-65), Physician and Politician — A738

2016, Nov. 4   **Litho.**   **Perf. 13¼x13½**
1601 A738 20p multi   1.25 .90

Mountains — A739

No. 1602: a, Matterhorn, Switzerland. b, Loma Isabel de Torres, Dominican Republic.

Perf. 13½x13¼

2016, Nov. 17   **Litho.**
1602 A739 60p Pair, #a-b   8.00 8.00

80th anniv. of relations between Dominican Republic and Switzerland.
See Switzerland Nos. 1617.

Specification of Dominican Republic National Anthem in National Constitution, 50th Anniv. — A740

2016, Nov. 28   **Litho.**   **Imperf.**
1603 A740 50p multi   3.50 3.50

Miguel de Cervantes (1547-1616), Writer — A741

2017, Jan. 31   **Litho.**   **Perf. 13¼x13½**
1604 A741 100p multi + label   4.50 4.50

BanReservas (Reserve Bank), 75th Anniv. — A742

2017, Mar. 2   **Litho.**   **Perf. 13¼x13½**
1605 A742 75p multi   3.25 3.25

Popes A743

No. 1606: a, Pope Emeritus Benedict XVI, denomination at LL. b, Pope Francis, denomination at LR. c, Pope Francis, denomination at LL. d, Pope Emeritus Benedict XVI, denomination at LR.

2017, Mar. 14   **Litho.**   **Perf. 13½**
1606 A743 60p Block of 4, #a-
    d   10.50 10.50

Francisco del Rosario Sánchez (1817-61), Leader in Dominican War of Independence — A744

2017, Mar. 29   **Litho.**   **Imperf.**
1607 A744 150p multi   6.50 6.50

Bridges A745

No. 1608: a, Mauricio Báez Bridge. b, Matías Ramón Mella Bridge. c, Rio Chavón Bridge. d, Hermanos Patiño Bridge.

2017, Apr. 24   **Litho.**   **Perf. 13½x13¼**
1608 A745 50p Block of 4, #a-d   8.50 8.50

Painters
and
Their
Paintings
A746

No. 1609: a, Silvano Lora (1931-2003). b, Domingo Líz (1931-2013), horiz. c, Gordas en Bicicletas, by Líz, horiz. d, Serie Concieno Ecologico, by Lora.

Perf. 13¼x13½, 13½x13¼ (horiz. stamps)

2017, Apr. 24   **Litho.**
1609 A746 25p Block of 4, #a-d   4.25 4.25

YMCA in Dominican
Republic, 50th
Anniv. — A747

2017, Apr. 28 Litho. *Perf. 13¼x13½*
1610 A747 50p multi   2.10 2.10

Miniature Sheet

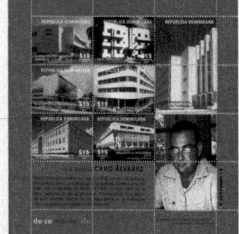

Buildings Designed by José Antonio
Caro Alvarez (1910-78) — A748

No. 1611: a, University of Santo Domingo Faculty of Medical Science Building, 1944. b, Menendez Building, 1941. c, Faculty of Engineering and Architecture Building, 1959. d, Rodriguez Building, 1949. e, Central Bank Building, 1956. f, National Library, 1971.

2017, May 9 Litho. *Perf. 13½x13¼*
1611 A748 15p Sheet of 6, #a-f,
+ 6 labels   4.00 4.00

Fe y Alegría
Organization in
Dominican Republic,
25th Anniv. — A749

2017, May 17 Litho. *Perf. 13¼x13½*
1612 A749 25p multi   1.10 1.10

Lions Clubs
International,
Cent. (in
2016) — A750

2017, May 21 Litho. *Perf. 13½x13¼*
1613 A750 100p multi   4.25 4.25

Casa de España
Organization,
Cent. — A751

2017, June 14 Litho. *Perf. 13½*
1614 A751 12p multi   .50 .50

Miniature Sheet

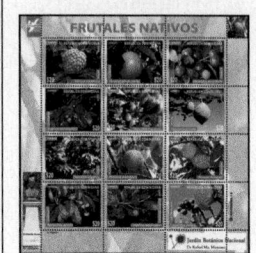

Fruit
A752

No. 1615: a, Annona squamosa. b, Chrysophyllum cainito. c, Malpighia punicifolia. d, Eugenia domingensis. e, Chrisobalanus icaco. f, Genipa americana. g, Spondias mombin. h, Mammea americana. i, Annona reticulata. j, Byrsonima spicata. k, Ziziphus rhodoxylon. l, Coccoloba uvifera.

Perf. 13½x13¼

2017, Sept. 12   **Litho.**
1615 A752 20p Sheet of 12,
#a-l   10.50 10.50

Miniature Sheets

Historic Maps of Hispaniola — A753

No. 1616, 10p — Map by: a, Christopher Columbus, 1493. b, Bologna, 1516. c, Benedetto Bordone, 1528. d, Giovanni B. Ramusio, 1534. e, Giacomo Gastaldi, 1548. f, Giacomo Ruscelli, 1561. g, Paolo Forlani, 1564. h, Ramusio, 1565. i, Bertelli Lafreri, 1566. j, Tomasso Porcacchi, 1572. k, Girolamo Ruscelli, 1580. l, Cornelius Wytfliet, 1597.
No. 1617, 10p — Map by: a, Laugenes, 1598. b, Metellus, 1598. c, Petrus Bertius, 1616. d, Arent Roggeveen, 1675. e, P. Coronelli, 1696. f, Guillaume de l'Isle, 1722-23. g, Emanuel Bowen, 1747. h, M. Bellin, 1754. i, M. Bonne, 1788. j, William Foden, 1795. k, I. Sonis, 1796. l, Tardieu, 1802.

2017, Sept. 26 Litho. *Perf. 13x13¼*
Sheets of 12, #a-l
1616-1617 A753 Set of 2   10.50 10.50

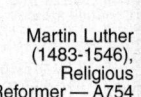

Martin Luther
(1483-1546),
Religious
Reformer — A754

2017, Oct. 9 Litho. *Perf. 13½x13¼*
1618 A754 100p multi   4.25 4.25
Protestant Reformation, 500th anniv.

Women's
Citizenship and
Suffrage, 75th
Anniv. — A755

2017, Nov. 7 Litho. *Perf. 13½x13¼*
1619 A755 75p multi   3.25 3.25

Manuel Corripio García (1908-2004),
Businessman, and His House — A756

2017, Nov. 29 Litho. *Perf. 13½*
1620 A756 20p multi   .85 .85
A vertical column of perforations runs through the center of No. 1620.

Miniature Sheet

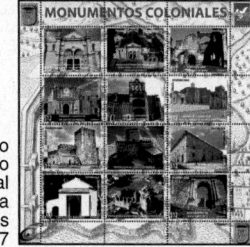

Santo
Domingo
Colonial
Era
Buildings
A757

No. 1621: a, Santa Maria de la Encarnacion Basilica Cathedral. b, Ruins of San Nicolás di Bari Hospital. c, Imperial Convent. d, Church of the Convent of Our Lady of Mercy. e, Ozama Fortress. f, Museum of the Royal Houses. g, Rosario Chapel. h, Ruins of Monastery of San Francisco.

2017, Dec. 11 Litho. *Perf. 13½*
1621 A757 12p Sheet of 8, #a-h,
+ 4 central labels   4.00 4.00

Jarabacoa — A758

2017, Dec. 20 Litho. *Perf. 13¼*
1622 A758 25p multi   1.10 1.10
International Year of Sustainable Tourism for Development.

Miniature Sheet

Tourist Attractions — A759

No. 1623: a, Lago Enriquillo, Bahoruco Province. b, Salinas Sand Dunes, Baní. c, Playo Macao, La Altagracia Province. d, Waterfall, Constanza. e, Cathedral of the Immaculate Conception, La Vega. f, Clock tower designed by Gustave Eiffel, Montecristi, vert. g, Bahia de las Aguilas, Pedernales Province. h, Lighthouse, Puerto Plata Province. i, Playa Rincón, Samaná Province. j, Cueva de las Maravillas, San Pedro de Macoris Province. k, St. James the Apostle Cathedral, Santiago de los Caballeros. l, Colonial City, Santo Domingo.

2017, Dec. 20 Litho. *Perf. 13½*
1623 A759 15p Sheet of 12, #a-l 7.50 7.50
America Issue.

Introduction of
Basketball in the
Dominican
Republic, Cent.
(in 2017) — A760

2018, Jan. 23 Litho. *Perf. 13x13¼*
1624 A760 25p multi   1.10 1.10
Dated 2017.

Vincentian
Charism, 400th
Anniv. (in
2017) — A761

2018, Jan. 25 Litho. *Perf. 13x13¼*
1625 A761 100p multi   4.25 4.25
Dated 2017.

Souvenir Sheet

Friendship Between Dominican
Republic and Peru — A762

No. 1626: a, Ramón Castilla y Marquesado (1797-1867), 20th President of Peru, and flag of Peru. b, Gregorio Luperón (1839-97), 20th President of Dominican Republic, flag of Dominican Republic.

2018, Feb. 7 Litho. *Perf. 13½*
1626 A762 50p Sheet of 2, #a-b 4.25 4.25
Dated 2017. See Peru No. 1957.

Miniature Sheet

Buildings Designed by Guillermo
González Sánchez (1900-70) — A763

No. 1627: a, Ramfis Park, 1936. b, Feria de la Paz (Peace Fair), 1955. c, Copello Building, 1938. d, Hotel Jaragua. e, Centro Social Obrero (Social Worker Center), 1945. f, Hotel Hamaca, 1949.

Perf. 13½x13¼

2018, Feb. 15   **Litho.**
1627 A763 15p Sheet of 6, #a-f,
+ 6 labels   3.75 3.75
Dated 2017.

Rotary
International in
Dominican
Republic, 75th
Anniv. — A764

2018, May 15 Litho. *Perf. 13½*
1628 A764 75p multi   3.00 3.00

Miniature Sheet

Buildings Designed by Humberto Ruiz Castillo (1897-1966) — A765

No. 1629: a, St. John Cosco Church, 1938. b, Santo Domingo College, 1939. c, San Rafael Chapel, 1942. d, Anatomy Faculty Building, University of Santo Domingo, 1945. e, Gonzalez Ramos Building, 1946. f, Alma Mater, University of Santo Domingo, 1955.

2018, May 29   Litho.   Perf. 13½x13¼
1629 A765 15p Sheet of 6, #a-f,
+ 6 labels   3.75 3.75

Inter-American Institute for Cooperation on Agriculture, 50th Anniv. — A766

Perf. 13½x13¼
2018, June 27   Litho.
1630 A766 50p multi   2.00 2.00

Miniature Sheet

23rd Central American and Caribbean Games, Barranquilla, Colombia — A767

No. 1631: a, Basketball. b, Baseball. c, Artistic gymnastics. d, Volleyball.

2018, July 4   Litho.   Perf. 13½x13¼
1631 A767 25p Sheet of 4, #a-d   4.00 4.00

Miniature Sheets

Artists and Their Works A768

No. 1632, 50p: a, Celeste Woss y Gil (1891-1985). b, Nude, by Woss y Gil. c, Mother Selling Dolls, by Cándido Bidó (1936-2011). d, Bidó.
No. 1633, 50p: a, Rooster, by Guillo Perez (1923-2014). b, Perez. c, Marianela Jiménez (1925-2008). d, Carnaval, by Jiménez.
No. 1634, 50p: a, Soucy de Pellerano (1928-2014). b, Maqui-barca del Progresso, sculpture by de Pellerano. c, Untitled work by Fernando Ureña Rib (1951-2014). d, Ureña Rib.

2018, July 18   Litho.   Perf. 13¼x13½
Sheets of 4, #a-d
1632-1634 A768   Set of 3   24.00 24.00

National Symphony Orchestra — A769

2018, Aug. 22   Litho.   Imperf.
1635 A769 100p multi   4.00 4.00

Miniature Sheets

Aviators and Flags of Their Countries — A770

No. 1636, 20p: a, Ramón Franco (1896-1938), Spain. b, Frank Andrés Féliz Miranda (1901-54), Dominican Republic. c, Charles Lindbergh (1902-74), United States. d, Juan Guillermo Villasana López (1891-1959), Mexico. e, Silvio Pettirossi (1887-1916), Paraguay. f, Jorge Antonio Chávez Dartnell (1887-1910), Peru. g, Cesáreo L. Berisso (1887-1971), Uruguay. h, Artur de Sacadura Cabral (1881-1924) and Carlos Viegas Gago Cutinho (1869-1959), Portugal, horiz.
No. 1637, 20p: a, Jorge Alejandro Newbery (1875-1914), Argentina, horiz. b, Rafael Pabón Cuevas (1903-34), Bolivia. c, Alberto Santos-Dumont (1873-1932), Brazil. d, Arturo Meriño Benítez (1888-1970), Chile. e, Camilo Daza Alvarez Mutiscua (1898-1975), Colombia. f, Domingo Rosillo del Toro (1878-1957), Cuba. g, Zoilo Hermógenes García (1881-1916), Dominican Republic. h, Cosme Rennella Barbatto (1890-1937), Ecuador.

Perf. 13¼x13½, 13½x13¼ (#1636h, 1637a)
2018, Oct. 3   Litho.
Sheets of 8, #a-h
1636-1637 A770   Set of 2   13.00 13.00

Spanish International Cooperation Agency in the Dominican Republic — A771

2018, Oct. 17   Litho.   Perf. 13½
1638 A771 60p multi   2.40 2.40

17th Congress of Aeronautical and Space History, Santo Domingo — A772

2018, Nov. 19   Litho.   Perf. 13½
1639 A772 25p multi   1.00 1.00

Dr. Salvador B. Gautier (1868-1938), First President of Dominican Republic Red Cross — A773

Perf. 13¼x13½
2018, Nov. 27   Litho.
1640 A773 100p multi   4.00 4.00

Miniature Sheet

Winning Art In Zero Hunger Generation Children's Stamp Design Contest — A774

No. 1641: a, Child licking bowl, by Anabelys Estévez. b, Child and plate of food, by Angela María Ramírez Ciriaco. c, Children watering seedling and dreaming of giving apples to other children, by Victor Manuel Pérez. d, Children on globe, by Anderson Alvarez Carpio.

2018, Dec. 12   Litho.   Perf. 13x13¼
1641 A774 25p Sheet of 4, #a-d   4.00 4.00

Miniature Sheet

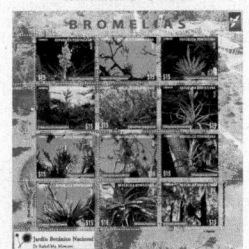

Bromeliads — A775

No. 1642: a, Bromelia pinguin. b, Captosis floribunda. c, Guzmania monestachya. d, Tillandsia baliophylla. e, Tillandsia compressa. f, Tillandsia fasciculata. g, Tillandsia hotteana. h, Tillandsia paucifolia. i, Tillandsia pruinosa. j, Vriesea capituligera. k, Vriesea incurva. l, Vriesea sintenisii.

2019, Feb. 26   Litho.   Perf. 13x13¼
1642 A775 15p Sheet of 12, #a-l   7.25 7.25

Expo-Independencia 2019 Numismatic and Philatelic Exhibition, Santo Domingo — A776

2019, Apr. 21   Litho.   Imperf.
1643 A776 25p multi   1.00 1.00

Cooperation Between the Dominican Republic and the European Union — A777

2019, May 8   Litho.   Perf. 13¼
1644 A777 60p multi   2.40 2.40

A778

A779

A780

A781

Santo Domingo Rotary Club, 50th Anniv. — A782

2019, May 24   Litho.   Perf. 13½x13¼
1645   Horiz. strip of 5   4.00 4.00
a.   A778 20p multi   .80   .80
b.   A779 20p multi   .80   .80
c.   A780 20p multi   .80   .80
d.   A781 20p multi   .80   .80
e.   A782 20p multi   .80   .80

Miniature Sheets

North and South American Icons of the Virgin Mary — A783

No. 1646, 50p — Icon from: a, Argentina. b, Bolivia. c, Brazil. d, Canada. e, Colombia. f, Costa Rica. g, Dominican Republic (Nuestra Señora de las Mercedes). h, Chile. i, Cuba. j, Ecuador. k, El Salvador. l, United States.
No. 1647, 50p — Icon from: a, Guatemala. b, Haiti. c, Honduras. d, Mexico. e, Nicaragua. f, Dominican Republic (Nuestra Señora de la Altagracia). g, Panama. h, Paraguay. i, Peru. j, Puerto Rico. k, Uruguay. l, Venezuela.

Perf. 13¼x13½
2019, June 13   Litho.
Sheets of 12, #a-l
1646-1647 A783   Set of 2   47.50 47.50

A784

Dominican Numismatic Society, 50th Anniv. — A785

Designs: 60p, Dominican Numismatic Society 50th anniversary emblem.
No. 1649 — Obverse and reverse of: a, King Ferdinand II era real coin (denomination at UR). b, Two reales silver coin minted in Santo Domingo (denomination at LR). c, 1844 quarter real coin (denomination at UL). d, 1937 half peso coin (denomination at LL).

2019, June 21   Litho.   Perf. 13½
1648 A784 60p multi   2.40 2.40

Perf. 13x13¼
1649 A785 20p Sheet of 4, #a-d   3.25 3.25

Dr. Zoraida Heredia Suncar (1917-2011), Educator — A786

2019, July 17   Litho.   Perf. 13¼x13
1650   A786   60p multi   2.40   2.40

Establishment of Diplomatic Relations Between the Dominican Republic and People's Republic of China — A787

2019, Aug. 2   Litho.   Imperf.
1651   A787   75p multi   3.00   3.00

Miniature Sheet

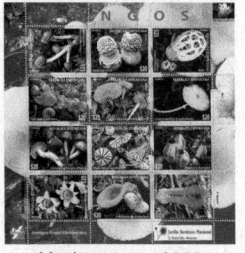

Mushrooms — A788

No. 1652: a, Chlorophyllum molybdites, vert. b, Amanita cruzii. c, Clathrus rose-ovolvatus, vert. d, Coockeina sulcipes. e, Entoloma aff. altissimum. f, Leucocoprinus fragilissimus. g, Leucopaxillus gracillimus. h, Marasmius tageticolor. i, Phallus indusiatus. j, Geastrum violaceum, vert. k, Phillipsia dom-ingensis. l, Laternea pusilla, vert.

Perf. 13½x13¼, 13¼x13½ (vert. stamps)
2019, Aug. 21   Litho.
1652   A788   20p Sheet of 12, #a-l   9.50   9.50

Mohandas K. Gandhi (1869-1948), Indian Nationalist Leader — A789

Perf. 13¼x13½
2019, Aug. 27   Litho.
1653   A789   100p multi   4.00   4.00

Alexander von Humboldt (1769-1859), Naturalist, and Andira Inermis — A790

Perf. 13¼x13½
2019, Sept. 18   Litho.
1654   A790   250p multi   9.75   9.75

A vertical column of perforations runs through the center of the stamp, with the denomination on the left side, and the country name on the right side.

Miniature Sheets

Corals A791

No. 1655, 20p: a, Plexaurella nutans. b, Madracis auretenra. c, Black fish over blue and red Montastraea cavernosa. d, Antipathes gracilis. e, Acropora palmata. f, Yellow Montastraea cavernosa. g, Orbicella annu-laris. h, Two fish over Colpophyllia natans. i, Iciligorgia schrammi. j, Fish and close-up view of Colpophyllia natans. k, Stylaster roseus. l, Mycetophyllia aliciae.

No. 1656, 20p: a, Acroporia cervicornis. b, Neospongodes portoricensis. c, Mycetophyllia ferox. d, Dendrogyra cylindrus. e, Pseudopter-ogorgia sp. f, Tubastraea coccinea. g, Antipathes caribbeana. h, Orbicella faveolata. i, Millepora complenata. j, Agaricia tenuifolia. k, Gorgonia ventalina. l, Helioseris cucullata.

2019, Oct. 9   Litho.   Perf. 13½x13¼
Sheets of 12, #a-l
1655-1656   A791   Set of 2   18.50   18.50

Color Television Broadcasting in Dominican Republic, 50th Anniv. — A792

2019, Nov. 7   Litho.   Perf. 13½x13¼
1657   A792   50p multi   1.90   1.90

Miniature Sheet

America Issue A793

No. 1658 — Native cuisine: a, Chicharrón de cerdo (pork rinds). b, Buñuelos de yuca con almíbar (yucca fritters with syrup). c, Chicharrón de pollo (fried chicken). d, Mangú (pureed plantains). e, Habichuelas con dulce (sweet beans). f, Sancocho siete carnes (stew with seven meats). g, Pastel en hoja (Domini-can tamales). h, Majarete (corn pudding). i, Chambre (meat and vegetable soup). j, Sopión o sancocho de habichuelas (bean soup). k, Plátano maduro al caldero (plantains in sweet syrup). l, Chivo liniero (goat stew).

Perf. 13½x13¼
2019, Nov. 14   Litho.
1658   A793   15p Sheet of 12, #a-l   7.00   7.00

Miniature Sheet

Paintings by Ramón Oviedo (1924-2015) — A794

No. 1659: a, Mi Mundo. b, 24 de Abril. c, Maternidad. d, Perrotoroburro.

Perf. 13½x13¼
2019, Nov. 29   Litho.
1659   A794   25p Sheet of 4, #a-d   4.00   4.00

First Catholic Mass in the Americas, 525th Anniv. — A795

No. 1660: a, Temple of the Americas, 1994. b, Church at La Isabela, 1494.

Perf. 13½x13¼
2019, Dec. 10   Litho.
1660   A795   60p Pair, #a-b   4.75   4.75

Miniature Sheet

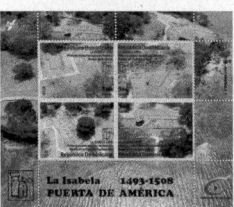

Founding of La Isabela (First Spanish Settlement in North America), 525th Anniv. (in 2018) — A796

No. 1661 — Various La Isabela archaelogi-cal sites with denomination at: a, LR. b, LL. c, UR. d, UL.

Perf. 13½x13¼
2019, Dec. 10   Litho.
1661   A796   60p Sheet of 4, #a-d   9.50   9.50

Order of the Blessed Virgin Mary of Mercy, 800th Anniv. — A797

Perf. 13¼x13½
2019, Dec. 11   Litho.
1662   A797   60p multi   2.40   2.40

Miniature Sheet

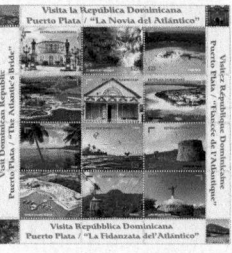

Puerto Plata Province Tourism A798

No. 1663: a, Parque Central Bandstand and statues, Puerto Plata. b, 27 Waterfalls of the Damajagua River. c, Punta Rucia. d, Cofresí. e, Victorian house, Puerto Plata. f, Playa Dorada. g, Sosua. h, Cabarete. i, Fuerte San Felipe. j, Cruise Terminal, Maimón. k, Aerial cable car, Puerto Plata. l, Christ the Redeemer statue, Loma Isabel de Torres.

2020, Jan. 14   Litho.   Perf. 13½x13¼
1663   A798   25p Sheet of 12, #a-l   12.00   12.00

Dated 2016.

A799

Dominican Republic Declaration of Independence, 175th Anniv. — A800

Designs: 15p, Oath of the Trinitarians, Masonic square and compass. 20p, Puerta de la Misericordia and General Matias Ramón Mella Castillo (1816-64). 25p, Puerta del Conde. 30p, Flag of the Dominican Republic, national heroes Francisco del Rosario Sánchez (1817-61), Juan Pablo Duarte (1813-76), and Mella.

150p, Dominican Republic coats of arms from 1844, 1848, 1865, 1889, 1898, 1905, 1913 and 2010.

2020, Feb. 5   Litho.   Perf. 13¼x13½
1664-1667   A799   Set of 4   3.50   3.50
Imperf
1668   A800   150p multi   6.00   6.00

Dated 2019.

First Census, Cent. — A801

2020, July 16   Litho.   Perf. 13¼x13½
1669   A801   100p multi   3.50   3.50

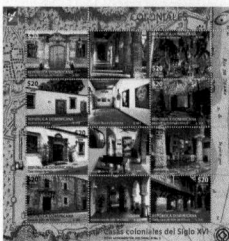

Domesticated Animals — A802

Designs: No. 1670, 20p, Cat. No. 1671, 20p, Dog. No. 1672, 20p, Horse. No. 1673, 20p, Hen and rooster.

2020, July 31   Litho.   Perf. 13½
1670-1673   A802   Set of 4   2.75   2.75

America issue.

Miniature Sheet

16th Century Colonial Houses of Santo Domingo A803

No. 1674: a, Rodrigo de Bastidas House. b, Patio of Rodrigo de Bastidas House. c, Quinta Dominica Art Gallery. d, Patio of Quinta Domi-nica. e, La Bricola Restaurant (house of Alonso de Peña). f, Patio of La Bricola. g, Juan de Villoria House. h, Patio of Juan de Villoria House.

2020, Aug. 4   Litho.   Perf. 13½x13¼
1674   A803   20p Sheet of 8, #a-h, + 4 central la-bels   5.50   5.50

María Victoria de la Cruz (1859-1967), Founder of Doña Chucha Girls' School Home — A804

Perf. 13½x13¼
2020, Sept. 30   Litho.
1675   A804   15p multi   .55   .55

Dated 2017.

Dominican School of Notaries, 50th Anniv. (in 2017) — A805

Perf. 13½x13¼
2020, Sept. 30   Litho.
1676   A805   20p multi   .70   .70

Musicians and Composers — A806

No. 1677: a, Salvador Sturla (1891-1975), musician. b, Luis Alberti (1906-76), musician. c, Juan Lockward (1915-2006), singer. d, Manuel Troncoso (1927-2012), composer.

Perf. 13¼x13½

2020, Sept. 30   Litho.
1677 A806 20p Block of 4, #a-d   2.75 2.75
     Dated 2017.

Juan Antonio Alix Rodríguez (1833-1918), Writer — A807

2020, Sept. 30   Litho.   **Imperf.**
1678 A807 100p multi   3.50 3.50
     Dated 2018.

Souvenir Sheet

Juan Hipolito Yrigoyen (1852-1933), President of Argentina — A808

2020, Oct. 28   Litho.   **Perf. 13¼x13**
1679 A808 100p multi + 2 labels   3.50 3.50
Order of Yrigoyen for Argentine ship 9 de Julio to fly Dominican Republic flag in protest of American occupation of the Dominican Republic, cent.

Dr. Angel Amado Pared Gómez (1917-2016), Organizer of Merchants in National District — A809

2020, Nov. 3   Litho.   **Perf. 13¼x13**
1680 A809 42p multi   1.50 1.50
A column of perforations was placed in the middle of the stamp.

Rosa Duarte Díez (1820-88), Independence Activist and Sister of Pres. Juan Pablo Duarte — A810

2020, Dec. 16   Litho.   **Perf. 13½**
1681 A810 60p multi   2.10 2.10

Manuel Bello Cabral (1927-91), Philatelic Publisher, and Dominican Republic No. C198 — A811

2021, Jan. 20   Litho.   **Perf. 13½**
1682 A811 multi   2.10 2.10
    Stamp Day. Dated 2020.

María Trinidad Sánhez (1794-1845), National Heroine — A812

2021, Mar. 9   Litho.   **Imperf.**
1683 A812 200p multi   7.00 7.00
     Dated 2020.

Ludwig van Beethoven (1770-1827), Composer A813

2021, Mar. 19   Litho.   **Perf. 13½**
1684 A813 250p multi   8.75 8.75
     Dated 2020.

Diplomatic Relations Between Dominican Republic and Morocco, 60th Anniv. — A814

No. 1685: a, 60p, Kasbah of the Oudaias, Rabat, Morocco. b, 72p, Alcázar de Cólon, Santo Domingo.

2021, Mar. 25   Litho.   **Perf. 13x13¼**
1685 A814   Horiz. pair, #a-b   4.75 4.75
   Dated 2020. See Morocco No. 1298.

Hotel Tortuga Bay and 50th Anniversary Emblem of Grupo Puntacana A815

2021, June 11   Litho.   **Perf. 13½**
1686 A815 42p multi   1.50 1.50
     Dated 2020.

Juan Pablo Duarte (1813-77), Giuseppe Garibaldi (1807-82) and Flags of Dominican Republic and Italy — A816

2021, July 7   Litho.   **Imperf.**
1687 A816 60p multi   2.10 2.10
Diplomatic relations between Dominican Republic and Italy. Dated 2019.

Gregorio Urbano Gilbert Suero (1898-1970), Guerilla Fighter Against United States Occupations of Dominican Republic — A817

2021, July 12   Litho.   **Perf. 13½**
1688 A817 100p multi   3.50 3.50

Dominican Academy of History, 90th Anniv. — A818

2021, Aug. 4   Litho.   **Perf. 13x13¼**
1689 A818 60p multi   2.10 2.10

Pedro Henriquez Ureña National Library, 50th Anniv. — A819

2021, Sept. 16   Litho.   **Perf. 13½**
1690 A819 50p multi   1.75 1.75

Architects — A820

Designs: No. 1691, 60p, Mario Rafael Lluberes Abreu (1906-67) and Herrera Báez Residence. No. 1692, 60p, Edgardo Vega Malagón (1924-99) and Banco Nacional de la Vivienda

2021, Nov. 4   Litho.   **Perf. 13¼x13**
1691-1692 A820   Set of 2   4.25 4.25
America issue. A column of perforations runs through the center of Nos. 1691 and 1692.

Miniature Sheet

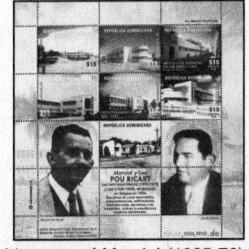

Architecture of Marcial (1905-76) and Leo Pou Ricart (1908-65) — A821

No. 1693: a, Dr. Martos Anti-tuberculosis Hospital, 1942. b, Education Secretariat building, 1944. c, Salomé Ureña Institute, 1944. d, Dr. Morgan Hospital, 1946. e, Odontology Faculty Building of the University of Santo Domingo, 1949. f, Men's Normal School, 1950.

2021, Nov. 4   Litho.   **Perf. 13½x13¼**
1693 A821 15p Sheet of 6, #a-f,
         + 6 labels   3.25 3.25

Larimar, National Mineral of the Dominican Republic — A822

2021, Nov. 22   Litho.   **Perf. 13¼x13**
1694 A822 20p multi   .70 .70

José Núñez de Cáceres (1772-1846), Leader of Independence Movement — A823

2021, Dec. 1   Litho.   **Perf. 13¼**
1695 A823 200p multi   7.00 7.00

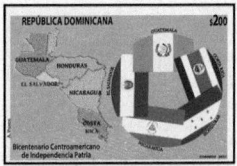

Independence of Central America, 200th Anniv. — A824

2021, Dec. 17   Litho.   **Imperf.**
1696 A824 200p multi   7.00 7.00

Independence of Mexico, 200th Anniv. — A825

Perf. 13½x13¼
2021, Dec. 21   Litho.
1697 A825 200p multi   7.00 7.00

Dr. Antonio Zaglul (1920-96), Psychiatrist — A826

2021, Dec. 23   Litho.   **Perf. 13¼**
1698 A826 100p multi   3.50 3.50

Type A6 Redrawn With Denominations in Pesos and "2020" Year Date — A827

Color of denomination numerals: 15p, Yellow green. 25p, Red. 45p, Bright mauve. 60p, Bister.

2022, Feb. 7   Litho.   **Rouletted 5**
1699-1702 A827   Set of 4   5.50 5.50
     Dated 2020.

Dominican Republic Coats of Arms — A828

Coat of arms from: No. 1703, 15p, 1844 (with cannons). No. 1704, 15p, 1844 (without cannons). No. 1705, 15p, 1848 (foliage around arms). No. 1706, 15p, 1848 (blue banner above arms). No. 1707, 15p, 1849. No. 1708, 15p, 1853. No. 1709, 15p, 1857. No. 1710,

15p, 1860. No. 1711, 15p, 1864. No. 1712, 15p, 1866. No. 1713, 15p, 1867. No. 1714, 15p, 1870. No. 1715, 15p, 1874. No. 1716, 15p, 1886. No. 1717, 15p, 1889. No. 1718, 15p, 1898. No. 1719, 15p, 1905. No. 1720, 15p, 1909. No. 1721, 15p, 1913. No. 1722, 15p, 1914. No. 1723, 15p, 1943. No. 1724, 15p, 1983. No. 1725, 15p, 2010.

2022, Feb. 7   Litho.   Perf. 13½
1703-1725 A828 Set of 23   13.00 13.00

Dated 2021.

Fire Fighting A829

No. 1726: a, Firefighters on aerial ladder at building fire. b, Rescue vehicle. c, Fire station, San Pedro de Macorís. d, Firefighter spraying water.

2022, Mar. 11   Litho.   Perf. 13x13¼
1726 A829 15p Block of 4, #a-d   2.25 2.25

SEMI-POSTAL STAMPS

Catalogue values for unused stamps in this section are for Never Hinged items.

Nos. 474-478 Surcharged in Red

Engraved and Lithographed
1957, Feb. 8   Unwmk.   Perf. 11½
Flags in National Colors

B1	A117	1c + 2c brn, lt bl, vio & mar	.40	.40
B2	A117	2c + 2c dk brn, lt bl & vio	.40	.40
B3	A117	3c + 2c red lilac & red	.40	.40
B4	A117	5c + 2c red orange & vio	.40	.40
B5	A117	7c + 2c green & violet	.50	.50

Nos. B1-B5,CB1-CB3 (8)   3.90 3.90

The surtax was to aid Hungarian refugees. A similar 25c surcharge was applied to the miniature sheets described in the footnote following No. 478. Value, 2 sheets, perf. and imperf., $45

Nos. 479-483 Surcharged in Red Orange

1957, Sept. 9   Photo.   Perf. 13½
Flags in National Colors

B6	A118	1c + 2c brown & brt bl	.30	.30
B7	A118	2c + 2c org ver & dk bl	.35	.35
B8	A118	3c + 2c dark blue	.40	.40
B9	A118	5c + 2c olive & dk bl	.55	.55
B10	A118	7c + 2c rose brn & dk bl	.60	.60

Nos. B6-B10,CB4-CB6 (8)   4.75 4.15

Cent. of the birth of Lord Baden Powell and the 50th anniv. of the Scout Movement. The surtax was for the Dominican Republic Boy Scouts.

A similar 5c surcharge was applied to the miniature sheets described in the footnote following No. 483. Value 4 sheets, perf. and imperf., medal and flag, $62.50

Types of Olympic Regular Issue, 1957, Surcharged in Carmine

a

b

1958, May 26   Engr. & Litho.
Flags in National Colors
Pink Paper

B11	A119(a)	1c + 2c red brown	.30	.30
B12	A119(b)	1c + 2c red brown	.30	.30
B13	A120(a)	2c + 2c gray brown	.40	.40
B14	A120(b)	2c + 2c gray brown	.40	.40
B15	A119(a)	3c + 2c violet	.40	.40
B16	A119(b)	3c + 2c violet	.40	.40
B17	A120(a)	5c + 2c red orange	.55	.55
B18	A120(b)	5c + 2c red orange	.55	.55
B19	A119(a)	7c + 2c Prus green	.65	.65
B20	A119(b)	7c + 2c Prus green	.65	.65

Nos. B11-B20,CB7-CB12 (16)   7.80 7.80

Surtax for the UN Relief and Works Agency for Palestine Refugees.

A similar 5c surcharge, plus marginal United Nations emblem and "UNRWA," was applied to the miniature sheets described in the footnote following No. 488. Value, 4 sheets, perf. and imperf., $20.

Nos. 501-505 Surcharged

Perf. 13½
1959, Apr. 13   Photo.   Unwmk.
Flags in National Colors

B21	A125	1c + 2c rose, indigo & ultra	.45	.45
B22	A125	1c + 2c brown & blue	.45	.45
B23	A125	3c + 2c gray, vio, blk & buff	.55	.55
B24	A125	5c + 2c rose, dk bl, brn & red	.70	.70
B25	A125	7c + 2c lt brn, dk bl & red	.80	.80

Nos. B21-B25,CB13-CB15 (8)   6.45 6.45

International Geophysical Year, 1957-58.
A similar 5c surcharge was applied to the miniature sheets described in the footnote following No. 505. Value, 2 sheets, perf. and imperf., $40.

Type of 1957 Surcharged in Red

Engraved and Lithographed
1959, Sept. 10   Unwmk.   Imperf.
Flags in National Colors

B26	A117	1c + 2c brn, lt bl, vio & mar	.40	.40
B27	A117	2c + 2c dk brn, lt bl & vio	.40	.40
B28	A117	3c + 2c red lilac & red	.45	.45
B29	A117	5c + 2c red org & vio	.45	.45
B30	A117	7c + 2c green & violet	.55	.55

Nos. B26-B30,CB16-CB18 (8)   4.85 4.85

3rd Pan American Games, Chicago, Aug. 27-Sept. 7, 1959.

Nos. 522-524 Surcharged in Red

1960, Apr. 7   Litho.   Perf. 12½
Center in Gray

B31	A135	5c + 5c red brn & yel grn	.35	.35
B32	A135	9c + 5c car & lt bl	.35	.35
B33	A135	13c + 5c org & grn	.80	.80

Nos. B31-B33,CB19-CB20 (5)   2.40 2.40

World Refugee Year, July 1, 1959-June 30, 1960. The surtax was for aid to refugees. Souvenir sheets exist perf. and imperf., containing one each of Nos. B31-B33 and CB19-CB20. Value, 2 sheets, perf. and imperf., $12.50

Nos. 525-529 Surcharged

1962, Jan. 8   Photo.   Perf. 13½
Flags in National Colors

B34	A136	1c + 2c red, yel grn & blk	.35	.35
B35	A136	2c + 2c org, grnsh bl & brn	.35	.35
B36	A136	3c + 2c henna brn & bl	.35	.35
B37	A136	5c + 2c brown & ultra	.35	.35
B38	A136	7c + 2c grn, bl & rose brn	.35	.35

Nos. B34-B38,CB21-CB23 (8)   3.10 3.10

15th anniv. (in 1961) of UNESCO.
A similar 5c surcharge was applied to the miniature sheets described in the footnote following No. 529. Value, 2 sheets, perf. and imperf., $20.

Anti-Malaria Type of 1962
1962, Apr. 29   Litho.   Perf. 12

B39	A141	10c + 2c brt pink & red lil	.50	.40
B40	A141	20c + 2c pale brn & brn	.75	.55

Freedom from Hunger Type of 1963
1963, Apr. 15   Unwmk.   Perf. 11½
Banner in Dark Blue & Red

B41	A148	2c + 1c green	.35	.25
B42	A148	5c + 2c brt rose lil	.35	.25
B43	A148	9c + 2c orange	.35	.25

Nos. B41-B43 (3)   1.05 .75

A souvenir sheet contains three imperf. stamps similar to Nos. B41-B43. Value, $1.50.

Nos. 591-593 Surcharged

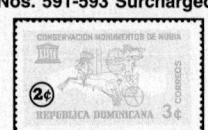

1964, Mar. 8   Perf. 12½

B44	A153	3c + 2c pale pink & ver	.35	.35
B45	A153	6c + 2c pale bl & ultra	.35	.35
B46	A153	9c + 2c pale rose & red brn	.35	.35

Nos. B44-B46,CB26-CB27 (5)   1.80 1.80

UNESCO world campaign to save historic monuments in Nubia.

Nos. 622-626 Surcharged

1966, Dec. 9   Litho.   Perf. 12½
Size: 31x21mm

B47	A164	1c + 2c multi	8.50	1.25
B48	A164	2c + 2c multi	8.50	1.25
B49	A164	3c + 2c multi	8.50	1.25
B50	A164	6c + 4c multi	8.50	1.25
B51	A164	8c + 4c multi	8.50	1.25

Nos. B47-B51,CB28-CB30 (8)   56.00 14.00

Surtax for victims of Hurricane Inez.

AIR POST STAMPS

Map of Hispaniola AP1

Perf. 11½
1928, May 31   Litho.   Unwmk.

C1	AP1	10c deep ultra	5.25	2.50

1930

C2	AP1	10c ocher	3.50	3.00
a.		Vert. pair, imperf. btwn.	600.00	
C3	AP1	15c scarlet	6.75	4.00
C4	AP1	20c green	3.25	.85
C5	AP1	30c redsh vio	6.75	4.50

Nos. C2-C5 (4)   20.25 12.35

Nos. C2-C5 have only "CENTAVOS" in lower panel. Issued: 10c, 20c, 1/24; 15c, 30c, 2/14.

1930

C6	AP1	10c light blue	1.75	.60
C7	AP1	15c blue green	3.25	1.00
C8	AP1	20c org brown	3.50	.85
a.		Horiz. pair, imperf. vert.	450.00	450.00
C9	AP1	30c brown	6.25	1.75

Nos. C6-C9 (4)   14.75 4.20

Issue dates: 10c, 15c, 20c, Sept.; 30c, Oct.

Batwing Sundial Erected in 1753 — AP2

1931-33   Perf. 12

C10	AP2	10c carmine	3.50	.50
C11	AP2	10c light blue	1.75	.50
C12	AP2	10c dp bl grn	6.25	2.75
C13	AP2	15c rose lilac	2.75	.50
C14	AP2	20c dark blue	6.25	2.25
a.		Numerals reading up at left and down at right	5.75	2.75
b.		Imperf., pair	250.00	
C15	AP2	30c turq grn	2.50	.25
C16	AP2	50c red brown	6.25	.50
C17	AP2	1p deep orange	10.00	2.75

Nos. C10-C17 (8)   39.25 10.00

Issued: No. C11, 7/2/32; No. C12, 5/28/33; others 8/16.

Airplane and Ozama Fortress — AP3

1933, Nov. 20

C18	AP3	10c dark blue	3.50	.60

Airplane and Trujillo Bridge — AP4

1934, Sept. 20

C19	AP4	10c dark blue	3.00	.50

Symbolic of Flight — AP5

1935, Apr. 29

C20	AP5	10c lt blue & dk blue	1.60	.50

AP6

1936, Feb. 11 *Perf. 11½*
C21 AP6 10c dk bl & turq grn 2.50 .50

Allegory of Flight — AP7

1936, Oct. 17
C22 AP7 10c dk bl, grnsh bl & turq bl 2.25 .40

Macoris Airport — AP8

1937, Oct. 22
C23 AP8 10c green 1.00 .25

Fleet of Columbus AP9

Air Fleet — AP10

Proposed Columbus Lighthouse AP11

1937, Nov. 9 *Perf. 12*
C24 AP9 10c rose red 1.75 1.40
C25 AP10 15c purple 1.40 .95
C26 AP11 20c dk bl & lt bl 1.40 1.25
C27 AP10 25c red violet 2.00 1.25
C28 AP11 30c yellow green 1.75 1.25
C29 AP10 50c brown 3.50 1.75
C30 AP11 75c dk olive grn 10.50 10.50
C31 AP9 1p orange 6.25 2.50
Nos. C24-C31 (8) 28.55 20.85

Goodwill flight to all American countries by the planes "Colon," "Pinta," "Nina" and "Santa Maria."

No. C30 was reproduced imperf. on No. 1019.

Pan American Clipper — AP12

1938, July 30
C32 AP12 10c green 1.25 .25

Trylon and Perisphere, Plane and Proposed Columbus Lighthouse AP13

1939, Apr. 30
C33 AP13 10c green & lt green 2.00 .85
New York World's Fair.

Airplane AP14

1939, Oct. 18
C34 AP14 10c green & dp green 1.60 .25
a. Pair, imperf. btwn. 450.00

Proposed Columbus Lighthouse, Plane and Caravels AP15

Christopher Columbus and Proposed Lighthouse AP16

Proposed Lighthouse AP17

Christopher Columbus AP18

Caravel AP19

1940, Oct. 12
C35 AP15 10c sapphire & lt bl 1.10 .60
C36 AP16 15c org brn & brn 1.60 1.00
C37 AP17 20c rose red & red 1.60 1.00
C38 AP18 25c brt red lil & red vio 1.60 .50
C39 AP19 50c green & lt green 3.00 1.75
Nos. C35-C39 (5) 8.90 4.85

Discovery of America by Columbus and proposed Columbus memorial lighthouse in Dominican Republic.

Posts and Telegraph Building, San Cristobal — AP20

1941, Feb. 21
C40 AP20 10c brt red lil & pale lil rose .50 .25

Globe, Wing and Letter — AP21

1942, Feb. 13
C41 AP21 10c dark violet brn .60 .30
C42 AP21 75c deep orange 3.25 2.00

Plane — AP22

1943, Sept. 1
C43 AP22 10c brt red lilac .40 .25
C44 AP22 20c dp blue & blue .40 .25
C45 AP22 25c yellow olive 5.75 3.25
Nos. C43-C45 (3) 6.55 3.75

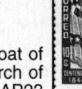

Plane, Flag, Coat of Arms and Torch of Liberty — AP23

1944, Feb. 27 *Perf. 11½*
Flag in Gray, Dark Blue, Carmine
C46 AP23 10c multicolored .35 .25
C47 AP23 20c multicolored .45 .25
C48 AP23 1p multicolored 2.00 1.50
Nos. C46-C48 (3) 2.80 2.00

Centenary of Independence. See No. 407 for souvenir sheet listing.

Communications Building, Ciudad Trujillo — AP24

1944, Nov. 12 *Litho.* *Perf. 12*
C49 AP24 9c yel grn & blue .25 .25
C50 AP24 13c dull brn & rose car .25 .25
C51 AP24 25c org & dull red .35 .25
b. Vert. pair, imperf. btwn. 45.00
C52 AP24 30c black & ultra .75 .65
Nos. C49-C52 (4) 1.60 1.40

Twenty booklets of 100 (25 panes of 4) of the 25c were issued. All booklets are still intact.

Communications Type
1945, Sept. 1
Center in Dark Blue and Carmine
C53 A92 7c deep yellow green .35 .25
C54 A92 12c red orange .40 .25
C55 A92 13c deep blue .50 .25
C56 A92 25c orange brown .90 .25
Nos. C53-C56 (4) 2.15 1.00

AP26 — Flags and National Anthem — AP27

Unwmk.
1946, Feb. 27 *Litho.* *Perf. 12*
Center in Dark Blue, Deep Carmine and Black
C57 AP26 10c carmine .95 .40
C58 AP26 15c blue 2.10 .85
C59 AP26 20c chocolate 2.50 .85
C60 AP26 35c orange 3.00 .95
C61 AP27 1p grn, yel grn & cit 25.00 10.00
Nos. C57-C61 (5) 33.55 13.05

Nos. C57-C61 exist imperf.

Map Type of Regular Issue
1946, Aug. 4
C62 A94 10c multicolored .75 .25
C63 A94 13c multicolored 1.35 .25

Waterfall Type of Regular Issue
1947, Mar. 18 *Litho.*
Center Multicolored
C64 A95 18c light blue 1.00 .50
C65 A95 23c carmine 1.60 .60
C66 A95 50c red violet 2.10 .60
C67 A95 75c chocolate 3.00 1.10
Nos. C64-C67 (4) 7.70 2.80

Palace Type of Regular Issue
1948, Feb. 27
C68 A96 37c orange brown 2.10 1.00
C69 A96 1p orange yellow 5.75 2.10

Ruins Type of Regular Issue
1949 *Unwmk.* *Perf. 11½*
C70 A97 7c ol grn & pale ol grn .40 .25
C71 A97 10c orange brn & buff .40 .25
C72 A97 15c brt rose & pale pink 1.25 .30
C73 A97 20c green & pale green 1.75 .60
Nos. C70-C73 (4) 3.80 1.40

Issue dates: 10c, Apr. 4; others, Apr. 13.

Las Carreras Monument — AP32

1949, Aug. 10
C74 AP32 10c red & pink .75 .25
Cent. of the Battle of Las Carreras.

> Catalogue values for unused stamps in this section, from this point to the end of the section, are for Never Hinged items.

Hotel Type of Regular Issue
Hotels: 12c, Montana. 37c, San Cristobal.

1950, Sept. 8
C75 A100 12c dk blue & blue .50 .25
C76 A100 37c carmine & pink 3.25 2.50

Map, Plane and Caduceus — AP34

1950, Oct. 2
C77 AP34 12c orange brn & yel 1.00 .25
13th Pan-American Health Conf. Exists imperf.

Hospital Type of Regular Issue
1952, Aug.
C78 A104 23c deep blue 1.20 1.20
C79 A104 29c carmine 3.25 2.25

Columbus Lighthouse and Plane — AP36

1953, Jan. 6 *Engr.* *Perf. 13*
C80 AP36 12c ocher .30 .25
C81 AP36 14c dark blue .30 .25
C82 AP36 20c black brown .70 .60
C83 AP36 23c deep plum .40 .40
C84 AP36 25c dark blue .95 .70
C85 AP36 29c deep green .70 .60
C86 AP36 1p red brown 2.00 1.25
a. Miniature sheet of 10 21.00 21.00
Nos. C80-C86 (7) 5.35 4.05

No. C86a is lithographed and contains Nos. 450-452 and C80-C86, in slightly different shades. Sheet measures 190x130mm and is imperf. with simulated perforations.
A miniature sheet similar to No. C86a, but measuring 200x163mm and in folder, exists. Value $100.

Ano Mariano Initials in Monogram — AP37

1954, Aug. 5 *Litho.* *Perf. 11½*
C87 AP37 8c claret .30 .25
C88 AP37 11c blue .35 .25
C89 AP37 33c brown orange 1.20 .60
Nos. C87-C89 (3) 1.85 1.10

Marian Year. Nos. C87-C89 exist imperf.

Rotary Type of Regular Issue
1955, Feb. 23 *Perf. 12*
C90 A110 11c rose red .50 .25

Flags — AP39

Portraits of General Hector B. Trujillo: 25c, In civilian clothes. 33c, In uniform.

1955, May 16   Engr.   Perf. 13½x13
C91 AP39 11c blue, yel & car   .80   .25
C92 AP39 25c rose violet   1.40   .30
C93 AP39 33c orange brown   2.00   .50
   Nos. C91-C93 (3)   4.20 1.05

The center of No. C91 is litho. 25th anniv. of the inauguration of the Trujillo era.

Fair Type of Regular Issue

1955, Dec. 20   Unwmk.   Perf. 13
C94 A112 11c vermilion   .60   .25

ICAO Type of Regular Issue

1956, Apr. 6   Litho.   Perf. 12½
C95 A114 11c ultra   1.25   .25

Tree Type of Regular Issue

Design: 13c, Mahogany tree.

1956, Dec. 8   Litho.   Perf. 11½x12
C96 A115 13c orange & green   2.25   .25

Type of Regular Issue, 1957

Olympic Winners and Flags: 11c, Paavo Nurmi, Finland. 16c, Ugo Frigerio, Italy. 17c, Mildred Didrikson ("Didrickson" on stamp), US.

Engraved and Lithographed
Perf. 11½, Imperf.
1957, Jan. 24   Unwmk.
Flags in National Colors
C97 A117 11c ultra & red org   .25   .25
C98 A117 16c carmine & lt grn   .30   .25
C99 A117 17c black, vio & red   .40   .25
   Nos. C97-C99 (3)   .95   .75

16th Olympic Games, Melbourne, Nov. 22-Dec. 8, 1956.
Souvenir sheets of 3 exist, perf. and imperf., containing Nos. C97-C99. Value, 2 sheets, perf. & imperf., $15.
For surcharges see Nos. CB1-CB3, CB16-CB18.

Type of Regular Issue

Olympic Winners and Flags: 11c, Robert Morrow, US, 100 & 200 meter dash. 16c, Chris Brasher, England, steeplechase. 17c, A. Ferreira Da Silva, Brazil, hop, step and jump.

Perf. 13½, Imperf.
1957, July 18   Photo.
Flags in National Colors
C100 A118 11c yellow grn & dk bl   .25   .25
C101 A118 16c lilac & dk blue   .30   .25
C102 A118 17c brown & blue grn   .40   .25
   Nos. C100-C102 (3)   .95   .75

1956 Olympic winners.
See note on miniature sheets following No. 483.
For surcharges see Nos. CB4-CB6.

Types of Regular Issue

Olympic Winners and Flags: 11c, Hans Winkler, Germany, individual jumping. 16c, Alfred Oerter, US, discus throw. 17c, Shirley Strickland, Australia, 800 meter hurdles.

Engraved and Lithographed
Perf. 13½, Imperf.
1957, Nov. 12   Unwmk.
Flags in National Colors
C103 A119 11c ultra   .25   .25
C104 A120 16c rose carmine   .40   .25
C105 A119 17c claret   .40   .25
   Nos. C103-C105 (3)   1.05   .75

1956 Olympic winners.
Miniature sheets of 3 exist, perf. and imperf., containing Nos. C103-C105. Value, 2 sheets, perf. and imperf., $5.50.
For surcharges see Nos. CB7-CB12.

Type of Regular Issue

Olympic Winners and Flags: 11c, Charles Jenkins, 400 & 800 meter run, and Thomas Courtney, 1,600 meter relay, US. 16c, Field hockey team, India. 17c, Yachting team, Sweden.

Perf. 13½, Imperf.
1958, Oct. 30   Unwmk.   Photo.
Flags in National Colors
C106 A125 11c blue, olive & brn   .30   .25
C107 A125 16c lt grn, org & dk bl   .40   .25
C108 A125 17c ver, blue & yel   .40   .25
   Nos. C106-C108 (3)   1.10   .75

1956 Olympic winners.
Miniature sheets of 3 exist, perf. and imperf., containing Nos. C106-C108. Value, 2 sheets, perf. and imperf., $3.
For surcharges see Nos. CB13-CB15.

Fair Type of Regular Issue

1958, Dec. 9   Litho.   Perf. 12½
C109 A127 9c gray   .30   .25
C110 A127 25c lt violet   .85   .40
   a.   Souv. sheet of 3, #C109-C110, 507, imperf.   2.25 2.25

Polo Type of Regular Issue

1959, May 15   Perf. 12
C111 A130 11c Dominican polo team   .40   .30

"San Cristobal" Plane — AP42

Perf. 11½
1960, Feb. 25   Unwmk.   Litho.
C112 AP42 13c org, bl, grn & gray   .50   .25

Dominican Civil Aviation.

Children and WRY Emblem AP43

1960, Apr. 7   Perf. 12½
C113 AP43 10c plum, gray & grn   .65   .30
C114 AP43 13c gray & green   .90   .30

World Refugee Year, 7/1/59-6/30/60.
For surcharges see Nos. CB19-CB20.

Olympic Type of Regular Issue

Olympic Winners: 11c, Pat McCormick, US, diving. 16c, Mithat Bayrack, Turkey, welterweight wrestling. 17c, Ursula Happe, Germany, 200 meter breast stroke.

Perf. 13½, Imperf.
1960, Sept. 14   Photo.
Flags in National Colors
C115 A136 11c blue, gray & brn   .35   .25
C116 A136 16c red, brown & ol   .35   .30
C117 A136 17c black, blue & ocher   .35   .40
   Nos. C115-C117 (3)   1.05   .95

17th Olympic Games, Rome, 8/25-9/11.
Miniature sheets of 3 exist, perf. and imperf., containing Nos. C115-C117. Value, 2 sheets, perf. and imperf., $3.75.
For surcharges see Nos. CB21-CB23.

Coffee-Cacao Type of Regular Issue

1961, Dec. 30   Litho.   Perf. 12½
C118 A140 13c orange ver   .35   .30
C119 A140 33c brt yellow   .80   .70
   Nos. C118-C119 exist imperf.

Anti-Malaria Type of Regular Issue

1962, Apr. 29   Unwmk.   Perf. 12
C120 A141 13c pink & red   .50   .25
C121 A141 33c org & dp org   .95   .50
   See Nos. CB24-CB25.

Type of Regular Issue

Designs: 13c, Broken fetters and laurel. 50c, Flag, torch and inscription.

1962, May 30   Perf. 12½
C122 A142 13c brn, yel, ol, ultra & red   .40   .30
C123 A142 50c rose lilac, ultra & red   1.40 1.00
   No. C122 exists imperf.

UPAE Type of Regular Issue

1962, Oct. 23   Perf. 12½
C124 A146 13c bright blue   .45   .45
C125 A146 22c dull red brown   .60   .50
   Nos. C124-C125 exist imperf.

Nouel Type of Regular Issue

Design: Frame altered with rosary and cross surrounding portrait.

1962, Dec. 18
C126 A147 13c blue & pale blue   .45   .25
C127 A147 25c vio & pale vio   .75   .50
   a.   Souv. sheet, #C126-C127, imperf   1.25 1.25
   Nos. C126-C127 exist imperf.

Sanchez, Duarte, Mella — AP44

1963, July 7   Litho.   Perf. 11½x12
C128 AP44 15c orange   .50   .25

120th anniv. of separation from Haiti.

World Map — AP45

1963, Oct. 25   Unwmk.   Perf. 12½
C129 AP45 10c gray & carmine   .45   .25

Cent. of Intl. Red Cross. Exists imperf.

Human Rights Type

1963, Dec. 10   Litho.
C130 A152 7c fawn & red brn   .30   .25
C131 A152 10c lt blue & blue   .30   .25
   Nos. C130-C131 exist imperf.

Ramses II Battling the Hittites (from Abu Simbel) — AP46

1964, Mar. 8   Perf. 12½
C132 AP46 10c brt violet   .30   .25
C133 AP46 13c yellow   .30   .25

UNESCO world campaign to save historic monuments in Nubia.
Nos. C132-C133 exist imperf.
For surcharges see Nos. CB26-CB27.

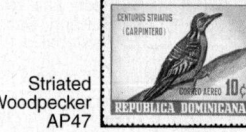

Striated Woodpecker AP47

1964, June 8   Litho.
C134 AP47 10c multicolored   5.75   .25

Type of Space Issue

Designs: 7c, Rocket leaving earth. 10c, Space capsule orbiting earth.

1964, July 28   Unwmk.   Perf. 12½
C135 A156 7c brt green   .30   .25
C136 A156 10c violet blue   .40   .30
   a.   Souvenir sheet   4.25 3.50

No. C136a contains 7c and 10c stamps similar to Nos. C135-C136 with simulated perforations.

UPAE Type of Regular Issue

Pres. John F. Kennedy — AP48

1964, Nov. 22   Perf. 11½
C137 AP48 10c buff & dk brown   .60   .25

President John F. Kennedy (1917-63). Sheets of 10 (5x2) and sheets of 50.

UPU Type of Regular Issue

1964, Dec. 5   Litho.   Perf. 12½
C138 A157 7c blue   .35   .25

ICY Type of Regular Issue

1965, Feb. 16   Unwmk.   Perf. 12½
C139 A158 10c lilac & violet   .45   .30

Basilica of Our Lady of Altagracia AP49

1965, Mar. 18   Unwmk.   Perf. 12½
C140 AP49 10c multicolored   .50   .25

Fourth Mariological Congress and the Eleventh International Marian Congress.

Abraham Lincoln — AP50

1965, Apr. 15   Litho.   Perf. 12½
C141 AP50 17c bright blue   .65   .40

Cent. of the death of Abraham Lincoln.

Stamp Centenary Type of 1965

Design: Stamp of 1865, (No. 2).

1965, Dec. 28   Perf. 12½
C142 A161 7c violet, lt grn & blk   .40   .25
C143 A161 10c yellow, lt grn & blk   .40   .30

ITU Emblem, Old and New Communication Equipment — AP51

1966, Apr. 6   Litho.   Perf. 12½
C144 AP51 28c rose pink & scar   .85   .85
C145 AP51 45c lt grn & dp grn   1.50 1.50

Cent. (in 1965) of the ITU.

Butterfly Type of Regular Issue

1966, Nov. 8   Litho.   Perf. 12½
Various Butterflies in Natural Colors
Size: 35x24mm
C146 A164 10c lt violet & violet   7.75   .75
C147 A164 50c org & dp org   10.00 1.50
C148 A164 75c pink & rose red   12.50 2.50
   Nos. C146-C148 (3)   30.25 4.75

For surcharges see Nos. CB28-CB30.

Altar Type of Regular Issue

1967, Jan. 18   Litho.   Perf. 11½
C149 A165 7c lt olive green   .35   .25
C150 A165 10c lilac   .35   .25
C151 A165 20c yellow brown   .45   .30
   Nos. C149-C151 (3)   1.15   .80

Chess Type of Regular Issue

Design: 10c, Pawn and Bishop.

1967, June 23   Litho.   Perf. 12½
C152 A167 10c ol, lt ol & blk   1.25   .30
   a.   Souvenir sheet   10.00 1.90

No. C152a contains 2 imperf. stamps similar to Nos. 636 and C152.

Alliance for Progress Type

1967, Sept. 16   Litho.   Perf. 12½
C153 A168 8c gray   .50   .30
C154 A168 10c blue   .60   .30

Cornucopia and Emblem — AP52

1967, Oct. 7
C155 AP52 12c multicolored   .75   .30
25th anniversary of the Inter-American Agriculture Institute.

Satellite Type of Regular Issue

1968, June 15   Typo.   Perf. 12
C156 A170 10c dp blue & multi   .35   .25
C157 A170 15c purple & multi   .50   .30

Boxing Type of Regular Issue

Designs: Two views of boxing match.

1968, June 29
C158 A171 7c orange yel & grn   .60   .25
C159 A171 10c gray & blue   .75   .25
See note after No. 641.

Lions Type of Regular Issue

1968, Aug. 9   Litho.   Perf. 11½
C160 A172 10c ultra & multi   .30   .25

Olympic Type of Regular Issue

Designs (Olympic Emblem and): 10c, Weight lifting. 33c, Pistol shooting.

1968, Nov. 12   Litho.   Perf. 11½
C161 A173 10c buff & multi   .35   .25
C162 A173 33c pink & multi   1.25   .75

Latin American Flags — AP53

1969, Jan. 25   Litho.   Perf. 12½
C163 AP53 10c pink & multi   .45   .25
7th Inter-American Savings and Loan Conference, Santo Domingo, Jan. 25-31.

Taino Art Type of Regular Issue

7c, Various vomiting spoons with human heads, vert. 10c, Female torso forming drinking vessel. 20c, Vase with human head, vert.

1969, Jan. 31   Litho.   Perf. 12½
C164 A175 7c lt bl, bl & lem   .40   .25
C165 A175 10c pink, ver & brn   .50   .25
C166 A175 20c yellow, org & brn   .60   .30
Nos. C164-C166 (3)   1.50   .80

COTAL Type of Regular Issue

10c, Airport of the Americas and COTAL emblem.

1969, May 25   Litho.   Perf. 12½
C167 A178 10c brown & pale fawn   .40   .25

ILO Type of Regular Issue

1969, June 27   Litho.   Perf. 12½
C168 A179 10c rose, red & black   .40   .25

Baseball Type of Regular Issue

Designs: 7c, Bleachers, Tetelo Vargas Stadium, horiz. 10c, Batter, catcher and umpire. 1p, Quisqueya Stadium, horiz.

1969, Aug. 15   Litho.   Perf. 12½
Size: 43x30mm (7c, 1p); 21x31mm (10c)

C169 A180 7c magenta & org   .55   .30
C170 A180 10c mar & rose red   .70   .30
C171 A180 1p violet blue & brn   5.00 3.50
Nos. C169-C171 (3)   6.25 4.10

Electrification Types of Regular Issue

Design: No. C172, Rio Haina steam plant. No. C173, Valdesa Dam.

1969   Litho.   Perf. 12
C172 A181 10c orange ver   .50   .25
C173 A182 10c multicolored   .55   .25
Issued: No. C172, Sept. 15; No. C173, Oct. 15.

Duarte Type of Regular Issue

1970, Jan. 26   Litho.   Perf. 12
C174 A183 10c brown & dk brown   .75   .25

Census Type of Regular Issue

Design: 10c, Buildings and census emblem.

1970, Feb. 6   Perf. 11
C175 A184 10c lt blue & multi   .75   .25

Sculpture Type of Regular Issue

Design: 10c, The Prisoner, by Abelardo Rodriguez Urdaneta, vert.

1970, Feb. 20   Litho.   Perf. 12½
C176 A186 10c bluish gray   .55   .25

Masonic Type of Regular Issue

1970, Mar. 2
C177 A187 10c brown   .30   .25

Satellite Type of Regular Issue

1970, May 25   Litho.   Perf. 12½
C178 A188 7c blue & gray   .40   .25

UPU Type of Regular Issue

1970, June 5   Perf. 11
C179 A189 10c yellow & brown   .40   .25

Education Year Type of Regular Issue

1970, June 26   Litho.   Perf. 12½
C180 A190 15c bright pink   .60   .25

Dancers — AP54

Design: 10c, UN emblem and wheel.

1970, Oct. 12   Litho.   Perf. 12½
C181 AP54 7c blue & multi   .35   .25
C182 AP54 10c pink & multi   .50   .25
1st World Exhib. of Books and Culture Festival, Santo Domingo, Oct. 11-Dec. 11.

Album, Globe and Emblem — AP55

1970, Oct. 26   Litho.   Perf. 11
C183 AP55 10c multicolored   .65   .25
EXFILCA 70, 2nd Interamerican Philatelic Exhibition, Caracas, Venezuela, 11/27-12/6.

Basilica of Our Lady of Altagracia — AP56

1971, Jan. 20   Litho.   Perf. 12½
C184 AP56 17c multicolored   1.00   .45
Inauguration of the Basilica of Our Lady of Altagracia.

Map of Dominican Republic, CARE Package — AP57

1971, May 28   Litho.   Perf. 12½
C185 AP57 10c blue & green   .45   .25
25th anniversary of CARE, a US-Canadian Cooperative for American Relief Everywhere.

Sports Type of Regular Issue

1971, Sept. 10   Perf. 11
C186 A195 7c Volleyball   .40   .25

Animal Type of Regular Issue

Design: 25c, Cock and grain.

1971, Sept. 29   Perf. 12½
C187 A196 25c black & multi   2.00   .35

Independence Type

10c, Dominican-Colombian flag of 1821.

1971, Dec. 1   Perf. 11
C188 A197 10c vio bl, yel & red   .75   .30

Christmas Type of Regular Issue

1971, Dec. 10   Litho.   Perf. 12½
C189 A198 10c Bell, 1493   .45   .25

UNICEF Type of Regular Issue

Design: UNICEF emblem & child on beach.

1971, Dec. 14   Perf. 11
C190 A199 15c multicolored   .80   .45

Book Year Type of Regular Issue

1972, Jan. 25   Litho.   Perf. 12½
C191 A200 12c lilac, dk bl & red   .75   .30

Magnifying Glass over Peru on Map of Americas — AP58

1972, Mar. 7   Litho.   Perf. 12
C192 AP58 10c blue & multi   .60   .30
EXFILIMA '71, 3rd Inter-American Philatelic Exposition, Lima, Peru, Nov. 6-14, 1971.

"Your Heart is your Health" — AP59

1972, Apr. 27   Litho.   Perf. 11
C193 AP59 7c red & multi   .50   .25
World Health Day.

Taino Art Type of 1972

Taino Art: 8c, Ritual vessel showing human figures. 10c, Trumpet (shell). 25c, Carved vomiting spoons. All horiz.

1972, May 10   Perf. 11
C194 A201 8c multicolored   .50   .25
C195 A201 10c lt blue & multi   .70   .25
C196 A201 25c multicolored   1.50   .45
Nos. C194-C196 (3)   2.70   .95

Telecommunications Type of Regular Issue

1972, May 17   Litho.   Perf. 12½
C197 A202 21c yellow & multi   1.00   .45

Exhibition Type of Regular Issue

1972, June 3
C198 A203 33c orange & multi   1.00   .55

Olympic Type of Regular Issue

1972, Aug. 25   Litho.   Perf. 12½
C199 A204 33c Running   1.25   .75

Club Type of Regular Issue

1972, Sept. 29   Litho.   Perf. 10½
C200 A205 20c blue & multi   .75   .25

Morel Type of Regular Issue

1972, Oct. 20   Litho.   Perf. 12½
C201 A206 10c multicolored   .50   .25

Bank Type of Regular Issue

25c, 1947 silver coin, entrance to the Mint.

1972, Oct. 23
C202 A207 25c ocher & multi   1.25   .55

"La Navidad" Fortress, 1492 — AP60

1972, Nov. 21   Litho.   Perf. 12½
C203 AP60 10c multicolored   .95   .25
Christmas 1972.

Sports Type of Regular Issue

Various sports; a, UL. b, UR. c, LL. d, LR.

1973, Mar. 30   Litho.   Perf. 13½x13
C204 A212 Block of 4   1.75 1.75
a.-d.   8c, any single   .30   .25
C205 A212 Block of 4   2.75 2.75
a.-d.   10c, any single   .50   .30

Easter Type 1973

10c, Belfry of Church of Our Lady of Help.

1973, Apr. 18   Litho.   Perf. 10½
C206 A213 10c multi, vert.   .75   .25

North and South America on Globe — AP61

1973, May 29   Litho.   Perf. 12
C207 AP61 7c multicolored   .45   .25
Pan-American Health Organization, 70th anniversary (in 1972).

WMO Type of Regular Issue

1973, Aug. 10   Litho.   Perf. 13½x13
C208 A214 7c green & multi   .50   .25

INTERPOL Emblem Police Scientist — AP62

1973, Sept. 28   Litho.   Perf. 10½
C209 AP62 10c vio bl, bl & emer   .60   .25
50th anniversary of International Criminal Police Organization.

Handicraft Type of Regular Issue

1973, Oct. 12
C210 A215 7c Sailing ship, mosaic   .75   .25
C211 A215 10c Maracas rattles, horiz.   1.00   .25

Christmas Type of Regular Issue

Design: 10c, Angels adoring Christ Child.

1973, Nov. 26   Litho.   Perf. 13½x13
C212 A216 10c multicolored   .50   .25

Scout Type of Regular Issue

21c, Scouts cooking, Lord Baden-Powell.

1973, Dec. 7   Litho.   Perf. 12
C213 A217 21c red & multi   1.25   .75

Sport Type of Regular Issue

10c, Olympic swimming pool and diver. 25c, Olympic Stadium, soccer and discus.

1974, Feb. 25   Litho.   Perf. 13½
C214 A218 10c blue & multi   .40   .25
C215 A218 25c multicolored   1.00   .25

The Last Supper — AP63

1974, June 27   Litho.   Perf. 13½
C216 AP63 10c multicolored   .65   .25

Holy Week 1974.

Bridge Type

Design: 10c, Higuamo Bridge.

1974, July 12   Perf. 12
C217 A221 10c multicolored   .65   .25

Diabetes Type

Map of Dominican Republic, Diabetics' Emblem and: 7c, Kidney. 33c, Eye & heart.

1974, Aug. 22   Litho.   Perf. 13
C218 A222 7c yellow & multi   .45   .25
C219 A222 33c lt blue & multi   2.00   .75

UPU Type

1974, Oct. 9   Litho.   Perf. 13½
C220 A223 7c Ships   1.75   .35
C221 A223 33c Jet   2.75   .75
   a.   Souvenir sheet of 4   7.50   7.50

No. C221a contains Nos. 727-728, C220-C221 forming continuous design.

Golfers and Championship Emblem AP64

20c, Golfer and Golf Association emblem.

1974, Oct. 24   Litho.   Perf. 13x13½
C222 AP64 10c green & multi   .50   .25
C223 AP64 20c green & multi   .80   .40

World Amateur Golf Championships.

Hand Holding Dove — AP65

1974, Dec. 3   Litho.   Perf. 12
C224 AP65 10c multicolored   .50   .25

Christmas 1974.

FAO Type

10c, Bee, beehive and barrel of honey.

1974, Dec. 5
C225 A227 10c multicolored   1.75   .25

Chrismon, Lamb, Candle and Palm — AP66

1975, Mar. 26   Litho.   Perf. 13½
C226 AP66 10c gold & multi   .65   .25

Holy Week 1975.

Spain No. 1, España 75 Emblem — AP67

1975, Apr. 10
C227 AP67 12c red, yel & blk   .65   .30

Espana 75, International Philatelic Exhibition, Madrid, Apr. 4-13.

Development Bank Type

1975, May 19   Litho.   Perf. 10½x10
C228 A230 10c rose car & multi   .60   .25

Three Satellites and Globe — AP68

1975, June 21   Litho.   Perf. 13½
C229 AP68 15c multicolored   .60   .35

Opening of first earth satellite tracking station in Dominican Republic.

Apollo Type

Design: 2p, Apollo-Soyuz link-up over earth.

1975, July 24   Perf. 13
        Size: 42x28mm
C230 A232 2p multicolored   6.00 4.00

Indian Chief Type

7c, Mayobanex. 8c, Cotubanama & Juan de Esquivel. 10c, Enriquillo & Mencia.

1975, Sept. 27   Litho.   Perf. 12
C231 A235 7c lt green & multi   .60   .25
C232 A235 8c orange & multi   .90   .30
C233 A235 10c gray & multi   1.00   .30
     Nos. C231-C233 (3)   2.50   .85

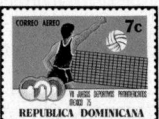

Volleyball — AP69

10c, Weight lifting and Games' emblem.

1975, Oct. 24   Litho.   Perf. 12
C234 AP69 7c blue & multi   .75   .25
C235 AP69 10c multicolored   1.25   .30

7th Pan-American Games, Mexico City, Oct. 13-26.

Christmas Type

Design: 10c, Dove and peace message.

1975, Dec. 12   Litho.   Perf. 13x13½
C236 A237 10c yellow & multi   .60   .25

Valdesia Dam — AP70

1976, Jan. 26   Litho.   Perf. 13
C237 AP70 10c multicolored   .50   .25

Holy Week Type 1976

Design: 10c, Crucifixion, by Eliezer Castillo.

1976, Apr. 14   Litho.   Perf. 13½
C238 A239 10c multicolored   .75   .30

Bicentennial Type and

George Washington, Independence Hall — AP71

Design: 10c, Hands holding maps of US and Dominican Republic.

1976, May 29   Litho.   Perf. 13½
C239 A241 10c vio bl, grn & blk   .60   .25
C240 AP71 75c black & orange   1.75 1.25

American Bicentennial; No. C240 also for Interphil 76 International Philatelic Exhibition, Philadelphia, Pa., May 29-June 6.

King Juan Carlos I and Queen Sofia — AP72

1976, May 31
C241 AP72 21c multicolored   1.25   .85

Visit of King Juan Carlos I and Queen Sofia of Spain.

Telephone Type

Design: 10c, Alexander Graham Bell and telephones, 1876 and 1976.

1976, July 15
C242 A243 10c multicolored   .65   .25

Duarte Types

10c, Scroll with Duarte letter and Dominican flag. 33c, Duarte return from Exile, by E. Godoy.

1976, July 20   Litho.   Perf. 13½
C243 A245 10c blue & multi   .65   .25
              Perf. 13x13½
C244 A244 33c brown & multi   2.00 1.10

Fire Engine — AP73

1976, Sept. 13   Litho.   Perf. 12
C245 AP73 10c multicolored   3.50   .30

Honoring firemen.

Radio Club Type

1976, Oct. 8   Litho.   Perf. 13½
C246 A247 10c blue & black   .60   .25

Various People — AP74

1976, Oct. 22   Litho.   Perf. 13½
C247 AP74 21c multicolored   .90   .55

Spanish heritage.

Olympic Games Type

1976, Oct. 22   Perf. 12
C248 A249 10c Running   .60   .25
C249 A249 25c Basketball   1.50   .75

Christmas Type

Design: 10c, Angel with bells.

1976, Dec. 8   Litho.   Perf. 13½
C250 A251 10c multicolored   .75   .30

Tourist Activities — AP75

Tourist publicity: 12c, Angling and hotel. 25c, Horseback riding and waterfall, vert.

1977, Jan. 7   Size: 36x36mm
C251 AP75 10c multicolored   .45   .25
   Size: 34x25½mm, 25½x34mm
C252 AP75 12c multicolored   .50   .25
C253 AP75 25c multicolored   1.00   .45
     Nos. C251-C253 (3)   1.95   .95

Championship Type

1977, Mar. 4   Litho.   Perf. 13½
C254 A253 10c yel grn & multi   .60   .25
C255 A253 25c lt brown & multi   1.50   .75

Holy Week Type 1977

Design: 10c, Belfry and open book.

1977, Apr. 18   Litho.   Perf. 13½x13
C256 A254 10c multicolored   .75   .25

Lions Type

1977, May 6   Perf. 13½x13
C257 A255 7c lt green & multi   .60   .25

Caravel under Sail — AP76

1977, July 16   Litho.   Perf. 13
C258 AP76 10c multicolored   .60   .30

Miss Universe Contest, held in Dominican Republic.

Melon Cactus — AP77

Design: 33c, Coccothrinax (tree).

1977, Aug. 19   Litho.   Perf. 12
C259 AP77 7c multicolored   1.00   .25
C260 AP77 33c multicolored   2.50 1.10

National Botanical Garden.

Chart and Factories — AP78

1977, Nov. 30   Litho.   Perf. 13x13½
C261 AP78 28c multicolored   1.00   .65

7th Interamerican Statistics Conference.

Animal Type

Congress Emblem and: 10c, "Dorado," red Roman stud bull. 25c, Flamingo, vert.

1977, Dec. 29   Litho.   Perf. 13
C262 A259 10c multicolored   3.00   .30
C263 A259 25c multicolored   5.00   .50

Spanish Heritage Type

21c, Window, Casa del Tostado, 16th cent.

1978, Jan. 19   Perf. 13x13½
        Size: 28x41mm
C264 A260 21c multicolored   .85   .55

Holy Week Type, 1978

7c, Facade, Santo Domingo Cathedral. 10c, Facade of Dominican Convent.

1978, Mar. 21   Litho.   Perf. 12
        Size: 27x36mm
C265 A261 7c multicolored   .50   .25
C266 A261 10c multicolored   1.00   .30

Schooner Duarte — AP79

1978, Apr. 15   Litho.   Perf. 13½
C267 AP79 7c multicolored   .70   .25

Dominican naval forces training ship.

Cardinal Type

1978, May 5   Litho.   Perf. 13
C268 A262 10c multicolored   .60   .25

Antenna — AP80

1978, May 17 **Litho.** *Perf. 13½*
C269 AP80 25c silver & multi 1.00 .55
10th World Telecommunications Day.

No. C1 and Map — AP81

1978, June 6
C270 AP81 10c multicolored .60 .25
1st Dominican Rep. airmail stamp, 50th anniv.

Globe, Soccer Ball, Emblem — AP82

33c, Soccer field, Argentina '78 emblem, globe.

1978, June 29
C271 AP82 12c multicolored .65 .35
C272 AP82 33c multicolored 1.40 1.00
11th World Cup Soccer Championship, Argentina, June 1-25.

Crown, Cross and Rosary Emblem — AP83

1978, July 11 *Perf. 13x13½*
C273 AP83 21c multicolored .85 .65
Congregation of the Merciful Sisters of Charity, centenary.

Sports Type

1978, July 21 **Litho.** *Perf. 13½*
C274 A265 7c Baseball, vert. 1.00 .25
C275 A265 10c Basketball, vert. 1.50 .25

Wright Brothers and Glider, 1902 — AP84

Designs: 7c, Diagrams of Flyer I and jet, vert. 13c, Diagram of air flow over wing. 45c, Flyer I over world map.

1978, Aug. 8 *Perf. 12*
C276 AP84 7c multicolored .25 .25
C277 AP84 10c multicolored .60 .25
C278 AP84 13c multicolored .85 .30
C279 AP84 45c multicolored 2.25 1.40
Nos. C276-C279 (4) 3.95 2.20
75th anniversary of first powered flight.

Tourist Type

Designs: 7c, Sun and musical instruments. 10c, Sun and plane over Santo Domingo.

1978, Sept. 12 **Litho.** *Perf. 12*
C280 A266 7c multicolored .65 .25
C281 A266 10c multicolored .90 .25

People and Globe — AP85

1978, Oct. 12 **Litho.** *Perf. 13½*
C282 AP85 21c multicolored .90 .70
Spanish heritage.

Dominican Republic and UN Flags — AP86

1978, Oct. 23 *Perf. 12*
C283 AP86 33c multicolored 1.25 .75
33rd anniversary of the United Nations.

Statue of the Virgin — AP87

1978, Dec. 5 **Litho.** *Perf. 12*
C284 AP87 10c multicolored .75 .30
Christmas 1978.

Pope John Paul II — AP88

1979, Jan. 25 **Litho.** *Perf. 13½*
C285 AP88 10c multicolored 3.75 3.25
Visit of Pope John Paul II to the Dominican Republic, Jan. 25-26.

Map of Beata Island — AP89

1979, Jan. 25 *Perf. 12*
C286 AP89 10c multicolored 1.50 .30
1st expedition of radio amateurs to Beata Is.

Year of the Child Type, 1979

Designs (ICY Emblem and): 7c, Children reading book. 10c, Symbolic head and protective hands. 33c, Hands and jars.

1979, Feb. 26
C287 A269 7c multicolored .40 .25
C288 A269 10c multicolored .60 .25
C289 A269 33c multicolored 1.75 1.10
Nos. C287-C289 (3) 2.75 1.60

Pope John Paul II Giving Benediction — AP90

1979, Apr. 9 **Litho.** *Perf. 13½*
C290 AP90 10c multicolored 4.00 1.25
Holy Week.

Adm. Juan Bautista Cambiaso — AP91

1979, Apr. 14 *Perf. 12*
C291 AP91 10c multicolored .60 .25
135th anniv. of the Battle of Tortuguero.

Map of Dominican Rep., Album, Magnifier — AP92

1979, Apr. 18
C292 AP92 33c multicolored 1.10 .75
EXFILNA, 3rd National Philatelic Exhibition, Apr. 18-22.

Flower Type

Designs: 7c, Passionflower. 10c, Isidorea pungens. 13c, Calotropis procera.

1979, May 17 **Litho.** *Perf. 12*
C293 A271 7c multicolored 1.00 .30
C294 A271 10c multicolored 1.50 .35
C295 A271 13c multicolored 2.50 .65
Nos. C293-C295 (3) 5.00 1.30

Cardiology Type, 1979

10c, Figure of man showing blood circulation.

1979, June 2 **Litho.** *Perf. 13½*
C296 A272 10c multi, vert. .75 .40

Sports Type

7c, Runner and Games' emblem, vert.

1979, June 20
C297 A273 7c multicolored 1.50 .30

Soccer Type

1979, Aug. 9 **Litho.** *Perf. 12*
C298 A273 10c Tennis, vert. .65 .30

Rowland Hill, Dominican Republic No. 1 — AP93

1979, Aug. 21 *Perf. 13½*
C299 AP93 2p multicolored 4.75 3.25
Sir Rowland Hill (1795-1879), originator of penny postage.

Electric Light Type

Design: 10c, "100" and light bulb, horiz.

1979, Aug. 27 *Perf. 13½*
C300 A275 10c multicolored .50 .30

Bird Type

Birds: 7c, Phaenicophilus palmarum. 10c, Calyptophilus frugivorus tertius. 45c, Icterus dominicensis.

1979, Sept. 12 **Litho.** *Perf. 12*
C301 A277 7c multicolored 2.75 .30
C302 A277 10c multicolored 3.75 .30
C303 A277 45c multicolored 9.50 1.00
Nos. C301-C303 (3) 16.00 1.60

Lions Type

10c, Melvin Jones, organization founder.

1979, Nov. 13 **Litho.**
C304 A278 10c multicolored .60 .30

Christmas Type

Christmas: 10c, Three Kings riding camels.

1979, Dec. 18 **Litho.** *Perf. 12*
C305 A279 10c multicolored .50 .25

Holy Week Type

1980, Mar. 27 **Litho.** *Perf. 12*
C306 A280 7c Crucifixion .40 .25
C307 A280 10c Resurrection .75 .55

Navy Day — AP94

1980, Apr. 15 **Litho.** *Perf. 13½*
C308 AP94 21c multicolored .75 .55

Dominican Philatelic Society, 25th Anniversary AP95

1980, Apr. 18
C309 AP95 10c multicolored .55 .30

Gold Type

1980, July 8 **Litho.** *Perf. 13½*
C310 A282 10c Drag line mining .75 .35
C311 A282 33c Mine 1.25 .55

Tourism Secretariat Emblem — AP96

1980, Aug. 26 **Litho.** *Perf. 13½*
C312 AP96 10c shown .45 .30
C313 AP96 33c Conf. emblem 1.60 1.10
World Tourism Conf., Manila, Sept. 27.

Iguana Type

Designs: 7c, American crocodile. 10c, Cuban rat. 25c, Manatee. 45c, Turtle.

1980, Aug. 30 *Perf. 12*
C314 A284 7c multi 2.00 .35
C315 A284 10c multi 2.40 .40
C316 A284 25c multi 3.75 .65
C317 A284 45c multi 5.25 .95
Nos. C314-C317 (4) 13.40 2.35

Painting Type

Designs: 10c, Abstract, by Paul Guidicelli, vert. 17c, Farmer, by Yoryi Morel, vert.

1980, Sept. 23 **Litho.** *Perf. 13½x13*
C318 A285 10c multi .60 .30
C319 A285 17c multi .90 .55

Visit of Radio Amateurs to Catalina Island — AP97

1980, Oct. 3
C320 AP97 7c multicolored .60 .50

Rotary International, 75th Anniversary AP98

Design: 10c, Globe, emblem, vert.

1980, Oct. 23 **Litho.** *Perf. 12*
C321 AP98 10c multi .60 .45
C322 AP98 33c shown 1.25 .85

Carrier Pigeons, UPU Emblem — AP99

1980, Oct. 31   **Perf. 13½**
C323 AP99 33c shown   .75 .50
C324 AP99 45c Pigeons, diff.   1.00 .65
C325 AP99 50c Pigeon, stamp   1.40 .75
   Nos. C323-C325 (3)   3.15 1.90

Souvenir Sheet
Imperf

C326 AP99 1.10p UPU emblem   2.00 2.00
   UPU cent. No. C326 contains one
48½x31mm stamp.

Christmas Type
1980, Dec. 5   Litho.   Perf. 13½
C327 A286 10c Holy Family   .65 .30

Christmas 1980.

Salcedo Type
Design: Map and arms of Salcedo.

1981, Jan. 14   Litho.   Perf. 13½
C328 A287 10c multicolored   .50 .25

AP100

Industrial Symbols, Seminar Emblem.

1981, Feb. 18   Litho.   Perf. 13½
C329 AP100 10c shown   .55 .30
C330 AP100 33c Seminar em-
            blem   .90 .55

CODIA Chemical Engineering Seminar.

National Games Type
1981, Mar. 31   Litho.   Perf. 13½
C331 A289 10c Baseball   2.50 .35

AP101

Design: Admiral Juan Alejandro Acosta.

1981, Apr. 15
C332 AP101 10c multicolored   .40 .25

Battle of Tortuguero anniversary.

13th World Telecommunications
Day — AP102

1981, May 16   Litho.   Perf. 12
C333 AP102 10c multicolored   .65 .25

Heinrich von
Stephan — AP103

1981, July 15   Litho.   Perf. 13½
C334 AP103 33c tan & lt red brn 1.10 .75

Birth sesquicentennial of UPU founder.

Worker in
Wheelchair — AP104

1981, July 24
C335 AP104 7c Stylized people   .50 .30
C336 AP104 33c shown   1.25 .75

Intl. Year of the Disabled.

EXPURIDOM '81
Intl. Stamp Show,
Santo Domingo,
July 31-Aug.
2 — AP105

1981, July 31
C337 AP105 7c multicolored   .75 .35

Bullet Holes in
Target,
Competition
Emblem — AP106

1981, Aug. 12
C338 AP106 10c shown   .35 .25
C339 AP106 15c Riflemen   .55 .30
C340 AP106 25c Pistol shooting 1.00 .65
   Nos. C338-C340 (3)   1.90 1.20

2nd World Sharpshooting Championship.

Exports — AP107

1981, Oct. 16   Litho.   Perf. 12
C341 AP107 7c Jewelry   .55 .25
C342 AP107 10c Handicrafts   .65 .30
C343 AP107 11c Fruit   .80 .30
C344 AP107 17c Vegetables   1.00 .35
   Nos. C341-C344 (4)   3.00 1.20

World Food
Day — AP108

1981, Oct. 16   Litho.   Perf. 13½
C345 AP108 10c Fruits   .75 .30
C346 AP108 50c Vegetables   1.75 1.40

5th Natl.
Games — AP109

1981, Dec. 5   Litho.   Perf. 13½
C347 AP109 10c Javelin, vert.   .45 .35
C348 AP109 50c Cycling   2.10 1.75

Orchids — AP110

7c, Encyclia cochleata. 10c, Broughtonia
domingensis. 25c, Encyclia truncata. 75c,
Elleanthus capitatus.

1981, Dec. 14
C349 AP110 7c multicolored   .85 .25
C350 AP110 10c multicolored   1.00 .30
C351 AP110 25c multicolored   1.60 .75
C352 AP110 75c multicolored   4.00 2.25
   Nos. C349-C352 (4)   7.45 3.55

Christmas Type
1981, Dec. 23
C353 A294 10c Dove, sun   .90 .45

Battle of
Tortuguero
Anniv. — AP111

Design: Naval Academy, cadets.

1982, Apr. 15   Litho.   Perf. 13½
C354 AP111 10c multi   .60 .30

1982 World Cup
Soccer — AP112

Designs: Various soccer players.

1982, Apr. 19
C355 AP112 10c multicolored   .60 .35
C356 AP112 21c multicolored   .75 .45
C357 AP112 33c multicolored   1.40 .90
   Nos. C355-C357 (3)   2.75 1.70

American Air Forces
Cooperation
System — AP113

1982, Apr. 12   **Perf. 12**
C358 AP113 10c multicolored   .70 .30

Scouting
Year — AP114

10c, Baden-Powell, vert. 15c, Globe. 25c,
Baden-Powell, scout, vert.

1982, Apr. 30   Litho.   Perf. 13½
C359 AP114 10c multi   .45 .25
C360 AP114 15c multi   .65 .30
C361 AP114 25c multi   .95 .45
   Nos. C359-C361 (3)   2.05 1.00

Dancers — AP115

7c, Emblem. 10c, Cathedral, Casa del Tostado, Santo Domingo.

1982, June 1   Litho.   Perf. 13½
C362 AP115 7c multi   .30 .25
C363 AP115 10c multi   .35 .25
C364 AP115 33c shown   1.75 .85
   Nos. C362-C364 (3)   2.40 1.35

Tourist Org. of the Americas, 25th Congress
(COTAL '82), Santo Domingo.

Espamer '82
Emblem — AP116

Espamer '82 Intl. Stamp Exhibition, San
Juan, Oct. 12-17: Symbolic stamps.

1982, July 5
C365 AP116 7c multi   .30 .25
C366 AP116 13c multi, horiz.   .50 .30
C367 AP116 50c multi   2.10 1.60
   Nos. C365-C367 (3)   2.90 2.15

Sports Type
1982, Aug. 13   Perf. 12, Imperf.
C368 A300 10c Basketball   1.00 .25
C369 A300 13c Boxing   1.50 .30
C370 A300 25c Gymnast   2.00 .45
   Nos. C368-C370 (3)   4.50 1.00

Harbor, by
Alejandro
Bonilla
AP117

Paintings: 10c, Portrait of a Woman, by Leopoldo Navarro. 45c, Amelia Francasci, by Luis
Desangles. 2p, Portrait, by Abelardo Rodriguez Urdaneta. 10c, 45c, 2p vert.

1982, Aug. 20   Perf. 13, Imperf.
C371 AP117 7c multicolored   .30 .25
C372 AP117 10c multicolored   .45 .30
C373 AP117 45c multicolored   2.10 1.40
C374 AP117 2p multicolored   9.00 6.00
   Nos. C371-C374 (4)   11.85 7.95

San Pedro de Macoris Type
1982, Aug. 26
   Size: 42x29mm
C375 A301 7c Lake   .75 .30

35th Anniv. of
Central
Bank — AP118

1982, Oct. 22   Litho.   Perf. 13½x13
C376 AP118 10c multicolored   .60 .35

490th Anniv. of
Discovery of
America — AP119

Designs: 7c, Map. 10c, Santa Maria, vert.
21c, Columbus, vert.

1982, Oct. 7   Litho.   Perf. 13½
C377 AP119 7c multi   1.25 .95
C378 AP119 10c multi   1.60 1.10
C379 AP119 21c multi   2.10 1.10
   Nos. C377-C379 (3)   4.95 3.15

Christmas Type
1982, Dec. 8
C380 A303 10c multicolored   .55 .35

French Alliance
Centenary — AP120

1983, Mar. 31   Litho.   Perf. 13½
C381 AP120 33c multicolored   .85 .55

Battle of
Tortuguero
Anniv. — AP121

Design: 15c, Frigate Mella-451.

1983, Apr. 15   Litho.   Perf. 13½
C382 AP121 15c multi   .95 .35

World Communications
Year — AP122

1983, May 6   Litho.   Perf. 13½
C383 AP122 10c dk blue & blue   .60 .30

AP123

1983, July 5   Litho.   Perf. 13½
C384 AP123 9c multicolored   .60 .35
Simon Bolivar (1783-1830).

AP124

7c, Gymnast, basketball. 10c, Highjump,
boxing. 15c, Baseball, weight lifting, bicycling.

1983, Aug. 22   Litho.   Perf. 12
C385 AP124 7c multi   .70 .25
C386 AP124 10c multi   .80 .25
C387 AP124 15c multi   1.00 .30
Nos. C385-C387 (3)   2.50 .80

9th Pan American Games, Caracas, Aug.
13-28.

491st Anniv. of
Discovery of
America — AP125

10c, Columbus' ships, map. 21c, Santa
Maria (trophy). 33c, Yacht Sotavento, vert.
50c, Ship models.

1983, Oct. 11   Litho.   Perf. 13½
C388 AP125 10c multi   1.25 .45
C389 AP125 21c multi   1.90 .75
C390 AP125 33c multi   2.10 .85
Nos. C388-C390 (3)   5.25 2.05

Size: 103x103mm
Imperf

C391 AP125 50c multi   15.00 15.00

10th Anniv. of
Latin American
Civil Aviation
Commission
AP126

1983, Dec. 7
C392 AP126 10c dark blue   .60 .35

Funeral
Procession, by
Juan Bautista
Gomez
AP127

Designs: 15c, Meeting of Maximo Gomez
and Jose Marti in Guayubin, by Enrique Garcia Godoy. 21c, St. Francis, by Angel
Perdomo, vert. 33c, Portrait of a Girl, by Adri-
ana Billini, vert.

1983, Dec. 26   Perf. 13½
C393 AP127 10c multicolored   .40 .25
C394 AP127 15c multicolored   .40 .25
C395 AP127 21c multicolored   .50 .25
C396 AP127 33c multicolored   .75 .25
Nos. C393-C396 (4)   2.05 1.00

Christmas
1983 — AP128

1983, Dec. 13   Litho.   Perf. 13½
C397 AP128 10c Bells, orna-
ments   .60 .25

AIR POST SEMI-POSTAL STAMPS

> Catalogue values for unused
> stamps in this section are for
> Never Hinged items.

**Nos. C97-C99 Surcharged in Red
like Nos. B1-B5
Engraved and Lithographed
1957, Feb. 8   Unwmk.   Perf. 11½
Flags in National Colors**
CB1 A117 11c + 2c ultra & red
org   .40 .40
CB2 A117 16c + 2c car & lt grn   .70 .70
CB3 A117 17c + 2c blk, vio & red   .70 .70
Nos. CB1-CB3 (3)   1.80 1.80

The surtax was to aid Hungarian refugees.
A similar 25c surcharge was applied to the
souvenir sheets described in the footnote following No. C99. Value, 2 sheets, perf. and
imperf., $17.50.

**Nos. C100-C102 Surcharged in Red
Orange like Nos. B6-B10
1957, Sept. 9   Photo.   Perf. 13½
Flags in National Colors**
CB4 A118 11c + 2c ygrn grn & dk
bl   .70 .50
CB5 A118 16c + 2c lilac & dk bl   .85 .70
CB6 A118 17c + 2c brn & bl grn   1.00 .75
Nos. CB4-CB6 (3)   2.55 1.95

See note after No. B10.
A similar 5c surcharge was applied to the
miniature sheets described in the footnote following No. 483. Value, 4 sheets, perf. &
imperf., medal and flag, $40.

**Types of Olympic Air Post Stamps,
1957, Surcharged in Carmine like
Nos. B11-B20
1958, May 26   Engr. & Litho.
Flags in National Colors
Pink Paper**
CB7 A119(a) 11c + 2c ultra   .40 .40
CB8 A119(b) 11c + 2c ultra   .40 .40
CB9 A120(a) 16c + 2c rose car   .55 .55
CB10 A120(b) 16c + 2c rose car   .55 .55
CB11 A119(a) 17c + 2c claret   .65 .65
CB12 A119(b) 17c + 2c claret   .65 .65
Nos. CB7-CB12 (6)   3.20 3.20

A similar 5c surcharge, plus marginal UN
emblem and "UNRWA," was applied to the
miniature sheets described in the footnote following No. C105. Value, 2 sheets, perf. and
imperf., $20.

**Nos. C106-C108 Surcharged like
Nos. B21-B25
1959, Apr. 13   Photo.   Perf. 13½
Flags in National Colors**
CB13 A125 11c + 2c blue, ol &
brn   .80 .80
CB14 A125 16c + 2c lt grn, org &
dk bl   1.10 1.10
CB15 A125 17c + 2c ver bl & yel   1.60 1.60
Nos. CB13-CB15 (3)   3.50 3.50

A similar 5c surcharge was applied to the
miniature sheets described in the footnote following No. C108. Value, 2 sheets, perf. and
imperf., $25.

**Type of Regular Issue 1957
Surcharged in Red like Nos. B26-
B30
Engraved and Lithographed
1959, Sept. 10   Imperf.
Flags in National Colors**
CB16 A117 11c + 2c ultra & red
org   .80 .80
CB17 A117 16c + 2c carmine & lt
grn   .90 .90
CB18 A117 17c + 2c black, vio &
red   .90 .90
Nos. CB16-CB18 (3)   2.60 2.60

**Nos. C113-C114 Surcharged in Red
like Nos. B31-B33
1960, Apr. 7   Litho.   Perf. 12½**
CB19 AP43 10c + 5c plum, gray &
grn   .35 .35
CB20 AP43 13c + 5c gray & green   .55 .55
World Refugee Year.
For souvenir sheets see note after No. B33.

Nos. C115-C117 Surcharged

Perf. 13½
**1962, Jan. 8   Unwmk.   Photo.
Flags in National Colors**
CB21 A136 11c + 2c blue, gray &
brn   .35 .35
CB22 A136 16c + 2c red, brn &
ol   .50 .50
CB23 A136 17c + 2c blk, bl &
ocher   .50 .50
Nos. CB21-CB23 (3)   1.35 1.35

See note after No. B38.
A similar 5c surcharge was applied to the
miniature sheets described in the footnote following No. C117. Value, 2 sheets, perf. and
imperf., $9.

Anti-Malaria Type of 1962
1962, Apr. 29   Litho.   Perf. 12
CB24 A141 13c + 2c pink & red   .50 .35
CB25 A141 33c + 2c org & dp
org   1.10 .75

Souvenir sheets exist, perf. and imperf. con-
taining one each of Nos. B39-B40, CB24-
CB25 and a 25c+2c pale grn and yel grn.
Value, 2 sheets, perf. and imperf., $7.50.

**Nos. C132-C133 Surcharged like
Nos. B44-B46
1964, Mar. 8**
CB26 AP46 10c + 2c brt violet   .35 .35
CB27 AP46 13c + 2c yellow   .40 .40

**Nos. C146-C148 Surcharged like
Nos. B47-B51
1966, Dec. 9   Litho.   Perf. 12½
Size: 35x24mm**
CB28 A164 10c + 5c multi   3.00 1.00
CB29 A164 50c + 10c multi   4.50 3.00
CB30 A164 75c + 10c multi   6.00 3.75
Nos. CB28-CB30 (3)   13.50 7.75

AIR POST OFFICIAL STAMPS

Nos. O13-O14
Overprinted in Blue

Unwmk.
1930, Dec. 3   Typo.   Perf. 12
CO1 O3 10c light blue   17.50 17.50
a. Pair, one without ovpt.   1,100.
CO2 O3 20c orange   17.50 17.50

SPECIAL DELIVERY STAMPS

Biplane — SD1

Perf. 11½
1920, Apr.   Unwmk.   Litho.
E1 SD1 10c deep ultra   6.75 1.40
a. Imperf., pair

Special
Delivery
Messenger
SD2

1925
E2 SD2 10c dark blue   21.00 5.75

SD3

1927
E3 SD3 10c red brown   6.75 1.40
a. "E EXPRESO" at top   55.00 55.00

Type of 1927
1941   Redrawn
E4 SD3 10c yellow green   3.00 3.25
E5 SD3 10c dark blue green   2.75 .60

The redrawn design differs slightly from SD3.
Issue dates: No. E4, Mar. 27; No. E5, Aug.
7.

Emblem of Communications — SD4

1945, Sept. 1   Perf. 12
E6 SD4 10c rose car, car & dk
bl   1.25 .25

> Catalogue values for unused
> stamps in this section, from this
> point to the end of the section, are
> for Never Hinged items.

SD5

1950   Litho.   Unwmk.
E7 SD5 10c multicolored   .70 .25
Exists imperf.

Modern Communications
System — SD6

1956, Aug. 18   Perf. 11½
E8 SD6 25c green   1.25 .30

Carrier
Pigeon — SD7

1967   Litho.   Perf. 11½
E9 SD7 25c light blue   .80 .30

Carrier Pigeon,
Globe — SD8

1978, Aug. 2   Litho.   Perf. 13½
E10 SD8 25c multicolored   1.10 .45

Messenger, Plane — SD9

1979, Nov. 30　　　　**Perf. 13½**
E11　SD9　25c multicolored　　　　.75　.45

Motorcycling SD10

1989, May　　**Litho.**　　**Perf. 13½**
E12　SD10　1p multicolored　　　2.50　1.10

Postman — SD11

1999　　**Litho.**　　**Perf. 13½x13¼**
E13　SD11　8p multicolored　　　3.25　2.75

INSURED LETTER STAMPS

Merino Issue of 1933 Surcharged in Red or Black

1935, Feb. 1　**Unwmk.**　　**Perf. 14**
G1　A35　8c on 7c ultra　　　.60　.25
　a.　Inverted surcharge　　18.00
G2　A35　15c on 10c org yel　　.65　.25
　a.　Inverted surcharge　　18.00
G3　A35　30c on 8c dk green　　2.25　.90
G4　A35　45c on 20c car rose (Bk)　　3.25　1.10
G5　A36　70c on 50c lemon　　7.75　1.75
　　　Nos. G1-G5 (5)　　14.50　4.25

Merino Issue of 1933 Surcharged in Red

1940
G6　A35　8c on ½c lt vio　　2.75　2.75
G7　A35　8c on 7c ultra　　3.25　3.25

Coat of Arms — IL1

1940-45　　**Litho.**　　**Perf. 11½**
Arms in Black
G8　IL1　8c brown red　　　.85　.25
　a.　8c dk red, no shading on inner frame　　1.10　.25
G9　IL1　15c dp orange ('45)　　1.75　.25
G10　IL1　30c dk green ('41)　　2.00　.25
　a.　30c yellow green　　2.00　.25
G11　IL1　45c ultra ('44)　　2.25　.30
G12　IL1　70c olive brn ('44)　　2.10　.30
　　　Nos. G8-G12 (5)　　8.95　1.35

See Nos. G13-G16, G24-G27.

Redrawn Type of 1940-45
1952-53　　　　**Arms in Black**
G13　IL1　8c car lake ('53)　　4.00　.50
G14　IL1　15c red orange ('53)　2.50　.75
G15　IL1　70c dp brown car　　9.50　1.75
　　　Nos. G13-G15 (3)　　16.00　3.00

Larger and bolder numerals on 8c and 15c. Smaller and bolder "70." There are many other minor differences in the design.

Type of 1940-45
1954　　**Arms in Black, 15x16mm**
G16　IL1　10c carmine　　　.85　.25

Coat of Arms — IL2

1955-69　Unwmk.　Litho.　Perf. 11½
Arms in Black, 13½x11½mm
G17　IL2　10c carmine rose　　.40　.25
G18　IL2　15c red orange ('56)　5.25　2.25
G19　IL2　20c red orange ('58)　1.25　.30
　a.　20c orange ('69)　　1.25　.30
　b.　20c orange, retouched ('69)　3.50　1.25
G20　IL2　30c dark green ('55)　2.00　.40
G21　IL2　40c dark green ('58)　2.10　.90
　a.　40c lt yellow grn ('62)　2.10　.45
G22　IL2　45c ultra ('56)　　4.00　3.75
G23　IL2　70c dp brn car ('56)　6.75　2.25
　　　Nos. G17-G23 (7)　　21.75　10.10

On No. G19b the horizontal shading lines of shield are omitted.
See Nos. G28-G37.

Type of 1940-45
Second Redrawing
1963　　　　**Perf. 12½**
Arms in Black, 17x16mm
G24　IL1　10c red orange　　1.25　.30
G25　IL1　20c orange　　　1.90　1.25

Third Redrawing
1966　　**Litho.**　　**Perf. 12½**
Arms in Black, 14x14mm
G26　IL1　10c violet　　　.40　.25
G27　IL1　40c orange　　　1.50　1.00

Type of 1955-62
1968　　**Litho.**　　**Perf. 11½**
Arms in Black, 13½x11½mm
G28　IL2　20c red　　　　2.50　1.00
G29　IL2　60c yellow　　　2.10　2.10

1973-76　　**Litho.**　　**Perf. 12½**
Arms in Black, 11x11mm
G30　IL2　10c car rose ('76)　　.50　.35
G31　IL2　20c yellow　　　1.40　.90
G32　IL2　20c orange ('76)　1.75　.50
G33　IL2　40c yel grn　　　1.60　1.00
　a.　40c green ('76)　　3.00　3.00
G34　IL2　70c blue　　　1.90　1.90
　　　Nos. G30-G34 (5)　　7.15　4.65

1973　　　　　　**Perf. 11½**
Arms in Black, 13½x11½mm
G35　IL2　10c dark violet　　.90　.30

1978, Aug. 9　　　**Perf. 10½**
Arms in Black, 11x11mm
G36　IL2　10c rose magenta　.45　.25
G37　IL2　40c bright green　1.75　1.50

IL3

1982-83　　**Litho.**　　**Perf. 10½**
Arms in Black
G38　IL3　10c deep magenta　.30　.25
G39　IL3　20c deep orange　.45　.30
G40　IL3　40c bluish green　1.00　.50
　　　Nos. G38-G40 (3)　　1.75　1.05

IL4

1986　　**Litho.**　　**Perf. 10½**
Arms in Black
G41　IL4　20c brt rose lilac　.35　.25
G42　IL4　60c orange　　1.20　.85
G43　IL4　1p light blue　2.10　1.40
G44　IL4　1.25p pink　　2.75　1.75
G45　IL4　1.50p vermilion　3.25　2.50
G46　IL4　3p light green　6.25　4.25
G47　IL4　3.50p olive bister　7.00　4.50
G48　IL4　4p yellow　　8.75　5.50
G49　IL4　4.50p lt blue grn　9.75　6.25
G50　IL4　5p brown olive　10.50　7.00
G51　IL4　6p gray　　12.50　8.50
G52　IL4　6.50p lt ultra　14.50　9.50
　　　Nos. G41-G52 (12)　78.90　52.25

Issue dates: Nos. G42-G43, G45, July 16. Nos. G46-G52, Sept. 2. Nos. G41, G44, Nov. 6.

Coat of Arms — IL5

1989-90　　**Litho.**　　**Perf. 13½**
Arms in Black
G53　IL5　20c brt lilac rose　.35　.25
G54　IL5　60c orange ('90)　1.00　.45
G55　IL5　1p sky blue　　1.60　.75
G56　IL5　1.25p lt salmon pink　1.90　.90
G57　IL5　1.50p dark red　2.40　1.40
　　　Nos. G53-G57 (5)　　7.25　3.75

"RD$" in lower left square on Nos. G55-G57.

IL6

1994, Oct.　　**Litho.**　　**Perf. 13½**
Arms in Black
G58　IL6　50c lilac rose　　.35　.25
G59　IL6　1p sky blue　　.50　.25
G60　IL6　1.50p red　　.65　.30
G61　IL6　2p pink　　.85　.50
G62　IL6　3p violet blue　1.40　.60
G63　IL6　5p yellow　　1.90　.90
G64　IL6　6p apple green　2.50　1.25
G65　IL6　8p green　　3.00　1.50
G66　IL6　10p silver gray　4.25　2.00
　　　Nos. G58-G66 (9)　　15.40　7.55

POSTAGE DUE STAMPS

D1

1901　　**Unwmk.**　**Typo.**　**Perf. 14**
J1　D1　2c olive gray　　.90　.25
J2　D1　4c olive gray　　1.10　.25
J3　D1　5c olive gray　　1.90　.30
J4　D1　10c olive gray　　3.25　.95
　　　Nos. J1-J4 (4)　　7.15　1.75

For surcharges and overprint see Nos. 162-165, 169-171.

1909　　　　　　**Wmk. 116**
J5　D1　2c olive gray　　1.50　.50
J6　D1　4c olive gray　　1.50　.50
J7　D1　5c olive gray　　2.00　.75
J8　D1　10c olive gray　　4.00　2.50
　　　Nos. J5-J8 (4)　　9.00　4.25

1913
J9　D1　2c olive green　　.60　.30
J10　D1　4c olive green　　.70　.40
J11　D1　6c olive green　　1.10　.50
J12　D1　10c olive green　　1.25　.60
　　　Nos. J9-J12 (4)　　3.65　1.80

1922　**Unwmk.**　**Litho.**　**Perf. 11½**
J13　D1　1c olive green　　.70　.70

D2

1942
J14　D2　1c dk red & pale pink　.40　.25
J15　D2　2c dk bl & pale bl　.40　.25
J16　D2　4c dk grn & pale grn　.40　.25
J17　D2　6c green & buff　.50　.25
J18　D2　8c yel org & pale yel　.50　.30
J19　D2　10c mag & pale pink　.75　.50
　　　Nos. J14-J19 (6)　　2.95　1.80

1955　　　　**Size: 20½x25mm**
J20　D2　2c dark blue　　1.40　1.00

D3

1959　　**Litho.**　　**Perf. 11½**
Size: 21x25½mm
J21　D3　1c dark car rose　1.25　1.25
J22　D3　2c dark blue　　1.25　1.25
J23　D3　4c green　　3.00　3.00
　　　Nos. J21-J23 (3)　　5.50　5.50

OFFICIAL STAMPS

Bastion of February 27 — O1

Unwmk.
1902, Feb. 25　**Litho.**　**Perf. 12**
O1　O1　2c scarlet & blk　.65　.30
O2　O1　5c dk blue & blk　.85　.25
O3　O1　10c yel grn & blk　1.00　.55
O4　O1　20c yellow & blk　1.25　.55
　a.　Imperf., pair　　11.00
　　　Nos. O1-O4 (4)　　3.75　1.65

For overprints and surcharge see Nos. 157-161.

Bastion of Feb. 27 — O2

Perf. 13½x13, 13½x14
1909-12　**Wmk. 116**　**Typo.**
O5　O2　1c blue grn & blk　.40　.25
O6　O2　2c scarlet & blk　.50　.30
O7　O2　5c dk blue & blk　1.00　.40
O8　O2　10c yel grn & blk ('12)　1.60　.95
O9　O2　20c orange & blk ('12)　2.75　2.25
　　　Nos. O5-O9 (5)　　6.25　4.15

The 2c, 5c are found in both perforations; 1c, 20c perf. 13½x13; 10c perf. 13½x14.
For overprints and surcharge see Nos. 177, 194-199.

Columbus Lighthouse — O3

1928　　**Unwmk.**　　**Perf. 12**
O10　O3　1c green　　.30　.30
O11　O3　2c red　　.30　.30
O12　O3　5c ultramarine　.35　.35
O13　O3　10c light blue　.40　.40
O14　O3　20c orange　　.60　.60
　　　Nos. O10-O14 (5)　　1.95　1.95

For overprints see Nos. CO1-CO2.

Proposed Columbus Lighthouse — O4

1937		Litho.	Perf. 11½	
O15	O4	3c dark purple	1.60	.50
O16	O4	7c indigo & blue	1.90	.60
O17	O4	10c orange yellow	2.25	.85
		Nos. O15-O17 (3)	5.75	1.95

Proposed Columbus Lighthouse — O5

1939-41

O18	O5	1c dp grn & lt grn	.90	.40
O19	O5	2c crim & pale pink	.90	.40
O20	O5	3c purple & lt vio	.90	.40
O21	O5	5c dk bl & lt bl ('40)	1.20	.60
O21A	O5	5c lt blue ('41)	2.40	1.25
O22	O5	7c brt bl & lt bl ('41)	2.10	.40
O23	O5	10c yel org & pale org ('41)	2.10	.60
O24	O5	20c org brn & buff ('41)	7.00	1.00
O25	O5	50c dp mag & pink ('41)	8.50	3.00
		Nos. O18-O25 (9)	26.00	8.05

Catalogue values for unused stamps in this section, from this point to the end of the section, are for Never Hinged items.

Type of 1939

1950			Redrawn
O26	O5	50c dp car & rose	10.00 2.00

The numerals "50" measure 3mm, and are close to left and right frames; numerals measure 4mm on No. O25. There are other minor differences.

Denominations in "Centavos Oro"

1950				
O27	O5	5c light blue	1.00	.40
O28	O5	10c yel & pale yel	1.25	.60
O29	O5	20c dl org brn & buff	2.50	2.25
		Nos. O27-O29 (3)	4.75	3.25

Letters of top inscription are 1½mm high.

Second Redrawing
Type of 1939-41 Denominations in "Centavos Oro"

1956		Unwmk.	Perf. 11½	
O30	O5	7c blue & lt blue	1.00	1.00
O31	O5	20c yellow brn & buff	2.50	2.50
O32	O5	50c red lil & brt pink	6.00	6.00
		Nos. O30-O32 (3)	9.50	9.50

The letters of top inscription are 2mm high, the trees at base of monument have been redrawn, etc. On No. O32 the numerals are similar to No. O26.

POSTAL TAX STAMPS

Santo Domingo after Hurricane — PT1

Hurricane's Effect on Capital — PT2

1930, Dec.		Unwmk. Litho.	Perf. 12	
RA1	PT1	1c green & rose	.25	.25
RA2	PT1	2c red rose	.25	.25
RA3	PT2	5c ultra & rose	.30	.25
RA4	PT2	10c yellow & rose	.40	.30
		Imperf		
RA5	PT1	1c green & rose	.40	.30
RA6	PT1	2c red & rose	.50	.30
RA7	PT2	5c ultra & rose	.60	.50
RA8	PT2	10c yellow & rose	.90	.75
		Nos. RA1-RA8 (8)	3.60	2.90

For surcharges see Nos. RAC1-RAC7.

Tête bêche Pairs

RA1a	PT1	1c green & rose	1.75	1.75
RA2a	PT1	2c red rose	1.75	1.50
RA3a	PT1	5c ultra & rose	1.75	2.10
RA4a	PT1	10c yellow & rose	2.10	2.10
RA5a	PT1	1c green & rose	1.75	1.75
RA6a	PT1	2c red & rose	1.75	1.75
RA7a	PT1	5c ultra & rose	2.10	2.10
RA8a	PT1	10c yellow & rose	2.10	2.10
		Nos. RA1a-RA8a (8)	15.05	15.15

Dr. Martos Sanatorium — PT3

1944, Apr. 1		Litho.	Perf. 11½	
RA9	PT3	1c dp bl, sl bl & red	.40	.30

Nurse and Child — PT4

1947, Apr. 1		Unwmk.		
RA10	PT4	1c dp bl, pale bl & car	.50	.30

Sanatorium of the Holy Help — PT5

1949, Apr. 1				
RA11	PT5	1c dp bl, pale bl & car	.35	.25

Youth Holding Banner — PT6

1950, Apr. 1			Perf. 11½	
RA12	PT6	1c dp bl, pale bl & car	.30	.25

"Suffer Little Children to Come Unto Me" — PT7

1950, Dec. 1			Perf. 12	
		Size: 22½x32mm		
RA13	PT7	1c lt bl & pale bl	1.25	.30
b.		Perf. 12½ ('52)	4.50	.25

Vertical line centering side borders merges into dots toward the bottom. See Nos. RA13A, RA17, RA19, RA26, RA32, RA35.
The tax was for child welfare.

1951, Dec. 1			Redrawn	
RA13A	PT7	1c lt blue & pale blue	6.25	.30

In the redrawn stamp, the standing child, a blonde in No. RA13, is changed to a brunette; more foliage has been added above child's head and to branches showing in upper right corner. Vertical dashes in side borders.

Tuberculosis Sanatorium, Santiago — PT8

1952, Apr. 1		Litho.	Perf. 11½	
RA14	PT8	1c lt blue & car	.30	.25

Sword, Serpent and Crab — PT9

1953, Feb. 1		Unwmk.	Perf. 12.	
RA15	PT9	1c carmine	.50	.30

The tax was for the Dominican League Against Cancer. See Nos. RA18, RA21, RA43, RA46, RA51, RA56, RA61, RA67, RA72, RA76, RA82, RA88, RA93, RA96.

Tuberculosis Dispensary for Children PT10

1953, Apr. 1		Litho.	Perf. 12½	
RA16	PT10	1c dp bl, pale bl & red	.40	.30

See No. RA22.

Jesus Type of 1950
Second Redrawing

1953, Dec. 1			Perf. 11½	
		Size: 22x31mm		
RA17	PT7	1c blue	.35	.25

Solid shading in sky reduced to a few scattered dots. Girl's left arm indicated. Rough white dots in side borders.

Cancer Type of 1952

1954, Oct. 1		Redrawn	Perf. 12½	
RA18	PT9	1c rose carmine	.30	.25
a.		1c red orange ('58)	.40	.25
b.		1c carmine ('70)	1.25	.25

Upper right serif of numeral "1" eliminated; diagonal line added through "C" and period removed; sword extended, placing top on a line with top of "1." Dots of background screen arranged diagonally. Many other differences.
The tax was for the Dominican League Against Cancer. No. RA18a exists imperf.
On No. RA18b background screen eliminates white outline of crab.

Jesus Type of 1950

1954, Dec. 1		Third Redrawing		
		Size: 23x32¾mm		
RA19	PT7	1c bright blue	.40	.30
a.		1c pale blue ('59)	.40	.30

Center completely screened. Tiny white horizontal rectangles in side borders.

Catalogue values for unused stamps in this section, from this point to the end of the section, are for Never Hinged items.

Lorraine Cross as Bell Clapper — PT11

1955, Apr. 1		Litho.	Perf. 11½x12	
RA20	PT11	1c black, yel & red	.50	.30

Cancer Type of 1952
Second Redrawing

1956, Oct. 1			Perf. 12½	
RA21	PT9	1c carmine	.70	.30
a.		1c red orange ('64)	1.25	.50

Similar to No. RA18, but dots of background screen arranged in vertical and horizontal rows. Outlines of central device, lettering and frame clearly delineated. "C" of cent-sign smaller. Upper claw in solid color.

TB Dispensary Type of 1953
Redrawn

1954, Apr. 1				
RA22	PT10	1c blue & red	.90	.25
a.		Red (cross) omitted	55.00	

No. RA22 has third color omitted; clouds added; bolder letters and numerals.

Angelita Trujillo — PT12

1955, Dec. 1		Unwmk.	Perf. 12½	
RA23	PT12	1c violet	.95	.30

The tax was for child welfare.

Lorraine Cross — PT13

1956, Apr. 1		Litho.	Perf. 11½	
RA24	PT13	1c blk, grn, lem & red	.50	.30

The tax was for the Anti-Tuberculosis League. Inscribed: B.C.G. (Bacillus Calmette-Guerin).

PT14

1957, Apr. 1				
RA25	PT14	1c red, blk, yel, grn & bl	.50	.30

Jesus Type of 1950
Fourth Redrawing

1956, Dec. 1		Unwmk.	Perf. 12	
		Size: 21¾x31¼mm		
RA26	PT7	1c blue	.40	.25

Thin white lines around numeral boxes. Girl's bouquet touches Jesus' sleeve. Tiny white squares or rectangles in side borders. Foliage at either side of "Era de Trujillo" panel.

PT15

1958, Apr. 1		Litho.	Perf. 12½	
RA27	PT15	1c brown car & red	.45	.25

1959, Apr. 1			Inscribed "1959"	
RA28	PT15	1c brown car & red	.45	.25

PT16

1960, Apr. 1		Litho.	Perf. 12	
RA29	PT16	1c bl, pale yel & red	.55	.30

PT17

1961, Apr. 1		Unwmk.	Perf. 11½	
RA30	PT17	1c blue & red	.40	.25

Nos. RA29-RA30: tax was for the Anti-Tuberculosis League.
See No. RA33.

PT18

Design: 1c, Maria de los Angeles M. de Trujillo and Housing Project.

1961, Aug. 1   Litho.   Perf. 12
RA31 PT18 1c carmine rose   .40   .25

The tax was for aid to the needy.
Nos. RA31-RA33 exist imperf.

Jesus Type of 1950
Fifth Redrawing
1961, Dec. 1   Unwmk.   Perf. 12½
RA32 PT7 1c blue   .40   .25

No. RA32 is similar to No. RA19, but "Era de Trujillo" has been replaced by a solid color panel.

Type of 1961 Dated "1962"
1962, Apr. 2   Perf. 12½
RA33 PT17 1c blue & red   .95   .30

Tax for the Anti-Tuberculosis League.

Man's Chest — PT19

1963, Apr. 1   Perf. 12x11½
RA34 PT19 1c ultra & red   .50   .30

Jesus Type of 1950
Sixth Redrawing
1963, Dec. 1   Perf. 11½
Size: 21¾x32mm
RA35 PT7 1c blue   .40   .25
a.   1c deep blue ('64)   .40   .25

No. RA35 is similar to No. RA26, but "Era de Trujillo" panel has been omitted.

Hibiscus — PT20

1966, Apr. 1   Litho.   Perf. 11½
RA36 PT20 1c emerald & car   .40   .25

Tax for the Anti-Tuberculosis League.

Domingoa
Nodosa — PT21

1967, Apr. 1   Litho.   Perf. 12½
RA37 PT21 1c lilac & red   1.00   .30

Tax for the Anti-Tuberculosis League.

Civil Defense
Emblem — PT22

1967, July 1   Litho.   Rouletted 13
RA38 PT22 1c multicolored   .40   .25

Tax for the Civil Defense Organization.

Boy, School and Yule
Bells — PT23

1967, Dec. 1   Litho.   Perf. 12½
RA39 PT23 1c rose red & pink   .50   .30

1968   Perf. 11
RA40 PT23 1c vermilion   .45   .25

No. RA40 has screened background; No. RA39, smooth background.
The tax was for child welfare.
See Nos. RA49A, RA52, RA57, RA62, RA68, RA73, RA77, RA81.

Hand Holding
Invalid — PT24

1968, Mar. 19   Litho.   Perf. 12½
RA41 PT24 1c green & yellow   .40   .25
a.   1c olive green & deep yellow,
perf. 11½x12 ('69)   .40   .25

The tax was for the rehabilitation of the handicapped. See Nos. RA47, RA50, RA54.

Dogbane — PT25

1968, Apr. 25   Litho.   Perf. 12½
RA42 PT25 1c emerald, yel & red .40 .25

The tax was for the Anti-Tuberculosis League. See Nos. RA45, RA49.

Redrawn Cancer Type of 1955
1968, Oct. 1   Litho.   Perf. 12
RA43 PT9 1c emerald   .40   .25

The tax was for the Dominican League against Cancer.

Schoolyard,
Torch — PT26

1969, Feb. 1   Litho.   Perf. 12½
RA44 PT26 1c light blue   .40   .25

Issued for Education Year 1969.

Flower Type of 1968
Design: No. RA45, Violets.
1969, Apr. 25   Litho.   Perf. 12½
RA45 PT25 1c emerald, lil & red   .70 .30

Tax for the Anti-Tuberculosis League.

Redrawn Cancer Type of 1955
1969, Oct. 1   Litho.   Perf. 11
RA46 PT9 1c brt rose lilac   .40   .25

Tax for Dominican League against Cancer.

Invalid Type of 1968
1970, Mar. 2   Perf. 12½
RA47 PT24 1c blue   .40   .25

The tax was for the rehabilitation of the handicapped.

Book, Sun and
Education Year
Emblem — PT27

1970, Feb. 6   Perf. 11
RA48 PT27 1c bright pink   .40   .25

International Education Year.

Flower Type of 1968
Design: 1c, Elleanthus capitatus; cross in upper left corner, denomination in lower right.
1970, Apr. 30   Perf. 11
RA49 PT25 1c emerald, red & yel 1.10 .30

Tax for Anti-Tuberculosis League.

Boy Type of 1967
1970, Dec. 1   Perf. 12½
RA49A PT23 1c orange   .45   .30

Communications
Emblem — PT28

1971, Jan. 2   Litho.   Perf. 11
Size: 17½x20½mm
RA49B PT28 1c vio bl & red
(white frame)   .55   .30

Tax was for Postal and Telegraph Communications School.
See Nos. RA53, RA58, RA63, RA69, RA78, RA91.

Invalid Type of 1968
1971, Mar. 1   Litho.   Perf. 11
RA50 PT24 1c brt rose lilac   .40   .25

Tax for rehabilitation of the handicapped.

Cancer Type of 1952
Third Redrawing
1971, Oct. 1   Perf. 11½
RA51 PT9 1c dp yellow green   .40   .25

Background of No. RA51 appears white and design stands out. No. RA43 has greenish background and design appears faint. Numeral "1" on No. RA51 is 3½mm high, on No. RA43 it is 3mm.

Boy Type of 1967
1971, Dec. 1   Litho.   Perf. 11
RA52 PT23 1c green   .45   .25

Communications Type of 1971
1972, Jan. 3   Litho.   Perf. 12½
Size: 19x22mm
RA53 PT28 1c dk bl & red (bl
frame)   .40   .25

Tax was for the Postal and Telegraph Communications School.

Invalid Type of 1968
1972, Mar. 1   Litho.   Perf. 11½
RA54 PT24 1c brown   .75   .25

Orchid — PT29

1972, Apr. 2   Perf. 11
RA55 PT29 1c lt grn, red & yel   1.60 .45

Tax was for the Anti-Tuberculosis League.

Redrawn Cancer Type of 1954-58
1972, Oct. 2   Perf. 12½
RA56 PT9 1c orange   .45   .25

Tax for Dominican League against Cancer.

Boy Type of 1967
1972, Dec. 1   Perf. 12
RA57 PT23 1c violet   .40   .25

Tax was for child welfare.

Communications Type of 1971
1973, Jan. 2   Perf. 10½
Size: 19x22mm
RA58 PT28 1c dk bl & red (red
frame)   .40   .25

Tax was for Postal and Telegraph Communications School.

Invalid — PT30

1973, Mar. 1   Litho.   Perf. 12½
Size: 21x25mm
RA59 PT30 1c olive   .40   .25

Tax was for the Dominican Rehabilitation Association. See Nos. RA66, RA70, RA74, RA79, RA86.

Hibiscus — PT31

1973, Apr. 17   Litho.   Perf. 10½
RA60 PT31 1c multicolored   1.20   .30

Tax was for Anti-Tuberculosis League. Exists imperf.

**Cancer Type of 1952 Redrawn and
"1973" Added**
1973, Oct. 1   Perf. 13½
RA61 PT9 1c olive green   .55   .30

Tax was for Dominican League Against Cancer.

Boy Type of 1967
1973, Dec. 1   Litho.   Perf. 13x13½
RA62 PT23 1c blue   .70   .25

Communications Type of 1971
1973, Nov. 3   Litho.   Perf. 10½
Size: 19x22mm
RA63 PT28 1c bl & red (lt grn
frame)   .40   .25

Tax was for Postal and Telegraph Communications School. Exists imperf.

Invalid Type of 1973
1974, Mar. 1   Litho.   Perf. 10½
Size: 22x27½mm
RA66 PT30 1c light ultra   .55   .30

See note after No. RA59.

**Cancer Type of 1952 Redrawn and
"1974" Added**
1974, Oct. 1   Perf. 12
RA67 PT9 1c orange   .55   .30

Tax for Dominican League Against Cancer.

Boy Type of 1967
1974, Dec. 2   Litho.   Perf. 11½
RA68 PT23 1c dk brown & buff   .40 .25

Communications Type of 1971
1974, Nov. 13   Perf. 10½
RA69 PT28 1c blue & red (yel
frame)   .40   .25

Invalid Type of 1973 Dated "1975"
1975, Mar. 1   Perf. 13½x13
Size: 21x32mm
RA70 PT30 1c olive brown   .55   .30

See note after No. RA59.

Catteeyopsis
Rosea — PT32

1975, Apr. 1   *Perf. 12*
RA71 PT32 1c blue & multi   1.40 .95
Tax was for Anti-Tuberculosis League.

**Cancer Type of 1952 Redrawn and
"1975" Added**

1975, Oct. 1   Litho.   *Perf. 12*
RA72 PT9 1c violet blue   .55 .30
Tax was for Dominican League Against Cancer. Exists imperf.

Boy Type of 1967

1975, Dec. 1   Litho.   *Perf. 12*
RA73 PT23 1c red orange   .40 .25
Tax was for child welfare.

Invalid Type of 1973 Dated "1976"

1976, Mar. 1   Litho.   *Perf. 12*
Size: 21x31mm
RA74 PT30 1c ultra   .55 .30
See note after No. RA59.

Oncidium
Colochilum — PT33

1976, Apr. 6   *Perf. 13x13½*
RA75 PT33 1c green & multi   1.00 .30
Tax was for Anti-Tuberculosis League.
See Nos. RA80, RA84.

**Cancer Type of 1952 Redrawn and
"1976" Added**

1976, Oct. 1   Litho.   *Perf. 13½*
RA76 PT9 1c green   .55 .30
Tax was for Dominican League Against Cancer.

Boy Type of 1967

1976, Dec. 1   Litho.   *Perf. 13½*
RA77 PT23 1c purple   .55 .30
Tax was for child welfare.

Communications Type of 1971
1977, Jan. 7   Litho.   *Perf. 10½*
Size: 19x22mm
RA78 PT28 1c blue & red (lil frame)   .40 .25
a.   Perf. 12½x10½   —   —
Tax was for Postal and Telegraph Communications School.

Invalid Type of 1973 Dated "1977"

1977, Mar. 11   *Perf. 12*
Size: 21x31mm
RA79 PT30 1c ultra   .55 .30
See note after No. RA59.

Orchid Type of 1976 Dated "1977"
Orchid: Oncidium variegatum.

1977, Apr. 22   Litho.   *Perf. 13½*
RA80 PT33 1c multicolored   1.25 .30
Tax was for Anti-Tuberculosis League.

Boy Type of 1967

1977, Dec. 27   Litho.   *Perf. 12*
RA81 PT23 1c emerald   .40 .25
Tax was for child welfare.

**Cancer Type of 1952 Redrawn and
"1977" Added**

1978, Oct. 2   Litho.   *Perf. 13½*
RA82 PT9 1c lilac rose   .55 .30
Tax for Dominican League Against Cancer.

Mother, Child,
Holly — PT34

1978, Dec. 1   Litho.   *Perf. 13½*
RA83 PT34 1c green   .40 .25
Tax was for child welfare.
See Nos. RA89, RA92, RA97.

Orchid Type of 1973 Dated "1978"
Flower: Yellow alder.

1979, Apr.   Litho.   *Perf. 13½*
RA84 PT33 1c lt blue & multi   1.10 .30
Tax was for Anti-Tuberculosis League.

University Seal — PT35

1979, Feb. 10   Litho.   *Perf. 13½*
RA85 PT35 2c ultra & gray   .40 .25
450th anniv. of University of Santo Domingo.

Invalid Type of 1973 Dated "1978"

1979, Mar. 1   Litho.   *Perf. 12*
RA86 PT30 1c emerald   .95 .30
See note after No. RA59.

Invalid — PT36

1980, Mar. 28   Litho.   *Perf. 13½*
RA87 PT36 1c olive & citron   .95 .30

**Cancer Type of 1952 Redrawn and
"1980" Added**

1980, Oct. 1
RA88 PT9 1c violet & dk pur   .40 .25

Mother and Child Type of 1978
1980, Dec. 1   Litho.   *Perf. 13½*
RA89 PT34 1c bright blue   .40 .25

Turnera Ulmifolia
(Marilope) — PT37

1981, Apr. 27   Litho.   *Perf. 12*
RA90 PT37 1c multicolored   .60 .25
Tax was for Anti-Tuberculosis League.
See Nos. RA98-RA99.

Communications Type of 1971
1981, Feb.   Litho.   *Perf. 10½*
RA91 PT28 1c blue & red (lt bl frame)   .75 .25

Mother and Child Type of 1978
1982, Dec. 1   Litho.   *Perf. 12x12½*
RA92 PT34 1c lt bluish green   .40 .25
Inscribed 1981.

**Cancer Type of 1952 Redrawn and
"1981" Added**

1982   Litho.   *Perf. 13½*
RA93 PT9 1c blue & dp blue   .95 .30

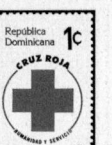

PT38

1983, Apr. 29   Litho.   *Perf. 12*
RA94 PT38 1c multicolored   .40 .25
Tax was for Red Cross.

Disabled — PT39

1984   Litho.   *Perf. 13½*
RA95 PT39 1c sky blue   .60 .25

**Cancer Type of 1952 Redrawn and
"1983" Added**

1983, Oct. 1   Litho.   *Perf. 13½*
RA96 PT9 1c lt bluish grn & dk grn   1.00 .25

Mother and Child Type of 1978
1983, Dec. 1   Litho.   *Perf. 12*
RA97 PT34 1c light green   1.00 .25
Inscribed 1983.

**Flower Type of 1981 Dated "1983"
or "1984"**

1983-85   Litho.   *Perf. 12x12½*
RA98 PT37 1c 1983   2.25 .25
RA99 PT37 1c 1984   2.25 .25
Issued: #RA98, 4/19/83; #RA99, 4/1/85.

POSTAL TAX AIR POST STAMPS

Postal Tax
Stamps
Surcharged in
Red or Gold

1930, Dec. 3   Unwmk.   *Perf. 12*
RAC1 PT2 5c + 5c blk & rose (R)   27.00 31.00
a.   Tête bêche pair   125.00
b.   "Habilitado Para" missing   52.50
RAC2 PT2 10c + 10c blk & rose (R)   27.00 31.00
a.   Tête bêche pair   125.00
b.   "Habilitado Para" missing   52.50
c.   Gold surcharge   95.00 95.00
d.   As "c," tête bêche pair   450.00
e.   As "c" and "b"   250.00

Nos. RAC1-RAC2 were on sale one day.

RAC4 PT2 5c + 5c ultra & rose (R)   6.75 6.75
a.   Tête bêche pair   45.00
b.   Inverted surcharge   42.50
c.   Tête bêche pair, inverted surcharge   600.00
d.   Pair, one without surcharge   190.00
e.   "Habilitado Para" missing   15.00
RAC5 PT2 10c + 10c yel & rose (G)   5.25 5.25
a.   Tête bêche pair   42.50
b.   "Habilitado Para" missing   18.00

Imperf

RAC6 PT2 5c + 5c ultra & rose (R)   6.75 6.75
a.   Tête bêche pair   52.50
b.   "Habilitado Para" missing   18.00
RAC7 PT2 10c + 10c yel & rose (G)   6.75 6.75
a.   Tête bêche pair   52.50
b.   "Habilitado Para" missing   18.00
Nos. RAC1-RAC7 (6)   79.50 87.50

It was obligatory to use Nos. RA1-RA8 and RAC1-RAC7 on all postal matter, in amounts equal to the ordinary postage.
This surtax was for the aid of sufferers from the hurricane of Sept. 3, 1930.

No. 261
Overprinted in
Green

1933, Oct. 11
RAC8 A32 2c scarlet   .50 .40
a.   Double overprint   9.00
b.   Pair, one without overprint   375.00

By official decree this stamp, in addition to the regular postage, had to be used on every letter, etc., sent by the internal air post service.

DUBAI

„dü-'bī

LOCATION — Oman Peninsula, Arabia, on Persian Gulf
GOVT. — Sheikdom under British protection
AREA — 1,500 sq. mi.
POP. — 60,000
CAPITAL — Dubai

Dubai is one of six Persian Gulf sheikdoms which join the United Arab Emirates which proclaimed its independence Dec. 2, 1971. See United Arab Emirates.

100 Naye Paise = 1 Rupee
100 Dirhams = 1 Riyal (1966)

Imperforate
Many issues were accompanied by smaller quantities of imperforate stamps.

Catalogue values for all unused stamps in this country are for Never Hinged items.

Hermit Crab — A1   Sheik Rashid bin Said al Maktum — A2

2np, 20np, Cuttlefish. 3np, 25np, Snail. 4np, 30np, Crab. 5np, 35np, Sea urchin. 10np, 50np, Sea shell. 1r, Fortress wall. 2r, View of Dubai. 3r, Fortress wall. 5r, View of Dubai.

Perf. 12x11½
1963, June 15   Litho.   Unwmk.

1	A1	1np dl bl & car rose	.30	.25
2	A1	2np lt bl & bis brn	.35	.25
3	A1	3np green & sepia	.35	.25
4	A1	4np pink & orange	.35	.25
5	A1	5np violet & blk	.35	.25
6	A1	10np brn org & blk	.35	.25
7	A1	15np gray ol & dp car	.70	.25
8	A1	20np rose red & org brn	.75	.40
9	A1	25np ap grn & red brn	.90	.40
10	A1	30np gray & red	1.50	.40
11	A1	35np dl lil & dl vio	1.50	.40
12	A1	50np org & sepia	2.25	.75
13	A1	1r brt bl & red org	6.00	1.50
14	A1	2r dull yel & brn	9.50	3.50
15	A1	3r rose car & blk	16.00	5.50
16	A1	5r grn & dl red brn	27.50	9.50

Perf. 12
17	A2	10r rose lake, grnsh bl & blk	60.00	19.00
		Nos. 1-17 (17)	128.65	43.10

Nos. 13-17 exist perf 10½. Values are much higher.

Dhows — A3

Designs: 2np, First-aid tent. 3np, Camel caravan. 4np, Butterfly.

1963, Sept. 1   Unwmk.   Perf. 12

18	A3	1np ultra, yel & red	.80	.35
19	A3	2np brn, yel & red	.80	.35
20	A3	3np red brn, org & red	.80	.35
21	A3	4np brn, brt grn & red	.80	.35
		Nos. 18-21,C9-C12 (8)	11.00	4.10

Intl. Red Cross, cent. Exist perf. 10½. Values, each $1.75.

Four imperf. souvenir sheets exist in the denominations and designs of Nos. C9-C12, with "Air-Mail" omitted and colors changed. Size: 119x99mm. Value $50.
For overprints see Nos. C52-C54.

A4

Anopheles Mosquito: 2np, Mosquito and entwined snakes. 3np, Mosquitoes over swamp.

1963, Dec. 20   Unwmk.   Perf. 12

22	A4	1np emer & red brn	.35	.25
23	A4	1np red & dark brn	.35	.25
24	A4	1np blue & carmine	.35	.25
25	A4	2np brn & orange	.35	.25
26	A4	2np carmine & blue	.35	.25
27	A4	3np org brn & blue	.35	.25
		Nos. 22-27,C13-C15 (9)	4.55	2.35

WHO drive to eradicate malaria.

A5

Designs: 1np, Scouts forming pyramid. 2np, Bugler. 3np, Cub Scouts. 4np, Scouts and bugler. 5np, Scouts presenting flag.

1964   Unwmk.

28	A5	1np dk brn & ocher	.25	.25
29	A5	2np car rose & sep	.25	.25
30	A5	3np blue & red org	.25	.25
31	A5	4np carmine & blue	.25	.25
32	A5	5np ind & bluish grn	.35	.25
		Nos. 28-32,C20-C24 (10)	6.35	3.20

11th Boy Scout Jamboree, Marathon, Greece, Aug., 1963.
For overprints see Nos. C47-C51.

Unisphere, New York Skyline and Dubai Harbor — A6

2np, 4np, 10np, Views of NYC and Dubai.

1964, Apr. 22   Litho.   Perf. 12

33	A6	1np dk bl & rose red	.25	.25
34	A6	2np dl red, lil rose & bl	.25	.25
35	A6	3np brown & green	.25	.25
36	A6	4np emer, brt grn & red	.25	.25
37	A6	5np ol, sl grn & lil	.25	.25
38	A6	10np brn org, red org & blk	.70	.50
		Nos. 33-38,C36-C38 (9)	6.15	4.05

New York World's Fair, 1964-65.

Gymnast A8

Designs: 2np, 5np, 20np, 40np, Various exercises on bar. 3np, 30np, Various exercises on vaulting horse. 4np, 10np, 1r, Various exercises on rings.

1964   Photo.   Perf. 14

43	A8	1np org brn & yel grn	.25	.25
44	A8	2np dk brn & grnsh bl	.25	.25
45	A8	3np ultra & org brn	.25	.25
46	A8	4np dk pur & yel	.25	.25
47	A8	5np ocher & dk bl	.25	.25
48	A8	10np brt bl & ocher	.25	.25
49	A8	20np ol & lil rose	.50	.25
50	A8	30np dk bl & car	.80	.25
51	A8	40np Prus grn & dl org	1.75	.50
52	A8	1r rose vio & grnsh bl	3.75	1.25
		Nos. 43-52 (10)	8.65	3.75

18th Olympic Games, Tokyo, Oct. 10-25, 1964. An imperf. miniature sheet contains a 67x67mm stamp similar to No. 52. Value $11.

Palace   Sheik Rashid bin
A9   Said
                A10

Designs: 20np, 25np, View of new Dubai. 35np, 40np, Bridge and dhow. 60np, 1r, Bridge. 1.25r, Minaret. 1.50r, 3r, Old Dubai.

1966, May 30   Photo.   Perf. 14x14½
Size: 23x18mm
53	A9	5np brown & indigo	.25	.25
54	A9	10np black & orange	.30	.25
55	A9	15np ultra & brown	.40	.25

Perf. 13
Size: 27½x20½mm
56	A9	20np blue & red brn	.50	.30
57	A9	25np org ver & ultra	.55	.40
58	A9	35np violet & emer	.75	.40
59	A9	40np grnsh bl & bl	1.10	.50

Perf. 14½
Size: 31½x24mm
60	A9	60np yel grn & org ver	1.75	1.00
61	A9	1r ultra & blue	2.75	1.50
62	A9	1.25r brn org & blk	3.00	2.00
63	A9	1.50r rose lil & yel grn	5.50	2.10
64	A9	3r dk ol bis & vio	10.00	4.00

Engr.
Perf. 14
65	A10	5r rose carmine	18.00	7.50
66	A10	10r dark blue	37.50	16.00
		Nos. 53-66 (14)	82.35	36.55

Nos. 53-62, 64-66 Overprinted with New Currency Names and Bars

1967
67	A9	5d on 5np	.30	.25
68	A9	10d on 10np	.35	.25
69	A9	15d on 15np	.50	.25
70	A9	20d on 20np	1.00	.25
71	A9	25d on 25np	1.25	.25
72	A9	35d on 35np	1.50	.25
73	A9	40d on 40np	1.75	.30
74	A9	60d on 60np	3.00	.40
75	A9	1r on 1r	4.00	.95
76	A9	1.25r on 1.25r	7.25	1.30
77	A9	3r on 3r	15.00	3.75
78	A10	5r on 5r	27.50	7.50
79	A10	10r on 10r	40.00	14.00
		Nos. 67-79 (13)	103.40	29.70

Sheik and   Dhow — A12
Falcon — A11

Litho. & Engr.
1967, Aug. 21   Perf. 13½
80	A11	5d dp car & org	1.10	.30
81	A11	10d sepia & green	1.25	.25
82	A11	20d dp cl & bl gray	1.40	.25
83	A11	35d slate & car	1.75	.30
84	A11	60d vio bl & emer	3.25	.50
85	A11	1r green & lilac	4.50	.50
86	A12	1.25r lt bl & claret	5.50	.65
87	A12	3r dull vio & claret	11.00	1.75
88	A12	5r brt grn & vio	22.50	3.75
89	A12	10r lil rose & grn	30.00	6.75
		Nos. 80-89 (10)	82.25	15.05

S. S. Bamora, 1914 — A13

35d, De Havilland 66 plane, 1930. 60d, S. S. Sirdhana, 1947. 1r, Armstrong Whitworth 15 "Atlanta," 1938. 1.25r, S. S. Chandpara, 1949. 3r, BOAC Sunderland amphibian plane, 1943. No. 96, Freighter Bombala, 1961, and BOAC Super VC10, 1967.

1969, Feb. 12   Litho.   Perf. 14x13½
90	A13	25d lt grn, bl & blk	.25	.25
91	A13	35d multicolored	.25	.25
92	A13	60d multicolored	.70	.25
93	A13	1r lil, blk & dl yel	1.15	.25
94	A13	1.25r gray, blk & dp org	1.60	.25
95	A13	3r pink, blk & bl grn	2.50	.35
		Nos. 90-95 (6)	6.45	1.60

Miniature Sheet
Imperf
96	A13	1.25r pink, blk & bl grn	16.00	16.00

60 years of postal service.

Mother and Children, by Rubens — A14

Arab Mother's Day: 60d, Madonna and Child, by Murillo. 1r, Mother and Child, by Francesco Mazzuoli. 3r, Madonna and Child, by Correggio.

1969, Mar. 21   Litho.   Perf. 13½
97	A14	60d silver & multi	.75	.25
98	A14	1r silver & multi	1.50	.25
99	A14	1.25r silver & multi	1.75	.25
100	A14	3r silver & multi	3.50	.45
		Nos. 97-100 (4)	7.50	1.20

Porkfish A15

1969, May 26   Litho.   Perf. 11
101	A15	60d shown	2.00	.35
102	A15	60d Spotted grouper	2.00	.35
103	A15	60d Moonfish	2.00	.35
104	A15	60d Sweetlips	2.00	.35
105	A15	60d Blue angel	2.00	.35
106	A15	60d Texas skate	2.00	.35
107	A15	60d Striped butterflyfish	2.00	.35
108	A15	60d Imperial angelfish	2.00	.35
a.		Block of 8, #101-108	35.00	
		Nos. 101-108 (8)	16.00	2.80

Nos. 101-108 printed in se-tenant blocks of 8, each sheet containing two such blocks.

Explorers and Map of Arabia — A16

1969, July 21   Litho.   Perf. 13½x13
109	A16	35d brown & green	1.50	.35
110	A16	60d vio & sepia	2.00	.45
111	A16	1r green & dl bl	5.50	.55
112	A16	1.25r gray & rose car	7.00	.65
		Nos. 109-112 (4)	16.00	2.00

European explorers of Arabia: Sir Richard Francis Burton (1821-1890), Charles Montagu Doughty (1843-1926), Johann Ludwig Burckhardt (1784-1817) and Wilfred Patrick Thesiger (1910-).

Construction of World's First Underwater Oil Storage Tank — A17

Designs: 20d, Launching of oil storage tank. 35d, Oil storage tank in place on ocean ground. 60d, Sheik Rashid bin Said, offshore drilling platform and monument commemorating first oil export. 1r, Offshore production platform and helicopter port.

1969, Oct. 13   Litho.   Perf. 11
113	A17	5d blue & multi	.30	.25
114	A17	20d blue & multi	1.00	.25
115	A17	35d blue & multi	1.90	.25
116	A17	60d blue & multi	2.75	.25
117	A17	1r blue & multi	4.00	.25
		Nos. 113-117 (5)	9.95	1.25

Astronauts Collecting Moon Rocks — A18

Designs: 1r, Astronaut at foot of ladder. 1.25r, Astronauts planting American flag.

1969, Dec. 15   Litho.   Perf. 14½
118		Strip of 3	3.75	1.00
a.	A18	60d multicolored	.40	.25
b.	A18	1r multicolored	.80	.25
c.	A18	1.25r multicolored (airmail)	1.50	.25

The 1.25r is inscribed "AIRMAIL."
Sizes: 60d and 1r, 28½x41mm; 1.25r, 60½x41mm.
See note after US No. C76.

Ocean Weather Ship Launching Radio Sonde, and Hastings Plane — A19

WMO Emblem and: 1r, Kew-type radio sonde, weather balloon and radar antenna. 1.25r, Tiros satellite and weather sounding rocket. 3r, Ariel satellite and rocket launching.

1970, Mar. 23   Litho.   Perf. 11
121	A19	60d dl grn, brn & blk	.40	.25
122	A19	1r brown & multi	.75	.25
123	A19	1.25r dk blue & multi	.90	.25
124	A19	3r multicolored	2.00	.30
		Nos. 121-124 (4)	4.05	1.05

10th World Meteorological Day.

UPU Headquarters and Monument, Bern — A20

60d, UPU monument, Bern, telecommunications satellite and London PO tower.

1970, May 20   Litho.   Perf. 13½x14
| 125 | A20 | 5d lt green & multi | .75 | .25 |
| 126 | A20 | 60d dp blue & multi | 1.90 | .25 |

UPU Headquarters opening, May 20.

Charles Dickens, London Skyline — A21

60d, Dickens' portrait, vert. 1.25r, Dickens & "Old Curiosity Shop." 3r, Bound volumes.

1970, July 23   Litho.   Perf. 13½
127	A21	60d olive & multi	.85	.25
128	A21	1r multicolored	1.00	.25
129	A21	1.25r buff & multi	1.20	.25
130	A21	3r multicolored	4.00	.50
		Nos. 127-130 (4)	7.05	1.25

Dickens (1812-70), English novelist.

The Graham Children, by William Hogarth A22

Paintings: 60d, Caroline Murat and her Children, by François Pascal Gerard, vert. 1r,

Napoleon with the Children on the Terrace in St. Cloud, by Louis Ducis.

1970, Oct. 1   Litho.   Perf. 13½
131	A22	35d multicolored	.75	.25
132	A22	60d multicolored	1.25	.25
133	A22	1r multicolored	2.00	.25
		Nos. 131-133 (3)	4.00	.75

Issued for Children's Day.

Sheik Rashid bin Said A23

Television Station A25

National Bank of Dubai — A24

Designs: 10d, Boat building. 20d, Al Maktum Bascule Bridge. 35d, Great Mosque, Dubai, vert. 1r, Dubai International Airport, horiz. 1.25r, Port Rashid harbor project, horiz. 3r, Rashid Hospital, horiz. 5r, Dubai Trade School, horiz.

Perf. 14x14½, 14½x14
1970-71   Litho.
134	A23	5d multi ('71)	.30	.25
135	A24	10d multi ('71)	.30	.25
136	A24	20d multi ('71)	.40	.25
137	A24	35d multi ('71)	.55	.25
138	A24	60d multicolored	.80	.25

Perf. 14
139	A25	1r multicolored	1.20	.25
140	A25	1.25r multicolored	1.20	.25
141	A25	3r multicolored	3.75	.25
142	A25	5r multicolored	6.00	.40
143	A25	10r multi ('71)	14.00	.85
		Nos. 134-143 (10)	28.50	3.25

Dubai Airport — A26

Designs: 1.25r, Airport entrance.

1971, May 15   Litho.   Perf. 13½x14
| 144 | A26 | 1r multicolored | 3.25 | .25 |
| 145 | A26 | 1.25r multicolored | 4.00 | .25 |

Opening of Dubai International Airport.

Map With Tracking Stations, Satellites — A27

1971, June 21   Litho.   Perf. 14½
| 146 | A27 | 60d multicolored | .60 | .30 |

Outer Space Telecommunications Cong., Paris, Mar. 29-Apr. 2. See Nos. C55-C56.

Fan, Scout Emblem, Map of Japan — A28

Designs: 1r, Boy Scouts in kayaks. 1.25r, Mountaineering. 3r, Campfire, horiz.

Perf. 14x13½, 13½x14
1971, Aug. 30   Litho.
147	A28	60d multicolored	.45	.25
148	A28	1r multicolored	.90	.25
149	A28	1.25r multicolored	1.15	.25
150	A28	3r multicolored	2.50	.30
		Nos. 147-150 (4)	5.00	1.05

13th Boy Scout World Jamboree, Asagiri Plain, Japan, Aug. 2-10.

Albrecht Dürer, Self-portrait — A29

1971, Oct. 18   Perf. 14x13½
| 151 | A29 | 60d gold & multi | .80 | .25 |

See Nos. C57-C59.

Boy in Meadow — A30

5r, Boys playing and UNICEF emblem.

1971, Dec. 11   Perf. 13½
| 152 | A30 | 60d multi | .45 | .25 |
| 153 | A30 | 5r multi, horiz. | 3.50 | .50 |

25th anniv. of UNICEF. See No. C60.

Ludwig van Beethoven — A31

Portrait: 10d, Leonardo da Vinci.

1972, Feb. 7
| 154 | A31 | 10d lt tan & multi | .30 | .25 |
| 155 | A31 | 35d lt tan & multi | .45 | .25 |

See Nos. C61-C62.

Olympic Emblems, Gymnast on Rings — A32

1972, July 31   Litho.   Perf. 13½
156	A32	35d shown	.55	.25
157	A32	40d Fencing	.65	.25
158	A32	65d Hockey	.25	
		Nos. 156-158,C65-C67 (6)	7.50	1.50

20th Olympic Games, Munich, 8/26-9/11.
Stamps of Dubai were replaced in 1972 by those of United Arab Emirates.

AIR POST STAMPS

Type of Regular Issue and

Peregrine Falcon — AP1

Design: A1, Falcon over bridge.

Perf. 12x11½, 11½x12
1963, June 15   Litho.   Unwmk.
C1	A1	20np dk red brn & lt blue	2.50	.35
C2	AP1	25np ol & blk brn	2.75	.45
C3	A1	30np red org & blk	3.25	.55
C4	AP1	40np grayish brn & dk violet	3.50	.65
C5	A1	50np emer & rose cl	4.25	.75
C6	AP1	60np brn org & blk	5.25	.85
C7	A1	75np vio & dp grn	6.50	1.00
C8	AP1	1r org & red brn	9.00	1.25
		Nos. C1-C8 (8)	37.00	5.85

Red Cross Type

Designs: 20np, Dhows. 30np, First-aid tent. 40np, Camel caravan. 50np, Butterfly.

1963, Sept. 1   Unwmk.   Perf. 12
C9	A3	20np brown, yel & red	1.40	.50
C10	A3	30np dk bl, buff & red	1.40	.50
C11	A3	40np black, yel & red	1.75	.60
C12	A3	50np vio, lt bl & red	3.25	1.10
		Nos. C9-C12 (4)	7.80	2.70

Malaria Type

Designs: 30np, Anopheles mosquito. 40np, Mosquito and coiled arrows. 70np, Mosquitoes over swamp.

1963, Dec. 20   Unwmk.   Perf. 12
C13	A4	30np purple & emer	.65	.25
C14	A4	40np red & dull grn	.75	.25
C15	A4	70np slate & citron	1.05	.35
		Nos. C13-C15 (3)	2.45	.85

Three imperf. souv. sheets exist containing 4 stamps each in changed colors similar to Nos. C13-C15. Value $30.

Wheat — AP2

40np, Wheat and palm tree. 70np, Hands holding wheat. 1r, Woman carrying basket.

1963, Dec. 30   Litho.
C16	AP2	30np vio bl & ocher	.50	.30
C17	AP2	40np red & olive	.75	.45
C18	AP2	70np green & orange	1.15	.65
C19	AP2	1r org brn & Prus bl	1.75	1.00
		Nos. C16-C19 (4)	4.15	2.40

Boy Scout Type

Designs: 20np, Human pyramid. 30np, Bugler. 40np, Cub Scouts. 70np, Scouts and bugler. 1r, Scouts presenting flag.

1964, Jan. 20
C20	A5	20np green & dk brn	.30	.25
C21	A5	30np lilac & ocher	.60	.25
C22	A5	40np vio bl & yel grn	.80	.30
C23	A5	70np dk grn & gray	1.40	.45
C24	A5	1r vio bl & red org	1.90	.70
		Nos. C20-C24 (5)	5.00	1.95

Five imperf. souv. sheets exist containing 4 stamps each in changed colors similar to Nos. C20-C24. Value $60.
For overprints see Nos. C47-C51.

John F. Kennedy and US Seal — AP3

1964, Jan. 15   Litho.
C25	AP3	75np grn & blk, lt grn	.90	.55
C26	AP3	1r ocher & blk, tan	1.25	.60
C27	AP3	1.25r mag & blk, gray	1.60	.85
		Nos. C25-C27 (3)	3.75	2.00

Pres. John F. Kennedy (1917-1963).
Nos. C25-C27 exist imperf. Value, set $9.50.
A souvenir sheet contains one imperf. 1.25r in buff and black with simulated perforations. Value $5.
For overprints see Nos. C52-C54.

Spacecraft — AP4

Designs: 1np, 5np, Ascending rocket, vert. 2np, 1r, Mercury capsule, vert. 4np, 2r, Twin spacecraft.

1964, Jan. 25   Unwmk.   Perf. 12

C28	AP4	1np emerald & org	.25	.25
C29	AP4	2np multicolored	.30	.25
C30	AP4	3np multicolored	.35	.25
C31	AP4	4np multicolored	.40	.25
C32	AP4	5np blue & orange	.45	.25
C33	AP4	1r vio bl, dp car & buff	1.25	.70
C34	AP4	1.50r vio bl, dp car & buff	2.00	1.25
C35	AP4	2r blue, yel & red	2.75	1.50
		Nos. C28-C35 (8)	7.75	4.70

Issued to honor the astronauts.
Nos. C28-C35 exist imperf. Value, set $10. An imperf. souvenir sheet contains one stamp similar to No. C35. Value $7.

New York World's Fair Type

Statue of Liberty and ships in Dubai harbor.

1964, Apr. 22   Litho.

C36	A6	75np gray bl, ultra & blk	.80	.40
C37	A6	2r gray grn, dk brn & bis	1.40	.80
C38	A6	3r dl grn, gray ol & dp org	2.00	1.10
		Nos. C36-C38 (3)	4.20	2.30

An imperf. souvenir sheet contains 2 stamps in Statue of Liberty design: 2r dark brown and rose carmine, and 3r ultramarine and gold. Value $10.

Scales and Flame — AP5

1964, Apr. 30   Litho.   Perf. 12

C39	AP5	35np bl, brn & scar	.60	.30
C40	AP5	50np lt bl, dk grn & scar	.75	.35
C41	AP5	1r grnsh bl, blk & scar	1.40	.60
C42	AP5	3r lt ultra, ultra, & scar	4.00	2.00
		Nos. C39-C42 (4)	6.75	3.25

15th anniv. of the Universal Declaration of Human Rights. An imperf. souvenir sheet contains one 3r light green, ultramarine and scarlet stamp. Value $7.50.

Nos. C20-C24 Overprinted in Red and Black (Shield in Red)

1964, June 20

C47	A5	20np green & dk brn	1.15	.40
C48	A5	30np lilac & ocher	1.35	.50
C49	A5	40np vio bl & yel grn	2.00	.75
C50	A5	70np dk grn & gray	3.25	1.50
C51	A5	1r vio bl & red org	4.50	2.00
		Nos. C47-C51 (5)	12.25	5.15

9th Winter Olympic Games, Innsbruck, Austria, Jan. 29-Feb. 9, 1964.
A similar but unauthorized overprint, with shield in black, exists on Nos. 28-32, C20-C24, and the five souvenir sheets mentioned below No. C24. The Dubai G.P.O. calls this black-shield overprint "bogus."

Nos. C25-C27 Overprinted in Brown or Green

1964, Sept. 15

C52	AP3	75np (Br)	2.00	2.00
C53	AP3	1r (G)	2.40	2.40
C54	AP3	1.25r (G)	3.00	3.00
		Nos. C52-C54 (3)	7.40	7.40

Pres. John F. Kennedy 48th birth anniv. The same overprint in black was applied to the souv. sheet noted after No. C27.

Communications Type

Designs: 1r, Intelsat 4, tracking station on globe and rocket. 5r, Eiffel Tower, Syncom 3 and Goonhilly radar station.

1971, June 21   Litho.   Perf. 14½

C55	A27	1r lt brown & multi	.60	.25
C56	A27	5r multicolored	3.00	.45

Portrait Type

1r, Newton. 1.25r, Avicenna. 3r, Voltaire.

1971, Oct. 18   Litho.   Perf. 14x13½

C57	A29	1r gold & multi	1.10	.25
C58	A29	1.25r gold & multi	1.40	.25
C59	A29	3r gold & multi	4.00	.50
		Nos. C57-C59 (3)	6.50	1.00

UNICEF Type

1r, Mother, children, UNICEF emblem.

1971, Dec. 11   Perf. 13½

C60	A30	1r gold & multi	1.00	.25

Portrait Type

75d, Khalil Gibran. 5r, Charles de Gaulle.

1972, Feb. 7   Litho.   Perf. 13½

C61	A31	75d lt tan & multi	.75	.25
C62	A31	5r lt tan & multi	5.25	.35

Infant Health Care — AP6

Design: 75d, Nurse supervising children at meal, and WHO emblem, vert.

1972, Apr. 7   Litho.   Perf. 14x13½

C63	AP6	75d multicolored	1.60	.25
C64	AP6	1.25r multicolored	2.40	.25

World Health Day.

Olympic Type

1972, July 31   Litho.   Perf. 13½

C65	A32	75d Water polo	1.50	.25
C66	A32	1r Steeplechase	1.75	.25
C67	A32	1.25r Running	2.25	.25
		Nos. C65-C67 (3)	5.50	.60

POSTAGE DUE STAMPS

Type of Regular Issue

Designs: 1np, 4np, 15np, Clam. 2np, 5np, 25np, Mussel. 3np, 10np, 35np, Oyster.

Perf. 12x11½

1963, June 15   Litho.   Unwmk.

J1	A1	1np gray grn & ver	1.00	.35
J2	A1	2np lemon & brt bl	1.50	.45
J3	A1	3np dl rose & green	1.75	.75
J4	A1	4np light grn & mag	2.50	1.00
J5	A1	5np vermilion & blk	3.00	1.25
J6	A1	10np citron & violet	3.50	1.50
J7	A1	15np brt ultra & ver	4.50	1.90
J8	A1	25np buff & olive grn	6.00	2.00
J9	A1	35np turq bl & dp org	6.50	2.75
		Nos. J1-J9 (9)	30.25	11.95

Sheik Rashid bin Said — D1

1972, May 22   Litho.   Perf. 14x14½

J10	D1	5d blk & gray grn	2.00	.70
J11	D1	10d vio bl, blk & bis	2.50	.85
J12	D1	20d sl grn, blk & brick red	4.25	1.50
J13	D1	30d grnsh gray, blk & lil	7.00	2.25
J14	D1	50d lilac, brn & bis	11.00	4.50
		Nos. J10-J14 (5)	26.75	9.85

EAST AFRICA & UGANDA PROTECTORATES

ˈēst ˈa-fri-kə and ü-ˈgan-də

prə-ˈtek-t̩ə-rəts

LOCATION — Central East Africa, bordering on the Indian Ocean
GOVT. — British Protectorate
AREA — 350,000 sq. mi. (approx.)
POP. — 6,503,507 (approx.)
CAPITAL — Mombasa

This territory, formerly administered by the British East Africa Colony, was divided between Kenya Colony and the Uganda Protectorate. See Kenya, Uganda and Tanzania.

16 Annas = 1 Rupee
100 Cents = 1 Rupee (1907)

Altered high value stamps of East Africa and Uganda are plentiful. Expertization by competent authorities is recommended.

A1   A2

King Edward VII

1903   Typo.   Wmk. 2   Perf. 14

1	A1	½a gray green	7.00	23.00
2	A1	1a car & black	3.00	2.00
3	A1	2a vio & dull vio	10.50	3.00
4	A1	2½a ultramarine	14.50	60.00
5	A1	3a gray grn & brn	30.00	75.00
6	A1	4a blk & gray grn	13.50	27.50
7	A1	5a org brn & blk	22.50	60.00
8	A1	8a pale blue & blk	28.00	50.00

Wmk. 1

9	A2	1r gray green	27.50	65.00
10	A2	2r vio & dull vio	95.00	100.00
11	A2	3r blk & gray grn	175.00	325.00
12	A2	4r lt green & blk	175.00	350.00
13	A2	5r car & black	175.00	350.00
14	A2	10r ultra & black	475.00	675.00
15	A2	20r ol gray & blk	850.00	1,950.
16	A2	50r org brn & blk	2,600.	4,750.
		Nos. 1-14 (14)	1,252.	2,166.

Nos. 9 and 14 are on both ordinary and chalky paper. Values are for examples on ordinary paper. Values are for the least expensive varieties. See *Scott Classic Specialized Catalogue of Stamps & Covers* for detailed listings.

1904-07   Wmk. 3   Chalky Paper

17	A1	½a gray green	16.00	3.75
18a	A1	1a car & black	11.00	1.00
19	A1	2a vio & dull vio	3.50	3.25
20	A1	2½a blue	10.00	37.50
a.		2½a blue & ultramarine	9.50	35.00
21	A1	3a gray grn & brn	4.75	45.00
22	A1	4a blk & gray grn	9.25	22.50
23	A1	5a org brn & blk	8.00	32.50
24a	A1	8a pale blue & blk	8.75	10.50
25	A2	1r gray green	35.00	75.00
26	A2	2r vio & dl vio	50.00	77.50
27	A2	3r blk & gray grn	100.00	160.00
28	A2	4r lt green & blk	140.00	200.00
29	A2	5r car & black	175.00	700.00
29A	A2	10r ultra & black	400.00	450.00
30	A2	20r ol gray & blk	875.00	1,600.
30A	A2	50r org brn & blk	2,750.	4,500.
		Nos. 17-29 (10)	541.50	1,320.

Nos. 17-19, 21-24 are on both ordinary and chalky paper. No. 20 is on ordinary paper. Values are for the least expensive varieties. See *Scott Classic Specialized Catalogue of Stamps & Covers* for detailed listings.

1907-08

31	A1	1c brown ('08)	3.00	.25
32	A1	3c gray green	22.50	.80
33	A1	6c carmine	3.25	.25
34	A1	10c citron & violet	13.00	10.00
35	A1	12c red vio & dl vio	12.00	3.50
36	A1	15c ultramarine	34.00	11.00
37	A1	25c blk & blue green	22.50	8.50
38	A1	50c org brn & green	20.00	17.50
39	A1	75c pale bl & gray blk ('08)	5.50	40.00
		Nos. 31-39 (9)	135.75	91.80

Nos. 31-33, 36 are on ordinary paper.
There are two dies of the 6c differing very slightly in many details.

King George V
A3   A4

1912-18   Ordinary Paper   Wmk. 3

40	A3	1c black	.40	2.10
41	A3	3c green	2.50	.75
a.		Booklet pane of 6		
42	A3	6c carmine	1.50	.70
a.		Booklet pane of 6		
43	A3	10c yel orange	2.50	.65
44	A3	12c gray	3.25	.65
45	A3	15c ultramarine	3.25	1.00

Chalky Paper

46	A3	25c scar & blk, *yel*	.65	1.60
47	A3	50c violet & black	1.90	1.60
48	A3	75c black, *green*	1.90	21.00
a.		75c black, *emerald*	13.50	65.00
b.		75c blk, *bl grn, olive back*	12.00	9.25
c.		75c blk, *emer, olive back*	50.00	175.00
49	A4	1r black, *green*	3.00	5.25
a.		1r black, *emerald*	6.00	60.00
50	A4	2r blk & red, *bl*	26.00	45.00
51	A4	3r gray grn & vio	32.50	130.00
52	A4	4r grn & red, *yel*	65.00	130.00
53	A4	5r dl vio & ultra	65.00	160.00
54	A4	10r grn & red, *grn*	260.00	375.00
55	A4	20r vio & blk, *red*	500.00	475.00
56	A4	20r bl & violet, *blue ('18)*	575.00	875.00
57	A4	50r gray grn & rose red	925.00	975.00
58	A4	100r blk & vio, *red*	9,750.	4,000.
59	A4	500r red & grn, *grn*	40,000.	
		Nos. 40-54 (15)	469.35	875.30

1914   Surface-colored Paper

60	A3	25c scarlet & blk, *yel*	.65	5.50
61	A3	75c black, *green*	1.25	19.50

Stamps of types A3 and A4 with watermark 4 are listed under Kenya, Uganda and Tanzania.
The 1r through 50r with revenue cancellations sell for minimal prices. The 100r and 500r were available for postage but were nearly always used fiscally.
For surcharge see No. 62.

No. 42 Surcharged

1919

62	A3	4c on 6c carmine	1.50	.25
a.		Double surcharge	160.00	250.00
b.		Without squares over old value	50.00	85.00
c.		Pair, one without surcharge	2,000.	2,250.
d.		Inverted surcharge	350.00	475.00

For later issues see Kenya, Uganda and Tanzania.
For stamps of East Africa and Uganda overprinted "G. E. A." see German East Africa.

EASTERN RUMELIA

ˈē-stərn rü-ˈmēl-yə

(South Bulgaria)

LOCATION — In southern Bulgaria
GOVT. — An autonomous unit of the Turkish Empire.
CAPITAL — Philippopolis (Plovdiv)

In 1885 the province of Eastern Rumelia revolted against Turkish rule and united with Bulgaria, adopting the new name of South Bulgaria. This union was assured by the Treaty of Bucharest in 1886, following the war between Serbia and Bulgaria.

40 Paras = 1 Piaster

Counterfeits of all overprints are plentiful.

Stamps of Turkey, 1876-84, Overprinted in Blue

No. 1

A2

A3

			Unwmk.	Perf. 13½	
1880					
1	A5	½pi on 20pa yel grn	67.50	57.50
a.		Horiz. pair, one without overprint		400.00
3	A2	10pa blk & rose	55.00	
4	A2	20pa vio & grn	87.50	67.50
6	A2	2pi blk & buff	115.00	100.00
7	A2	5pi red & bl	450.00	500.00
8	A3	10pa blk & red lil	57.50	

Nos. 3 & 8 were not placed in use. Inverted and double overprints of all values exist.

Same, with Extra Overprint "R. O."

9	A3	10pa blk & red lil	97.50	95.00

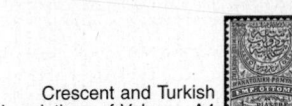

Crescent and Turkish Inscriptions of Value — A4

1881		**Typo.**	**Perf. 13½**	
10	A4	5pa blk & olive	17.00	1.35
11	A4	10pa blk & green	65.00	1.35
12	A4	20pa blk & rose	1.75	1.25
13	A4	1pi blk & blue	5.75	4.50
14	A4	5pi rose & blue	57.50	82.50

Tête bêche pairs, imperforates and all perf. 11½ examples of Nos. 10-14 were not placed in use, and were found only in the remainder stock. This is true also of a 10pa cliché in the 20pa plate, and of a cliché of Turkey No. 63 in the 1pi plate. See the *Scott Classic Catalogue*.

1884			**Perf. 11½**	
15	A4	5pa lil & pale lil	.75	.45
16	A4	10pa grn & pale grn	.25	.45
17	A4	20pa car & pale rose	.55	
18	A4	1pi bl & pale bl	1.15	
19	A4	5pi brn & pale brn	400.00	

Nos. 17-19 were not placed in use, and were found only in the remainder stock. Nos. 15-19 imperf. are from remainders. See the *Scott Classic Catalogue* for perf 13½ listings. For overprints see Turkey Nos. 542-545.

South Bulgaria

Counterfeits of all overprints are plentiful.

Nos. 10-14 Overprinted in Two Types

a

b

Type a — Four toes on each foot.
Type b — Three toes on each foot.

Blue Overprint

1885		**Unwmk.**	**Perf. 13½**	
20	A4 (a)	5pa blk & olive	325.00	375.00
21	A4 (a)	10pa blk & grn	875.00	825.00
22	A4 (a)	20pa blk & rose	325.00	—
23	A4 (a)	1pi blk & blue	37.50	72.50
24	A4 (a)	5pi rose & blue	1,100.	

See the *Scott Classic Catalogue* for Nos. 22-23, type b, No. 24, type a, and No. 22, perf 11½, types a and b.

Black Overprint

24B	A4 (a)	20pa blk & rose	275.00	—
25	A4 (a)	1pi blk & blue	55.00	115.00
26	A4 (b)	5pi rose & bl	675.00	—

See the *Scott Classic Catalogue* for No. 25 type b.

Same Overprint on Nos. 15-17
Blue Overprint
Perf. 11½

27	A4 (b)	5pa lil & pale lil, type "b"	22.50	57.50
28	A4 (b)	10pa grn & pale grn	40.00	75.00
29	A4 (b)	20pa car & pale rose	275.00	375.00

Black Overprint
Perf. 13½

30	A4 (b)	5pa lil & pale lil	40.00	67.50

Perf. 11½

31	A4 (a)	10pa grn & pale grn	42.50	85.00
32	A4 (b)	20pa car & pale rose	55.00	65.00

See the *Scott Classic Catalogue* for detailed listings of Nos. 27-32.

Nos. 10-17 Handstamped in Black in Two Types

a

b

Type a — First letter at top circular.
Type b — First letter at top oval.

1885			**Perf. 13½**	
33	A4 (b)	5pa blk & olive	300.00	250.00
34	A4 (b)	10pa blk & grn	225.00	250.00
35	A4 (b)	20pa blk & rose	72.50	85.00
36	A4 (a)	1pi blk & bl	87.50	115.00
37	A4 (a)	5pi rose & blue, type "a"	2,500.	—

Perf. 13½

38	A4 (a)	5pa lil & pale lil	26.00	44.00

Perf. 11½

39	A4 (a)	10pa grn & pale grn	29.00	35.00
40	A4 (a)	20pa car & pale rose	29.00	50.00

See the *Scott Classic Catalogue* for Nos. 38-40, type b, and No. 38, perf 11½, types a and b.
Nos. 20-40 exist with inverted and double handstamps. Overprints in unlisted colors are proofs.
The stamps of South Bulgaria were superseded in 1886 by those of Bulgaria.

EASTERN SILESIA

ˈē-stərn sī-ˈlē-zh ē-ə

LOCATION — In central Europe
GOVT. — Austrian crownland
AREA — 1,987 sq. mi.
POP. — 680,422 (estimated 1920)
CAPITAL — Troppau

After World War I, this territory was occupied by Czechoslovakia and eventually was divided between Poland and Czechoslovakia, the dividing line running through Teschen.

100 Heller = 1 Krone
100 Fennigi = 1 Marka

Plebiscite Issues

Stamps of Czechoslovakia 1918-20, Overprinted in Black, Blue, Violet or Red

1920		**Unwmk.**	**Imperf.**	
1	A2	1h dark brown	.25	.30
2	A1	3h red violet	.25	.25
3	A2	5h blue green	23.50	22.50
4	A2	15h red	11.50	11.00
5	A1	20h blue green	.25	.25
6	A1	25h dull violet	.75	.75
7	A1	30h bister (R)	.25	.25
8	A1	40h red orange	.30	.30
9	A2	50h dull violet	.60	.45
10	A2	50h dark blue	2.60	1.50
11	A2	60h orange (Bl)	.75	.75
12	A2	75h slate (R)	.50	.75
13	A2	80h olive grn (R)	.50	.75
14	A1	100h brown	1.10	1.10
15	A2	120h gray blk (R)	1.60	2.25
16	A1	200h ultra (R)	1.60	2.00
17	A2	300h green (R)	6.25	7.50
18	A1	400h purple (R)	2.60	3.00
20	A2	500h red brn (Bl)	5.25	6.00
a.		Black overprint	6.25	9.00
21	A1	1000h violet (Bl)	13.00	13.50
a.		Black overprint	62.50	75.00
		Nos. 1-21 (20)	73.40	75.15

Perf. 11½, 13¾

22	A2	1h dark brown	.25	.25
23	A2	5h blue green	.30	.25
24	A2	10h yellow green	.30	.25
a.		Imperf.	260.00	210.00
25	A2	15h red	.50	.25
26	A2	20h rose	.50	.35
a.		Imperf.	300.00	250.00
27	A2	25h dull violet	.50	.35
28	A2	30h red violet (Bl)	.35	.35
29	A2	60h orange (Bl)	.50	.50
30	A1	200h ultra (R)	3.00	3.00
		Nos. 22-30 (9)	6.20	5.55

The letters "S. O." are the initials of "Silésie Orientale."
Forged cancellations are found on Nos. 1-30.

Overprinted in Carmine or Violet

31	A4	500h sl, *grysh* (C)	40.00	
32	A4	1000h blk brn, *brnsh*	40.00	

Excellent counterfeits of this overprint exist.

Stamps of Poland, 1919, Overprinted

1920			**Perf. 11½**	
41	A10	5f green	.25	.25
42	A10	10f red brown	.25	.25
43	A10	15f light red	.25	.25
44	A11	25f olive green	.25	.25
45	A11	50f blue green	.25	.25

Overprinted

46	A12	1k deep green	.25	.25
47	A12	1.50k brown	.25	.25
48	A12	2k dark blue	.25	.25
49	A13	2.50k dull violet	.30	.25
50	A14	5k slate blue	.50	.25
		Nos. 41-50 (10)	2.80	2.50

SPECIAL DELIVERY STAMPS

Czechoslovakia Special Delivery Stamps Ovptd. in Blue

1920		**Unwmk.**	**Imperf.**	
E1	SD1	2h red violet, *yel*	.25	.25
a.		Black overprint	4.75	.80
E2	SD1	5h yellow green, *yel*	.25	.25
a.		Black overprint	8.00	5.00

Nos. E1-E2a exist on white paper.

POSTAGE DUE STAMPS

Czechoslovakia Postage Due Stamps Overprinted In Blue or Red

1920		**Unwmk.**	**Imperf.**	
J1	D1	5h deep bis (Bl)	.25	.25
a.		Black overprint	72.50	62.50
J2	D1	10h deep bister	.25	.25
J3	D1	15h deep bister	.25	.25
J4	D1	20h deep bister	.25	.25
J5	D1	25h deep bister	.25	.25
J6	D1	30h deep bister	.25	.25
J7	D1	40h deep bister	.50	.25
J8	D1	50h deep bister	2.60	3.00
J9	D1	100h blk brn (R)	2.60	3.00
J10	D1	500h gray grn (R)	5.75	4.50
J11	D1	1000h purple (R)	8.50	11.50
		Nos. J1-J11 (11)	21.45	23.75

Forged cancellations exist.

NEWSPAPER STAMPS

Czechoslovakia Newspaper Stamps Overprinted in Black like Nos. 1-30

1920		**Unwmk.**	**Imperf.**	
P1	N1	2h gray green	.30	.30
P2	N1	6h red	.25	.25
P3	N1	10h dull violet	.40	.25
P4	N1	20h blue	.65	.25
P5	N1	30h gray brown	.65	.25
		Nos. P1-P5 (5)	2.25	1.30

ECUADOR

'e-kwə-,dor

LOCATION — Northwest coast of South America, bordering on the Pacific Ocean
GOVT. — Republic
AREA — 116,270 (?) sq. mi.
POP. — 12,562,496 (1999 est.)
CAPITAL — Quito

The Republic of Ecuador was so constituted on May 11, 1830, after the Civil War that separated the original members of the Republic of Colombia, founded by Simon Bolivar by uniting the Presidency of Quito with the Viceroyalty of New Grenada and the Captaincy of Venezuela. The Presidency of Quito became the Republic of Ecuador.

8 Reales = 1 Peso
100 Centavos = 1 Sucre (1881)
100 Cents = 1 Dollar (2000)

Catalogue values for unused stamps in this country are for Never Hinged items, beginning with Scott 453 in the regular postage section, Scott C147 in the airpost section, Scott CO19 in the airpost officials section, Scott O201 in the officials section, Scott RA60 in the postal tax section, and all entries in the Galapagos section.

Watermarks

Wmk. 117 — Liberty Cap   Wmk. 127 — Quatrefoils

Wmk. 233 — "Harrison & Sons, London" in Script Letters

Wmk. 340 — Alternating Interlaced Wavy Lines

Wmk. 367 — Liberty Cap, Emblem, Inscription

Wmk. 377 — Interlocking Circles

Wmk. 395 — Emblem, Inscription

Coat of Arms
A1   A2

1865-72 Unwmk. Typo. Imperf.
Quadrille Paper

1	A1	1r yellow ('72)	60.00	55.00

Wove Paper

2	A1	½r ultra	40.00	20.00
a.		½r gray blue ('67)	40.00	15.00
b.		Batonne paper ('70)	50.00	25.00
c.		Blue paper ('72)	250.00	100.00
3	A1	1r buff	25.00	18.00
a.		1r orange buff	30.00	20.00
4	A1	1r yellow	25.00	15.00
a.		1r olive yellow ('66)	32.50	22.50
b.		Laid paper	175.00	110.00
c.		Half used as ½r on cover		900.00
d.		Batonne paper	40.00	30.00
5	A1	1r green	300.00	55.00
a.		Half used as ½r on cover		900.00
6	A2	4r red ('66)	500.00	200.00
a.		4r red brown ('66)	700.00	200.00
b.		Arms in circle	500.00	250.00
c.		Printed on both sides	550.00	—
d.		Half used as 2r on cover		1,600.
		Nos. 1-6 (6)	950.00	363.00

Letter paper embossed with arms of Ecuador was used in printing a number of sheets of Nos. 2, 4-6.
On the 4r the oval holding the coat of arms is usually 13½-14mm wide, but on about one-fifth of the stamps in the sheet it is 15-15½mm wide, almost a circle.
The 2r, 8r and 12r, type A1, are bogus.
Proofs of the ½r, type A1, are known in black and green.
An essay of type A2 shows the condor's head facing right.

1871-72 Blue-surface Paper

7	A1	½r ultra	50.00	25.00
8	A1	1r yellow	300.00	100.00

Unofficial reprints of types A1-A2 differ in color, have a different sheet makeup and lack gum. Type A1 reprints usually have a double frameline at left. All stamps on blue paper with horiz. blue lines are reprints.

A3   A4

1872 White Paper Litho. Perf. 11

9	A3	½r blue	30.00	5.00
10	A4	1r orange	40.00	7.00
11	A3	1p rose	5.00	25.00
		Nos. 9-11 (3)	75.00	37.00

The 1r surcharged 4c is fraudulent.

A5   A6

A7   A8

A9   A10

1881, Nov. 1   Engr.   Perf. 12

12	A5	1c yellow brn	.40	.25
13	A6	2c lake	.40	.25
14	A7	5c blue	10.00	.50
15	A8	10c orange	.40	.25
16	A9	20c gray violet	.40	.25
17	A10	50c blue green	2.00	3.00
		Nos. 12-17 (6)	13.60	4.50

The 1c surcharged 3c, and 20c surcharged 5c are fraudulent.
For overprints see Nos. O1-O6.

No. 17 Surcharged in Black

1883, Apr.

18	A10	10c on 50c blue grn	50.00	30.00
a.		Double surcharge		

Dangerous forgeries exist.

A12   A13

A14   A15

1887

19	A12	1c blue green	.50	.40
20	A13	2c vermilion	1.00	.40
21	A14	5c blue	3.00	.50
22	A15	80c olive green	6.00	15.00
		Nos. 19-22 (4)	10.50	16.30

For overprints see Nos. O7-O10.

President Juan Flores — A16

1892

23	A16	1c orange	.30	1.00
24	A16	2c dk brown	.30	1.00
25	A16	5c vermilion	.30	1.00
26	A16	10c green	.30	1.00
27	A16	20c red brown	.30	1.00
28	A16	50c maroon	.30	2.00
29	A16	1s blue	.30	4.00
30	A16	5s purple	1.00	8.00
		Nos. 23-30 (8)	3.10	19.00

The issues of 1892, 1894, 1895 and 1896 were printed by the Hamilton Bank Note Co., New York, to the order of N. F. Seebeck, who held a contract for stamps with the government of Ecuador.
No. 30 in green is said to be an essay or color trial.
For surcharges and overprints see Nos. 31-37, O11-O17.

Nos. 29 and 30 Surcharged in Black

1893

Surcharge Measures 25½x2½mm

31	A16	5c on 1s blue	6.00	6.00
32	A16	5c on 5s redsh pur	10.00	9.00
a.		Double surcharge		

Surcharge Measures 24x2¼mm

33	A16	5c on 1s blue	3.00	3.00
a.		Double surcharge, one inverted		
34	A16	5c on 5s purple	12.00	10.00
a.		Double surcharge, one invtd.		

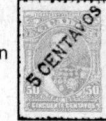

Nos. 28-30 Surcharged in Black

35	A16	5c on 50c maroon	2.00	2.00
a.		Inverted surcharge		5.00
36	A16	5c on 1s blue	2.50	2.00
37	A16	5c on 5s purple	10.00	10.00
		Nos. 31-37 (7)	45.50	42.00

Pres. Juan Flores — A19

38	A19	5c on 5s lake	4.00	4.00

It is stated that No. 38 was used exclusively as a postage stamp and not for telegrams.

Pres. Vicente Rocafuerte — A20

Dated "1894"

1894 Various Frames Perf. 12

39	A20	1c blue	.40	.40
40	A20	2c yellow brn	.40	.40
41	A20	5c green	.40	.40
b.		Perf. 14	6.00	2.00
42	A20	10c vermilion	.70	.60
43	A20	20c black	1.10	.70
44	A20	50c orange	6.00	2.00
45	A20	1s carmine	9.50	4.00
46	A20	5s dark blue	12.00	6.00
		Nos. 39-46 (8)	30.50	14.50

1895 Same, Dated "1895"

47	A20	1c blue	.90	.70
48	A20	2c yellow brn	.90	.70
49	A20	5c green	.70	.50
50	A20	10c vermilion	.70	.40
51	A20	20c black	1.00	1.00
52	A20	50c orange	3.50	2.25
53	A20	1s carmine	21.00	8.00
54	A20	5s dark blue	8.50	4.00
		Nos. 47-54 (8)	37.20	17.55

Reprints of the 2c, 10c, 50c, 1s and 5s of the 1894-95 issues are generally on thick paper. Original issues are on thin to medium thick paper. To distinguish reprints from originals, a comparison of paper thickness, paper color, gum, printing clarity and direction of paper weave is necessary. Value 20 cents each.
For overprints see Nos. 77-112, O20-O33, O50-O91.

A21   A22

A23   A24

A25   A26

A27   A28

1896   Wmk. 117

55	A21	1c dk green	.70	.60
56	A22	2c red	.70	.40
57	A23	5c blue	.70	.40
58	A24	10c bister brn	.60	.90
59	A25	20c orange	1.40	2.00
60	A26	50c dark blue	5.00	3.00

61	A27	1s yellow brn	4.00	4.00
62	A28	5s violet	14.00	5.50
		Nos. 55-62 (8)	*27.10*	*16.80*

Unwmk.

62A	A21	1c dk green	1.00	.40
62B	A22	2c red	1.10	.40
62C	A23	5c blue	1.10	.70
62D	A24	10c bister brn	.70	1.40
62E	A25	20c orange	6.00	5.50
62F	A26	50c dark blue	2.00	2.75
62G	A27	1s yellow brn	6.00	8.00
62H	A28	5s violet	15.00	6.00
		Nos. 62A-62H (8)	*32.90*	*25.15*

Reprints of Nos. 55-62H are on very thick paper, with paper weave direction vertical. Value 20 cents each.

For surcharges and overprints see Nos. 74, 76, 113-114, O34-O49.

Vicente Roca, Diego Noboa and José Olmedo
A28a

General Juan Francisco Elizalde
A28b

Perf. 11½

1896, Oct. 9 Unwmk. Litho.

63	A28a	1c rose	.55	.55
64	A28b	2c blue	.55	.55
65	A28a	5c green	.75	.75
66	A28b	10c ocher	.75	.75
67	A28a	20c red	1.10	3.25
68	A28b	50c violet	1.75	4.75
69	A28a	1s orange	3.25	8.00
		Nos. 63-69 (7)	*8.70*	*18.60*

Success of the Liberal Party in 1845 & 1895.
For overprints see Nos. 115-125.

A29

Black Surcharge

1896, Nov. *Perf. 12*

70	A29	1c on 1c ver, "1893-1894"	1.00	.60
a.		Inverted surcharge	2.50	2.00
b.		Double surcharge	8.00	7.00
71	A29	2c on 2c bl, "1893-1894"	2.00	1.75
a.		Inverted surcharge	4.00	3.50
72	A29	5c on 10c org, "1887-1888"	2.00	.60
a.		Inverted surcharge	4.00	1.75
b.		Double surcharge	7.00	4.00
c.		Surcharged "2cts"	1.00	.80
d.		"1893-1894"	6.00	5.00
73	A29	10c on 4c brn, "1887-1888"	2.00	1.10
a.		Inverted surcharge	4.00	1.75
b.		Double surcharge	6.00	3.50
c.		Double surcharge, one inverted		
d.		Surcharged "1 cto"	2.00	2.75
e.		"1891-1892"	17.00	13.50
		Nos. 70-73 (4)	*7.00*	*4.05*

Similar surcharges of type A29 include:
Dated "1887-1888" — 1c on 1c blue green, 1c on 2c red, 1c on 4c brown, 1c on 10c yellow; 2c on 2c red, 2c on 10c yellow; 10c on 1c green.
Dated "1891-1892" — 1c on 1c blue green, 1c on 4c brown.
Dated "1893-1894" — 2c on 10c yellow; 10c on 1c vermilion, 10c on 10s black.
For overprints see Nos. O18-O19.

Nos. 59-60 Surcharged in Black or Red

1896, Oct. Wmk. 117

74	A25	5c on 20c orange	40.00	40.00
76	A26	10c on 50c dk bl (R)	50.00	50.00
a.		Double surcharge		

The surcharge is diag., horiz. or vert.

Nos. 39-54 Overprinted

On Issue of 1894

1897 Unwmk.

77	A20	1c blue	2.25	2.25
78	A20	2c yellow brn	1.90	1.30
79	A20	5c green	.90	.90
80	A20	10c vermilion	2.75	2.25
81	A20	20c black	3.00	2.75
82	A20	50c orange	6.50	3.25
83	A20	1s carmine	19.00	6.50
84	A20	5s dark blue	110.00	90.00
		Nos. 77-84 (8)	*146.30*	*109.20*

On Issue of 1895

85	A20	1c blue	6.00	5.50
86	A20	2c yellow brn	2.25	2.25
87	A20	5c green	1.90	1.60
88	A20	10c vermilion	7.00	6.00
89	A20	20c black	1.90	1.75
90	A20	50c orange	32.50	13.00
91	A20	1s carmine	14.50	7.50
92	A20	5s dark blue	14.50	14.50
		Nos. 85-92 (8)	*80.55*	*52.10*

Nos. 39-54 Overprinted

On Issue of 1894

93	A20	1c blue	1.40	.90
94	A20	2c yellow brn	1.20	.75
95	A20	5c green	.60	.50
96	A20	10c vermilion	3.50	1.75
97	A20	20c black	3.75	2.50
98	A20	50c orange	7.00	2.75
99	A20	1s carmine	13.00	8.50
100	A20	5s dark blue	115.00	85.00
		Nos. 93-100 (8)	*145.45*	*102.65*

On Issue of 1895

101	A20	1c blue	3.25	1.60
102	A20	2c yellow brn	1.60	1.60
103	A20	5c green	1.75	1.40
104	A20	10c vermilion	5.50	4.50
105	A20	20c black	5.00	1.20
106	A20	50c orange	1.75	1.75
107	A20	1s carmine	8.00	7.00
108	A20	5s dark blue	9.50	9.50
		Nos. 101-108 (8)	*36.35*	*28.15*

Overprints on Nos. 77-108 are to be found reading upward from left to right and downward from left to right, as well as inverted.

Overprinted

1897 On Issue of 1894

109	A20	10c vermilion	—	—

On Issue of 1895

110	A20	2c yellow brn	—	—
111	A20	1s carmine	—	—
112	A20	5s dark blue	—	—

Nos. 56, 59 Overprinted like Nos. 93-108

1897, June Wmk. 117

113	A22	2c red	100.00	100.00
114	A25	20c orange	—	100.00

Many forged overprints on Nos. 77-114 exist, made on original stamps and reprints.

Stamps or Types of 1896 Overprinted in Black

1897 Unwmk. *Perf. 11½*

115	A28a	1c rose	3.75	3.75
116	A28b	2c blue	3.00	3.00
117	A28b	10c ocher	3.00	3.00
118	A28a	1s yellow	15.00	15.00
		Nos. 115-118 (4)	*24.75*	*24.75*

No. 63 Overprinted in Black

1897

119	A28a	1c rose	.60	.50

Nos. 63-66 Overprinted in Black

1897

122	A28a	1c rose	4.50	4.00
123	A28b	2c blue	4.50	4.00
124	A28a	5c green	4.50	4.00
125	A28b	10c yellow	4.50	4.00
a.		Double overprint	10.50	9.50
		Nos. 122-125 (4)	*18.00*	*16.00*

The 20c, 50c and 1s with this overprint in black and all values of the issue overprinted in blue are reprints.

Overprint Inverted

122a	A28a	1c	6.00	5.50
123a	A28b	2c	6.00	5.50
124a	A28a	5c	6.00	5.50
125b	A28b	10c	6.00	5.50

Coat of Arms — A33

1897, June 23 Engr. *Perf. 14-16*

127	A33	1c dk yellow grn	.35	.25
128	A33	2c orange red	.35	.25
129	A33	5c lake	.35	.25
130	A33	10c dk brown	.35	.25
131	A33	20c yellow	.45	.40
132	A33	50c dull blue	.45	.65
133	A33	1s gray	.90	1.25
134	A33	5s dark lilac	4.00	5.00
		Nos. 127-134 (8)	*7.20*	*8.30*

No. 135 No. 136

1899, May

135	A33	1c on 2c orange red	3.00	1.50
136	A33	5c on 10c brown	2.50	1.00
a.		Double surcharge		

Luis Vargas Torres
A36

Abdón Calderón
A37

Juan Montalvo
A38

José Mejia
A39

Santa Cruz y Espejo
A40

Pedro Carbo
A41

José Joaquin Olmedo
A42

Pedro Moncayo
A43

1899 *Perf. 12½-16*

137	A36	1c gray blue & blk	.40	.25
a.		Horiz. pair, imperf. vert.		
138	A37	2c brown lil & blk	.40	.25
139	A38	5c lake & blk	.70	.25
140	A39	10c reddsh lil & blk	.70	.25
141	A40	20c green & blk	.70	.25
142	A41	50c lil rose & blk	1.75	.25
143	A42	1s ocher & blk	8.00	2.75
144	A43	5s lilac & blk	14.50	7.50
		Nos. 137-144 (8)	*27.15*	*12.05*

1901

145	A36	1c scarlet & blk	.45	.25
146	A37	2c green & blk	.45	.25
147	A38	5c gray lil & blk	.45	.25
148	A39	10c dp blue & blk	.50	.25
149	A40	20c gray & blk	.50	.25
150	A41	50c lt blue & blk	1.75	.95
151	A42	1s brown & blk	6.00	2.75
152	A43	5s gray blk & blk	9.00	5.75
		Nos. 145-152 (8)	*19.10*	*10.70*

In July, 1902, following the theft of a quantity of stamps during a fire at Guayaquil, the Government authorized the governors of the provinces to handstamp their stocks. Many varieties of these handstamps exist.

Other control marks were used in 1907.

For overprints see Nos. O103-O106, O167.

A44

Surcharged on Revenue Stamp Dated 1901-1902

1903-06 *Perf. 14, 15*

153	A44	1c on 5c gray lil ('06)	.75	.40
154	A44	1c on 20c gray ('06)	10.00	4.50
155	A44	1c on 25c yellow	1.50	.40
a.		Double surcharge		
156	A44	1c on 1s bl ('06)	77.50	50.00
157	A44	3c on 5c gray lil ('06)	10.00	4.00
158	A44	3c on 20c gray ('06)	25.00	15.00
159	A44	3c on 25c yel ('06)	24.00	15.00
159A	A44	3c on 1s blue ('06)	3.75	2.25
		Nos. 153-159A (8)	*152.50*	*91.55*

Counterfeits are plentiful.
See Nos. 191-197.

Capt. Abdón Calderón
A45 A46

1904, July 31 *Perf. 12*

160	A45	1c red & blk	.45	.30
161	A45	2c blue & blk	.50	.35
162	A46	5c yellow & blk	1.90	1.00
163	A45	10c red & blk	6.00	2.00
164	A45	20c blue & blk	10.00	8.00
165	A46	50c yellow & blk	85.00	120.00
		Nos. 160-165 (6)	*103.85*	*131.65*

Centenary of the birth of Calderón.

Presidents

Vicente Roca
A47

Diego Noboa
A48

Francisco Robles A49

José M. Urvina A50

García Moreno A51

Jerónimo Carrión A52

Javier Espinoza A53

Antonio Borrero A54

1907, July *Perf. 14, 15*
166	A47	1c red & blk	1.00	.25
167	A48	2c pale blue & blk	2.00	.25
168	A49	3c orange & blk	3.00	.25
169	A50	5c lilac rose & blk	3.75	.25
170	A51	10c dp blue & blk	7.50	.25
171	A52	20c yellow grn & blk	10.00	.35
172	A53	50c violet & blk	22.50	.70
173	A54	1s green & blk	30.00	2.00
		Nos. 166-173 (8)	79.75	4.30

The stamps of the 1907 issue frequently have control marks similar to those found on the 1899 and 1901 issues. These marks were applied to distinguish the stamps issued in the various provinces and to serve as a check on local officials.

Locomotive — A55

García Moreno A56

Gen. Eloy Alfaro A57

Abelardo Moncayo A58

Archer Harman A59

James Sivewright A60

Mt. Chimborazo — A61

1908, June 25
174	A55	1c red brown	1.10	2.10
175	A56	2c blue & blk	1.30	2.25
176	A57	5c claret & blk	2.75	5.25
177	A58	10c ocher & blk	1.75	2.75
178	A59	20c green & blk	1.75	3.75

179	A60	50c gray & blk	1.75	3.75
180	A61	1s black	3.50	8.00
		Nos. 174-180 (7)	13.90	27.85

Opening of the Guayaquil-Quito Railway.

José Mejía Vallejo A62

Principal Exposition Building A70

Designs: 2c, Francisco J. E. Santa Cruz y Espejo. 3c, Francisco Ascásubi. 5c, Juan Salinas. 10c, Juan Pio de Montúfar, el Marques de Selva Alegre. 20c, Carlos de Montúfar. 50c, Juan de Dios Morales. 1s, Manuel R. de Quiroga.

1909, Aug. 10 *Perf. 12*
181	A62	1c green	.35	.65
182	A62	2c blue	.35	.65
183	A62	3c orange	.35	.75
184	A62	5c claret	.35	.75
185	A62	10c yellow brn	.45	.75
186	A62	20c gray	.45	1.10
187	A62	50c vermilion	.45	1.10
188	A62	1s olive grn	.45	1.40
189	A70	5s violet	1.25	2.75
		Nos. 181-189 (9)	4.45	9.90

National Exposition of 1909.

No. 187 Surcharged

1909
190	A62	5c on 50c vermilion	.90	.75

Revenue Stamps Surcharged as in 1903
1910 *Perf. 14, 15*
Stamps Dated 1905-1906
191	A44	1c on 5c green	2.25	1.75
192	A44	5c on 20c blue	9.50	2.00
193	A44	5c on 25c violet	18.00	3.50

Stamps Dated 1907-1908
194	A44	1c on 5c green	.40	.40
195	A44	5c on 20c blue	14.00	9.50
196	A44	5c on 25c violet	1.20	.40

Stamp Dated 1909-1910
197	A44	5c on 20c blue	80.00	60.00
		Nos. 191-197 (7)	125.35	77.55

Presidents

Roca A71

Noboa A72

Robles A73

Urvina A74

Moreno A75

Borrero A76

1911-28 *Perf. 12*
198	A71	1c scarlet & blk	.80	.25
199	A71	1c orange ('16)	.80	.25
200	A71	1c lt blue ('25)	.40	.25
201	A72	2c blue & blk	1.10	.25
202	A72	2c green ('16)	1.10	.25
203	A72	2c dk violet ('25)	1.10	.25
204	A73	3c orange & blk ('13)	2.25	.30
205	A73	3c black ('15)	1.50	.25
206	A74	5c scarlet & blk	1.90	.25
207	A74	5c violet ('15)	1.90	.25

208	A74	5c rose ('25)	.70	.25
209	A74	5c dk brown ('28)	.70	.25
210	A75	10c dp blue & blk	2.25	.25
211	A75	10c dp blue ('15)	2.25	.25
212	A75	10c yellow grn ('25)	.70	.25
213	A75	10c black ('28)	1.60	.25
214	A76	1s green & blk	12.00	1.50
215	A76	1s orange & blk ('27)	8.00	.25
		Nos. 198-215 (18)	41.05	5.80

For overprints see Nos. 260-262, 264-265, O107-O122, O124-O134, O156-O157, O160-O162, O164-O166, O168-O173, O175-O178, O183-O184, O189, RA1.

A77

1912 *Perf. 14, 15*
216	A77	1c on 1s green	1.00	1.00
217	A77	2c on 2s carmine	2.50	1.50
218	A77	2c on 5s dull blue	1.50	1.50
219	A77	2c on 10s yellow	5.00	5.00
a.		Inverted surcharge	16.00	12.00
		Nos. 216-219 (4)	10.00	9.00

No. 216 exists with narrow "V" and small "U" in "UN" and Nos. 217, 218 and 219 with "D" with serifs or small "O" in "DOS."

Enrique Váldez A78

Jerónimo Carrión A79

Javier Espinoza — A80

1915-17 *Perf. 12*
220	A78	4c red & blk	.75	.25
221	A79	20c green & blk ('17)	5.00	.25
222	A80	50c dp violet & blk	10.00	.45
		Nos. 220-222 (3)	15.75	.95

For overprints see Nos. O123, O135, O163, O174.

Olmedo A86

Monument to "Fathers of the Country" A95

Laurel Wreath and Star — A104

Designs: 2c, Rafael Ximena. 3c, Roca. 4c, Luis F. Vivero. 5c, Luis Febres Cordero. 6c, Francisco Lavayen. 7c, Jorge Antonio de Elizalde. 8c, Baltazar Garcia. 9c, Jose de Antepara. 15c, Luis Urdaneta. 20c, Jose M. Villamil. 30c, Miguel Letamendi. 40c, Gregorio Escobedo. 50c, Gen. Antonio Jose de Sucre. 60c, Juan Illingworth. 70c, Roca. 80c, Rocafuerte. 1s, Simon Bolivar.

1920
223	A86	1c yellow grn	.35	.25
224	A86	2c carmine	.35	.25
225	A86	3c yellow brn	.35	.25
226	A86	4c myrtle green	.55	.25
227	A86	5c pale blue	.55	.25
228	A86	6c red orange	.90	.30
229	A86	7c brown	2.25	.75
230	A86	8c apple green	1.25	.35
231	A86	9c lake	4.25	1.50
232	A95	10c lt blue	1.50	.25
233	A86	15c dk gray	2.25	.35
234	A86	20c dk violet	2.25	.25
235	A86	30c brt violet	4.25	1.40

236	A86	40c dk brown	7.50	2.10
237	A86	50c dk green	5.25	.55
238	A86	60c dk blue	9.50	2.10
239	A86	70c bluish gray	16.00	4.75
240	A86	80c orange yel	16.50	4.75
241	A104	90c green	17.00	4.75
242	A86	1s pale blue	24.00	8.50
		Nos. 223-242 (20)	116.80	33.90

Cent. of the independence of Guayaquil.
For overprints and surcharges see Nos. 263, 274-292, O136-O155, O179-O182, O185-O188.

No. RA12 Overprinted in Black

POSTAL

1925
259	PT6	20c bister brown	4.00	1.50

Stamps of 1915-25 Overprinted in Black or Red Upright (1c, 3c, 5c) or Inverted (2c, 4c, 10c)

1926
260	A71	1c lt blue	12.50	10.50
261	A72	2c dk violet	12.50	10.50
262	A73	3c black (R)	12.50	10.50
263	A86	4c myrtle green	12.50	10.50
264	A74	5c rose	17.50	10.50
265	A75	10c yellow grn	17.50	10.50
		Nos. 260-265 (6)	85.00	63.00

Quito-Esmeraldas railway opening.
Upright overprints on 2c, 4c, 10c and inverted overprints on 1c, 3c, 5c sell for more.

Nos. RA10-RA12 Overprinted in Black

POSTAL

1927
266	PT6	1c olive green	.50	.25
a.		"POSTAI"	1.40	.85
b.		Double overprint	2.00	.85
c.		Inverted overprint	2.00	.85
267	PT6	2c deep green	.50	.25
a.		"POSTAI"	1.40	.85
b.		Double overprint	2.00	.85
268	PT6	20c bister brown	1.00	.25
a.		"POSTAI"	8.50	5.00
		Nos. 266-268 (3)	2.00	.75

Quito Post Office — A109

1927, June
269	A109	5c orange	.50	.25
270	A109	10c dark green	.70	.25
271	A109	20c violet	.80	.25
		Nos. 269-271 (3)	2.00	.75

Opening of new Quito P.O.
For overprint see No. O190.

No. RA12 Overprinted in Dark Blue

POSTAL

1928
273	PT6	20c bister brown	.50	.25
a.		Double overprint, one inverted	2.00	.70

See No. 339 for 10c with same overprint.

Nos. 235, 239-240 Ovptd. in Red Brown and Srchd. in Bluish Black

 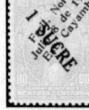

1928, July 8

274	A86	10c on 30c violet	16.00	16.00
275	A86	50c on 70c bluish		
		gray	20.00	20.00
276	A86	1s on 80c org yel	22.50	22.50
		Nos. 274-276 (3)	58.50	58.50

Quito-Cayambe railway opening.

Stamps of 1920
Surcharged

1928, Oct. 9

277	A86	1c on 1c yel grn	15.00	15.00
278	A86	1c on 2c car	.30	.30
279	A86	2c on 3c yel brn	2.25	2.25
a.		Dbl. surch., one reading up	30.00	30.00
280	A86	2c on 4c myr grn	1.50	1.50
281	A86	2c on 5c lt blue	.60	.45
a.		Dbl. surch., one reading up	30.00	30.00
282	A86	2c on 7c brown	75.00	75.00
283	A86	5c on 6c red org	.40	.30
a.		"5 ctvos." omitted	37.50	37.50
284	A86	10c on 7c brown	1.25	1.25
285	A86	20c on 8c apple grn	.35	.30
a.		Double surcharge		
286	A95	40c on 10c blue	4.25	4.25
287	A86	40c on 15c dk gray	1.25	1.25
288	A86	50c on 20c dk vio	13.25	13.25
289	A86	1s on 40c dk brown	4.50	4.50
290	A86	5s on 50c dk green	5.25	5.25
291	A86	10s on 60c dk blue	19.50	19.50

With Additional Surcharge
in Red

292	A86	10c on 2c on 7c		
		brn	.55	.55
a.		Red surcharge double	30.00	30.00
		Nos. 277-292 (16)	145.20	144.90

National Assembly of 1928.
Counterfeit overprints exist of Nos. 277-291.

A111

Surcharged in Various Colors

1928, Oct. 31			*Perf. 14*	
293	A111	5c on 20c gray lil		
		(Bk)	3.00	1.75
294	A111	10c on 20c gray lil		
		(R)	3.00	1.75
295	A111	20c on 1s grn (O)	3.00	1.75
296	A111	50c on 1s grn (Bl)	3.75	1.40
297	A111	1s on 1s grn (V)	4.75	1.75
298	A111	5s on 2s red (G)	15.00	9.00
299	A111	10s on 2s red (Br)	18.00	12.00
a.		Black surcharge	15.00	10.00
		Nos. 293-299 (7)	50.50	29.40

Quito-Otavalo railway opening.
See Nos. 586-587.

No. RA11 Overprinted
in Red

1929			*Perf. 12*	
302	PT6	2c deep green	.50	.25

There are two types of overprint on No. 302 differing slightly.

A112

1929			**Red Overprint**	
303	A112	1c dark blue	.50	.25
a.		Overprint reading down	.75	.50

See Nos. 586-587.

Plowing
A113

Cultivating
Cacao
A114

Cacao Pod
A115

Growing
Tobacco
A116

Exportation of
Fruits — A117

Landscape — A118

Loading Sugar
Cane — A119

Scene in
Quito — A120

Scene in Quito
A121

Olmedo
A122

Monument to
Simón
Bolívar — A125

Designs: 2s, Sucre. 5s, Bolivar.

1930, Aug. 1			*Perf. 12½*	
304	A113	1c yellow & car	.30	.25
305	A114	2c yellow & grn	.30	.25
306	A115	5c dp grn & vio brn	.35	.25
307	A116	6c yellow & red	.45	.25
308	A117	10c orange & ol grn	.45	.25
309	A118	16c red & yel grn	.55	.25
310	A119	20c ultra & yel	.90	.25
311	A120	40c orange & sepia	1.10	.35
312	A121	50c orange & sepia	1.10	.40
313	A122	1s dp green & blk	4.25	.45
314	A122	2s dk blue & blk	6.50	2.00
315	A122	5s dk violet & blk	11.50	3.00
316	A125	10s car rose & blk	40.00	6.50
		Nos. 304-316 (13)	67.75	14.45

Centenary of founding of republic.
For surcharges and overprints see Nos. 319-320, 331-338, RA25, RA33, RA43.

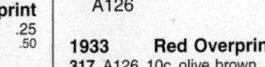

A126

1933		**Red Overprint**	*Perf. 15*	
317	A126	10c olive brown	1.15	.25

A127

Blue Overprint

318	A127	10c olive brown	.70	.25
a.		Inverted overprint	5.00	5.00

For overprint see No. 339.

Nos. 307, 309 Surcharged in Black

1933

319	A116	5c on 6c yellow & red	1.00	.25
320	A118	10c on 16c red & yel		
		grn	2.00	.25
a.		Inverted overprint	4.00	4.00

Landscape
A128

Mt.
Chimborazo
A129

1934-45			*Perf. 12*	
321	A128	5c violet	3.00	.55
322	A128	5c blue	3.00	.55
323	A128	5c dark brown	3.00	.55
323A	A128	5c slate blk ('45)	3.00	.55
324	A128	10c rose	3.00	.55
325	A128	10c dark green	3.00	.55
326	A128	10c brown	3.00	.55
327	A128	10c orange	3.00	.55
328	A128	10c olive green	3.00	.55
329	A128	10c gray blk ('35)	3.00	.55
329A	A128	10c red lilac ('44)	3.00	.55

Perf. 14

330	A129	1s carmine rose	3.25	.55
		Nos. 321-330 (12)	36.25	6.60

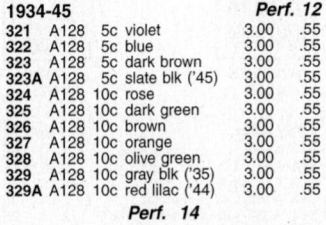

Stamps of 1930 Srchd.
or Ovptd. in various
colors

1935			*Perf. 12½*	
331	A116	5c on 6c (Bl)	.90	.35
332	A116	10c on 6c (G)	1.25	.35
333	A119	20c (R)	1.75	.35
334	A120	40c (G)	2.50	.35
335	A121	50c (G)	3.00	.45
336	A122	1s on 5s (Gold)	7.00	1.25
337	A122	2s on 5s (Gold)	9.50	1.75
338	A125	5s on 10s (Bl)	12.00	5.00
		Nos. 331-338,C35-C38 (12)	87.90	29.85

Unveiling of a monument to Bolivar at Quito, July 24, 1935.

A129a

1935, Oct. 13 | **Photo.** | *Perf. 11½x11* | |
|---|---|---|---|---|
| 338A | A129a | 5c ultra & black | .50 | .25 |
| 338B | A129a | 10c org & blue | .50 | .25 |
| 338C | A129a | 40c dk car & red | .50 | .30 |
| 338D | A129a | 1S blue grn & | | |
| | | red | .60 | .70 |
| 338E | A129a | 2S violet & red | 1.10 | 1.20 |
| | | *Nos. 338A-338E,C38A-C38E (10)* | 8.60 | 7.60 |

Columbus Day. Nos. 338A-338E and C38A-C38E were prepared by the Sociedad Colombista Panamericana and were sold by the Ecuadorian post office through Oct. 30.

**Telegraph Stamp Overprinted
Diagonally in Red like No. 273**

1935			*Perf. 14½*	
339	A126	10c olive brown	.75	.25

Map of
Galápagos
Islands
A130

Galapagos
Land
Iguana
A131

Galápagos
Tortoise
A132

Charles R.
Darwin
A133

Columbus
A134

Island
Scene
A135

1936			*Perf. 14*	
340	A130	2c black	1.25	.25
341	A131	5c olive grn	1.50	.25
342	A132	10c brown	3.00	.30
343	A133	20c dk violet	3.50	.45
344	A134	1s dk carmine	6.25	.85
345	A135	2s dark blue	9.75	1.40
		Nos. 340-345 (6)	25.25	3.50

Cent. of the visit of Charles Darwin to the Galápagos Islands, Sept. 17, 1835.
For overprints see Nos. O191-O195.

**Tobacco Stamp Overprinted in
Black**

1936			*Rouletted 7*	
346	PT7	1c rose red	.50	.25
a.		Horiz. pair, imperf. vert.		
b.		Double surcharge		

No. 346 is similar to type PT7 but does not include "CASA CORREOS."

Louis Godin,
Charles M. de la
Condamine and
Pierre
Bouguer — A136

Portraits: 5c, 20c, Antonio Ulloa, La Condamine and Jorge Juan.

1936		**Engr.**	*Perf. 12½*	
347	A136	2c deep blue	.50	.30
348	A136	5c dark green	.50	.30
349	A136	10c deep orange	.50	.30
350	A136	20c violet	.80	.30
351	A136	50c dark red	1.25	.30
		Nos. 347-351,C39-C42 (9)	6.60	2.60

Bicentenary of Geodesical Mission to Quito.

Independence Monument — A137

1936			*Perf. 13½x14*	
352	A137	2c green	2.25	1.25
353	A137	5c dark violet	2.25	1.25
354	A137	10c carmine rose	2.25	1.25
355	A137	20c black	2.25	1.25
356	A137	50c blue	3.25	2.10
357	A137	1s dark red	3.75	1.25
		Nos. 352-357,C43-C48 (12)	46.00	40.35

1st Intl. Philatelic Exhibition at Quito.

INAUGURACION
MONUMENTO
A BOLIVAR
5 ctvs.
QUITO, 24 DE
JULIO DE 1935

Coat of Arms — A138

Overprint in Black or Red

1937 Perf. 12½
359 A138 5c olive green 2.00 .30
360 A138 10c dark blue (R) 2.00 .25

For overprint see No. 562.

Andean Landscape A139

Atahualpa, the Last Inca A140

Hat Weavers A141

Coast Landscape A142

Gold Washing — A143

1937, Aug. 19 Perf. 11½
361 A139 2c green .50 .25
362 A140 5c deep rose .50 .25
363 A141 10c blue .50 .25
364 A142 20c deep rose 1.50 .30
365 A143 1s olive green 2.00 .35
  Nos. 361-365 (5) 5.00 1.40

For overprints see Nos. O196-O200.

"Liberty" Carrying Flag of Ecuador A144

Engraved and Lithographed
1938, Feb. 22 Perf. 12
Center Multicolored
366 A144 2c blue .25 .25
367 A144 5c violet .35 .25
368 A144 10c black .55 .25
369 A144 20c brown .65 .25
370 A144 50c black 1.10 .25
371 A144 1s olive blk 1.75 .30
372 A144 2s dk brn 3.25 .55
  Nos. 366-372,C57-C63 (14) 22.40 4.50

US Constitution, 150th anniversary.
For overprints and surcharges see Nos.
413-415, 444-446, RA46, RA52.

A145

A146

A147

A148

Designs: 10c, Winged figure holding globe.
50c, Cactus, winged wheel. 1s, "Communications." 2s, "Construction."

Perf. 13, 13x13½
1938, Oct. 30 Engr.
373 A145 10c bright ultra .40 .25
374 A146 50c deep red violet .40 .25
375 A147 1s copper red .70 .25
376 A148 2s dark green 1.10 .25
  Nos. 373-376 (4) 2.60 1.00

Progress of Ecuador Exhibition.
For overprints see Nos. C105-C113.

Parade of Athletes — A149

Runner A150

Basketball A151

Wrestlers A152

Diver A153

1939, Mar. Perf. 12
377 A149 5c carmine rose 3.00 .55
378 A150 10c deep blue 3.50 .65
379 A151 50c gray olive 5.75 .85
380 A152 1s dull violet 7.75 .85
381 A153 2s dull olive green 12.50 .95
  Nos. 377-381,C65-C69 (10) 78.35 6.15

First Bolivarian Games (1938), Bogota.

Dolores Mission — A154

1939, June 16 Perf. 12½x13
382 A154 2c blue green .50 .25
383 A154 5c rose red .50 .25
384 A154 10c ultra .50 .25
385 A154 50c yellow brown 1.20 .25
386 A154 1s black 1.90 .25
387 A154 2s purple 1.25 .40
  Nos. 382-387,C73-C79 (13) 11.25 3.40

Golden Gate International Exposition.
For surcharges see Nos. 429, 436.

Trylon and Perisphere — A155

1939, June 30
388 A155 2c lt olive green .80 .35
389 A155 5c red orange .80 .35
390 A155 10c ultra .80 .35
391 A155 50c slate gray 1.10 .35
392 A155 1s rose carmine 1.90 .35
393 A155 2s black brown 2.25 .40
  Nos. 388-393,C80-C86 (13) 16.55 4.20

New York World's Fair.
For surcharge see No. 437.

Flags of the 21 American Republics — A156

1940 Perf. 12
394 A156 5c dp rose & blk 1.00 .25
395 A156 10c dk blue & blk .40 .25
396 A156 50c Prus green & blk .60 .25
397 A156 1s dp violet & blk 1.00 .30
  Nos. 394-397,C87-C90 (8) 8.30 2.75

Pan American Union, 50th anniversary.

Francisco J. E. Santa Cruz y Espejo — A157

1941, Dec. 15
398 A157 30c blue 1.25 .25
399 A157 1s red orange 2.50 .35
  Nos. 398-399,C91-C92 (4) 21.50 1.30

Exposition of Journalism held under the
auspices of the Natl. Newspaper Men's Union.

Francisco de Orellana A158

Gonzalo Pizarro A159

View of Guayaquil A160

View of Quito A161

1942, Jan. 30
400 A158 10c sepia .90 .35
401 A159 40c deep rose 2.50 .35
402 A160 1s violet 3.50 .35
403 A161 2s dark blue 4.50 .45
  Nos. 400-403,C93-C96 (8) 23.45 3.35

400th anniv. of the discovery and exploration of the Amazon River by Orellana.

Remigio Crespo Toral — A162

1942 Perf. 13½
404 A162 10c green .60 .25
405 A162 50c brown 1.00 .25
  Nos. 404-405,C97 (3) 2.85 1.00

Alfredo Baquerizo Moreno — A163

1942
406 A163 10c green .25 .25

Mt. Chimborazo — A164

1942-47 Perf. 12
407 A164 30c red brown 1.50 .30
407A A164 30c lt blue ('43) 1.50 .30
407B A164 30c red orange ('44) 1.50 .30
407C A164 30c green ('47) 1.50 .30
  Nos. 407-407C (4) 6.00 1.20

View of Guayaquil — A165

1942-44
408 A165 20c red 1.50 .25
408A A165 20c deep blue ('44) 1.50 .25

Gen. Eloy Alfaro A166

Devil's Nose A167

President Alfaro (1842-1912): 30c, Military
College. 1s, Montecristi, Alfaro's birthplace.

1942
409 A166 10c dk rose & blk .60 .25
410 A167 20c ol blk & red brn .60 .25
411 A167 30c ol gray & grn .75 .25
412 A167 1s slate & salmon 1.80 .25
  Nos. 409-412,C98-C101 (8) 20.15 4.40

Nos. 370-372 Overprinted in Red Brown

1943, Apr. 15 Perf. 11½
413 A144 50c multicolored .65 .65
414 A144 1s multicolored 1.25 1.25
415 A144 2s multicolored 2.75 2.75
  Nos. 413-415,C102-C104 (6) 14.65 10.25

Visit of US Vice-Pres. Henry A. Wallace.

"30 Centavos" — A170

1943 **Black Surcharge** Perf. 12½
416 A170 30c on 50c red brn 1.00 .25
  a. Without bars 1.00 .25

Map Showing US and Ecuador A171

1943, Oct. 9 Perf. 12
417 A171 10c dull violet .75 .50
418 A171 20c red brown .75 .50
419 A171 30c orange .75 .50
420 A171 50c olive green .90 .60
421 A171 1s deep violet 1.00 .65
422 A171 10s olive bister 8.25 5.25
  Nos. 417-422,C114-C118 (11) 32.70 15.10

Good will tour of Pres. Arroyo del Rio in
1942.

1944, Feb. 7
423 A171 10c yellow green .65 .45
424 A171 20c rose pink .65 .45
425 A171 30c dark gray brown .65 .45
426 A171 50c deep red lilac .65 .45
427 A171 1s olive gray 1.00 .45
428 A171 10s red orange 10.50 6.00
  Nos. 423-428,C119-C123 (11) 24.90 13.40

For surcharges see Nos. B1-B6.

No. 385 Surcharged in Black

1944 **Unwmk.** Perf. 12½x13
429 A154 30c on 50c yel brn 2.00 .25

Archbishop Federico González Suárez, Birth Cent. — A172

1944 — Perf. 12

430	A172	10c deep blue	.40	.25
431	A172	20c green	.40	.25
432	A172	30c dk violet brn	.50	.25
433	A172	1s dull violet	.90	.25

Nos. 430-433,C124-C127 (8)   15.50   4.30

Air Post Stamps Nos.
C76 and C83
Surcharged in Black

1944 — Perf. 12½x13

434	AP15	30c on 50c rose vio	.40	.25
435	AP16	30c on 50c sl grn	.40	.25

Nos. 382 and 388
Surcharged in Black

1944-45

436	A154	5c on 2c bl grn	.50	.25
a.		Double surcharge	4.00	
437	A155	5c on 2c lt ol grn ('45)	.50	.25

Government Palace,
Quito — A173

1944 — Engr. — Perf. 11

438	A173	10c dark green	.50	.25
439	A173	30c blue	.50	.25

See Nos. C128-C130, C221. For
surcharges see Nos. 452, RAC1-RAC2.

Symbol of the Red
Cross — A174

1945, Apr. 25 — Perf. 12
Cross in Rose

440	A174	30c bister brown	1.90	.35
441	A174	1s red brown	2.75	.45
442	A174	5s turq green	4.75	1.10
443	A174	10s scarlet	13.00	3.00

Nos. 440-443,C131-C134 (8)   58.40   14.75

International Red Cross, 80th anniversary.

Nos. 370 to 372 Overprinted in Dark Blue and Gold

1945, Oct. 2 — Perf. 11½
Center Multicolored

444	A144	50c black	.80	.70
a.		Double overprint	22.50	
445	A144	1s olive black	1.40	1.40
446	A144	2s dark brown	2.75	2.50
a.		Double overprint	22.50	

Nos. 444-446,C139-C141 (6)   10.45   8.25

Visit of Pres. Juan Antonio Rios of Chile.

General Antonio José
de Sucre, 150th Birth
Anniv. — A175

1945, Nov. 14 — Engr. — Perf. 12

447	A175	10c olive	.55	.25
448	A175	20c red brown	.55	.25
449	A175	40c olive gray	.55	.25
450	A175	1s dark green	1.10	.35
451	A175	2s sepia	2.25	.75

Nos. 447-451,C142-C146 (10)   13.20   6.10

No. 438 Surcharged
in Blue

1945 — Perf. 11

452	A173	20c on 10c dark green	.50	.25
a.		Fancy bar omitted		

> **Catalogue values for unused stamps in this section, from this point to the end of the section, are for Never Hinged items.**

Map of Pan-American
Highway and Arms of
Loja — A176

1946, Apr. 22 — Engr. — Perf. 12

453	A176	20c red brown	.75	.40
454	A176	30c bright green	.75	.45
455	A176	1s bright ultra	.75	.45
456	A176	5s deep red lilac	2.50	1.50
457	A176	10s scarlet	4.75	2.00

Nos. 453-457,C147-C151 (10)   19.35   7.95

Torch of
Democracy
A177

Popular
Suffrage
A178

Flag of
Ecuador
A179

Pres. José
M. Velasco
Ibarra
A180

1946, Aug. 9 — Unwmk. — Perf. 12½

458	A177	5c dark blue	.35	.25
459	A178	10c Prus green	.35	.25
460	A179	20c carmine	.45	.25
461	A180	30c chocolate	.65	.25

Nos. 458-461,C152-C155 (8)   5.00   2.20

Revolution of May 28, 1944, 2nd anniv.

"30 Ctvs." — A181

1946 — Black Surcharge

462	A181	30c on 50c red brown	.65	.25

For overprint see No. 484.

Nos. CO13-CO14
With Additional Ovpt.
in Black

1946 — Perf. 11½

463	AP7	10c chestnut	.60	.25
464	AP7	20c olive black	.60	.25

Instructor and
Student — A182

1946, Sept. 16 — Perf. 12½

465	A182	10c deep blue	.40	.50
466	A182	20c chocolate	.40	.50
467	A182	30c dark green	.40	.50
468	A182	50c bluish blk	.55	.65
469	A182	1s dark red	1.10	1.00
470	A182	10s dark violet	6.50	1.90

Nos. 465-470,C156-C160 (11)   21.00   9.75

Campaign for adult education.

Mariana de
Jesus
Paredes y
Flores
A183

Urn
A184

1946, Nov. 28

471	A183	10c black brown	.35	.25
472	A183	20c green	.35	.25
473	A183	30c purple	.35	.25
474	A184	1s rose brown	.45	.30

Nos. 471-474,C161-C164 (8)   5.00   3.10

300th anniv. of the death of the Blessed
Mariana de Jesus Paredes y Flores.

Pres.
Vicente
Rocafuerte
A185

Jesuits'
Church Quito
A186

45c, 50c, 80c, F.J.E. de Santa Cruz y
Espejo.

1947, Nov. 27 — Perf. 12

475	A185	5c redsh brown	.30	.25
476	A185	10c sepia	.30	.25
477	A185	15c gray black	.30	.25
478	A186	20c redsh brown	.35	.25
479	A186	30c red violet	.60	.25
480	A186	40c brt ultra	.75	.25
481	A185	45c dk slate grn	1.00	.30
482	A185	50c olive black	1.05	.30
483	A185	80c orange red	1.50	.35

Nos. 475-483,C165-C171 (16)   10.35   4.20

For overprints and surcharges see Nos.
489, 496, 525-527, C215.

Type of 1946, Overprinted "POSTAL" in Black but Without Additional Surcharge

1948 — Engr.

484	A181	10c orange	.50	.25

Andrés Bello — A188

1948, Apr. 21 — Perf. 13

485	A188	20c lt blue	.40	.25
486	A188	30c rose carmine	.40	.25
487	A188	40c blue green	.40	.25
488	A188	1s black brown	.80	.25

Nos. 485-488,C172-C174 (7)   4.30   1.75

83rd anniversary of the death of Andrés
Bello (1781-1865), educator.

No. 480 Overprinted in
Black

1948, May 24 — Perf. 12

489	A186	40c bright ultra	.60	.35

See No. C175.

Flagship of
Columbus — A189

1948 — Perf. 14

490	A189	10c dark blue green	.50	.25
491	A189	20c brown	.50	.25
492	A189	30c dark purple	1.20	.25
493	A189	50c dark claret	1.60	.25
494	A189	1s ultra	2.40	.40
495	A189	5s carmine	6.50	.80

Nos. 490-495,C176-C180 (11)   25.65   7.55

Issued to publicize the proposed Columbus
Memorial Lighthouse near Ciudad Trujillo,
Dominican Republic.

No. 483 Overprinted in
Blue, "MANANA"
Reading Down

1948 — Perf. 12

496	A185	80c orange red	.25	.25

Issued to publicize the National Fair of
Today and Tomorrow, 1948. See No. C181.

Telegrafo I in
Flight — A190

1948 — Engr. — Perf. 12½

497	A190	30c red orange	.70	.25
498	A190	40c rose lilac	.70	.25
499	A190	60c violet blue	.70	.25
500	A190	1s brown red	.70	.25
501	A190	3s brown	2.25	.35
502	A190	5s gray black	2.60	.35

Nos. 497-502,C182-C187 (12)   14.95   3.50

25th anniversary (in 1945) of the first postal
flight in Ecuador.

Book and Pen — A191

1948, Oct. 12 — Unwmk. — Perf. 14

503	A191	10c deep claret	.60	.30
504	A191	20c brown	.60	.30
505	A191	30c dark green	1.25	.30
506	A191	50c red	2.00	.30
507	A191	1s purple	3.00	.45
508	A191	10s dull blue	8.00	1.25

Nos. 503-508,C188-C192 (11)   32.45   9.65

Campaign for adult education.

A192

Franklin D. Roosevelt
and Two of "Four
Freedoms" — A193

1948, Oct. 24 — Perf. 12½

509	A192	10c rose brn & gray	.50	.30
510	A192	20c brn ol & bl	.60	.40
511	A193	30c ol bis & car rose	.60	.40
512	A193	40c red vio & sep	.75	.40
513	A193	1s org brn & car	.80	.50

Nos. 509-513,C193-C197 (10)   8.50   3.70

Maldonado
and Map
A194

Riobamba
Aqueduct
A195

Maldonado
on Bank of
Riobamba
A196

Pedro V.
Maldonado
A197

1948, Nov. 17　　Engr.　　Unwmk.
514 A194　5c gray blk & ver　　　.50　.25
515 A195　10c car & gray blk　　.60　.25
516 A196　30c bis brn & ultra　　.70　.25
517 A195　40c sage grn & vio　　.90　.25
518 A194　50c grn & car　　　1.20　.30
519 A197　1s brn & slate bl　　1.50　.35
　　Nos. 514-519,C198-C201 (10)　9.70　2.65

Bicentenary of the death of Pedro Vicente
Maldonado, geographer.

For overprints and surcharges see Nos.
537-540.

　A198

Miguel de
Cervantes
Saavedra — A199

1949, May 2　　　Perf. 12½x12
520 A198　30c dk car rose &
　　　　　dp ultra　　　　.75　.25
521 A199　60c bis & brn vio　　1.25　.30
522 A198　1s grn & rose car　　1.75　.25
523 A199　2s gray blk & red
　　　　　brn　　　　　3.25　.30
524 A198　5s choc & aqua　　6.50　1.25
　　Nos. 520-524,C202-C206 (10)　25.75　5.95

400th anniv. of the birth of Miguel de
Cervantes Saavedra, novelist, playwright and
poet.

No. 480 Surcharged in
Carmine

1949, June 15　　　Perf. 12
525 A186　10c on 40c brt ultra　.55　.25
526 A186　20c on 40c brt ultra　.75　.25
　a.　　Double surcharge
527 A186　30c on 40c brt ultra　.75　.25
　　Nos. 525-527,C207-C209 (6)　4.15　1.50

2nd Natl. Eucharistic Cong., Quito, 6/49.
No. 526 exists se-tenant with No. 527.

Monument on
Equator — A200

1949, June　　Engr.　Perf. 12½x12
528 A200　10c deep plum　　　.50　.25
　For overprint see No. 536.

No. 542 Surcharged in
Black and Carmine

1949　　　　Perf. 12x12½
529 A203　10c on 50c green　　.60　.25
530 A203　20c on 50c green　　.60　.25
531 A203　30c on 50c green　　.70　.25
　　Nos. 529-531,C210-C213 (7)　6.60　2.25

Universal Postal Union, 75th anniversary.

Consular Service Stamps
Surcharged in Black

Arms of Ecuador — R1

1949　　　　　　Perf. 12
532 R1　20c on 25c red brown　.85　.25
533 R1　30c on 50c gray　　　.85　.25

For other overprints and surcharges on type
R1 see Nos. 544-549, 566-570, C214 C245,
C249-C252, RA60-RA62, RA72.

Nos. RA49A and RA55
Overprinted in Black — a

1950　　　Unwmk.　　Perf. 12
534 PT18　5c green　　　　　.45　.25
535 PT21　5c blue　　　　　.45　.25

Overprint 15mm on No. 534.

Nos. 528 and 517 to
519 Ovptd. or Srchd. in
Black or Carmine

1950, Feb. 10　　　Perf. 12½x12
536 A200　10c dp plum　　　.50　.50
**　　　　　　Perf. 12½**
537 A195　20c on 40c sage grn
　　　　　& vio　　　　1.00　1.00
538 A195　30c on 40c sage grn
　　　　　& vio　　　　1.25　1.25
539 A194　50c grn & car　　2.00　2.00
540 A197　1s brn & slate bl
　　　　　(C)　　　　2.50　2.50

No. C220 Overprinted
in Carmine

Overprint 15mm long
**　　　Perf. 11**
541 A173　10s violet　　　　6.00　3.00
　　Nos. 536-541,C216-C220 (11)　33.00　22.25
　Nos. 536-541 publicize adult education.

San Pablo Lake — A203

**　　　　　　Perf. 12x12½**
1950, May　　Engr.　　Unwmk.
542 A203　50c green　　　　.60　.25
　　For surcharges see Nos. 529-531.

Consular Service Stamp
Surcharged Vertically in
Black

1950　　　　　Perf. 12
544 R1　30c on 50c gray　　.60　.25

Consular Service Stamps
Overprinted or Surcharged in Black

b　　　　　　c

d　　　　　　e

f　　　　　　g

1951　　Unwmk.　　Perf. 12
545 R1 (b)　5c on 10c car rose　.60　.25
546 R1 (c)　10c car car rose　　.60　.25
547 R1 (d)　10c car rose　　　.60　.25
548 R1 (e)　20c on 25c red brn　.60　.25
549 R1 (e)　30c on 50c gray　　.60　.25
550 R2 (f)　40c on 25c blue　　.60　.25
551 R2 (g)　50c on 25c blue　　.60　.25
　　Nos. 545-551 (7)　　　4.20　1.75

See Nos. 552-554, C233-C234, C246-
C248, RA67.

Consular Service Stamps
Surcharged in Black

1951
552 R2　20c on 25c blue　　.50　.25
553 R2　30c on 25c blue　　.50　.25

Adult education. See Nos. C225-C226.

Consular Service Stamp
Surcharged in Black

1951
554 R2　$0.30 on 50c car rose　.60　.25

Reliquary of St. Mariana
and Vatican — A204

**　　　　　Perf. 12½x12**
1952, Feb.　　Engr.　　Unwmk.
555 A204　10c emer & red brn　1.00　.70
556 A204　20c dp bl & pur　　1.00　.70
557 A204　30c car & bl grn　　1.00　.70
　　Nos. 555-557,C227-C230 (7)　6.65　3.30

Issued to publicize the canonization of Mariana de Jesus Paredes y Flores.

Presidents Galo
Plaza and Harry
Truman — A205

2s, Pres. Plaza addressing US Congress.

1952, Mar. 26　　　Perf. 12
558 A205　1s rose car & gray blk　.75　.60
559 A205　2s dl bl & sepia　　1.90　.90
　　Nos. 558-559,C231-C232 (4)　5.65　3.70

1951 visit of Pres. Galo Plaza y Lasso to the
US.

R3

Fiscal Stamps Srchd. or
Ovptd. Horiz. in Carmine
or Black

Type of 1937 Overprinted
Diagonally

1952　　Unwmk.　　Engr.　Perf. 12
560 R3　20c on 30c dp bl (C)　.80　.25
561 R3　30c deep blue　　　.80　.25
562 A138　50c purple　　　.80　.25
　　Nos. 560-562 (3)　　　2.40　.75

For overprints and surcharge see Nos.
RA68-RA69, RA71.

Pres. José M.
Urvina, Slave and
"Liberty" — A206

Hyphen-hole Perf. 7x6½
1952　　　　　　Litho.
563 A206　20c red & green　　.70　.45
564 A206　30c red & vio bl　　.90　.45
565 A206　50c blue & car　　1.50　.45
　　Nos. 563-565,C236-C239 (7)　18.10　3.15

Centenary of abolition of slavery in Ecuador.
Counterfeits exist.

Consular Service Stamps
Surcharged in Black — h

1952-53　　Unwmk.　　Perf. 12
566 R1　10c on 20s blue ('53)　.85　.25
567 R1　20c on 10s gray ('53)　.85　.25
568 R1　20c on 20s blue　　.85　.25
569 R1　30c on 10s gray ('53)　.85　.25
570 R1　30c on 20s blue　　.85　.25
　　Nos. 566-570 (5)　　　4.25　1.25

Similar surcharges of 60c and 90c on the
20s blue are said to be bogus.

Teacher and
Students
A207

New Citizens
Voting
A208

Designs: 10c, Instructor with student. 30c,
Teaching the alphabet.

1953, Apr. 13   Engr.
571 A207 5c lt bl .35 .25
572 A207 10c dk car rose .55 .25
573 A208 20c brt brn org .60 .25
574 A208 30c dp red lil .90 .25
  Nos. 571-574,C240-C241 (6) 5.55 1.50

1952 adult education campaign.

A209

1953   Black Surcharge
575 A209 40c on 50c purple 1.00 .25

Cuicocha
Lagoon — A210

Designs: 10c, Equatorial Line monument. 20c, Quininde countryside. 30c, Tomebamba river. 40c, La Chilintosa rock. 50c, Iliniza Mountains.

Frames in Black

1953   Engr.   Perf. 13x12½
576 A210 5c brt bl .60 .50
577 A210 10c brt grn .60 .50
578 A210 20c purple .60 .50
579 A210 30c brown .60 .50
580 A210 40c orange .60 .50
581 A210 50c dp car 1.10 .50
  Nos. 576-581 (6) 4.10 3.00

A211

Carlos Maria Cardinal de la Torre and arches.

1954, Jan.   Photo.   Perf. 8½
582 A211 30c blk & ver .70 .65
583 A211 50c blk & rose lil .70 .65
  Nos. 582-583, C253-C255 (5) 4.20 2.35

1st anniv. of the elevation of Archbishop de la Torre to Cardinal.

A212

1954, Apr. 22
584 A212 30c blk & gray 1.50 1.40
585 A212 50c blk & yel 1.50 1.40
  Nos. 584-585,C256-C260 (7) 7.30 4.80

Queen Isabella I (1451-1504) of Spain, 500th birth anniv.

Type of 1929 Overprint
Larger, No Letterspacing

1954-55   Unwmk.   Perf. 12
586 A112 5c ol grn ('55) .80 .25
587 A112 10c orange .80 .25

The normal overprint on Nos. 586-587 reads up. It also exists reading down.

Indian
Messenger — A213

1954, Aug. 2   Litho.   Perf. 11
588 A213 30c dk brn 1.00 .25

Day of the Postal Employee. See No. C263.

Products of
Ecuador — A214

1954, Sept. 24   Photo.
589 A214 10c orange .45 .25
590 A214 20c vermilion .45 .25
591 A214 30c rose pink .45 .25
592 A214 40c dk gray grn .70 .25
593 A214 50c yel brn .90 .25
  Nos. 589-593 (5) 2.95 1.25

José Abel
Castillo — A215

Perf. 11½x11

1955, Oct. 19   Engr.   Unwmk.
594 A215 30c olive bister .65 .25
595 A215 50c dk gray .65 .25
  Nos. 594-595,C282-C286 (7) 11.00 2.10

30th anniv. of the 1st flight of the "Telegrafo I" and to honor Castillo, aviation pioneer.

Babahoyo River Los
Rios — A216

Designs: 5c, Palms, Esmeraldas. 10c, Fishermen, Manabi. 30c, Guayaquil, Guayas. 50c, Pital River, El Oro. 70c, Cactus, Galapagos Isls. 80c, Orchids, Napo-Pastaza. 1s, Aguacate Mission, Zamora-Chinchipe. 2s, Jibaro Indian, Morona-Santiago.

1955-56   Photo.   Perf. 13
596 A216 5c yel grn ('56) 1.50 .30
597 A216 10c blue ('56) 1.50 .30
598 A216 20c brown 1.50 .30
599 A216 30c dk gray 1.50 .30
600 A216 50c blk grn 1.50 .30
601 A216 70c ol ('56) 1.50 .30
602 A216 80c dk gray ('56) 3.75 .30
603 A216 1s org ('56) 2.00 .30
604 A216 2s rose red ('56) 3.75 .30
  Nos. 596-604 (9) 18.50 2.70

See Nos. 620-630, 670, C288-C297, C310-C311.

Brother Juan Adam
Schwarz, S. J. — A217

1956, Aug. 27   Engr.   Perf. 13½
605 A217 5c yel grn .55 .25
606 A217 10c org red .55 .25
607 A217 20c lt vio .55 .25
608 A217 30c dk grn .55 .25
609 A217 40c blue .55 .25
610 A217 50c dp ultra .55 .25
611 A217 70c orange .55 .25
  Nos. 605-611,C302-C305 (11) 6.85 2.75

Bicentennial of printing in Ecuador and honoring Brother Juan Adam Schwarz, S.J.

Andres
Hurtado de
Mendoza
A218

Gil Ramirez
Davalos
A219

Designs: 20c, Brother Vincent Solano.

1957, Apr. 7   Unwmk.   Perf. 12
612 A218 5c dk bl, pink .80 .25
613 A219 10c grn, grnsh .80 .25
614 A218 20c choc, buff .80 .25
  a. Souvenir sheet of 4, imperf. 3.50 3.50
  Nos. 612-614,C312-C314 (6) 3.45 1.50

4th cent. of the founding of Cuenca.
No. 614a contains 2 5c gray & 2 20c brown red stamps in designs similar to #612, 614. It was printed on white ungummed paper.

A220

Design: 40c, 50c, 2s, Francisco Marcos, Gen. Pedro Alcantara Herran and Santos Michelena.

1957, Sept. 5   Engr.   Perf. 14½x14
615 A220 40c yellow .40 .25
616 A220 50c ultra .40 .25
617 A220 2s dk red 1.00 .25
  Nos. 615-617 (3) 1.80 .75

7th Postal Congress of the Americas and Spain (in 1955).

Souvenir Sheets

Various
Railroad
Scenes
A221

1957   Litho.   Perf. 10½x11
618 A221 20c Sheet of 5 9.25 4.25
619 A221 30c Sheet of 5 9.25 4.25

Issued to commemorate the opening of the Quito-Ibarra-San Lorenzo railroad.
Nos. 618-619 contain 2 orange yellow, 1 ultramarine and 2 carmine stamps, each in a different design.

Scenic Type of 1955-56.

Designs as before, except: 40c, as 70c. 90c, as 80c. No. 629, San Pablo, Imbabura.

1957-58   Photo.   Perf. 13
620 A216 5c light blue 1.75 .25
621 A216 10c brown 1.75 .25
622 A216 20c crimson rose 1.75 .25
623 A216 20c yel green 1.75 .25
624 A216 30c rose red 2.50 .25
625 A216 40c chalky blue 1.75 .25
626 A216 50c lt vio 2.50 .25
627 A216 90c brt ultra 1.75 .25
628 A216 1s dark brown 1.75 .25
629 A216 1s gray blk ('58) 1.75 .25
630 A216 2s brown 2.75 .25
  Nos. 620-630 (11) 21.75 2.75

Blue and Yellow
Macaw — A222

Birds: 20c, Red-breasted toucan. 30c, Condor. 40c, Black-tailed and sword-tailed hummingbirds.

Perf. 13½x13

1958, Jan. 7   Litho.   Unwmk.
Birds in Natural Colors
634 A222 10c red brn 1.40 .25
635 A222 20c dk gray 1.40 .25
636 A222 30c brt yel grn 3.50 .25
637 A222 40c red org 3.50 .25
  Nos. 634-637 (4) 9.80 1.00

Carlos Sanz de
Santamaria
A223

Richard M.
Nixon and
Flags
A224

No. 640, Dr. Ramon Villeda Morales, flags. 2.20s, José Carlos de Macedo Soares, horizontal flags.

1958   Perf. 12
Flags in Red, Blue, Yellow & Green
638 A223 1.80s dl vio .65 .25
639 A224 2s dk brn .65 .25
640 A224 2s dk brn .65 .25
641 A223 2.20s blk brn .65 .25
  Nos. 638-641 (4) 2.60 1.00

Visits: Colombia's Foreign Minister Dr. Carlos Sanz de Santamaria; US Vice Pres. Nixon, May 9-10; Pres. Ramon Villeda Morales of Honduras; Brazil's Foreign Minister José Carlos de Macedo Soares. See Nos. C419-C421. For overprints and surcharges see Nos. 775-775C, C419-C421, C460.

Locomotive of
1908 — A225

Garcia
Moreno, Jose
Caamano, L.
Plaza and
Eloy Alfaro
A226

Design: 50c, Diesel locomotive.

Perf. 13½x14, 14
1958, Aug. 9   Photo.   Unwmk.
642 A225 30c brn blk .30 .25
643 A225 50c dk car .40 .25
644 A226 5s dk brn 1.80 .70
  Nos. 642-644 (3) 2.50 1.20

Guayaquil-Quito railroad, 50th anniv.

Cardinal — A227

Birds: 30c, Andean cock-of-the-rock. 50c, Glossy cowbird. 60c, Red-fronted Amazon.

1958   Litho.   Perf. 13½x13
Birds in Natural Colors
645 A227 20c bluish grn, blk & red 1.40 .25
646 A227 30c buff, blk & brt bl 1.65 .25
647 A227 50c org, blk & grn 1.90 .55
648 A227 60c pale rose, blk & bluish grn 3.75 .55
  Nos. 645-648 (4) 8.70 1.60

UNESCO Building
and Eiffel Tower,
Paris — A228

1958, Nov. 3   Engr.   Perf. 12½
649 A228 80c brown .65 .25

UNESCO Headquarters in Paris opening, Nov. 3.

Globe and Satellites — A229

1958, Dec. 20 Photo. Perf. 14x13½
650 A229 1.80s dark blue   1.25 .45

International Geophysical Year, 1957-58.
For overprints see Nos. 718, C422.

Virgin of Quito — A230

1959, Sept. 8   Unwmk.   Perf. 13
651 A230 5c ol grn   .30 .25
652 A230 10c yel brn   .30 .25
653 A230 20c purple   .30 .25
654 A230 30c ultra   .30 .25
655 A230 80c dk car rose   .30 .25
　　　Nos. 651-655 (5)   1.50 1.25

See No. C290. For surcharges and overprint see Nos. 695-699.

Uprooted Oak Emblem — A231

1960, Apr. 7   Litho.   Perf. 14x13
656 A231 80c rose car & grn   .60 .25

World Refugee Year, 71/59-630/60.
For overprints see Nos. 709, 719, O205.

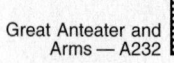

Great Anteater and Arms — A232

Animals: 40c, Tapir and map. 80c, Spectacled bear and arms. 1s, Puma and map.

1960, May 14   Photo.   Perf. 13
657 A232 20c org, grn & blk   .60 .25
658 A232 40c yel grn, bl grn & brn   .90 .25
659 A232 80c bl, blk & red brn   1.50 .25
660 A232 1s Prus bl, plum & ocher   2.75 .60
　　　Nos. 657-660 (4)   5.75 1.35

Founding of the city of Baeza, 4th cent.
See Nos. 676-679.

Hotel Quito — A233

No. 662, Dormitory, Catholic University. No. 663, Dormitory, Central University. No. 664, Airport, Quito. No. 665, Overpass on Highway to Quito. No. 666, Security Bank. No. 667, Ministry of Foreign Affairs. No. 668, Government Palace. No. 669, Legislative Palace.

Perf. 11x11½
1960, Aug. 8   Engr.   Unwmk.
661 A233 1s dk pur & redsh brn   .55 .25
662 A233 1s dk bl & brn   .55 .25
663 A233 1s blk & red   .55 .25
664 A233 1s dk bl & ultra   .55 .25
665 A233 1s dk pur & dk car rose   .55 .25
666 A233 1s blk & ol bis   .55 .25
667 A233 1s dk pur & turq   .55 .25
668 A233 1s dk bl & grn   .55 .25
669 A233 1s blk & vio   .55 .25
　　　Nos. 661-669 (9)   4.95 2.25

11th Inter-American Conference, Quito.
For surcharges see Nos. 700-708.

Type of Regular Issue, 1955-56
Souvenir Sheet

Design: Orchids, Napo-Pastaza.

1960   Photo.   Perf. 13
Yellow Paper
670 Sheet of 2   5.00 5.00
　a. A216 80c deep violet   .85 .45
　b. A216 90c deep green   .85 .45

25th anniv. of Asociacion Filatelica Ecuatoriana. Marginal inscription in silver. Exists with silver inscription omitted.

"Freedom of Expression" A234

Manabi Bridge A235

10c, "Freedom to vote." 20c, "Freedom to work." 30c, Coins, "Monetary stability."

1960, Aug. 29   Litho.   Perf. 13
671 A234 5c dk bl   .80 .25
672 A234 10c lt vio   .80 .25
673 A234 20c orange   .80 .25
674 A234 30c bluish grn   .80 .25
675 A235 40c brn & bluish grn   .80 .25
　　　Nos. 671-675 (5)   4.00 1.25

Achievements of President Camilo Ponce Enriquez. See Nos. C370-C374.

Animal Type of 1960

Animals: 10c, Collared peccary. 20c, Kinkajou. 80c, Jaguar. 1s, Mountain coati.

Unwmk.
1961, July 13   Photo.   Perf. 13
676 A232 10c grn, rose red & blk   .60 .25
677 A232 20c vio, grnsh bl & brn   1.10 .25
678 A232 80c red org, dl yel & blk   1.70 .55
679 A232 1s org brn & pale bl grn   2.20 .65
　　　Nos. 676-679 (4)   5.60 1.70

Founding of the city of Tena, 400th anniv.

Graphium Pausianus — A236

Butterflies: 30c, Papilio torquatus leptalea. 50c, Graphium molops molops. 80c, Battus lycidas.

1961, July 13   Litho.   Perf. 13½
680 A236 20c pink & multi   .70 .25
681 A236 30c lt ultra & multi   1.20 .25
682 A236 50c org & multi   1.40 .25
683 A236 80c bl grn & multi   2.40 .25
　　　Nos. 680-683 (4)   5.70 1.00

See Nos. 711-713.

Galapagos Islands Nos. L1-L3 Overprinted in Black or Red

1961, Oct. 31   Photo.   Perf. 12
684 A1 20c dk brn   1.00 .25
685 A2 50c violet   1.00 .25
686 A1 1s dk ol grn (R)   2.40 1.50
　　　Nos. 684-686, C389-C391 (6)   10.25 3.25

Establishment of maritime biological stations on Galapagos Islands by UNESCO. Overprint arranged differently on 20c, 1s.
See Nos. C389-C391.

Daniel Enrique Proano School — A237

Designs: 60c, Loja-Zamora highway, vert. 80c, Aguirre Abad College, Guayaquil. 1s, Army quarters, Quito.

Perf. 11x11½, 11½x11
1962, Jan. 10   Engr.   Unwmk.
687 A237 50c dl bl & blk   .50 .25
688 A237 60c ol grn & blk   .50 .25
689 A237 80c org red & blk   .50 .25
690 A237 1s rose lake & blk   .50 .25
　　　Nos. 687-690 (4)   2.00 1.00

Pres. Arosemena, Flags of Ecuador, US — A238

Designs (Arosemena and): 10c, Flags of Ecuador. 20c, Flags of Ecuador and Panama.

1963, July 1   Litho.   Perf. 14
691 A238 10c buff & multi   .30 .25
692 A238 20c multi   .30 .25
693 A238 60c multi   .30 .25
　　　Nos. 691-693, C409-C411 (6)   3.05 1.60

Issued to commemorate Pres. Carlos J. Arosemena's friendship trip, July 1962.
Imperfs exist. Value $9.

Protection for The Family — A239

1963, July 9   Unwmk.   Perf. 14
694 A239 10c ultra, red, gray & blk   .25 .25

Social Insurance, 25th anniv. See No. C413.

No. 655 Ovptd. or Srchd. in Black or Blue

1963   Photo.   Perf. 13
695 A230 10c on 80c dk car rose   .35 .25
696 A230 20c on 80c dk car rose   .35 .25
697 A230 50c on 80c dk car rose   .35 .25
698 A230 60c on 80c dk car rose (Bl)   .35 .25
699 A230 80c dk car rose   .40 .25
　　　Nos. 695-699 (5)   1.80 1.25

Nos. 661-669 Surcharged

1964, Apr. 20   Engr.   Perf. 11x11½
700 A233 10c on 1s dk pur & redsh brn   .65 .25
701 A233 10c on 1s dk pur & turq   .65 .25
702 A233 20c on 1s dk bl & brn   .65 .25
703 A233 20c on 1s dk bl & grn   .65 .25
704 A233 30c on 1s dk pur & dk car rose   .65 .25
705 A233 40c on 1s blk & ol bis   .65 .25
706 A233 60c on 1s blk & red   .65 .25
707 A233 80c on 1s dk bl & ultra   .65 .25
708 A233 80c on 1s blk & vio   .65 .25
　　　Nos. 700-708 (9)   5.85 2.25

No. 656 Overprinted in Black or Light Ultramarine

1964   Litho.   Perf. 14x13
709 A231 80c rose car & grn   5.00 1.25

Butterfly Type of 1961

Butterflies: Same as on Nos. 680, 682-683.

1964, June   Litho.   Perf. 13½
711 A236 20c brt grn & multi   .80 .25
712 A236 50c sal pink & multi   1.60 .25
713 A236 80c lt red brn & multi   3.25 .25
　　　Nos. 711-713 (3)   5.65 .75

Alliance for Progress Emblem, Agriculture and Industry — A240

Designs: 50c, Emblem, gear wheels, mountain and seashore. 80c, Emblem, banana worker, fish, factory and ship.

1964, Aug. 26   Unwmk.   Perf. 12
715 A240 40c bis brn & vio   .35 .25
716 A240 50c red org & blk   .35 .25
717 A240 80c bl & dk brn   .55 .25
　　　Nos. 715-717 (3)   1.25 .75

Issued to publicize the Alliance for Progress which aims to stimulate economic growth and raise living standards in Latin America.

No. 650 Overprinted in Red

1964   Photo.   Perf. 14x13½
718 A229 1.80s dark blue   2.75 2.25

No. 656 Overprinted

1964, July   Litho.   Perf. 14x13
719 A231 80c block of 4   4.00 4.00

Organization of American States.

World Map and Banana Tree — A241

1964, Oct. 26   Perf. 12½x12
720 A241 50c dk brn, gray & gray ol   .30 .25
721 A241 80c blk, org & gray ol   .30 .25

Issued to publicize the Banana Conference, Oct.-Nov. 1964. See Nos. C427-C428a.

King Philip II of Spain and Map of Upper Amazon River — A242

Designs (Map and): 20c, Juan de Salinas de Loyola. 30c, Hernando de Santillan.

1964, Dec. 6   Litho.   Perf. 13½
722 A242 10c rose, blk & buff   .40 .25
723 A242 20c bl grn, blk & buff   .40 .25
724 A242 30c bl, blk & buff   .40 .25
　　　Nos. 722-724 (3)   1.20 .75

4th centenary of the establishment of the Royal High Court in Quito.

Pole Vaulting — A243

1964, Dec. 16   **Perf. 14x13½**
725 A243 80c vio bl, yel grn &
    brn   .35   .25

18th Olympic Games, Tokyo, Oct. 10-25.
See Nos. C432-C434.

Peter Fleming and
Two-toed Sloth — A244

Designs: 20c, James Elliot and armadillo.
30c, T. Edward McCully, Jr., and squirrel. 40c,
Roger Youderian and deer. 60c, Nathaniel
(Nate) Saint and plane over Napo River.

1965   **Unwmk.**   **Perf. 13½**
726 A244 20c emerald & multi   1.00   .25
727 A244 30c yellow & multi   1.00   .25
728 A244 40c lilac & multi   1.00   .25
729 A244 60c multi   1.00   .25
730 A244 80c multi   1.00   .25
    Nos. 726-730 (5)   5.00   1.25

Issued in memory of five American Protestant missionaries, killed by the Auca Indians,
1/8/56.
Issue dates: 80c, May 11; others, July 8.

Juan B.
Vázquez and
Benigno Malo
College
A245

1965, June 6   **Litho.**   **Perf. 14**
731 A245 20c blk, yel & vio bl   .35   .25
732 A245 60c blk, red, yel & vio
    bl   .35   .25
733 A245 80c blk, emer, yel &
    vio bl   .35   .25
    Nos. 731-733 (3)   1.05   .75

Centenary (in 1964) of the founding of
Benigno Malo National College.

National Anthem,
Juan Leon Mera
and Antonio
Neumane — A246

1965, Aug. 10   **Litho.**   **Perf. 13½**
734 A246 50c pink & blk   .30   .25
735 A246 80c lt grn & blk   .40   .25
736 A246 5s bis & blk   .95   .25
737 A246 10s lt ultra & blk   1.75   .90
    Nos. 734-737 (4)   3.40   1.75

Cent. of the national anthem. The name of
the poet Juan Leon Mera is misspelled on the
stamps.
For surcharges see Nos. 766C, 766H.

Torch and Athletes (Shot Put, Discus,
Javelin and Hammer Throw)
A247

50c, 1s, Runners. 60c, 1.50s, Soccer.

1965, Nov. 20   **Perf. 12x12½**
738 A247 40c org, gold, & blk   .30   .25
739 A247 50c org ver, gold &
    blk   .30   .25
740 A247 60c bl, gold & blk   .30   .25
741 A247 80c brt yel grn, gold
    & blk   .50   .25
742 A247 1s lt vio, gold & blk   .50   .25
743 A247 1.50s brt pink, gold &
    blk   .85   .50
    Nos. 738-743,C435-C440 (12)   6.90   3.75

Issued to publicize the 5th Bolivarian
Games, held at Guayaquil and Quito.
For surcharges see Nos. 766B, 766D,
C449.

Stamps of
1865 — A248

1965, Dec. 30   **Litho.**   **Perf. 13½**
**Stamps of 1865 in Yellow,
Ultramarine & Green**
744 A248 80c rose red   .40   .25
745 A248 1.30s rose lilac   .45   .25
746 A248 2s chocolate   .60   .25
747 A248 4s black   .90   .25
    a. Souv. sheet, #744-747, imperf.   4.00   4.00
    Nos. 744-747 (4)   2.35   1.00

Cent. of Ecuadorian postage stamps.

The postal validity of some of the following sets has been questioned.

ITU
Centenary —
A248a

No. 748, Telstar. No. 748A, Syncom. No.
748B, Relay. No. 748C, Luna 3. No. 748D,
Echo II. No. 748E, E. Branly, Marconi, Bell, E.
Belin.

1966, Jan. 27   **Litho.**   **Perf. 12x12½**
748 A248a 10c multi   .30   .25
748A A248a 1s multi   .30   .25
748B A248a 80c multi   .30   .25
748C A248a 1.50s multi   .50   .35
748D A248a 3s multi   2.25   1.25
    f. Souv. sheet of 3, #748,
      748B, 748D, perf.
      14x12½   17.50
748E A248a 4s multi   2.25   1.50
    g. Souv. sheet of 3, #748A,
      748C, 748E, perf.
      14x12½   17.50
    Nos. 748-748E (6)   5.90   3.85

1.50s, 3s, 4s are airmail.
Nos. 748Df, 748Eg are printed on surface
colored paper. Exist imperf. Value, each $20.

Space
Exploration
A248b

10c, Edward White's space walk, June 8,
1965. 1s, Gemini 5, Aug. 21, 1965. 1.30s,
Solar system. 2s, Charles Conrad, L. Gordon
Cooper, Gemini 5, Aug. 21-29, 1965. 2.50s,
Gemini 6. 3.50s, Alexei L. Leonov's space
walk, Mar. 18, 1965.

1966, Jan. 27   **Perf. 12x12½**
749 A248b 10c multi   .30   .25
749A A248b 1s multi   .40   .25
749B A248b 1.30s multi   .40   .25
749C A248b 2s multi   1.40   .65
749D A248b 2.50s multi   1.40   .65
749E A248b 3.50s multi   3.25   2.50
    f. Souv. sheet of 3, #749,
      749B, 749E, perf.
      14x12½   15.00   10.00
    Nos. 749-749E (6)   7.15   4.55

1.30s, 2s, 2.50s, 3.50s are airmail.
No. 749Ef is printed on surface colored
paper. Exists imperf. Value $15.

Dante's
Dream by
Rossetti
A248c

Designs: 80c, Dante and Beatrix by Hol-
liday. 2s, Galileo Galilei, 400th birth cent., vert.
3s, Dante, 700th birth cent., vert.

1966, June   **Perf. 13½x14, 14x13½**
750 A248c 10c multicolored   .30   .25
750A A248c 80c multicolored   .30   .25
750B A248c 2s multicolored   3.00   1.50
750C A248c 3s multicolored   3.00   1.60
    d. Souv. sheet of 3, #750,
      750A, 750C, perf.
      12x12½   18.00   18.00
    Nos. 750-750C (4)   6.60   3.60

Nos. 750A-750B are airmail. No. 750Cd
exists imperf. Value $18.

Pavonine
Quetzal — A249

Birds: 50c, Blue-crowned motmot. 60c,
Paradise tanager. 80c, Wire-tailed manakin.

1966, June 17   **Litho.**   **Perf. 13½**
Birds in Natural Colors
751 A249 40c dl rose & blk   1.60   .25
751A A249 50c sal & blk   1.60   .25
751B A249 60c lt ocher & blk   1.60   .25
751C A249 80c lt bl & blk   1.60   .25
    Nos. 751-751C,C441-C448 (12)   31.70   6.25

For surcharges see Nos. 766E-766F, C450,
C455-C457.

Pope Paul
VI — A249a

Pope Paul VI and: 1.30s, Nativity. 3.50s, Virgin of Merced.

1966, June 24   **Perf. 12½x12**
752 A249a 10c multicolored   .30   .25
752A A249a 1.30s multicolored   .90   .35
752B A249a 3.50s multicolored   2.50   .75
    c. Souv. sheet of 3, #752,
      perf. 14x13½, 752A-
      752B, perf. 12½x12   15.00   15.00
    Nos. 752-752B (3)   3.70   1.35

Nos. 752A-752B are airmail.
No. 752Bc is printed on surface colored
paper. Exists imperf. Value $18.

Sir Winston
Churchill,
(1874-1965)
A249b

Famous Men: 10c, Dag Hammarskjold, vert.
1.50s, Albert Schweitzer, vert. 2.50s, John F.
Kennedy, vert. 4s, Churchill, Kennedy.

Perf. 14x13½, 13½x14
1966, June 24
753 A249b 10c vio bl, brn
    & blk   .30   .25
753A A249b 1s ver, bl &
    blk   .40   .25
753B A249b 1.50s brn, lil rose
    & blk   .90   .30
753C A249b 2.50s ver, bl &
    blk   2.25   1.00
753D A249b 4s bl, blk &
    brn   2.50   1.50
    e. Souv. sheet of 3, #753,
      753B, 753D   30.00   27.50
    Nos. 753-753D (5)   6.35   3.30

Nos. 753C-753D are airmail.
No. 753De is printed on surface colored
paper. 10c stamp is perf. 14x13½, 1.50s is
perf. 14x13½x14x12, 4s is perf.
12x12½x13x12½. Exists imperf. Value $30.

History of
Summer
Olympics
A249c

No. 754, Long jump. No. 754A, Wrestling.
No. 754B, Discus, javelin. No. 754C, Chariot
racing. No. 754D, High jump. No. 754E,
Discus.

1966, June 27   **Perf. 12x12½**
754 A249c 10c multi   .30   .25
754A A249c 10c multi   .30   .25
754B A249c 80c multi   .35   .25
754C A249c 1.30s multi   1.40   .45
754D A249c 3s multi   2.25   .90
    f. Souv. sheet of 3, #754,
      754B, 754D   12.00   5.00

754E A249c 3.50s multi   3.50   1.10
    g. Souv. sheet of 3, #754A,
      754C, 754E   12.50   5.00
    Nos. 754-754E (6)   8.10   3.20

Nos. 754C-754D are airmail.
Nos. 754Df, 754Eg are printed on surface
colored paper.
Nos. 754Df and 754Eg exist imperf. Value
$13.50.

1968 Winter
Olympics,
Grenoble
A249d

Designs: 10c, Speedskating. 1s, Ice hockey.
1.50s, Ski jumping. 2s, Cross country skiing.
2.50s, Downhill skiing. 4s, Figure skating.

1966, June 27   **Perf. 14**
755 A249d 10c multi   .25   .25
755A A249d 1s multi   .40   .25
755B A249d 1.50s multi   .60   .30
755C A249d 2s multi   1.20   .45
755D A249d 2.50s multi   1.60   1.25
755E A249d 4s multi   2.00   1.50
    f. Souv. sheet of 3, #755, 755B,
      755E, perf. 14x13½   8.50   6.00
    Nos. 755-755E (6)   6.05   4.00

Nos. 755B-755E are airmail.
No. 755Ef is printed on surface colored
paper. Exists imperf. Value same as perf.

French-American Cooperation in
Space — A249e

Designs: 1.50s, French satellite D-1, Mt.
Gros observatory, vert. 4s, John F. Kennedy,
satellites.

1966   **Perf. 13½x14, 14x13½**
756 A249e 10c multicolored   .25   .25
756A A249e 1.50s multicolored   1.75   1.10
756B A249e 4s multicolored   4.25   2.25
    c. Sheet of 3, #756-756B   15.00   12.00
    Nos. 756-756B (3)   6.30   3.60

Nos. 756A-756B are airmail.
No. 756Bc exists imperf. Value same as
perf.

Italian
Space
Program —
A249n

Designs: 10c, San Marco satellite. 1.30s,
San Marco satellite, diff. 3.50s, Leonardo da
Vinci, Moon, and Johannes Kepler.

1966   **Litho.**   **Unwmk.**   **Perf. 14**
757 A249n 10c multi   .25   .25
757A A249n 1.30s multi   .75   .45
757B A249n 3.50s multi   2.00   1.10
    c. Souvenir sheet of 3, #757,
      757A, 757B   13.00   8.00
    Nos. 757- (3)   3.00   1.80

Nos. 757A and 757B are airmail. No. 757Bc
is printed on paper with a gray pattern, and
exists imperforate on paper printed with a
green pattern. Value same as perf.

Moon Exploration
A249f

Designs: 10c, Surveyor. 80c, Luna 10. 1s,
Luna 9. 2s, Astronaut flight trainer. 2.50s,
Ranger 7. 3s, Lunar Orbiter 1.

1966　　　　　　　　　　Perf. 14

758	A249f	10c multi	.25	.25
758A	A249f	80c multi	.25	.25
758B	A249f	1s multi	.25	.25
758C	A249f	2s multi	.80	.45
758D	A249f	2.50s multi	1.00	.75
758E	A249f	3s multi	1.20	.90
f.		Sheet of 3, #758, 758A, 758E	12.00	6.00
		Nos. 758-758E (6)	3.75	2.85

Nos. 758C-758E are airmail. Stamps in No. 758Ef have colored pattern in border.

No. 758Ef exists imperf. Value same as perf.

1968 Summer Olympics, Mexico City A249g

Paintings by Mexican artists: 10c, Wanderer by Diego Rivera. 1s, Workers by Jose Orozco. 1.30s, Pres. Juarez by Orozco. 2s, Mother and Child by David Siqueiros. 2.50s, Two Women by Rivera. 3.50s, New Democracy by Siqueiros.

1967, Mar. 13　　　　　　Perf. 14

759	A249g	10c multicolored	.25	.25
759A	A249g	1s multicolored	.55	.25
759B	A249g	1.30s multicolored	.80	.35
759C	A249g	2s multicolored	1.00	.60
759D	A249g	2.50s multicolored	1.20	1.00
759E	A249g	3.50s multicolored	2.25	2.00
f.		Sheet of 3, #759, 759B, 759E	15.00	
		Nos. 759-759E (6)	6.05	4.45

Nos. 759B-759E are airmail.

No. 759f is printed on surface colored paper that differs slightly from Nos. 759-759E. Exists imperf. Value same as perf.

1968 Summer Olympics, Mexico City A249h

No. 760, Soccer. No. 760A, Hurdles. No. 760B, Track. No. 760C, Fencing. No. 760D, High jump. No. 760E, Swimming.

1967, Mar. 13

760	A249h	10c multi	.25	.25
760A	A249h	10c multi	.25	.25
760B	A249h	80c multi	.25	.25
760C	A249h	1.50s multi	.75	.30
760D	A249h	3s multi	1.50	1.00
f.		Souv. sheet of 3, #760A, 760B, 760D	15.00	7.50
760E	A249h	4s multi	3.25	1.50
g.		Souv. sheet of 3, #760, 760C, 760E	12.00	7.00
		Nos. 760-760E (6)	6.25	3.55

Nos. 760C-760E are airmail.

Nos. 760f-760g are printed on surface colored paper. Exist imperf. Value same as perf.

4th Natl. Eucharistic Congress A249i

Paintings: 10c, Madonna and Child by unknown artist. 60c, Holy Family by Rodriguez. 80c, Madonna and Child by Samaniego. 1s, Good Shepherd by Samaniego. 1.50s, Assumption of the Virgin by Vargas. 2s, Man in Prayer by Santiago.

10s, Chalice, eucharist, church, wheat.

1967, May 10

761	A249i	10c multicolored	.30	.25
761A	A249i	60c multicolored	.60	.30
761B	A249i	80c multicolored	.90	.40
761C	A249i	1s multicolored	.90	.50
761D	A249i	1.50s multicolored	1.60	.75
761E	A249i	2s multicolored	2.75	.75
		Nos. 761-761E (6)	7.05	2.85

Souvenir Sheet

761F	A249i	10s multi	7.50	6.50

Nos. 761D-761E are airmail. Frames and inscriptions vary greatly.

No. 761F exists imperf. with an orange margin color. Value, same.

Madonna and Child Enthroned by Guido Reni — A249j

Paintings of the Madonna and Child by: 40c, van Hemesen. 50c, Memling. 1.30s, Durer. 2.50s, Raphael. 3s, Murillo.

1967, May 25　　　　　Perf. 14x13½

762	A249j	10c multicolored	.25	.25
762A	A249j	40c multicolored	.25	.25
762B	A249j	50c multicolored	.25	.25
762C	A249j	1.30s multicolored	.70	.30
762D	A249j	2.50s multicolored	1.75	.95
762E	A249j	3s multicolored	2.75	1.20
		Nos. 762-762E (6)	5.95	3.20

Nos. 762C-762E are airmail.

Portrait of a Young Woman by Rogier van der Weyden — A249k

Designs: 1s, Helene Fourment by Rubens. 1.50s, Venetian Woman by Durer. 2s, Lady Sheffield by Gainsborough. 2.50s, Suzon by Manet. 4s, Lady with a Unicorn by Raphael.

1967, Sept. 9　　　　　Perf. 14x13½

763	A249k	10c multicolored	.30	.25
763A	A249k	1s multicolored	.60	.30
763B	A249k	1.50s multicolored	1.40	.50
763C	A249k	2s multicolored	1.90	.65
763D	A249k	2.50s multicolored	2.75	.80
763E	A249k	4s multicolored	3.25	1.25
f.		Sheet of 3, #763, 763B, 763E, perf. 14	18.00	8.00
		Nos. 763-763E (6)	10.20	3.75

Nos. 763B-763E are airmail.
Stamps in No. 763f have colored pattern in border. Exists imperf. Value same as perf.

John F. Kennedy, 50th Birth Anniv. — A249l

JFK and: No. 764A, Dag Hammarskjold. 80c, Pope Paul VI. 1.30s, Konrad Adenauer. 3s, Charles de Gaulle. 3.50s, Winston Churchill.

Perf. 14x13½, 13½x14
1967, Sept. 11

764	A249l	10c lil, brn & bl	.25	.25
764A	A249l	10c yel, brn & sky bl	.25	.25
764B	A249l	80c yel, brn & sal	.25	.25
764C	A249l	1.30s yel, brn & pink	2.00	.75
764D	A249l	3s yel, brn & yel grn	2.90	1.25
764E	A249l	3.50s yel, brn & bl	4.00	1.75
		Nos. 764-764E (6)	9.65	4.50

Souvenir Sheets

764F		Sheet of 3	19.00	8.00
h.		like #764, 35x27mm		
i.		like #764B, 35x27mm		
j.		like #764D, 35x27mm		
764G		Sheet of 3	19.00	8.00
k.		like #764A, 35x27mm		
l.		like #764C, 35x27mm		
m.		like #764E, 35x27mm		

Nos. 764C-764E are airmail. Nos. 764A-764E horiz. Stamps in Nos. 764F-764G have colored pattern in border.

Nos. 764F and 764G exist imperf. Values same as perf.

Christmas A249m

Designs: No. 765A, Children's procession. 40c, Candlelight procession. 50c, Children singing. 60c, Processional. 2.50s, Christmas celebration.

1967, Dec. 29　　　　　Perf. 13x14

765	A249m	10c multi	.40	.25
765A	A249m	10c multi	.40	.25
765B	A249m	40c multi	.40	.25
765C	A249m	50c multi	.40	.25
765D	A249m	60c multi	.40	.25
765E	A249m	2.50s multi	11.00	9.75
		Nos. 765-765E (6)	13.00	11.00

No. 765E is airmail. See Nos. 768-768F.

Various Surcharges on Issues of 1956-66
1967-68

766	AP72	30c on 1.10s (C337)	.35	.25
766A	AP66	40c on 1.70s (C292)	.35	.25
766B	A247	40c on 3.50s (C438)	.35	.25
766C	A246	50c on 5s (736) ('68)	.35	.25
766D	A247	80c on 1.50s (743)	.40	.25
766E	A249	80c on 2.50s (C445)	.40	.25
766F	A249	1s on 4s (C447)	.50	.25
766G	AP66	1.30s on 1.90s (C293)	.65	.55
766H	A246	2s on 10s (737) ('68)	.80	.25
		Nos. 766-766H,C449-C450 (11)	4.95	3.15

The surcharge on Nos. 766B-766C, 766E and 766G-766H includes "Resello." The obliteration of old denomination and arrangement of surcharges differ on each stamp.

Bust of Peñaherrera, Central University, Quito — A250

50c, Law books. 80c, Open book, laurel, horiz.

Perf. 12x12½, 12½x12
1967, Dec. 29　　　　　Litho.

767	A250	50c brt grn & blk	.25	.25
767A	A250	60c rose & blk	.25	.25
767B	A250	80c rose lil & blk	.25	.25
		Nos. 767-767B,C451-C452 (5)	1.35	1.25

Cent. (in 1964) of the birth of Dr. Victor Manuel Peñaherrera (1864-1932), author of the civil and criminal codes of Ecuador.

Christmas Type of 1967

Native Christian Art: 10c, Mourning of the Death of Christ, by Manuel Chili. 80c, Ascension of the Holy Virgin, vert. 1s, The Holy Virgin. 1.30s, Coronation of the Holy Virgin, by Bernardo Rodriguez, vert. 1.50s, Madonna and Child with the Heavenly Host, vert. 2s, Madonna and Child, by Manuel Samaniego, vert. 3s, Immaculate Conception, by Bernardo de Legranda, vert. 3.50s, Passion of Christ, by Chili, vert. 4s, The Holy Virgin of Quito, by de Legranda, vert.

1968 Jan. 19　Perf. 13½x14, 14x13½

768	A249m	10c multi	.25	.25
768A	A249m	80c multi	.25	.25
768B	A249m	1s multi	.25	.25
768C	A249m	1.30s multi	.25	.25
768D	A249m	1.50s multi	.50	.30
768E	A249m	2s multi	.80	.75
		Nos. 768-768E (6)	2.30	2.05

Souvenir Sheet
Perf. 14

768F		Sheet of 3	19.00	8.00
g.		A249m 3s multicolored		
h.		A249m 3.50s multicolored		
i.		A249m 4s multicolored		

Nos. 768C-768F are airmail. No. 768F exists imperf. Value same.

Tourism Year — A250a

20c, Woman from Otavalo. 30c, Colorado Indian. 40c, Petroglyph of a cat. 50c, Petroglyph of a mythological predator. 60c, Woman in a bazaar. 80c, 1s, 1.30s, Petroglyphs, diff. 1.50s, Colonial street, Quito. 2s, Amulet.

1968, Apr. 1　　　　Perf. 13½x14

769	A250a	20c multicolored	.30	.25
769A	A250a	30c multicolored	.30	.25
769B	A250a	40c multicolored	.30	.25
769C	A250a	50c multicolored	.30	.25
769D	A250a	60c multicolored	.30	.25
769E	A250a	80c multicolored	.30	.25
769F	A250a	1s multicolored	.35	.25
769G	A250a	1.30s multicolored	.30	.25
769H	A250a	1.50s multicolored	.35	.25
769I	A250a	2s multicolored	.40	.25
		Nos. 769-769I (10)	3.20	2.50

Eleventh Congress of the Confederation of Latin American Tourist Organizations (COTAL). Nos. 769G-769I are airmail.

Otto Arosemena Gomez — A251

Design: 1s, Page from the Constitution.

1968, May 9　Litho.　Perf. 13½x14

770	A251	80c lil & multi	.35	.25
770A	A251	1s multi	.35	.25
		Nos. 770-770A,C453-C454 (4)	1.45	1.00

First anniversary of the administration of Pres. Otto Arosemena Gomez.

Lions Emblem — A252

1968, May 24　Litho.　Perf. 13½x14

771	A252	80c multi	.35	.25
771A	A252	1.30s multi	.35	.25
771B	A252	2s pink & multi	.40	.25
c.		Souvenir sheet of 1	4.75	4.75
		Nos. 771-771B (3)	1.10	.75

50th anniv. (in 1967) of Lions Intl.
No. 771c contains one 5s 39x49mm stamp. Exists imperf. Value same as perf.

Pope Paul VI, Visit to Latin America A252a

39th Intl. Eucharistic Congress, Bogota, Colombia A252b

60c, Pope Paul VI, vert. 1s, Madonna by Botticelli. 1.30s, Pope Paul VI with flags of South American nations. 2s, Madonna and Child by Durer.

1969   Perf. 13½x14, 14x13½

772	A252a	40c multicolored	.35	.25
772A	A252a	60c multicolored	.45	.25
772B	A252b	1s multicolored	1.25	.30
772C	A252b	1.30s multicolored	.90	.40
e.		Souv. sheet of 3, #772, 772A, 772C, imperf.	4.00	2.50
772D	A252b	2s multicolored	1.90	.75
f.		Souv. sheet of 2, #772B, 772D, imperf.	4.75	2.50
		Nos. 772-772D (5)	4.85	1.95

Nos. 772C-772D are airmail. Nos. 772-772f overprinted in silver with the national coat of arms.

Madonna with the Angel by Rogier van der Weyden — A252c

Paintings by various artists showing the life of the Virgin Mary: 40c, Annunciation of the Lord, by van der Weyden. 60c, Presentation of the Lord, by van der Weyden. 1s, Holy Family, by Raphael. 1.30s, Adoration of the Shepherds, by Bonifazio Veronese. 2s, Adoration of the Magi, by van der Weyden

1969   Perf. 14x13½, 13½x14

773	A252c	40c shown	.25	.25
773A	A252c	60c multi	.25	.25
773B	A252c	1s multi	.35	.25
773C	A252c	1.30s multi	1.25	.65
e.		Souv. sheet of 2, #773B-773C, imperf.	6.25	2.50
773D	A252c	2s multi	2.00	.80
f.		Souv. sheet of 3, #773-773A, 773D, imperf.	6.25	2.50
		Nos. 773-773D (5)	4.10	2.20

Nos. 773-773Df overprinted in silver with the national coat of arms. Sizing of No. 773Df stamps, side stamps are 25mm x 50mm; center stamp is 54.5mm x 50mm. Nos. 773C-773D are airmail.

Nos. C331 and C326 Surcharged in Violet and Dark Blue

a

b

1969, Jan. 10   Perf. 11½, 14x13½

774	AP79 (a)	40c on 1.30s (V)	.60	.25
774A	AP76 (b)	50c on 1.30s (DBl)	.60	.25

Types of 1958

No. 775 & 775B Srchd. and Ovptd. in Plum and Black	No. 775A Srchd. and Ovptd. in Plum and Black

No. 775C Overprinted in Red & Black

Design: Ignacio Luis Arcaya, Foreign Minister of Venezuela.

1969, Mar.   Litho.   Perf. 12
Flags in Red, Blue and Yellow

775	A223	50c on 2s sepia	.35	.25
775A	A223	80c on 2s sepia	.35	.25
775B	A223	1s on 2s sepia	.35	.25
775C	A223	2s sepia	.35	.25
		Nos. 775-775C,C455-C457 (7)	3.05	1.75

Nos. 775-775C were not issued without overprint. The obliteration of old denomination on No. 775A is a small square around a star. Overprint is plum, except for the black small coat of arms on right flag.

Map of Ecuador and Oriental Region — A253

Surcharge typographed in Dark Blue, Red Brown, Black or Lilac

1969   Litho.   Perf. 14

776	A253	20c on 30c (DBl)	.40	.25
776A	A253	40c on 30c (RBr)	.40	.25
777	A253	50c on 30c (DBl)	.40	.25
778	A253	60c on 30c (DBl)	.40	.25
778A	A253	60c on 30c (Bk)	.45	.40
778B	A253	80c on 30c (DBl)	—	20.00
779	A253	80c on 30c (Bk)	.40	.25
780	A253	1s on 30c (L)	.40	.25
780A	A253	1s on 30c (DBl)	1.35	.80
781	A253	1.30s on 30c (Bk)	.60	.25
782	A253	1.50s on 30c (Bk)	.60	.25
783	A253	2s on 30c (DBl)	.75	.25
784	A253	3s on 30c (Bk)	.85	.25
784A	A253	4s on 30c (DBl)	2.40	2.00
785	A253	4s on 30c (Bk)	.90	.25
786	A253	5s on 30c (Bk)	1.20	.35
		Nos. 776-786 (16)	11.50	26.30

Not issued without surcharge.

M. L. King, John and Robert Kennedy — A254

1969-70   Typo.   Perf. 12½

787	A254	4s blk, bl, grn & buff	.65	.25
		Perf. 13½		
788	A254	4s blk, lt bl & grn ('70)	.65	.25

In memory of John F. Kennedy, Robert F. Kennedy and Martin Luther King, Jr.

Thecla Coronata — A255

Butterflies: 20c, Papilio zabreus. 30c, Heliconius chestertoni. 40c, Papilio pausanias. 50c, Pereute leucodrosime. 60c, Metamorpha dido. 80c, Morpho cypris. 1s, Catagramma astarte.

1970   Litho.   Perf. 12½

789	A255	10c buff & multi	3.25	.45
790	A255	20c lt grn & multi	3.25	.45
791	A255	30c lt blu & multi	3.25	.25
792	A255	40c lt bl & multi	3.25	.25
793	A255	50c gold & multi	3.25	.25
794	A255	60c salmon & multi	3.25	.25
795	A255	80c silver & multi	3.25	.25
796	A255	1s lt grn & multi	3.25	.25

Same, White Background
Perf. 13½

797	A255	10c multi	3.25	.45
798	A255	20c multi	3.25	.45
799	A255	30c multi	3.25	.45
800	A255	40c multi	3.25	.25
801	A255	50c multi	3.25	.25
802	A255	60c multi	3.25	.25
803	A255	80c multi	3.25	.25
804	A255	1s multi	3.25	.25
		Nos. 789-804,C461-C464 (20)	66.00	6.20

Surcharged Revenue Stamps — A256

1970, June 16   Litho.   Perf. 14
Red Surcharge

805	A256	1s on 1s light blue	.30	.25
806	A256	1.30s on 1s light blue	.30	.25
807	A256	1.50s on 1s light blue	.35	.30
808	A256	2s on 1s light blue	.40	.25
809	A256	5s on 1s light blue	.80	.30
810	A256	10s on 1s light blue	1.60	.55
		Nos. 805-810 (6)	3.75	1.90

Surcharged Revenue Stamps — A257

1970   Typo.   Perf. 12
Black Surcharge

811	A257	60c on 1s violet	.35	.25
812	A257	80c on 1s violet	.35	.25
813	A257	1s on 1s violet	.35	.25
814	A257	1.10s on 1s violet	.35	.25
815	A257	1.30s on 1s violet	.35	.25
816	A257	1.50s on 1s violet	.40	.25
817	A257	2s on 1s violet	.40	.25
818	A257	2.20s on 1s violet	.45	.25
819	A257	3s on 1s violet	.55	.25
		Nos. 811-819 (9)	3.55	2.25

1970

820	A257	1.10s on 2s green	.35	.25
821	A257	1.30s on 2s green	.35	.25
822	A257	1.50s on 2s green	.40	.25
823	A257	2s on 2s green	.40	.25
824	A257	3.40s on 2s green	.60	.25
825	A257	5s on 2s green	.90	.25
826	A257	10s on 2s green	1.40	.25
827	A257	20s on 2s green	2.40	.70
828	A257	50s on 2s green	6.00	2.25
		Nos. 820-828 (9)	12.80	4.70

1970

829	A257	3s on 5s blue	.60	.25
830	A257	5s on 5s blue	.70	.35
831	A257	10s on 40s orange	1.35	.65
		Nos. 829-831 (3)	2.65	1.25

In the surcharge applied to Nos. 811-831, the word "POSTAL" is not locked into horizontal and vertical position relative to the "1970". On some stamps the "P" is directly below the numeral "1", on others the "O" is below the "1". The top of "POSTAL" can vary from 1mm-8mm from the bottom of the date.

Arms of Zamora Chinchipe — A258

Design: 1s, Arms and flag of Esmeraldas.

1971   Litho.   Perf. 10½

832	A258	50c pale yel & multi	.30	.25
833	A258	1s sal & multi	.30	.25
		Nos. 832-833,C465-C469 (7)	3.90	2.00

Flags of Ecuador and Chile — A259

1971, Sept.   Perf. 12½

840	A259	1.30s blk & multi	.30	.25
		Nos. 840,C481-C482 (3)	.90	.75

Visit of Pres. Salvador Allende of Chile, Aug. 24.

Ismael Pérez Pazmiño — A260

1971, Sept. 16   Perf. 12x11½

841	A260	1s grn & multi	.35	.25
		Nos. 841,C485-C486 (3)	1.15	.75

"El Universo," newspaper founded by Ismael Pérez Pazmiño, 50th anniv.

CARE Package — A261

1971-72   Perf. 12½

842	A261	30c lilac ('72)	.35	.25
843	A261	40c emerald ('72)	.35	.25
844	A261	50c blue	.35	.25
845	A261	60c carmine	.35	.25
846	A261	80c lt brn ('72)	.35	.25
		Nos. 842-846 (5)	1.75	1.25

25th anniversary of CARE, a US-Canadian Cooperative for American Relief Everywhere.

Flags of Ecuador and Argentina — A262

1972   Perf. 11½

847	A262	1s blk & multi	.30	.25
		Nos. 847,C491-C492 (3)	1.20	.80

Visit of Lt. Gen. Alejandro Agustin Lanusse, president of Argentina, Jan. 25.

Jesus Giving Keys to St. Peter, by Miguel de Santiago — A263

Ecuadorian Paintings: 1.10s, Virgin of Mercy, Quito School. 2s, Virgin Mary, by Manuel Samaniego.

1972, Apr. 24   Litho.   Perf. 14x13½

848	A263	50c black & multi	.30	.25
849	A263	1.10s black & multi	.40	.30
850	A263	2s black & multi	.60	.50
a.		Souvenir sheet of 3	2.50	2.50
		Nos. 848-850,C494-C495 (5)	2.90	1.95

No. 850a contains 3 imperf. stamps similar to Nos. 848-850.

1972, May 4

Ecuadorian Statues: 50c, Our Lady of Sorrow, by Caspicara. 1.10s, Nativity, Quito School, horiz. 2s, Virgin of Quito, anonymous.

851	A263	50c blk & multi	.35	.25
852	A263	1.10s blk & multi	.45	.25
853	A263	2s blk & multi	.60	.50
a.		Souv. sheet of 3	2.90	2.40
		Nos. 851-853,C496-C497 (5)	3.05	2.00

Letters of "Ecuador" 3mm high on Nos. 851-853, 7mm high on Nos. 848-850. No. 853a contains 3 imperf. stamps similar to Nos. 851-853.

A264

Designs: 30c, Gen. Juan Ignacio Pareja. 40c, Juan José Flores. 50c, Leon de Febres Cordero. 60c, Ignacio Torres. 70c, Francisco de Paula Santander. 1s, José M. Cordova.

1972, May 24   Perf. 12½

854	A264	30c blue & multi	.35	.25
855	A264	40c blue & multi	.35	.25
856	A264	50c blue & multi	.35	.25
857	A264	60c blue & multi	.35	.25

ECUADOR

858	A264	70c blue & multi	.35	.25
859	A264	1s blue & multi	.35	.25

Nos. 854-859,C498-C503 (12) 7.50 4.10

Sesquicentennial of the Battle of Pichincha and the liberation of Quito.

A265

Designs: 2s, Woman Wearing Poncho. 3s, Striped poncho. 5s, Embroidered poncho. 10s, Metal vase.

1972, July   Photo.   Perf. 13

860	A265	2s multicolored	.35	.25
861	A265	3s multicolored	.60	.25
862	A265	5s multicolored	.75	.40
863	A265	10s dp blue & multi	1.75	.90
a.		Souvenir sheet of 4	4.00	4.00

Nos. 860-863,C504-C507 (8) 6.95 3.60

Handicraft of Ecuador. No. 863a contains 4 imperf. stamps similar to Nos. 860-863.

Sucre Statue, Santo Domingo — A266

1.80s, San Agustin Convent. 2.30s, Plaza de la Independencia. 2.50s, Bolivar statue, La Alameda. 4.75s, Chapel door.

1972, Dec. 6   Litho.   Perf. 11½

864	A266	1.20s yel & multi	.40	.25
865	A266	1.80s yel & multi	.40	.25
866	A266	2.30s yel & multi	.45	.25
867	A266	2.50s yel & multi	.60	.25
868	A266	4.75s yel & multi	.90	.30

Nos. 864-868,C518-C524 (12) 8.85 3.95

Sesquicentennial of the Battle of Pichincha.

Radar Station — A267

1973, Apr. 5   Wmk. 367

| 869 | A267 | 1s multicolored | .40 | .25 |

Inauguration of earth telecommunications station, Oct. 19, 1972.

Blue-footed Boobies — A268

Designs: 40c, Blue-faced booby. 50c, Oyster-catcher. 60c, California sea lions. 70c, Galapagos giant tortoise. 1s, California sea lion.

Wmk. 367, Unwmkd. (#872)

1973   Litho.   Perf. 11½x12

870	A268	30c shown	.55	.30
871	A268	40c multicolored	.55	.30
872	A268	50c multicolored	.55	.30
873	A268	60c multicolored	1.10	.30
874	A268	70c multicolored	1.25	.30
875	A268	1s multicolored	1.75	.90

Nos. 870-875,C527-C528 (8) 9.95 2.40

Elevation of Galapagos Islands to a province of Ecuador.
Issue dates: 50c, Oct. 3; others Aug. 16.

Black-chinned Mountain Tanager — A269

Birds of Ecuador: 2s, Moriche oriole. 3s, Toucan barbet, vert. 5s, Masked crimson tanager, vert. 10s, Blue-necked tanager, vert.

Perf. 11x11½, 11½x11

1973, Dec. 6   Litho.   Unwmk.

876	A269	1s brick red & multi	.65	.25
877	A269	2s lt blue & multi	1.10	.25
878	A269	3s lt green & multi	1.10	.25
879	A269	5s pale lilac & multi	2.40	.65
880	A269	10s pale yel grn & multi	4.75	1.40

Nos. 876-880 (5) 10.00 2.80

Two souvenir sheets exist: one contains 2 imperf. stamps similar to Nos. 876-877 with yellow margin and black inscription; the other 3 stamps similar to Nos. 878-880; gray margin and black inscription including "Aereo." Both sheets dated "1972." Size: 143x84mm. Value, each $9.50.

Marco T. Varea, Botanist — A270

Portraits: 60c, Pio Jaramillo Alvarado, writer. 70c, Prof. Luciano Andrade M. No. 883, Marco T. Varea, botanist. No. 884, Dr. Juan Modesto Carbo Noboa, medical researcher. No. 885, Alfredo J. Valenzuela. No. 886, Capt. Edmundo Chiriboga G. 1.20s, Francisco Campos R., scientist. 1.80s, Luis Vernaza Lazarte, philanthropist.

1974   Unwmk.   Perf. 12x11½

881	A270	60c crimson rose	.40	.25
882	A270	70c lilac	.40	.25
883	A270	1s ultra	.30	.25
884	A270	1s orange	.30	.25
885	A270	1s emerald	.30	.25
886	A270	1s brown	.30	.25
887	A270	1.20s apple green	.40	.25
889	A270	1.80s lt blue	.50	.25

Nos. 881-889 (8) 2.90 2.00

Arcade — A271

Designs: 30c, Monastery, entrance. 40c, Church. 50c, View of Church through gate, vert. 60c, Chapel, vert. 70c, Church and cemetery, vert.

Perf. 11½x12, 12x11½

1975, Feb. 4   Litho.

896	A271	20c yellow & multi	.35	.25
897	A271	30c yellow & multi	.35	.25
898	A271	40c yellow & multi	.35	.25
899	A271	50c yellow & multi	.35	.25
900	A271	60c yellow & multi	.35	.25
901	A271	70c yellow & multi	.35	.25

Nos. 896-901 (6) 2.10 1.50

Colonial Monastery, Tilipulo, Cotopaxi Province.

Angel Polibio Chaves, Founder of Bolivar Province — A272

Portrait: No. 903, Emilio Estrada Ycaza (1916-1961), archeologist.

1975   Litho.   Perf. 12x11½

902	A272	80c violet bl & lt bl	.35	.25
903	A272	80c vermilion & pink	.35	.25

Issue dates: No. 902, 2/21; No. 903, 3/25.

R. Rodriguez Palacios and A. Duran Quintero — A273

1975, Apr. 1   Litho.   Perf. 12x11½

| 910 | A273 | 1s multicolored | .30 | .25 |

Nos. 910,C547-C548 (3) 1.00 .75

Meeting of the Ministers for Public Works of Ecuador and Colombia, July 27, 1973.

"Woman of Action" — A274

Design: No. 912, "Woman of Peace."

1975, June

911	A274	1s yellow & multi	.40	.25
912	A274	1s blue & multi	.50	.25

International Women's Year 1975.

Planes, Soldier and Ship — A275

1975, July 9   Perf. 11½x12

| 913 | A275 | 2s multicolored | .45 | .25 |

3 years of Natl. Revolutionary Government.

Hurdling — A276

Designs: Modern sports drawn Inca style.

1975, Sept. 11   Litho.   Perf. 11½

914	A276	20c shown	.55	.40
915	A276	20c Chess	.55	.40
916	A276	30c Basketball	.55	.40
917	A276	30c Boxing	.55	.40
918	A276	40c Bicycling	.55	.40
919	A276	40c Steeplechase	.55	.40
920	A276	50c Soccer	.55	.40
921	A276	50c Fencing	.55	.40
922	A276	60c Golf	.55	.40
923	A276	60c Vaulting	.55	.40
924	A276	70c Judo (standing)	.55	.40
925	A276	70c Wrestling	.55	.40
926	A276	80c Swimming	.55	.40
927	A276	80c Weight lifting	.55	.40
928	A276	1s Table Tennis	.55	.40
929	A276	1s Paddle ball	.55	.40

Nos. 914-929,C554-C558 (21) 12.50 7.90

3rd Ecuadorian Games.

Genciana — A277

Ecuadorian plants — 20c, Phragmipedium caudatum, vert. 40c, Bromeliaceae cactacceae, vert. 50c, Cochlioda vulcanica. 60c, Odontoglossum hallii. 80c, Pitahaya flowering cactus. 1s, Odontoglossum cirrhosum.

Perf. 12x11½, 11½x12

1975, Nov. 18   Litho.

930	A277	20c multicolored	.25	.25
931	A277	30c shown	.25	.25
932	A277	40c multicolored	.35	.35
933	A277	50c multicolored	.35	.35
934	A277	60c multicolored	.45	.40
935	A277	80c multicolored	.45	.40
936	A277	1s multicolored	.75	.50

Nos. 930-936,C559-C563 (12) 7.20 5.35

Venus, Chorrera Culture A278

Female Mask, Tolita Culture A279

Designs: 30c, Venus, Valdivia Culture. 40c, Seated man, Chorrera Culture. 50c, Man with poncho, Panzaleo Culture (late). 60c, Mythical head, Cashaloma Culture. 80c, Musician, Tolita Culture. No. 943, Chief Priest, Mantefia Culture. No. 945, Ornament, Tolita Culture. No. 946, Angry mask, Tolita Culture.

1976, Feb. 12   Litho.   Perf. 11½

937	A278	20c multicolored	.45	.30
938	A278	30c multicolored	.45	.30
939	A278	40c multicolored	.45	.30
940	A278	50c multicolored	.45	.30
941	A278	60c multicolored	.45	.30
942	A278	80c multicolored	.45	.30
943	A278	1s multicolored	.45	.30
944	A279	1s multicolored	.45	.30
945	A279	1s multicolored	.45	.30
946	A279	1s multicolored	.45	.30

Nos. 937-946,C568-C572 (15) 8.65 4.90

Archaeological artifacts.

Strawberries — A280

1976, Mar. 30

| 947 | A280 | 1s blue & multi | .45 | .30 |

Nos. 947,C573-C574 (3) 2.05 1.05

25th Flower and Fruit Festival, Ambato.

Carlos Amable Ortiz (1859-1937) — A281

No. 949, Sixto Maria Duran (1875-1947). No. 950, Segundo Cueva Celi (1901-1969). No. 951, Cristobal Ojeda Davila (1910-1952). No. 952, Luis Alberto Valencia (1918-1970).

1976, Mar. 15   Litho.   Perf. 11½

948	A281	1s ver & multi	.40	.25
949	A281	1s orange & multi	.40	.25
950	A281	1s lt green & multi	.40	.25
951	A281	1s blue & multi	.40	.25
952	A281	1s lt brn & multi	.40	.25

Nos. 948-952 (5) 2.00 1.25

Ecuadorian composers and musicians.

Institute Emblem — A282

1977, Aug. 15   Litho.   Perf. 11½x12

| 953 | A282 | 2s multicolored | .40 | .25 |

11th General Assembly of Pan-American Institute of Geography and History, Quito, Aug. 15-30. See Nos. C597-C597a.

Hands Holding Rotary Emblem — A283

1977, Aug. 31   Litho.   Perf. 12

954	A283	1s multicolored	.30	.25
955	A283	2s multicolored	.50	.25

Souvenir Sheets
Imperf

956	A283	5s multicolored	1.25	1.25
957	A283	10s multicolored	1.50	1.50

Rotary Club of Guayaquil, 50th anniv.

José Peralta — A284

Design: 2.40s, Peralta statue.

1977 Litho. Perf. 11½
958 A284 1.80s multi .35 .25
959 A284 2.40s multi .35 .25
Nos. 958-959,C609 (3) 1.25 .75

José Peralta (1855-1937), writer.

Blue-faced Booby — A285

Galapagos Birds: 1.80s, Red-footed booby. 2.40s, Blue-footed boobies. 3.40s, Gull. 4.40s, Galapagos hawk. 5.40s, Map of Galapagos Islands and boobies, vert.

Perf. 11½x12, 12x11½
1977, Nov. 29 Litho.
960 A285 1.20s multi .50 .25
961 A285 1.80s multi .70 .25
962 A285 2.40s multi 1.15 .25
963 A285 3.40s multi 1.60 .25
964 A285 4.40s multi 2.40 .30
965 A285 5.40s multi 3.25 .30
Nos. 960-965 (6) 9.60 1.60

Dr. Corral Moscoso Hospital, Cuenca — A286

1978, Apr. 12 Litho. Perf. 11½x12
966 A286 3s multicolored .30 .25
Nos. 966,C613-C614 (3) 2.15 1.00

Inauguration (in 1977) of Dr. Vicente Corral Moscoso Regional Hospital, Cuenca.

Surveyor Plane over Ecuador — A287

1978, Apr. 12 Litho. Perf. 11½
967 A287 6s multicolored .75 .35
Nos. 967,C619-C620 (3) 3.85 2.65

Military Geographical Institute, 50th anniv.

Latin-American Lions Emblem — A288

1978, May 24
968 A288 3s multi .60 .25
969 A288 4.20s multi .90 .25
Nos. 968-969,C621-C623 (5) 5.65 2.40

7th meeting of Latin American Lions, Jan. 25-29.

70th Anniversary Emblem — A289

1978, Sept. Litho. Perf. 11½
970 A289 4.20s gray & multi .70 .30

70th anniversary of Filanbanco (Philanthropic Bank). See No. C626.

Goalmouth and Net A290

Designs: 1.80s, "Gauchito" and Games emblem, vert. 4.40s, "Gauchito," vert.

1978, Nov. 1 Litho. Perf. 12
971 A290 1.20s multi .30 .25
972 A290 1.80s multi .30 .25
973 A290 4.40s multi .70 .25
Nos. 971-973,C627-C629 (6) 3.65 2.05

11th World Cup Soccer Championship, Argentina, June 1-25.

Symbols for Male and Female — A291

1979, Feb. 15 Litho. Perf. 12x11½
974 A291 3.40s multi .75 .30

Inter-American Women's Commission, 50th anniversary.

Emblem — A292

1979, June 21 Litho. Perf. 11½x12
975 A292 4.40s multi .45 .30
976 A292 5.40s multi .55 .30

Ecuadorian Mortgage Bank, 16th anniv.

Street Scene, Quito — A293

Perf. 12x11½
1979, Aug. 3 Litho. Unwmk.
977 A293 3.40s multi .35 .25
Nos. 977,C651-C653 (4) 8.00 3.70

Natl. heritage: Quito & Galapagos Islands.

Jose Joaquin de Olmedo (1780-1847), Physician — A294

1980, Apr. 29 Litho. Perf. 12x11½
978 A294 3s multi .35 .25
979 A294 5s multi .55 .40
Nos. 978-979,C662 (3) 2.15 1.30

First Pres. of Free State of Guayaquil, 1820.

Chief Enriquillo, Dominican Republic — A295

Indo-American Tribal Chiefs: 3.40s, Guaycaypuro, Venezuela. No. 982, Abayuba, Uruguay. No. 983, Atlacatl, Salvador.

Wmk. 367, Unwmkd. (#981-983)
1980, May 12
980 A295 3s multi .70 .35
981 A295 3.40s multi .90 .40
982 A295 5s multi 1.75 .55
983 A295 5s multi 1.75 .55
Nos. 980-983,C663-C678 (20) 46.35 11.75

King Juan Carlos and Queen Sofia, Visit to Ecuador — A296

Perf. 11½x12
1980, May 18 Unwmk.
984 A296 3.40s multi .55 .30
See No. C679.

Cofan Indian, Napo Province — A297

3.40s, Zuleta man, Imbabura. 5s, Chota woman, Imbabura.

1980, June 10 Litho. Perf. 12x11½
985 A297 3s shown .55 .25
986 A297 3.40s multicolored .55 .25
987 A297 5s multicolored .85 .30
Nos. 985-987,C681-C684 (7) 8.70 4.55

Basilica, Our Lady of Mercy Church, Quito — A298

1980, July 7 Litho. Perf. 11½
988 A298 3.40s shown .45 .25
989 A298 3.40s Balcony .45 .25
989A A298 3.40s Dome and cupolas .45 .25

Sizes: 91x116mm, 116x91mm
Imperf
990 A298 5s multi 1.75 1.60
990A A298 5s multi, horiz. 1.75 1.60
990B A298 5s multi 1.75 1.60
Nos. 988-990B,C685-C691 (13) 15.60 10.05

Virgin of Mercy, patron saint of Ecuadorian armed forces. No. 990 contains designs of Nos. C686, C685, 989. No. 990A contains designs of Nos. C688, C691, C690. No. 990B contains designs of Nos. C689, C687, 989A, 988.

Olympic Torch and Rings — A299

Perf. 12x11½
1980, July 19 Wmk. 395
991 A299 5s multi .70 .25
992 A299 7.60s multi .80 .30
Nos. 991-992,C695-C696 (4) 3.65 2.05

Souvenir Sheet
Imperf
993 A299 30s multi 7.00 6.75

22nd Summer Olympic Games, Moscow, July 19-Aug. 3.
No. 993 contains vignettes in designs of Nos. 991 and C695.

Coronation of Virgin of Cisne, 50th Anniv. — A300

1980 Litho. Perf. 11½
994 A300 1.20s shown .30 .25
995 A300 3.40s Different statue .60 .30

J.J. Olmedo, Father de Velasco, Flags of Ecuador and Riobamba, Constitution A301

1980, Sept. 20 Litho. Perf. 11½
996 A301 3.40s multi .30 .25
997 A301 5s multi .80 .40
Nos. 996-997,C700-C701 (4) 3.00 1.35

Souvenir Sheet
Imperf
998 A301 30s multi 6.00 3.00

Constitutional Assembly of Riobamba sesquicentennial. No. 998 contains vignettes in designs of #996-997.

Young Indian Girl — A302

Perf. 12x11½
1980, Oct. 9 Litho. Wmk. 395
999 A302 1.20s multi .25 .25
1000 A302 3.40s multi .55 .25
Nos. 999-1000,C703-C704 (4) 3.00 1.45

Democratic government, 1st anniversary.

OPEC Emblem — A303

1980, Nov. 8 Perf. 11½x12
1001 A303 3.40s multi .50 .25

20th anniversary of OPEC. See No. C706.

Decorative Hedges, Capitol Gardens, Carchi — A304

1980, Nov. 21 Perf. 13
1002 A304 3s multi .50 .25
Nos. 1002,C707-C708 (3) 3.95 1.55

Carchi province centennial.

Cattleya Maxima — A305

Orchids: 3s, Comparattia speciosa. 3.40s, Cattleya iricolor.

1980, Nov. 22 Perf. 11½x12
1003 A305 1.20s shown .75 .25
1004 A305 3s multicolored 1.00 .30
1005 A305 3.40s multicolored 1.10 .35
Nos. 1003-1005,C709-C712 (7) 21.60 5.20

Souvenir Sheet
Imperf
1006 A305 20s multi 14.00 10.00

No. 1006 contains vignettes in designs of Nos. 1003-1005.

Pope John Paul II and Children A306

1980, Dec. 27 Perf. 12
1007 A306 3.40s multi .60 .30
Nos. 1007,C715-C716 (3) 2.85 1.40

Christmas and visit of Pope John Paul II.

Carlos and Jorge Mantilla Ortega, Editors of El Comercio A307

El Comercio Newspaper, 75th Anniv.: 3.40s, Editors Cesar & Carlos Mantilla Jacome.

1981, Jan. 6
1008 A307 2s multi .40 .25
1009 A307 3.40s multi .65 .25

Soldier on Map of Ecuador — A308

1981, Mar. 10 Litho. Perf. 13
1010 A308 3.40s shown .30 .25
1011 A308 3.40s Pres. Roldos .30 .25
  a. Pair, #1010-1011 1.50 .90

National defense.

Theodore E. Gildred and Ecuador I — A309

1981, Mar. 31 Litho. Perf. 13
1012 A309 2s lt bl & blk .40 .25

Ecuador-US flight, 50th anniv.

A310

1981, Apr. 10
1013 A310 2s multi .80 .25

Octavio Cordero Palacios (1870-1930), humanist.

Radio Station HCJB, 50th Anniv. — A311

1981 Litho. Perf. 13
1014 A311 2s multi .30 .30
  Nos. 1014,C721-C722 (3) 3.30 1.85

Virgin of Dolorosa — A312

1981, Apr. 30 Litho. Perf. 12
1015 A312 2s shown .45 .25
1016 A312 2s San Gabriel College Church .45 .25

Miracle of the painting of the Virgin of Dolorosa at San Gabriel College, 75th anniv.

Dr. Rafael Mendoza Aviles Bridge Inauguration A313

1981, July 25 Perf. 13
1017 A313 2s multi .45 .25

Pablo Picasso (1881-1973), Painter — A313a

1981, Oct. 26 Litho. Imperf.
1017A A313a 20s multi 3.00 2.75
  Nos. 1017A,C728-C731 (5) 9.55 7.50

No. 1017A contains design of No. C728, additional portrait.

World Food Day — A314

1981, Dec. 31 Litho. Perf. 13½x13
1018 A314 5s multi .60 .25

See No. C732.

Transnave Shipping Co. 10th Anniv. — A315

1982, Jan. 21 Litho. Perf. 13
1019 A315 3.50s Freighter Isla Salango .70 .25

Intl. Year of the Disabled — A316

1982, Feb. 25
1020 A316 3.40s Man in wheel- chair .40 .25
  Nos. 1020,C733-C734 (3) 2.10 1.10

Arch — A317

1982, May Litho. Perf. 13
1021 A317 2s shown .45 .25
1022 A317 3s Houses .60 .25

Miniature Sheet
Perf. 12½ on 2 Sides
1023 Sheet of 4, 18th cent. map of Quito 4.50 3.50
  a.-d. A317 6s multi .90 .50

QUITEX '82, 4th Natl. Stamp Exhib., Quito, Apr. 16-22. No. 1023 contains 4 48x31mm stamps.

Juan Montalvo Birth Sesqui. — A318

1982 Perf. 13
1024 A318 2s Portrait .35 .25
1025 A318 3s Mausoleum .35 .25
  Nos. 1024-1025,C735 (3) 1.95 1.15

American Air Forces Cooperation System — A319

1982
1026 A319 5s Emblem .75 .35

4th World Swimming Champ., Guayaquil — A320

1982, July 30
1027 A320 1.80s Stadium .30 .25
1028 A320 3.40s Water polo .35 .25
  Nos. 1027-1028,C736-C737 (4) 2.85 1.55

A321

1982, Dec. Litho. Perf. 13
1029 A321 5.40s shown .45 .25
1030 A321 6s Statue .60 .25

Juan L. Mera (1832-?), Writer, by Victor Mideros.

A322

1983, Mar. 28 Litho. Perf. 13
1031 A322 2s multi .75 .25

St. Teresa of Jesus of Avila (1515-82).

Sea Lions A323

Flamingoes A324

1983, June 17 Litho. Perf. 13
1032 A323 3s multi 1.40 .25
1033 A324 5s multi 2.25 .25

Ecuadorian rule over Galapagos Islds., sesqui. (3s); Charles Darwin (1809-1882).

Pres. Rocafuerte A325

Simon Bolivar A326

Juan Montalvo Birth Sesqui. — A318

Perf. 13x13½
1983, Aug. 26 Litho. Wmk. 395
1034 A325 5s Statue .25 .25
1035 A325 20s Portrait .85 .35
1036 A326 20s Portrait .85 .35
  Nos. 1034-1036 (3) 1.95 .95

Vicente Rocafuerte Bejarano, president, 1833-39 (Nos. 1034-1035).

A327

1983, Sept. 3
1037 A327 5s River .80 .25
1038 A327 10s Dam 1.20 .85

Size: 110x89mm
Imperf
1039 A327 20s Dam, river 3.50 2.50
  Nos. 1037-1039 (3) 5.50 3.60

Paute hydroelectric plant opening. No. 1039 is airmail.

World Communication Year — A328

Wmk. 395
1983, Oct. 11 Litho. Perf. 13
1040 A328 2s multi .75 .30

World Communication Year.

A329

1983, Sept. Litho. Perf. 13
1041 A329 3s multi .75 .30

Cent. of Bolivar and El Oro Provinces (1984).

A330

1984, Mar. Litho. Perf. 13
1042 A330 15s Engraving .75 .45

Atahualpa (1497-1529), last Incan ruler.

A331

Christmas 1983 — A331a

Creche figures: No. 1043, Jesus & the teachers. No. 1044, Three kings. No. 1045, Holy Family. No. 1046, Priest.

Perf. 13½x13, 13x13½
1984, July 7 Litho.
1043 A331 5s multicolored .30 .25
1044 A331 5s multicolored .30 .25
1045 A331 5s multicolored .30 .25
1046 A331a 6s multicolored .30 .25
  Nos. 1043-1046 (4) 1.20 1.00

Foreign Policy of Pres. Hurtado — A332

State visits: 8s, Brazil. 9s, PRC. 24s, UN. 28s, USA. 29s, Venezuela. 37s, Latin American Economic Conf., Quito.

1984, July 10   **Perf. 13½x13**
1047	A332	8s multicolored	.40	.25
1048	A332	9s multicolored	.50	.25
1049	A332	24s multicolored	1.20	.75
1050	A332	28s multicolored	1.60	.80
1051	A332	29s multicolored	1.60	.80
1052	A332	37s multicolored	1.90	1.25
	Nos. 1047-1052 (6)		7.20	4.10

Miguel Diaz Cueva (1884-1942), Lawyer — A333

1984, Aug. 8   **Litho.**   **Perf. 13½x13**
1053	A333	10s multicolored	.90	.30

1984 Winter Olympics — A334

Designs: 2s, Emblem. 4s, Ice skating, right leg in air. 6s, Ice skating, left leg in air. 10s, Skiing. 20s, Figure skating.

Perf. 13x13½, 12x11½ (6s)
1984, Aug. 15
1054	A334	2s multi	.40	.25
1055	A334	4s multi	.40	.25
1056	A334	6s multi	.40	.25
1057	A334	10s multi	.70	.25
	Nos. 1054-1057 (4)		1.90	1.00

Size: 90x100mm
Imperf
1057A	A334	20s multi	40.00	17.50

No. 1057A is airmail.

Manned Flight Bicentenary — A335

3s, Montgolfier. 6s, Charlier's balloon, Paris, 1789. 20s, Graf Zeppelin, Montgolfier.

1984, Aug. 15   **Perf. 13x13½**
1058	A335	3s multicolored	.25	.25
1059	A335	6s multicolored	.50	.25

Souvenir Sheet
1060	A335	20s multi	2.50	1.50

No. 1060 is airmail and contains one imperf. stamp (50x37mm).

SAN MATEO '83, Esmeraldas A336

8s, La Marimba folk dance. 15s, La Marimba, 8 dancers in white.

1984   **Litho.**   **Perf. 13**
1061	A336	8s multi	1.75	.25

Size: 89x110mm
Imperf
1061A	A336	15s multi	2.25	1.50

No. 1061A is airmail.

Jose Maria de Jesus Yerovi (b. 1824), 4th Archbishop of Quito — A337

1984
1062	A337	5s multi	.75	.30

Canonization of Brother Miguel — A338

Designs: 9s, Academy of Languages. 24s, Vatican City, vert. 28s, Home of Brother Miguel.

1984   **Litho.**   **Perf. 13**
1063	A338	9s multi	.40	.25
1064	A338	24s multi	1.10	.60

Imperf
Size: 110x90mm
1065	A338	28s multi	3.50	1.50
	Nos. 1063-1065 (3)		5.00	2.35

No. 1065, airmail, has black control number.

State Visit of Pope John Paul II — A339

Designs: 1.60s, Papal arms. 5s, Blessing crowd. 9s, World map, itinerary. 28s, Pope waving. 29s, Portrait. 30s, Pope holding crosier.

1985, Jan. 23   **Litho.**   **Perf. 13x13½**
1066	A339	1.60s multi	1.00	.25
1067	A339	5s multi	1.00	.25
1068	A339	9s multi	1.00	.25
1069	A339	28s multi	2.50	.40
1070	A339	29s multi	3.00	.40

Size: 90x109mm
Imperf
1071	A339	30s multi	8.00	6.00
	Nos. 1066-1071 (6)		16.50	7.55

Beatification of Mercedes de Jesus Molina — A340

Paintings, sculpture: 1.60s, Portrait. 5s, Czestochowa Madonna. 9s, Alborada Madonna. 20s, Mercedes de Jesus, children.

1985, Jan. 23
1072	A340	1.60s multi	.35	.25
1073	A340	5s multi	.35	.25
1074	A340	9s multi	.60	.25

Size: 90x110mm
Imperf
1075	A340	20s multi	3.50	3.00
	Nos. 1072-1075 (4)		4.80	3.75

Visit of Pope John Paul II, birth bimillennium of the Virgin Mary.

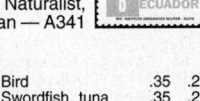

Samuel Valarezo Delgado, Naturalist, Politician — A341

1985, Feb.
1076	A341	2s Bird	.35	.25
1077	A341	3s Swordfish, tuna	.35	.25
1078	A341	6s Portrait	.60	.25
	Nos. 1076-1078 (3)		1.30	.75

ESPANA '84, Madrid — A342

Designs: 6s, Emblem. 10s, Spanish royal family. 15s, Retiro Park, exhibition site.

1985, Apr. 25   **Perf. 13½x13**
1079	A342	9s multi	.35	.25
1080	A342	10s multi	.60	.25

Size: 110x90mm
Imperf
1081	A342	15s multi	1.90	1.50

Dr. Pio Jaramillo Alvarado (1884-1968), Historian — A343

1985, May 17
1082	A343	6s multi	.75	.25

Ingenio Valdez Sugar Refinery A344

Designs: 50s, Sugar cane, emblem. 100s, Rafael Valdez Cervantes, founder.

1985, June   **Litho.**   **Perf. 13**
1082A	A344	50s multi	1.25	.50
1082B	A344	100s multi	2.75	1.00

Size: 110x90mm
Imperf
1083	A344	30s multi	1.50	1.50
	Nos. 1082A-1083 (3)		5.50	3.00

Chamber of Commerce, 10th Anniv. — A345

50s, Natl. and American Statues of Liberty.

1985, Aug. 15   **Perf. 13½x13**
1084	A345	24s multicolored	.95	.30
1085	A345	28s multicolored	1.05	.45

Size: 110x90mm
Imperf
1086	A345	50s multicolored	2.40	2.25
	Nos. 1084-1086 (3)		4.40	3.00

Natl. Philatelic Assoc., AFE, 50th Anniv. — A346

1985, Aug. 25   **Perf. 12**
1087	A346	25s AFE emblem	.85	.45
1088	A346	30s No. 357, horiz.	1.20	.50

Guayaquil Fire Dept., 150th Anniv. — A347

6s, Steam fire pump, 1882. 10s, Fire Wagon, 1899. 20s, Anniv. emblem, natl. flag.

1985, Oct. 10   **Perf. 13½x13**
1089	A347	6s multi	.45	.25
1090	A347	10s multi	.75	.25
1091	A347	20s multi	1.50	.75
	Nos. 1089-1091 (3)		2.70	1.25

Natl. Infant Survival Campaign — A348

1985, Oct.   **Perf. 13x13½**
1092	A348	10s Boy, girl, tree	.75	.30

1st Natl. Phil. Cong., Quito, Nov. 25-28 — A349

20th cent. illustrations, natl. cultural collection: 5s, Supreme Court, Quito, by J. M. Roura. 10s, Riobamba Cathedral, by O. Munaz. 15s, House of 100 Windows, by J. M. Roura, horiz. 20s, Rural cottage near Cuenca, by J. M. Roura.

No. 1097: a, Stampless cover, 1779, Riobamba. b, Hand press, 1864, Quito. c, Postrider, 1880, Cuenca. d, Monoplane, 1st airmail flight, 1919, Guayaquil.

1985, Nov.   **Perf. 13x13½, 13½x13**
1093	A349	5s multi	.25	.25
1094	A349	10s multi	.60	.25
1095	A349	15s multi	.70	.40
1096	A349	20s multi	1.00	.50
	Nos. 1093-1096 (4)		2.55	1.40

Souvenir Sheet
1097		Sheet of 4	1.25	1.25
a.-d.		A349 5s, any single	.25	.25

AFE, 50th anniv. No. 1097 contains 53x42mm stamps, perf. 13x12½ on 2 sides.

10th Bolivarian Games, Cuenca — A350

Designs: 10s, Boxing. 25s, Women's gymnastics. 30s, Discus.

1985, Nov.   **Perf. 13½x13**
1098	A350	10s multi	.45	.25
1099	A350	25s multi	.75	.30
1100	A350	30s multi	.90	.45
	Nos. 1098-1100 (3)		2.10	1.00

BAE Calderon, Navy Cent. — A351

Military anniv.: No. 1102, Fighter plane, Air Force 65th anniv. No. 1103, Army & paratroops emblems, Special Forces 30th anniv.

1985, Dec.   **Perf. 13½x13**
1101	A351	10s multi	.60	.30
1102	A351	10s multi	.60	.30
1103	A351	10s multi	.60	.30
	Nos. 1101-1103 (3)		1.80	.90

UN, 40th Anniv. — A352

1985, Oct.   **Litho.**   **Perf. 13**
1104	A352	10s UN flag	.55	.30
1105	A352	20s Natl. flag	.55	.30

Size: 110x90mm
Imperf
1106	A352	50s UN Building	1.60	1.50
	Nos. 1104-1106 (3)		2.70	2.10

No. 1106 is airmail.

Christmas — A353

Designs: 5s, Little girl riding donkey. 10s, Baked goods. 15s, Little boy riding donkey.

1985, Nov.
1107	A353	5s multicolored	.25	.25
1108	A353	10s multicolored	.50	.30
1109	A353	15s multicolored	.70	.50

Size: 90x110mm
Imperf
1110	A353	30s like 5s	2.00	1.50
		Nos. 1107-1110 (4)	3.45	2.55

Indigenous Flowers — A354

Designs: 24s, Embotrium grandiforum. 28s, Topobea sp. 29s, Befaria resinosa mutis.

1986, Feb.
1111	A354	24s multi	1.10	.30
1112	A354	28s multi	1.60	.30
1113	A354	29s multi	2.10	.40

Size: 110x90mm
Imperf
1114	A354	15s multi	7.00	3.50
		Nos. 1111-1114 (4)	11.80	4.50

No. 1114 contains designs of Nos. 1111, 1113, 1112; black control number.

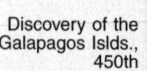

Discovery of the Galapagos Islds., 450th Anniv. — A355

Map of the Islands — A356

Designs: 10s, Land iguana. 20s, Sea lion. 30s, Frigate birds. 40s, Penguins. 50s, Giant tortoise. 100s, Charles Darwin. 200s, Bishop Tomas de Berlenga, discoverer.

1986, Feb. 12
1115	A355	10s multi	.55	.30
1116	A355	20s multi	1.10	.65
1117	A355	30s multi	1.75	1.10
1118	A355	40s multi	2.25	1.50
1119	A355	50s multi	2.75	1.75
1120	A355	100s multi	5.50	3.75
1121	A355	200s multi	11.00	7.00

Perf. 12½ on 2 Sides
1122	A356	Sheet of 4	13.00	13.00
a.-d.		50s, any single	1.75	1.75
		Nos. 1115-1122 (8)	37.90	29.05

No. 1122 contains 53x42mm stamps.

Inter-American Development Bank, 25th Anniv. — A357

5s, Antonio Ortiz Mena, pres. 1971-88. 10s, Felipe Herrera, pres. 1960-71. 50s, Emblem.

1986, Mar. 6
1123	A357	5s multicolored	.45	.25
1124	A357	10s multicolored	.65	.25
1125	A357	50s multicolored	1.25	.80
		Nos. 1123-1125 (3)	2.35	1.30

Guayaquil Tennis Club, 75th Anniv. — A358

Designs: No. 1126, Emblem. No. 1127, Francisco Segura Cano, vert. No. 1128, Andres Gomez Santos, vert.

1986, Mar. 7
1126	A358	10s multicolored	.60	.30
1127	A358	10s multicolored	.60	.30
1128	A358	10s multicolored	.60	.30
		Nos. 1126-1128 (3)	1.80	.90

1986 World Cup Soccer Championships, Mexico — A359

1986, May 5
1129	A359	5s Shot	.35	.25
1130	A359	10s Block	.80	.25

An imperf. stamp exists picturing flags, player and emblem. Value $9.50.

Meeting of Presidents Cordero and Betancourt of Colombia, Feb. 1985 — A360

1986   Litho.   Perf. 13½x13
1131	A360	20s Presidents	.60	.30
1132	A360	20s Embracing	.60	.30

Exports — A361

35s, No. 1137c, Shrimp. 40s, No. 1137b, Tuna. 45s, No. 1137a, Sardines. No. 1137d, MICIP emblem.

1986, Apr. 12
1133	A361	35s ultra & ver	1.10	.40
1134	A361	40s red & yel grn	1.10	.40
1135	A361	45s car & dk yel	1.25	.60

Perf. 12½ on 2 Sides
1137		Sheet of 4	2.75	2.50
a.-d.		A361 10s, any single	.40	.40
		Nos. 1133-1137 (4)	6.20	3.90

No. 1137 contains 4 53x42mm stamps.

A362

La Condamine's First Geodesic Mission, 250th Anniv. — A363

Designs: 10s, La Condamine. 15s, Maldonado. 20s, Middle of the World, Quito.
No. 1141a, Triangulation map for determining equatorial meridian, 1736. No. 1141b, Partial map of the Maranon & Amazon Rivers, by Samuel Fritz, 1743-1744. No. 1141c, Base of measurement, Yaruqui plains. No. 1141d, Caraburo & Dyambaru Pyramids near Quito. No. 1141 has a continuous design.

1986, July 10   Litho.   Perf. 13½x13
1138	A362	10s multicolored	.45	.25
1139	A362	15s multicolored	.55	.30
1140	A362	20s multicolored	.65	.30
		Nos. 1138-1140 (3)	1.65	.85

Souvenir Sheet
Perf. 12½ on 2 Sides
1141	A363	Sheet of 4	3.25	3.25
a.-d.		10s any single	.45	.45

Chambers of Commerce — A364

1986   Litho.   Perf. 13½x13
1142	A364	10s Pichincha	.45	.25
1143	A364	10s Cuenca	.45	.25
1144	A364	10s Guayaquil	.45	.25
		Nos. 1142-1144 (3)	1.35	.75

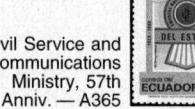

Civil Service and Communications Ministry, 57th Anniv. — A365

Organization emblems: 5s, State railway. 10s, Post office. 15s, Communications. 20s, Ministry of Public Works.

1986, Dec.   Litho.   Perf. 13x13½
1145	A365	5s multicolored	.25	.25
1146	A365	10s multicolored	.35	.25
1147	A365	15s multicolored	.65	.25
1148	A365	20s multicolored	.75	.55
		Nos. 1145-1148 (4)	2.00	1.30

A366

1987, Feb. 16   Litho.   Perf. 13x13½
1149	A366	5s multi	.65	.25

Chamber of Agriculture of the 1st Zone, 50th anniv.

Col. Luis Vargas Torres (d. 1887) — A367

Combat unit, c. 1885 — A367a

A367b

No. 1152a, Torres & his mother, Delfina. No. 1152b, Letter to Delfina written by Torres during imprisonment, 1882. No. 1152c, Arms of Ecuador & combat unit.

Litho. & Typo.
1988, Jan. 6   Perf. 13
1150	A367	50s yel grn, blk & gold	1.25	.80
1151	A367a	100s ver, gold & ultra	2.75	1.40

Size: 95x140mm
Perf. 12 on One or Two Sides
1152	A367b	Block of 3	7.50	7.50
a.-c.		100s any single	1.50	1.50
		Nos. 1150-1152 (3)	11.50	9.70

Sizes: Nos. 1152a, 1152c, 95x28mm, No. 1152b, 95x83mm.

Founding of Guayaquil, 450th Anniv. — A368

15s, Street in Las Penas. 30s, Rafael Mendoza Aviles Bridge. 40s, Francisco de Orellana (c. 1490-1546), Spanish explorer, founder, & reenactment of landing, 1538.

1988, Feb. 19   Litho.   Perf. 13
1153	A368	15s multi, vert.	.35	.25
1154	A368	30s multi	.60	.25
1155	A368	40s multi	.70	.25
		Nos. 1153-1155 (3)	1.65	.75

Social Security Foundation (IESS), 60th Anniv. — A369

1988, Mar. 11
1156	A369	50s shown	.90	.55
1157	A369	100s multi, diff.	1.90	1.10

Dr. Pedro Moncayo y Esparza (1807-1888), Author, Politician — A370

Designs: 10s, Yaguarcocha Lake. 20s, Residence. 100s, Full-length portrait.

1988, Apr. 28   Litho.   Perf. 14x13½
1158	A370	10s multicolored	.25	.25
1159	A370	15s shown	.35	.25
1160	A370	20s multicolored	.35	.25

Size: 89x110mm
Imperf
1161	A370	100s multi	1.60	1.50
		Nos. 1158-1161 (4)	2.55	2.25

A371

Avianca Airlines, 60th Anniv. — A372

10s, Junkers F-13. 20s, Dornier Wal seaplane. 30s, Ford 5AT trimotor. 40s, Boeing 247-D. 50s, Boeing 720-059B. 100s, Douglas DC-3. 200s, Boeing 727-200. 300s, Sikorsky S-38.

1988, May 12   Litho.   Perf. 14x13½
1162	A371	10s shown	.35	.25
1163	A371	20s multi	.35	.25
1164	A371	30s multi	.45	.25
1165	A371	40s multi	.55	.25
1166	A371	50s multi	.65	.45
1167	A371	100s multi	1.50	.60
1168	A371	200s multi	2.75	1.50
1169	A371	300s multi	4.75	2.00

Perf. 13½x14
1170	A372	500s shown	7.25	3.75
		Nos. 1162-1170 (9)	18.60	9.30

San Gabriel College, 125th Anniv. — A373

15s, Contemporary facility. 35s, College entrance, 19th cent.

1988, July 25   Litho.   Perf. 14x13½
1171 A373 15s multicolored   .35   .25
1172 A373 35s multicolored   .85   .30

A374

Military Geographical Institute, 60th Anniv. — A375

25s, Planetarium. 50s, Zeiss projector. 60s, Anniv. emblem. 500s, Creation, mural by E. Kingman.

1988, July 25   Perf. 12½ on 2 Sides
Size of No. 1173: 110x90mm
1173 A374 Block of 4   2.25   2.25
a.-d.   5s any single   .30   .30

Perf. 13½
1174 A375 25s multi   .55   .30
1175 A375 50s multi   1.00   .30
1176 A375 60s multi   1.25   .40
1177 A375 500s multi   7.75   3.75
   Nos. 1173-1177 (5)   12.80   7.00

In 1996 Nos. 1174, 1183, 1265 were surcharged 800s, 2600s, 400s respectively. Only a few sets were sold to the public. The balance were sold by postal employees at greatly inflated prices.

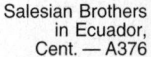

Salesian Brothers in Ecuador, Cent. — A376

Designs: 10s, St. John Bosco (1815-88), vert. 50s, 1st Salesian Cong. in Ecuador. 100s, Bosco, Salesian Brothers monument and Andes Mountains.

1988, July 29   Litho.   Perf. 13½
1178 A376 10s multi   .30   .25
1179 A376 50s multi   1.05   .40

Size: 89x110mm
Imperf
1180 A376 100s multi   2.60   1.60
   Nos. 1178-1180 (3)   3.95   2.25

Francisco Coello, Founder — A377

Social Services Council, Guayaquil, Cent. — A378

Designs: 20s, Eduardo Arosemena, 1st Director. 45s, Emblem.
No. 1184: a, Flag: a, Emblem (upper left portion). b, Emblem (upper right portion). c, Emblem (lower left portion) and "100 ANOS." d, Emblem (lower right portion) and "DE TRADICION DE FE, AMPARO Y ESPERANZA."

1988, Nov. 24   Litho.   Perf. 13½x14
1181 A377 15s shown   .25   .25
1182 A377 20s multicolored   .35   .25
1183 A377 45s multicolored   .70   .25

Size: 110x90mm
Perf. 12½ on 2 Sides
1184 A378 Block of 4   1.75   1.75
a.-d.   10s any single   .25   .25
   Nos. 1181-1184 (4)   3.05   2.50

For surcharge see note following No. 1177.

A379

Azuay Bank, 75th Anniv. — A380

Perf. 14x13½, 13½x14
1989, Mar. 1   Litho.
1185 A379 20s shown   .40   .25
1186 A379 40s multi, vert.   .50   .25

Size: 90x110mm
Imperf
1187 A380 500s shown   11.00   2.75
   Nos. 1185-1187 (3)   11.90   3.25

1988 Summer Olympics, Seoul — A381

Character trademark demonstrating sports.

1989, Mar. 20   Perf. 13½x14
1188 A381 10s Running   .30   .25
1189 A381 20s Boxing   .30   .25
1190 A381 30s Cycling   .50   .25
1191 A381 40s Shooting   .50   .25
1192 A381 100s Diving   1.25   .65
1193 A381 200s Weight lifting   2.25   1.40
1194 A381 300s Tae kwon do   3.50   2.10

Size: 90x110mm
Imperf
1195 A381 200s Emblems   3.50   3.25
   Nos. 1188-1195 (8)   12.10   8.40

RUMINAHUI '88 — A382

Designs: 50s, Bird, by Joaquin Tinta, vert. 70s, Matriz Church, Sangolqui. 300s, Monument to Ruminahui in Sangolqui, Pichincha.

Perf. 14x13½, 13½x14
1989, May 2   Litho.   Wmk. 395
1196 A382 50s multi   .90   .30
1197 A382 70s multi   1.25   .45

Size: 90x111mm
Imperf
1198 A382 300s multi   6.75   2.10
   Nos. 1196-1198 (3)   8.90   2.85

Cantonization, 50th anniv.

Benjamin Carrion Mora, Educator — A383

50s, Portrait, vert. 70s, Loja landscape. 1000s, University. 200s, Portrait, diff.

Perf. 13½x14, 14x13½
1989, May 10   Litho.
1199 A383 50s multi   .45   .25
1200 A383 70s multi   .65   .25
1201 A383 1000s multi   10.50   5.25

Size: 110x90mm
Imperf
1202 A383 200s multi   2.00   2.00
   Nos. 1199-1202 (4)   13.60   7.75

2nd Intl. Art Biennial — A384

Prize-winning art: 40s, The Gilded Frame, by Myrna Baez. 70s, Paraguay III, by Carlos Colorabino, vert. 100s, Ordinance establishing the art exhibition. 180s, Modulation 892, by Julio Le Parc, vert.

Perf. 14x13½, 13½x14, Imperf. (100s)
1989, June 2   Litho.
Size of No. 1205: 110x90mm
1203 A384 40s multi   .55   .25
1204 A384 70s multi   1.10   .25
1205 A384 100s multi   2.25   .75
1206 A384 180s multi   1.75   .95
   Nos. 1203-1206 (4)   5.65   2.20

Guayaquil Chamber of Commerce, Cent. — A385

50s, Founder Ignacio Molestina, vert. 200s, Flags. 300s, Headquarters. 500s, Flags, diff.

Perf. 13½x14, 14x13½, Imperf. (No. 1208)
1989, June 20   Litho.
Size of No. 1208: 110x91mm
1207 A385 50s multi   .85   .35
1208 A385 200s multi   3.50   2.00
1209 A385 300s multi   2.50   2.25
1210 A385 500s multi   1.75   1.50
   Nos. 1207-1210 (4)   8.60   6.10

French Revolution, Bicent. — A386

20s, French natl. colors, anniv. emblem. 50s, Cathedral fresco. 100s, Rooster. 200s, Symbols of the revolution. 600s, Story board showing events of the revolution.

1989, July 11   Perf. 13½x14, 14x13½
1211 A386 20s multi, vert.   .25   .25
1212 A386 50s multi   .55   .25
1213 A386 100s multi, vert.   .90   .45

Size: 90x110mm
Imperf
1214 A386 200s multi, vert.   1.75   1.75
1215 A386 600s multi, vert.   6.75   6.75
   Nos. 1211-1215 (5)   10.20   9.45

Ministry of Public Works and Communications — A388

No. 1216a, MOP emblem, 2-lane roadway. No. 1216b, State railway emblem, train. No. 1216c, Postal service emblem, airmail cover. No. 1216d, Telecommunications (IETEL) emblem, wall telephone. No. 1217, MOP, IETEL, postal service & state railway emblems. 100s, IETEL emblem. 200s, MOP emblem.

1989, July 7   Perf. 12½ on 2 Sides
1216 A387 Block of 4   2.00   2.00
a.-d.   50s any single   .40   .40

Perf. 13½x14
1217 A388 50s shown   .45   .25
1218 A388 100s multi   .90   .55
1219 A388 200s multi   1.90   1.10
   Nos. 1216-1219 (4)   5.25   3.90

MOP, 60th anniv.; national communications, 105th anniv. (No. 1216d, 100s).

A389

Designs: 10s, Medical volunteer, vert. 200s, Two volunteers.

1989, Sept. 14   Litho.   Perf. 13½
1220 A389 10s multi   .25   .25
1221 A389 30s shown   .25   .25
1222 A389 200s multi   2.00   .85
   Nos. 1220-1222 (3)   2.50   1.85

Natl. Red Cross, Intl. Red Cross and Red Crescent Societies, 125th Annivs.

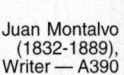

Juan Montalvo (1832-1889), Writer — A390

Designs: 50s, Mausoleum, Ambato. 100s, Portrait (detail). No. 1225, Monument, Ambato. No. 1226, Portrait.

1989, Nov. 11   Litho.   Perf. 14x13½
1223 A390 50s multi   .45   .25
1224 A390 100s multi   1.25   .65
1225 A390 200s multi   2.10   1.40

Size: 90x110mm
Imperf
1226 A390 200s multi   1.75   1.75
   Nos. 1223-1226 (4)   5.55   4.05

America Issue — A391

UPAE emblem and pre-Columbian pottery: 200s, La Tolita incensory, vert. 300s, Warrior (plate).

1990, Mar. 6   Litho.   Perf. 13½
1227 A391 200s multi   2.10   1.25
1228 A391 300s multi   3.25   2.00

Dated 1989.

Dr. Luis Carlos Jaramillo Leon, Founder — A392

No. 1233a, Dr. Leon. Nos. 1230, 1233b, Federico Malo Andrade, honorary president. 130s, No. 1233c, Roberto Crespo Toral, 1st president. 200s, Alfonso Jaramillo Leon, founder.

1990, Jan. 17   Litho.   Perf. 13½
1229 A392 100s shown   .90   .60
1230 A392 100s multicolored   .90   .60
1231 A392 130s multicolored   1.25   .75
1232 A392 200s multicolored   1.75   1.25

Size: 91x38mm
Perf. 12½ Horiz. on 1 or 2 sides
1233 A392 Block of 3   3.00   3.00
a.-c.   100s any single   .50   .50
   Nos. 1229-1233 (5)   7.80   6.20

Chamber of Commerce, 70th anniversary.

World Cup Soccer,
Italy — A393

Designs: No. 1235, Soccer player. No. 1236, Map of Italy, trophy. No. 1237, Player, flags. No. 1238, World Cup Trophy.

1990, July 12		**Litho.**	**Perf. 13½**	
1234	A393	100s shown	.60	.25
1235	A393	200s multi	1.25	.60
1236	A393	300s multi	1.90	.90

Imperf
Size: 110x90mm

1237	A393	200s multi	1.75	1.75

Size: 60x90mm

1238	A393	300s multi	2.50	2.50
	Nos. 1234-1238 (5)		8.00	6.00

Nos. 1235-1236, 1238 vert.

A394

Design: 200s, Church tower, book.

1990, June 12			**Perf. 13½**	
1239	A394	100s multi	.70	.25
1240	A394	200s multi	1.25	.60

College of St. Mariana, cent.

A395

Tourism: No. 100s, No. 1244c, Iguana. 200s, No. 1244b, La Compania Church, Quito. 300s, No. 1244a, Old man from Vilcabamba. No. 1244d, Locomotive.

1990, Sept. 7		**Litho.**	**Perf. 13½**	
1241	A395	100s multi	.85	.25
1242	A395	200s multi, vert.	1.75	.55
1243	A395	300s multi	2.50	.75

Size: 111x90mm
Perf. 12½ on 2 sides

1244		Block of 4	7.50	3.25
a.-d.	A395	100s any single	.35	.30
	Nos. 1241-1244 (4)		12.60	4.80

A396

National Census: 100s, No. 1248a, People and house. 200s, No. 1248b, Map. 300s, No. 1248c, Census breakdown, pencil.

1990, Sept. 1			**Perf. 13½**	
1245	A396	100s multicolored	.60	.25
1246	A396	200s multi, horiz.	1.25	.55
1247	A396	300s multicolored	1.75	.75

Size: 109x88mm
Perf. 12½ on 2 sides

1248		Block of 3	1.90	1.90
a.-c.	A396	100s any single	.30	.30
	Nos. 1245-1248 (4)		5.50	3.45

A397

1990, Nov. 2		**Litho.**	**Perf. 14**	
1249	A397	200s Flags	2.25	.55
1250	A397	300s shown	2.90	.75

Organization of Petroleum Exporting Countries (OPEC), 30th anniv.

A398

Designs: No. 1251, Emblem. No. 1252, Four wooden parrots. No. 1253, Wooden parrots, diff.

1990, Oct. 31			**Perf. 13½x14**	
1251	A398	200s multi	1.25	.55
1252	A398	300s multi	1.90	.75

Size: 92x110mm
Imperf

1253	A398	200s multi	2.10	2.10
	Nos. 1251-1253 (3)		5.25	3.40

Artisans' Organization, 25th anniv.

Flowers — A399

Wmk. 395

1990, Nov. 12		**Litho.**	**Perf. 13½**	
1254	A399	100s Sobralia	1.25	.25
1255	A399	100s Blakea, vert.	1.25	.25
1256	A399	100s Cattleya, vert.	1.25	.25
1257	A399	100s Loasa, vert.	1.25	.25
	Nos. 1254-1257 (4)		5.00	1.00

Discovery of
America, 500th
Anniv. (in
1992) — A400

Designs: 100s, Ancient dwelling. 200s, Mangrove swamp.

1990, Dec. 31		**Litho.**	**Perf. 13½**	
1258	A400	100s multi	.70	.25
1259	A400	200s multi	1.60	.35

Natl. Union of
Journalists, 50th
Anniv. — A401

Designs: 300s, Eugenio Espejo, writer. 400s, Union emblem.

1991, Feb. 28				
1260	A401	200s shown	1.10	.70
1261	A401	300s multicolored	1.75	.80
1262	A401	400s multicolored	1.90	1.10
	Nos. 1260-1262 (3)		4.75	2.60

Radio Quito, 50th
Anniv. — A402

Designs: 200s, Man with microphone, vert. 500s, Family listening to radio.

1991, Apr. 10				
1263	A402	200s multicolored	.85	.35
1264	A402	500s multicolored	1.75	.95

Dr. Pablo A. Suarez,
Birth Cent. — A403

1991, Sept. 16		**Wmk. 395**		
1265	A403	70s multicolored	.75	.25

Dated 1990.
For surcharge see note following No. 1177. Value $20.

America
Issue — A404

UPAEP emblem and: 200s, Columbus' ships. 500s, Columbus, landing in America.

1991, Oct. 18		**Litho.**	**Perf. 13½x13**	
1266	A404	200s multicolored	1.25	.65
1267	A404	500s multicolored	2.25	1.25

Cultural Artifacts — A405

Designs: 100s, Cat censer. 200s, Statue of old man's head. 300s, Zoomorphic statue.

Wmk. 395

1991, Nov. 14		**Litho.**	**Perf. 13½**	
1268	A405	100s multi	.55	.25
1269	A405	200s multi	1.05	.35
1270	A405	300s multi	1.90	.60
	Nos. 1268-1270 (3)		3.50	1.20

Dated 1990. See No. 1291.

A406

Design: 500s, Woman in profile.

1991			**Perf. 13**	
1271	A406	300s shown	1.10	.55
1272	A406	500s multicolored	2.00	1.00

Day of Non-violence Toward Women.

Jacinto Jijon y
Caamano,
Archaeologist, Birth
Cent. — A407

1991, Dec. 11			**Perf. 13½**	
1273	A407	200s Portrait, vert.	.80	.35
1274	A407	300s shown	1.20	.55

Pres. Rodrigo Borja, Ecuador and
Pres. Jaime Paz Zamora, Bolivia
A408

1991, Dec. 10			**Perf. 14x13½**	
1275	A408	500s multicolored	2.00	1.00

Pres.
Rodrigo
Borja's
Visit to the
UN
A409

Designs: 1000s, Flags, world map.

		Wmk. 395		
1992, Jan. 24		**Litho.**	**Perf. 14**	
1276	A409	100s multicolored	.40	.25
1277	A409	1000s multicolored	3.00	1.60

Battle of
Jambeli,
50th Anniv.
A410

No. 1278, Gunboat Calderon and Capt. Raphael Moran Valverde. No. 1279, Dispatch boat Atahualpa and Ens. Victor Naranjo Fiallo. No. 1280, Valverde, Fiallo and ships.

1992, Apr. 7				
1278	A410	300s multicolored	.65	.40
1279	A410	500s multicolored	1.35	.90

Size: 110x90mm
Imperf

1280	A410	500s multicolored	3.00	2.40
	Nos. 1278-1280 (3)		5.00	3.70

Galapagos Islands
Wildlife — A411

Designs: No. 1281, Giant tortoise. No. 1282, Galapagos penguin, vert. No. 1283, Zalophus californianus, vert. No. 1284, Swallow-tailed gull. No. 1285, Fregata minor. No. 1286, Land iguana.

1992, Apr. 9		**Litho.**	**Perf. 13½**	
1281	A411	100s multicolored	1.75	.80
1282	A411	100s multicolored	1.75	.80
1283	A411	100s multicolored	1.75	.80
1284	A411	100s multicolored	1.75	.80
1285	A411	100s multicolored	1.75	.80
1286	A411	100s multicolored	1.75	.80
	Nos. 1281-1286 (6)		10.50	4.80

Vicente Rocafuerte
National College,
150th Anniv. (in
1991) — A412

Designs: 400s, Vicente Rocafuerte.

Perf. 14x13½

1992, Apr. 29		**Litho.**	**Wmk. 395**	
1287	A412	200s shown	.85	.35
1288	A412	400s multicolored	1.40	.65

Eloy Alfaro (1842-1912),
President — A413

Designs: 300s, Portrait, vert.

Perf. 13½x14, 14x13½

1992, Aug. 26		**Litho.**	**Wmk. 395**	
1289	A413	300s multicolored	.90	.70
1290	A413	700s multicolored	1.60	1.00

Cultural Artifacts Type of 1991

Designs: 400s, Ceremonial mask.

1992, Sept. 6		**Litho.**	**Perf. 13½**	
1291	A405	400s multi	1.60	.75

Dated 1990.

Discovery of
America, 500th
Anniv. — A414

Designs: 200s, Sailing ship. 400s, Columbus, map, vert.

Wmk. 395

1992, Oct. 15		**Litho.**	**Perf. 13½**	
1292	A414	200s multi	.75	.50
1293	A414	400s multi	1.40	.85

Andres F. Cordova
(b. 1892) — A415

1992, Nov. 17		**Litho.**	**Perf. 13½**	
1294	A415	300s multicolored	1.20	.60

Beatification of Narcisa of Jesus — A416

1992, Nov. 30   *Perf. 13½*
1295 A416 100s multicolored   .75 .30

A417

Christmas: 300s, Infant Jesus of Saqueo, 18th cent. 600s, Stable scene, Infant Jesus asleep on hay.

1992, Dec. 14   *Perf. 13½*
1296 A417 300s multicolored   1.20 .60
1297 A417 600s multicolored   2.00 1.25

A418

1992, Dec. 29
1298 A418 200s multicolored   1.05 .45

Father Juan de Velasco, Death Bicent.

Frogs — A419

No. 1299, Agalychnis spurelli. No. 1300, Atelopus bomolochos. No. 1301, Gastrotheca plumbea. No. 1302, Hyla picturata. No. 1303, Dendrobates sp. No. 1304, Sphaenorhyncus lacteus.

     Perf. 13½x14
1993, Jan. 28   **Litho.**   **Wmk. 395**
1299 A419 300s multi   .75 .35
1300 A419 300s multi   .75 .35
1301 A419 600s multi   1.75 .90
1302 A419 600s multi   1.75 .90
1303 A419 900s multi   2.00 1.40
1304 A419 900s multi   2.00 1.40
    Nos. 1299-1304 (6)   9.00 5.30

A420

1993, Feb. 16   **Litho.**   *Perf. 13x13½*
1305 A420 300s blue   .80 .25

J. Roberto Paez, (1893-1983), co-founder of social security.

Francisco Robles (1811-93) — A421

1993, Mar. 16   *Perf. 13½x14*
1306 A421 500s No. 168   1.50 .55

National Police — A422

     Perf. 13½x14
1993, Mar. 25   **Litho.**   **Wmk. 395**
1307 A422 300s multicolored   1.00 .60

Pres. Jose Maria Velasco Ibarra (1893-1979) A423

     Perf. 14x13½
1993, Mar. 31   **Litho.**   **Wmk. 395**
1308 A423 500s multicolored   1.50 .55

Insects — A424

150s, Fulgora laternaria. 200s, Semiotus ligneus. 300s, Taeniotes pulverulenta. 400s, Danaus plexippus. 600s, Erotylus onagga. 700s, Xylocopa darwini.

     Wmk. 395
1993, May 27   **Litho.**   *Perf. 13½*
1309 A424 150s multi   .75 .25
1310 A424 200s multi   1.00 .25
1311 A424 300s multi   1.50 .45
1312 A424 400s multi   2.00 .60
1313 A424 600s multi   3.00 .95
1314 A424 700s multi   3.25 1.10
    Nos. 1309-1314 (6)   11.50 3.60

A425

     Wmk. 395
1993, May 31   **Litho.**   *Perf. 13½*
1315 A425 1000s multicolored   3.00 1.50

Pedro Fermin Cevallos Villacreces (1812-93), historian and founder of Academy of Language.

First Latin-American Children's Peace Assembly, Quito — A426

1993, June 7
1316 A426 300s multicolored   .95 .45

Juan Benigno Vela Hervas (1843-97), Jurist — A427

     Perf. 13x13½
1993, July 8   **Litho.**   **Wmk. 395**
1317 A427 2000s multicolored   4.50 3.00

Guillermo Bustamante, Birth Cent. — A428

1993, Sept. 23   *Perf. 13½*
1318 A428 1500s multicolored   3.75 1.75

University of Ecuador School of Medicine, 300th Anniv. — A429

     Perf. 14x13½
1993, Sept. 7   **Litho.**   **Wmk. 395**
1319 A429 300s multicolored   1.00 .45

Maldonado-La Condamine Amazon Expedition, 250th Anniv. — A430

Designs: 150s, Cinchona cordifolia. 200s, Pedro V. Maldonado, 1500s, Charles La Condamine (1701-74), explorer.

1993, Aug. 20
1320 A430 150s multicolored   .35 .25
1321 A430 200s multicolored   .50 .25
1322 A430 1500s multicolored   4.25 2.10
    Nos. 1320-1322 (3)   5.10 2.60

A431

     Wmk. 395
1993, Nov. 27   *Perf. 13*
1323 A431 500s multicolored   1.20 .55

Dr. Carlos A. Arroyo del Rio, birth cent.

Endangered Species — A432

400s, Dinomys branickii, horiz. 800s, Ara severa.

1993, Oct. 15   *Perf. 13½x13, 13x13½*
1324 A432 400s multicolored   1.90 .60
1325 A432 800s multicolored   2.75 1.25
     America issue.

Christmas — A433

600s, Holy Family, 18th cent. Tagua miniatures. 900s, Mother and child, vert.

     Wmk. 395
1993, Dec. 1   **Litho.**   *Perf. 13*
1326 A433 600s multicolored   1.40 .90
1327 A433 900s multicolored   2.25 1.40

Intl. Year of the Family — A434

     Wmk. 395
1994, Jan. 18   **Litho.**   *Perf. 13*
1328 A434 300s grn, blk & org   .60 .35

A435

1994, Jan. 25
1329 A435 500s multicolored   1.75 .90

Dr. Julio Tobar Donoso, birth cent.

Orchids — A436

No. 1330, Dracula hirtzii. No. 1331, Sobralia dichotoma. No. 1332, Encyclia pulcherrima. No. 1333, Lepanthes delhierroi. No. 1334, Masdevallia rosea. No. 1335, Telipogon andicola.

     Wmk. 395
1994, Feb. 7   **Litho.**   *Perf. 13½*
1330 A436 150s multicolored   .50 .25
1331 A436 150s multicolored   .50 .25
1332 A436 300s multicolored   1.00 .40
1333 A436 300s multicolored   1.00 .40
1334 A436 600s multicolored   2.00 .90
1335 A436 600s multicolored   2.00 .90
    Nos. 1330-1335 (6)   7.00 3.10

First Convention on the Conservation of Andean Orchids.

Federico Gonzalez Suarez (1844-1917) — A437

1994, Apr. 12   *Perf. 13*
1336 A437 200s multicolored   .75 .25

Scouting in Ecuador — A438

1994, Jan. 11
1337 A438 400s multicolored   1.25 .60

Dr. Miguel Egas Cabezas (1823-94) — A439

     Wmk. 395
1994, Mar. 10   **Litho.**   *Perf. 13*
1338 A439 100s multicolored   .75 .25

Father Aurelio Espinosa, Birth Cent. — A440

1994, July 12
1339 A440 200s multicolored   .70 .45

A441

Nos. 1341, 1343d, Mascot. 900s, Player.

No. 1343: a, Emblem. b, "COPA MUNDIAL FUTBOL '94," emblem. c, "COPA MUNDIAL, USA 94."

Wmk. 395
1994, June 10   **Litho.**   *Perf. 13*
1340 A441 300s shown   1.25   .60
1341 A441 600s Mascot   2.40 1.25
1342 A441 900s Soccer player   3.75 1.75

Perf. 12 on 2 Sides
1343 A441 600s Block of 4,
      #a.-d.   9.75 7.50
   Nos. 1340-1343 (4)   17.15 11.10

1994 World Cup Soccer Championships, US. No. 1343 contains two 50x25mm stamps, two 50x51mm stamps.

Ecuador in Antarctica — A442

1994, July 19   *Perf. 13*
1344 A442 600s Outpost   2.25 1.10
1345 A442 900s Ship, B/1 Orion   3.50 1.75

ILO, 75th Anniv. — A443

1994   **Litho.**   **Wmk. 395**   *Perf. 13*
1346 A443 100s multicolored   .50   .25

Ecuadorian Culture Center, 50th Anniv. — A444

700s, Benjamin Carrion, vert. 900s, Cultural center.

1994
1347 A444 700s multi   2.40 1.40
1348 A444 900s multi   3.50 1.60

Natl. Lottery, Cent. — A445

1994
1349 A445 1000s multicolored   3.75 1.75

Junior World Cycling Championships, Quito — A446

Design: No. 1351, Stylized cyclist, vert.

Wmk. 395
1994, June 22   **Litho.**   *Perf. 13*
1350 A446 300s shown   .75   .35
1351 A446 400s multi   1.00   .50

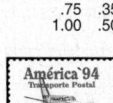
Postal Transportation — A447

America Issue: No. 1352, Van, airplane, ship, horiz. No. 1353, Airplane, mail bag.

1994
1352 A447 600s multicolored   .90   .40
1353 A447 600s multicolored   1.20   .50

Christmas — A448

No. 1354, Simulated stamp showing globe circled by envelope, horiz. No. 1355, Nativity.

1994
1354 A448 600s multicolored   1.10   .75
1355 A448 900s multicolored   1.60   .85

Juan Leon Mera, Death Cent.
A449   A450

Wmk. 395
1994, Dec. 21   **Litho.**   *Perf. 13*
1356 A449 600s Mera's home   1.00   .65
1357 A450 900s multicolored   2.25 1.40

Gen. Antonio Jose de Sucre (1795-1830) — A451

Designs: 2000s, Portrait at right. 3000s, In military uniform.

Perf. 14x13½
1995, Mar. 14   **Litho.**   **Wmk. 395**
1358 A451 1500s shown   3.25 1.75
1359 A451 2000s multi   4.50 2.50

Size: 80x105
Imperf
1360 A451 3000s multi   5.00 5.50
  Nos. 1358-1360 (3)   12.75 9.75

Beatification of Josemaria Escriva, 3rd Anniv. — A452

1995, May 17   *Perf. 13x13½*
1361 A452 900s multicolored   2.00   .90

Gen. Eloy Alfaro (1842-1912), Alfarista Revolution, Cent. — A453

1995, June 5   *Perf. 13½x13*
1362 A453 800s multicolored   1.40   .80

A454

Conflict Between Ecuador & Peru — A455

Designs: 200s, Soldier writing to children. 400s, Hand holding flag of Ecuador. 800s, Soldier in wilderness.

1995, July   *Perf. 13½, 13 (#1364)*
1363 A454 200s multicolored   .50   .25
1364 A455 400s multicolored   1.00   .45
1365 A454 800s multicolored   1.75   .90
  Nos. 1363-1365 (3)   3.25 1.60

CARE, 50th Anniv. A456

1995, July 14   *Perf. 13½*
1366 A456 400s Girl, vert.   .60   .30
1367 A456 800s shown   1.75 1.00

CAF (Andes Development Corporation), 25th Anniv. — A457

1995, Aug. 22   *Perf. 13*
1368 A457 1000s multicolored   2.75 1.25

Virgin of Cisne — A458

1995, Sept. 2   **Litho.**   *Perf. 13*
1369 A458 500s multi   .75   .50

A459

1995, Sept. 28
1370 A459 400s multicolored   .85   .45

Natl. Institute of Children and Families (INNFA), 35th anniv.

UN, 50th Anniv. — A460

Wmk. 395
1995, Oct. 6   **Litho.**   *Perf. 13*
1371 A460 1000s bl, blk & bis   1.90 1.00

Intl. Decade for Natural Disaster Reduction — A461

Civil defense emblem and: No. 1372, House surrounded by flood waters. No. 1373, Family leaving site of erupting volcano. No. 1374, People under table during earthquake. No. 1375, Couple planting seedlings on hillside. No. 1376, Man reading instruction booklet for natural disaster preparation.

1995, Oct. 11
1372 A461 1000s multicolored   2.00 1.00
1373 A461 1000s multicolored   2.00 1.00
1374 A461 1000s multicolored   2.00 1.00
1375 A461 1000s multicolored   2.00 1.00
1376 A461 1000s multicolored   2.00 1.00
  Nos. 1372-1376 (5)   10.00 5.00

FAO, 50th Anniv. — A462

1995, Oct. 16
1377 A462 1300s multicolored   2.75 1.50

Women's Culture Club, 50th Anniv. — A463

1995, Oct. 20
1378 A463 1500s multicolored   2.75 1.50

29th Assembly of Inter-America Philatelic Federation, Quito — A464

1995, Nov. 11
1379 A464 1000s blue & red   1.75 1.00

A465

Christmas: 2000s, Santa, sleigh, reindeer on top of world. 2600s, Man on decorated horse, children.

Wmk. 395
1995, Dec.   **Litho.**   *Perf. 13*
1380 A465 2000s multicolored   5.00 2.40
1381 A465 2600s multicolored   6.00 2.40

A466

Indigenous Birds: No. 1382, Aglaiocercus kingi.
No. 1383: a, Coeligena torquata. b, Phaethornis superciliosus. c, Ocreatus underwoodii. d, Oreotrochilus chimborazo. e, Aglaiocercus coelestis.

1995, Dec.
1382 A466 1000s multicolored   2.25   .85
1383 A466 1000s Strip of 5,
      #a.-e.   11.25 6.25

Ecuadoran Air Force, 75th Anniv. — A467

1995, Dec.
1384 A467 1000s multicolored   1.90   .85

Year of Folk Music — A468

2000s, Julio Jaramillo (1935-78), musician, composer. 3000s, Jaramillo, wall.

1996, Jan. 16   **Litho.**   *Perf. 13*
1385 A468 2000s multicolored   3.75 2.00
Imperf
1386 A468 3000s multicolored   5.00 4.25

Advancement of Ecuador, 4 Year Program — A469

Designs show symbols for: 1500s, Mail delivery. 2000s, Customs crossing. 2600s, Telecommunications. 3000p, Ports.

Wmk. 395

1996, July 23		**Litho.**	**Perf. 13**	
1387	A469	1000s multicolored	1.75	.80
1388	A469	1500s multicolored	2.75	1.25
1389	A469	2000s multicolored	3.25	1.75
1390	A469	2600s multicolored	4.50	1.90
a.		Pair, #1388, #1390	8.00	8.00
b.		Pair, #1389, #1390	8.50	8.50
1391	A469	3000s multicolored	5.50	3.00
a.		Pair, #1387, #1391	8.00	8.00
b.		Pair, #1389, #1391	9.50	9.50
		Nos. 1387-1391 (5)	*17.75*	*8.70*
		Nos. 1390a-1391b (4)	*34.00*	*34.00*

Nos. 1387-1391 were issued in strips of 2 each.

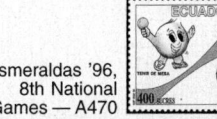

Esmeraldas '96, 8th National Games — A470

Mascot depicting two sports on each stamp: No. 1392, Tennis, boxing. No. 1393, Basketball, socccer. 600s, Racketball, swimming. 800s, Weight lifting, karate. 1000s, Volleyball, gymnastics. 1200s, Athletics, judo. No. 1398, Chess, wrestling.
No. 1399, Mascot holding flag, emblem, surrounded by flags.

1996, July 30				
1392	A470	400s multicolored	.55	.25
1393	A470	400s multicolored	.55	.25
1394	A470	600s multicolored	.90	.45
a.		Pair, #1392, #1394	1.50	1.50
1395	A470	800s multicolored	1.25	.60
a.		Pair, #1394-1395	2.25	2.25
1396	A470	1000s multicolored	1.60	.75
a.		Pair, #1393, #1396	2.40	2.40
b.		Pair, #1395-1396	3.00	3.00
1397	A470	1200s multicolored	1.75	.95
1398	A470	2000s multicolored	3.25	1.40
		Nos. 1392-1398 (7)	*9.85*	*4.65*
		Nos. 1394a-1396b (4)	*9.15*	*9.15*

Size: 120x100mm

1399	A470	2000s multicolored	4.00	3.50

Nos. 1392-1396 were printed in strips of 2 each.

Civil Aviation, 50th Anniv. — A471

1996, Aug. 8				
1400	A471	2000s multicolored	3.00	1.25

1996 Summer Olympic Games, Atlanta — A472

Atlanta Games emblem and: 1000s, Mascot carrying torch. No. 1402, Emblem of Olympic Committee of Ecuador. 3000s, Jefferson Perez, vert.
No. 1404, Perez, gold medalist, 20-kilometer walk, walking.

1996				
1401	A472	1000s multicolored	2.00	.75
1402	A472	2000s multicolored	4.00	2.25
a.		Pair, #1401-1402	6.00	6.00
1403	A472	3000s multicolored	5.00	2.50
		Nos. 1401-1403 (3)	*11.00*	*5.50*

Size: 100x120mm

Imperf

1404	A472	2000s multicolored	4.50	3.50

Fight Against Drug Abuse — A473

1996	**Litho.**	**Wmk. 395**	**Perf. 13**	
1408	A473	2000s multicolored	4.00	2.00

Dr. Eduardo Salazar Gomez, Birth Cent. — A474

1996				
1409	A474	1000s multicolored	2.25	1.25

Catholic University, Quito, 50th Anniv. — A475

Designs: 400s, Outside view of building, horiz. 800s, Entrance.

1996				
1410	A475	400s multicolored	.90	.45
1411	A475	800s multicolored	1.75	.85

Junior Chamber International — A476

2000s, Children's faces, horiz.

1996				
1412	A476	2000s multi	4.00	2.75
1413	A476	2600s shown	5.00	3.50

Catholic University, Quito, 50th Anniv. — A477

1996, Nov.				
1414	A477	2000s multicolored	4.00	2.00

The Universe Daily Newspaper, 75th Anniv. — A478

1996, Dec.				
1415	A478	2000s multicolored	3.75	2.00

Private Technical University, Loja — A479

1996, Dec. 9				
1416	A479	4700s multicolored	9.00	5.50

UNICEF, 50th Anniv. — A480

1996, Dec. 11				
1417	A480	2000s multicolored	3.50	2.25

Christmas — A481

Children's paintings: 600s, Merry Chrismas All Over the World. 800s, World of Peace and Love. 2000s, Christmas.

1996, Dec. 19				
1418	A481	600s multicolored	1.25	1.00
1419	A481	800s multicolored	1.75	1.25

Size: 51x31mm

Perf. 13½

1420	A481	2000s multicolored	4.50	2.50
		Nos. 1418-1420 (3)	*7.50*	*4.75*

Preserving the Ecological System — A482

America '95: 1000s, Voltur grypus. 1500s, Harpia harpyja, vert.

1996, Dec. 30			**Perf. 13**	
1421	A482	1000s multicolored	2.25	1.50
1422	A482	1500s multicolored	3.50	2.00

Typical Children's Costumes — A483

America '96: No. 1423, "Bordando" girl, Zuleta. No. 1424, Girl from Otavalo.

1996, Dec. 30				
1423	A483	2600s multicolored	5.25	1.75
1424	A483	2600s multicolored	5.25	4.25
a.		Pair, #1423-1424	14.00	12.50

Mejia Natl. Institute, Cent. — A484

Design: Jose Mejia Lequerica, building.

1997, Jan. 10				
1425	A484	1000s multicolored	2.00	1.25

Army Polytechnical School, 75th Anniv. — A485

Wmk. 395

1997, June 16	**Typo.**		**Perf. 13**	
1426	A485	400s multicolored	1.25	.75

Natl. Experimental College, Ambato, 50th Anniv. — A486

1997, June 20				
1427	A486	600s multicolored	1.50	1.00

Vicente Rocafuerte (1783-1847), First Constitutional President of Ecuador — A487

1997, July 1				
1428	A487	400s multicolored	1.25	.75

49th Intl. Congress of the Americanists A488

1997, July 3				
1429	A488	2000s multicolored	4.50	3.25

Butterflies — A489

Designs: 400s, Actinote equatoria. 600s, Dismorphia amphione. 800s, Marpesia corinna. 2000s, Marpesia berania. 2600s, Morpho helenor.

1997, July 21				
1430	A489	400s multicolored	1.05	.80
1431	A489	600s multicolored	1.30	1.00
1432	A489	800s multicolored	1.75	1.25
1433	A489	2000s multicolored	4.25	3.25
1434	A489	2600s multicolored	6.00	4.75
		Nos. 1430-1434 (5)	*14.35*	*11.05*

Air Club of Ecuador, 66th Anniv. — A490

1997, July 23				
1435	A490	2600s multicolored	5.75	3.00

Orchids — A491

400s, Epidendrum secundum. 600s, Epidendrum. 800s, Oncidium cultratrum. 2000s, Oncidium sp mariposa. 2600s, Pleurothalis corrulensis.

1997, Aug. 14	**Litho.**		**Perf. 13**	
1436	A491	400s multicolored	1.05	.80
1437	A491	600s multicolored	1.30	1.00
1438	A491	800s multicolored	1.75	1.25
1439	A491	2000s multicolored	4.25	3.25
1440	A491	2600s multicolored	6.00	4.75
		Nos. 1436-1440 (5)	*14.35*	*11.05*

Rocks and Minerals — A492

Designs: 400s, Quartz. 600s, Chalcopyrite. 800s, Gold. 2000s, Petrified wood. 2600s, Pyrite.

1997, Oct. 6	**Litho.**		**Perf. 13**	
1441	A492	400s multi	1.05	.80
1442	A492	600s multi	1.30	1.00
1443	A492	800s multi	1.75	1.25
1444	A492	2000s multi	4.25	3.25
1445	A492	2600s multi	6.00	4.75
		Nos. 1441-1445 (5)	*14.35*	*11.05*

A493

Christmas (Children's designs): 400s, Santa as postman delivering letters over world. 2600s, Star on Christmas tree reaching for letters, airplane under tree. 3000s, Child dreaming of angels carrying letters.

1997, Dec. 22	**Litho.**		**Perf. 13**	
1446	A493	400s multicolored	.95	.80
1447	A493	2600s multicolored	5.25	4.75
1448	A493	3000s multicolored	6.50	5.50
		Nos. 1446-1448 (3)	*12.70*	*11.05*

America Issue — A494

Designs: 800s, Life of a Postman. 2000s, On bicycle.

1997, Dec. 29
1449	A494	800s multi	1.50	1.00
1450	A494	2000s multi	4.50	2.50

Intl. Women's Day — A495

Matilde Hidalgo de Procel (1889-1974), physician, social reformer.

1998, Mar. 6   Litho.   Perf. 13
1451	A495	2000s multicolored	4.25	3.25

Dr. Misael Acosta Solis, Botanist — A496

Wmk. 395
1998, Apr. 22   Litho.   Perf. 13
1452	A496	2000s multicolored	7.00	5.50

Organization of American States (OAS), 50th Anniv. — A497

1998, Apr. 30
1453	A497	2600s multicolored	4.25	3.25

1998 World Cup Soccer Championships, France — A498

Designs: 2600s, Trophy, mascot, vert. 3000s, Two players, trophy.

1998, May
1454	A498	2000s multicolored	3.25	2.25
1455	A498	2600s multicolored	4.00	2.75
1456	A498	3000s multicolored	4.75	3.25
		Nos. 1454-1456 (3)	12.00	8.25

Flowers — A499

600s, Gypsophila paniculata. 800s, Banana flowers. 2000s, Roses. 2600s, Asters.

1998, June
1457	A499	600s multicolored	1.10	.60
1458	A499	800s multicolored	1.40	.90
1459	A499	2000s multicolored	3.25	2.25
1460	A499	2600s multicolored	4.00	2.75
		Nos. 1457-1460 (4)	9.75	6.50

Galapagos Flora — A500

Designs: 600s, Jasminocereus thouarsii. 1000s, Cordia lutea lamarck. 2600s, Momordica charantia.

1998, July
1461	A500	600s multicolored	.90	.60
1462	A500	1000s multicolored	1.50	1.00
1463	A500	2600s multicolored	4.00	2.75
		Nos. 1461-1463 (3)	6.40	4.35

Tourism — A501

Designs: 600s, St. Augustine Church, Quito. 800s, Monument to the Heroes of the Independence, Guayaquil. 2000s, Equator Monument, Quito. 2600s, Mojanda Lake.

1998, July
1464	A501	600s multi, vert.	.90	.60
1465	A501	800s multi, vert.	1.20	.90
1466	A501	2000s multi	2.75	2.25
1467	A501	2600s multi	3.50	2.75
		Nos. 1464-1467 (4)	8.35	6.50

Emiliano Ortega Espinosa (1898-1974), Educator — A502

Perf. 13¼x13, 13x13¼
1998   Litho.   Wmk. 395
1468	A502	400s shown	.75	.50
1469	A502	4700s Portrait, vert.	10.00	8.25

Carlos Cueva Tamariz (1898-1991), Educator — A503

Perf. 13x13¼
1998, Nov.   Litho.   Wmk. 395
1470	A503	2600s multicolored	4.50	3.50

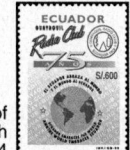

Radio Club of Guayaquil, 75th Anniv. — A504

Wmk. 395
1998, Nov. 20   Litho.   Perf. 13
1471	A504	600s multicolored	1.00	.90

6th South American Games — A505

Designs: 400s, Mascot. 1000s, Games poster, tennis rackets, hurdles, sailing, hammer throw, bowling, boxing. 2600s, Mascot, parallel bars, wrestling, judo, fencing, running, swimming, shooting, cycling.

1998
1472	A505	400s multicolored	.90	.50
1473	A505	1000s multicolored	1.50	1.00
1474	A505	2600s multicolored	4.00	2.75
		Nos. 1472-1474 (3)	6.40	4.25

Paintings by Eduardo Kingman (1913-85) — A506

Designs: 600s, Ecuadoran Woman, vert. 800s, World Without Answers.

1998, Dec. 10
1475	A506	600s multicolored	1.25	.65
1476	A506	800s multicolored	1.90	1.00

Manuela Sáenz (1797-1856), Mistress of Simon Bolívar — A507

1999, Jan. 19
1477	A507	1000s multicolored	2.00	.95

America issue. Exists imperf. Value, $25.

Christmas — A508

Children's drawings: 1000s, Santa posting letters on tree. 2600s, People holding up giant letter, vert. 3000s, Santas parachuting with letters, nativity scene, tree, vert.

1998, Dec. 22
1478	A508	1000s multicolored	1.40	.95
1479	A508	2600s multicolored	3.75	2.50
1480	A508	3000s multicolored	4.00	2.75
		Nos. 1478-1480 (3)	9.15	6.20

Los Tayos Caves — A509

Design: 1000s, Man in cave, vert.

1999, Feb. 25   Litho.   Perf. 13
1481	A509	1000s multi	1.50	.90
1482	A509	2600s shown	4.50	2.50

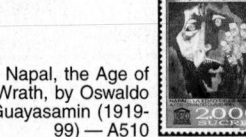

Napal, the Age of Wrath, by Oswaldo Guayasamin (1919-99) — A510

Wmk. 395
1999, May 12   Litho.   Perf. 13
1483	A510	2000s multicolored	3.75	2.10

Iberoamerica art exhibition.

Universal Day of Human Rights — A511

1999, May 28
1484	A511	4000s multicolored	6.75	4.50

Eloy Alfaro Superior Military College, Cent. — A512

5200s, Cannon, monument, flags, buildings. 9400s, Honor Guard, modern building.

1999, June 4
1485	A512	5200s multicolored	8.00	7.00
1486	A512	9400s multicolored	13.50	11.50

Puyo, 100th Anniv. — A513

Designs: a, Bromeliad. b, Ara chloroptera.

1999, June 2
1487	A513	4000s Pair, #a.-b.	12.50	10.00

Dr. Rafael Barahona Andrade (1827-98) — A514

Perf. 13¼x13
1999, June 17   Litho.   Wmk. 395
1488	A514	5200s multi	8.00	4.50

Generals — A515

Designs: 2000s, Manuel Antonio de Luzarraga y Echezurria (1776-1859). 4000s, Tomas Carlos Wright (1799-1868).

1999, Aug. 11   Perf. 13x13¼
1489-1490	A515	Set of 2	11.00	6.00

Galapagos Islands Flora and Fauna — A516

No. 1491, vert.: a, Phoenicopterus ruber. b, Buteo galapagoensis. c, Amblyrhynchus cristatus. d, Conolophus subcristatus. e, Opuntia galapageia. f, Pyrocephalus rubinus. g, Sula nebouxii. h, Sula dactylatra. i, Scalesia villosa. j, G. elephantopus abingdoni.

No. 1492: a, Brachycereus nesioticus. b, Dendroica petechia. c, Nannopterum harrisi. d, Tursiops truncatus. e, Pentaceraster cumingi. f, G. elephantopus porteri. g, Microlophus albemarlensis. h, Arctocephalus galapagoensis. i, Spheniscus mendiculus. j, Geospiza scandens.

Perf. 13x13¼, 13¼x13
1999, Sept. 3	**Litho.**		**Wmk. 395**	
1491		Strip of 10	90.00	75.00
a.-j.	A516	7000s Any single	5.50	1.75
1492		Strip of 10	175.00	125.00
a.-j.	A516	15,000s Any single	12.00	5.00

Intl. Year of Older Persons — A517

Designs: No. 1493, 1000s, Hands of child and old person. No. 1494, 1000s, Emblem.

Perf. 13¼x13
1999, Sept. 22   Litho.   Wmk. 395
1493-1494	A517	Set of 2	3.00	1.75

SOS Children's Villages, 50th Anniv. — A518

a, 2000s, Two children. b, 2000s, One child.

1999, Sept. 30
1495	A518	Pair, #a-b	5.00	2.50

America Issue, A World Without Arms A519

No. 1496: a, World map. b, Tree, bird, Earth.

Perf. 13¼x13
1999, Dec. 11   Litho.   Wmk. 395
1496	A519	4000s Pair, #a-b	12.50	10.00

UPU, 125th
Anniv. — A520

Designs: 1000s, Ecuadorian Postal Service mascot, vert. 4000s, Dove with letter, vert. 8000s, UPU emblem.

Perf. 13¼x12¾

1999, Dec. 11		**Litho.**	**Wmk. 395**	
1497	A520	1000s multi	.75	.45
1498	A520	4000s multi	3.00	1.75
1499	A520	8000s multi	5.75	4.00
	Nos. 1497-1499 (3)		9.50	6.20

Ecuador as Secretary General of Permanent South Pacific Commission — A521

Design: León Dormido.

Perf. 13x13¼

1999, Dec. 21		**Litho.**	**Wmk. 395**	
1500	A521	7000s multi	7.00	5.50

Machala Tourism — A522

Designs: No. 1501, Banana flower and city. No. 1502, vert.: a, Monument to banana plantation workers. b, City Hall.

1999, Dec. 28		**Perf. 13¼x13, 13x13¼**		
1501	A522	3000s multi	3.25	1.60
1502	A522	3000s multi, #a-b	6.50	3.25

EMELEC Soccer Team A523

No. 1503: a, Jorge Bolanos. b, Carlos Raffo. No. 1504, EMELEC team photo, 1957. No. 1505, Player, vert.

Perf. 13¼x13, 13¼x13

2000, Jan. 7			**Litho.**	
1503	A523	1000s Pair, #a-b	4.00	2.25
1504	A523	2000s multi	4.00	1.50
1505	A523	2000s multi	4.00	1.50

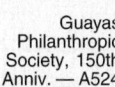

Guayas Philanthropic Society, 150th Anniv. — A524

Designs: 1000s, Building. 2000s, Founder Juan Maria Martinez Coello. 4000s, Emblem.

Perf. 13¼x13

2000, Jan. 19		**Litho.**	**Wmk. 395**	
1506-1508	A524	Set of 3	4.00	1.50

Dual Nationality Day — A525

2000, Jan. 24		**Perf. 13x13¼**		
1509	A525	7000s multi	3.00	1.50

Cuenca, World Heritage Site — A526

No. 1510: a, Buildings. b, Puente Roto and Tomebamba River. c, Church bell gable, Concepcion Monastery. d, Cathedral and city skyline. e, San José Church.

2000, Mar. 24		**Perf. 13¼x13**		
1510		Strip of 5	7.00	6.00
a.-e.	A526	4000s Any single	.75	.50

Nicolas Lapentti, Tennis Player — A527

2000, Mar. 26		**Perf. 13x13¼**		
1511	A527	8000s multi	3.00	1.50

Birds — A528

No. 1512: a, Diglossa cyanea. b, Oreotrochilus chimborazo. c, Trogon personatus. d, Colibri coruscans. e, Atlapetes rufinucha.

2000, Apr. 7				
1512		Horiz. strip of 5	14.00	11.50
a.-e.	A528	8000s Any single	2.50	1.50

Relocation of Riobamba, Bicent. — A529

Designs: No. 1513, Mt. Chimborazo. No. 1514: a, Riobamba Cathedral. b, Statue of Pedro Vicente Maldonado.

2000, Apr. 13		**Perf. 13¼x13, 13x13¼**		
1513	A529	8000s multi	3.00	1.00
1514	A529	8000s Pair, #a-b	5.25	3.50

Gen. Eloy Alfaro, Founder of Natl. Music Conservatory — A530

2000, Apr. 19		**Perf. 13x13¼**		
1515	A530	10,000s multi	3.75	1.60

Natl. Music Conservatory, cent.

Climbing of Mt. Everest by Ivan Vallejo Ricaurte — A531

2000, May 23		**Perf. 13¼x13**		
1516	A531	8000s multi	3.50	2.00

100 Cents=1 Dollar

Dolores Sucre Fiscal College, 50th Anniv. — A532

Perf. 13x13¼

2000		**Litho.**	**Wmk. 395**	
1517	A532	32c multi	2.50	1.25

Training Ship Guayas — A533

2000, July 5		**Perf. 13x13¼**		
1518	A533	68c multi	2.00	.80

Imperf

Size: 90x110mm

1519	A533	$1 multi	7.00	3.25

Battle of Jambeli, 59th Anniv., Navy Day — A534

2000		**Perf. 13¼x13**		
1520	A534	16c multi	1.50	.25

Guayaquil Civic Renovation — A535

2000, July		**Perf. 13x13¼**		
1521	A535	84c multi	6.75	3.75

Megaptera Novaeangliae A536

2000, Aug. 3		**Perf. 13¼x13**		
1522	A536	84c multi	7.50	4.25

Imperf

Size: 90x110mm

1523	A536	$1 Two whales	10.00	5.75

American and Caribbean Dog Show, Quito — A537

2000, Aug.		**Perf. 13¼x13**		
1524	A537	68c multi	4.50	2.25

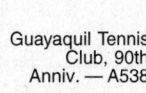

Guayaquil Tennis Club, 90th Anniv. — A538

2000, Aug.			**Wmk. 395**	
1525	A538	84c multi	5.50	2.50

Alberto Spencer, Soccer Player — A539

2000		**Perf. 13x13¼**		
1526	A539	68c multi	5.00	2.50

Imperf

Size: 69x99mm

1527	A539	$1 Spencer, crowd	7.50	4.50

2000 Summer Olympics, Sydney — A540

Ecuadoran team emblem, Games emblem and: 32c Mascots. 68c, Runner Jefferson Perez Marchista. 84c, Weight lifter Boris Burov, Olympic flag, horiz.

2000, Sept.	**Perf. 13x13¼, 13¼x13**			
1528-1530	A540	Set of 3	12.00	6.00

Salinas Yacht Club, 60th Anniv. — A541

Designs: No. 1531a, Lighthouse, vert. Nos. 1531b, 1533, Sailboat, vert. 68c, Sailboats, fisherman, waterskier, scuba diver.

2000, Oct.		**Perf. 13x13¼**		
1531	A541	32c Horiz. pair, #a-b	3.75	2.75

Perf. 13¼x13

1532	A541	68c multi	4.00	2.75

Imperf

Size: 69x100mm

1533	A541	$1 multi	6.00	4.50

Inter-American Development Bank, 40th Anniv. — A542

Designs: No. 1534a, 68c, No. 1536a, 25c, Salsipuedes Bridge, Felipe Herrera. No. 1534b, 68c, No. 1536b, 25c, Daule-Peripa Dam, Antonio Ortiz Mena. No. 1535a, 84c, No. 1536c, 25c, Enrique Iglesias, Ucubamba Water Treatment Plant. No. 1535b, 84c, No. 1536d, 25c, Bank emblem, History Museum, Quito.

2000, Oct. 27		**Perf. 13¼x13**		
Horiz. Pairs, #a-b				
1534-1535	A542	Set of 2	17.50	10.00
Rouletted 14 on 2 sides				
1536	A542	25c Sheet of 4, #a-d	7.00	3.75

Size of Nos. 1536a-1536b, 75x48mm; Nos. 1536c-1536d, 75x42mm.

National Union of Journalists A543

2000, Nov. 1		**Perf. 13¼x13**		
1537	A543	16c multi	1.35	.25

Civil Registry, Cent. A544

No. 1538: a, People, flag, computer. b, Fingerprint, family.

2000, Oct. 27		**Perf. 13x13¼**		
1538	A544	68c Horiz. pair, #a-b	9.00	4.50

Mama Negra Festival, Latacunga — A545

No. 1539: a, Mama Negra with doll. b, Man in Moor King costume.

2000, Nov.   **Perf. 13x13¼**
1539 A545 32c Horiz. pair, #a-b   4.75 2.75
Imperf
Size: 100x68mm
1540 A545 $1 Mama Negra, doll, diff.   6.50 3.00

Ministry of Labor, 75th Anniv. — A546

2000, Nov. 15   **Perf. 13x13¼**
1541 A546 68c multi   4.50 2.25

Intl. Fruits and Flowers Festival, Ambato, 50th Anniv. — A547

No. 1542, horiz.: Design inside "0" of 50 — a, Tungurahua Volcano. b, Aerial view of Ambato.
No. 1544, horiz.: Design inside "0" of 50 — a, Flower. b, Fruit.

2000, Nov.   **Perf. 13¾**
1542 A547 32c Vert. pair, #a-b   4.25 2.10
1543 A547 84c shown   5.75 2.75
1544 A547 84c Vert. pair, #a-b   12.00 6.00
   Nos. 1542-1544 (3)   22.00 10.85
Imperf
Size: 68x100mm
1545 A547 $1 Ambato   6.25 3.00

Christmas — A548

Children's art by — No. 1546, 68c: a, Giannina Rhor Isaias. b, Josue Remache Romero.
No. 1547, 84c: a, Maria Cedeño Bazurtto. b, Juan Alban Salazar.
$1, Walther Carvache.

2000, Dec. 15   **Perf. 13¼x13**
Horiz. Pairs, #a-b
1546-1547 A548   Set of 2   21.50 11.00
Imperf
Size: 100x69mm
1548 A548 $1 multi   6.25 3.00

Expoflores Flower Producer and Exporter Association — A549

2000   **Perf. 13x13¼**
1549 A549 68c multi   5.00 2.50

Man's Chapel, Guayasamin A550

2000   **Perf. 13¼x13**
1550 A550 16c multi   1.45 .25

Spanish Chamber of Commerce in Ecuador, 80th Anniv. — A551

2000, Dec.   **Perf. 13x13¼**
1551 A551 16c multi   1.40 .25

Intl. Volunteers Year — A552

2000   **Wmk. 395**
1552 A552 16c multi   1.40 .25

Restoration of Bolivar Theater, Quito — A553

Designs: 16c, Piano, banquet room. 32c, Stage, orchestra, horiz.

2000, Dec.   **Perf. 13x13¼, 13¼x13**
1553-1554 A553   Set of 2   3.75 1.75

Spondylus Princeps — A554

2000, Dec. 16   **Perf. 13¾**
1555 A554 84c multi   5.50 3.00
Imperf
Size: 69x99mm
1556 A554 $1 multi   7.00 3.50

America Issue, Fight Against AIDS A555

No. 1557: a, Strands. b, Earth.

2000   **Perf. 13x13¼**
1557 A555 84c Horiz. pair, #a-b   13.50 7.50

Guayas Province Red Cross, 90th Anniv. — A556

2000   **Perf. 13¼x13**
1558 A556 16c multi   1.25 .60

Guayas Sports Federation, 78th Anniv. — A557

2000, Dec.   **Perf. 13x13¼**
1559 A557 16c multi   1.40 .60

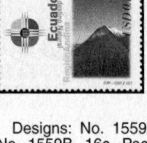

Landscapes A557a

Designs: No. 1559A, 16c, Andean region. No. 1559B, 16c, Pacific coast. 32c, Tourism emblem. 68c, Amazonia. 84c, Galápagos Islands.

2001, Jan. 24   **Litho.**   **Wmk. 395**
1559A A557a 16c multi   1.25 .60
1559B A557a 16c multi   1.25 .60
1559C A557a 32c multi   2.50 1.10
1559D A557a 68c multi   4.75 2.40
1559E A557a 84c multi   4.75 2.40
   Nos. 1559A-1559E (5)   14.50 7.10

Guayas Soccer Team, 50th Anniv. — A558

2001, Mar. 8   **Perf. 13¼x13**
1560 A558 68c multi   4.50 2.50

Census — A558a   Census — A558b

Perf. 12¾x13¼
2001, Mar. 12   **Litho.**   **Wmk. 395**
1560A A558a 68c multi   4.50 4.50
1560B A558b 68c multi   4.50 4.50
  c.   Horiz. pair, #1560A-
     1560B   10.00 10.00

Dr. Raúl Clemente Huerta — A559

2001, Apr. 4   **Perf. 13¼x13**
1561 A559 68c multi   5.25 2.75

Dr. Antonio J. Quevedo, Birth Cent. — A560

2001, Apr. 5   **Litho.**
1562 A560 84c multi   6.00 3.25

Military Geographic Institute — A560a

No. 1562A: b, Soldier, building. c, Computer, printing press.

Perf. 13¼x12¾
2001, Apr. 11   **Litho.**   **Wmk. 395**
1562A A560a 68c Vert. pair, #b-
   c   11.00 6.00

Automobile Club of Ecuador, 50th Anniv. — A561

2001, May 15   **Wmk. 395**
1563 A561 84c multi   6.50 3.25

San Francisco de Peleusí Church, Azogues — A561a

Perf. 12¾x13¼
2001, May   **Litho.**   **Wmk. 395**
1563A A561a 84c multi   6.00 3.25

Women's Training Institute — A562

2001, Apr. 10   **Perf. 13x13¼**
1564 A562 84c multi   6.00 3.25

Intl. Women's Day — A563

No. 1565: a, Woman, child, corn. b, Woman, emblem.

2001, Apr. 2   **Perf. 13¼x13**
1565 A563 84c Vert. pair, #a-b   12.50 6.25

Secular Education at Manuela Cañizares University, Cent. — A564

2001, Mar. 29   **Wmk. 395**
1566 A564 84c multi   6.00 3.25

Ecuador Merchant Marines, Cent. — A565

2001, Jan. 2001   **Perf. 13x13¼**
1567 A565 16c multi   1.25 .60

Ambato Technical University, 32nd Anniv. — A566

No. 1568: a, Building. b, Painting.

2001   **Perf. 13¼x13**
1568 A566 32c Vert. pair, #a-b   5.00 2.75

Galapagos Islands Scenes A567

No. 1569: a, Española Island (shown). b, San Cristobal Island. c, Bartolome Island. d,

Española Island, diff. e, Bartolome and Santiago Islands.
  $1, Bird on rock, Española Island.

2001, Feb. 17		**Perf. 13¾**
1569	Horiz. strip of 5	6.00 3.00
a.-e.	A567 16c Any single	.50 .25

Imperf
Size: 100x70mm

1570 A567 $1 multi	8.00 4.00

Alexander von Humboldt (1769-1859), Naturalist — A568

2001, June 14 Litho.		**Wmk. 395**
1571 A568 84c multi		6.00 3.00

Ecuadorian Atomic Energy Commission — A568a

2001, Aug. 3 Litho.		**Perf. 12¾x13¼**
1571A A568a 70c multi		5.50 2.75

Lebanese Union, 80th Anniv. — A569

No. 1572: a, Building and emblem. b, Emblem.

2001, Aug. 30		**Perf. 13¼x13**
1572 A569 16c Horiz. pair, #a-b		2.75 1.50

Manta Port Authority A570

No. 1573: a, Emblem. b, Ships in port.

2001, Sept. 28		
1573 A570 68c Horiz. pair, #a-b		9.50 5.00

Esmereldas Province Tourism — A571

No. 1574: a, Beach. b, Musicians and dancers on beach.

2001		
1574 A571 86c Horiz. pair, #a-b		11.75 6.25

Latin American Writers A572

No. 1575: a, Claudia Lars (1899-1974), Salvadoran poet. b, Federico Proaño (1848-94), Ecuadoran journalist.

2001, Aug. 28		**Perf. 13x13¼**
1575 A572 86c Horiz. pair, #a-b		12.50 6.75

Andean Condor Preservation — A573

No. 1576: a, Condor and chick. b, Condor heads, FRAPZOO emblem.
  $1, Condor in flight, FRAPZOO emblem.

2001, July 23		**Perf. 13x13¼**
1576 A573 86c Horiz. pair, #a-b		14.50 6.25

Imperf
Size: 68x99mm

1577 A573 $1 multi	7.50 3.75

Ecuador — Peru Peace Accords — A574

No. 1578: a, Map of Ecuador and Peru. b, Soldier. c, Flags of military obeservers. d, Amazon River. e, Men in field.

2001, May 22		**Perf. 13¼x13**
1578	Horiz. strip of 5	22.50 11.00
a.-e.	A574 68c Any single	4.00 2.00

Archidona Canton — A575

No. 1579: a, Phragmipedium orchid. b, Saimiri sciureus. c, B. macrophylla. d, Church. e, Kichwa Indian family.

2001, Apr. 28		**Perf. 13x13¼**
1579	Vert. strip of 5	25.00 15.00
a.-e.	A575 84c Any single	5.00 2.40

Ecotourism in Baños — A576

No. 1580: a, Orchid. b, Basilica, Baños. c, Tungurahua Volcano. d, Pailon del Diablo Waterfall. e, Statue of Virgin of Rosario de Agua Santa.
  $1, Pailon del Diablo Waterfall, orchid.

2001		**Perf. 13¼x13**
1580	Horiz. strip of 5	27.50 13.50
a.-e.	A576 86c Any single	5.00 2.40

Imperf
Size: 68x99mm

1581 A576 $1 multi	7.50 3.75

Guayas Educational Journalists Association, 30th Anniv. — A577

		Perf. 13¼x13
2001, Oct. 15 Litho.		**Wmk. 395**
1582 A577 16c multi		1.25 .60

Foundation for Development of Cattle Ranching, 15th Anniv. — A578

2001, Aug. 15		**Perf. 13x13¼**
1583 A578 16c multi		1.40 .60

City Gates, Loja — A579

2001		**Perf. 13¼x13**
1584 A579 32c multi		2.50 1.25

Quito Municipal District Directorate of Security — A580

2001, Nov. 26		
1585 A580 68c multi		4.75 2.50

Salvador Bustamante Celi (1876-1935), Musician — A581

2001		
1586 A581 68c multi		5.00 2.75

Marcel Laniado de Wind (1927-98), First Pres. of Natl. Modernization Council — A582

2001, Aug. 6		**Perf. 13x13¼**
1587 A582 70c multi		5.25 2.75

Bernardino Cardinal Echeverria (1912-2000) — A583

2001, Nov. 14		
1588 A583 84c multi		6.00 3.25

José Joaquin Olmedo (1780-1847), Statesman and Poet — A584

2001, Nov. 8		
1589 A584 84c multi		6.25 3.25

El Angel Ecological Reserve — A585

No. 1590: a, Paja de Paramo. b, Frailejón.

2001		**Perf. 13¼x13**
1590 A585 16c Horiz. pair, #a-b		2.75 1.40

Yahuarcocha Race Track — A586

No. 1591: a, Race track and lake. b, Lake.

2001, Nov. 30		
1591 A586 68c Horiz. pair, #a-b		10.00 5.00

World Food Day A587

No. 1592: a, Wheat ears. b, Food baskets.

2001, Nov. 5		
1592 A587 84c Horiz. pair, #a-b		12.50 6.25

Art of Voroshilov Bazante — A588

No. 1593: a, Spatial composition. b, Abstract, artists name at LR. c, Urban landscape. d, Abstract, diff., "Abstracto" at UL, denomination at LL. e, Abstract, denomination at LR.

2001, Nov.		
1593	Horiz. strip of 5	25.00 12.50
a.-e.	A588 84c Any single	4.50 2.50

Wilson Popenoe Private Foundation — A589

2001, Nov. 19 Litho.		**Perf. 13¼x13**
1594 A589 16c multi		1.40 .60

FAO Food Program — A590

2001, Aug. 15		
1595 A590 84c multi		6.00 3.25

Rotary District 4400, 75th Anniv. — A591

2001, Nov. 30		**Perf. 13x13¼**
1596 A591 84c multi		6.00 3.25

Pres. Camilo Ponce Enriquez (1912-76) — A592

2001		
1597 A592 84c multi		6.00 3.25

Pedro Vicente Maldonado (1702-48), Geographer — A593

2001, Dec. 12		
1598 A593 84c multi		6.00 3.25

Otonga Foundation A595

No. 1599: a, Frog on branch. b, Mustela frenata.

2001, Oct. 31		
1599 A595 16c Horiz. pair, #a-b		2.50 1.40

Tourism in Zaruma A596

No. 1600: a, Virgen del Carmen. b, Orchid.

2001, Dec. 12		**Perf. 13¼x13**
1600 A596 68c Horiz. pair, #a-b		10.00 5.00

Radio HCJB, 70th Anniv. A597

No. 1601: a, Microphone. b, Announcer.

2001, Dec. 21
1601 A597 68c Horiz. pair, #a-b   10.00 5.00

Tennis — A598

No. 1602: a, Davis Cup. b, K. Lapentti, G. Lapentti, L.A. Morejón, A. Intriago and R. Viver. c, Francisco Guzman and Miguel Olvera. d, Pancho Segura. e, Andres Gomez.

2001, Nov. 1
1602   Horiz. strip of 5   24.00 12.00
a.-e.   A598 68c Any single   4.50   2.25

Church Paintings of Wilfrido Martínez A599

No. 1603: a, San Francisco (artist's name is vert.). b, Guapulo. c, San Francisco (artist's name is horiz.). d, La Compania. e, El Rosario.

2002, Apr. 9   Perf. 13¾
1603   Horiz. strip of 5   25.00 13.50
a.-e.   A599 90c Any single   5.00   2.50

First Judicial Summit of the Americas, Quito — A600

**   Perf. 13¼x13**
2002, Jan. 8   Litho.   Wmk. 395
1604 A600 68c multi   5.00   2.50

Union Club, Guayaquil — A601

2002, Apr. 25   Perf. 13x13¼
1605 A601 90c multi   5.75   2.75

South American Soccer Confederation — A602

Designs: 25c, Confederation Pres. Nicolás Leoz. 40c, Confederation emblem, soccer players. 70c, Emblem of Emelec team.

2002, Jan. 29
1606-1608 A602   Set of 3   9.00   5.00

World Conservation Union — A603

Designs: 70c, Fish, man's head. 85c, Leopard, man, horiz.
$1, Bird, animals, women and children, horiz.

2002, Feb. 21 Perf. 13x13¼, 13¼x13
1609-1610 A603   Set of 2   10.00 5.75
Imperf
Size: 100x70mm
1611 A603 $1 multi   7.50   3.75

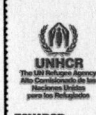

UN High Commissioner for Refugees — A604

Designs: 70c, Emblem. 85c, Child. $1, Refugees carrying belongings, horiz.

2002, Feb. 28   Perf. 13x13¼
1612-1613 A604   Set of 2   10.00 5.75
Imperf
Size: 100x70mm
1614 A604 $1 multi   7.50   3.75

Ecuadorian Educational Credit and Scholarship Institute — A605

No. 1615: a, Student using microscope. b, Emblem.

2002, Apr. 30   Perf. 13x13¼
1615 A605 25c Horiz. pair, #a-b   2.75 1.50

Cuenca Soccer Team A606

No. 1616: a, Team photo. b, Emblem, player dribbling.

2002, Apr. 19   Perf. 13¼x13
1616 A606 25c Horiz. pair, #a-b   3.00 1.50

Imbabura Province History A607

No. 1617: a, Building. b, Statue.

2002, Mar. 27   Perf. 13x13¼
1617 A607 40c Horiz. pair, #a-b   5.50 3.00

Crucita A608

No. 1618: a, Parachutist with sun on horizon. b, Prachutist above beach.

2002, Mar. 28   Perf. 13¼x13
1618 A608 40c Horiz. pair, #a-b   6.00 3.00

Mountains — A609

No. 1619: a, Mt. Altar (trees in foreground). b, Mt. Chimborazo. c, Mt. Carihuayrazo. d, Mt. Altar (lake in foreground). e, Mt. Cubillin.

2002, Apr. 19
1619   Horiz. strip of 5   29.00 15.00
a.-e.   A609 90c Any single   5.00   2.25

Endangered Frogs — A610

No. 1620: a, Atelopus bomolochos. b, Atelopus longirostris. c, Atelopus pachydermus. d, Atelopus arthuri. e, Atelopus sp.
$1, Atelopus ignescens.

2002, Mar. 25   Perf. 13¼x13
1620   Horiz. strip of 5   29.00 15.00
a.-e.   A610 $1.05 Any single   5.00   2.25
Imperf
Size: 100x70mm
1621 A610 $1 multi   9.00   8.00

National Anti-narcotics Police — A611

No. 1622: a, Policeman and dog. b, Emblem.

**   Perf. 13x13¼**
2002, Apr. 23   Litho.   Wmk. 395
1622 A611 40c Horiz. pair, #a-b   6.00 3.00

2002 World Cup Soccer Championships, Japan and Korea — A612

Designs: 90c, Ecuadorian Soccer Federation emblem, vert. $1.05, $2, Emblem, team photo, players in action.

2002, Apr. 28 Perf. 13x13¼, 13¼x13
1623-1624 A612   Set of 2   8.50   4.50
Imperf
Size: 100x70mm
1625 A612 $2 multi   8.50   4.50

Dr. Servio Aguirre Villamagua, Forest Conservationist — A613

No. 1626: a, Aguirre. b, Plant.

2002, May 22   Perf. 13¼x13
1626 A613 40c Horiz. pair, #a-b   4.00 2.00

Food and Agriculture Organization in Ecuador, 50th Anniv. — A614

2002, May 30
1627 A614 $1.05 multi   5.00   2.50

Galapagos Islands Fauna — A615

No. 1628: a, Grapsus grapsus. b, Conolophus subcristatus.
No. 1629, vert.: a, Sula sula websteri. b, Phoenicopterus ruber.
No. 1630, Amblyrhynchus cristatus.
No. 1631, vert.: a, Pair of Zalophus californianus wollebacki. b, One Zalophus californianus wollebacki.
No. 1632, Sula nebouxii excisa, vert.
No. 1633, vert.: a, Sula dactylatra granti. b, Emblem of Iberoamerican Summit on Tourism and Environment.
$2, Bird, tourists, tourist ship.

2002, May 31 Perf. 13¼x13, 13x13¼
1628 A615   25c Horiz. pair,
                        #a-b   3.00   1.50
1629 A615   40c Horiz. pair,
                        #a-b   4.00   2.00
1630 A615   90c multi   6.00   3.00
1631 A615   90c Horiz. pair,
                        #a-b   9.00   4.50
1632 A615 $1.05 multi   5.00   2.50
1633 A615 $1.05 Horiz. pair,
                        #a-b   10.00   5.00
     Nos. 1628-1633 (6)   37.00 18.50

Imperf
Size: 100x68mm
1634 A615 $2 multi   10.00   7.00

Ministry of Foreign Relations — A616

2002, June 5   Perf. 13x13¼
1635 A616 90c multi   4.50   2.25

Army Polytechnic School, 80th Anniv. — A617

2002, June 13   Perf. 13¼x13
1636 A617 25c multi   1.60   .90

Military Engineers, Cent. — A618

Designs: No. 1637, 40c, Castle of Engineering. No. 1638, 40c, Castle of Engineering, Military engineers in action, vert.
$2, Castle of Engineering, engineers in action, emblems of military groups.

**   Perf. 13¼x13, 13x13¼**
2002, June 19   Set of 2   4.00   2.00
1637-1638 A618
Imperf
Size: 100x68mm
1639 A618 $2 multi   9.00   4.50

Dr. Alfredo Pérez Guerrero (1901-66), Academic — A619

2002, July 4   Perf. 13x13¼
1640 A619 25c multi   1.75   .90

20th Anniv. of Ecuador's Second Place Finish In World Taekwondo Championships A620

2002, July 18   Perf. 13¼x13
1641 A620 40c multi   2.00   1.00

Orellana Province A621

No. 1642: a, Three native men. b, Man in tree.

2002, July 30   Wmk. 395
1642 A621 25c Horiz. pair, #a-b   3.00 1.50

CARE in Ecuador, 40th Anniv. A622

No. 1643: a, Two children. b, Boy.

2002, July 30   Perf. 13x13¼
1643 A622 90c Horiz. pair, #a-b   9.00 4.50

Macará Region — A623

2002, Aug. 10   *Perf. 13¼x13*
1644 A623 40c multi   2.00 1.00

Intl. Organization for Migration, 50th Anniv. — A624

2002, Aug. 18   *Perf. 13x13¼*
1645 A624 $1.05 multi   5.00 2.50

Quito Philharmonic Society, 50th Anniv. — A625

2002, Aug. 29
1646 A625 25c multi   1.60 .90

Comptroller General, 75th Anniv. — A625a

Perf. 13x13¼
2002, Sept. 26   *Litho.*   *Wmk. 395*
1646A A625a 40c multi   2.00 1.00

Second World Meeting of Mountain People — A626

No. 1647 — Emblem of World Meeting and: a, Mountain. b, Group of people. c, Houses in valley. d, Town. e, Other emblems.

2002, Sept. 18
1647   Horiz. strip of 5   24.00 11.00
a.-e. A626 90c Any single   4.00 2.00

Pujili Dancer — A627

Perf. 13x13¼
2002, Oct. 14   *Litho.*   *Wmk. 395*
1648 A627 $1.05 multi   5.00 2.50

Paintings of Milton Estrella Gavidia A628

No. 1649 — Various paintings with background colors of: a, Blue violet. b, Brown violet. c, Olive green. d, Blue. e, Gray lilac.

Wmk. 395
2002, May 17   *Litho.*   *Perf. 13¾*
1649   Horiz. strip of 5   24.00 11.00
a.-e. A628 90c Any single   4.00 2.00

Paintings of Leonardo Hidalgo — A629

No. 1650: a, La Dolorosa. b, El Hombre Cargando su Fruto. c, Frida Kahlo. d, El Hombre Fuerte del Mar. e, Jesus.

Wmk. 395
2002, Oct. 3   *Litho.*   *Perf. 13¾*
1650   Horiz. strip of 5   22.50 11.00
a.-e. A629 90c Any single   4.00 2.00

Pan-American Health Organization, Cent. — A630

2002, Dec. 2   *Perf. 13¼x12¾*
1651 A630 $1.05 multi   4.75 2.50

Lo Nuestro Art Exhibition — A631

No. 1652: a, Wall with six works of art. b, Walls with 16 works of art.

2002, Dec. 15
1652 A631 25c Horiz. pair, #a-b   2.50 1.25

Catholic University, 40th Anniv. — A632

2002, Dec. 18
1653 A632 40c multi   2.00 1.00

America Issue — UNESCO World Heritage Sites A633

No. 1654: a, Cupola of San Blas Church, Cuenca. b, Society of Jesus Church, Quito.

2002, Dec. 18   *Perf. 12¾x13¼*
1654 A633 25c Horiz. pair, #a-b   3.00 1.50
Dated 2001.

America Issue — Youth, Education and Literacy — A634

No. 1655: a, Students and blackboard. b, Toddler and books.

2002, Dec. 18   *Perf. 13¼x12¾*
1655 A634 25c Horiz. pair, #a-b   3.00 1.50

Second Meeting of South American Presidents, Guayaquil — A635

No. 1656: a, Meeting emblem. b, Emblem, presidents and flags.

2003, Jan. 13
1656 A635 $1.05 Horiz. pair, #a-b   6.00 4.00

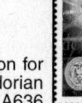

Papal Benediction for Ecuadorian Emigrants — A636

2003, Jan. 24   *Perf. 12¾x13¼*
1657 A636 $1.05 multi   4.75 2.25
Size: 68x100mm
Imperf
1658 A636 $2 multi   8.50 4.50

World Vision — A637

2003, Feb. 6   *Perf. 12¾x13¼*
1659 A637 40c multi   1.90 .95

Intl. Women's Day — A638

2003, Mar. 8   *Wmk. 395*
1660 A638 $1.05 multi   5.00 2.50

Agustin Cueva Vallejo (1820-73), Physician — A639

2003, Mar. 13   *Litho.*
1661 A639 40c multi   1.90 .95

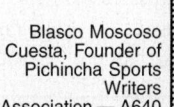

Blasco Moscoso Cuesta, Founder of Pichincha Sports Writers Association — A640

2003, Mar. 14
1662 A640 25c multi   1.50 .75

Cuenca Artisan Products — A641

No. 1663: a, Azuay University domes. b, Tinware. c, Jewelry. d, Fireworks. e, Saddles.
No. 1664: a, Engraving. b, Metallurgy. c, Baskets. d, Embroidery. e, Ceramics.
$2, Assorted products.

2003, Mar. 27   *Perf. 13¼x12¾*
1663   Horiz. strip of 5   6.00 3.00
a.-e. A641 25c Any single   1.00 .50
1664   Horiz. strip of 5   22.50 11.00
a.-e. A641 $1.05 Any single   4.00 2.00
Size: 100x68mm
Imperf
1665 A641 $2 multi   9.00 4.50

Flora and Fauna — A642

No. 1666: a, Curculionidae. b, Lycidae. c, Acridoidea. d, Arachnidae. e, Liliacea.

2003, Apr. 4   *Perf. 13¼x12¾*
1666   Horiz. strip of 5   22.50 11.00
a.-e. A642 $1.05 Any single   4.00 2.00

Military Geographic Institute, 75th Anniv. — A643

Designs: No. 1667, 40c, No. 1669, $2, Painting by Eduardo Kingman. No. 1668, 40c, Institute emblem, vert.

Perf. 13¼x12¾, 12¾x13¼
2003, Apr. 11
1667-1668 A643   Set of 2   3.50 1.75
Size: 100x68mm
Imperf
1669 A643 $2 multi   9.00 4.50

Galápagos Marine Reserve — A644

Designs: 40c, Stylized butterfly.
No. 1671, $1.05, horiz.: a, Sphyrna lewini. b, Chelonia mydas agassisi.
No. 1672, $1.05, horiz.: a, Xanthichthys mento. b, Zanclus cornutus.
$2, Tubastrea coccinea, horiz.

Perf. 12¾x13¼, 13¼x12¾
2003, May 9
1670 A644 40c multi   1.75 .90
Horiz. Pairs, #a-b
1671-1672 A644   Set of 2   17.50 8.75
Size: 100x68mm
Imperf
1673 A644 $2 multi   9.00 4.50

Intl. Tourism Trade Fair of Ecuador — A645

No. 1674: a, Monkey in tree. b, Birds. c, Embroidery. d, Mountain. e, Hat seller on beach.

2003, May 14   *Perf. 13¼x12¾*
1674   Vert. strip of 5   6.00 3.00
a.-e. A645 25c Any single   1.00 .50

Artifacts of Pre-Columbian Cultures — A646

No. 1675, 25c: a, Gold bell with monkey. b, Amphora.
No. 1676, 25c: a, Sculpture of a man. b, Three-footed pot.

Perf. 13x13¼
2003, May 16   *Litho.*   *Wmk. 395*
Horiz. pairs, #a-b
1675-1676 A646   Set of 2   4.50 2.25

Central Bank of Ecuador — A647

No. 1677, vert.: a, Tolita Culture mask. b, Guayaquil Historic Park.
$1.05, Pumapungo Museum.

Perf. 13x13¼, 13¼x13
2003, June 5   *Litho.*
1677 A647   25c Horiz. pair,
       #a-b   1.75 .75
1678 A647 $1.05 multi   3.00 1.40

Philately and Guayaquil — A648

No. 1679, horiz.: a, British consular cover to Veracruz with British stamp and cancel. b, Stampless cover.

No. 1680, horiz.: a, SCADTA first flight cover. b, French consular cover to Lima with French stamps and cancels.

$1.05, Philatelic magazines.

$2, Guayaquil Philatelic Club emblem, Ecuadoran stamps, horiz.

2003, July 22   *Perf. 13¾*
1679 A648 40c Vert. pair, #a-
        b   3.50 1.60
1680 A648 40c Vert. pair, #a-
        b   3.50 1.60
1681 A648 $1.05 multi   4.25 2.00
    Nos. 1679-1681 (3)   11.25 5.20

        Size: 100x69mm
           Imperf

1682 A648 $2 multi   8.50 4.50

Guayaquil Urban Renewal — A649

No. 1683: a, Punta Cerro Santa Ana. b, Plaza Colón. c, Malecón Gardens. d, Crystal Palace. e, Plaza de San Francisco.

2003, July 26   *Perf. 13¼x13*
1683   Horiz. strip of 5 19.00 9.50
a.-e. A649 90c Any single   3.50 1.75

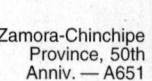

World Bird Festival — A650

Designs: No. 1684, $1.05, Geranoaetus melanoleucus. No. 1685, $1.05, Harpia harpyja, vert.

2003, Sept. 2 *Perf. 13¼x13, 13x13¼*
1684-1685 A650 Set of 2 9.00 4.50

Zamora-Chinchipe Province, 50th Anniv. — A651

No. 1686: a, Shown. b, Eira barbara. c, Boa constrictor. d, Tapirus terrestris. e, Psophia crepitans.

2003, Nov. 7   *Perf. 13¼x13*
1686   Vert. strip of 5 6.00 3.00
a.-e. A651 25c Any single 1.00 .50

America Issue — Flora and Fauna A652

No. 1687: a, Semnornis ramphastinus. b, Bomarea glaucescens.

       Perf. 13x13¼
2003, Nov. 1 *Litho.* *Wmk. 395*
1687 A652 $1.05 Horiz. pair,
        #a-b   7.50 3.75

Selection of Quito as World Heritage Site, 25th Anniv. — A653

Churches: 40c, El Sagrario. No. 1689a, La Compañia de Jesus. No. 1689b, Santa Barbara. $1.05, San Francisco, vert.

2003, Nov. 1 *Perf. 13¼x13, 13x13¼*
1688 A653 40c multi   1.25 .60
1689 A653 90c Horiz. pair,
        #a-b   6.00 3.00
1690 A653 $1.05 multi   3.75 1.90
    Nos. 1688-1690 (3) 11.00 5.50

Christmas — A654

Children's art by: No. 1691a, Stephanie Pacheco. No. 1691b, Sebastián Tejada. 40c, María Claudia Iturralde, vert. 90c, Luis Antonio Ortega. $1.05, Angel Andrés Castro, vert.

2003, Nov. 1
1691 A654 25c Horiz. pair,
        #a-b   1.90 .95
1692 A654 40c multi   1.50 .75
1693 A654 90c multi   3.50 1.75
1694 A654 $1.05 multi   3.75 1.90
    Nos. 1691-1694 (4) 10.65 5.35

Treasures of Guayaquil Municipal Museum — A655

No. 1695: a, Santiago de Guayaquil Act of Independence. b, Punaes ceremonial stone. c, Proclamation of Mariano Donoso. d, Tzantzas. e, Manteño-Huancavilca totem.

2003, Dec. 1   *Perf. 13¼x13*
1695   Horiz. strip of 5 7.00 3.50
a.-e. A655 40c Any single 1.25 .65

Selection of Galapagos Islands as World Heritage Site, 25th Anniv. — A656

No. 1696: a, Zalophus californianus wollebacki. b, Fregata minor palmerstoni. c, Sula nebouxxi excisa. d, Isla Bartolomé. e, Two Sula nebouxxi excisa shaped as "25."

2003, Nov. 26   *Perf. 13x13¼*
1696   Horiz. strip of 5 7.00 3.50
a.-e. A656 40c Any single 1.25 .65

Army Aviation Instruction, 50th Anniv. — A657

No. 1697, 40c: a, Mountain, airplanes, emblem. b, Airplane in flight, men on ground. No. 1698, 40c, horiz.: a, Helicopter and soldiers. b, Airplanes, mountain, people.

2004, Jan. 21 *Perf. 13x13¼, 13¼x13*
     Horiz. pairs, #a-b
1697-1698 A657 Set of 2 6.00 3.00

Military Geographical Institute's Role in National Development A658

2004, Apr. 14   *Perf. 13¼x13*
1699 A658 $1.05 multi   3.25 1.90

Commander Rafael Morán Valverde, Military Hero — A659

2004, Apr. 5   *Perf. 13x13¼*
1700 A659 $1.05 multi   3.75 1.90

Intl. Philately Day A660

No. 1701: a, Ecuador #2, Greece #1. b, Cover with six stamps.

$2, Various stamps, tongs, magnifying glass, stamp catalogues.

2004, May 6   *Perf. 13¼x13*
1701 A660 75c Horiz. pair, #a-b 6.00 3.00

        Imperf
    Size: 100x68mm
1702 A660 $2 multi   7.50 3.75

Ecuadorian Volleyball Federation — A661

     Perf. 13x13¼
2004, May 27 *Litho.* *Wmk. 395*
1703 A661 75c multi   3.00 1.50

2004 Miss Universe Pageant — A662

2004, May 29   *Perf. 13¾*
1704 A662 75c multi   3.00 1.50

Sculpture by Mario Tapia — A663

No. 1705: a, Adolescencia. b, Beato Chaminade. c, Delfin de Galapagos. d, Pelicano. e, Homenaje a Carlo Vidano.
$2, Similar to No. 1705b.

2004, June 1   *Perf. 13¼x13*
1705   Horiz. strip of 5 16.00 8.00
a.-e. A663 90c Any single 2.25 1.10

        Imperf
    Size: 100x69mm
1706 A663 $2 multi   9.00 4.50

Pedro Vicente Maldonado (1704-48), Cartographer — A664

2004, June 25   *Perf. 13¼x13*
1707 A664 90c multi   3.25 1.50

Dr. Agustín Cueva Tamariz (1903-79) — A665

2004, June 30   *Litho.*
1708 A665 90c multi   3.25 1.50

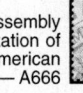

34th General Assembly of the Organization of American States — A666

2004, July 4   *Wmk. 395*
1709 A666 75c multi   3.00 1.50

Dr. Angel Felicísmo Rojas (b. 1909), Writer — A667

2004, July 11
1710 A667 50c multi   2.00 1.00

Ecuadoran and Spanish Postal Money Orders — A668

2004, Aug. 3   *Perf. 13¼x13*
1711 A668 $1.05 multi   3.50 1.90

2004 Summer Olympics, Athens — A669

No. 1712 — 2004 Summer Olympics emblem, Ecuadoran Olympic Committee emblem and: a, 2004 Olympics mascots. b, Alexandra Escobar Guerrero.

2004, Aug. 3   *Perf. 13x13¼*
1712 A669 $1.05 Horiz. pair,
        #a-b   7.50 3.75

Ecuador Orchid Association, 30th Anniv. — A670

Designs: 25c, Cattleya maxima. $1.05, Epidendrum bracteolatum.

2004, Sept. 30
1713-1714 A670 Set of 2 5.00 2.50

Guayaquil Symphony Orchestra — A671

      Perf. 13x13¼
2004, Nov. 19 *Litho.* *Wmk. 395*
1715 A671 90c multi   3.25 1.50

Christmas — A672

Children's art: 40c, Christmas stocking with envelopes. $1.05, Santa Claus giving letter to Christmas tree, horiz.

2004, Dec. 12   Perf. 13x13¼, 13¼x13
1716-1717 A672   Set of 2   5.25 2.50

America Issue - Environmental Protection — A673

Designs: 40d, Buddha and trees. $1.05, Mother Earth.

2004, Dec. 23   Perf. 13x13¼
1718-1719 A673   Set of 2   5.25 2.50

Galapagos Islands Fauna — A674

Designs: 40c, Chelonoidis abingdonii. 90c, Amblyrhynchus cristatus, vert. $2.15, Sula granti. $3, Fregata magnifiscens. $2, Creagrus furcatus, vert.

2005, Feb. 18   Perf. 13¼x13, 13x13¼
1720-1723 A674   Set of 4   24.00 12.00
Imperf
Size: 68x98mm
1724 A674 $2 multi   7.50 3.75

El Mercurio Newspaper, 80th Anniv. — A675

Designs: $1.25, Masthead. $2, Dr. Nicanor Merchan Bermeo, newspaper co-founder. $2.25, Miguel Merchan Ochoa.

2005, Mar. 4   Perf. 13¼x13, 13x13¼
1725-1727 A675   Set of 3   21.50 11.00

Tourism — A676

2005, Mar. 22   Perf. 13¼x13
1728 A676 $3.75 multi   14.00 7.00

Ecuadorian Chess Federation, 25th Anniv. — A677

2005, Apr. 1   Perf. 13x13¼
1729 A677 $1.25 multi   5.00 2.50

Ecuadorian Olympic Academy, 25th Anniv. — A678

Perf. 13x13¼
2005, June 20   Litho.   Wmk. 395
1730 A678 $1.25 shown   4.50 2.50

Imperf
Size: 69x100mm
1731 A678 $2 Emblems   8.50 4.50

Rotary International, Cent. — A679

Rotary emblem and: 40c, Man on Mt. Chimborazo. 90c, People on Mt. Cotopaxi. $2, Man on Mt. Shisha Pangma, Nepal.

2005, June 29   Perf. 13¼x13
1732-1734 A679   Set of 3   12.50 6.25

Guayaquil Conference, 183rd Anniv. — A680

No. 1735 — Guayaquil Philatelic Club emblem and: a, José de San Martín, Argentina #1. b, Simón Bolívar, Venezuela #1. $2, Bolívar, San Martín, monument.

2005, July 22   Perf. 13¼x13
1735 A680 90c Horiz. pair, #a-b   7.50 3.75
Imperf
Size:98x68mm
1736 A680 $2 multi   9.00 4.50

Intl. Year of Books and Reading — A681

Perf. 13x13¼
2005, July 22   Litho.   Wmk. 395
1737 A681 25c multi   1.25 .60

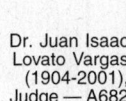

Dr. Juan Isaac Lovato Vargas (1904-2001), Judge — A682

Perf. 13¼x13
2005, July 28   Litho.   Wmk. 395
1738 A682 $1.25 multi   5.75 3.00

Mountain and Eastern Cattleman's Association — A683

No. 1739 — Emblem and: a, Mountains. b, Head of cow.

2005, Aug. 4   Perf. 13x13¼
1739 A683 40c Horiz. pair, #a-b   3.00 3.00

University Sports League of Quito, 75th Anniv. — A684

No. 1740: a, University Sports League Stadium. b, 1969 University Sports League soccer team. c, Emblem. d, Children playing at school. e, Statue of emblem, League Country Club.
$2, Soccer shirt, vert.

2005, Aug. 4   Perf. 13¼x13
1740   Horiz. strip of 5   8.00 4.00
a.-e. A684 40c Any single   1.40 .70
Imperf
Size: 68x98mm
1741 A684 $2 multi   8.00 4.50

15th Bolivarian Games, Armenia and Pereira — A685

2005, Aug. 8   Perf. 13¼x13
1742 A685 25c multi   1.25 .60

A686

Design: 1938 South American Swimming Champions, Trophy and Swimming Federation Emblem.

2005, Aug. 8   Litho.
1743 A686 25c multi   1.25 .60

First Ecuadoran victory in international sports competition.

Virgin of Cisne — A687

2005, Sept. 6   Perf. 13¾
1744 A687 $1.25 multi   5.50 3.00

History of the Ecuadoran Army — A688

No. 1745: a, Troops in Esmeraldas, 1916. b, Military school cadets, 1928. c, Cayambe Battalion. d, Arms and Grandsons of Gen. Eloy Alfaro. e, Imbabura Battalion.
$2, Battle for emancipation of Guayaquil.

2005, Sept. 15   Perf. 13¼x13
1745   Horiz. strip of 5   7.50 4.00
a.-e. A688 40c Any single   1.00 .50
Imperf
Size: 98x67mm
1746 A688 $2 multi   8.00 4.50

Carchi Province Arms — A689

No. 1747: a, Tulcán Canton. b, Bolívar Canton.
No. 1748: a, Carchi Province. b, Huaca Canton. c, Mira Canton. d, Espejo Canton. e, Montúfar Canton.

2005, Sept. 26   Perf. 13x13¼
1747   Horiz. pair   3.00 1.50
a.-b. A689 40c Either single   1.40 .70
1748   Horiz. strip of 5   7.50 3.75
a.-e. A689 40c Any single   1.40 .70

Tourism A690

No. 1749: a, Cerro Santa Ana, Guayaquil. b, Esmereldas. c, Misahualli. d, Tsunki Shuar, Pastaza.
No. 1750: a, Cisne Church, Loja. b, Ingapirca Ruins. c, Seal, Galapagos Islands. d, Sea turtle, Galapagos Islands.

Perf. 13¼x13
2005, Sept. 26   Litho.   Wmk. 395
1749 A690 30c Block of 4, #a-d   5.00 2.50
1750 A690 40c Block of 4, #a-d   6.50 3.25

St. Mariana de Jesús Paredes y Flores — A691

2005, Oct. 19
1751 A691 25c multi   1.10 .60

Popes Reigning in 2005 A692

No. 1752: a, $1.25, Pope John Paul II (1920-2005). b, $2, Pope Benedict XVI.

2005, Oct. 19
1752 A692   Horiz. pair, #a-b   12.50 6.25

Cenepa War With Peru, 10th Anniv. A693

No. 1753: a, Mirage F1-JA airplanes. b, Cessna A-37B airplanes. c, Kfir-C2 airplanes. d, Lt. Col. Carlos Uscategui and airplane.

2005, Oct. 26
1753 A693 $1.25 Block of 4, #a-d   19.00 11.00

First Guayaquil to Cuenca Airmail Flight, 85th Anniv. — A694

No. 1754: a, 25c, Tail of Telegrafo I airplane, flight manager José Abel Castillo. b, $1, Front of Telegrafo I airplane, pilot Elia Liut.

2005, Nov. 12
1754 A694   Horiz. pair, #a-b   5.00 2.75

Ecuadorian Armed Forces in United Nations Peacekeeping Forces — A695

No. 1755: a, Female soldier. b, Two soldiers wearing helmets. c, Soldiers with flags. d, United Nations and Ecuadorian flags, beret of Peacekeeping forces.

2005, Nov. 25   Perf. 13x13¼
1755 A695 75c Block of 4, #a-d   11.50 6.00

Christmas
A696

No. 1756 — Children's drawings by: a, Pamela Alejandra Castillo Rocha. b, Kira Cedeño. c, Silvia Moran Burgos. d, Carol Garcia.

2005, Nov. 25
1756 A696 $1.25 Block of 4,
#a-d   20.00 11.00

19th Cent. Watercolors of Ecuadorians
A697

No. 1757: a, Water bearer. b, Indian governor's wife. c, Dancer. d, Cuenca Indian. e, Municipal council piper. f, Indian carrying skyrockets. g, Woman (Mina gigante). h, Majordomo. i, Society woman (Chola pinganilla). j, Street sweeper.

2005, Nov. 30   *Perf. 13¾*
1757   Block of 10   12.50 6.25
a.-j.   A697 25c Any single   1.00 .50

Publication of Don Quixote, 400th Anniv. — A698

No. 1758 — Drawings of Don Quixote and: a, Windmills. b, Tree.

2005, Dec. 7   *Perf. 13x13¼*
1758 A698 $2 Horiz. pair, #a-b   15.00 8.50

Colonial Religious Art
A699

Colonial Religious Art
A700

No. 1759: a, St. Joseph and Baby Jesus. b, Resurrected Christ. c, Virgin of Quito. d, St. Augustine.
No. 1760: $2, The Divine Shepherd.

2005, Dec. 9
1759 A699 40c Block of 4, #a-d   5.50 3.00

Souvenir Sheet
Imperf
1760 A700 $2 multi   8.00 4.50

El Comercio Newspaper, Cent. (in 2006) — A701

"100" and: No. 1761, Statue at LL, newspaper masthead. No. 1762a, Statue at LR. No. 1762b, Statue in "0." No. 1763, Statue in seal. No. 1764, Statue at LL, newspaper masthead, simulated perforations.

Perf. 13¼x13
2006, Jan. 2   Litho.   Wmk. 395
1761 A701 40c multi   1.75 .85
1762 A701 40c Horiz. pair, #a-b   3.25 1.60
     Size: 55x35mm
     Perf. 13¾
1763 A701 50c multi   2.00 1.00
   Nos. 1761-1763 (3)   7.00 3.45
     Size: 100x69mm
     Imperf
1764 A701 $2 multi   8.00 4.00
     Dated 2006.

Quito Tourism — A702

2006, Jan. 11   *Perf. 13¼x13*
1765 A702 25c multi   1.25 .60
     Dated 2005.

35th Latin American and Caribbean Lions' Club Forum, Quito — A703

Color of oceans: 90c, White. $2, Orange.

2006, Jan. 19   *Perf. 13x13¼*
1766 A703 90c multi   3.75 2.00
     Size: 68x99mm
     Imperf
1767 A703 $2 multi   7.50 4.00

Biodiversity of Puyo — A704

Designs: $1, Cromacris sp. $1.20, Desmodus rotundus.

2006, Mar. 22   *Perf. 13¼x13*
1768-1769 A704 Set of 2   9.50 5.00

America Issue, Fight Against Poverty — A705

Various Pre-Columbian Guayasamin figurines: 40c, 80c, $1, $1.20.

2006, Feb. 12
1770-1773 A705 Set of 4   13.50 7.25

Benito Juarez (1806-72), President of Mexico — A706

2006, Mar. 21   *Perf. 13x13¼*
1774 A706 $1.20 multi   5.00 2.50

Manteña Raft — A707

2006, Mar. 23   *Perf. 13¼x13*
1775 A707 $1 multi   4.00 2.25

Straw Hat Makers — A708

Designs: No. 1776, 40c, Hat maker. No. 1777, 40c, Hat maker wearing hat, vert.

2006, Apr. 8   *Perf. 13¼x13, 13x13¼*
1776-1777 A708   Set of 2   3.50 1.90

Federation of University Students — A709

2006, Apr. 21   *Perf. 13x13¼*
1778 A709 30c multi   1.25 .60

Miracle of Colegio San Gabriel, Cent. — A710

2006, Apr. 21   Wmk. 395
1779 A710 80c multi   3.50 1.90

Ibarra, 400th Anniv. — A711

2006, Apr. 28   *Perf. 13¼x13*
1780 A711   20c shown   .95 .25
     Size: 68x100mm
     Imperf
1781 A711 $2.50 Painting, diff.   10.50 5.50

Baltazara Calderon — A712

2005, May 16   *Perf. 13x13¼*
1782 A712 $1 multi   4.00 2.25

18th Cent. Military Uniforms — A713

No. 1783: a, Compañia Fija de Quito. b, Dragones de Quito. c, Infanteria de Quito. d, Dragones de Guayaquil (gray horse). e, Dragones de Guayaquil (brown horse).

2006, May 18   *Perf. 13¾*
1783   Horiz. strip of 5   4.25 2.10
a.-e.   A713 20c Any single   .70 .25

Mushrooms and Fauna of Podocarpus Park — A714

Designs: 20c, Basidiomicetes. 25c, Tremarctus ornatus. 90c, Harpya harpyja, vert.

Perf. 13¼x13, 13x13¼
2006, May 22   Litho.   Wmk. 395
1784-1786 A714   Set of 3   6.00 3.00

Wolfgang Amadeus Mozart (1756-91), Composer — A715

2006, May 31   *Perf. 13¼x13*
1787 A715 20c multi   .80 .25

UNICEF, 60th Anniv. — A716

Designs: 75c, Child, butterfly, and sun. $1, Children and books.

Perf. 13¼x13
2006, June 1   Litho.   Wmk. 395
1788-1789 A716   Set of 2   7.00 4.00

Eloy Alfaro Military School — A717

2006, June 5
1790 A717 80c multi   3.25 1.90

Banco Pichincha, Cent. — A718

Designs: No. 1791, 1906 1-sucre banknote. No. 1792 — First bank building: a, Denomination at left. b, Denomination at right.

2006, June 8
1791 A718 40c shown   1.80 .90
1792 A718 40c Horiz. pair, #a-b   3.75 1.90

2006 World Cup Soccer Championships, Germany — A719

FIFA emblem and: 40c, World Cup. 80c, 2006 World Cup emblem. $1, Mascot. $1.20, World Cup and flags of competing countries.

Perf. 13¼x13
2006, June 9   Litho.   Wmk. 395
1793-1796 A719   Set of 4   12.50 7.25

World Cup Type of 2006
Perf. 13¼x13
2006, June 9   Litho.   Wmk. 395
Stamps Without FIFA Emblem
With Inscription "COPA MONDIAL
de la FIFA"

1796A	A719	40c Like #1793	16.00	16.00
1797	A719	80c Like #1794	5.25	5.25
1797A	A719	$1 Like #1795	6.75	6.75
1797B	A719	$1.20 Like #1795	8.00	8.00
		Nos. 1796A-1797B (4)	36.00	36.00

2006   Litho.   Wmk. 395   *Imperf.*
Size: 60x40mm
Designs: No. 1797C, Like #1796. No. 1797D, Similar to #1796, but with scores of Ecuador team's first round victories.

1797C	A719	$2 multi	8.00	4.00
1797D	A719	$2 multi	8.00	4.00

A720

Plaza de Mayo Mothers of Argentina — A721

Perf. 13¼x13
2006, June 19   Litho.   Wmk. 395

1798	A720	80c multi	3.50	1.90

Imperf

1799	A721	$2.50 multi	10.50	5.50

Machala Canton, 182nd Anniv. — A722

2006, June 20   Perf. 13¼x13

1800	A722	30c multi	1.25	.60

Machala Canton, 182nd Anniv. A723

Flags of 2006 World Cup Soccer Championship participants, FIFA emblem and: No. 1801, Flag of Ecuador. No. 1802, Soccer shoes and ball.

2006   Litho.   Wmk. 395   *Imperf.*

1801	A723	$2 multi	8.00	4.00
1802	A723	$2 multi	8.00	4.00

2006 World Cup Soccer Championships, Germany.

Garibaldi Italian Assistance Society — A724

2006, July 7   Perf. 13x13¼

1803	A724	90c multi	4.00	2.00

Municipal Railroads — A725

Designs: No. 1804, $1, Steam locomotive. No. 1805, $1, Steam locomotive, vert.

Perf. 13¼x13, 13x13¼
2006, July 20   Litho.   Wmk. 395

1804-1805	A725	Set of 2	8.00	8.00

Souvenir Sheet

Municipal Railroads — A726

Wmk. 395
2006, July 20   Litho.   *Imperf.*

1806	A726	$2 multi	8.00	4.00

Simón Bolívar Experimental College A727

Bolívar A728

2006, July 25   Litho.   Perf. 13x13¼

1807	A727	20c multi	.80	.25

Imperf

1808	A728	$10 multi	40.00	20.00

Spondylus Shell Carvings in National Institute of Cultural Heritage — A729

Designs: 25c, Necklace. No. 1810, vert.: a, Figurine of trader. b, Figurine of fishermen in boat.

2006, July 26   Perf. 13¼x13, 13x13¼

1809	A729	25c multi	1.25	.75
1810	A729	$1 Horiz. pair, #a-b	7.50	8.00

Indian Postal Runner and Ecuador Post Emblem — A730

Background colors: 25c, White. 30c, Dark blue. 40c, Black. 60c, Beige. 80c, Olive green

2006, Aug. 5   Perf. 13x13¼

1811-1815	A730	Set of 5	9.00	5.00

Ecuadorian Olympic Committee — A731

2006, Aug. 15   Litho.

1816	A731	30c multi	1.25	.60

Writers — A732

Designs: $1, Jorge Icaza (1906-78). $1.20, Pablo Palacio (1906-47).

2006, Sept. 18   Wmk. 395

1817-1818	A732	Set of 2	9.00	5.00

Ecuadorian Food — A733

No. 1819: a, Bandera Manabi. b, Viche de Manabi.

2006, Sept. 23   Perf. 13¼x13

1819	A733	$1 Horiz. pair, #a-b	8.50	4.25

Orchids — A734

No. 1820: a, Caucaea olivaceum. b, Cyrtochilum macranthum. c, Miltoniopsis vexillaria. d, Odontoglossum harryanum. e, Cyrtochilum pastasae. f, Cyrtochilum loxense. g, Cyrtochilum eduardii. h, Odontoglossum epidendroides. i, Cyrtochilum retusum. j, Cyrtochilum geniculatum. $2, Cyrtochilum macranthum, diff.

2006, Sept. 29   Perf. 13x13¼

1820		Block of 10	12.00	6.50
a.-j.	A734	30c Any single	1.00	.60

Imperf
Size: 66x95mm

1821	A734	$2 multi	8.50	4.25

America Issue, Energy Conservation A735

Background color: $1, Brown. $1.20, Blue.

2006, Oct. 4   Perf. 13¼x13

1822-1823	A735	Set of 2	9.00	5.00

Natural Fiber Art, by Giti Neuman — A736

Designs: No. 1824, En la Ventana. No. 1825: a, Forma en Movimiento. b, Caminantes. No. 1826, horiz.: a, Caminando. b, Cabezas Huecas.

2006, Oct. 4   Perf. 13x13¼, 13¼x13

1824	A736	30c multi	1.00	.60
1825	A736	30c Vert. pair, #a-b	2.50	1.40
1826	A736	30c Horiz. pair, #a-b	2.50	1.40
		Nos. 1824-1826 (3)	6.00	3.40

Tourism in Otavalo — A737

Designs: 25c, El Lechero tree. 30c, El Jordan Church. 75c, Young girl, vert. $1, Costume for El Coraza Festival, vert.

2006, Oct. 18   Perf. 13¼x13, 13x13¼

1827-1830	A737	Set of 4	10.00	5.25

Eruption of Tungurahua Volcano — A738

No. 1831: a, Ash cloud above volcano. b, Lava flowing down volcano.

2006, Oct. 20   Perf. 13x13¼

1831	A738	$1 Horiz. pair, #a-b	8.00	4.25

Urban Renewal of Guayaquil — A739

No. 1832: a, Municipal Palace, denomination at left. b, Municipal Palace, denomination at right. c, Vulcan forge. d, José Joaquín de Olmedo Airport. e, Bus station.

2006, Oct. 24   Perf. 13¼x13

1832		Horiz. strip of 5	19.00	11.00
a.-e.	A739	$1 Any single	3.50	1.90

Radio Station HCJB, 75th Anniv. — A740

2006, Oct. 26   Wmk. 395

1833	A740	$1 multi	4.50	2.25

Millennium Development Objectives of the United Nations — A741

2006, Oct. 27   Perf. 13¾

1834	A741	$2 multi	8.50	4.25

Pres. Galo Plaza Lasso (1906-87) — A742

Designs: 40c, Photograph. 80c, Tree.

2006, Oct. 27   Perf. 13x13¼

1835-1836	A742	Set of 2	5.00	2.50

German Shepherd Breeding Association A743

2006, Oct. 28   Litho.   Perf. 13¼x13

1837	A743	$1 multi	4.00	2.25

Military Parachuting, 50th Anniv. — A744

Designs: 20c, Soldiers. 40c, Soldiers and airplane. 60c, Soldier and troop emblem. 80c, Paratrooper in air.

Perf. 13¼x13, 13x13¼
2006, Oct. 31   Litho.   Wmk. 395

1838-1841	A744	Set of 4	8.00	4.25

Galapagos Islands
Fauna — A745

No. 1842, horiz.: a, Sea turtle. b, Sea gull. c,
Marine iguana. d, Blue-footed boobies. e, Sea
lion.
80c, Flamingo. $1, Crab. $1.20, Fish.

2006, Nov. 1
1842 A745   30c Horiz. strip of
                    5, #a-e   6.50   3.25
1843 A745   80c multi   3.25   1.60
1844 A745 $1 multi   4.00   2.00
1845 A745 $1.20 multi   5.00   2.50
        Nos. 1842-1845 (4)   18.75   9.35

Christmas — A746

2006, Nov. 28   Perf. 13x13¼
1846 A746   80c multi   3.25   1.60

Monsignor Juan I. Larrea Holguín
(1927-2006) — A747

No. 1847: a, In bishop's robes. b, In judicial
robes.

2006, Dec. 8   Perf. 13¾
1847 A747   40c Horiz. pair, #a-b   3.50   1.90

Freemasonry — A748

Designs: 25c, Masonic altar, beehive. 40c,
Compass and square.

2006, Dec. 11   Perf. 13x13¼
1848-1849 A748   Set of 2   3.00   1.50

Quito Zoo
Animals
A749

No. 1850: a, Parrot. b, Frog.
No. 1851: a, Harpy eagle. b, Jaguar.
$2, Parrot on branch.

2006, Dec. 11   Perf. 13x13¼
1850 A749   60c Horiz. pair, #a-b   5.25   2.40
1851 A749   80c Horiz. pair, #a-b   7.00   3.25
Imperf
Size: 40x65mm
1852 A749 $2 multi   8.50   4.25

Erotic and Fertility
Figurines — A750

Designs: 10c, Nursing mother. 20c, Copu-
lating couple. $1.20, Pregnant woman. $2,
Man with erect penis.

2006, Dec. 12   Perf. 13x13¼
1853-1856 A750   Set of 4   14.50   7.50

Admiral Juan
Illingworth Naval
Museum — A751

Emblem of Ecuador Navy and Illingworth:
20c, On rope ladder, 1880. 25c, As Marine
Guard, 1854.

2006, Dec. 15   Litho.
1857-1858 A751   Set of 2   2.00   1.00

Colors of Ecuador
Flag — A752

2006, Dec. 15   Wmk. 395
1859 A752 $10 multi   35.00 19.00

Postmen and
Bicycles — A753

Color of photograph: 20c, Gray brown. 40c,
Gray blue. 80c, Red.

2006, Dec. 17   Perf. 13¼x13
1860-1862 A753   Set of 3   6.00   3.00

Pets — A754

Designs: 25c, Puppy. 40c, Dog, vert. 50c,
Cat with brown and blue eyes, vert. 80c, Dog
running. $1, Cat with blue eyes, vert.

2006, Dec. 17   Perf. 13¼x13, 13x13¼
1863-1867 A754   Set of 5   12.00   6.00

Cuenca
Biennale — A755

Art by: 5c, Alexander Apóstol. 15c, Ricardo
González Elias, vert.

2006, Dec. 20
1868-1869 A755   Set of 2   1.00   .25

Independence Monument, 50th
Anniv. — A756

No. 1870: a, Head of statue. b, Entire
statue.

2006, Dec. 21   Perf. 13¾
1870 A756   20c Horiz. pair, #a-b   1.80   .90

Quito Fair — A757

Designs: No. 1871, Matador Manolo Caena.
No. 1872 — Matadors: a, Sebastián Cas-
tella. b, El Juli.
No. 1873, horiz. — Quito Bull Ring: a, At
right. b, At left.
$3, Sculpture of Jesus, horiz.

Perf. 13x13¼, 13¼x13
2006, Dec. 27   Litho.
1871 A757   50c multi   2.25   1.25
1872 A757   50c Horiz. pair, #a-b   4.00   2.10
1873 A757   50c Horiz. pair, #a-b   4.00   2.10
        Nos. 1871-1873 (3)   10.25   5.45
Litho. With Foil Application
Imperf
Size: 65x40mm
1874 A757 $3 multi   12.00   6.50

Pirates — A758

No. 1875, vert.: a, Jolly Roger flag, ship, sea
lions. b, Sea lions, ships. c, Ships, Jolly roger
flag. d, Armed pirate on ship. e, Ship, Jolly
Roger flag.
No. 1876: a, Map of Galapagos Islands,
Jolly Roger flag, Sir Francis Drake. b, Ship,
map, skull.
$1, Ship, map, skull, William Dampier.

Perf. 13x13¼, 13¼x13
2006, Dec. 27   Litho.
1875 A758   30c Horiz. strip of 5,
                    #a-e   7.25   3.50
1876 A758   40c Horiz. pair, #a-b   3.75   1.90
1877 A758 $1 multi   5.00   2.50
        Nos. 1875-1877 (3)   16.00   7.90

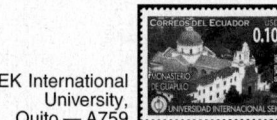

SEK International
University,
Quito — A759

Perf. 13¼x13
2006, Dec. 29   Wmk. 395
1878 A759   10c multi   .75   .40

Scouting,
Cent. — A760

Scout emblem and: 25c, Circles. $2, Scout
and circles.

Perf. 13x13¼
2007, Mar. 29   Litho.   Wmk. 395
1879-1880 A760   Set of 2   8.00   4.00

Hispanic-American
Poetry Festival — A761

2007, Apr. 19
1881 A761   10c multi   .75   .30

Cuenca, 450th
Anniv. — A762

Designs: 40c, Casa de los Arcos (Arch
House). 75c, Vergel Plaza. 80c, Tomebamba
River Gorge, horiz. $3, Cathedral of the
Immaculate Conception.

2007, Apr. 27   Perf. 13x13¼, 13¼x13
1882-1885 A762   Set of 4   15.00   8.75

Prehistoric
Animals — A763

Designs: No. 1886, 80c, Megatherium. No.
1887, 80c, Smilodon, horiz.

2007, May 10
1886-1887 A763   Set of 2   5.75   3.75

Beetles — A764

Designs: No. 1888, Golopha eaucus.
No. 1889: a, Chrysophora chrysochlora. b,
Dynastes hercules.

2007, May 10   Perf. 13¼x13
1888 A764   40c multi   1.50   .75
1889 A764   40c Horiz. pair, #a-b   3.00   1.50

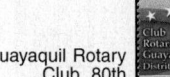

Guayaquil Rotary
Club, 80th
Anniv. — A765

2007, June 1   Wmk. 395
1890 A765   25c multi   .90   .45

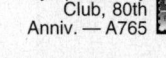

America Issue,
Education For
All — A766

Designs: 40c, Children on school bus. 80c,
Girl doing geometry work. $1, Children flying
kites, vert. $1.20, Student in wheelchair, vert.
$2, Girl and handprints, vert.

2007, June 6   Perf. 13¼x13, 13x13¼
1891-1894 A766   Set of 4   12.00   6.00
Imperf
Size: 40x65mm
1895 A766 $2 multi   7.50   3.75

Naval Institute of
Oceanography, 75th
Anniv. — A767

Antarctic research: 10c, Penguin, ship. $3,
Scientists and scientific equipment, horiz.

2007, July 18   Perf. 13x13¼
1896 A767   10c multi   .40   .30
Perf. 12
Size: 52x32mm
1897 A767 $3 multi   11.00   5.50

Central
Bank of
Ecuador,
80th
Anniv.
A768

2007, Aug. 28   Perf. 12
1898 A768 $2 multi   7.50   3.75

Guayaquil Firefighters — A769

Various firefighers at fires: 5c, 10c, 15c, 25c, $1. 25c and $1 are horiz.

2007, Oct. 10 *Perf. 13x13¼, 13¼x13*
1899-1903 A769 Set of 5 5.50 2.75

Breast Cancer Prevention A770

2007, Oct. 15 *Perf. 13¼x13*
1904 A770 $3 multi 10.25 5.50

Guayaquil Tourism — A771

Designs: 5c, Las Peñas. 10c, Lighthouse, Santa Ana Hill. 15c, El Velero Bridge. 25c, Mercado Sur, horiz. $1, June 5 Bridge, horiz.

2007, Oct. 23 *Perf. 13x13¼, 13¼x13*
1905-1909 A771 Set of 5 5.50 2.25

Cuenca Chamber of Industries, 70th Anniv. — A772

2007, Oct. 25 *Perf. 13¼x13*
1910 A772 $1.20 multi 4.00 2.10

Operation Smile — A773

2007, Nov. 16 *Litho.*
1911 A773 $1 multi 3.75 1.90

Vistazo Magazine, 50th Anniv. — A774

2007, Nov. 29 *Perf. 12*
1912 A774 20c multi .85 .25

Galapagos Islands Fauna — A775

Designs: 40c, Sea turtle. 80c, Penguin. $1, Dolphin. $1.20, Tropicbird.

2007, Nov. 30 *Perf. 13¼x13*
1913-1916 A775 Set of 4 12.00 6.00
Compare with type A780.

Comptroller General, 80th Anniv. — A776

2007, Dec. 3 *Perf. 12*
1917 A776 20c multi .75 .25

2007 Pan American Games, Rio de Janeiro — A777

No. 1918 — Athletes and text noting gold medalists: a, Alexandra Escobar. b, Seledina Nieve. c, Jefferson Perez. d, Xavier Moreno. e, Under-18 soccer team.

2007, Dec. 18 *Perf. 13x13¼*
1918 Horiz. strip of 5 6.75 3.00
a.-e. A777 40c Any single 1.25 .60

Christmas — A778

No. 1919: a, The Annunciation. b, The Three Magi. c, Nativity. d, Flight into Egypt.

2007, Dec. 20 *Perf. 13¼x13*
1919 A778 20c Block of 4, #a-d 3.00 1.40

Guayas Province Transit Commission, 60th Anniv. — A779

Perf. 13x13¼
2008, Jan. 29 *Litho.* *Wmk. 395*
1920 A779 $1 multi 3.00 1.90

Galapagos Islands — A780

Map of islands and: 40c, Pelecanus occidentalis. 80c, Aetobatus narinari. $1, Carcharhinus galapagensis. $1.20, San Cristóbal Windmill Project.

2008, Mar. 18 *Perf. 13¼x13*
1921-1924 A780 Set of 4 10.50 6.00
Compare with Type A775.

Free Maternity and Infant Care A781

2008, Mar. 28 *Perf. 12*
1925 A781 $1 multi 3.75 1.90

Guayaquil Port Authority, 50th Anniv. — A782

2008, Apr. 8
1926 A782 20c multi .75 .25

Tungurahua Chamber of Industry, 80th Anniv. — A783

Wmk. 395
2008, Apr. 24 *Litho.* *Perf. 12*
1927 A783 $3 multi 9.00 5.50

Father Carlos Crespi (1891-1982) — A784

2008, Apr. 30
1928 A784 $2 multi 7.25 3.00

Santiago de Guayaquil Medallion — A785

2008, June 3
1929 A785 30c multi 1.00 .55
Intl. Philately Day.

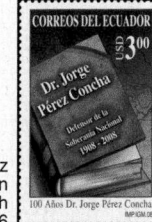

Jorge Pérez Concha, Historian and Diplomat, Birth Cent. — A786

2008, June 4
1930 A786 $3 multi 10.00 5.50

Los Pinos College, Quito, 40th Anniv. — A787

2008, June 6
1931 A787 20c multi .75 .25

Guayaquil-Quito Railway, Cent. — A788

Ecuador No. 174 and: 56c, Steam locomotive. $5, Steam locomotives, Gabriel García Moreno and Gen. Eloy Alfaro.

2008, June 23 *Perf. 12*
1932 A788 56c multi 1.75 1.00
Imperf
Size: 100x70mm
1933 A788 $5 multi 15.00 9.00

Polytechnic School of the Coast, 50th Anniv. — A789

Wmk. 395
2008, July 28 *Litho.* *Perf. 12*
1934 A789 32c multi 1.00 .55

Latin American Youth Year A790

2008, Aug. 20
1935 A790 30c multi 1.00 .55

Ecuadorian Cacao — A791

No. 1936: a, Cacao pod, UL corner of #306. b, Cacao flower, UR corner of #306. c, Cacao processing, LL corner of #306. d, Cacao pods and beans, chocolate candy, LR corner of #306.

2008, Oct. 1 *Perf. 13¼x13*
1936 A791 56c Block of 4, #a-d 7.00 4.00

Meridiano Newspaper, 25th Anniv. — A792

2008, Oct. 22 *Perf. 13x13¼*
1937 A792 60c multi 2.00 1.00

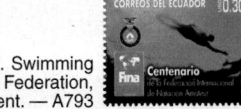

Intl. Swimming Federation, Cent. — A793

No. 1938: a, World Map. b, Ecuadorian swimmer. 30c, Swimmer from underwater.

2008, Oct. 31 *Perf. 13¼x13*
1938 A793 24c Horiz. pair, #a-b 1.25 .60
1939 A793 30c multi .70 .30

Office of the Procurator General, 80th Anniv. — A794

2008, Nov. 11   *Perf. 13x13¼*
1940 A794 25c multi   .60 .25

Guayaquil Chamber of Construction, 40th Anniv. — A795

2008, Nov. 27   *Perf. 13¼x13*
1941 A795 $1 multi   2.50 1.10

New Constitution — A796

Flag and: 32c, Sun behind clouds. $5, People, vert.

2008, Nov. 29   *Perf. 12*
1942 A796 32c multi   .75 .30

Size: 66x95mm
Imperf
1943 A796 $5 multi   10.00 6.00

Santiago de Guayaquil Municipal Museum, Cent. — A797

No. 1944: a, Old musuem building. b, New museum building with murals.
$2, Entrance to old musuem building.

2008, Dec. 16   *Perf. 13¼x13*
1944 A797 60c Horiz. pair, #a-b   3.25 1.50
1945 A797 $2 multi   5.25 2.50

Friendship Between Ecuador and Japan, 90th Anniv. — A798

No. 1945: a, Cotopaxi Volcano, Ecuador. b, Mt. Fuji, Japan.

2008, Dec. 17
1946 A798 30c Horiz. pair, #a-b   1.50 .75

America Issue, National Festivals A799

No. 1947 — Festival of Sts. Peter and Paul: a, Dancers. b, Guitarist.
No. 1948, vert. — Diablada Pillareña: a, Figure with red mask. b, Figure with black mask.

2008, Dec. 23   *Perf. 13¼x13*
1947 A799 20c Horiz. pair, #a-b   1.00 .50

Perf. 13x13¼
1948 A799 $1 Horiz. pair, #a-b   5.00 2.50

Christmas — A800

Various creche figurines of Holy Family and animals with background color of: 30c, Blue.
No. 1949: a, Green. b, Yellow brown.

2008, Dec. 23   *Perf. 13¼x13*
1949 A800 30c multi   .75 .30
1950 A800 80c Horiz. pair, #a-b   4.00 2.00

A801

A802

A803

A804

Jacchigua National Folk Ballet — A805

Perf. 13¼x13
2009, Feb. 18   Litho.   **Wmk. 395**
1951   Horiz. strip of 5   11.00 6.00
   a.   A801 $1 multi   2.00 1.00
   b.   A802 $1 multi   2.00 1.00
   c.   A803 $1 multi   2.00 1.00
   d.   A804 $1 multi   2.00 1.00
   e.   A805 $1 multi   2.00 1.00

Preservation of Polar Regions and Glaciers — A806

Designs: 20c, Feet of polar bear. 80c, Earth in water.

2009, Mar. 31
1952-1953 A806   Set of 2   2.40 1.25

A807

Tourism — A808

Designs: No. 1954, Babahoyo River, Los Ríos Province. No. 1955, Ingapirca Ruins, Cañar Province. No. 1956, Rafters on Quijos River, Napo Province. No. 1957, Marimba group, Esmeraldas Province. $1.25, Tulcán cemetery, Carchi Province. $2, Train and Mt. Chimborazo, Chimborazo Province. $3, Alcea rosea flowers, Morona-Santiago Province. $5, Acrocinus longimanus, Sucumbíos Province.
No. 1962: a, Like #1954. b, Like #1957. c, Like #1958. d, Like #1955. e, Like #1959. f, Like #1956. g, Like #1960. h, Like #1961.
No. 1963: a, Equator Monument, Pichincha Province. b, Colorado Indians, Santo Domingo de los Tsáchilas Province. c, Los Frailes Beach, Manabí Province. d, Banana plantation, El Oro Province. e, Arctocephalus galapagoensis, Galápagos Province. f, Cuicocha Lake, Imbabura Province. g, Harpia harpyja, Pastaza Province. h, Shuar community, Orellana Province.
No. 1964: a, Bolívar and San Martín Monument, Guayas Province. b, The Lovers of Sumpa, Santa Elena Province. c, Pillaro devil, Tungurahua Province. d, Mt. Cotopaxi, Cotopaxi Province. e, Guaranga Indian Monument, Bolívar Province. f, Virgin of Cisne, Loja Province. g, Tomebamba River, Azuay Province. h, Leopardus pardalis, Zamora Province.

Perf. 13¼x13
2009   Litho.   **Wmk. 395**
1954   A807   25c multi   .50 .25
1955   A807   50c multi   1.00 .60
1956   A807   75c multi   1.40 .90
1957   A807 $1 multi   2.00 1.25
1958   A807 $1.25 multi   2.40 1.50
1959   A807 $2 multi   3.75 2.40
1960   A807 $3 multi   5.75 3.50
1961   A807 $5 multi   9.50 6.00
  Nos. 1954-1961 (8)   26.30 16.40

Booklet Stamps
Self-Adhesive
Die Cut
Unwmk.

1962   Booklet pane of 8 + 2 labels   12.50
  a.-b.   A808 25c Either single   .60 .25
  c.-d.   A808 50c Either single   1.25 .50
  e.-f.   A808 75c Either single   1.75 .75
  g.-h.   A808 $1 Either single   2.50 1.00
1963   Booklet pane of 8 + 2 labels   12.50
  a.-b.   A808 25c Either single   .60 .25
  c.-d.   A808 50c Either single   1.25 .50
  e.-f.   A808 75c Either single   1.75 .75
  g.-h.   A808 $1 Either single   2.50 1.00
1964   Booklet pane of 8 + 2 labels   12.50
  a.-b.   A808 25c Either single   .60 .25
  c.-d.   A808 50c Either single   1.25 .50
  e.-f.   A808 75c Either single   1.75 .75
  g.-h.   A808 $1 Either single   2.50 1.00
  Nos. 1962-1964 (3)   37.50

Issued: Nos. 1954-1961, 4/29; Nos. 1962-1964, July.
See Nos. 1985-2000, 2021-2022.

Intl. Philately Day — A809

Perf. 13¼x13
2009, May 6   **Wmk. 395**
1965 A809 75c multi   1.60 .90

Icons of Santa Clara Monastery — A810

No. 1966: a, Angel. b, Jesus Christ. c, Pensive child. d, Protective Virgin. e, Virgin of Quito.

2009, June 9   *Perf. 13x13¼*
1966   Horiz. strip of 5   12.50 6.00
  a.-e.   A810 $1 Any single   2.00 1.00

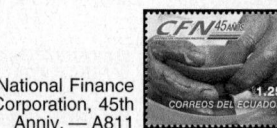

National Finance Corporation, 45th Anniv. — A811

2009, June 22   *Perf. 13¼x13*
1967 A811 $1.25 multi   3.00 1.50

Ambato Electric Company, 50th Anniv. — A812

2009, June
1968 A812 $1 multi   2.50 1.25

Paute-Molino Dam, 25th Anniv. — A813

2009, July 22
1969 A813 $2 multi   5.00 2.50

El Telégrafo Newspaper, 125th Anniv. — A814

2009, July 30   *Perf. 12*
1970 A814 $1.75 multi   4.25 2.10

Call for Independence, Bicent. — A815

Nos. 1971 and 1972 — Doves, butterflies, bell and: a, Open mouth. b, Monument.

2009, Aug. 14   *Perf. 13¼x13*
1971 A815 $3 Horiz. pair, #a-b   14.50 7.25

Souvenir Sheet
With Horizontal Blue Stripe Added to Middle of Stamps
1972 A815 $3 Sheet of 2, #a-b   14.50 7.25

Call for Independence, Bicent. — A816

Serpentine Die Cut 12½x12¼
2009, Aug. 14   Litho.   Unwmk.
Self-Adhesive
Printed on Cork
1973 A816 $3.50 multi   8.25 4.25

Chinese Benevolent Society, Cent. — A817

No. 1974: a, Galápagos tortoise. b, Giant panda.

Perf. 13¼x13
2009, Aug. 18   **Wmk. 395**
1974 A817 25c Horiz. pair, #a-b   1.40 .60

Famous People — A818

No. 1975: a, Carlos Silva Pareja (1909-68), musician. b, Tránsito Amaguaña (1909-2009), Indian rights advocate. c, Demetrio Aguilera Malta (1909-81), writer, diplomat. d, Carlos Zevallos Menéndez (1909-81), archaeologist. e, Humberto Salvador Guerra (1909-82), writer.

2009, Aug. 28   Litho.
1975   Horiz. strip of 5   3.00 1.50
  a.-e.   A818 25c Any single   .50 .25

Ecuadorian Olympic Committee, 50th Anniv. — A819

Designs: No. 1976, 25c, Shooting, cycling, equestrian, wrestling, archery, and basketball. No. 1977, 25c, Diving, running, weight lifting, tennis, boxing and soccer, vert.

2009, Oct. 17   *Perf. 13¼x13, 13x13¼*
1976-1977 A819   Set of 2   1.25 .60

Exportation of Cooperative Open Banking Information System — A820

Perf. 13¼x13

2009, Nov. 5	**Litho.**		**Wmk. 395**
1978	A820	50c multi	1.25 1.00

Loja National University, 150th Anniv. A821

Wmk. 395

2009, Nov. 27	**Litho.**		**Perf. 12**
1979	A821	$2 multi	5.00 2.50

Independence, Bicent. — A822

No. 1980: a, Juan Pío Montúfar (1758-1818), Chairman of Supreme Council of Government. b, José Mejía Lequerica (1777-1813), representative to Cortes of Cadiz. c, Eugenio Espejo (1747-95), journalist, medical pioneer. d, Manuela Cañizares (1769-1814), patriot. e, Bicentenary emblem.

2009, Nov. 28			
1980		Horiz. strip of 5	9.00 4.50
a.-e.	A822	75c Any single	1.50 .75

Charles Darwin (1809-82), Naturalist — A824

No. 1982 — Darwin and: a, Phoenicopterus ruber. b, Ardea herodias. c, Calandria galapagosa. d, Conolopus marthae. e, Sula granti. f, Rhincodon typus. g, Zalophus wollebaeki. h, Phalacrocorax harrisi. i, Geochelone nigra abingdoni. Nos. 1982a-1982h are 35x35mm, No. 1982i is 38mm diameter.

Perf. 13¾x14

2009, Nov. 30			**Unwmk.**
		Granite Paper	
1981	A823	$5 multi	11.00 6.00

Perf. 13¼ ($1), 13¾ ($2)

1982	A824	Sheet of 9	24.00 12.00
a.-h.		$1 Any single	2.00 1.00
i.		$2 multi	4.00 2.00

Christmas — A825

Perf. 13¼x13

2009, Dec. 10			**Wmk. 395**
1983	A825	$1 multi	2.50 1.25

America Issue, Toys and Games A826

No. 1984: a, Paddle and ball. b, Go-cart.

2009, Dec. 18			
1984	A826	$1 Horiz. pair, #a-b	5.25 2.50

Tourism Type of 2009

Designs: No. 1985, The Lovers of Sumpa, Santa Elena Province. No. 1986, Colorado Indians, Santo Domingo de los Tsáchilas Province. No. 1987, Shuar community, Orellana Province. No. 1988, Guaranga Indian Monument, Bolívar Province. No. 1989, Banana plantation, El Oro Province. No. 1990, Virgin of Cisne, Loja Province. No. 1991, Pillaro devil, Tungurahua Province. No. 1992, Equator Monument, Pichincha Province. No. 1993, Cuicocha Lake, Imbabura Province. $1.75, Bolívar and San Martín Monument, Guayas Province. No. 1995, Tomebamba River, Azuay Province. No. 1996, Leopardus pardalis, Zamora Province. No. 1997, Los Frailes Beach, Manabí Province. No. 1998, Harpia harpyja, Pastaza Province. No. 1999, Arctocephalus galapagoensis, Galápagos Province. $5, Mt. Cotopaxi, Cotopaxi Province.

Wmk. 395, 377 (#1986-1987, 1989, 1992, 1993, 1997-1999)

2010-11		**Litho.**	**Perf. 13¼x13**	
1985	A807	25c multi	.50	.25
1986	A807	25c multi	.50	.25
1987	A807	25c multi	.50	.25
1988	A807	50c multi	1.00	.50
1989	A807	50c multi	1.00	.50
1990	A807	$1 multi	2.00	1.00
1991	A807	$1.25 multi	2.50	1.25
1992	A807	$1.25 multi	2.50	1.25
1993	A807	$1.25 multi	2.50	1.25
1994	A807	$1.75 multi	3.50	1.75
1995	A807	$2 multi	4.00	2.00
1996	A807	$2 multi	4.00	2.00
1997	A807	$2 multi	4.00	2.00
1998	A807	$3 multi	6.00	3.00
1999	A807	$3 multi	6.00	3.00
2000	A807	$5 multi	10.00	5.00
		Nos. 1985-2000 (16)	50.50	25.25

Issued: Nos. 1985, 1988, 1991, 1995, 1/20; Nos. 1990, 1994, 1996, 2000, 4/12; Nos. 1986, 1992, 1997, 1998, 9/30; Nos. 1987, 1989, 1993, 1999, 1/24/11.

Miniature Sheet

First Unmanned Ecuadorian Airship — A827

No. 2001: a, $1, Pilot with remote-control device (40x18mm). b, $1, Airship over coastline (40x18mm). c, $1, Airship and mountain (40x18mm). d, $3, Airship (115x42mm).

Wmk. 395

2010, Feb. 7	**Litho.**		**Perf. 14**
2001	A827	Sheet of 4, #a-d	15.00 6.00

Ecuadorian Red Cross, Cent. — A828

No. 2002: a, Old ambulance, blood drop inscribed "Ayuda." b, New ambulance, blood drop inscribed "Cuida." c, Modern Red Cross hard hat, blood drop inscribed "Salva." d, Old Red Cross hard hat, blood drop inscribed "Vida."

Perf. 13¼x13

2010, Mar. 18			**Wmk. 395**
2002	A828	50c Block of 4, #a-d	4.50 2.00

Birds A829

No. 2003: a, Tachycineta albiventer. b, Momotus momota. c, Semnornis ramphastinus. d, Aulacorhynchus haematopygus.

No. 2004, horiz.: a, Ramphocelus carbo. b, Tangara vitriolina.

2010, Apr. 16	**Wmk. 395**		**Perf. 14**
2003	A829	25c Block of 4, #a-d	2.50 1.00

Souvenir Sheet

Perf. 13¼x13

2004	A829	$1.50 Sheet of 2, #a-	
		b	6.25 3.00

No. 2004 contains two 38x27mm stamps. Birdpex 2010, Antwerp, Belgium (No. 2004).

Tall Ships in Velas Sudamérica 2010 — A830

No. 2005, vert. (27x38mm) — Various knots, ships and flags: a, Cisne Branco, Brazil. b, Libertad, Argentina. c, Sagres, Portugal. d, Capitán Miranda, Uruguay. e, Europa, Netherlands. f, Esmerelda, Chile. g, Gloria, Colombia. h, Simón Bolívar, Venezuela. i, Cuauhtémoc, Mexico. j, Juan Sebastián Elcano, Spain.

$1, Training Ship Guayas, Ecuador.

Perf. 13x13¼

2010, May 7			**Wmk. 377**
2005		Block of 10	15.00 7.50
a.-j.	A830	75c Any single	1.50 .75
		Perf. 12	
2006	A830	$1 shown	2.00 1.00

Miniature Sheet

Manuela Sáenz (c. 1797-1856), Mistress of Simón Bolívar — A831

Litho. with Foil Application

2010, May 24			**Imperf.**
2007	A831	$3 multi	6.00 3.00

See Venezuela No. 1707.

2010 World Cup Soccer Championships, South Africa — A832

No. 2008 — Emblem of 2010 World Cup, soccer player, ball and: a, Lion. b, Elephant. c, Zebra.

$5, Mascot of 2010 World Cup, giraffe.

2010, June 9	**Litho.**		**Perf. 13¼x13**
2008		Horiz. strip of 3	6.00 3.00
a.-c.	A832	$1 Any single	2.00 1.00

Souvenir Sheet

Imperf

2009	A832	$5 multi	10.00 5.00

No. 2009 contains one 45x36mm stamp with simulated perforations. Animals on No. 2009 have blurred appearance, but have a three-dimensional appearance when seen through 3-D glasses.

Creation of Tungurahua Province, 150th Anniv. — A833

No. 2010: a, Atelopus ignescens. b, Mt. Tungurahua, flag at Parque de la Familia. c, Casa del Portal Museum.

Perf. 13¼x13

2010, July 1			**Wmk. 377**
2010		Horiz. strip of 3	1.75 .75
a.-c.	A833	25c Any single	.50 .25

Las Floristas, by Camilo Egas A834

2010, July 21			**Perf. 12**
2011	A834	$1.25 multi	2.50 1.25

Campaign against illegal trafficking in historical objects.

Souvenir Sheet

Massacre of Patriots, Bicent. — A835

No. 2012: a, Soldier with sword threatening woman, man and child. b, Soldier threatening to shoot man.

2010, Aug. 2			**Perf. 13x13¼**
2012	A835	$2 Sheet of 2, #a-b, +	
		central label	8.00 4.00

Souvenir Sheet

Philatelic Firsts of Ecuador A836

No. 2013: a, First postmark of Ecuador, 1770, emblem of Philatelic Association of Ecuador. b, First Ecuadorian stamps (#2, 3, 5, 6), emblem of Intl. Federation of Philately. c, Cover from first SCADTA flight, 1928, emblem of 2010 Philatelic Association of Ecuador Expo.

2010, Aug. 25			**Perf. 13¼x13**
2013	A836	$1 Sheet of 3, #a-c	6.00 3.00

Philatelic Association of Ecuador, 75th anniv., and its admission to Intl. Federation of Philately.

Organization of Petroleum Exporting Countries, 50th Anniv. — A837

2010, Sept. 14	**Wmk. 377**		**Perf. 12**
2014	A837	50c multi	1.00 .50

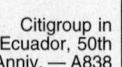

Citigroup in
Ecuador, 50th
Anniv. — A838

2010, Oct. 7 **Perf. 13¼x13**
2015 A838 $1 multi 2.50 1.00

General Directorate of Civil
Registration, Identification and
Certification — A839

2010, Oct. 29 **Litho.** **Perf. 12**
2016 A839 50c multi 1.40 .50

America Issue,
National
Symbols — A840

No. 2017 — National: a, Flag. b, Coat of
arms. c, Anthem.

2010, Nov. 24 **Perf. 13¼x13**
2017 Horiz. strip of 3 6.00 3.00
  a.-c. A840 $1 Any single 2.00 1.00

Christmas — A841

2010, Dec. 3 **Perf. 13x13¼**
2018 A841 $2 multi 5.00 2.00

San José-La Salle
College, Guayaquil,
Cent. — A842

2010, Dec. 16 **Litho.** **Wmk. 377**
2019 A842 25c multi .85 .25

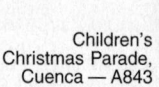

Children's
Christmas Parade,
Cuenca — A843

2010, Dec. 21 **Perf. 13¼x13**
2020 A843 50c multi 1.25 .50

Tourism Type of 2009

No. 2021 — Galapagos Islands fauna: a,
Fregata magnificens. b, Sula dactylatra. c,
Sphenisciforme. d, Sula nebouxi. e,
Conolophus subcristatus. f, Geochelone nigra.
g, Chelonia mydas agassisi. h, Oxycirrhites
typus.
No. 2022 — Galapagos Islands sites and
fauna: a, Bartolomé Island, denomination at L.
b, Bartolomé Island, denomination at R. c,
Zoluphus wallebaeki, denomination at L. d,
Zoluphus wallebaeki, denomination at R. e,
Darwin's Arch, denomination at L. f, Darwin's
Arch, denomination at R. g, Amblyrhynchus
cristatus, denomination at L. h,
Amblyrhynchus cristatus, denomination at R.

2011, Mar. 18 **Unwmk.** **Die Cut**
Self-Adhesive
2021 Booklet pane of 8 + 2
   labels 12.50
  a.-b. A808 25c Either single .50 .25
  c.-d. A808 50c Either single 1.00 .50
  e.-f. A808 75c Either single 1.50 .75
  g.-h. A808 $1 Either single 2.00 1.00
  i. Booklet pane of 8, #a-h, with lilac pane margins 10.00

2022 Booklet pane of 8 + 2
   labels 12.50
  a.-b. A808 25c Either single .50 .25
  c.-d. A808 50c Either single 1.00 .50
  e.-f. A808 75c Either single 1.50 .75
  g.-h. A808 $1 Either single 2.00 1.00
  i. Booklet pane of 8, #a-h, with lilac pane margins 10.00

  Issued: Nos. 2021i, 2022i, 1/13/12. Nos.
2021 and 2022 have gray pane margins.

Souvenir Sheet

Postal Union of the Americas, Spain
and Portugal (UPAEP), Cent. — A844

2011, Mar. 18 **Wmk. 377** **Perf. 12**
2023 A844 $3 multi 7.00 3.00

Souvenir Sheet

Yuri
Gagarin,
First
Man in
Space,
50th
Anniv.
A845

2011, May 6 **Perf. 13x13¼**
2024 A845 $5 multi 10.00 5.00

Intl. Year
of Forests
A846

No. 2025, 50c: a, Chinchona officinalis. b,
Ceiba tichistandra.
No. 2026, 75c, horiz.: a, Jacaranda sp. b,
Prosopis sp.

2011, May 19 **Perf. 13x13¼, 13¼x13**
Horiz. pairs, #a-b
2025-2026 A846 Set of 2 5.00 2.50

Pichincha Chamber of Industries and
Production, 75th Anniv.
A847

Wmk. 377
2011, June 16 **Litho.** **Perf. 12**
2027 A847 $2 multi 4.00 4.00

Christopher
Columbus College,
Guayaquil,
Cent. — A848

2011, July 7 **Perf. 13¼x13**
2028 A848 $1 multi 2.00 2.00

National Telecommunications
Day — A849

No. 2029: a, First Bell telephone, 1876. b,
Western Electric magneto wall telephone,
1894. c, Ericsson wall pay telephone, 1970. d,
Apple iPhone, 2011.

2011, July 8
2029 A849 50c Block of 4, #a-d 4.00 4.00

Miniature Sheet

Seven
Wonders
of Quito
A850

No. 2030: a, Basilica of the National Vow. b,
Virgin of the Panecillo. c, Chimbacalle Railway
Station. d, San Francisco Convent. e, Inde-
pendence Plaza. f, Church of the Society of
Jesus. g, Sanctuary of the Virgin of El
Quinche.

2011, Sept. 8
2030 A850 75c Sheet of 7, #a-
     g, + label 10.50 10.50

Quito, 2011 American Capital of Culture.

Yasuni- ITT
Initiative — A851

No. 2031 — Reptiles: a, Chelonoidis den-
ticulata. b, Anolis trachyderma. c, Thecadacty-
lus solimoensis. d, Epicrates cenchria. e, Den-
dropsophus bifurcus. f, Osteocephalus
taurinus. g, Ranitomeya ventrimaculata. h,
Melanosuchus niger.
No. 2032: a, Clavija procera. b, Duguetia
hadrantha. c, Hymenaea oblongifolia. d, Con-
narus ruber. e, Fungi. f, Theobroma speci-
osum. g, Brownea gradiceps. h, Apeiba
membranacea.

Unwmk.
2011, Sept. 20 **Litho.** **Die Cut**
Self-Adhesive
2031 Booklet pane of 8 + 2
   labels 11.00
  a.-b. A851 25c Either single .50 .25
  c.-d. A851 50c Either single 1.00 .50
  e.-f. A851 75c Either single 1.50 .75
  g.-h. A851 $1 Either single 2.00 1.00
2032 Booklet pane of 8 + 2
   labels 11.00
  a.-b. A851 25c Either single .50 .25
  c.-d. A851 50c Either single 1.00 .50
  e.-f. A851 75c Either single 1.50 .75
  g.-h. A851 $1 Either single 2.00 1.00

See Nos. 2061-2062.

Intl. Year
For
People
of
African
Descent
A852

No. 2033 — Musical instruments: a,
Marimba. b, Guasá. c, Maracas. d, Cununos.

Perf. 13¼x13
2011, Sept. 26 **Litho.** **Wmk. 395**
2033 A852 $1 Block of 4, #a-d 8.00 4.00

Flowers — A853

Designs: 25c, Passiflora manicata. $2, Pas-
siflora pinnatistipula. $3, Herrania balaensis.
$5, Passiflora arborea.

Perf. 13x13¼
2011, Sept. 26 **Litho.** **Wmk. 377**
2034-2037 A853 Set of 4 20.50 20.50

Trains
A854

Railroad
Stations
A855

No. 2038 — Locomotives: a, 1992 GEC
Alsthon. b, 1900 Baldwin. c, 1900 Baldwin,
diff. d, 1935 Baldwin. e, 1992 GEC Alsthon on
hillside. f, Front of 1992 GEC Alsthon. g, 1953
Baldwin. h, Baldwin XXXX.
No. 2039 — Stations at: a, Machachi. b,
Latacunga. c, Sibambe. d, Durán. e, El
Tambo. f, Riobamba. g, Chimbacalle. h,
Boliche.

2011, Oct. 3 **Unwmk.** **Die Cut**
Self-Adhesive
2038 Booklet pane of 8 + 2
   labels 11.00
  a.-b. A854 25c Either single .50 .25
  c.-d. A854 50c Either single 1.00 .50
  e.-f. A854 75c Either single 1.50 .75
  g.-h. A854 $1 Either single 2.00 1.00
2039 Booklet pane of 8 + 2
   labels 11.00
  a.-b. A855 25c Either single .50 .25
  c.-d. A855 50c Either single 1.00 .50
  e.-f. A855 75c Either single 1.50 .75
  g.-h. A855 $1 Either single 2.00 1.00

Exports
A856

No. 2040: a, Wicker basket. b, Chocolate. c,
Wooden automobile. d, Hats. e, Textiles. f,
Leather goods. g, Filigree. h, Tagua carvings.

Perf. 13¼x13
2011, Oct. 11 **Wmk. 395**
2040 A856 50c Block of 8, #a-h,
    + central label 9.00 8.00

Intl. Day for Disaster
Reduction — A857

No. 2041: a, Volcano eruption. b, Landslide.
c, Flood, d, Earthquake.

2011, Oct. 12 **Perf. 13¼**
2041 A857 $1.25 Block of 4,
    #a-d 12.50 10.00

Mail Boxes and Postal
Transportation — A858

Designs: No. 2042, $1.75, 1928 mailbox,
bicycle. No. 2043, $1.75, 2011 mailbox,
motorcycle.
$5, Mailbox, Post Office Bay, Galápagos
Islands, vert.

Perf. 13½x13¾
2011, Nov. 28 **Wmk. 377**
2042-2043 A858 Set of 2 8.00 7.00
Souvenir Sheet
Perf. 13x13¼
2044 A858 $5 multi 12.50 10.00

America issue. No. 2044 contains one
28x38mm stamp.

Christmas
A859

No. 2045: a, Holy Family. b, Angel.

2011, Nov. 29   *Perf. 13½x13¾*
2045 A859 $1 Horiz. pair, #a-b   4.00 4.00

2011 Pan-American Games, Guadalajara, Mexico — A860

Emblem, sports equipment and athletes: a, Karate. b, Weight lifting. c, Kayaking. d, Boxing. e, Rollerblading.

2011, Nov. 30
2046   Horiz. strip of 5   3.00 2.50
a.-e. A860 25c Any single   .50 .50

Guayaquil Chamber of Industries, 75th Anniv. A861

2011, Dec. 14   **Wmk. 377**
2047 A861 $2 multi   4.00 4.00

Ecuador Cancer Society, 60th Anniv. — A862

2011, Dec. 19   *Perf. 13¼x13*
2048 A862 75c multi   1.50 .75

Pres. Luis Cordero (1833-1912) A864

2012, Mar. 1   *Perf. 13¾x13½*
2051 A864 $1 multi   2.00 2.00

Flowers — A865

Designs: $1, Barnadesia spinosa. $2, Bixa orellana. $3, Espeletia pycnophylla. $5, Brugmansia sanguinea.

Perf. 13½x13¾
2012, Mar. 28   **Unwmk.**
2052-2055 A865   Set of 4   22.00 22.00

Souvenir Sheets

Sinking of the Titanic, Cent. A866

Designs: No. 2056, $4, Titanic, sepia-toned image. No. 2056, $4, Titanic and Olympic at dock.

Perf. 13¾x13½
2012, Apr. 20   **Wmk. 377**
2056-2057 A866   Set of 2   16.00 16.00

Bananas A867

Perf. 13½x13¾
2012, May 17   **Litho.**   **Wmk. 377**
2058 A867 $2 multi   4.00 4.00

Banco de Machala, 50th anniv.

Catholic University of Santiago, Guayaquil, 50th Anniv. — A868

2012, May 31   *Perf. 13¾*
2059 A868 $1 multi   2.00 2.00

Miniature Sheet

Guayaquil Tourist Attractions — A869

No. 2060: a, Hemiciclo la Rotonda (monument honoring meeting of Simón Bolívar and José de San Martín). b, Malecón del río Guayas (Guayas River Walk). c, Metropolitan Cathedral. d, Torre del Reloj (Clock Tower). e, Malecón del Salado (Salado Walk). f, Edificio del Municipio (City Hall). g, Las Peñas Cerro Santa Ana (Santa Ana Hill).

2012, June 8   **Wmk. 377**
2060 A869 75c Sheet of 7, #a-g, + label   14.00 10.50

Yasuni-ITT Type of 2011
No. 2061 — Flora and fauna: a, Dasypodidae. b, Saimiri sciureus. c, Tettigoniidae. d, Automeris postalbida. e, Brownea sp. f, Aristolochia sp. g, Hypsiboas sp. h, Hypsiboas geographicus.
No. 2062 — Birds: a, Morphnus guianensis. b, Sarcorhamphus papa. c, Ara ararauna. d, Harpia harpyja. e, Trochilidae sp. f, Ramphastos tucanus. g, Pteroglossus pluricinctus. h, Pionus menstruus.

2012, June 11   **Unwmk.**   *Die Cut*
Self-Adhesive
2061   Booklet pane of 8 + 2 labels   11.00
a.-b. A851 25c Either single   .50 .50
c.-d. A851 50c Either single   1.00 1.00
e.-f. A851 75c Either single   1.50 1.50
g.-h. A851 $1 Either single   2.00 2.00
2062   Booklet pane of 8 + 2 labels   11.00
a.-b. A851 25c Either single   .50 .50
c.-d. A851 50c Either single   1.00 1.00
e.-f. A851 75c Either single   1.50 1.50
g.-h. A851 $1 Either single   2.00 2.00

Galapagos Islands Landscapes and Fauna — A870

No. 2063: a, Rocks in surf. b, Head of Amblyrhynchus cristatus. c, Numenius phaeopus. d, South Plaza Island. e, Pinnacle Rock, Bartolomé Island. f, Sula nebouxi. g, Chelonoidis sp. h, Kicker Rock (Leon Dormido), San Cristóbal Island.
No. 2064: a, Zalophus wollebaeki. b, Geospiza magnirostris. c, Sula granti. d, Fregata magnificens. e, Microlophus bivittatus. f, Spheniscus mendiculus. g, Anas bahamensis. h, Sphyrna lewini.

2012, July 11   **Unwmk.**   *Die Cut*
Self-Adhesive
Water Droplets on Blue Depicted in Frames Around Stamps
2063   Booklet pane of 8   11.00
a.-b. A870 25c Either single   .50 .25
c.-d. A870 50c Either single   1.00 .50
e.-f. A870 75c Either single   1.50 .75
g.-h. A870 $1 Either single   2.00 1.00
i. Booklet pane of 8, #a-h, with pane margins depicting rocks   10.00
2064   Booklet pane of 8   11.00
a.-b. A870 25c Either single   .50 .25
c.-d. A870 50c Either single   1.00 .50
e.-f. A870 75c Either single   1.50 .75
g.-h. A870 $1 Either single   2.00 1.00
i. Booklet pane of 8, #a-h, with pane margins depicting rocks   10.00

Issued: Nos. 2063i, 2064i, 10/8. See Nos. 2094-2095.

Guayas Sports Federation, 90th Anniv. — A871

No. 2065: a, Shooting (tiro). b, Wrestling (lucha). c, Kayaking (canotaje). d, Boxing (boxeo). e, Weight lifting (pesas).

Perf. 13¾x13½
2012, July 25   **Wmk. 377**
2065   Horiz. strip of 5   5.00 2.50
a.-e. A871 50c Any single   1.00 .50

A872

Legacy of the Revolution of 1895 — A873

No. 2066: a, Ecuador #129, Matilde Huerta, first Ecuadoran female postal official, 1895. b, Bolívar College, Tulcán, first lay college, 1896. c, Civil Registration Law, 1900. d, School of Fine Arts, Quito, 1904. e, Opening of Guayaquil-Quito Railroad, 1908. f, Founding of Guayaquil Worker's Society, 1903. g, Creation of Independence Plaza, Quito, 1909. h, Map of South America, José Marti, Eloy Alfaro, and Augusto César Sandino, 1911.
$3, Alfaro, locomotive.

2012, July 31   *Perf. 13¾x13½*
2066 A872 25c Sheet of 8, #a-h   4.00 2.00

Souvenir Sheet
Imperf
2067 A873 $3 multi   6.00 3.00

Enrique Gil Gilbert (1912-73), Writer — A874

2012, Aug. 8   *Perf. 13¾x13½*
2068 A874 $1 multi   2.00 1.00

Souvenir Sheet

Steamship Ecuador — A875

No. 2069 — Emblem of 2012 Ecuador Philatelic Society Stamp Exposition and: a, Ship's stern and flag. b, Ship's bow.

Litho. (Foil Application in Margin)
2012, Aug. 16   *Perf. 13½x13¾*
2069 A875 $3 Sheet of 2, #a-b, gold inscription in sheet margin   15.00 6.00
c. As #2069, silver inscription in sheet margin   15.00 6.00
d. As #2069, red metallic inscription in sheet margin   15.00 6.00

Miniature Sheet

Moths — A876

No. 2070: a, Getta baetifica. b, Sematura diana. c, Xylophanes pyrrhus. d, Leucanella contempta.

Perf. 13¾x13½
2012, Aug. 28   **Litho.**
2070 A876 50c Sheet of 4, #a-d   4.50 2.00

Quito Chamber of Construction, 50th Anniv. — A877

Construction materials: No. 2071, $1, Timber (madera). No. 2072, $1, Bamboo (guadua). No. 2073, $1, Wattle (bahareque). No. 2074, $1, Compacted mud (tapial).

2012, Sept. 4   *Perf. 13½x13¾*
2071-2074 A877   Set of 4   10.50 4.00

America Issue — A878

Myths and legends: No. 2075, $2, Legend of Ayer. No. 2076, $2, Legend of the Rooster of the Cathedral, vert.

Perf. 13¾x13½, 13½x13¾
2012, Sept. 17
2075-2076 A878   Set of 2   4.75 4.00

Nelson Estupiñán Bass (1912-2002), Writer — A879

2012, Sept. 20   *Perf. 13¾x13½*
2077 A879 $2 multi   5.00 2.00

Alexander von Humboldt (1769-1859), Naturalist — A880

Denominations: 50c, $2.

2012, Sept. 26   **Wmk. 377**
2078-2079 A880 Set of 2   5.00 2.50
Friendship between Ecuador and Germany, 125th anniv.

A881   Trains — A882

No. 2080: a, Baldwin No. 3 Ingenio Valdez. b, Baldwin No. 2 Inés María. c, Baldwin No. 12 C.F.F.E. d, Baldwin No. 37 G&Q. e. Baldwin No. 7 G&Q. f, Baldwin No. 3 Quito-Esmeraldas train. g, Baldwin No. 2 Yaguachi train. h, Baldwin No. 1 Curaray train.

No. 2081: a, Baldwin No. 53. b, Gec Alsthom No. 2408. c, Gec Alsthom No. 2405. d, Baldwin No. 17. e, Baldwin No. 58. f, Gec Alsthom No. 2407 and station. g, Gec Alsthom No. 2404. h, Gec Alsthom No. 2407.

No. 2082: a, Baldwin No. 58, diff. b, Gec Alsthom No. 2404, diff. c, Gec Alsthom No. 2406. d, Baldwin No. 53, diff. e, Gec Alsthom No. 2402. f, Baldwin No. 58 on bridge. g, Baldwin No. 17, diff. h, Gec Alsthom No. 2405, diff.

2012, Oct. 8   Unwmk.   Die Cut
Self-Adhesive
2080   Booklet pane of 8   11.00
a.-b. A881 25c Either single   .50   .25
c.-d. A881 50c Either single   1.00   .50
e.-f. A881 75c Either single   1.50   .75
g.-h. A881 $1 Either single   2.00   1.00
2081   Booklet pane of 8   11.00
a.-b. A882 25c Either single   .50   .25
c.-d. A882 50c Either single   1.00   .50
e.-f. A882 75c Either single   1.50   .75
g.-h. A882 $1 Either single   2.00   1.00
2082   Booklet pane of 8   11.00
a.-b. A882 25c Either single   .50   .25
c.-d. A882 50c Either single   1.00   .50
e.-f. A882 75c Either single   1.50   .75
g.-h. A882 $1 Either single   2.00   1.00

Jesuit Institutions — A883

Schools: No. 2083, $1, Unidad Educativa Borja, 75th anniv. No. 2084, $1, Unidad Educativa San Felipe Neri, 175th anniv. No. 2085, $1.25, Colegio San Gabriel, 150th anniv. $5, Jesuit church and emblem.

Perf. 13¾x13½
2012, Oct. 29   Wmk. 377
2083-2085 A883   Set of 3   9.00 3.25
Size: 100x70mm
Imperf
2086 A883 $5 multi   10.00 10.00
Permanent return of Jesuits to Ecuador, 150th anniv.

Renovation of Guayas Government Palace — A884

2012, Nov. 6   Perf. 13½x13¾
2087 A884 $5 multi   13.00 10.00

Ecuadorian Army's Communications Group, 50th Anniv. — A885

No. 2088: a, Indian messenger. b, Men and wagon transporting radiotelegraphic station, 1924. c, Bicycle messengers, 1932. d, Communication transmission school building, 1942.

2012, Nov. 14
2088   Horiz. strip of 4   2.50 2.00
a.-d. A885 25c Any single   .50   .50

Guayaquil Beneficence Council, 125th Anniv. — A886

2012, Nov. 27   Perf. 13¾x13½
2089 A886 $3 multi   7.50 6.00

Miniature Sheet

Guayas Tourism A887

No. 2090: a, Crucifix. b, Rock climbers. c, Fishermen in boats. d, Rice farmer. e, Cacao farmer. f, Sugar processing.

2012, Nov. 29
2090 A887 75c Sheet of 6, #a-f,
           + 2 labels   10.50 9.00

Christmas — A888

Icons: No. 2091, $1, Bethlehem Portal, Concepción Monastery, Quito. No. 2092, $1, Mystery, Carmen Alto Monastery, Quito.

2012, Dec. 3   Wmk. 377
2091-2092 A888   Set of 2   4.50 4.00

Military Leaders A889

No. 2093: a, Gen. Eloy Alfaro (1842-1912). b, Col. Carlos Concha Torres (1864-1919). c, Col. Luis Vargas Torres (1855-87).

2012, Dec. 14   Rouletted 13½
2093   Horiz. strip of 3   9.00 7.50
a.-c. A889 $1.25 Any single   2.50 2.50

Galapagos Islands Type of 2012

No. 2094: a, Rock with carving of face, Isla Floreana. b, Phoebastria irrorata. c, Carcharhinus galapagensis. d, Chelonia mydas. e, Pterophyllum scalare. f, Sleeping Lion Rock, San Cristóbal. g, Flower. h, Isla Plaza Sur.

No. 2095: a, Fregata magnificens. b, Post barrel, Post Office Bay, Isla Floreana. c, Camarhynchus pallidus. d, Pyrocephalus rubinus. e, Buteo galapagoensis. f, Isla Bartolomé. g, Red reef fish. h, Vicente Roca Point.

2013, Jan. 16   Unwmk.   Die Cut
Self-Adhesive
2094   Booklet pane of 8   11.00
a.-b. A870 25c Either single   .50   .50
c.-d. A870 50c Either single   1.00   1.00
e.-f. A870 75c Either single   1.50   1.50
g.-h. A870 $1 Either single   2.00   2.00
2095   Booklet pane of 8   11.00
a.-b. A870 25c Either single   .50   .50
c.-d. A870 50c Either single   1.00   1.00
e.-f. A870 75c Either single   1.50   1.50
g.-h. A870 $1 Either single   2.00   2.00

Miniature Sheet

TAME Airlines, 50th Anniv. A890

No. 2096: a, DC-3. b, DC-6B. c, Avro 748. d, Electra II. e, Boeing 727-200. f, Embraer E-190. g, Airbus A320. h, ATR 42-500.

2013, Feb. 8   Wmk. 377   Perf. 13½
2096 A890 25c Sheet of 8, #a-h,
           + central label   5.50 4.00

Hat Making A891

No. 2097: a, Unfinished hats (orange panel). b, Hat maker (blue panel). c, Hat maker, diff. (red panel).

2013, Mar. 18   Perf. 13¼
2097   Horiz. strip of 3   3.50 3.00
a.-c. A891 50c Any single   1.00 1.00

Scout Group No. 14, Guayaquil, 50th Anniv. — A892

Litho. With Foil Application
Perf. 13½x13¾
2013, June 21   Wmk. 377
2098 A892 $1 multi   2.50 2.00

Launch of Pegasus NEE-01 (First Ecuadorian Satellite) — A893

Perf. 13¾x13½
2013, June 28   Litho.
2099 A893 $2 multi   4.50 4.00

Diplomatic Relations Between Dominican Republic and Ecuador, 75th Anniv. A894

2013, July 2   Perf. 13½x13¾
2100 A894 $1 multi   2.00 2.00

Popes Francis and Benedict XVI A895

Litho. With Foil Application
2013, July 3   Wmk. 377
2101 A895 $5 multi   10.00 10.00

June 24, 2012 Death of Pinta Island Tortoise, Lonesome George — A896

Lonesome George and: $3, Surf spray. $25, Trees.

Litho. With Grit Affixed
Perf. 13½x13¼
2013, July 4   Unwmk.
2102 A896 $3 multi   6.00 6.00
Litho.
Wmk. 377
Size: 91x71mm
Imperf
2103 A896 $25 multi   52.50 50.00

Dr. Ricardo Descalzi (1912-90), Writer and Physician — A897

Perf. 13½x13¾
2013, Aug. 1   Litho.   Wmk. 377
2104 A897 $3 multi   6.50 6.00

Volcanos — A898

No. 2105: a, Mt. Chimborazo. b, Mt. Cotopaxi. c, Mt.Tungurahua.

Perf. 13¾x13½
2013, Aug. 21   Litho.   Wmk. 377
2105   Horiz. strip of 3   1.75 1.50
a.-c. A898 25c Any single   .50   .50

Flower With Black and White Faces, Dr. Martin Luther King, Jr. — A899

Perf. 13¾x13½
2013, Oct. 22   Litho.   Wmk. 377
2106 A899 $1 multi   2.00 2.00
America issue (campaign against discrimination).

Royal Audience of Quito, 450th Anniv. — A900

Designs: 25c, Hernando de Santillán y Figueroa (1519-75), First President of the Royal Audience of Quito. $5, Map of the Royal Audience of Quito.

Perf. 13¾x13½

2013, Nov. 13 Litho. Wmk. 377
2107 A900 25c multi .60 .50

Size: 74x94mm

Imperf

2108 A900 $5 multi 10.00 10.00

Ecuadorian Presence in the Antarctic, 25th Anniv. — A901

No. 2109: a, Pygoscelis papua. b, Leptonychotes weddellii. c, Catharacta lonnbergi.

Wmk. 377

2013, Nov. 21 Litho. Perf. 13½
2109 Horiz. strip of 3 3.00 3.00
a.-c. A901 50c Any single 1.00 1.00

Miniature Sheet

Christmas — A902

No. 2110: a, Annunciation (Primer día). b, Visitation of St. Elizabeth (Segundo día). c, St. Joseph's dream (Tercer día). d, Journey to Bethlehem (Cuarto día). e, Arrival at the inn (Quinto día). f, Star of Bethlehem (Sexto día). g, Shepherds (Séptimo día). h, Angels (Octavo día). i, Holy Family (Noveno día).

Perf. 13½x13¼

2013, Nov. 29 Litho. Wmk. 377
2110 A902 25c Sheet of 9, #a-i 5.50 4.50

Intl. Year of Quinoa — A903

No. 2111: a, Chenopodium quinoa. b, Amaranthus caudatus. c, Lupinus mutabilis.

Perf. 13¾x13½

2013, Dec. 16 Litho. Wmk. 377
2111 Horiz. strip of 3 12.00 12.00
a.-c. A903 $2 Any single 4.00 4.00

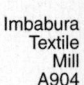

Imbabura Textile Mill A904

No. 2112: a, Workers near weaving machines. b, Workers near machines with thread spools.

Rouletted 12¼

2014, Jan. 27 Litho. Wmk. 377
2112 A904 $1 Horiz. pair, #a-b 4.00 4.00

Resolution of Ecuador-Peru Border Dispute, 15th Anniv. — A905

Rouletted 12¼

2014, Jan. 30 Litho. Wmk. 377
2113 A905 $5 multi 10.00 10.00

Presidents of Ecuador — A906

No. 2114: a, Juan José Flores A. (1800-64). b, Vicente Rocafuerte B. (1783-1847). c, Vicente Roca R. (1792-1858). d, Diego Noboa A, (1789-1870). e, José M. Urbina V. (1808-91). f, Francisco Robles G. (1811-93). g, Gabriel García M. (1821-75). h, Jerónimo Carrión P. (1804-73). i, Javier Espinosa E. (1815-70). j, Antonio Borrero C. (1827-1911). k, Ignacio de Vientemilla V. (1828-1908). l, José M. Camaño (1837-1900). m, Antonio Flores J. (1833-1915). n, Luis Cordero C. (1833-1912). o, Eloy Alfaro D. (1842-1912). p, Leonidas Plaza G. (1865-1932). q, Lizardo García S. (1844-1937). r, Emilio Estrada C. (1855-1911). s, Alfredo Baquerizo M. (1859-1951). t, José L. Tamayo T. (1858-1947). u, Gonzalo S. córdova R. (1863-1928). v, Isidro Ayora C. (1879-1978). w, Juan D. Martínez M. (1875-1955). x, José M. Velasco I. (1893-1979). y, Aurelio Mosquera N. (1883-1939). z, Carlos A. Arroyo (1893-1969). aa, Mariano Suárez V. (1897-1980). ab, Carlos J. Arosemena T. (1888-1952). ac, Galo Plaza L. (1906-87). ad, Camilo Ponce E. (1912-76). ae, Carlos J. Arosemena M. (1919-2004). af, Otto Arosemena G. (1925-84). ag, Jaime Roldós A. (1940-81). ah, León Febres Cordero R. (1931-2008).

Perf. 13¾x13½

2014, Apr. 1 Litho. Wmk. 377
2114 Sheet of 34 + label 20.00 17.00
a.-ah. A906 25c Any single .50 .50

Hugo R. Chávez (1954-2013), President of Venezuela — A907

Perf. 13¾x13½

2014, Apr. 14 Litho. Wmk. 377
2115 A907 50c multi 1.00 1.00

Parade of Tall Ships, Manabí A908

No. 2116 — Ship and national flag: a, Cisne Branco, Brazil. b, Cuauhtémoc, Mexico. c, Gloria, Colombia. d, Libertad, Argentina. e, Esmerelda, Chile. f, Guayas, Ecuador. g, Simón Bolívar, Venezuela.

Perf. 13½x13¾

2014, May 3 Litho. Wmk. 377
2116 Sheet of 7 + label 10.50 10.50
a.-g. A908 75c Any single 1.50 1.50

Intl. Philately Day A909

Magnifying glass over: $2, Ecuadorian stamps. $3, Text from El Nacional.

2014, May 22 Litho. Perf. 13½x13¾
2117 A909 $2 multi 4.00 4.00

Size: 90x70mm

Wmk. 395

Imperf

2118 A909 $3 multi 6.00 6.00

Regional Platform for Disaster Risk Reduction in the Americas, Guayaquil A910

Perf. 13½x13¾

2014, May 27 Litho. Wmk. 377
2119 A910 $1 multi 2.00 2.00

2014 World Cup Soccer Championships, Brazil — A911

Designs: 50c, Stadium and stylized Ecuador soccer player. $3, Stylized Ecuador soccer player in stadium, Christ the Redeemer Statue, Rio de Janeiro, horiz. $5, Soccer player and field, horiz.

Perf. 13½x13¾, 13¾x13½

2014, June 18 Litho. Wmk. 377
2120-2121 A911 Set of 2 7.00 7.00

Size: 55x35mm

Imperf

2122 A911 $5 multi 10.00 10.00

Pancho Segura, Ecuadorian-born Tennis Player — A912

Designs: 25c, Segura on tennis court as young man. $5, Segura, tennis ball and racquet, Ecuadoran flag.

Perf. 13½x13¾

2014, July 25 Litho. Wmk. 377
2123-2124 A912 Set of 2 10.50 10.50

Intl. Year of Family Farming — A913

Designs: 75c, Woman near tree. $1, Woman spinning yarn from wool. $2, Man pulling down cacao pod from tree.

Perf. 13¾x13½

2014, Aug. 11 Litho. Wmk. 377
2125-2127 A913 Set of 3 8.50 7.50

2014 Latin American Integration Association Expo, Montevideo, Uruguay — A914

Perf. 13½x13¾

2014, Aug. 28 Litho. Wmk. 377
2128 A914 $3 multi 6.00 6.00

Mural by Oswaldo Guayasamín — A915

No. 2129: a, Denomination at left. b, Denomination at right.

Perf. 13¾x13½

2014, Aug. 29 Litho. Wmk. 377
2129 A915 25c Horiz. pair, #a-b 1.00 1.00

Latin American Parliament, 50th anniv.

Luis Vernaza Hospital, 450th Anniv. A916

No. 2130: a, Hospital building. b, Doctor examining patient.

Perf. 13½x13¾

2014, Sept. 10 Litho. Wmk. 377
2130 A916 50c Horiz. pair, #a-b 2.75 2.00

Miniature Sheet

Scorpions — A917

No. 2131: a, Centruroides margaritatus. b, Teuthraustes atramentarius. c, Tityus asthenes. d, Tityus crassicauda. e, Tityus ythieri.

Perf. 13¾x13½

2014, Sept. 30 Litho. Wmk. 377
2131 A917 $5 Sheet of 5, #a-e, + label 50.00 50.00

Yachay University Buildings — A918

No. 2132: a, Capitular Building. b, Library.

Perf. 13¾x13½

2014, Oct. 21 Litho. Wmk. 377
2132 A918 $2 Horiz. pair, #a-b 11.00 8.00

Oryx Leucoryx, Vultur Gryphus, Flags of Ecuador and Qatar — A919

Litho. With Foil Application
Perf. 13½x13¾

2014, Oct. 22 Wmk. 377
2133 A919 $10 multi 20.00 20.00

See Qatar No. 1101.

Manuela Espejo (c. 1757-c. 1829), Writer — A920

Litho. With Foil Application
Perf. 13½x13¾

2014, Oct. 28 Wmk. 377
2134 A920 $5 metallic blue & blue 13.00 10.00

America issue.

Electricity Generation Projects — A921

Designs: 75c, Baba Dam. $1.25, Wind generators, Villonaco. $2, Mazar Dam.

Perf. 13½x13¾

2014, Oct. 31 Litho. Wmk. 377
2135-2137 A921 Set of 3 8.00 8.00

Fall of the Berlin Wall, 25th Anniv. — A922

Perf. 13¾x13½
2014, Nov. 10   Litho.   Wmk. 377
2138 A922 75c multi   1.50 1.50

Christmas — A923

Designs: 50c, Ivory creche figurines, 18th cent. $1, Wood carving of Infant Jesus, by Caspicara, vert.

Perf. 13¾x13½, 13½x13¾
2014, Nov. 25   Litho.   Wmk. 377
2139-2140 A923 Set of 2   3.00 3.00

Miniature Sheet

Cuenca Tourist Attractions — A924

No. 2141: a, Rio Tomebamba. b, Mayor's office (Alcaldía). c, Benigno Malo College. d, Interamerican Artisans Center. e, New Cathedral. f, Azuay Provincial Court. g, Plaza de las Flores.

Perf. 13¾x13½
2014, Dec. 2   Litho.   Wmk. 377
2141 A924 75c Sheet of 7, #a-g, + label   10.50 10.50

Miniature Sheet

First Ecuadorian Postage Stamps, 150th Anniv. — A925

No. 2142: a, Emilia Rivadeneira (1839-1916), engraver. b, Printing press, Ecuador #3. c, Printing press, Ecuador #2. d, Printing press, Ecuador #5. e, Manuel Rivadeneira (1814-94), printer.

Litho. With Foil Application
Perf. 13¾x13½
2015, Mar. 19   Wmk. 377
2142 A925 $5 Sheet of 5, #a-e, + 4 labels   65.00 50.00

Insects — A926

No. 2143: a, Antianthe expansa. b, Heteronotus abbreviatus. c, Cyphonia clavata. d, Guayaquila gracilicornis. e, Stegaspis frondiia. f, Thuris depressus. g, Tritropidia galeata. h, Membracis mexicana.

Unwmk.
2015, Apr. 21   Litho.   Die Cut
Self-Adhesive
2143   Booklet pane of 8   10.00
a.-b.   A926 25c Either single   .50   .50
c.-d.   A926 50c Either single   1.00 1.00
e.-f.   A926 75c Either single   1.50 1.50
g.-h.   A926 $1 Either single   2.00 2.00

Pres. Sixto Durán Ballén and Dove — A927

Perf. 13½x13¾
2015, May 15   Litho.   Wmk. 377
2144 A927 $1.25 multi   2.50 2.50

Insects — A928

No. 2145: a, Alchisme grossa. b, Membracis foliata. c, Cladonota apicalis. d, Cyphonia trifida. e, Adippe histrio.

Perf. 13½x13¾
2015, May 28   Litho.   Wmk. 377
2145   Horiz. strip of 5   30.00 30.00
a.-e.   A928 $3 Any single   6.00 6.00

Cattle — A929

Breeds: 75c, Aberdeen Angus. $1.25, Brahman. $3, Holstein Friesian.

Perf. 13½x13¾
2015, June 2   Litho.   Wmk. 377
2146-2148 A929 Set of 3   14.50 10.00
Eradication of hoof-and-mouth disease in Ecuador.

Renovation of San Francisco Monastery, Quito — A930

Designs: 25c, Friar Jodoco Ricke baptizing indigenous people. 50c, Icon of Jesus, San Francisco Church. $1, San Francisco Church and Plaza. $1.75, Franciscan monk making beer. $2, Religious procession.

Perf. 13½x13¾
2015, June 11   Litho.   Wmk. 377
2149-2153 A930 Set of 5   13.00 11.00

Birds — A931

Designs: 25c, Grallaria ridgelyi. 50c, Amazona lilacina. $1, Atlapetes pallidiceps. $2, Pyrrhura albipectus. $3, Chaetocercus berlepschi.

Perf. 13½x13¾
2015, June 16   Litho.   Wmk. 377
2154-2158 A931 Set of 5   15.00 13.50

Visit of Pope Francis to Ecuador — A932

Perf. 13¾x13½
2015, June 30   Litho.   Wmk. 377
2159 A932 $3 multi   8.50 6.00

Litho. With Foil Application
Size: 100x70mm
Imperf
2160 A932 $5 Pope Francis, diff.   14.00 10.00

Official Registrar, 120th Anniv. — A933

Perf. 13¾x13½
2015, Sept. 1   Litho.   Wmk. 377
2161 A933 $1.50 multi   3.25 3.00

Famous People — A934

No. 2162: a, Antonio Bastidas y Carranza (1615-81), poet. b, Raúl Clemente Huerta (1915-91), politician. c, Morayma Ofyr Carvajal (1915-51), writer. d, José Modesto Espinosa (1833-1915), writer. e, José Cuero y Caicedo (1735-1815), bishop of Quito.

Perf. 13¾x13½
2015, Sept. 22   Litho.   Wmk. 377
2162   Horiz. strip of 5   13.50 12.50
a.-e.   A934 $1.25 Any single   2.50 2.50

Miniature Sheet

ExpoAFE,150th Anniv. — A935

No. 2163: a, Argentina #594, flag of Argentina. b, Unissued Bolivia stamp of 1863, flag of Bolivia. c, Brazil #3252c, flag of Brazil. d, Canada #322, flag of Canada. e, Chile #348A, flag of Chile. f, Colombia #C56, flag of Colombia. g, Costa Rica #1, flag of Costa Rica. h, Cuba #432, flag of Cuba. i, Ecuador #306, flag of Ecuador. j, El Salvador #509, flag of El Salvador. k, Cover of *El Coleccionista Ecuatoriano*, emblem of Ecuadorian Philatelic Association. l, Block of six of Ecuador #2, ExpoAFE 80th anniv. emblem. m, Cover to Lima, emblem of ExpopAFE thematic stamp exhibition. n, Cover depicting airplane, emblem of FIAF thematic stamp exhibition. o, Postal card, FIAF emblem. p, Spain #345, flag of Spain. q, United States #C3a, flag of United States. r, Guatemala #21, flag of Guatemala. s, Mexico #246, flag of Mexico. t, Panama #214, flag of Panama. u, Paraguay #407, flag of Paraguay. v, Peru #C338, flag of Peru. w, St. Pierre & Miquelon #136, flag of St. Pierre & Miquelon. x, Uruguay #1167, flag of Uruguay. y, Venezuela #C9, flag of Venezuela.

Perf. 13½x13¾
2015, Sept. 29   Litho.   Wmk. 377
2163 A935   Sheet of 25   40.00 37.50
a.-y.   75c Any single   1.50 1.50

Birds — A936

No. 2164: a, Tangara florida. b, Acropternis orthonyx. c, Pipreola jucunda. d, Pionopsitta pyrilia. e, Semnornis ramphastinus. f, Trogon chionurus. g, Pipra filicauda. h, Dacnis egregia.
No. 2165: a, Thryothorus nigricapillus. b, Neomorphus radiolosus. c, Phoenicircus nigricollis. d, Tangara gyrola. e, Aegolius harrisii. f, Grallaricula lineifrons. h, Melanopareia elegans. h, Piculus rivolii.

Unwmk.
2015, Oct. 20   Litho.   Die Cut
Self-Adhesive
2164   Booklet pane of 8   11.00
a.-b.   A936 25c Either single   .50   .50
c.-d.   A936 50c Either single   1.00 1.00
e.-f.   A936 75c Either single   1.50 1.50
g.-h.   A936 $1 Either single   2.00 2.00
2165   Booklet pane of 8   11.00
a.-b.   A936 25c Either single   .50   .50
c.-d.   A936 50c Either single   1.00 1.00
e.-f.   A936 75c Either single   1.50 1.50
g.-h.   A936 $1 Either single   2.00 2.00

Don Quixote in Art A937

No. 2166, $1 — Depictions of Don Quixote by: a, Carlos Monsalve. b, Ernesto Saá Sevilla.
No. 2167, $1.50 — Depictions of Don Quixote by: a, Oswaldo Viteri. b, Vilma Vargas.
No. 2168, $1.75, horiz. — Depictions of Don Quixote by: a, Joaquín Pinto. b, Karlomán Villota.

Perf. 13½x13¾, 13¾x13½
2015, Oct. 30   Litho.   Wmk. 377
Horiz. Pairs, #a-b
2166-2168 A937 Set of 3   17.00 17.00

A938

A939

Tourism — A940

No. 2169: a, Chelonia mydas. b, Vicugna vicugna. c, Paleosuchus trigonatus. d, Megaptera novaeangliae. e, Marine iguana. $5, Tortoise, caiman, whale, condor.
No. 2171: a, Corallus batesii. b, San Rafael Waterfall. c, Dasyatis brevis. d, Gardner Bay Beach, Española Island, Galapagos Islands. e, Ceratophrys stolzmanni. f, Ship on Guayas River. g, Coeligena torquata. h, El Vado, Cuenca.
No. 2172: a, Hippocampus ingens. b, Amblyrhynchus cristatus. c, Prionurus laticlavius. d, Fregata magnificens. e, Spheniscus mendiculus. f, Boats near Isabela Island, Galapagos Islands. g, Roca Pináculo, Bartolomé Island, Galapagos Islands. h, Boats near Plaza Islands, Galapagos Islands.

Perf. 13¾x13½
2015, Nov. 11   Litho.   Wmk. 377
2169   Horiz. strip of 5   10.00 10.00
a.-e.   A938 $1 Any single   2.00 2.00
Imperf
2170 A939 $5 multi   10.00 10.00
Self-Adhesive
Unwmk.
Die Cut
2171   Booklet pane of 8   11.00
a.-b.   A940 25c Either single   .50   .50
c.-d.   A940 50c Either single   1.00 1.00
e.-f.   A940 75c Either single   1.50 1.50
g.-h.   A940 $1 Either single   2.00 2.00
2172   Booklet pane of 8   11.00
a.-b.   A940 25c Either single   .50   .50
c.-d.   A940 50c Either single   1.00 1.00
e.-f.   A940 75c Either single   1.50 1.50
g.-h.   A940 $1 Either single   2.00 2.00

Campaign to End Violence Against Women — A941

Perf. 13¾x13½
2015, Nov, 25   Litho.   Wmk. 377
2173 A941 $5 multi   10.00 10.00
See Dominican Republic No. 1583, Guatemala No. 717, El Salvador No. 1747, Venezuela No. 1731.

Campaign Against Human Trafficking — A942

Perf. 13½x13¾
2015, Nov. 22   Litho.   Wmk. 377
2174 A942 $1.50 multi   3.50 3.00
America Issue.

Christmas — A943

Perf. 13½x13¾
2015, Dec. 3   Litho.   Wmk. 377
2175 A943 $2 multi   4.00 4.00

Yachay, City of Knowledge — A944

Perf. 13¾x13½
2016, Mar. 31   Litho.   Wmk. 377
2176 A944 $2 multi   5.50 4.00

Amphibians — A945

No. 2177: a, Epipedobates anthonyi. b, Hyloscirtus princecharlesi, c, Oophaga sylvatica. d, Ceratophrys stolzmanni. e, Gastrotheca riobambae. f, Hyalinobatrachium aureoguttatum. g, Hypsiboas picturatus. h, Atelopus balios.

Unwmk.
2016, Mar. 31   Litho.   Die Cut
Self-Adhesive
2177   Booklet pane of 8   12.50
a.-b. A945 25c Either single   .50   .50
c.-d. A945 50c Either single   1.00 1.00
e.-f. A945 75c Either single   1.50 1.50
g.-h. A945 $1 Either single   2.00 2.00

Quito Central Lions Club, 70th Anniv. — A946

Perf. 13½x13¾
2016, Apr. 27   Litho.   Wmk. 377
2178 A946 $5 multi   14.00 10.00

Ecuador Postal Service, 185th Anniv. A947

No. 2179: a, Chasqui (relay messenger). b, Postman on bicycle. c, Postal worker on motorcycle. d, Old Quito Post Office, 185th anniv. emblem.

Perf. 13½x13¾
2016, May 25   Litho.   Wmk. 377
2179 A947 10c Block of 4, #a-d   1.50   .80

Miniature Sheet

2016 Summer Olympics, Rio de Janeiro — A948

No. 2180: a, Swimming. b, Running. c, Weight lifting. d, Boxing.

Perf. 13¾x13½
2016, Aug. 16   Litho.   Wmk. 377
2180 A948 $1.25 Sheet of 4,
       #a-d   10.00 10.00

Colegio Intisana, Quito, 50th Anniv. — A949

Perf. 13½x13¾
2016, Oct. 24   Litho.   Wmk. 377
2181 A949 $2 multi   5.75 4.00

Jamaica Letter, by Simón Bolívar, 200th Anniv. (in 2015) A950

No. 2182: a, Portrait of Bolívar, by Antonio Salguero. b, Jamaica Letter, ribbon in colors of Ecuadorian flag.

Perf. 13½x13¾
2016, Oct. 28   Litho.   Wmk. 377
2182 A950 $10 Horiz. pair, #a-
       b   55.00 40.00

Coca Codo Sinclair Hydroelectric Project — A951

Designs: $1.25, Dam. $1.50, Compensating reservoir. $1.75, Generators.

Perf. 13¾x13½
2016, Oct. 25   Litho.   Wmk. 377
2183-2185 A951   Set of 3   13.00 9.00

Flowers — A952

No. 2186: a, Cyrtocaucaea. b, Masdevallia. c, Hippeastrum sp. d, Gentianella hirculus. e, Bomarea caldasii.

Perf. 13¾x13½
2016, Nov. 12   Litho.   Wmk. 395
2186   Horiz. strip of 5   12.00 10.00
a.-e. A952 $1 Any single   2.00 2.00

Third French-Ecuadorian Geodesic Mission — A953

No. 2187: a, Drawing of people near globe. b, Mt. Chimborazo.

Perf. 13¾x13½
2016, Nov. 14   Litho.   Wmk. 377
2187 A953 10c Horiz. pair, #a-b   .75   .40

Society for Protection of Children — A954

Perf. 13½x13¾
2016, Nov. 22   Litho.   Wmk. 377
2188 A954 $5 multi   14.00 10.00

Santa Elena Petroleum Ancón Oil Well — A955

Perf. 13¾x13½
2016, Nov. 30   Litho.   Wmk. 377
2189 A955 30c multi   .75   .60

Christmas — A956

No. 2190: a, Shepherd and sheep, volcano. b, Star of Bethlehem, Andean village. c, Annunciation, Galapagos turtle. d, Three Magi in Ecuadorian Indian costumes. e, Afro-American Holy Family.

Perf. 13¾x13½
2016, Dec. 12   Litho.   Wmk. 377
2190   Horiz. strip of 5   27.50 20.00
a.-e. A956 $2 Any single   4.00 4.00

Union of South American Nations Summit, Quito — A957

Perf. 13¾x13½
2016, Dec. 22   Litho.   Wmk. 377
2191 A957 $3 multi   8.50 6.00

Ecuadorian Institute for Promotion of Exportation and Investment — A958

No. 2192: a, Dam, emblem for 2016 Ecuador Investment Summit. b, Spiral and "love life." c, Hats. d, Cacao pods. e, Onions, bananas, herbs, shrimp.

Perf. 13½x13¾
2016, Dec. 29   Litho.   Wmk. 377
2192   Horiz. strip of 5   15.00 10.00
a.-e. A958 $1 Any single   2.00 2.00

A959

Schools A960

No. 2193: a, Hands, emblem of Ecuador University of Arts. b, Book, quill pen, emblem of National University of Ecuador.
No. 2194: a, Buckminsterfullerene molecule, emblem for Yachay Tech. b, Frog, emblem for Amazon Regional University.

Perf. 13½x13¾
2016, Dec. 30   Litho.   Wmk. 377
2193 A959 $3 Horiz. pair, #a-b 17.00 12.00
2194 A960 $3 Horiz. pair, #a-b 17.00 12.00

Carnival, Guaranda — A961

No. 2195: a, Aerial view of Guaranda. b, Guitarist.

Perf. 13¾x13½
2017, Feb. 24   Litho.
2195 A961 $1 Horiz. pair, #a-b   5.00 4.00

Ants — A962

No. 2196: a, Atta cephalotes (Hormiga arriera). b, Eciton hamatum (Hormiga legionaria). c, Daceton armigerum (Hormiga cazadora). d, Acanthoponera minor (Conga enana). e, Ectatomma tuberculatum (Hormiga rugosa). f, Gigantiops destructor (Hormiga ojona). g, Neoponera villosa (Hormiga peluda). h, Cephalotes atratus (Cabezona negra).
No. 2197: a, Cephalotes spinosus (Hormiga paracaidista). b, Odontomachus hastatus (Hormiga mandibula). c, Pheidole xanthogaster (Hormiga zanahoria). d, Myrmelachista ruszkii (Hormiga limón). e, Leptogenys pucuna (Hormiga de Lattke). f, Eciton rapax (Hormiga rapaz). g, Paraponera clavata (Conga). h, Camponotus sericeiventris (Hormiga aterciopelada).

Unwmk.
2017, Mar. 31   Litho.   Die Cut
Self-Adhesive
2196   Booklet pane of 8   16.00
a.-b. A962 25c Either single   .50   .50
c.-d. A962 50c Either single   1.00 1.00
e.-f. A962 75c Either single   1.50 1.50
g.-h. A962 $1 Either single   2.00 2.00
2197   Booklet pane of 8   16.00
a.-b. A962 25c Either single   .50   .50
c.-d. A962 50c Either single   1.00 1.00
e.-f. A962 75c Either single   1.50 1.50
g.-h. A962 $1 Either single   2.00 2.00

Miniature Sheet

World Philately Day A963

No. 2198: a, Emblem of Olympic and Sports Philatelic Association of Ecuador. b, 1883 cover with Ecuador #18. c, 1895 cover with Guaranda provisional surcharge stamps. d, 1896 cover with bisected Seebeck stamp and other Ecuador stamps.

Litho., Litho With Foil Application (#2198a)

Perf. 13¾x13½

2017, May 18   **Wmk. 377**

2198 A963 $2.50 Sheet of 4,
     #a-d   32.50 20.00

German School,
Quito,
Cent. — A964

Perf. 13¼x13

2017, Oct. 3   **Litho.**   **Wmk. 377**

2199 A964 $5 multi   16.00 10.00

Darwin and Wolf
Islands Marine
Sanctuary — A965

No. 2200: a, Darwin Island and Darwin
Arch. b, Sphyrna lewini. c, Rhincodon typus. d,
Aetobatus narinari. e, Darwin Arch. f, Chelonia
mydas. g, Delphinus delphis. h, Sula nebouxii.

Unwmk.

2017, Oct. 24   **Litho.**   **Die Cut**

Self-Adhesive

2200   Booklet pane of 8   17.00
   a.-b.   A965 25c Either single   .50   .50
   c.-d.   A965 50c Either single   1.00   1.00
   e.-f.   A965 75c Either single   1.50   1.50
   g.-h.   A965 $1 Either single   2.00   2.00

Amazon Regional Economic
Development Institute
(ECORAE) — A966

No. 2201: a, Communication between Amazon cultures. b, Bridge, Morona-Santiago
Province.

Perf. 13¼x13

2017, Nov. 2   **Litho.**   **Wmk. 377**

2201 A966 $2.50 Horiz. pair,
     #a-b   16.00 10.00

A967

Tourism — A968

No. 2202: a, Train, Guamote Canton. b,
Chimborazo Volcano. c, San Rafael Waterfall.
d, San Lorenzo Beach. e, Negra Beach.
No. 2203: a, Caucaea nubigena. b, Handroanthus chrysanthus. c, Sula granti. d,
Podocnemis expansa. e, Oreotrochilus. f,
Cuyabeno River. g, Los Frailes Beach. h, San
Francisco Church, Quito.

Perf. 13¼x13

2017   **Wmk. 377**

2202   Horiz. strip of 5   37.50 30.00
   a.-e.   A967 $3 Any single   6.00   6.00

Self-Adhesive

Unwmk.

Die Cut

2203   Booklet pane of 8   12.50
   a.-b.   A968 25c Either single   .50   .50
   c.-d.   A968 50c Either single   1.00   1.00
   e.-f.   A968 75c Either single   1.50   1.50
   g.-h.   A968 $1 Either single   2.00   2.00

America issue. Issued: No. 2202, 12/27; No.
2203, 11/27.

Christmas — A969

Perf. 13x13¼

2017, Dec. 18   **Litho.**   **Wmk. 377**

2204 A969 $2 multi   4.50 4.00

Eugenio Espejo
National Prize — A970

Perf. 13x13¼

2017, Dec. 21   **Litho.**   **Wmk. 377**

2205 A970 $10 multi   31.00 20.00

15th Interamerican
Scout Jamboree,
Ecuador — A971

Perf. 13x13¼

2017, Dec. 29   **Litho.**   **Wmk. 377**

2206 A971 $5 multi   12.50 10.00

Souvenir Sheet

Locomotives — A972

No. 2207: a, Model of Sapucai locomotive.
b, Baldwin steam locomotive.

Perf. 13¼x13

2018, Apr. 27   **Litho.**   **Wmk. 377**

2207 A972 $2.50 Sheet of 2,
     #a-b, + 2 labels   10.00 10.00

Joint Issue between Ecuador & Paraguay.
See Paraguay No. 3083.

Spiders — A973

No. 2208: a, Micrathena pilaton. b, Patrera
fulvastra.
No. 2209: a, Argiope argentata. b,
Chrysometa tenuipes.
No. 2210: a, Micrathena raimondi. b,
Micrathena pichincha.
$5, Linothele quori.

Perf. 13x13¼

2018, May 9   **Litho.**   **Wmk. 377**

2208   Horiz. pair   1.20   .80
   a.-b.   A973 20c Either single   .40   .40
2209   Horiz. pair   3.00   2.00
   a.-b.   A973 50c Either single   1.00   1.00
2210   Horiz. pair   12.00   8.00
   a.-b.   A973 $2 Either single   4.00   4.00
2211 A973 $5 multi   15.00 10.00
   Nos. 2208-2211 (4)   31.20 20.80

A974

Domesticated
Animals — A975

No. 2212: a, Lama glama. b, Cavia porcellus. c, Bos primigenius taurus. d, Ovis
orientalis aries. e, Equus ferus caballus.
No. 2213: a, Anser anser. b, Gallus gallus.
c, Canis lupus familiaris. d, Felis silvestris
catus. e, Capra aegagrus hircus. f, Oryctolagus cuniculus. g, Equus ferus caballus. h,
Lama glama.

Perf. 13¼x13

2018, May 18   **Litho.**   **Wmk. 377**

2212   Horiz. strip of 5   30.00 20.00
   a.-e.   A974 $2 Any single   4.00   4.00

Self-Adhesive

Unwmk.

Die Cut

2213   Booklet pane of 8   12.50
   a.-b.   A975 25c Either single   .50   .50
   c.-d.   A975 50c Either single   1.00   1.00
   e.-f.   A975 75c Either single   1.50   1.50
   g.-h.   A975 $1 Either single   2.00   2.00

University of Azuay,
50th Anniv. — A976

Designs: $3, Emblem. $5, Emblem and
trees, horiz.

Perf. 13x13¼

2018, June 14   **Litho.**   **Wmk. 377**

2214 A976 $3 multi   9.00 6.00

Imperf

Size: 96x71mm

2215 A976 $5 multi   15.00 10.00

Nelson Mandela
(1918-2013),
President of South
Africa, and Flag of
South
Africa — A977

Perf. 13x13¼

2018, July 18   **Litho.**   **Wmk. 377**

2216 A977 $10 multi   30.00 20.00

Miniature Sheet

Diplomatic Relations Between Ecuador
and Japan, Cent. — A978

No. 2217: a, Kinkaku-ji Temple, Kyoto,
Japan. b, Torii, Itsukushima Shrine, Miyajima,
Japan. c, Church of the Society of Jesus,
Quito. d, Darwin's Arch, Galapagos Islands.

Wmk. 377

2018, Aug. 13   **Litho.**   **Perf. 13**

2217 A978 $2.50 Sheet of 4,
     #a-d   30.00 20.00

Volcanoes — A979

No. 2218: a, Corazón Volcano. b, Imbabura
Volcano. c, Cotacachi Volcano.

Wmk. 377

2018, Aug. 20   **Litho.**   **Perf. 13**

2218   Horiz. strip of 3   15.00 12.00
   a.-c.   A979 $2 Any single   4.00   4.00

Souvenir Sheet

12th Latin American Botanical
Congress, Quito — A980

Perf. 13¾x13½

2018, Aug. 29   **Litho.**   **Wmk. 377**

2219 A980 $4 multi   10.00 8.00

A981

Green Tourism — A982

No. 2220: a, Amblyrhynchus cristatus. b,
Mount Carihuairazo. c, Machalilla National
Park. d, Paleosuchus trigonatus.
No. 2221: a, Zalophus wollebaeki. b, Isabela
Island. c, Chalcostigma herrani. d, Espelitia
plants, Páramo el Angel Ecological Reserve.
e, Oophaga sylvatica. f, Cayapas Mataje
Reserve. g, Cebuella pygmaea. h, Lake, Orellana Province.

Perf. 13¾x13½

2018, Sept. 13   **Litho.**   **Wmk. 377**

2220 A981 $2 Block of 4, #a-d 25.00 16.00

Self-Adhesive

Die Cut

Unwmk.

2221   Booklet pane of 8   15.00
   a.-b.   A982 25c Either single   .50   .50
   c.-d.   A982 50c Either single   1.00   1.00
   e.-f.   A982 75c Either single   1.50   1.50
   g.-h.   A982 $1 Either single   2.00   2.00

A983   A984

Image of the
Motherland Mural,
by Oswaldo
Guayasamín
A985

Perf. 13¾x13½

2018, Sept. 18   **Litho.**   **Wmk. 377**

2222   Horiz. strip of 3   9.50 6.00
   a.   A983 $1 multi   2.00 2.00
   b.   A984 $1 multi   2.00 2.00
   c.   A985 $1 multi   2.00 2.00

Christmas — A986

No. 2223: a, Buildings. b, Magi on camels.
c, Holy Family. d, Angel with horn. e, Shepherd and sheep.

Perf. 13¾x13½

2018, Nov. 30   **Litho.**   **Wmk. 377**

2223   Horiz. strip of 5   1.25 1.25
   a.-e.   A986 10c Any single   .25   .25

Miniature Sheet

Scientific Contributions of San Francisco University, Quito — A987

No. 2224: a, 25c, Rhincodon typus. b, 50c, Geospiza magnirostri. c, 75c, Oreotrochilus cyanolaemus. d, $1, Tiputinia foetida. e, $1.25, Cebuella pygmaea. f, $1.50, Vaccinium floribundum. g, $2, Microlophus bivittatus. h, $2.50, Chimerella mariaelenae. i, $5, University crest.

Perf. 13½x13¾

2018, Dec. 11	**Litho.**		**Wmk. 377**
2224	A987	Sheet of 9, #a-i	32.50 29.50

A988

Cotacachi-Cayapas Ecological Reserve, 50th Anniv. — A989

No. 2225: a, Podiceps occipitalis. b, Odocoileus virginiannus. c, Cuicocha Lake. d, Elaenia albiceps. e, Epidendrum jamiesonis.

No. 2226: a, Eira barbara. b, Tremarctos ornatus. c, Geranoaetus melanoleucus. d, Anisgomathus igniventris. e, Eriocnemis nigrivestis. f, Cerro Pilavo. g, Bomarea glaucenscens. h, Vaccinium floribundum.

Perf. 13¾x13½

2018, Dec. 27	**Litho.**	**Wmk. 377**
2225	Horiz. strip of 5	32.50 30.00
a.-e.	A988 $3 Any single	6.00 6.00

Self-Adhesive
Unwmk.
Die Cut

2226	Booklet pane of 8	12.50
a.-b.	A989 25c Either single	.50 .50
c.-d.	A989 50c Either single	1.00 1.00
e.-f.	A989 75c Either single	1.50 1.50
g.-h.	A989 $1 Either single	2.00 2.00

National Development Plan — A990

Perf. 13¾x13½

2018	**Litho.**	**Wmk. 377**
2227	A990 $5 multi	16.50 10.00

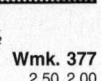

2019 Global Forum on Miigration and Development, Quito — A991

Perf. 13¾x13½

2019, Apr. 8	**Litho.**	**Wmk. 377**
2228	A991 $1 multi	2.50 2.00

Birds — A992

No. 2229: a, Turdus fuscater. b, Zonotrichia capensis. c, Sicalis flaveola. d, Thraupis bonariensis. e, Mimus gilvus. f, Pyrocephalus rubinus. g, Diglossa sittoides. h, Notiochleidon cyanoleuca.

No. 2230: a, Sporophila luctuosa. b, Dendroica fusca. c, Thraupis episcopus. d, Zenaida auriculata. e, Camptostoma obsoletum. f, Patagona gigas. g, Pheucticus chrysogaster. h, Euphonia cyanocephala.

Unwmk.

2019, May 2	**Litho.**		**Die Cut**

Self-Adhesive

2229	Booklet pane of 8	10.00	
a.-b.	A992 25c Either single	.50	.50
c.-d.	A992 50c Either single	1.00	1.00
e.-f.	A992 75c Either single	1.50	1.50
g.-h.	A992 $1 Either single	2.00	2.00
2230	Booklet pane of 8	10.00	
a.-b.	A992 25c Either single	.50	.50
c.-d.	A992 50c Either single	1.00	1.00
e.-f.	A992 75c Either single	1.50	1.50
g.-h.	A992 $1 Either single	2.00	2.00

Frogs — A993

No. 2231: a, Hyalinobatrachium pellucidum. b, Nymphargus anomalus. c, Nymphargus cochranae. d, Nymphargus grandisonae facing forward. e, Nymphargus griffithsi facing left. f, Sachatamia albomaculata. g, Sachatamia ilex. h, Overhead view of Teratohyla pulverata.

No. 2232: a, Centrolene ballux. b, Centrolene buckleyi. c, Centrolene condor. d, Centrolene heloderma. e, Chimerella mariaelenae. f, Espadarana callistomma. g, Espadarana prosoblepon. h, Overhead view of Hyalinobatrachium aureoguttatum.

No. 2233: a, Cochranella balionota. b, Cochranella litoralis. c, Cochranella mache. d, Nymphargus grandisonae facing right. e, Underside view of Hyalinobatrachium aureoguttatum. f, Underside view of Teratohyla pulverata. g, Underside view of Nymphargus griffithsi. h, Two Terarohyla spinosa.

Unwmk.

2019, May 29	**Litho.**		**Die Cut**

Self-Adhesive

2231	Booklet pane of 8	16.50	
a.-b.	A993 25c Either single	.50	.50
c.-d.	A993 50c Either single	1.00	1.00
e.-f.	A993 75c Either single	1.50	1.50
g.-h.	A993 $1 Either single	2.00	2.00
2232	Booklet pane of 8	16.50	
a.-b.	A993 25c Either single	.50	.50
c.-d.	A993 50c Either single	1.00	1.00
e.-f.	A993 75c Either single	1.50	1.50
g.-h.	A993 $1 Either single	2.00	2.00
2233	Booklet pane of 8	16.50	
a.-b.	A993 25c Either single	.50	.50
c.-d.	A993 50c Either single	1.00	1.00
e.-f.	A993 75c Either single	1.50	1.50
g.-h.	A993 $1 Either single	2.00	2.00
	Nos. 2231-2233 (3)	49.50	

Paintings by Oswaldo Guayasamín (1919-99) — A994

No. 2234: a, Manos del Mendigo (Hands of a Beggar). b, Manos de la Ternura (Hands of Tenderness). c, Autoretrato (Self-portrait). d, Manos de la Oración (Hands in Prayer). e, Manos de la Esperanza (Hands of Hope).

Perf. 13½x13¾

2019, June 28	**Litho.**	**Wmk. 377**
2234	Horiz. strip of 5	29.50 20.00
a.-e.	A994 $2 Any single	4.00 4.00

National Symphony Orchestra, 70th Anniv. — A995

Perf. 13¾x13½

2019, Sept. 12	**Litho.**	**Wmk. 377**
2235	A995 25c multi	.50 .50

A996

No. 2236: a, Telipogon humboldtiana. b, Dichaea bonplandiana. c, Flowers and Alexander von Humboldt (1769-1859), naturalist and explorer. d, Caucaea kunthiana. e, Telipogon montufariana.

	Wmk. 377	
2019, Sept. 26	**Litho.**	**Perf. 13¾**
2236	Horiz. strip of 5	12.50 10.00
a.-e.	A996 $1 Any single	2.00 2.00

A997

A998

A999

A1000

Items in Mindalae Ethnohistoric and Crafts Museum of Ecuador, Quito — A1001

No. 2237 — Inscription: a, Pirotecnia Festiva. b, Máscara Andina. c, Fiesta Andina. d, Aya Huma de Imbabura. e, Máscara de Tigua. f, Máscara Lobo Andino. g, Rondador Andino. h, Danzante de Corpus Christi.

No. 2238 — Inscription: a, Shigra Andina. b, Shakap Shuar. c, Canasto Zápara. d, Cesta Huaorani. e, Peinilla Achuar. f, Collar Amazónico. g, Canasto Epera. h, Tambor Andino.

No. 2239 — Inscription: a, Shigras de Simiatug. b, Bordado de Zuleta. c, Fajas Andinas. d, Ikat de Gualaceo. e, Tapiz de Salasaca. f, Chal de Imbabura. g, Máscara afro del Chota. h, Coquero del Carchi.

No. 2240 — Inscription: a, Rostro Manteño. b, Murciélago Jama Coaque. c, Zarigüeya Manteña. d, Hombre Pájaro Ancestral. e, Jaguar Jama Coaque. f, Emplumado Jama Coaque. g, Mujer Chorrera. h, Mindalae Tolita.

No. 2241 — Inscription: a, Banco Chamánico Shiwiar. b, Boa Quichua. c, Tinaja Quichua. d, Supai Quichua. e, Ollas Huaorani. f, Mukawa Quichua. g, Arte Plumario. h, Tawasapa Shuar.

Unwmk.
2019, Oct. 22   Litho.   Die Cut
Self-Adhesive

2237	A997	Booklet pane of 8	10.00	
a.-b.		25c Either single	.50	.50
c.-d.		50c Either single	1.00	1.00
e.-f.		75c Either single	1.50	1.50
g.-h.		$1 Either single	2.00	2.00
2238	A998	Booklet pane of 8	10.00	
a.-b.		25c Either single	.50	.50
c.-d.		50c Either single	1.00	1.00
e.-f.		75c Either single	1.50	1.50
g.-h.		$1 Either single	2.00	2.00
2239	A999	Booklet pane of 8	10.00	
a.-b.		25c Either single	.50	.50
c.-d.		50c Either single	1.00	1.00
e.-f.		75c Either single	1.50	1.50
g.-h.		$1 Either single	2.00	2.00
2240	A1000	Booklet pane of 8	10.00	
a.-b.		25c Either single	.50	.50
c.-d.		50c Either single	1.00	1.00
e.-f.		75c Either single	1.50	1.50
g.-h.		$1 Either single	2.00	2.00
2241	A1001	Booklet pane of 8	10.00	
a.-b.		25c Either single	.50	.50
c.-d.		50c Either single	1.00	1.00
e.-f.		75c Either single	1.50	1.50
g.-h.		$1 Either single	2.00	2.00
		Nos. 2237-2241 (5)	50.00	

Miniature Sheet

Tiputini Biodiversity Station, 25th Anniv. — A1002

No. 2242: a, 25c, Amorphochilus schnablii. b, 50c, Anoura peruana. c, 75c, Desmodus rotundus. d, $1, Diclidurus albus. e, $1.25, Eumops maurus. f, $1.50, Noctilio albiventris. g, $1.75, Sphaeronycteris toxophyllum. h, $3, Trachops cirrhosus. i, $5, Emblem of Tiputini Biodiversity Station.

Perf. 13½x13¾
2019, Oct. 29   Litho.   Wmk. 377
2242	A1002	Sheet of 9, #a-i	30.00	30.00

Elias Cedeño Jerves (1902-71), Poet — A1003

Perf. 13¾x13½
2019, Nov. 20   Litho.   Wmk. 377
2243	A1003	$5 multi	15.00	10.00

A1004

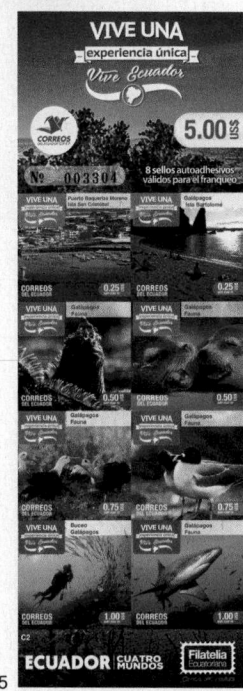

A1005

No. 2244: a, Driftwood on beach. b, Bicyclist near Cotopaxi. c, Cuyabeno River. d, Land iguana, Galapagos Islands. e, Canyon explorers near Puyo.

No. 2245: a, Puerto Baquerizo Moreno, Isla San Cristóbal. b, Isla Bartolomé, Galapagos Islands. c, Iguana, Galapagos Islands. d, Sea lions, Galapagos Islands. e, Albatrosses, Galapagos Islands. f, Two Swallow-tailed gulls, Galapagos Islands. g, Diver and school of fish in Galapagos Islands waters. h, Shark in Galapagos Islands waters.

No. 2246: a, Train on bridge. b, Cuenca. c, Guayaquil. d, Whale breaching water. e, Head of reptile, Yasuní National Park. f, Butterflies, Zamora. g, Rafters on Pastaza River. h, Montubio Rodeo, Pimocha.

Perf. 13¾x13½
2019, Nov. 22   Litho.   Wmk. 377
2244		Horiz. strip of 5	50.00	30.00
a.-e.	A1004	$3 Any single	6.00	6.00

Booklet Stamps
Self-Adhesive
Die Cut
Unwmk.
2245	A1005	Booklet pane of 8	15.00	
a.-b.		25c Either single	.50	.50
c.-d.		50c Either single	1.00	1.00
e.-f.		75c Either single	1.50	1.50
g.-h.		$1 Either single	2.00	2.00
2246	A1006	Booklet pane of 8	15.00	
a.-b.		25c Either single	.50	.50
c.-d.		50c Either single	1.00	1.00
e.-f.		75c Either single	1.50	1.50
g.-h.		$1 Either single	2.00	2.00

Tourism A1006

Traditional Dishes — A1007

No. 2247 — Inscriptions: a, Trilogía de helados, jucho, canelazo y colada morada. b, Sudado de mariscos con piña y curry ecuatoriano. c, Cascarita de cerdo con tubérculos del páramo. d, Sopa de los siete mares. e, Seco de chivo. f, Brocheta de chontacuro. g, Caldo de patas. h, Pangora fría de aconcito. i, Maito de paiche y palmito. j, Dulces típicos.

Perf. 13¾x13½
2019, Nov. 26   Litho.   Wmk. 377
2247		Block of 10	25.00	15.00
a.-j.	A1007	75c Any single	1.50	1.50

America issue.

Christmas — A1008

No. 2248: a, Village in circle. b, Angel and people. c, Christmas tree. d, Three candles. e, Angel.

Perf. 13½x13¾
2019, Dec. 3   Litho.   Wmk. 377
2248		Horiz. strip of 5	32.50	20.00
a.-e.	A1008	$2 Any single	4.00	4.00

Baños de Agua Santa Tourism A1009

No. 2249: a, Treehouse. b, Cara de Perro hiker. c, Bridge over Pailón del Diablo Waterfall. d, Las Antenas Mountains. e, Basilica, Baños de Agua Santa. f, Bridge jumper. g, Thermal baths. h, Hikers near Cascada del Silencio.

Unwmk.
2019, Dec. 26   Litho.   Die Cut
Self-Adhesive
2249	A1009	Booklet pane of 8	17.00	
a.-b.		25c Either single	.50	.50
c.-d.		50c Either single	1.00	1.00
e.-f.		75c Either single	1.50	1.50
g.-h.		$1 Either single	2.00	2.00

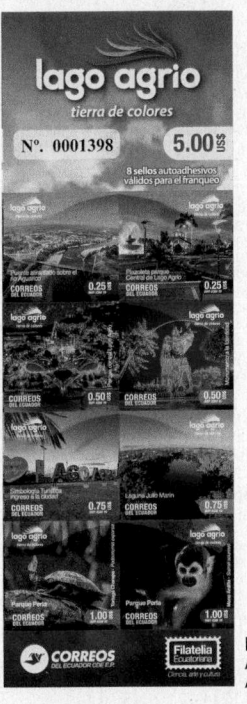

lago agrio
tierra de colores

Nº 0001398   5.00 USD

8 sellos autoadhesivos
válidos para el franqueo

Lake
Agrio
A1010

No. 2250: a, Aguarico River cable-stayed bridge. b, Central plaza in Lago Agrio. c, Central plaza in Lago Agrio at night. d, Monument, Plaza de Toros, Lago Agrio. e, Lago Agrio town sign. f, Julio Marín Lagoon. g, Turtle and butterfly in Perla Park. h, Saimin sciureus.

	2020	Litho.	Unwmk.	*Die Cut*
		Self-Adhesive		
2250	A1010	Booklet pane of 8	10.00	
a.-b.		25c Either single	.50	.50
c.-d.		50c Either single	1.00	1.00
e.-f.		75c Either single	1.50	1.50
g.-h.		$1 Either single	2.00	2.00

SEMI-POSTAL STAMPS

Nos. 423-428 Surcharged in Carmine or Blue

1944, May 9		Unwmk.	*Perf. 12*	
B1	A171	10c + 10c yel grn (C)	.60	.30
B2	A171	20c + 20c rose pink	.60	.30
B3	A171	30c + 20c dk gray brn	.60	.30
B4	A171	50c + 20c dp red lil	1.20	.60
B5	A171	1s + 50c ol gray (C)	2.00	1.00
B6	A171	10s + 2s red orange	7.00	3.50
		Nos. B1-B6 (6)	12.00	6.00

The surtax aided Mendez Hospital.

AIR POST STAMPS

In 1928-30, the internal airmail service of Ecuador was handled by the Sociedad Colombo-Alemana de Transportes Aereos ("SCADTA") under government sanction. During this period SCADTA issued stamps which were the only legal franking for airmail service except that handled under contract with Pan American-Grace Airways. SCADTA issues are Nos. C1-C6, C16-C25, CF1-CF2.

Colombla Air Post
Stamps of 1923
Surcharged in Carmine

"Provisional" at 45 degree Angle

Perf. 14x14½

1928, Aug. 28			Wmk. 116	
C1	AP6	50c on 10c green	110.00	70.00
C2	AP6	75c on 15c car	210.00	160.00
C3	AP6	1s on 20c gray	70.00	42.50
C4	AP6	1½s on 30c blue	45.00	35.00
C5	AP6	3s on 60c brown	85.00	52.50
		Nos. C1-C5 (5)	520.00	360.00

"Provisional" at 41 degree Angle

1929, Mar. 20				
C1a	AP6	50c on 10c green	125.00	110.00
C2a	AP6	75c on 15c carmine	225.00	175.00
C3a	AP6	1s on 20c gray	225.00	175.00
		Nos. C1a-C3a (3)	575.00	460.00

| C6 | AP6 | 50c on 10c green | *700.00* | *1,700.* |

A 75c on 15c carmine with "Cts." between the surcharged numerals exists. There is no evidence that it was regularly issued or used. For overprints see Nos. CF1-CF1a.

Plane over River
Guayas — AP1

Unwmk.

1929, May 5		Engr.	*Perf. 12*	
C8	AP1	2c black	.40	.25
C9	AP1	5c carmine rose	.40	.25
C10	AP1	10c deep brown	.40	.25
C11	AP1	20c dark violet	.90	.25
C12	AP1	50c deep green	1.60	.45
C13	AP1	1s dark blue	6.00	2.75
C14	AP1	5s orange yellow	25.00	11.00
C15	AP1	10s orange red	135.00	57.50
		Nos. C8-C15 (8)	169.70	72.70

Establishment of commercial air service in Ecuador. The stamps were available for all forms of postal service and were largely used for franking ordinary letters.

Nos. C13-C15 show numerals in color on white background. Counterfeits of No. C15 exist.

See Nos. C26-C31. For overprints and surcharge see Nos. C32-C38, C287, CO1-CO12.

Jesuit
Church La
Compania
AP2

Mount
Chimborazo
AP3

Wmk. 127

1929, Apr. 1		Litho.	*Perf. 14*	
C16	AP2	50c red brown	4.50	2.25
C17	AP2	75c green	4.50	2.25
C18	AP2	1s rose	7.00	2.25
C19	AP2	1½s gray blue	7.00	2.25
C20	AP2	2s violet	11.50	4.50
C21	AP2	3s brown	11.50	4.50
C22	AP3	5s lt blue	50.00	15.00
C23	AP3	10s lt red	100.00	32.50
C24	AP3	15s violet	160.00	65.00
C25	AP3	25s olive green	225.00	75.00
		Nos. C16-C25 (10)	581.00	205.50

For overprint see No. CF2.

Plane Type of 1929

1930-44		Unwmk.	Engr.	*Perf. 12*	
C26	AP1	1s carmine lake		6.50	.55
C27	AP1	1s green ('44)		1.00	.25
C28	AP1	5s olive green		10.00	3.75
C29	AP1	5s purple ('44)		2.00	.25
C30	AP1	10s black		30.00	5.50
C31	AP1	10s brt ultra ('44)		4.50	.30
		Nos. C26-C31 (6)		54.00	10.60

Nos. C26-C31 show numerals in color on white background.

For surcharge see No. C287.

Nos. C26, C28, C30
Ovptd. in Various
Colors

1930, June 4				
C32	AP1	1s car lake (Bk)	22.50	22.50
a.		Double ovpt. (R Br + Bl)	75.00	
C33	AP1	5s olive grn (Bl)	22.50	22.50
C34	AP1	10s black (R Br)	22.50	22.50
		Nos. C32-C34 (3)	67.50	67.50

Flight of Capt. Benjamin Mendez from Bogota to Quito, bearing a crown of flowers for the tomb of Grand Marshal Sucre.

Air Post Official
Stamps of 1929-30
Ovptd. in Various
Colors or Srchd.
Similarly in Upper &
Lower Case

1935, July 24				
C35	AP1	50c deep green (Bl)	12.50	5.00
C36	AP1	50c olive brn (R)	12.50	5.00
C37	AP1	1s on 5s ol grn (Bk)	12.50	5.00
a.		Double surcharge	95.00	
C38	AP1	2s on 10s black (R)	12.50	5.00
		Nos. C35-C38 (4)	50.00	20.00

Unveiling of a monument to Bolívar at Quito, July 24th, 1935.

 AP5

1935, Oct. 13		Photo.	*Perf. 11½x11*	
C38A	AP5	5c ultra & red	.50	.30
C38B	AP5	10c brown & black	.50	.50
C38C	AP5	50c green & red	.50	.50
C38D	AP5	1S carmine & blue	1.50	1.20
C38E	AP5	5S gray grn & red	2.40	2.40
		Nos. C38A-C38E (5)	5.40	4.90

Columbus Day. Nos. C38A-338E and C38A-C38E were prepared by the Sociedad Colombista Panamericana and were sold by the Ecuadorian post office through Oct. 30. Nos. C38B-C38E exist imperf.

Geodesical Mission Issue
Type of Regular Issue and Nos. 349-351 Overprinted in Blue or Black

1936, July 3			*Perf. 12½*	
C39	A136	10c deep orange (Bl)	.60	.25
C40	A136	20c violet (Bk)	.60	.25
C41	A136	50c dark red (Bl)	.60	.25
C42	A136	70c black	1.25	.35
		Nos. C39-C42 (4)	3.05	1.10

For surcharge see No. RA42.

Philatelic Exhibition Issue
Type of Regular Issue Overprinted
"AEREA"

1936, Oct. 20			*Perf. 13½x14*	
C43	A137	2c rose	5.00	5.00
C44	A137	5c brown orange	5.00	5.00
C45	A137	10c brown	5.00	5.00
C46	A137	20c ultra	5.00	5.00
C47	A137	50c red violet	5.00	5.00
C48	A137	1s green	5.00	5.00

Condor and
Plane — AP6

			Perf. 13½	
C49	AP6	70c orange brown	2.25	.50
C50	AP6	1s dull violet	2.25	.50
		Nos. C43-C50 (8)	34.50	31.00

Nos. C43-C50 were issued for the 1st Intl. Phil. Exhib. at Quito.

Condor over "El
Altar" — AP7

1937-46			*Perf. 11½, 12*	
C51	AP7	10c chestnut	5.00	.25
C52	AP7	20c olive black	6.50	.25
C53	AP7	40c rose car ('46)	6.50	.25
C54	AP7	70c black brown	9.00	.25
C55	AP7	1s gray black	14.00	.25
C56	AP7	2s dark violet	24.00	.65
		Nos. C51-C56 (6)	65.00	1.90

Issue dates: 40c, Oct. 7; others, Aug. 19. For overprints see Nos. 463-464, CO13-CO17.

Portrait of Washington, American
Eagle and Flags — AP8

Engraved and Lithographed

1938, Feb. 9			*Perf. 12*	
		Center Multicolored		
C57	AP8	2c brown	.40	.25
C58	AP8	5c black	.40	.25
C59	AP8	10c brown	.40	.25
C60	AP8	20c dark blue	.80	.25
C61	AP8	50c violet	1.75	.25
C62	AP8	1s black	3.25	.25
C63	AP8	2s violet	7.50	.90
		Nos. C57-C63 (7)	14.50	2.40

150th anniv. of the US Constitution.

In 1947, Nos. C61-C63 were overprinted in dark blue: "Primero la Patria!" and plane. These revolutionary propaganda stamps were later renounced by decree. Value $20.

For overprints see Nos. C102-C104, C139-C141.

No. RA35 Surcharged in
Red

1938, Nov. 16			*Perf. 13½*	
C64	PT12	65c on 3c ultra	.40	.25

A national airmail concession was given to the Sociedad Ecuatoriano de Transportes Aereos (SEDTA) in July, 1938. No. RA35 was surcharged for SEDTA postal requirements. SEDTA operated through 1940.

Army
Horseman
AP9

Woman
Runner
AP10

Tennis
AP11

Boxing
AP12

Olympic Fire — AP13

1939, Mar.		Engr.	*Perf. 12*	
C65	AP9	5c lt green	1.60	.25
C66	AP10	10c salmon	2.25	.25
C67	AP11	50c redsh brown	11.50	.25
C68	AP12	1s black brown	13.50	.45
C69	AP13	2s rose carmine	17.00	1.10
		Nos. C65-C69 (5)	45.85	2.30

First Bolivarian Games (1938).

Plane over
Chimborazo — AP14

1939, May 1 *Perf. 13x12½*
C70 AP14 1s yellow brown .40 .25
C71 AP14 2s rose violet .70 .25
C72 AP14 5s black 1.90 .25
  Nos. C70-C72 (3) 3.00 .75

Golden Gate Bridge and
Mountain Peak — AP15

1939 *Perf. 12½x13*
C73 AP15 2c black .40 .25
C74 AP15 5c rose red .40 .25
C75 AP15 10c indigo .40 .25
C76 AP15 50c rose violet .40 .25
C77 AP15 1s chocolate .80 .25
C78 AP15 2s yellow brown 1.00 .25
C79 AP15 5s emerald 2.00 .25
  Nos. C73-C79 (7) 5.40 1.75

Golden Gate International Exposition.
For surcharge & overprint see Nos. 434, CO18.

Empire State Building
and Mountain
Peak — AP16

1939
C80 AP16 2c brown orange .65 .30
C81 AP16 5c dark carmine .65 .25
C82 AP16 10c indigo .65 .30
C83 AP16 50c slate green .65 .30
C84 AP16 1s deep orange 1.30 .30
C85 AP16 2s dk red violet 1.50 .30
C86 AP16 5s dark gray 3.50 .30
  Nos. C80-C86 (7) 8.90 2.05

New York World's Fair.
For surcharge see No. 435.

Map of the Americas
and Airplane — AP17

1940, July 9
C87 AP17 10c red org & blue .45 .25
C88 AP17 70c sepia & blue .45 .25
C89 AP17 1s copper brn & blue .90 .25
C90 AP17 10s black & blue 3.50 .95
  Nos. C87-C90 (4) 5.30 1.70

Pan American Union, 50th anniversary.

Journalism Type
1941, Dec. 15
C91 A157 3s rose carmine 5.75 .25
C92 A157 10s yellow orange 12.00 .45

See note after No. 399.

Old Map of | Panoramic
South | View of
America | Amazon
Showing | River
Amazon | AP20
River |
AP19

Designs: 70c, Gonzalo de Pineda. 5s, Painting of the expedition.

1942, Jan. 30
C93 AP19 40c black & buff 1.90 .25
C94 AP19 70c olive 2.90 .25
C95 AP20 3s dark green 3.25 .25
C96 AP19 5s rose 4.00 1.10
  Nos. C93-C96 (4) 12.05 1.85

See note after No. 403.

Remigio Crespo Toral Type
1942, Sept. 1 *Perf. 13½*
C97 A162 10c dull violet 1.25 .50

Alfaro Types
70c, Gen. Eloy Alfaro. 1s, Devils's Nose. 3s, Military College. 5s, Montecristi, Alfaro's birthplace.

1943, Feb. 16 *Perf. 12*
C98 A166 70c dk rose & blk 1.90 .50
C99 A167 1s ol blk & red brn 3.25 .75
C100 A167 3s ol gray & grn 4.50 1.10
C101 A167 5s slate & salmon 6.75 1.30
  Nos. C98-C101 (4) 16.40 3.40

**Nos. C61-C63 Overprinted in Red
Brown**

1943, Apr. 15 *Perf. 11½*
Center Multicolored
C102 AP8 50c violet 2.75 1.50
C103 AP8 1s black 3.25 1.60
C104 AP8 2s violet 4.00 2.50
  Nos. C102-C104 (3) 10.00 5.60

Visit of US Vice-Pres. Henry A. Wallace.

**Nos. 374-376 Overprinted "AEREO
LOOR A BOLIVIA JUNIO 11-1943"
(like Nos. C111-C113)**

1943, June 11 *Perf. 13*
C105 A146 50c dp red violet .40 .25
C106 A147 1s copper red .60 .25
C107 A148 2s dark green .70 .25
  Nos. C105-C107 (3) 1.70 .75

Visit of Pres. Eurique Penaranda of Bolivia.
Vertical overprints on Nos. C105-C106.

**Nos. 374-376 Overprinted "AEREO
LOOR A PARAGUAY JULIO 5-1943"
(like Nos. C111-C113)**

1943, July 5
C108 A146 50c dp red violet .45 .25
  a. Double overprint 75.00
C109 A147 1s copper red 1.10 .50
C110 A148 2s dark green 1.50 .70
  Nos. C108-C110 (3) 3.05 1.45

Visit of Pres. Higinio Morinigo of Paraguay.
Vertical overprints on Nos. C108-C109.

Nos. 374-376
Overprinted in Black

1943, July 23
C111 A146 50c dp red violet .45 .25
C112 A147 1s copper red .65 .25
C113 A148 2s dark green .75 .25
  Nos. C111-C113 (3) 1.85 .75

Issued to commemorate the visit of President Isaias Medina Angarita of Venezuela. Vertical overprint on Nos. C111-C112.
See Nos. C105-C110.

President
Arroyo del
Rio
Addressing
US Congress
AP26

1943, Oct. 9 *Perf. 12*
C114 AP26 50c dark brown 1.00 .50
C115 AP26 70c brt rose 1.30 .50
C116 AP26 1s dark blue 1.50 .65
C117 AP26 5s dark green 3.50 1.20
C118 AP26 10s olive black 13.00 4.25
  Nos. C114-C118 (5) 20.30 7.10

Good will tour of Pres. Arroyo del Rio in 1942.
For surcharges see Nos. CB1-CB5.

1944, Feb. 7
C119 AP26 50c dp red lilac .90 .65
C120 AP26 70c red brown 1.75 .65
C121 AP26 3s turq green 1.75 .65

C122 AP26 5s brt ultra 2.90 1.40
C123 AP26 10s scarlet 3.50 1.60
  Nos. C119-C123 (5) 10.80 4.95
  Nos. C114-C123 (10) 31.10 12.05

Church of San
Francisco,
Quito — AP27

1944, Feb. 13
C124 AP27 70c turq green 1.90 .45
C125 AP27 1s olive 1.90 .45
C126 AP27 3s red orange 4.25 1.10
C127 AP27 5s carmine rose 5.25 1.30
  Nos. C124-C127 (4) 13.30 3.30

Palace Type
1944 **Engr.** *Perf. 11*
C128 A173 3s orange 1.00 .25
C129 A173 5s dark brown 1.75 .25
C130 A173 10s dark red 4.00 .25
  Nos. C128-C130 (3) 6.75 .75

See No. C221. For overprints and surcharges see Nos. 541, C136-C138, C210-C213, C218-C220, C223-C224, C277-C279.

Red Cross Type
1945, Apr. 25 **Unwmk.** *Perf. 12*
Cross in Rose
C131 A174 2s deep blue 4.00 1.10
C132 A174 3s green 4.50 1.25
C133 A174 5s dark violet 6.50 1.75
C134 A174 10s carmine rose 21.00 5.75
  Nos. C131-C134 (4) 36.00 9.85

No. RA55 Surcharged
in Black

1945, June 8
C135 PT21 40c on 5c blue 1.00 .25
  a. Double surcharge 10.00

Counterfeits exist.

Nos. C128-C130
Overprinted in Green

1945, Sept. 6 *Perf. 11*
C136 A173 3s orange 1.00 .50
  a. Inverted overprint 50.00
  b. Double overprint 50.00
C137 A173 5s dark brown 1.25 .65
C138 A173 10s dark red 3.25 1.25
  Nos. C136-C138 (3) 5.50 2.40

**Nos. C61-C63 Overprinted in Dark
Blue and Gold like Nos. 444-446**
1945, Oct. 2 *Perf. 12*
Center Multicolored
C139 AP8 50c violet 1.40 .25
C140 AP8 1s black 1.60 1.50
C141 AP8 2s violet 2.50 1.90
  Nos. C139-C141 (3) 5.50 3.65

Visit of Pres. Juan Antonio Rios of Chile.

Monument to
Liberty — AP30

1945, Nov. 14 **Engr.**
C142 AP30 30c blue .45 .25
C143 AP30 40c rose carmine .45 .25
C144 AP30 1s dull violet 1.30 .55
C145 AP30 3s gray black 2.50 1.40
C146 AP30 5s purple brown 3.50 1.90
  Nos. C142-C146 (5) 8.20 4.35

Gen. Antonio Jose de Sucre, 150th birth anniv.

Catalogue values for unused stamps in this section, from this point to the end of the section, are for Never Hinged items.

Highway Type
1946, Apr. 22 **Unwmk.**
C147 A176 1s carmine rose .85 .40
C148 A176 2s violet 1.10 .55
C149 A176 3s turq green 1.90 .60
C150 A176 5s red orange 2.25 .80
C151 A176 10s dark blue 3.75 .80
  Nos. C147-C151 (5) 9.85 3.15

Revolution Types
1946, Aug. 9 *Perf. 12½*
C152 A177 40c deep claret .35 .25
C153 A178 1s sepia .35 .25
C154 A179 2s indigo .90 .25
C155 A180 3s olive green 1.60 .45
  Nos. C152-C155 (4) 3.20 1.20

National Union of
Journalists, Initials and
Quill Pen — AP36

1946, Sept. 16
C156 AP36 50c dull purple .75 .50
C157 AP36 70c dark green .90 .65
C158 AP36 3s red 1.50 .80
C159 AP36 5s indigo 2.00 1.00
C160 AP36 10s chocolate 6.50 1.75
  Nos. C156-C160 (5) 11.65 4.70

Campaign for adult education.

The Blessed | "Lily of
Mariana | Quito"
Teaching | AP38
Children |
AP37

1946, Nov. 28 **Unwmk.**
C161 AP37 40c chocolate .30 .25
C162 AP37 60c dark green .40 .35
C163 AP38 3s orange yellow .80 .60
C164 AP38 5s green 2.00 .85
  Nos. C161-C164 (4) 3.50 2.05

300th anniv. of the death of the Blessed Mariana de Jesus Paredes y Flores.

Rocafuerte Type
60c-1.10s, Jual de Velasco. 1.30s-2s, Riobamba Irrigation Canal.

1947, Nov. 27 *Perf. 12*
C165 A185 60c dark green .30 .25
C166 A185 70c purple .30 .25
C167 A185 1s black brown .30 .25
C168 A185 1.10s car rose .30 .25
C169 A185 1.30s deep blue .40 .25
C170 A185 1.90s olive bister 1.20 .25
C171 A185 2s olive green 1.40 .25
  Nos. C165-C171 (7) 4.20 1.75

For overprints and surcharges see Nos. C175, C181, C207-C209, C215, C216-C217, C222, C235.

Bello Type
1948, Apr. 21 *Perf. 13*
C172 A188 60c magenta .55 .25
C173 A188 1.30s dk blue grn .95 .25
C174 A188 1.90s dk rose car .80 .25
  Nos. C172-C174 (3) 2.30 .75

No. C166 Overprinted in
Black

1948, May 24 *Perf. 12*
C175 A185 70c purple .65 .35

Columbus — AP42

1948, May 26   *Perf. 14*
C176	AP42	50c olive green	.25 .25
C177	AP42	70c rose carmine	.50 .40
C178	AP42	3s ultra	1.60 1.10
C179	AP42	5s brown	2.60 1.60
C180	AP42	10s deep violet	8.00 2.00
	Nos. C176-C180 (5)		12.95 5.35

See note after No. 495.

No. C169 Overprinted in Carmine like No. 496 (MANANA reads up)

1948, Aug. 26   **Unwmk.**   *Perf. 12*
C181	A185	1.30s deep blue	.40 .25

National Fair of Today and Tomorrow, 1948.

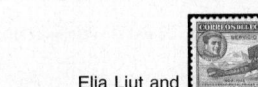

Elia Liut and Telegrafo I — AP43

1948, Sept. 10   *Perf. 12½*
C182	AP43	60c rose red	.85 .25
C183	AP43	1s green	.85 .25
C184	AP43	1.30s deep claret	.85 .25
C185	AP43	1.90s deep violet	.85 .25
C186	AP43	2s dark brown	1.30 .30
C187	AP43	5s blue	2.60 1.60
	Nos. C182-C187 (6)		7.30 1.80

25th anniv. (in 1945) of the 1st postal flight in Ecuador.

Teacher and Pupils — AP44

1948, Oct. 12   *Perf. 14*
C188	AP44	50c violet	1.50 .60
C189	AP44	70c deep blue	1.50 .60
C190	AP44	3s dark green	2.50 1.25
C191	AP44	5s red	4.00 1.90
C192	AP44	10s brown	7.50 2.50
	Nos. C188-C192 (5)		17.00 6.85

Campaign for adult education.

AP45

Franklin D. Roosevelt and Two of "Four Freedoms" — AP46

1948, Oct. 24   *Perf. 12½*
C193	AP45	60c emer & org brn	.50 .25
C194	AP45	1s car rose & slate	.75 .30
C195	AP46	1.50s grn & red brn	.90 .55
C196	AP46	2s red & black	1.00 .30
C197	AP46	5s ultra & blk	2.10 .30
	Nos. C193-C197 (5)		5.25 1.70

Maldonado Types

1948, Nov. 17
C198	A196	60c dp org & rose car	.95 .25
C199	A197	90c red & gray blk	.95 .25
C200	A196	1.30s pur & dp org	1.20 .25
C201	A197	2s dp bl & dull grn	1.20 .25
	Nos. C198-C201 (4)		4.30 1.00

See note after No. 519.

Juan Montalvo and Cervantes AP47   Don Quixote AP48

1949, May 2   **Engr.**   *Perf. 12½x12*
C202	AP47	1.30s ol brn & ultra	3.00 2.50
C203	AP48	1.90s grn & rose car	1.00 .30
C204	AP47	3s vio & org brn	1.50 .30
C205	AP48	5s red & gray blk	2.75 .25
C206	AP47	10s red lil & aqua	4.00 .25
	Nos. C202-C206 (5)		12.25 3.60

400th anniv. of the birth of Miguel de Cervantes Saavedra, novelist, playwright and poet, and the 60th anniv. of the death of Juan Montalvo (1832-89), Ecuadorean writer. For surcharges see Nos. C225-C226.

No. C168 Surcharged in Blue

1949, June 15   *Perf. 12*
C207	A185	50c on 1.10s car rose	.60 .25
C208	A185	60c on 1.10s car rose	.60 .25
C209	A185	90c on 1.10s car rose	.90 .25
	Nos. C207-C209 (3)		2.10 .75

2nd Eucharistic Cong., Quito, June 1949.

No. C128 Surcharged in Black

1949, Oct. 11   *Perf. 11*
C210	A173	60c on 3s orange	.80 .40
a.		Double surcharge	30.00
C211	A173	90c on 3s orange	.90 .30
C212	A173	1s on 3s orange	1.10 .40
C213	A173	2s on 3s orange	1.90 .40
	Nos. C210-C213 (4)		4.70 1.50

"SUCRE(S)" in capitals on Nos. C212-C213. 75th anniv. of the UPU.

Consular Service Stamps Type of 1949 Surcharged in Black

1950   **Unwmk.**   *Perf. 12*
C214	R1	60c on 50c gray	.75 .25
a.		Double surcharge	15.00

No. C170 Surcharged with New Value in Black
C215	A185	90c on 1.90s ol bis	.75 .25

See Nos. 475-483, 532-533.

Nos. C168, C128-C129 and Type of 1944 Srchd. or Ovptd. in Black or Carmine

1950, Feb. 10   *Perf. 12*
C216	A185	50c on 1.10s	1.75 1.75
C217	A185	70c on 1.10s	2.25 1.75

    Perf. 11
C218	A173	3s orange	3.25 3.00
C219	A173	5s dark brown (C)	5.00 2.50
C220	A173	10s violet (C)	7.50 3.00
	Nos. C216-C220 (5)		19.75 12.00

Issued to publicize adult education. For overprint see No. 541.

Govt. Palace Type of 1944

1950, May 15   **Engr.**   *Perf. 11*
C221	A173	10s violet	2.00 .25

For surcharges see Nos. C277-C279.

No. C169 Surcharged with New Value in Black

1950   *Perf. 12*
C222	A185	90c on 1.30s dp blue	.30 .25

See No. C235.

Nos. C128-C129 Overprinted in Black

1951, July 28   **Unwmk.**   *Perf. 11*
C223	A173	3s orange	1.25 .90
C224	A173	5s dark brown	2.50 1.25

20,000th crossing of the equator by Pan American-Grace Airways planes.

Nos. C202-C203 Surcharged in Black

1951   **Unwmk.**   *Perf. 12½x12*
C225	AP47	60c on 1.30s	.30 .25
C226	AP48	1s on 1.90s	.30 .25
a.		Inverted surcharge	20.00

Issued to publicize adult education.

St. Mariana de Jesus — AP50

1952, Feb. 15   **Engr.**
C227	AP50	60c plum & aqua	.65 .30
C228	AP50	90c dk grn & lt ultra	.90 .30
C229	AP50	1s car & dk grn	1.00 .30
C230	AP50	2s indigo & rose lil	1.10 .30
	Nos. C227-C230 (4)		3.65 1.20

Canonization of Mariana de Jesus Paredes y Flores.

Plaza Visit to US Issue

3s, as No. 558. 5s, as No. 559.

1952, Mar. 26   *Perf. 12*
C231	A205	3s lilac & bl grn	.75 .45
C232	A205	5s red brn & ol gray	2.25 1.75
a.		Souv. sheet of 2, #C231-C232	4.50 9.00

Consular Service Stamps Surcharged in Black

1952   **Unwmk.**   *Perf. 12*
C233	R2	60c on 1s green	.35 .25
C234	R2	1s on 1s green	.35 .25

Type R2 illustrated above No. 545.

No. C169 Surcharged with New Value in Carmine
C235	A185	90c on 1.30s dp bl	.35 .25
	Nos. C233-C235 (3)		1.05 .75

See No. C222.

Pres. José M. Urvina and Allegory of Freedom — AP52

Hyphen-hole Perf. 7x6½

1952, Nov. 18   **Litho.**
C236	AP52	60c rose red & blue	3.75 .45
C237	AP52	90c lilac & red	3.75 .60
C238	AP52	1s orange & green	3.75 .30
C239	AP52	2s red brn & blue	3.75 .45
	Nos. C236-C239 (4)		15.00 1.80

Centenary of abolition of slavery in Ecuador. Counterfeits exist.

Torch of Knowledge — AP53

Design: 2s, Aged couple studying alphabet.

Unwmk.

1953, Apr. 13   **Engr.**   *Perf. 12*
C240	AP53	1s dark blue	1.40 .25
C241	AP53	2s red orange	1.75 .25

1952 adult education campaign.

Globe Showing Part of Western Hemisphere — AP54

1953, June 5   *Perf. 12½x12*
C242	AP54	60c orange yellow	.30 .25
C243	AP54	90c dark blue	.40 .30
C244	AP54	3s carmine	.70 .45
	Nos. C242-C244 (3)		1.40 1.00

Issued to publicize the crossing of the equator by the Pan-American highway.

Consular Service Stamps Surcharged in Black

a   b

1953-54   *Perf. 12*
C245	R1 (a)	60c on 2s brown	.35 .25
C246	R2 (a)	60c on 5s sep ('54)	.35 .25
C247	R2 (a)	70c on 5s sep ('54)	.35 .25
C248	R2 (a)	90c on 50c car rose ('54)	.35 .25
C249	R1 (b)	1s on 2s brown	.35 .25
C250	R1 (a)	1s on 2s brn ('54)	.35 .25
C251	R1 (a)	2s on 2s brn ('54)	.65 .25
C252	R1 (a)	3s on 5s vio ('54)	.90 .25
	Nos. C245-C252 (8)		3.65 2.00

Surcharge is horizontal on Nos. C245-C248.

Carlos Maria Cardinal de la Torre — AP55

1954, Jan. 13   **Photo.**   *Perf. 8½*
Center in Black
C253	AP55	60c rose lilac	.55 .30
C254	AP55	90c green	.90 .30
C255	AP55	3s orange	1.35 .45
	Nos. C253-C255 (3)		2.80 1.05

1st anniv. of the elevation of Archbishop de la Torre to Cardinal.

Queen Isabella I — AP56

1954, Apr. 22
C256	AP56	60c dk grn & grn	.55 .40
C257	AP56	90c lil rose	.55 .40
C258	AP56	1s blk & pale lil	.55 .40
C259	AP56	2s blk brn & pale bl	.75 .40
C260	AP56	5s blk brn & sepia	1.90 .40
	Nos. C256-C260 (5)		4.30 2.00

See note with No. 585.

Post Office, Guayaquil AP57

1954, May 19   **Engr.**   *Perf. 12½x12*
Black Surcharge
C261	AP57	80c on 20c red	.35 .25
C262	AP57	1s on 20c red	.35 .25

25th anniversary of Pan American-Grace Airways' operation in Ecuador.

Plane, Gateway and Wheel — AP58

Unwmk.
1954, Aug. 2　　Litho.　　Perf. 11
C263　AP58　80c blue　　　　　.40　.25

Day of the Postal Employee.

San Pablo Lagoon — AP59

1954, Sept. 24　　　　Photo.
C264　AP59　60c orange　　　.35　.25
C265　AP59　70c rose pink　　.35　.25
C266　AP59　90c dp grn　　　.35　.25
C267　AP59　1s dk gray grn　.35　.25
C268　AP59　2s blue　　　　　.45　.25
C269　AP59　3s yel brn　　　.85　.25
　　Nos. C264-C269 (6)　　2.70　1.50

 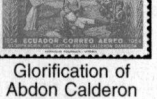

Glorification of Abdon Calderon Garaicoa AP60

Capt. Calderon AP61

1954, Oct. 1
C270　AP60　80c rose pink　　.45　.25
C271　AP61　90c blue　　　　　.45　.25

150th anniversary of the birth of Capt. Abdon Calderon Garaicoa.

El Cebollar College AP62

Brother Miguel Instructing Boys AP63

Designs: 90c, Francisco Febres Cordero (Brother Miguel). 2.50s, Tomb of Brother Miguel. 3s, Monument to Brother Miguel.

1954, Dec. 3　　Unwmk.　　Perf. 11
C272　AP62　70c dk grn　　　.25　.25
C273　AP63　80c dk brn　　　.25　.25
C274　AP63　90c dk gray bl　.25　.25
C275　AP63　2.50s indigo　　.45　.25
C276　AP62　3s lil rose　　　.55　.35
　　Nos. C272-C276 (5)　　1.75　1.35

Centenary of the birth of Francisco Febres Cordero (Brother Miguel).

No. C221 Surcharged in Various Colors

1955, May 25
C277　A173　1s on 10s vio (Bk)　.30　.25
C278　A173　1.70s on 10s vio (C)　.40　.25
C279　A173　4.20s on 10s vio (Br)　.65　.35
　　Nos. C277-C279 (3)　　　1.35　.85

Denomination in larger type on No. C279. National Exhibition of Daily Periodicals.

"La Rotonda," Guayaquil, and Rotary Emblem — AP64

Design: 90c, Eugenio Espejo hospital, Quito, and Rotary emblem.

1955, July 9　　Engr.　　Perf. 12½
C280　AP64　80c dark brown　　.30　.25
C281　AP64　90c dark green　　.50　.35

50th anniv. of the founding of Rotary Intl.

José Abel Castillo — AP65

2s, 5s, José Abel Castillo, Map of Ecuador.

1955, Oct. 19　　　　Perf. 11x11½
C282　AP65　60c chocolate　　1.20　.25
C283　AP65　90c light olive green　1.35　.25
C284　AP65　1s lilac　　　　　1.50　.25
C285　AP65　2s vermilion　　　1.90　.30
C286　AP65　5s ultra　　　　　3.75　.55
　　Nos. C282-C286 (5)　　　9.70　1.60

See note after No. 595.

No. C29 Surcharged in Black

1955, Oct. 24　　　　Perf. 12
C287　AP1　1s on 5s purple　　.75　.25

A similar surcharge on No. C29, set in two lines with letters 5mm high and no X's or black-out line of squares, was privately applied.

San Pablo, Imbabura — AP66

50s, Rumichaca Caves. 1.30s, Virgin of Quito. 1.50s, Cotopaxi Volcano. 1.70s, Tungurahua Volcano, Tungurahua. 1.90s, Guanacos. 2.40s, Mat market. 2.50s, Ruins at Ingapirca. 4.20s, El Carmen, Cuenca, Azuay. 4.80s, Santo Domingo Church.

1956, Jan. 2　　Photo.　　Perf. 13
C288　AP66　50c slate blue　　2.75　.25
C289　AP66　1s ultra　　　　　2.75　.25
C290　AP66　1.30s crimson　　4.25　.25
C291　AP66　1.50s dp grn　　　2.75　.25
C292　AP66　1.70s yel brn　　1.75　.25
C293　AP66　1.90s olive　　　3.50　.25
C294　AP66　2.40s red org　　3.75　.25
C295　AP66　2.50s violet　　　3.75　.25
C296　AP66　4.20s black　　　4.75　.25
C297　AP66　4.80s yel org　　7.50　.30
　　Nos. C288-C297 (10)　　37.50　2.55

See Nos. C310-C311. For surcharges see Nos. 766A, 766G.

Honorato Vazquez — AP67

1956, May 28　　　　　　Engr.
Various Portraits
C298　AP67　1s yellow green　　.50　.25
C299　AP67　1.50s red　　　　　.50　.25
C300　AP67　1.70s bright blue　.50　.25
C301　AP67　1.90s slate blue　.50　.25
　　Nos. C298-C301 (4)　　　2.00　1.00

Birth centenary (in 1955) of Honorato Vazquez, statesman.

Title Page of First Book — AP68

1956, Aug. 27　　Unwmk.　　Perf. 13½
C302　AP68　1s black　　　　.75　.25
C303　AP68　1.70s slate bl　.75　.25
C304　AP68　2s blk brn　　　.75　.25
C305　AP68　3s redsh brn　　.75　.25
　　Nos. C302-C305 (4)　　3.00　1.00

Bicentenary of printing in Ecuador.

Hands Reaching for UN Emblem — AP69

1956, Oct. 24　　　　　Perf. 14
C307　AP69　1.70s red org　　1.10　.25

10th anniv. of the UN (in 1955). See No. C319. For overprint see No. C426.

Coat of Arms and Basketball Player — AP70

Designs: 1.70s, Map of South America with flags and girl basketball players.

1956, Dec. 28　Photo.　Perf. 14½x14
C308　AP70　1s red lilac　　.85　.25
C309　AP70　1.70s deep green　.85　.25

6th South American Women's Basketball Championship, Aug. 1956.

Scenic Type of 1956
1957, Jan. 2　　　　　Perf. 13
C310　AP66　50c bl grn　　1.75　.25
C311　AP66　1s orange　　1.75　.25

Type of Regular Issue, 1957
Designs: 50c, Map of Cuenca, 16th century. 80c, Cathedral of Cuenca. 1s, Modern City Hall.

Unwmk.
1957, Apr. 7　　Photo.　　Perf. 12
C312　A219　50c brn, cr　　　.35　.25
　a.　Souvenir sheet of 4　1.00　1.00
C313　A219　80c red, bluish　.35　.25
C314　A219　1s pur, yel　　　.35　.25
　a.　Souvenir sheet of 3　2.00　2.00
　　Nos. C312-C314 (3)　　1.05　.75

No. C312a contains 4 imperf. 50c stamps similar to No. 613, but inscribed "AEREO" and printed in green. The sheet is printed on white ungummed paper.
No. C314a contains 3 imperf. stamps in designs similar to Nos. C312-C314, but with colors changed to orange (50c), brown (80c), violet (1s). The sheet is printed on white ungummed paper.

Gabriela Mistral — AP71

Unwmk.
1957, Sept. 18　　Litho.　　Perf. 14
C315　AP71　2s lt bl, blk & red　.55　.25

Issued to honor Gabriela Mistral (1889-1957), Chilean poet and educator. See Nos. C406-C407.

Arms of Espejo, Carchi — AP72

Arms of Cantons: 2s, Montufar. 4.20s, Tulcan.

1957, Nov. 16　　Perf. 14½x13½
Coat of Arms Multicolored
C316　AP72　1s carmine　　　.55　.25
C317　AP72　2s black　　　　.55　.25
C318　AP72　4.20s ultra　　　1.00　.25
　　Nos. C316-C318 (3)　　2.10　.75

Province of Carchi.
See Nos. C334-C337, C355-C364, C392-C395. For surcharge see No. 766.

Redrawn UN Type of 1956
1957, Dec. 10　　Engr.　　Perf. 14
C319　AP69　2s greenish blue　.75　.25

Honoring the UN. Dates, as on No. C307, are omitted; inscribed: "Homenaje a las Naciones Unidas."

Mater Dolorosa, San Gabriel College — AP73

No. C321, 1s, Door of San Gabriel College, Quito.

1958, Apr. 27　　Engr.　　Perf. 14
C320　AP73　30c rose cl, dp rose　.40　.25
C321　AP73　30c rose cl, dp rose　.40　.25
　a.　Pair, #C320-C321　　.85　.60
C322　AP73　1s dk bl, lt bl　.40　.25
C323　AP73　1.70s dk bl, lt bl　.40　.25
　a.　Pair, #C322-C323　　.85　.60

Miracle of San Gabriel College, Quito, 50th anniv.

Rafael Maria Arizaga (1858-1933), Writer — AP74

1958, July 21　　　　　Litho.
C324　AP74　1s multi　　　　.75　.30

See Nos. C343, C350, C412.

Daule River Bridge — AP75

1958, July 25　　Engr.　Perf. 13½x14
C325　AP75　1.30s green　　.70　.25

Issued to commemorate the opening of the River Daule bridge in Guayas province. See Nos. C367-C369.

Basketball Player — AP76

1958, Sept. 1　　Photo.　Perf. 14x13½
C326　AP76　1.30s dk grn & lt brn　.70　.45

South American basketball championships. For surcharge see No. 774A.

Symbolical of the Eucharist — AP77

Design: 60c, Cathedral of Guayaquil.

1958, Sept. 25　　Litho.　　Unwmk.
C327　AP77　10c vio & buff　.55　.30
C328　AP77　60c org & vio brn　.55　.30
C329　AP77　1s brn & lt bl　.55　.30
　　Nos. C327-C329 (3)　1.65　.90

Souvenir Sheet

Symbolical of the Eucharist — AP78

Perf. 13½x14

C330 AP78   Sheet of 4   2.75 2.25
a.-d.   40c dark blue, any single   .25   .25

3rd National Eucharistic Congress.

Stamps of 1865 and 1920 — AP79

Designs: 2s, Stamps of 1920 and 1948. 4.20s, Municipal museum and library.

1958, Oct. 8   Photo.   Perf. 11½
Granite Paper

C331 AP79 1.30s grn & brn red   .40   .25
C332 AP79 2s bl & vio   .75   .30
C333 AP79 4.20s dk brn   .95   .40
   Nos. C331-C333 (3)   2.10   .95

National Philatelic Exposition (EXFIGUA), Guayaquil, Oct. 4-14.
For surcharge see No. 774.

Coat of Arms Type of 1957
Province of Imbabura

Arms of Cantons: 50c, Cotacachi. 60c, Antonio Ante. 80c, Otavalo. 1.10s, Ibarra.

1958, Nov. 9   Litho.   Perf. 14½x13½
Coats of Arms Multicolored

C334 AP72 50c blk & red   .55   .25
C335 AP72 60c blk, bl & red .55   .25
C336 AP72 80c blk & yel   .55   .25
C337 AP72 1.10s blk & red   .55   .25
   Nos. C334-C337 (4)   2.20 1.00

Charles V — AP80

Engr. & Photo.

1958, Dec. 12   Perf. 14x13½

C338 AP80 2s brn red & dk brn   .55   .30
C339 AP80 4.20s dk gray & red brn .65   .45

400th anniv. of the death of Charles V, Holy Roman Emperor.

Paul Rivet — AP81

1958, Dec. 29   Photo.   Perf. 11½
Granite Paper

C340 AP81 1s brown   .75   .30

Issued in honor of Paul Rivet (1876-1958), French anthropologist.

1959, May 6

Portrait: 2s, Alexander von Humboldt.

C341 AP81 2s slate   .70   .25

Cent. of the death of Alexander von Humboldt, German naturalist and geographer.

Front Page of "El Telegrafo" AP82

1959, Feb.   Litho.   Perf. 13½
C342 AP82 1.30s bl grn & blk   .70   .25

75th anniv. of Ecuador's oldest newspaper.

Portrait Type of 1958

José Luis Tamayo (1858-1947), lawyer.

1959, June 26   Unwmk.   Perf. 14
Portrait Multicolored

C343 AP74 1.30s lt grn, bl & sal   .70   .30

El Sagrario & House of Manuela Canizares AP83

Condor AP84

Designs: 80c, Hall at San Agustin. 1s, First words of the constitutional act. 2s, Entrance to Cuartel Real. 4.20s, Allegory of Liberty.

Unwmk.
1959, Aug. 28   Photo.   Perf. 14

C344 AP83 20c ultra & lt brn   .35   .25
C345 AP83 80c brt bl & dp org   .35   .25
C346 AP83 1s dk red & dk ol   .35   .25
C347 AP84 1.30s brt bl & org   .35   .25
C348 AP84 2s ultra & org brn   .35   .25
C349 AP84 4.20s scar & brt bl   .75   .45
   Nos. C344-C349 (6)   2.50 1.70

Sesquicentennial of the revolution.

Portrait Type of 1958

1s, Alfredo Baquerizo Moreno (1859-1951), statesman.

1959, Sept. 26   Litho.   Perf. 14
C350 AP74 1s gray, red & salmon   .50   .30

Pope Pius XII — AP85

1959, Oct. 9   Unwmk.   Perf. 14½
C351 AP85 1.30s multi   .70   .30

Issued in memory of Pope Pius XII.

Flags of Argentina, Bolivia, Brazil, Guatemala, Haiti, Mexico and Peru — AP86

Flags of: 80c, Chile, Costa Rica, Cuba, Dominican Republic, Panama, Paraguay, United States. 1.30s, Colombia, Ecuador, Honduras, Nicaragua, Salvador, Uruguay, Venezuela.

1959, Oct. 12   Perf. 13½.
C352 AP86 50c multi   .25   .25
C353 AP86 80c yel, red & bl   .30   .25
C354 AP86 1.30s multi   .40   .25
   Nos. C352-C354 (3)   .95   .75

Organization of American States.
For overprints see Nos. C423-C425, CO19-CO21.

Arms of the Cantons Type of 1957
Province of Pichincha

10c, Rumiñahui. 40c, Pedro Moncayo. 1s, Mejia. 1.30s, Cayambe. 4.20s, Quito.

Perf. 14½x13½
1959-60   Unwmk.   Litho.
Coat of Arms Multicolored

C355 AP72 10c blk & dk red ('60)   .50   .30
C356 AP72 40c blk & yel   .50   .30
C357 AP72 1s blk & brn ('60)   .50   .30
C358 AP72 1.30s blk & grn ('60)   .50   .30
C359 AP72 4.20s blk & org   .50   .30
   Nos. C355-C359 (5)   2.50 1.50

Province of Cotopaxi

40c, Pangua. 60c, Pujili. 70c, Saquisili. 1s, Salcedo. 1.30s, Latacunga.

1960   Coat of Arms Multicolored

C360 AP72 40c blk & car   .40   .25
C361 AP72 60c blk & bl   .40   .25
C362 AP72 70c blk & turq   .40   .25
C363 AP72 1s blk & red org .40   .25
C364 AP72 1.30s blk & org   .45   .25
   Nos. C360-C364 (5)   2.05 1.25

Flags of American Nations AP87

1960, Feb. 23   Perf. 13x12½
C365 AP87 1.30s multi   .40   .25
C366 AP87 2s multi   .40   .25

11th Inter-American Conference, Feb. 1960.

Bridge Type of 1958.

Bridges: No. C367, Juntas. No. C368, Saracay. 2s, Railroad bridge, Ambato.

1960   Litho.   Perf. 13½
C367 AP75 1.30s chocolate   .30   .25

Photo.   Perf. 12½
C368 AP75 1.30s emerald   .30   .25
C369 AP75 2s brown   .50   .25
   Nos. C367-C369 (3)   1.10   .75

Building of three new bridges.

Bahia-Chone Road — AP88

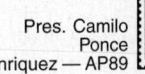

Pres. Camilo Ponce Enriquez — AP89

Designs: 4.20s, Public Works Building, Cuenca. 5s, El Coca airport. 10s, New Harbor, Guayaquil.

1960, Aug.   Litho.   Perf. 14
C370 AP88 1.30s blk & dl yel   .30   .25
C371 AP88 4.20s rose car & lt grn .45   .45
C372 AP88 5s dk brn & yel   .65   .55
C373 AP88 10s dk bl & bl   1.50   .55

Perf. 11x11½
C374 AP89 2s org brn & blk   2.25   .30
   Nos. C370-C374 (5)   5.15 2.10

Nos. C370-C374 publicize the achievements of Pres. Camilo Ponce Enriquez (1956-1960).
Issued: Nos. C370-C373, 8/24; No. C374, 8/31.

Red Cross Building, Quito and Henri Dunant — AP90

1960, Oct. 5   Unwmk.   Perf. 13x14
C375 AP90 2s rose vio & car   .70   .25

Centenary (in 1959) of Red Cross idea.
For overprint see No. C408.

El Belen Church, Quito — AP91

1961, Jan. 14   Perf. 12½
C376 AP91 3s multi   .75   .25

Ecuador's participation in the 1960 Barcelona Philatelic Congress.

Map of Ecuador and Amazon River System AP92

1961, Feb. 27   Litho.   Perf. 10½
C377 AP92 80c salmon, claret & grn   .35   .25
C378 AP92 1.30s gray, slate & grn   .55   .25
C379 AP92 2s beige, red & grn   .75   .25
   Nos. C377-C379 (3)   1.65 .75

Amazon Week, and the 132nd anniversary of the Battle of Tarqui against Peru.

Juan Montalvo, Juan Leon Mera, Juan Benigno Vela — AP93

1961, Apr. 13   Unwmk.   Perf. 13
C380 AP93 1.30s salmon & blk   .75   .25

Centenary of Tungurahua province.

Hugo Ortiz G. — AP94

Design: No. C382, Ortiz monument.

1961, May 25   Perf. 14x14½
C381 AP94 1.30s grnsh bl, blk & yel   .45   .25
C382 AP94 1.30s grnsh bl, pur, ol & brn .45   .25

Lt. Hugo Ortiz G., killed in battle 8/2/41.

Condor and Airplane Stamp of 1936 — AP95

1.30s, Map of South America and stamp of 1865. 2s, Bolivar monument stamp of 1930.

Perf. 10½
1961, May 25   Litho.   Unwmk.
Size: 41x28mm
C383 AP95 80c org & vio   .40   .25
Size: 41x34mm
C384 AP95 1.30s bl, yel, ol & car   .60   .35
Size: 40½x37mm
C385 AP95 2s car rose & blk   1.00   .35
   Nos. C383-C385 (3)   2.00   .95

Third National Philatelic Exhibition, Quito, May 25-June 3, 1961.

Arms of Los Rios and Egret — AP96

1961, May 27　　Perf. 14½x13½
Coat of Arms Multicolored
C386　AP96　2s bl & blk　　　.75　.30
Centenary (in 1960) of Los Rios province.

Gabriel Garcia
Moreno — AP97

1961, Sept. 24　Unwmk.　Perf. 12
C387　AP97　1s bl, brn & buff　.75　.25
Centenary of the restoration of national integrity.

Remigio Crespo
Toral — AP98

1961, Nov. 3　Unwmk.　Perf. 14
C388　AP98　50c multi　　　.65　.25
Centenary of the birth of Remigio Crespo Toral, poet laureate of Ecuador.

Galapagos Islands Nos. LC1-LC3 Overprinted in Black or Red (Similar to #684-686)
"ESTACION DE BIOLOGIA MARITIMA DE GALAPAGOS" and " UNESCO 1961"

1961, Oct. 31　Photo.　Perf. 12
C389　A1　1s dp bl　　　1.30　.30
　a.　"de Galapagos" on top line　6.00　6.00
C390　A1　1.80s rose vio　　1.80　.40
　a.　UNESCO emblem omitted　6.00　6.00
C391　A1　4.20s blk (R)　　2.75　.60
　　　Nos. C389-C391 (3)　5.85　1.25
Establishment of maritime biological stations on Galapagos Islands by UNESCO.

Arms of the Cantons Type of 1957
Province of Tungurahua
50c, Pillaro. 1s, Pelileo. 1.30s, Baños. 2s, Ambato.

Perf. 14½x13½
1962, Mar. 30　Litho.　Unwmk.
Coats of Arms Multicolored
C392　AP72　50c black　　　.25　.25
C393　AP72　1s black　　　.35　.25
C394　AP72　1.30s black　　.45　.25
C395　AP72　2s black　　　.75　.25
　　　Nos. C392-C395 (4)　1.80　1.00

AP99

Designs: 1.30s, 2s, Pres. Arosemena and Prince Philip, Arms of Ecuador and Great Britain and Equator Monument.

Perf. 14x13½
1962, Feb. 17　　Wmk. 340
C396　AP99　1.30s bl, sepia, red & yel　　.40　.25
C397　AP99　2s multi　　　.60　.25
Visit of Prince Philip, Duke of Edinburgh, to Ecuador, Feb. 17-20, 1962.

Mountain
Farming — AP100

Perf. 12½
1963, Mar. 21　Unwmk.　Litho.
C398　AP100　30c emer, yel & blk　.30　.25
C399　AP100　3s dl red, grn & org　.70　.25
C400　AP100　4.20s bl, blk & yel　1.10　.55
　　　Nos. C398-C400 (3)　2.10　1.05
FAO "Freedom from Hunger" campaign.
Exist imperf. Value $32.50.

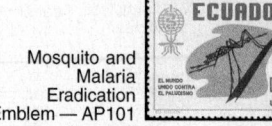

Mosquito and
Malaria
Eradication
Emblem — AP101

1963, Apr. 17　Unwmk.　Perf. 12½
C401　AP101　50c multi　　　.35　.25
C402　AP101　80c multi　　　.35　.25
C403　AP101　2s multi　　　.50　.25
　　　Nos. C401-C403 (3)　1.20　.75
WHO drive to eradicate malaria.

Stagecoach and
Jet Plane — AP102

1963, May 7　　　Litho.
C404　AP102　2s org & car rose　.40　.30
C405　AP102　4.20s claret & ultra　.70　.50
1st Intl. Postal Conference, Paris, 1863.

Type of 1957 Inscribed "Islas Galapagos," Surcharged with New Value and Overprinted "Ecuador" in Black or Red

1963, June 19　Unwmk.　Perf. 14
C406　AP71　5s on 2s gray, dk bl & red　　1.10　.80
C407　AP71　10s on 2s gray, dk bl & red (R)　2.00　1.60
The basic 2s exists without surcharge and overprint. No. C407 exists with "ECUADOR" omitted, and with both "ECUADOR" and "10 SUCRES" double.

No. C375 Overprinted: "1863-1963/Centenario/de la Fundación/ de la Cruz Roja/Internacional"

1963, June 21　Photo.　Perf. 13x14
C408　AP90　2s rose vio & car　.70　.25
Intl. Red Cross, centenary.

Type of Regular Issue, 1963
Arosemena and: 70c, Flags of Ecuador. 2s, Flags of Ecuador, Panama. 4s, Flags of Ecuador, US.

1963, July 1　Litho.　Perf. 14
C409　A238　70c pale bl & multi　.30　.25
C410　A238　2s pink & multi　　.60　.25
C411　A238　4s lt bl & multi　1.25　.35
　　　Nos. C409-C411 (3)　2.15　.85
Imperfs exist. Value $15.

Portrait Type of 1958
Portrait: 2s, Dr. Mariano Cueva (1812-82).

Unwmk.
1963, July 4　Litho.　Perf. 14
C412　AP74　2s lt grn & multi　.70　.25

Social Insurance
Symbol — AP103

1963, July 9　　　Litho.
C413　AP103　10s brn & multi　1.10　.90
25th anniversary of Social Insurance.
Exists imperf. Value $9.

Mother and
Child — AP104

1963, July 28　　　Perf. 12½
C414　AP104　1.30s org, dk bl & blk　.45　.25
C415　AP104　5s gray, red & brn　.75　.60
7th Pan-American and South American Pediatrics Congresses, Quito.

Simon Bolivar
Airport,
Guayaquil — AP105

1963, July 25　　　Perf. 14
C416　AP105　60c gray　　.35　.25
C417　AP105　70c dl grn　　.40　.25
C418　AP105　5s brn vio　　.60　.35
　　　Nos. C416-C418 (3)　1.35　.85
Opening of Simon Bolivar Airport, Guayaquil, July 15, 1962.
Exist imperf. Value $4.50.

Nos. 638, 640-641 Overprinted "AEREO"

1964　　　　　Perf. 12
Flags in National Colors
C419　A223　1.80s dl vio　　.60　.35
C420　A224　2s dk brn　　.60　.35
C421　A223　2.20s blk brn　　.60　.35
　　　Nos. C419-C421 (3)　1.80　1.05
On 1.80s and 2.20s, "AEREO" is vertical, reading down.

No. 650 Overprinted in Gold: "FARO DE COLON / AEREO"

1964　Photo.　Perf. 14x13½
C422　A229　1.80s dk bl　　3.00　2.00

Nos. C352-C354 Overprinted

1964　　Litho.　Perf. 13½
C423　AP86　50c bl & multi　　.80　.45
C424　AP86　80c yel & multi　.80　.45
C425　AP86　1.30s pale grn & multi　.80　.45
　　　Nos. C423-C425 (3)　2.40　1.35

No. C307 Overprinted: "DECLARACION / DERECHOS HUMANOS / 1964 / XV-ANIV"
Unwmk.

1964, Sept. 29　Engr.　Perf. 14
C426　AP69　1.70s red org　　.70　.25
15th anniversary (in 1963) of the Universal Declaration of Human Rights.

Banana Type
1964, Oct. 26　Litho.　Perf. 12½x12
C427　A241　4.20s blk, bis & gray ol　.40　.30
C428　A241　10s blk, scar & gray ol　.70　.50
　a.　Souv. sheet of 4　3.25　3.00
No. C428a contains imperf. stamps similar to Nos. 720-721 and C427-C428.

John F.
Kennedy,
Flag-draped
Coffin and
John
Jr. — AP106

1964, Nov. 22　Litho.　Perf. 14
C429　AP106　4.20s multi　1.25　.95
C430　AP106　5s multi　　1.60　1.25
C431　AP106　10s multi　　3.00　1.60
　a.　Souv. sheet of 3　10.00　10.00
　　　Nos. C429-C431 (3)　5.85　3.80
President John F. Kennedy (1917-63).
No. C431a contains stamps similar to Nos. C429-C431, imperf.

Olympic Type
1.30s, Gymnast, vert. 1.80s, Hurdler. 2s, Basketball.

Perf. 13½x14, 14x13½
1964, Dec. 16　　　Unwmk.
C432　A243　1.30s vio bl, ver & brn　.45　.25
C433　A243　1.80s vio bl & multi　.45　.25
C434　A243　2s red & multi　　.45　.25
　a.　Souv. sheet of 4　3.75　3.25
　　　Nos. C432-C434 (3)　1.35　.75
No. C434a contains stamps similar to Nos. 725 and C432-C434, imperf.

Sports Type
Torch and Athletes: 2s, 3s, Diver, gymnast, wrestlers and weight lifter. 2.50s, 4s, Bicyclists. 3.50s, 5s, Jumpers.

1965, Nov. 20　Litho.　Perf. 12x12½
C435　A247　2s bl, gold & blk　.65　.25
C436　A247　2.50s org, gold & blk　.65　.25
C437　A247　3s brt pink, gold & blk　.65　.25
C438　A247　3.50s lt vio, gold & blk　.70　.65
C439　A247　4s brt yel grn, gold & blk　.70　.25
C440　A247　5s red org, gold & blk　.80　.35
　a.　Souv. sheet of 12　12.00　12.00
　　　Nos. C435-C440 (6)　4.15　2.00
No. C440a contains 12 imperf. stamps similar to Nos. 738-743 and C435-C440.
For surcharges see Nos. 766B, C449.

Bird Type
Birds: 1s, Yellow grosbeak. 1.30s, Black-headed parrot. 1.50s, Scarlet tanager. 2s, Sapphire quail-dove. 2.50s, Violet-tailed sylph. 3s, Lemon-throated barbet. 4s, Yellow-tailed oriole. 10s, Collared puffbird.

1966, June 17　Litho.　Perf. 13½
Birds in Natural Colors
C441　A249　1s lt red brn & blk　1.10　.25
C442　A249　1.30s pink & blk　1.10　.25
C443　A249　1.50s pale grn & blk　1.10　.25
C444　A249　2s sal & blk　　2.75　.45
C445　A249　2.50s lt yel grn & blk　2.75　.45
C446　A249　3s sal & blk　　3.75　.65
C447　A249　4s gray & blk　　5.00　.85
C448　A249　10s beige & blk　7.75　2.10
　　　Nos. C441-C448 (8)　25.30　5.25
For surcharges see Nos. 766E-766F, C450, C455-C457.

Nos. C436 and C443 Surcharged 1967
C449　A247　80c on 2.50s multi　.40　.35
C450　A249　80c on 1.50s multi　.40　.25
Old denomination on No. C449 is obliterated with heavy bar; the surcharge on No. C450 includes "Resello" and an ornament over old denomination.

Peñaherrera
Monument,
Quito — AP107

Design: 2s, Peñaherrera statue.

1967, Dec. 29　Litho.　Perf. 12x12½
C451　AP107　1.30s blk & org　.30　.25
C452　AP107　2s blk & lt ultra　.30　.25
See note after No. 767B.

Arosemena Type
1.30s, Inauguration. 2s, Pres. Arosemena speaking in Punta del Este.

1968, May 9　Litho.　Perf. 13½x14
C453　A251　1.30s multi　　.35　.25
C454　A251　2s multi　　　.40　.25

No. C448 Srchd. in
Plum, Dark Blue or
Green

1969, Jan. 9   Litho.   Perf. 13½

Bird in Natural Colors

C455	A249	80c on 10s beige (P)	.55	.25
C456	A249	1s on 10s beige (DBl)	.55	.25
C457	A249	2s on 10s beige (G)	.55	.25
		Nos. C455-C457 (3)	1.65	.75

"Operation Friendship" — AP108

1969-70   Typo.   Perf. 13½

C458	AP108	2s yel, blk, red & lt bl	.30	.25
a.		Perf. 12½	.30	.25
C459	AP108	2s bl, blk, car & yel ('70)	.30	.25

Friendship campaign. Medallion background on Nos. C458 and C458a is blue; on No. C459, yellow.

No. C459 exists imperf. Value, $7.50.

No. 639 Surcharged in Gold "S/. 5 AEREO" and Bar

1969, Nov. 25   Litho.   Perf. 12

C460	A224	5s on 2s multi	2.00	.75

Butterfly Type

Butterflies: 1.30s, Morpho peleides. 1.50s, Anartia amathea.

1970   Litho.   Perf. 12½

C461	A255	1.30s multi	3.50	.25
C462	A255	1.50s pink & multi	3.50	.25

Same, White Background

1970   Perf. 13½

C463	A255	1.30s multi	3.50	.25
C464	A255	1.50s multi	3.50	.25

Arms Type

Provincial Arms and Flags: 1.30s, El Oro. 2s, Loja. 3s, Manabi. 5s, Pichincha. 10s, Guayas.

1971   Litho.   Perf. 10½

C465	A258	1.30s pink & multi	.30	.25
C466	A258	2s multi	.40	.25
C467	A258	3s multi	.55	.30
C468	A258	5s multi	.70	.30
C469	A258	10s multi	1.35	.40
		Nos. C465-C469 (5)	3.30	1.50

Presentation of the Virgin — AP109

Art of Quito: 1.50s, Blessed Anne at Prayer. 2s, St. Theresa de Jesus. 2.50s, Altar of Carmen, horiz. 3s, Descent from the Cross. 4s, Christ of St. Mariana de Jesus. 5s, Shrine of St. Anthony. 10s, Cross of San Diego.

1971   Perf. 11½

Inscriptions in Black

C473	AP109	1.30s multi	.25	.25
C474	AP109	1.50s multi	.25	.25
C475	AP109	2s multi	.25	.25
C476	AP109	2.50s multi	.40	.25
C477	AP109	3s multi	.50	.25
C478	AP109	4s multi	.65	.25
C479	AP109	5s multi	.65	.35
C480	AP109	10s multi	1.25	.65
		Nos. C473-C480 (8)	4.20	2.50

Pres. Allende and Chilean Flag — AP110

2.10s, Pres. José M. Velasco Ibarra of Ecuador, Pres. Salvador Allende of Chile, national flags.

1971, Aug. 24   Perf. 12½

C481	AP110	2s multi	.30	.25
C482	AP110	2.10s multi	.30	.25

Visit of Pres. Salvador Allende of Chile, Aug. 24.

Globe and Emblem — AP111

1971

C483	AP111	5s black	1.10	.45
C484	AP111	5.50s dl pur & blk	1.10	.45

Opening of Postal Museum, Aug. 24, 1971. Exist imperf. Value $7.50.

Pazmiño Type

1971, Sept. 16   Perf. 12x11½

C485	A260	1.50s grn & multi	.35	.25
C486	A260	2.50s grn & multi	.45	.25

AP112

Designs: 5s, Map of Americas. 10s, Converging roads and map. 20s, Map of Americas and Equator. 50s, Mountain road and monument on Equator.

1971   Perf. 11½

C487	AP112	5s org & multi	.80	.30
C488	AP112	10s org & blk	1.25	.55
C489	AP112	20s blk, bl & brt rose	2.00	1.00
C490	AP112	50s bl, blk & gray	3.25	1.50
		Nos. C487-C490 (4)	7.30	3.35

11th Pan-American Road Congress. Issued: 5s, 10s, 50s, 11/15; 20s, 11/22. No. C488 exists imperf. Value $8.

AP113

Design: 3s, Arms of Ecuador and Argentina. 5s, Presidents José M. Velasco Ibarra and Alejandro Agustin Lanusse.

1972

C491	AP113	3s blk & multi	.30	.25
C492	AP113	5s blk & multi	.60	.30

Visit of Lt. Gen. Alejandro Agustin Lanusse, president of Argentina, Jan. 25.

Flame, Scales, Map of Americas — AP114

1972, Apr. 24   Litho.   Perf. 12½

C493	AP114	1.30s bl & red	.50	.25

17th Conference of the Interamerican Federation of Lawyers, Quito, Apr. 24.

Religious Paintings Type of Regular Issue

Ecuadorian Paintings: 3s, Virgin of the Flowers, by Miguel de Santiago. 10s, Virgin of the Rosary, by Quito School.

1972, Apr. 24   Perf. 14x13½

C494	A263	3s blk & multi	.40	.35
C495	A263	10s blk & multi	1.20	.55
a.		Souv. sheet of 2, #C494-C495	1.90	1.90

1972, May 4

Ecuadorian Statues: 3s, St. Dominic, Quito School. 10s, St. Rosa of Lima, by Bernardo de Legarda.

C496	A263	3s blk & multi	.45	.35
C497	A263	10s blk & multi	1.20	.55
a.		Souv. sheet of 2, #C496-C497	2.50	2.10

Letters of "Ecuador" 3mm high on Nos. C496-C497, 7mm high on Nos. C494-C495.

Portrait Type

Designs (Generals, from Paintings): 1.30s, José Maria Saenz. 3s, Tomás Wright. 4s, Antonio Farfan. 5s, Antonio José de Sucre. 10s, Simon Bolivar. 20s, Arms of Ecuador.

1972, May 24

C498	A264	1.30s bl & multi	.35	.25
C499	A264	3s bl & multi	.35	.25
C500	A264	4s bl & multi	.45	.25
C501	A264	5s bl & multi	.65	.30
C502	A264	10s bl & multi	1.20	.55
C503	A264	20s bl & multi	2.40	1.00
		Nos. C498-C503 (6)	5.40	2.60

Artisan Type

Handicraft of Ecuador: 2s, Woman wearing flowered poncho. 3s, Striped poncho. 5s, Poncho with roses. 10s, Gold sunburst sculpture.

1972, July   Photo.   Perf. 13

C504	A265	2s multi	.35	.25
C505	A265	3s multi	.60	.25
C506	A265	5s multi	.95	.45
C507	A265	10s org red & multi	1.60	.90
a.		Souv. sheet of 4, #C504-C507	4.00	4.00
		Nos. C504-C507 (4)	3.50	1.80

Epidendrum Orchid AP115

1972   Photo.   Perf. 12½

C508	AP115	4s shown	.90	.90
C509	AP115	6s Canna	1.40	1.40
C510	AP115	10s Jimson weed	2.00	2.00
a.		Souv. sheet of 3, #C508-C510	9.00	6.00
		Nos. C508-C510 (3)	4.30	4.30

Exists imperf.

Oil Drilling Towers — AP116

1972, Oct. 17   Litho.   Perf. 11½

C511	AP116	1.30s bl & multi	.50	.25

Ecuadorian oil industry.

Coat of Arms — AP117

Arms Multicolored

1972, Nov. 18   Litho.   Perf. 11½

C512	AP117	2s black	.25	.25
C513	AP117	3s black	.25	.25
C514	AP117	4s black	.35	.25
C515	AP117	4.50s black	.35	.25
C516	AP117	6.30s black	.80	.30
C517	AP117	6.90s black	.80	.30
		Nos. C512-C517 (6)	2.80	1.60

Pichincha Type

Designs: 2.40s, Corridor, San Agustin. 4.50s, La Merced Convent. 5.50s, Column base. 6.30s, Chapter Hall, San Agustin. 6.90s, Interior, San Agustin. 7.40s, Crucifixion, Cantuña Chapel. 7.90s, Decorated ceiling, San Agustin.

1972, Dec. 6   Wmk. 367

C518	A266	2.40s yel & multi	.40	.25
C519	A266	4.50s yel & multi	.60	.30
C520	A266	5.50s yel & multi	.60	.30
C521	A266	6.30s yel & multi	.90	.35
C522	A266	6.90s yel & multi	.90	.35
C523	A266	7.40s yel & multi	1.35	.55
C524	A266	7.90s yel & multi	1.35	.55
		Nos. C518-C524 (7)	6.10	2.65

UN Emblem — AP118

1973, Mar. 23   Unwmk.

C525	AP118	1.30s lt bl & blk	.70	.25

25th anniversary of the Economic Committee for Latin America (CEPAL).

OAS Emblem — AP119

1973, Apr. 14   Wmk. 367

C526	AP119	1.50s multi	.65	.25
a.		Unwatermarked	.65	.25

Day of the Americas and "Philately for Peace."

Bird Type

Designs: 1.30s, Blue-footed booby. 3s, Brown pelican.

1973   Unwmk.   Perf. 11½x11

C527	A268	1.30s multi	2.10	.30
C528	A268	3s multi	2.10	.30

Presidents Lara and Caldera — AP120

1973, June 15   Wmk. 367

C529	AP120	3s multi	.70	.30

Visit of Venezuela Pres. Rafael Caldera, Feb. 5-7.

Silver Coin, 1934 — AP121

Ecuadorian Coins: 10s, Silver coin, obverse. 50s, Gold coin, 1928.

Unwmk.

1973, Dec. 14   Photo.   Perf. 14

C530	AP121	5s multi	.60	.40
C531	AP121	10s multi	1.00	.60
C532	AP121	50s multi	4.50	2.50
a.		Souvenir sheet of 3	8.00	7.25
		Nos. C530-C532 (3)	6.10	3.50

No. C532a contains one each of Nos. C530-C532; Dated "1972." Exists imperf. Value, same.

A gold marginal overprint was applied in 1974 to No. C532a (perf. and imperf.): "X Campeonato Mundial de Football / Munich - 1974." Value, each $75.

A carmine overprint was applied in 1974 to No. C532a (perf. and imperf.): "Seminario de Telecommunicaciones Rurales, / Septiembre-1974 / Quito-Ecuador" and ITU emblem. Value, each $12.

Globe, OPEC Emblem, Oil Derrick — AP122

1974, June 15   Litho.   Perf. 11½

C533	AP122	2s multi	.45	.30

Meeting of Organization of Oil Exporting Countries, Quito, June 15-24.

Ecuadorian Flag, UPU
Emblem — AP123

1974, July 15   Litho.   Perf. 11½
C534 AP123 1.30s multi   .65 .25
 Centenary of Universal Postal Union.
Two 25s souvenir sheets exist. These were
sold on a restricted basis. Value, each $75.

Teodoro Wolf
AP124

Capt.
Edmundo
Chiriboga
AP125

1974   Litho.   Perf. 12x11½
C535 AP124 1.30s blk & ultra   .35 .25
C536 AP125 1.50s gray   .40 .25
 Teodoro Wolf, geographer; Edmundo
Chiriboga, national hero.
 Issued: No. C535, 11/29; No. C536, 12/4.

Congress
Emblem — AP126

1974, Dec. 8   Litho.   Perf. 11½x12
C537 AP126 5s bl & multi   .70 .30
 8th Inter-American Postmasters' Cong.,
Quito.

Map of Americas and
Coat of Arms — AP127

1975, Feb. 1   Perf. 12x11½
C538 AP127 3s bl & multi   .70 .30
 EXFIGUA Stamp Exhibition and 5th General
Assembly of Federation Inter-Americana de
Filatelia, Guayaquil, Nov. 1973.

Prominent
Ecuadorians — AP128

 No. C539, Manuel J. Calle, Journalist. No.
C540, Leopoldo Benites V., president of UN
General Assembly, 1973-74; No. C541, Adolfo
H. Simmonds G. (1892-1969), journalist; No.
C542, Juan de Dios Martinez Mera, President
of Ecuador, birth centenary.

1975   Perf. 12x11½
C539 AP128 5s lilac rose   .60 .30
C540 AP128 5s gray   .60 .30
C541 AP128 5s violet   .60 .30
C542 AP128 5s blk & rose red   .60 .30
  Nos. C539-C542 (4)   2.40 1.20

Pres.
Guillermo
Rodriguez
Lara
AP129

1975   Unwmk.   Perf. 12
C546 AP129 5s vermilion & blk   .85 .30
 State visit of Pres. Guillermo Rodriguez
Lara to Algeria, Romania and Venezuela.

Meeting Type of 1975

 1.50s, Rafael Rodriguez Palacios & Argelino
Duran Quintero meeting at border in
Rumichaca. 2s, Signing border agreement.

1975, Apr. 1   Litho.   Perf. 12x11½
C547 A273 1.50s multi   .35 .25
C548 A273 2s multi   .35 .25

Sacred Heart
(Painting)
AP130

Quito
Cathedral
AP131

 Design: 2s, Monstrance.

1975, Apr. 28 Litho. Perf. 12x11½
C549 AP130 1.30s yel & multi   .35 .25
C550 AP130 2s bl & multi   .40 .25
C551 AP131 3s multi   .50 .25
  Nos. C549-C551 (3)   1.25 .75
 3rd Bolivarian Eucharistic Congress, Quito,
June 9-16, 1974.

J. Delgado
Panchana
with Trophy
AP132

J. Delgado
Panchana
Swimming
AP133

Perf. 12x11½, 11½x12
1975, June 12   Unwmk.
C552 AP132 1.30s bl & multi   .45 .25
C553 AP133 3s blk & multi   .50 .25
 Jorge Delgado Panchana, South American
swimming champion, 1971 and 1974.

Sports Type of 1975

1975, Sept. 11   Litho.   Perf. 11½
C554 A276 1.30s Tennis   .45 .30
C555 A276 2s Target shooting   .60 .30
C556 A276 2.80s Volleyball   .70 .30
C557 A276 3s Raft with sails   .70 .30
C558 A276 5s Mask   1.25 .30
  Nos. C554-C558 (5)   3.70 1.50

Flower Type of 1975

 Designs: 1.30s, Pitcairnia pungens. 2s,
Scarlet sage. 3s, Amaryllis. 4s, Opuntia
quitense. 5s, Bomarea.

1975, Nov. 18 Litho. Perf. 11½x12
C559 A277 1.30s multi   .35 .35
C560 A277 2s multi   .55 .35
C561 A277 3s multi   .75 .50
C562 A277 4s multi   1.10 .75
C563 A277 5s multi   1.60 .90
  Nos. C559-C563 (5)   4.35 2.85

Tail
Assemblies
and Emblem
AP134

Planes over
Map of
Ecuador
AP135

1975, Dec. 17   Litho.   Perf. 11½
C564 AP134 1.30s bl & multi   .45 .30
C565 AP135 3s multi   .55 .30
 TAME, Military Transport Airline, 13th anniv.

Benalcázar
Statue — AP136

1976, Feb. 6   Litho.   Perf. 11½
C566 AP136 2s multi   .50 .25
C567 AP136 3s multi   .50 .25
 Sebastián de Benalcázar (1495-1550),
Spanish conquistador, founder of Quito.

Archaeology Type of 1975

 1.30s, Seated man, Carchi Culture. 2s,
Funerary urn, Tuncahuan Culture. 3s, Priest,
Bahia de Caraquez Culture. 4s, Snail's shell,
Cuasmal Culture. 5s, Bowl supported by figu-
rines, Guangala Culture.

1976, Feb. 12   Litho.   Perf. 11½
C568 A278 1.30s multi   .40 .30
C569 A278 2s multi   .50 .30
C570 A278 3s multi   .75 .30
C571 A278 4s multi   1.10 .50
C572 A278 5s multi   1.40 .50
  Nos. C568-C572 (5)   4.15 1.90

Fruit Type of 1976

1976, Mar. 30
C573 A280 2s Apples   .50 .30
C574 A280 5s Rose   1.10 .45

Lufthansa
Jet — AP137

1976, June 25   Litho.   Perf. 12
C575 AP137 10s bl & multi   1.50 .50
 Lufthansa, 50th anniversary.
 An imperf. 20s miniature sheet exists, simi-
lar to No. C575 enlarged, with overprinted
black bar covering line below "Lufthansa."
Size: 90x115mm. Value, $32.50.

Projected PO,
Quito — AP138

1976, Aug. 10   Litho.   Perf. 12
C576 AP138 5s blk & multi   .60 .25
 Design for new General Post Office, Quito.

Fruit Peddler — AP139

 No. C578, Longshoreman. No. C579, Cer-
ros del Carmen & Santa Ana, hills of Guayaquil, horiz. No. C580, Sebastián de Belal-
cázar. No. C581, Francisco de Orellana. No.
C582, Chief Guayas & his wife Quila.

1976, July 25
C577 AP139 1.30s red & multi   .40 .25
C578 AP139 1.30s red & multi   .40 .25
C579 AP139 1.30s red & multi   .40 .25
C580 AP139 2s red & multi   .40 .25
C581 AP139 2s red & multi   .40 .25
C582 AP139 2s red & multi   .40 .25
  Nos. C577-C582 (6)   2.40 1.50
 Founding of Guayaquil, 441st anniversary.

Emblem and
Laurel — AP140

1976, Aug. 9
C583 AP140 1.30s yel & multi   .65 .25
 Bolivarian Soc. of Ecuador, 50th anniv.

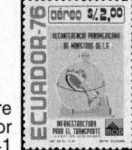

Western Hemisphere
and Equator
Monument — AP141

1976, Sept. 6
C584 AP141 2s multi   .60 .25
Souvenir Sheet
Imperf
C585 AP141 5s multi   3.75 4.00
 3rd Conf. of Pan-American Transport Ministers, Quito, Sept. 6-11. No. C585 contains
design similar to No. C584 with black denomination and red control number in margin.

Congress
Emblem — AP142

1976, Sept. 27 Litho.   Perf. 11½
C586 AP142 1.30s bl & multi   .40 .25
C587 AP142 3s bl & multi   .50 .30
Souvenir Sheet
Imperf
C588 AP142 10s bl & multi   2.10 1.00
 10th Inter-American Congress of the Con-
struction Industry, Quito, Sept. 27-30.

George Washington
AP143

 American Bicentennial: 5s, Naval battle,
Sept. 23, 1779, in which the Bonhomme Richard, commanded by John Paul Jones,
defeated and captured the Serapis, British
man-of-war, off Yorkshire coast, horiz.

1976, Oct. 18   Perf. 12
C589 AP143 3s blk & multi   .70 .30
C590 AP143 5s red brn & yel   1.30 .60

Dr. Hideyo
Noguchi — AP144

1976   Litho.   Perf. 11½
C591 AP144 3s yel & multi   .40 .25
 Dr. Hideyo Noguchi (1876-1928), bacteriolo-
gist (at Rockefeller Institute). A 10s imperf.
miniature sheet exists in same design without
"Aereo." Size: 95x114mm. Value $6.

Luis Cordero — AP145

1976, Dec.   Litho.   Perf. 11½
C592 AP145 2s multi   .70 .25
Luis Cordero (1833-1912), president of Ecuador.

Mariuxi Febres Cordero — AP146

1976, Dec.   Perf. 11½
C593 AP146 3s multi   .70 .25
Mariuxi Febres Cordero, South American swimming champion.

Flags and Monument — AP147

1976, Nov. 9   Perf. 12
C594 AP147 3s multi   .50 .25
Miniature Sheet
Imperf
C595 AP147 5s multi   2.50 1.50
2nd Meeting of the Agriculture Ministers of the Andean Countries, Quito, Nov. 8-10.

Sister Catalina — AP148

1977, June 17   Litho.   Perf. 12x11½
C596 AP148 1.30s blk & pale salmon   .70 .30
Sister Catalina de Jesus Herrera (1717-1795), writer.

Congress Hall, Quito — AP149

1977, Aug. 15   Litho.   Perf. 12x11½
C597 AP149 5s multi   .60 .30
  a.   10s souvenir sheet   2.00 2.00
11th General Assembly of Pan-American Institute of Geography and History, Quito, Aug. 15-30. No. C597a contains the designs of types A282 and AP149 without denominations and with simulated perforations.

Pres. Alfonso López Michelsen, Flag of Colombia — AP150

Designs: 5s, Pres. López Michelsen of Colombia, Pres. Alfredo Poveda Burbano of Ecuador and aide. 7s, as 5s, vert. 9s, 10s, Presidents with aides.

1977, Sept. 13   Perf. 12
C598 AP150 2.60s multi   .60 .25
C599 AP150 5s multi   .90 .30
C600 AP150 7s multi   1.10 .40
C601 AP150 9s multi   1.35 .60
Imperf
C602 AP150 10s multi   2.00 1.00
  Nos. C598-C602 (5)   5.95 2.55
Meeting of the Presidents of Ecuador and Colombia and Declaration of Putumayo, Feb. 25, 1977. Nos. C598-C602 are overprinted in multiple fluorescent, colorless rows: INSTITUTO GEOGRAFICO MILITAR GOBIERNO DEL ECUADOR.

Ceramic Figure, Tolita Culture — AP151

9s, Divine Shepherdess, sculpture by Bernardo de Legarda. 11s, The Fruit Seller, sculpture by Legarda. 20s, Sun God, pre-Columbian gold mask.

1977, Aug. 24   Perf. 12
C603 AP151 7s gold & multi   1.35 .30
C604 AP151 9s gold & multi   1.75 .35
C605 AP151 11s gold & multi   2.25 .70
  Nos. C603-C605 (3)   5.35 1.35
Souvenir Sheet
Gold Embossed
Imperf
C606 AP151 20s vio, bl, blk & gold   8.00 3.50
Central Bank of Ecuador, 50th anniversary. Nos. C603-C605 overprinted like Nos. C598-C602.

Lungs — AP152

1977, Oct. 5   Litho.   Perf. 12x11½
C607 AP152 2.60s multi   .65 .25
3rd Cong. of the Bolivarian Pneumonic Soc. and cent. of the founding of the medical faculty of the University of Guayaquil.

Brother Miguel, St. Peter's, Rome — AP153

1977
C608 AP153 2.60s multi   .50 .25
Beatification of Brother Miguel.

Peralta Type
2.60s, Titles of works by Peralta & his bookmark.
1977   Perf. 11½
C609 A284 2.60s multi   .55 .25

Broadcast Tower — AP154

1977, Dec. 2   Litho.   Perf. 12x11½
C610 AP154 5s multi   .50 .45
9th World Telecommunications Day.

Remigio Romero y Cordero (1895-1967), Poet — AP155

1978, Mar. 2   Litho.   Perf. 12½x11½
C611 AP155 3s multi   .50 .25
C612 AP155 10.60s multi   .65 .30
Imperf
C612A AP155 10s multi   1.60 1.40
  Nos. C611-C612A (3)   2.75 1.95
No. C612A contains a vignette similar to Nos. C611-C612.

Dr. Vicente Corral Moscoso — AP156

5s, Hospital emblem with Caduceus.
1978, Apr. 12   Litho.   Imperf.
C613 AP156 5s multi   .60 .25
Perf. 12x11½
C614 AP156 7.60s multi   1.25 .50
Inauguration (in 1977) of Dr. Vicente Corral Moscoso Regional Hospital, Cuenca.

Faces — AP157

Designs: 9s, Emblems and flags of Ecuador. 10s, 11s, Hands reaching for light.
1978, Mar. 17
C615 AP157 7s multicolored   .80 .25
C616 AP157 9s multicolored   1.10 .25
C617 AP157 11s multicolored   1.40 .25
Imperf
C618 AP157 10s multicolored   1.75 1.25
  Nos. C615-C618 (4)   5.05 2.00
Ecuadorian Social Security Institute, 50th anniv.

Geographical Institute Type
7.60s, Plane over map of Ecuador with mountains.
1978, Apr. 12   Litho.   Perf. 11½
C619 A287 7.60s multi   1.10 .55
Imperf
C620 A287 10s multi   2.00 1.75
No. C620 contains 2 vignettes with simulated perforations in designs of Nos. 967 and C619.

Lions Type
1978   Perf. 11½
C621 A288 5s multi   .75 .25
C622 A288 6.20s multi   .90 .40
Imperf
C623 A288 10s multi   2.50 1.25
  Nos. C621-C623 (3)   4.15 1.90
No. C623 contains a vignette similar to Nos. C621-C622.

San Martin — AP158

1978, Apr. 13   Litho.   Perf. 12
C624 AP158 10.60s multi   1.60 .50
Imperf
C625 AP158 10s multi   2.25 1.75
Gen. José de San Martin (1778-1850), soldier and statesman. No. C625 contains a vignette similar to No. C624.

Bank Type
Design: 5s, Bank emblem.
1978, Sept.   Litho.   Perf. 11½
C626 A289 5s gray & multi   .60 .30

Soccer Type
Designs: 2.60s, "Gauchito" and Games' emblem. 5s, "Gauchito." 7s, Soccer ball. 9s, Games' emblem, vert. 10s, Games' emblem.
1978, Nov. 1   Perf. 12
C627 A290 2.60s multi   .35 .25
C628 A290 7s multi   .85 .40
C629 A290 9s multi   1.15 .65
Imperf
C630 A290 5s blk & bl   6.00 6.00
C631 A290 10s blk & bl   6.00 6.00
  Nos. C627-C631 (5)   14.35 13.30

Bernardo O'Higgins — AP159

1978, Nov. 11   Litho.   Perf. 12x11½
C632 AP159 10.60s multi   1.00 .30
Imperf
C633 AP159 10s multi   1.50 .90
Gen. Bernardo O'Higgins (1778-1842), Chilean soldier and statesman. No. C633 contains a vignette similar to No. C632.

Old Men of Vilcabamba — AP160

1978, Nov. 11   Perf. 12x11½
C634 AP160 5s multi   .75 .30
Vilcabamba, valley of longevity.

Humphrey — AP161

1978, Nov. 27   Litho.   Perf. 12x11½
C635 AP161 5s multi   .75 .30
Hubert H. Humphrey (1911-1978), Vice President of the US.

Virgin and Child — AP162

Children's Drawings: 4.60s, Holy Family. 6.20s, Candle and children.
1978
C636 AP162 2.20s multi   .40 .25
C637 AP162 4.60s multi   .60 .25
C638 AP162 6.20s multi   .95 .40
  Nos. C636-C638 (3)   1.95 .90
Christmas 1978.

Village, by Anibal
Villacis — AP163

Ecuadorian Painters: No. C640, Mountain
Village, by Gilberto Almeida. No. C641, Bay,
by Roura Oxandaberro. No. C642, Abstract,
by Luis Molinari. No. C643, Statue, by
Oswaldo Viteri. No. C644, Tools, by Enrique
Tabara.

1978, Dec. 9   *Perf. 12*
C639 AP163 5s multi   .60   .25
C640 AP163 5s multi   .60   .25
C641 AP163 5s multi   .60   .25
C642 AP163 5s multi   .60   .25
C643 AP163 5s multi   .60   .25
C644 AP163 5s multi   .60   .25
  Nos. C639-C644 (6)   3.60 1.50

House and
Monument
AP164

Design: 3.40s, Monument, vert.

1979, Feb. 27   Litho.   *Perf. 12*
C645 AP164 2.40s multi   .45   .25
C646 AP164 3.40s multi   .45   .25

Imperf
C647 AP164 10s multi   1.40   .90
  Nos. C645-C647 (3)   2.30 1.40

Sesquicentennial of Battle of Portete and
Tarqui. No. C647 contains vignettes similar to
Nos. C645-C646.

Fish and Ship — AP165

7s, Map of Ecuador & Galapagos showing
territorial waters. 9s, Map of South America
with west-coast territorial waters.

Perf. 12x11½, 11½x12
1979, July 23   Litho.   Wmk. 367
C648 AP165 5s multi   .75   .25
C649 AP165 7s multi, horiz.   1.00   .35
C650 AP165 9s multi   1.40   .50
  Nos. C648-C650 (3)   3.15 1.10

Declaration of 200-mile territorial limit, 25th
anniversary.

National Heritage Type
Designs: 10.60s, Bells in Quito clock tower,
horiz. 13.60s, Aerial view of Galapagos coast.

1979, Aug. 3   *Perf. 12x11½*
C651 A293 10.60s multi   1.25   .60
C652 A293 13.60s multi   1.40   .75

Size: 115x91mm
Imperf
Unwmk.
C653 A293 10s multi   5.00 2.10
  Nos. C651-C653 (3)   7.65 3.45

National heritage: Quito and Galapagos
Islands. No. C653 contains vignettes similar to
Nos. 977, C651-C652.

Flags of Ecuador and
U.S. — AP166

1979, Aug.   Wmk. 367   *Perf. 11½x12*
C654 AP166 7.60s multi   .60   .50
C655 AP166 10.60s multi   .90   .75

Size: 115x91mm
Imperf
Unwmk.
C656 AP166 10s multi   1.30   .75
  Nos. C654-C656 (3)   2.80 2.00

5th anniv. of Ecuador-US Chamber of Commerce. No. C656 contains vignettes similar to
Nos. C654-C655.

Smiling Girl, IYC
Emblem — AP167

Perf. 12x11½
1979, Sept. 7   Litho.   Wmk. 367
C657 AP167 10s multi   1.15   .40

International Year of the Child.

Citizens and Flag
of
Ecuador — AP168

Design: 10.60s, Pres. Jaime Roldos Aguilera, flag of Ecuador, vert.

Perf. 11½
1979, Sept. 27   Litho.   Unwmk.
C658 AP168 7.60s multi   1.00   .45

Wmk. 367
C659 AP168 10.60s multi   1.25   .40

Restoration of democracy to Ecuador.

Ecuador Coat of Arms,
Olympic Rings and
Eagle — AP169

Perf. 12x11½
1979, Nov. 23   Unwmk.
C660 AP169 28s multi   2.25 1.25

5th National Games, Cuenca.

CIESPAL Building,
Quito — AP170

Perf. 11½x12½
1979, Dec. 26   Wmk. 367
C661 AP170 10.60s multi   1.05   .40

Opening of Ecuadorian Institute of Engineers building.

Olmedo Type
Perf. 12x11½
1980, Apr. 29   Litho.   Unwmk.
C662 A294 10s multi   1.25   .65

Tribal Chief Type
Indo-American Tribal Chiefs: No. C663,
Cuauhtemoc, Mexico. No. C664, Lempira,
Honduras. No. C665, Nicaragua. No. C666,
Lambaré, Paraguay. No. C667, Urraca, Pan-
ama. No. C668, Anacaona, Haiti. #C669, Cau-
polican, Chile. No. C670, Tacun-Uman, Guate-
mala. No. C671, Calarca, Colombia. No.
C672, Garabito, Costa Rica. No. C673,
Hatuey, Cuba. No. C674, Camarao, Brazil.
No. C675, Tehuelche, Argentina. No. C676,
Tupaj Katri, Bolivia. 17.80s, Sequoyah, US.
22.80s, Ruminahui, Ecuador.

Wmk. 367 (#C663, C667), Unwmkd.
1980, May 12
C663 A295 7.60s multi   1.75   .45
C664 A295 7.60s multi   1.75   .45
C665 A295 7.60s multi   1.75   .45
C666 A295 10s multi   2.10   .50
C667 A295 10s multi   2.10   .50
C668 A295 10.60s multi   2.10   .50
C669 A295 10.60s multi   2.10   .50
C670 A295 10.60s multi   2.10

C671 A295 12.80s multi   3.00   .65
C672 A295 12.80s multi   3.00   .65
C673 A295 12.80s multi   3.00   .65
C674 A295 13.60s multi   3.00   .65
C675 A295 13.60s multi   3.00   .65
C676 A295 13.60s multi   3.00   .65
C677 A295 17.80s multi   3.50   .75
C678 A295 22.80s multi   4.00 1.40
  Nos. C663-C678 (16)   41.25 9.90

Royal Visit Type
Perf. 11½x12
1980, May 18   Unwmk.
C679 A296 10.60s multi   .75   .40

Pichincha Provincial
Development Council
Building — AP171

1980, June 1   Perf. 12x11½
C680 AP171 10.60s multi   1.40   .60

Progress in Pichincha Province.

Indian Type
Designs: 7.60s, Salasaca boy, Tungurahua.
10s, Amula woman, Chimborazo. 10.60s,
Canar woman, Canar. 13.60s, Colorado
Indian, Pichincha.

1980, June 10   Litho.   Perf. 12x11½
C681 A297 7.60s multi   1.25   .75
C682 A297 10s multi   1.50   .85
C683 A297 10.60s multi   1.75   .90
C684 A297 13.60s multi   2.25 1.25
  Nos. C681-C684 (4)   6.75 3.75

Virgin of Mercy Type
Designs: No. C685, Cupola, cloisters. No.
C686, Gold screen. No. C687, Quito from
basilica tower. No. C688, Retable. No. C689,
Pulpit. No. C690, Cupola. No. C691, Statue of
Virgin.

1980, July 7   Litho.   Perf. 11½
C685 A298 7.60s multi   1.00   .50
C686 A298 7.60s multi   1.00   .50
C687 A298 7.60s multi   1.00   .50
C688 A298 10.60s multi   1.25   .60
C689 A298 10.60s multi   1.25   .60
C690 A298 13.60s multi   1.75   .90
C691 A298 13.60s multi   1.75   .90
  Nos. C685-C691 (7)   9.00 4.50

Nos. C685-C691 are vert.

UPU
Monument — AP172

Design: 17.80s, Mail box, 1880.

1980, July 7   Perf. 12
C692 AP172 10.60s multi   1.50   .75
C693 AP172 17.80s multi   2.50 1.25

Souvenir Sheet
C694 AP172 25s multi   3.50 3.00

UPU membership cent. No. C694 contains
designs of C692 and C693, horiz., perf. 11½.

Olympic Type.
Design: 10.60s, 13.60s, Moscow '80
emblem, Olympic rings.

Perf. 12x11½
1980, July 19   Wmk. 395
C695 A299 10.60s multi   .90   .65
C696 A299 13.60s multi   1.25   .85

Souvenir Sheet
C697 A299 30s multi   7.50 7.00

No. C697 contains vignettes in designs of
Nos. 991 and C695.

Marshal Sucre, by
Marco Sales — AP173

1980
C698 AP173 10.60s multi   1.10   .60

Marshal Antonio Jose de Sucre, death
sesquicentennial.

Rotary International,
75th
Anniversary — AP174

1980, Aug. 4   *Perf. 11½*
C699 AP174 10s multi   1.50   .50

Riobamba Type
Design: 7.60s, 10.60s, Monstrance,
Riobamba Cathedral, vert.

1980, Sept. 20   Litho.   *Perf. 11½*
C700 A301 7.60s multi   .80   .30
C701 A301 10.60s multi   1.10   .40

Souvenir Sheet
Imperf
C702 A301 30s multi   2.25 2.25

No. C702 contains vignettes in designs of
Nos. 996 and C701.

Democracy Type
7.60s, 10.60s, Pres. Aguilera and voter.

Perf. 12x11½
1980, Oct. 9   Litho.   Wmk. 395
C703 A302 7.60s multi   .95   .45
C704 A302 10.60s multi   1.25   .50

Souvenir Sheet
Imperf
C705 A302 15s multi   1.75 1.50

No. C705 contains vignettes in designs of
Nos. 999 and C703.

OPEC Type
20th Anniversary of OPEC: 7.60s, Men
holding OPEC emblem, vert.

1980, Nov. 8   *Perf. 11½x12*
C706 A303 7.60s multi   .60   .45

Carchi Province Type
10.60s, Governor's Palace, vert. 17.80s,
Victory Museum, Central Square, vert.

1980, Nov. 21   *Perf. 13*
C707 A304 10.60c multi   1.35   .50
C708 A304 17.80s multi   2.10   .80

Orchid Type
Designs: No. C709, Anguloa uniflora. No.
C710, Scuticaria salesiana. C711, Helcia
sanguinolenta, vert. No. C712, Anguloa
virginalis.

Perf. 12x11½, 11½x12
1980, Nov. 22
C709 A305 7.60s multi   2.25   .60
C710 A305 10.60s multi   3.25   .35
C711 A305 50s multi   5.75 1.10
C712 A305 100s multi   7.50 2.25
  Nos. C709-C712 (4)   18.75 4.30

Souvenir Sheets
Imperf
C713 A305 20s multi   7.50 5.25
C714 A305 20s multi   7.50 5.25

Nos. C713-C714 contain vignettes in
designs of Nos. C709, C711 and C710, C712
respectively.

Christmas Type
7.60s, Pope blessing crowd. 10.60s,
Portrait.

1980, Dec. 27   *Perf. 12*
C715 A306 7.60s multi, vert.   1.00   .50
C716 A306 10.60s multi, vert.   1.25   .60

Isidro Cueva — AP175

1980, Nov. 20   ***Perf. 13***
C717 AP175 18.20s multi   2.50 1.25
Dr. Isidro Ayora Cueva, former president, birth centenary.

Simon Bolivar, by Marco Salas — AP176

1980, Dec. 17   ***Perf. 11½***
C718 AP176 13.60s multi   2.00 1.00
Simon Bolivar death sesquicentennial.

Turtle, Galapagos Islands — AP177

100s, Oldest Ecuadorian mail box, 1793.

1981, Feb. 12   **Litho.**   ***Perf. 13***
C719 AP177 50s multi   6.50 4.00
C720 AP177 100s multi, vert.   8.00 5.00

HCJB Type
1981   **Litho.**   ***Perf. 13***
C721 A311 7.60s Emblem,
          horiz.   1.25 .65
C722 A311 10.60s Emblem, diff.   1.75 .90

Soccer Players — AP178

1981, July 8
C723 AP178 7.60s Emblem   1.10 .45
C724 AP178 10.60s shown   1.40 .45
C725 AP178 13.60s World Cup   1.75 .75
   Nos. C723-C725 (3)   4.25 1.65

Souvenir Sheets
C726 AP178 20s multi   3.50 3.50
C727 AP178 20s multi   3.50 3.50
1982 World Cup Soccer Championship. Nos. C726-C727 contain vignettes in designs of Nos. C723 and C725 respectively.

Picasso Type
7.60s, Still-life. 10.60s, First Communion, vert. 13.60s, Las Meninas, vert.

1981, Oct. 26   **Litho.**   ***Perf. 13***
C728 A313a 7.60s multi   .90 .45
C729 A313a 10.60s multi   1.25 .60
C730 A313a 13.60s multi   1.40 .70

Size: 110x90mm
Imperf
C731 A313a 20s multi   3.00 3.00
   Nos. C728-C731 (4)   6.55 4.75
No. C731 contains designs of Nos. C730, C729.

World Food Day Type
1981, Dec. 31   **Litho.**   ***Perf. 13x13½***
C732 A314 10.60s Farming, vert. 1.40 .70

IYD Type
Designs: No. C733, Emblem. No. C734, Man with crutch.

1982, Feb. 25   **Litho.**   ***Perf. 13***
C733 A316 7.60s multi   .75 .30
C734 A316 10.60s multi   .95 .55

Montalvo Type
1982   **Litho.**   ***Perf. 13***
C735 A318 5s Home, horiz.   1.25 .65

Swimming Type
1982, July 30
C736 A320 10.20s Emblem, vert. .95 .45
C737 A320 14.20s Diving, vert. 1.25 .60

Pres. Jaime Roldos, (1940-81), Mrs. Martha Roldos, Independence Monument, Quito — AP179

1983, May 25   **Litho.**   ***Perf. 12***
C738 AP179 13.60s multi   .85 .50

Souvenir Sheet
Imperf
C739 AP179   20s multi   1.75 2.00

AIR POST SEMI-POSTAL STAMPS

Nos. C119-C123 Surcharged in Blue or Red

1944, May 9   **Unwmk.**   ***Perf. 12***
CB1 AP26 50c + 50c   7.00 3.50
CB2 AP26 70c + 30c   7.00 3.50
CB3 AP26 3s + 50c (R)   7.00 3.50
CB4 AP26 5s + 1s (R)   7.00 3.50
CB5 AP26 10s + 2s   7.00 3.50
   Nos. CB1-CB5 (5)   35.00 17.50
The surtax aided Mendez Hospital.

AIR POST REGISTRATION STAMPS

Issued by Sociedad Colombo-Alemana de Transportes Aereos (SCADTA)

Nos. C3 and C3a Overprinted in Carmine

1928-29   **Wmk. 116**   ***Perf. 14x14½***
CF1 AP6 1s on 20c (#C3)   110.00 100.00
  a.   1s on 20c (#C3a) ('29)   140.00 110.00

No. C18 Overprinted in Black

1929, Apr. 1   **Wmk. 127**   ***Perf. 14***
CF2 AP2 1s rose   85.00 55.00

AIR POST OFFICIAL STAMPS

Nos. C8-C15 Overprinted in Red or Black

1929, May   **Unwmk.**   ***Perf. 12***
CO1 AP1 2c black (R)   1.00 .50
CO2 AP1 5c carmine rose   1.00 .50
CO3 AP1 10c deep brown   1.00 .50
CO4 AP1 20c dark violet   1.00 .50
CO5 AP1 50c deep green   4.00 2.00
CO6 AP1 1s dark blue   4.00 2.00
  a.   Inverted overprint   240.00

CO7 AP1 5s orange yellow   18.00 7.75
CO8 AP1 10s orange red   210.00 75.00
   Nos. CO1-CO8 (8)   240.00 88.75
Establishment of commercial air service in Ecuador.
Counterfeits of No. CO8 exist.
See Nos. CO9-CO12. For overprints and surcharges see No. C35.

1930, Jan. 9
CO9 AP1 50c olive brown   3.50 1.75
CO10 AP1 1s carmine lake   4.50 2.25
CO11 AP1 5s olive green   11.00 5.50
CO12 AP1 10s black   21.00 10.50
   Nos. CO9-CO12 (4)   40.00 20.00
For surcharges and overprint see Nos. C32-C34, C36-C38.

Air Post Stamps of 1937 Overprinted in Black

1937, Aug. 19
CO13 AP7 10c chestnut   .50 .25
CO14 AP7 20c olive black   .50 .25
CO15 AP7 70c black brown   .60 .25
CO16 AP7 1s gray black   .70 .25
CO17 AP7 2s dark violet   .70 .30
   Nos. CO13-CO17 (5)   3.00 1.30
For overprints see Nos. 463-464.

No. C79 Overprinted in Black

1940, Aug. 1   ***Perf. 12½x13***
CO18 AP15 5s emerald   2.00 .60

> **Catalogue values for unused stamps in this section, from this point to the end of the section, are for Never Hinged items.**

Nos. C352-C354 Overprinted

1964   ***Perf. 13½***
CO19 AP86 50c multi   2.00 .85
CO20 AP86 80c multi   2.00 .85
CO21 AP86 1.30s multi   2.00 .85
   Nos. CO19-CO21 (3)   6.00 2.55

SPECIAL DELIVERY STAMPS

SD1

SD1a

1928   **Unwmk.**   ***Perf. 12***
E1 SD1 2c on 2c blue   8.00 9.00
  a.   "DOS CVTOS." inverted   35.00 37.50
E2 SD1a 5c on 2c blue   7.00 9.00
E3 SD1a 10c on 2c blue   7.00 6.00
  a.   "10 CENTAVOS" inverted   21.00 25.00
E4 SD1a 20c on 2c blue   10.00 9.00
E5 SD1a 50c on 2c blue   12.00 9.00
   Nos. E1-E5 (5)   44.00 42.00
No. E1 surcharge reads "CTVOS". Nos. E2-E5 surcharge reads "CENTAVOS".

No. RA49A Surcharged in Red

1945
E6 PT18 20c on 5c green   3.00 2.00

LATE FEE STAMP

No. RA49A Surcharged in Black

1945   **Unwmk.**   ***Perf. 12***
I1 PT18 10c on 5c green   1.00 1.00

POSTAGE DUE STAMPS

Numeral — D1

1896   **Engr.**   **Wmk. 117**   ***Perf. 12***
J1 D1 1c blue green   6.00 6.50
J2 D1 2c blue green   6.00 6.50
J3 D1 5c blue green   6.00 6.50
J4 D1 10c blue green   6.00 6.50
J5 D1 20c blue green   6.00 8.50
J6 D1 50c blue green   6.00 13.00
J7 D1 100c blue green   6.00 17.00
   Nos. J1-J7 (7)   42.00 64.50
Reprints are on very thick paper with distinct watermark and vertical paper-weave direction. Value 15c each.

Unwmk.
J8 D1 1c blue green   5.00 6.00
J9 D1 2c blue green   5.00 6.00
J10 D1 5c blue green   5.00 6.00
J11 D1 10c blue green   5.00 6.00
J12 D1 20c blue green   5.00 7.50
J13 D1 50c blue green   5.00 10.50
J14 D1 100c blue green   5.00 15.00
   Nos. J8-J14 (7)   35.00 57.00

Coat of Arms — D2

1929
J15 D2 5c deep blue   .40 .40
J16 D2 10c orange yellow   .40 .40
J17 D2 20c red   .60 .60
   Nos. J15-J17 (3)   1.40 1.40

Numeral — D3

Perf. 13½
1958, Nov.   **Unwmk.**   **Litho.**
J18 D3 10c bright lilac   .40 .40
J19 D3 50c emerald   .40 .40
J20 D3 1s maroon   .50 .40
J21 D3 2s red   .60 .40
   Nos. J18-J21 (4)   1.90 1.60

OFFICIAL STAMPS

Regular Issues of 1881 and 1887 Handstamped in Black

1886　　**Unwmk.**　　*Perf. 12*

O1	A5	1c yellow brown	2.50	2.50
O2	A6	2c lake	3.00	3.00
O3	A7	5c blue	6.75	8.75
O4	A8	10c orange	5.25	3.25
O5	A9	20c gray violet	5.25	5.25
O6	A10	50c blue green	15.00	11.50
		Nos. O1-O6 (6)	37.75	34.25

1887

O7	A12	1c green	3.25	2.50
O8	A13	2c vermilion	3.25	3.25
O9	A14	5c blue	5.25	2.50
O10	A15	80c olive green	17.50	10.00
		Nos. O7-O10 (4)	29.25	18.25

Nos. O1-O10 are known with red hand-stamp but these are believed to be speculative.

The overprint on the 1886-87 issues is handstamped and is found in various positions.

Flores — O1

1892　　**Carmine Overprint**

O11	O1	1c ultramarine	.25	.40
O12	O1	2c ultramarine	.25	.40
O13	O1	5c ultramarine	.25	.40
O14	O1	10c ultramarine	.25	.60
O15	O1	20c ultramarine	.25	.90
O16	O1	50c ultramarine	.25	.90
O17	O1	1s ultramarine	.35	1.00
		Nos. O11-O17 (7)	1.85	4.60

Arms — O1a

1894

O18	O1a	1c slate green (R)	15.00	
O19	O1a	2c lake (Bk)	20.00	

Nos. O18 and O19 were not placed in use.

Rocafuerte — O2

Dated "1894"

1894　　**Carmine Overprint**

O20	O2	1c gray black	.60	1.00
O21	O2	2c gray black	.60	.60
O22	O2	5c gray black	.60	.60
O23	O2	10c gray black	.75	1.00
O24	O2	20c gray black	1.00	1.00
O25	O2	50c gray black	3.75	3.75
O26	O2	1s gray black	6.00	6.00
		Nos. O20-O26 (7)	13.30	13.95

Dated "1895"

1895　　**Carmine Overprint**

O27	O2	1c gray black	5.25	5.25
O28	O2	2c gray black	7.50	7.50
O29	O2	5c gray black	1.50	1.50
O30	O2	10c gray black	7.50	7.50
O31	O2	20c gray black	11.00	10.50
O32	O2	50c gray black	75.00	75.00
O33	O2	1s gray black	3.75	3.75
		Nos. O27-O33 (7)	111.50	111.00

Reprints of 1894-95 issues are on very thick paper with paper weave found both horizontal and vertical for all denominations. Values: Nos. O20-O26, 35c each; O27-O33, 20c each. Generally they are blacker than originals.
For overprints see Nos. O50-O91.

Types of 1896 Overprinted in Carmine

1896　　**Wmk. 117**

O34	A21	1c olive bister	1.00	1.00
O35	A22	2c olive bister	1.00	1.00
O36	A23	5c olive bister	1.00	1.00
O37	A24	10c olive bister	1.00	1.00
O38	A25	20c olive bister	1.00	1.00
O39	A26	50c olive bister	1.00	1.00

O40	A27	1s olive bister	3.00	3.00
O41	A28	5s olive bister	6.00	6.00
		Nos. O34-O41 (8)	15.00	15.00

Reprints of Nos. O34-O41 are on thick paper with vertical paper weave direction.

Unwmk.

O42	A21	1c olive bister	3.00	3.00
O43	A22	2c olive bister	3.00	3.00
O44	A23	5c olive bister	3.00	3.00
O45	A24	10c olive bister	3.00	3.00
O46	A25	20c olive bister	3.00	3.00
O47	A26	50c olive bister	3.00	3.00
O48	A27	1s olive bister	7.50	7.50
O49	A28	5s olive bister	10.50	10.50
		Nos. O42-O49 (8)	36.00	36.00

Reprints of Nos. O42-O49 all have overprint in black. Value 20 cents each.

Nos. O20-O26 Overprinted

1897-98

O50	O2	1c gray black	20.00	20.00
O51	O2	2c gray black	35.00	35.00
O52	O2	5c gray black	200.00	200.00
O53	O2	10c gray black	30.00	30.00
O54	O2	20c gray black	20.00	20.00
O55	O2	50c gray black	35.00	35.00
O56	O2	1s gray black	55.00	55.00
		Nos. O50-O56 (7)	395.00	395.00

Nos. O20-O26 Overprinted

O57	O2	1c gray black	4.00	4.00
O58	O2	2c gray black	9.00	9.00
O59	O2	5c gray black	90.00	90.00
O60	O2	10c gray black	100.00	100.00
O61	O2	20c gray black	25.00	25.00
O62	O2	50c gray black	15.00	15.00
O63	O2	1s gray black	165.00	165.00
		Nos. O57-O63 (7)	408.00	408.00

Nos. O20-O26 Overprinted

O64	O2	1c gray black	40.00	40.00
O65	O2	2c gray black	40.00	40.00
O66	O2	5c gray black	40.00	40.00
O67	O2	10c gray black	40.00	40.00
O68	O2	20c gray black	40.00	40.00
O69	O2	50c gray black	40.00	40.00
O70	O2	1s gray black	40.00	40.00
		Nos. O64-O70 (7)	280.00	280.00

Nos. O27-O33 Overprinted in Black like Nos. O50-O56

O71	O2	1c gray black	20.00	20.00
O72	O2	2c gray black	20.00	20.00
O73	O2	5c gray black	20.00	20.00
O74	O2	10c gray black	20.00	20.00
O75	O2	20c gray black	30.00	30.00
O76	O2	50c gray black	275.00	275.00
O77	O2	1s gray black	100.00	100.00
		Nos. O71-O77 (7)	485.00	485.00

Nos. O27-O33 Overprinted

O78	O2	1c gray black	35.00	35.00
O79	O2	2c gray black	30.00	30.00
O80	O2	5c gray black	30.00	30.00
O81	O2	10c gray black	32.50	32.50
O82	O2	20c gray black	42.50	42.50
O83	O2	50c gray black	30.00	30.00
O84	O2	1s gray black	30.00	30.00
		Nos. O78-O84 (7)	230.00	230.00

Nos. O27-O33 Overprinted like #O64-O70

O85	O2	1c gray black	90.00	90.00
O86	O2	2c gray black	20.00	20.00
O87	O2	5c gray black	80.00	80.00
O88	O2	10c gray black	80.00	80.00
O89	O2	20c gray black	140.00	140.00

O90	O2	50c gray black	85.00	85.00
O91	O2	1s gray black	165.00	165.00
		Nos. O85-O91 (7)	660.00	660.00

Many forged overprints of Nos. O50-O91 exist, made on the original stamps and reprints.

O3

1898-99　　*Perf. 15, 16*

Black Surcharge

O92	O3	5c on 50c lilac	10.00	10.00
a.		Inverted surcharge	25.00	25.00
O93	O3	10c on 20s org	15.00	15.00
a.		Double surcharge	40.00	30.00
O94	O3	10c on 50c lilac	140.00	140.00
O95	O3	20c on 50c lilac	30.00	30.00
O96	O3	20c on 50s green	30.00	30.00
		Nos. O92-O96 (5)	225.00	225.00

Green Surcharge

O97	O3	5c on 50c lilac	10.00	10.00
a.		Double surcharge		
b.		Double surcharge, blk and grn	12.00	
c.		Same as "b," blk surch. invtd.	5.00	

1899　　**Red Surcharge**

O98	O3	5c on 50c lilac	10.00	10.00
a.		Double surcharge	20.00	
b.		Dbl. surch., blk and red	25.00	
O99	O3	20c on 50s green	15.00	15.00
a.		Inverted surcharge	40.00	
b.		Dbl. surch., red and blk	60.00	

Similar Surcharge in Black Value in Words in Two Lines

O100	O3	1c on 5c blue	650.00	

Red Surcharge

O101	O3	2c on 5c blue	1,150.	
O102	O3	4c on 20c blue	800.00	

Types of Regular Issue of 1899 Ovptd. in Black

1899　　*Perf. 14, 15*

O103	A37	2c orange & blk	.70	1.60
O104	A39	10c orange & blk	.70	1.60
O105	A40	20c orange & blk	.50	2.50
O106	A41	50c orange & blk	.50	3.25
		Nos. O103-O106 (4)	2.40	8.95

For overprint see No. O167.

The above overprint was applied to remainders of the postage stamps of 1904 with the idea of increasing their salability. They were never regularly in use as official stamps.

Regular Issue of 1911-13 Overprinted in Black

1913　　*Perf. 12*

O107	A71	1c scarlet & blk	3.50	3.50
O108	A72	2c blue & blk	3.50	3.50
O109	A73	3c orange & blk	2.25	2.25
O110	A74	5c scarlet & blk	4.50	4.50
O111	A75	10c blue & blk	4.50	4.50
		Nos. O107-O111 (5)	18.25	18.25

Regular Issue of 1911-13 Overprinted

1916-17　　**Overprint 22x3½mm**

O112	A72	2c blue & blk	25.00	18.00
O113	A74	5c scarlet & blk	25.00	18.00
O114	A75	10c blue & blk	15.00	12.00
		Nos. O112-O114 (3)	65.00	48.00

Overprint 25x4mm

O115	A71	1c scarlet & blk	1.10	1.10
O116	A72	2c blue & blk	1.60	1.60
a.		Inverted overprint	5.00	5.00
O117	A73	3c orange & blk	1.00	1.00
O118	A74	5c scarlet & blk	1.60	1.60
O119	A75	10c blue & blk	1.60	1.60
		Nos. O115-O119 (5)	6.90	6.90

Same Overprint On Regular Issue of 1915-17

O120	A71	1c orange	1.40	1.40
O121	A72	2c green	1.40	1.40
O122	A73	3c black	2.25	2.25
O123	A78	4c red & blk	2.25	2.25
a.		Inverted overprint	15.00	
O124	A74	7c violet	1.40	1.40
O125	A75	10c blue	2.75	2.75
O126	A79	20c green & blk	15.00	15.00
		Nos. O120-O126 (7)	26.45	26.45

Regular Issues of 1911-17 Overprinted in Black or Red

O127	A71	1c orange	.90	.90
O128	A72	2c green	.70	.70
O129	A73	3c black (Bk)	.90	.90
O130	A73	3c black (R)	.90	.70
a.		Inverted overprint	15.00	
O131	A78	4c red & blk	.90	.90
O132	A74	7c violet	1.75	.90
O133	A75	10c blue & blk	4.50	1.75
O134	A75	10c blue	.90	.90
O135	A79	20c green & blk	4.50	1.75
		Nos. O127-O135 (9)	15.95	9.40

Regular Issue of 1920 Overprinted

1920

O136	A86	1c green	1.25	1.25
a.		Inverted overprint	17.00	
O137	A86	2c carmine	1.00	1.00
a.		Inverted overprint	5.00	
O138	A86	3c yellow brn	1.25	1.25
O139	A86	4c dark green	2.00	2.00
a.		Inverted overprint	17.00	—
O140	A86	5c blue	2.00	2.00
O141	A86	6c orange	1.25	1.25
O142	A86	7c brown	2.00	2.00
O143	A86	8c yellow green	2.50	2.50
O144	A86	9c red	3.25	3.25
O145	A95	10c blue	2.00	2.00
O146	A86	15c gray	11.00	11.00
O147	A86	20c deep violet	14.50	14.50
O148	A86	30c violet	17.00	17.00
O149	A86	40c dark brown	21.00	21.00
O150	A86	50c dark green	14.50	14.50
O151	A86	60c dark blue	17.00	17.00
O152	A86	70c bluish gray	17.00	17.00
O153	A86	80c yellow	21.00	21.00
O154	A104	90c green	21.00	21.00
O155	A86	1s blue	45.00	45.00
		Nos. O136-O155 (20)	217.50	217.50

Cent. of the independence of Guayaquil.

Stamps of 1911 Overprinted

1922

O156	A71	1c scarlet & blk	9.00	9.00
O157	A72	2c blue & blk	4.50	4.50

Revenue Stamps of 1919-1920 Overprinted like Nos. O156 and O157

1924

O158	PT3	1c dark blue	2.00	2.00
O159	PT3	2c green	12.50	12.50

Regular Issues of 1911-17 Overprinted

1924
O160	A71	1c orange	7.00	7.00
a.		Inverted overprint	15.00	

Overprinted in Black or Red

O161	A72	2c green	.60	.60
O162	A73	3c black (R)	.80	.80
O163	A78	4c red & blk	1.25	1.25
O164	A74	5c violet	1.25	1.25
O165	A76	10c deep blue	1.25	1.25
O166	A76	1s green & blk	7.00	7.00
	Nos. O160-O166 (7)		19.15	19.15

No. O106 with Additional Overprint

1924 *Perf. 14, 15*
O167	A41	50c orange & blk	2.25	2.25

Nos. O160-O167 exist with inverted overprint.

No. 199 Overprinted

1924 *Perf. 12*
O168	A71	1c orange	5.50	5.50

Regular Issues of 1911-25 Overprinted

1925
O169	A71	1c scarlet & blk	10.00	4.25
a.		Inverted overprint	15.00	
O170	A71	1c orange	.60	.60
a.		Inverted overprint	4.00	
O171	A72	2c green	.60	.60
a.		Inverted overprint	4.00	
O172	A73	3c black (Bk)	.60	.60
O173	A73	3c black (R)	1.10	1.10
O174	A78	4c red & blk	.60	.60
O175	A74	5c violet	.80	.80
O176	A74	5c rose	.80	.80
O177	A75	10c deep blue	.60	.60
	Nos. O169-O177 (9)		15.70	9.95

Regular Issues of 1916-25 Ovptd. Vertically Up or Down

1927, Oct.
O178	A71	1c orange	2.00	2.00
O179	A86	2c carmine	2.00	2.00
O180	A86	3c yellow brown	2.00	2.00
O181	A86	4c myrtle green	2.00	2.00
O182	A86	5c pale blue	2.00	2.00
O183	A75	10c yellow green	2.00	2.00
	Nos. O178-O183 (6)		12.00	12.00

Regular Issues of 1920-27 Overprinted

1928
O184	A71	1c lt blue	1.25	1.25
O185	A86	2c carmine	1.25	1.25
O186	A86	3c yellow brown	1.25	1.25
a.		Inverted overprint	5.00	
O187	A86	4c myrtle green	1.25	1.25
O188	A86	5c lt blue	1.25	1.25
O189	A75	10c yellow green	1.25	1.25
O190	A109	20c violet	11.00	2.50
a.		Overprint reading up	3.50	2.25
	Nos. O184-O190 (7)		18.50	10.00

The overprint is placed vertically reading down on No. O190.

Regular Issue of 1936 Overprinted in Black

1936 *Perf. 14*
O191	A131	5c olive green	1.50	1.50
O192	A132	10c brown	1.50	1.50
O193	A133	20c dark violet	1.90	.70
O194	A134	1s dark carmine	2.25	1.10
O195	A135	2s dark blue	2.50	1.75
	Nos. O191-O195 (5)		9.65	6.55

The overprint is placed vertically reading up on No. O192.

Regular Postage Stamps of 1937 Overprinted in Black

1937 *Perf. 11½*
O196	A139	2c green	.40	.40
O197	A140	5c deep rose	.40	.40
O198	A141	10c blue	.40	.40
O199	A142	20c deep rose	.40	.40
O200	A143	1s olive green	.40	.40
	Nos. O196-O200 (5)		2.00	2.00

> Catalogue values for unused stamps in this section, from this point to the end of the section, are for Never Hinged items.

Tobacco Stamp, Overprinted in Black

1946 **Unwmk.** *Rouletted*
O201	PT7	1c rose red	1.75	1.75

Communications Building, Quito — O4

1947 **Unwmk.** **Litho.** *Perf. 11*
O202	O4	30c brown	.60	.40
O203	O4	30c greenish blue	.60	.40
a.		Imperf., pair		
O204	O4	30c purple	.60	.40
	Nos. O202-O204 (3)		1.80	1.20

Nos. O202 to O204 overprinted "Primero la Patria!" and plane in dark blue were issued in August, 1947, by a revolutionary group. They were later repudiated by decree.

No. 719 with Additional Diagonal Overprint

1964 *Perf. 14x13*
O205	A231	80c block of 4	6.00	6.00

The "OEA" overprint covers four stamps, the "oficial" overprint is applied to every stamp.

A set of 20 imperforate items in the above Roosevelt design, some overprinted with the initials of various government ministries, was released in 1949. Later that year a set of 8 miniature sheets, bearing the same design plus a marginal inscription, "Presidencia (or Vicepresidencia) de la Republica," and a frame-line were released. In the editors' opinion, information justifying the listing of these issues has not been received.

POSTAL TAX STAMPS

Roca — PT1

1920 **Unwmk.** *Perf. 12*
RA1	PT1	1c orange	.75	.30
a.		Double overprint	10.00	

PT2   PT3

RA2	PT2	1c red & blue	1.10	.25
a.		"de" inverted	10.50	5.25
b.		Double overprint	10.00	.60
c.		Inverted overprint	10.00	.60
RA3	PT3	1c deep blue	1.25	.25
a.		Inverted overprint	6.00	1.00
b.		Double overprint	6.00	1.00

For overprints see Nos. O158-O159.

PT4   PT5

Red or Black Surcharge or Overprint
Stamp Dated 1911-1912
RA4	PT4	20c deep blue	—	30.00

Stamp Dated 1913-1914
RA5	PT4	20c deep blue (R)	2.25	.35

Stamp Dated 1917-1918
RA6	PT4	20c olive green (R)	6.50	.55
a.		Dated 1919-20	25.00	25.00
RA7	PT5	1c on 2c green	.90	.25

Stamp Dated 1911-1912
RA8	PT5	1c on 5c green	.90	.25
a.		Double surcharge		

Stamp Dated 1913-1914
RA9	PT5	1c on 5c green	8.00	.55
a.		Double surcharge	12.00	4.00

On Nos. RA7, RA8 and RA9 the surcharge is placed upward or downward. For surcharges see Nos. RA15-RA16.

Post Office — PT6

1920-24 *Engr.*
RA10	PT6	1c olive green	.40	.25
RA11	PT6	1c deep green	.40	.25
RA12	PT6	20c bister brn ('24)	1.75	.25

RA13	PT6	2s violet	11.50	3.25
RA14	PT6	5s blue	20.00	5.75
	Nos. RA10-RA14 (5)		34.05	9.75

For overprints and surcharge see Nos. 259, 266-268, 273, 302, RA17, RA28.

Revenue Stamps of 1917-18 Srchd. Vertically in Red reading up or down

1921-22
RA15	PT5	20c on 1c dk blue	55.00	6.50
RA16	PT5	20c on 2c green	55.00	6.50

No. RA12 Surcharged in Green

1924
RA17	PT6	2c on 20c bis brn	.60	.25
a.		Inverted surcharge	14.00	5.00
b.		Double surcharge	4.00	2.00

CASA—CORREOS

PT7

1924 *Rouletted 7*
RA18	PT7	1c rose red	.90	.25
a.		Inverted overprint	3.50	

Similar Design, Eagle at left
Perf. 12
RA19	PT7	2c blue	.90	.25
a.		Inverted overprint	3.50	1.75

For overprints and surcharges see Nos. 346, O201, RA32, RA34, RA37, RA44-RA45, RA47.

PT8

Inscribed "Timbre Fiscal"
1924
RA20	PT8	1c yellow	4.50	.85
RA21	PT8	2c dark blue	1.40	.35

Inscribed "Region Oriental"
RA22	PT8	1c yellow	.70	.30
RA23	PT8	2c dark blue	1.40	.35
	Nos. RA20-RA23 (4)		8.00	1.85

Overprint on No. RA22 reads down or up.

Revenue Stamp Overprinted in Blue

1934
RA24		2c green	.50	.25
a.		Blue overprint inverted	3.50	1.75
b.		Blue ovpt. dbl., one invtd.	4.00	1.25

Postage Stamp of 1930 Overprinted in Red
Perf. 12½
RA25	A119	20c ultra & yel	.50	.25

Telegraph Stamp Overprinted in Red, like No. RA24, and Surcharged diagonally in Black

1934 *Perf. 14*
RA26		2c on 10c olive brn	.70	.25
a.		Double surcharge	5.50	

Overprint Blue, Surcharge Red
RA27		2c on 10c olive brn	.70	.25

PT9

1934-36 **Perf. 12**
RA28 PT9 2c green　　　　.60 .25
　a. Both overprints in red ('36)　.60 .25
Postal Tax stamp of 1920-24, overprinted in red "POSTAL" has been again overprinted "CASA de Correos y Teleg. de Guayaquil" in black.

PT10

1934 **Photo.** **Wmk. 233**
Perf. 14½x14
RA29 PT10 2c yellow green　　.50 .25
For the rebuilding of the GPO at Guayaquil.
For surcharge see No. RA31.

Symbols of Post
and Telegraph
Service — PT11

1935
RA30 PT11 20c claret　　　　.50 .25
For the rebuilding of the GPO at Guayaquil.

No. RA29 Surcharged in
Red and Overprinted in
Black

1935
RA31 PT10 3c on 2c yel grn　.40 .25
　a. Double surcharge
　b. Inverted surcharge (R)　4.50
Social and Rural Workers' Insurance Fund.

Tobacco Stamp Surcharged in Black

1936 **Unwmk.** **Rouletted 7**
RA32 PT7 3c on 1c rose red　　.60 .25
　a. Lines of words reversed　2.00 .25
　b. Horiz. pair, imperf. vert.
Issued for the Social and Rural Workers' Insurance Fund.

No. 310 Overprinted in
Black

1936 **Perf. 12½**
RA33 A119 20c ultra & yel　　.60 .25
　a. Double overprint

Tobacco Stamp Surcharged in Black

1936 **Rouletted 7**
RA34 PT7 3c on 1c rose red　　.60 .25
Social and Rural Workers' Insurance Fund.

Worker — PT12

1936 **Engr.** **Perf. 13½**
RA35 PT12 3c ultra　　　　　.40 .25
Social and Rural Workers' Insurance Fund.
For surcharges see Nos. C64, RA36, RA53-RA54.

Surcharged in Black

1936
RA36 PT13 5c on 3c ultra　　.60 .25
This combines the 2c for the rebuilding of the post office with the 3c for the Social and Rural Workers' Insurance Fund.

National Defense Issue
Tobacco Stamp Surcharged in Black

1936 **Rouletted 7**
RA37 PT7 10c on 1c rose　　.90 .25
　a. Double surcharge

Symbolical of
Defense — PT14

1937-42 **Perf. 12½**
RA38 PT14 10c deep blue　　.90 .25
A 1s violet and 2s green exist in type PT14.
For surcharge see No. RA40.

Overprinted or Surcharged in Black

PT15

1937 **Engr. & Typo.** **Perf. 13½**
RA39 PT15 5c lt brn & red　2.00 .25
　d. Inverted overprint　20.00
1942 **Perf. 12, 11½**
RA39A PT15 20c on 5c rose
　　pink &
　　red　　75.00 20.00
RA39B PT15 20c on 1s yel
　　brn & red　75.00 20.00
　e. Surcharge omitted　　—
RA39C PT15 20c on 2s grn
　　& red　75.00 20.00
　Nos. RA39A-RA39C (3)　225.00 60.00
A 50c dark blue and red exists.

No. RA38 Surcharged in
Red

1937 **Engr.** **Perf. 12½**
RA40 PT14 5c on 10c dp
　　blue　1.10 .25

Map of
Ecuador — PT16

1938 **Perf. 14x13½**
RA41 PT16 5c carmine
　　rose　.70 .25
Social and Rural Workers' Insurance Fund.

No. C42 Surcharged in Red

1938 **Perf. 12½**
RA42 A136 20c on 70c black　1.10 .25

No. 307 Surcharged in
Red

1938
RA43 A116 5c on 6c yel & red　.40 .25
This stamp was obligatory on all mail from Nov. 23rd to 30th, 1938. The tax was for the Intl. Union for the Control of Cancer.

Tobacco Stamp Surcharged in Black

1939 **Rouletted**
RA44 PT7 5c on 1c rose　　.70 .25
　a. Double surcharge
　b. Triple surcharge

Tobacco Stamp Surcharged in Blue

1940
RA45 PT7 5c on 1c rose red　1.00 .25
　a. Double surcharge　3.50 3.50

No. 370 Surcharged in Carmine

1940 **Perf. 11½**
RA46 A144 20c on 50c blk &
　　multi　.50 .25
　a. Double surcharge, one invert-
　　ed

Tobacco Stamp Surcharged in Black

1940 **Rouletted**
RA47 PT7 20c on 1c rose red　6.00 .50

Farmer
Plowing — PT17

1940 **Perf. 13x13½**
RA48 PT17 5c carmine rose　.70 .25

Communication
Symbols — PT18

1940-43 **Perf. 12**
RA49 PT18 5c copper brown　.70 .25
RA49A PT18 5c green ('43)　.70 .25
For overprint and surcharges see #534, E6, I1.

Pursuit Planes — PT19

1941 **Perf. 11½x13**
RA50 PT19 20c ultra　1.10 .25
The tax was used for national defense.

Warrior Shielding
Women — PT20

1942-46 **Engr.** **Perf. 12**
RA51 PT20 20c dark blue　1.10 .25
RA51A PT20 40c blk brn ('46)　1.10 .25
The tax was used for national defense.
A 20c carmine, 20c brown and 30c gray exist lithographed in type PT20.

No. 370 Surcharged in Carmine

1942 **Perf. 11½**
RA52 A144 20c on 50c multi　1.10 .25
　a. Double surcharge　10.00

No. RA35 Surcharged in
Red

1943 **Perf. 13½**
RA53 PT12 5c on 3c ultra　.60 .25

No. RA53 with Additional
Surcharge in Black

1943
RA54 PT12 5c on 5c on 3c ultra　1.10 .25

Peons — PT21

1943 **Perf. 12**
RA55 PT21 5c blue　.90 .25
The tax was for farm workers.
For overprint & surcharge see #535, C135.

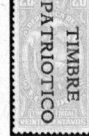

Revenue Stamp (as No.
RA64) Overprinted or
Surcharged in Black

1943 **Perf. 12½**
RA56 20c red orange　75.00 1.50

Revenue Stamp (as No.
RA64) Overprinted or
Surcharged in Black

1943 **Perf. 12**
RA57 20c on 10c orange　2.25 .25
　a. Double surcharge

Coat of Arms — PT22

1943   **Perf. 12½**
RA58 PT22 20c orange red   .70   .25
   The tax was for national defense.

No. RA58 Surcharged in Black

1944
RA59 PT22 30c on 20c org red   .70   .25
   a.   Double surcharge   20.00

> **Catalogue values for unused stamps in this section, from this point to the end of the section, are for Never Hinged items.**

Consular Service Stamps Surcharged in Black

1951   **Unwmk.**   **Perf. 12**
RA60 R1 20c on 1s red   .60   .25
RA61 R1 20c on 2s brown   .60   .25
RA62 R1 20c on 5s violet   .60   .25
   Nos. RA60-RA62 (3)   1.80   .75

Teacher and Pupils in Schoolyard — PT23

1952   **Engr.**   **Perf. 13**
RA63 PT23 20c blue green   .60   .25

Revenue Stamp Overprinted — PT24

1952   **Perf. 12**
RA64 PT24 40(c) olive green   1.10   .25
   For overprints & surcharges see #RA56-RA57

Woman Holding Flag — PT25

1953   **Perf. 12½**
RA65 PT25 40c ultra   1.25   .25

Telegraph Stamp Surcharged in Black — PT26

1954   **Unwmk.**   **Perf. 13**
RA66 PT26 20c on 30c red brn   1.00   .25

Revenue Stamps Surcharged or Overprinted Horizontally in Black

PT26a   PT26b

PT26c

1954   **Unwmk.**   **Perf. 12**
RA67 PT26a 10c on 25c blue   1.25   .25
RA68 PT26b 10c on 50c org red   1.25   .25
RA69 PT26c 10c carmine   1.25   .25
   Nos. RA67-RA69 (3)   3.75   .75

Telegraph Stamp Surcharged — PT27

1954   **Perf. 13**
RA70 PT27 10c on 30c red brn   2.25   .25

Revenue Stamp Overprinted in Black

1954   **Perf. 12**
RA71 R3 20c olive black   1.75   .25

Consular Service Stamp Surcharged in Black

1954
RA72 R1 20c on 10s gray   1.75   .25

Young Student at Desk — PT28

Imprint: "Heraclio Fournier.-Vitoria"

1954   **Photo.**   **Perf. 11**
RA73 PT28 20c rose pink   1.25   .25
   See No. RA76.

Globe, Ship, Plane — PT29

1954   **Engr.**   **Perf. 12**
RA74 PT29 10c dp magenta   2.25   .25

Soldier Kissing Flag — PT30

1955   **Photo.**   **Perf. 11**
RA75 PT30 40c blue   2.25   .25
   See No. RA77.

Types of 1954-55 Redrawn.
Imprint: "Thomas de la Rue & Co. Ltd."

1957   **Unwmk.**   **Perf. 13**
RA76 PT28 20c rose pink   1.10   .25
               Perf. 14x14½
RA77 PT30 40c blue   2.25   .25
   No. RA77 is inscribed "Republica del Ecuador."

The above stamp is believed to have been used only for fiscal purposes.

AIR POST POSTAL TAX STAMPS

No. 438 Surcharged in Black or Carmine

1945   **Unwmk.**   **Perf. 11**
RAC1 A173 20c on 10c dk grn   .75   .25
   a.   Pair, one without surcharge   90.00
RAC2 A173 20c on 10c dk grn   .75   .25
     (C)
   Obligatory on letters and parcel post carried on planes in the domestic service.

Liberty, Mercury and Planes — PTAP1

1946   **Engr.**   **Perf. 12**
RAC3 PTAP1 20c orange brown   .75   .25

GALAPAGOS ISLANDS

Issued for use in the Galapagos Islands (Columbus Archipelago), a province of Ecuador, but were commonly used throughout the country.

> Catalogue values for unused stamps in this section are for Never Hinged items.

Sea Lions — A1   Map — A2

Design: 1s, Marine iguana.

Unwmk.
1957, July 15   **Photo.**   **Perf. 12**
L1 A1 20c dark brown   1.50   .30
L2 A2 50c violet   1.00   .30
L3 A1 1s dull olive green   4.75   .80
   Nos. L1-L3 (3)   7.25   1.40
   Nos. L1-L3,LC1-LC3 (6)   18.50   3.65

   125th anniv. of Ecuador's possession of the Galapagos Islands, and publicizing the islands.
   See Nos. LC1-LC3. For overprints see Nos. 684-686, C389-C391.

GALAPAGOS AIR POST STAMPS

Type of Regular Issue

1s, Santa Cruz Island. 1.80s, Map of Galapagos archipelago. 4.20s, Galapagos giant tortoise.

Unwmk.
1957, July 19   **Photo.**   **Perf. 12**
LC1 A1 1s deep blue   1.25   .30
LC2 A1 1.80s rose violet   2.50   .70
LC3 A1 4.20s black   7.50   1.25
   Nos. LC1-LC3 (3)   11.25   2.25
   For overprints see Nos. C389-C391.

Redrawn Type of Ecuador, 1956
1959, Jan. 3   **Engr.**   **Perf. 14**
LC4 AP69 2s lt olive green   1.25   .70

   Issued to honor the United Nations. See note after No. C407.

EGYPT

ˈē-jəpt

LOCATION — Northern Africa, bordering on the Mediterranean and the Red Sea
GOVT. — Republic
AREA — 386,900 sq. mi.
POP. — 61,404,000 (1997 est.)
CAPITAL — Cairo

Modern Egypt was a part of Turkey until 1914 when a British protectorate was declared over the country and the Khedive was deposed in favor of Hussein Kamil under the title of sultan. In 1922 the protectorate ended and the reigning sultan was declared king of the new monarchy. Egypt became a republic on June 18, 1953. Egypt merged with Syria in 1958 to form the United Arab Republic. Syria left this union in 1961. In 1971 Egypt took the name of Arab Republic of Egypt.

   40 Paras = 1 Piaster
   1000 Milliemes = 100 Piasters = 1 Pound (1888)
   1000 Milliemes = 1 Pound (1953)
   1000 Milliemes = 100 Piasters = 1 Pound (1982)

> **Catalogue values for unused stamps in this country are for Never Hinged items, beginning with Scott 241 in the regular postage section, Scott B1 in the semipostal section, Scott C38 in the airpost section, Scott CB1 in the airpost semi-postal section, Scott E5 in the special delivery section, Scott J40 in the postage due section, Scott M16 in the military stamps section, Scott O60 in the officials section, Scott N1 in the occupation section, Scott NC1 in the occupation airpost section, Scott NE1 in the occupation special delivery section, and Scott NJ1 in the occupation postage due section.**

Watermarks

Wmk. 118 — Pyramid and Star   Wmk. 119 — Crescent and Star

Wmk. 120 — Triple Crescent and Star   Wmk. 195 — Multiple Crown and Arabic F

"F" in watermark stands for Fuad.

Wmk. 315 — Multiple Eagle

Wmk. 318 — Multiple Eagle and "Misr"

Wmk.
328 — U
A R

Wmk.
342 —
Coat of
Arms,
Multiple

Values for unused stamps are for examples with original gum as defined in the catalogue introduction. Very fine examples of Nos. 1-15 will have perforations that are clear of the framelines but with the design noticeably off center. Well centered stamps are extremely scarce and will command substantial premiums.

Turkish Numerals

١ ٢ ٣ ٤ ٥
1 2 3 4 5

٧ ٧ ٨ ٩ ٠
6 7 8 9 0

Turkish Suzerainty

A1   A2

A3   A4

A5   A6

A7

Surcharged in Black
Wmk. 118

1866, Jan. 1   Litho.   Perf. 12½

1	A1	5pa greenish gray	62.50	37.50
a.		Imperf., pair	250.00	
b.		Pair, imperf. between	400.00	
c.		Perf. 12½x13	82.50	62.50
d.		Perf. 13	325.00	370.00
2	A2	10pa brown	75.00	37.50
a.		Imperf., pair	210.00	
b.		Pair, imperf. between	550.00	
c.		Perf. 13	300.00	340.00
d.		Perf. 12½x15	325.00	350.00
e.		Perf. 12½x13	100.00	65.00
3	A3	20pa blue	105.00	40.00
a.		Imperf., pair	300.00	
b.		Pair, imperf. between	500.00	
c.		Perf. 12½x13	140.00	95.00
d.		Perf. 13	575.00	375.00
4	A4	2pi yellow	125.00	52.50
a.		Imperf.	150.00	125.00
b.		Imperf. vert. or horiz., pair	525.00	450.00
c.		Perf. 12½x15	210.00	
d.		Diagonal half used as 1pi on cover		3,000.
e.		Perf. 12½x13, 13x12½	200.00	75.00
f.		Pair, imperf. between	650.00	550.00
5	A5	5pi rose	325.00	250.00
a.		Imperf.	425.00	375.00
b.		Imperf. vert. or horiz., pair	1,300.	
d.		Inscription of 10pi, imperf.	1,100.	950.00
e.		Perf. 12½x13, 13x12½	350.00	275.00

f.		As "d," perf. 12½x15	1,050.	1,000.
g.		Perf. 13	850.00	
6	A6	10pi slate bl	375.00	325.00
a.		Imperf.	550.00	450.00
b.		Pair, imperf. between	2,750.	
c.		Perf. 12½x13, 13x12½	575.00	575.00
d.		Perf. 13	2,000.	

Unwmk.
Typo.

7	A7	1pi rose lilac	80.00	6.00
a.		Imperf.	125.00	
b.		Horiz. pair, imperf. vert.	525.00	
c.		Perf. 12½x13, 13x12½	110.00	25.00
d.		Perf. 13	475.00	325.00
e.		Perf. 12½x15	350.00	
		Nos. 1-7 (7)	1,148.	748.50

Single imperforates of types A1-A10 are sometimes simulated by trimming wide-margined examples of perforated stamps.

No. 4d must be dated between July 16 and July 31, 1867.

Proofs of Nos. 1-7 are on smooth white paper, unwatermarked and imperforate. Proofs of No. 7 are on thinner paper than No. 7a.

Sphinx and
Pyramid — A8

Perf. 15x12½

1867   Litho.   Wmk. 119

8	A8	5pa orange	42.50	11.00
a.		Imperf.	250.00	
b.		Horiz. pair, imperf between	200.00	
c.		Vert. pair, imperf between	—	
9	A8	10pa lilac ('69)	70.00	11.00
a.		10pa violet	95.00	14.00
b.		Half used as 5pa on newspaper piece		900.00
11	A8	20pa yel grn ('69)	135.00	14.00
a.		20pa blue green	135.00	17.00
13	A8	1pi rose red	27.50	1.10
a.		Imperf., pair	150.00	
b.		Pair, imperf. between	325.00	
d.		Rouletted	70.00	
e.		1pi lake red	175.00	32.50
14	A8	2pi blue	150.00	18.00
a.		Imperf.	325.00	
b.		Horiz. pair, imperf. vert.	525.00	
d.		Perf. 12½	275.00	
15	A8	5pi brown	375.00	200.00
		Nos. 8-15 (6)	800.00	255.10

There are 4 types of each value, so placed that any block of 4 contains all types.

A9

Clear Impressions
Thick Opaque Paper
Typographed by the Government at Boulac
Perf. 12½x13½ Clean-cut

1872   Wmk. 119

19	A9	5pa brown	10.00	5.50
20	A9	10pa lilac	9.00	3.75
21	A9	20pa blue	67.50	4.75
22	A9	1pi rose red	72.50	2.25
h.		Half used as 20pa on cover		750.00
23	A9	2pi dull yellow	100.00	15.00
j.		Half used as 1p on cover		1,200.
24	A9	2½pi dull violet	95.00	25.00
25	A9	5pi green	325.00	42.50
i.		Tête bêche pair	8,000.	
		Nos. 19-25 (7)	679.00	98.75

Perf. 13½ Clean-cut

19a	A9	5pa brown	27.50	10.00
20a	A9	10pa dull lilac	7.00	3.50
21a	A9	20pa blue	95.00	22.00
22a	A9	1pi rose red	95.00	4.00
23a	A9	2pi dull yellow	20.00	4.50
24a	A9	2½pi dull violet	800.00	225.00
25a	A9	5pi green	325.00	62.50

Litho.

21m	A9	20pa blue, perf. 12½x13½	160.00	80.00
21n	A9	20pa blue, perf. 13½	250.00	65.00
21p	A9	20pa blue, imperf.	—	
21q	A9	20pa blue, pair, imperf. between	—	2,000.
22m	A9	1pi rose red, perf. 12½x13½	550.00	20.00
22n	A9	1pi rose red, perf. 13½	875.00	50.00

A10

Blurred Impressions
Thinner Paper
Perf. 12½ Rough

1874-75   Typo.   Wmk. 119

26	A10	5pa brown ('75)	22.50	3.75
e.		Imperf.	200.00	200.00
f.		Vert. pair, imperf. horiz.	1,000.	—
g.		Tête bêche pair	45.00	45.00
20b	A9	10pa gray lilac	16.00	3.75
g.		Tête bêche pair	225.00	225.00
21b	A9	20pa gray blue	105.00	4.00
k.		Half used as 10pa on cover		
22b	A9	1pi vermilion	12.00	1.75
f.		Imperf.	—	150.00
g.		Tête bêche pair	150.00	125.00
23b	A9	2pi yellow	90.00	5.75
i.		Tête bêche pair	600.00	600.00
24b	A9	2½pi deep violet	9.25	6.25
e.		Imperf.	—	
f.		Tête bêche pair	600.00	600.00
25b	A9	5pi yellow green	65.00	22.50
e.		Imperf.	400.00	

No. 26f normally occurs tête-bêche.

Perf. 13½x12½ Rough

26c	A10	5pa brown	24.00	4.50
i.		Tête bêche pair	62.50	62.50
20c	A9	10pa gray lilac	37.50	3.50
i.		Tête bêche pair	225.00	225.00
21c	A9	20pa gray blue	11.00	3.75
h.		Pair, imperf. between	350.00	
22c	A9	1pi vermilion	90.00	3.25
i.		Tête bêche pair	500.00	500.00
23c	A9	2pi yellow	10.00	6.25
g.		Tête bêche pair	500.00	500.00
k.		Half used as 1pi on cover		4,000.

Perf. 12½x13½ Rough

23d	A9	2pi yellow ('75)	80.00	17.00
h.		Tête bêche pair	1,250.	
24d	A9	2½pi dp violet ('75)	80.00	20.00
i.		Tête bêche pair	1,150.	800.00
25d	A9	5pi yel grn ('75)	375.00	300.00

Nos. 24b, 24d
Surcharged in Black

1879, Jan. 1   Perf. 12½ Rough

27	A9	5pa on 2½pi dull vio	10.00	12.00
a.		Imperf.	450.00	450.00
b.		Tête bêche pair	7,500.	
c.		Inverted surcharge	125.00	75.00
d.		Perf. 12½x13½ rough	12.00	12.00
e.		As "d," tête bêche pair	7,500.	
f.		As "d," inverted surcharge	150.00	150.00
28	A9	10pa on 2½pi dull vio	12.50	12.50
a.		Imperf.	400.00	400.00
b.		Tête bêche pair	2,500.	
c.		Inverted surcharge	125.00	82.50
d.		Perf. 12½x13½ rough	17.00	17.00
e.		As "d," tête bêche pair	3,000.	
f.		As "d," inverted surcharge	150.00	125.00

A11   A12

A13   A14

A15   A16

1879-1902   Typo.   Perf. 14x13½
Ordinary Paper

29	A11	5pa brown	4.25	1.25
30	A12	10pa violet	57.50	5.00
31	A12	10pa lilac rose ('81)	70.00	10.00
32	A12	10pa gray ('82)	8.00	1.75
33	A12	10pa green ('84)	2.50	2.00
34	A13	20pa ultra	67.50	2.25
35	A13	20pa rose ('84)	22.00	1.25
36	A14	1pi rose	42.50	.30
37	A14	1pi ultra ('84)	5.75	.30
38	A15	2pi orange yel	42.50	1.50
39	A15	2pi orange brn	27.50	.50
40	A16	5pi green	77.50	11.50
41	A16	5pi gray ('84)	25.00	.50
		Nos. 29-41 (13)	452.50	38.10

Nos. 29-31, 35-41 imperf are proofs.
Nos. 37, 39, 41, exist on both ordinary and chalky paper. See *Scott Classic Specialized Catalogue of Stamps & Covers* for detailed listings.
For overprints see Nos. 42, O6-O7.

A17

1884, Feb. 1

42	A17	20pa on 5pi green	14.00	2.25
a.		Inverted surcharge	70.00	62.50
b.		Double surcharge	—	

A18   A19

A20   A21

A22   A23

1888-1906   Ordinary Paper

43	A18	1m pale brown ('02)	3.50	.25
44	A19	2m green ('02)	3.00	.25
45	A19	3m maroon ('92)	8.00	2.25
46	A20	3m yel org ('02)	5.75	.25
48	A22	5m carmine rose	6.50	.25
49	A23	10p purple ('89)	35.00	1.00
		Nos. 43-49 (6)	61.75	4.25

Chalky Paper

43a	A18	1m pale brown ('02)	4.00	.25
44a	A19	2m green ('02)	1.25	.25
46a	A20	3m yel org ('02)	3.00	.25
47	A21	4m brown red ('06)	4.75	.25
a.		Half used as 2m on cover		
48b	A22	5m rose ('02)	3.00	.25
49b	A23	10p mauve ('02)	22.50	.55

Nos. 43-44, 47-48 imperf are proofs.
For overprints see Nos. O2-O5, O8-O10, O14-O15.

Boats on
Nile
A24

Cleopatra
A25

Ras-el-
Tin
Palace
A26

Giza
Pyramids
A27

Sphinx
A28

Colossi of
Thebes
A29

Pylon of
Karnak and
Temple of
Khonsu
A30

Citadel at
Cairo
A31

Rock
Temple of
Abu Simbel
A32

Aswan Dam
A33

Perf. 13½x14

1914, Jan. 8 **Wmk. 119**
Chalk-surfaced Paper

50	A24	1m olive brown	1.25	.80
51	A25	2m dp green	3.75	.25
52	A26	3m orange	3.50	.50
53	A27	4m red	4.50	.75
54	A28	5m lake	4.25	.25
a.		Booklet pane of 6	250.00	
55	A29	10m dk blue	7.50	.40

Perf. 14

56	A30	20m olive grn	8.00	.70
57	A31	50m red violet	24.00	1.10
58	A32	100m black	25.00	1.40
59	A33	200m plum	42.50	4.00
		Nos. 50-59 (10)	124.25	10.15

All values of this issue exist imperforate on both watermarked and unwatermarked paper but are not known to have been issued in that condition.

See Nos. 61-69, 72-74. For overprints and surcharge see Nos. 60, 78-91, O11-O13, O16-O27, O30.

British Protectorate

No. 52 Surcharged

1915, Oct. 15

60	A26	2m on 3m orange	1.25	2.25
a.		Inverted surcharge	250.00	250.00

Scenic Types of 1914 and

Statue of Ramses II
A34   A35

1921-22 **Wmk. 120** **Perf. 13½x14**
Chalk-surfaced Paper

61	A24	1m olive brown	1.50	3.00
62	A25	2m dp green	9.00	4.75
63	A26	2m red ('22)	6.00	2.50
64	A26	3m orange	9.00	6.00
65	A27	4m green ('22)	8.00	6.50
66	A28	5m lake	7.00	1.75
67	A28	5m pink	14.00	.25
68	A29	10m dp blue	12.00	.70
69	A29	10m lake ('22)	3.50	.70
70	A34	15m indigo ('22)	10.00	.30
71	A35	15m indigo ('22)	40.00	5.00

Perf. 14

72	A30	20m olive green	12.50	.40
73	A31	50m maroon	10.00	1.25
74	A32	100m black	95.00	7.50
		Nos. 61-74 (14)	237.50	40.60

For overprints see Nos. O28-O29.

Independent Kingdom

Stamps of 1921-22
Overprinted

1922, Oct. 10

78	A24	1m olive brown	1.50	1.10
a.		Inverted overprint	475.00	450.00
b.		Double overprint	225.00	—
79	A25	2m red	1.10	.65
a.		Double overprint	225.00	
80	A26	3m orange	2.25	1.10
81	A27	4m green	1.50	1.00
b.		Inverted overprint	225.00	
82	A28	5m pink	2.75	.25
83	A29	10m lake	2.75	.25
84	A34	15m indigo	5.75	1.10
85	A35	15m indigo	4.50	1.10

Perf. 14

86	A30	20m olive green	6.00	1.10
a.		Inverted overprint	200.00	—
b.		Double overprint	300.00	—
87	A31	50m maroon	9.00	1.10
a.		Inverted overprint	400.00	500.00
88	A32	100m black	22.50	1.25
a.		Inverted overprint	500.00	160.00
b.		Double overprint	400.00	250.00
		Nos. 78-88 (11)	59.60	10.00

Same Overprint on Nos. 58-59
Wmk. Crescent and Star (119)

90	A32	100m black	90.00	50.00
91	A33	200m plum	30.00	1.60

Proclamation of the Egyptian monarchy.
The overprint signifies "The Egyptian Kingdom, March 15, 1922." It exists in four types, one lithographed and three typographed on Nos. 78-87, but lithographed only on Nos. 88-91.

A36

King
Fuad — A37

Wmk. 120
1923-24 **Photo.** **Perf. 13½**
Size 18x22½mm

92	A36	1m orange	.35	.25
93	A36	2m black	1.10	.25
94	A36	3m brown	1.00	.65
a.		Imperf., pair	225.00	
95	A36	4m yellow grn	.90	.50
96	A36	5m orange brn	.45	.25
a.		Imperf., pair	50.00	
97	A36	10m rose	2.00	.25
98	A36	15m ultra	3.25	.25

Perf. 14
Size: 22x28mm

99	A36	20m dk green	6.25	.25
100	A36	50m myrtle grn	10.00	.25
101	A36	100m red violet	25.00	.55
102	A36	200m violet ('24)	45.00	2.00
a.		Imperf., pair	325.00	
103	A37	£1 ultra & dk vio ('24)	175.00	27.50
a.		Imperf., pair	1,750.	
		Nos. 92-103 (12)	270.30	32.95

For overprints & surcharge see Nos. 167, O31-O38.

Thoth Carving Name of King Fuad — A38

1925, Apr. **Litho.** **Perf. 11**

105	A38	5m brown	11.00	6.00
106	A38	10m rose	22.50	12.50
107	A38	15m ultra	22.50	14.00
		Nos. 105-107 (3)	56.00	32.50

International Geographical Congress, Cairo.
Nos. 106-107 exist with both white and yellowish gum.

Oxen
Plowing — A39

1926 **Wmk. 195** **Perf. 13x13½**

108	A39	5m lt brown	3.00	2.00
109	A39	10m brt rose	2.75	2.00
110	A39	15m dp blue	3.00	2.00
111	A39	50m Prus green	14.00	5.00
112	A39	100m brown vio	22.50	8.00
113	A39	200m brt violet	32.50	17.50
		Nos. 108-113 (6)	77.75	36.50

12th Agricultural and Industrial Exhibition at Gezira.
For surcharges see Nos. 115-117.

King Fuad — A40

Perf. 14x14½
1926, Apr. 2 **Photo.** **Wmk. 120**

114	A40	50p brn vio & red vio	140.00	22.50

58th birthday of King Fuad.
For overprint and surcharge see Nos. 124, 166.

Nos. 111-113 Surcharged

Perf. 13x13½
1926, Aug. 24 **Wmk. 195**

115	A39	5m on 50m Prus green	2.50	2.50
116	A39	10m on 100m brn vio	2.50	2.50
117	A39	15m on 200m brt vio	2.50	2.50
a.		Double surcharge	300.00	
		Nos. 115-117 (3)	7.50	7.50

Ship of
Hatshepsut
A41

1926, Dec. 9 **Litho.** **Perf. 13x13½**

118	A41	5m brown & blk	3.00	1.40
119	A41	10m dp red & blk	3.50	1.50
120	A41	15m dp blue & blk	4.00	1.50
		Nos. 118-120 (3)	10.50	4.40

International Navigation Congress, Cairo.
For overprints see Nos. 121-123.

Nos. 118-120, 114
Overprinted — a

No. 114
Overprinted — b

1926, Dec. 21

121	A41	(a)	5m	300.00	250.00
122	A41	(a)	10m	300.00	250.00
123	A41	(a)	15m	300.00	250.00

Perf. 14x14½
Wmk. 120

124	A40	(b)	50p	1,600.	875.00

Inauguration of Port Fuad opposite Port Said.
Nos. 121-123 have a block over "Le Caire" at lower left.
Forgeries of Nos. 121-124 exist.

Branch of
Cotton — A42

Perf. 13x13½
1927, Jan. 25 **Wmk. 195**

125	A42	5m dk brown & sl grn	1.75	.80
126	A42	10m dp red & slate grn	2.75	1.50
127	A42	15m dp blue & slate grn	3.50	1.50
		Nos. 125-127 (3)	8.00	3.80

International Cotton Congress, Cairo.

King Fuad
A43   A44

A45   A46

Type I   Type II

Early printings of the seven values indicated were printed from plates with screens of vertical dots in the vignettes (type I). All values were printed later from plates with screens of diagonal dots (type II).

Perf. 13x13½
1927-37 **Wmk. 195** **Photo.**
Type II

128	A43	1m orange	.35	.25
a.	Type I		3.25	.60
129	A43	2m black	.35	.25
a.	Type I		11.00	6.00
130	A43	3m olive brn	.35	.55
a.	Type I		2.50	1.00
131	A43	3m dp green ('30)	.65	.25
132	A43	4m yellow grn	1.25	1.10
a.	Type I		65.00	12.50
133	A43	4m brown ('30)	1.10	.55
134	A43	4m dp green ('34)	.85	.40
135	A43	5m dk red brn ('29)	.95	.40
a.	Type I		3.50	1.00
136	A43	10m dk red ('29)	1.40	.25
a.	10m orange red, type I		2.50	.45
137	A43	10m purple ('34)	3.75	.25
138	A43	13m car rose ('32)	1.50	.40
139	A43	15m ultra	2.50	.25
a.	Type I		12.00	.65
140	A43	15m dk violet ('34)	5.25	.25
141	A43	20m ultra ('34)	9.25	.30

Perf. 13½x14

142	A44	20m olive grn	3.25	.40
143	A44	20m ultra ('32)	7.50	.25
144	A44	40m olive brn ('32)	4.25	.25
145	A44	50m Prus green	3.50	.25
a.		50m greenish blue	6.00	.35

146	A44	100m brown vio	10.00 .35
a.		100m claret	14.00 .50
147	A44	200m deep violet	9.00 1.25

Printings of Nos. 142, 145 and 146, made in 1929 and later, were from new plates with stronger impressions and darker colors.

Perf. 13x13½

148	A45	500m choc & Prus bl, entirely photo ('32)	100.00 25.00
a.		Frame litho, vignette photo	125.00 11.50
149	A46	£1 dk grn & org brn, entirely photo ('37)	125.00 8.25
a.		Frame litho, vignette photo	140.00 7.00
		Nos. 128-149 (22)	292.00 41.45

Statue of Amenhotep, Son of Hapu — A47

1927, Dec. 29 Photo. Perf. 13½x13

150	A47	5m orange brown	1.50 1.00
151	A47	10m copper red	2.00 1.00
152	A47	15m deep blue	3.25 1.00
		Nos. 150-152 (3)	6.75 3.00

Statistical Congress, Cairo.

Imhotep A48

Mohammed Ali Pasha A49

1928, Dec. 15

153	A48	5m orange brown	1.10 .65
154	A49	10m copper red	1.25 .65

Intl. Congress of Medicine at Cairo and the cent. of the Faculty of Medicine at Cairo.

Prince Farouk — A50

1929, Feb. 11 Litho.

155	A50	5m choc & gray	2.00 1.40
156	A50	10m dull red & gray	3.00 1.50
157	A50	15m ultra & gray	3.00 1.50
158	A50	20m Prus blue & gray	3.50 1.50
		Nos. 155-158 (4)	11.50 5.90

Ninth birthday of Prince Farouk.
Nos. 155-158 with black or brown centers are trial color proofs. They were sent to the UPU, but were never placed on sale to the public, although some are known used.

Tomb Fresco at El-Bersheh A51

1931, Feb. 15 Perf. 13x13½

163	A51	5m brown	1.50 1.00
164	A51	10m copper red	2.50 1.75
165	A51	15m dark blue	3.50 2.00
		Nos. 163-165 (3)	7.50 4.75

14th Agricultural & Industrial Exhib., Cairo.

Nos. 114 and 103 Surcharged in Black

1932 Wmk. 120 Perf. 14x14½

166	A40	50m on 50p	20.00 3.00

Perf. 14

167	A37	100m on £1	250.00 190.00

Locomotive of 1852 — A52

Perf. 13x13½

1933, Jan. 19 Litho. Wmk. 195

168	A52	5m shown	14.00 8.00
169	A52	13m 1859	21.00 12.00
170	A52	15m 1862	21.00 12.00
171	A52	20m 1932	21.00 12.00
		Nos. 168-171 (4)	77.00 44.00

International Railroad Congress, Heliopolis.

Commercial Passenger Airplane — A56

Dornier Do-X — A57

Graf Zeppelin — A58

1933, Dec. 20 Photo.

172	A56	5m brown	7.50 4.00
173	A56	10m brt violet	17.50 12.00
174	A57	13m brown car	20.00 15.00
175	A57	15m violet	20.00 13.00
176	A58	20m blue	25.00 20.00
		Nos. 172-176 (5)	90.00 64.00

International Aviation Congress, Cairo.

A59

Khedive Ismail Pasha — A60

1934, Feb. 1 Perf. 13½

177	A59	1m dp orange	.60 1.10
178	A59	2m black	.60 1.10
179	A59	3m brown	.75 1.25
180	A59	4m blue green	1.25 .40
181	A59	5m red brown	1.40 .25
182	A59	10m violet	2.50 .35
183	A59	13m copper red	4.00 2.25
184	A59	15m dull violet	4.50 1.75
185	A59	20m ultra	3.00 .40
186	A59	50m Prus blue	9.50 .65
187	A59	100m olive grn	9.50 1.25
188	A59	200m dp violet	75.00 7.25

Perf. 13½x13

189	A60	50p brown	225.00 95.00
190	A60	£1 Prus blue	400.00 150.00
		Nos. 177-190 (14)	737.60 263.00

10th Congress of UPU, Cairo.

King Fuad — A61

1936-37 Perf. 13½

191	A61	1m dull orange	.55 .90
192	A61	2m black	1.75 .25
193	A61	4m dk green	2.00 .25
194	A61	5m chestnut	1.40 .55
195	A61	10m purple ('37)	2.50 .35
196	A61	15m brown violet	2.75 .50
197	A61	20m sapphire	3.25 .35
		Nos. 191-197 (7)	14.20 3.15

Entrance to Agricultural Building A62

Agricultural Building A63

Design: 15m, 20m, Industrial Building.

1936, Feb. 15 Perf. 13½x13

198	A62	5m brown	1.75 1.25

Perf. 13x13½

199	A63	10m violet	2.00 1.50
200	A63	13m copper red	3.25 2.50
201	A63	15m dark violet	1.75 1.25
202	A63	20m blue	3.75 2.25
		Nos. 198-202 (5)	12.50 8.75

15th Agricultural & Industrial Exhib., Cairo.

Signing of Treaty A65

1936, Dec. 22 Perf. 11x11½

203	A65	5m brown	.80 .80
204	A65	15m dk violet	1.00 1.00
205	A65	20m sapphire	1.75 1.75
		Nos. 203-205 (3)	3.55 3.55

Signing of Anglo-Egyptian Treaty, Aug. 26, 1936.

King Farouk — A66

1937-44 Wmk. 195 Perf. 13x13½

206	A66	1m brown org	.30 .25
207	A66	2m vermilion	.30 .25
208	A66	3m brown	.30 .25
209	A66	4m green	.30 .25
210	A66	5m red brown	.50 .25
211	A66	6m lt yel grn ('40)	.60 .25
212	A66	10m purple	.30 .25
213	A66	13m rose car	.60 .35
214	A66	15m dk vio brn	.50 .25
215	A66	20m blue	.75 .35
216	A66	20m lil gray ('44)	.75 .25
		Nos. 206-216 (11)	5.20 2.95

For overprints see Nos. 301, 303, 345, 348, 360E, N3, N6, N8, N22, N25, N27.

Medal for Montreux Conf. — A67

1937, Oct. 15 Perf. 13½x13

217	A67	5m red brown	.75 .55
218	A67	15m dk violet	1.25 1.10
219	A67	20m sapphire	1.50 1.25
		Nos. 217-219 (3)	3.50 2.90

Intl. Treaty signed at Montreux, Switzerland, under which foreign privileges in Egypt were to end in 1949.

Eye of Ré — A68

1937, Dec. 8 Perf. 13½x13½

220	A68	5m brown	1.25 .80
221	A68	15m dk violet	1.50 .90
222	A68	20m sapphire	1.75 1.00
		Nos. 220-222 (3)	4.50 2.70

15th Ophthalmological Congress, Cairo, December, 1937.

King Farouk, Queen Farida A69

1938, Jan. 20 Perf. 11

223	A69	5m red brown	6.50 5.00

Royal wedding of King Farouk and Farida Zulficar.

Inscribed: "11 Fevrier 1938"

1938, Feb. 11

224	A69	£1 green & sepia	200.00 150.00

King Farouk's 18th birthday.
No. 224 is valued CTO; postally used examples: Value, $300.

Cotton Picker — A70

1938, Jan. 26 Perf. 13½x13

225	A70	5m red brown	.75 .75
226	A70	15m dk violet	2.25 1.50
227	A70	20m sapphire	2.00 1.75
		Nos. 225-227 (3)	5.00 4.00

18th International Cotton Congress at Cairo.

Pyramids of Giza and Colossus of Thebes — A71

1938, Feb. 1 Perf. 13x13½

228	A71	5m red brown	1.40 1.00
229	A71	15m dk violet	2.00 1.25
230	A71	20m sapphire	2.25 1.25
		Nos. 228-230 (3)	5.65 3.50

Intl. Telecommunication Conf., Cairo.

Branch of Hydnocarpus A72

1938, Mar. 21 Perf. 13x13½

231	A72	5m red brown	1.50 1.25
232	A72	15m dk violet	2.25 1.25
233	A72	20m sapphire	2.50 1.25
		Nos. 231-233 (3)	6.25 3.75

International Leprosy Congress, Cairo.

King Farouk and Pyramids — A73

King Farouk
A74   **A75**

Backgrounds: 40m, Hussan Mosque. 50m, Cairo Citadel. 100m, Aswan Dam. 200m, Cairo University.

1939-46   **Photo.**   **Perf. 14x13½**
234	A73	30m gray	.75	.25
a.		30m slate gray	.75	.25
234B	A73	30m ol grn ('46)	.80	.25
235	A73	40m dk brown	.85	.25
236	A73	50m Prus green	1.00	.25
237	A73	100m brown vio	1.40	.50
238	A73	200m dk violet	5.00	.50

Perf. 13½x13
239	A74	50p green & sep	11.00	4.00
240	A75	£1 dp bl & dk brn	26.00	7.00
		Nos. 234-240 (8)	46.80	13.00

For £1 with A77 portrait, see No. 269D. See Nos. 267-269D. For overprints see Nos. 310-314, 316, 355-358, 360, 363-364, N13-N19, N32-N38.

> Catalogue values for unused stamps in this section, from this point to the end of the section, are for Never Hinged items.

King Fuad — A76

1944, Apr. 28   **Perf. 13½x13**
241 A76 10m dk violet   .50 .25
8th anniv. of the death of King Fuad.

King Farouk — A77

1944-50   **Wmk. 195**   **Perf. 13½x13**
242	A77	1m yellow brn ('45)	.45	.25
243	A77	2m red org ('45)	.45	.25
244	A77	3m sepia ('46)	1.00	1.00
245	A77	4m dp green ('45)	.45	.25
246	A77	5m red brown ('46)	.45	.25
247	A77	10m dp violet	.45	.25
247A	A77	13m rose red ('50)	12.00	4.25
248	A77	15m dk violet ('45)	1.25	.25
249	A77	17m olive grn	1.25	.25
250	A77	20m dk gray ('45)	1.40	.25
251	A77	22m dp blue ('45)	1.40	.25
		Nos. 242-251 (11)	20.55	7.50

For overprints see Nos. 299-300, 302, 304-309, 343-344, 346-347, 349-354, 360B, 361-362, N1-N2, N4-N5, N7, N9-N12, N20-N21, N23-N24, N26, N28-N31.

King Farouk — A78

1945, Feb. 10   **Perf. 13½x13**
252 A78 10m deep violet   .40 .25
25th birthday of King Farouk.

Khedive Ismail Pasha — A79

1945, Mar. 2   **Photo.**
253 A79 10m dark olive   .35 .25
50th anniv. of death of Khedive Ismail Pasha.

Flags of Arab Nations — A80

1945, July 29
254 A80 10m violet   .35 .25
255 A80 22m dp yellow grn   .45 .25
League of Arab Nations Conference, Cairo, Mar. 22, 1945.

Flags of Egypt and Saudi Arabia — A81

Perf. 13x13½
1946, Jan. 10   **Wmk. 195**
256 A81 10m dp yellow grn   .35 .25
Visit of King Ibn Saud, Jan. 1946.

Citadel, Cairo — A82

1946, Aug. 9
257 A82 10m yel brn & dp yel grn   .40 .25
Withdrawal of British troops from Cairo Citadel, Aug. 9, 1946.

King Farouk and Inchas Palace, Cairo — A83

2m, Prince Abdullah, Yemen. 3m, Pres. Bechara el-Khoury, Lebanon. 4m, King Abdul Aziz ibn Saud, Saudi Arabia. 5m, King Faisal II, Iraq. 10m, Amir Abdullah ibn Hussein, Jordan. 15m, Pres. Shukri el Kouatly, Syria.

1946, Nov. 9
258	A83	1m dp yellow grn	.60	.25
259	A83	2m sepia	.60	.25
260	A83	3m deep blue	.60	.25
261	A83	4m brown orange	.60	.25
262	A83	5m brown red	.60	.25
263	A83	10m dark gray	.75	.25
264	A83	15m deep violet	.75	.25
		Nos. 258-264 (7)	4.50	1.75

Arab League Cong. at Cairo, May 28, 1946.

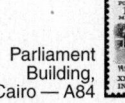

Parliament Building, Cairo — A84

1947, Apr. 7   **Photo.**
265 A84 10m green   .35 .25
36th conf. of the Interparliamentary Union, Apr. 1947.

Raising Egyptian Flag over Kasr-el-Nil Barracks — A85

1947, May 6   **Perf. 13½x13**
266 A85 10m dp plum & yel grn   .40 .25
Withdrawal of British troops from the Nile Delta.

Farouk Types 1939 Redrawn and

King Farouk — A85a

1947-51   **Wmk. 195**   **Perf. 14x13½**
267	A73	30m olive green	.75	.25
268	A73	40m dk brown	.60	.25
269	A73	50m Prus grn ('48)	.90	.25
269A	A73	100m dk brn vio ('49)	6.00	.90
269B	A73	200m dk vio ('49)	14.00	1.40

Perf. 13½x13
269C	A85a	50p green & sep ('51)	27.50	9.50
269D	A75	£1 dp bl & dk brn ('50)	37.50	3.75
		Nos. 267-269D (7)	87.25	16.30

The king faces slightly to the left and clouds have been added in the sky on Nos. 267-269B. Backgrounds as in 1939-46 issue. Portrait on £1 as on type A77.
For overprints see Nos. 315, 359.

Field and Branch of Cotton — A86

Perf. 13½x13
1948, Apr. 1   **Wmk. 195**
270 A86 10m olive green   .65 .25
Intl. Cotton Cong. held at Cairo in Apr. 1948.

Map and Infantry Column — A87

1948, June 15   **Perf. 11½x11**
271 A87 10m green   1.40 .25
Arrival of Egyptian troops at Gaza, 5/15/48.

Ibrahim Pasha (1789-1848) A88

1948, Nov. 10   **Perf. 13½x13**
272 A88 10m brn red & dp grn   .40 .25

Statue, "The Nile" A89   **Protection of Industry and Agriculture A90**

Perf. 13x13½
1949, Mar. 1   **Photo.**   **Wmk. 195**
273	A89	1m dk green	.40	.25
274	A89	10m purple	1.00	.25
275	A89	17m crimson	1.00	.25
276	A89	22m deep blue	1.00	.45

Perf. 11½x11
277	A90	30m dk brown	1.50	.60
		Nos. 273-277 (5)	4.90	1.80

Souvenir Sheets
Photo. & Litho.
Imperf
278		Sheet of 4	3.75	3.75
a.		A89 1m red brown	.75	.75
b.		A89 10m dark brown	.75	.75
c.		A89 17m brown orange	.75	.75
d.		A89 22m dark Prussian green	.75	.75
279		Sheet of 2	3.75	3.75
a.		A90 10m violet gray	1.60	1.60
b.		A90 30m red orange	1.60	1.60

16th Agricultural & Industrial Expo., Cairo.

Mohammed Ali and Map — A93

Perf. 11½x11
1949, Aug. 2   **Photo.**   **Wmk. 195**
280 A93 10m orange brn & grn   .60 .25
Centenary of death of Mohammed Ali.

Globe — A94

1949, Oct. 9   **Perf. 13½x13**
281	A94	10m rose brown	1.00	.60
282	A94	22m violet	2.00	.90
283	A94	30m dull blue	2.75	1.20
		Nos. 281-283 (3)	5.75	2.70

75th anniv. of the UPU.

Scales of Justice — A95

1949, Oct. 14   **Perf. 13x13½**
284 A95 10m deep olive green   .40 .25
End of the Mixed Judiciary System, 10/14/49.

Desert Scene — A96

1950, Dec. 27
285 A96 10m violet & red brn   .90 .75
Opening of the Fuad I Institute of the Desert.

Fuad I
University — A97

1950, Dec. 27
286 A97 22m dp green & claret　　.90　.75
Founding of Fuad I University, 25th anniv.

Globe and
Khedive Ismail
Pasha — A98

1950, Dec. 27
287 A98 30m claret & dp grn　　.90　.75
75th anniv. of Royal Geographic Society of Egypt.

Picking Cotton — A99

1951, Feb. 24
290 A99 10m olive green　　　.40　.35
International Cotton Congress, 1951.

King
Farouk
and
Queen
Narriman
A100

1951, May 6　Photo.　Perf. 11x11½
291 A100 10m green & red brn　3.00　2.25
　a.　Souvenir sheet　　　17.50　19.00
Marriage of King Farouk and Narriman Sadek, May 6, 1951.

Stadium Entrance
A101

Arms of
Alexandria
and Olympic
Emblem
A102

King
Farouk — A103

1951, Oct. 5　Perf. 13x13½, 13½x13
292 A101 10m brown　　　1.10　1.10
293 A102 22m dp green　　1.40　1.40
294 A103 30m blue & dp grn　1.40　1.40
　a.　Souvenir sheet of 3, #292-
　　　294　　　　　　14.00　16.00
　　Nos. 292-294 (3)　　3.90　3.90
Issued to publicize the first Mediterranean Games, Alexandria, Oct. 5-20, 1951.

Winged Figure and
Map — A105

Designs: 22m, King Farouk and Map. 30m, King Farouk and Flag.

Dated "16 Oct. 1951"
1952, Feb. 11　　Perf. 13½x13
296 A105 10m dp green　　.75　.40
297 A105 22m plum & dp grn　1.00　.75
298 A105 30m green & brown　1.25　.95
　a.　Souvenir sheet of 3, #296-
　　　298　　　　　　14.00　14.00
　　Nos. 296-298 (3)　　3.00　2.10
Abrogation of the Anglo-Egyptian treaty.

Stamps of 1937-51
Overprinted in Various
Colors

**　　　Perf. 13x13½**
1952, Jan. 17　　Wmk. 195
299 A77　1m yellow brown　.85　.25
300 A77　2m red org (Bl)　.35　.25
301 A66　3m brown (Bl)　.35　.50
302 A77　4m dp green (RV)　.35　.25
303 A66　6m lt yel grn (RV)　1.25　1.25
304 A77　10m dp vio (C)　.45　.25
305 A77　13m rose red (C)　1.75　1.60
306 A77　15m dk violet (C)　2.75　1.75
307 A77　17m olive grn (C)　2.00　.35
308 A77　20m dk gray (RV)　1.60　.35
309 A77　22m dp blue (C)　3.00　3.00
No. 244, the 3m sepia, exists with this overprint but was not regularly issued or used.

Same Overprint,
24½mm Wide, on
Nos. 267 to 269B

310 A73　30m olive grn (DkBl)　3.75　.25
　a.　Black overprint　　2.25　1.00
311 A73　40m dk brown (G)　.90　.25
312 A73　50m Prus grn (C)　1.75　.25
313 A73　100m dk brn vio (C)　3.00　.50
314 A73　200m dk violet (C)　15.00　2.25

Same Overprint, 19mm
Wide, on Nos. 269C-
269D

315 A85a 50p grn & sep (C)　25.00　8.00
316 A75　£1 dp bl & dk brn
　　　　　　(Bl)　　　45.00　9.00
　　Nos. 299-316 (18)　109.10　30.30
The overprint translates: King of Egypt and the Sudan, Oct. 16, 1951.
Overprints in colors other than as listed are color trials.

Egyptian Flag — A106

**　　　Perf. 13½x13**
1952, May 6　Photo.　Wmk. 195
317 A106 10m org yel, dp bl &
　　　　　dp grn　　　1.00　.25
　a.　Souvenir sheet of 1　7.50　5.25
Issued to commemorate the birth of Crown Prince Ahmed Fuad, Jan. 16, 1952.

"Dawn of New Era"
A107

Symbolical
of Egypt
Freed
A108

Designs: 10m, "Egypt" with raised sword. 22m, Citizens marching with flag.
Dated: "23 Juillet 1952"

Perf. 13x13½, 13½x13
1952, Nov. 23
318 A107　4m dp green & org　.35　.25
319 A107 10m dp grn & cop brn　.35　.75
320 A108 17m brn org & dp grn　.75　.90
321 A108 22m choc & dp grn　1.25　.60
　　Nos. 318-321 (4)　　2.70　2.50
Change of government, July 23, 1952.

Republic

Farmer
A109

Soldier
A110

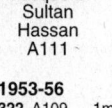
Mosque of
Sultan
Hassan
A111

Queen
Nefertiti
A112

1953-56　　　　Perf. 13x13½
322 A109　1m red brown　.50　.25
323 A109　2m dk lilac　.35　.25
324 A109　3m brt blue　.50　.45
325 A109　4m dk green　.35　.25
326 A110 10m dk brown
　　　　　("Defence")　.40　.40
327 A110 10m dk brown
　　　　　("Defense")　.80　.25
328 A110 15m gray　.55　.25
329 A110 17m dk grnsh blue　.75　.25
330 A110 20m purple　.35　.25
**　　　　　Perf. 13¼x13¾**
331 A111 30m dull green　.35　.25
332 A111 32m brt blue　.90　.25
333 A111 35m violet ('55)　1.10　.25
334 A111 37m gldn brn ('56)　1.75　.60
335 A111 40m red brown　.90　.25
336 A111 50m violet brn　1.75　.25
337 A112 100m henna brn　2.75　.30
338 A112 200m dk grnsh blue　4.50　.75
339 A112 500m purple　12.00　1.75
340 A112　£1 dk grn, blk &
　　　　　red　　　22.50　3.25
　　Nos. 322-340 (19)　53.05　10.50
Nos. 327-330 are inscribed "Defense."
See No. 490. For overprints and surcharges see Nos. 460, 500, N44-N56, N72.

Stamps of 1939-51
Overprinted in Black

1953　　Perf. 13x13½, 13½x13
343 A77　1m yellow brn　.35　.25
344 A77　2m red orange　.35　.25
345 A66　3m brown　.75　.75
346 A77　3m sepia　.35　.25
347 A77　4m dp green　.35　.25
348 A66　6m lt yel grn　.35　.25
349 A77　10m dp violet　.35　.25
350 A77　13m rose red　1.00　1.00
351 A77　15m dk violet　.75　.25
352 A77　17m olive grn　.75　.25
353 A77　20m dk gray　.90　.25
354 A77　22m deep blue　1.25　.25
355 A73　30m ol grn
　　　　　(#267)　　.75　.35
356 A73　50m Prus grn
　　　　　(#269)　　1.20　.35
357 A73　100m dk brn vio
　　　　　(#269A)　　2.00　.75
358 A73　200m dk vio
　　　　　(#269B)　　7.50　1.60
359 A85a 50p grn & sepia　19.00　7.00
360 A75　£1 dp bl & dk
　　　　　brn
　　　　　(#269D)　　24.00　4.75
　　Nos. 343-360 (18)　61.95　19.05
No. 206 with this overprint is a forgery.

Same Overprint on Nos. 300, 303-
305, 311 and 314
360B A77　2m red orange　.40　.25
360E A66　6m lt yel grn　35.00
361 A77　10m dp violet　4.00　4.00
362 A77　13m rose red　1.25　.75
363 A73　40m dk brown　6.00　.75
364 A73 200m dk violet　4.00　.75
　　Nos. 360B,361-364 (5)　15.65　6.65
Practically all values of Nos. 343-364 exist with double overprint. Other values of the 1952

---

overprinted issue are known only with counterfeit bars.

Symbols of
Electronic
Progress
A113

1953, Nov. 23　Photo.　Perf. 13x13½
365 A113 10m brt blue　　.75　.50
Electronics Exposition, Cairo, Nov. 23.

Crowd Acclaiming the
Republic — A114

Design: 30m, Crowd, flag and eagle.

**　　　Perf. 13½x13**
1954, June 18　　Wmk. 195
366 A114 10m brown　　.55　.25
367 A114 30m deep blue　.90　.60
Proclamation of the republic, 1st anniv.

Farmer — A115

1954-55　　　Perf. 13x13½
368 A115　1m red brown　.35　.25
369 A115　2m dark lilac　.35　.25
370 A115　3m brt blue　.35　.25
371 A115　4m dk green ('55)　1.25　.95
372 A115　5m dp car ('55)　.35　.25
　　Nos. 368-372 (5)　2.65　1.95
For overprints see Nos. N39-N43.

Egyptian Flag,
Map — A116

Design: 35m, Bugler, soldier and map.

1954, Nov. 4　　Perf. 13½x13
373 A116 10m rose vio & grn　.50　.30
374 A116 35m ver, blk & bl grn　.80　.70
Agreement of Oct. 19, 1954, with Great Britain for the evacuation of the Suez Canal zone by British troops.

Arab Postal Union Issue

Globe — A117

1955, Jan. 1
375 A117　5m yellow brn　.60　.30
376 A117 10m green　.60　.50
377 A117 37m violet　1.25　.95
　　Nos. 375-377 (3)　2.45　1.75
Founding of the Arab Postal Union, 7/1/54.
For overprints see Nos. 381-383.

Paul P. Harris and
Rotary Emblem — A118

35m, Globe, wings and Rotary emblem.

Perf. 13½x13
1955, Feb. 23 **Wmk. 195**
378 A118 10m claret 1.10 .35
379 A118 35m blue 1.50 .75
50th anniv. of the founding of Rotary Intl.

Nos. 375-377
Overprinted

1955, Nov. 1
381 A117 5m yellow brown 1.00 .80
382 A117 10m green 1.25 1.00
383 A117 37m violet 1.75 1.25
Nos. 381-383 (3) 4.00 3.05
Arab Postal Union Congress held at Cairo, Mar. 15, 1955.

Map of Africa and Asia, Olive Branch and Rings A119

Globe, Torch, Dove and Olive Branch A120

1956, July 29 **Perf. 13x13½, 13½x13**
384 A119 10m chestnut & green .40 .25
385 A120 35m org yel & dull pur 1.00 .70
Afro-Asian Festival, Cairo, July, 1956.

Map of Suez Canal and Ship — A121

Perf. 11½x11
1956, Sept. 26 **Wmk. 195**
386 A121 10m blue & buff .60 .60
Nationalization of the Suez Canal, July 26, 1956. See No. 393.

Queen Nefertiti — A122

1956, Oct. 15 **Perf. 13½x13**
387 A122 10m dark green 1.40 1.25
Intl. Museum Week (UNESCO), Oct. 8-14.

Egyptians Defending Port Said — A123

1956, Dec. 20 **Litho.** **Perf. 11x11½**
388 A123 10m brown violet 1.00 .75
Honoring the defenders of Port Said.

No. 388 Overprinted in Carmine Rose

1957, Jan. 14
389 A123 10m brown violet 1.00 .60
Evacuation of Port Said by British and French troops, Dec. 22, 1956.

Old and New Trains — A124

1957, Jan. 30 **Photo.** **Perf. 13x13½**
390 A124 10m red violet & gray 1.10 1.00
100th anniv. of the Egyptian Railway System (in 1956).

Mother and Children — A125

1957, Mar. 21
391 A125 10m crimson .90 .35
Mother's Day, 1957.

Battle Scene — A126

Perf. 13x13½
1957, Mar. 28 **Wmk. 195**
392 A126 10m bright blue .40 .35
Victory over the British at Rosetta, 150th anniv.

Type of 1956; New Inscriptions in English
1957, Apr. 15 **Perf. 11½x11**
393 A121 100m blue & yel grn 1.60 1.25
Reopening of the Suez Canal.
No. 393 is inscribed: "Nationalisation of Suez Canal Co. Guarantees Freedom of Navigation" and "Reopening 1957."

Map of Gaza Strip — A127

Perf. 13½x13
1957, May 4 **Photo.** **Wmk. 195**
394 A127 10m Prus blue 1.50 .70
"Gaza Part of Arab Nation."
For overprint see No. N57.

Al Azhar University A128

1957, Apr. 27 **Perf. 13x13½**
New Arabic Date in Red
395 A128 10m brt violet .50 .40
396 A128 15m violet brown .80 .60
397 A128 20m dark gray 1.30 .90
Nos. 395-397 (3) 2.60 1.90
Millenary of Al Azhar University, Cairo.

Shepheard's Hotel, Cairo — A129

Perf. 13½x13
1957, July 20 **Wmk. 195**
398 A129 10m brt violet .70 .45
Reopening of Shepheard's Hotel, Cairo.

Gate, Palace and Eagle — A130

Perf. 11½x11
1957, July 22 **Wmk. 315**
399 A130 10m yellow & brown .70 .40
First meeting of New National Assembly.

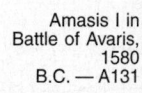

Amasis I in Battle of Avaris, 1580 B.C. — A131

Designs: No. 401, Sultan Saladin, Hitteen, 1187 A. D. No. 402, Louis IX of France in chains, Mansourah, 1250, vert. No. 403, Map of Middle East, Ein Galout, 1260. No. 404, Port Said, 1956.

Inscribed: "Egypt Tomb of Aggressors 1957"
1957, July 26 **Perf. 13x13½, 13½x13**
400 A131 10m carmine rose 1.50 1.50
401 A131 10m dk olive grn 1.50 1.50
402 A131 10m brown violet 1.50 1.50
403 A131 10m grnsh blue 1.50 1.50
404 A131 10m yellow brown 1.50 1.50
Nos. 400-404 (5) 7.50 7.50
No. 400 exists with Wmk. 195.

Ahmed Arabi Speaking to the Khedive — A132

Perf. 13x13½
1957, Sept. 16 **Wmk. 315**
405 A132 10m deep violet .80 .25
75th anniversary of Arabi Revolution.

Hafez Ibrahim — A133

Portrait: No. 407, Ahmed Shawky.

1957, Oct. 14 **Perf. 13½x13**
406 A133 10m dull red brn .30 .25
407 A133 10m olive green .30 .25
a. Pair, #406-407 1.00 1.00
25th anniv. of the deaths of Hafez Ibrahim and Ahmed Shawky, poets.

MiG and Ilyushin Planes — A134

Design: No. 409, Viscount plane.

1957, Dec. 19 **Perf. 13x13½**
408 A134 10m ultra .70 .50
409 A134 10m green .70 .50
a. Pair, #408-409 1.60 1.60
25th anniv. of the Egyptian Air Force and of Misrair, the Egyptian airline.

Pyramids, Dove and Globe — A135

1957, Dec. 26 **Photo.** **Wmk. 315**
410 A135 5m brown orange .60 .40
411 A135 10m green .60 .30
412 A135 15m brt violet .50 .40
Nos. 410-412 (3) 1.70 1.10
Afro-Asian Peoples Conf., Cairo, 12/26-1/2.

Farmer's Wife A136 — Ramses II A137

1957-58 **Wmk. 315** **Perf. 13½**
413 A136 1m blue green ('58) .30 .25
414 A137 10m violet .30 .25

"Industry" — A138

1958 **Wmk. 318**
415 A136 1m lt blue green .30 .25
416 A138 5m brown .35 .25
417 A137 10m violet .60 .25
Nos. 413-417 (5) 1.85 1.25
See Nos. 438-444, 474-488, 535. For overprints see Nos. N58-N63, N66-N68, N75, N77-N78.

Cyclists — A139

Perf. 13½x13
1958, Jan. 12 **Wmk. 315**
418 A139 10m lt red brown .65 .45
5th Intl. Bicycle Race, Egypt, Jan. 12-26.

Mustafa Kamel — A140

1958, Feb. 10 **Photo.** **Wmk. 318**
419 A140 10m blue gray .80 .25
50th anniversary of the death of Mustafa Kamel, orator and politician.

United Arab Republic

Linked Maps of Egypt and Syria — A141

Perf. 11½x11

1958, Mar. 22   **Wmk. 318**
436 A141 10m yellow & green   .75   .25

Birth of United Arab Republic. See No. C90.
See also Syria-UAR Nos. 1 and C1.

Cotton — A142

1958, Apr. 5   **Perf. 13½x13**
437 A142 10m Prussian blue   .35   .25

Intl. Fair for Egyptian Cotton, Apr., 1958.

Types of 1957-58 Inscribed "U.A.R. EGYPT" and

Princess Nofret — A143

Designs: 1m, Farmer's wife. 2m, Ibn-Tulun's Mosque. 4m, 14th century glass lamp (design lacks "1963" of A217). 5m, "Industry" (factories and cogwheel). 10m, Ramses II. 35m, "Commerce" (eagle, ship and cargo).

1958   **Perf. 13½x14**
438 A136 1m crimson .30 .30
439 A138 2m blue .25 .25
440 A143 3m dk red brown .25 .25
441 A217 4m green .30 .25
442 A138 5m brown .30 .25
443 A137 10m violet .85 .30
444 A138 35m lt ultra 3.75 .45
   Nos. 438-444 (7) 6.00 2.05

See Nos. 474-488, 532-533, N62-N68, N75-N78.

Qasim Amin — A144

1958, Apr. 23   **Perf. 13½x13**
445 A144 10m deep blue   .60   .25

50th anniversary of the death of Qasim Amin, author of "Emancipation of Women."

Doves, Broken Chain and Globe — A145

1958, June 18
446 A145 10m violet   .60   .25

5th anniv. of the republic and to publicize the struggle of peoples and individuals for freedom.
For overprint see No. N69.

Cement Industry — A146

UAR Flag A147

Industries: No. 448, Textile. No. 449, Iron & steel. No. 450, Petroleum (Oil). No. 451, Electricity and fertilizers.

Perf. 13½x13

1958, July 23   **Photo.**   **Wmk. 318**
447 A146 10m red brown .40 .25
448 A146 10m blue green .40 .25
449 A146 10m bright red .40 .25
450 A146 10m olive green .40 .25
451 A146 10m dark blue .40 .25
  a.   Strip of 5, #447-451 2.75 2.75

Souvenir Sheet
Imperf
452 A147 50m grn, dp car & blk 16.00 14.00

Revolution of July 23, 1952, 6th anniv.

Sayed Darwich — A148

1958, Sept. 15   **Perf. 13½x13**
453 A148 10m violet brown   .50   .25

35th anniv. of the death of Sayed Darwich, Arab composer.

Hand Holding Torch, Broken Chain and Flag — A149

1958, Oct. 14   **Photo.**   **Wmk. 318**
454 A149 10m carmine rose   .40   .25

Establishment of the Republic of Iraq. See Syria-UAR No. 13.

Maps and Cogwheels A150

1958, Dec. 8   **Perf. 13x13½**
455 A150 10m blue   .50   .25

Issued to publicize the Economic Conference of Afro-Asian Countries, Cairo, Dec. 8.

Ovptd. in Red in English and Arabic in 3 Lines "Industrial and Agricultural Production Fair"
1958, Dec. 9
456 A150 10m lt red brown   .50   .25

Issued to publicize the Industrial and Agricultural Production Fair, Cairo, Dec. 9.

Dr. Mahmoud Azmy and UN Emblem — A151

1958, Dec. 10
457 A151 10m dull violet .45 .25
458 A151 35m green 1.00 .75

10th anniv. of the signing of the Universal Declaration of Human Rights.
For overprints see Nos. N70-N71.

University Building, Sphinx, "Education" and God Thoth — A152

1958, Dec. 21   **Photo.**   **Wmk. 318**
459 A152 10m grnsh black   .40   .25

50th anniversary of Cairo University.

No. 337 Surcharged

1959, Jan. 20   **Wmk. 195**   **Perf. 13½**
460 A112 55m on 100m henna brn 3.00 .75

For overprint see No. N72.

Emblem — A153

1959, Feb. 2   **Perf. 13x13½**
461 A153 10m lt olive green   .35   .25

Afro-Asian Youth Conf., Cairo, Feb. 2.

See Syria UAR issues for stamps of designs A141, A149, A154, A156, A157, A162, A170, A172, A173, A179 with denominations in piasters (p).

Arms of UAR — A154

Perf. 13½x13
1959, Feb. 22   **Photo.**   **Wmk. 318**
462 A154 10m green, blk & red   .35   .25

First anniversary, United Arab Republic. See Syria UAR No. 17.

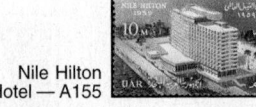

Nile Hilton Hotel — A155

1959, Feb. 22   **Perf. 13x13½**
463 A155 10m dark gray   .35   .25

Opening of the Nile Hilton Hotel, Cairo.

Globe, Radio and Telegraph A156

1959, Mar. 1
464 A156 10m violet   .40   .25

Arab Union of Telecommunications. See Syria-UAR Nos. C20-C21.

United Arab States Issue

Flags of UAR and Yemen — A157

1959, Mar. 8
465 A157 10m sl grn, car & blk   .35   .25

First anniversary of United Arab States. See Syria-UAR No. 16.

Oil Derrick and Pipe Line — A158

Perf. 13½x13
1959, Apr. 16   **Litho.**   **Wmk. 318**
466 A158 10m lt bl & dk bl   .65   .25

First Arab Petroleum Congress, Cairo.

Railroad — A159

Designs: No. 468, Bus on highway. No. 469, River barge. No. 470, Ocean liner. No. 471, Telecommunications on map. No. 472, Stamp printing building, Heliopolis. No. 472A, Ship, train, plane and motorcycle mail carrier.

1959, July 23   **Photo.**   **Perf. 13x13½**
Frame in Gray
467 A159 10m maroon 1.10 .50
468 A159 10m green 1.10 .50
469 A159 10m violet 1.10 .50
470 A159 10m dark blue 1.10 .50
471 A159 10m dull purple 1.10 .50
472 A159 10m scarlet 1.10 .50
   Nos. 467-472 (6) 6.60 3.00

Souvenir Sheet
Imperf
472A A159 50m green & red   12.00 12.00

No. 472A for the 7th anniv. of the Egyptian revolution of 1952 and was sold only with 5 sets of Nos. 467-472.

Globe, Swallows and Map — A160

1959, Aug. 8   **Perf. 13½x13**
473 A160 10m lake brn   .40   .25

Convention of the Assoc. of Arab Emigrants in the US.

Types of 1953-58 without "Egypt" and

St. Simon's Gate, Bosra, Syria — A161

Designs: 1m, Farmer's wife. 2m, Ibn-Tulun's Mosque. 3m, Princess Nofret. 4m, 14th century glass lamp (design lacks "1963" of A217). 5m, "Industry" (factories and cogwheel). 10m, Ramses II. 15m, Omayyad Mosque, Damascus. 20m, Lotus vase, Tutankhamun treasure. 35m, Eagle, ship and cargo. 40m, Scribe statue. 45m, Saladin's citadel, Aleppo. 55m, Eagle, cotton and wheat. 60m, Dam and factory. 100m, Eagle, hand, cotton and grain. 200m, Palmyra ruins, Syria. 500m, Queen Nefertiti, inscribed "UAR" (no ovpt.).

Perf. 13½x14, 14x13½
1959-60   **Wmk. 328**   **Photo.**
474 A136 1m vermilion .25 .25
475 A138 2m dp blue ('60) .25 .25
476 A143 3m maroon .25 .25
477 A217 4m green ('60) .25 .25
478 A138 5m black ('60) .25 .25
479 A137 10m dk ol grn .30 .25
480 A138 15m deep claret .30 .25
481 A138 20m crimson ('60) .90 .25
482 A161 30m brown vio .65 .25
483 A138 35m lt vio bl ('60) .75 .25
484 A143 40m sepia 1.10 .25
485 A161 45m lil gray ('60) 2.25 .35
486 A138 55m brt blue grn 2.00 .25
487 A138 60m dp purple ('60) 2.75 .25
488 A138 100m org & sl grn ('60) 2.25 .30
489 A161 200m lt blue & mar 4.50 .50

490 A112 500m dk gray & red
('60) 14.00 1.60
Nos. 474-490 (17) 33.00 6.00
See Nos. 532-535.

Shield and
Cogwheel — A162

Perf. 13½x13
1959, Oct. 20 Photo. Wmk. 328
491 A162 10m brt car rose .35 .25
Issued for Army Day, 1959.
See Syria-UAR No. 32.

Cairo
Museum — A163

1959, Nov. 18 Perf. 13x13½
492 A163 10m olive gray .40 .25
Centenary of Cairo museum.

Abu Simbel Temple of
Ramses II — A164

1959, Dec. 22 Perf. 11x11½
493 A164 10m lt red brn, *pnksh* .70 .30
Issued as propaganda to save historic monuments in Nubia threatened by the construction of Aswan High Dam.

Postrider, 12th
Century — A165

1960, Jan. 2 Perf. 13x13½
494 A165 10m dark blue .35 .25
Issued for Post Day, Jan. 2.

Hydroelectric
Power Station,
Aswan
Dam — A166

1960, Jan. 9
495 A166 10m violet blk .35 .25
Inauguration of the Aswan Dam hydroelectric power station, Jan. 9.

A167

10m, Arabic and English Description of Aswan High Dam. 35m, Architect's Drawing of Aswan High Dam.

1960, Jan. 9 Perf. 11x11½
496   10m claret .75 .60
497   35m claret 1.10 .75
a. A167 Pair, #496-497 2.00 2.00

Start of work on the Aswan High Dam.

Symbols of Agriculture
and Industry — A169

1960, Jan. 16 Perf. 13½x13
498 A169 10m gray grn & sl grn .35 .25
Industrial and Agricultural Fair, Cairo.

Arms and Flag — A170

1960, Feb. 22 Photo. Wmk. 328
499 A170 10m green, blk & red .35 .25
2nd anniversary of the proclamation of the United Arab Republic.
See Syria-UAR No. 38.

No. 340 Overprinted in
Red

1960 Wmk. 195 Perf. 13½
500 A112 £1 dk grn, blk & red 19.00 4.25

"Art" — A171

Perf. 13½x13
1960, Mar. 1 Wmk. 328
501 A171 10m brown .35 .25
Issued to publicize the 3rd Biennial Exhibition of Fine Arts in Alexandria.

Arab League
Center,
Cairo — A172

1960, Mar. 22 Photo. Perf. 13x13½
502 A172 10m dull grn & blk .35 .25
Opening of Arab League Center and Arab Postal Museum, Cairo.
See Syria-UAR No. 40.

Refugees
Pointing to Map
of
Palestine — A173

1960, Apr. 7
503 A173 10m orange ver .55 .30
504 A173 35m Prus blue .80 .65
World Refugee Year, 7/1/59-6/30/60.
See Nos. N73-N74. See also Syria-UAR Nos. 43-44.

Weight Lifter — A174

Stadium, Cairo — A175

Sports: No. 506, Basketball. No. 507, Soccer. No. 508, Fencing. No. 509, Rowing. 30m, Steeplechase, horiz. 35m, Swimming, horiz.

Perf. 13½x13
1960, July 23 Photo. Wmk. 328
505 A174 5m gray .60 .30
506 A174 5m brown .60 .30
507 A174 5m dp claret .60 .30
508 A174 10m brt carmine .60 .30
509 A174 10m gray green .60 .30
a. Vert. or horiz. strip, #505-509 3.75
510 A174 30m purple .85 .50
511 A174 35m dark blue 1.10 .60
Nos. 505-511 (7) 4.95 2.60
Souvenir Sheet
Imperf
512 A175 100m car & brown 3.25 3.25
Nos. 505-511 for the 17th Olympic Games, Rome, Aug. 25-Sept. 11.

Dove and UN
Emblem — A176

35m, Lights surrounding UN emblem, horiz.

Perf. 13½x13
1960, Oct. 24 Wmk. 328
513 A176 10m purple .25 .25
514 A176 35m brt rose .50 .30
15th anniversary of United Nations.

Abu
Simbel
Temple
of Queen
Nefertari
A177

Perf. 11x11½
1960, Nov. 14 Photo. Wmk. 328
515 A177 10m ocher, *buff* .80 .50
Issued as propaganda to save historic monuments in Nubia and in connection with the UNESCO meeting, Paris, Nov. 14.

Model Post
Office — A178

1961, Jan. 2 Perf. 13x13½
516 A178 10m brt car rose .40 .25
Issued for Post Day, Jan. 2.

Eagle, Fasces and
Victory Wreath — A179

1961, Feb. 22 Perf. 13½x13
517 A179 10m dull violet .35 .25
3rd anniversary of United Arab Republic.
See Syria-UAR No. 50.

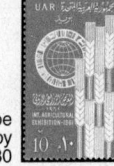

Wheat and Globe
Surrounded by
Flags — A180

1961, Mar. 21 Wmk. 328
518 A180 10m vermilion .35 .25
Intl. Agricultural Exhib., Cairo, 3/21-4/20.

Patrice Lumumba and
Map — A181

1961, Mar. 30 Perf. 13½x13
519 A181 10m black .35 .25
Africa Day, Apr. 15 and 3rd Conf. of Independent African States, Cairo, Mar. 25-31.

Reading Braille and
WHO Emblem — A182

1961, Apr. 6 Photo.
520 A182 10m red brown .35 .25
WHO Day. See Nos. B21, N80.

Tower of Cairo — A183

1961, Apr. 11 Perf. 13½x13
521 A183 10m grnsh blue .35 .25
Opening of the 600-foot Tower of Cairo, on island of Gizireh. See No. C95.

Arab Woman and Son,
Palestine Map — A184

1961, May 15 Wmk. 328
522 A184 10m brt green .45 .30
Issued for Palestine Day.
See No. N79.

Symbols of
Industry and
Electricity
A185

Chart and Workers — A186

No. 524, New buildings and family. No. 525, Ship, train, bus and radio. No. 526, Dam, cotton and field. No. 527, Hand holding candle and family.

1961, July 23   Photo.   Perf. 13x13½
523 A185 10m dp carmine   .65   .30
524 A185 10m brt blue   .65   .30
525 A185 10m dk vio brown   .65   .30
526 A185 35m dk green   .85   .40
527 A185 35m brt purple   .85   .40
    Nos. 523-527 (5)   3.65 1.70

Souvenir Sheet
Imperf
528 A186 100m red brown   4.00 3.75
    9th anniv. of the revolution.

Map of Suez Canal and Ships — A187

Perf. 11½x11
1961, July 26   Unwmk.
529 A187 10m olive   .50   .30
    Suez Canal Co. nationalization, 5th anniv.

Various Enterprises of Misr Bank — A188

Perf. 13x13½
1961, Aug. 22   Wmk. 328
530 A188 10m red brn, *pnksh*   .35   .25
    The 41st anniversary of Misr Bank.

Flag, Ship's Wheel and Battleship — A189

1961, Aug. 29   Photo.   Perf. 13½x13
531 A189 10m deep blue   .45   .25
    Issued for Navy Day.

Type A136 Redrawn, Type A138, Type A217 and

Eagle of Saladin over Cairo — A190

Designs: 1m, Farmer's wife. 4m, 14th cent. glass lamp. 35m, "Commerce."

1961, Aug. 31   Unwmk.   Perf. 11½
532 A136 1m blue   .25   .25
533 A217 4m olive   .25   .25
534 A190 10m purple   .40   .25
535 A138 35m slate blue   .70   .25
    Nos. 532-535 (4)   1.60 1.00

Smaller of two Arabic inscriptions in new positions: 1m, at right above Egyptian numeral; 4m, upward to spot beside waist of lamp; 35m, upper left corner below "UAR." On 4m, "UAR" is 2mm deep instead of 1mm. "Egypt" omitted as in 1959-60.

UN Emblem, Book, Cogwheel, Corn — A191

Design: 35m, Globe and cogwheel, horiz.

Perf. 13½x13
1961, Oct. 24   Photo.   Wmk. 328
536 A191 10m black & ocher   .30   .25
537 A191 35m blue grn & brn   .65   .35
    UN Technical Assistance Program and 16th anniv. of the UN.
    See Nos. N81-N82.

Trajan's Kiosk, Philae A192

1961, Nov. 4   Unwmk.   Perf. 11½
    Size: 60x27mm
538 A192 10m dp vio blue   .85   .40
    15th anniv. of UNESCO, and to publicize UNESCO's help in safeguarding the monuments of Nubia.

Palette, Brushes, Map of Mediterranean — A193

1961, Dec. 14   Wmk. 328   Perf. 13½
539 A193 10m dk red brown   .35   .25
    Issued to publicize the 4th Biennial Exhibition of Fine Arts in Alexandria.

Atom and Educational Symbols — A194

1961, Dec. 18
540 A194 10m dull purple   .35   .25
    Issued to publicize Education Day.
    See No. N83.

Arms of UAR — A195

1961, Dec. 23   Unwmk.   Perf. 11½
541 A195 10m brt pink, brt grn & blk   .35   .25
    Victory Day. See No. N84.

Sphinx at Giza — A196

1961, Dec. 27   Perf. 11x11½
542 A196 10m black   .55   .35
    Issued to publicize the "Sound and Light" Project, the installation of floodlights and sound equipment at the site of the Pyramids and Sphinx.

Post Office Printing Plant, Nasser City — A197

1962, Jan. 2   Photo.   Perf. 11½x11
543 A197 10m dk brown   .40   .25
    Issued for Post Day, Jan. 2.

Map of Africa, King Mohammed V of Morocco and Flags — A198

1962, Jan. 4   Perf. 11x11½
544 A198 10m indigo   .35   .25
    African Charter, Casablanca, 1st anniv.

Girl Scout Saluting and Emblem — A199

Perf. 13x13½
1962, Feb. 22   Wmk. 328
545 A199 10m bright blue   .95   .30
    Egyptian Girl Scouts' 25th anniversary.

Arab Refugees, Flag and Map — A200

1962, Mar. 7   Perf. 13½x13
546 A200 10m dark slate green   .40   .25
5th anniv. of the liberation of the Gaza Strip. See No. N85.

Mother and Child — A201

1962, Mar. 21   Photo.
547 A201 10m dk violet brn   .40   .25
    Issued for Arab Mother's Day, Mar. 21.

Map of Africa and Post Horn — A202

1962, Apr. 23   Wmk. 328
548 A202 10m crimson & ocher   .40   .30
549 A202 50m dp blue & ocher   .80   .55
    Establishment of African Postal Union.

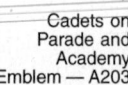

Cadets on Parade and Academy Emblem — A203

1962, June 18   Perf. 13x13½
550 A203 10m green   .35   .25
    Egyptian Military Academy, 150th anniv.

Malaria Eradication Emblem — A204

1962, June 20   Perf. 13½x13
551 A204 10m dk brown & red   .25   .25
552 A204 35m dk green & blue   .70   .50
    WHO drive to eradicate malaria.
    See Nos. N87-N88.

Theodor Bilharz — A205

1962, June 24   Perf. 11x11½
553 A205 10m brown orange   .55   .25
    Dr. Theodor Bilharz (1825-1862), German physician who first described bilharziasis, an endemic disease in Egypt.

Patrice Lumumba and Map of Africa — A206

1962, July 1   Photo.   Wmk. 342
554 A206 10m rose & red   .35   .25
    Issued in memory of Patrice Lumumba (1925-61), Premier of Congo.

Hand on Charter — A207

1962, July 10   Perf. 11x11½
555 A207 10m brt blue & dk brn .35   .25
    Proclamation of the National Charter.

"Birth of the Revolution" A208

Symbolic Designs: No. 557, Proclamation (Scroll and book). No. 558, Agricultural Reform (Farm and crescent). No. 559, Bandung Conference (Dove, globe and olive branch). No. 560, Birth of UAR (Eagle and flag). No. 561, Industrialization (cogwheel, factory, ship and bus). No. 562, Aswan High Dam. No. 563, Social Revolution (Modern buildings and emblem). 100m, Arms of UAR, emblems of Afro-Asian and African countries and UN.

1962, July 23   Perf. 11½
556 A208 10m brn, dk red brn & pink   .40   .30
557 A208 10m dk blue & sepia   .40   .30
558 A208 10m sepia & brt bl   .40   .30
559 A208 10m olive & dk ultra   .40   .30
560 A208 10m grn, blk & red   .40   .30
561 A208 10m brn org & indigo   .40   .30
562 A208 10m brn org & vio blk .40   .30
563 A208 10m orange & blk   .40   .30
    Nos. 556-563 (8)   3.20 2.40

Souvenir Sheets
Perf. 11½
564 A208 100m grn, pink, red & blk   2.75 2.50
    10th anniv. of the revolution.

No. 564 exists imperf. Same value.

Mahmoud Moukhtar, Museum and Sculpture A209

1962, July 24   **Perf. 11½x11**
565 A209 10m lt vio bl & olive   .40   .25
   Opening of the Moukhtar Museum, Island of Gezireh. The sculpture is "La Vestale de Secrets" by Moukhtar.

Flag of Algeria and Map of Africa Showing Algeria — A210

1962, Aug. 15   **Perf. 11x11½**
566 A210 10m multicolored   .35   .25
   Algeria's independence, July 1, 1962.

Rocket, Arms of UAR and Atom Symbol — A211

1962, Sept. 1   Photo.   Wmk. 342
567 A211 10m brt grn, red & blk   .45   .25
   Launching of UAR rockets.

Rifle and Target A212

Map of Africa, Table Tennis Paddle, Net and Ball A213

1962, Sept. 18   **Perf. 11½**
568 A212 5m green, blk & red   .55   .45
569 A213 5m green, blk & red   .55   .45
   a. Pair, #568-569   1.25 1.25
570 A212 10m bister, bl & dk grn   .65   .55
571 A213 10m bister, bl & dk grn   .65   .55
   a. Pair, #570-571   1.50 1.50
572 A212 35m dp ultra, red & blk   1.50 1.50
573 A213 35m dp ultra, red & blk   1.50 1.50
   a. Pair, #572-573   3.25 3.25
      Nos. 568-573 (6)   5.40 5.00
   38th World Shooting Championships and the 1st African Table Tennis Tournament. Types A212 and A213 are printed se-tenant at the base.

Dag Hammarskjold and UN Emblem — A214

Perf. 11½x11
1962, Oct. 24   Photo.   Wmk. 342
Portrait in Slate Blue
574 A214 5m deep lilac   .65   .25
575 A214 10m olive   .75   .25
576 A214 35m deep ultra   1.10 .50
      Nos. 574-576 (3)   2.50 1.00
   Dag Hammarskjold, Secretary General of the UN, 1953-61, and 17th anniv. of the UN.
See Nos. N89-N91.

Queen Nefertari Crowned by Isis and Hathor — A215

1962, Oct. 31   **Perf. 11½**
577 A215 10m blue & ocher   1.25   .40
   Issued to publicize the UNESCO campaign to safeguard the monuments of Nubia.

Jet Trainer, Hawker Hart Biplane and College Emblem — A216

1962, Nov. 2   **Perf. 11½x11**
578 A216 10m bl, dk bl & crim   .40   .25
   25th anniversary of Air Force College.

14th Century Glass Lamp and "1963" — A217

1963, Feb. 20   **Perf. 11x11½**
579 A217 4m dk brn, grn & car   .35   .25
   Issued for use on greeting cards.
See Nos. 441, 477, 533, N76, N92. For overprint see No. N65.

Yemen Flag and Hand with Torch — A218

1963, Mar. 14   Photo.   Wmk. 342
580 A218 10m olive & brt car   .45   .25
   Establishment of Yemen Arab Republic.

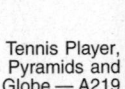

Tennis Player, Pyramids and Globe — A219

Perf. 11½x11
1963, Mar. 20   **Unwmk.**
581 A219 10m gray, blk & brn   .75   .30
   Intl. Lawn Tennis Championships, Cairo.

Cow, UN and FAO Emblems A220

Designs: 10m, Corn, wheat and emblems, vert. 35m, Wheat, corn and emblems.

Perf. 11½x11, 11x11½
1963, Mar. 21   **Wmk. 342**
582 A220 5m violet & dp org   .45   .30
583 A220 10m ultra & yel   .55   .30
584 A220 35m blue, yel & blk   .75   .75
      Nos. 582-584 (3)   1.75 1.35
   FAO "Freedom from Hunger" campaign.
See Nos. N93-N95.

Centenary Emblem — A221

Design: 35m, Globe and emblem.

1963, May 8   Unwmk.   Perf. 11x11½
585 A221 10m lt blue, red & mar   .30   .25
586 A221 35m lt blue & red   .85   .85
   Centenary of the Red Cross.
See Nos. N96-N97.

Arab Socialist Union Emblem — A222

50m, Tools, torch & symbol of National Charter.

Wmk. 342
1963, July 23   Photo.   Perf. 11½
587 A222 10m slate & rose pink   .35   .25
Souvenir Sheets
Perf. 11½
588 A222 50m vio bl & org yel   2.25 2.25
   11th anniv. of the revolution and to publicize the Arab Socialist Union.
No. 588 exists imperf. Same value.

Television Station, Cairo, and Screen — A223

1963, Aug. 1   **Perf. 11½x11**
589 A223 10m dk blue & yel   .35   .25
   2nd Intl. Television Festival, Alexandria, 9/1-10.

Queen Nefertari — A224

Designs: 10m, Great Hypostyle Hall, Abu Simbel. 35m, Ramses in moonlight.

Size: 25x42mm (5m, 35m); 28x61mm (10m)
Wmk. 342
1963, Oct. 1   Photo.   Perf. 11
590 A224 5m brt vio blue & yel   .65   .40
591 A224 10m gray, blk & red org   .75   .45
592 A224 35m org yel & blk   1.60 .85
      Nos. 590-592 (3)   3.00 1.70
   UNESCO world campaign to save historic monuments in Nubia.
See Nos. N98-N100.

Swimmer and Map of Suez Canal — A225

1963, Oct. 15
593 A225 10m blue & sal rose   .35   .25
   Intl. Suez Canal Swimming Championship.

Ministry of Agriculture A226

Perf. 11½x11
1963, Nov. 20   **Wmk. 342**
594 A226 10m multicolored   .35   .25
   50th anniv. of the Ministry of Agriculture.

Modern Building and Map of Africa and Asia — A227

1963, Dec. 7
595 A227 10m multicolored   .35   .25
   Afro-Asian Housing Congress, Dec. 7-12.

Scales, Globe, UN Emblem — A228

1963, Dec. 10
596 A228 5m dk green & yel   .30   .25
597 A228 10m blue, gray & blk   .35   .25
598 A228 35m rose red, pink & red   .85   .45
      Nos. 596-598 (3)   1.50 .95
   15th anniv. of the Universal Declaration of Human Rights.
See Nos. N101-N103.

Sculpture, Arms of Alexandria and Palette with Flags — A229

1963, Dec. 12   **Perf. 11x11½**
599 A229 10m pale bl, dk bl & brn   .35   .25
   Issued to publicize the 5th Biennial Exhibition of Fine Arts in Alexandria.

Lion and Nile Hilton Hotel A230

Vase, 13th Century A231

Pharaoh Userkaf (5th Dynasty) — A232

Designs: 1m, Long Necked Mamluke glass bottle, 14th century. 2m, Ivory headrest. 3m, Pharaonic calcite boat. 4m, Minaret and gate. 5m, Nile and Aswan High Dam. 10m, Eagle of Saladin over pyramids. 15m, Window, Ibn Tulun's mosque. No. 608, Mitwalli Gate, Cairo. 35m, Nefertari. 40m, Tower Hotel. 55m, Sultan Hassan's Mosque. 60m, Courtyard, Al Azhar University. 200m, Head of Ramses II. 500m, Funerary mask of Tutankhamun.

1964-67   Unwmk.   Photo.   Perf. 11
Size: Nos. 608, 612, 19x24mm; others, 24x29mm

600 A231 1m citron & ultra   .25   .25
601 A231 2m magenta & bis   .25   .25
602 A230 3m sal, org & bl   .25   .25
603 A235 4m och, blk & ultra   .35   .25
604 A231 5m brn & brt blue   .25   .25
   a. 5m brown & dark blue   .50   .25
605 A231 10m green, dk brn & lt brn .30   .25
606 A230 15m ultra & yel   .30   .25
607 A231 20m brn org & blk   .90   .25
608 A231 20m lt olive grn ('67)   1.60 .25
609 A231 30m yellow & brown   .75   .25

610	A231	35m sal, och & ultra	.90	.25
611	A231	40m ultra & yellow	1.75	.40
612	A231	55m brt red lil ('67)	2.00	.25
613	A231	60m grnsh bl & yel brn	1.25	.55

Wmk. 342

614	A232	100m dk vio brn & sl	3.50	.85
615	A232	200m bluish blk & yel brn	8.00	1.00
616	A232	500m ultra & dp org	17.50	3.25
		Nos. 600-616 (17)	40.10	9.05

Nos. 603 & N107 lack the vertically arranged dates which appear at lower right on No. 619.
See Nos. N104-N116.

HSN Commission Emblem — A233

Perf. 11x11½

1964, Jan. 10　　Wmk. 342
617 A233 10m dull bl, dk bl & yel　.35　.25

1st conf. of the Commission of Health, Sanitation and Nutrition.

Arab League Emblem A234

1964, Jan. 13　　Perf. 11
618 A234 10m brt green & blk　.35　.25

1st meeting of the Heads of State of the Arab League, Cairo, January.
See No. N117.

Minaret at Night — A235

1964　　Unwmk.　　Perf. 11
619 A235 4m emerald, blk & red　.35　.25

Issued for use on greeting cards.
See Nos. 603, N107, N118.

Old and New Dwellings and Map of Nubia — A236

Perf. 11½x11

1964, Feb. 27　　Photo.　　Wmk. 342
620 A236 10m dull vio & yel　.35　.25

Resettlement of Nubian population.

Map of Africa and Asia and Train — A237

1964, Mar. 21
621 A237 10m dull bl, dk bl & yel　.90　.50

Asian Railway Conference, Cairo, Mar. 21.

Ikhnaton and Nefertiti with Children — A238

1964, Mar. 21　　Perf. 11x11½
622 A238 10m dk brown & ultra　.90　.30

Issued for Arab Mother's Day, Mar. 21.

APU Emblem — A239

1964, Apr. 1　　Photo.　　Wmk. 342
623 A239 10m org brn & bl, sal　.35　.25

Permanent Office of the APU, 10th anniv.
See No. N119.

WHO Emblem — A240

1964, Apr. 7
624 A240 10m dk blue & red　.35　.25

World Health Day (Anti-Tuberculosis).
See No. N120.

Statue of Liberty, World's Fair Pavilion and Pyramids A241

1964, Apr. 22　　Perf. 11½x11
625 A241 10m brt green & ol, grysh　.35　.25

New York World's Fair, 1964-65.

Nile and Aswan High Dam — A242

1964, May 15　　Unwmk.　　Perf. 11½
626 A242 10m black & blue　.35　.25

The diversion of the Nile.

"Land Reclamation" A243

A423a

Design: No. 628, "Electricity," Aswan High Dam hydroelectric station. No. 628A, Aswan High Dam before and after diversion of the Nile.

1964, July 23　　Perf. 11½
627 A243 10m yellow & emer　.35　.25
628 A243 10m green & blk　.35　.25

Souvenir Sheet
Imperf
628A A243a 50m blue & black　2.00 2.00

Land reclamation and hydroelectric power due to the Aswan High Dam.

Map of Africa and 34 Flags A244

1964, July 17　　Photo.
629 A244 10m brn, brt bl & blk　.40　.25

Assembly of Heads of State and Government of the Organization for African Unity at Cairo in July.

Jamboree Emblem A245

Design: No. 631, Emblem of Air Scouts.

1964, Aug. 28　　Unwmk.　　Perf. 11½
630 A245 10m red, grn & blk　.60　.40
631 A245 10m green & red　.60　.40
a.　Pair, #630-631　2.50 2.50

The 6th Pan Arab Jamboree, Alexandria.

Flag of Algeria — A246

1964, Sept. 5　　Perf. 11½x11
Flags in Original Colors

632	A246	10m Algeria	.75	.40
633	A246	10m Iraq	.75	.40
634	A246	10m Jordan	.75	.40
635	A246	10m Kuwait	.75	.40
636	A246	10m Lebanon	.75	.40
637	A246	10m Libya	.75	.40
638	A246	10m Morocco	.75	.40
639	A246	10m Saudi Arabia	.75	.40
640	A246	10m Sudan	.75	.40
641	A246	10m Syria	.75	.40
642	A246	10m Tunisia	.75	.40
643	A246	10m UAR	.75	.40
644	A246	10m Yemen	.75	.40
		Nos. 632-644 (13)	9.75	5.20

2nd meeting of the Heads of State of the Arab League, Alexandria, Sept. 1964.

World Map, Dove, Olive Branches and Pyramids A247

1964, Oct. 5　　Perf. 11½
645 A247 10m slate blue & yel　.35　.25

Conference of Heads of State of Non-Aligned Countries, Cairo, Oct. 1964.

Pharaonic Athletes — A248

Designs from ancient decorations: 10m, Four athletes, vert. 35m, Wrestlers, vert. 50m, Pharaoh in chariot hunting.

Perf. 11½x11, 11x11½
1964, Oct. 10　　Photo.　　Unwmk.
Sizes: 39x22mm, 22x39mm

646	A248	5m lt green & org	.40	.25
647	A248	10m slate bl & lt brn	.45	.25
648	A248	35m dull vio & lt brn	1.10	.75

Size: 58x24mm

649	A248	50m ultra & brn org	1.75	1.00
		Nos. 646-649 (4)	3.70	2.25

18th Olympic Games Tokyo, Oct. 10-25.

Emblem, Map of Africa and Asia — A249

1964, Oct. 10　　Perf. 11x11½
650 A249 10m violet & yellow　.35　.25

First Afro-Asian Medical Congress.

Map of Africa, Communication Symbols — A250

1964, Oct. 24
651 A250 10m green & dp sepia　.35　.25

Pan-African and Malagasy Posts and Telecommunications Cong., Cairo, Oct. 24-Nov. 6.

Horus and Facade of Nefertari Temple, Abu Simbel — A251

Ramses II — A252

Designs: 35m, A god holding rope of life, Abu Simbel. 50m, Isis of Kalabsha, horiz.

1964, Oct. 24　　Perf. 11½, 11x11½

652	A251	5m grnsh bl & yel brn	.70	.35
653	A252	10m sepia & brt yel	1.10	.40
654	A251	35m brown org & indigo	2.50	1.25
		Nos. 652-654 (3)	4.30	2.00

Souvenir Sheet
Imperf
655 A252 50m olive & vio blk　15.00 15.00

"Save the Monuments of Nubia" campaign.
No. 655 contains one horiz. stamp.

Emblems of Cooperation, Rural Handicraft and Women's Work — A253

Perf. 11½x11
1964, Dec. 8　　Photo.　　Unwmk.
656 A253 10m yellow & dk blue　.35　.25

25th anniv. of the Ministry of Social Affairs.

UN, UNESCO Emblems, Pyramids — A254

1964, Dec. 24　　Perf. 11x11½
657 A254 10m ultra & yellow　.35　.25

Issued for UNESCO Day.

Minaret, Mardani Mosque — A255

1965, Jan. 20   Photo.   Perf. 11
658 A255 4m blue & dk brown   .35   .25

Issued for use on greeting cards. See No. N121.

Police Emblem over City — A256

Perf. 11x11½
1965, Jan. 25   Wmk. 342
659 A256 10m dp sepia & yellow   .85   .40

Issued for Police Day.

Oil Derrick and Emblem — A257

1965, Mar. 16   Photo.
660 A257 10m dk brown & yellow   .45   .25

5th Arab Petroleum Congress and the 2nd Arab Petroleum Exhibition.

Flags and Emblem of the Arab League — A258

Design: 20m, Arab League emblem, horiz.

1965, Mar. 22   Wmk. 342
661 A258 10m green, red & blk   .80   .40
662 A258 20m ultra & brown   1.00   .55

20th anniversary of the Arab League. See Nos. N122-N123.

Red Crescent and WHO Emblem — A259

1965, Apr. 7   Photo.
663 A259 10m blue & crimson   .55   .35

World Health Day (Smallpox: Constant Alert). See No. N124.

Dagger in Map of Palestine — A260

1965, Apr. 9   Perf. 11x11½
664 A260 10m black & red   1.50   .35

Deir Yassin massacre, Apr. 9, 1948. See No. N125.

ITU Emblem, Old and New Communication Equipment A261

1965, May 17   Perf. 11½x11
665 A261 5m violet blk & yel   .40   .30
666 A261 10m red & yellow   .65   .30
667 A261 35m dk blue, ultra & yel   1.75   .80
Nos. 665-667 (3)   2.80   1.40

Cent. of the ITU. See Nos. N126-N128.

Library Aflame and Lamp — A262

1965, June 7   Photo.   Wmk. 342
668 A262 10m black, grn & red   .60   .25

Burning of the Library of Algiers, 6/7/62.

Sheik Mohammed Abdo (1850-1905), Mufti of Egypt — A263

1965, July 11   Perf. 11x11½
669 A263 10m Prus blue & bis brn   .35   .25

Pouring Ladle (Heavy Industry) — A264

President Gamal Abdel Nasser and Emblems of Arab League, African Unity Organization, Afro-Asian Countries and UN — A265

No. 670, Search for off-shore oil. No. 672, Housing, construction in Nasser City (diamond shaped).

1965, July 23   Perf. 11½
670 A264 10m indigo & lt blue   .85   .50
671 A264 10m brown & yellow   .85   .50
672 A264 10m yel brn & blk   .85   .50
673 A265 100m lt green & blk   5.75   3.25
Nos. 670-673 (4)   8.30   4.75

13th anniversary of the revolution. The 100m was printed in sheets of six, consisting of two singles and two vertical pairs. Margins and gutters contain multiple UAR coat of arms in light green. Size: 240x330mm.

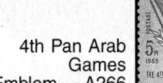

4th Pan Arab Games Emblem — A266

Map and Emblems of Previous Games A267

No. 675, Swimmers Zeitun & Abd el Gelil, arms of Alexandria. 35m, Race horse "Saadoon."

Perf. 11½x11; 11½ (#676)
1965, Sept. 2   Photo.   Wmk. 342
674 A266 5m blue & red   .40   .40
675 A266 10m dp blue & dk brn   .65   .30
676 A267 10m org brn & dp bl   .80   .45
677 A266 35m green & brown   1.40   1.00
Nos. 674-677 (4)   3.25   2.15

4th Pan Arab Games, Cairo, Sept. 2-11. No. 675 for the long-distance swimming competition at Alexandria, a part of the Games.

Map of Arab Countries, Emblem of Arab League and Broken Chain — A268

1965, Sept. 13   Photo.   Perf. 11½
678 A268 10m brown & yellow   .40   .25

3rd Arab Summit Conf., Casablanca, 9/13.

Land Forces Emblem and Sun — A269

Perf. 11x11½
1965, Oct. 20   Wmk. 342
679 A269 10m bister brn & blk   .65   .30

Issued for Land Forces Day.

Map of Africa, Torch and Olive Branches A270

1965, Oct. 21   Perf. 11½
680 A270 10m dull pur & car rose   .40   .25

Assembly of Heads of State of the Organization for African Unity.

Ramses II, Abu Simbel, and ICY Emblem A271

Pillars, Philae, and UN Emblem A272

Designs: 35m, Two Ramses II statues, Abu Simbel and UNESCO emblem. 50m, Cartouche of Ramses II and ICY emblem, horiz.

Wmk. 342
1965, Oct. 24   Photo.   Perf. 11½
681 A271 5m yellow & slate grn   1.00   .50
682 A272 10m blue & black   2.00   .50
683 A271 35m dk violet & yel   3.75   2.00
Nos. 681-683 (3)   6.75   3.00

Souvenir Sheet
Imperf
684 A272 50m brt ultra & dk brn   5.00   4.00

Intl. cooperation in saving the Nubian monuments. No. 684 also for the 20th anniv. of the UN. No. 684 contains one 42x25mm stamp.

Al-Maqrizi, Buildings and Books — A273

Perf. 11½x11
1965, Nov. 20   Photo.   Wmk. 342
685 A273 10m olive & dk slate grn   .40   .25

Ahmed Al-Maqrizi (1365-1442), historian.

Flag of UAR, Arms of Alexandria and Art Symbols — A274

1965, Dec. 16   Perf. 11x11½
686 A274 10m multicolored   .40   .25

6th Biennial Exhibition of Fine Arts in Alexandria, Dec. 16, 1965-Mar. 31, 1966.

Parchment Letter, Carrier Pigeon and Postrider — A275

1966, Jan. 2   Wmk. 342   Perf. 11½
687 A275 10m multicolored   .80   .25
Nos. 687,CB1-CB2 (3)   8.30   6.50

Post Day, Jan. 2.

Lamp and Arch — A276

1966, Jan. 10   Unwmk.   Perf. 11
688 A276 4m violet & dp org   .40   .25

Issued for use on greeting cards.

Exhibition Poster — A277

Perf. 11x11½
1966, Jan. 27   Wmk. 342
689 A277 10m lt blue & blk   .40   .25

Industrial Exhibition, Jan. 29-Feb.

Arab League
Emblem — A278

1966, Mar. 22   Photo.   Wmk. 342
690 A278 10m brt yellow & pur   .40   .25
Arab Publicity Week, Mar. 22-28.

Printed Page and
Torch — A279

1966, Mar. 25   Perf. 11x11½
691 A279 10m dp orange & sl
      blue   .40   .25
Centenary of the national press.

Traffic Signal at
Night — A280

1966, May 4   Photo.   Wmk. 342
692 A280 10m green & red   .85   .25
Issued for Traffic Day.

Hands Holding Torch,
Flags of UAR &
Iraq — A281

1966, May 26   Perf. 11x11½
693 A281 10m dp claret, rose red
      & brt grn   .40   .25
Friendship between UAR and Iraq.

Workers and UN
Emblem — A282

Perf. 11½x11
1966, June 1   Wmk. 342
694 A282 5m blue grn & blk   .35   .25
695 A282 10m brt rose lil & grn   .40   .25
696 A282 35m orange & black   1.25   .85
      Nos. 694-696 (3)   2.00   1.35
50th session of the ILO.

Mobilization Dept.
Emblem, People and
City — A283

1966, June 30   Perf. 11x11½
697 A283 10m dull pur & brn   .35   .25
Population sample, May 31-June 16.

"Salah el Din,"
Crane and
Cogwheel
A284

Present-day Basket Dance and
Pharaonic Dance — A285

No. 699, Transfer of first stones of Abu
Simbel. No. 700, Development of Sinai (map
of Red Sea area and Sinai Peninsula). No.
701, El Maadi Hospital and nurse with patient.

Wmk. 342
1966, July 23   Photo.   Perf. 11½
698 A284 10m orange & multi   .65   .30
699 A284 10m brt green & multi   .65   .30
700 A284 10m yellow & multi   .65   .30
701 A284 10m lt blue & multi   .65   .30
      Nos. 698-701 (4)   2.60   1.20

Souvenir Sheet
Imperf
702 A285 100m multicolored   5.00   3.75
14th anniv. of the revolution.

Suez Canal Headquarters, Ships and
Map of Canal — A286

1966, July 26   Perf. 11½
703 A286 10m blue & crimson   1.10   .50
Suez Canal nationalization, 10th anniv.

Cotton, Farmers
with Plow and
Tractor — A287

Perf. 11½x11
1966, Sept. 9   Photo.   Wmk. 342
704 A287 5m shown   .35   .25
705 A287 10m Rice   .35   .25
706 A287 35m Onions   1.10   .90
      Nos. 704-706 (3)   1.80   1.40
Issued for Farmer's Day.

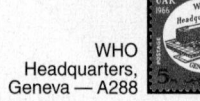

WHO
Headquarters,
Geneva — A288

Designs: 10m, UN refugee emblem. 35m,
UNICEF emblem.

Perf. 11½x11
1966, Oct. 24   Wmk. 342
707 A288 5m olive & brt pur   .40   .25
708 A288 10m orange & brt pur   .40   .25
709 A288 35m lt blue & brt pur   .90   .80
      Nos. 707-709 (3)   1.70   1.30
21st anniversary of the United Nations.
See Nos. N129-N131.

World Map and
Festival
Emblem — A289

1966, Nov. 8   Photo.
710 A289 10m brt purple & yellow   .55   .25
5th Intl. Television Festival, Nov. 1-10.

Arms of UAR,
Rocket and
Pylon — A290

1966, Dec. 23   Wmk. 342   Perf. 11½
711 A290 10m brt grn & car rose   .55   .25
Issued for Victory Day.
See No. N132.

Jackal — A291

35m, Alabaster head from Tutankhamun
treasure.

1967, Jan. 2   Photo.
712 A291 10m slate, yel & brn   1.50   .35
713 A291 35m bl, dk vio & ocher   2.75   .70
Issued for Post Day, Jan. 2.

Carnations — A292

1967, Jan. 10   Unwmk.   Perf. 11
714 A292 4m citron & purple   .50   .25
Issued for use on greeting cards.

Workers Planting
Tree — A293

Perf. 11x11½
1967, Mar. 15   Wmk. 342
715 A293 10m brt green & blk vio   .40   .25
Issued to publicize the Tree Festival.

Gamal el-Dine el-
Afaghani and Arab
League Emblem — A294

1967, Mar. 22   Photo.   Wmk. 342
716 A294 10m dp green & dk brn   .40   .25
Arab Publicity Week, Mar. 22-28.
See No. N133.

Census Emblem,
Man, Woman
and
Factory — A295

1967, Apr. 23   Perf. 11½x11
717 A295 10m black & dp org   .40   .25
First industrial census.

Brickmaking Fresco, Tomb of
Rekhmire, Thebes, 1504-1450
B.C. — A296

1967, May 1   Photo.   Wmk. 342
718 A296 10m olive & orange   .55   .30
Issued for Labor Day, 1967.
See No. N134.

Ramses
II and
Queen
Nefertari
A297

Design: 35m, Shooting geese, frieze from
tomb of Atet at Meidum, c. 2724 B. C.

Perf. 11½x11
1967, June 7   Photo.   Wmk. 342
719 A297 10m multicolored   1.00   .50
720 A297 35m dk green & org   4.25   1.40
      Nos. 719-720,C113-C115 (5)   13.60   6.15
Issued for International Tourist Year, 1967.

President Nasser,
Crowd and Map
of
Palestine — A298

1967, June 22   Perf. 11½
721 A298 10m dp org, yel & ol   2.75   1.50
Issued to publicize Arab solidarity for "the
defense of Palestine."

Souvenir Sheet

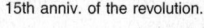

National
Products
A299

1967, July 23   Wmk. 342   Imperf.
722 A299 100m multicolored   4.00   3.50
15th anniv. of the revolution.

Salama Higazi — A300

Perf. 11x11½
1967, Oct. 14   Photo.   Wmk. 342
723 A300 20m brown & dk blue   .80   .40
50th anniversary of the death of Salama
Higazi, pioneer of Egyptian lyric stage.

Stag on Ceramic
Disk — A301

Design: 55m, Apse showing Christ in Glory,
Madonna and Saints, Coptic Museum, and
UNESCO Emblem.

1967, Oct. 24   Perf. 11½
724 A301 20m dull rose & dk bl   .95   .40
725 A301 55m dk slate grn & yel   1.75   .85
      Nos. 724-725,C117 (3)   4.20   2.15
22nd anniv. of the UN.

Savings Bank and Postal Authority Emblems A302

1967, Oct. 31   *Perf. 11½x11*
726 A302 20m sal pink & dk blue   .60 .30
International Savings Day.

Rose — A303

Unwmk.
1967, Dec. 15   **Photo.**   *Perf. 11*
727 A303 5m green & rose lilac   .50 .25
Issued for use on greeting cards.

Pharaonic Dress — A304

Designs: Various pharaonic dresses from temple decorations.

Perf. 11x11½
1968, Jan. 2   **Wmk. 342**
728 A304 20m brown, grn & buff   1.40 .35
729 A304 55m lt grn, yel & sepia   2.25 .85
730 A304 80m dk brn, bl & brt
       rose   3.75 1.25
   Nos. 728-730 (3)   7.40 2.45
Issued for Post Day, Jan. 2.
See Nos. 752-755.

Aswan High Dam and Power Lines — A305

1968, Jan. 9
731 A305 20m yel, bl & dk brn   .35 .25
1st electricity generated by the Aswan Hydroelectric Station.

Alabaster Vessel, Tutankhamun Treasure A306

Capital of Coptic Limestone Pillar A307

Perf. 11x11½, 11½
1968, Jan. 20   **Photo.**   **Wmk. 342**
732 A306 20m dk ultra, yel & brn   .75 .30
733 A307 80m lt grn, dk pur & ol
       grn   1.60 1.00
2nd International Festival of Museums.

Girl, Moon and Paint Brushes — A308

1968, Feb. 15   *Perf. 11x11½*
734 A308 20m brt blue & black   .40 .30
7th Biennial Exhibition of Fine Arts, Alexandria, Feb. 15.

Cattle and Veterinarian A309

Perf. 11½x11
1968, May 4   **Photo.**   **Wmk. 342**
735 A309 20m brown, yel & grn   .75 .25
8th Arab Veterinary Congress, Cairo.

Human Rights Flame — A310

Perf. 11x11½
1968, July 1   **Photo.**   **Wmk. 342**
736 A310 20m citron, crim & grn   .50 .25
737 A310 60m sky blue, crim &
       grn   1.00 .90
International Human Rights Year, 1968.

Open Book with Symbols of Science, Victory Election Result — A311

Workers, Cogwheel with Coat of Arms and Open Book — A312

1968, July 23   *Perf. 11½*
738 A311 20m rose red & sl grn   .50 .25
Souvenir Sheet
Imperf
739 A312 100m lt grn, org & pur   3.25 3.00
16th anniversary of the revolution.

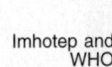

Imhotep and WHO Emblem — A313

No. 741, Avicenna and WHO emblem.

Perf. 11½x11
1968, Sept. 1   **Photo.**   **Wmk. 342**
740 A313 20m blue, yel & brn   1.10 .55
741 A313 20m yellow, bl & brn   1.10 .55
   a. Pair, #740-741   3.00 3.00
20th anniv. of the WHO. Nos. 740-741 printed in checkerboard sheets of 50 (5x10).

Table Tennis — A314

Perf. 11x11½
1968, Sept. 20   **Photo.**   **Wmk. 342**
742 A314 20m lt green & dk brn   .90 .35
First Mediterranean Table Tennis Tournament, Alexandria, Sept. 20-27.

Factories and Fair Emblem — A315

1968, Oct. 20   **Wmk. 342**   *Perf. 11½*
743 A315 20m bl gray, red & sl bl   .45 .25
Cairo International Industrial Fair.

Temples of Philae A316

Refugees, Map of Palestine, Refugee Year Emblem — A317

55m, Temple at Philae & UNESCO emblem.

1968, Oct. 24   **Photo.**
744 A316 20m multicolored   1.25 .30
745 A317 30m multicolored   1.75 .85
746 A317 55m lt blue, yel & blk   3.00 1.10
   Nos. 744-746 (3)   6.00 2.25
Issued for United Nations Day, Oct. 24.

Egyptian Boy Scout Emblem — A318

1968, Nov. 1
747 A318 10m dull org & vio bl   .80 .30
50th anniversary of Egyptian Boy Scouts.

Pharaonic Sports — A319

Design: 30m, Pharaonic sports, diff.

1968, Nov. 1
748 A319 20m pale ol, pale sal &
       blk   .80 .25
749 A319 30m pale blue, buff &
       pur   1.25 .75
19th Olympic Games, Mexico City, 10/12-27.

Aly Moubarak — A320

1968, Nov. 9   *Perf. 11½*
750 A320 20m green, brn & bister   .55 .25
Aly Moubarak (1823-93), founder of the modern educational system in Egypt.

Lotus — A321

1968, Dec. 11   **Photo.**   **Wmk. 342**
751 A321 5m brt blue, grn & yel   .55 .25
Issued for use on greeting cards.

Ramses IV — A322

Pharaonic Dress: No. 753, Ramses III. No. 754, Girl carrying basket on her head. 55m, Queen of the New Empire in transparent dress.

1969, Jan. 2   **Photo.**   *Perf. 11½*
752 A322 5m blue & multi   .75 .30
753 A322 20m blue & multi   1.25 .50
754 A322 20m blue & multi   1.50 .60
755 A322 55m blue & multi   3.75 1.75
   Nos. 752-755 (4)   7.25 3.15
Issued for Post Day, Jan. 2.

Hefni Nassef — A323

Portrait: No. 757, Mohammed Farid.

Perf. 11x11½
1969, Mar. 2   **Photo.**   **Wmk. 342**
756 A323 20m purple & brown   .55 .30
757 A323 20m emerald & brown   .55 .30
   a. Pair, #756-757   1.25 1.25
50th anniv. of the death of Hefni Nassef (1860-1919) writer and government worker, and Mohammed Farid (1867-1919), lawyer and Speaker of the Nationalist Party.

Teacher and Children — A324

1969, Mar. 2   *Perf. 11x11½*
758 A324 20m multicolored   .55 .25
Arab Teacher's Day.

ILO Emblem and Factory Chimneys — A325

1969, Apr. 11   Photo.   Wmk. 342
759 A325 20m brown, ultra & car   .55 .25
50th anniv. of the ILO.

A326

Design: Flag of Algeria, Africa Day and Tourist Year Emblems.

Perf. 11½x11
1969, May 25   Litho.   Wmk. 342
760 A326 10m Algeria   .95 .55
761 A326 10m Botswana   .95 .55
762 A326 10m Burundi   .95 .55
763 A326 10m Cameroun   .95 .55
764 A326 10m Cent. Afr. Rep.   .95 .55
765 A326 10m Chad   .95 .55
766 A326 10m Congo (Brazzaville)   .95 .55
767 A326 10m Congo (Kin-
shassa)   .95 .55
768 A326 10m Dahomey   .95 .55
769 A326 10m Equatorial
Guinea   .95 .55
770 A326 10m Ethiopia   .95 .55
771 A326 10m Gabon   .95 .55
772 A326 10m Gambia   .95 .55
773 A326 10m Ghana   .95 .55
774 A326 10m Guinea   .95 .55
775 A326 10m Ivory Coast   .95 .55
776 A326 10m Kenya   .95 .55
777 A326 10m Lesotho   .95 .55
778 A326 10m Liberia   .95 .55
779 A326 10m Libya   .95 .55
780 A326 10m Malagasy   .95 .55
781 A326 10m Malawi   .95 .55
782 A326 10m Mali   .95 .55
783 A326 10m Mauritania   .95 .55
784 A326 10m Mauritius   .95 .55
785 A326 10m Morocco   .95 .55
786 A326 10m Niger   .95 .55
787 A326 10m Nigeria   .95 .55
788 A326 10m Rwanda   .95 .55
789 A326 10m Senegal   .95 .55
790 A326 10m Sierra Leone   .95 .55
791 A326 10m Somalia   .95 .55
792 A326 10m Sudan   .95 .55
793 A326 10m Swaziland   .95 .55
794 A326 10m Tanzania   .95 .55
795 A326 10m Togo   .95 .55
796 A326 10m Tunisia   .95 .55
797 A326 10m Uganda   .95 .55
798 A326 10m UAR   .95 .55
799 A326 10m Upper Volta   .95 .55
800 A326 10m Zambia   .95 .55
Nos. 760-800 (41)   38.95 22.55

El Fetouh Gate, Cairo — A327

Sculptures from the Egyptian Museum, Cairo — A328

Millenary of Cairo A329

No. 802, Al Azhar University. No. 803, The Citadel. No. 805, Sculptures, Coptic Museum. No. 806, Glass plate and vase, Fatimid dynasty, Islamic Museum.
No. 807: a, Islamic coin. b, Fatimist era jewelry. c, Copper vase. d, Coins and plaque.

Perf. 11½x11
1969, July 23   Photo.   Wmk. 342
801 A327 10m dk brown &
multi   .55 .25
802 A327 10m green & multi   .55 .25

---

803 A327 10m blue & multi   .55 .25
Perf. 11½
804 A328 20m yellow grn &
multi   .95 .40
805 A328 20m dp ultra & multi   .95 .40
806 A328 20m brown & multi   .95 .40
Nos. 801-806 (6)   4.50 1.95

Souvenir Sheet
807 A329 Sheet of 4   15.00 14.00
a. 20m dark blue & multi   2.50 2.00
b. 20m lilac & multi   2.50 2.00
c. 20m yellow & multi   2.50 2.00
d. 20m dark green & multi   2.50 2.00
Millenium of the founding of Cairo.

African Development Bank Emblem — A330

Perf. 11x11½
1969, Sept. 10   Photo.   Wmk. 342
808 A330 20m emerald, yel & vio   .40 .25
African Development Bank, 5th anniv.

Pharaonic Boat and UN Emblem — A331

Temple of Philae Inundated and UNESCO Emblem — A332

Design: 5m, King and Queen from Abu Simbel Temple and UNESCO Emblem (size: 21x38mm).

Perf. 11x11½, 11½x11
1969, Oct. 24   Photo.   Wmk. 342
809 A332 5m brown & multi   .45 .30
810 A331 20m yellow & ultra   1.40 .55
Perf. 11½
811 A332 55m yellow & multi   1.60 .75
Nos. 809-811 (3)   3.45 1.60
Issued for United Nations Day.

Ships of 1869 and 1967 and Maps of Africa and Suez Canal A333

1969, Nov. 15   Perf. 11½x11
812 A333 20m lt blue & multi   1.50 .55
Centenary of the Suez Canal.

Cairo Opera House and Performance of Aida — A334

1969, Nov. 15
813 A334 20m multicolored   1.00 .45
Centenary of the Cairo Opera House.

Crowd with Egyptian and Revolutionary Flags — A335

1969, Nov. 15   Perf. 11½x11
814 A335 20m brt grn, dull lil &
red   1.00 .45
Revolution of 1919.

Ancient Arithmetic and Computer Cards — A336

Perf. 11½x11
1969, Dec. 17   Photo.   Wmk. 342
815 A336 20m multicolored   .55 .30
Intl. Congress for Scientific Accounting, Cairo, Dec. 17-19.

Poinsettia — A337

1969, Dec. 24   Unwmk.   Perf. 11
816 A337 5m yellow, grn & car   .30 .25
Issued for use on greeting cards.

Sakkara Step Pyramid A338

El Fetouh Gate, Cairo A339

Fountain, Sultan Hassan Mosque, Cairo A340

King Khafre (Ruled c. 2850 B.C.) A341

Designs: 5m, Al Azhar Mosque. 10m, Luxor Temple. 50m, Qaitbay Fort, Alexandria.

Wmk. 342 (20m, £1), Unwmkd.
Photo.; Engr. (20m, 55m)
1969-70   Perf. 11
817 A338 1m multi ('70)   .30 .40
818 A338 5m multi ('70)   .50 .25
819 A338 10m multi ('70)   .50 .25
820 A339 20m dark brown   2.25 .35
821 A338 50m multi ('70)   2.25 .50
822 A340 55m slate green   3.50 .30
Perf. 11½
Photo. & Engr.
823 A341 £1 org & sl grn
('70)   40.00 9.50
Nos. 817-823 (7)   49.30 11.55
See Nos. 889-891, 893-897, 899, 901-902, 904.

Veiled Women, by Mahmoud Said — A342

Perf. 11x11½
1970, Jan. 2   Photo.   Wmk. 342
824 A342 100m blue & multi   3.50 3.00
Post Day. Sheet of 8 with 2 panes of 4.

Parliament, Scales, Globe and Laurel — A343

1970, Feb. 2   Perf. 11½x11
825 A343 20m blue, vio bl &
ocher   .75 .25
Intl. Conf. of Parliamentarians on the Middle East Crisis, Cairo, Feb. 2-5.

Map of Arab League Countries, Flag and Emblem — A344

Perf. 11½x11
1970, Mar. 22   Photo.   Wmk. 342
826 A344 30m brn org, grn & dk
pur   .65 .40
Arab League, 25th anniv. See No. B42.

Mena House and Sheraton Hotel — A345

1970, Mar. 23
827 A345 20m olive, org & bl   .55 .25
Centenary of Mena House and the inauguration of the Cairo Sheraton Hotel.

Manufacture of Medicine — A346

1970, Apr. 20
828 A346 20m brown, yel & bl   1.25 .35
Production of medicines in Egypt, 30th anniv.

Mermaid — A347

1970, Apr. 20   Perf. 11x11½
829 A347 20m orange, blk & ultra   .65 .25
8th Biennial Exhibition of Fine Arts, Alexandria, March 12.

Misr Bank and Talaat Harb — A348

1970, May 7   Photo.   Wmk. 342
830 A348 20m multicolored   .65 .25
50th anniversary of Misr Bank.

ITU Emblem — A349

1970, May 17   Perf. 11x11½
831 A349 20m dk brn, yel & dull
bl   .65 .25
World Telecommunications Day.

UPU Headquarters, Bern — A350

1970, May 20   *Perf. 11½x11*
832 A350 20m multicolored   .80   .35
   Inauguration of the UPU Headquarters in Bern. See No. C128.

Basketball Player and Map of Africa A351

UPU, UN and U.P.A.F. Emblems A352

   No. 834, Soccer player, map of Africa & cup, horiz.

Perf. 11x11½, 11½x11
1970, May 25   **Photo.**   **Wmk. 342**
833 A351 20m lt blue, yel & brn   1.25   .40
834 A351 20m yellow & multi   .80   .35
835 A352 20m ocher, grn & blk   .70   .25
   Nos. 833-835 (3)   2.75 1.00

   Africa Day. No. 833 also for the 5th African basketball championship for men; No. 834 the annual African Soccer championship; No. 835 publicizes the African Postal Union seminar.

Fist and Freed Bird — A353

1970, July 23   **Photo.**   *Perf. 11*
836 A353 20m lt green, org & blk   .95   .25

Souvenir Sheet
Imperf
837 A353 100m lt blue, dp org & blk   3.25 2.40
   18th anniv. of the revolution.

Al Aqsa Mosque on Fire — A354

1970, Aug. 21   **Wmk. 342**   *Perf. 11*
838 A354 20m multicolored   1.25   .40
839 A354 60m brt blue & multi   2.75 1.60
   1st anniv. of the burning of Al Aqsa Mosque, Jerusalem.

Standardization Emblems A355

1970, Oct. 14   **Wmk. 342**   *Perf. 11*
840 A355 20m yellow, ultra & grn   .75   .25
   World Standards Day and 25th anniv. of the Intl. Standardization Organization, ISO.

UN Emblem, Scales and Dove — A356

Temple at Philae — A357

Child, Education Year and UN Emblems — A358

   Designs: 10m, UN emblem. No. 845, 2nd Temple at Philae (denomination at left).

Perf. 11 (5m), 11½ (others)
1970, Oct. 24   **Photo.**   **Wmk. 342**
841 A356 5m lt bl, rose lil & sl   .25   .25
842 A357 10m yel, brn & lt bl   .25   .25
843 A358 20m slate & multi   .65   .30
844 A357 55m brn, bl & ocher   1.10   .75
845 A357 55m brn, bl & ocher   1.10   .75
   a.   Strip of 3, #842, 844-845   4.00 4.00
   Nos. 841-845,B43 (6)   4.25 3.10

   25th anniv. of the UN. No. 843 also for Intl. Education Year; Nos. 842, 844-845, the work of UNESCO in saving the Temples of Philae. No. 845a printed in sheets of 35 (15 No. 842, 10 each Nos. 844-845). Nos. 844-845 show continuous picture of the Temples at Philae.

Gamal Abdel Nasser — A359

1970, Nov. 6   **Wmk. 342**   *Perf. 11*
846 A359 5m sky blue & blk   .25   .25
847 A359 20m gray green & multi   .55   .25
   Nos. 846-847,C129-C130 (4)   4.55 2.15
   Gamal Abdel Nasser (1918-70), Pres. of Egypt.

Medical Association Building — A360

   No. 849, Old & new National Library. No. 850, Egyptian Credo (Nasser quotation). No. 851, Engineering Society, old & new buildings. No. 852, Government Printing Offices, old & new buildings.

1970, Dec. 20   **Photo.**   *Perf. 11*
848 A360 20m yel, grn & brn   .80   .40
849 A360 20m green & multi   .80   .40
850 A360 20m lt blue & brn   .80   .40
851 A360 20m blue, yel & brn   .80   .40
852 A360 20m blue, yel & brn   .80   .40
   a.   Strip of 5, #848-852   4.50 4.25

   50th anniv. of Egyptian Medical Assoc. (No. 848); cent. of Natl. Library (No. 849); Egyptian Engineering Assoc. (No. 851); sesqui. of Government Printing Offices (No. 852).

Map and Flags of UAR, Libya, Sudan — A361

1970, Dec. 27   *Perf. 11½*
853 A361 20m lt grn, car & blk   .75   .25
   Signing of the Charter of Tripoli affirming the unity of UAR, Libya & the Sudan, 12/27/70.

Qalawun Minaret — A362

   Designs (Minarets): 10m, As Saleh. 20m, Isna. 55m, Al Hakim.

1971, Jan. 2   **Wmk. 342**   *Perf. 11*
854 A362 5m green & multi   .60   .25
855 A362 10m green & multi   1.25   .40
856 A362 20m green & multi   2.50   .80
857 A362 55m green & multi   4.00 2.25
   a.   Strip of 4, #854-857 + label   10.00 9.00

   Post Day, 1971.
   See Nos. 905-908, 932-935.

Gamal Abdel Nasser — A363

   Design: Nos. 860a-860b, Portrait facing right.

Photogravure and Engraved
1971   **Wmk. 342**   *Perf. 11½*
858 A363 200m brn vio & dk bl   5.00 1.25
859 A363 500m blue & black   12.00 3.25

Souvenir Sheet
Imperf
860   Sheet of 2   13.00 13.00
   a.   A363 100m lt green & black   4.00 2.75
   b.   A363 200m blue & black   6.00 4.50

   No. 860 commemorates inauguration of the Aswan High Dam, which is shown in margin. Issued: No. 860, 1/15; Nos. 858-859, 2/1. See No. 903.

Cotton and Globe — A364

1971, Mar. 6   **Photo.**   *Perf. 11½x11*
861 A364 20m lt grn, blue & brn   .65   .25
   Egyptian cotton.

Arab Countries, and Arab Postal Union Emblem — A365

1971, Mar. 6   **Wmk. 342**
862 A365 20m lt bl, org & sl grn   .65   .25
   9th Arab Postal Cong., Cairo, 3/6-25. See No. C131.

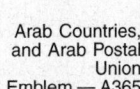

Cairo Fair Emblem — A366

1971, Mar. 6   *Perf. 11x11½*
863 A366 20m plum, blk & org   .65   .25
   Cairo International Fair, March 2-23.

Nesy Ra, Apers Papyrus and WHO Emblem — A367

Perf. 11½x11
1971, Apr. 30   **Photo.**   **Wmk. 342**
864 A367 20m yellow bis & pur   1.25   .30
   World Health Organization Day.

Gamal Abdel Nasser — A368

1971, May 1   *Perf. 11*
865 A368 20m purple & bl gray   .90   .30
866 A368 55m blue & purple   2.75   .95

Map of Africa, Telecommunications Symbols — A369

1971, May 17   *Perf. 11½x11*
867 A369 20m blue & multi   .65   .25
   Pan-African telecommunications system.

Wheelwright A370

Hand Holding Wheat and Laurel A371

Candle Lighting Africa A372

Perf. 11x11½
1971, July 23   **Photo.**   **Wmk. 342**
868 A370 20m yellow & multi   .60   .25
869 A371 20m tan, grn & ocher   .60   .25

Souvenir Sheet
Imperf
870 A372 100m blue & multi   6.00 4.75
   19th anniv. of the July Revolution. No. 870 contains one stamp with simulated perforations in gold.

Arab Postal Union Emblem — A373

1971, Aug. 3   *Perf. 11½*
871 A373 20m black, yel & grn   .65   .25
   25th anniv. of the Conf. of Sofar, Lebanon, establishing the APU. See No. C135.

Arab Republic of Egypt

Three Links — A374

Perf. 11½x11
1971, Sept. 28   **Photo.**   **Wmk. 342**
872 A374 20m gray, org brn & blk   .65   .30
   Confederation of Arab Republics (Egypt, Syria and Libya). See No. C136.

Gamal Abdel Nasser — A375

1971, Sept. 28   **Perf. 11x11½**
873 A375 5m slate grn & vio
　　　　 brn .45 .25
874 A375 20m violet brn & ultra .65 .25
875 A375 30m ultra & brown 1.25 .75
876 A375 55m brown & emerald 2.10 1.10
　　 Nos. 873-876 (4) 4.45 2.35

Death of Pres. Gamal Abdel Nasser, 1st anniv.

Blood Donation — A376

1971, Oct. 24
877 A376 20m green & carmine 1.10 .25
"Blood Saves Lives."

Princess Nursing Child, UNICEF Emblem A377

Submerged Pillar, Philae, UNESCO Emblem A379

Equality Year Emblem — A378

Perf. 11x11½, 11½x11
1971, Oct. 24   **Photo.**   **Wmk. 342**
878 A377 5m buff, blk & org brn .55 .30
879 A378 20m red brn, grn, yel &
　　　　 blk .90 .30
880 A379 55m black, lt bl, yel &
　　　　 brn 2.25 .30
　　 Nos. 878-880,C137 (4) 5.45 1.35

UN Day. No. 878 honors UN Intl. Children's Fund; No. 879 for Intl. Year Against Racial Discrimination; No. 880 honors UNESCO.

Postal Traffic Center, Alexandria A380

1971, Oct. 31   **Perf. 11½x11**
881 A380 20m blue & bister 1.00 .30
Opening of Postal Traffic Center in Alexandria.

Sunflower — A381

1971, Nov. 13   **Perf. 11**
882 A381 5m lt blue & multi .45 .25
For use on greeting cards.

Abdalla El Nadim — A382

1971, Nov. 14   **Perf. 11x11½**
883 A382 20m green & brown .65 .25
Abdalla El Nadim (1845-1896), journalist, publisher, connected with Orabi Revolution.

Section of Earth's Crust, Map of Africa on Globe — A383

1971, Nov. 27   **Perf. 11½x11**
884 A383 20m ultra, yel & brn 1.25 .25
75th anniv. of Egyptian Geological Survey and Intl. Conference, Nov. 27-Dec. 1.

Postal Union Emblem, Letter and Dove — A384

55m, African Postal Union emblem and letter.

1971, Dec. 2
885 A384 5m multicolored .45 .25
886 A384 20m olive, blk & org .90 .25
887 A384 55m red, blk & blue 2.00 1.10
　　 Nos. 885-887,C138 (4) 4.75 2.00
10th anniversary of African Postal Union.

Money and Safe Deposit Box — A385

1971, Dec. 23   **Perf. 11½**
888 A385 20m rose, brn & grn .85 .30
70th anniversary of Postal Savings Bank.

Types of 1969-70, 1971 Inscribed "A. R. Egypt" and

Ramses II — A385a

Designs as before and: No. 894, King Citi I. No. 897, View of Alexandria. No. 898, Queen Nefertari. No. 900, Sphinx and Middle Pyramid. 100m, Cairo Mosque. 200m, Head of Pharaoh Userkaf.

Wmk. 342 (892A, 901-904)
1972-76   **Photo.**   **Unwmk.**   **Perf. 11**
889 A338 1m multi .25 .25
890 A338 1m dk brn ('73) .30 .25
891 A338 5m multi .40 .25
892 A385a 5m olive ('73) .45 .25
892A A385a 5m bister ('76) .45 .25
893 A338 10m multi .70 .25
894 A338 10m lt brn ('73) .70 .25
895 A339 20m olive 1.10 .25
896 A339 20m purple ('73) 1.10 .25
897 A339 50m multi 2.25 .30
898 A385a 50m dull bl ('73) 2.25 .30
899 A340 55m red lilac 4.00 .50
900 A340 55m green ('74) 2.00 .50
901 A339 100m lt blue, dp
　　　　 org & blk 3.00 .70
Perf. 11½
Photo. & Engr.
902 A341 200m yel grn &
　　　　 brn 6.75 1.50
903 A363 500m bl & choc 17.50 4.00
904 A341 £1 org & sl grn 32.50 9.00
　　 Nos. 889-904 (17) 75.70 19.45

Minaret Type of 1971

5m, West Minaret, Nasser Mosque. 20m, East Minaret, Nasser Mosque. 30m, Minaret, Al Gawli Mosque. 55m, Minaret, Ibn Tulun Mosque.

Wmk. 342
1972, Jan. 2   **Photo.**   **Perf. 11**
905 A362 5m dk green & multi .45 .25
906 A362 20m dk green & multi 1.25 .25
907 A362 30m dk green & multi 2.75 .50
908 A362 55m dk green & multi 3.75 1.50
a. Strip of 4, #905-908 + label 11.00 3.50
Post Day, 1972.

Police Emblem and Activities A386

1972, Jan. 25   **Perf. 11½**
909 A386 20m dull blue, brn &
　　　　 yel 2.25 .35
Police Day 1972.

UNESCO, UN and Book Year Emblems — A387

1972, Jan. 25   **Perf. 11x11½**
910 A387 20m lt yel grn, vio bl &
　　　　 yel 1.10 .25
International Book Year 1972.

Alexandria Biennale — A388

1972, Feb. 15   **Wmk. 342**   **Perf. 11½**
911 A388 20m black, brt rose &
　　　　 yel .85 .30
9th Biennial Exhibition of Fine Arts, Alexandria, Mar., 1972.

Fair Emblem — A389

1972, Mar. 5   **Perf. 11x11½**
912 A389 20m blue, org & yel
　　　　 grn 1.10 .30
International Cairo Fair.

Abdel Moniem Riad — A390

1972, Mar. 21   **Photo.**   **Wmk. 342**
913 A390 20m blue & brown 1.25 .30
In memory of Brig. Gen. Abdel Moniem Riad (1919-1969), military hero.

Bird Feeding Young — A391

1972, Mar. 21   **Perf. 11½**
914 A391 20m yellow & multi 1.00 .25
Mother's Day.

Tutankhamun A392

Design: 55m, Back of chair with king's name and symbols of eternity.

1972, May 22   **Unwmk.**
915 A392 20m gray, blk &
　　　　 ocher 2.25 .65
916 A392 55m purple & yellow 6.25 1.75
　　 Nos. 915-916,C142-C143 (4) 28.50 13.40
Discovery of the tomb of Tutankhamun by Howard Carter & Lord Carnarvon, 50th anniv. See No. C144.

Queen Nefertiti — A393

Wmk. 342
1972, May 22   **Photo.**   **Perf. 11½**
917 A393 20m red, blk & gold 1.25 .30
Soc. of the Friends of Art, 50th anniv.

Map of Africa — A394

1972, May 25   **Perf. 11x11½**
918 A394 20m purple, bl & brn .75 .30
Africa Day.

Atom Symbol, "Faith and Science" — A395

Design: No. 920, Egyptian coat of arms.

1972, July 23   **Perf. 11½**
919 A395 20m blue, claret & blk 1.10 .30
920 A395 20m ol grn, gold & blk 1.10 .30
20th anniversary of the revolution.

Boxing, Olympic and Motion Emblems A396

Designs (Olympic and Motion Emblems and): 10m, Wrestling. 20m, Basketball.

1972, Aug. 17   *Perf. 11½x11*
921 A396 5m blue & multi .35 .25
922 A396 10m yellow & multi .50 .25
923 A396 20m ver & multi .60 .30
Nos. 921-923,C149-C152 (7) 6.65 3.70
20th Olympic Games, Munich, 8/26-9/11.

Flag of Confederation of Arab Republics — A397

1972, Sept. 1   Wmk. 342   *Perf. 11½*
924 A397 20m carmine, bis & blk .85 .30
Confederation of Arab Republics, 1st anniv.

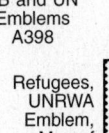

Red Crescent, TB and UN Emblems A398

Heart and WHO Emblem A399

Refugees, UNRWA Emblem, Map of Palestine A400

Design: 55m, Inundated Temple of Philae, UNESCO emblem.

Perf. 11x11½ (#925), 11½ (#926, 928), 11 (#927)

1972, Oct. 24   Photo.
925 A398 10m brn org, red & bl .55 .30
926 A399 20m green, yel & blk 1.00 .40
927 A400 30m lt bl, pur & lt brn 3.00 .75
928 A399 55m brn, gold & bluish gray 3.25 1.00
Nos. 925-928 (4) 7.80 2.45

UN Day. No. 925 is for the 14th Regional Tuberculosis Conf., Cairo, 1972; No. 926 World Health Month; No. 927 publicizes aid to refugees and No. 928 the UN campaign to save the Temples at Philae.

Morning Glory — A401

1972, Oct. 24   *Perf. 11*
929 A401 10m yel, lilac & grn .65 .25
For use on greeting cards.

"Seeing Eye" — A402

1972, Nov. 30   *Perf. 11½*
930 A402 20m multicolored 1.00 .25
Social Work Day.

Sculling Race, View of Luxor A403

1972, Dec. 17   Wmk. 342   *Perf. 11*
931 A403 20m blue & brown 1.40 .40
3rd Nile Intl. Rowing Festival, Dec. 1972.

Minaret Type of 1971
10m, Al Maridani, 1338. 20m, Bashtak, 1337. 30m, Qusun, 1330. 55m, Al Gashankir, 1306.

1973, Jan. 2
Frame in Bright Yellow Green
932 A362 10m multicolored .80 .25
933 A362 20m multicolored 1.25 .30
934 A362 30m multicolored 2.75 .75
935 A362 55m multicolored 3.75 2.00
a. Strip of 4, #932-935 + Label 11.00 10.00
Post Day, 1973.

Cairo Fair Emblem — A404

Perf. 11½x11
1973, Mar. 21   Photo.   Wmk. 342
936 A404 20m gray & multi .55 .25
International Cairo Fair.

Family — A405

1973, Mar. 21   *Perf. 11x11½*
937 A405 20m multicolored .65 .25
Family planning.

Sania Girls' School and Hoda Sharawi — A406

Perf. 11½x11
1973, July 15   Photo.   Wmk. 342
938 A406 20m ultra & green .65 .25
Centenary of education for girls and 50th anniversary of the Egyptian Women's Union, founded by Hoda Sharawi.

Rifaa el Tahtawi — A407

1973, July 15   *Perf. 11x11½*
939 A407 20m brt green, ol & brn .70 .30
Centenary of the death of Rifaa el Tahtawi, champion of democracy and principal of language school.

Omar Makram A408

Abdel Rahman al Gabarti, Historian A409

"Reconstruction and Battle" — A410

No. 941, Mohamed Korayem, martyr.

1973, July 23
940 A408 20m yel grn, bl & brn .65 .30
941 A408 20m lt grn, bl & brn .65 .30
942 A409 20m ocher & brown .65 .30
Nos. 940-942 (3) 1.95 .90

Souvenir Sheet
Imperf
943 A410 110m gold, bl & blk 3.25 3.00
Revolution establishing the republic, 21st anniv.

Grain, Cow, FAO Emblem — A411

Perf. 11½x11
1973, Oct. 24   Wmk. 342
944 A411 10m brn, dk bl & yel grn .65 .25
10th anniv. of the World Food Org.

Inundated Temples at Philae — A412

1973, Oct. 24   *Perf. 11½*
945 A412 55m blue, pur & org 4.00 1.40
UNESCO campaign to save the temples at Philae.

Bank Building — A413

1973, Oct. 24
946 A413 20m brn org, grn & blk .75 .30
75th anniv. of the National Bank of Egypt.

Rose — A414

1973, Oct. 24   *Perf. 11*
947 A414 10m blue & multi .55 .25
For use on greeting cards.

Human Rights Flame — A415

Perf. 11x11½
1973, Dec. 8   Photo.   Wmk. 342
948 A415 20m yel grn, dk bl & car .75 .25
25th anniversary of the Universal Declaration of Human Rights.

Taha Hussein — A416

1973, Dec. 10
949 A416 20m dk blue, brn & emer .75 .25
Dr. Taha Hussein (1893-1973), "Father of Education" in Egypt, writer, philosopher.

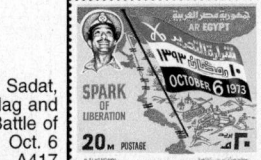

Pres. Sadat, Flag and Battle of Oct. 6 A417

1973, Dec. 23   *Perf. 11x11½*
950 A417 20m yellow, blk & red 1.25 .60
October War against Israel (crossing of Suez Canal by Egyptian forces, Oct. 6, 1973). See No. 959.

WPY Emblem and Chart — A418

1974, Mar. 21   Wmk. 342   *Perf. 11*
951 A418 55m org, grn & dk bl 1.10 .50
World Population Year.

Cairo Fair Emblem — A419

1974, Mar. 21   Photo.
952 A419 20m blue & multi .65 .25
Cairo International Fair.

Nurse and Medal of Angels of Ramadan 10 — A420

1974, May 15   *Perf. 11½*
953 A420 55m multicolored 2.00 .65
Nurses' and World Hospital Day.

Workers, Relief Carving from Queen
Tee's Tomb, Sakhara
A421

1974, May 15　　　　　　*Perf. 11*
954 A421 20m yellow, blue & brn　.85　.30
Workers' Day.

Pres. Sadat, Troops
Crossing Suez
Canal — A422

"Reconstruction," Map of
Suez Canal and New
Building — A423

Sheet of
Aluminum — A424

Design: 110m, Pres. Sadat's "October
Working Paper," symbols of science and
development.

1974, July 23　Photo.　*Perf. 11x11½*
955 A422 20m multicolored　　.75　.40
956 A423 20m blue, gold & blk　.75　.40
　　　　　　Perf. 11½
957 A424 20m plum & silver　　.75　.40
　　Nos. 955-957 (3)　　　2.25 1.20
Souvenir Sheet
Imperf
958 A424 110m green & multi　3.75 3.75

22nd anniv. of the revolution establishing
the republic and for the end of the October
War. No. 958 contains one 52x59mm stamp.

Pres. Sadat
and
Flag — A425

　　　　Perf. 11x11½
1974, Oct. 6　　　　　Wmk. 342
959 A425 20m yellow, blk & red　1.50　.75
1st anniv. of Battle. See No. 950.

Palette and
Brushes — A426

1974, Oct. 6　　　　　*Perf. 11½*
960 A426 30m purple, yel & blk　1.00　.40
6th Exhibition of Plastic Art.

Teachers and
Pupils — A427

1974, Oct. 6　　　　*Perf. 11x11½*
961 A427 20m multicolored　　.75　.25
Teachers' Day.

Souvenir Sheet

UPU Monument, Bern — A428

1974, Oct. 6　　　　　　*Imperf.*
962 A428 110m gold & multi　5.50 5.00
Cent. of the UPU.

Emblems,
Cogwheel
and Calipers
A429

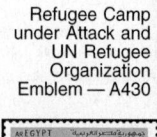

Refugee Camp
under Attack and
UN Refugee
Organization
Emblem — A430

Child and UNICEF
Emblem
A431

Temple
of
Philae
A432

1974, Oct. 24　*Perf. 11½, 11x11½*
963 A429 10m black, bl & yel　.55　.25
964 A430 20m dp org, bl & blk　.85　.25
965 A431 30m green, bl & brn　1.25　.40
966 A432 55m blue, bl & yel　3.00　.85
　　Nos. 963-966 (4)　　5.65 1.75

UN Day. World Standards Day (10m); Pal-
estinian refugee repatriation (20m); Family
Planning (30m); Campaign to save Temple of
Philae (55m).

Calla Lily — A433

1974, Nov. 7　　　　　*Perf. 11*
967 A433 10m ultra & multi　.55　.25
For use on greeting cards.

10m-coins,
Smokestacks and
Grain — A434

1974, Nov. 7　　　　*Perf. 11½x11*
968 A434 20m yel grn, dk bl & sil　.60　.25
International Savings Day.

Organization
Emblem and
Medical
Services — A435

1974, Nov. 7　　　　　*Perf. 11½*
969 A435 30m vio, red & gold　.90　.30
Health Insurance Organization, 10th anniv.

Mustafa
Lutfy El
Manfalouty
A436

Abbas
Mahmoud El
Akkad
A437

　　　Perf. 11x11½
1974, Dec. 8　　Photo.　Wmk. 342
970 A436 20m blue blk & brn　.55　.30
971 A437 20m brown & bl blk　.55　.30
　a.　Pair, #970-971　　1.30 1.30

Arab writers; El Manfalouty (1876-1924) and
El Akkad (1889-1964).

Goddess
Maat Facing
God Thoth
A438

Fish-shaped
Vase — A439

Pharaonic
Golden
Vase — A440

Sign of Life,
Mirror — A441

　　　　Wmk. 342
1975, Jan. 2　Photo.　　*Perf. 11½*
972 A438　20m silver & multi　1.00　.30
973 A439　30m multicolored　1.25　.30
974 A440　55m multicolored　1.75 1.00
975 A441 110m blue & multi　3.00 1.75
　　Nos. 972-975 (4)　　7.00 3.35

Post Day 1975. Egyptian art works from
12th-5th centuries B.C.

Om Kolthoum — A442

　　　　Perf. 11½
1975, Mar. 3　　Photo.　Unwmk.
976 A442 20m brown　　　.85　.25
In memory of Om Kolthoum, singer.

Crescent, Globe, Al
Aqsa and
Kaaba — A443

1975, Mar. 25
977 A443 20m multicolored　　.85　.25
Mohammed's Birthday.

Cairo Fair
Emblem — A444

　　　Perf. 11x11½
1975, Mar. 25　　　　**Wmk. 342**
978 A444 20m multicolored　　.65　.25
International Cairo Fair.

Kasr El Ainy
Hospital WHO
Emblem — A445

　　　Perf. 11½x11
1975, May 7　　Photo.　Wmk. 342
979 A445 20m dk brown & blue　.85　.25
World Health Organization Day.

Children
Reading
Book
A446

Children
and Line
Graph
A447

1975, May 7　　　　*Perf. 11x11½*
980 A446 20m multicolored　　1.00　.40
981 A447 20m multicolored　　1.00　.40
Science Day.

Suez Canal, Globe, Ships, Pres.
Sadat
A448

1975, June 5　　　　　*Perf. 11½*
982 A448 20m blue, brn & blk　.85　.30
　Nos. 982,C166-C167 (3)　5.35 2.90
Reopening of the Suez Canal, June 5.

Belmabgoknis
Flowers — A449

1975, July 30　Photo.　Wmk. 342
983 A449 10m green & blue　　.65　.25
For use on greeting cards.

Sphinx and
Pyramids
Illuminated
A450

Rural
Electrification
A451

Map of
Egypt
with
Tourist
Sites
A452

1975, July 23
984 A450 20m black, org & grn .75 .25
985 A451 20m dk blue & brown .75 .25
Perf. 11
986 A452 110m multicolored 5.75 5.00
Nos. 984-986 (3) 7.25 5.50

23rd anniversary of the revolution establishing the republic. No. 986 printed in sheets of 6 (2x3). Size: 71x80mm.

Volleyball — A453

No. 988, Running. No. 989, Torch and flag bearers. No. 990, Basketball. No. 991, Soccer.

1975, Aug. 2 Photo. Perf. 11x11½
987 A453 20m shown .90 .45
988 A453 20m multicolored .90 .45
989 A453 20m multicolored .90 .45
990 A453 20m multicolored .90 .45
991 A453 20m multicolored .90 .45
a. Strip of 5, #987-991 5.75 5.75

6th Arab School Tournament.

Egyptian Flag and
Tanks — A454

1975 Photo. Unwmk. Perf. 11½
992 A454 20m multicolored 1.40 .40
**Two-line Arabic Inscription
in Bottom Panel, "M" over "20"**
992A A454 20m multicolored 1.40 .40

No. 992 for 2nd anniv. of October War against Israel, "The Spark;" No. 992A, the Intl. Symposium on October War against Israel 1973, Cairo University, Oct. 27-31.
Issue dates: No. 992, Oct. 6; No. 992A, Oct. 24.

Arrows
Pointing to
Fluke, and
Emblems
A455

Submerged
Wall and
Sculpture,
UNESCO
Emblem
A456

Perf. 11x11½
1975, Oct. 24 Wmk. 342
993 A455 20m multicolored .95 .40
994 A456 55m multicolored 2.50 1.25

UN Day. 20m for Intl. Conf. on Schistosomiasis (Bilharziasis); 55m for UNESCO help in saving temples at Philae. See Nos. C169-C170.

Pharaonic Gate,
University
Emblem — A457

1975, Nov. 15 Photo. Wmk. 342
995 A457 20m multicolored .55 .25

Ain Shams University, 25th anniversary.

Al Biruni — A458

Arab Philosophers: No. 997, Al Farabi and lute. No. 998, Al Kanady, book and compass.

1975, Dec. 23 Photo. Perf. 11x11½
996 A458 20m blue, brn & grn 1.50 .50
997 A458 20m blue, brn & grn 1.50 .50
998 A458 20m blue, brn & grn 1.50 .50
Nos. 996-998 (3) 4.50 1.50

Ibex (Prow) — A459

Post Day (from Tutankhamun's Tomb): 30m, Lioness. 55m, Cow's head (Goddess Hawthor). 110m, Hippopotamus' head (God Horus).

1976, Jan. 2 Unwmk. Perf. 11½
999 A459 20m multicolored 4.75 2.00
Wmk. 342
1000 A459 30m brown, gold
& ultra 7.50 2.50
1001 A459 55m multicolored 12.50 6.50
1002 A459 110m multicolored 18.00 13.50
Nos. 999-1002 (4) 42.75 24.50

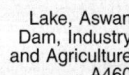

Lake, Aswan
Dam, Industry
and Agriculture
A460

Perf. 11½x11
1976, Jan. 27 Photo. Wmk. 342
1003 A460 20m multicolored .90 .25

Filling of lake formed by Aswan High Dam.

Fair Emblem — A461

1976, Mar. 15 Perf. 11x11½
1004 A461 20m orange & purple .50 .25
9th International Cairo Fair, Mar. 8-27.

Commemorative
Medal — A462

1976, Mar. 15 Wmk. 342
1005 A462 20m olive, yel & blk .60 .25
11th Biennial Exhibition of Fine Arts, Alexandria.

Hands Shielding
Invalid — A463

1976, Apr. 7 Photo. Perf. 11½
1006 A463 20m dk grn, lt grn &
yel .65 .30
Founding of Faithfulness and Hope Society.

Eye and WHO
Emblem — A464

1976, Apr. 7
1007 A464 20m dk brn, yel & grn .85 .25
World Health Day: "Foresight prevents blindness."

Pres. Sadat,
Legal
Department
Emblem — A465

Perf. 11½x11
1976, May 15 Photo. Wmk. 342
1008 A465 20m olive & multi .65 .30
Centenary of State Legal Department.

Scales of
Justice — A466

1976, May 15 Perf. 11x11½
1009 A466 20m carmine, blk &
grn .60 .30
5th anniversary of Rectification Movement.

Al-Ahram Front
Page, First
Issue — A467

Perf. 11½x11
1976, June 25 Photo. Wmk. 342
1010 A467 20m bister & multi .65 .30
Centenary of Al-Ahram newspaper.

World Map,
Pres. Sadat
and
Emblems
A468

1976, July 23 Perf. 11x11½
1011 A468 20m bl, blk & yel .85 .35
Size: 240x216mm
Imperf
1012 A468 110m bl, brn & yel 7.00 6.75
24th anniv. of the revolution. No. 1012 design is similar to No. 1011.

Scarborough
Lily — A469

1976, Sept. 10 Photo. Perf. 11
1013 A469 10m multicolored .55 .25
For use on greeting cards.

Reconstruction of Sinai
by Irrigation
A470

Abu Redice
Oil Wells
and
Refinery
A471

1976, Oct. 6 Perf. 11x11½
1014 A470 20m multicolored .85 .40
1015 A471 20m multicolored .85 .40
Size: 65x77mm
1016 A472 110m grn, bl & blk 7.50 7.00
October War against Israel, 3rd anniv.

Unknown
Soldier,
Memorial
Pyramid
for
October
War
A472

Papyrus with Children's Animal
Story — A473

Al Aqsa Mosque,
Palestinian
Refugees
A474

55m, Isis, from Philae Temple, UNESCO emblem, vert. 110m, UNESCO emblem & "30."

Perf. 11½, 11½x11
1976, Oct. 24 Photo. Wmk. 342
1017 A473 20m dk bl, bis & brn .65 .30
1018 A474 30m brn, grn & blk .80 .35
1019 A474 55m dk blue & bister 1.50 .50
1020 A474 110m lt grn, vio bl &
red 2.50 1.40
Nos. 1017-1020 (4) 5.45 2.55

30th anniversary of UNESCO.

Census Chart — A475

1976, Nov. 22 Photo. Perf. 11½x11
1021 A475 20m multicolored .65 .25
10th General Population and Housing Census.

A476

Nile and commemorative medal.

1976, Nov. 22 Perf. 11x11½
1022 A476 20m green & brown .65 .25
Geographical Soc. of Egypt, cent. (in 1975).

A477

Post Day: 20m, Akhnaton. 30m, Akhnaton's daughter. 55m, Nefertiti, Akhnaton's wife. 110m, Akhnaton, front view.

1977, Jan. 2 Photo. Perf. 11x11½
1023 A477 20m multicolored .65 .30
1024 A477 30m multicolored .65 .35
1025 A477 55m multicolored 1.10 .55
1026 A477 110m multicolored 3.50 1.50
Nos. 1023-1026 (4) 5.90 2.70

Policeman, Emblem and Emergency Car — A478

Perf. 11½x11
1977, Feb. 25 Photo. Wmk. 342
1027 A478 20m multicolored 1.10 .30
Police Day.

Map of Africa, Arab League Emblem — A479

1977, Mar 7 Perf. 11x11½
1028 A479 55m multicolored .90 .50
First Afro-Arab Summit Conference, Cairo.

Fair Emblem, Pharaonic Ship — A480

1977, Mar. 7 Perf. 11½x11
1029 A480 20m green, blk & red .65 .30
10th International Cairo Fair.

King Faisal — A481

1977, Mar. 22 Photo. Perf. 11x11½
1030 A481 20m indigo & brown .65 .25
King Faisal Ben Abdel-Aziz Al Saud of Saudi Arabia (1906-1975).

Healthy and Crippled Children — A482

1977, Apr. 12 Wmk. 342
1031 A482 20m multicolored .95 .30
National campaign to fight poliomyelitis.

APU Emblem, Members' Flags — A483

1977, Apr. 12 Perf. 11½
1032 A483 20m blue & multi .45 .25
1033 A483 30m gray & multi .65 .25
25th anniv. of Arab Postal Union (APU).

Children's Village — A484

Perf. 11½x11
1977, May 7 Photo. Wmk. 342
1034 A484 20m multicolored .55 .35
1035 A484 55m multicolored 1.25 .70
Inauguration of Children's Village, Cairo.

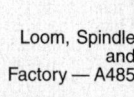

Loom, Spindle and Factory — A485

1977, May 7
1036 A485 20m multicolored .55 .25
Egyptian Spinning and Weaving Company, El Mehalla el Kobra, 50th anniv.

Satellite, Globe, ITU Emblem — A486

1977, May 17 Perf. 11x11½
1037 A486 110m dk blue & multi 2.00 .50
World Telecommunications Day.

Flag and "25" — A487

Egyptian Flag and Eagle A488

Perf. 11½x11
1977, July 23 Photo. Wmk. 342
1038 A487 20m silver, car & blk .65 .25

Perf. 11x11½
1039 A488 110m multicolored 3.00 3.00
25th anniversary of July 23rd Revolution. No. 1039 printed in sheets of six. Size: 75x83mm.

Saad Zaghloul — A489

Perf. 11x11½
1977, Aug. 23 Photo. Wmk. 342
1040 A489 20m dk green & dk brn .40 .25
Saad Zaghloul, leader of 1919 Revolution, 50th death anniversary.

Archbishop Capucci, Map of Palestine — A490

1977, Sept. 1
1041 A490 45m emerald & blue 1.10 .50
Palestinian Archbishop Hilarion Capucci, jailed by Israel in 1974.

Bird-of-Paradise Flower — A491

1977, Sept. 3
1042 A491 10m multicolored .45 .25
For use on greeting cards.

Proclamation Greening the Land — A492

Perf. 11x11½
1977, Sept. 25 Photo. Wmk. 342
1043 A492 20m multicolored .50 .25
Agrarian Reform Law, 25th anniversary.

Soldier, Tanks, Medal of Oct. 6 — A493

Anwar Sadat A494

1977, Oct. 6 Perf. 11½x11
1044 A493 20m multicolored .55 .25
Unwmk.
Perf. 11
1045 A494 140m dk brn, gold & red 8.50 8.50
October War against Israel, 4th anniv. No. 1045 printed in sheets of 16.

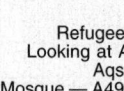

Refugees Looking at Al Aqsa Mosque — A495

Goddess Taueret and Spirit of Flight (Horus) A496

Mural Relief, Temple of Philae A497

Wmk. 342
1977, Oct. 24 Photo. Perf. 11
1046 A495 45m grn, red & blk .80 .35
1047 A496 55m dp blue & yel 1.50 .45
1048 A497 140m ol bis & dk brn 2.50 1.25
Nos. 1046-1048 (3) 4.80 2.05
United Nations Day.

Electric Trains, First Egyptian Locomotive A498

1977, Oct. 22
1049 A498 20m multicolored 1.75 .40
125th anniversary of Egyptian railroads.

Film and Eye — A499

1977, Nov. 16 Perf. 11½x11
1050 A499 20m gray, blk & gold .75 .25
50th anniversary of Egyptian cinema.

Natural Gas Well and Refinery — A500

1977, Nov. 17 Photo.
1051 A500 20m multicolored 1.25 .30
National Oil Festival, celebrating the acquisition of Sinai oil wells.

Pres. Sadat and Dome of the Rock — A501

Perf. 11½x11

1977, Dec. 31   Photo.   Wmk. 342
1052 A501 20m green, brn & blk   .60 .25
1053 A501 140m green, blk & brn   2.00 .80

Pres. Sadat's peace mission to Israel.

Ramses II — A502

Post Day: 45m, Queen Nefertari, bas-relief.

1978, Jan. 2   Perf. 11½
1054 A502 20m green, blk & gold   .85 .40
1055 A502 45m orange, blk & ol   1.75 .90

Post Day 1978.

Water Wheels, Fayum A503

Flying Duck, from Floor in Ikhnaton's Palace A504

5m, Birdhouse, 10m, Statue of Horus. 20m, 30m, Al Rifa'i Mosque, Cairo. 50m, Monastery of Baramus, Wadi el Natrun. 55m, Ruins of Edfu Temple. 70m, 80m, Bridge of Oct. 6. 85m, Medum pyramid. 100m, Facade, El Morsi Mosque, Alexandria. 200m, Column, Alexandria, Sphinx. 500m, Arabian stallion.

Wmk. 342, Unwmkd. (30m, 70m, 80m)

1978-85   Perf. 11½
1056 A503 1m slate blue   .25 .25
  a.   Unwmkd. ('79)   .25 .25
  b.   1m gray ('83)   .25 .25
  c.   1m gray, unwmkd. ('83)   .25 .25
1057 A503 5m lt brn   .25 .25
  a.   5m dull brn, unwmkd. (79)   .25 .25
1058 A503 10m brt green   .25 .25
  a.   Unwmkd. ('79)   .25 .25
1059 A503 20m dk brown   .25 .25
  b.   Unwmkd. ('79)   .25 .25
1059A A503 30m sepia   .60 .50
  c.   Wmk. 342 ('82)
1060 A503 50m lt blue   .25 .25
  a.   Unwmkd. ('79)   .25 .25
  b.   Unwmkd., brt blue ('87)   .25 .25
1061 A503 55m olive   .25 .25
1062 A503 70m olive ('79)   .40 .25
1062A A503 80m olive ('82)   .50 .30
1063 A503 85m dp purple   .70 .30
  a.   Unwmkd. ('85)   .70 .35
1064 A503 100m yel brn   .95 .30
  a.   Unwmkd. ('85)   1.25 .40
1065 A503 200m lt bl & ind   2.25 .80
  a.   Unwmkd. ('85)   2.25 .85
1066 A504 500m multicolored   7.00 2.00
  a.   Unwmkd. ('85)   7.00 2.00
1067 A504 £1 multicolored   11.00 4.00
  a.   Unwmkd. ('85)   11.00 4.00
    Nos. 1056-1067 (14)   24.90 9.95

Issued: 500m, £1, 2/27/78; 70m, 8/22/79; others, 7/23/78.

Fair Emblem and Wheat — A505

1978, Mar. 15   Perf. 11½
1072 A505 20m multicolored   .45 .25

11th Cairo International Fair, Mar. 11-25.

Emblem, Kasr El Ainy School — A506

1978, Mar. 18   Perf. 11½x11
1073 A506 20m lt blue, blk & gold   .55 .25

Kasr El Ainy School of Medicine, 150th anniv.

A507

No. 1074, Soldiers and Emblem. No. 1075, Youssef El Sebai.

1978, Mar. 30   Perf. 11x11½
1074   20m multicolored   .50 .30
1075   20m bister brown   .50 .30
  a.   A507 Pair, #1074-1075   1.25 1.25

Youssef El Sebai, newspaper editor, assassinated on Cyprus and in memory of the commandos killed in raid on Cyprus.

Biennale Medal, Statue for Entrance to Port Said — A509

1978, Apr. 1   Perf. 11½
1076 A509 20m blue, grn & blk   .55 .25

12th Biennial Exhibition of Fine Arts, Alexandria.

Child with Smallpox, UN Emblem — A510

1978, Apr. 7   Photo.   Perf. 11½
1077 A510 20m multicolored   .55 .35

Eradication of smallpox.

Heart & Arrow, UN Emblem — A511

1978, Apr. 7   Wmk. 342
1078 A511 20m multicolored   .55 .35

Fight against hypertension.

Anwar Sadat — A512

1978, May 15   Photo.   Perf. 11½x11
1079 A512 20m grn, brn & gold   .65 .30

7th anniversary of Rectification Movement.

Social Security Emblem A513

1978, May 16   Perf. 11
1080 A513 20m lt green & dk brn   .35 .25

General Organization of Insurance and Pensions (Social Security), 25th anniversary.

New Cities on Map of Egypt A514

Map of Egypt and Sudan, Wheat A515

Wmk. 342
1978, July 23   Photo.   Perf. 11½
1081 A514 20m multicolored   .85 .30
1082 A515 45m multicolored   1.75 .50

26th anniversary of July 23rd revolution.

Symbols of Egyptian Ministries — A516

1978, Aug. 28 Photo. Perf. 11½x11
1083 A516 20m multicolored   .65 .30

Centenary of Egyptian Ministerial System.

Pres. Sadat and "Spirit of Egypt" Showing Way — A517

1978, Oct. 6   Photo.   Perf. 11x11½
1084 A517 20m multicolored   .85 .30

October War against Israel, 5th anniv.

Fight Against Racial Discrimination Emblem A518

Kobet al Sakra Mosque, Refugee Camp A519

Dove and Human Rights Emblem — A520

UN Day: 55m, Sanctuary of Isis at Philae and UNESCO emblem, horiz.

Perf. 11, 11½ (45m)
1978, Oct. 24   Photo.   Wmk. 342
1085 A518 20m multicolored   .45 .25
1086 A519 45m multicolored   .90 .50
1087 A518 55m multicolored   1.00 .50
1088 A520 140m multicolored   2.25 1.00
    Nos. 1085-1088 (4)   4.60 2.35

Pilgrims, Mt. Arafat and Holy Kaaba A521

1978, Nov. 7   Photo.   Perf. 11
1089 A521 45m multicolored   1.00 .40

Pilgrimage to Mecca.

Tahtib Horse Dance — A522

1978, Nov. 7
1090 A522 10m multicolored   .50 .25
1091 A522 20m multicolored   .50 .25

For use on greeting cards.

UN Emblem, Globe and Grain — A523

1978, Nov. 11   Photo.   Perf. 11½
1092 A523 20m green, dk bl & yel   .45 .25

Technical Cooperation Among Developing Countries Conf., Buenos Aires, Sept. 1978.

Pipes, Map and Emblem of Sumed Pipeline — A524

1978, Nov. 11
1093 A524 20m brown, bl & yel   .65 .25

Inauguration of Sumed pipeline from Suez to Alexandria, 1st anniversary.

Mastheads — A525

1978, Dec. 24   Perf. 11x11½
1094 A525 20m brown & black   .65 .25

El Wakea el Masriya newspaper, 150th anniv.

Abu el Walid — A526

1978, Dec. 24
1095 A526 45m brt grn & indigo   .85 .30

800th death anniv. of Abu el Walid ibn Rashid.

Helwan Observatory and Sky — A527

1978, Dec. 30   **Wmk. 342**
1096 A527 20m multicolored   .95   .35
Helwan Observatory, 75th anniversary.

Second Daughter of Ramses II A528

Ramses Statues, Abu Simbel, and Cartouches A529

1979, Jan. 2   **Photo.**   **Perf. 11**
1097 A528 20m brown & yellow   .65   .30

Perf. 11½x11
1098 A529 140m multicolored   2.25   .80
Post Day 1979.

Book, Reader and Globe — A530

Perf. 11½x11
1979, Feb. 1   **Photo.**   **Wmk. 342**
1099 A530 20m yel grn & brn   .45   .25
Cairo 11th International Book Fair.

Wheat, Globe, Fair Emblem A531

Perf. 11x11½
1979, Mar. 17   **Photo.**   **Unwmk.**
1100 A531 20m blue, org & blk   .50   .25
12th Cairo International Fair, Mar.-Apr.

Skull, Poppy, Agency Emblem A532

1979, Mar. 20   **Perf. 11**
1101 A532 70m multicolored   1.90   .65
Anti-Narcotics General Administration, 50th anniv.

Isis Holding Horus — A533

1979, Mar. 21
1102 A533 140m multicolored   3.25   1.00
Mother's Day.

World Map and Book A534

Perf. 11x11½
1979, Mar. 22   **Wmk. 342**
1103 A534 45m yellow, bl & brn   .55   .25
Cultural achievements of the Arabs.

Pres. Sadat's Signature, Peace Doves — A535

Wmk. 342
1979, Mar. 31   **Photo.**   **Perf. 11½**
1104 A535   70m brt green & red   1.25   .45
1105 A535 140m yel grn & red   2.25   1.00
Signing of Peace Treaty between Egypt and Israel, Mar. 26.

1979, May 26   **Photo.**   **Perf. 11½**
1106 A535 20m yellow & dk brn   .55   .30
Return of Al Arish to Egypt.

Honeycomb with Food Symbols — A536

1979, May 15
1107 A536 20m multicolored   .35   .25
8th anniversary of movement to establish food security.

Coins, 1959, 1979 — A537

Perf. 11½x11
1979, June 1   **Wmk. 342**   **Photo.**
1108 A537 20m yellow & gray   .45   .25
25th anniversary of the Egyptian Mint.

Egypt No. 1104 under Magnifying Glass A538

1979, June 1   **Perf. 11**
1109 A538 20m green, blk & brn   .55   .25
Philatelic Society of Egypt, 50th anniversary.

Book, Atom Symbol, Rising Sun — A539

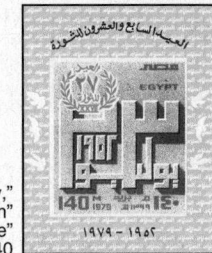

"23 July," "Revolution" and "Peace" A540

Perf. 11½x11
1979, July 23   **Wmk. 342**
1110 A539 20m multicolored   .50   .25
Miniature Sheet
Imperf
1111 A540 140m multicolored   3.75   3.75
27th anniversary of July 23rd revolution.

Musicians — A541

1979, Aug. 22   **Perf. 11½**
1112 A541 10m multicolored   .25   .25
For use on greeting cards.

Dove over Map of Suez Canal — A542

Wmk. 342
1979, Oct. 6   **Photo.**   **Perf. 11½**
1113 A542 20m blue & brown   .65   .30
October War against Israel, 6th anniv.

Prehistoric Mammal Skeleton, Map of Africa — A543

Perf. 11½x11
1979, Oct. 9   **Photo.**   **Wmk. 342**
1114 A543 20m multicolored   2.00   .35
Egyptian Geological Museum, 75th anniv.

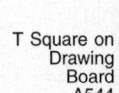

T Square on Drawing Board A544

1979, Oct. 11   **Perf. 11**
1115 A544 20m multicolored   .65   .25
Engineers Day.

Human Rights Emblem Over Globe A545

Boy Balancing IYC Emblem A546

Perf. 11½
1979, Oct. 24   **Photo.**   **Unwmk.**
1116 A545   45m multicolored   .65   .30
1117 A546 140m multicolored   1.50   1.25
UN Day and Intl. Year of the Child.

International Savings Day — A547

1979, Oct. 31
1118 A547 70m multicolored   1.00   .45

A548

Design: Shooting championship emblem.

1979, Nov. 16
1119 A548 20m multicolored   .65   .25
20th International Military Shooting Championship, Cairo.

International Palestinian Solidarity Day — A549

1979, Nov. 29   **Perf. 11x11½**
1120 A549 45m multicolored   .85   .30

Dove Holding Olive Branch, Rotary Emblem, Globe — A550

1979, Dec. 3   **Photo.**   **Perf. 11½**
1121 A550 140m multicolored   1.60   1.00
Rotary Intl., 75th anniv,; Cairo Rotary Club, 50th anniv.

Arms Factories, 25th Anniversary A551

Perf. 11½x11
1979, Dec. 23   **Photo.**   **Wmk. 342**
1122 A551 20m lt olive grn & brn   .55   .25

Aly El Garem (1881-1949) — A552

Poets: No. 1124, Mahmoud Samy El Baroudy (1839-1904).

1979, Dec. 25   **Perf. 11x11½**
1123 A552 20m dk brn & yel brn   .50   .30
1124 A552 20m brn & dk brn   .50   .30
a.   Pair, #1123-1124   1.25   1.25

Pharaonic Capital — A553

Post Day: Various Pharaonic capitals.

1980, Jan. 2   **Unwmk.**   **Perf. 11½**
1125 A553 20m multicolored   .45   .30
1126 A553 45m multicolored   .65   .65
1127 A553 70m multicolored   1.00   .75
1128 A553 140m multicolored   2.75   1.50
    a.   Strip of 4, #1125-1128   6.50   .650

Golden Goddess of Writing, Fair Emblem — A554

1980, Feb. 2   **Photo.**   **Perf. 11½**
1129 A554 20m multicolored   1.10   .25
   12th Cairo Intl. Book Fair, Jan. 24-Feb. 4.

Exhibition Catalogue and Medal — A555

1980, Feb. 2
1130 A555 20m multicolored   .60   .30
   13th Biennial Exhibition of Fine Arts, Alexandria.

13th Cairo International Fair — A556

1980, Mar. 8   **Photo.**   **Perf. 11x11½**
1131 A556 20m multicolored   .60   .25

Kiosk of Trajan A557

   a, Kiosk of Trajan. b, Temple of Korasy, entry at right. c, Temple of Ksalabsha, carvings on frame. d, Temple of Philae, 5 columns..

1980, Mar. 10   **Perf. 11½**
1132   Strip of 4 + label   5.50   5.50
   a.-d. A557 70m, any single   1.10   .85
   UNESCO campaign to save Nubian monuments, 20th anniversary. Shown on stamps are Temples of Philae, Kalabsha, Korasy.

Physicians' Day — A558

1980, Mar. 18   **Perf. 11x11½**
1133 A558 20m multicolored   .60   .25

Rectification Movement, 9th Anniversary A559

1980, May 15   **Photo.**   **Wmk. 342**
1134 A559 20m multicolored   .60   .25

Re-opening of Suez Canal, 5th Anniversary — A560

1980, June 5   **Perf. 11½**
1135 A560 140m multicolored   1.50   1.00

Prevention of Cruelty to Animals Week — A561

1980, June 5
1136 A561 20m lt yel grn & gray   .85   .25

Industry Day — A562

Perf. 11½x11
1980, July 12   **Photo.**   **Wmk. 342**
1137 A562 20m multicolored   .55   .25

Leaf with Text — A563

Family Protection Emblem A564

1980, July 23   **Perf. 11½**
1138 A563 20m multicolored   .60   .25
       Souvenir Sheet
       Imperf
1139 A564 140m multicolored   3.75   3.75
   July 23rd Revolution, 28th anniv.; Social Security Year.

Erksous Seller and Nakrazan Player — A565

Perf. 11½
1980, Aug. 8   **Unwmk.**   **Photo.**
1140 A565 10m multicolored   .50   .25
    For use on greeting cards.

October War Against Israel, 7th Anniv. A566

1980, Oct. 6   **Litho.**
1141 A566 20m multicolored   .75   .25

Islamic and Coptic Columns — A567

International Telecommunications Union Emblem — A568

Wmk. 342
1980, Oct. 24   **Photo.**   **Perf. 11½**
1142 A567 70m multicolored   .80   .60
1143 A568 140m multicolored   1.60   1.25
   UN Day. Campaign to save Egyptian monuments (70m), Intl. Telecommunications Day (140m).

Hegira (Pilgrimage Year) — A569

1980, Nov. 9   **Litho.**   **Perf. 11x11½**
1144 A569 45m multicolored   .70   .30

Opening of Suez Canal Third Branch — A570

Perf. 11½x11
1980, Dec. 16   **Photo.**   **Wmk. 342**
1145 A570 70m multicolored   1.10   .60

Mustafa Sadek El-Rafai (1880-1927), Writer — A571

   No. 1147, Ali Mustafa Mousharafa (1898-1950), mathematician (with glasses). No. 1148, Ali Ibrahim (1880-1947), surgeon.

1980, Dec. 23   **Perf. 11x11½**
1146 A571 20m green & brown   .50   .30
1147 A571 20m green & brown   .50   .30
1148 A571 20m green & brown   .50   .30
   a.   Strip of 3, #1146-1148   2.00   2.00
    See Nos. 1178-1179.

Perf. 11½
1981, Jan. 2   **Unwmk.**
1149 A572 70m shown   1.25   .50
1150 A572 70m Scarab, reverse   1.25   .50
    Post Day.

von Stephan, UPU — A573

Perf. 11x11½
1981, Jan. 7   **Wmk. 342**
1151 A573 140m grnsh bl & dk brn   1.75   .70
   Heinrich von Stephan (1831-97), founder of UPU.

13th Cairo International Book Fair — A574

1981, Feb. 1   **Perf. 11½x11**
1152 A574 20m multicolored   .60   .25

14th Cairo International Fair, Mar. 14-28 — A575

Perf. 11x11½
1981, Mar. 14   **Photo.**   **Wmk. 342**
1153 A575 20m multicolored   .60   .25

Rural Electrification Authority, 10th Anniversary A576

1981, Mar. 18
1154 A576 20m multicolored   .60   .25

Veterans' Day — A577

1981, Mar. 26
1155 A577 20m multicolored   .60   .25

Intl. Dentistry Conf., Cairo — A578

Perf. 11x11½
1981, Apr. 14   **Photo.**   **Wmk. 342**
1156 A578 20m red & olive   .60   .25

Trade Union Emblem — A579

Perf. 11x11½
1981, May 1   Photo.   Wmk. 342
1157 A579 20m brt blue & dk brn   .60   .25

International Confederation of Arab Trade Unions, 25th anniv.

Nurses' Day — A580

1981, May 12
1158 A580 20m multicolored   .60   .25

Irrigation Equipment (Electrification Movement) A581

1981, May 15   *Perf. 11½*
1159 A581 20m multicolored   .60   .25

Air Force Day — A582

Perf. 11x11½
1981, June 30   Photo.   Wmk. 342
1160 A582 20m multicolored   .60   .25

A583

Designs: No. 1161, Flag Surrounding Map of Suez Canal. No. 1162, Emblems.

Wmk. 342
1981, July 23   Photo.   *Perf. 11½*
1161 A583 20m multicolored   .60   .25
1162 A583 20m multicolored   .60   .25

July 23rd Revolution, 29th anniv.; Social Defense Year.

Lotus — A584

Wmk. 342
1981, July 29   Photo.   *Perf. 11*
1163 A584 10m multicolored   .60   .25

For use on greeting cards.

Kemal Ataturk — A585

1981, Aug. 10   *Perf. 11x11½*
1164 A585 140m dp bluish grn, brn   2.25 1.25

Orabi Revolution Centenary — A586

20m, Orabi Pasha, Leader of Egyptian Force.

Perf. 11x11½
1981, Sept. 9   Photo.   Wmk. 342
1165 A586 20m dp bluish grn, brn   .60   .25

A587

1981, Sept. 14
1166 A587 45m ochre, blk, brn   .85   .25

World Muscular Athletics Championships, Cairo.

A588

Perf. 11x11½
1981, Sept. 26   Photo.   Wmk. 342
1167 A588 45m multicolored   .60   .25

Ministry of Industry and Mineral Resources, 25th anniv.

20th Intl. Occupational Health Congress, Cairo — A589

1981, Sept. 28   *Perf. 11½x11*
1168 A589 20m multicolored   .60   .25

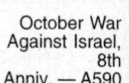

October War Against Israel, 8th Anniv. — A590

1981, Oct. 6
1169 A590 20m multicolored   .65   .25

World Food Day — A591

13th World Telecommunications Day — A592

Intl. Year of the Disabled A593

Fight Against Apartheid A594

Perf. 11½x11, 11x11½
1981, Oct. 24   Photo.   Wmk. 342
1170 A591 10m multicolored   .45   .25
1171 A592 20m multicolored   .60   .25
1172 A593 45m multicolored   .80   .55
1173 A594 230m multicolored   3.75 1.10
   Nos. 1170-1173 (4)   5.60 2.15

United Nations Day.

Pres. Anwar Sadat (1917-81) A595

Perf. 11x11½
1981, Nov. 14   Unwmk.
1174 A595 30m multicolored   1.25   .75
1175 A595 230m multicolored   5.50 3.00

Establishment of Shura Council — A596

Perf. 11½x11
1981, Dec. 12   Photo.   Wmk. 342
1176 A596 45m purple & yellow   .60   .30

Agricultural Credit and Development Bank, 50th Anniv. — A597

1981, Dec. 15   *Perf. 11x11½*
1177 A597 20m multicolored   .50   .25

Famous Men Type of 1980

30m, Ali el-Ghayati (1885-1956), journalist. 60m, Omar Ebn sl-Fared (1181-1234), Sufi poet.

Perf. 11x11½
1981, Dec. 21   Photo.   Wmk. 342
1178 A571 30m green & brown   .40   .30
1179 A571 60m green & brown   .65   .45
  a.   Pair, #1178-1179   1.50 1.50

20th Anniv. of African Postal Union — A598

1981, Dec. 21   *Perf. 11½x11*
1180 A598 60m multicolored   .95   .35

14th Cairo Intl. Book Fair — A599

1982, Jan. 28
1181 A599 3p brown & yellow   .65   .25

Arab Trade Union of Egypt, 25th Anniv. — A600

1982, Jan. 30
1182 A600 3p multicolored   .45   .25

Khartoum Branch of Cairo University, 25th Anniv. — A601

Perf. 11½x11
1982, Mar. 4   Wmk. 342
1183 A601 6p blue & green   .75   .35

15th Cairo Intl. Fair — A602

1982, Mar. 13   *Perf. 11x11½*
1184 A602 3p multicolored   .60   .25

50th Anniv. of Al-Ghardaka Marine Biological Station — A603

Fish of the Red Sea: 10m, Lined butterfly fish. 30m, Blue-banded sea perch. 60m, Batfish. 230m, Blue-spotted boxfish.

1982, Apr. 24   Litho.   *Perf. 11½x11*
1185   10m multicolored   .90   .60
1186   30m multicolored   1.10   .70
1187   60m multicolored   1.50   .90
1188   230m multicolored   3.50 2.00
  a.   A603 Block of 4, #1185-1188   7.50 7.50

Liberation of the Sinai — A604

1982, Apr. 25   Photo.   *Perf. 11x11½*
1189 A604 3p multicolored   .65   .25

50th Anniv. of Egypt Air — A605

1982, May 7   Photo.   *Perf. 11½x11*
1190 A605 23p multicolored   3.25 2.25

Minaret — A606

Al Azhar Mosque A607

a, shown. b, Two terraces. c, Three terraces. d, Two turrets at top.

Perf. 11x11½
1982, June 28   Photo.   Wmk. 342
1191   Strip of 4 + label   5.00 5.00
  a.-d.   A606 6p any single, multi   .75   .55

Souvenir Sheet
Unwmk.   *Imperf.*
1192 A607 23p multicolored   6.25 6.25
Al Azhar Mosque millennium.
No. 1192 airmail.

Dove — A608

Flower in Natl. Colors A609

Perf. 11x11½
1982, July 23   Photo.   Wmk. 342
1193 A608 3p multicolored   .50 .25
Souvenir Sheet
Imperf
1194 A609 23p multicolored   4.00 4.00
30th anniv. of July 23rd Revolution.

World Tourism Day — A610

Design: Sphinx, pyramid of Cheops, St. Catherine's Tower.

Perf. 11½x11
1982, Sept. 27   Photo.   Wmk. 342
1195 A610 23p multicolored   3.50 2.25

October War Against Israel, 9th Anniv. — A611

1982, Oct. 6
1196 A611 3p Memorial, map   .65 .25

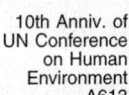

Biennale of Alexandria Art Exhibition — A612

1982, Oct. 17   *Perf. 11x11½*
1197 A612 3p multicolored   .60 .25

10th Anniv. of UN Conference on Human Environment A613

2nd UN Conference on Peaceful Uses of Outer Space, Vienna, Aug. 9-21 — A614

Scouting Year — A615

TB Bacillus Centenary A616

Perf. 11½x11, 11½ (A615)
1982, Oct. 24
1198 A613 3p multicolored   .50 .35
1199 A614 6p multicolored   .80 .55
1200 A615 6p multicolored   1.10 .55
1201 A616 8p multicolored   1.25 .75
Nos. 1198-1201 (4)   3.65 2.20
United Nations Day.

50th Anniv. of Air Force — A617

1982, Nov. 2   *Perf. 11½x11*
1202 A617 3p Jet, plane   .70 .25

Ahmed Chawki (1868-1932) and Hafez Ibrahim (1871-1932), Poets — A618

Perf. 11½x11
1982, Nov. 25   Photo.   Wmk. 342
1203 A618 6p multicolored   .65 .50

Natl. Research Center, 25th Anniv. — A619

1982, Dec. 12   Photo.   *Perf. 11x11½*
1204 A619 3p red & blue   .70 .30

50th Anniv. of Arab Language Society — A620

1982, Dec. 25   *Perf. 11½x11*
1205 A620 6p multicolored   .80 .50

Year of the Aged — A621

1982, Dec. 25   *Perf. 11x11½*
1206 A621 23p multicolored   3.25 2.00

Post Day — A622

1983, Jan. 2   *Perf. 11½*
1207 A622 3p multicolored   .60 .25

15th Cairo Intl. Book Fair — A623

Perf. 11x11½
1983, Jan. 25   Photo.   Wmk. 342
1208 A623 3p blue & red   .65 .25

Police Day — A624

1983, Jan. 25   *Perf. 11½x11*
1209 A624 3p multicolored   .65 .25

16th Cairo Intl. Fair — A625

Perf. 11x11½
1983, Mar. 2   Photo.   Wmk. 342
1210 A625 3p multicolored   .65 .30

5th UN African Map Conf., Cairo — A626

1983, Mar. 2
1211 A626 3p lt green & blue   .70 .30

A627

Design: African ministers of transport, communications and planning, 3rd conference.

1983, Mar. 8   *Perf. 11½x11*
1212 A627 23p green & blue   1.75 1.00

Victory in African Soccer Cup — A628

1983, Mar. 20   *Perf. 11x11½*
1213 A628 3p Heading   .55 .30
1214 A628 3p Kick   .55 .30
a.   Pair, #1213-1214   1.25 1.25

World Health Day and Natl. Blood Donation Campaign — A629

Perf. 11x11½
1983, Apr. 2   Photo.   Wmk. 342
1215 A629 3p olive & red   .70 .25

Org. of African Trade Union Unity — A630

Perf. 11½x11
1983, Apr. 21   Photo.   Wmk. 342
1216 A630 3p multicolored   .65 .30

1st Anniv. of Sinai Liberation — A631

1983, Apr. 25   *Perf. 11x11½*
1217 A631 3p multicolored   .70 .30

75th Anniv. of Entomology Society — A632

3p, Emblem (Holy Scarab).

1983, May 23
1218 A632 3p blue & black   .70 .30

Chrysanthemums A633

1983, June 11   Photo.   *Perf. 11½x11*
1219 A633 20m green & org red   .40 .25
For use on greeting cards.

5th African Handball Championship, Cairo — A634

Perf. 11½x11
1983, July 22   Photo.   Wmk. 342
1220 A634 6p brown & dk grn   .65 .30

31st Anniv. of Revolution — A635

1983, July 23   *Perf. 11½*
1221 A635 3p multicolored   .45 .25

Simon Bolivar (1783-1830) — A636

1983, Aug.   *Perf. 11x11½*
1222 A636 23p brown & dull grn 1.75 1.00

Centenary of Arrival of Natl. Hero Orabi in Ceylon — A637

3p, Map, Orabi, El-Zahra School.

Perf. 11½x11
1983, Aug. 25   Photo.   Wmk. 342
1223 A637 3p multicolored   .55 .25

Islamic Vase, Museum Building — A638

1983, Sept. 14   Photo.   Perf. 11½x11
1224 A638 3p yel brn & dk brn   .85 .30
Reopening of Islamic Museum.

October War Against Israel, 10th Anniv. — A639

1983, Oct. 6   Perf. 11½
1225 A639 3p multicolored   .70 .25

2nd Pharaonic Race — A640

1983, Oct. 17   Perf. 11½
1226 A640 23p multicolored   2.25 1.25

United Nations Day — A641

1983, Oct. 24   Photo.   Perf. 11
1227 A641 3p IMO, ships, horiz.   .60 .25
1228 A641 6p ITU, UPU   .75 .50
1229 A641 6p FAO, UN, grain   .75 .50
1230 A641 23p UN, ocean   2.50 1.75
Nos. 1227-1230 (4)   4.60 3.00

4th World Karate Championship, Cairo — A642

1983, Nov.   Photo.   Perf. 13
1231 A642 3p multicolored   .70 .30

Intl. Palestinian Cooperation Day — A643

1983, Nov. 29   Photo.   Perf. 13x13½
1232 A643 6p Dome of the Rock   1.00 .30

75th Anniv. of Faculty of Fine Arts, Cairo — A644

1983, Nov. 30   Photo.   Perf. 13
1233 A644 3p multicolored   .55 .25

75th Anniv. of Cairo University — A645

1983, Nov. 30   Perf. 11x11½
1234 A645 3p multicolored   .55 .25
   a.   Perf. 13¼x12¾

Intl. Egyptian Society of Mother and Child Care — A646

1983, Nov. 30   Perf. 11½x11
1235 A646 3p multicolored   .55 .25

Org. of African Unity, 20th Anniv. — A647

1983, Dec. 20   Photo.   Wmk. 342
Perf. 11x11½
1236 A647 3p multicolored   .55 .25

World Heritage Convention, 10th Anniv. — A648

1983, Dec. 24
1237 A648   Strip of 3   2.25 2.25
   a.   3p Wood carving, Islamic   .70 .45
   b.   3p Coptic tapestry   .70 .45
   c.   3p Ramses II Thebes   .70 .45

Post Day — A649

Restored Forts: 6p, Quatbay. 23p, Mosque, Salah El-Din.

1984, Jan. 2   Perf. 13
1238 A649 6p multicolored   .80 .45
1239 A649 23p multicolored   2.50 1.25

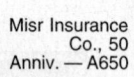

Misr Insurance Co., 50 Anniv. — A650

1984, Jan. 14   Perf. 11½x11
1240 A650 3p multicolored   .55 .30

16th Cairo Intl. Book Fair — A651

Perf. 13½x13
1984, Jan. 26   Photo.   Wmk. 342
1241 A651 3p multicolored   .55 .25

17th Cairo Intl. Fair — A652

Perf. 11½x11
1984, Mar. 10   Photo.   Wmk. 342
1242 A652 3p multicolored   .55 .30

25th Anniv. of Asyut University — A653

1984, Mar. 10   Perf. 11x11½
1243 A653 3p multicolored   .55 .25

75th Anniv. of Cooperative Unions — A654

1984, Mar. 17
1244 A654 3p multicolored   .55 .25

World Theater Day A655

Mahmoud Mokhtar (1891-1934), Sculptor A656

Perf. 11x11½, 11½x11
1984, Mar. 27   Photo.   Unwmk.
1245 A655 3p Masks   .55 .25
1246 A656 3p Pride of the Nile   .55 .25

World Health Day and Fight Against Polio — A657

Perf. 11½x11
1984, Apr. 7   Photo.   Wmk. 342
1247 A657 3p Polio vaccine   1.00 .30

2nd Anniv. of Sinai Liberation — A658

1984, Apr. 25
1248 A658 3p Doves, map   .55 .25

Africa Day — A659

Perf. 12½x13½
1984, May 25   Photo.   Wmk. 342
1249 A659 3p Map, UN emblem   .55 .25

Satellite, Waves — A660

1984, May 31   Perf. 11x11½
1250 A660 3p multicolored   .55 .25
Radio broadcasting in Egypt, 50th anniv.

Carnations — A661

1984, June 1
1251 A661 2p red & green   .45 .25
For use on greeting cards.

Intl. Cairo Arab Arts Biennale — A662

1984, June 1   Perf. 13½x12½
1252 A662 3p multicolored   .55 .25

July Revolution, 32nd Anniv. — A663

3p, Atomic energy, agriculture.

Wmk. 342
1984, July 23   Photo.   Perf. 11
1253 A663 3p multicolored   .55 .25

A664

1984 Summer Olympics: a, Boxing. b, Basketball. c, Volleyball. d, Soccer.

1984, July 28
1254   Strip of 4 + label   5.75 5.75
   a.-d.   A664 3p any single   .45 .25
Size: 130x80mm
Imperf
1255 A664 30p like No. 1254   4.25 4.25

A665

Wmk. 342
1984, Aug. 13   Photo.   Perf. 11
1256 A665 3p bl & multi   .55 .25
1257 A665 23p grn & multi   2.50 1.40
2nd Genl. Conference of Egyptians Abroad, Aug. 11-15, Cairo.

Youth Hostels, 30th
Anniv. — A666

1984, Sept. 22   Photo.   Wmk. 342
1258 A666 3p Youths, emblem   .55 .25

Egypt Tour Co., 50th
Anniv. — A667

1984, Sept. 27
1259 A667 3p Emblem, sphinx   .60 .25

October War Against
Israel, 11th
Anniv. — A668

1984, Oct. 6
1260 A668 3p Map, eagle   .55 .25

Egypt-Sudan
Unity — A669

1984, Oct. 12
1261 A669 3p Map of Nile, arms   .55 .25

UN Day — A670

Perf. 13½x12½
1984, Oct. 24   Photo.   Wmk. 342
1262 A670 3p UNICEF Emblem,
child   .55 .25

UN campaign for infant survival.

Tanks, Emblem — A671

1984, Nov. 10
1263 A671 3p multicolored   .60 .25
Military Equipment Exhibition, Cairo, Nov. 10-14.

Tolon Mosque,
Egypt — A672

1984, Dec. 23   Photo.   Perf. 11½x11
1264 A672 3p multicolored   .65 .25
Ahmed Ebn Tolon (A.D. 835-884), Gov. of Egypt, founder of Kataea City.

A673

1984, Dec. 23   Perf. 11x11½
1265 A673 3p multicolored   .55 .25
Kamel el-Kilany (1897-1959), author.

Globe and Congress
Emblem — A674

Perf. 11x11½
1984, Dec. 26   Photo.   Wmk. 342
1266 A674 3p lt blue, ver & blk   .65 .25
29th Intl. Congress on the History of Medicine, Dec. 27, 1984-Jan. 1, 1985, Cairo.

Academy of the
Arts, 25th
Anniv. — A675

1984, Dec. 31   Perf. 13
1267 A675 3p Emblem in spotlights   .60 .25

A676

Design: Pharaoh Receiving Message, Natl. Postal Museum, Cairo.

1985, Jan. 2   Perf. 11½x11
1268 A676 3p brown, lt bl & ver   .65 .25
Postal Museum, 50th anniv.

Intl. Union of
Architects, 15th
Conference, Jan.
14-Feb.
15 — A677

1985, Jan. 20
1269 A677 3p multicolored   .60 .25

Seated Pharaonic
Scribe — A678

1985, Jan. 22   Perf. 11x11½
1270 A678 3p brt org & dk blue grn   .70 .30
17th Intl. Book Fair, Jan. 22-Feb. 3, Cairo.

Wheat, Cogwheels, Fair
Emblem — A679

1985, Mar. 9   Perf. 13½x13
1271 A679 3p multicolored   .60 .25
18th Intl. Fair, Mar. 9-22, Cairo.

Return of Sinai to
Egypt, 3rd
Anniv. — A680

1985, Apr. 25   Wmk. 342   Litho.
1272 A680 5p multicolored   1.00 .30

Ancient Artifacts — A681

A681a

A681b

A681c
A681d

A681e
A681f

A681g
A681h

A681i
A681j

A681k
A681l

A681m
A681n

A681o

Designs: 1p, God Mout, limestone sculpture, 360-340 B.C. 2p, No. 1281, Five wading birds, bas-relief. 3p, No. 1276, Seated statue, Ramses II, Temple of Luxor. No. 1276A, Vase. 8p, 15p, Slave bearing votive fruit offering, mural. 10p, Double-handled flask. 11p, Sculpted head of woman. No. 1282, Pitcher.

30p, 50p, Decanter. 35p, Temple of Karnak carved capitals. £1, Mosque.

1985-90   Photo.   Unwmk.   Perf. 11½
1273	A681	1p brown olive	.40	.25
1274	A681a	2p brt grnsh bl	.40	.25
1275	A681b	3p yel brn	.40	.25
1276	A681c	5p dk violet	.50	.25
1276A	A681d	5p bister	.40	.25
1277	A681e	8p pale ol grn, sep & brn	.75	.25
1278	A681f	10p dk vio & bl	.60	.25
1279	A681g	11p blksh pur	.90	.30
1280	A681h	15p pale yel, sep & brn	1.40	.30
1281	A681i	20p yel grn	.60	.30
1282	A681j	20p dk grn & yel	.60	.30
1283	A681k	30p ol bis & buff	.70	.30
1284	A681l	35p sep & pale yel	1.00	.60
1285	A681m	50p vio & buff	1.25	.50
1285A	A681n	£1 brn & buff	3.00	1.25
1286	A681o	£2 sepia & yel	6.00	2.00
	Nos. 1273-1286 (16)		18.90	7.60

No. 1276A is 18x23mm.
No. 1278 exists dated "1990."
See Nos. 1467, 1470, 1472.
Issued: 1p, 2p, 3p, No. 1276, 8p, 11p, 15p, 5/1/85; 35p, 7/7/85; No. 1281, 4/1/86; 10p, 10/1/89; £2, 12/1/89; No. 1282, 2/1/90; 30p, 50p, 2/5/90; £1, 2/8/90; No. 1276A, 12/15/90.

Helwan University
School of Music,
50th
Anniv. — A682

1985, May 15
1287 A682 5p multicolored   .75 .30

El-Moulid Bride, Folk
Doll — A683

1985
1288 A683 2p orange & multi   .50 .25
1289 A683 5p red & multi   .60 .30
Festivals 1985. Issued: 2p, 6/11; 5p, 8/10. For use on greeting cards.

A684

Winning teams: a, b, Cairo Sports Stadium. c, El-Zamalek Club, white uniform, 1983. d, Natl. Club, red uniform, 1984. e, El-Mokawiloon Club (Arab Contractor Club), orange uniform, 1984.

1985, June 17   Perf. 13½x13
1290   Strip of 5   5.50 5.50
  a.-e. A684 5p any single   .80 .50
1985 Africa Cup Soccer Championships. Cairo Sports Stadium, 25th anniv. Nos. 1290a-1290b have continuous design.

A685

1985, July 23   Perf. 11½x11
1291 A685 5p blue, brn & yel   .80 .30
Egyptian Television, 25th anniv. Egyptian Revolution, 33rd anniv.

Suez Canal Reopening, 10th Anniv. A686

Perf. 13x13½
1985, July 23   **Litho.**   **Wmk. 342**
1292 A686 5p multicolored   .80 .30
Egyptian Revolution, 33rd anniv.

Ahmed Hamdi Memorial Underwater Tunnel — A687

1985, July 23   **Perf. 13½x13**
1293 A687 5p blue, vio & org   .60 .25
Egyptian Revolution, 33rd anniv.

Souvenir Sheet

Aswan High Dam, 25th Anniv. A688

Wmk. 342
1985, July 23   **Photo.**   **Imperf.**
1294 A688 30p multicolored   4.00 4.00

Heart, Map, Olive Laurel, Conference Emblem — A689

1985, Aug. 10   **Litho.**   **Perf. 13½x13**
1295 A689 15p multicolored   1.25 .85
Egyptian Emigrants, 3rd general conference, Aug. 10-14, Cairo.

Natl. Tourism Ministry, 50th Anniv. A690

1985, Sept. 10   **Perf. 13x13½**
1296 A690 5p multicolored   .55 .30

October War Against Israel, 12th Anniv. A691

1985, Oct. 6
1297 A691 5p multicolored   .60 .30

Air Scouts Assoc., 30th Anniv. A692

1985, Oct. 15   **Photo.**   **Perf. 11½**
1298 A692 5p Emblem   .80 .30

UN Day, Meteorology Day — A693

5p, UN emblem, weather map.

1985, Oct. 24
1299 A693 5p multicolored   .55 .25

UN, 40th Anniv. — A694

1985, Oct. 24
1300 A694 15p multicolored   1.25 .85

Intl. Youth Year — A695

1985, Oct. 24
1301 A695 5p multicolored   .55 .25

A696

1985, Oct. 24
1302 A696 15p blue & int blue   1.25 .85
Intl. Communications Development Program.

2nd Intl. Dentistry Conference — A697

Emblem, hieroglyphics of Hassi Raa, 1st known dentist.

1985, Oct. 29   **Perf. 11x11½**
1303 A697 5p beige & pale bl vio   .75 .30

Emblem, Squash Player — A698

1985, Nov. 18   **Photo.**   **Perf. 11½**
1304 A698 5p multicolored   .65 .25
1985 World Squash Championships, Nov. 18-Dec. 4.

A699

1985, Nov. 2   **Litho.**   **Perf. 13½x13**
1305 A699 5p multicolored   .55 .30
4th Intl. Conference on the Biography and Sunna of Mohammed.

A700

1985, Dec. 1   **Photo.**   **Perf. 11x11½**
1306 A700 5p multicolored   .55 .25
1st Conference on the Development of Vocational Training.

Natl. Olympic Committee, 75th Anniv. — A701

1985, Dec. 28   **Photo.**   **Perf. 13x13½**
1307 A701 5p multicolored   .60 .30

18th Intl. Book Fair, Cairo — A702

1986, Jan. 21   **Perf. 11x11½**
1308 A702 5p Pharaonic scribe   .55 .25

CODATU III — A703

1986, Jan. 26   **Perf. 11½**
1309 A703 5p lt ol grn, ver & grnsh bl   .55 .25
3rd Intl. Conference on Urban Transportation in Developing Countries, Cairo.

Central Bank, 25th Anniv. A704

1986, Jan. 30   **Perf. 13x13½**
1310 A704 5p multicolored   .55 .25

Cairo Postal Traffic Center Inauguration A705

1986, Jan. 30   **Perf. 11½x11**
1311 A705 5p blue & dk brown   .55 .25

Pharaonic Mural, Btah Hotteb's Tomb at Saqqara — A706

1986, Feb. 27   **Photo.**   **Perf. 11½x11**
1312 A706 5p yel, gldn brn & brn   .70 .35
Faculty of Commerce, Cairo Univ., 75th anniv.

Cairo Intl. Fair, Mar. 8-21 — A707

1986, Mar. 8   **Litho.**   **Perf. 13½x13**
1313 A707 5p multicolored   .55 .25

Queen Nefertiti, Sinai — A708

Perf. 13x13½
1986, Apr. 25   **Litho.**   **Wmk. 342**
1314 A708 5p multicolored   .70 .30
Return of the Sinai to Egypt, 4th anniv.

Ministry of Health, 50th Anniv. — A709

1986, Apr. 10   **Perf. 13½x13**
1315 A709 5p multicolored   .55 .30

1986 Census A710

1986, May 26   **Photo.**   **Perf. 11½**
1316 A710 15p brn, grnsh bl & yel bis   1.00 .50

Egypt, Winner of African Soccer Cup — A711

No. 1317, English inscription below cup. No. 1318, Arabic inscription below cup.

1986, May 31   **Perf. 13½x13**
1317 A711 5p multicolored   .65 .45
1318 A711 5p multicolored   .65 .45
   a.   Pair, #1317-1318   1.50 1.50

Festivals, Roses — A712

1986, June 2   **Perf. 11½**
1319 A712 5p multicolored   .55 .25
For use on greeting cards.

World Environment
Day — A713

15p, Emblem, smokestacks.

1986, June 5   *Perf. 13½x13*
1320 A713 15p multicolored   1.25 .50

July 23rd
Revolution, 34th
Anniv. — A714

1986, July 23   Litho.   Perf. 13
1321 A714 5p gray grn, scar & yel
bis   .60 .25

6th African Roads
Conference, Cairo,
Sept. 22-26 — A715

Perf. 13½x13
1986, Sept. 21   Litho.   Wmk. 342
1322 A715 15p multicolored   1.25 .55

October War
Against Israel,
13th
Anniv. — A716

1986, Oct. 6   Litho.   Perf. 13
1323 A716 5p multicolored   1.00 .30

Engineers'
Syndicate, 40th
Anniv. — A717

1986, Oct. 11   Photo.   Perf. 11½
1324 A717 5p lt blue, brn & pale
grn   .55 .25

Workers' Cultural
Education Assoc., 25th
Anniv. — A718

1986, Oct. 11   Perf. 11x11½
1325 A718 5p orange & rose vio .55 .25

Intl. Peace Year — A719

1986, Oct. 24
1326 A719 5p blue, grn & pale sal .55 .25

First Oil Well in Egypt,
Cent. — A720

1986, Nov. 7   Photo.   Perf. 11½
1327 A720 5p dull grn, blk & pale
yel   .65 .25

UN Child Survival
Campaign
A721

1986, Nov. 20   Litho.   Perf. 13
1328 A721 5p multicolored   .60 .25

Ahmed Amin,
Philosopher — A722

1986, Dec. 20   Perf. 11½
1329 A722 5p pale grn, pale yel &
brn   .55 .25

National Theater, 50th
Anniv. — A723

1986, Dec. 20   Perf. 13½x13
1330 A723 5p multicolored   .55 .25

Post
Day — A724

Step Pyramid, Saqqara, King Zoser.

Perf. 13x13½
1987, Jan. 2   Litho.   Wmk. 342
1331 A724 5p multicolored   .65 .30

19th Intl. Book
Fair,
Cairo — A725

1987, Jan. 25   Litho.   Perf. 13
1332 A725 5p multicolored   .60 .30

5th World
Conference on
Islamic Education
A726

Wmk. 342
1987, Mar. 8   Litho.   Perf. 13
1333 A726 5p multicolored   .55 .25

20th Intl. Fair,
Cairo — A727

5p, Good workers medal.

1987, Mar. 21   Photo.   Perf. 11½
1334 A727 5p multicolored   .55 .25

Veteran's
Day — A728

1987, Mar. 26
1335 A728 5p multicolored   .55 .30

Intl. Gardens
Inauguration,
Nasser
City — A729

1987, Mar. 30   Litho.   Perf. 13
1336 A729 15p multicolored   1.10 .60

World Health
Day — A730

No. 1337, Mother feeding child. No. 1338,
Oral rehydration therapy.

1987, Apr. 7   Photo.   Perf. 11½
1337 A730 5p multicolored   .55 .30
Litho.
Perf. 13
1338 A730 5p multicolored   .55 .30

A731

Natl. Team Victory at 1986 Intl. Soccer
Championships — A732

Trophies: No. 1339a, Al Ahly Cup. No.
1339b, National Cup. No. 1339c, Al Zamalek
Cup. No. 1340, Natl. flag, Cairo Stadium and
trophies pictured on No. 1339.

1987, Apr. 19   Litho.   Perf. 13½x13
1339 A731   Strip of 3   1.75 1.75
a.-c.   5p any single   .55 .30
Size: 115x85mm
Imperf
1340 A732 30p multicolored   4.00 4.00

A733

Salah El Din Citadel, Pharoah's Is., Sinai.

1987, Apr. 25
1341 A733 5p sky blue & lt brown .65 .30
Return of the Sinai to Egypt, 5th anniv.

Festivals — A734

1987, May 21   Photo.   Perf. 11½
1342 A734 5p Dahlia   .55 .25

Cultural
Heritage
Exhibition
A735

1987, June 17   Litho.   Perf. 13x13½
1343 A735 15p multicolored   1.00 1.00

Tourism
Year
A736

a, Column and Sphinx, Alexandria. b, St.
Catherine's Monastery, Mt. Sinai. c, Colossi of
Thebes. d, Temple of Theban Triad, Luxor.

1987, June 18
1344 A736   Block of 4   5.25 5.25
a.-d.   15p any single   1.10 .90
See No. C187.

Loyalty
Day — A737

1987, June 26   Perf. 13
1345 A737 5p multicolored   .55 .25

General Intelligence Service, 32nd anniv.

Industry-Agriculture Exhibition — A738

1987, July 23   Photo.   Perf. 11½
1346 A738 5p grn, dull org & blk .55 .25

Intl. Year of Shelter for the Homeless — A739

1987, Sept. 2   Litho.   Perf. 13
1347 A739 5p multicolored   .55   .25
World Architects' Day.

Aida, Performed at Al Ahram Pyramid, Giza — A740

Radamis and troops returning from Ethiopia.

1987, Sept. 21
1348 A740 15p multicolored   1.50   .65
Size: 70x70mm
Imperf
1349 A740 30p multicolored   10.00 10.00

Greater Cairo Subway Inauguration A741

1987, Sept. 27   Perf. 13x13½
1350 A741 5p multicolored   1.20   .30

Industry Day — A742

1987, Oct. 1   Perf. 13
1351 A742 5p multicolored   .55   .25

Battle of Hettin, 800th Anniv. — A743

1987, Oct. 6   Photo.   Perf. 11x11½
1352 A743 5p multicolored   .70   .30

UPU Emblem — A744

Perf. 11½
1987, Oct. 24   Unwmk.   Photo.
1353 A744 5p multicolored   .55   .25
UN Executive Council, 40th anniv.; UPU Consultative Council, 30th anniv.

16th Art Biennial of Alexandria — A745

1987, Nov. 7   Litho.   Perf. 13½x13
1354 A745 5p multicolored   .55   .25

Second Intl. Defense Equipment Exhibition, Cairo, Nov. 9-13 — A746

Perf. 13x13½
1987, Nov. 9   Litho.   Unwmk.
1355 A746 5p multicolored   .60   .25

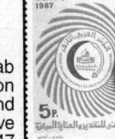

2nd Pan-Arab Congress on Anaesthesia and Intensive Care — A747

Unwmk.
1987, Dec. 1   Litho.   Perf. 13
1356 A747 5p multicolored   .65   .30

Intl. Orthopedic and Traumatology Conference — A748

1987, Dec. 1   Perf. 13½x13
1357 A748 5p gray, red brn & bl   .55   .25

Selim Hassan (1887-1961), Egyptologist, and Hieroglyphs A749

Abdel Hamid Badawi (1887-1965), Jurist, and Scales of Justice A750

1987, Dec. 30   Perf. 13½x13
Litho.   Unwmk.
1358 A749 5p multicolored   .55   .25
1359 A750 5p multicolored   .55   .25

Stamp Day 1988 A751

Pyramids of the Pharaohs and: a, Cheops. b, Chefren. c, Mycerinus. No. 1360 has a continuous design.

1988, Jan. 2
1360 A751   Strip of 3   5.50   5.50
a.-c.   15p, any single   1.40   .90

Afro-Asian Peoples Solidarity Organization, 30th Anniv. A752

1988, Jan. 10   Perf. 13x13½
1361 A752 15p multicolored   1.00   .55

20th Intl. Book Fair, Cairo — A753

1988, Jan. 26   Perf. 13½x13
1362 A753 5p multicolored   .55   .25

Martrans (Natl. Shipping Line), 25th Anniv. — A754

Unwmk.
1988, Mar. 3   Litho.   Perf. 13
1363 A754 5p multicolored   .85   .25

Cairo Intl. Fair — A755

1988, Mar. 12   Photo.   Perf. 11½x11
1364 A755 5p multicolored   .55   .25

World Health Day 1988: Diabetes — A756

Perf. 11x11½
1988, Apr. 7   Photo.   Unwmk.
1365 A756 5p multicolored   .55   .25

Prince, Fig Tree — A757

1988, Apr. 17   Perf. 11½
1366 A757 5p grn, brn org & brn   .55   .25
1988 Festival. For use on greeting cards.

African Postal Union, 25th Anniv. A758

1988, Apr. 23   Litho.   Perf. 13x13½
1367 A758 15p brt blue   1.00   1.00

Oppose Racial Discrimination — A759

1988, May 25   Photo.   Perf. 11½
1368 A759 5p multicolored   .50   .25

Taw Fek-Hakem (1902-1987), Playwright, Novelist — A760

1988, Aug. 5   Photo.   Perf. 11½
1369 A760 5p brt grn bl & org brn   .60   .25
See Nos. 1383-1384, 1479-1480, 1486, 1500-1502, 1543-1546.

Faculty of Art Education, 50th Anniv. — A761

Perf. 11½
1988, Sept. 10   Photo.   Unwmk.
1370 A761 5p multicolored   .50   .25

A762

1988 Summer Olympics, Seoul — A763

1988, Sept. 17   Litho.   Perf. 13
1371 A762 15p multicolored   1.25   1.25
Size: 96x91mm
Imperf.
1372 A763 30p multicolored   6.25   6.25
No. 1371 is airmail.

October War Against Israel, 15th Anniv. A764

Perf. 13x13½
1988, Oct. 6   Litho.   Unwmk.
1373 A764 5p multicolored   .55   .35

A765

Opening of the Opera House A766

1988, Oct. 10   Perf. 11½
1374 A765 5p multicolored   .55   .30
Size: 112x75mm
Imperf
1375 A766 50p multicolored   3.50   3.50

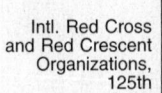

Intl. Red Cross and Red Crescent Organizations, 125th Annivs. — A767

Perf. 11½
1988, Oct. 24   Photo.   Unwmk.
1376 A767 5p green, blk & red   .50 .25

WHO, 40th Anniv. — A768

1988, Oct. 24   Perf. 11x11½
1377 A768 20p multicolored   1.25 1.10

Naguib Mahfouz, 1988 Nobel Prize Winner for Literature
A769

1988, Nov. 7   Litho.   Perf. 13x13½
1378 A769 5p multicolored   .50 .25
See No. C190.

Arab Scouting Organization, 75th Anniv.
A770

1988, Nov. 10
1379 A770 25p multicolored   1.25 1.25

Return of Taba to Egypt
A771

1988, Nov. 15
1380 A771 5p multicolored   .50 .25

Intl. Conference on Orthopedic Surgery, Cairo, Nov. 15-18 — A772

1988, Nov. 15   Photo.   Perf. 11½x11
1381 A772 5p pale yel, brt yel grn & brn   .60 .25

A773

1988, Dec. 3   Perf. 11½
1382 A773 5p multicolored   .50 .25
Ministry of Agriculture, 75th anniv.

A774

Famous Men: No. 1383, Mohamed Hussein Hekal (1888-1956), author, politician. No. 1384, Ahmed Lotfi El Sayed (1872-1963), educator, politician.

Perf. 13½x13
1988, Dec. 29   Litho.   Unwmk.
1383 A774 5p green & red brn   .45 .25
1384 A774 5p green & red brn   .45 .25
  a. Pair, #1383-1384   1.00 1.00

Stamp Day — A775

Statues: 5p, Statue of K. Abr, a priest, 5th cent. No. 1386, Queen Nefert, 4th Dynasty. No. 1387, King Ra Hoteb, 4th Dynasty.

1989, Jan. 2
1385 A775 5p multicolored   .50 .30
1386 A775 25p multicolored   1.60 1.00
1387 A775 25p multicolored   1.60 1.00
  a. Pair, #1386-1387   3.50 3.50
  Nos. 1385-1387 (3)   3.70 2.30

A776

1989, Jan. 10
1388 A776 5p dull green   .55 .25
Jawaharlal Nehru (1889-1964), 1st Prime Minister of independent India.

Nile Hilton Hotel, 30th Anniv.
A777

1989, Feb. 22   Litho.   Perf. 13x13½
1389 A777 5p multicolored   .45 .25

Return of Taba to Egypt — A778

Unwmk.
1989, Mar. 15   Litho.   Perf. 13
1390 A778 5p multicolored   .45 .25

2nd Stage of Cairo Subway — A779

1989, Apr. 12   Litho.   Perf. 13
1391 A779 5p multicolored   1.00 .30

Lantern — A780

1989, May 4   Photo.   Perf. 11½
1392 A780 5p multicolored   .45 .25
1989 Festival. For use on greeting cards.

1st Arab Olympic Day — A781

1989, May 24
1393 A781 5p tan, blk & dull grn   .50 .25

Interparliamentary Union, Cent. — A782

Pyramids and the Parliament Building, Cairo.

1989, June 29   Litho.   Perf. 13x13½
1394 A782 25p shown   1.60 1.25
Size: 87x76mm
Imperf
1395 A782 25p multi, diff.   2.75 2.75

French Revolution, Bicent.
A783

1989, July 14   Photo.   Perf. 11½
1396 A783 25p multicolored   1.50 1.25
No. 1396 is an airmail issue.

African Development Bank, 25th Anniv. — A784

Perf. 11½
1989, Oct. 1   Photo.   Unwmk.
1397 A784 10p multicolored   .45 .25

A785

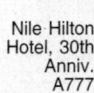

October War Against Israel, 16th Anniv. — A786

1989, Oct. 6   Perf. 13
1398   Strip of 3   1.50 1.50
  a. A785 10p shown   .50 .25
  b. A786 10p shown   .50 .25
  c. A785 10p Battle scene   .50 .25
See No. 1424.

Aga Khan Award for Architecture — A788

Perf. 11½
1989, Oct. 15   Photo.   Unwmk.
1400 A788 35p multicolored   1.25 .60

Natl. Health Insurance Plan, 25th Anniv. — A789

1989, Oct. 24
1401 A789 10p blk, gray & ver   .50 .25

World Post Day — A790

1989, Oct. 24   Perf. 11x11½
1402 A790 35p blue, blk & brt yel 1.00 .50

Statues of Memnon, Thebes
A791

Perf. 11½
1989, Nov. 12   Photo.   Unwmk.
1403 A791 10p lt vio, blk & brt yel grn   .50 .25
Intl. Cong. & Convention Assoc. (ICCA) annual convention, Nov. 11-18, Cairo.

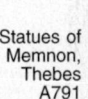

Cairo University School of Agriculture, Cent. — A792

1989, Nov. 15
1404 A792 10p pale grn, blk & brt yel   .45 .25

Cairo Intl. Conference Center — A793

1989, Nov. 20   Perf. 11½x11
1405 A793 5p multicolored   .45 .25

Road Safety Soc., 20th Anniv.
A794

1989, Nov. 20   Perf. 11½
1406 A794 10p multicolored   .45 .25

Alexandria University, 50th Anniv. — A795

1989, Nov. 30   *Perf. 11x11½*
1407 A795 10p pale blue & tan   .45   .25

Portrait of Pasha, Monument in Opera Square, Cairo — A796

Perf. 11½x11
1989, Dec. 31   *Photo.*   *Unwmk.*
1408 A796 10p multicolored   .45   .25
Ibrahim Pasha (d. 1838), army commander from 1825 to 1828.

Famous Men
A797   A798

1989, Dec. 31   *Perf. 11x11½*
1409 A797 10p grn & dk ol grn   .45   .25
1410 A798 10p golden brown   .45   .25
Abd El-Rahman El-Rafei (b. 1889), historian (No. 1409); Abdel Kader El Mazni (b. 1889), man of letters (No. 1410).
See Nos. 1431-1432.

Statue of Priest Ranofr A799   Relief Sculpture of Betah Hoteb A800

1990, Jan. 2   *Perf. 13½x13*
1411 A799 30p multicolored   1.00   .40
1412 A800 30p multicolored   1.00   .40
   a.   Pair, #1411-1412   2.75   2.75
Stamp Day.

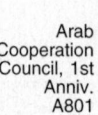

Arab Cooperation Council, 1st Anniv. A801

Perf. 13x13½
1990, Feb. 16   *Photo.*   *Unwmk.*
1413 A801 10p multicolored   .45   .25
1414 A801 35p multicolored   1.25   .60

Emblem, Conference Center — A802

Perf. 13½x13
1990, Mar. 10   *Litho.*   *Unwmk.*
1415 A802 10p brt yel grn, red & blk   .50   .25

Size: 80x59mm
Imperf
1416 A802 30p multicolored   1.50   1.50
African Parliamentary Union 13th general conference, Mar. 10-15.

Road Safety Emblems — A803

1990, Mar. 19   *Photo.*   *Perf. 11x11½*
1417 A803 10p multicolored   .60   .25
Intl. Conference on Road Safety & Accidents in Developing Countries, Mar. 19-22.

Egyptian Wild Daisies — A804

1990, Apr. 24   *Perf. 11½*
1418 A804 10p multicolored   .45   .25
1990 Festival. For use on greeting cards.

Sinai Liberation, 8th Anniv. — A805

1990, Apr. 25
1419 A805 10p blue, blk & yel grn   .50   .25

World Cup Soccer Championships, Italy — A806

1990, May 26   *Litho.*   *Perf. 13½x13*
1420 A806 10p multicolored   .40   .25
Souvenir Sheet
Imperf
1421 A806 50p Flags, trophy   2.25   2.25

World Basketball Championships, Argentina — A807

1990, Aug. 8   *Perf. 13½x13*
1422 A807 10p multicolored   .50   .25

Natl. Population Council, 5th Anniv. — A808

Perf. 13½x13
1990, Sept. 15   *Perf. 13½x13*
1423 A808 10p brown & yel grn   .50   .25

October War Against Israel Type
1990, Oct. 6   *Litho.*   *Perf. 13x13½*
1424   Strip of 3   1.75   1.75
  a.   A785 10p Bunker, tank   .40   .25
  b.   A786 10p like #1398b   .40   .25
  c.   A785 10p Troops with flag, flame thrower   .40   .25

Egyptian Postal Service, 125th Anniv. A809

1990, Oct. 9
1425 A809 10p lt blue, blk & red   .50   .25

Dar El Eloum Faculty, Cent. — A810

1990, Oct. 13   *Litho.*   *Perf. 13*
1426 A810 10p multicolored   .45   .25

UN Development Program, 40th Anniv. A811

ITU, 125th Anniv. — A812

1990, Oct. 24   *Perf. 11½*
1427 A811 30p yel, bl grn & yel grn   .90   .30
Perf. 13
1428 A812 30p multicolored   .90   .30
UN Day.

Ras Mohammed Natl. Park — A813

Designs: a, Crown butterfly fish. b, Lionfish. c, Twobar anemone fish. d, Grouper.

1990, Dec. 22   *Litho.*   *Perf. 13*
1429 A813   Block of 4   3.50   3.50
  a.-b.   10p any single   .50   .30
  c.-d.   20p any single   .80   .40

Day of the Disabled — A814

1990, Dec. 15   *Photo.*   *Perf. 11*
1430 A814 10p multicolored   .50   .25

Mohamed Fahmy Abdel Meguid Bey, Medical Reformer A815   Nabaweya Moussa (1890-1951), Educator A816

Perf. 11x11½
1990, Dec. 30   *Unwmk.*
1431 A815 10p Prus bl, brn & org   .40   .25
1432 A816 10p grn, org brn & blk   .40   .25

Stamp Day — A817

1991, Jan. 1   *Litho.*   *Perf. 13½x13*
1433 A817   5p No. 1   .30   .25
1434 A817 10p No. 2   .45   .25
1435 A817 20p No. 3   .60   .40
  a.   Strip of 3, #1433-1435   1.75   1.75
See Nos. 1443-1446, 1459-1460.

Veterinary Surgeon Syndicate, 50th Anniv. A818

1991, Feb. 28   *Photo.*   *Perf. 11½*
1436 A818 10p multicolored   .45   .25

Syndicate of Journalists, 50th Anniv. A819

1991, Apr.   *Photo.*   *Perf. 11½*
1437 A819 10p multicolored   .40   .25

Narcissus — A820

1991, Apr. 13
1438 A820 10p multicolored   .40   .25
1991 Festival. For use on greeting cards.

Giza Zoo, Cent. — A821

1991, June 15   *Litho.*   *Imperf.*
Size: 80x63mm
1439 A821 50p multicolored   4.00   4.00

Mahmoud Mokhtar (1891-1934), Sculptor A822

Mohamed Nagi (1888-1956), Painter — A823

Perf. 13x13½, 13½x13

1991, June 11   Litho.
1440 A822 10p multicolored   .40   .25
1441 A823 10p multicolored   .40   .25

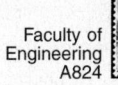

Faculty of Engineering
A824

1991, June 30   **Perf. 13x13½**
1442 A824 10p multicolored   .40   .25

Stamp Day Type

Designs: No. 1443, No. 5. No. 1444, No. 4. No. 1445, No. 7. No. 1446, Sphinx, pyramid, No. 6.

1991, July 23   **Perf. 13**
1443 A817 10p orange & blk   .40   .25
1444 A817 10p yellow & blk   .40   .25
1445 A817 10p lilac & blk   .40   .25
  a.   Strip of 3, #1443-1445   1.40   1.40

Size: 80x60mm
Imperf
1446 A817 50p multicolored   2.25   1.75
  Nos. 1443-1446 (4)   3.45   2.50

Mohamed Abdel el Wahab, Musician — A825

1991, Aug. 28   **Perf. 13**
1447 A825 10p multicolored   .55   .25

5th Africa Games, Cairo
A826

No. 1448, Karate, judo. No. 1449, Table tennis, field hockey, tennis. No. 1450, Running, gymnastics, swimming. No. 1451, Soccer, basketball, shooting. No. 1452, Boxing, wrestling, weightlifting. No. 1453, Handball, cycling, volleyball. No. 1454, Games mascot, vert. No. 1455, Mascot, emblem, torch.

Perf. 13x13½

1991, Sept.   Litho.   Unwmk.
1448 A826 10p multicolored   .40   .25
1449 A826 10p multicolored   .40   .25
  a.   Pair, #1448-1449   .90   .90
1450 A826 10p multicolored   .40   .25
1451 A826 10p multicolored   .40   .25
  a.   Pair, #1450-1451   .90   .90
1452 A826 10p multicolored   .40   .25
1453 A826 10p multicolored   .40   .25
  a.   Pair, #1452-1453   .90   .90

Perf. 13½x13
1454 A826 10p multicolored   .45   .25

Size: 80x60mm
Imperf
1455 A826 50p multicolored   1.75   1.75
  Nos. 1448-1455 (8)   4.60   3.50

Intl. Statistics Institute, 48th Session — A827

1991, Sept. 9
1456 A827 10p multicolored   .40   .25

Opening of Dar Al Eftaa Religious Center — A828

1991, Oct. 1   Litho.   **Perf. 13**
1457 A828 10p multicolored   .40   .25

October War Against Israel, 18th Anniv. A829

1991, Oct. 6   **Perf. 13x13½**
1458 A829 10p multicolored   .55   .25

Stamp Day Type

Designs: 10p, No. 6. £1, Stamp exhibition emblem, hieroglyphics, pyramids, sphinx.

1991, Oct. 7   **Perf. 13**
1459 A817 10p blue & black   .50   .25

Size: 90x60mm
Imperf
1460 A817 £1 multicolored   5.50   5.50

Natl. Philatelic Exhibition, Cairo, 10/7-12 (No. 1460). No. 1460 sold only with £1 admission ticket at exhibition.

Ancient Artifacts Type of 1985
Perf. 11½x11

1990-92   Unwmk.   Photo.
Size: 18x23mm
1467 A681 10p like #1278   .60   .25
1470 A681 30p like #1283   1.00   1.00
1472 A681 50p like #1285   1.75   1.75
  Nos. 1467-1472 (3)   3.35   3.00

  Issued: 10p, 1/20/90; 30p, 9/1/91; 50p, 7/11/92.

United Nations Day — A830

No. 1477, Brick hands housing people. No. 1478, Woman learning to write, fingerprint, vert.

Perf. 13x13½, 13½x13
1991, Oct. 24   Litho.
1476 A830 10p shown   .40   .25
1477 A830 10p multicolored   .40   .25
1478 A830 10p multicolored   .40   .25
  Nos. 1476-1478 (3)   1.20   .75

Famous Men Type of 1988
Inscribed "1991"

Designs: No. 1479, Dr. Zaki Mubarak (1891-1952), writer and poet. No. 1480, Abd El Kader Hamza (1879-1941), journalist.

1991, Dec. 23 Photo. **Perf. 13½x13**
1479 A760 10p olive brown   .40   .25
1480 A760 10p gray   .40   .25

A831   Post Day — A832

1992, Jan. 2   Litho.   **Perf. 13**
1481 A831 10p shown   .40   .25
1482 A831 45p Bird mosaic   1.00   1.00

Perf. 14
1483 A832 70p shown   1.75   1.75
  Nos. 1481-1483 (3)   3.15   3.00

Nos. 1482-1483 are airmail.

Police Day — A833

1992, Jan. 25   **Perf. 14**
1484 A833 10p multicolored   .40   .25

25th Cairo Intl. Fair — A834

1992, Feb. 15   Litho.   **Perf. 14**
1485 A834 10p multicolored   .40   .25

Famous Men Type of 1988
Inscribed "1992"

10p, Sayed Darwish (1882-1923), musician.

1992, Mar. 17 Photo. **Perf. 14x13½**
1486 A760 10p dull org & olive   .40   .25

Festivals — A835

1992, Mar. 18   **Perf. 11½**
1487 A835 10p Egyptian hoopoe   .40   .25
  For use on greeting cards.

World Health Day — A836

1992, Apr. 20   Litho.   **Perf. 13**
1488 A836 10p multicolored   .50   .25

Aswan Dam, 90th Anniv. — A837

1992, July   Litho.   **Perf. 13**
1489 A837 10p No. 487   .50   .25

20th Arab Scout Jamboree A838

1992, July 10   **Perf. 13x13½**
1490 A838 10p multicolored   .50   .25

A839

70p, Summer Games' emblem.

1992, July 20   **Perf. 13½x13**
1491 A839 10p multicolored   .45   .25

Size: 80x60mm
Imperf
1492 A839 70p multicolored   5.00   2.50
  1992 Summer Olympics, Barcelona.

El Helal Magazine, Cent. — A840

1992, Sept. 14 Litho. **Perf. 13½x13**
1493 A840 10p multicolored   .45   .25

Alexandria World Festival
A841

1992, Sept. 27   **Perf. 13x13½**
1494 A841 70p multicolored   1.60   1.60

Congress of Federation of World and American Travel Companies, Cairo
A842

1992, Sept. 20
1495 A842 70p multicolored   1.50   1.50

World Post Day — A843

1992, Oct. 9   Litho.   **Perf. 13**
1496 A843 10p dk bl, lt bl & blk   .45   .25

Children's Day — A844

1992, Oct. 24   Litho.   **Perf. 13½x13**
1497 A844 10p multicolored   .55   .25

Intl. Conference on Food, Agriculture and World Health — A845

1992, Oct. 24   **Perf. 13**
1498 A845 70p multicolored   1.50   1.50

A846

1992, Nov. 21　　　**Perf. 13½x13**
1499 A846 10p multicolored　　.50　.25
　　20th Arab Scout Conference, Cairo.

Famous Men Type of 1988
Inscribed "1992"

No. 1500, Talaat Harb, economist. No. 1501, Mohamed Taymour, writer. No. 1502, Dr. Ahmed Zaki Abu Shadi (with glasses), physician & poet.

1992, Dec. 23　**Photo.**　**Perf. 13½x13**
1500 A760 10p blue & brown　.40　.25
1501 A760 10p citron & blue gray　.40　.25
1502 A760 10p citron & blue gray　.40　.25
　a.　Pair, #1501-1502　　.90　.90
　　Nos. 1500-1502 (3)　　1.20　.75

A847

Pharaohs: 10p, Sesostris I. 45p, Amenemhet III. 70p, Hur I.

1993, Jan. 2　**Litho.**　**Perf. 13½x13**
1503 A847 10p brown & yellow　.45　.25
1504 A847 45p brown & yellow　.75　.65
1505 A847 70p brown & yellow　1.20　1.00
　a.　Strip of 3, #1503-1505　3.00　3.00
　　Post Day.

25th Intl. Book Fair, Cairo — A848

1993, Jan. 26　**Litho.**　**Perf. 13½x13**
1506 A848 15p multicolored　　.40　.25

A849　　　 **A849a**

A849b　　　　**A849c**

A849d　　　　**A849e**

A849f　　　　**A849g**

A849h

Artifacts: A849, Bust. A849a, Sphinx. A849b, Bust of princess. A849c, Ramses II. A849d, Queen Ti. A849e, Horemheb. A849f, As A849b. A849g, Amenhotep III. £1, Head of a woman. £2, Woman wearing headdress. £5, Pharaonic capital.

Photo., Litho. (#1511)
1993-99　**Unwmk.**　**Perf. 11½x11,**
1507 A849　5p multi　　.55　.25
1508 A849a 15p brn & bis　.55　.25
1509 A849a 15p brn & bis　.30　.25
1510 A849b 25p brn & org
　　　　　brn　　　　.35　.25
1511 A849c 55p blk & bl　.90　.50

Size: 21x25mm
Perf. 11¼
1512 A849　5p dp cl &
　　　　　brick red　.50　.25
1513 A849d　5p brown　.30　.25
　a.　Wmk. 342　　.30
1514 A849a 15p brn & bis　.50　.25
1515 A849e 20p blk & gray　.30　.25
　a.　Wmk. 342　　.30
1516 A849f 25p brn & org
　　　　　brn　　　.70　.30
1517 A849f 25p black brown　.30　.25
1518 A849c 55p blk & lt bl　.60　.60
1519 A849g 75p blk & brn　.90　.80

Perf. 11½
1520 A849h　£1 slate & blk　2.25　2.25
1521 A849h　£2 brn & grn　5.00　5.00
1521A A849h £5 brn & gold　10.00 10.00
　　Nos. 1507-1521A (16)　24.00 21.70

Warning: Avoid using watermark fluid on Nos. 1513-1513a and 1515-1515a. Images will be adversely affected.
Body of Sphinx on Nos. 1509, 1514 stops above value, and extends through value on No. 1508.
Issued: Nos. 1507-1508, 2/1; No. 1509, 3/10; £1, £2, 4/1; No. 1511, 7/1/93; £5, 8/1/93; Nos. 1512, 1514, 1518, 10/30/94; No. 1516, 6/25/94; 20p, 2/1/97; 75p, 3/25/97; No. 1517, 1998; Nos. 1513a, 1515a, 1999.
See Nos. C204-C206.

Architects' Association, 75th Anniv. A850

1993, Feb. 28　**Litho.**　**Perf. 13x13½**
1522 A850 15p multicolored　　.45　.25

New Building for Ministry of Foreign Affairs — A851

1993, Mar. 15　　　**Perf. 13**
1523 A851 15p multicolored　　.45　.25
1524 A851 80p multicolored　1.50　1.50
　　Diplomacy Day (No. 1523). No. 1524 is airmail.

Feasts — A852

1993, Mar. 20　**Litho.**　**Perf. 13x13½**
1525 A852 15p Opuntia　　.45　.25
　　For use on greeting cards.

Newspaper, Le Progres Egyptien, Cent. A853

1993, Apr. 15　**Litho.**　**Perf. 13x13½**
1526 A853 15p multicolored　　.40　.25

A854

1993, May 15　**Litho.**　**Perf. 13½x13**
1527 A854 15p multicolored　　.50　.25
　　World Telecommunications Day.

A855

1993, June 15　**Litho.**　**Perf. 13½x13**
1528 A855 15p multicolored　　.45　.25
　　UN Conference on Human Rights, Vienna.

Organization of African Unity — A856

1993, June 26　　　**Perf. 13**
1529 A856 15p yel grn & multi　.45　.25
1530 A856 80p red violet & multi 1.10 1.10
　　No. 1530 is airmail.

World PTT Conference, Cairo — A857

1993, Sept. 4　**Litho.**　**Perf. 13**
1531 A857 15p multicolored　　.45　.25

Salah El-Din El Ayubi (1137-1193), Dome of the Rock — A858

1993, Sept. 4
1532 A858 55p multicolored　1.10 1.10

A859

1993, Oct. 6
1533 A859 15p multicolored　　.50　.25
　　October War Against Israel, 20th Anniv.

A860

1993, Oct. 12　　　**Perf. 13½x13**
1534 A860 15p cream & multi　.45　.25
1535 A860 55p silver & multi　1.10　.55
1536 A860 80p gold & multi　1.50　.85

Imperf
Size: 90x70mm
1537 A860 80p multicolored　2.00 2.00
　　Nos. 1534-1537 (4)　　5.05 3.65
　　Pres. Mohamed Hosni Mubarak, Third Term.

Reduction of Natural Disasters — A861

1993, Oct. 24　**Litho.**　**Perf. 13**
1538 A861 80p multicolored　　1.10 1.10

Electricity in Egypt, Cent. — A862

1993, Oct. 24　　　**Perf. 13½x13**
1539 A862 15p multicolored　　.45　.25

Intl. Conference on Big Dams, Cairo A863

1993, Nov. 19　**Litho.**　**Perf. 13**
1540 A863 15p multicolored　　.45　.25

35th Military Intl. Soccer Championship — A864

1993, Dec. 1　**Litho.**　**Perf. 13½x13**
1541 A864 15p orange & multi　.40　.25
1542 A864 15p Trophy, emblem　.40　.25
　　9th Men's Junior World Handball Championship (No. 1542).

Famous Men Type of 1988
Inscribed "1993"

No. 1543, Abdel Azis Al-Bishry. No. 1544, Mohammad Farid Abu Hadid. No. 1545, Mahmud Beyram el-Tunsi. No. 1546, Ali Moubarak.

1993, Dec. 25　　　**Perf. 13½x13**
1543 A760 15p blue　　.40　.25
1544 A760 15p blue black　.40　.25
1545 A760 15p light violet　.40　.25
1546 A760 15p green　　.40　.25
　　Nos. 1543-1546 (4)　1.60 1.00

EGYPT

Post Day — A865

15p, Amenhotep III. 55p, Queen Hatshepsut. 80p, Thutmose III.

1994, Jan. 2
1547 A865 15p multicolored .45 .25
1548 A865 55p multicolored 1.10 .30
1549 A865 80p multicolored 1.75 .40
Nos. 1547-1549 (3) 3.30 .95

Congress of
Egyptian
Sedimentary
Geology
Society
A866

1994, Jan. 4   Litho.   Perf. 13x13½
1550 A866 15p multicolored .45 .25

Birds — A867

1994, Mar. 3   Litho.   Perf. 13
1551 A867 Block of 4, #a.-d. 2.75 2.75
a. 15p Egyptian swallow .45 .30
b. 15p Fire crest .45 .30
c. 15p Rose-ringed parrot .45 .30
d. 15p Goldfinch .45 .30
Festivals 1994.

Arab Scouting, 40th
Anniv. — A868

1994, Mar. 25   Perf. 13½x13
1552 A868 15p multicolored .45 .25

27th Cairo Intl.
Fair — A869

1994, Apr. 9   Litho.   Perf. 13½x13
1553 A869 15p multicolored .45 .25

A870

1994, Apr. 15   Litho.   Perf. 13
1554 A870 15p green & brown .45 .25
1994 African Telecommunications Exhibition, Cairo.

A871

1994, Apr. 30   Litho.   Perf. 13
1555 A871 15p grn, blk & blue .45 .25
Natl. Afforestation Campaign.

5th Arab Energy
Conference,
Cairo. — A872

1994, July 5   Litho.   Perf. 13
1556 A872 15p multicolored .45 .25

Signing of Washington Accord for
Palestinian Self-Rule in Gaza and
Jericho
A873

1994, May 4   Litho.   Perf. 13
1557 A873 15p multicolored .60 .25

18th Biennial
Art
Exhibition,
Alexandria
A874

1994, May 21
1558 A874 15p yel, blk & gray .45 .25

Organization of African
Unity — A875

1994, May 25
1559 A875 15p multicolored .45 .25

Natl. Reading
Festival
A876

1994, June 15
1560 A876 15p multicolored .45 .25

ILO, 75th
Anniv. — A877

1994, June 28   Litho.   Perf. 13½x13
1561 A877 15p multicolored .45 .25

Intl. Conference on Population and
Development, Cairo
A878

15p, Conference, UN emblems. 80p, Drawings, hieroglyphics, conference emblem.

1994, Sept. 5   Litho.   Perf. 13
1562 A878 15p multi .45 .25
1563 A878 80p multi, vert. 1.10 .75
No. 1563 is airmail.

World Junior Squash
Championships — A879

1994, Sept. 14   Litho.   Perf. 13
1564 A879 15p multicolored .45 .25

World Post
Day — A880

1994, Oct. 9   Litho.   Perf. 13
1565 A880 15p multicolored .50 .25

Intl. Red Cross & Red
Crescent Societies,
75th Anniv. — A881

1994, Oct. 24
1566 A881 80p multicolored 1.50 .90

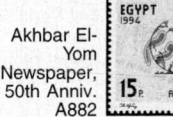

Akhbar El-
Yom
Newspaper,
50th Anniv.
A882

1994, Nov. 11
1567 A882 15p multicolored .45 .25

African Field Hockey Club
Championships — A883

1994, Nov. 14   Litho.   Perf. 13
1568 A883 15p multicolored .45 .25

A884

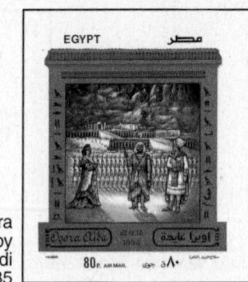

Opera
Aida, by
Verdi
A885

1994, Nov. 26
1569 A884 15p multicolored .45 .25
Imperf
Size: 58x69mm
1570 A885 80p multicolored 2.25 2.25
No. 1570 is airmail.

Intl. Olympic
Committee,
Cent. — A886

1994, Dec. 10   Perf. 13
1571 A886 15p multicolored .45 .25

Egyptian Youth
Hostels Assoc., 40th
Anniv. — A887

1994, Dec. 24
1572 A887 15p multicolored .45 .25

Intl. Speed
Ball
Federation,
10th Anniv.
A888

1994, Dec. 25
1573 A888 15p multicolored .45 .25

African Development
Bank, 30th
Anniv. — A889

1994, Dec. 26
1574 A889 15p multicolored .45 .25

Opening of
Suez
Canal,
125th
Anniv.
A890

Design: 80p, Map, inaugural ceremony.

1994, Dec. 27
1575 A890 15p multicolored .65 .25
1576 A890 80p multicolored 1.25 .75
No. 1576 is airmail.

Famous Men — A891

No. 1577, Hassan Fathy, engineer. No. 1578, Mahmoud Taimour, writer.

1994, Dec. 29
1577	A891	15p multicolored	.40	.25
1578	A891	15p multicolored	.40	.25

Post Day — A892

15p, Statue of Akhenaton. 55p, Golden mask of King Tutankhamun. 80p, Statue of Nefertiti.

1995, Jan. 2   Litho.   Perf. 13½x13
1579	A892	15p multicolored	.50	.25
1580	A892	55p multicolored	1.10	.40
1581	A892	80p multicolored	1.50	.50
		Nos. 1579-1581 (3)	3.10	1.15

World Tourism Organization, 20th Anniv. A893

1995, Jan. 2   Perf. 13x13½
1582	A893	15p multicolored	.45	.25

Festivals A894

1995, Feb. 25   Litho.   Perf. 13x13½
1583	A894	15p multicolored	.45	.25

For use on greeting cards.

Egyptian Women's Day — A895

1995, Mar. 16   Litho.   Perf. 13x13½
1584	A895	15p multicolored	.45	.25

Arab League, 50th Anniv. — A896

1995, Mar. 22   Perf. 13½x13
1585	A896	15p blue & multi	.45	.25
1586	A896	55p green & multi	.75	.75

Sheraton Hotel, Cairo, 25th Anniv. A897

1995, Mar. 28   Perf. 13x13½
1587	A897	15p multicolored	.45	.25

Misr Bank, 75th Anniv. — A898

1995, May 7   Litho.   Perf. 13½x13
1588	A898	15p multicolored	.50	.25

World Telecommunications Day — A899

1995, May 31   Perf. 13x13½
1589	A899	80p multicolored	1.00	.50

Wilhelm Roentgen (1845-1923), Discovery of the X-Ray, Cent. — A900

1995, May   Litho.   Perf. 13½x13
1590	A900	15p multicolored	.50	.25

Membership in World Heritage Committee, 20th Anniv. (in 1994) — A901

Artifacts from the Shaft of Luxor: No. 1591, Goddess Hathor. No. 1592, God Atoum. 80p, God Amon and Horemheb.

1995, July 23   Litho.   Perf. 13½x13
1591		15p multicolored	.45	.25
1592		15p multicolored	.45	.25
a.		A901 Pair, #1591-1592	1.10	1.10
1593	A901	80p multicolored	1.10	1.10
		Nos. 1591-1593 (3)	2.00	1.60

No. 1592a is a continuous design. No. 1593 is airmail.

21st Intl. Conference on Pediatrics, Cairo — A902

1995, Sept. 10   Litho.   Perf. 13
1594	A902	15p multicolored	.50	.25

Intl. Ozone Day — A903

1995, Sept. 16   Litho.   Perf. 13x12½
1595	A903	15p green & multi	.45	.25
1596	A903	55p brown & multi	.90	.45
1597	A903	80p blue & multi	1.40	.55
		Nos. 1595-1597 (3)	2.75	1.25

See Nos. 1622-1623, 1824.

World Tourism Day — A904

1995, Sept. 25   Perf. 12½x13
1598	A904	15p multicolored	1.00	.25

Government Printing House, 175th Anniv. — A905

1995, Sept. 27
1599	A905	15p multicolored	.45	.25

Sun Verticality on Abu Simbel Temple — A906

1995, Oct. 22   Litho.   Perf. 12½x13
1600	A906	15p multicolored	.95	.30

Opening of New Esna Dam — A907

1995, Nov. 25   Perf. 12½
1601	A907	15p multicolored	.75	.30

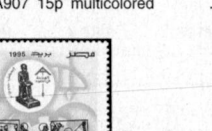

Egyptian Engineers Assoc., 75th Anniv. — A908

1995, Dec. 20   Perf. 13
1602	A908	15p multicolored	.45	.25

A909

Famous entertainers.

1995, Dec. 9   Litho.   Perf. 13x12½
1603	A909	15p Abdel Halim Hafez	.40	.25
1604	A909	15p Youssef Wahbi	.40	.25
1605	A909	15p Naquib el-Rihani	.40	.25
		Nos. 1603-1605 (3)	1.20	.75

A910

1995, Dec. 23   Litho.   Perf. 13x12½
1606	A910	15p multicolored	.45	.25

Motion Pictures, cent.

Post Day — A911

Ancient paintings: 55p, Man facing right. 80p, Man facing left. 100p, Playing flute, dancers.

1996, Jan. 2   Litho.   Perf. 13½x13
1607		55p multicolored	1.10	.60
1608		80p multicolored	1.50	.90
a.		A911 Pair, Nos. 1607-1608	2.75	2.75

Imperf
Size: 88x72mm
1609	A911	100p multicolored	3.00	3.00

Nos. 1607-1608 are airmail.

Feasts — A912

1996, Feb. 15   Perf. 12½
1610	A912	15p Blue convolvulus	.45	.25
1611	A912	15p Red poppies	.45	.25
a.		Pair, No. 1610-1611	.95	.95

For use on greeting cards.

A913

1996, Mar. 13   Litho.   Perf. 13x12½
1612	A913	15p pink & multi	.40	.25
1613	A913	80p brown & multi	.90	.60

Summit of Peace Makers, Sharm al-Sheikh. No. 1613 is airmail.

A914

1996, Mar. 16
1614	A914	15p multicolored	.45	.25

29th Intl. Fair, Cairo.

Egyptian Geological Survey, Cent. — A915

1996, Mar. 18   Perf. 12½x13
1615	A915	15p multicolored	.45	.25

A916

1996, Apr. 11   Litho.   Perf. 13x12½
1616	A916	15p blue & multi	.45	.25
1617	A916	80p pink & multi	.95	.50

Signing of African Nuclear Weapon-Free Zone Treaty.

A917

1996, Apr. 20   Litho.   Perf. 13x12½
1618	A917	15p multicolored	.45	.25

Egyptian Society of Accountants and Auditors, 50th anniv.

General Census — A918

1996, May 4
1619 A918 15p multicolored .45 .25

A919

1996 Summer Olympics, Atlanta: 15p, Atlanta 1996 emblem. £1, Emblem surrounded by sports pictograms.

1996, July 15 Litho. Perf. 13x12½
1620 A919 15p lilac & multi .50 .25
  Size: 63x103mm
  Imperf
1621 A919 £1 black & multi 2.75 2.75
 No. 1621 is airmail.

Intl. Ozone Day Type of 1995
1996, Sept. 16 Litho. Perf. 13x12½
1622 A903 15p pink & multi .40 .25
1623 A903 80p gray & multi 1.10 .55
 No. 1623 is airmail.
 See Nos. 1595-1597, 1824.

A920

1996, Sept. 19
1624 A920 80p multicolored .75 .45
 2nd Alexandria World Festival.

A921

1996, Sept. 21
1625 A921 15p grn, blk & bl .45 .25
 Scientific Research and Technology Academy, 25th anniv.

A922

1996, Oct. 7 Perf. 12½x13
1626 A922 15p multicolored .50 .25
 Opening of 2nd Line of Greater Cairo Subway System.

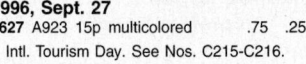

Rowing Festival — A923

1996, Sept. 27
1627 A923 15p multicolored .75 .25
 Intl. Tourism Day. See Nos. C215-C216.

Courts of the State Council, 50th Anniv. — A924

1996, Nov. 2 Litho. Perf. 12½x13
1628 A924 15p blue & claret .45 .25

A925

1996, Nov. 4 Perf. 13x12½
1629 A925 15p yel, blk & blue .40 .25
 25th World Conference of Intl. Federation of Training and Development Organizations.

A926

 Cairo Economic Summit (MENA): £1, Graph, earth, gear, olive branch, wheat.

1996, Nov. 12 Litho. Perf. 13x12½
1630 A926 15p shown .45 .25
  Size: 65x45mm
  Imperf
1631 A926 £1 multicolored 1.75 1.75
 No. 1631 is airmail.

A927

1996, Nov. 13 Perf. 13x12½
1632 A927 15p multicolored .45 .25
 1996 World Food Summit, Rome.

A928

 National Day of El-Gharbia Governorate: Al Sayd Ahmed El-Badawy mosque, Tanta.

1996, Nov. 16
1633 A928 15p multicolored .45 .25

A929

 Famous artists: No. 1634, Ali El-Kassar. No. 1635, George Abyad. No. 1636, Mohamed Kareem. No. 1637, Fatma Roshdi.

1996, Dec. 28 Litho. Perf. 13x12½
1634 A929 20p black .45 .25
1635 A929 20p red brown .45 .25
1636 A929 20p brown .45 .25
1637 A929 20p black .45 .25
  Nos. 1634-1637 (4) 1.80 1.00
 See Nos. 1666-1669.

A930

1997, Jan. 2
1638 A930 20p multicolored .45 .25
  Size: 61x80mm
  Imperf
1639 A930 £1 multicolored 2.00 2.00
 Post Day; Discovery of Tutankhamun's tomb, 75th anniv.
 No. 1639 is airmail.

Police Day — A931

1997, Jan. 25 Litho. Perf. 13x13½
1640 A931 20p multicolored .45 .25

Feasts — A932

1997, Feb. 1 Perf. 13
1641 A932 20p Pink asters .40 .25
1642 A932 20p White asters .40 .25
 a. Pair, #1641-1642 .95 .95
 For use on greeting cards.

World Civil Defense Day — A933

1997, Mar. 10 Litho. Perf. 13x13½
1643 A933 20p multicolored .45 .25

30th Cairo Intl. Fair — A934

1997, Mar. 19 Perf. 13½x13
1644 A934 20p multicolored .45 .25

Mahmoud Said, Photographer, Artist, Birth Cent. — A935

The City, By Mahmoud Said — A936

1997, Apr. 12 Litho. Perf. 12½
1645 A935 20p multicolored .45 .25
  Size: 80x60mm
  Imperf
1646 A936 £1 multicolored 1.25 1.25
 No. 1646 is airmail.

Institute of African Research and Studies, 50th Anniv. — A937

1997, May 27 Litho. Perf. 13
1647 A937 75p multicolored .65 .65

New Headquarters of State Information Service — A938

1997, Aug. 16 Litho. Perf. 12½
1648 A938 20p multicolored .45 .25

A939

 £1, Mascot, soccer ball, playing field, emblems.

1997, Sept. 4 Perf. 13x12½
1649 A939 20p multicolored .45 .25
1650 AP81 75p multicolored .70 .65
  Size: 75x55mm
  Imperf
1651 A939 £1 multicolored 1.75 1.75
 Nos. 1650-1651 are airmail. Under 17 FIFA World Soccer Championships, Egypt.

A940

1997, Sept. 16 Perf. 13
1652 A940 20p lt bl grn & multi .60 .30
1653 A940 £1 pink & multi 1.60 1.25
 Montreal Protocol on Substances that Deplete the Ozone Layer, 10th anniv. No. 1653 is airmail.

Completion of Second Stage of Metro Line No. 2 — A941

1997, Sept. 27 Perf. 12½x13
1654 A941 20p multicolored .45 .25

Premiere in Egypt of Opera Aida, by Verdi, 125th Anniv. — A942

1997, Oct. 12 Perf. 13
1655 A942 20p multicolored .60 .25
  Size: 80x75mm
  Imperf
1656 A942 £1 like #1655 4.00 4.00
 No. 1656 is airmail.

Queen Nefertari — A943

1997, Oct. 25   Litho.   Perf. 13
1657 A943 £1 multicolored   1.25 1.25
a.   Perf. 14 1/4x14   —   —

A944

1997, Nov. 17   Litho.   Perf. 13
1658 A944 20p multicolored   .50   .25
Intl. Congress of Orthopedics, Cairo.

A945

Designs: 20p, Goddess Selket. £1, Scarab, baboon pendant.

1997, Nov. 22   Perf. 13x12½
1659 A945 20p black & gold   .50   .25
Size: 73x62mm
Imperf
1660 A945 £1 multicolored   1.50 1.50
No. 1660 is airmail. Discovery of King Tutanhkamen's tomb, 75th anniv.

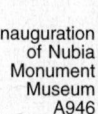

Inauguration of Nubia Monument Museum A946

1997, Nov. 23   Perf. 13
1661 A946 20p multicolored   .95   .25

Arab Land Bank, 50th Anniv. — A947

1997, Dec. 10   Perf. 12½
1662 A947 20p multicolored   .60   .25

5th Pan Arab Congress on Anesthesia and Intensive Care — A948

1997, Dec. 9   Litho.   Perf. 13
1663 A948 20p multicolored   .45   .25

El Salaam Canal A949

1997, Dec. 28
1664 A949 20p multicolored   .60   .25
Liberation of Sinai, 15th anniv.

Famous Artists Type of 1996 and

A950

1997, Dec. 23   Litho.   Perf. 13x12½
1665 A950 20p blue   .40   .25
1666 A929 20p Zaky Tolaimat   .40   .25
1667 A929 20p Ismael Yassen   .40   .25
1668 A929 20p Zaky Roustom   .40   .25
1669 A929 20p Soliman Naguib   .40   .25
a.   Strip of 5, #1665-1669   2.00 2.00

A951

Post Day: 20p, King Tutankhamun's guard. 75p, King Ramses III. £1, Cover of King Tutankhamun's coffin.

1998, Jan. 2   Perf. 13
1670 A951 20p multicolored   .45   .25
1671 A951 75p multicolored   1.10   .65
Size: 26x43mm
1672 A951 £1 multicolored   1.75   .85
Nos. 1671-1672 are airmail.

Feasts A952

1998, Jan. 20
1673   20p multicolored   .40   .25
1674   20p multicolored   .40   .25
a.   A952 Pair, #1673-1674   .80   .80
For use on greeting cards.

Intl. Cairo Fair — A954

1998, Mar. 11   Litho.   Perf. 13
1675 A954 20p multicolored   .50   .25

Natl. Bank of Egypt, Cent. — A955

1998, Mar. 12
1676 A955 20p multicolored   .50   .25

Tutankhamun A956

Thutmose IV A957

1998   Litho.   Perf. 13½x12½
1677 A956 £2 pink & multi   1.75 1.75
1677A A956 £2 Like #1677, with   —   —
              white back-
              ground
b.   Perf. 14x14 7/8   —   —
1678 A957 £5 purple & black   5.00 3.75
Nos. 1677-1678 (3)   6.75 5.50
Issued: £2, 4/23; £5, 3/23.

A958

1998, Apr. 14   Perf. 13
1679 A958 20p green & multi   .45   .25
1680 A958 75p blue & multi   1.10   .75
Size: 70x52mm
Imperf
1681 A958 £1 Natl. flags, map,
              trophy   1.50 1.00
Egypt, winners of 21st African Cup of Nations soccer competition.
Nos. 1680-1681 are airmail.

Egyptian Satellite "Nile Sat" — A959

1998, May 30   Litho.   Perf. 13
1682 A959 20p multicolored   .50   .25

World Environment Day — A960

1998, June 5
1683 A960 20p shown   .60   .25
Size: 43x62mm
Imperf
1684 A960 £1 Fauna, emblems   3.75 3.75
No. 1684 is airmail.

A961

1998, June 14
1685 A961 20p blue & black   .40   .25
1686 A961 £1 yel, grn & blk   1.10   .80
Dr. Ahmed Zewail, winner of Franklin Institute award.
No. 1686 is airmail.

A962

Imam Sheikh Mohamed Metwalli Al-Shaarawi.

1998, July 15
1687 A962 20p buff & multi   .40   .25
1688 A962 £1 green & multi   1.10   .80
No. 1688 is airmail.

Day of the Nile Flood — A963

1998, Sept. 12   Litho.   Perf. 13
1689 A963 20p multicolored   .50   .25

A964

1998, Sept. 30   Litho.   Perf. 13
1690 A964 20p multicolored   .50   .25
Chemistry Administration, cent.

October War Against Israel, 25th Anniv. — A965

1998, Oct. 6   Litho.   Perf. 13
1691 A965 20p multicolored   .60   .25
Size: 50x70mm
Imperf
1692 A965 £2 like No. 1691   3.25 3.25
No. 1692 is airmail.

Egyptian Survey Authority, Cent. A966

1998, Oct. 15   Perf. 13
1693 A966 20p multicolored   .50   .25

Cairo University, 90th Anniv. A967

1998, Dec. 7   Litho.   Perf. 13
1694 A967 20p multicolored   .50   .25

A968

1998, Dec. 17   Litho.   Perf. 13
1695 A968 20p multicolored   .45   .25
Egyptian trade unions, cent.

A970

Post Day (19th Dynasty): 20p, Queen Nefertari, Goddess Isis. 125p, God Osiris, Goddess Isis.

1999, Jan. 2   Litho.   Perf. 13
1696 A970 20p multicolored   .50 .25

Size: 41x61mm
Imperf
1697 A970 125p multicolored   2.00 2.00
No. 1697 is airmail.

Feasts
A971

1999, Jan. 5   Perf. 13
1698   20p multicolored   1.00 .30
1699   20p multicolored   .40 .25
a. A971 Pair, #1698-1699   1.75 1.75
For use on greeting cards.

Intl. Women's
Day — A973

1999, Mar. 7   Litho.   Perf. 13
1700 A973 20p multicolored   .50 .25

Cairo Intl. Fair — A974

1999, Mar. 9
1701 A974 20p multicolored   .50 .25

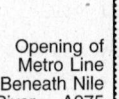

Opening of
Metro Line
Beneath Nile
River — A975

1999, Apr.   Litho.   Perf. 13
1702 A975 20p multicolored   .60 .25

A976

UPU, 125th
Anniv. — A977

1999, Apr. 21
1703 A976 20p shown   .45 .25
1704 A976 £1 multi   1.25 .85
1705 A977 125p shown   1.50 1.20

Size: 50x70mm
Imperf
1706 A977 125p multi   2.10 2.10
Nos. 1703-1706 (4)   5.30 4.40
Nos. 1704-1706 are airmail.

A978

1999, May 8   Perf. 13
1707 A978 20p green & multi   .45 .25
1708 A978 125p buff, red & multi   1.25 1.00
Geneva Conventions, 50th anniv. No. 1708 is airmail.

A980

1999, May 20   Litho.   Perf. 13¾
1710 A980 20p green & multi   .45 .25
1711 A980 £1 buff & multi   .95 .85
African Development Bank, 35th Meeting, Cairo. No. 1711 is airmail.

16th Men's Handball World
Championship — A981

20p, Stylized player with ball, pyramids. 1£, Mascot with ball, Sphinx, pyramids, globe. 125p, Mascot with ball, goalie, pyramids.

1999, June 1   Perf. 13
1712 A981 20p multicolored   .45 .25
1713 A981 £1 multicolored   .90 .85
1714 A981 125p multicolored   1.10 1.00
Nos. 1712-1714 (3)   2.45 2.10
Nos. 1713-1714 are airmail.

Goddess Selket — A982

1999, June 23   Litho.   Perf. 13
1715 A982 25p multicolored   .40 .25
See Nos. 1750, 1754.

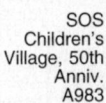

SOS
Children's
Village, 50th
Anniv.
A983

1999, June 23   Perf. 12¾x13¼
1716 A983 20p grn, blk & blue   .45 .25
1717 A983 125p pale yel, blk & bl   1.25 1.10
No. 1717 is airmail.

A984

No. 1718, Sameera Moussa (1917-52), Physicist. No. 1719, Aisha Abdul Rahman (1913-98), writer. No. 1720, Ahmed Eldemerdash Touny (1907-97), member of Intl. Olympic Committee.

1999   Litho.   Perf. 13x12¾
1718 A984 20p multicolored   .45 .25
1719 A984 20p multicolored   .45 .25
1720 A984 20p multicolored   .45 .25
Nos. 1718-1720 (3)   1.35 .75
Issued: Nos. 1718-1719, 7/23; No. 1720, 8/13.
See Nos. 1730-1733.

A985

1999, Oct. 5   Litho.   Perf. 13x12¾
1721 A985 20p org & multi   .45 .25
1722 A985 £1 silver & multi   .90 .85
1723 A985 125p gold & multi   1.10 1.00
Imperf
1724 A985 125p multicolored   2.00 2.00
Nos. 1721-1724 (4)   4.45 4.10
Pres. Hosni Mubarak, 4th term. Nos. 1722-1724 are airmail.

A986

1999, Nov. 15   Litho.   Perf. 13¼x13
Background Color
1725 A986 20p green   .45 .25
1726 A986 £1 red vio   .90 .85
1727 A986 125p purple   1.10 1.00
Nos. 1725-1727 (3)   2.45 2.10
Intl. Year of the Elderly. Nos. 1726-1727 are airmail.

A987

1999, Nov. 20
1728 A987 20p multi   .50 .25
Children's Day.

Famous People Type of 1999

No. 1730, Farid El Attrash (1913-76), singer, movie star. No. 1731, Laila Mourad (1918-95), singer, movie star. No. 1732, Anwar Wagdi (1911-55), actor, director. No. 1733, Asia Dagher (1901-86), actor, producer.

1999, Dec. 30   Litho.   Perf. 13x12¾
1730 A984 20p lt bl & blk   .40 .25
1731 A984 20p lt bl & blk   .40 .25
1732 A984 20p lt bl & blk   .40 .25
1733 A984 20p lt bl & blk   .40 .25
Nos. 1730-1733 (4)   1.60 1.00

Millennium — A989

20p, "1999" & "2000." 125p, Countdown of years. £2, Holy Family, Virgin Tree.

2000, Jan. 1   Perf. 13x12¾
1734 A989 20p multi   .45 .25
1735 A989 125p multi   1.25 1.10

Size: 70x50mm
Imperf
1736 A989 £2 multi, horiz.   4.00 4.00
Nos. 1734-1736 (3)   5.70 5.35
Nos. 1735-1736 are airmail.

A990   Post
Day — A991

2000, Jan. 2   Perf. 13¼x12¾
1737 A990 20p multi   .50 .25
1738 A991 20p multi   .50 .25
a.   Pair, #1737-1738   1.25 1.25

Size: 70x50mm
Imperf
1739 A991 125p Chariot, horiz.   2.00 2.00
Nos. 1737-1739 (3)   3.00 2.50

Ain Shams
University,
50th Anniv.
A992

2000, Jan. 3   Perf. 13¼x13
1740 A992 20p multi   .50 .25

Festivals
A993   A994

2000, Jan. 5   Perf. 13x13¼
1741 A993 20p multi   .40 .25
1742 A994 20p multi   .40 .25
a.   Pair, #1741-1742   .90 .90
For use on greeting cards.

A995

2000, Jan. 20   Perf. 13¼x13
1743 A995 20p multi   .50 .25
Islamic Development Bank, 25th anniv.

A996

2000, Feb. 28   **Perf. 13¼x12¾**
1744 A996 125p multi   1.25 1.25
   Common Market for Eastern and Southern Africa Economic Conference.

Death of Om Kolthoum, 25th Anniv. — A997

2000, Mar. 11   **Perf. 13¼x13**
1745 A997 20p grnsh yel & blk   .50 .25

8th Intl. Congress of Egyptologists — A998

2000, Mar. 28   **Perf. 13x13¼**
1746 A998 20p multi   .50 .25

Europe-Africa Summit, Cairo — A999

2000, Apr. 3   **Perf. 13¼x13**
1747 A999 125p multi   1.25 1.25

Group of 15 Developing Nations, 10th Summit, Cairo A1000

Perf. 12¾x13¼
2000, June 19   **Litho.**
1748 A1000 125p multi   1.25 1.25

Goddess Selket Type of 1999 and

Scene from 20th Dynasty A1003

Nofret, Wife of Rahotep A1004

King Seostris A1005

Princess Merit Aton A1006

20th Dynasty A1007

Pyramid at Snefru A1008

Wife of Sheikh-el-Balad A1009

King Psusennes I A1010

King Tutankhamun A1011

Obelisk of Ramses II A1011a

Temple of Karnak — A1012

Without Dots

With Dots

Perf. 12¾x13¼, 11¼ (#1750A, 1752-1755, 1757), 11x11½ (#1758-1760), 13¼x12¾ (#1756, 1761, 1763)
Photo., Litho. (#1750, 1750A, 1751, 1754, 1754A, 1761, 1763)

2000-2002
1750	A982	10p multi, type I	.40	.25
1750A	A982	10p multi, Type II	3.00	3.00
1751	A1003	10p multi	.40	.25
1752	A1004	20p multi	.40	.25
a.		With dot pattern in headdress and on chest and face ('07)	—	—
1753	A1005	25p multi	.40	.25
1754	A982	30p multi, Type I	.60	.45
1754A	A982	30p multi, Type II	—	—
1755	A1006	30p multi	.50	.35
1756	A1007	50p multi	.65	.45
1757	A1008	£1 multi	.60	.25
1758	A1009	110p multi	1.25	.95
1759	A1010	125p multi	1.40	1.00
1760	A1011	150p multi	1.75	1.25
1761	A1011a	225p multi	2.75	2.00

1763	A1012	£5 multi	5.75	5.50
a.	Perf. 14x14¼		—	—
	Nos. 1750-1763 (15)		19.85	16.20

   Issued: 20p, 6/25; No. 1750, 3/25/01; Nos. 1750A, 1754A, 2007; No. 1754, 6/11/01. Nos. 1751, 1755, 225p, 5/25/02; 110p, 6/4/02; 125p, 6/20/02; 150p, 6/15/02; £5, 6/1/02. 25p, 50p, £1, 6/30/02.
   Type I (Nos. 1750, 1754), has "Goddess" in smaller type than "Silakht." Type II (No. 1750A, 1754A), has "Goddess" and "Silakht" in type the same height.
   See No. 2174 for smaller stamp of type A1010.

Intl. Day Against Drug Abuse A1013

Perf. 12¾x13¼
2000, June 26   **Litho.**
1764 A1013 20p multi   .50 .25
    See No. 1796.

Natl. Insurance Company, Cent. — A1014

125p, Emblem, building, horiz.

Perf. 13¼x12¾
2000, Aug. 20   **Litho.**
1765 A1014 20p shown   .50 .25
Imperf
Size: 96x75mm
1766 A1014 125p multi   2.25 2.25

2000 Summer Olympics, Sydney — A1015

   Background colors: 20p, Light blue. 125p, Pink.

2000, Sept. 9   **Perf. 13¼x12¾**
1767-1768 A1015   Set of 2   1.75 1.50
    No. 1768 is airmail.

Productive Cooperative Union, 25th Anniv. A1016

2000, Sept. 15   **Perf. 12¾x13¼**
1769 A1016 20p multi   .50 .25

Opening of Fourth Stage of Second Cairo Subway Line A1017

2000, Oct. 7
1770 A1017 20p multi   .60 .25

World Post Day A1018

2000, Oct. 9
1771 A1018 125p multi   1.40 1.40

Solidarity with Palestinians — A1019

   Palestinian Authority flag and: 20p, Dome of the Rock, Jerusalem, vert. No. 1773, 125p, shown. No. 1774, 125p, Dome of the Rock, father and boy, vert.

Perf. 13¼x12¾, 12¾x13¼
2000, Nov. 29
1772-1774 A1019   Set of 3   3.25 3.25
    No. 1774 is airmail.

Opening of El-Ferdan Railway Bridge A1020

2000, Dec. 2   **Perf. 12¾x13¼**
1775 A1020 20p multi   .70 .25

Disabled Person's Day — A1021

2000, Dec. 9   **Perf. 13¼x12¾**
1776 A1021 20p multi   .50 .25

Opening of Al-Azhar Professorial Building A1022

2000, Dec. 10   **Perf. 12¾x13¼**
1777 A1022 20p multi   .50 .25

Famous Egyptians — A1023

   No. 1778: a, Karem Mahmoud, artist (yellow background). b, Mahmoud El-Miligi, artist (green background). c, Mohamed Fawzi, musician (pink background). d, Hussein Riyad, artist (lilac background). e, Abdel Wares Asser, artist (light blue background).

2000, Dec. 24   **Perf. 13¼x12¾**
1778   Horiz. strip of 5   2.00 2.00
a.-e. A1023 20p Any single   .40 .40

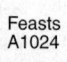
Feasts A1024

a, Red and yellow flowers. b, Purple flowers.

Perf. 12¾x13¼

2000, Dec. 23   Litho.
1779 A1024 20p Pair, #a-b   .90   .90

For use on greeting cards.

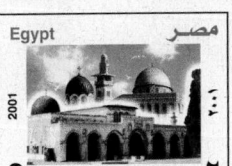

Jerusalem, City of Peace — A1025

2001, Jan. 1   *Imperf.*
1780 A1025 £2 multi   2.00 2.00

Post Day
A1026

Ancient Egyptian art: 20p, 8 standing figures. No. 1782, 125p, 3 large standing figures.

2001, Jan. 2   *Perf. 12¾x13¼*
1781-1782 A1026   Set of 2   1.75 1.75

Imperf

Size: 80x60mm

1783 A1026 125p Chariot   2.00 2.00

No. 1782 is airmail.

Arab Labor
Organization, 36th
Anniv. — A1027

Perf. 13¼x12¾

2001, Feb. 10   Litho.
1784 A1027 20p multi   .50 .25

Postal Savings Bank,
Cent. — A1028

2001, Mar. 1
1785 A1028 20p multi   .50 .25

Natl. Council
for Women,
1st Anniv.
A1029

Background colors: 30p, Pink. 125p, Blue.

2001, Mar. 16   *Perf. 12¾x13¼*
1786-1787 A1029   Set of 2   2.00 1.40

No. 1787 is airmail.

Cairo Intl.
Fair — A1030

2001, Mar. 21   *Perf. 13¼x12¾*
1788 A1030 30p multi   .50 .25

Helwan
University,
25th Anniv.
A1031

2001, May 4   *Perf. 12¾x13¼*
1789 A1031 30p multi   .50 .25

Inauguration
of
Alexandria
Library
A1032

2001, May 20
1790 A1032 125p multi   1.40 1.25

African Conference on
the Future of
Children — A1033

Background color: 30p, Blue. 125p, Red.

2001, May 28   *Perf. 13¼x12¾*
1791-1792 A1033   Set of 2   1.75 1.40

No. 1792 is airmail.

World Environment
Day — A1034

2001, June 5   Litho.   *Perf. 13¼x12¾*
1793 A1034 125p multi   1.40 1.25

World Military Soccer
Championships
A1035

Designs: 30p, Emblem. 125p, Emblem and map.

Perf. 13¼x12¾

2001, June 21   Litho.
1794-1795 A1035   Set of 2   1.75 1.50

**Intl. Day Against Drug Abuse Type
of 2000**

2001, June 26   *Perf. 12¾x13¼*
1796 A1013 30p multi   .50 .25

Egypt's Victory in World Military
Soccer Championships — A1036

2001, July 6   Litho.   *Imperf.*
1797 A1036 125p multi   1.75 1.75

Egyptian Railways,
150th Anniv.
A1037

2001, July 12   *Perf. 12¾x13¼*
1798 A1037 30p multi   .75 .25

Poets
A1038

No. 1799: a, Aziz Abaza Pasha (1898-73), blue background. b, Ahmed Rami (1892-1981), pink background.

2001, July 28   *Perf. 13¼x12¾*
1799 A1038 30p Horiz. pair, #a-b   .80 .80

Intl. Volunteers
Year — A1039

2001, Aug. 18
1800 A1039 125p multi   1.40 1.10

Ismailia Folklore
Festival — A1040

2001, Aug. 20
1801 A1040 30p multi   .60 .25

Satellite Telecommunications Ground
Stations, 25th Anniv. — A1041

2001, Sept. 8   *Perf. 12¾x13¼*
1802 A1041 30p multi   .60 .25

Year of Dialogue
Among
Civilizations — A1042

Designs: No. 1803, 125p, Emblem. No. 1804, 125p, UN emblem, globe, symbols of various civilizations, horiz.

Perf. 13¼x12¾, 12¾x13¼

2001, Oct. 9
1803-1804 A1042   Set of 2   3.00 2.50

Opening of Suez Canal Bridge
A1043

No. 1805: a, 30p, Bridge, ship. b, 125p, Bridge, road.
No. 1806, Bridge, ship and flags of Egypt and Japan.

2001, Oct. 10   *Perf. 12¾x13¼*
1805 A1043   Horiz. pair, #a-b   1.75 1.75

Imperf

Size: 81x60mm

1806 A1043 125p multi   2.00 2.00

Ancient Gold
Masks
A1044

Designs: No. 1807, 30p, Mask of San Xing Dui, China, green background. No. 1808, 30p, Funerary mask of King Tutankhamun, brown background.

2001, Oct. 12   *Perf. 12¾x13¼*
1807-1808 A1044   Set of 2   .80 .60

See People's Republic of China 3141-3142.

Opening of Azhar
Tunnels,
Cairo — A1045

2001, Oct. 28   *Perf. 13¼x12¾*
1809 A1045 30p multi   .60 .25

El-Menoufia University,
25th Anniv. — A1046

2001, Nov. 25
1810 A1046 30p multi   .60 .25

Feasts
A1047

No.1811: a, Black and white bird on branch. b, Sea gulls. c, Parrot. d, Blue bird on branch.

2001, Dec. 5
1811 A1047 30p Block of 4, #a-d   2.50 2.00

For use on greeting cards.

Musicians — A1048

No. 1812: a, Zakaria Ahmed (1896-1961) with scarf around neck (4). b, Riyadh El-Sonbati (1908-81) with glasses with rectangular lenses (3). c, Mahmoud El-Sherif (1912-90) (2). d, Mohamed El-Kasabgi (1898-1966) with glasses with round lenses (1). Stamp numbers, shown in parentheses, are found at the bottom center in Arabian script.

2001, Dec.
1812 A1048 30p Horiz. strip of 4   2.00 1.40

Painting From Tomb of Anhur Khawi
A1049

Painting from Tomb of Irinefer
A1050

2002, Jan. 2   Litho.   Perf. 12¾x13¼
1813 A1049 30p multi   .45 .25
Imperf
Size: 79x60mm
1814 A1050 125p multi   2.25 2.25
Post Day.

Intl. Nephrology Congress — A1051

2002, Jan. 16   Litho.   Perf. 13¼x12¾
1815 A1051 30p multi   .45 .25

Police Day, 50th Anniv.
A1052

2002, Jan. 25   Perf. 12¾x13¼
1816 A1052 30p multi   .45 .25
Imperf
Size: 79x50mm
1817 A1052 30p multi   1.60 1.50

Return of Sinai to Egypt, 20th Anniv. — A1053

2002, Apr. 25   Perf. 13¼x12¾
1818 A1053 30p multi   .60 .25

Cairo Bank, 50th Anniv. — A1054

2002, May 15
1819 A1054 30p multi   .50 .25

Weight Lifters
A1055

No. 1820: a, Ibrahim Shams, 1948 (weights over head). b, Khidre el Touney, 1936 (weights at knees).

2002, June 1
1820 A1055 30p Horiz. pair, #a-b   .80 .80

Al Akhbar Newspaper, 50th Anniv.
A1056

2002, June 15   Perf. 12¾x13¼
1821 A1056 30p multi   .45 .25

Nos. 318-321 and Egyptian Arms
A1057

2002, July 23   Litho.   Imperf.
1822 A1057 125p multi   1.40 1.40
July 23rd Revolution, 50th anniv.

Aswan Dam, Cent.
A1058

No. 1823: a, Dam. b, Dam and buildings.

2002, Aug. 15   Perf. 12¾x13¼
1823 A1058 30p Horiz. pair, #a-b   .90 .90

Intl. Ozone Day — A1059

2002, Sept. 16   Perf. 13¼x12¾
1824 A1059 125p multi   1.40 1.25
See Nos. 1595-1597, 1622-1623.

18th Intl. Conference on Road Safety, Cairo — A1060

2002, Sept. 22
1825 A1060 30p multi   .50 .25

17th Congress of Ear-Nose-Throat (ENT) Associations — A1061

2002, Sept. 28
1826 A1061 30p multi   .50 .25
17th Congress of Intl. Federation of Otorhinolaryngological Societies, Cairo.

World Post Day — A1062

2002, Oct. 9
1827 A1062 125p multi   1.10 1.10

Opening of Alexandria Library
A1063

Ancient Alexandria Library — A1064

Designs: 30p, Library exterior. 125p, Pillar, sun on horizon, vert.

Perf. 12¾x13¼, 13¼x12¾
2002, Oct. 16
1828-1829 A1063 Set of 2   1.75 1.50
Size: 60x80mm
Imperf
1830 A1064 125p multi   1.60 1.60

Hassan Faek, Actor
A1065

Aziza Amir, Actress
A1066

Farid Shawki, Actor
A1067

Mary Mounib, Actress
A1068

2002, Nov. 23   Perf. 13¼x12¾
1831   Horiz. strip of 4   1.75 1.60
  a. A1065 30p tan & black   .40 .25
  b. A1066 30p tan & black   .40 .25
  c. A1067 30p tan & black   .40 .25
  d. A1068 30p tan & black   .40 .25

A1069   A1070

A1071

Birds — A1072

2002, Dec. 3   Perf. 13¼x12¾
1832   Block of 4   1.75 1.60
  a. A1069 30p multi   .40 .25
  b. A1070 30p multi   .40 .25
  c. A1071 30p multi   .40 .25
  d. A1072 30p multi   .40 .25

Egyptian Museum, Cent.
A1073

125p, Entrance, statue of Cheops.

2002, Dec. 11   Perf. 12¾x13¼
1833 A1073 30p shown   .50 .25
Size: 80x60mm
Imperf
1834 A1073 125p multi   1.40 1.40

Opening of Aswan Suspension Bridge — A1074

No. 1835: a, Bridge and support cables. b, Bridge towers.

2002, Dec. 17   Perf. 12¾x13¼
1835 A1074 30p Horiz. pair, #a-b   .90 .90

Suez Canal University, 25th Anniv. — A1075

2002, Dec. 29   Perf. 13¼x12¾
1836 A1075 30p multi   .45 .25

Toshka Land Reclamation Project
A1076

2002, Dec. 31   Perf. 12¾x13¼
1837 A1076 30p multi   .45 .25

A1077

A1078

Post
Day — A1079

2003, Jan. 2
1838	A1077	30p multi	.45	.25
1839	A1078	30p multi	.45	.25
1840	A1079	125p multi	1.10	1.00
Nos. 1838-1840 (3)			2.00	1.50

Cairo Intl.
Communications and
Information Technology
Fair — A1080

2003, Jan. 12   Litho.   Perf. 13¼x12¾
1841	A1080	30p multi	.50	.25

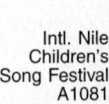

Intl. Nile
Children's
Song Festival
A1081

Background color: 30p, Brown. 125p,
Green.

2003, Jan. 28   Perf. 12¾x13¼
1842-1843	A1081	Set of 2	1.50	1.25

Intl. Table Tennis
Championships — A1082

Background color: 30p, Blue. 125p, Orange.

2003, Feb. 3
1844-1845	A1082	Set of 2	1.50	1.25

Tenth Intl. Building and
Construction
Conference — A1083

Background color: 30p, Orange. 125p, Blue.

2003, Apr. 1   Perf. 13¼x12¾
1846-1847	A1083	Set of 2	1.50	1.10

Arab
Lawyer's
Union, 60th
Anniv.
A1084

Background color: 30p, Blue. 125p, Lilac.

2003, Apr. 25   Perf. 12¾x13¼
1848-1849	A1084	Set of 2	1.40	1.10

Inauguration
of First Phase
of Smart
Village Project
A1085

Denomination color: 30p, White. 125p, Yellow. £1, White.

2003, July 1   Perf. 12¾x13¼
1850-1851	A1085	Set of 2	1.50	1.50
		Size: 79x59mm		
		Imperf		
1852	A1085	£1 multi	1.50	1.50

Writers
A1086

No. 1853: a, Ihsan Abdul Qudous (1919-90)
(wearing checked tie). b, Youssef Idris (1927-
91) (wearing solid tie).

2003, July 28   Perf. 13¼x12¾
1853	A1086	30p Horiz. pair, #a-b	.90	.90

African Men's
Basketball
Championships
A1087

Background color: 30p, Black. 125p, Blue.

2003, Aug. 12
1854-1855	A1087	Set of 2	1.50	1.10

Natl. Institute of Astronomical and
Geophysical Research, Cent.
A1088

2003, Sept. 7   Perf. 12¾x13¼
1856	A1088	30p multi	.60	.30

World
Tourism
Day — A1089

Denomination color: 30p, White. 125p, Red.

Perf. 12¾x13¼

2003, Sept. 27   Litho.
1857-1858	A1089	Set of 2	1.50	1.10

Egypt's Bid for Hosting
2010 World Cup
Soccer Championships
A1090

Designs: 30p, Emblem, vert. 125p, Emblem,
funerary mask of King Tutankhamun.

Perf. 13¼x12¾, 12¾x13¼

2003, Sept. 27
1859-1860	A1090	Set of 2	1.50	1.10

October War Against
Israel, 30th
Anniv. — A1091

2003, Oct. 6   Perf. 13¼x12¾
1861	A1091	30p multi	1.00	.30

World Post
Day — A1092

2003, Oct. 9
1862	A1092	125p multi	1.00	.80

National Bar
Association, 91st
Anniv. — A1093

2003, Oct. 30
1863	A1093	30p multi	.60	.25

Festivals
A1094

No. 1864: a, Pink orchids. b, White rose. c,
Red rose. d, Sunflower.

2003, Nov. 23   Perf. 14
1864	A1094	30p Block of 4, #a-d	1.50	1.50

For use on greeting cars.

Film
Directors
A1095

No. 1865: a, Salah Abou Seif (balding man
with open collar). b, Kamal Selim (round eyeglasses) c, Henri Barakat (square eyeglasses). d, Hassan El Emam.

2003, Dec. 1   Perf. 13¼x12¾
1865	A1095	30p Horiz. strip of 4, #a-d	1.50	1.50

El Gomhoreya
Newspaper, 50th
Anniv. — A1096

2003, Dec. 7
1866	A1096	30p multi	.50	.25

Cairo Bourse,
Cent.
A1097

2003, Dec. 7   Perf. 12¾x13¼
1867	A1097	30p multi	.45	.25

Mrs. Suzanne Mubarak, Emblems of
Fifth E-9 Ministerial Review Meeting
and UNESCO
A1098

Background color: 30p, Blue. 125p, Orange.
£2, Blue.

Perf. 12¾x13¼
2003, Dec. 18   Litho.
1868-1869	A1098	Set of 2	1.50	1.10
		Imperf		
		Size: 79x60mm		
1870	A1098	£2 multi	2.00	2.00

Delta International
Bank, 25th
Anniv. — A1099

Background color: 30p, Green. 125p, Blue.
£2, Green and blue, horiz.

2004, Jan. 1   Perf. 12¾x13¼
1871-1872	A1099	Set of 2	1.40	1.00
		Imperf		
		Size: 80x60mm		
1873	A1099	£2 multi	2.00	2.00

Post
Day — A1100

Denominations: 30p, 125p.

2004, Jan. 2   Perf. 12¾x13¼
1874-1875	A1100	Set of 2	1.50	1.25

Eighth Intl. Telecommunications
Conference — A1101

2004, Jan. 17
1876	A1101	30p multi	.80	.30

Treasures of
Egypt — A1102

No. 1877: a, Sinai. b, Pyramids at dusk. c,
Egyptian Bedouin. d, Red Sea corals. e, Suez
Canal, Ferdinand-Marie de Lesseps, Khedive
Ismail. f, Ramadan lanterns. g, Nile felucca. h,
White Western Desert. i, Maydum Pyramid.

No. 1878: a, St. Catherine Monastery, Sinai.
b, Icon of Sts. Paul and Anthony. c, Mosque of
Muhammad Ali. d, Lamp, Old Cairo. e,
Emblem of Sultan Qaytbay. f, Minaret, Cairo.
g, Mosque of al-Azhar. h, Coptic priest and
icon, Cairo. i, Ben Ezra Synagogue.

No. 1879: a, Ankh. b, Rosetta Stone. c, Sarcophagus of Ahmes Meritamun. d, Stela of
Amenmhat. e, Sphinx. f, Udjat. g, Canopic jars

of Tutankhamun. h, Cartouche of Tutankhamun. i, Egyptian scribe.
No. 1880: a, Sphinx, diff. b, Queen Nefertiti. c, Tutankhamun.

2004, Jan. 22   Litho.   Perf. 13x13¼

1877	Booklet pane of 9	2.25	—
a.-i.	A1102 30p Any single	.40	.25
1878	Booklet pane of 9	8.25	—
a.-i.	A1102 125p Any single	.90	.80

Litho. & Embossed, Litho. & Embossed With Foil Application (£10)

1879	Booklet pane of 9	13.50	—
a.-i.	A1102 £2 Any single	1.50	1.25

Perf. 13¼

1880	Booklet pane of 3	15.00	—
a.-b.	A1102 £5 Either single, 38x51mm	3.75	3.75
c.	A1102 £10 gold & multi, 38x51mm	7.00	7.00
	Complete booklet, #1877-1880	39.00	

Complete booklet sold for £80.

Morkos Hanna
A1103

Ahmed Lotfi
A1104

Mahmoud Abu el Nasr
A1105

Abd el Aziz Fahmy
A1106

Ibrahim el Helbawi
A1107

Makram Ebeid
A1108

Mohammad Naguib el Gharabli
A1109

Mohammad Bassiouni
A1110

Mohammad Hafez Ramadan
A1111

Mohammad Abu Shadi
A1112

Mahmoud Fahmi Goundia
A1113

Kamel Youssof Saleh
A1114

Abd el Hamid Abd el Hakk
A1115

Mohammad Ali Allouba
A1116

Kamel Sedki Beck
A1117

Bar Association Emblem
A1118

Abd el Rahman el Rafei
A1119

Abd el Fattah el Shalkany
A1120

Mohammad Sabri Abu Alam
A1121

Omar Omar
A1122

Sameh Ashour
A1123

Ahmed el Khawaga
A1124

Abd el Aziz el Shorgabi
A1125

Mostafa el Baradei
A1126

2004, Feb.   Litho.   Perf. 13¼x12¾

1881	Block of 25	8.75	8.75
a.	A1103 30p bright blue & black	.35	.25
b.	A1104 30p bright blue & black	.35	.25
c.	A1105 30p bright blue & black	.35	.25
d.	A1106 30p bright blue & black	.35	.25
e.	A1107 30p bright blue & black	.35	.25
f.	A1108 30p pink & black	.35	.25
g.	A1109 30p pink & black	.35	.25
h.	A1110 30p pink & black	.35	.25
i.	A1111 30p pink & black	.35	.25
j.	A1112 30p pink & black	.35	.25
k.	A1113 30p orange & black	.35	.25
l.	A1114 30p orange & black	.35	.25
m.	A1115 30p orange & black	.35	.25
n.	A1116 30p orange & black	.35	.25
o.	A1117 30p orange & black	.35	.25
p.	A1118 30p green & multi	.35	.25
q.	A1119 30p green & black	.35	.25
r.	A1120 30p green & black	.35	.25
s.	A1121 30p green & black	.35	.25
t.	A1122 30p green & black	.35	.25
u.	A1118 30p dark blue & multi	.35	.25
v.	A1123 30p dark blue & black	.35	.25
w.	A1124 30p dark blue & black	.35	.25
x.	A1125 30p dark blue & black	.35	.25
y.	A1126 30p dark blue & black	.35	.25

National Bar Association, 92nd anniv.

IBM Corporation in Egypt, 50th Anniv. — A1127

2004, Feb. 24
1882   A1127 30p multi   .60   .25

Cairo Rotary Club, 75th Anniv. — A1128

2004, Mar. 11
1883   A1128 30p multi   .60   .25

Egyptian Victory in Regional Computer Programming and Information Technology Competition — A1129

2004, Mar. 15
1884   A1129 30p multi   .60   .25

National Women's Day — A1130

Background colors: 30p, Blue. 125p, Red orange.

2004, Mar. 16   Litho.
1885-1886   A1130 Set of 2   1.50   1.00

Anti-Narcotics General Administration, 75th Anniv. — A1131

2004, Mar. 20   Perf. 12¾x13¼
1887   A1131 30p multi   .75   .30

Imperf
Size: 80x60mm
1888   A1131 125p multi   1.50   1.50

Orphan's Day — A1132

2004, Apr. 2   Perf. 13¼x12¾
1889   A1132 30p multi   .60   .25
Compare with Types A1169 and A1199.

Telecom Africa Fair and Conference, Cairo A1133

2004, May 4   Perf. 12¾x13¼
1890   A1133 30p multi   .60   .25

Egyptian Philatelic Society, 75th Anniv. — A1134

Designs: 30p, Emblem. 125p, Emblem, stamp, magnifying glass, tongs.

2004, May 20   Perf. 13¼x12¾
1891   A1134 .30p multi   .60   .25

Imperf
Size: 80x60mm
1892   A1134 125p multi   1.50   1.50

State Information Service, 50th Anniv. A1135

2004, May 30   Perf. 12¾x13¼
1893   A1135 30p multi   .75   .25

Tenth Radio and Television Festival, Cairo — A1136

Designs: 30p, Festival emblem, green background. £1, Festival emblem, brown background. 125p, Sphinx, festival emblem, film, horiz. £2, Like 125p, horiz.

Perf. 13¼x12¾, 12¾x13¼
2004, June 1
1894-1896 A1136 Set of 3   2.00 2.00
Imperf
Size: 80x60mm
1897 A1136 £2 multi   2.00 2.00

Pres. Hosni Mubarak, "Education for
All" Arab Regional Conference
Emblem
A1137

Stylized Children,
Emblems — A1138

Perf. 12¾x13¼, 13¼x12¾
2004, June 1
1898 A1137 30p yel & multi   .35 .25
1899 A1137 125p red org & multi   .60 .60
1900 A1138 125p multi   .60 .60
  Nos. 1898-1900 (3)   1.55 1.45
Imperf
Size: 80x60mm
1901 A1137 £2 blue & multi   1.75 1.75

Construction and
Housing Bank, 25th
Anniv. — A1139

2004, June 24   Perf. 13¼x12¾
1902 A1139 30p multi   .60 .25

2004 Summer
Olympics,
Athens — A1140

Background color: 30p, Gray. 150p, Orange
yellow.

Perf. 13¼x12¾
2004, Aug. 13   Litho.
1903-1904 A1140 Set of 2   1.50 1.40

Scouting in
Egypt, 90th
Anniv.
A1141

2004, Aug. 15   Perf. 12¾x13¼
1905 A1141 30p multi   .80 .30

14th Intl. Folklore
Festival,
Ismailia — A1142

2004, Aug. 24   Perf. 13¼x12¾
1906 A1142 30p multi   .70 .25

Administrative
Attorneys, 50th
Anniv. — A1143

2004, Sept. 16   Perf. 13¼x12¾
1907 A1143 30p multi   .60 .25
Imperf
Size: 60x80mm
1908 A1143 £1 multi   1.50 1.50

Egyptian
National
Archives,
50th Anniv.
A1144

2004, Sept. 20   Perf. 12¾x13¼
1909 A1144 30p multi   .75 .25

Light and
Hope
Society, 50th
Anniv.
A1145

2004, Sept. 26
1910 A1145 30p multi   .70 .25

General Arab
Journalists Union, 10th
Conference — A1146

2004, Oct. 2   Perf. 13¼x12¾
1911 A1146 125p multi   1.00 .80

Telecom
Egypt, 150th
Anniv.
A1146a

2004, Oct. 3 Litho.   Perf. 12¾x13¼
1911A A1146a 30p multi   18.50 18.50
  No. 1911A was withdrawn from sale after a
few days as anniversary emblem was
incorrect.

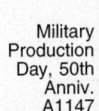

Military
Production
Day, 50th
Anniv.
A1147

2004, Oct. 6   Perf. 12¾x13¼
1912 A1147 30p multi   .90 .30

World Post
Day — A1148

2004, Oct. 9
1913 A1148 150p multi   1.10 1.00

Egyptian Youth Hostels
Association, 50th
Anniv. — A1149

2004, Oct. 20   Perf. 13¼x12¾
1914 A1149 30p multi   .80 .25

Rose
A1150

Songbird
A1151

  Perf. 12¾x13¼
2004, Nov. 10   Litho.
1915 A1150 30p multi   .50 .25
  Perf. 13¼x12¾
1916 A1151 30p multi   .50 .25

24th Arab
Scouting
Congress
A1152

2004, Nov. 27   Perf. 12¾x13¼
1917 A1152 30p multi   .65 .25

Arab
Scouting
Organization,
50th Anniv.
A1153

2004, Dec. 4
1918 A1153 30p multi   .65 .25

Islamic Art Museum
Foundation,
Cent. — A1154

2004, Dec. 15   Perf. 13¼x12¾
1919 A1154 30p multi   .65 .25

FIFA (Fédération Internationale de
Football Association), Cent.
A1155

2004, Dec. 15   Perf. 12¾x13¼
1920 A1155 150p multi   1.25 1.00

Fekri Abaza
(1896-1979),
Journalist
A1156

Abd El
Rahman El
Sharqawi
(1920-87),
Journalist
A1157

2004, Dec. 28   Perf. 13¼x12¾
1921 A1156 30p multi   .40 .25
1922 A1157 30p multi   .40 .25

Telecom
Egypt, 150th
Anniv.
A1158

Color of central panel: 30p, White. 125p,
Gray.

2004, Dec. 30   Perf. 12¾x13¼
1923-1924 A1158 Set of 2   1.50 1.10

First Sale of
Natural Gas
to Jordan
A1159

2005, Jan. 1
1925 A1159 30p multi   .90 .30

Post Day — A1160

2005, Jan. 2   Perf. 13¼x12¾
1926 A1160 30p multi   .80 .30

Opening of Om El Massrean — El
Moneib Subway Line, Cairo
A1161

2005, Jan. 16   Perf. 12¾x13¼
1927 A1161 30p multi   .65 .30
Imperf
Size: 80x59mm
1928 A1161 150p multi   1.40 1.40

Police Day — A1162

Pres. Hosni Mubarak and flag stripes
aligned: 30p, Vertically. £1, Horizontally.

2005, Jan. 25   Perf. 13¼x12¾
1929 A1162 30p multi   .60 .25
Imperf
Size: 80x59mm
1930 A1162 £1 multi   1.25 1.25

El Mohandes
Insurance Company,
25th Anniv. — A1163

2005, Jan. 26   *Perf. 13¼x12¾*
1931 A1163 30p multi   .65 .30

9th Intl.
Telecommunications
and Information
Conference,
Cairo — A1164

2005, Feb. 1
1932 A1164 30p multi   .65 .25

7th University Youth
Week — A1165

2005, Feb. 5
1933 A1165 30p multi   .65 .25

Rotary International,
Cent. — A1166

2005, Feb. 23   *Litho.*
1934 A1166 30p multi   .75 .30

38th Intl. Fair,
Cairo — A1167

2005, Mar. 15
1935 A1167 30p multi   .50 .25

Arab League, 60th
Anniv. — A1168

2005, Mar. 22
1936 A1168 30p multi   .55 .25

Orphan's
Day — A1169

2005, Apr. 2
1937 A1169 30p multi   .70 .30
Compare with Types A1132 and A1199. See
also Nos. 2035, 2053.

Heliopolis
Foundation,
Cent.
A1170

2005, May 5   *Perf. 12¾x13¼*
1938 A1170 30p multi   .65 .25

National Center of
Social and
Criminological
Research, 50th
Anniv. — A1171

2005, May 22   *Litho.*   *Perf. 13¼x12¾*
1939 A1171 30p multi   .70 .30

Egyptian-European
Association
Agreement, 1st
Anniv. — A1172

2005, June 1
1940 A1172 150p multi   .90 .50

World
Environment
Day — A1173

2005, June 5   *Perf. 12¾x13¼*
1941 A1173 30p multi   .80 .30

World Summit on the
Information Society,
Tunis — A1174

2005, July 31   *Litho.*   *Perf. 13¼x12¾*
1942 A1174 150p multi   1.40 1.40

Ministry of Youth, 50th
Anniv. — A1175

Background colors: 30p, Green. 125p, Olive
green.

2005, Aug. 13
1943-1944 A1175   Set of 2   1.25 1.10

Presidential
Elections — A1176

2005, Sept. 7
1945 A1176 30p multi   .65 .30

13th World Psychiatry
Congress,
Cairo — A1177

Designs: 30p, Emblem. 150p, Emblem and
funerary mask of King Tutankhamun, horiz.

2005, Sept. 10   *Perf. 13¼x12¾*
1946 A1177 30p multi   .65 .30

Imperf
Size: 80x60mm
1947 A1177 150p multi   1.90 1.90

World
Literacy
Day — A1178

2005, Sept. 24   *Perf. 12¾x13¼*
1948 A1178 30p multi   .70 .30

Re-election of Pres.
Hosni
Mubarak — A1179

2005, Sept. 27   *Perf. 13¼x12¾*
1949 A1179 30p multi   .60 .25

Mohamed El-Baradei,
Director General of
Intl. Atomic Energy
Agency — A1180

Background colors: 30p, Blue green. 150p,
Rose lilac.

2005, Oct. 8
1950-1951 A1180   Set of 2   1.75 1.50
Awarding of 2005 Nobel Peace Prize to El-
Baradei and IAEA.

World Post
Day — A1181

Denominations: 30p, 150p.

2005, Oct. 9
1952-1953 A1181   Set of 2   1.40 1.25

Intl. Year of Sports and
Physical
Education — A1182

2005, Oct. 24
1954 A1182 150p multi   1.25 1.00

United
Nations, 60th
Anniv.
A1183

2005, Oct. 24   *Perf. 12¾x13¼*
1955 A1183 150p multi   1.25 1.00

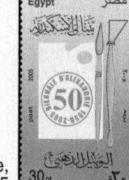

Festivals — A1184

2005, Nov. 1   *Perf. 13¼x12¾*
1956 A1184 30p multi   .70 .30

Alexandria Biennale,
50th Anniv. — A1185

2005, Dec. 1
1957 A1185 30p multi   .65 .30

K-8 Training
Airplane
A1186

Denominations: 30p, 150p.

2005, Dec. 26   *Perf. 12¾x13¼*   *Litho.*
1958-1959 A1186   Set of 2   2.00 1.50

Saved Mekawi,
Musician
A1187

Mohamed El
Mogi (1923-
95), Musician
A1188

Kamal El Taweel, Composer A1189

Ali Ismael (1921-75), Composer A1190

Mohamed Roshdi, Folk Singer — A1191

2005, Dec. 31
1960   Horiz. strip of 5   1.75 1.75
   a.   A1187 30p green & multi   .30 .25
   b.   A1188 30p blue & multi   .30 .25
   c.   A1189 30p lilac & black   .30 .25
   d.   A1190 30p org & black   .30 .25
   e.   A1191 30p brt org & black   .30 .25

Post Day — A1192

2006, Jan. 2
1961   A1192 30p multi   .75 .30

25th Africa Cup of Nations Soccer Tournament — A1193

2006, Jan. 20
1962   A1193 30p multi   .60 .25

Arab University Youth Week A1194

2006, Feb. 4   *Perf. 12¾x13¼*
1963   A1194 30p multi   .55 .25

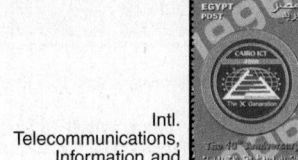

Intl. Telecommunications, Information and Networking Exhibition, Cairo — A1195

2006, Feb. 5   *Perf. 13¼x12¾*
1964   A1195 30p multi   .55 .25

Pres. Hosni Mubarak Holding African Cup of Nations A1196

2006, Feb. 10   *Perf. 12¾x13¼*
1965   A1196   30p multi   .75 .35
      Size: 80x60mm
      Imperf
1966   A1196 150p multi   1.75 1.60

Information and Decision Support Center, 20th Anniv. — A1197

2006, Mar. 27   *Perf. 13¼x12¾*
1967   A1197 30p multi   .55 .25

Total Solar Eclipse of March 29, 2006 A1198

2006, Mar. 29   *Perf. 12¾x13¼*
1968   A1198   30p multi   .55 .35
      Size: 82x60mm
      Imperf
1969   A1198 150p multi   2.25 1.90

Orphan's Day — A1199

2006, Apr. 2   *Perf. 13¼x12¾*
1970   A1199 30p multi   .70 .30
    Compare with types A1132 and A1169. See also Nos. 2035, 2053.

Gamal Hemdan (1928-93), Geographical Historian — A1200

2006, Apr. 16
1971   A1200 30p lilac & black   .55 .30

Abd El-Rahman ibn Khaldun (1332-1406), Historian — A1201

2006, May 27
1972   A1201 30p multi   .70 .30

World Environment Day — A1202

Designs: 30p, Stone pillar in White Desert. 150p, Trees in desert.

2006, June 5   *Perf. 12¾x13¼*
1973-1974 A1202   Set of 2   1.50 1.25

Diplomatic Relations Between Egypt and People's Republic of China, 50th Anniv. — A1203

No. 1975, £1.50: a, Abu Simbel Temple, Egypt. b, South Gate Pavilion, China.

2006, July 13   Litho.   *Perf. 12*
1975 A1203   Horiz. pair, #a-b,
         + central label   1.75 1.75
   c.   Souvenir sheet, #1975   25.00 25.00

Military Academy Headquarters, Heliopolis, 50th Anniv. — A1204

2006, July 19   *Perf. 12¾x13¼*
1976 A1204 30p multi   .70 .30

Nationalization of the Suez Canal, 50th Anniv. — A1205

2006, July 26   *Perf. 13¼x12¾*
1977 A1205 30p multi   .55 .25

World Post Day — A1206

Denominations: 30p, 150p.

2006, Oct. 9
1978-1979 A1206   Set of 2   1.50 1.25

China - Africa Summit — A1206a

No. 1979A: b, Chinese mask. c, African mask.

2006, Nov. 5   Litho.   *Perf. 12*
1979A A1206a   Horiz. pair with
          central label   2.25 2.25
   b.-c.   £1.50 Either single   .80 .60

National Housing Census — A1207

2006, Nov. 21   Litho.   *Perf. 13¼x13*
1980 A1207 30p multi   .55 .25

Al-Ahram Newspaper — A1208

No. 1981: a, Newspaper headquarters. b, Newspaper emblem. 150p, Headquarters and emblem.

2006, Nov. 26   *Perf. 13x13¼*
1981 A1208   30p Horiz. pair, #a-
         b, + central
         label   1.00 1.00
      Imperf
      Size: 80x60mm
1982 A1208 150p multi   1.00 1.00

Egyptian Initiative to Support Lebanon A1209

2006, Dec. 27   *Perf. 13x13¼*
1983 A1209 150p multi   1.00 1.00

Feasts A1210

2006, Dec. 30
1984 A1210 30p multi   .45 .25

Post Day — A1211

2007, Jan. 2
1985 A1211 30p multi   .45 .25

Ali El Kassar (1888-1957), Artist — A1212

2007, Jan. 15   *Perf. 13¼x13*
1986 A1212 30p multi   .45 .25

Automobile and Touring Club of Egypt A1213

2007, Jan. 14 Litho.   *Perf. 12¾x13¼*
1987 A1213   30p multi   .55 .30
      Imperf
      Size: 80x60mm
1988 A1213 150p multi   1.50 1.50

Police Day — A1214

2007, Jan. 25   *Perf. 12¾x13¼*
1989 A1214   30p multi   .55 .30
      Imperf
      Size: 80x60mm
1990 A1214 150p multi   1.00 1.00

Rededication of National Library A1215

2007, Feb. 25   *Perf. 12¾x13¼*
1991 A1215 30p multi   .55 .30

Arabic Language Academy, 75th Anniv. — A1216

2007, Mar. 17　　　**Perf. 13¼x12¾**
1992 A1216 30p multi　　　　　.55　.30

World Health Day — A1217

2007, Apr. 7　Litho.　Perf. 12¾x13¼
1993 A1217 30p multi　　　　　.55　.30

Egyptian Trade Union Federation, 50th Anniv. — A1218

2007, May 1　　　**Perf. 13¼x12¾**
1994 A1218 30p multi　　　　　.45　.25

Egypt Air, 75th Anniv. A1219

Anniversary emblem and: 30p, Biplane. 150p, Biplane and jet.

2007, May 7　　　**Perf. 12¾x13¼**
1995-1996 A1219　Set of 2　1.00　.75

Return of Sinai to Egypt, 25th Anniv. A1220

No. 1997: a, Monastery of St. Catherine. b, Salah el Din Castle. c, Sharm el-Sheikh. d, Oasis of Nabq.

2007, Apr. 25　Litho.　Perf. 12¾x13¼
1997 A1220 30p Block of 4, #a-d 1.90 1.25

Mevlana Jalal ad-Din Rumi (1207-73), Islamic Philosopher — A1221

2007, May 8　　　**Perf. 13¼x12¾**
1998 A1221 150p multi　　　　.55　.30

World Environment Day — A1222

Designs: 30p, Sinai baton blue butterfly. 150p, Melting ice, horiz.

Perf. 13¼x12¾, 12¾x13¼
2007, June 5
1999-2000 A1222　Set of 2　1.50　.75

Scouting, Cent. A1223

2007, June 6　　　**Perf. 12¾x13¼**
2001 A1223 150p multi　　　　1.25　.80

EuroMed Postal Conference, Marseille, France A1224

2007, July 9
2002 A1224 150p multi　　　　1.10　.75

Diplomatic Relations Between Egypt and Nepal, 50th Anniv. A1225

2007, July 16
2003 A1225 150p multi　　　　1.10　.75

Egyptian Air Force, 75th Anniv. A1226

2007, Oct. 14　Litho.　Perf. 13x13¼
2004 A1226 30p multi　　　　　.55　.25

A1227

11th Arab Games A1228

2007, Oct. 26　Litho.　Perf. 13¼x12¾
2005 A1227 150p multi　　　　1.25　.90
Imperf
Size: 95x75mm
2006 A1228 150p multi　　　　1.25 1.00

Assiut University, 50th Anniv. — A1229

2007, Nov. 27　　　**Perf. 13¼x12¾**
2007 A1229 30p brn & blk　　　.45　.25

Hafez Ibrahim (1872-1932), Poet — A1230

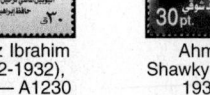

Ahmed Shawky (1868-1932), Poet — A1231

2007, Dec. 16
2008 A1230 30p multi　　　　　.45　.25
2009 A1231 30p multi　　　　　.45　.25

A 150p stamp issued in December 2007 depicting riders on horses on a beach with a se-tenant label was created exclusively for the Utopia Resort in Marsa Alam. The resort sold the stamps to its guests.

Egyptian Handball Federation, 50th Anniv. — A1232

2007, Dec. 30
2010 A1232 30p multi　　　　　.50　.25

Musicians A1233

2008, Jan. 1　　　**Perf. 12¾x13¼**
2011 A1233 30p multi　　　　　.45　.25

Post Day A1234

2008, Feb. 7　Litho.　Imperf.
2012 A1234 150p multi　　　　1.00 1.00

Africa Cup of Nations Soccer Championships, Ghana — A1235

2008, Feb. 10　　　**Perf. 13¼x13**
2013 A1235 30p multi　　　　　.45　.25

Wadi El-Hitan UNESCO World Heritage Site — A1236

No. 2014: a, Whale bones on ground. b, Reconstructed whale skeleton.

2008, Feb. 10　　　**Perf. 13x13¼**
2014　Horiz. pair with central label　1.00 1.00
a.-b.　A1236 30p Either single　.45　.25

Cairo University, Cent. — A1237

2008, Apr. 14　　　**Perf. 13¼x13**
2015 A1237 30p multi　　　　　.45　.25

Land Mine Clearance in Northwest Egypt A1238

No. 2016 — Map and: a, Amputee surrounded by land mines. b, Hand, "no land mines" symbol, vert.

Perf. 13x13¼, 13¼x13 (#2016b)
2008, Apr. 22
2016 A1238 150p Pair, #a-b　1.10 1.10

Telecom Africa Conference — A1239

2008, May 12　　　**Perf. 13¼x13**
2017 A1239 30p multi　　　　　.45　.25

World Environment Day — A1240

Background colors: 30p, Blue. 150p, Lilac.

2008, June 5
2018-2019 A1240　Set of 2　1.00　.70

Faculty of Fine Arts, Cent. A1241

No. 2020 — Background color: a, 30p, Blue. b, 150p, Green.

2008, June 21　Litho.　Perf. 13¼x13
2020 A1241　Horiz. pair, #a-b　1.25 1.25

Pan African Postal Union Plenipotentiary Conference, Cairo — A1242

2008, June 28　　　**Perf. 13x13¼**
2021 A1242 150p multi　　　　1.25　.60

Egypt Air Joining Star Alliance A1243

2008, July 11
2022 A1243 150p multi   1.25   .85

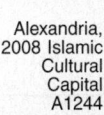

Alexandria, 2008 Islamic Cultural Capital A1244

2008, July 26
2023 A1244 150p multi   .85   .60

Arab Post Day A1245

No. 2024 — Emblem and: a, World map, pigeon. b, Camel caravan.

2008, Aug. 3
2024   Horiz. pair   2.00 2.00
a.-b. A1245 150p Either single   .75   .60

24th Universal Postal Union Congress, Geneva, Switzerland A1246

2008, Aug. 4   Litho.   Perf. 12¾x13¼
2025 A1246 150p multi   1.00   .75

Men's Sports Education Faculty, 50th Anniv. — A1247

2008, Oct. 15   Litho.   Perf. 13¼x13
2026 A1247 30p multi   .50   .30

Postech 2008 Intl. Postal Technology Conference, Sharm El-Sheikh A1248

Map and: 30p, Queen Nefertari holding Postech 2008 emblem. 150p, Statue of King Tutankhamun, hand holding Postech emblem.

Perf. 12¾x13¼
2008, Nov. 17   Litho.
2027-2028 A1248   Set of 2   1.40   .90

Egyptian Cooperative Movement, Cent. — A1249

2008, Dec. 22   Perf. 13¼x12¾
2029 A1249 30p multi   .45   .25

Natl. Telecommunications Institute, 25th Anniv. — A1250

2008, Dec. 31
2030 A1250 30p multi   .55   .30

Natl. Sports Council — A1251

2009, Mar. 3   Perf. 13¼x12¾
2031 A1251 150p multi   .95   .75

Constitutional Judiciary, 40th Anniv. — A1252

Designs: 30p, Emblem, text below. 150p, Emblem, text at right, horiz.

2009, Mar. 7   Perf. 13¼x12¾
2032 A1252 30p multi   .65   .40

Size:80x60mm
Imperf
2033 A1252 150p multi   1.00 1.00

Intl. Francophone Day — A1253

2009, Mar. 20   Perf. 12¾x13¼
2034 A1253 150p multi   .95   .55

Orphan's Day — A1254

2009, Apr. 3   Perf. 13¼x12¾
2035 A1254 150p multi   1.00   .60

Compare with Types A1132, A1169 and A1199. See also No. 2053.

Intl. Labor Organization, 90th Anniv. — A1255

2009, Apr. 21   Perf. 12¾x13¼
2036 A1255 150p multi   .90   .60

Suzanne Mubarak Women's International Peace Movement — A1256

2009, May 14   Perf. 13¼x12¾
2037 A1256 150p multi   .75   .55

Yehia Hakki (1905-92), Writer A1257

2009, May 11   Litho.   Perf. 12¾x13¼
2038 A1257 150p multi   .95   .55

Nobel Laureates From Africa A1258

No. 2039: a, Ahmed Zewail, Chemistry, 1999. b, Bishop Desmond Tutu, Peace, 1984. c, Wangari Maathai, Peace 2004. d, Anwar al-Sadat, Peace, 1978. e, Naguib Mahfouz, Literature, 1988. f, Allan M. Cormack, Physiology or Medicine, 1979. g, Nelson Mandela, Peace, 1993. h, Wole Soyinka, Literature, 1986. i, Sydney Brenner, Physiology or Medicine, 2002. j, F.W. de Klerk, Peace, 1993. k, Nadine Gordimer, Literature, 1991. l, Max Theiler, Physiology or Medicine, 1951. m, Mohamed El Baradei, Peace, 2005. n, Albert Luthuli, Peace, 1960. o, Kofi Annan, Peace, 2001. p, J.M. Coetzee, Literature, 2003.

2009, June 9
2039   Sheet of 16, #a-p, +
9 labels   22.50 22.50
a.-p. A1258 150p Any single   .95   .75

Fourth Extraordinary Session of the Pan-African Postal Union Plenipotentiary Conference, Cairo.

Fifteenth Non-Aligned Movement Summit, Sharm el-Sheikh — A1259

2009, July 15   Perf. 13¼x12¾
2040 A1259 150p multi   .55   .55

Opening of Mubarak Public Library, Damanhour A1260

2009, May 7   Litho.   Perf. 13x13¼
2041 A1260 150p multi   .95   .70

Jerusalem, Capital of Arab Culture — A1261

2009, Aug. 3   Perf. 13¼x13
2042 A1261 150p multi   .95   .75

FIFA Under-20 World Cup Soccer Championships, Egypt — A1262

No. 2042 — Tournament emblem, trophy and flag of participating team: a, Paraguay. b, Brazil. c, Uruguay. d, Germany. e, Nigeria. f, South Korea. g, Venezuela. h, Ghana. i, United Arab Emirates. j, South Africa. k, Egypt. l, Spain. m, Italy. n, Hungary. o, Czech Republic. p, Costa Rica.

2009, Oct. 5   Perf. 13x13¼
2043   Sheet of 16, #a-p, +
9 labels   19.50 19.50
a.-p. A1262 150p Any single   .95   .75

Fourth Ministerial Conference of Forum on China-African Cooperation, Sharm El Sheikh A1263

2009, Nov. 8
2044 A1263 150p multi   .95   .75

Fourth Meeting of Internet Governance Forum, Sharm El Sheikh A1264

2009, Nov. 15
2045 A1264 150p multi   .95   .75

Luxor Governate — A1264a

2009, Dec. 9   Litho.   Perf. 12¾x13¼
2045A A1264a 250p multi   1.25 1.25

Egyptian Society of Political Economy, Statistics and Legislation, Cent. A1265

2009, Dec. 19
2046 A1265 150p multi   .95   .95

Pharmaceutical Industry Drug Holding Company, 75th Anniv. — A1266

Background colors: 30p, Pink, yellow and pale green. 150p, Green.

2009, Dec. 19   Perf. 13¼x13
2047-2048 A1266   Set of 2   .95   .95

Egyptian Stock Exchange, 125th Anniv. A1267

Stock Exchange Building with anniversary emblem at left in: 30p, Gold and white. 150p, Gold (75x30mm).

2009, Dec. 21   **Perf. 13x13¼**
2049-2050 A1267   Set of 2   .95   .95

Pan-African Postal Union, 30th Anniv. A1268

2010, Jan. 18
2051 A1268   150p multi   .85   .85

National Council for Women, 10th Anniv. A1269

2010, Mar. 16
2052 A1269   30p multi   .65   .65

Orphan's Day — A1270

2010, Jan. 4   **Litho.**   **Perf. 13¼x12¾**
2053 A1270   30p multi   .55   .55
   Compare with Types A1132, A1169 and A1199. See also No. 2035.

Edfu Temple A1271

2010, Jan. 5   **Perf. 12¾x13¼**
2054 A1271   250p multi   1.50   1.50

Aswan High Dam, 50th Anniv. A1272

No. 2055 — Part of dam: a, 30p. b, £1.

2010, Jan. 15
2055 A1272   Horiz. pair, #a-b   1.50   1.50

Arab League Center, 50th Anniv. A1273

2010, Mar. 22
2056 A1273   200p multi   1.25   1.25

Egyptian Soccer Team, 2010 Winner of African Cup of Nations A1274

No. 2057 — Pyramid, African Cup of Nations, tournament emblems and: a, 30p, Crocodile mascot. b, 200p, Eagle mascot. c, 250p, Antelope mascot.
No. 2058 — Soccer players, African Cup of nations, years of Egyptian championships, horiz.

2010, Jan. 31   **Litho.**   **Perf. 13¼x12¾**
2057 A1274   Horiz. strip of
       3, #a-c   4.50   4.50
     Size: 80x60mm
       Imperf
2058 A1274   250p multi   1.50   1.50

Egyptian Gazette, 130th Anniv. — A1275

2010, Apr. 20   **Perf. 13¼x12¾**
2059 A1275   30p multi   .55   .55

Egypt Pavilion, Expo 2010, Shanghai A1276

2010, May 1   **Litho.**   **Perf. 12¾x13¼**
2060 A1276   £2.50 multi   1.75   1.75

Opening of Road to Red Sea — A1277

2010, May 27   **Perf. 13¼x12¾**
2061 A1277   £1 multi   .95   .95

World Environment Day A1278

2010, June 5   **Perf. 12¾x13¼**
2062 A1278   £2.50 multi   1.50   1.50

Tawfiq al-Hakim (1898-1987), Writer — A1279

2010, June 6   **Litho.**   **Perf. 13¼x12¾**
2063 A1279   150p multi   .95   .95
Second Egyptian Post Innovation Meeting.

Reading for All, 20th Anniv. — A1280

2010, June 21
2064 A1280   £1 multi   .95   .95

Egyptian Television, 50th Anniv. — A1281

2010, July 21
2065 A1281   £1.50 multi   1.25   1.25

Alexandria, 2010 Captial of Arab Tourism — A1282

2010, July 22   **Perf. 12¾x13¼**
2066 A1282   150p multi   1.25   1.25

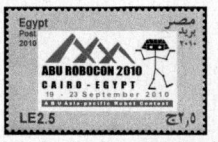

2010 Asia-Pacific Broadcasting Union Robotics Competition, Cairo A1283

2010, Sept. 19
2067 A1283   £2.50 multi   1.50   1.50

2010 Euromed Postal Conference, Alexandria A1284

2010, Sept. 28
2068 A1284   £2.50 multi   1.75   1.75

Alabaster Canopic Jar — A1285

2010, Oct. 8   **Perf. 13¼x12¾**
2069 A1285   £2.50 multi   1.75   1.75
   See Slovakia No. 601.

Second Arab University Games, Cairo — A1286

2010, Oct. 17   **Perf. 13¼x12¾**
2070 A1286   30p multi   .55   .55

World Statistics Day — A1287

2010, Oct. 20
2071 A1287   30p multi   .55   .55

Reopening of Museum of Islamic Art, Cairo — A1288

No. 2072: a, 30p, Goblet. £2, Bas-relief. £2.50, Plate with antelope design.

2010, Oct. 25
2072 A1288   Horiz. strip of 3,
       #a-c   2.50   2.50

Egyptian Olympic Committee, Cent. — A1289

2010, Dec. 11
2073 A1289   30p multi   .60   .60

Information and Decision Support Center, 25th Anniv. A1290

2010, Dec. 20   **Perf. 12¾x13¼**
2074 A1290   30p multi   .55   .55

Cairo Stadium, 50th Anniv. A1291

2010, Dec. 30   *Imperf.*
2075 A1291   £2.50 multi   1.50   1.50

Post Day — A1292

No. 2076 — Egyptian stamps: a, #3. b, #57. c, #107. d, #183. e, #271. f, #321. g, #386. h, #389. i, #873. j, #C1.

2011, Jan. 2   **Perf. 13**
2076   Block of 10   5.50   5.50
  a.-h.   A1292 30p Any single   .40   .30
  i.   A1292 £2 multi   1.00   .75
  j.   A1292 £2.50 multi   1.25   1.00

Cairo Tower, 50th Anniv. A1293

No. 2077 — Tower: a, 30p, In daylight. b, £2.50, At night.

2011, Apr. 11   **Perf. 13¼x12¾**
2077 A1293   Horiz. pair, #a-b   2.25   2.25

World Environment
Day — A1294

2011, June 5
2078 A1294 £2.50 multi   1.50 1.50

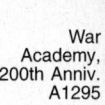

War
Academy,
200th Anniv.
A1295

2011, July 20   *Perf. 12¾x13¼*
2079 A1295 30p multi   .80 .80

Rivers
A1296

No. 2080: a, 30p, Pyramids, Nile River. b,
30p, Downtown Singapore, Singapore River.
c, £2, Ancient Egyptian boat, Nile River. d, £2,
Modern boat, Singapore River. e, £2.50, Cairo
skyline, yellow flowers, Nile River. f, £2.50,
Singapore buildings, pink flowers, Singapore
River.

2011, Oct. 17
2080 A1296 Block of 6, #a-f   3.25 3.25
See Singapore Nos. 1513-1515.

Post Day
A1297

No. 2081: a, Dove, flowers, Egypt Post
emblem. b, Post office, air mail envelopes. c,
Eye of Horus, flowers, Egypt Post emblem.

2012, Jan. 2   *Perf. 13¼x12¾*
2081 A1297 £2.50 Horiz. strip of
3, #a-c   2.50 2.50

Temple — A1297a

2011   **Litho.**   *Perf. 11¼*
2081D A1297a £2.50 multi   — —

January 25 Revolution, 1st
Anniv. — A1298

2012, Jan. 25   *Imperf.*
2082 A1298 £2.50 multi   .85 .85

Pope Shenouda III of Alexandria
(1923-2012) — A1299

2012, Mar. 17   *Imperf.*
2083 A1299 £5 multi   1.75 1.75

Diplomatic Relations Between Egypt
and Azerbaijan, 20th Anniv. — A1300

No. 2084: a, Arches and Maiden Tower,
Baku, Azerbaijan. b, Sphinx and Pyramids,
Egypt.

2012, May 28   *Perf. 12¾x13¼*
2084 A1300 £2.50 Horiz. pair,
#a-b   1.75 1.75

Environment
Day — A1301

2012, June 5   *Perf. 13¼x12¾*
2085 A1301 £2 multi   .70 .70

A1302

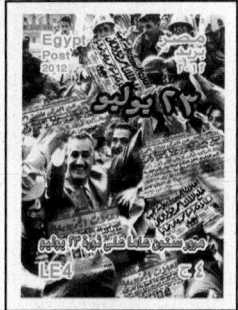

Overthrow of King Farouk by Gamal
Abdel Nasser, 60th Anniv. — A1303

2012, July 23   *Perf. 12¾x13¼*
2086 A1302 £2 multi   .65 .65
        Imperf
2087 A1303 £4 multi   1.40 1.40

2012 Summer
Olympics,
London — A1304

No. 2088 — Mascot and: a, Cycling. b, Running. c, Emblem of 2012 Summer Olympics. d,
Basketball. e, Soccer.

2012, July 27   *Perf. 13¼x12¾*
2088   Horiz. strip of 5   4.25 4.25
a.-e. A1304 £2.50 Any single   .85 .85

Arab Postal
Day — A1305

2012, Aug. 3   *Perf. 12¾x13¼*
2089 A1305 £3 multi   1.00 1.00

Festivals
A1306

No. 2090: a, Rider on blue gray horse,
heads of white and black horses. b, Two riders, black horse, head of brown horse. c, Rider
on brown horse.

2012, Aug. 18   *Perf. 13¼x12¾*
2090 A1306 £1 Horiz. strip of 3,
#a-c   1.00 1.00

Lawyers
Trade Union,
Cent.
A1307

2012, Sept. 12   *Perf. 12¾x13¼*
2091 A1307 £1 multi   .35 .35

Tourism and
Sustainable
Energy — A1308

2012, Sept. 27   *Perf. 13¼x12¾*
2092 A1308 £1 multi   .35 .35

Helwan University Art
Education Faculty,
75th Anniv. — A1309

2012, Nov. 12   **Litho.**
2093 A1309 £2 multi   .65 .65

Post Day
A1310

No. 2094: a, Ancient Egyptian art with Isis
seated at right, envelopes. b, Lotus flowers.
funerary mask of King Tutankhamun. c,
Ancient Egyptian art with Isis seated at left.

2013, Jan. 2   *Perf. 13¼x13*
2094 A1310 £3 Horiz. strip of 3,
#a-c   3.00 3.00

January 25th
Revolution,
2nd Anniv.
A1311

2013, Jan. 25   *Perf. 13x13¼*
2095 A1311 £1 multi   .30 .30

Victory of Egyptian
Team at African Cup
of Nations Youth
Soccer
Championships
A1312

2013, Apr. 24   *Perf. 13¼x13*
2096 A1312 £3 multi   .90 .90

Return of
Sinai to
Egypt,
31st
Anniv.
A1313

No. 2097 — Various tourist attractions and
Sinai Peninsula map showing: a, Northwestern section. b, Northeastern section. c, Southwestern section. d, Southeastern section.

2013, Apr. 25   *Perf. 13x13¼*
2097 A1313 £2 Block of 4, #a-d 2.40 2.40

World Environment
Day — A1314

2013, June 5   *Perf. 13¼x13*
2098 A1314 £3 multi   .85 .85

July 23rd
Revolution,
61st Anniv.
A1315

2013, July 23 Litho. *Perf. 12¾x13¼*
2099 A1315 £3 multi   .85 .85

Day of the Nile Inundation — A1316

2013, Aug. 25 Litho.   *Imperf.*
2100 A1316 £4 multi   1.25 1.25

Intl. Islamic Council for
Da'wa and
Relief — A1317

        Perf. 13¼x12¾
2013, Sept. 21   **Litho.**
2101 A1317 £2 multi   .60 .60

World Tourism
Day — A1318

Perf. 13¼x12¾
2013, Sept. 27   Litho.
2102   A1318   £3 multi   .90   .90

A1319

October War
Against
Israel, 40th
Anniv.
A1320

2013, Oct. 6   Litho.   **Perf. 12¾x13¼**
2103   A1319   £1 multi   .30   .30
2104   A1320   £4 multi   1.25   1.25

Thutmosis
III — A1321

Thutmosis
III —
A1321a

Sculptures of Egyptian
Pharaohs — A1322

Designs: £1, Senusret I. £3, Ramesses II.
£4, Akhenaten.

2013-20   Litho.   **Perf. 11¼**
2105   A1321   50p org & multi   .25   .25
2106   A1321   50p grn & multi   .25   .25
Perf. 11x11½
2107   A1322   £1 multi   .30   .30
2108   A1322   £3 lil & multi   .90   .90
2108A   A1322   £3 blue & multi   —   —
2109   A1322   £4 brn & multi   1.25   1.25
2109A   A1322   £4 rose brn &   —   —
          multi

**Star Punched Out in Upper Left
Corner**
Perf. 13½x14
2109B   A1321a   50p multi ('20)   2.95   2.95
    Nos. 2105-2109A (7)
Issued: Nos. 2105-2109A, 10/7. See Nos.
2174-2175.

World Post
Day — A1323

2013, Oct. 9   Litho.   **Perf. 12¾x13¼**
2110   A1323   £4 multi   1.25   1.25

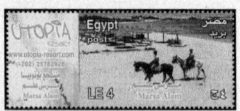

Tourists on Horseback, Utopia Resort,
Marsa Alam — A1324

Old Town, Hurghada — A1325

Madinat Makadi Resort,
Hurghada — A1326

Perf. 12¾x13¼
2013, Dec. 17   Litho.
2111   A1324   £4 multi   1.25   1.25
2112   A1325   £4 multi   1.25   1.25
2113   A1326   £4 multi   1.25   1.25
    Nos. 2111-2113 (3)   3.75   3.75

Nile
Meter,
by M.
Sabry
A1327

2014, Jan. 2   Litho.   Imperf.
2114   A1327   £4 multi   1.25   1.25
     Post Day.

January 25th
Revolution,
3rd Anniv.
A1328

2014, Jan. 25   Litho.   **Perf. 12¾x13¼**
2115   A1328   £2 multi   .60   .60

Intl. Women's
Day — A1329

2014, Mar. 8   Litho.   **Perf. 12¾x13¼**
2116   A1329   £2 multi   .60   .60

World
Heritage
Day
A1330

No. 2117: a, Two women. b, Men and
camel. c, Men playing board game. d, Man,
pottery in windows.

2014, Apr. 18   Litho.   **Perf. 12¾x13¼**
2117   A1330   £1 Block of 4 #a-d   1.25   1.25

Diversion
of the
Nile
River,
50th
Anniv.
A1331

2014, May 15   Litho.   Imperf.
2118   A1331   £4 multi   1.10   1.10

African
Regional
Postal
Training
Center
A1332

2014, June 1   Litho.   **Perf. 12¾x13¼**
2119   A1332   £2 multi   .55   .55

Day of the
African Child
A1333

Perf. 12¾x13¼
2014, June 17   Litho.
2120   A1333   £3 multi   .85   .85

Euromed Postal Emblem and
Mediterranean Sea — A1334

2014, July 9   Litho.   **Perf. 13x13¼**
2121   A1334   £4 multi   1.10   1.10

July 23rd Revolution,
62nd Anniv. — A1335

2014, July 23   Litho.   **Perf. 13¼x13**
2122   A1335   £2 multi   .55   .55

Start of Construction on Second Suez
Canal — A1336

No. 2123: a, Suez Canal emblem, ship, map
of northern portion of canal. b, Map of central
portion of canal, ships near locks of Panama
Canal. c, Map of southern portion of canal,
Administration building, ship.

2014, Aug. 5   Litho.   **Perf. 13¼x13**
2123   A1336   £2 Horiz. strip of
        3, #a-c   55.00   37.50
No. 2123 was withdrawn shortly after the
error in stamp design (the Suez Canal has no
locks) was made known to Egypt Post.

General Arab
Insurance Federation,
50th Anniv. — A1337

50th anniversary emblem: No. 2124, Above
map of Arab countries. No. 2125, To left of
map of Arab countries.

2014, Sept. 1   Litho.   **Perf. 13¼x13**
2124   A1337   £4 multi   1.10   1.10
Imperf
Size: 90x70mm
2125   A1337   £4 multi   1.10   1.10

Start of Construction on New Suez
Canal — A1338

No. 2126: a, Map of canal, Adminisration
Building, ship in canal. b, Map of canal, ship
approaching canal. c, Suez Canal emblem,
ship in canal.

2014, Sept. 16   Litho.   **Perf. 13¼x13**
2126   A1338   £2 Horiz. strip of 3,
         #a-c   1.75   1.75
No. 2126 replaces the hastily withdrawn No.
2123. First day covers of No. 2126 show the
Aug. 5 first day cancel of No. 2123, though the
stamps were printed after the discovery of the
design error on No. 2123.

Shali Siwa
Oasis
A1339

Perf. 12¾x13¼
2014, Sept. 27   Litho.
2127   A1339   £4 multi   1.10   1.10

October War
Against
Israel, 41st
Anniv.
A1340

2014, Oct. 6   Litho.   **Perf. 12¾x13¼**
2128   A1340   £2 multi   .55   .55

World Post
Day — A1341

2014, Oct. 9   Litho.   **Perf. 13¼x12¾**
2129   A1341   £4 multi   1.10   1.10

Scouting in
Egypt, Cent.
A1342

2014, Oct. 15   Litho.   **Perf. 12¾x13¼**
2130   A1342   £1.25 multi   .35   .35

Arabic Calligraphy — A1343

2014, Dec. 6   Litho.   Imperf.
2131   A1343   £5 multi   1.40   1.40

Central Agency for
Public Mobilization and
Statistics,
Cent. — A1344

2014, Dec. 8   Litho.   **Perf. 13¼x12¾**
2132   A1344   £3 multi   .85   .85

Birds
A1345

No. 2133, £1.25: a, Palm dove. b, Hoopoe. c, Roller. d, Bee-eater. e, Sooty falcon. f, Golden oriole.

Perf. 13¼x12¾
2014, Dec. 10   **Litho.**
2133 A1345   Block of 6, #a-f, + 3
             central labels   2.10 2.10

Re-opening of National Theater A1346

Perf. 12¾x13¼
2014, Dec. 20   **Litho.**
2134 A1346   £1.50 multi   .45 .45

A1347

Amenhotep, Son of Hapu — A1347a

2015-20   **Litho.**   **Perf. 11¼**
2135 A1347   £3 multi   .85 .85
  a.   Perf. 13x13¼ ('15)
Perf. 13½x14
Star Punched Out in Upper Left Corner
2135B A1347a £3 multi ('20)   —   —

A1348

Egyptian Post, 150th Anniv. A1349

2015, Jan. 2   Litho.   Perf. 12¾x13¼
2136 A1348   £1.50 multi   .45 .45
Imperf
2137 A1349   £4 multi   1.10 1.10

January 25 Revolution, 4th Anniv. A1350

2015, Jan. 25   Litho.   Perf. 12¾x13¼
2138 A1350   £2 multi   .55 .55

Faten Hamama (1931-2015), Actress — A1351

2015, Mar. 8   Litho.   Perf. 13¼x12¾
2139 A1351   £3 black   .80 .80

Egypt Economic Development Conference A1352

Perf. 12¾x13¼
2015, Mar. 13   **Litho.**
2140 A1352   £2 multi   .55 .55

26th Arab Summit, Sharm el-Sheikh — A1353

Perf. 13¼x12¾
2015, Mar. 23   **Litho.**
2141 A1353   £3 multi   .80 .80

International Telecommunication Union, 150th Anniv. — A1354

2015, May 17   Litho.   Perf. 12¾x13¼
2142 A1354   £4 multi   1.10 1.10

Dar al-Ifta al-Misriyyah Educational Institute, 120th Anniv. A1355

2015, June 1   Litho.   Perf. 12¾x13¼
2143 A1355   £2 multi   .55 .55

July 23rd Revolution, 63rd Anniv. A1356

2015, July 23   Litho.   Perf. 12¾x13¼
2144 A1356   £2 multi   .55 .55

Campaign to Save the Nile River A1357

2015, July 25   Litho.   Perf. 12¾x13¼
2145 A1357   £2 multi   .55 .55

A1358

New Suez Canal A1359

2015, Aug. 6   Litho.   Perf. 12¾x13¼
2146   Horiz. strip of 3   2.40 2.40
  a. A1358 £3 lilac & multi   .80 .80
  b. A1358 £3 beige & multi   .80 .80
  c. A1358 £3 lt blue green & multi .80 .80
Imperf
2147 A1359   £4 multi   1.10 1.10

Poets A1360

No. 2148: a, Fouad Hadad (1927-85). b, Salah Jaheen (1930-86). c, Abd el Rahman El Abnody (1938-2015).

Perf. 13¼x12¾
2015, Aug. 10   **Litho.**
2148 A1360   £2 Horiz. strip of 3,
             #a-c   1.60 .80

Food and Agricultural Organization, 70th Anniv. A1361

2015, Oct. 1   Litho.   Perf. 12¾x13¼
2149 A1361   £3 multi   .80 .40

October War With Israel, 42nd Anniv. A1362

2015, Oct. 6   Litho.   Perf. 12¾x13¼
2150 A1362   £2 multi   .50 .25

A1363

Federation of Afro-Asian Insurers and Reinsurers, 50th Anniv. — A1364

2015, Oct. 12   Litho.   Perf. 13¼x12¾
2151 A1363   £4 multi   1.00 .50
Imperf
2152 A1364   £4 multi   1.00 .50

World Statistics Day — A1365

2015, Oct. 20   Litho.   Perf. 12¾x13¼
2153 A1365   £3 multi   .75 .35

Yacht "Mahrousa," 150th Anniv. — A1366

Perf. 12¾x13¼
2015, Dec. 15   **Litho.**
2154 A1366   £2 multi   .55 .55

Al-Ahram Newspaper, 140th Anniv. — A1367

Perf. 13¼x12¾
2015, Dec. 20   **Litho.**
2155 A1367   £2 multi   .55 .55

Helwan University Faculty of Applied Arts, 175th Anniv. A1368

Perf. 12¾x13¼
2015, Dec. 31   **Litho.**
2156 A1368   £2 multi   .55 .55

A1369

First Egyptian Postage Stamps, 150th Anniv. A1370

No. 2157: a, Egypt #4-7, dove, boat. b, Egyptian man on donkey. c, Egypt #1-3, Egyptian man on camel. £4, Emblem of Philatelic Society of Egypt, dove, boat, train, mail carrier on bicycle, mail box.

2016, Jan. 1   Litho.   Perf. 13¼x12¾
2157 A1369   £2 Horiz. strip of 3,
             #a-c   1.60 1.60
Imperf
2158 A1370   £4 multi   1.10 1.10

Syndicate of Journalists, 75th Anniv. — A1371

Perf. 13¼x12¾
2016, Mar. 31   **Litho.**
2159 A1371   £3 multi   .70 .70

Famous Men A1372

No. 2160: a, United Nations emblem and Boutros Boutros-Ghali (1922-2016), United Nations Secretary-General. b, Muhammad Husayn Haykal (1888-1956), Minister of Education.

2016, May 31   Litho.   Perf. 13¼x12¾
2160 A1372   £2 Horiz. pair, #a-b .90 .90

World Day to Combat Drugs A1373

Perf. 12¾x13¼

2016, June 26 Litho.
2161 A1373 £2 multi .45 .45

Egypt Nos. 356, 374, 386, 388 and 393 A1374

2016, July 23 Litho. *Imperf.*
2162 A1374 £4 multi .90 .90
July 23 Revolution, 64th anniv.

Arab Postal Day A1375

No. 2163 — Area behind denomination in: a, White. b, Green.

2016, Aug. 3 Litho. **Perf. 12¾x13¼**
2163 A1375 £3 Horiz. pair, #a-b 1.40 1.40

Gezera Youth Center — A1376

Perf. 13¼x12¾

2016, Aug. 15 Litho.
2164 A1376 £2 multi .45 .45

Relocation of Abu Simbel Temples, 50th Anniv. — A1377

No. 2165: a, Moving of statues. b, Man wearing glasses. c, Face of Ramesses II statue.

Perf. 13¼x12¾

2016, Aug. 18 Litho.
2165 A1377 £2 Horiz. strip of 3, #a-c 1.40 1.40

World Tourism Day A1378

No. 2166: a, Hanging Church, Cairo. b, Al-Moez Street, Cairo. c, Philae Temple, Aswan. d, Qaitbay Castle, Alexandria.

Perf. 12¾x13¼

2016, Sept. 27 Litho.
2166 A1378 £2 Block of 4, #a-d 1.90 1.90

October War Against Israel, 43rd Anniv. A1379

2016, Oct. 6 Litho. **Perf. 12¾x13¼**
2167 A1379 £2 multi .45 .45

Egyptian Parliament, 150th Anniv. — A1380

2016, Oct. 22 Litho. **Perf. 12¾x13¼**
2168 A1380 £2 multi + label .45 .45

Ahmed Zewail (1946-2016), 1999 Nobel Laureate in Chemistry A1381

2016, Oct. 25 Litho. **Perf. 12¾x13¼**
2169 A1381 £2 multi .45 .45

Actors A1382

No. 2170: a, Mahmoud Abd El-Aziz (1946-2016). b, Nour El-Sherif (1946-2015). c, Ahmed Zaki (1949-2005).

Perf. 13¼x12¾ Syncopated

2016, Nov. 27 Litho.
2170 A1382 £2 Horiz. strip of 3, #a-c .70 .70

Miniature Sheet

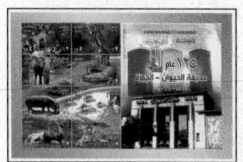

Giza Zoo, 125th Anniv. A1383

No. 1383: a, Barbary sheep. b, Giraffe. c, Elephant. d, Crocodile. e, Hippopotamus. f, Pelicans. g, Lion. h, Tiger.

2016, Dec. 2 Litho. **Perf. 12¾x13¼**
2171 A1383 £2 Sheet of 8, #a-h 1.90 1.90

World Day of the Arabic Language — A1384

No. 2172: a, £1, Arabic calligraphy. b, £2, Arabic calligraphy, diff., circle arc at left. c, £2, Arabic calligraphy, diff., circle arc at right.

2016, Dec. 18 Litho. **Perf. 11½**
2172 A1384 Horiz. strip of 3, #a-c .55 .55

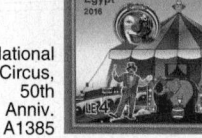

National Circus, 50th Anniv. A1385

2016, Dec. 25 Litho. *Imperf.*
2173 A1385 £4 multi .45 .45

Sculptures of Egyptian Pharaohs Type of 2013

Designs: 125p, Pseusennes I (image used on #1759). £4, Akhenaten.

2017 Litho. **Perf. 11¼**
2174 A1321 125p multi — —
2175 A1321 £4 multi — —

Dendera Temple — A1385a

Perf. 12¾x13¼

2017, Nov. 19 Litho.
2176 A1385a £5 multi .60 .60

Central Agency for Public Mobilization and Statistics — A1386

Perf. 13¼x12¾ Syncopated

2017, Apr. 10 Litho.
2177 A1386 £2 multi .25 .25

Modern Egypt Heritage, 150th Anniv. A1387

Perf. 12¾x13¼ Syncopated

2017, July 5 Litho.
2178 A1387 £2 multi .25 .25

July 23 Revolution, 65th Anniv. A1388

Perf. 12¾x13¼ Syncopated

2017, July 23 Litho.
2179 A1388 £4 multi .45 .45

General Sports Union for Businesses, 50th Anniv. — A1389

Perf. 13¼x12¾ Syncopated

2017, Sept. 14 Litho.
2180 A1389 £2 multi .25 .25

Forum on Heavenly Religions, Sharm el Sheikh — A1390

Perf. 13¼x12¾ Syncopated

2017, Sept. 28 Litho.
2181 A1390 £4 multi .45 .45

October War Against Israel, 44th Anniv. A1391

Perf. 12¾x13¼ Syncopated

2017, Oct. 6 Litho.
2182 A1391 £2 multi .25 .25
No. 2182 has simulated perfs to look like a label is attached.

A1392

Discovery of Abu Simbel Temples, 200th Anniv. — A1393

Perf. 12¾x13¼ Syncopated

2017, Oct. 21 Litho.
2183 A1392 £4 multi .45 .45

Size: 90x70mm

Imperf

2184 A1393 £5 multi .60 .60

Egyptian Women's Year A1394

Perf. 12¾x13¼ Syncopated

2017, Dec. 10 Litho.
2185 A1394 £2 multi .25 .25

The National Post Organization of Egypt has declared as "illegal" miniature sheets of 3 depicting Renaissance painters and miniature sheets of 4 depicting Coins, Napoleonic Wars, High Speed Trains, and the 2018 Winter Olympics.

Post Day — A1395

Perf. 13¼x12¾ Syncopated

2018, Jan. 2 Litho.
2186 A1395 £2.50 multi .30 .30

2018 World Cup Soccer Championships, Russia — A1396

Designs: £2.50, World Cup trophy, silhouette of soccer player dribbling ball. £5, World Cup trophy, soccer ball, player kicking ball, horiz.

Perf. 13¼x12¾ Syncopated

2018, June 14 Litho.
2187 A1396 £2.50 multi .30 .30
Size: 90x70mm
Imperf
2188 A1395 £5 multi .55 .55

Luxor Temple — A1397

2018, Sept. 12 Litho. **Perf. 11¼**
2189 A1397 £2.50 multi .30 .30

October War
Against
Israel, 45th
Anniv.
A1398

Perf. 12¾x13¼ Syncopated
2018, Oct. 6 Litho.
2190 A1398 £4 multi .45 .45

Ministry of
Culture, 60th
Anniv.
A1399

2018, Oct. 14 Litho. Perf. 12¾x13¼
2191 A1399 £2.50 multi .30 .30

Post
Day — A1400

Perf. 12¾x13¼ Syncopated
2019, Jan. 2 Litho.
2192 A1400 £3 multi .35 .35

Cairo
International
Book Fair,
50th Anniv.
A1401

2019, Jan. 23 Litho. Perf. 12¾x13¼
2193 A1401 £2.50 multi .30 .30

Egyptian
Chairmanship
of African
Union
A1402

Perf. 12¾x13¼ Syncopated
2019, Feb. 10 Litho.
2194 A1402 £4 multi .45 .45

National Institute of Oceanography
and Fisheries, Cent. — A1403

Perf. 12¾x13¼ Syncopated
2019, Feb. 12 Litho.
2195 A1403 £3 multi .35 .35

International Women's
Day — A1405

Perf. 13¼x12¾ Syncopated
2019, Mar. 8 Litho.
2198 A1405 £4 multi .50 .50

Saad Zaghloul (1859-1927), Leader of
1919 Egyptian Revolution and Prime
Minister
A1406

Perf. 12¾x13¼ Syncopated
2019, Mar. 9 Litho.
2199 A1406 £4 multi .50 .50

Return of Sinai to
Egypt, 37th
Anniv. — A1407

Perf. 13¼x12¾ Syncopated
2019, Apr. 25 Litho.
2200 A1407 £4 multi .50 .50

Labor Day — A1408

Perf. 13¼x12¾ Syncopated
2019, May 1 Litho.
2201 A1408 £5 multi .60 .60

World
Telecommunications
Day — A1410

Perf. 13¼x12¾ Syncopated
2019, May 17 Litho.
2203 A1410 £5 multi .60 .60

World Environment
Day — A1411

Perf. 13¼x12¾ Syncopated
2019, June 5 Litho.
2204 A1411 £4 multi .50 .50

A1412

Africa Cup of Nations Soccer
Tournament, Egypt — A1413

No. 2205 — Silhouettes of Egyptian buildings and: a, Flags of African countries on map
of Africa, emblem of African Cup of Nations. b,
Arabic text in red, "2019" in violet. c, Mascot
and African Cup of Nations.

Perf. 13¼x12¾ Syncopated
2019, June 21 Litho.
2205 A1412 £4 Horiz. strip of 3,
#a-c 1.50 1.50
Imperf
2206 A1413 £5 multi .60 .60

Traditional Costumes — A1414

No. 2207 — Euromed Postal emblem and:
a, Man and woman dancing, ship's wheel and
anchor. b, Women in robes. c, Women in
ancient Egyptian costumes.

Perf. 13¼x12¾ Syncopated
2019, July 8 Litho.
2207 A1414 £4 Horiz. strip of 3,
#a-c 1.50 1.50

July 23rd Revolution,
67th Anniv. — A1415

Perf. 13¼x12¾ Syncopated
2019, July 23 Litho.
2208 A1415 £4 multi .50 .50

Egyptian Team's Victory at World
Under-19 Handball
Championships — A1416

Perf. 12¾x13¼ Syncopated
2019, Aug. 16 Litho.
2209 A1416 £5 multi .60 .60

Egyptian Philatelic
Society, 90th
Anniv. — A1417

Perf. 13¼x12¾ Syncopated
2019, Sept. 9 Litho.
2210 A1417 £5 multi .65 .65

Egypt as Host of
African Space
Agency — A1418

Perf. 13¼x12¾ Syncopated
2019, Sept. 19 Litho.
2211 A1418 £5 multi .65 .65

Cairo University
School of Law, 150th
Anniv. — A1419

Perf. 13¼x12¾ Syncopated
2019, Sept. 23 Litho.
2212 A1419 £5 multi .65 .65

Opening of the Suez
Canal, 150th
Anniv. — A1420

Perf. 13¼x12¾ Syncopated
2019, Oct. 3 Litho.
2213 A1420 £5 multi .65 .65

October War Against
Israel, 46th
Anniv. — A1421

Perf. 13¼x12¾ Syncopated
2019, Oct. 6 Litho.
2214 A1421 £5 multi .65 .65

World Post
Day — A1422

Perf. 12¾x13¼ Syncopated
2019, Oct. 9 Litho.
2215 A1422 £5 multi .65 .65

Dome of the Rock, Jerusalem, Doves,
and Flag of Palestinian Authority
A1423

Perf. 12¾x13¼ Syncopated
2019, Oct. Litho.
2216 A1423 £5 multi .65 .65

Supreme Constitutional
Court, 50th
Anniv. — A1424

Perf. 13¼x12¾ Syncopated
2019, Oct. Litho.
2217 A1424 £5 multi .65 .65

Mohandas K. Gandhi (1869-1948),
Indian Nationalist Leader
A1425

Perf. 12¾x13¼ Syncopated
2019, Nov. 6   Litho.
2218 A1425 £5 multi   .65   .65

International Civil
Aviation Organization,
75th Anniv. — A1426

Perf. 13¼x12¾ Syncopated
2019, Dec, 7   Litho.
2219 A1426 £5 blue   .65   .65

Ministry of Social
Solidarity, 80th
Anniv. — A1427

2019   Litho.   Perf. 11½
2220 A1427 £5 multi   .65   .65

Post Day
A1428

Perf. 13¼x12¾ Syncopated
2020, Jan. 2   Litho.
2221 A1428 £5 multi   .65   .65

Pan-African Postal
Union, 40th
Anniv. — A1429

Perf. 13¼x12¾ Syncopated
2020, Jan. 18   Litho.
2222 A1429 £5 multi   .65   .65

International
Organization of La
Francophonie, 50th
Anniv. — A1430

Perf. 13¼x12¾ Syncopated
2020, Mar. 20   Litho.
2223 A1430 £5 multi   .65   .65

Arab League, 75th
Anniv.— A1431

Perf. 13¼x12¾ Syncopated
2020, Mar. 22   Litho.
2224 A1431 £5 multi   .65   .65

Economic
Census — A1432

Perf. 13¼x12¾ Syncopated
2020, Mar. 31   Litho.
2225 A1432 £4 multi   .50   .50

Government
Printing Offices,
200th Anniv.
— A1432a

Perf. 12¾x13¼ Syncopated
2020, July 16   Litho.
2225A A1432a £5 multi   —   —

October War
Against Israel,
47th
Anniv. — A1433

2020, Oct. 6   Litho.   Perf. 11½
2226 A1433 £4 multi   .50   .50

Misr Bank,
Cent.
A1434

Perf. 13x13¼ Syncopated
2020   Litho.
2227 A1434 £5 multi   .65   .65

World Statistics
Day — A1435

Perf. 13¼x13 Syncopated
2020   Litho.
2228 A1435 £4 multi   .50   .50
Country name is spelled incorrectly.

Tribute to Medical
Professionals
Combatting COVID-
19 — A1436

Perf. 13¼x13 Syncopated
2020, Nov. 1   Litho.
2229 A1436 £5 multi   .65   .65

United Nations,
75th
Anniv. — A1437

2020, Oct. 24   Litho.   Perf. 11½
2230 A1437 £5 multi   .65   .65

Egyptian
Engineers
Society,
Cent.
A1438

Perf. 13x13¼ Syncopated
2020, Dec. 3   Litho.
2231 A1438 £4 multi   .50   .50

Post
Day — A1439

Perf. 13½x14 Syncopated
2021, Jan. 2   Litho.
2232 A1439 £5 multi   .65   .65

2021 Men's World
Handball
Championships,
Egypt — A1440

Perf. 14x13½ Syncopated
2021, Jan. 13   Litho.
2233 A1440 £5 multi   .65   .65

Police
Day — A1441

Perf. 13½x14 Syncopated
2021, Jan. 25   Litho.
2234 A1441 £5 multi   .65   .65

Diplomatic Relations Between Egypt
and the Philippines, 75th Anniv.
A1442

Perf. 13x13¼ Syncopated
2021, Mar. 3   Litho.
2235 A1442 £5 multi   .65   .65

Martyr's
Day
A1443

No. 2236: a, General Abd El Moniem Riad
(1919-69). b, Monument.

Perf. 13¼x13 Syncopated
2021, Mar. 9   Litho.
2236 A1443 £4 Horiz. pair, #a-b   1.10   1.10

A1444

A1445

Golden Parade of the
Pharaohs — A1446

No. 2237 — Walls with hieroglyphs and: a,
QR code, left side of emblem. c, Central part
of emblem. d, Right side of emblem.
No. 2238: a, Hatshepsut. b, Thutmose II, c,
Thutmose I. d, Merytamon. e, Amenhotep I. f,
Ahmose-Nefertari. g, Seqenenre. h, Amenho-
tep III. i, Thutmose IV. j, Amenhotep II. k, Thut-
mose III. l, Merenptah. m, Ramesses II. n,
Sety I. o, Tiye. p, Ramesses IX. q, Ramesses
VI. r, Ramesses V. s, Ramesses IV. t,
Ramesses III. u, Siptah. v, Sety II.
No. 2239, Museums and procession,
emblem and QR code.

Perf. 13¼x12¾ Syncopated
2021, Apr. 3   Litho.
2237 A1444 £5 Horiz. strip of   1.90   1.90
           3, #a-c
2238 A1445 £5 Sheet of 22,
           #a-v, + 6
           central la-
           bels   14.00 14.00
Size: 120x79mm
Imperf
2239 A1446 £5 multi   .65   .65
Move of 22 pharaoh mummies from Egyptian Museum to National Museum of Egyptian
Civilization.

Museums — A1447

No. 2240 — QR code and: a, Mohamed
Mahmoud Khalil Museum, Giza, and
Mohamed Mahmoud Khalil Pasha (1877-
1941), Prime minister of Egypt. b, National
Museum of Egyptian Civilization, Cairo. c,
Baron Empain Palace, Heliopolis. d, Royal
Carriages Museum, Cairo.

Perf. 13½x13¾ Syncopated
2021, Apr. 18   Litho.
2240 A1447 £5 Block of 4, #a-d   —   —
World Heritage Day.

Sinai
Liberation
Day, 39th
Anniv.
A1448

Perf. 12¾x13¼ Syncopated
2021, Apr. 25   Litho.
2241 A1448 £5 multi

Labor Day — A1449

Perf. 13¼x12¾ Syncopated
2021, May 1   Litho.
2242 A1449 £5 multi   —   —

World Telecommunication and
Information Society Day — A1450

Perf. 13½x13¾ Syncopated
2021, May 17   Litho.
2243 A1450 £5 multi   —   —

Misr Life Insurance
Company, 120th
Anniv. — A1451

Perf. 13¼x13 Syncopated
2021, May 20   Litho.
2244 A1451 £5 multi   —   —

World Environment Day — A1452

2021, June 5   Litho.   *Imperf.*
2245 A1452 £5 multi   —   —

Good Life to All
Egyptians Presidential
Initiative — A1453

Perf. 13¼x13 Syncopated
2021, June 30   Litho.
2246 A1453 £5 multi   —   —

Good Life to All Egyptians
Campaign — A1454

2021, June 30   Litho.   *Imperf.*
2247 A1454 £5 multi   —   —

July 23rd Revolution,
69th Anniv. — A1455

Perf. 13¼x13 Syncopated
2021, July 23   Litho.
2248 A1455 £5 multi   —   —

2020 Summer
Olympics,
Tokyo — A1456

Perf. 14x13½ Syncopated
2021, July 23   Litho.
2249 A1456 £5 multi   —   —

The 2020 Summer Olympics were postponed until 2021 because of the COVID-19 pandemic.

World Day
Against Human
Trafficking
A1457

Perf. 14x13½ Syncopated
2021, July 30   Litho.
2250 A1457 £5 multi   —   —

Establishment of
Egypt University
of Informatics
A1458

Perf. 14x13½ Syncopated
2021, Aug. 5   Litho.
2251 A1458 £5 multi   —   —

Egyptian Medalists at 2020 Summer
Olympics — A1459

2021, Aug. 8   Litho.   *Imperf.*
2252 A1459 £5 multi   —   —

The 2020 Summer Olympics were postponed until 2021 because of the COVID-19 pandemic.

International
Youth
Day — A1460

Perf. 14x13½ Syncopated
2021, Aug. 13   Litho.
2253 A1460 £5 multi   —   —

Egyptian Medalists at the 2020
Summer Paralympics, Tokyo — A1461

2021, Sept. 2   Litho.   *Imperf.*
2254 A1461 £5 multi   —   —

The 2020 Summer Paralympics were postponed until 2021 because of the COVID-19 pandemic.

World Tourism
Day — A1462

Perf. 14x13½ Syncopated
2021, Sept. 27   Litho.
2255 A1462 £10 multi   —   —

Egyptian
Judiciary
Day — A1463

Perf. 12¾x13¼ Syncopated
2021, Oct. 1   Litho.
2256 A1463 £5 multi   —   —

Field Marshal Mohamed Hussein
Tantawi (1935-2021) — A1464

2021, Oct. 6   Litho.   *Perf. 14*
2257 A1464 £5 multi   —   —

October War
Against
Israel, 48th
Anniv. —
A1465

Perf. 13¼x14 Syncopated
2021, Oct. 6   Litho.
2258 A1465 £5 multi   —   —

Sports
Culture
A1466

Perf. 12¾x13¼ Syncopated
2021, Oct.   Litho.
2259 A1466 £5 multi   —   —

Restoration of the Avenue of the
Sphinxes — A1467

No. 2260: a, Sphinx statues facing right. b, "Luxor" and QR code. c, Sphinx statues facing left.

Perf. 13½x13 Syncopated
2021, Nov. 25   Litho.
2260 A1467   £5 Horiz. strip of 3,   —   —
      #a-c

First Public
Film
Presentation,
125th Anniv.
(in 2020)
A1468

2021, Nov. 26   Litho.   *Perf. 13½x14*
2261 A1468 £5 multi   —   —

Post
Day — A1469

2022, Jan. 2   Litho.   *Perf. 11½*
2262 A1469 £10 multi   —   —

Miniature Sheet

World
Youth
Forum,
Sharm
el-Sheikh
A1470

No. 2263: a. Flowers, youths, ankhs, QR code (100x100mm). b, Ankh, olive branch in ellipse (58x38mm). c, Olive branch, sun over pyramid (58x38mm). d, Youths and sun over pyramid in diamond (58x58mm). e, Greek key border in circle, sun over pyramid (58x58mm).

2022, Jan. 10   Litho.   *Perf. 14*
2263 A1470 £5 Sheet of 5, #a-e   —   —

Independence,
Cent. — A1472

Perf. 14x13½ Syncopated
2022, Mar. 15   Litho.
2265 A1472 £10 multi   —   —

Cairo,
2022
Capital
of
Islamic
Culture
A1474

2022, Apr. 10   Litho.   *Perf. 14x13½*
2267 A1474 £10 multi   —   —

Ain Shams
University Faculty
of Medicine, 75th
Anniv. — A1476

Perf. 14x13½ Syncopated

2022		Litho.
2270	A1476	£10 multi	—	—

SEMI-POSTAL STAMPS

> Catalogue values for unused
> stamps in this section are for
> Never Hinged items.

Princess Ferial — SP1

Perf. 13½x14

1940, May 17	Photo.	Wmk. 195
B1	SP1 5m + 5m copper brown	4.50 1.25

No. B1 Overprinted in
Green

1943, Nov. 17

B2	SP1 5m + 5m	14.00	9.00
a.	Arabic date "1493"	300.00	300.00

The surtax on Nos. B1 and B2 was for the
children's fund.

First Postage
Stamp of
Egypt — SP2

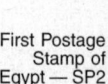

King
Fuad — SP3

No. B4, Khedive Ismail Pasha. No. B6, King
Farouk.

Perf. 13¼x13½

1946, Feb. 28		Wmk. 195
B3	SP2 1m + 1m gray	.40 .25
B4	SP3 10m + 10m violet	.50 .25
B5	SP3 17m + 17m brown	.50 .40
B6	SP3 22m + 22m yel grn	.75 .60
a.	Souv. sheet, #B3-B6, perf. 8½	85.00 85.00
b.	As "a," imperf.	85.00 85.00
	Nos. B3-B6 (4)	2.15 1.50

80th anniv. of Egypt's 1st postage stamp.
Nos. B6a, B6b measure 129x171mm.

Goddess
Hathor,
King Men-
kau-Re
(Mycerinus)
and
Jackalheaded
Goddess
SP7

Ramesseum,
Thebes
SP8

Queen
Nefertiti
SP9

Funerary
Mask of
King
Tutankhamun
SP10

Perf. 13½x13¼, 13¼x13½

1947, Mar. 9		Wmk. 195
B9	SP7 5m + 5m slate	1.75 .80
B10	SP8 15m + 15m dp blue, perf. 13¼x13½	2.00 1.00
B11	SP9 30m + 30m henna brn	2.50 1.75
B12	SP10 50m + 50m brown	3.50 2.25
	Nos. B9-B12 (4)	9.75 5.80

Intl. Exposition of Contemporary Art, Cairo.

Boy Scout
Emblem — SP11

Scout Emblems: 20m+10m, Sea Scouts.
35m+15m, Air Explorers.

1956, July 25	Photo.	Perf. 13½x13
B13	SP11 10m + 10m green	1.00 .55
B14	SP11 20m + 10m ultra	1.50 .85
B15	SP11 35m + 15m blue	2.00 1.25
	Nos. B13-B15 (3)	4.50 2.65

2nd Arab Scout Jamboree, Alexandria-
Aboukir, 1956.
Souvenir sheets, perf. and imperf., contain
one each of Nos. B13-B15. Size: 118x158mm.
Values: $1,750 unused each, $1,100 used
each.

Ambulance
SP12

1957, May 13	Perf. 13x13½
B16	SP12 10m + 5m rose red	.80 .55

50th anniv. of the Public Aid Society.

United Arab Republic

Eye and Map of Africa,
Europe and
Asia — SP13

Perf. 13½x13

1958, Mar. 1	Photo.	Wmk. 318
B17	SP13 10m + 5m orange	1.25 1.00

1st Afro-Asian Cong. of Ophthalmology,
Cairo.
The surtax was for centers to aid the blind.

Postal Emblem — SP14

1959, Jan. 2

B18	SP14 10m + 5m bl grn, red & blk	.40 .30

Post Day. The surtax went to the social fund
for postal employees.
See Syria UAR issues No. B1 for similar
stamp with denominations in piasters (p).

Children and UN
Emblem — SP15

1959, Oct. 24   **Wmk. 328**

B19	SP15 10m + 5m brown lake	.60 .30
B20	SP15 35m + 10m dk blue	.90 .40

Issued for International Children's Day and
to honor UNICEF.

Braille Type of Regular Issue, 1961

1961, Apr. 6	Perf. 13½x13
B21	A182 35m + 15m yel & brn	.80 .50

Arab League Building,
Cairo, and
Emblem — SP16

1962, Mar. 22	Photo.	Wmk. 328
B22	SP16 10m + 5m gray	.60 .40

Arab Publicity Week, Mar. 22-28.
See No. N86.

Postal
Emblem
SP17

Stamp of
1866
SP18

1963, Jan. 2	Wmk. 342	Perf. 11½
B23	SP17 20m + 10m brt grn, red & blk	1.25 1.25
B24	SP18 40m + 20m blk & brn org	1.75 1.75
B25	SP18 40m + 20m brn org & blk	1.75 1.75
a.	Pair, #B24-B25	4.00 4.00
	Nos. B23-B25 (3)	4.75 4.75

Post Day, Jan. 2 and 1966 exhibition of the
FIP.

Arms of UAR and
Pyramids — SP19

1964, Jan. 2	Wmk. 342	Perf. 11
B26	SP19 10m + 5m org yel & grn	1.75 1.00
B27	SP19 80m + 40m grnsh bl & blk	3.00 1.75
B28	SP19 115m + 55m org brn & blk	4.00 2.25
	Nos. B26-B28 (3)	8.75 5.00

Issued for Post Day. Jan. 2.

Type of 1963 and

SP20

Postal
Emblem
— SP20a

No. B30, Emblem of Postal Secondary
School. 80m+40m, Postal emblem, gear-
wheel, laurel wreath.

Perf. 11½

1965, Jan. 2	Unwmk.	Photo.
B29	SP20 10m + 5m lt grn & car	1.00 .50
B30	SP20 10m + 5m ultra, car & blk	1.00 .50
B31	SP20a 80m + 40m rose, brt grn & blk	2.75 2.00
	Nos. B29-B31 (3)	4.75 3.00

Issued for Post Day, Jan. 2. No. B31 also
publicizes the Stamp Centenary Exhibition.

Souvenir Sheet

Stamps
of Egypt,
1866
SP21

1966, Jan. 2	Wmk. 342	Imperf.
B32	SP21 140m + 60m blk, sl bl & rose	4.50 4.50

Post Day, 1966, and cent. of the 1st Egyptian postage stamps.

Pharaonic
"Mediator" — SP22

Design: 115m+40m, Pharaonic guard.

1967, Jan. 2	Wmk. 342	Perf. 11½
B33	SP22 80m + 20m multi	3.75 2.75
B34	SP22 115m + 40m multi	6.00 3.50

Issued for Post Day, Jan. 2.

Grand Canal, Doges' Palace, Venice,
and Santa Maria del Fiore, Florence
SP23

115m+30m, Piazzetta and Campanile, Venice, and Palazzo Vecchio, Florence.

Perf. 11½x11

1967, Dec. 9	Photo.	Wmk. 342
B35	SP23 80m + 20m grn, yel & brn	1.75 1.25
B36	SP23 115m + 30m ol, yel & sl bl	2.75 2.00

The surtax was to help save the cultural
monuments of Venice and Florence, damaged
in the 1966 floods.

Boy and Girl — SP24

Design: No. B38, Five children and arch.

Wmk. 342

1968, Dec. 11   Photo.   Perf. 11
B37 SP24 20m + 10m car, bl & lt
           brn   .80 .60
B38 SP24 20m + 10m vio bl, sep
           & lt grn   .80 .60

Children's Day & 22nd anniv. of UNICEF.

Emblem and Flags of
Arab League — SP25

1969, Mar. 22   Perf. 11x11½
B39 SP25 20m + 10m multi   .80 .60

Arab Publicity Week, Mar. 22-28.

Refugee
Family — SP26

1969, Oct. 24   Photo.   Perf. 11½
B40 SP26 30m + 10m multi   .80 .60

Issued for United Nations Day.

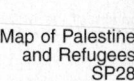

Men of Three
Races, Human
Rights
Emblem — SP27

1970, Mar. 21   Perf. 11½x11
B41 SP27 20m + 10m multi   1.00 .75

Issued to publicize the International Day for the Elimination of Racial Discrimination.

Arab League Type

1970, Mar. 22   Wmk. 342
B42 A344 20m + 10m bl, grn &
            brn   .90 .60

Map of Palestine
and Refugees
SP28

Perf. 11½x11

1970, Oct. 24   Photo.   Wmk. 342
B43 SP28 20m + 10m multi   .90 .80

25th anniv. of the UN and to draw attention to the plight of the Palestinian refugees.

Arab Republic of Egypt

Blind Girl, WHO and
Society
Emblems — SP29

1973, Oct. 24   Photo.   Perf. 11x11½
B44 SP29 20m + 10m blue &
            gold   .85 .75

25th anniv. of WHO and for the Light and Hope Soc., which educates and helps blind girls.

Map of Africa, OAU
Emblem — SP30

Perf. 11x11½

1973, Dec. 8   Photo.   Wmk. 342
B45 SP30 55m + 20m multi   2.25 1.50

Organization for African Unity, 10th anniv.

Social Work Day
Emblem — SP31

1973, Dec. 8
B46 SP31 20m + 10m multi   .75 .65

Social Work Day.

Jihan al
Sadat
Consoling
Wounded
Man — SP32

1974, Mar. 21   Wmk. 342   Perf. 11
B47 SP32 20m + 10m multi   1.25 .90

Faithfulness and Hope Society.

Afghan
Solidarity — SP33

Wmk. 342

1981, July 15   Photo.   Perf. 11½
B48 SP33 20m + 10m multi   1.00 .75

Size: 30x25mm

1981   Photo.   Perf. 11½
B49 SP33 20m + 10m multi   4.25 3.75

Map of Sudan, Dunes,
Dead Tree — SP34

1986, Mar. 25   Photo.   Perf. 13x13½
B50 SP34 15p + 5p multi   1.75 1.25

Fight against drought and desertification of the Sudan. Surtax for drought relief.

Organization of
African Unity,
25th
Anniv. — SP35

1988, May 25   Litho.   Perf. 13
B51 SP35 15p +10p multi   1.25 1.00

AIR POST STAMPS

Mail Plane in
Flight — AP1

Perf. 13x13½

1926, Mar. 10   Wmk. 195   Photo.
C1 AP1 27m deep violet   32.50 32.50

1929, July 17
C2 AP1 27m orange brown   10.00 2.50

Zeppelin Issue

No. C2 Surcharged in Blue or Violet

1931, Apr. 6
C3 AP1 50m on 27m (Bl)   90.00 77.50
  a. "1951" instead of "1931" 125.00 115.00
C4 AP1 100m on 27m (V)   90.00 82.50

Airplane over
Giza
Pyramids — AP2

1933-38   Litho.   Perf. 13x13½
C5   AP2 1m orange & blk   .30 .50
C6   AP2 2m gray & blk   .80 1.50
C7   AP2 2m org red & blk
           ('38)   2.75 2.00
C8   AP2 3m ol brn & blk   .60 .35
C9   AP2 4m green & blk   .90 .90
C10 AP2 5m dp brown & blk   .75 .25
C11 AP2 6m dk green & blk   1.50 1.25
C12 AP2 7m dk blue & blk   1.25 1.00
C13 AP2 8m violet & blk   .80 .25
C14 AP2 9m dp red & blk   2.00 1.50
C15 AP2 10m violet & brn   .75 .70
C16 AP2 20m dk green & brn .60 .25
C17 AP2 30m dull blue & brn .75 .25
C18 AP2 40m dp red & brn   15.00 .60
C19 AP2 50m orange & brn   13.00 .25
C20 AP2 60m gray & brn   6.00 1.10
C21 AP2 70m dk blue & bl
            grn   3.50 1.00
C22 AP2 80m ol brn & bl grn 3.50 1.00
C23 AP2 90m org & bl grn   4.00 1.00
C24 AP2 100m vio & bl grn   9.00 .80
C25 AP2 200m dp red & bl grn 15.00 1.75
      Nos. C5-C25 (21)   82.75 18.20

See Nos. C34-C37. For overprint see No. C38.

Type of 1933

1941-43   Photo.
C34 AP2 5m copper brn ('43) .30 .30
C35 AP2 10m violet   .55 .30
C36 AP2 25m dk vio brn ('43) .55 .30
C37 AP2 30m green   .70 .30
      Nos. C34-C37 (4)   2.10 1.20

Catalogue values for unused stamps in this section, from this point to the end of the section, are for Never Hinged items.

No. C37 Overprinted in Black

1946, Oct. 1
C38 AP2 30m green   .85 .40
  a. Double overprint   425.00 —
  b. Inverted overprint   425.00 —

Middle East Intl. Air Navigation Congress, Cairo, Oct. 1946.

King Farouk,
Delta Dam and
DC-3
Plane — AP3

Perf. 13x13½

1947, Feb. 19   Photo.   Wmk. 195
C39 AP3 2m red orange   .30 .85
C40 AP3 3m dk brown   .30 1.00
C41 AP3 5m red brown   .30 .30
C42 AP3 7m dp yellow org   .60 .30
C43 AP3 8m green   .60 .90
C44 AP3 10m violet   .60 .30
C45 AP3 20m brt blue   .90 .30
C46 AP3 30m brown violet   1.20 .30
C47 AP3 40m carmine rose   2.00 .75
C48 AP3 50m Prus green   2.50 .85
C49 AP3 100m olive green   5.00 2.50
C50 AP3 200m dark gray   11.00 5.00
      Nos. C39-C50 (12)   25.30 13.35

For overprints see Nos. C51-C64, C67-C89, NC1-NC30.

Nos. C49 and C50 Surcharged in Black

1948, Aug. 23
C51 AP3 13m on 100m   .60 .55
C52 AP3 22m on 200m   .85 .85
  a. Date omitted

Inaugural flights of "Services Aeriens Internationaux d'Egypte" from Cairo to Athens and Rome, Aug. 23, 1948.

Nos. C39 to C50 Overprinted in Various Colors

Overprint 27mm Wide

1952, Jan. Wmk. 195 Perf. 13x13½
C53 AP3 2m red orange (Bl)   .45 .30
C54 AP3 3m dark brown (R)   1.60 1.25
C55 AP3 5m red brown   .55 .55
C56 AP3 7m dp yel org (Bl)   .85 .50
C57 AP3 8m green (R)   2.50 1.60
C58 AP3 10m violet (G)   1.75 1.60
C59 AP3 20m brt blue (R)   4.25 2.50
C60 AP3 30m brown vio (G)   1.90 1.60
C61 AP3 40m carmine rose   4.00 2.50
C62 AP3 50m Prus green (R)   4.25 2.75
C63 AP3 100m olive green   7.50 3.75
C64 AP3 200m dark gray (R)   15.00 7.50
      Nos. C53-C64 (12)   44.60 26.40

See notes after No. 316.

Delta Dam and
Douglas DC-
3 — AP4

1953   Photo.
C65 AP4 5m red brown   .60 .60
C66 AP4 15m olive green   1.50 1.25

For overprints see Nos. NC31-NC32.

Nos. C39-C49 Overprinted in Black

1953
C67   AP3 2m red orange   3.00 3.00
C68   AP3 3m dk brown   1.25 1.25
C69   AP3 5m red brown   1.60 1.60
C70   AP3 7m dp yellow org   .60 .60
C71   AP3 8m green   2.00 2.00
C72   AP3 10m violet   32.50 37.50
C73   AP3 20m brt blue   2.10 .60
C74   AP3 30m brown violet   1.60 1.00
C75   AP3 40m carmine rose   3.00 1.90
C76   AP3 50m Prus green   5.00 2.00
C77   AP3 100m olive green   9.25 4.75
C77A AP3 200m gray   55.00

No. C77A is in question. It is not known postally used.

Nos. C53-C64 Overprinted in Black with Three Bars to Obliterate Portrait

1953

C78	AP3	2m red orange	.90	.50
C79	AP3	3m dark brown	1.90	1.60
C80	AP3	5m red brown	.50	.35
C82	AP3	8m green	1.10	2.50
C83	AP3	10m violet	.90	2.00
C85	AP3	30m brown violet	2.00	2.00
C87	AP3	50m Prus green	4.25	1.60
C88	AP3	100m olive green	6.25	3.75
C89	AP3	200m dark gray	12.50	12.50
		Nos. C78-C89 (9)	30.30	26.80

Practically all values of Nos. C67-C89 exist with double overprint. The 7m, 20m and 40m with this overprint have been considered forgeries. Values: 7m, $8 mint and used; 20m, $5 mint and used; 40m, $20 mint, $25 used.

United Arab Republic
Type of Regular Issue

Perf. 11½x11

1958, Mar. 22   Photo.   Wmk. 318

C90	A141	15m ultra & red brn	.65	.30

Pyramids at Giza — AP5

Al Azhar University — AP6

Designs: 15m, Colossi of Memnon, Thebes. 90m, St. Catherine Monastery, Mt. Sinai.

1959-60   Wmk. 328   Perf. 13x13½

C91	AP5	5m bright red	.35	.25
C92	AP5	15m dk dull violet	.40	.35
C93	AP6	60m dk green	.95	.60
C94	AP3	90m brown car ('60)	2.00	1.25
		Nos. C91-C94 (4)	3.70	2.45

Nos. C91-C93 exist imperf. See Nos. C101, C105, NC33.

Tower of Cairo Type, Redrawn

1961, May 1   Perf. 13½x13

C95	A183	50m bright blue	1.10	.55

Top inscription has been replaced by two airplanes.

Weather Vane, Anemometer and UN World Meteorological Organization Emblem — AP7

Perf. 11½x11

1962, Mar. 23   Photo.   Unwmk.

C96	AP7	60m yellow & dp blue	2.00	1.00

2nd World Meteorological Day, Mar. 23.

Patrice Lumumba and Map of Africa — AP8

Perf. 13½x13

1962, July 1   Wmk. 328

C97	AP8	35m multicolored	.65	.40

Patrice Lumumba (1925-61), Premier of Congo.

Maritime Station, Alexandria AP9

Designs: 30m, International Airport, Cairo. 40m, Railroad Station, Luxor.

1963, Mar. 18   Perf. 13x13½

C98	AP9	20m dark brown	.70	.30
C99	AP9	30m carmine rose	.95	.40
C100	AP9	40m black	1.50	1.00
		Nos. C98-C100 (3)	3.15	1.70

Type of 1959-60 and

Temple of Queen Nefertari, Abu Simbel AP10

Arch and Tower of Cairo AP11

Designs: 80m, Al Azhar University seen through arch. 140m, Ramses II, Abu Simbel.

Perf. 11½x11, 11x11½

1963-65   Photo.   Wmk. 342

C101	AP6	80m vio blk & brt bl	3.75	1.60
C102	AP10	115m brown & yel	4.00	1.50
C103	AP10	140m pale vio, blk & org red	4.00	2.00

Unwmk.

C104	AP11	50m vio brn & brt bl	2.25	1.00
C105	AP6	80m vio bl & lt bl	3.75	1.60
		Nos. C101-C105 (5)	17.75	7.70

Issued: 50m, 11/2/64; No. C105, 2/13/65; others, 10/24/63.
See Nos. NC34-NC36.

Weather Vane, Anemometer and WMO Emblem — AP12

Perf. 11½x11

1965, Mar. 23   Wmk. 342

C106	AP12	80m dk blue & rose lil	2.75	1.50

Fifth World Meteorological Day.
See No. NC37.

Game Board from Tomb of Tutankhamun AP13

1965, July 1   Photo.   Unwmk.

C107	AP13	10m yellow & dk blue	2.00	.45

See No. NC38.

Temples at Abu Simbel AP14

1966, Apr. 28   Wmk. 342   Perf. 11½

C108	AP14	20m multicolored	1.10	.55
C109	AP14	80m multicolored	2.50	1.75

Issued to commemorate the transfer of the temples of Abu Simbel to a hilltop, 1963-66.

Scout Camp and Jamboree Emblem — AP15

1966, Aug. 10   Perf. 11½x11

C110	AP15	20m olive & rose	1.60	.50

7th Pan-Arab Boy Scout Jamboree, Good Daim, Libya, Aug. 12.

St. Catherine Monastery, Mt. Sinai — AP16

1966, Nov. 30   Photo.   Wmk. 342

C111	AP16	80m multicolored	2.25	1.75

St. Catherine Monastery, Sinai, 1400th anniv.

Cairo Airport — AP17

1967, Apr. 26   Perf. 11½x11

C112	AP17	20m sky bl, sl grn & lt brn	1.00	.40

Hotel El Alamein and Map of Nile Delta — AP18

Intl. Tourist Year: 80m, The Virgin's Tree, Virgin Mary and Child. 115m, Fishing in the Red Sea.

1967, June 7   Wmk. 342   Perf. 11½

C113	AP18	20m dull pur, sl grn & dl org	1.10	.50
C114	AP18	80m blue & multi	2.50	1.50
C115	AP18	115m brown, org & bl	4.75	2.25
		Nos. C113-C115 (3)	8.35	4.25

Oil Derricks, Map of Egypt — AP19

1967, July 23   Photo.

C116	AP19	50m org & bluish blk	1.25	.85

15th anniversary of the revolution.

Type of Regular Issue, 1967

Design: 80m, Back of Tutankhamun's throne and UNESCO emblem.

1967, Oct. 24   Wmk. 342   Perf. 11½

C117	A301	80m blue & yellow	1.50	.90

Koran AP20

1968, Mar. 25   Wmk. 342   Perf. 11½

C118	AP20	30m lilac, bl & yel	1.25	1.00
C119	AP20	80m lilac, bl & yel	2.25	1.25
a.		Pair, #C118-C119 + label	4.50	3.50

1400th anniv. of the Koran. Nos. C118-C119 are printed in miniature sheets of 4 containing 2 each of Nos. C118-C119.

St. Mark and St. Mark's Cathedral — AP21

1968, June 25   Wmk. 342   Perf. 11½

C120	AP21	80m brt grn, dk brn & dp car	1.75	1.00

Martyrdom of St. Mark, 1900th anniv. and the consecration of St. Mark's Cathedral, Cairo.

AP22

Design: No. C121, Map of United Arab Airlines and Boeing 707. No. C122, Ilyushin 18 and routes of United Arab Airlines.

1968-69   Photo.   Perf. 11½x11

C121	AP22	55m blue, ocher & car	1.75	.90
C122	AP22	55m bl, yel & vio blk ('69)	1.25	.90

1st flights of a Boeing 707 and an Ilyushin 18 for United Arab Airlines.

Mahatma Gandhi, Arms of India and UAR — AP23

1969, Sept. 10   Perf. 11x11½

C123	AP23	80m lt blue, ocher & brn	4.00	1.75

Mohandas K. Gandhi (1869-1948), leader in India's fight for independence.

Imam El Boukhary — AP24

1969, Dec. 27   Photo.   Wmk. 342

C124	AP24	30m lt ol & dk brn	.70	.25

1100th anniv. of the death of the Imam El Boukhary (824-870), philosopher and writer.

Azzahir Beybars Mosque — AP25

1969, Dec. 27   Engr.   Perf. 11½x11

C125	AP25	30m red lilac	.70	.25

700th anniv. of the founding of the Azzahir Beybars Mosque, Cairo.

Lenin (1870-1924) — AP26

Perf. 11x11½

1970, Apr. 22   Photo.   Wmk. 342

C126	AP26	80m lt grn & brn	2.00	1.25

Phantom Fighters and Destroyed Factory — AP27

1970, May 1   Perf. 11½x11

C127	AP27	80m yel, grn & dk vio brn	2.00	1.00

Issued to commemorate the destruction of the Abu-Zaabal factory by Israeli planes.

UPU Type of Regular Issue

1970, May 20   Photo.   Wmk. 342

C128	A350	80m multicolored	1.40	.85

Nasser and Burial Mosque AP28

1970, Nov. 6   Wmk. 342   Perf. 11
C129 AP28 30m olive & blk   1.00 .40
C130 AP28 80m brown & blk   2.75 1.25
Gamal Abdel Nasser (1918-70), Pres. of Egypt.

Postal Congress Type
Perf. 11½x11
1971, Mar. 6   Photo.   Wmk. 342
C131 A365 30m lt ol, org & sl grn   .90 .45

Nasser, El Rifaei and Sultan Hussein Mosques AP29

Designs: 85m, Nasser and Ramses Square, Cairo. 110m, Nasser, Sphinx and pyramids.

Perf. 11½x11
1971, July 1   Photo.   Wmk. 342
C132 AP29 30m multicolored   2.50 .80
C133 AP29 85m multicolored   4.50 1.25
C134 AP29 110m multicolored 5.75 2.50
  Nos. C132-C134 (3)   12.75 4.55

APU Type of Regular Issue
1971, Aug. 3   Wmk. 342   Perf. 11½
C135 A373 30m brown, yel & bl   1.40 .50

Arab Republic of Egypt Confederation Type
Perf. 11½x11
1971, Sept. 28   Photo.   Wmk. 342
C136 A374 30m gray, sl grn & dk
           pur   1.25 .50

Al Aqsa Mosque and Woman — AP30

Wmk. 342
1971, Oct. 24   Photo.   Perf. 11½
C137 AP30 30m bl, yel, brn &
           grn   1.75 .45
25th anniv. of the UN (in 1970) and return of Palestinian refugees.

Postal Union Type
30m, African Postal Union emblem & letter.
1971, Dec. 2   Perf. 11½x11
C138 A384 30m green, blk & bl   1.40 .40

Aida, Triumphal March — AP31

1971, Dec. 23   Wmk. 342   Perf. 11½
C139 AP31 110m dk brn, yel & sl
           grn   5.75 3.00
Centenary of the first performance of the opera Aida, by Giuseppe Verdi.

Globe, Glider, Rocket Club Emblem — AP32

1972, Feb. 11   Perf. 11x11½
C140 AP32 30m blue, ocher &
           yel   1.50 .50
International Aerospace Education Conference, Cairo, Jan. 11-13.

St. Catherine's Monastery on Fire — AP33

Perf. 11½x11
1972, Feb. 15   Unwmk.
C141 AP33 110m dp car, org &
           blk   4.75 4.00
The burning of St. Catherine's Monastery in Sinai Desert, Nov. 30, 1971.

Tutankhamun in Garden — AP34

Tutankhamun, from 2nd Sarcophagus — AP35

Design: No. C143, Ankhesenamun.
1972, May 22   Photo.   Perf. 11½
C142   110m brn org, bl & grn 10.00 5.50
C143   110m brn org, bl & grn 10.00 5.50
  a. AP34 Pair, #C142-C143   26.00 22.50

Souvenir Sheet
Imperf
C144 AP35 200m gold & multi   32.50 32.50
50th anniv. of the discovery of the tomb of Tutankhamun.

Souvenir Sheet

Flag of Confederation of Arab Republics — AP36

1972, July 23   Photo.   Imperf.
C145 AP36 110m gold, dp car &
           blk   4.50 4.25
20th anniversary of the revolution.

Temples at Abu Simbel — AP37

Designs: 30m, Al Azhar Mosque and St. George's Church. 110m, Pyramids at Giza.

1972   Wmk. 342   Perf. 11½x11
C146 AP37 30m blue, brn &
           buff   2.50 .40
C147 AP37 85m bl, brn &
           ocher   3.50 1.75
C148 AP37 110m multicolored   5.25 1.75
  Nos. C146-C148 (3)   11.25 3.90
Issued: Nos. C146, C148, 11/22; No. C147, 8/1.

Olympic Type of Regular Issue
Olympic and Motion Emblems and: No. C149, Handball. No. C150, Weight lifting. 50m, Swimming. 55m, Gymnastics. All vertical.

1972, Aug. 17   Perf. 11x11½
C149 A396 30m multicolored   .80 .40
C150 A396 30m yellow & multi .80 .40
C151 A396 50m blue & multi   1.60 1.00
C152 A396 55m multicolored   2.00 1.10
  Nos. C149-C152 (4)   5.20 2.90

Champollion, Rosetta Stone, Hieroglyphics AP38

1972, Oct. 16
C153 AP38 110m gold, grn & blk 7.50 2.50
Sesquicentennial of the deciphering of Egyptian hieroglyphics by Jean-François Champollion.

World Map, Telephone, Radar, ITU Emblem AP39

1973, Mar. 21   Photo.   Perf. 11
C154 AP39 30m lt bl, dk bl & blk .90 .25
5th World Telecommunications Day.

Karnak Temple, Luxor — AP40

1973, Mar. 21
C155 AP40 110m dp ultra, blk &
           rose   4.75 2.50
Sound and light at Karnak.

Hand Dripping Blood and Falling Plane — AP41

1973, May 1   Perf. 11x11½
C156 AP41 110m multicolored   6.25 3.00
Israeli attack on Libyan civilian plane, Feb. 1973.

WMO Emblem, Weather Vane — AP42

1973, Oct. 24   Perf. 11x11½
C157 AP42 110m blue, gold &
           pur   3.00 1.75
Cent. of intl. meteorological cooperation.

Refugees, Map of Palestine — AP43

1973, Oct. 24   Perf. 11½
C158 AP43 30m dk brn, yel & bl 1.60 .50
Plight of Palestinian refugees.

INTERPOL Emblem — AP44

Perf. 11x11½
1973, Dec. 8   Photo.   Wmk. 342
C159 AP44 110m black & multi 3.75 2.00
Intl. Criminal Police Organization, 50th anniv.

Postal and UPU Emblems — AP45

Post Day (UPU Emblems and): 30m, APU emblem. 55m, African Postal Union emblem. 110m, UPU emblem.

Size: 26x46½mm
1974, Jan. 2   Unwmk.   Perf. 11
C160 AP45 20m gray, red & blk   .45 .25
C161 AP45 30m sal, blk & pur   .65 .25
C162 AP45 55m emerald, blk &
           brt mag   1.25 .85

Size: 37x37½mm
Perf. 11½
C163 AP45 110m lt bl, blk & gold 1.75 1.50
  Nos. C160-C163 (4)   4.10 2.85

Solar Bark of Khufu (Cheops) AP46

Wmk. 342
1974, Mar. 21   Photo.   Perf. 11½
C164 AP46 110m blue, gold &
           brn   3.75 2.25
Solar Bark Museum.

Hotel Meridien — AP47

1974, Oct. 6   Perf. 11½x11
C165 AP47 110m multicolored   2.25 1.25
Opening of Hotel Meridien, Cairo.

Suez Canal Type of 1975
1975, June 5   Perf. 11½
C166 A448 30m bl, yel grn &
           ind   1.75 .60
C167 A448 110m indigo & blue 2.75 2.00

Irrigation Commission Emblem — AP48

1975, July 20
C168 AP48 110m orange & dk
grn					2.25 1.25

9th Intl. Congress on Irrigation and Drainage, Moscow, and 25th anniv. of the Intl. Commission on Irrigation and Drainage.

Refugees and UNWRA
Emblem
AP49

Woman and
IWY
Emblem
AP50

Perf. 11x11½
1975, Oct. 24		**Photo.**		**Wmk. 342**
C169 AP49 30m multicolored		1.40 .50
Unwmk.
C170 AP50 110m olive, org & blk 3.50 2.00

UN Day. 30m publicizes UN help for refugees; 110m is for Intl. Women's Year 1975.

Step Pyramid,
Sakhara, and
Entrance
Gate — AP51

Designs: 45m, 60m, Plane over Giza Pyramids. 140m, Plane over boats on Nile.

Perf. 11½x11
1978-82		**Photo.**		**Wmk. 342**
C171	AP51	45m yel & brown		.60 .25
	b.	Unwatermarked
C171A	AP51	60m olive		2.00 1.00
	c.	Unwatermarked
C172	AP51	115m blue & brn		1.10 .55
C173	AP51	140m blue & pur		2.00 1.00
C173A	AP51	185m bl, sep &
			gray brn		5.00 2.25
	Nos. C171-C173A (5)		10.70 5.05

Issued: 60m, 1/15/82; 185m, 1982; others, 1/1/78.

Flyer and UN ICAO
Emblem — AP52

Perf. 11x11½
1978, Dec. 30	**Photo.**	**Wmk. 342**
C174 AP52 140m blue, blk & brn 2.50 1.25
75th anniversary of 1st powered flight.

Seeing Eye
Medallion
AP53

Perf. 11½x11
1981, Oct. 1	**Photo.**	**Wmk. 342**
C175 AP53 230m multicolored		2.50 1.25

Hilton Ramses Hotel
Opening — AP54

Perf. 11x11½
1982, Mar. 15	**Photo.**	**Wmk. 342**
C176 AP54 18½p multi		2.00 1.00

Temple of Horus,
Edfu — AP55

Designs: 15p, like 6p. 18½p, 25p, Statue of Akhnaton, Thebes, hieroglyphics, vert. 23p, 30p, Giza pyramids.

Perf. 11½x11, 11x11½
1985		**Photo.**		**Wmk. 342**
C177	AP55	6p lt blue & dk bl
			grn		1.00 .40
C178	AP55	15p grnsh bl &
			brn		1.75 .50
	a.	Unwatermarked			—
C179	AP55	18½p grn, sep & dp
			yel		2.00 1.25
C180	AP55	23p grnsh bl, sep
			& yel bis		2.50 1.50
C181	AP55	25p lt bl, sep &
			yel bis		2.10 .95
	a.	Unwmkd. ('87)		2.75 1.10
C182	AP55	30p grnsh bl, sep
			& org yel		2.10 .85
	a.	Unwmkd. ('87)		2.75 1.10
	Nos. C177-C182 (6)		11.45 5.45

Issued: 6p, 18½p, 23p, 3/1; 15p, 25p, 30p, 5/1.
See No. C236.

Post Day
AP56

Narmer Board, oldest known hieroglyphic inscriptions: No. C183a, Tablet obverse. No. C183b, Reverse.

1986, Jan. 2	**Photo.**	**Perf. 13½x13**
C183 AP56 Pair		2.50 2.50
a.-b.	15p any single		1.10 1.00

Map, Jet, AFRAA
Emblem — AP57

1986, Apr. 7	**Photo.**	**Perf. 11½**
C184 AP57 15p blue, yel & blk	1.25 .50
African Airlines Assoc., 18th General Assembly, Cairo, Apr. 7-10.

World Food
Day — AP58

UNESCO,
40th Anniv.
AP59

Perf. 13½x13, 13x13½
1986, Oct. 24			**Litho.**
C185 AP58 15p multicolored		1.00 1.00
C186 AP59 15p multicolored		1.00 1.00
UN Day.

Tourism
Year
AP60

Design: Column and Sphinx in Alexandria, St. Catherine's Monastery in Mt. Sinai, Colossi of Thebes and Temple of Theban Triad in Luxor.

Unwmk.
1987, Sept. 30	**Litho.**	*Imperf.*
Size: 140x90mm
C187 AP60 30p multicolored		4.25 4.25
See No. 1344.

Palestinian
Uprising
AP61

1988, Sept. 28	**Litho.**	**Perf. 12x13½**
C188 AP61 25p multicolored		1.60 1.40

UN
Day — AP62

1988, Oct. 20	**Litho.**	**Perf. 13x13½**
C189 AP62 25p multicolored		1.60 1.40

Nobel Prize Type of 1988
1988, Nov. 7
C190 A769 25p multicolored		1.60 1.40

Arab Cooperation
Council — AP63

1989, May 10	**Litho.**	**Perf. 13½x13**
C191 AP63 25p Flags		1.25 .55
Size: 89x80mm
Imperf
C192 AP63 50p Flags, seal		3.50 3.50

Architecture and
Art — AP64

1989-91		**Photo.**	**Perf. 11x11½**
C193	AP64	20p Balcony		.75 .45
C194	AP64	25p Brazier		1.10 .60
C195	AP64	35p shown		1.25 .75
C196	AP64	45p Tapestry		1.60 .75
C197	AP64	45p like #C195		1.40 .40
C198	AP64	50p Stag (dish)		2.00 1.00
C199	AP64	55p 4 animals
			(plate)		1.90 .90
C200	AP64	60p like #C198		2.25 1.25
C201	AP64	65p like #C198		2.50 1.50
C202	AP64	70p like #C193		2.50 1.50
C203	AP64	85p like #C199		3.00 1.75
	Nos. C193-C203 (11)		20.25 10.85

Issued: 35p, 60p, 10/1/89; 55p, 1/1/90; No. C197, C202, 1/25/91; 65p, 85p, 7/20/91; others, 4/1/89.

AP65

Funerary Mask of
King Tutankhamun
AP66

King
Tutankhamun
AP66a

No. C205, 21mm between "EGYPT" and Arabic text at top.
No. C205A, 17mm between "Egypt" and Arabic text at top ('00).

1993-2000		**Litho.**	**Perf. 11½**
C204	AP65	55p black & sepia	2.00 .95
C205	AP66	80p black & drab	3.25 1.25
C205A	AP66	80p black & sepia	— 1.25
		Photo.
		Perf. 11x11¼
C206	AP66a	£1 black & brown	1.50 1.25
	b.	Wmk. 342		2.00 1.25
	Nos. C204-C206 (4)		6.75 3.45

Issued: 55p, 80p, 3/1/93; £1, 1997; No. C206b, 1999.
See No. C231.

ICAO, 50th
Anniv. — AP67

1994, Sept. 16	**Litho.**	**Perf. 13**
C207 AP67 80p multicolored		1.00 .45

Intl. Year of
the Family
AP68

1994, Oct. 24	**Litho.**	**Perf. 13**
C208 AP68 80p multicolored		1.50 1.00

Arab League
for Education,
Culture, &
Science
Organization
AP69

1995, July 25	**Litho.**	**Perf. 13x13½**
C209 AP69 55p multicolored		.80 .50

UN Organizations, 50th
Anniv. — AP70

Perf. 12½x13, 13x12½
1995, Oct. 24			**Litho.**
C210	AP70	80p UN		2.00 1.00
C211	AP70	80p FAO		2.00 1.00
C212	AP70	80p UNESCO, vert.	2.00 1.00
	Nos. C210-C212 (3)		6.00 3.00

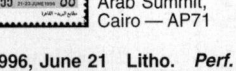

Arab Summit,
Cairo — AP71

1996, June 21	**Litho.**	**Perf. 13x12½**
C213 AP71 55p multicolored		.70 .30

16th Intl.
Conference on
Irrigation and
Drainage,
Cairo — AP72

1996, Sept. 15 Litho. Perf. 12½x13
C214 AP72 80p multicolored   1.10 1.10

Intl. Tourism
Day — AP73

1996, Sept. 27   Perf. 13
C215 AP73 80p multicolored   1.50 .60

Arabian Horse
Day — AP74

1996, Sept. 27   Perf. 13x12½
C216 AP74 55p grn, blk & gray   1.00 .35

World Post Day — AP75

1996, Oct. 9 Litho. Perf. 13x12½
C217 AP75 80p multicolored   1.25 .60

AP76

1996, Oct. 24
C218 AP76 55p multicolored   .70 .40
Cairo, Arab cultural capital of 1996.

UNICEF, 50th
Anniv. — AP77

1996, Oct. 24
C219 AP77 80p multicolored   1.10 .55

World Meteorological
Day — AP78

1997, Mar. 23 Litho. Perf. 13x12½
C220 AP78 £1 multicolored   1.75 1.00

Thutmose III — AP79

1997, Mar. 25 Photo. Perf. 11x11½
C221 AP79 75p blk, bl & gray   1.10 1.10

Heinrich von
Stephan
(1831-97)
AP80

1997, Apr. 15   Litho.   Perf. 13
C222 AP80 £1 multicolored   1.60 1.25

AP81

1997, Sept. 11
C223 AP81 £1 multicolored   1.00 .90
98th Intl. Parliamentary Conference, Cairo.

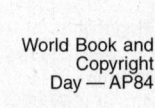

AP82

1997, Sept. 10   Litho.   Perf. 13
C224 AP82 75p multicolored   1.00 .90
1997 Egyptian Team, top medal winners of
8th Pan Arab Games, Beirut, Lebanon.

AP83

1997, Sept. 27   Perf. 13x12½
C225 AP83 £1 multicolored   1.90 1.00
Sarabas (180-211), mumified Egyptian.

World Book and
Copyright
Day — AP84

1997, Oct. 24 Litho. Perf. 12½x13
C226 AP84 £1 multicolored   1.75 1.00

African Ministries of
Transport and
Communications, 11th
Conference — AP85

1997, Nov. 22 Litho. Perf. 13x12½
C227 AP85 75p multicolored   .80 .70

Arab Scout
Movement, 85th
Anniv. — AP86

1997, Nov. 24   Perf. 12½x13
C228 AP86 75p multicolored   1.00 .90

8th G-15 Summit
Meeting — AP87

1998, May 11   Litho.   Perf. 13
C229 AP87 £1 multicolored   1.10 .90

Lighthouse of
Alexandria — AP88

1998, May 20   Litho.   Perf. 13
C230 AP88 £1 multicolored   1.75 1.00

King Tut Type of 1997
1998, July 25 Litho. Perf. 11x11¼
C231 AP66a 125p Tutankhamun   1.75 1.25
   a.   Wmk. 342 ('99)   5.50 4.00

Arab Post Day — AP90

1998, Aug. 3   Perf. 13
C232 AP90 £1 multicolored   1.10 .90

World Post
Day — AP91

1998, Oct. 9   Litho.   Perf. 13
C233 AP91 125p multicolored   1.40 1.25

67th Interpol Meeting,
Cairo — AP92

1998, Oct. 22
C234 AP92 125p multicolored   1.40 1.25

AP93

1998, Oct. 24
C235 AP93 125p multicolored   1.40 1.25
Universal Declaration of Human Rights,
50th anniv.

Statue of Akhnaton Type of 1985
1998   Litho.   Perf. 13
C236 AP55 25p lt bl, brn & tan   1.75 1.00

AP94

1999, Oct. 12 Litho. Perf. 13x12¾
C237 AP94 125p multicolored   2.25 1.75
Performance of opera "Aida" at the Pyramids.

AP95

1999, Oct. 16
C238 AP95 125p multicolored   2.50 1.75
Discovery of the Rosetta Stone, bicent.

World Tourism
Day — AP96

Perf. 13¼x12¾
2000, Sept. 27   Litho.
C239 AP96 125p multi   1.50 1.25

Awarding of Nobel Prize for Chemistry
to Dr. Ahmed Zewail — AP97

1999, Dec. 10   Imperf.
C240 AP97 125p multi   2.00 2.00

UN High
Commissioner for
Refugees, 50th
Anniv. — AP98

2000, Dec. 13
C241 AP98 125p multi   1.50 1.25

AIR POST SEMI-POSTAL STAMPS

> Catalogue values for unused stamps in this section are for Never Hinged items.

United Arab Republic

Pharaonic Mail
Carriers and
Papyrus
Plants — SPAP1

Design: 115m+55m, Jet plane, world map and stamp of Egypt, 1926 (No. C1).

			Wmk. 342	
1966, Jan. 2	**Photo.**		**Perf. 11½**	
CB1	SPAP1	80m + 40m multi	3.25	2.75
CB2	SPAP1	115m + 55m multi	4.25	3.50
a.	Pair, #CB1-CB2		10.00	8.00

Post Day, Jan. 2.

SPECIAL DELIVERY STAMPS

Motorcycle
Postman — SD1

		Perf. 13x13½		
1926, Nov. 28	**Photo.**		**Wmk. 195**	
E1	SD1	20m dark green	35.00	9.50
1929, Sept.				
E2	SD1	20m brown red & black	6.75	1.75

Inscribed "Postes Expres"
1943-44			**Litho.**	
E3	SD1	26m brn red & gray blk	6.75	6.75
E4	SD1	40m dl brn & pale gray ('44)	6.00	4.00

For overprints see Nos. E5, NE1.

> Catalogue values for unused stamps in this section, from this point to the end of the section, are for Never Hinged items.

No. E4 Overprinted in Black

1952, Jan.   **Overprint 27mm Wide**
E5 SD1 40m dl brn & pale gray   3.50 2.00

See notes after No. 316.

POSTAGE DUE STAMPS

D1

	Wmk. Crescent and Star (119)			
1884, Jan. 1	**Litho.**		**Perf. 10½**	
J1	D1	10pa red	57.50	9.50
a.	Horiz. pair, imperf. vert.		175.00	
J2	D1	20pa red	175.00	50.00
J3	D1	1pi red	145.00	52.50
J4	D1	2pi red	240.00	12.50
J5	D1	5pi red	20.00	65.00
	Nos. J1-J5 (5)		637.50	189.50
1886, Aug. 1			**Unwmk.**	
J6	D1	10pa red	75.00	17.50
a.	Horiz. pair, imperf. vert.		150.	
J7	D1	20pa red	260.00	50.00
J8	D1	1pi red	37.50	10.00
a.	Pair, imperf. between		225.00	150.00
J9	D1	2pi red	37.50	5.00
a.	Pair, imperf. between		200.00	
	Nos. J6-J9 (4)		410.00	82.50

D2

1888, Jan. 1			**Perf. 11½**	
J10	D2	2m green	22.50	27.50
a.	Horiz. pair, imperf. between		250.00	225.00
J11	D2	5m rose red	45.00	27.50
J12	D2	1pi blue	145.00	40.00
a.	Pair, imperf. between		325.00	
J13	D2	2pi yellow	155.00	20.00
J14	D2	5pi gray	240.00	210.00
a.	Period after "PIASTRES"		325.00	250.00
	Nos. J10-J14 (5)		607.50	325.00

Excellent counterfeits of #J1-J14 are plentiful.

There are 4 types of each of Nos. J1-J14, so placed that any block of 4 contains all types.

D3

		Perf. 14x13½		
1889	**Wmk. 119**		**Typo.**	
J15	D3	2m green	10.00	.70
a.	Half used as 1m on cover		400.00	
J16	D3	4m maroon	3.75	.70
J17	D3	1pi ultra	7.75	.70
J18	D3	2pi orange	7.50	1.00
a.	Half used as 1p on cover			
	Nos. J15-J18 (4)		29.00	3.10

Nos. J15-J18 exist on both ordinary and chalky paper. Imperf. examples of Nos. J15-J17 are proofs.

Black Surcharge

Type I — D4

1898				
J19	D4	3m on 2pi orange	2.10	6.25
a.	Inverted surcharge		67.50	90.00
b.	Pair, one without surcharge			
f.	Double surcharge		250.00	

There are two types of this surcharge. In type I, the spacing between the last two Arabic characters at the right is 2mm. In type II, this spacing is 3mm, and there is an added sign on top of the second character from the right. See *Scott Classic Specialized Catalogue of Stamps & Covers* for detailed listing.

D5   D6

1921	**Wmk. 120**		**Perf. 14x13½**	
J20	D5	2m green	3.75	6.75
J21	D5	4m vermilion	7.50	19.00
J22	D6	10m deep blue	12.50	25.00
	Nos. J20-J22 (3)		23.75	50.75

1921-22				
J23	D5	2m vermilion	1.00	2.25
J24	D5	4m green	6.00	2.00
J25	D6	10m lake ('22)	6.50	1.50
	Nos. J23-J25 (3)		13.50	5.75

Nos. J18, J23-J25
Overprinted

1922, Oct. 10			**Wmk. 119**	
J26	D3	2pi orange	7.50	10.50
a.	Overprint right side up		32.50	32.50
			Wmk. 120	
J27	D5	2m vermilion	1.00	3.25
J28	D5	4m green	1.60	3.25
J29	D6	10m lake	2.75	2.00
	Nos. J26-J29 (4)		12.85	19.00

Overprint on Nos. J26-J29 is inverted.

Arabic Numeral — D7

		Perf. 13x13½		
1927-56	**Litho.**		**Wmk. 195**	
		Size: 18x22½mm		
J30	D7	2m slate	.85	.50
J31	D7	2m orange ('38)	1.00	1.10
J32	D7	4m gray green	.85	.55
J33	D7	4m ol brn ('32)	8.00	5.25
J34	D7	5m brown	4.25	1.10
J35	D7	6m grn gray ('41)	2.75	2.10
J36	D7	8m brn vio	1.60	.65
J37	D7	10m brick red ('29)	1.25	.35
a.	10m deep red		1.90	1.00
J38	D7	12m rose lake ('41)	1.90	3.75
J38A	D7	20m dk red ('56)	2.50	2.50
		Perf. 13½x14		
		Size: 22x28mm		
J39	D7	30m purple	5.25	3.75
	Nos. J30-J39 (11)		30.20	21.60

See Nos. J47-J59. For overprints see Nos. J40-J46, NJ1-NJ7.

> Catalogue values for unused stamps in this section, from this point to the end of the section, are for Never Hinged items.

Postage Due Stamps and
Type of 1927 Overprinted
in Various Colors

1952, Jan. 16			**Perf. 13x13½**	
J40	D7	2m orange (Bl)	1.60	1.60
J41	D7	4m green	1.60	1.60
J42	D7	6m gray grn (RV)	1.90	1.90
J43	D7	8m brn vio (Bl)	2.50	2.50
J44	D7	10m dl rose (Bl)	4.25	3.50
a.	10m brown red (Bk)		4.00	3.75
J45	D7	12m rose lake (Bl)	2.10	2.10
		Perf. 14		
J46	D7	30m purple (C)	3.50	3.50
	Nos. J40-J46 (7)		17.45	16.70

See notes after No. 316.

United Arab Republic

1960	**Wmk. 318**		**Perf. 13x13½**	
		Size: 18x22½mm		
J47	D7	2m orange	1.00	1.00
J48	D7	4m light green	1.50	1.50
J49	D7	6m green	2.50	2.50
J50	D7	8m brown vio	5.00	5.00
J51	D7	12m rose brown	12.00	10.00
J52	D7	20m dull rose brn	2.00	.50
		Perf. 14		
		Size: 22x28mm		
J53	D7	30m violet	12.00	6.00
	Nos. J47-J53 (7)		36.00	26.50
1962	**Wmk. 328**		**Perf. 13x13½**	
		Size: 18x22½mm		
J54	D7	2m salmon	1.00	1.00
J55	D7	4m light green	1.50	1.50
J56	D7	10m red brown	2.50	2.50
J57	D7	12m rose brown	5.00	5.00
J58	D7	20m dull rose brn	11.00	11.00

		Perf. 14		
		Size: 22x28mm		
J59	D7	30m light violet	16.00	16.00
	Nos. J54-J59 (6)		37.00	37.00

D8

1965	**Unwmk.**	**Photo.**	**Perf. 11**	
J60	D8	2m org & vio blk	1.25	1.00
J61	D8	8m lt bl & dk bl	1.50	1.50
J62	D8	10m yel & emer	2.25	1.50
J63	D8	20m lt bl & vio blk	2.75	2.25
J64	D8	40m org & emer	4.75	2.00
	Nos. J60-J64 (5)		12.50	8.25

MILITARY STAMPS

The "British Forces" and "Army post" stamps were special issues provided at a reduced rate for the purchase and use by the British military forces in Egypt and their families for ordinary letters sent to Great Britain and Ireland by a concessionary arrangement made with the Egyptian government. From Nov. 1, 1932 to Feb. 29, 1936, in order to take advantage of the concessionary rate, it was mandatory to use #M1-M11 by affixing them to the backs of envelopes. An "Egypt Postage Prepaid" handstamp was applied to the face of the envelopes. Envelopes bearing these stamps were to be posted only at British military post boxes. Envelopes bearing the 1936-39 "Army Post" stamps (#M12-M15, issued by the Egyptian Postal Administration) also were sold at the concessionary rate and also were to be posted only at British military post boxes. The "Army Post" stamps were withdrawn in 1941, but the concession continued without the use of special stamps. The concession was finally canceled in 1951.

Imperf examples of Nos. M1-M4, M6, M9 (without overprint) and M10 are proofs.

M1

		Unwmk.		
1932, Nov. 1	**Typo.**		**Perf. 11**	
M1	M1	1pi red & blue	70.00	4.50

For similar design see No. M3.

M2

1932, Nov. 26	**Typo.**		**Perf. 11½**	
M2	M2	3m blk, *sage grn*	57.50	80.00

See Nos. M4, M6, M10.

M3

1933, Aug.	**Typo.**		**Perf. 11**	
M3	M3	1pi red & blue	47.50	1.10

Camel Type of 1932
1933, Nov. 13	**Typo.**		**Perf. 11½**	
M4	M2	3m brown lake	40.00	57.50

M4

1934, June 1   Photo.   Perf. 14½x14
M5 M4 1pi bright carmine   40.00   1.25
    See Nos. M7-M8. For overprint and
surcharge see Nos. M9, M11.

Camel Type of 1932
1934, Nov. 17   Typo.   Perf. 11½
M6 M2 3m deep blue   30.00 30.00

Type of 1934
1934, Dec. 5   Photo.   Perf. 14½x14
M7 M4 1pi green   6.00   6.00

Type of 1934
1935, Apr. 24   Perf. 13½x14
M8 M4 1pi bright carmine   2.90   3.75

Type of 1934 Overprinted in Red

1935, May 6   Perf. 14
M9 M4 1pi ultramarine   350.00 275.00

Camel Type of 1932
1935, Nov. 23   Typo.   Perf. 11½
M10 M2 3m vermilion   30.00 45.00

No. M8 Surcharged

1935, Dec. 16   Photo.   Perf. 13½x14
M11 M4 3m on 1pi brt car   40.00 100.00

Fuad Type of 1927

Inscribed "Army
Post" — M5

1936, Mar. 1   Wmk. 195
M12 M5   3m green   2.50   2.50
M13 M5 10m carmine   7.00   .25

King Farouk — M6

1939, Dec. 16   Perf. 13½x14
M14 M6   3m green   6.00 12.00
M15 M6 10m carmine rose   8.00   .25

> Catalogue values for unused
> stamps in this section, from this
> point to the end of the section, are
> for Never Hinged items.

United Arab Republic

Arms of UAR and Military
Emblems — M7

Perf. 11x11½
1971, Apr. 15   Photo.   Wmk. 342
M16 M7 10m purple   .75   .50

OFFICIAL STAMPS

O1

Wmk. Crescent and Star (119)
1893, Jan. 1   Typo.   Perf. 14x13½
O1 O1 orange brown   3.75   .25
    No. O1 exists on ordinary and chalky paper.
Imperf. examples of No. O1 are proofs.

Regular Issues of 1884-93 Overprinted

1907
O2 A18 1m brown   2.40   .35
O3 A19 2m green   4.25   .25
O4 A20 3m orange   4.75   1.25
O5 A22 5m car rose   7.75   .25
O6 A14 1pi ultra   4.75   .25
O7 A16 5pi gray   17.00   6.00
         Nos. O2-O7 (6)   40.90   8.35
    Nos. O2-O3, O5-O7 imperf. are proofs.

No. 48 Overprinted

1913
O8 A22 5m carmine rose   9.50   .70
 a.   Inverted overprint   90.00
 b.   No period after "S"   65.00 19.00

Regular Issues Overprinted

1914-15   On Issues of 1888-1906
O9 A19 2m green   5.00 10.00
 a.   Inverted overprint   42.50 42.50
 b.   Double overprint   450.00
 c.   No period after "S"   16.00 16.00
O10 A21 4m brown red   7.50   5.50
 a.   Inverted overprint   225.00 160.00

On Issue of 1914
O11 A24 1m olive brown   2.50   5.00
 a.   No period after "S"   14.00 30.00
O12 A26 3m orange   3.75   6.00
 a.   No period after "S"   16.00 30.00
O13 A28 5m lake   4.75   2.75
 a.   No period after "S"   17.50 26.00
 b.   Two periods after "S"   17.50 26.00
         Nos. O9-O13 (5)   23.50 29.25

Regular Issues Overprinted

1915, Oct.   On Issues of 1888-1906
O14 A19 2m green   5.50   5.00
 a.   Inverted overprint   24.00 24.00
 b.   Double overprint   30.00
O15 A21 4m brown red   11.00 11.00

On Issue of 1914
O16 A28 5m lake   15.00   1.75
 a.   Pair, one without overprint   325.00
         Nos. O14-O16 (3)   31.50 17.75

Nos. 50, 63, 52, 67 Overprinted

1922   Wmk. 120
O17 A24 1m olive brown   4.25 16.00
O18 A25 2m red   10.00 24.00
O19 A26 3m orange   77.50 150.00
O20 A28 5m pink   21.00   6.00
         Nos. O17-O20 (4)   112.75 196.00

Regular Issues of 1921-22 Overprinted

1922
O21 A24 1m olive brn   1.50   3.25
O22 A25 2m red   2.00   4.50
O23 A26 3m orange   3.25   5.00
O24 A27 4m green   7.00   9.00
 a.   Two periods after "H" none
        after "S"   175.00 175.00
O25 A28 5m pink   4.00   1.00
 a.   Two periods after "H" none
        after "S"   75.00 75.00
O26 A29 10m deep blue   7.00   8.00
O27 A29 10m lake ('23)   10.00   4.00
 a.   Two periods after "H" none
        after "S"   100.00 100.00

O28 A34 15m indigo   8.00   7.00
O29 A35 15m indigo   160.00 160.00
 a.   Two periods after "H" none
        after "S"   250.00 250.00
O30 A31 50m maroon   20.00 18.00

Regular Issue of 1923 Overprinted in Black or Red

1924   Perf. 13½x14
O31 A36 1m orange   2.10   2.25
O32 A36 2m gray (R)   2.75   3.50
O33 A36 3m brown   6.75   6.75
O34 A36 4m yellow green   8.50   8.50
O35 A36 5m orange brown   2.00   1.05
O36 A36 10m rose   5.50   4.00
O37 A36 15m ultra   9.25   6.75

Perf. 14
O38 A36 50m myrtle green   25.00 13.50
         Nos. O31-O38 (8)   61.85 46.30

O2

Perf. 13x13½
1926-35   Litho.   Wmk. 195
Size: 18½x22mm
O39 O2 1m lt orange   1.05   .55
O40 O2 2m black   .70   .40
O41 O2 3m olive brn   2.00   1.35
O42 O2 4m lt green   1.75   1.60
O43 O2 5m brown   2.10   .55
O44 O2 10m dull red   5.25   .55
O45 O2 10m brt vio ('34)   3.00   .60
O46 O2 15m dp blue   5.25   1.25
O47 O2 15m brown vio ('34)   5.25   1.10
O48 O2 20m dp blue ('35)   5.50   1.60

Perf. 13½
Size: 22½x27½mm
O49 O2 20m olive green   7.50   2.75
O50 O2 50m myrtle green   10.00   2.00
         Nos. O39-O50 (12)   49.35 14.30

O3

1938, Dec.   Size: 22½x19mm
O51 O3 1m orange   .35   .35
O52 O3 2m red   .35   .35
O53 O3 3m olive brown   1.60   1.60
O54 O3 4m yel green   1.00   1.00
O55 O3 5m brown   .50   .50
O56 O3 10m brt violet   .60   .60
O57 O3 15m rose violet   1.60   1.60
O58 O3 20m blue   1.60   1.60

Perf. 14x13½
Size: 26½x22mm
O59 O3 50m myrtle green   3.75   3.00
         Nos. O51-O59 (9)   11.35 10.60

> Catalogue values for unused
> stamps in this section, from this
> point to the end of the section, are
> for Never Hinged items.

Nos. O51 to O59 Overprinted in Various Colors

Overprint 19mm Wide

1952, Jan.   Perf. 13x13½
O60 O3 1m orange (Br)   2.10   2.10
O61 O3 2m red (Br)   2.10   2.10
O62 O3 3m olive brn (Bl)   2.50   2.50
O63 O3 4m yel green (Bl)   2.50   2.50
O64 O3 5m brown (Bl)   2.50   2.50
O65 O3 10m brt violet (Bl)   2.50   2.50
O66 O3 15m rose violet (Bl)   3.00   3.00
O67 O3 20m blue   3.75   3.75

Overprint 24½mm Wide
Perf. 14x13½
O68 O3 50m myrtle grn (RV)   8.00   8.00
         Nos. O60-O68 (9)   28.95 28.95
    See notes after No. 316.

United Arab Republic

O4

Perf. 13x13½
1959   Litho.   Wmk. 318
O69 O4 10m brown violet   .65   .25
O70 O4 35m chalky blue   1.75   .30

1962-63   Wmk. 328
O71 O4 1m orange ('63)   .30   .30
O72 O4 4m yel grn ('63)   .60   .60
O73 O4 5m brown   .60   .25
O74 O4 10m dk brown   .75   .30
O75 O4 35m dark blue   2.25   .50
O76 O4 50m green   3.50   .50
O77 O4 100m violet ('63)   7.00   1.75
O78 O4 200m rose red ('63)   15.00   8.00
O79 O4 500m gray ('63)   22.50 15.00
         Nos. O71-O79 (9)   52.50 27.30

Arms of UAR — O5

Perf. 11½x11
1966-68   Unwmk.   Photo.
O80 O5 1m ultra   .25   .25
O81 O5 4m brown   .25   .25
O82 O5 5m olive   .30   .25
O83 O5 10m brown blk   1.00   .35
O84 O5 20m magenta   .60   .30
O85 O5 35m dk purple   1.00   .35
O86 O5 50m orange   1.10   .45
O87 O5 55m dk purple   1.10   .45

Wmk. 342
O88 O5 100m brt grn & brick
         red   2.25   1.00
O89 O5 200m blue & brick red   4.50   2.00
O90 O5 500m olive & brick red   15.00   9.00
         Nos. O80-O90 (11)   22.35 11.90

1969   Wmk. 342
O91 O5 10m magenta   1.10   .65

Arab Republic of Egypt

Arms of Egypt — O6

Wmk. 342
1972, June 30   Photo.   Perf. 11
O92 O6 1m black & vio blue   .30   .25
 a.   1m black & light blue ('75)   .25   .25
O93 O6 10m black & car   .65   .30
 a.   10m black & rose red ('76)   .25   .25
O94 O6 20m black & olive   .90   .40
O95 O6 50m black & orange   .60   .55
O96 O6 55m black & purple   3.00   1.00

1973
O97 O6 20m lilac & sepia   .90   .40
 a.   20m purple & light brown ('76)   2.50   .70
O98 O6 70m black & grn ('79)   .85   .45

1982   Photo.   Unwmk.   Perf. 11
O99 O6 30m purple & brown   .60   .30
O100 O6 60m black & orange   .70   .30
O101 O6 80m black & green   .95   .35
         Nos. O92-O101 (10)   9.45   4.30

    Issued: 30m, 2/12; 60m, 2/24; 80m, 2/18.

Arms of Egypt — O7

1985-89   Photo.   Perf. 11½
Size: 21x25mm
O102 O7 1p vermilion   .25   .25
O103 O7 2p brown   .25   .25
O104 O7 3p sepia   .25   .25
O105 O7 5p orange yel   .35   .30
O106 O7 8p green   .70   .35
O107 O7 10p brown olive   .25   .25

O108	O7	15p dull violet	1.50	.70
O109	O7	20p blue	.85	.80
O110	O7	25p red	1.50	1.00
O111	O7	30p dull violet	.90	.70
O112	O7	50p green	2.25	2.25
O113	O7	60p myrtle green	2.00	1.40
		Nos. O102-O113 (12)	11.05	8.50

Issued: 1p, 3p, 5p, 8p, 15p, 5/1/85; 20p, 50p, 4/88; 10p, 30p, 60p, 12/1/89; 2p, 25p, 1989.

1991-99 Wmk. 342 Perf. 11½x11
Size: 18x22mm

O114	O7	5p orange yellow	.25	.25
O115	O7	10p brown violet	.25	.25
O116	O7	15p brown	.25	.25
O117	O7	20p blue	.35	.25
O118	O7	20p violet	.25	.25
O119	O7	25p purple	.45	.25
O120	O7	30p dk violet	.50	.25
O121	O7	50p green	.80	.60
O122	O7	55p red	.70	.55
O123	O7	75p brown	.75	.55
O124	O7	£1 green blue	1.25	.75
O125	O7	£2 green	2.50	1.50
		Nos. O114-O125 (12)	8.30	5.70

Issued: 10p, 30p, 7/1/91; 50p, 12/1/91; 55p, 4/1/93; £1, £2, 3/22/94; No. O123, 75p, 2/1/97; No. O118, 4/11/99.

Arms Type of 1985-89
Perf. 11½x11
2001-02? Photo. Unwmk.
Size: 18x22mm

O126	O7	5p orange yellow	—	—
O127	O7	10p brown	2.75	.50
O128	O7	20p dark blue	—	—
O129	O7	25p purple	—	—
O130	O7	30p violet	3.75	.60
O131	O7	75p olive brown	—	—
O132	O7	£1 greenish blue	—	—

Issued: Nos. O126-O129, O131-O132, 3/25/01; No. O130, 2002?.

Arms Type of 1985-89
Perf. 11½x11
2018, Aug. 16 Photo. Unwmk.
Size: 18x22mm

O133	O7	50p brown	.25	.25
O134	O7	£2.50 Prus blue	.30	.30
O135	O7	£3 blksh pur	.35	.35
O136	O7	£4 dark brown	.45	.45
O137	O7	£5 green	.55	.55
		Nos. O133-O137 (5)	1.90	1.90

OCCUPATION STAMPS

Catalogue values for unused stamps in this section are for Never Hinged items.

For Use in Palestine

Stamps of 1939-46 Overprinted in Red, Green or Black — a

Perf. 13x13½, 13½x13
1948, May 15 Wmk. 195

N1	A77	1m yellow brn (G)	.35	.35
N2	A77	2m red org (G)	.35	.35
N3	A66	3m brown (G)	.35	.35
N4	A77	4m dp green	.35	.35
N5	A77	5m red brown (Bk)	.35	.35
N6	A66	6m lt yel grn (Bk)	.35	.35
N7	A77	10m dp violet	.35	.35
N8	A66	13m rose car (G)	2.00	2.50
N9	A77	15m dk violet	.45	.45
N10	A77	17m olive green	.45	.45
N11	A77	20m dk gray	.45	.45
N12	A77	22m deep blue	.50	.50
N13	A74	50pi green & sep	30.00	30.00
N14	A75	£1 dp bl & dk brn	50.00	50.00

The two lines of the overprint are more widely separated on Nos. N13 and N14.

Nos. 267-269, 237 and 238 Ovptd. in Red — b

Perf. 14x13½

N15	A73	30m olive green	1.25	1.25
N16	A73	40m dark brown	1.60	1.60
N17	A73	50m Prus green	3.00	3.00
N18	A73	100m brown violet	5.00	5.00
N19	A73	200m dark violet	15.00	15.00
		Nos. N1-N19 (19)	112.15	112.65

Overprint arranged to fit size of stamps.

Nos. N1-N19 Overprinted in Black with Three Bars to Obliterate Portrait
Perf. 13x13½, 13½x13, 14x13½
1953 Wmk. 195

N20	A77	1m yellow brown	.70	.70
N21	A77	2m red orange	.70	.70
N22	A66	3m brown	.70	.70
N23	A77	4m deep green	.70	.70
N24	A77	5m red brown	.70	.70
N25	A66	6m lt yel grn	.80	.80
N26	A77	10m deep violet	.85	.85
N27	A66	13m rose carmine	.90	.90
N28	A77	15m dark violet	.95	.95
N29	A77	17m olive green	.95	.95
N30	A77	20m dark gray	1.10	1.10
N31	A77	22m deep blue	1.45	1.45
N32	A73	30m olive green	1.45	1.45
N33	A73	40m dark brown	2.60	2.60
N34	A73	50m Prus green	8.00	8.00
N35	A73	100m brown violet	17.00	17.00
N36	A73	200m dark violet	40.00	40.00
N37	A74	50pi green & sepia	80.00	75.00
N38	A75	£1 dp bl & dk brn	170.00	170.00
		Nos. N20-N38 (19)	329.55	324.55

Regular Issue of 1953-55 Overprinted Type "a" in Blue or Red
1954-56 Perf. 13x13½

N39	A115	1m red brown	.50	.50
N40	A115	2m dark lilac	.50	.50
N41	A115	3m brt blue (R)	.50	.50
N42	A115	4m dark green (R)	.50	.50
N43	A115	5m deep carmine	.50	.50
N44	A110	10m dark brown	.50	.50
N45	A110	15m gray (R)	.50	.50
N46	A110	17m dk grnsh bl (R)	.50	.50
N47	A110	20m purple (R) ('54)	.65	.65

Nos. 331-333 and 335-340 Overprinted in Blue or Red — c

Perf. 13½

N48	A111	30m dull green (R)	.90	.90
N49	A111	32m brt blue (R)	1.00	1.00
N50	A111	35m violet (R)	1.30	1.30
N51	A111	40m red brown	2.00	2.00
N52	A111	50m violet brown	2.50	2.50
N53	A112	100m henna brown	6.00	6.00
N54	A112	200m dk grnsh bl (R)	20.00	20.00
N55	A112	500m purple (R)	70.00	70.00
N56	A112	£1 dk grn, blk & red (R) ('56)	115.00	115.00
		Nos. N39-N56 (18)	223.35	223.35

Type of 1957 Overprinted in Red — d

1957 Wmk. 195 Perf. 13½x13

N57	A127	10m blue green	5.00	5.00

Nos. 414-417 Overprinted Type "d" in Red
1957-58 Wmk. 315 Perf. 13½

N58	A137	10m violet	3.25	3.25

Wmk. 318

N59	A136	1m lt bl grn ('58)	.65	.65
N60	A138	5m brown ('58)	.65	.65
N61	A137	10m violet ('58)	.95	.95
		Nos. N58-N61 (4)	5.50	5.50

United Arab Republic

Nos. 438-444 Overprinted in Red or Green

Perf. 13½x14
1958 Wmk. 318 Photo.

N62	A136	1m crimson	.40	.40
N63	A138	2m blue	.40	.40
N64	A143	3m dk red brn (G)	.40	.40
N65	A217	4m green	.40	.40
N66	A138	5m brown	.40	.40
N67	A137	10m violet	.50	.40
N68	A138	35m lt ultra	3.50	3.25
		Nos. N62-N68 (7)	6.00	5.65

Freedom Struggle Type of 1958 Overprint in Red

1958 Perf. 13½x13

N69	A145	10m dark brown	2.25	2.25

Declaration of Human Rights Type of 1958 Overprinted in Green

1958 Perf. 13½x13

N70	A151	10m rose violet	3.50	3.50
N71	A151	35m red brown	8.50	8.50

No. 460 Overprinted in Green

1959 Wmk. 195 Perf. 13½

N72	A112	55m on 100m henna brn	4.25	4.25

World Refugee Year Type "PALESTINE" Added in English and Arabic to Stamps of Egypt

OS1

1960 Wmk. 328 Perf. 13x13½

N73	OS1	10m orange brown	.80	.80
N74	OS1	35m dk blue gray	1.75	1.50

Type of Regular Issue 1957-63
1960 Perf. 13½x14

N75	A136	1m brown orange	.40	.40
N76	A217	4m olive gray	.40	.40
N77	A138	5m dk dull pur	.40	.40
N78	A137	10m dk olive grn	.40	.40
		Nos. N75-N78 (4)	1.60	1.60

Palestine Day Type
1961, May 15 Perf. 13½x13

N79	A184	10m purple	1.00	1.00

WHO Day Type
1961 Wmk. 328 Perf. 13½x13

N80	A182	10m blue	1.30	.75

U.N.T.A.P. Type
1961, Oct. 24

N81	A191	10m dk blue & org	.55	.55
N82	A191	35m vermilion & blk	.80	.80

Education Day Type
1961, Dec. 18 Photo. Perf. 13½

N83	A194	10m red brown	.55	.55

Victory Day Type
1961, Dec. 23 Unwmk. Perf. 11½

N84	A195	10m brn org & brn	.45	.45

Gaza Strip Type
Perf. 13½x13
1962, Mar. 7 Wmk. 328

N85	A200	10m red brown	.45	.45

Arab Publicity Week Type
1962, Mar. 22 Perf. 13½x13

N86	SP16	10m dark purple	.35	.35

Anti-Malaria Type
1962, June 20 Photo.

N87	A204	10m brn & dk car rose	.50	.50
N88	A204	35m black & yellow	.60	.60

Hammarskjold Type
1962, Oct. 24 Wmk. 342
Portrait in Slate Blue
Perf. 11x11½

N89	A214	5m bright rose	.40	.40
N90	A214	10m brown	.50	.50
N91	A214	35m blue	.80	.80
		Nos. N89-N91 (3)	1.70	1.70

Lamp Type of Regular Issue
Perf. 11x11½
1963, Feb. 20 Unwmk.

N92	A217	4m dk brn, org & ultra	.35	.35

"Freedom from Hunger" Type
Perf. 11½x11, 11x11½
1963, Mar. 21 Wmk. 342

N93	A220	5m blue grn & brn org	.35	.35
N94	A220	10m olive & yellow	.45	.45
N95	A220	35m lt pur, yel & blksh pur	.65	.65
		Nos. N93-N95 (3)	1.45	1.45

Red Cross Centenary Type
Designs: 10m, Centenary emblem, bottom panel added. 35m, Globe and emblem, top and bottom panels added.

1963, May 8 Unwmk. Perf. 11x11½

N96	A221	10m blue & brt red	.35	.35
N97	A221	35m brt red & blue	.60	.60

"Save Abu Simbel" Type, 1963
1963, Oct. 15 Wmk. 342 Perf. 11

N98	A224	5m black & yellow	.40	.40
N99	A224	10m gray, blk & yellow	.50	.50
N100	A224	35m org yel, vio & pur	1.25	.95
		Nos. N98-N100 (3)	2.15	1.85

Human Rights Type
1963, Dec. 10 Photo. Perf. 11½x11

N101	A228	5m dk brown & yellow	.35	.35
N102	A228	10m dp claret, gray & blk	.40	.40
N103	A228	35m lt grn, pale grn & blk	.95	.95
		Nos. N101-N103 (3)	1.70	1.70

Types of Regular Issue
1964 Unwmk. Perf. 11

N104	A231	1m citron & lt vio	.40	.40
N105	A230	2m orange & slate	.40	.40
N106	A230	3m blue & ocher	.40	.40
N107	A235	4m ol gray, ol, brn & rose	.40	.40
N108	A230	5m rose & brt blue	.40	.40
a.		5m rose & dark blue	1.25	1.25
N109	A231	10m ol, rose & brn	.40	.40
N110	A230	15m lilac & yellow	.50	.50
N111	A230	20m brown blk & ol	.80	.80
N112	A231	30m dp org & ind	1.60	1.60
N113	A231	35m buff, ocher & emer	1.40	1.40
N114	A231	40m ultra & emer	1.75	1.75
N115	A231	60m grnsh bl & brn org	2.50	2.50

Wmk. 342

N116	A232	100m bluish blk & yel brn	3.50	3.50
		Nos. N104-N116 (13)	14.45	14.45

Arab League Council Type
1964, Jan. 13 Photo.

N117	A234	10m olive & black	.35	.35

Minaret Type
1964 Unwmk. Perf. 11

N118	A235	4m ol, red brn & red	.35	.35

Arab Postal Union Type
1964, Apr. 1 Wmk. 342 Perf. 11

N119	A239	10m emer & ultra, *lt grn*	.35	.35

WHO Type
1964, Apr. 7

N120	A240	10m violet blk & red		

Minaret Type

1965, Jan. 20	Unwmk.	Perf. 11	
N121	A255	4m green & dk brn	.35 .35

Arab League Type

1965, Mar. 22	Wmk. 342	Perf. 11	
N122	A258	10m green, red & blk	.35 .35
N123	A258	20m green & brown	.35 .35

World Health Day Type

1965, Apr. 7	Wmk. 342	Perf. 11	
N124	A259	10m brt green & crim	.35 .35

Massacre Type

1965, Apr. 9		Photo.	
N125	A260	10m slate blue & red	.60 .60

ITU Type

1965, May 17	Wmk. 342	Perf. 11	
N126	A261	5m sl grn, sl bl & yel	.40 .40
N127	A261	10m car, rose red & gray	.50 .50
N128	A261	35m vio bl, ultra & yel	1.40 .95
		Nos. N126-N128 (3)	2.30 1.85

United Nations Type

5m, WHO Headquarters, Geneva. 10m, UN Refugee emblem. 35m, UNICEF emblem.

1966, Oct. 24	Wmk. 342	Perf. 11	
N129	A288	5m rose & brt pur	.35 .35
N130	A288	10m yel brn & brt pur	.40 .40
N131	A288	35m brt green & brt pur	.80 .80
		Nos. N129-N131 (3)	1.55 1.55

Victory Day Type
Wmk. 342

1966, Dec. 23		Photo.	Perf. 11½
N132	A290	10m olive & car rose	.40 .40

Arab Publicity Week Type
Perf. 11x11½

1967, Mar. 22	Photo.	Wmk. 342	
N133	A294	10m vio blue & brn	.35 .35

Labor Day Type
Perf. 11½x11

1967, May 1	Photo.	Wmk. 342	
N134	A296	10m olive & sepia	.35 .35

OCCUPATION AIR POST STAMPS

Catalogue values for unused stamps in this section are for Never Hinged items.

Nos. C39-C50 Overprinted Type "b" in Black, Carmine or Red

Nos. NC1-NC12 Overprinted in Black, Carmine or Red

		Perf. 13x13½	
1948, May 15			Wmk. 195
NC1	AP3	2m red org (Bk)	.75 .75
NC2	AP3	3m dk brn (C)	.75 .75
NC3	AP3	5m red brn (Bk)	.75 .75
NC4	AP3	7m dp yel org (Bk)	1.05 1.05
NC5	AP3	8m green (C)	1.05 1.05
NC6	AP3	10m violet	1.20 1.20
NC7	AP3	20m brt bl	1.90 1.90
NC8	AP3	30m brn vio (Bk)	4.50 4.50
NC9	AP3	40m car rose (Bk)	3.00 3.00
NC10	AP3	50m Prus grn	4.00 4.00
NC11	AP3	100m olive grn	6.75 6.75
NC12	AP3	200m dark gray	34.00 34.00
		Nos. NC1-NC12 (12)	59.70 59.70

Nos. NC1-NC12 Overprinted in Black with Three Bars to Obliterate Portrait

1953			
NC13	AP3	2m red org	1.90 1.90
NC14	AP3	3m dk brn	1.20 1.20
NC15	AP3	5m red brn	20.00 20.00
NC16	AP3	7m dp yel org	1.25 1.25
NC17	AP3	8m green	3.75 3.75
NC18	AP3	10m violet	3.75 3.75
NC19	AP3	20m brt bl	3.75 3.75
NC20	AP3	30m brn vio	3.75 3.75
NC21	AP3	40m car rose	6.75 6.75

NC22	AP3	50m Prus grn	28.00 28.00
NC23	AP3	100m olive grn	115.00 115.00
NC24	AP3	200m dk gray	15.00 15.00
		Nos. NC13-NC24 (12)	204.10 204.10

Nos. NC1-NC3, NC6, NC10, NC11 with Additional Overprint in Various Colors

1953			
NC25	AP3	2m red org (Bk + Bl)	1.00 1.00
NC26	AP3	3m dk brn (Bk + RV)	19.00 19.00
NC27	AP3	5m red brn (Bk)	2.75 2.75
NC28	AP3	10m vio (R + G)	28.00 28.00
NC29	AP3	50m Prus grn (R + RV)	8.75 8.75
NC30	AP3	100m ol grn (R + Bk)	62.50 62.50
		Nos. NC25-NC30 (6)	122.00 122.00

Nos. C65-C66 Overprinted Type "b" in Black or Red

1955		Wmk. 195	Perf. 13x13½
NC31	AP4	5m red brn	7.00 5.75
NC32	AP4	15m ol grn (R)	10.00 8.25

United Arab Republic

OAP1

Designs: 80m, Al Azhar University. 115m, Temple of Queen Nefertari, Abu Simbel. 140m, Ramses II, Abu Simbel.

Perf. 11½x11

1963, Oct. 24			Wmk. 342
NC33	OAP1	80m blk & brt bl	2.50 2.50
NC34	OAP1	115m blk & yel	3.50 3.50
NC35	OAP1	140m bl, ultra & org red	4.00 4.00
		Nos. NC33-NC35 (3)	10.00 10.00

Cairo Tower Type, 1964

1964, Nov. 2	Unwmk.	Perf. 11x11½	
NC36	AP11	50m dl vio & lt bl	1.25 1.25

World Meteorological Day Type

1965, Mar. 23		Wmk. 342	Perf. 11
NC37	AP12	80m dk bl & org	3.00 3.00

Tutankhamun Type of 1965

1965, July 1		Photo.	Perf. 11
NC38	AP13	10m brn org & brt grn	1.75 1.75

OCCUPATION SPECIAL DELIVERY STAMP

Catalogue values for unused stamps in this section are for Never Hinged items.

No. E4 Overprinted Type "b" in Carmine

1948		Wmk. 195	Perf. 13x13½
NE1	SD1	40m dl brn & pale gray	12.50 12.50

OCCUPATION POSTAGE DUE STAMPS

Catalogue values for unused stamps in this section are for Never Hinged items.

Postage Due Stamps of Egypt, 1927-41, Overprinted Type "a" in Black or Rose

1948		Wmk. 195	Perf. 13x13½
NJ1	D7	2m orange	2.25 2.40
NJ2	D7	4m green (R)	1.60 2.00
NJ3	D7	6m gray green	1.60 2.00

NJ4	D7	8m brown violet	1.60 2.00
NJ5	D7	10m brick red	1.60 2.00
NJ6	D7	12m rose lake	1.60 2.00

Overprinted Type "b" in Red
Perf. 14
Size: 22x28mm

NJ7	D7	30m purple	5.00 9.00
		Nos. NJ1-NJ7 (7)	15.25 21.40

ELOBEY, ANNOBON & CORISCO

ˌel-ə-ˈbā, ˌan-ə-ˈbän and kə-ˈris-ˌkō

LOCATION — A group of islands near the Guinea Coast of western Africa.
GOVT. — Spanish colonial possessions administered as part of the Continental Guinea District. A second district under the same governor-general included Fernando Po.
AREA — 13¾ sq. mi.
POP. — 2,950 (estimated 1910)
CAPITAL — Santa Isabel

100 Centimos = 1 Peseta

King Alfonso XIII — A1

1903	Unwmk.	Typo.	Perf. 14
Control Numbers on Back			
1	A1	¼c carmine	.75 .55
2	A1	½c dk violet	.75 .55
3	A1	1c black	.75 .55
4	A1	2c red	.75 .55
5	A1	3c dk green	.75 .55
6	A1	4c dk blue grn	.75 .55
7	A1	5c violet	.75 .55
8	A1	10c rose lake	1.50 1.60
9	A1	15c orange buff	4.50 1.75
10	A1	25c dark blue	7.75 6.00
11	A1	50c red brown	9.00 10.50
12	A1	75c black brn	9.00 14.50
13	A1	1p orange red	15.00 20.00
14	A1	2p chocolate	40.00 60.00
15	A1	3p dp olive grn	60.00 75.00
16	A1	4p claret	140.00 100.00
17	A1	5p blue green	165.00 110.00
18	A1	10p dull blue	300.00 165.00
		Nos. 1-18 (18)	757.00 568.20
		Set, never hinged	1,500.

Dated "1905"

1905		Control Numbers on Back	
19	A1	1c carmine	1.25 .70
20	A1	2c dp violet	5.00 .70
21	A1	3c black	1.25 .70
22	A1	4c dull red	1.25 .70
23	A1	5c dp green	1.25 .70
24	A1	10c blue grn	4.50 .90
25	A1	15c violet	5.00 4.75
26	A1	25c rose lake	5.00 4.75
27	A1	50c orange buff	9.00 7.25
28	A1	75c dark blue	9.00 7.25
29	A1	1p red brown	18.50 16.00
30	A1	2p black brn	20.00 22.50
31	A1	3p orange red	20.00 23.00
32	A1	4p dk brown	150.00 72.50
33	A1	5p bronze grn	160.00 80.00
34	A1	10p claret	350.00 225.00
		Nos. 19-34 (16)	761.00 467.40
		Set, never hinged	1,500.

Nos. 19-22 Surcharged in Black or Red

1906			
35	A1	10c on 1c rose (Bk)	11.50 6.50
a.		Inverted surcharge	11.50 6.50
b.		Value omitted	30.00 16.00
c.		Frame omitted	16.00 7.50
d.		Double surcharge	11.50 6.50
e.		Surcharged "15 cents"	30.00 16.00
f.		Surcharged "25 cents"	52.50 22.50
g.		Surcharged "50 cents"	37.50 22.50
h.		"1906" omitted	17.50 7.50
36	A1	15c on 2c dp vio (R)	11.50 6.50
a.		Frame omitted	12.50 6.50
b.		Surcharged "25 cents"	16.00 9.00
c.		Double surcharge	11.50 6.50
d.		Inverted surcharge	11.50 6.50
37	A1	25c on 3c blk (R)	11.50 6.50
a.		Inverted surcharge	11.50 6.50
b.		Double surcharge	11.50 6.50
c.		Surcharged "15 cents"	16.00 6.50
d.		Surcharged "50 cents"	25.00 11.00

38	A1	50c on 4c red (Bk)	11.50 6.50
a.		Inverted surcharge	11.50 6.50
b.		Value omitted	35.00 17.50
c.		Frame omitted	17.50 8.00
d.		Double surcharge	11.50 6.50
e.		"1906" omitted	17.50 8.00
g.		Surcharged "10 cents"	32.50 16.00
h.		Surcharged "25 cents"	32.50 16.00
		Nos. 35-38 (4)	46.00 26.00

Eight other surcharges were prepared but not issued: 10c on 50c, 75c, 1p, 2p and 3p; 15c on 50c and 5p; 50c on 5c.

Exist with surcharges in different colors; #35 in blue, red or violet; #36 in black or violet; #37 in black or violet; #38 in blue, violet or red. Value, set of 10, $135.

King Alfonso XIII — A2

1907		Control Numbers on Back	
39	A2	1c dk violet	.50 .45
40	A2	2c black	.50 .45
41	A2	3c red orange	.50 .45
42	A2	4c dk green	.50 .45
43	A2	5c blue green	.50 .45
44	A2	10c violet	5.50 5.50
45	A2	15c carmine	1.60 1.75
46	A2	25c orange	1.60 1.75
47	A2	50c blue	1.60 1.75
48	A2	75c brown	6.00 2.75
49	A2	1p black brn	9.00 4.75
50	A2	2p orange red	12.00 8.00
51	A2	3p dk brown	12.00 9.00
52	A2	4p bronze grn	18.00 8.50
53	A2	5p claret	22.00 10.00
54	A2	10p rose	45.00 27.50
		Nos. 39-54 (16)	136.80 83.50
		Set, never hinged	350.00

Stamps of 1907 Surcharged

1908-09		Black Surcharge	
55	A2	5c on 3c red org ('09)	2.25 1.25
56	A2	5c on 4c dk grn ('09)	2.25 1.25
57	A2	5c on 10c violet	4.50 5.00
58	A2	25c on 10c violet	30.00 15.00
		Nos. 55-58 (4)	39.00 22.50
		Set, never hinged	70.00

1910		Red Surcharge	
59	A2	5c on 1c dark violet	1.75 .90
60	A2	5c on 2c black	1.75 .90

Nos. 55-60 exist with surcharge inverted (value set, $125 unused or used); with double surcharge, one black, one red (value set, $300 unused or used); with "PARA" omitted (value set, $150.00 unused or used).

The same 5c surcharge was also applied to Nos. 45-54, but these were not issued (value set, $250).

In 1909, stamps of Spanish Guinea replaced those of Elobey, Annobon and Corisco.

Revenue stamps surcharged as above were unauthorized although some were postally used.

For postally valid examples similar to the item shown above see Rio de Oro Nos. 44-45 and Spanish Guinea Nos. 98-101C.

For revenue stamps with the arms at the left surcharged for postal use see Spanish Guinea Nos. 8A-8J.

EPIRUS

i-ˈpī-rəs

LOCATION — A region of southeastern Europe, now divided between Greece and Albania.

During the First Balkan War (1912-13), this territory was occupied by the Greek army, and the local Greek majority wished to be united with Greece. Italy and Austria-Hungary favored its inclusion in the newly created Albania, however, which both powers expected to dominate. Greek forces were withdrawn subsequently in early 1914. The local population resisted inclusion in Albania and established the Autonomous Republic of Northern Epirus on Feb. 28, 1914. Resistance to Albanian control continued until October, when Greece reoccupied the country. Northern Epirus was administered as an integral part of Greece, and it was expected that Greece's annexation of the territory would become official following World War I. Instead, in 1916, Italian pressure and its own military reverses in Anatolia caused Greece to withdraw from Epirus and to formally cede the territory to Albania.

100 Lepta = 1 Drachma

Chimarra Issue

Double-headed Eagle, Skull and Crossbones — A1

Handstamped
1914, Feb. 10   Unwmk.   Imperf.
Control Mark in Blue
Without Gum

1	A1	1 l black & blue	475.00 250.00
a.		Tête-bêche pair	3,000.
2	A1	5 l blue & red	475.00 250.00
3	A1	10 l red & blk	475.00 250.00
4	A1	25 l blue & red	475.00 250.00
		Nos. 1-4 (4)	1,900. 1,000.

All values exist without control mark. This mark is a solid blue oval, about 12x8mm, containing the colorless Greek letters "SP," the first two letters of Spiromilios, the Chimarra commander.

All four exist with denomination inverted and the 1 l, 5 l and 10 l with denomination double.

The values above are for the first printing on somewhat transparent shiny, white, thin, wove paper, which is sometimes known as "rice paper."

A second printing was made from original handstamps, on similar thin wove paper, but not transluscent, known as "Spetsiotis Reprints." Value, unused or canceled to order, each $55. Later printings were made from original handstamps on other papers, generally thicker and whiter, sometimes surfaced. Value, unused or canceled to order, each $45.

Values above are for genuine stamps expertized by knowledgeable authorities. Most of the stamps offered as Nos. 1-4 in the marketplace are forgeries. Most resemble the stamps from the second reprinting, but the designs differ in details of the lettering, monogram and skull. Such forgeries have only nominal commercial value.

Some experts question the official character of this issue.

Argyrokastro Issues
Stamps of Turkey surcharged "AUTONOMOUS EPIRUS" and new denominations in several formats in Greek currency.

On Turkish stamps of 1908

No. 4A

No. 4B

1914, Mar. 2

4A	A19	1d on 2½pi (#137)	11.00 12.50
4B	A19	2d on 2½pi (#137)	11.00 12.50

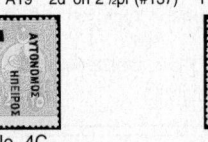
No. 4C   No. 4D

4C	A19	5d on 25pi (#140)	80.00 92.50
4D	A19	5d on 50pi (#141)	127.50 140.00

On Turkish stamps of 1909-10

4E	A21	5 l on 5pa (#151)	80.00 —

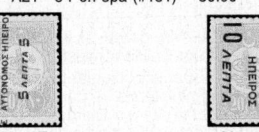
No. 4F   No. 4G

4F	A21	5 l on 10pa (#152)	3.50 4.00
4G	A21	10 l (oval "O") on 20pa (#153)	2.50 2.75
a.		Double surcharge	80.00

No. 4H   No. 4I

4H	A21	10 l (round "O") on 20pa (#153)	2.50 2.75
a.		Double surcharge	80.00
4I	A21	20 l on 1pi (#154)	2.50 2.75
a.		Double surcharge	80.00

No. 4J   No. 4K

4J	A21	25 l on 1pi (#154)	2.50 2.75
a.		Double surcharge	80.00
4K	A21	40 l on 2pi (#155)	3.50 3.75

No. 4L   No. 4M

4L	A21	80 l on 2pi (#155)	3.50 3.75
4M	A21	1d on 5pi (#157)	13.00 14.00

No. 4N   No. 4O

4N	A21	2d on 5pi (#157)	13.00 14.00
4O	A21	5d on 10pi (#158)	80.00 92.50
a.		Double surcharge	
4P	A21	5d on 10pa (#152)	135.00 170.00
4Q	A21	5d on 20pa (#153)	135.00 170.00
4R	A21	5d on 1pi (#154)	135.00 170.00
4RR	A21	5d on 2½pi (#156)	135.00 170.00
4S	A21	5d on 50pi (#160)	135.00 170.00

On Turkish stamps of 1909-11 (with "Béhié")

4T	A21	5 l on 10pa (#161)	80.00
4U	A21	10 l (oval "O") on 20pa (#162)	80.00
4V	A21	10 l (round "O") on 20pa (#162)	80.00
4W	A21	20 l on 1pi (#163)	80.00
4X	A21	25 l on 1pi (#163)	80.00
4Y	A21	40 l on 2pi (#164)	80.00
4Z	A21	80 l on 2pi (#164)	80.00
4AA	A21	5d on 10pa (#161)	135.00
4BB	A21	5d on 20pa (#162)	135.00
4CC	A21	5d on 1pi (#163)	135.00
4CA	A21	5d on 2pi (#164)	135.00

On Turkish Printed Matter stamps of 1910-11

No. 4DD

No. 4EE

4DD	A21	30 l on 2pa on 5pa (#P67)	87.50
4EE	A21	50 l on 2pa on 5pa (#P67)	87.50

No. 4FF

4FF	A21	30 l on 2pa (#P68)	2.50 2.75
4GG	A21	50 l on 2pa (#P68)	2.50 2.75

Provisional Government Issues

Infantryman with Rifle
A2   A3

Serrate Roulette 13½

1914, Mar.				**Litho.**
5	A2	1 l orange	.50	1.00
a.		Imperf., pair	60.00	
6	A2	5 l green	.50	1.00
a.		Imperf., pair	60.00	
7	A3	10 l carmine	.50	1.00
8	A3	25 l deep blue	.50	1.00
9	A2	50 l brown	1.50	1.50
10	A2	1d violet	2.25	2.50
11	A2	2d blue	14.00	14.00
12	A2	5d gray green	18.00	19.00
		Nos. 5-12 (8)	37.75	41.00

Issue dates: 10 l, 25 l, Mar. 5; balance of set, Mar. 26.

Flag of Epirus — A5

1914, Aug. 28

15	A5	1 l brown & blue	.35 .40
16	A5	5 l green & blue	.35 .40
17	A5	10 l rose red & blue	.40 .65
18	A5	25 l dk blue & blue	1.00 1.10
19	A5	1 l violet & blue	1.00 1.10
20	A5	1d carmine & blue	5.75 6.50
21	A5	2d orange & blue	1.50 2.25
b.		Double impression, one inverted	1,000.
22	A5	5d dk green & blue	9.50 11.00
a.		Double impression	1,000.
		Nos. 15-22 (8)	19.85 23.40

Nos. 16 and 21 exist with the blue color inverted.

Koritsa Issue

A7

1914, Sept. 25

26	A7	25 l dk blue & blue	6.00 5.25
27	A7	50 l violet & blue	12.00 13.50

Nos. 26 and 27 were issued at Koritsa (Korce) to commemorate that city's occupation by Epirot forces.

Chimarra Issues

King Constantine I — A8

1914, Oct.

28	A8	1 l yellow green	135.00 77.50
29	A8	2 l red	120.00 42.50
30	A8	5 l dark blue	120.00 77.50

31	A8	10 l orange brown	80.00 30.00
32	A8	20 l carmine	87.50 62.50
33	A8	25 l gray blue	115.00 77.50
33A	A8	50 l yellow green	170.00 90.00
33B	A8	1d carmine	170.00 90.00
33C	A8	2d pale yellow green	255.00 125.00
33D	A8	5d orange brown	425.00 290.00
		Nos. 28-33D (10)	1,678. 962.50

Nos. 28-33D were printed by Papachrysanthou, Athens. The papermaker's watermark "PARCHIMINE JOHANNOT" appears on some stamps in the set.

1911-23 Issues of Greece Overprinted

1914, Aug. 24			**Perf. Perf. 11½**
34	A24	1 l green	55.00 62.50
35	A25	2 l carmine	45.00 52.50
36	A24	3 l vermilion	45.00 52.50
37	A26	5 l green	45.00 52.50
38	A24	10 l carmine	60.00 65.00
39	A25	20 l slate	80.00 87.50
40	A25	25 l blue	175.00 185.00
41	A26	50 l violet brn	220.00 225.00
		Nos. 34-41 (8)	725.00 782.50

The 2 l and 3 l are engraved stamps of the 1911-21 issue; the others are lithographed stamps of the 1912-23 issue.

Overprint reads: "Greek Chimarra 1914."

Stamps of this issue are with or without a black monogram (S.S., for S. Spiromilios) in manuscript. Counterfeits are plentiful.

Moschopolis Issue

Arms
A9

Ancient Epirot Coins/Medals
A10

1914, Sept.		**Engr.**	**Perf. 14½**
42	A9	1 l yellow brown	.75 3.50
43	A9	2 l black	.75 3.50
44	A9	3 l yellow	.75 3.50
45	A9	5 l green	.75 3.50
46	A9	10 l red	.75 3.50
47	A9	25 l deep blue	.75 3.50
48	A9	30 l violet	.75 3.50
49	A9	40 l olive gray	.75 3.50
50	A9	50 l violet black	.75 3.50
51	A10	1d yellow brown & olive	5.00 11.50
52	A10	2d carmine & gray	6.00 11.50
53	A10	3d gray green & red brown	5.00 11.50
54	A10	5d olive & yellow brown	5.00 11.50
55	A10	10d orange & blue	5.00 14.50
56	A10	25d violet & black	5.00 20.00
		Nos. 42-56 (15)	37.75 112.00

Nos. 42-56 were privately printed in early 1914. In June 1914, the Epirots occupied Moschopolis (Voskopoj), and these stamps were authorized for use by the local military commander in Sept. After the occupation of Moschopolis by Greek forces in Nov., remaining stocks of this issue were sent to Athens, where they were destroyed in 1931.

All values exist imperf., and all but the 5 l and 10 l stamps exist in different colors. For details, see the *Scott Classic Specialized Catalogue of Stamps and Covers.*

The 1d exists with center omitted. Value $100. The 1d, 2d, 10d and 25d exist with center inverted. Values, each $65.

Stamps of the following designs were locals, privately produced. Issued primarily for propaganda and for philatelic purposes, their postal use is in dispute. The 1917 and 1920 designs are fantasy items, created long after Epirus was annexed by Albania.

From 1914: 1st design, 3 varieties. 2nd design, 6 varieties. 3rd design, 7 varieties.

From 1917: 4th design, 8 varieties, + 1 surcharged; perforated and imperforate.

From 1920: 5th design, 4 varieties.

OCCUPATION STAMPS

Issued under Greek Occupation

Greek Occupation
Stamps of 1913
Overprinted
Horizontally

Serrate Roulette 13½

1914-15		**Black Overprint**	**Unwmk.**	
N1	O1	1 l brown	.90	.90
b.		Inverted overprint	25.00	25.00
c.		Double overprint	25.00	25.00
d.		Double overprint, one inverted	25.00	25.00
N2	O2	2 l red	.90	.90
b.		2 l rose	1.35	1.35
c.		As #N2, inverted overprint	25.00	25.00
d.		As "b", inverted overprint	32.50	32.50
e.		As #N2, double overprint	26.00	32.50
f.		As "b", double overprint	32.50	32.50
g.		As #N2, double overprint, one inverted	25.00	25.00
N4	O2	3 l orange	.90	.90
b.		Inverted overprint	20.00	17.50
c.		Double overprint	20.00	17.50
d.		Double overprint, one inverted	26.00	26.00
N5	O1	5 l green	2.50	2.50
b.		Inverted overprint	37.50	37.50
N6	O1	10 l rose red	3.00	3.00
a.		Double overprint	52.50	52.50
b.		Double overprint	52.50	52.50
N7	O1	20 l violet	7.00	7.00
a.		Inverted overprint	52.50	52.50
b.		Double overprint	87.50	67.50
N8	O2	25 l pale blue	3.00	3.25
N9	O1	30 l gray green	14.50	15.00
N10	O2	40 l indigo	19.50	21.00
N11	O1	50 l dark blue	22.00	24.00
N12	O2	1d violet brown	140.00	150.00
a.		Inverted overprint	325.00	225.00
b.		Double overprint	400.00	300.00
		Nos. N1-N12 (11)	214.20	228.45

Red Overprint

N1a	O1	1 l brown	5.75
N2a	O2	2 l red	5.75
N4a	O2	3 l orange	5.75
N5a	O1	5 l green	5.75

Nos. N1a-N5a were not issued. Exist canceled.

Regular Issues of Greece, 1911-23, Ovptd. Reading Up

On Issue of 1911-21

1916			**Engr.**	
N17	A24	3 l vermilion	11.50	11.50
a.		Overprint reading down	15.00	
N18	A26	30 l carmine rose	52.50	40.00
a.		Overprint reading down	225.00	
N18B	A25	40 l dark blue	—	—
N19	A27	1d ultra	85.00	85.00
N20	A27	2d vermilion	95.00	95.00
N21	A27	3d carmine rose	130.00	130.00
N22	A27	5d ultra	—	—
a.		Double overprint	1,300.	—
b.		Overprint reading down	725.00	
		Nos. N17-N22 (6)	374.00	361.50

On Issue of 1912-23

1916			**Litho.**	
N23	A24	1 l green	2.75	2.75
b.		Overprint reading down	10.00	
N24	A25	2 l carmine	2.75	2.75
a.		Double overprint	13.00	
b.		Overprint reading down	10.00	
N25	A24	3 l vermilion	2.75	2.75
a.		Double overprint	13.00	
b.		Overprint reading down	15.00	
N26	A26	5 l green	2.75	2.75
a.		Double overprint	15.00	
b.		Overprint reading down	15.00	
N27	A24	10 l carmine	2.75	2.75
a.		Double overprint	15.00	
b.		Overprint reading down	15.00	
N28	A25	20 l slate	2.75	2.75
a.		Double overprint	17.50	
N29	A25	25 l blue	3.75	3.75
a.		Double overprint	30.00	
N30	A26	30 l rose	22.00	22.00
a.		Overprint reading down	250.00	
N31	A25	40 l indigo	16.50	16.50
a.		Overprint reading down	475.00	
N32	A26	50 l violet brown	26.50	26.50
		Nos. N23-N32 (10)	85.25	85.25

In each sheet, there are two varieties in the overprint. For listings, see the *Scott Classic Catalogue*.
Counterfeits exist of Nos. N1-N32.
Postage stamps issued in 1940-41, during Greek occupation, are listed under Greece.

EQUATORIAL GUINEA

ē-kwə-'tō-ē-əl 'gi-nē

LOCATION — Gulf of Guinea, West Africa
GOVT. — Republic
AREA — 10,832 sq. mi.
POP. — 465,746 (1999 est.)
CAPITAL — Malabo

The Spanish provinces Fernando Po and Rio Muni united and became independent as the Republic of Equatorial Guinea, on Oct. 12, 1968.

100 Centimos = 1 Peseta
100 centimos = 1 ekuele, bipkwele is plural (1973)
100 centimes = 1 CFA franc (1985)

> **Catalogue values for all unused stamps in this country are for Never Hinged items.**

Clasped Hands and Laurel — A1

Unwmk.

1968, Oct. 12		**Photo.**	**Perf. 13**	
1	A1	1p dp bl, gold & sep	.35	.35
2	A1	1.50p dk grn, gold & brn	.35	.35
3	A1	6p cop red, gold & brn	.35	.35
		Nos. 1-3 (3)	1.05	1.05

Attainment of independence, Oct. 12, 1968.

Pres. Francisco Macias Nguema — A2

1970, Jan. 27			**Perf. 13x12½**	
4	A2	50c dl org, brn & crim	.25	.25
5	A2	1p pink, grn & lil	.25	.25
6	A2	1.50p pale ol, brn & bl grn	.25	.25
7	A2	2p buff, grn & ol	.25	.25
8	A2	2.50p pale grn, dk grn & dk bl	.30	.25
9	A2	10p bis, Prus bl & vio brn	1.00	.25
10	A2	25p gray, blk & brn	2.10	.25
		Nos. 4-10 (7)	4.40	1.75

Pres. Macias Nguema and Cock — A3

1971, Apr.		**Photo.**	**Perf. 13**	
11	A3	3p lt bl & multi	.25	.25
12	A3	5p buff & multi	.30	.25
13	A3	10p pale lilac & multi	.75	.25
14	A3	25p pale grn & multi	1.50	.35
		Nos. 11-14 (4)	2.80	1.10

2nd anniv. of independence, Oct. 12, 1970.

Torch, Bow and Arrows A4

1972		**Photo.**	**Perf. 11½**	
15	A4	50p ocher & multi	1.50	.55

"3rd Triumphal Year."

> **Upon achieving independence from Spain in 1968, Francisco Macias Nguema was elected the first president of Equatorial Guinea. By May 1971, Nguema controlled a government that essentially performed no functions except internal security. From 1972 to 1979, the country's main post office was padlocked and completely inoperative. Nonetheless, European agents continued to produce postage stamps for Equatorial Guinea that were promoted by so-called press releases from Madrid, Spain.**
>
> **With the exception of Nos. 16-25, the editors question whether any of the stamps described below could have reached Equatorial Guinea or been placed on sale in that country. As such, they do not meet the criteria for listing in the Scott catalogue. See the Catalogue Listing Policy section in the catalogue introduction for additional details.**

Apollo 15, set of seven, 1p, 3p, 5p, 8p, 10p, airmail 15p, 25p, plus two airmail semi-postal gold foil perf. 200p+25p, imperf. 250p+50p, and two souv. sheets, perf. 25p+200p, imperf. 50p+250p, issued Jan. 28. Nos. 7201-7211.

1972 Winter Olympics, Sapporo, set of seven, 1p, 2p, 3p, 5p, 8p, airmail 15p, 50p, plus two airmail semi-postal gold foil perf., imperf., 200p+25p, 250p+50p, and two souv. sheets, perf. 200p+25p, imperf. 250p+50p, issued Feb. 3, 1972. Nos. 7212-7222.

Christmas, paintings, set of seven, 1p, 3p, 5p, 8p, 10p, airmail 15p, 25p, plus two airmail semi-postal gold foil perf. 200p+25p, imperf. 250p+50p, and two souv. sheets, perf. 25p+200p, imperf. 50p+250p (Virgin and Child by da Vinci, Murillo, Raphael, Mabuse, van der Weyden, Durer), issued Feb. 20. Nos. 7223-7233.

Easter, set of seven, 1p, 3p, 5p, 8p, 10p, airmail 15p, 25p, plus two airmail semi-postal gold foil perf., imperf., 200p+25p, 250p+50p (designs by Velazquez and El Greco), two souv. sheets, perf. (25p, 200p), and imperf. 250p+50p, issued Apr. 28. Nos. 7234-7244.

1972 Summer Olympics, Munich, set of seven, 1p, 2p, 3p, 5p, 8p, airmail 15p, 50p, plus two airmail semi-postal souv. sheets, perf. 200p+25p, imperf. 250p+50p, and presentation folder with two gold foil, perf. 200p+25p, imperf. 250p+50p, issued May 5, 1972. Nos. 7245-7255.

Gold Medal Winners, Sapporo, set of seven, 1p, 2p, 3p, 5p, 8p, airmail 15p, 50p, plus 12 airmail semi-postal gold foil perf. 200p+25p (6), imperf. 250p+50p (6), imperf. souv. sheet 250p+50p, and perf. souv. sheet of two (25p, 200p), issued May 25. Nos. 7256-7276.

Black Gold Medal Winners, Munich, set of seven, 1p, 2p, 3p, 5p, 8p, airmail 15p, 50p, plus 18 gold foil airmail semi-postal perf. 200p+25p (9), imperf. 250p+50p (9), and two souv. sheets, perf. 200p+25p, imperf. 250p+50p, issued June 26. Nos. 7277-72103.

Olympic Games, Regatta in Kiel and Oberschleissheim, set of seven, 1p, 2p, 3p, 5p, 8p, airmail 15p, 50p, plus four airmail semi-postal gold foil, perf. 200p+25p (2), imperf. 250p+50p (2), and two souv. sheets, perf. 200p+25p, imperf. 250p+50p, issued July 25. Nos. 72104-72116.

1972 Summer Olympics, Munich, set of seven, 1p, 2p, 3p, 5p, 8p, airmail 15p, 50p, plus two airmail semi-postal souv. sheets, perf. 200p+25p, imperf. 250p+50p, issued Aug. 10, 1972; and 20 gold foil, perf. 200p+25p (10), imperf. 250+50p (10), issued Aug. 17. Nos. 72117-72145.

Olympic Equestrian Events, set of seven, 1p, 2p, 3p, 5p, 8p, airmail 15p, 50p, plus two airmail semi-postal souv. sheets, perf. 200p+25p, imperf. 250p+50p, two gold foil, perf. 200p+25p, imperf. 250p+50p, four gold foil souv. sheets of two, 200p+25p (2 perf., 2 imperf.), and 16 souv. sheets, perf. 200p+25p (8), imperf. 250p+50p (8), issued Aug. 24. Nos. 72146-72176.

Japanese Railroad Cent. (locomotives), set of seven, 1p, 3p, 5p, 8p, 10p, airmail 15p, 25p, plus 2 airmail semi-postal souv. sheets, perf. 200p+25p, imperf. 250p+50p, 11 gold foil souv. sheets of 1, perf. 200p+25p (9), imperf. 200p+25p (2), and 2 souv. sheets of 2, perf., imperf., 200p+25p, issued Sept. 21. Nos. 72177-72198.

Gold Medal Winners, Munich, set of seven, 1p, 2p, 3p, 5p, 8p, airmail 15p, 50p, plus two airmail semi-postal souv. sheets, perf. 200p+25p, imperf. 250p+50p, and four gold foil souv. sheets, perf. 200p+25p (2), imperf. 250p+50p (2), issued Oct. 30. Nos. 72199-72211.

Christmas and 500th Birth Anniv. of Lucas Cranach, Madonnas and Christmas seals, set of seven, 1p, 3p, 5p, 8p, 10p, airmail 15p, 25p (Giotto, Schongauer, Fouquet, de Morales, Fini, David, Sassetta), plus two airmail semi-postal souv. sheets, perf. 200p+25p, imperf. 250p+50p, 12 gold foil souv. sheets, perf. 200p+25p (6), imperf. 250p+50p (6), two souv. sheets of two, perf., imperf., 200p+25p, and ovptd. 200p+25p stamp, issued Nov. 22. Nos. 72212-72234.

American and Russian Astronaut Memorial, set of seven, 1p, 3p, 5p, 8p, 10p, airmail 15p, 25p, plus two airmail semi-postal souv. sheets, perf. 200p+25p, imperf. 250p+50p, and four gold foil ovptd. "Apollo 16 and 17" perf. 200p+25p (2), imperf. 250p+50p (2), issued Dec. 14. Nos. 72235-72247.

United Natl. Workers' Party Emblem — A5

1973		Litho.	Perf. 13½x13	
16	A5	1p multi	.25	.25
17	A5	1.50p multi	.25	.25
18	A5	2p multi	.25	.25
19	A5	4p multi	.30	.25
20	A5	5p multi	.40	.25
		Nos. 16-20 (5)	1.45	1.25

Natl. Independence, 4th Anniv. — A6

Pres. Macias Nguema and: 1.50p, Agriculture. 2p, 4p, Education. 3p, 5p, Natl. defense.

1973			Perf. 13½	
21	A6	1.50p multi	.25	.25
22	A6	2p multi	.25	.25
23	A6	3p multi	.35	.25
24	A6	4p multi	.40	.25
25	A6	5p multi	.60	.35
		Nos. 21-25 (5)	1.85	1.35

1973
Transatlantic Yacht Race, set of seven, 1p, 2p, 3p, 5p, 8p, airmail 15p, 50p, and two airmail semi-postal souv. sheets, perf. 200p+25p, imperf. 250p+50p, issued Jan. 22. Nos. 7301-7309.

Renoir paintings, set of seven, 1p, 2p, 3p, 5p, 8p, airmail 15p, 50p, plus two airmail semi-postal gold foil, perf. 200p+25p, imperf. 250p+50p, and two souv. sheets, perf. 200p+25p, imperf. 250p+50p, issued Feb. 22. Nos. 7310-7320.

Conquest of Venus (spacecraft), set of seven, 1p, 3p, 5p, 8p, 10p, airmail 5p, 25p, and two airmail semi-postal souv. sheets, perf. 200p+25p, imperf. 250p+50p, issued Mar. 22. Nos. 7321-7329.

Apollo 11-17 Flights, gold foil airmail semi-postal souv. sheets, perf. 200p+25p (7), 250p+50p (7), and four souv. sheets of two, perf. 200p+25p (2), imperf. 250p+50p (2), issued Mar. 22. Nos. 7330-7347.

Easter, paintings, set of seven, 1p, 3p, 5p, 8p, 10p, airmail 15p, 25p (Verrocchio, Perugino, Tintoretto, Witz, Pontormo), plus two airmail semi-postal souv. sheets, perf. 200p+25p, imperf. 250p+50p, and four gold foil issue of 1972 souv. sheets ovptd., perf. 200p+25p (2), imperf. 250p+50p (2), issued Apr. 25. Nos. 7348-7360.

Copernicus, 500th birth anniv. (US and USSR space explorations), four gold foil airmail semi-postal souv. sheets, perf. 200p+25p (2), imperf. 250p+50p (2), issued May 15. Nos. 7361-7364.

Tour de France bicycle race, set of seven, 1p, 2p, 3p, 5p, 8p, airmail 15p, 50p, and two airmail semi-postal souv. sheets, perf. 200p+25p, imperf. 250p+50p, issued May 22. Nos. 7365-7373.

Paintings, set of seven, 1p, 2p, 3p, 5p, 8p, airmail 15p, 50p, and two airmail semi-postal souv. sheets, 200p+25p, imperf. 250p+50p, issued June 29. Nos. 7374-7382.

1974 World Cup Soccer Championships, Munich, set of nine, 5c, 10c, 15c, 20c, 25c, 55c, 60c, airmail 5p, 70p, and two airmail souv. sheets, perf. 130p, imperf. 200p, issued Aug. 30. Nos. 7383-7393.

Rubens paintings, set of seven, 1p, 2p, 3p, 5p, 8p, airmail 15p, 50p, and two airmail semi-postal souv. sheets, perf. (25p, 200p), imperf. (50p, 250p), issued Sept. 23. Nos. 7394-73102.

1974 World Cup Soccer Championships, Munich, four gold foil airmail souv. sheets, perf. 130e (2), imperf. 200e (2), and two souv. sheets of two, perf. 130e, imperf. 200e, issued Oct. 24. Nos. 73103-73108.

Christmas, paintings, set of seven, 1p, 3p, 5p, 8p, 10p, airmail 15p, 25p, and two airmail semi-postal souv. sheets, perf. 200p+25p, imperf. 250p+50p (Nativity, by van der Weyden, Bosco, de Carvajal, Mabuse, Lucas Jordan, P. Goecke, Maino, Fabriano, Lochner), issued Oct. 30. Nos. 73109-73117.

Apollo Program and J.F. Kennedy, two gold foil airmail semi-postals, perf. 200p+25p, imperf. 250p+50p, and two souv. sheets, perf. 200p+25p, imperf. 250p+50p, issued Nov. 10. Nos. 73118-73121.

World Cup Soccer (famous players), set of nine, 30c, 35c, 40c, 45c, 50c, 65c, 70c, airmail 8p, 60p, and two airmail souv. sheets, perf. 130p, imperf. 200p, issued Nov. 20. Nos. 73122-73132.

Princess Anne's Wedding, six gold foil airmail souv. sheets, perf., imperf., two sheets of one, each 250e, one sheet of two 250e, issued Dec. 17. Nos. 73133-73141.

Pablo Picasso Memorial (Blue Period paintings), set of seven, 30c, 35c, 40c, 45c, 50c, airmail 8e, 60e, and two airmail souv. sheets, perf. 130e, imperf. 200e, issued Dec. 20. Nos. 73142-73150.

1974
Copernicus, 500th birth anniv., set of seven, 5c, 10c, 15c, 20c, 4e, airmail 10e, 70e, two airmail souv. sheets, perf. 130e, imperf. 200e, issued Feb. 8, 1974; eight gold foil airmail souv. sheets, perf. 130e (3), 250e, imperf. 200e (3), 300e, and four souv. sheets of two, perf. 250e (2), imperf. 250e (2), issued Apr. 10. Nos. 7401-7421.

World Cup Soccer Championships (final games), set of nine, 75c, 80c, 85c, 90c, 95c, 1e, 1.25e, airmail 10e, 50e, and two airmail souv. sheets, perf. 130e, imperf. 200e, issued Feb. 28. Nos. 7422-7432.

Easter, paintings, set of seven, 1p, 3p, 5p, 8p, 10p, airmail 15p, 25p (Fra Angelico, Castagno, Allori, Multscher, della Francesca, Pleydenwurff, Correggio), and two airmail semi-postal souv. sheets, perf. 200p+25p, imperf. 250p+50p, issued Mar. 27. Nos. 7433-7441.

Holy Year 1975 (famous churches), set of seven, 5c, 10c, 15c, 20c, 3.50e, airmail 10e, 70e, and two airmail souv. sheets, perf. 130e, imperf. 200e, issued Apr. 11. Nos. 7442-7450.

World Cup Soccer (contemporary players), set of nine, 1.50, 1.75, 2, 2.25, 2.50, 3, 3.50e, airmail 10e, 60e, and 2 airmail souv. sheets of 2, (2x65e), imperf. (2x100e), issued Apr. 30. Nos. 7451-7461.

UPU Cent. (transportation from messenger to rocket), set of seven, 60c, 70c, 80c, 1e, 1.50e, airmail 30e, 50e, and two airmail souv. sheets, perf. 225e, imperf. (150e, 150e), issued May 30; three airmail deluxe souv. sheets, 130e, and 2x130e, issued June 8. Nos. 7462-7472A.

Picasso Memorial (Pink Period paintings), set of seven, 55c, 60c, 65c, 70c, 75c, airmail 10e, 50e, and two airmail souv. sheets, perf. 130e, imperf. 200e, issued June 28. Nos. 7473-7481.

World Cup Soccer Championships, gold foil airmail souv. sheets, four sheets of one, 130e (2), 250e (2), two sheets of two (2x130e; 2x250e), issued July 8. Nos. 7482-7487.

Aleksander Solzhenitsyn, two gold foil airmail souv. sheets, perf. 250e, imperf. 300e, issued July 25. Nos. 7488-7489.

Opening of American West, set of seven, 30c, 35c, 40c, 45c, 50c, airmail 8p, 60p, and two souv. sheets, perf. 130p, imperf. 200p, issued July 30. Nos. 7490-7498.

Flowers, set of 14, 5c, 10c, 15c, 20c, 25c, 1p, 3p, 5p, 8p, 10p, airmail 5p, 15p, 25p, 70p, and 4 airmail souv. sheets, perf. 130p, 25p+200p, imperf. 200p, 50p+250p, issued Aug. 20. Nos. 7499-74116.

Christmas, set of seven, 60c, 70c, 80c, 1e, 1.50e, airmail 30e, 50e, and two souv. sheets, perf. 225e, imperf. 300e, issued Sept. 16. Nos. 74117-74125.

Barcelona Soccer Team, 75th anniv., set of seven, 1e, 3e, 5e, 8e, 10e, airmail 15e, 60e, miniature sheet of seven plus label, two airmail souv. sheets, perf. 200e, imperf. 300e, and two gold foil airmail souv. sheets, perf., imperf., 200e each, issued Sept. 25. Nos. 74126-74137.

UPU Cent. and ESPANA 75, set of seven, 1.25e, 1.50e, 1.75e, 2e, 2.25e, airmail 35e, 60e, and 2 airmail souv. sheets, perf. 225e, imperf. 300e, issued Oct. 9; 6 gold foil sheets, perf. 250e, 250e, 2x250e, imperf. 300e, 300e, 2x300e, issued Oct. 14. Nos. 74138-74152.

Nature Protection
Australian Animals, set of seven, 80c, 85c, 90c, 95c, 1e, airmail 15e, 40e, and two airmail souv. sheets, perf. 130e, imperf. 200e, issued Oct. 25. Nos. 74153-74161.

African Animals, set of seven, 55c, 60c, 65c, 70c, 75c, airmail 10e, 70e, and two airmail souv. sheets, perf. 130e, imperf. 200e, issued Nov. 6. Nos. 74162-74170.

Australian and South American Birds, set of 14, 1.25p, 1.50p, 1.75p, 2p, 2.25p, 2.50p, 2.75p, 3p, 3.50p, 4p, airmail 20p, 25p, 30p, 35p, and four souv. sheets, perf. 130p (2), imperf. 200p (2), issued Nov. 26. Nos. 74171-74188.

Endangered Species, set of 15, 10c, 15c, 20c, 25c, 30c, 35c, 40c, 45c, 50c, 55c, 60c, 1e, 2e, airmail 10e, 70e, se-tenant in sheet of 15, issued Dec. 17. Nos. 74189-74203.

Monkeys, various species, set of 16, 5c, 10c, 15c, 20c, 25c, 30c, 35c, 40c, 45c, 50c, 55c, 60c, 1e, 2e, airmail 10e, 70e, se-tenant in sheet of 16, issued Dec. 27. Nos. 74204-74219.

Cats, various species, set of 16, 5c, 10c, 15c, 20c, 25c, 30c, 35c, 40c, 45c, 50c, 55c, 60c, 1e, 2e, airmail 10e, 70e, se-tenant in sheet of 16, issued Dec. 27. Nos. 74220-74235.

Fish, various species, set of 16, 5c, 10c, 15c, 20c, 25c, 30c, 35c, 40c, 45c, 50c, 55c, 60c, 1e, 2e, airmail 10e, 70e, se-tenant in sheet of 16, issued Dec. 27. Nos. 74236-74251.

Butterflies, various species, set of 16, 5c, 10c, 15c, 20c, 25c, 30c, 35c, 40c, 45c, 50c, 55c, 60c, 1e, 2e, airmail 10e, 70e, se-tenant in sheet of 16, issued Dec. 27. Nos. 74252-74267.

1975
Picasso Memorial (paintings from last period), set of seven, 5c, 10c, 15c, 20c, 25c, airmail 5e, 70e, and two souv. sheets, perf. 130e, imperf. 200e, issued Jan. 27. Nos. 7501-7509.

ARPHILA 75 Phil. Exhib., Paris, 8 gold foil airmail souv. sheets: perf. 3 sheets of 1 250e, 1 sheet of 2 250e,

imperf. 3 sheets of 1 300e, 1 sheet of 2 300e, issued Jan. 27. Nos. 7510-7517.

Easter and Holy Year 1975, set of seven, 60c, 70c, 80c, 1e, 1.50e, airmail 30e, 50e, and two airmail souv. sheets, perf. 225e, imperf. 300e, issued Feb. 15. Nos. 7518-7526.

1976 Winter Olympics, Innsbruck, set of 11, 5c, 10c, 15c, 20c, 25c, 30c, 35c, 40c, 45c, 25e, 70e, two airmail souv. sheets, perf. 130e, imperf. 200e, and two gold foil airmail souv. sheets, 1 sheet of 1 250e, 1 sheet of 2 250e, issued Mar. 10. Nos. 7527-7541.

Don Quixote, set of seven, 30c, 35c, 40c, 45c, 50c, airmail 25e, 60e, and two airmail souv. sheets, perf. 130e, imperf. 200e, issued Apr. 4. Nos. 7542-7550.

American Bicent. (1st issue), set of nine, 5c, 20c, 40c, 75c, 2e, 5e, 8e, airmail 25e, 30e, and two airmail souv. sheets, perf. 130e, imperf. 200e, issued Apr. 30. Nos. 7551-7561.

American Bicent. (2nd issue), set of nine, 10c, 30c, 50c, 1e, 3e, 6e, 10e, airmail 12e, 40e, and two airmail souv. sheets, perf. 130e, imperf. 200e, issued Apr. 30. Nos. 7562-7572.

American Bicent. (Presidents), set of 18, 5c, 10c, 20c, 30c, 40c, 50c, 75c, 1e, 2e, 3e, 5e, 6e, 8e, 10e, airmail 12e, 25e, 30e, 40e, four airmail souv. sheets, perf. 225e (2), imperf. 300e (2), and six embossed gold foil airmail souv. sheets, perf. 200e, 200e, 2x200e, imperf. 300e, 300e, 2x300e, issued July 4. Nos. 7573-75100.

Bull Fight, set of seven, 80c, 85c, 90c, 95c, 8e, airmail 35e, 40e, and two airmail souv. sheets, perf. 130e, imperf. 200e, issued May 26. Nos. 75101-75109.

Apollo-Soyuz Space Project, set of 11, 1e, 2e, 3e, 5e, 5.50e, 7e, 7.50e, 9e, 15e, airmail 20e, 30e, and two airmail souv. sheets, perf. 225e, imperf. 300e, issued June 20, 1975; airmail souv. sheet, perf. 250e, issued July 17. Nos. 75110-75123.

Famous Painters, Nudes, set of 16, 5c, 10c, 15c, 20c, 25c, 30c, 35c, 40c, 45c, 50c, 55c, 60c, 1e, 2e, airmail 10e, 70e (Egyptian Greek, Roman, Indian art, Goes, Durer, Liss, Beniort, Renoir, Gauguin, Stenlen, Picasso, Modigliani, Matisse, Padua), se-tenant in sheet of 16, and 20 airmail embossed gold foil souv. sheetlets, perf. 200p+25p (10), imperf. 250p+50p (10), issued Aug. 10. Nos. 75124-75159.

Conquerors of the Sea, set of 14, 30c, 35c, 40c, 45c, 50c, 55c, 60c, 65c, 70c, 75c, airmail 8p, 10p, 50p, 60p, and four airmail souv. sheets, perf. 130p (2), imperf. 200p (2), issued Sept. 5. Nos. 75160-75177.

Christmas and Holy Year, 1975, set of seven, 60c, 70c, 80c, 1e, 1.50e, airmail 30e, 50e (Jordan, Barocci, Vereycke, Rubens, Mengs, Del Castillo, Cavedone), two airmail souv. sheets, perf. 225e, imperf. 300e, plus four embossed gold foil souv. sheets, perf. 200e (2), imperf. 300e (2), and two gold foil miniature sheets of two, perf. 200e+200e, imperf. 300e+300e, issued Oct. Nos. 75178-75192.

President Macias, IWY, set of eight, 1.50e, 3e, 3.50e, 5e, 7e, 10e, airmail 100e, 300e, and two imperf. airmail souv. sheets (world events), 100e (US 2c Yorktown), 300e, issued Dec. 25. Nos. 75193-75202.

1976
Cavalry Uniforms, set of seven, 5c, 10c, 15c, 20c, 25c, airmail 5p, 70p, and two airmail souv. sheets, perf. 130p, imperf. 200p, issued Feb. 2. Nos. 7601-7609.

1976 Winter Olympics, Innsbruck, set of 11, 50c, 55c, 60c, 65c, 70c, 75c, 80c, 85c, 90c, airmail 35e, 60e, and two airmail souv. sheets, perf. 130e, imperf. 200e, issued Feb. Nos. 7610-7622.

1976 Summer Olympics, Montreal, Ancient to Modern Games, set of seven, 50c, 60c, 70c, 80c, 90c, airmail 35e, 60e, and two airmail souv. sheets, perf. 225e, imperf. 300e, issued Feb. Nos. 7623-7631.

1976 Summer Olympics, Montreal, set of seven, 50c, 60c, 70c, 80c, 90c, airmail 30e, 60e, plus two airmail souv. sheets, perf. 225e, imperf. 300e, four embossed gold foil airmail souv. sheets, per. 250e (2), imperf. 300e (2), and two imperf. miniature sheets of two, perf. 2x250e, imperf. 2x300e, issued Mar. 5. Nos. 7632-7646.

El Greco, paintings, set of seven, 1e, 3e, 5e, 8e, 10e, airmail 15e, 25e, and two airmail semi-postal souv. sheets, perf. 200e+25e, imperf. 250e+50e, issued Apr. 5. Nos. 7647-7655.

1976 Summer Olympics, modern games, set of 11, 50c, 55c, 60c, 65c, 70c, 75c, 80c, 85c, 90c, airmail 35e, 60e, plus two airmail souv. sheets, perf. 225e, imperf. 300e, four embossed gold foil airmail souv. sheets, perf. 250e (2), imperf. 300e (2), and two miniature sheets of two, perf. 2x250e, imperf. 2x300e, issued May 7. Nos. 7656-7674.

UN 30th Anniv., airmail souv. sheet, 250e, issued June. No. 7675.

Contemporary Automobiles, set of seven, 1p, 3p, 5p, 8p, 10p, airmail 15p, 25p, and two airmail semi-postal souv. sheets, perf. 200p+25p, imperf. 250p+50p, issued June 10. Nos. 7675-7684.

Nature Protection

European Animals, set of seven, 5c, 10c, 15c, 20c, 25c, airmail 5p, 70p, and two airmail souv. sheets, perf. 130p, imperf. 200p, issued July 1. Nos. 7685-7693.

Asian Animals, set of seven, 30c, 35c, 40c, 45c, 8p, airmail 50c, 60p, and two airmail souv. sheets, perf. 130p, imperf. 200p, issued Sept. 20. Nos. 7694-74102.

Asian Birds, set of seven, 55c, 60c, 65c, 70c, 75c, airmail 10p, 50p, and two airmail souv. sheets, perf. 130p, imperf. 200p, issued Sept. 20. Nos. 76103-76111.

European Birds, set of seven, 5c, 10c, 15c, 20c, 25c, airmail 5p, 70p, and two airmail souv. sheets, perf. 130p, imperf. 200p, issued Sept. 20. Nos. 76112-76120.

North American Birds, set of seven, 80c, 85c, 90c, 95c, 1p, airmail 15p, 40p, and two airmail souv. sheets, perf. 130p, imperf. 200p, issued Sept. 20. Nos. 76121-76129.

Motorcycle Aces, set of 16, two each 1e, 2e, 3e, 4e, 5e, 10e, 30e, 40e, in se-tenant blocks of eight diff. values, issued July 22. Nos. 76130-76145.

1976 Summer Olympics, Montreal, set of five, 10e, 25e se-tenant strip of 3, airmail 200e, and imperf. airmail souv. sheet, 300e, issued Aug. 7. Nos. 76146-76151.

South American Flowers, set of seven, 30c, 35c, 40c, 45c, 50c, airmail 8p, 60p, and two airmail souv. sheets, perf. 130p, imperf. 200p, issued Aug. 16. Nos. 76152-76160.

Oceania, set of seven, 80c, 85c, 90c, 95c, 1p, airmail 15p, 40p, and two airmail souv. sheets, perf. 130p, imperf. 200p, issued 1976. Nos. 76161-76169.

1977

Butterflies, set of seven, 80c, 85c, 90c, 95c, 8e, airmail 35e, 40e, and two airmail souv. sheets, perf. 130e, imperf. 200e, issued Jan. Nos. 7701-7709.

Madrid Real, 75th Anniv., set of nine, 2e, 4e, 5e, 8e, 10e, 15e, airmail 20e, 35e, 150e, issued Jan. Nos. 7710-7718.

Ancient Carriages, set of 16, 5c, 10c, 15c, 20c, 25c, 30c, 35c, 40c, 45c, 50c, 55c, 60c, 1e, 2e, airmail 10e, 70e, issued Feb. Nos. 7719-7734.

Chinese Art, set of seven, 60c, 70c, 80c, 1e, 1.50e, airmail 30e, 50e, and two airmail souv. sheets, perf. 130e, imperf. 200e, issued Feb. Nos. 7735-7743.

African Masks, set of seven, 5c, 10c, 15c, 20c, 25c, airmail 5e, 70e, and two airmail souv. sheets, perf. 130e, imperf. 200e, issued Mar. Nos. 7744-7752.

North American Animals, set of seven, 1.25e, 1.50e, 1.75e, 2e, 2.25e, airmail 20e, 50e, and two airmail souv. sheets, perf. 130e, imperf. 200e, issued 1977. Nos. 7753-7761.

World Cup Soccer Championships, Argentina '78 (famous players), set of eight, 2e, 4e, 5e, 8e, 10e, 15e, airmail 20e, 35e, and two airmail souv. sheets, perf. 150e, imperf. 250e, issued July 25. Nos. 7762-7771.

World Cup Soccer (famous teams), se-tenant set of eight, 2e, 4e, 5e, 8e, 10e, 15e, airmail 20e, 35e, and two gold foil embossed souv. sheets, 500e (AMPHILEX '77, Cutty Sark, Concorde), airmail 500e (World Cup), issued Aug. 25.Nos. 7772-7781.

Napoleon, Life and Battle Scenes, se-tenant sheet of 16, 5c, 10c, 15c, 20c, 25c, 30c, 35c, 40c, 45c, 50c, 55c, 60c, 1e, 2e, airmail 10e, 70e, issued Aug. 20. Nos. 7782-7797.

Napoleon, Military Uniforms, se-tenant sheet of 16, 5c, 10c, 15c, 20c, 25c, 30c, 35c, 40c, 45c, 50c, 55c, 60c, 1e, 2e, airmail 10e, 70e, issued Aug. 20. Nos. 7798-77113.

South American Animals, set of seven, 2.50e, 2.75e, 3e, 3.50e, 4e, airmail 25e, 35e, and two airmail souv. sheets, perf. 130e, imperf. 200e, issued Aug. Nos. 77114-77122.

USSR Space Program, 20th Anniv., set of eight, 2e, 4e, 5e, 8e, 10e, 15e, airmail 20e, 35e, and two airmail souv. sheets, imperf. 150e, perf. 250e, issued Dec. 15. Nos. 77123-77132.

1978

Ancient Sailing Ships, set of 12, 5c, 10c, 15c, 20c, 25c, airmail 5e, 70e, also 5e, 10e, 20e, 25e, 70e, plus four airmail souv. sheets, perf. 150e, 225e, imperf. 250e, 300e, and two embossed gold foil airmail souv. sheets, perf., imperf., 500e, issued Jan. 6. Nos. 7801-7818.

1980 Winter Olympics, Lake Placid, set of five, 5e, 10e, 20e, 25e, airmail 70e, two airmail souv. sheets, perf. 150e, imperf. 250e, and two embossed gold foil airmail souv. sheets, perf., imperf., 500e, issued Jan. 17. Nos. 7819-7827.

1980 Summer Olympics, Moscow, set of eight, 2e, 3e, 5e, 8e, 10e, 15e, airmail 30e, 50e, two airmail souv. sheets, perf. 150e, imperf. 250e, and two embossed gold foil airmail souv. sheets, perf., imperf., 500e, issued Jan. 17. Nos. 7828-7839.

1980 Summer Olympic Water Games, Tallinn, set of five, 5e, 10e, 20e, 25e, airmail 70e, two airmail souv. sheets, perf. 150e, imperf. 250e, and two embossed gold foil airmail souv. sheets, perf., imperf., 500e, issued Jan. 17. Nos. 7840-7848.

Eliz. II Coronation, 25th Anniv., set of eight, 2e, 5e, 8e, 10e, 12e, 15e, airmail 30e, 50e, and two airmail souv. sheets, perf. 150e, imperf. 250e, issued Apr. 25. Nos. 7849-7858.

English Knights of 1200-1350 A.D., set of seven, 5e, 10e, 15e, 20e, 25e, airmail 15e, 70e, and two airmail souv. sheets, perf. 130e, imperf. 200e, issued Apr. 25. Nos. 7859-7867.

Old Locomotives, set of seven, 1e, 2e, 3e, 5e, 10e, airmail 25e, 70e, and two airmail souv. sheets, perf. 150e, imperf. 250e, issued Aug. Nos. 7868-7876.

Prehistoric Animals, set of seven, 30e, 35e, 40e, 45e, 50e, airmail 25e, 60e, and airmail souv. sheets, 130e, 200e, issued Aug. Nos. 7877-7884, 7884A.

Francisco Goya, "Maja Vestida," airmail souv. sheet, 150e, issued Aug. No. 7885.

Peter Paul Rubens — UNICEF, airmail souv. sheet, 250e, issued Aug. No. 7886.

Europa — CEPT — Europhila '78, airmail souv. sheet, 250e, issued Aug. No. 7887.

30th Intl. Stamp Fair, Riccione, airmail souv. sheet, 150e, issued Aug. Nos. 7888.

Eliz. II Coronation, 25th anniv., airmail souv. sheet of three, 150e, issued CEPT, airmail souv. sheet, 250e, issued Aug. Nos. 7890.

World Cup Soccer Championships, Argentina '78 and Spain '82, airmail souv. sheet, 150e, issued Aug. Nos. 7891.

Christmas, Titian painting, "The Virgin," airmail souv. sheet, 150e, issued Aug. Nos. 7892.

Natl. Independence, 5th Anniv. (in 1973) — A7

1979   **Perf. 13x13½**

26	A7	1e	Ekuele coin	1.10 .25

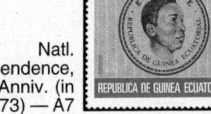

Natl. Independence, 5th Anniv. (in 1973) — A8

1e, Port Bata. 1.50e, State Palace. 2b, Central Bank, Bata. 2.50b, Nguema Biyogo Bridge. 3b, Port, palace, bank, bridge.

1979

27	A8	1e multicolored	.25	.25
28	A8	1.50e multicolored	.25	.25
29	A8	2b multicolored	.30	.30
30	A8	2.50b multicolored	.35	.35
31	A8	3b multicolored	.60	.60
		Nos. 27-31 (5)	1.75	1.75

Pres. Nguema — A9

1979   **Perf. 13½x13**

32	A9	1.50e multi	.50	.35

United Natl. Workers's Party (PUNT), 3rd Congress.

Independence Martyrs — A10

1e, Enrique Nvo. 1.50e, Salvador Ndongo Ekang. 2b, Acacio Mane.

1979

33	A10	1e multicolored	.30	.30
34	A10	1.50e multicolored	.35	.35
35	A10	2b multicolored	.45	.45
		Nos. 33-35 (3)	1.10	1.10

Agricultural Experiment Year — A11

1979   **Perf. 13x13½**

36	A11	1e multi	.65	.25
37	A11	1.50e multi, diff.	.95	.35

Independence Martyrs   Natl. Coat of
A12   Arms
                         A13

5b, Obiang Esono Nguema. 15b, Fernando Nvara Engonga. 25b, Ela Edjodjomo Mangue. 35b, Obiang Nguema Mbasogo, president. 50b, Hipolito Micha Eworo.

1981, Mar.   **Photo.**   **Perf. 13½x12½**

38	A12	5b multicolored	.40	.25
39	A12	15b multicolored	.40	.25
40	A12	25b multicolored	.40	.25
41	A12	35b multicolored	.55	.25
42	A12	50b multicolored	.80	.30
43	A13	100b multicolored	1.60	.45
		Nos. 38-43 (6)	4.15	1.75

Dated 1980.

Christmas 1980 — A14

1981, Mar. 30   **Perf. 13½**

44	A14	8b Cathedral, infant	.30	.25
45	A14	25b Bells, youth	.35	.25

Dated 1980.

Souvenir Sheet

Pres. Obiang Nguema Mbasogo A15

1981, Aug. 30   **Litho.**   **Imperf.**

46	A15	400b multi	5.00	2.25

State Visit of King Juan Carlos of Spain A16

50b, Government reception. 100b, Arrival at airport. 150b, King, Pres. Mbasogo, vert.

Perf. 13x13½, 13½x13

1981, Nov. 30

47	A16	50b multicolored	.90	.25
48	A16	100b multicolored	1.75	.50
49	A16	150b multicolored	2.75	.75
		Nos. 47-49 (3)	5.40	1.50

State Visit of Pope John Paul II A17

100b, Papal and natl. arms. 200b, Pres. Mbasogo greeting Pope. 300b, Pope, vert.

1982, Feb. 18
50	A17	100b multicolored	1.50	.80
51	A17	200b multicolored	3.25	1.60
52	A17	300b multicolored	4.75	2.40
		Nos. 50-52 (3)	9.50	4.80

Christmas
1981 — A18

1982, Feb. 25　　　　　**Photo.**
53	A18	100b Carolers, vert.	1.25	.40
54	A18	150b Magi, African youth	1.90	.70

Dated 1981.

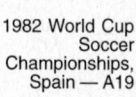

1982 World Cup
Soccer
Championships,
Spain — A19

40b, Emblem. 60b, Naranjito character trademark. 100b, World Cup trophy. 200b, Players, palm tree, emblem.

1982, June 13　　　　　**Perf. 13½**
55	A19	40b multicolored	.45	.25
56	A19	60b multicolored	.70	.35
57	A19	100b multicolored	1.25	.60
58	A19	200b multicolored	2.50	1.10
		Nos. 55-58 (4)	4.90	2.30

Fauna — A20

1983, Feb. 4　　　　　**Litho.**
59	A20	40b Gorilla	.75	.25
60	A20	60b Hippopotamus	1.25	.40
61	A20	80b Atherurus africanus	1.75	.50
62	A20	120b Felis pardus	2.75	.75
		Nos. 59-62 (4)	6.50	1.90

Dated 1982.

Christmas
1982 — A21

1983, Feb. 25　　　　　**Photo.**
63	A21	100b Stars	.95	.35
64	A21	200b King offering frank-incense	2.25	.75

Dated 1982.

World
Communications
Year — A22

Designs: 150b, Postal runner. 200b, Microwave station, drummer.

1983, July 18　　　　　**Litho.**
65	A22	150b multicolored	1.00	.45
66	A22	200b multicolored	2.25	.80

Banana
Trees — A23

1983, Oct. 8
67	A23	300b shown	3.25	1.00
68	A23	400b Forest, vert.	4.50	1.40

Christmas
1983 — A24

Designs: 80b, Folk dancer, musical instruments. 100b, Holy Family.

1984
69	A24	80b multicolored	1.00	.35
70	A24	100b multicolored	1.25	.50

Dated 1983.

Constitution of
State
Powers — A25

Scales of justice, fundamental lawbook and various maps.

1984, Feb. 15
71	A25	50b Annobon and Bioko	.60	.30
72	A25	100b Mainland regions	1.40	.65

Inscription at the UR on No. 71 reads "Region Insular". No. 71 also exists with inscription reading "Regiones Insulares".

Turtle Hunting, Rio
Muni — A26

1984, May 1
73	A26	125b Hunting Whales, horiz.	1.75	.75
74	A26	150b shown	2.00	.85

World Food Day — A27

1984, Sept.
75	A27	60b Papaya	1.25	.50
76	A27	80b Malanga	1.50	.65

Abstract Wood-
Carved Figurines
and Art — A28

Designs: 25b, *Black Gazelle* and *Anxiety.* 30b, *Black Gazelle,* diff., and *Woman.* 60b, *Man and woman,* vert. 75b, *Poster,* vert. 100b, *Mother and Child,* vert. 150b, *Man and Woman,* diff., and *Bust of a Woman.*

1984, Nov. 15
77	A28	25b multi	.25	.25
78	A28	30b multi	.35	.25
79	A28	60b multi	.75	.35
80	A28	75b multi	1.00	.40
81	A28	100b multi	1.50	.50
82	A28	150b multi	2.00	.90
		Nos. 77-82 (6)	5.85	2.65

Christmas — A29

60b, Mother and child, vert. 100b, Musical instruments.

1984, Dec. 24
83	A29	60b multicolored	.75	.25
84	A29	100b multicolored	1.25	.55

Immaculate
Conception
Missions,
Cent. — A30

50fr, Emblem, vert. 60fr, Map, nun and youths, vert. 80fr, First Guinean nuns. 125fr, Missionaries landing at Bata Beach, 1885.

1985, Apr.　　　　　**Perf. 14**
85	A30	50fr multi	.45	.25
86	A30	60fr multi	.60	.25
87	A30	80fr multi	.90	.30
88	A30	125fr multi	1.40	.60
		Nos. 85-88 (4)	3.35	1.40

Jose Mavule
Ndjong, First
Postmaster
A31

1985, July　　　　　**Perf. 13½**
89	A31	50fr Postal emblem, vert.	1.00	.25
90	A31	80fr shown	1.75	.55

Equatorial Guinea Postal Service.

Christmas — A32

Designs: 40fr, Nativity. 70fr, Folk band, dancers, mother and child.

1985, Dec.
91	A32	40fr multicolored	.65	.25
92	A32	70fr multicolored	1.10	.35

Nature
Conservation
A33

15fr, Crab, snail. 35fr, Butterflies, bees, birds. 45fr, Flowering plants. 65fr, Spraying and harvesting cacao.

1985
93	A33	15fr multicolored	.30	.25
94	A33	35fr multicolored	.85	.30
95	A33	45fr multicolored	.85	.30
96	A33	65fr multicolored	1.25	.45
		Nos. 93-96 (4)	3.25	1.30

Folklore — A34

10fr, Ndowe dance, Mekuyo, horiz. 50fr, Fang dance, Mokom. 65fr, Cacha Bubi, Bisila. 80fr, Fang dance, Ndong-Mba.

1986, Apr. 15
97	A34	10fr multicolored	.25	.25
98	A34	50fr multicolored	.60	.25
99	A34	65fr multicolored	.90	.30
100	A34	80fr multicolored	1.00	.40
		Nos. 97-100 (4)	2.75	1.20

A35

1986 World Cup Soccer Championships, Mexico: Various soccer plays.

1986, June 25
101	A35	50fr multi, horiz.	.30	.25
102	A35	100fr multi, horiz.	.80	.30
103	A35	150fr multi	1.25	.45
104	A35	200fr multi	1.60	.60
		Nos. 101-104 (4)	3.95	1.60

Christmas — A36

Designs: 100fr, Musical instruments, horiz. 150fr, Holy Family, lamb.

1986, Dec. 12
105	A36	100fr multicolored	1.10	.35
106	A36	150fr multicolored	1.60	.60

Conf. of the Union of
Central African
States — A37

Designs: 80fr, Flags, map. 100fr, Emblem, map, horiz.

1986, Dec. 29
107	A37	80fr multicolored	.90	.35
108	A37	100fr multicolored	1.25	.40

Campaign
Against
Hunger — A38

1987, June 5
109	A38	60fr Chicken	.65	.25
110	A38	80fr Fish	.95	.35
111	A38	100fr Wheat	1.25	.45
		Nos. 109-111 (3)	2.85	1.05

Intl. Peace
Year — A39

1987, July 15　　**Litho.**　　**Perf. 13½**
112	A39	100fr shown	.85	.40
113	A39	200fr Hands holding dove	1.90	.80

Stamp Day
1987 — A40

1987, Oct. 5　　**Litho.**　　**Perf. 13½**
114	A40	150fr shown	1.25	.50
115	A40	300fr Posting envelope	2.25	.90

Christmas 1987 — A41

Mother and child (wood carvings).

1987, Dec. 22　　**Litho.**　　**Perf. 13½**
116	A41	80fr multi	1.00	.35
117	A41	100fr multi, diff.	1.40	.45

Climbing Palm
Tree — A42

75fr, Woman carrying fish. 150fr, Chopping down trees.

1988, May 4　　**Litho.**　　**Perf. 13½**
118	A42	50fr shown	.45	.25
119	A42	75fr multicolored	.65	.35
120	A42	150fr multicolored	1.40	.65
		Nos. 118-120 (3)	2.50	1.25

Democratic Party — A43

40fr, Crest. 75fr, Torch, motto, horiz. 100fr, Torch, flag, weaving, horiz.

1988, Nov. 16
121	A43	40fr multicolored	.40	.25
122	A43	75fr multicolored	.65	.30
123	A43	100fr multicolored	.95	.40
		Nos. 121-123 (3)	2.00	.95

Cultural Revolution Day — A44

Geometric shapes.

1988, June 4
124	A44	35fr shown	.40	.25
125	A44	50fr Squares, sphere	.60	.25
126	A44	100fr Bird	1.00	.40
		Nos. 124-126 (3)	2.00	.90

Christmas — A45

1988, Dec. 22
127	A45	50fr shown	.55	.25
128	A45	100fr Mother and child	1.20	.40

Natl. Independence, 20th Anniv. — A46

Designs: 10fr, Lumber on truck. 35fr, Folk dancers. 45fr, Officials on dais.

1989, Apr. 14   Litho.   Perf. 14
129	A46	10fr multicolored	.35	.25
130	A46	35fr multicolored	.40	.35
131	A46	45fr multicolored	.55	.40
		Nos. 129-131 (3)	1.30	1.00

Youths Bathing, Ilachi Falls — A47

25fr, Waterfall in the jungle. 60fr, Boy drinking from fruit, boys swimming at Luba Beach.

1989, July 7   Perf. 13½
132	A47	15fr shown	.45	.25
133	A47	25fr multicolored	.50	.25
134	A47	60fr multicolored	.75	.40
		Nos. 132-134 (3)	1.70	.90

1st Congress of the Democratic Party of Equatorial Guinea — A48

1989, Oct. 23   Litho.   Perf. 13½
135	A48	25fr shown	.35	.25
136	A48	35fr Torch, vert.	.60	.25
137	A48	40fr Pres. Nguema, vert.	.70	.25
		Nos. 135-137 (3)	1.65	.75

Christmas — A49

1989, Dec. 18   Litho.   Perf. 13½
138	A49	150fr shown	1.60	.50
139	A49	300fr Nativity, horiz.	2.00	.75

Boy Scouts — A50

Designs: 100fr, Lord Baden-Powell. 250fr, Salute. 350fr, Bugler.

1990, Mar. 23   Litho.   Perf. 13
140	A50	100fr multi	1.50	.50
141	A50	250fr multi	3.50	1.10
142	A50	350fr multi	4.75	1.50
		Nos. 140-142 (3)	9.75	3.10

World Cup Soccer Championships, Italy — A51

Designs: 100fr, Soccer player, map. 250fr, Goalkeeper. 350fr, Trophy.

1990, June 8   Litho.   Perf. 13
143	A51	100fr multicolored	.60	.35
144	A51	250fr multicolored	1.50	.65
145	A51	350fr multicolored	2.00	1.00
		Nos. 143-145 (3)	4.10	2.00

Musical Instruments of the Ndowe People — A52

Instruments of the: 250fr, Fang. 350fr, Bubi.

1990, June 19
146	A52	100fr multicolored	.50	.30
147	A52	250fr multicolored	1.50	.75
148	A52	350fr multicolored	2.00	1.00
		Nos. 146-148 (3)	4.00	2.05

Discovery of America, 500th Anniv. (in 1992) — A53

Designs: 170fr, Arrival in New World. 300fr, Columbus' fleet.

1990, Oct. 10
149	A53	170fr multicolored	2.00	.60
150	A53	300fr multicolored	2.50	1.00

Christmas — A54

1990, Dec. 23   Litho.   Perf. 13½
151	A54	170fr shown	1.00	.45
152	A54	300fr Bubi tribesman	2.00	.90

1992 Summer Olympics, Barcelona — A55

1991, Apr. 22   Litho.   Perf. 13½x14
153	A55	150fr Tennis	1.25	.75
154	A55	250fr Cycling	2.25	1.25

Souvenir Sheet
155	A55	500fr Equestrian	20.00	20.00

La Maja Desnuda by Goya — A56

Designs: 250fr, Eve by Durer, vert. 350fr, The Three Graces by Rubens, vert.

1991, May 6   Litho.   Perf. 14
156	A56	150fr shown	1.50	.50
157	A56	250fr multicolored	2.75	1.00
158	A56	350fr multicolored	3.75	1.25
		Nos. 156-158 (3)	8.00	2.75

Madrillus Sphinx — A57

1991, July 1   Litho.   Perf. 13½x14
159	A57	25fr shown	2.50	1.25
160	A57	25fr Face	2.50	1.25
161	A57	25fr Seated	2.50	1.25
162	A57	25fr Walking, horiz.	2.50	1.25
		Nos. 159-162 (4)	10.00	5.00

World Wildlife Fund.

Discovery of America, 500th Anniv. — A58

Captains, ships: 150fr, Vicente Yanez Pinzon, Nina. 260fr, Martin Alonso Pinzon, Pinta. 350fr, Christopher Columbus, Santa Maria.

1991   Litho.   Perf. 13½x14
163	A58	150fr multicolored	1.50	.60
164	A58	250fr multicolored	2.75	1.00
165	A58	350fr multicolored	3.75	1.50
		Nos. 163-165 (3)	8.00	3.10

Locomotives A59

150fr, Electric, Japan, 1932. 250fr, Steam, US, 1873. 500fr, Steam, Germany, 1841.

1991, Sept. 10
166	A59	150fr multicolored	1.00	.50
167	A59	250fr multicolored	2.50	.75

Souvenir Sheet
168	A59	500fr multicolored	22.50	22.50

1992 Summer Olympics, Barcelona — A60

1992, Feb. 12   Litho.   Perf. 13½x14
169	A60	200fr Basketball	1.75	.75
170	A60	300fr Swimming	2.50	1.10

Souvenir Sheet
171	A60	400fr Baseball	22.50	22.50

Souvenir Sheet

Discovery of America, 500th Anniv. — A61

Columbus: a, 300fr, Departing from Palos, Spain. b, 500fr, Landing in New World.

1992, Apr. 8
172	A61	Sheet of 2, #a.-b.	22.50	22.50

Motion Pictures, Cent. — A61a

Scenes from movies: 100fr, Humphrey Bogart, Ingrid Bergman, Dooley Wilson in "Casablanca," 1942. 250fr, "Viridiana," 1961. 350fr, Laurel and Hardy in "Sons of the Desert," 1933.

1992, Sept.   Litho.   Perf. 14
172C	A61a	100fr multicolored	1.00	.65
172D	A61a	250fr multicolored	1.50	1.00
172E	A61a	350fr multicolored	2.50	1.50
		Nos. 172C-172E (3)	5.00	3.15

Mushrooms — A62

75fr, Termitomyces globulus. 125fr, Termitomyces le testui. 150fr, Termitomyces robustus.

1992, Nov.   Litho.   Perf. 14x13½
173	A62	75fr multicolored	1.00	.25
174	A62	125fr multicolored	1.50	.50
175	A62	150fr multicolored	2.00	.65
		Nos. 173-175 (3)	4.50	1.40

A62a

Wildlife Protection: 150fr, Halcyon malimbicus. 250fr, Corythaeola cristata. 500fr, Mariposa nymphalidae, horiz.

1992   Litho.   Perf. 14x13½
175A	A62a	150fr multicolored	2.50	1.00
175B	A62a	250fr multicolored	4.25	1.50

Souvenir Sheet
Perf. 13½x14
175C	A62a	500fr multicolored	25.00	25.00

Virgin and Child with Virtuous Saints, by Claudio Coello (c. 1635-1693) A63

Paintings, by Jacob Jordaens (1593-1678): 300fr, Apollo Conquering Marsias. 400fr, Meleager and Atalanta.

1993, Mar.   Litho.   Perf. 13½x14
176	A63	200fr multicolored	2.25	.75
177	A63	300fr multicolored	3.00	1.10

Souvenir Sheet
178	A63	400fr multicolored	20.00	20.00

1992 Olympic Gold Medalists — A64

Designs: 100fr, Quincy Watts, 400-meter dash, US. 250fr, Martin Lopez Zubero, swimming, Spain. 350fr, Petra Kronberger, women's slalom, Austria. 400fr, Flying Dutchman class yachting, Spain.

1993   Litho.   Perf. 13½x14
179	A64	100fr multicolored	.90	.35
180	A64	250fr multicolored	2.25	.75
181	A64	350fr multicolored	3.25	1.00
182	A64	400fr multicolored	4.00	1.25
		Nos. 179-182 (4)	10.40	3.35

Scene from Romeo and Juliet, by Tchaikovsky A65

Design: 200fr, Scene from Faust, by Charles-Francois Gounod (1818-93).

1993, June   Litho.   Perf. 13½x14
183 A65 100fr multicolored   1.40   .40
184 A65 200fr multicolored   2.40   .65

First Ford Gasoline Engine, Cent. — A66

1993   Perf. 13½x14, 14x13½
185 A66 200fr First Ford vehicle   2.00   .75
186 A66 300fr Ford Model T   2.75   1.00
187 A66 400fr Henry Ford, vert.   4.00   1.25
     Nos. 185-187 (3)   8.75   3.00

25th Anniv. of Independence A67

Designs: 150fr, Pres. Obiang Nguema Mbasogo, vert. 250fr, Cargo ship, map, communications . 300fr, Hydroelectric plant, Riaba. 350fr, Bridge.

Perf. 14x13½, 13½x14
1993, Oct. 12   Litho.
188 A67 150fr multicolored   1.10   .50
189 A67 250fr multicolored   1.90   .75
190 A67 300fr multicolored   2.50   .85
191 A67 350fr multicolored   3.00   .95
     Nos. 188-191 (4)   8.50   3.05

1994 World Cup Soccer Championships, US — A68

Designs: 200fr, German team, 1990 champions. 300fr, Rose Bowl Stadium, Pasadena, Calif. 500fr, Player kicking ball, vert.

1994 Litho.   Perf. 13½x14, 14x13½
192 A68 200fr multicolored   1.35   .50
193 A68 300fr multicolored   1.90   .70
194 A68 500fr multicolored   3.50   1.20
     Nos. 192-194 (3)   6.75   2.40

First Manned Moon Landing, 25th Anniv. — A69

Designs: 500fr, Lunar module, Eagle. 700fr, "Buzz" Aldrin, Michael Collins, Neil Armstrong. 900fr, Footprint on moon, astronaut.

1994   Perf. 13½x14
195 A69 500fr multicolored   2.75   1.10
196 A69 700fr multicolored   4.25   1.50
197 A69 900fr multicolored   6.50   2.00
     Nos. 195-197 (3)   13.50   4.60

Dinosaurs — A70

Designs: 300fr, Chasmosaurus. 500fr, Tyrannosaurus rex. 700fr, Triceratops. 800fr, Styracosaurus, deinonychus.

1994
198 A70 300fr multicolored   2.00   .65
199 A70 500fr multicolored   3.25   1.10
200 A70 700fr multicolored   6.00   1.60
     Nos. 198-200 (3)   11.25   3.35
          Souvenir Sheet
201 A70 800fr multicolored   21.00 21.00

Famous Men — A71

Designs: 300fr, Jean Renoir (1894-1979), French film director. 500fr, Ferdinand de Lesseps (1805-94), French diplomat, promoter of Suez Canal. 600fr, Antoine de Saint Exupery (1900-44), French aviator, writer. 700fr, Walter Gropius (1883-1969), architect.

1994   Litho.   Perf. 13½x14
202 A71 300fr multicolored   2.25   .75
203 A71 500fr multicolored   3.75   1.40
204 A71 600fr multicolored   4.50   1.50
205 A71 700fr multicolored   5.50   2.00
     Nos. 202-205 (4)   16.00   5.65

Establishment of The Bauhaus, 75th anniv. (No. 205).

Minerals — A72

1994   Litho.   Perf. 13½x14
206 A72 300fr Aurichalcite   2.50   .90
207 A72 400fr Pyromorphite   3.50   1.25
208 A72 600fr Fluorite   5.00   1.75
209 A72 700fr Halite   6.00   2.00
     Nos. 206-209 (4)   17.00   5.90

Domestic Animals — A73

Designs: a, Cat. b, Dog. c, Pig.

1995   Litho.   Perf. 13½x14
210   Strip of 3, #a.-c.   8.50   8.50
a.-c. A73 500fr Any single   1.60   1.40

Butterflies & Orchids — A74

a, Hypolimnas salmacis. b, Myrina silenus. c, Palla ussheri. d, Pseudacraea boisduvali.

1995
211   Strip of 4, #a.-d.   14.00 14.00
a.-d. A74 400fr Any single   2.75   1.50

Anniversaries A75

Designs: a, 350fr, End of World War II, 50th Anniv. b, 450fr, UN, 50th anniv. c, 600fr, Sir Rowland Hill, birth bicent.

1995   Litho.   Perf. 13½x14
212   Strip of 3, #a.-c.   11.00 11.00
a. A75 350fr multi   2.50   1.25
b. A75 450fr multi   3.25   1.50
c. A75 600fr multi   4.00   2.25

Trains — A76

Designs: No. 213a, English steam engine. b, German diesel engine. c, Japanese Shinkansen train.
800fr, Swiss electric locomotive.

1995
213   Strip of 3, #a.-c.   13.00 13.00
a.-c. A76 500fr Any single   2.75   2.25
          Souvenir Sheet
214 A76 800fr multicolored   11.00 11.00

Formula 1 Driving Champions A77

Designs: a, Juan Manuel Fangio. b, Ayrton Senna. c, Jim Clark. d, Jochen Rindt.

1995   Litho.   Perf. 14
215   Strip of 4, #a.-d.   12.00 12.00
a.-d. A77 400fr Any single   2.25   1.50

Motion Pictures, Cent. — A78

Designs: a, Marilyn Monroe. b, Elvis Presley. c, James Dean. d, Vittorio de Sica.

1996   Litho.   Perf. 14
216   Strip of 4, #a.-d.   9.00   9.00
a.-d. A78 350fr Any single   1.50   1.50

Famous People — A79

Designs: a, Alfred Nobel (1833-96), inventor, philanthropist. b, Anton Bruckner (1824-96), composer. c, Abraham and Three Angels, by Giovanni B. Tiepolo (1696-1770).
800fr, Family of Charles IV, by Francisco de Goya, (1746-1828).

1996
217   Strip of 3, #a.-c.   13.50 13.50
a.-c. A79 500fr Any single   2.75   2.00
          Souvenir Sheet
218 A79 800fr multicolored   8.00   7.75

Chess — A80

Designs: a, World Chess Festival for youth and children, Minorca, Spain. b, Women's World Chess Championship, Jaén, Spain. c, Men's World Chess Championship, Karpov versus Kamsky, Elista, Kalmyk. d, Chess Olympiad, Yerevan, Armenia.

1996   Litho.   Perf. 14
219   Strip of 4, #a.-d.   14.00 14.00
a.-d. A80 400fr Any single   3.00   1.50

1996 Summer Olympic Games, Atlanta — A81

Designs: a, Olympic Stadium, Athens, 1896. b, Cycling. c, Tennis. d, Equestrian show jumping.

1996   Litho.   Perf. 14
220   Strip of 4, #a.-d.   10.00 10.00
a.-d. A81 400fr Any single   1.75   1.50

Ships — A82

Designs: a, Paddle steamer with sails, 19th cent. b, Bark "Galatea," 1896. c, Modern ferry.

1996
221   Strip of 3, #a.-c.   12.00 12.00
a.-c. A82 500fr Any single   2.75   2.00

Franz Schubert (1797-1828), Composer — A83

Miguel de Cervantes (1547-1616), Novelist — A84

Designs: a, shown. b, Chinese Lunar New Year, 1997, (Year of the Ox). c, Johannes Brahms (1833-97), composer.

1997, Apr. 23   Litho.   Perf. 14
222   Strip of 3, #a.-c.   10.00 10.00
a.-c. A83 500fr Any single   2.50   2.00
          Souvenir Sheet
223 A84 800fr multicolored   11.00 11.00

Mushrooms A85

a, Sparassis laminosa. b, Amanita pantherina. c, Morchella esculenta. d, Aleuria aurantia.

1997
224   Strip of 4, #a.-d.   13.50 13.50
a.-d. A85 400fr Any single   2.25   1.75

1998 World Cup Soccer Championships, France — A86

Designs: a, Players with ball on field. b, Stadium. c, Kicking ball.

1997   Litho.   Perf. 14
225   Strip of 3, #a.-c.   7.00   7.00
a.-c. A86 300fr Any single   1.50   1.10

Fauna — A88

a, Snake. b, Snail. c, Turtle. d, Monitor lizard.

1998   Litho.   Perf. 14
230   Strip of 4, #a.-d.   14.00 14.00
a.-d. A88 400fr Any single   2.25   1.50

A89

Military Uniforms: a, Alsace Regiment, French Infantry, 18th cent. b, English Marine, 18th cent. c, Georgian Hussars Regiment, Russian Calvary, 18th cent. d, Prussian Artillery, 19th cent.

1998
231   Strip of 4, #a.-d.   10.00 10.00
a.-d. A89 400fr Any single   1.75   1.50

A90

Easter (Museum paintings): a, Crucifixion of Christ, by Velázquez. b, Adoration of the Magi, by Rubens. c, Holy Family, by Michelangelo.

1999   Litho.   Perf. 14
232   Strip of 3, #a.-c.   10.00 10.00
a.-c.   A90 500fr Any single   2.25 2.00

Orchids — A91

Designs: a, Angraecum eburneum. b, Paphiopedilum insigne. c, Ansellia africana. d, Cattleya leopoldii.

1999
233   Strip of 4, #a.-d.   16.00 16.00
a.-d.   A91 400fr Any single   3.00 1.50

Birth and Death Anniversaries — A92

No. 234: a, 750fr, Portrait of Frederic Chopin (1810-49), by Eugene Delacroix. b, 100fr, Christ Crowned With Thorns, by Anthony Van Dyck (1599-1641). c, 250fr, Portrait of Johann Wolfgang von Goethe (1749-1832), by Joseph Carl Stieler. d, 500fr, Jacques-Etienne Montgolfiere (1745-1799) and balloon.

1999   Litho.   Perf. 14x13¾
234   Horiz. strip of 4, #a-d   11.00 11.00
a.   A92 750fr multi   4.00 3.00
b.   A92 100fr multi   .45   .35
c.   A92 250fr multi   1.25 1.10
d.   A92 500fr multi   2.75 2.00

Parrots — A93

No. 235: a, Aratinga guarouba. b, Ara ambigua. c, Anodorhynchus hyacinthinus. 800fr, Alisterus amboinensis.

1999
235   Vert. strip of 3, #a-c   13.00 13.00
a.-c.   A93 500fr any single   3.00 2.25
Souvenir Sheet
236   A93 800fr multi   11.00 11.00

Economic and Monetary Community of Central Africa Week (CEMAC) — A93a

Designs: 100fr, Map of Africa, flags of member nations.

1999   Litho.   Perf. 14½
236A   A93a 100fr multi

An additional stamp was issued in this set. The editors would like to examine any example.

Locomotives A94

No. 237: a, Swiss. b, German. c, Japanese.

2000   Litho.   Perf. 13¾x14
237   Horiz. strip of 3   12.00 12.00
a.-c.   A94 500fr Any single   3.00 2.50
Souvenir Sheet
238   A94 800fr AVE Train   7.25 7.25

Butterflies — A95

a, Fabriciana nìobe. b, Palaeochrysophanus hippothoe. c, Inachis io. d, Apatura iris.

2000
239   Horiz. strip of 4   16.00 16.00
a.-d.   A95 400fr Any single   3.00 1.75

UPU, 125th Anniv. (in 1999) — A96

2000   Litho.   Perf. 13¾
240   A96 400fr multi   3.00 2.60

Mushrooms A97

No. 241: a, Gyroporus cyanescens. b, Terfezia arenaria. c, Battarrea stevenii. d, Amanita muscaria.

2001   Litho.   Perf. 13¾
241   Horiz. strip of 4   12.00 12.00
a.-d.   A97 400fr Any single   2.25 1.75

Fire Trucks — A98

No. 242: a, Truck, 1915. b, Tanker, 1943. c, Ladder truck, 1966. d, Merryweather pumper, 1888.

2001
242   Horiz. strip of 4   13.00 13.00
a.-d.   A98 400fr Any single   2.50 2.00

Soldiers — A99

No. 243: a, Infantry officer, 1700. b, Harquebusier, 1534. c, Musketeer, 17th cent. d, Fusilier, 1815.

2001   Litho.   Perf. 14x13¾
243   Horiz. strip of 4   12.00 12.00
a.-d.   A99 400fr Any single   2.50 1.75

Prehistoric Animals — A100

No. 244: a, Carnotaurus sastrei. b, Iberomesornis romerali. c, Troodon. 800fr, Diplodocus carnegiei.

2001
244   Horiz. strip of 3   12.00 12.00
a.-c.   A100 500fr Any single   3.00 2.50
Souvenir Sheet
245   A100 800fr multi   10.00 10.00

Millennium A101

Designs: No. 246, 200fr, Intl. Conference Center. No. 247, 200fr, Offshore petroleum exploration. No. 248, 200fr, Women's Plaza, Malabo.
400fr, Statue at Intl. Conference Center, vert.

2001   Litho.   Perf. 13¾x14
246-248 A101   Set of 3   10.50 10.50
Souvenir Sheet
Perf. 14x13¾
249   A101 400fr multi   7.75 7.75

Flora — A102

No. 250: a, Alstonia congensis. b, Harongana madagascariensis. c, Caloncoba glauca. d, Cassia occidentalis.

2002   Perf. 14x13¾
250   Horiz. strip of 4   12.00 12.00
a.-d.   A102 400fr Any single   2.60 2.10

Automobiles A103

No. 251: a, 1924 Rochet Schneider 20,000. b, 1930 Bugatti T49. c, 1931 Ford Model A. d, 1925 Alfa Romeo RLSS.

2002   Perf. 13¾x14
251   Vert. strip of 4   12.00 12.00
a.-d.   A103 400fr Any single   2.60 2.10

Butterflies A104

No. 252: a, Papilio menestheus canui. b, Papilio policenes. c, Papilio tyndaraeus. d, Papilio zalmoxis.

2002
252   Strip of 4   12.00 12.00
a.-d.   A104 400fr Any single   2.60 2.10

Famous Men — A105

No. 253: a, Victor Hugo (1802-85), writer. b, Santiago Ramón y Cajal (1852-1934), histologist. c, Emile Zola (1840-1902), writer.

2002
253   Horiz. strip of 3   7.25 7.25
a.-c.   A105 400fr Any single   1.90 1.75

2002 World Cup Soccer Championships, Japan and Korea — A106

No. 254: a, Player with yellow shirt with knee on ground. b, Stadium. c, Player with yellow shirt on ground.

2002
254   Horiz. strip of 3   11.00 11.00
a.-c.   A106 500fr Any single   3.00 2.75
Souvenir Sheet

2002 Chess Olympiad, Bled, Slovenia — A107

2002
255   A107 800fr multi   7.50 7.50

Anniversaries and Events — A108

No. 256: a, Painting by Henri de Toulouse-Lautrec (1864-1901). b, Year of Dialogue Among Civilizations. c, Giuseppe Verdi (1813-1901), composer.

2004 ?   Litho.   Perf. 14x13¾
256   Vert. strip of 3   8.00 8.00
a.-c.   A108 400fr Any single   2.50 2.50

Dated 2001. Stamps did not appear in philatelic market until 2004.

Anniversaries and Events — A109

No. 257: a, Tour de France bicycle race, cent. b, Painting by Vincent van Gogh (1853-90). c, Wright Brothers and Wright Flyer.

2004 ?   Perf. 13¾x14
257   Horiz. strip of 3   10.00 10.00
a.   A109 400fr multi   2.75 2.75
b.   A109 500fr multi   3.25 3.25
c.   A109 600fr multi   4.00 4.00

Dated 2003. Stamps did not appear in philatelic market until 2004.

Minerals — A110

2004 ?
258   Vert. strip of 4   12.00 12.00
a.   A110 400fr Realgar   2.25 2.25
b.   A110 450fr Gypsum   2.75 2.75
c.   A110 550fr Red quartz   3.25 3.25
d.   A110 600fr Chrysoberyl   3.50 3.50

Dated 2003. Stamps did not appear in philatelic market until 2004.

Lighthouses — A111

Designs: a, Marina Lighthouse, Luba, Equatorial Guinea. b, La Plata Lighthouse, Spain. c, Prodecao Lighthouse, Luba. d, Torre de Hércules, Spain.

2004 ?   Perf. 14x13¾
259   Horiz. strip of 4   12.50 12.50
a.   A111 400fr multi   2.50 2.50
b.   A111 450fr multi   2.75 2.75
c.   A111 550fr multi   3.00 3.00
d.   A111 600fr multi   3.75 3.75

Dated 2003. Stamps did not appear in philatelic market until 2004.

Space Shuttle Columbia Accident — A112

No. 260: a, Rocket lift-off. b, Rocket on launch pad. c, Flight crew patch. 1000fr, View of earth from outer space.

2004 ?
260	Vert. strip of 3	10.50	10.50
a.	A112 500fr multi	3.00	3.00
b.	A112 600fr multi	3.25	3.25
c.	A112 700fr multi	3.75	3.75

Souvenir Sheet
261	A112 1000fr multi	8.00	8.00

Dated 2003. Stamps did not appear in philatelic market until 2004.

Motorcycles A113

No. 262: a, 1944-47 Soriano Tigre. b, 1970 Derbi 50 Grand Prix. c, 1938 DKW 250 with sidecar. 1000fr, Harley-Davidson VRSCA V-Rod.

2004 ?   **Perf. 13¾x14**
262	Horiz. strip of 3	8.50	8.50
a.	A113 450fr multi	2.00	2.00
b.	A113 500fr multi	2.50	2.50
c.	A113 550fr multi	3.00	3.00

Souvenir Sheet
263	A113 1000fr multi	7.50	7.50

Dated 2003. Stamps did not appear in philatelic market until 2004.

Souvenir Sheet

Wedding of Spanish Prince Felipe and Letizia Ortiz Rocasolano — A114

2004   Litho.   Perf. 13¾x14
264	A114 1400fr multi	11.00	11.00

2004 Summer Olympics, Athens — A115

2004
265	Horiz. strip of 4	10.00	10.00
a.	A115 400fr Basketball	1.90	1.90
b.	A115 450fr Track	2.25	2.25
c.	A115 550fr Tennis	2.75	2.75
d.	A115 600fr Cycling	3.00	3.00

2004 Anniversaries — A116

No. 266: a, FIFA (Fédération Internationale de Football Association), cent. b, Pablo Neruda (1904-73), poet. c, Anton Dvorak (1841-1904), composer.

2005 ?   Litho.   Perf. 14x13¾
266	Vert. strip of 3	10.00	10.00
a.	A116 450fr multi	2.75	2.75
b.	A116 500fr multi	3.00	3.00
c.	A116 550fr multi	3.50	3.50

Dated 2004. Stamps did not appear in philatelic marketplace until 2005.

Airplanes A117

No. 267: a, Concorde. b, Airbus A340-600. c, Boeing 747-400. d, Eurofighter C-16 Typhoon.

2005 ?   Perf. 13¾x14
267	Vert. strip of 4	11.00	11.00
a.	A117 400fr multi	2.00	2.00
b.	A117 450fr multi	2.50	2.50
c.	A117 500fr multi	2.75	2.75
d.	A117 600fr multi	3.25	3.25

Dated 2004. Stamps did not appear in philatelic marketplace until 2005.

Churches — A118

No. 268: a, Cathedral, Pisa, Italy. b, Notre-Dame-la-Grande Church, Poitiers, France. c, Speyer Cathedral, Germany. d, Cathedral, Santiago de Compostela, Spain.

2005   Perf. 14x13¾
268	Horiz. strip of 4	12.00	12.00
a.	A118 400fr multi	2.00	2.00
b.	A118 450fr multi	2.50	2.50
c.	A118 550fr multi	3.00	3.00
d.	A118 600fr multi	3.25	3.25

Paintings by Salvador Dali (1904-89) — A119

Various unnamed paintings.

2005   Perf. 14x13¾
269	Vert. strip of 3	10.00	10.00
a.	A119 500fr multi	2.50	2.50
b.	A119 600fr multi	3.00	3.00
c.	A119 700fr multi	3.50	3.50

Souvenir Sheet
270	A119 1000fr multi	9.00	9.00

Art and Architecture A120

No. 271: a, Statue of African Woman, Malabo. b, Building, Bioko Sur. c, Eyi Muan Ndong, troubador.

2005   Litho.   Perf. 13¾x14
271	Horiz. strip of 3	8.00	8.00
a.	A120 450fr multi	2.25	2.25
b.	A120 550fr multi	2.60	2.60
c.	A120 600fr multi	3.00	3.00

Trains — A121

No. 272: a, Tren Basculante. b, Tren Talgo Pendular. c, Tren Electrotrén. d, Tren T. A. F.

2005
272	Strip of 4	11.00	11.00
a.	A121 400fr multi	2.10	2.10
b.	A121 450fr multi	2.25	2.25
c.	A121 550fr multi	3.00	3.00
d.	A121 600fr multi	3.25	3.25

Publication of Don Quixote, 400th Anniv. — A122

No. 273: a, Emblem. b, Don Quixote and Sancho Panza riding. c, Quixote catching falling Panza. d, Quixote on horse, windmill.

2005   Perf. 14x13¾
273	Horiz. strip of 4	11.00	11.00
a.	A122 400fr multi	2.10	2.10
b.	A122 450fr multi	2.25	2.25
c.	A122 550fr multi	3.00	3.00
d.	A122 600fr multi	3.25	3.25

Famous People — A123

No. 274: a, Christopher Columbus (1451-1506), explorer. b, Federico García Lorca (1898-1936), poet. c, Wolfgang Amadeus Mozart (1756-91), composer.

2006   Perf. 13¾x14
274	Horiz. strip of 3	11.00	11.00
a.	A123 450fr multi	3.00	3.00
b.	A123 550fr multi	3.50	3.50
c.	A123 600fr multi	3.75	3.75

Pope Benedict XVI — A124

No. 275: a, Coat of Arms. b, St. Peter's Basilica. 1000fr, Pope Benedict XVI.

2006
275	Vert. pair	6.00	6.00
a.	A124 450fr multi	2.50	2.50
b.	A124 550fr multi	3.50	3.50

Souvenir Sheet
276	A124 1000fr multi	7.00	7.00

Tourism — A125

No. 277: a, Road from Boloko to Luba. b, Malabo Intl. Airport Terminal. c, Sculpture, Avenida de Juan Pablo II. d, National Parliament.

2006   Litho.   Perf. 13¾x14
277	Strip of 4	12.00	12.00
a.	A125 400fr multi	2.40	2.40
b.	A125 450fr multi	2.60	2.60
c.	A125 550fr multi	3.25	3.25
d.	A125 600fr multi	3.50	3.50

Spain, 2006 World Basketball Champions — A126

No. 278: a, Emblem of Spanish Basketball Federation. b, Basketball and hoop. c, Players.

2006   Perf. 14x13¾
278	Vert. strip of 3	10.00	10.00
a.	A126 450fr multi	2.50	2.50
b.	A126 550fr multi	3.25	3.25
c.	A126 600fr multi	3.50	3.50

Christmas A127

No. 279 — Baby and: a, People and drummer. b, People. c, People and airplane.

2006   Perf. 13¾x14
279	Horiz. strip of 3	9.00	9.00
a.	A127 450fr multi	2.25	2.25
b.	A127 550fr multi	3.00	3.00
c.	A127 600fr multi	3.25	3.25

European Economic Community, 50th Anniv. — A128

No. 280: a, Orchard, Spain. b, Mountain, France. c, Farm fields, Italy. d, Village, Germany.

2007   Litho.   Perf. 13¾x14
280	Horiz. strip of 4	13.00	13.00
a.	A128 450fr multi	2.25	2.25
b.	A128 500fr multi	2.75	2.75
c.	A128 550fr multi	3.00	3.00
d.	A128 600fr multi	3.25	3.25

Locomotives in Madrid Train Museum — A129

No. 281: a, Steam locomotive 242F-2009. b, Diesel locomotive 1615. c, Electric locomotive 6101. d, Talgo II train. 1000fr, Steam locomotive, diff.

2007
281	Strip of 4	13.00	13.00
a.	A129 450fr multi	2.25	2.25
b.	A129 500fr multi	2.75	2.75
c.	A129 600fr multi	3.50	3.50
d.	A129 650fr multi	3.75	3.75

Souvenir Sheet
282	A129 1000fr multi	5.75	5.75

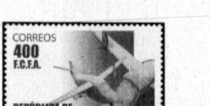

Native Toys — A130

2007   Litho.   Perf. 13¾x14
283	Horiz. strip of 4	10.00	10.00
a.	A130 400fr Airplane	2.00	2.00
b.	A130 450fr Car	2.40	2.40
c.	A130 500fr Scooter	2.60	2.60
d.	A130 550fr Songo game	3.00	3.00

Flora — A131

No. 284: a, Artocarpus communis. b, Hibiscus sabdariffa. c, Spathodea campanulata. d, Theobroma cacao.

2007   Litho.   Perf. 13¾x14
284	Horiz. strip of 4	12.00	12.00
a.	A131 400fr multi	2.25	2.25
b.	A131 450fr multi	2.60	2.60
c.	A131 550fr multi	3.25	3.25
d.	A131 600fr multi	3.50	3.50

African Children — A132

No. 285: a, Child and basket. b, Five children and toy cars. c, Six children and net.

2008   Litho.   Perf. 13¾
285	Horiz. strip of 3	8.50	8.50
a.	A132 400fr multi	2.50	2.50
b.	A132 450fr multi	2.75	2.75
c.	A132 500fr multi	3.00	3.00

2008 African Cup of Nations Soccer Championships, Ghana — A133

No. 286 — Emblem and: a, Soccer ball and player's foot. b, Soccer ball being caught. c, Goalie. d, Goalie, diff.

2008
286	Horiz. strip of 4	12.00	12.00
a.	A133 400fr multi	2.50	2.50
b.	A133 450fr multi	2.75	2.75
c.	A133 500fr multi	3.00	3.00
d.	A133 600fr multi	3.50	3.50

Flora and Fauna — A134

No. 287: a, Sitatunga. b, Passiflora quadrangularis. c, Pachylobus edulis.

2008
287	Horiz. strip of 3	8.00	8.00
a.	A134 450fr multi	2.25	2.25
b.	A134 500fr multi	2.60	2.60
c.	A134 600fr multi	3.00	3.00

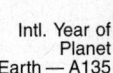

Intl. Year of Planet Earth — A135

No. 288: a, Seedlings. b, Parched earth. c, Waterfall.

2008
288	Horiz. strip of 3	7.50	7.50
a.	A135 400fr multi	2.25	2.25
b.	A135 450fr multi	2.40	2.40
c.	A135 550fr multi	2.75	2.75

Declaration of the Rights of Children, 50th Anniv. — A136

No. 289: a, Child drinking glass of milk. b, Children playing with ball. c, Children reading. d, Child coloring.

2009, Mar. 27   **Litho.**   **Perf. 14x13¾**
289	Horiz. strip of 4	11.00	11.00
a.	A136 400fr multi	2.00	2.00
b.	A136 500fr multi	2.75	2.75
c.	A136 550fr multi	3.00	3.00
d.	A136 600fr multi	3.25	3.25

Women's Soccer — A137

No. 290: a, Cheering crowd. b, Soccer ball hitting net. c, Players battling for ball. d, Corner of field.

2009, May 14   **Litho.**   **Perf. 13¾**
290	Vert. strip of 4	13.00	13.00
a.	A137 475fr multi	2.50	2.50
b.	A137 550fr multi	3.00	3.00
c.	A137 600fr multi	3.25	3.25
d.	A137 650fr multi	3.50	3.50

Medicinal Plants — A138

No. 291: a, Asystasia gangetica. b, Bryophyllum pinnatum. c, Solanum torvum. 1000fr, Cassia alata.

2009, Aug. 14
291	Vert. strip of 3	10.00	10.00
a.	A138 400fr multi	2.75	2.75
b.	A138 450fr multi	3.25	3.25
c.	A138 550fr multi	3.75	3.75

Souvenir Sheet
292	A138 1000fr multi	7.25	7.25

Christmas — A139

No. 293 — Paintings: a, Birth of Christ, by Federico Barocci. b, Adoration of the Kings, by J. B. Maíno. c, Adoration of the Shepherds, by Maíno. d, Nativity, by Master of Sopetrán.

2009, Sept. 25
293	Horiz. strip of 4	11.00	11.00
a.	A139 400fr multi	2.00	2.00
b.	A139 450fr multi	2.75	2.75
c.	A139 500fr multi	3.00	3.00
d.	A139 550fr multi	3.25	3.25

Paintings by Joaquin Sorolla y Bastida — A140

No. 294: a, Paseo a Orillas del Mar. b, El Balandrito. c, La Hora del Baño. d, Self-portrait.

Perf. 13¾x13¼
2010, Mar. 15   **Litho.**
294	Horiz. strip of 4	14.00	14.00
a.	A140 475fr multi	2.75	2.75
b.	A140 575fr multi	3.50	3.50
c.	A140 625fr multi	3.75	3.75
d.	A140 675fr multi	4.00	4.00

Architecture A141

No. 295: a, La Paz Medical Center, Bata. b, Gepetrol Building, Malabo. c, Gecotel Building, Bata. d, Central African Economic and Monetary Community Parliament Building, Malabo.

2010, June 15
295	Horiz. strip of 4	14.00	14.00
a.	A141 475fr multi	2.75	2.75
b.	A141 575fr multi	3.50	3.50
c.	A141 625fr multi	3.75	3.75
d.	A141 675fr multi	4.00	4.00

2010 World Cup Soccer Championships, South Africa — A142

No. 296: a, Emblem of 2010 tournament. b, Mascot. c, World Cup. d, Colors of Spain, World Cup champions.

2010   **Litho.**   **Perf. 13¼x13¾**
296	Horiz. strip of 4	14.00	14.00
a.	A142 475fr multi	2.75	2.75
b.	A142 575fr multi	3.50	3.50
c.	A142 625fr multi	3.75	3.75
d.	A142 675fr multi	4.00	4.00

Miniature Sheet

Christmas — A143

No. 297: a, 375fr, Adoration of the Shepherds, by Anton Rafael Mengs. b, 425fr, Adoration of the Magi, by Diego Velázquez. c,

475fr, Nativity, by Hans Memling. d, 525fr, Adoration of the Shepherds, by El Greco.

2010
297	A143	Sheet of 4, #a-d	12.00	12.00

Intl. Women's Day, Cent. — A144

No. 298 — Stylized woman as: a, Doctor. b, Police officer. c, Chemist. d, Chef.

2011   **Perf. 13¾x14**
298	Horiz. strip of 4	16.00	16.00
a.	A144 525fr black	3.25	3.25
b.	A144 625fr green	3.75	3.75
c.	A144 675fr red violet	4.25	4.25
d.	A144 725fr blue	4.50	4.50

Intl. Year of Chemistry — A145

No. 299 — Emblem and: a, Chemical glassware. b, Molecular model and textbook. c, Children in school. d, Water.

2011   **Perf. 14x13¾**
299	Horiz. strip of 4	16.00	16.00
a.	A145 525fr multi	3.25	3.25
b.	A145 625fr multi	3.75	3.75
c.	A145 675fr multi	4.25	4.25
d.	A145 725fr multi	4.50	4.50

Gustavo Adolfo Bécquer (1836-70), Poet — A146

No. 300: a, Drawing of Woman. b, Windows of Veruela Monastery. c, Portrait of Bécquer by his brother, Valeriano.

2011
300	Horiz. strip of 3	11.00	11.00
a.	A146 525fr multi	3.00	3.00
b.	A146 625fr multi	3.75	3.75
c.	A146 675fr multi	4.00	4.00

Christmas A147

No. 301 — Christmas-themed paintings by: a, Nicolás Francés. b, Fra Angelico. c, Luca di Tommè. d, Jaume Serra.

2011   **Perf. 13¾x14**
301	Horiz. strip of 4	13.00	13.00
a.	A147 525fr multi	2.60	2.60
b.	A147 625fr multi	3.00	3.00
c.	A147 675fr multi	3.25	3.25
d.	A147 725fr multi	3.50	3.50

Paintings by Juan Gris (1887-1927) — A148

Various paintings.

2012   **Perf. 14x13¾**
302	Horiz. strip of 4	12.00	12.00
a.	A148 525fr multi	2.40	2.40
b.	A148 625fr multi	2.75	2.75
c.	A148 675fr multi	3.00	3.00
d.	A148 725fr multi	3.25	3.25

Spices — A149

No. 303: a, Xylopia aethiopica. b, Piper guineense. c, Capsicum frutescens. d, Zingiber officinale.

2012
303	Horiz. strip of 4	12.00	12.00
a.	A149 525fr multi	2.40	2.40
b.	A149 625fr multi	2.75	2.75
c.	A149 675fr multi	3.00	3.00
d.	A149 725fr multi	3.25	3.25

Sports — A150

No. 304: a, Gymnastics. b, Table tennis. c, Running. d, Kayaking.

2012   **Perf. 14x13¾**
304	Horiz. strip of 4	12.00	12.00
a.	A150 525fr multi	2.40	2.40
b.	A150 625fr multi	2.75	2.75
c.	A150 675fr multi	3.00	3.00
d.	A150 725fr multi	3.25	3.25

Christmas A151

No. 305 — Religious painting by: a, Pietro de Lignis. b, Francisco and Rodrigo de Osona. c, Pietro da Cortona. d, Hans Memling.

2012   **Perf. 14x13¾**
305	Horiz. strip of 4	12.00	12.00
a.	A151 525fr multi	2.40	2.40
b.	A151 625fr multi	2.75	2.75
c.	A151 675fr multi	3.00	3.00
d.	A151 725fr multi	3.25	3.25

Tourist Areas — A152

No. 306: a, Sipopo. b, Luba. c, Mbini. d, Bata.

2013   **Perf. 13¾x13¼**
306	Horiz. strip of 4	12.00	12.00
a.	A152 550fr multi	2.50	2.50
b.	A152 600fr multi	2.75	2.75
c.	A152 650fr multi	3.00	3.00
d.	A152 700fr multi	3.25	3.25

Intl. Red Cross, 150th Anniv. — A153

No. 307: a, Students in classroom. b, Man carrying large pot on head. c, Red Cross worker. d, Flags on building.

2013   **Perf. 13¾x14**
307	Horiz. strip of 4	12.00	12.00
a.	A153 550fr multi	2.50	2.50
b.	A153 600fr multi	2.75	2.75
c.	A153 650fr multi	3.00	3.00
d.	A153 700fr multi	3.25	3.25

Pope John XXIII (1881-1963) — A154

No. 307: a, Pope John XXIII. b, Pope John XXIII, diff. c, Pope John XXIII, diff. d, Arms of Pope John XXIII.

2013　　　　　　　　*Perf. 13¼x13¾*
308　　Horiz. strip of 4　　　12.00　12.00
a. A154 550fr multi　　　　2.60　2.60
b. A154 600fr multi　　　　2.75　2.75
c. A154 650fr multi　　　　3.00　3.00
d. A154 700fr multi　　　　3.50　3.50

Christmas — A155

No. 308: a, Nativity. b, Adoration of the Magi. c, Nativity, diff. d, Nativity, diff.

2013　　　　　　　　*Perf. 13¼x13¾*
309　　Horiz. strip of 4　　　12.00　12.00
a. A155 550fr multi　　　　2.60　2.60
b. A155 600fr multi　　　　2.75　2.75
c. A155 650fr multi　　　　3.00　3.00
d. A155 700fr multi　　　　3.50　3.50

Bolondo-Mbini Bridge — A156

Various views of bridge.

2014　　Litho.　　*Perf. 13¼x13¾*
310　　Horiz. strip of 4　　　11.50　11.50
a. A156 600fr multi　　　　2.50　2.50
b. A156 650fr multi　　　　2.75　2.75
c. A156 700fr multi　　　　3.00　3.00
d. A156 750fr multi　　　　3.25　3.25

Intl. Year of Family Farms — A157

No. 311: a, Hands leveling earth. b, Woman tending cows. c, Woman tending goats. d, Farmer inspecting crops.

2014　　Litho.　　*Perf. 13¾x13¼*
311　　Horiz. strip of 4　　　11.50　11.50
a. A157 600fr multi　　　　2.50　2.50
b. A157 650fr multi　　　　2.75　2.75
c. A157 700fr multi　　　　3.00　3.00
d. A157 750fr multi　　　　3.25　3.25

Religious Paintings by El Greco (1541-1614) — A158

No. 312: a, St. Andrew and St. Francis. b, Christ Carrying the Cross. c, St. Peter. d, The Disrobing of Christ.

2014　　Litho.　　*Perf. 13¼x13¾*
312　　Horiz. strip of 4　　　11.50　11.50
a. A158 600fr multi　　　　2.50　2.50
b. A158 650fr multi　　　　2.75　2.75
c. A158 700fr multi　　　　3.00　3.00
d. A158 750fr multi　　　　3.25　3.25

Christmas A159

No. 313: a, Adoration of the Shepherds, by Bartolomé Esteban Murillo. b, Adoration of the Magi, by Peter Paul Rubens. c, Adoration of the Magi, by Luis de Morales. d, Adoration of the Shepherds, by de Morales.

2014　　Litho.　　*Perf. 13¼x13¾*
313　　Horiz. strip of 4　　　11.50　11.50
a. A159 600fr multi　　　　2.50　2.50
b. A159 650fr multi　　　　2.75　2.75
c. A159 700fr multi　　　　3.00　3.00
d. A159 750fr multi　　　　3.25　3.25

Sipopo Congress Center, Malabo — A160

No. 314: a, Seats and video screen in meeting hall (29x41mm). b, Seats in auditorium (29x41mm). c, Building exterior (29x41mm). d, Building entrance (58x41mm).

2015　　Litho.　　*Perf. 13¼x13¾*
314　　Horiz. strip of 4　　　14.50　14.50
a. A160 650fr multi　　　　2.25　2.25
b. A160 700fr multi　　　　2.40　2.40
c. A160 750fr multi　　　　2.60　2.60
d. A160 2100fr multi　　　7.25　7.25

Paintings of Women by Federico de Madrazo y Kuntz (1815-94) — A161

No. 315 — Various women wearing: a, Blue dress. b, White dress. c, Lilac dress. d, Black dress.

2015　　Litho.　　*Perf. 13¾*
315　　Horiz. strip of 4　　　9.25　9.25
a. A161 600fr multi　　　　2.00　2.00
b. A161 650fr multi　　　　2.25　2.25
c. A161 700fr multi　　　　2.40　2.40
d. A161 750fr multi　　　　2.60　2.60

International Year of Light — A162

No. 316: a, Fiber optic cord connector. b, Ends of optical fibers. c, Ends of optical fibers, diff. d, Close-up of ends of bound optical fibers.

2015　　Litho.　　*Perf. 13¾x13¼*
316　　Horiz. strip of 4　　　8.75　8.75
a. A162 600fr multi　　　　2.00　2.00
b. A162 650fr multi　　　　2.10　2.10
c. A162 700fr multi　　　　2.25　2.25
d. A162 750fr multi　　　　2.40　2.40

Christmas — A163

No. 317 — Various Nativity paintings by unknown artists from: a, Prado, Madrid. b, Museum of Fine Arts, Bilbao. c, Prado, diff. d, Museum of Fine Arts, diff.

2015　　Litho.　　*Perf. 13¼x13¾*
317　　Horiz. strip of 4　　　8.75　8.75
a. A163 600fr multi　　　　2.00　2.00
b. A163 650fr multi　　　　2.10　2.10
c. A163 700fr multi　　　　2.25　2.25
d. A163 750fr multi　　　　2.40　2.40

Paintings by Hieronymus Bosch (c.1450-1516) — A164

No. 318 — Details of paintings: a, Garden of Earthly Delights (left panel). b, Garden of Earthly Delights (center panel). c, The Hay Wagon (center panel). d, St. John the Baptist in the Wilderness.

2016　　Litho.　　*Perf. 13¾*
318　　Horiz. strip of 4　　　8.75　8.75
a. A164 600fr multi　　　　2.00　2.00
b. A164 650fr multi　　　　2.25　2.25
c. A164 700fr multi　　　　2.40　2.40
d. A164 750fr multi　　　　2.60　2.60

Miguel de Cervantes (1547-1616), Writer — A165

No. 319 — Various paintings from Prado Museum, Madrid.

2016　　Litho.　　*Perf. 13¾*
319　　Horiz. strip of 4　　　8.75　8.75
a. A165 600fr multi　　　　2.00　2.00
b. A165 650fr multi　　　　2.25　2.25
c. A165 700fr multi　　　　2.40　2.40
d. A165 750fr multi　　　　2.60　2.60

Flora and Fauna — A166

No. 320: a, Hibisco (hibiscus). b, Geranio de la jungla (jungle geranium). c, Pangolín arborícola (tree pangolin). d, Barbasco guineano (Vogel's tephrosia).

2016　　Litho.　　*Perf. 13¾x14*
320　　Horiz. strip of 4　　　8.75　8.75
a. A166 600fr multi　　　　1.90　1.90
b. A166 650fr multi　　　　2.10　2.10
c. A166 700fr multi　　　　2.25　2.25
d. A166 750fr multi　　　　2.40　2.40

Christmas — A167

Various paintings depicting the Nativity from the Prado Museum, Madrid.

2016　　Litho.　　*Perf. 14x13¾*
321　　Horiz. strip of 4　　　8.75　8.75
a. A167 600fr multi　　　　1.90　1.90
b. A167 650fr multi　　　　2.10　2.10
c. A167 700fr multi　　　　2.25　2.25
d. A167 750fr multi　　　　2.40　2.40

International Year for Sustainable Tourism for Development — A168

No. 322: a, Bicyclist walking bicycle. b, Boat near dock. c, Cyclist on trail. d, Canoers.

2017　　Litho.　　*Perf. 13¾*
322　　Horiz. strip of 4　　　9.50　9.50
a. A168 600fr multi　　　　2.10　2.10
b. A168 650fr multi　　　　2.25　2.25
c. A168 700fr multi　　　　2.40　2.40
d. A168 750fr multi　　　　2.60　2.60

Paintings by Bartolomé Esteban Murillo (1617-82) — A169

No. 323: a, Leander and St. Bonaventure. b, Saints Justa and Rufina. c, Christ the Good Shepherd. d, Immaculate Conception.

2017　　Litho.　　*Perf. 13¾*
323　　Horiz. strip of 4　　　9.50　9.50
a. A169 600fr multi　　　　2.10　2.10
b. A169 650fr multi　　　　2.25　2.25
c. A169 700fr multi　　　　2.40　2.40
d. A169 750fr multi　　　　2.60　2.60

Malabo National Park — A170

No. 324: a, Bridge. b, Sculptures. c, Island. d, Park entrance.

2017　　Litho.　　*Perf. 13¾*
324　　Horiz. strip of 4　　　10.00　10.00
a. A170 600fr multi　　　　2.25　2.25
b. A170 650fr multi　　　　2.40　2.40
c. A170 700fr multi　　　　2.60　2.60
d. A170 750fr multi　　　　2.75　2.75

Christmas — A171

Various unattributed Nativity paintings from the Prado Museum.

2017　　Litho.　　*Perf. 13¾*
325　　Horiz. strip of 4　　　10.00　10.00
a. A171 600fr multi　　　　2.25　2.25
b. A171 650fr multi　　　　2.40　2.40
c. A171 700fr multi　　　　2.60　2.60
d. A171 750fr multi　　　　2.75　2.75

Paintings by Tintoretto (1518-94) A172

No. 326: a, Christ Washing the Feet of His Disciples. b, The Queen of Sheba and Solomon. c, Susanna and the Elders. d, Esther Before Ahasuerus.

2018　　Litho.　　*Perf. 13¾*
326　　Horiz. strip of 4　　　9.75　9.75
a. A172 600fr multi　　　　2.10　2.10
b. A172 650fr multi　　　　2.40　2.40
c. A172 700fr multi　　　　2.50　2.50
d. A172 750fr multi　　　　2.75　2.75

 A173

Independence, 50th Anniv. — A174

No. 326: a, Mongomo Basilica. b, Coat of arms of Equatorial Guinea. c, Presidential Palace. d, President Teodoro Obiang Nguema Mbasogo.
1000fr, Pres. Obiang, diff.

2018　　Litho.　　*Perf. 13¾*
327　　Horiz. strip of 4　　　9.75　9.75
a. A173 600fr multi　　　　2.10　2.10
b. A173 650fr multi　　　　2.40　2.40
c. A173 700fr multi　　　　2.50　2.50
d. A173 750fr multi　　　　2.75　2.75

Souvenir Sheet
Perf. 13¾x13½
328　A174 1000fr multi　　　3.50　3.50

Items Made by Artisans — A175

No. 329: a, Decorated gourds. b, Comb. c, Basket. d, Carved wooden shelf.

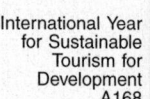

2018   **Litho.**   **Perf. 13¾**
329   Horiz. strip of 4   9.50   9.50
   a.   A175 600fr multi   2.10   2.10
   b.   A175 650fr multi   2.25   2.25
   c.   A175 700fr multi   2.40   2.40
   d.   A175 750fr multi   2.60   2.60

Christmas — A176

Various unnamed works of religious art from the Prado, Madrid.

2018   **Litho.**   **Perf. 13¾**
330   Horiz. strip of 4   9.50   9.50
   a.   A176 600fr multi   2.10   2.10
   b.   A176 650fr multi   2.25   2.25
   c.   A176 700fr multi   2.40   2.40
   d.   A176 750fr multi   2.60   2.60

SPECIAL DELIVERY STAMPS

Archer with Crossbow — SD1

1971, Oct. 12   **Photo.**   **Perf. 12½x13**
E1   SD1 4p blue & multi   .75   .25
E2   SD1 8p rose & multi   1.25   .35

3rd anniversary of independence.

ERITREA

ˌer-ə-ˈtrē-ə

LOCATION — In northeast Africa, bordering on the Red Sea, Sudan, Ethiopia and Djibouti.
GOVT. — Independent state
AREA — 45,300 (?) sq. mi.
POP. — 3,984,723 (1999 est.)
CAPITAL — Asmara

Formerly an Italian colony, Eritrea was incorporated as a State of Italian East Africa in 1936.

Under British occupation (1941-52) until it became part of Ethiopia as its northernmost region. Eritrea became independent May 24, 1993.

100 Centesimi = 1 Lira
100 cents = 1 birr (1991)
100 cents = 1 nakfa (1997)

> **Catalogue values for unused stamps in this country are for Never Hinged items, beginning with Scott 200 in the regular postage section.**

All used values to about 1916 are for postally used stamps. From 1916-1934, used values in italics are for postally used stamps. CTO's, for stamps valued postally used, sell for about the same as unused, hinged stamps.

Watermark

Wmk. 140 — Crown

Stamps of Italy Overprinted

    a   b

1892   **Wmk. 140**   **Perf. 14**
Overprinted Type "a" in Black
1   A6   1c bronze grn   6.00   12.00
  a.   Inverted overprint   725.00   750.00
  b.   Double overprint   2,150.
    Never hinged   3,200.
  c.   Vert. pair, one without
    overprint   4,800.
    Never hinged   7,250.
2   A7   2c org brn   3.75   6.00
  a.   Inverted overprint   725.00   750.00
  b.   Double overprint   2,150.
    Never hinged   3,200.
3   A33   5c green   75.00   16.00
  a.   Inverted overprint   9,500.   4,275.
    Never hinged   13,500.

Overprinted Type "b" in Black
4   A17   10c claret   100.00   15.00
5   A17   20c orange   185.00   12.00
6   A17   25c blue   675.00   50.00
7   A25   40c brown   7.50   27.50
8   A26   45c slate grn   7.50   30.00
9   A27   60c violet   7.50   60.00
10   A28   1 l brn & yel   37.50   75.00
11   A38   5 l bl & rose   300.00   500.00
    Nos. 1-11 (11)   1,405.   803.50
    Set, never hinged   3,600.

1895-99
Overprinted type "a" in Black
12   A39   1c brown ('99)   12.50   9.00
13   A40   2c org brn ('99)   3.00   1.85
14   A41   5c green   3.00   1.90
  a.   Inverted overprint   500.00   4,500.
Overprinted type "b" in Black
15   A34   10c claret ('98)   3.00   1.90
16   A35   20c orange   3.00   2.50
17   A36   25c blue   3.00   3.75
18   A37   45c olive grn   24.00   22.00
    Nos. 12-18 (7)   51.50   42.90
    Set, never hinged   130.00

1903-28
Overprinted type "a" in Black
19   A42   1c brown   1.25   1.10
  a.   Inverted overprint   125.00   100.00
20   A43   2c orange brn   1.25   .55
21   A44   5c blue green   35.00   .50
22   A45   10c claret   40.00   .55
23   A45   20c orange   6.00   1.00
24   A45   25c blue   340.00   13.75
  a.   Double overprint   1,400.   —
25   A45   40c brown   375.00   22.00
26   A45   45c olive grn   6.00   7.50
27   A45   50c violet   135.00   25.00
28   A46   75c dk red & rose ('28)   85.00   6.00
29   A46   1 l brown & grn   5.00   .75
30   A46   1.25 l bl & ultra ('28)   37.50   3.00
31   A46   2 l dk grn & org ('25)   85.00   100.00
32   A46   2.50 l dk grn & org ('28)   250.00   75.00
33   A46   5 l blue & rose   24.00   35.00
    Nos. 19-33 (15)   1,426.   291.80
    Set, never hinged   3,700.

Surcharged in Black

1905
34   A45   15c on 20c orange   100.00   18.50
    Never hinged   250.00

1908-28
Overprinted type "a" in Black
35   A48   5c green   .90   .85
36   A48   10c claret ('09)   .90   .85
37   A48   15c slate ('20)   17.00   11.00
38   A49   20c green ('25)   24.50   11.00
39   A49   20c lilac brn ('28)   8.50   3.00
40   A49   25c blue ('09)   5.00   2.00
41   A49   30c gray ('25)   24.00   15.00
42   A49   40c brown ('16)   75.00   30.00
43   A49   50c violet ('16)   30.00   1.60
44   A49   60c brown car ('18)   21.00   21.50
  a.   Printed on both sides   2,000.
45   A49   60c brown org ('28)   135.00   240.00
46   A51   10 l gray grn & red ('16)   340.00   625.00
    Nos. 35-46 (12)   681.80   961.80
    Set, never hinged   1,970.

See No. 53.

A1

Government Building at Massaua — A2

1910-29   **Unwmk.**   **Engr.**   **Perf. 13½**
47   A1   15c slate   500.00   24.00
  a.   Perf. 11 ('29)   50.00   55.00
    Never hinged   125.00
48   A2   25c dark blue   12.50   13.50
  a.   Perf. 12   925.00   925.00

For surcharges see Nos. 51-52.

   A3   Farmer Plowing — A4

1914-28
49   A3   5c green   2.50   2.00
  a.   Perf. 11 ('28)   250.00   75.00
    Never hinged   625.00
50   A4   10c carmine   12.00   13.50
  a.   Perf. 11 ('28)   21.00   42.50
    Never hinged   52.50
  b.   Perf. 13½x14   55.00   55.00

No. 47 Surcharged in Red or Black

1916
51   A1   5c on 15c slate (R)   8.50   13.00
52   A1   20c on 15c slate   3.75   3.75
  a.   "CEN" for "CENT"   27.50   30.00
  b.   "CENT" omitted   160.00   160.00
  c.   "ENT"   44.00   44.00
    Set, never hinged   31.00

Italy No. 113 Overprinted in Black — f

1921   **Wmk. 140**   **Perf. 14**
53   A50   20c brown orange   3.75   11.00
    Never hinged   9.00

Victory Issue
Italian Victory Stamps of 1921 Overprinted type "f" 13mm long

1922
54   A64   5c olive green   1.90   6.00
55   A64   10c red   1.90   5.50
56   A64   15c slate green   1.90   8.50
57   A64   25c ultra   1.90   8.50
    Nos. 54-57 (4)   7.60   28.50
    Set, never hinged   27.00

Somalia Nos. 10-16 Overprinted In Black   g

1922   **Wmk. 140**
58   A1   2c on 1b brn   5.00   14.75
  a.   Pair, one missing "ERI-TREA"   2,450.
59   A1   5c on 2b bl grn   5.00   10.25
60   A2   10c on 1a claret   5.00   2.25
61   A2   15c on 2a brn org   5.00   2.25
62   A2   25c on 2½a blue   5.00   2.25
63   A2   50c on 5a yellow   20.00   10.25
  a.   "ERITREA" double   950.00

64   A2   1 l on 10a lilac   20.00   18.50
  a.   "ERITREA" double   1,850.   950.00
  b.   Pair, one missing "ERI-TREA"   3,750.
    Nos. 58-64 (7)   65.00   60.50
    Set, never hinged   160.00

See Nos. 81-87.

Propagation of the Faith Issue
Italy Nos. 143-146 Overprinted

1923
65   A68   20c ol grn & brn org   11.00   45.00
66   A68   30c claret & brn org   11.00   45.00
67   A68   50c vio & brn org   7.00   52.50
68   A68   1 l bl & brn org   7.00   82.50
    Nos. 65-68 (4)   36.00   225.00
    Set, never hinged   90.00

Fascisti Issue

Italy Nos. 159-164 Overprinted in Red or Black — j

1923   **Unwmk.**   **Perf. 14**
69   A69   10c dk green (R)   12.00   17.00
70   A69   30c dk violet (R)   12.00   17.00
71   A69   50c brown carmine   12.00   23.50
    Wmk. 140
72   A70   1 l blue   12.00   42.50
73   A70   2 l brown   12.00   52.50
74   A71   5 l black & blue (R)   12.00   80.00
    Nos. 69-74 (6)   72.00   232.50
    Set, never hinged   180.00

Manzoni Issue
Italy Nos. 165-170 Overprinted in Red

1924   **Perf. 14**
75   A72   10c brown red & blk   12.00   62.50
76   A72   15c blue grn & blk   12.00   62.50
77   A72   30c black & slate   12.00   62.50
78   A72   50c org brn & blk   12.00   62.50
79   A72   1 l blue & blk   75.00   375.00
80   A72   5 l violet & blk   375.00   2,750.
    Nos. 75-80 (6)   498.00   3,375.
    Set, never hinged   1,240.

On Nos. 79 and 80 the overprint is placed vertically at the left side.

Somalia Nos. 10-16 Overprinted type "g" in Blue or Red
Bars over Original Values in Black

1924
81   A1   2c on 1b brn   17.00   22.50
  a.   Pair, one without "ERI-TREA"   2,750.
82   A1   5c on 2b bl grn (R)   17.00   14.00
83   A2   10c on 1a rose red   8.50   12.00
84   A2   15c on 2a brn org   8.50   13.50
  a.   Pair, one without "ERI-TREA"   2,750.
  b.   "ERITREA" inverted   1,950.   2,000.
85   A2   25c on 2½a bl (R)   8.50   8.50
  a.   Double surcharge   1,475.
86   A2   50c on 5a yellow   8.50   16.00
87   A2   1 l on 10a lil (R)   22.50   22.50
    Nos. 81-87 (7)   76.50   109.00
    Set, never hinged   195.00

Stamps of Italy, 1901-08 Overprinted type "j" in Black

1924

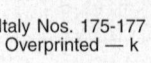

88	A42	1c brown	8.50	8.75
a.		Inverted overprint	250.00	
b.		Vertical pair, one without ovpt.	1,850.	
89	A43	2c orange brown	6.25	7.50
b.		Vertical pair, one without ovpt.	1,850.	
90	A48	5c green	8.50	8.75
		Nos. 88-90 (3)	23.25	25.00
		Set, never hinged	60.00	

Victor Emmanuel Issue

Italy Nos. 175-177
Overprinted — k

1925-26   **Unwmk.**   *Perf. 11*

91	A78	60c brown car	2.25	9.25
a.		Perf. 13½	12.50	37.50
92	A78	1 l dark blue	2.25	14.50
a.		Perf. 13½	24,000.	9,300.
		Never hinged	36,000.	

                Perf. 13½

93	A78	1.25 l dk blue ('26)	4.00	32.50
a.		Perf. 11	8.00	40.00
		Nos. 91-93 (3)	8.50	56.25
		Set, never hinged	21.50	

Saint Francis of Assisi Issue
Italian Stamps of 1926 Overprinted

1926   **Wmk. 140**   *Perf. 14*

94	A79	20c gray green	2.40	14.00
95	A80	40c dark violet	2.40	14.00
96	A81	60c red violet	2.40	25.00

Overprinted in Red

          Unwmk.   *Perf. 11*

97	A82	1.25 l dark blue	2.40	36.00

                Perf. 14

98	A83	5 l + 2.50 l ol grn	8.00	72.50
		Nos. 94-98 (5)	17.60	161.50
		Set, never hinged	42.50	

Italian Stamps of 1926 Overprinted type "f" in Black

1926   **Wmk. 140**   *Perf. 14*

99	A46	75c dk red & rose	70.00	20.00
a.		Double overprint	450.00	
100	A46	1.25 l blue & ultra	40.00	20.00
101	A46	2.50 l dk green & org	175.00	72.50
		Nos. 99-101 (3)	285.00	112.50
		Set, never hinged	710.00	

Volta Issue

Type of Italy, 1927,
Overprinted — o

1927

102	A84	20c purple	6.50	35.00
103	A84	50c deep orange	9.50	23.50
a.		Double overprint	160.00	
104	A84	1.25 l brt blue	14.00	57.50
		Nos. 102-104 (3)	30.00	116.00
		Set, never hinged	75.00	

Italian Stamps of 1925-28 Overprinted type "a" in Black

1928-29

105	A86	7½c lt brown ('29)	24.00	72.50
106	A86	50c brt violet	87.50	65.00
		Set, never hinged	270.00	

Italian Stamps of 1927-28 Overprinted type "f"

1928-29

107	A86	50c brt violet	72.50	60.00
		Never hinged	175.00	

          Unwmk.   *Perf. 11*

107A	A85	1.75 l deep brown	95.00	47.50
		Never hinged	240.00	

Italy No. 192 Overprinted type "o"

1928   **Wmk. 140**   *Perf. 14*

108	A85	50c brown & slate	24.00	12.00
		Never hinged	60.00	

Monte Cassino Issue

Types of 1929
Issue of Italy
Overprinted in
Red or Blue

1929   *Perf. 14*

109	A96	20c dk green (R)	6.50	18.50
110	A96	25c red orange (Bl)	6.50	18.50
111	A98	50c + 10c crim (Bl)	6.50	23.50
112	A98	75c + 15c ol brn (R)	6.50	23.50
113	A96	1.25 l + 25c dl vio (R)	14.50	42.50
114	A98	5 l + 1 l saph (R)	14.50	47.50

          Unwmk.

115	A100	10 l + 2 l gray brn	14.50	70.00
		Nos. 109-115 (7)	69.50	244.00
		Set, never hinged	170.00	

Royal Wedding Issue

Type of Italian
Stamps of 1930
Overprinted

1930   **Wmk. 140**

116	A101	20c yellow green	2.60	7.50
117	A101	50c + 10c dp org	1.90	9.25
118	A101	1.25 l + 25c rose red	1.90	19.00
		Nos. 116-118 (3)	6.40	35.75
		Set, never hinged	17.50	

Lancer
A5

Scene in Massaua
A6

2c, 35c, Lancer. 5c, 10c, Postman. 15c, Lineman. 25c, Askari (infantryman). 2 l, Railroad viaduct. 5 l, Asmara Deghe Selam. 10 l, Camels.

1930   **Wmk. 140**   **Litho.**   *Perf. 14*

119	A5	2c brt bl & blk	4.75	20.00
120	A5	5c dk vio & blk	8.00	2.40
121	A5	10c yel brn & blk	8.00	1.25
122	A5	15c dk grn & blk	8.00	1.60
123	A5	25c gray grn & blk	8.00	1.25
124	A5	35c red brn & blk	12.50	35.00
125	A6	1 l dk bl & blk	8.00	1.25
126	A6	2 l choc & blk	12.50	35.00
127	A6	5 l ol grn & blk	24.00	52.50
128	A6	10 l dl bl & blk	32.50	100.00
		Nos. 119-128 (10)	126.25	250.25
		Set, never hinged	300.00	

Ferrucci Issue
Types of Italian Stamps of 1930
Overprinted type "f" in Red or Blue

1930

129	A102	20c violet (R)	5.25	5.25
130	A103	25c dk green (R)	5.25	5.25
131	A103	50c black (R)	5.25	12.00
132	A103	1.25 l dp blue (R)	5.25	18.00

133	A104	5 l + 2 l dp car (Bl)	17.00	37.50
		Nos. 129-133 (5)	38.00	78.00
		Set, never hinged	95.00	

Virgil Issue
Types of Italian Stamps of 1930
Overprinted in Red or Blue

1930   **Photo.**

134	A106	15c violet black	1.00	9.50
135	A106	20c org brn	1.00	3.75
136	A106	25c dark green	1.00	3.75
137	A106	30c lt brown	1.00	3.75
138	A106	50c dull violet	1.00	3.75
139	A106	75c rose red	1.00	7.50
140	A106	1.25 l gray blue	1.00	9.50

       Unwmk.   **Engr.**

141	A106	5 l + 1.50 l dk vio	6.75	47.50
142	A106	10 l + 2.50 l ol brn	6.75	72.50
		Nos. 134-142 (9)	20.50	161.50
		Set, never hinged	46.80	

Saint Anthony of Padua Issue
Types of Italian Stamps of 1931
Overprinted type "f" in Blue, Red or Black

1931   **Photo.**   **Wmk. 140**

143	A116	20c brown (Bl)	2.00	18.00
144	A116	25c green (R)	2.00	7.00
145	A118	30c gray brn (Bl)	2.00	7.00
146	A118	50c dl violet (Bl)	2.00	7.00
147	A120	1.25 l slate bl (R)	3.00	14.00

       Unwmk.   **Engr.**

148	A121	75c black (R)	3.00	19.00
149	A122	5 l + 2.50 l dk brn (Bk)	6.75	80.00
		Nos. 143-149 (7)	20.75	178.00
		Set, never hinged	44.00	

Victor Emmanuel III — A13

1931   **Photo.**   **Wmk. 140**

150	A13	7½c olive brown	1.40	5.25
151	A13	20c slate bl & car	1.40	.25
152	A13	30c ol grn & brn vio	1.40	.25
153	A13	40c bl & yel grn	2.40	.50
154	A13	50c bis brn & ol	1.40	.25
155	A13	75c carmine rose	4.75	.25
156	A13	1.25 l vio & indigo	5.75	5.25
157	A13	2.50 l dull green	5.75	12.00
		Nos. 150-157 (8)	24.25	24.00
		Set, never hinged	60.00	

Camel
A14

Temple
Ruins
A18

Designs: 2c, 10c, Camel. 5c, 15c, Shark fishery. 25c, Baobab tree. 35c, Pastoral scene. 2 l, African elephant. 5 l, Eritrean man. 10 l, Eritrean woman.

1934   **Photo.**   **Wmk. 140**

158	A14	2c deep blue	2.40	4.75
159	A14	5c black	4.00	.40
160	A14	10c brown	4.00	.35
161	A14	15c orange brn	4.75	1.60
162	A14	25c gray green	4.00	.35
163	A14	35c purple	12.50	9.50
164	A18	1 l dk blue gray	.80	.35
165	A18	2 l olive black	35.00	3.25
166	A18	5 l carmine rose	19.00	6.50
167	A18	10 l red orange	27.50	22.50
		Nos. 158-167 (10)	113.95	49.55
		Set, never hinged	275.00	

Abruzzi Issue

Types of 1934
Issue Overprinted
in Black or Red

1934

168	A14	10c dull blue (R)	22.50	29.00
169	A14	15c blue	16.00	29.00
170	A14	35c green (R)	9.50	29.00
171	A14	1 l copper red	9.50	29.00
172	A14	2 l rose red	27.50	29.00
173	A18	5 l purple (R)	19.00	57.50
174	A18	10 l olive grn (R)	19.00	70.00
		Nos. 168-174 (7)	123.00	272.50
		Set, never hinged	293.00	

Grant's
Gazelle — A22

1934   **Photo.**

175	A22	5c ol grn & brn	5.50	22.50
176	A22	10c yel brn & blk	5.50	22.50
177	A22	20c scar & indigo	5.50	20.00
178	A22	50c dk vio & brn	5.50	20.00
179	A22	60c org brn & ind	5.50	27.50
180	A22	1.25 l dk bl & grn	5.50	47.50
		Nos. 175-180 (6)	33.00	160.00
		Set, never hinged	80.00	

Second Colonial Arts Exhibition, Naples.
See Nos. C1-C6.

> **Catalogue values for unused stamps in this section, from this point to the end of the section, are for Never Hinged items.**

Between 1981 and 1986 unofficial labels appeared showing such non-Eritrean subjects as the British royal weddings, Queen Mother, Queen's birthday, and the Duke & Duchess of York. These labels are not listed.

In 1978, two sets of stamps were issued for use within liberated areas of Eritrea and to publicize the liberation effort. A May 26 set of 5c, 10c, 80c and 1b commemorated the 8th anniv. of the Eritrean People's Liberation Front (EPLF). An August 1 set of 80c, 1b, 1.50b featured the Future of Eritrea theme. A September 1, 1991 set of 5c, 15c and 20c was issued with a Freedom Fighter design in orange and black almost identical to design A24. Although the 80c from the 1st 1978 issue was available at the Asmara post office in late 1992 and early 1993, there is no evidence that any of these stamps were available at the time of independence. Thus these stamps are more properly considered locals and provisionals.

A23

Designs: Freedom fighter with EPLF flags.

1991, Jan. 16   **Typo.**   *Perf. 11 rough*

192	A23	5c lt bl, blk & org	30.00	40.00
193	A23	15c pale green, blk & org	30.00	40.00
194	A23	20c pale yel, blk & org	30.00	40.00
195	A23	3b silver, blk & org	25.00	25.00
196	A23	5b gold, blk & org	25.00	25.00

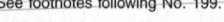

See footnotes following No. 199.

A24

1993, Feb. 1 Litho. Perf. 10

197	A24	5c lt bl, blk & org	25.00 25.00
198	A24	15c pale grn, blk & org	25.00 25.00
199	A24	20c pale yel, blk & org	25.00 25.00

Nos. 192-199 commemorate 30 years of the war for national liberation.

Nos. 192-199 were issued for local use, and became valid for international mail on Sept. 13, 1993.

Referendum for Independence — A25

Designs: 15c, Placing ballot in box. 60c, Group of arrows pointing right, one pointing left. 75c, Signs indicating "yes" & "no." 1b, Candle burning. 2b, Peace dove, horn over country map.

Perf. 14x15

1993, Apr. 22 Litho. Wmk. 373

200	A25	15c multicolored	1.50 1.50
201	A25	60c multicolored	2.75 2.75
202	A25	75c multicolored	4.00 4.00
203	A25	1b multicolored	7.50 7.50
204	A25	2b multicolored	10.00 10.00
		Nos. 200-204 (5)	25.75 25.75

Natl. Flag — A26

1993 Litho. Perf. 11 rough
Blue Border

205	A26	5c multicolored	2.50 .50
206	A26	20c multicolored	—
207	A26	35c multicolored	4.25 2.00
208	A26	50c multicolored	11.00 2.50
209	A26	70c multicolored	3.50 3.50
210	A26	80c multicolored	3.50 4.00

The border of the 40c, No. 215, is similar to that of this issue but it was issued with next set. And the type face of the "0.40" matches that set.

1994 Litho. Perf. 11 rough
Color of Border

211	A26	5c brown	2.00 1.50
212	A26	15c red	2.00 1.50
213	A26	20c gold	15.00 —
214	A26	25c lt blue	2.00 1.50
215	A26	40c blue	15.00 15.00
216	A26	60c yellow	3.00 2.00
217	A26	70c purple	3.00 2.25
218	A26	3b light green	7.50 6.00
219	A26	5b silver	9.00 6.00

Flag & Map — A27

1994, Sept. 2 Litho. Perf. 13½x14
Color of Border

220	A27	5c deep yellow	.45 .40
221	A27	10c yellow green	.50 .45
222	A27	20c salmon	.70 .65
223	A27	25c red	1.25 1.25
224	A27	40c lilac rose	1.40 1.25
225	A27	60c blue green	1.50 1.25
226	A27	70c dark green	1.60 1.50
227	A27	1b yellow	1.60 1.50
228	A27	2b orange	1.75 1.50
229	A27	3b blue violet	1.90 1.75
230	A27	5b red lilac	2.25 2.00
231	A27	10b pale violet	3.75 3.50
		Nos. 220-231 (12)	18.65 17.00

See Nos. 277A-277D.

World Tourism Organization, 20th Anniv. — A29

Perf. 14x13½, 13½x14
1995, Jan. 2 Litho.

232	A29	10c Fishing from boat	1.50 1.50
233	A29	35c Monument, vert.	1.50 1.50
234	A29	85c Winding road	3.00 3.00
235	A29	2b Stone dwelling, vert.	5.00 5.00
		Nos. 232-235 (4)	11.00 11.00

Fish — A30

Designs: 30c, Horned butterflyfish. 55c, Gonochaetodon larvatus. 70c, Shrimp lobster. 1b, Bluestripe snapper.

1995, Apr. 1 Perf. 14x13½

236	A30	30c multicolored	.60 .60
237	A30	55c multicolored	.85 .85
238	A30	70c multicolored	1.25 1.25
239	A30	1b multicolored	1.50 1.50
		Nos. 236-239 (4)	4.20 4.20

Independence Day — A31

Designs: 25c, Breaking chains, mountain, buildings, animals. 40c, Raising natl. flag, vert. 70c, Three men, holding natl. flag, sword, vert. 3b, Natl. flag, fireworks, vert.

Perf. 14x13½, 13½x14
1995, May 23 Litho.

240	A31	25c multicolored	.40 .40
241	A31	40c multicolored	.45 .45
242	A31	70c multicolored	.70 .70
243	A31	3b multicolored	1.40 1.40
		Nos. 240-243 (4)	2.95 2.95

Future Development Plan — A32

1995, Aug. 28 Litho. Perf. 13

244	A32	60c Building bridge	.60 .60
245	A32	80c Trees	.75 .75
246	A32	90c Rural village	.90 .90
247	A32	1b Camels	1.00 1.00
		Nos. 244-247 (4)	3.25 3.25

A33

1995, Oct. 23 Perf. 13½x14

248	A33	40c shown	.30 .30
249	A33	60c Tree, emblem	.40 .40
250	A33	70c Dove, "50," emblem	.50 .50
251	A33	2b like No. 248	2.25 2.25
		Nos. 248-251 (4)	3.45 3.45

UN, 50th anniv.

A34

COMESA, Committee for Economic Growth and Development in Southern Africa: 40c, Map of African member countries. 50c, Tree with country names on branches. 60c, Emblem, 3b, Emblem surrounded by country flags, horiz.

1995, Oct. 2 Perf. 13½x14, 14x13½

252	A34	40c multicolored	.30 .30
253	A34	50c multicolored	.50 .50
254	A34	60c multicolored	.60 .60
255	A34	3b multicolored	2.25 2.25
		Nos. 252-255 (4)	3.65 3.65

FAO, 50th Anniv. — A35

5c, Food bowl with world map on it, spoon. 25c, Men with tractor. 80c, Mother bird feeding chicks. 3b, Vegetables in horn of plenty.

1995, Dec. 18 Litho. Perf. 13x14

256	A35	5c multicolored	.40 .40
257	A35	25c multicolored	.40 .40
258	A35	80c multicolored	.80 .80
259	A35	3b multicolored	2.50 2.50
		Nos. 256-259 (4)	4.10 4.10

Endangered Fauna — A36

No. 260: a, Green monkey. b, Aardwolf. c, Dugong. d, Maned rat.

Beisa oryx: No. 261: a, With young. b, One facing left. c, Two with heads together. d, One facing right.

White-eyed gull: No. 262: a, Preening. b, In flight. c, Two standing. d, One facing right.

1996, July 15 Litho. Perf. 14

260-262	A36	3b Set of 3 strips	26.00 26.00

Nos. 260-262 were each issued in sheets of 12 stamps, containing three strips of four stamps, Nos. a.-d. No. 261 for World Wildlife Fund.

Martyrs Day — A37

1996, June 17 Litho. Perf. 13½x14

263	A37	40c People, flag	.40 .40
264	A37	60c At grave	.40 .40
265	A37	70c Mother, child	.80 .80
266	A37	80c Planting crops	1.00 1.00
		Nos. 263-266 (4)	2.60 2.60

1996 Summer Olympic Games, Atlanta — A38

No. 267, Cycling. No. 268, Basketball, vert. No. 269, Volleyball, vert. No. 270, Soccer.

No. 271, vert: a, Volleyball. b, Laurel wreath. c, Basketball. d, Torch. e, Cycling, yellow shirt. f, Torch, diff. g, Cycling, green shirt. h, Gold medal. i, Soccer.

Each 10b: No. 272, Soccer, vert. No. 273, Cycling, vert.

1996, Nov. 20 Litho. Perf. 14

267-270	A38	3b Set of 4	7.50 7.50
271	A38	2b Sheet of 9, #a.-i.	11.00 11.00

Souvenir Sheets

272-273	A38	Set of 2	11.00 11.00

UNICEF, 50th Anniv. — A39

UNICEF emblem and: 40c, Mother with child. 55c, Nurse helping child. 60c, Weighing baby. 95c, Boy with one leg walking with crutch.

1996, Dec. 9 Litho. Perf. 14x13½

274	A39	40c multicolored	.45 .45
275	A39	55c multicolored	.45 .45
276	A39	60c multicolored	1.00 1.00
277	A39	95c multicolored	1.00 1.00
		Nos. 274-277 (4)	2.90 2.90

Flag and Map Type of 1994 Redrawn With Islands Added on Map at Lower Right

1996, Dec. 25 Litho. Perf. 13½x14
Color of Border

277A	A27	20c salmon	— —
277B	A27	40c lilac rose	— —
277C	A27	60c blue green	— —
277D	A27	3b blue violet	— —

Revival of Eritrea Railway — A40

Designs: 40c, Repairing track. 55c, Steam train arriving at station. 60c, Train shuttle transporting people. 95c, Train tunnel.

1997, Jan. 10

278	A40	40c multicolored	.50 .50
279	A40	55c multicolored	.50 .50
280	A40	60c multicolored	.50 .50
281	A40	95c multicolored	1.50 1.50
		Nos. 278-281 (4)	3.00 3.00

National Service — A41

40c, Service members, speaker's platform, flags, vert. 55c, People looking over mountainside, vert. 60c, People digging ditches. 95c, Man standing on mountain top, overlooking valley, lake.

1996, Dec. 28 Perf. 13½x14, 14x13½

282	A41	40c multicolored	.75 .75
283	A41	55c multicolored	.75 .75
284	A41	60c multicolored	1.25 1.25
285	A41	95c multicolored	2.00 2.00
		Nos. 282-285 (4)	4.75 4.75

Butterflies and Moths — A42

1b, Pieris napi. 2b, Heliconius melpomerie. 4b, Ornithoptera goliath. 8b, Heliconius astraea.

No. 290, vert, each 3b: a, Psaphis eusehemoides. b, Papilio brookiana. c, Parnassius charitonius. d, Morpho cypris. e, Dariaus plexippus. f, Precis octavia. g, Teinopalpus imperialis. h, Samia gloreri. i, Automeris nyctimene.

No. 291, each 3b: a, Papilio polymnestar. b, Ornithoptera paradiseo. c, Graphium marcellus. d, Panaxia quadripuntcaria. e, Cardui japonica. f, Papilio childrence. g, Philosamea cynthis. h, Actias luna. i, Heticopis acit.

Each 10b: No. 292, Papilio glaucus. No. 293, Parnassius phoebus.

1997, June 16 Litho. Perf. 14

286-289	A42	Set of 4	12.00 12.00

Sheets of 9

290-291	A42	3b Set of 2	
		Sheets, #a.-i.	30.00 30.00

Souvenir Sheets

292-293	A42	10b Set of 2	
		Sheets	15.00 15.00

Environmental Protection — A43

1997, Aug. 15 Litho. Perf. 14x13½

294	A43	60c Irrigation	.90 .90
295	A43	90c Reforestation	.90 .90
296	A43	95c Preventing erosion	2.00 2.00
		Nos. 294-296 (3)	3.80 3.80

Marine Life — A44

No. 297, each 3n: a, Sergeant major, white tipped reef shark. b, Hawksbill turtle, devil ray (e). c, Surgeonfish. d, Red sea houndfish, humpback whale (a, g). e, Devil ray (b, f, h). f, Devil ray (e, c), two-banded clownfish. g, Long-nosed butterflyfish. h, Red sea houndfish (g), yellow sweetlips (i). i, White moray eel.

No. 298, each 3n: a, Masked butterflyfish. b, Suckerfish (a), whale shark (a). c, Sunrise dottyback, bluefin trevally (a). d, Moon wrasse (a), purple moon angel (a), two-banded anemonefish. e, Lionfish (b, f). f, White tipped shark, sand diver fish. g, Golden jacks (d), lunar tailed grouper. h, Batfish (e, i). i, Black triggerfish.

Each 10n: No. 299, Powder-blue surge-onfish. No. 300, Twin-spot wrasse.

1997, Dec. 29   Litho.   Perf. 14
Sheets of 9, #a.-i.
297-298   A44   Set of 2   20.00 20.00

Souvenir Sheets
299-300   A44   Set of 2 Sheets   12.50 12.50

A45

Natl. Constitution: 10c, Speaker, crowd seated beneath tree. 40c, Dove, scales of justice. 85c, Hands holding constitution.

1997, Oct. 24   Litho.   Perf. 13½x14
301-303   A45   Set of 3   3.50 3.50

A46

Birds — No. 304, each 3n: a, African darter (b, d, e). b, White-headed vulture (e). c, Egyptian vulture (f). d, Yellow-billed hornbill (g). e, Helmeted guineafowl (d, f). f, Secretary bird (d, e, i). g, Martial eagle (h). h, Bateleur eagle (i). i, Red-billed queleas.

No. 305, each 3n: a, Black-headed weaver. b, Abyssinian roller (c, f). c, Abyssinian ground hornbill (b, e, f). d, Lichtenstein's sandgrouse. e, Erckel's francolin (d, g, h). f, Arabian bustard (e, i). g, Chestnut-backed finch-lark. h, Desert lark. i, Bifasciated lark.

Each 10n: #306, Peregrine falcon. #307, Hoopoe.

1998, Mar. 16   Litho.   Perf. 14
Sheets of 9, #a.-i.
304-305   A46   Set of 2   25.00 25.00

Souvenir Sheets
306-307   A46   Set of 2 Sheets   12.00 12.00

Dwellings — A47

1998, July 1   Litho.   Perf. 13½x14
308   A47   50c Highlanders   1.50 1.50
309   A47   60c Lowlanders   1.50 1.50
310   A47   85c Danakils (Afars)   1.50 1.50
     Nos. 308-310 (3)   4.50 4.50

Traditional Hair Styles — A48

1998, Nov. 23   Litho.   Perf. 13½x14
311   A48   10c Cunama   .30   .30
312   A48   50c Tignnys   .60   .60
313   A48   85c Bilen   1.00 1.00
314   A48   95c Tigre   1.25 1.25
     Nos. 311-314 (4)   3.15 3.15
         Dated 1997.

A49

Traditional Musical Instruments: 15c, Chirawata. 60c, Imbilta, malaket, shambeko. 75c, Kobero. 85c, K'rar.

1998, Dec. 28   Litho.   Perf. 13½x14
315   A49   15c multicolored   .35   .35
316   A49   60c multicolored   .60   .60
317   A49   75c multicolored   .80   .80
318   A49   85c multicolored   1.00 1.00
     Nos. 315-318 (4)   2.75 2.75

A50

1999, May 25   Litho.   Perf. 13¼x14
319   A50   60c green & multi   .60   .60
320   A50   1n red & multi   1.00 1.00
321   A50   3n blue & multi   4.00 4.00
     Nos. 319-321 (3)   5.60 5.60
      Independence, 8th Anniv.

1997 Introduction of Nakfa Currency — A51

Bank notes: 10c, 1 Nakfa. 60c, 5 Nakfa. 80c, 10 Nakfa. 1n, 20 Nakfa. 2n, 50 Nakfa. 3n, 100 Nakfa.

1999, Nov. 8   Litho.   Perf. 13¼
322   A51   10c multicolored   .45   .45
323   A51   60c multicolored   .60   .60
324   A51   80c multicolored   .75   .75
325   A51   1n multicolored   1.00 1.00
326   A51   2n multicolored   2.00 2.00
327   A51   3n multicolored   3.50 3.50
     Nos. 322-327 (6)   8.30 8.30

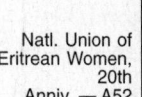
Natl. Union of Eritrean Women, 20th Anniv. — A52

Designs: 5c, Woman and child, vert. 10c, Three women. 25c, Women and flag. 1n, Woman with binoculars.

Perf. 13¼x14, 14x13¼
1999, Nov. 26
328   A52   5c multicolored   .35   .35
329   A52   10c multicolored   .35   .35
330   A52   25c multicolored   .50   .50
331   A52   1n multicolored   .75   .75
     Nos. 328-331 (4)   1.95 1.95

A53

Marine Life — A54

No. 332, each 3n: a, Coachwhip ray. b, Sulfur damselfish. c, "Gray moray." d, Sabre squirrelfish. e, Rusty parrotfish. f, "Striped eel catfish."

No. 333, each 3n: a, Spangled emperor. b, Devil scorpionfish. c, Crown squirrelfish. d, Vanikoro sweeper. e, Sergeant major. f, Giant manta.

No. 334, each 3n: a, Chilomycterus spilostylus. b, Dascyllus marginatus. c, Balistapus undulatus. d, Pomacanthus semicirculatus. e, Rhinecanthus assasi. f, Millepora.

No. 335, each 3n: a, Epinephalus fasciata. b, Pygoplites diacanthus. c, Cephalopholis miniata. d, Centropyge eibli. e, Ostracion cubicus. f, Heniochus acuminatus.

Each 10n: No. 336, Centropyge flavissimus. No. 337, Larabicus quadrilineatus. No. 338, Anthias squamipinnis. 15n, Pomacanthus maculosus.

2000, Apr. 17   Litho.   Perf. 14
Sheets of 6, #a.-f.
332-333   A53   Set of 2   13.50 13.50
334-335   A54   Set of 2   13.50 13.50

Souvenir Sheets
336-338   A54   Set of 3   15.00 15.00
339   A54   15n multi   6.00 6.00

Illustrations on Nos. 332c and 332f were switched.

A55

Flag and: 5c, Man with sword. 10c, Ship Denden Assab. 25c, Independence Day festivities. 60c, Soldiers and barracks. 1n, Finger, heart and map. 2n, People under tree. 3n, Ballot box. 5n, Eritrean seal, military plane, tank, ship. 7n, Seal. 10n, Ten-nakfa note.

Perf. 13¾x13¼
2000, Mar. 17   Litho.
Denominations in Sans-Serif Type
340-349   A55   Set of 10   16.00 16.00
      See Nos. 363A-363F.

Worldwide Fund for Nature (WWF) — A56

Proteles cristatus: a, Laying down. b, Pair in den. c, Walking. d, Close-up.

2001, Oct. 1   Litho.   Perf. 14
350   A56   3n Block or strip of 4,
          #a-d   4.50 4.50

Wild Animals A57

No. 351, 3n: a, Salt's dik-dik. b, Klipspringer. c, Greater kudu. d, Soemmering's gazelle. e, Dorcas gazelle. f, Somali wild ass.

No. 352, 3n: a, Aardvark. b, Black-backed jackal. c, Striped hyena. d, Spotted hyena. e, East African leopard. f, African elephant.

2001, Oct. 29   Sheets of 6, #a-f
351-352   A57   Set of 2   10.00 10.00

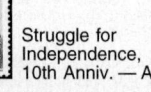
Struggle for Independence, 10th Anniv. — A58

Designs: 20c, Women, flag, jewelry. 60c, Doves, stylized flag, vert. 1n, Bees, honeycomb, flag, vert. 3n, Men with sticks, vert.

Perf. 13x13¼, 13¼x13
2001, May 23   Litho.
353-356   A58   Set of 4   3.00 3.00

Liberation of Nakfa, 25th Anniv. — A59

Designs: 50c, Denden. 1n, Town of Nakfa, 1977 (77x27mm). 3n, First Organizational Congress of the Eritrean People's Liberation Front (77x27mm).

2002, Mar. 23   Litho.   Perf. 14x13¼
357-359   A59   Set of 3   2.00 2.00

Martyr's Day — A60

Designs: 1n, People and map. 2n, Hand, map of Badma area, and flag. 3n, Map and ship. 5n, Dove, map and dead man (49x29mm, triangular).

Perf. 14x13¼, 13½ (5n)
2002, June 20
360-363   A60   Set of 4   4.50 4.50

Type of 2000 Redrawn
Flag and: 30c, People under tree. 45c, Man with sword. 50c, Independence Day festivities. 60c, Soldiers and barracks. 75c, Ship Denden Assab. 3n, Ballot box.

2002, Oct. 21   Litho.   Perf. 13¼x14¼
Denominations in Serifed Type
363A   A55   30c multi   —   —
363B   A55   45c multi   —   —
363C   A55   50c multi   —   —
363D   A55   60c multi   —   —
363E   A55   75c multi   —   —
363F   A55   3n multi   —   —

Denominations on Nos. 340-349 are in sans-serif type.

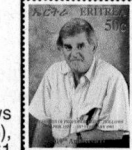
Dr. Fred C. Hollows (1929-93), Ophthalmologist — A61

Designs: 50c, Portrait. 1n, Hollows wearing ophthalmological equipment. 2n, Hollows with man.

2003, Feb. 10   Perf. 13¼x14
364-366   A61   Set of 3   2.00 2.00

Eritrea — People's Republic of China Diplomatic Relations, 10th Anniv. — A62

2003, May 24   Perf. 12
367   A62   4.50n multi   2.50 2.50

Eritrean postal authorities have declared "illegal" the following items:

Sheetlet of nine 5n stamps depicting Trains;

Sheetlets of nine 3n stamps depicting Marilyn Monroe (two different), Dogs, The Beatles "Yellow Submarine," September 11 firefighters, Brigitte Bardot, Grace Kelly, Sophia Loren, Golf etiquette, Sexy actresses, Sexy models, Boris Vallejo nudes, Dorian Cleavenger, Michael Möbius, Olivia, Ricky Carralero, Concorde;

Sheetlets of six stamps with various denominations depicting Lighthouses (with Rotary emblem) (two different), Hopper paintings (two different), Vettriano paintings (two different), Marilyn Monroe (two different), Elvgren pin-ups (two different), Teddy bears (two different);

Sheetlets of six 3n stamps depicting Van Gogh paintings, Paintings of nudes;

Sheetlets of five 3n stamps depicting Corot paintings, Pisarro paintings, Renoir paintings, Elvis Presley, Marilyn Monroe;

Sheetlets of four stamps with various denominations depicting Pandas (with Scouting emblem), Crocodiles (with Scouting emblem), Buffalos (with Rotary emblem), Elephants (with Rotary emblem), Monkeys (with Scouting emblem), Lizards (with Scouting emblem), Snakes (with Scouting Emblem), Turtles (with Rotary emblem), Wild cats (with Scouting emblem), Birds of prey (with Rotary emblem), Fowl (with Rotary emblem), Parrots (with Scouting emblem), Penguins (with Rotary emblem), Fish (with Rotary emblem), Marine life (with Scouting emblem), Mushrooms (with Rotary emblem), Butterflies (with Scouting emblem), Bees (with Scouting emblem), Spiders (with Scouting emblem);

Sheetlets of four 3n stamps depicting Dinosaurs (with Scouting emblem), Dinosaurs (with Rotary emblem) Elephants (with Scouting emblem), Elephants (with Rotary emblem), Horses (with Scouting emblem), Horses (with Rotary emblem), Birds (with Scouting emblem), Birds (with Rotary emblem), Penguins (with Scouting emblem), Penguins (with Rotary emblem), Orchids (with Scouting emblem), Orchids (with Rotary emblem), Butterflies (with Scouting emblem), Butterflies (with Rotary emblem), Cars (with Scouting emblem), Cars (with Rotary emblem), Motorcycles (with Scouting emblem), Motorcycles (with Rotary emblem), Trains (with Scouting emblem), Trains (with Rotary emblem);

Sheetlets of three 5n stamps depicting Dinosaurs (with Rotary emblem) (two different), Pandas;

Strips of three 5n stamps depicting Steam trains (four different);

Souvenir sheet with one 8n stamp depicting Steam Trains (with Rotary emblem) (two different), Dinosaurs (with Rotary emblem), Pandas (with Scouting emblem), Elephants (with Scouting emblem), Tigers (with Scouting emblem), Birds of prey (with Scouting emblem);

Souvenir sheets with one 5n stamp depicting Marilyn Monroe (six different), Lighthouses (with Rotary emblem) (four different), Teddy bears (four different), Hopper paintings (two different), Vettriano paintings (two different).

Eritrean Railway
A63

Independence Celebrations
A63a

Massawa
A63b

2003 Litho. *Perf. 14x13¼*
Denomination Color
368	A63	5c Prussian blue	.25	.25
369	A63	10c greenish blk	.25	.25
370	A63	15c lilac	.25	.25
371	A63	35c violet	.25	.25
372	A63	50c orange	.25	.25
373	A63	90c olive green	.25	.25
374	A63	1n red	.25	.25
375	A63	2n blue violet	.55	.55
376	A63	10n red	2.75	2.75
376A	A63a	50n white	12.00	12.00
376B	A63b	75n white	18.00	18.00
376C	A63	100n white	24.00	24.00

Nos. 368-376C (12) 59.05 59.05
Issued: 50n, 75n, 100n, 8/29.

Liberation of Massawa, 14th Anniv. — A64

Designs: 40c, Tanks as fountains. 50c, Boat with soldiers.
No. 379: a, 3n, Crashed airplane, people, soldiers in shallow water. b, 3n, Tank, soldier, flag, boat. c, 4n, People, buildings at shore.

2004
377-378	A64	Set of 2	1.00	1.00

Miniature Sheet
379	A64	Sheet of 3, #a-c	4.00	4.00

Man and Camels — A65

Man and Cattle — A66

Highland Woman, Child and Camel — A67

2004, July 12 Litho. *Perf. 12*
Frame Color
380	A65	20c violet blue	.25	.25
381	A65	25c red violet	.25	.25
382	A65	40c brown	.25	.25
383	A66	50c red	.25	.25
384	A66	55c green	.25	.25
385	A66	60c light blue	.25	.25
386	A67	80c olive green	.50	.50
387	A67	1n orange	.50	.50
388	A67	4.50n blue	1.25	1.25

Nos. 380-388 (9) 3.75 3.75

A68

A69

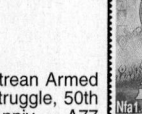
Eritrean Armed Struggle, 50th Anniv. — A77

Perf. 13¼x14, 14x13¼
2006, Jan. 5 Litho.
389	A68	1.50n multi	.25	.25
390	A69	6n multi	.80	.80
391	A70	25n multi	3.50	3.50

Nos. 389-391 (3) 4.55 4.55

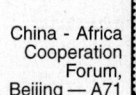
China - Africa Cooperation Forum, Beijing — A71

2006, Nov. 3 Litho. *Perf. 12*
392	A71	7n multi	.95	.95

African Soccer Confederation, 50th Anniv. — A72

Anniversary emblem and: 3n, Eritrean soccer players and flags. 5n, Soccer field. 10n, Soccer players in action.

2007, May 29 Litho. *Perf. 13x13¼*
393-395	A72	Set of 3	2.40	2.40

Soldiers Carrying Flag — A73

2008, Dec. 31 Litho. *Perf. 14x13¼*
Denomination Color
396	A73	15c dark blue	.25	.25
397	A73	35c green	.25	.25
398	A73	50c orange	.25	.25
399	A73	70c red	.25	.25
400	A73	75c blue	.25	.25
401	A73	90c brown	.25	.25
402	A73	1.50n red violet	.25	.25
403	A73	2n indigo	.25	.25
404	A73	3n org yellow	.40	.40
405	A73	5n gray	.65	.65
406	A73	10n yel green	1.25	1.25

Nos. 396-406 (11) 4.30 4.30

Eritrean National Festival — A74

Ethnic groups in costume: 5c, Afars. 10c, Bilens. 30c, Hedarebs. 95c, Kunamas. 1n, Naras. 1.50n, Rashaidas. 4n, Sahos. 7n, Tigres. 8n, Tigrinyas.

2010, Nov. 15
407-415	A74	Set of 9	4.25	4.25

Independence, 20th Anniv. — A75

Designs: 70c, Eritrean flag, stylized people defining border. 95c, Map of Eritrea, hand holding torch, vert. 8n, Map of Africa, flag of Eritrea, vert.

2011, Mar. 24 *Perf. 14x13¼, 13¼x14*
416-418	A75	Set of 3	2.00	2.00

Eritrean Martyr's Day, 20th Anniv. — A76

Designs: 80c, Eritreans and woman holding shining square. 9n, Woamn and child lighting candles

2011, June 17 *Perf. 13¾x13¼*
419-420	A76	Set of 2	2.10	2.10

Designs: 1.50n, Arm holding rifle, "50," flame, stylized people. 7n, Flame, arms holding rifles.

2011, Sept. 3 *Perf. 13¼x14*
421-422	A77	Set of 2	1.75	1.75

Miniature Sheet

Diplomatic Relations Between Eritrea and People's Republic of China, 20th Anniv. — A78

No. 423: a, 1n, Mosque, Nakfa, Eritrea. b, 1n, Harbor, Massawa, Eritrea. c, 1.50n, Pagoda and bridge, Yan'an, People's Republic of China. d, 1.50n, Harbor, Qingdao, People's Republic of China. e, 7n, Buildings, Asmara, Eritrea. f, 7n, Camels. g, 10n, Buildings, Datong, People's Republic of China. h, 10n, Antelopes.

2013, May 27 Litho. *Perf. 12*
423	A78	Block of 8, #a-h	8.50	8.50
i.		Souvenir sheet of 8, #423a-423h	8.50	8.50

Gelaalo — A79

2013, June 27 Litho. *Perf. 13x13¼*
Frame Color
424	A79	55c orange yellow	.50	.50
425	A79	60c green	.55	.55
426	A79	70c purple	.60	.60
427	A79	80c blue	.70	.70
428	A79	90c red	.80	.80
429	A79	90c olive yellow	.85	.85
430	A79	1.50n yellow brown	1.40	1.40
431	A79	50n light blue	42.50	42.50

Nos. 424-431 (8) 47.90 47.90

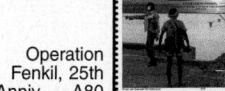
Operation Fenkil, 25th Anniv. — A80

Designs: 3n, Soldiers watching man in water. 7n, Tank in Massawa. 10n, Soldiers watching people in boats.

Perf. 13¼x13¾
2015, Feb. 10 Litho.
432-434	A80	Set of 3	4.25	4.25

A81

Monuments and Statues — A70

Liberation of
Eritrea, 25th
Anniv. — A82

2016   Litho.   Perf. 14x14¼
435 A81 7n multi   1.40 1.40
436 A82 8n multi   1.60 1.60

Souvenir Sheet

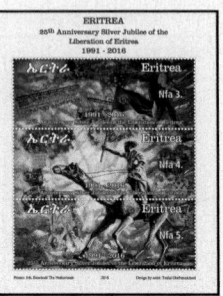

Liberation of Eritrea, 25th
Anniv. — A83

No. 437: a, 3n, Eritrean flag. b, 4n,
Flagbearer and camel's head. c, 5n, Body of
camel.

2016   Litho.   Perf. 14x13½
437 A83 Sheet of 3, #a-c   2.75 2.75

SEMI-POSTAL STAMPS

Many issues of Italy and Italian Colonies include one or more semipostal denominations. To avoid splitting sets, these issues are generally listed as regular postage, airmail, etc., unless all values carry a surtax.

Italy Nos. B1-B3 Overprinted type "f"

1915-16   Wmk. 140   Perf. 14
B1 SP1 10c + 5c rose   4.00 16.00
  a.   "EPITREA"   32.50 45.00
  b.   Inverted overprint   800.00 800.00
B2 SP2 15c + 5c slate   32.50 27.50
B3 SP2 20c + 5c orange   4.75 35.00
  a.   "EPITREA"   80.00 110.00
  b.   Inverted overprint   800.00 800.00
  c.   Pair, one with ovpt.   4,500.
      Nos. B1-B3 (3)   41.25 78.50
      Set, never hinged   102.00

No. B2 Surcharged

1916
B4 SP2 20c on 15c+5c
          slate   32.50 35.00
      Never hinged   80.00
  a.   "EPITREA"   80.00 110.00
  b.   Pair, one without over-
        print   2,000.

Counterfeits exist of the minor varieties of
Nos. B1, B3-B4.

Holy Year Issue
Italy Nos. B20-B25 Overprinted in
Black or Red

1925   Perf. 12
B5 SP4 20c + 10c dk grn &
          brn   4.00 24.00
B6 SP4 30c + 15c dk brn &
          brn   4.00 27.50
  a.   Double overprint

B7 SP4 50c + 25c vio & brn   4.00 24.00
B8 SP4 60c + 30c dp rose &
          brn   4.00 32.50
  a.   Inverted overprint
B9 SP8 1 l + 50c dp bl &
          vio (R)   4.00 40.00
B10 SP8 5 l + 2.50 l org brn
          & vio (R)   4.00 60.00
      Nos. B5-B10 (6)   24.00 208.00
      Set, never hinged   60.00

Colonial Institute Issue

"Peace" Substituting
Spade for Sword — SP1

1926   Typo.   Perf. 14
B11 SP1 5c + 5c brown   1.20   9.50
B12 SP1 10c + 5c olive grn   1.20   9.50
B13 SP1 20c + 5c blue grn   1.20   9.50
B14 SP1 40c + 5c brown red   1.20   9.50
B15 SP1 60c + 5c orange   1.20   9.50
B16 SP1 1 l + 5c blue   1.20 20.00
      Nos. B11-B16 (6)   7.20 67.50
      Set, never hinged   18.00

The surtax of 5c on each stamp was for the
Italian Colonial Institute.

Italian Semi-Postal
Stamps of 1926
Overprinted

1927   Unwmk.   Perf. 11½
B17 SP10 40c + 20c dk brn
          & blk   4.00 45.00
B18 SP10 60c + 30c brn
          red & ol
          brn   4.00 45.00
B19 SP10 1.25 l + 60c dp bl
          & blk   4.00 65.00
B20 SP10 5 l + 2.50 l dk
          grn & blk   6.50 100.00
      Nos. B17-B20 (4)   18.50 255.00
      Set, never hinged   46.00

The surtax on these stamps was for the
charitable work of the Voluntary Militia for Italian National Defense.

Fascism and
Victory — SP2

1928 Wmk. 140 Typo.   Perf. 14
B21 SP2 20c + 5c blue grn   3.25 14.00
B22 SP2 30c + 5c red   3.25 14.00
B23 SP2 50c + 10c purple   3.25 24.00
B24 SP2 1.25 l + 20c dk blue   4.00 32.50
      Nos. B21-B24 (4)   13.75 84.50
      Set, never hinged   34.00

The surtax was for the Society Africana
d'Italia, whose 46th anniv. was commemorated by the issue.

Types of Italian Semi-Postal Stamps
of 1928 Overprinted type "f"

1929   Unwmk.   Perf. 11
B25 SP10 30c + 10c red &
          blk   4.75 27.50
B26 SP10 50c + 20c vio &
          blk   4.75 30.00
B27 SP10 1.25 l + 50c brn &
          bl   7.25 52.50
B28 SP10 5 l + 2 l olive
          grn & blk   7.25 100.00
      Nos. B25-B28 (4)   24.00 210.00
      Set, never hinged   60.00

Surtax for the charitable work of the Voluntary Militia for Italian Natl. Defense.

Types of Italian Semi-Postal Stamps
of 1930 Overprinted type "f" in
Black or Red

1930   Perf. 14
B29 SP10 30c + 10c dk
          grn & bl
          grn (Bk)   35.00 65.00
B30 SP10 50c + 10c dk
          grn & vio   35.00 100.00
B31 SP10 1.25 l + 30c ol
          brn & red
          brn   35.00 100.00

B32 SP10 5 l + 1.50 l ind
          & grn   120.00 275.00
      Nos. B29-B32 (4)   225.00 540.00
      Set, never hinged   560.00

Surtax for the charitable work of the Voluntary Militia for Italian Natl. Defense.

Agriculture — SP3

1930   Photo.   Wmk. 140
B33 SP3 50c + 20c ol brn   4.00 25.00
B34 SP3 1.25 l + 20c dp bl   4.00 25.00
B35 SP3 1.75 l + 20c green   4.00 27.50
B36 SP3 2.55 l + 50c purple   9.50 45.00
B37 SP3 5 l + 1 l dp car   9.50 67.50
      Nos. B33-B37 (5)   31.00 190.00
      Set, never hinged   76.00

Italian Colonial Agricultural Institute, 25th
anniv. The surtax aided that institution.

AIR POST STAMPS

Desert
Scene — AP1

Design: 80c, 1 l, 2 l, Plane and globe.

Wmk. Crowns (140)
1934, Oct. 17   Photo.   Perf. 14
C1 AP1 25c sl bl & org
          red   5.50 22.50
C2 AP1 50c grn & indigo   5.50 20.00
C3 AP1 75c brn & org red   5.50 20.00
C4 AP1 80c org brn & ol
          grn   5.50 22.50
C5 AP1 1 l scar & ol grn   5.50 27.50
C6 AP1 2 l dk bl & brn   5.50 47.50
      Nos. C1-C6 (6)   33.00 160.00
      Set, never hinged   81.00

Second Colonial Arts Exhibition, Naples.

Plowing — AP3

Plane and
Cacti — AP6

Designs: 25c, 1.50 l, Plowing. 50c, 2 l, Plane over mountain pass. 60c, 5 l, Plane and trees. 75c, 10 l, Plane and cacti. 1 l, 3 l, Bridge.

1936   Photo.
C7 AP3 25c deep green   4.75   4.75
C8 AP3 50c dark brown   3.25   .35
C9 AP3 60c brn org   6.50 16.00
C10 AP6 75c org brn   4.75   1.60
C11 AP3 1 l deep blue   1.60   .35
C12 AP3 1.50 l purple   6.50   .85
C13 AP3 2 l gray blue   6.50   3.25
C14 AP3 3 l copper red   25.00 27.50
C15 AP3 5 l green   19.00   8.00
C16 AP6 10 l rose red   45.00 27.50
      Nos. C7-C16 (10)   122.85 90.15
      Set, never hinged   300.00

AIR POST SEMI-POSTAL STAMPS

King Victor
Emmanuel
III — SPAP1

1934 Wmk. 140 Photo. Perf. 14
CB1 SPAP1 25c + 10c
          ol grn   9.50 27.50
CB2 SPAP1 50c + 10c
          brn   9.50 27.50
CB3 SPAP1 75c + 15c
          car   9.50 27.50
CB4 SPAP1 80c + 15c
          brnsh
          blk   9.50 27.50
CB5 SPAP1 1 l + 20c
          redsh
          brn   9.50 27.50
CB6 SPAP1 2 l + 20c
          bl   9.50 27.50
CB7 SPAP1 3 l + 25c
          vio   27.50 125.00
CB8 SPAP1 5 l + 25c
          org   27.50 125.00
CB9 SPAP1 10 l + 30c
          lil   27.50 125.00
CB10 SPAP1 25 l + 2 l
          grn   27.50 125.00
      Nos. CB1-CB10 (10)   167.00 665.00
      Set, never hinged   410.00

65th birthday of King Victor Emmanuel III and the nonstop flight from Rome to Mogadiscio. Used values are for stamps canceled to order.

AIR POST SEMI-POSTAL OFFICIAL
STAMP

Type of Air Post Semi-Postal
Stamps, 1934, Overprinted in Black

1934   Wmk. 140   Perf. 14
CBO1 SPAP1 25 l + 2 l cop
          red   2,800.
      Never hinged   5,500.

SPECIAL DELIVERY STAMPS

Special Delivery Stamps of Italy,
Overprinted type "a"

1907   Wmk. 140   Perf. 14
E1 SD1 25c rose red   24.00 20.00
      Never hinged   60.00
  a.   Double overprint

1909
E2 SD2 30c blue & rose   145.00 240.00
      Never hinged   375.00

1920
E3 SD1 50c dull red   4.00 24.00
      Never hinged   10.00

"Italia" — SD1

1924   Engr.   Unwmk.
E4 SD1 60c dk red & brn   6.50 24.00
  a.   Perf. 13½   14.00 40.00
E5 SD1 2 l dk blue & red   17.50 27.50
      Set, never hinged   59.00

For surcharges see Nos. E6-E8.

Nos. E4 and E5 Surcharged in Dark
Blue or Red

v

w

1926
E6 SD1 70c on 60c (Bl)   6.50 16.00
E7 SD1 2.50 l on 2 l (R)   17.50 27.50
      Set, never hinged   60.00

Type of 1924 Surcharged in Blue or Black

1927-35   *Perf. 11*

E8	SD1	1.25 l on 60c dk red & brn (Bl)	16.00	4.00
		Never hinged	40.00	
a.		Perf. 14 (Bl) ('35)	110.00	24.00
		Never hinged	275.00	
b.		Perf. 11 (Bk) ('35)	9,500.	1,250.
		Never hinged	14,500.	
c.		Perf. 14 (Bk) ('35)	400.00	65.00
		Never hinged	1,000.	

AUTHORIZED DELIVERY STAMP

Authorized Delivery Stamp of Italy, No. EY2, Overprinted Type "f" in Black

1939-41   **Wmk. 140**   *Perf. 14*

EY1	AD2	10c dk brown ('41)	.80	
		Never hinged	2.00	
a.		10c reddish brown	27.50	47.50
		Never hinged	72.50	

On No. EY1a, which was used in Italian East Africa, the overprint hits the figures "10." On No. EY1, which was sold in Rome, the overprint falls above the 10's.

POSTAGE DUE STAMPS

Postage Due Stamps of Italy Overprinted type "a" at Top

1903   **Wmk. 140**   *Perf. 14*

J1	D3	5c buff & mag	24.00	47.50
a.		Double overprint	550.00	
J2	D3	10c buff & mag	16.00	47.50
J3	D3	20c buff & mag	16.00	32.50
J4	D3	30c buff & mag	24.00	35.00
J5	D3	40c buff & mag	80.00	72.50
J6	D3	50c buff & mag	87.50	72.50
J7	D3	60c buff & mag	24.00	72.50
J8	D3	1 l blue & mag	16.00	40.00
J9	D3	2 l blue & mag	200.00	180.00
J10	D3	5 l blue & mag	325.00	340.00
J11	D3	10 l blue & mag	3,600.	875.00
		Never hinged	7,200.	
		Set, #J1-J10, never hinged	1,600.	

Same with Overprint at Bottom

1920-22

J1b	D3	5c buff & magenta	4.75	16.00
c.		Numeral and ovpt. inverted	550.00	550.00
J2a	D3	10c buff & magenta	8.00	16.00
J3a	D3	20c buff & magenta	950.00	475.00
J4a	D3	30c buff & magenta	65.00	65.00
J5a	D3	40c buff & magenta	47.50	52.50
J6a	D3	50c buff & magenta	24.00	47.50
J7a	D3	60c buff & magenta	24.00	47.50
J8a	D3	1 l buff & magenta	40.00	47.50
J9a	D3	2 l blue & magenta	1,900.	1,450.
J10a	D3	5 l blue & magenta	475.00	350.00
J11a	D3	10 l blue & magenta	47.50	100.00
		Set, never hinged	7,125.	

1903   **Wmk. 140**

J12	D4	50 l yellow	875.00	300.00
J13	D4	100 l blue	475.00	180.00
		Set, never hinged	2,700.	

1927

J14	D3	60c buff & brown	160.00	240.00
		Never hinged	325.00	

Postage Due Stamps of Italy, 1934, Overprinted type "j" in Black

1934

J15	D6	5c brown	.80	16.00
J16	D6	10c blue	.80	3.25
J17	D6	20c rose red	4.00	4.75
a.		Inverted overprint	—	
J18	D6	25c green	4.00	6.50
J19	D6	30c red orange	4.00	16.00
J20	D6	40c black brown	4.00	16.00
J21	D6	50c violet	4.00	2.40
J22	D6	60c black	8.00	24.00
J23	D7	1 l red orange	4.00	3.25
a.		Inverted overprint	550.00	
J24	D7	2 l green	16.00	47.50
J25	D7	5 l violet	28.00	55.00
J26	D7	10 l blue	32.50	65.00
J27	D7	20 l carmine rose	40.00	72.50
a.		Inverted overprint	550.00	
		Nos. J15-J27 (13)	150.10	332.15
		Set, never hinged	375.00	

PARCEL POST STAMPS

These stamps were used by affixing them to the way bill so that one half remained on it following the parcel, the other half staying on the receipt given the sender. Most used halves are right halves. Complete stamps were obtainable canceled, probably to order. Both unused and used values are for complete stamps.

Parcel Post Stamps of Italy, 1914-17, Overprinted type "j" in Black on Each Half

1916   **Wmk. 140**   *Perf. 13½*

Q1	PP2	5c brown	145.00	225.00
Q2	PP2	10c deep blue	2,600.	4,250.
		Never hinged	5,250.	
Q3	PP2	25c red	290.00	350.00
Q4	PP2	50c orange	72.50	225.00
Q5	PP2	1 l violet	145.00	225.00
Q6	PP2	2 l green	110.00	225.00
Q7	PP2	3 l bister	875.00	625.00
Q8	PP2	4 l slate	875.00	625.00
		Set #Q1, Q3-Q8, never hinged	5,200.	

Halves Used, Each

Q1	4.25
Q2	85.00
Q3	5.50
Q4	3.00
Q5	3.00
Q6	8.50
Q7	19.00
Q8	19.00

Overprinted type "f" on Each Half

1917-24

Q9	PP2	5c brown	3.25	8.00
Q10	PP2	10c deep blue	3.25	8.00
Q11	PP2	20c black	3.25	8.00
Q12	PP2	25c red	3.25	8.00
Q13	PP2	50c orange	6.50	12.00
Q14	PP2	1 l violet	6.50	12.00
Q15	PP2	2 l green	6.50	12.00
Q16	PP2	3 l bister	6.50	12.00
Q17	PP2	4 l slate	6.50	20.00
Q18	PP2	10 l rose lil ('24)	87.50	190.00
Q19	PP2	12 l red brn ('24)	240.00	375.00
Q20	PP2	15 l olive grn ('24)	240.00	375.00
Q21	PP2	20 l brn vio ('24)	325.00	525.00
		Nos. Q9-Q21 (13)	938.00	1,565.
		Set, never hinged	1,860.	

Halves Used, Each

Q9	1.20
Q10	1.20
Q11	1.20
Q12	1.20
Q13	1.20
Q14	1.20
Q15	1.60
Q16	4.25
Q17	4.25
Q18	8.50
Q19	12.50
Q20	12.50
Q21	17.00

Parcel Post Stamps of Italy, 1927-39, Overprinted type "f" on Each Half

1927-37

Q21A	PP3	10c dp blue ('37)	8,750.	1,250.
		Never hinged	13,500.	
Q22	PP3	25c red ('37)	550.00	72.50
Q23	PP3	30c ultra ('29)	4.00	24.00
Q24	PP3	50c org ('36)	725.00	47.50
Q25	PP3	60c red ('29)	4.00	24.00
Q26	PP3	1 l brn vio ('36)	325.00	47.50
a.		1 l lilac	400.00	47.50
Q27	PP3	2 l grn ('36)	325.00	47.50
Q28	PP3	3 l bister	9.50	40.00
Q29	PP3	4 l gray	9.50	40.00
Q30	PP3	10 l rose lil ('36)	525.00	800.00
Q31	PP3	20 l lilac brn ('36)	525.00	800.00
		Nos. Q22-Q31 (10)	3,002.	
		Set, never hinged	6,000.	
		Nos. Q21A-Q31 (11)		3,193.

Halves Used, Each

Q21A	27.50
Q22	1.20
Q23	.65
Q24	1.70
Q25	.85
Q26	1.25
Q26a	1.25
Q27	1.25
Q28	1.25
Q29	1.25
Q30	37.50
Q31	37.50

ESTONIA

e-ˈstō-nē-ə

LOCATION — Northern Europe, bordering on the Baltic Sea and the Gulf of Finland
GOVT. — Independent republic
AREA — 17,462 sq. mi.
POP. — 1,408,523 (1999 est.)
CAPITAL — Tallinn

Formerly a part of the Russia empire, Estonia declared its independence in 1918. In 1940 it was incorporated in the Union of Soviet Socialist Republics.
Estonia declared the restoration of its independence from the USSR on Aug. 20, 1991. Estonian independence was recognized by the Soviet Union on Sept. 6, 1991.

100 Kopecks = 1 Ruble (1918, 1991)
100 Penni = 1 Mark (1919)
100 Sents = 1 Kroon (1928, 1992)
100 Cents = 1 Euro (2011)

> Catalogue values for unused stamps in this country are for Never Hinged items, beginning with Scott 200 in the regular postage section, Scott B60 in the semi-postal section, and Scott F1 in the registration section.

Watermark

Wmk. 207 — Arms of Finland in the Sheet

Watermark covers a large part of sheet.

A1   A2

1918-19   **Unwmk.**   **Litho.**   *Imperf.*

1	A1	5k pale red	.95	.80
2	A1	15k bright blue	.95	.80
3	A2	35k brown ('19)	.80	.80
a.		Printed on both sides	200.00	
b.		35k olive	80.00	80.00
4	A2	70p olive grn ('19)	1.60	2.00
		Nos. 1-4 (4)	4.30	4.40

Nos. 1-4 exist privately perforated.

Russian Stamps of 1909-17 Handstamped in Violet or Black

1919, May 7   *Perf. 14, 14½x15, 13½*

8	A14	1k orange	8,000.	8,000.
9	A14	2k green	45.00	45.00
10	A14	3k red	52.50	52.50
11	A14	5k claret	45.00	45.00
12	A15	10k dk bl (Bk)	85.00	85.00
13	A15	10k dk bl	500.00	500.00
14	A14	10k on 7k lt bl	2,400.	2,400.
15	A11	15k red brn & bl	67.50	67.50
16	A11	25k grn & vio	80.00	80.00
17	A11	35k red brn & grn	7,000.	7,000.
18	A8	50k vio & grn	190.00	190.00
19	A9	1r pale brn, brn & org	325.00	325.00
20	A13	10r scar, yel & gray	12,000.	12,000.

Imperf

21	A14	1k orange	62.50	62.50
22	A14	2k green	2,000.	2,000.
23	A14	3k red	85.00	85.00
24	A9	1r pale brn, brn & red org	475.00	475.00
25	A12	3½r mar & grn	2,000.	2,000.
26	A13	5r dk bl, grn & pale bl	2,750.	2,750.

Provisionally issued at Tallinn. This overprint has been extensively counterfeited. Values are for genuine examples competently expertized. No. 20 is always creased.

Gulls — A3

1919, May 13   *Imperf.*

27	A3	5p yellow	2.50	5.50

A4   A5   A6

A7   Viking Ship — A8

1919-20   *Perf. 11½*

28	A4	10p green	.45	.80

Imperf

29	A4	5p orange	.25	.25
30	A4	10p green	.25	.25
31	A5	15p rose	.25	.30
32	A6	35p blue	.25	.30
33	A7	70p dl vio ('20)	.25	.30
34	A8	1m bl & blk brn	4.25	1.60
a.		Gray granite paper ('20)	1.60	.80
35	A8	5m org yel & blk	6.25	4.75
a.		Gray granite paper ('20)	3.25	1.25
36	A8	15m yel grn & vio ('20)	4.00	2.40
37	A8	25m ultra & blk brn ('20)	6.50	5.50
		Nos. 28-37 (10)	22.70	16.45
		Set, never hinged	32.50	

The 5m exists with inverted center. Not a postal item.
See Nos. 76-77. For surcharges see Nos. 55, 57.

Skyline of Tallinn — A9

1920-24   **Pelure Paper**   *Imperf.*

39	A9	25p green	.30	.40
40	A9	25p yellow ('24)	.30	.30
41	A9	35p rose	.40	.40
42	A9	50p green ('21)	.60	.25
43	A9	1m vermilion	1.25	.80
44	A9	2m blue	.80	.40
45	A9	2m ultramarine	1.00	1.25
46	A9	2.50m blue	1.25	.80
		Nos. 39-46 (8)	5.90	4.60
		Set, never hinged	16.50	

Nos. 39-46 with sewing machine perforation are unofficial.
For surcharge see No. 56.

Stamps of 1919-20 Surcharged

1920   *Imperf.*

55	A5	1m on 15p rose	.50	.50
56	A9	1m on 35p rose	.70	.80
57	A7	2m on 70p dl vio	.85	.80
		Nos. 55-57 (3)	2.05	2.10
		Set, never hinged	4.25	

Weaver
A10

Blacksmith
A11

1922-23　　　Typo.　　　Imperf.
58	A10	½m orange ('23)	2.75	8.00
59	A10	1m brown ('23)	4.75	11.00
60	A10	2m yellow green	4.75	8.00
61	A10	2½m claret	5.50	8.00
62	A11	5m rose	8.00	8.00
63	A11	9m red ('23)	12.00	24.00
64	A11	10m deep blue	5.50	16.00
		Nos. 58-64 (7)	43.25	83.00
		Set, never hinged	110.00	

1922-25　　　　　　　　Perf. 14
65	A10	½m orange ('23)	1.25	.80
66	A10	1m brown ('23)	2.40	.80
67	A10	2m yellow green	2.40	.40
68	A10	2½m claret	4.75	.80
69	A10	3m blue green ('24)	2.00	.40
70	A11	5m rose	2.75	.40
71	A11	9m red ('23)	4.75	1.60
72	A11	10m deep blue	6.00	.40
73	A11	12m red ('25)	6.00	1.75
74	A11	15m plum ('25)	8.00	1.40
75	A11	20m ultra ('25)	22.00	.80
		Nos. 65-75 (11)	62.30	9.55
		Set, never hinged	130.00	

See No. 89. For surcharges see Nos. 84-88.

Viking Ship Type of 1920
1922, June 8　　　Perf. 14x13½
76	A8	15m yel grn & vio	20.00	.80
77	A8	25m ultra & blk brn	20.00	3.25
		Set, never hinged	80.00	

Map of
Estonia — A13

1923-24　　Paper with Lilac Network
78	A13	100m ol grn & bl	24.00	3.50

Paper with Buff Network
79	A13	300m brn & bl ('24)	80.00	17.50
		Set, never hinged	210.00	

For surcharges see Nos. 106-107.

National Theater,
Tallinn — A14

Paper with Blue Network
1924, Dec. 9　　　Perf. 14x13½
81	A14	30m violet & blk	10.00	4.00

Paper with Rose Network
1924　　　　　　　　　
82	A14	70m car rose & blk	15.00	8.00
		Set, never hinged	50.00	

For surcharge see No. 105.

Vanemuine Theater,
Tartu — A15

Paper with Lilac Network
1927, Oct. 25
83	A15	40m dp bl & ol brn	10.00	3.50
		Never hinged	20.00	

Stamps of 1922-25
Surcharged in New
Currency in Red or Black

1928　　　　　　　　Perf. 14
84	A10	2s yellow green	1.25	1.25
85	A11	5s rose red (B)	1.25	1.25
86	A11	10s deep blue	2.40	1.25
a.		Imperf., pair	2,000.	16,000.
87	A11	15s plum (B)	3.75	1.25
88	A11	20s ultra	3.75	1.25
		Nos. 84-88 (5)	12.40	6.25
		Set, never hinged	30.00	

10th anniversary of independence.

3rd Philatelic Exhibition Issue
Blacksmith Type of 1922-23
1928, July 6
89	A11	10m gray	3.00	6.00
		Never hinged	6.00	

Sold only at Tallinn Philatelic Exhibition.
Exists imperf. Value $1,000.

Arms — A16

Paper with Network in Parenthesis
1928-40　　　　Perf. 14, 14½x14
90	A16	1s dk gray (bl)	.50	.25
a.		Thick gray-toned laid paper ('40)	10.00	27.50
91	A16	2s yel grn (org)	.50	.25
92	A16	4s grn (brn) ('29)	1.10	.25
93	A16	5s red (grn)	.70	.25
a.		5 feet on lowest lion	45.00	32.50
94	A16	8s vio (buff) ('29)	2.75	.25
95	A16	10s lt bl (lilac)	1.75	.25
96	A16	12s crimson (grn)	1.75	.25
97	A16	15s yel (blue)	2.75	.25
98	A16	15s car (gray) ('35)	12.00	1.50
99	A16	20s slate bl (red)	3.75	.25
100	A16	25s red vio (grn) ('29)	9.00	.25
101	A16	25s bl (brn) ('35)	10.00	1.50
102	A16	40s red org (bl) ('29)	5.75	.80
103	A16	60s gray (brn) ('29)	10.00	.80
104	A16	80s brn (bl) ('29)	12.00	1.60
		Nos. 90-104 (15)	74.30	8.70
		Set, never hinged	160.00	

Types of 1924 Issues Surcharged

1930, Sept. 1　　　Perf. 14x13½
Paper with Green Network
105	A14	1k on 70m car & blk	16.00	5.50

Paper with Rose Network
106	A13	2k on 300m brn & bl	32.50	16.00

Paper with Blue Network
107	A13	3k on 300m brn & bl	60.00	27.50
		Nos. 105-107 (3)	108.50	49.00
		Set, never hinged	215.00	

University
Observatory
A17

University
of Tartu
A18

Paper with Network as in Parenthesis
1932, June 1　　　　Perf. 14
108	A17	5s red (yellow)	6.00	.80
109	A18	10s light bl (lilac)	4.00	.80
110	A17	12s car (blue)	10.00	4.00
111	A18	20s dk bl (green)	6.00	1.60
		Nos. 108-111 (4)	26.00	7.20
		Set, never hinged	57.50	

University of Tartu tercentenary.

Narva Falls — A19

1933, Apr. 1　Photo.　　Perf. 14x13½
112	A19	1k gray black	6.50	3.00
		Never hinged	14.00	

See No. 149.

Ancient Bard Playing
Harp — A20

Paper with Network as in Parenthesis
1933, May 29　Typo.　　Perf. 14
113	A20	2s green (orange)	1.60	.30
114	A20	5s red (green)	2.75	.30
115	A20	10s blue (lilac)	3.50	.30
		Nos. 113-115 (3)	7.85	.90
		Set, never hinged	17.00	

Tenth National Song Festival.
Nos. 113-115 exist imperf. Value $125.

Woman Harvester — A21

1935, Mar. 1　Engr.　　Perf. 13½
116	A21	3k black brown	.80	6.50
		Never hinged	1.75	

Pres. Konstantin
Päts — A22

1936-40　　　Typo.　　Perf. 14
117	A22	1s chocolate	.80	.40
118	A22	2s yellow green	.80	.40
119	A22	3s dp org ('40)	8.00	8.00
120	A22	4s rose vio	1.60	.80
121	A22	5s lt blue grn	2.00	.40
122	A22	6s rose lake	1.60	.40
123	A22	6s dp green ('40)	40.00	55.00
124	A22	10s greenish blue	2.00	.40
125	A22	15s crim rose ('37)	2.40	.40
126	A22	15s dp bl ('40)	4.00	3.25
127	A22	18s dp car ('39)	17.50	6.25
128	A22	20s brt vio	4.00	.40
129	A22	25s dk bl ('38)	12.00	1.60
130	A22	30s bister ('38)	18.00	1.60
131	A22	30s ultra ('39)	24.00	6.25
132	A22	50s org brn	8.75	1.60
133	A22	60s brt pink	20.00	5.50
		Nos. 117-133 (17)	167.45	92.65
		Set, never hinged	340.00	

St. Brigitta
Convent
Entrance
A23

Ruins of
Convent,
Pirita River
A24

Front View
of Convent
A25

Seal of
Convent
A26

Paper with Network as in Parenthesis
1936, June 10　　　Perf. 13½
134	A23	5s green (buff)	.60	1.60
135	A24	10s blue (lil)	.60	1.60
136	A25	15s red (org)	1.75	4.75
137	A26	25s ultra (brn)	3.00	8.00
		Nos. 134-137 (4)	5.95	15.95
		Set, never hinged	12.00	

St. Brigitta Convent, 500th anniversary.

Harbor at
Tallinn — A27

1938, Apr. 11　Engr.　　Perf. 14
138	A27	2k blue	.80	8.00
		Never hinged	1.75	

Friedrich R.
Faehlmann
A28

Friedrich R.
Kreutzwald
A29

1938, June 15　Typo.　　Perf. 13½
139	A28	5s dark green	.40	.80
140	A29	10s deep brown	.40	.80
141	A29	15s dark carmine	.80	5.50
142	A28	25s ultra	1.25	7.25
a.		Sheet of 4, #139-142	10.00	80.00
		Nos. 139-142 (4)	2.85	14.35
		Set, never hinged	8.00	

Society of Estonian Scholars centenary.

Hospital at
Pärnu — A30

Beach
Hotel — A31

1939, June 20　Typo.　Perf. 14x13½
144	A30	5s dark green	1.60	1.60
145	A31	10s deep red violet	.80	1.60
146	A30	18s dark carmine	1.25	5.50
147	A31	30s deep blue	1.60	7.25
a.		Sheet of 4, #144-147	16.00	87.50
		Nos. 144-147 (4)	5.25	15.95
		Set, never hinged	11.00	

Cent. of health resort and baths at Pärnu.

Narva Falls Type of 1933
1940, Apr. 15　　　　　Engr.
149	A19	1k slate green	1.40	12.00
		Never hinged	2.75	

The sky consists of heavy horizontal lines
and the background consists of horizontal and
vertical lines.

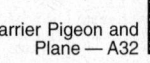
Carrier Pigeon and
Plane — A32

1940, July 30　　　　　Typo.
150	A32	3s red orange	.25	.25
151	A32	10s purple	.25	.25
152	A32	15s rose brown	.25	.25
153	A32	30s dark blue	1.60	1.25
		Nos. 150-153 (4)	2.35	2.00
		Set, never hinged	4.75	

Centenary of the first postage stamp.
The 15s exists imperf. Value $6.25.

Natl. Arms — A40

1991, Oct. 1　Litho.　　Perf. 13x12½
200	A40	5k salmon & red	.30	.30
201	A40	10k lt grn & dk bl grn	.30	.30
202	A40	15k lt bl & dk bl	.30	.30
203	A40	30k vio & gray	.35	.35
204	A40	50k org & brn	.40	.40
205	A40	70k pink & purple	.50	.50
206	A40	90k pur & rose lilac	.60	.60

Size: 20½x27mm
Engr.
Perf. 12½ Horiz.
207	A40	1r dark brown	.75	.75
208	A40	2r lt bl & dk bl	1.50	1.50
		Nos. 200-208 (9)	5.00	5.00

See Nos. 211-213, 215, 216, 230, 299-301,
314-314A, 317, 333-334, 339-340. For
surcharge, see No. 217.

A41

Perf. 13½x14, 14x13½

1991, Nov. 1   Litho.
209 A41 1.50r Flag, vert.   1.10 1.10
210 A41 2.50r shown   1.90 1.90

National Arms — A42

1992, Mar. 16   Litho.   Perf. 13x12½
211 A42 E (1r) lemon   .25   .25
212 A42 I (20r) blue green   .85   .85
213 A42 A (40r) blue   1.90 1.90
      Nos. 211-213 (3)   3.00 3.00

No. 211 was valid for postage within Estonia. No. 212 was valid for postage within Europe. No. 213 was valid for overseas mail. See Nos. 214, 219, 220, 224-229.

Arms Types of 1991-1992 and

No. 202 Surcharged

Natl. Arms — A42a

Perf. 14, 13x12½ (#214, 217, 219-220)

1992-96
214 A42   E (10s) orange   .25   .25
215 A40   10s blue & gray   .25   .25
216 A40   50s gray & brt bl   .25   .25
   a.   Perf. 13x13¼
217 A40   60s on 15k #202   .25   .25
218 A40   60s lilac & olive   .25   .25
219 A42   I (1k) emerald   .75   .75
220 A42   A (2k) violet blue   1.50 1.50
221 A42a 5k bis & red vio   1.25 1.25
   a.   5k yel orange & red violet 2.75 2.75
222 A42a 10k turq blue &
             dp ol   2.50 2.50
223 A42a 20k pale lilac &
             slate grn   4.25 4.25
      Nos. 214-223 (10)   11.50 11.50

Coil Stamps
Engr.
Size: 20½x27mm
Perf. 12½ Horiz.
224 A42 X (10s) brown   .30   .30
225 A42 X (10s) olive   .30   .30
226 A42 X (10s) black   .30   .30
227 A42 Z (30s) red lilac   .30   .30
228 A42 Z (30s) red   .30   .30
229 A42 Z (30s) dark blue   .30   .30
Litho.
230 A40 60s lilac brown   .30   .30
      Nos. 224-230 (7)   2.10 2.10

Issued: Nos. 214, 219-220, 6/22; No. 224, 8/29; No. 225, 9/25; No. 226, 10/31; No. 227, 11/16; No. 228, 12/1; No. 229, 12/22; No. 230, 1/8/93; No. 217, 3/5/93; 10s, 50s, 3/23 1993; 10k, 5/25/93; 5k, 7/7/93; No. 218, 8/5/93; 20k, 9/8/93; No. 221a, 9/19/96; No. 216a, 3/5/96.
See note after No. 213. Nos. 224-229 were valid for postage within Estonia.
See No. F1.

A44

Birds of the Baltic shores.

1992, Oct. 3   Litho. & Engr.   Perf. 13
Booklet Stamps
231 A44 1k Pandion haliaetus   .65   .65
232 A44 1k Limosa limosa   .65   .65
233 A44 1k Mergus merganser   .65   .65
234 A44 1k Tadorna todorna   .65   .65
   a. Booklet pane of 4, #231-234   2.60 2.60

See Latvia Nos. 332-335a, Lithuania Nos. 427-430a and Sweden Nos. 1975-1978a.

A45

1992, Dec, 15   Litho.   Perf. 14
235 A45 30s gray & multi   .30   .30
236 A45 2k light brown & multi   .70   .70

Christmas.
Exist on ordinary and fluorescent paper. Values are for former. Value for set on fluorescent paper, $30.

Friendship — A46

1993, Feb. 8   Litho.   Perf. 14
237 A46 1k multicolored   .30   .30
   a. Booklet pane of 6   1.80

See Finland No. 906.

First Republic, 75th
Anniv. — A47

1993, Feb. 16   Perf. 13x13½
238 A47 60s black & multi   .25   .25
239 A47 1k violet & multi   .25   .25
240 A47 2k blue & multi   .50   .50
      Nos. 238-240 (3)   1.00 1.00

First Baltic Sea
Games — A48

60s, Wrestling. 1k +25s, Viking ship, map. 2k, Shot put with rock.

1993, June 9   Litho.   Perf. 13½x14
241 A48 60s multi   .25   .25
242 A48 1k +25s multi   .30   .30
243 A48 2k multi   .45   .45
      Nos. 241-243 (3)   1.00 1.00

Tallinn Castle — A49

Designs: 1k, Toolse Castle. No. 245, Paide Castle, vert. No. 246, Purtse Castle. No. 247, Haapsalu Castle and Cathedral. 2.70k, Narva Fortress. 2.90k, Haapsalu Cathedral. 3k, Monks' Tower, Kiiu. 3.20k, Rakvere Castle. 4k, Kuressaare Castle. 4.80k, Viljandi Castle.

1993-97   Litho.   Perf. 14
244 A49 1k gray & black   .45   .45
245 A49 2k tan & brown   .45   .45
246 A49 2.50k lt vio & dk vio   .55   .55
247 A49 2.50k gray   .55   .55
248 A49 2.70k lt blue & dk blue   .55   .55
249 A49 2.90k lt grn & dk grn   .60   .60
250 A49 3k rose & brown   .60   .60
251 A49 3k lt grn & dk grn   .85   .85
252 A49 4k lt gray vio & gray
             vio   .90   .90
253 A49 4.80k dull org & brn   .95   .95
      Nos. 244-253 (10)   6.45 6.45

Issued: 1k, 2/22/94; 2k, 10/12/93; 2.70k, 12/10/93; 2.90k, 12/23/93; 3k, 3/31/94; 3.20, 12/28/94; 4k, 9/20/94; No. 246, 1/25/96; 247, 7/25/96; 4.80k, 1/21/97.

First Estonian
Postage Stamp, 75th
Anniv. — A50

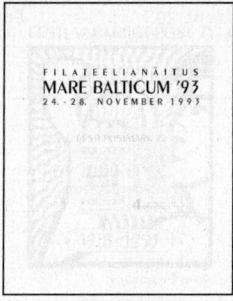

No. 260a

1993, Nov. 13   Litho.   Perf. 14
259 A50 1k multicolored   .40   .40
Souvenir Sheet
Imperf
260 A50 4k multicolored   3.00 3.00
   a. Ovptd. in sheet margin   11.50 11.50
      No. 260 sold for 5k.

Christmas — A51

80s, Haapsalu Cathedral. 2k, Tallinn Church.

1993, Nov.   Litho.   Perf. 14
261 A51 80s red   .25   .25
262 A51 2k blue, vert.   .40   .40
      See Nos. 279-280.

Lydia Koidula — A52

1993, Dec. 14   Litho.   Perf. 14
263 A52 1k multicolored   .35   .35

1994 Winter Olympics,
Lillehammer — A53

1994, Jan. 26
264 A53 1k +25s Ski jumping   .40   .40
265 A53 2k Speed skating   .50   .50

Festival Badges — A54

1k+25s, Tartu, 1869. 2k, Tallinn, 1923. 3k, Tallinn, 1969.
15k, Anniversary badge.

1994, May 31   Litho.   Perf. 13½x14
266 A54 1k +25s olive & multi   .25   .25
267 A54 2k blue & brown   .45   .45
268 A54 3k brown, buff & bister   .60   .60
      Nos. 266-268 (3)   1.30 1.30
Souvenir Sheet
269 A54 15k multicolored   3.00 3.00

All Estonian Song Festival, 125th anniv.

Flying Squirrel — A55

1994, June 27   Litho.   Perf. 13½x14
270 A55 1k shown   .40   .40
271 A55 2k On leafy branch   .50   .50
272 A55 3k In fir tree   .85   .85
273 A55 4k With young   1.10 1.10
      Nos. 270-273 (4)   2.85 2.85
      World Wildlife Fund.

A56

Europa (Estonian Inventions): 1k, Rotating horizontal millstones, by Aleksander Mikiver. 2.70k, First mini-camera, by Walter Zapp.

1994, July 19
274 A56 1k multicolored   .25   .25
275 A56 2.70k multicolored   .50   .50

Folk Costumes — A57

1994, Aug. 23   Litho.   Perf. 14
276 A57 1k Jamaja   .25   .25
277 A57 1k Mustjala   .25   .25

See Nos. 286-287, 303-304, 325-326, 347-348, 369-370, 476-477, 497-498, 524-525.

Estonian Art Museum,
75th Anniv. — A58

1994, Sept. 27   Litho.   Perf. 13½
278 A58 1.70k multicolored   .35   .35

Christmas Type of 1993

Designs: 1.20k, Ruhnu Church, vert. 2.50k, Urvaste Church.

1994, Nov. 15   Litho.   Perf. 14
279 A51 1.20k brown   .30   .30
280 A51 2.50k green   .55   .55

For surcharge see No. B63.

Intl. Year of the
Family — A59

1994, Oct. 18
281 A59 1.70k multicolored   .40   .40

A60

Gustavus II Adolphus (1594-1632), King of Sweden.

1994, Dec. 9
282 A60 2.50k lilac   1.00 1.00

Matsalu Nature Reserve — A61

1995, Jan. 26   Litho.   Perf. 14
283 A61 1.70k Branta leucopsis   .35 .35
284 A61 3.20k Anser anser   .60 .60

FAO, 50th Anniv. — A62

Farm Laborer's Family at Table, by Efraim Allsalu.

1995, Feb. 28   Litho.   Perf. 14
285 A62 2.70k multicolored   .55 .55

Folk Costumes Type of 1994
1995, Mar. 30   Litho.   Perf. 14
286 A57 1.70k Muhu couple   .40 .40
287 A57 1.70k Three Muhu girls   .40 .40

A63

Via Baltica Highway Project: Nos. 288, 289a, Beach Hotel, Parnu. No. 289b, Castle, Bauska, Latvia. No. 289c, Kaunas, Lithuania.

1995, Apr. 20   Litho.   Perf. 14
288 A63 1.70k multicolored   .45 .45

Souvenir Sheet
289 A63 3.20k Sheet of 3, #a.-c.   2.00 2.00
See Latvia Nos. 394-395, Lithuania Nos. 508-509.

A64

1995, Apr. 20   Litho.   Perf. 14
290 A64 2.70k multicolored   .75 .75
Europa. Liberation of Nazi Concentration Camps, 50th anniv.

UN, 50th Anniv. — A65

1995, June 1   Litho.   Perf. 14
291 A65 4k multicolored   .75 .75

Pakri Lighthouse — A66

1995, July 5   Litho.   Perf. 14
292 A66 1.70k multicolored   .45 .45
See Nos. 309, 318, 338, 356, 388-389, 408, 434, 452, 501-502.

Vanemuine Theater, 125th Anniv. — A67

1995, Aug. 14   Litho.   Perf. 14
293 A67 1.70k multicolored   .45 .45

Louis Pasteur (1822-95) — A68

1995, Sept. 20   Litho.   Perf. 14
294 A68 2.70k multicolored   .60 .60

Miniature Sheet

Finno-Ugric Peoples — A69

Ethnographic object, languages: a, 2.50k, Drawing on shaman's drum, Saami. b, 3.50k, Duck-shaped brooch, Mordva, Mari. c, 4.50k, Duck-feet necklace pendant, Udmurdi, Komi. d, 2.50k, Khanty band ornament, Ungari, Mansi, Handi. e, 3.50k, Bronze amulet, Neenetsi, Eenetsi, Nganassaani, Solkupi, Kamassi. f, 4.50k, Karelian writing on birchbark, Eesti, Vadia, Soome, Liivi, Isuri, Karjala, Vespa.

1995, Oct. 17   Litho.   Perf. 14
295 A69 Sheet of 6, #a.-f.   4.00 4.00

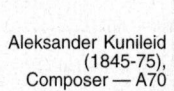

Aleksander Kunileid (1845-75), Composer — A70

1995, Nov. 1   Engr.   Perf. 12½ Horiz.
296 A70 2k dark blue black   .45 .45

Christmas — A71

Churches: 2k, St. Martin's, Türi. 3.50k, Charles' Church of the Toompea Congregation, Tallinn.

1995, Nov. 15   Litho.   Perf. 14
297 A71   2k yellow orange   .55 .55
298 A71 3.50k dull carmine   .95 .95
See Nos. 315-316, 331.

Natl. Arms Type of 1991
1995, Oct. 26   Litho.   Perf. 14
299 A40 20s blue green & black   .25 .25
300 A40 30s gray & magenta   .25 .25
301 A40 80s lilac & blue black   .25 .25
  a. Perf. 13   .25 .25
    Nos. 299-301 (3)   .75 .75
No. 301a issued in 1996.

Submarine Lembit — A72

1996, Feb. 29   Litho.   Perf. 14
302 A72 2.50k multicolored   .65 .65
See No. 308, 328.

Folk Costume Type of 1994
1996, Mar. 26   Litho.   Perf. 14
303 A57 2.50k Emmaste   .65 .65
304 A57 2.50k Reigi   .65 .65

A73

Designs: a, 2.50k, First gold medal, 1896. b, 3.50k, Alfred Neuland, weight lifter, first to win gold medal for Estonia, 1920. c, 4k, Cyclist.

1996, Apr. 25   Litho.   Perf. 14
305 A73 Sheet of 3, #a.-c.   2.00 2.00
Modern Olympic Games, Cent. & 1996 Summer Olympics, Atlanta.

A74

Europa: Marie Under (1883-1980), poet.

1996, May 10
306 A74 2.50k multicolored   1.00 1.00

Radio, Cent. — A75

1996, June 27   Litho.   Perf. 14
307 A75 3.50k Guglielmo Marconi   .90 .90

Ship Type of 1996
Design: Icebreaker, Suur Toll.

1996, Aug. 30   Litho.   Perf. 14
308 A72 2.50k multicolored   .65 .65

Lighthouse Type of 1995
1996, Sept. 25   Litho.   Perf. 14
309 A66 2.50k Vaindloo   .70 .70

Estonian Narrow Gauge Railway, Cent. — A76

Designs: 3.20k, Class Gk steam locomotive. 3.50k, DeM 1 diesel motor wagon. 4.50k, Class Sk steam locomotive.

1996, Oct. 17   Litho.   Perf. 14
310 A76 3.20k multicolored   .70 .70
311 A76 3.50k multicolored   .75 .75
312 A76 4.50k multicolored   .85 .85
    Nos. 310-312 (3)   2.30 2.30
See No. 397.

Christmas — A77

1996, Nov. 27   Litho.   Perf. 14
313 A77 2.50k multicolored   .60 .60

Natl. Arms Type of 1991
1996-97   Perf. 14
314 A40 3.30k lilac and claret   1.25 1.25
    Perf. 13x13¼
314A A40 3.30k blue & lt claret   1.25 1.25
    Issued: No. 314, 12/2; No. 314A, 12/10/97.

Church Type of 1995
Christmas: 3.30k, Harju-Madise Church. 4.50k, Holy Spirit Church, Tallinn.

1996, Dec. 12
315 A71 3.30k blue   .70 .70
316 A71 4.50k pink   .85 .85

Natl. Arms Type of 1991
1996, Oct. 24   Litho.   Perf. 13½
317 A40 2.50k grn & dark grn   1.25 1.25

Lighthouse Type of 1995
1997, Feb. 11   Litho.   Perf. 14
318 A66 3.30k Ruhnu   .75 .75

Tallinn Zoo A78

a, Haliaeetus pelagicus. b, Mustela lutreola. c, Aegypius monachus. d, Panthera pardus orientalis. e, Diceros bicornis. f, Capra cylindricornis.

1997, Mar. 26   Litho.   Perf. 14
319 A78 3.30k Sheet of 6, #a.-f.   3.50 3.50

Heinrich von Stephan (1831-97), Founder of UPU — A79

1997, Apr. 8   Litho.   Perf. 14
320 A79 7k black & bister   1.25 1.25

Goldspinners Fairy Tale — A80

1997, May 5   Litho.   Perf. 14
321 A80 4.80k multicolored   1.00 1.00
Europa.

A81

No. 323: a, like #322. b, Linijkugis, 17th cent. c, Kurenas, 16th cent.

1997, May 10
322 A81 3.30k multicolored   .70 .70
    Perf. 14x14½
323 A81 4.50k Sheet of 3, #a.-c.   5.25 5.25
    Maasilinn ship, 16th cent.
See Latvia Nos. 443-444, Lithuania Nos. 571-572.

Folk Costume Type of 1994
1997, June 10   Litho.   Perf. 14
325 A57 3.30k Ruhnu   .55 .55
326 A57 3.30k Vormsi   .55 .55

One Kroon Coin — A82

1997, June 12   Litho.   Perf. 14
327 A82 50k bl grn, blk & gray   9.00 9.00
See Nos. 345, 363, 391.

Ship Type of 1996
Design: Four-masted barkentine, Tormilind.

1997, July 2
328 A72 5.50k multicolored   .90 .90

Stone Bridge, Tartu — A83

1997, Sept. 16   Litho.   Perf. 14
329 A83 3.30k multicolored   .65 .65

Wastne Testament, Estonian Bible Translation, 1686 — A84

1997, Oct. 14   Litho.   Perf. 14
330 A84 3.50k multicolored   .65 .65

Church Type of 1995
Christmas: St. Anne's, Halliste.

1997, Nov. 27   Litho.   Perf. 14
331 A71 3.30k brown   .65 .65

Christmas — A85

1997, Dec. 3
332 A85 2.90k Elves   .60 .60

Natl. Arms Type of 1991
1998, Jan. 19   Litho.   Perf. 13x13½
333 A40 3.10k lt violet & rose   .60 .60
334 A40 3.60k lt blue & ultra   .70 .70
a.   3.60k gray & vio bl   .80 .80
Issued: No. 334a, 8/4/98.

1998 Winter Olympic Games, Nagano — A86

1998, Jan. 28   Litho.   Perf. 14
335 A86 3.60k multicolored   .70 .70

Republic of Estonia, 80th Anniv. A87

1998, Feb. 6   Litho.   Imperf.
336 A87 7k Proclamation, arms   1.40 1.40

Eduard Wiiralt (1898-1954), Print Artist — A88

Various sections of print, "Hell," showing faces: a, 3.60k, shown. b, 3.60k, Explosion coming from center figure. c, 5.50k, Cat on top of one figure's head. d, 5.50k, Faces within faces.

1998, Feb. 18   Perf. 14
337 A88 Sheet of 4, #a.-d.   4.00 4.00

Lighthouse Type of 1995
1998, Mar. 12   Litho.   Perf. 14
338 A66 3.60k Kunda   .70 .70

Natl. Arms Type of 1991
1998, Mar. 16   Perf. 13
339 A40 10s grn bl & brn blk   .25 .25
340 A40 4.50k pale orange & brick red   .80 .80
Issued: 10s, 3/25/97; 4.50k, 3/16/98.

A88a

1998, Apr. 16   Litho.   Perf. 14
341 A88a 7k multicolored   1.30 1.30
1998 World Cup Soccer Championship, France.

St. John's Day — A89

1998, May 5   Litho.   Perf. 14
342 A89 5.20k multi   1.25 1.25
Europa.

Use of Lübeck Charter in Tallinn, 750th Anniv. — A90

1998, June 1
343 A90 4.80k multicolored   .95 .95

Beautiful Homes Year — A91

1998, June 16   Litho.   Perf. 14
344 A91 3.60k multicolored   .85 .85

One Kroon Coin Type of 1997
1998, June 18
345 A82 25k green, gray & black   4.75 4.75

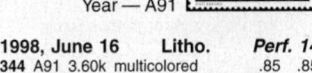
A92

1998, Aug. 4   Litho.   Perf. 14
346 A92 5.50k multicolored   1.00 1.00
470 Class World Yachting Championships.

Folk Costume Type of 1994
1998, Aug. 21   Litho.   Perf. 14
347 A57 3.60k Kihnu couple   .65 .65
348 A57 3.60k Kihnu family   .65 .65

A93

1998, Sept. 3
349 A93 3.60k yel, blue & blk   .70 .70
Juhan Jaik (1899-1948), author.

Tallinn Zoo — A94
Design: Panthera tigris altaica.

1998, Sept. 17
350 A94 3.60k multicolored   .70 .70
See No. 357.

Estonian Post, 80th Anniv. — A95

1998, Oct. 22   Litho.   Perf. 14
351 A95 3.60k multicolored   .75 .75

Military Aid from Finland, 90th Anniv. — A96

1998, Nov. 5   Litho.   Perf. 14
352 A96 4.50k Freedom Cross   .85 .85

Christmas — A97

1998, Nov. 26   Litho.   Perf. 14
353 A97 3.10k Santa, child, vert.   .60 .60
354 A97 5k shown   .90 .90

Friedrich Robert Faehlmann, Founder of Learned Estonian Society, Birth Bicent. — A98

1998, Dec. 2
355 A98 3.60k multicolored   .70 .70

Lighthouse Type of 1995
1999, Jan. 20   Litho.   Perf. 14
356 A66 3.60k Vilsandi   .70 .70

Tallinn Zoo Type of 1998
1999, Feb. 18   Litho.   Perf. 14
357 A94 3.60k Uncia uncia   .70 .70

Council of Europe, 50th Anniv. — A99

1999, Mar. 24   Litho.   Perf. 14
358 A99 5.50k multicolored   1.00 1.00

Estonian Pres. Lennart Meri, 70th Birthday — A100

1999, Mar. 29
359 A100 3.60k multicolored   .70 .70

Tolkuse Bog — A101

1999, Apr. 27   Litho.   Perf. 14
360 A101 5.50k multicolored   1.25 1.25
Europa.

Bank of Estonia, 80th Anniv. — A102

1999, May 3   Litho.   Perf. 14
361 A102 5k multicolored   1.00 1.00

Olustvere Manor — A103

1999, June 1
362 A103 3.60k multicolored   .70 .70
See Nos. 395, 414, 433, 456, 490, 520, 551, 562, 603, 627, 648.

One Kroon Coin Type of 1997
1999, June 18   Litho.   Perf. 14
363 A82 100k bl, bister & blk   17.00 17.00

Estonian Natl. Anthem — A104

1999, June 30   Litho.   Perf. 14
364 A104 3.60k multicolored   .70 .70
No. 364 is printed se-tenant with label.

Tower on Suur Munamägi, Highest Point in Baltic Countries — A105

1999, July 17
365 A105 5.20k multicolored   1.00 1.00

A106

Families holding hands and: 3.60k, Estonian flag.
No. 367: a, like #366. b, Latvian flag. c, Lithuanian flag.

1999, Aug. 23   Litho.   Perf. 14
366 A106 3.60k multicolored   .70 .70
Souvenir Sheet
367 A106 5.50k Sheet of 3, #a.-c.   3.00 3.00
Baltic Chain, 10th Anniv.
See Latvia Nos.493-494, Lithuania Nos. 639-640.

A107

1999, Sept. 23   Litho.   Perf. 14x13¾
368 A107 7k multicolored   1.40 1.40
UPU, 125th Anniv.

Folk Costumes Type of 1994
1999, Oct. 12   Litho.   Perf. 13¾x14
369 A57 3.60k Setu couple   .65 .65
370 A57 5k Setu man, boy   .90 .90

Three Lions — A108

Perf. 13x13¼, 13¾x14 (#371, 373, 374, 378-382)
1999-2002   Litho.
371 A108 10s brn & dk brn   .30 .30
372 A108 30s lt bl & dk bl   .30 .30
a.   Perf. 13¾x14   .30 .30
b.   As No. 372, with two "1999" year dates   — —

373	A108	30s blue & slate blue, dated 2003	.30	.30
374	A108	50s ol & dk grn	.30	.30
375	A108	1k brn & fawn	.30	.30
376	A108	2k gray	.50	.50
377	A108	3.60k sky bl & dk bl	.75	.75

a.   bright blue green ('00)   .75   .75

378	A108	4.40k grn & bl grn	1.00	.80

a.   Inscribed "2001"   1.00   .80
b.   Inscribed "2002"   1.00   .80

379	A108	4.40k bl grn & brt bl grn, wide 2001 date	1.00	.30
380	A108	4.40k Prus bl & lt bl, narrow 2001 date	1.00	.30
381	A108	4.40k grn & lt grn, dated 2002	1.00	.30
382	A108	4.40k grn & apple grn, dated 2002	1.00	.30
382A	A108	4.40k ol grn & apple grn, dated 2003	1.00	.35
382B	A108	5k grn & lt grn, dated "2001"	1.30	1.30

a.   Inscribed "2002"   1.20   1.20
b.   Inscribed "2004"   .75   .75

382C	A108	6k bis & yel	1.50	1.50
382D	A108	6.50k pale org & org	1.50	1.50
382E	A108	8k lake & pink	1.75	1.75

Nos. 371-382E (17)   14.80   11.15

Issued: 30s, 2k, 11/4; No. 377, 10/22; No. 377a, 3/31/00; No. 378, 8/21/00; 6k, 10/12/00; 6.50k, 10/5/00; 8k, 10/19/00; No. 372a: 4/17/01; 1k, 5k, 8/28/01; 10s, 2/2/02. 50s, 1/7/03; No. 373, 3/11/03; No. 379, 4/17/01; No. 380, 9/24/01; No. 381, 2/2/02; No. 382, 11/14/02; No. 382A, 3/11/03.

The background color of No. 379 is bolder than that on No. 380. The additional year date on No. 372b is at left below the paw of the lower lion and is found on one cliché (No. 83) of the sheet.

See Nos. 467, 472-474.

Christmas — A109

1999, Nov. 25   **Litho.**   **Perf. 14x13¾**
383   A109   3.10k multicolored   .60   .60

A110

1999, Nov. 25   **Perf. 13¾x14**
384   A110   7k multicolored   1.25   1.25
1st public Christmas tree in Tallinn, 1441.

Christmas Lottery — A110a

1999, Dec. 1   **Litho.**   **Perf. 14x13¾**
384A   A110a   3.10k + 1.90k multi   1.75   1.75

A111

1999, Dec. 14   **Litho.**   **Perf. 13¾x14**
385   A111   5.50k Millennium   1.10   1.10

2000 Census — A112

2000, Jan. 5
386   A112   3.60k multicolored   .70   .70

Tartu Peace Treaty, 80th Anniv. — A113

2000, Feb. 2   **Litho.**   **Perf. 14x13¾**
387   A113   3.60k multi   .70   .70

Lighthouse Type of 1995
2000, Feb. 25
388   A66   3.60k Ristna   .65   .65
389   A66   3.60k Kopu   .65   .65
a.   Pair, #388-389   1.30   1.30

Congress, 10th Anniv. — A114

2000, Mar. 9   **Perf. 13¾x14**
390   A114   3.60k multi   .65   .65

One Kroon Coin Type of 1997
2000, Mar. 14   **Perf. 14x13¾**
391   A82   10k red, sil & blk   1.75   1.75

Cornflower (Natl. Flower) — A115

2000, Apr. 7
392   A115   4.80k multi   .85   .85

Natl. Book Year — A116

2000, Apr. 22   **Perf. 13¾x14**
393   A116   3.60k multi   .65   .65
First book printed in Estonian language, 475th anniv.

Europa, 2000
Common Design Type
2000, May 9
394   CD17   4.80k multi   1.25   1.25

Manor Type of 1999
2000, May 23   **Litho.**   **Perf. 14x13¾**
395   A103   3.60k Palmse Hall   .70   .70

Tallinn Zoo — A117

2000, June 13   **Litho.**   **Perf. 14x13¾**
396   A117   3.60k Naemorhedus caudatus   .70   .70

Railway Type of 1996
4.50k, Viljandi-Tallinn Railway, cent.
2000, June 30
397   A76   4.50k multi   .80   .80

9th Intl. Finno-Ugric Congress — A118

2000, Aug. 1
398   A118   5k multi   1.00   1.00

2000 Summer Olympics, Sydney — A119

2000, Sept. 5   **Litho.**   **Perf. 13¾x14**
399   A119   8k multi   1.50   1.50

Folk Costume Type of 1994
Designs: 4.40k, Hargla. 8k, Polva.
2000, Sept. 12
400-401   A57   Set of 2   2.25   2.25

August Mälk (1900-87), Writer — A120

2000, Sept. 20   **Perf. 14x13¾**
402   A120   4.40k multi   .80   .80

Lake Peipus Fish — A121

No. 403: a, Osmerus eperlanus spirinchus. b, Stizostedion lucioperka.

2000, Oct. 25
403   Horiz. pair + central label   2.50   2.50
a.-b.   A121 6.50k Any single   1.10   1.10
See Russia No. 6607.

Souvenir Sheet

Estonian Bookplates, Cent. — A122

Various bookplates. Denominiations in: a, LR. b, UR.

2000, Nov. 11   **Perf. 13¾x14**
404   A122   6k Sheet of 2, #a-b   2.25   2.25

Christmas — A123

3.60k, Horn and bow. 6k, Ornament.

2000, Nov. 29   **Perf. 14x13¾**
405-406   A123   Set of 2   1.60   1.60

Erki Nool, Olympic Decathlon Champion — A124

2001, Jan. 10   **Litho.**   **Perf. 14x13¾**
407   A124   4.40k multi   .75   .75

Lighthouse Type of 1995
2001, Jan. 24
408   A66   4.40k Mohni   .80   .80

Valentine's Day — A125

2001, Feb. 6   **Litho.**   **Perf. 13¾x14**
409   A125   4.40k multi   .80   .80

Stenbock House, Seat of Government — A126

2001, Feb. 20   **Perf. 14x13¾**
410   A126   6.50k multi   1.10   1.10

Souvenir Sheet

Paintings of Johann Köler (1826-99) — A127

No. 411: a, Girl on the Spring, 1858-62. b, Eve of the Pomegranate, 1879-80.

2001, Feb. 27
411   A127   4.40k Sheet of 2, #a-b   1.50   1.50

European Year of Languages — A128

2001, Mar. 6
412   A128   4.40k multi   .85   .85

Vanellus Vanellus — A129

2001, Apr. 4   **Perf. 12¾x13**
413   A129   4.40k multi   .85   .85
See No. 435.

Manor Type of 1999
2001, Apr. 17   **Perf. 14x13¾**
414   A103   4.40k Laupa Hall   .80   .80

Europa — A130

2001, May 9   **Perf. 13¾x14**
415   A130   6.50k multi   1.30   1.30

Kalev Sports Association, Cent. — A131

2001, May 24
416   A131   6.50k multi   1.25   1.25

Pärnu, 750th
Anniv. — A132

2001, June 5   Litho.   Perf. 14x13¾
417   A132   4.40k multi   .85   .85

Illustrations from
Pokuland, by Edgar
Valter — A133

Characters and — No. 418: a, Lake. b, Owl.
c, Crane. d, Bird in nest.
No. 419: a, Fence. b, Flowers. c, Dog. d,
Moon.

2001, June 19
418   Booklet pane of 4   2.75
a.-d.   A133 3.60k Any single   .75   .75
419   Booklet pane of 4   3.75
a.-d.   A133 4.40k Any single   .90   .90
             Booklet, #418-419   7.25

Entire booklet sold for 35k, 3k of which went
to the Pokuland Project of the Estonian Nature
Fund.

Restoration of
Independence, 10th
Anniv. — A134

2001, Aug. 7   Perf. 13¾x14
420   A134   4.40k multi   .85   .85

Establishment of St.
Mary's Land, 800th
Anniv. — A135

2001, Aug. 15   Perf. 14x13¾
421   A135   6.50k multi   1.25   1.25

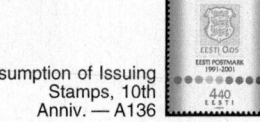

Resumption of Issuing
Stamps, 10th
Anniv. — A136

2001, Sept. 4   Perf. 13¾x14
422   A136   4.40k #200   .85   .85

Baltic Coast
Landscapes — A137

Designs: 4.40k, No. 424a, Lahemaa. No.
424b, Vidzeme. No. 424c, Palanga.

2001, Sept. 15   Perf. 14x13¾
423   A137   4.40k multi   .90   .90
Souvenir Sheet
Perf. 13¼x13½
424   Sheet of 3   3.50   3.50
a.-c.   A137 6k Any single   1.10   1.10

No. 424 contains three 35x29mm stamps.
See Lithuania Nos.
See Latvia Nos. 534-535, Lithuania Nos.
698-699.

Tallinn Zoo — A138

2001, Oct. 4   Perf. 14x13¾
425   A138   4.40k Alligator sinensis   .90   .90

Estonia 26/9 Racing
Car — A139

2001, Oct. 23
426   A139   6k multi   1.15   1.15

Folk Costume Type of 1994

Designs: 4.40k, Paistu woman. 7.50k,
Tarvastu man.

2001, Nov. 7   Litho.   Perf. 13¾x14
427-428   A57   Set of 2   2.25   2.25

A140

Christmas — A141

Perf. 13¾x14, 14x13¾
2001, Nov. 22
429   A140   3.60k multi   .70   .70
430   A141   6.50k multi   1.40   1.40

Radio Broadcasting in
Estonia, 75th
Anniv. — A142

2001, Dec. 4   Perf. 14x13¾
431   A142   4.40k multi   .90   .90

2002 Winter
Olympics, Salt Lake
City — A143

2002, Jan. 10   Litho.   Perf. 14x13¾
432   A143   8k multi   1.40   1.40

Manor Type of 1999
2002, Jan. 22
433   A103   4.40k Sangaste Hall   .80   .80

Lighthouse Type of 1995
2002, Feb. 20
434   A66   4.40k Laidunina   .80   .80

Bird Type of 2001
Design: Passer domesticus and Passer
montanus.

2002, Mar. 7   Perf. 12¾x13
435   A129   4.40k multi   .80   .80

Spring
Flowers — A144

2002, Mar. 20   Perf. 14x13¾
436   A144   4.40k multi   .80   .80

Estonian
Puppet
Theater,
50th Anniv.
A145

2002, Mar. 27   Perf. 13¾x14
437   A145   4.40k multi + label   .80   .80

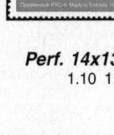

PTO-4 Training
Airplane — A146

2002, Apr. 10   Perf. 14x13¾
438   A146   6k multi   1.10   1.10

Andrus Veerpalu,
Gold Medalist at
2002 Winter
Olympics — A147

2002, Apr. 12
439   A147   4.40k multi   .80   .80

Tartu University Anniversaries — A148

No. 440: a, Main building, 1806-09, founding
act of 1632. b, University Library, 1982, text
from Biblia Latina.

2002, Apr. 24
440   A148   4.40k Horiz. pair, #a-b,
              + central label   2.25   2.25

Europa — A149

2002, May 9   Perf. 12¾x13
441   A149   6.50k multi   1.60   1.60

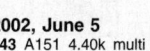

Re-adoption of
Constitution, 10th
Anniv. — A150

2002, May 23   Perf. 13¾x14
442   A150   4.40k multi   .80   .80

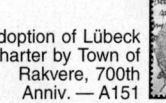

Adoption of Lübeck
Charter by Town of
Rakvere, 700th
Anniv. — A151

2002, June 5
443   A151   4.40k multi   .80   .80

Souvenir Sheet

Re-introduction of the Kroon, 10th
Anniv. — A152

No. 444 — Portraits from bank notes: a,
Lydia Koidula, poet. b, Carl Rober Jakobson,
journalist.

2002, June 10   Perf. 14x13¾
444   A152   4.40k Sheet of 2, #a-b   2.00   2.00

Souvenir Sheet

Adamson-Eric (1902-68),
Painter — A153

Denomination at: a, LL. b, LR. c, UL. d, UR.

2002, Aug. 8   Litho.   Perf. 14x13¾
445   A153   4.40k Sheet of 4, #a-d   3.00   3.00

Sus
Scrofa — A154

2002, Aug. 21   Perf. 12¾x13
446   A154   4.40k multi   .80   .80

Limestone,
Estonia's National
Stone — A155

2002, Sept. 18
447   A155   4.40k multi   .80   .80

Folk Costume Type of 1994

Designs: 4.40k, Kolga-Jaani women. 5.50k,
Suure-Jaani boy and girl.

2002, Oct. 1   Perf. 13¾x14
448-449   A57   Set of 2   1.60   1.60

A156

Christmas — A157

Perf. 14x13¾, 13¾x14
2002, Nov. 20   Litho.
450   A156   3.60k Reindeer   .60   .60
451   A157   6.50k Christmas tree   1.15   1.15

Lighthouse Type of 1995
2003, Jan. 15   Perf. 14x13¾
452   A66   4.40k Keri   .80   .80

Anton Hansen
Tammsaare (1878-
1940),
Novelist — A158

2003, Jan. 30   Litho.   Perf. 14x13¾
453   A158   4.40k multi   .80   .80

Pica Pica — A159

2003, Feb. 13   *Perf. 12¾x13*
454 A159 4.40k multi   .80 .80
See Nos. 485, 509, 540, 566, 595, 625.

Spring Flowers
A160

No. 455: a, Tulips. b, Helleborus purpurascens. c, Narcissus poeticus. d, Crocus vernus.

2003, Mar. 20   *Perf. 13¾x14*
455 A160 4.40k Sheet of 4, #a-d   7.00 7.00
e.   Booklet pane, like #455, without
        date in margin   3.25   —
        Complete booklet, #455e   3.25
See No. 484.

Manor Type of 1999
2003, Apr. 9   *Perf. 14x13¾*
456 A103 4.40k Alatskivi Hall   .80 .80

Pres. Arnold Rüütel,
75th Birthday — A161

2003, Apr. 24
457 A161 4.40k multi + label   .90 .90

Europa — A162

2003, May 8   *Perf. 13¾x14*
458 A162 6.50k multi   1.60 1.60

Tartu University
Botanical Gardens,
Bicent. — A163

**2003, June 11 Litho. *Perf. 14x13¾*
459 A163 4.40k multi   .90 .90

14th Junior World
Orienteering
Championships
A164

2003, June 27
460 A164 7.50k multi   1.25 1.25

Circumnavigation of Adam Johann von
Krusenstern (1770-1846) — A165

2003, Aug. 6   *Perf. 12½*
461 A165 8k multi   1.40 1.40

Phoca
Hispida — A166

2003, Aug. 27   *Perf. 12¾x13*
462 A166 4.40k multi   .80 .80

Adm. Fabian
Gottlieb von
Bellingshausen
(1778-1852)
A167

2003, Sept. 10
463 A167 8k multi   1.75 1.75

Ancient
Trade
Routes
A168

Map and: No. 464, 6.50k, Silver coin of Prince Volodymyr Sviatoslavovych, Slavic warship with sail. No. 465, 6.50k, Arrival of Scandinavian Seamen, coin of Danish King Svend Estridsen.

2003, Sept. 10   *Perf. 11½*
464-465 A168   Set of 2   2.10 2.10
See Ukraine No. 524.

Three Lions Type of 1999-2002
**2003-04 Litho. *Perf. 13¾x14*
467 A108 20s blk & gray   .30 .30
472 A108 4.40k ol grn & apple
                grn   .80 .80
473 A108 5k dk grn & apple
                grn, dated 2004   .90 .90
474 A108 5.50k dk grn & yel grn   1.00 1.00
Issued: 20s, 4.40k, 8/22; 5k, 1/20/04; 5.50k, 3/25/04.

Folk Costume Type of 1994
Designs: 4.40k, Aksi woman and girl. 6.50k, Otepää man, woman and girl.

**2003, Oct. 9 Litho. *Perf. 13¾x14*
476-477 A57   Set of 2   1.90 1.90

A169

Christmas — A170

2003, Nov. 26   *Perf. 14x13¾*
478 A169 3.60k multi   .70 .70
479 A170 6k multi   .90 .90

Souvenir Sheet

Friedrich Reinhold Kreutzwald (1803-
82), Writer — A171

No. 480: a, 4.40k, Illustration by Kristjan Raud of "Voyage to the End of the World," from "Kalevipoeg," by Kreutzwald. b, 6.50k, Portrait of Kreutzwald.

2003, Dec. 4   *Perf. 13x12¾*
480 A171   Sheet of 2, #a-b   2.10 2.10

Lighthouse Type of 1995
**2004, Jan. 7 Litho. *Perf. 14x13¾*
481 A66 4.40k Sorgu   .85 .85

Canis
Lupus — A172

2004, Feb. 3   *Perf. 12¾x13*
482 A172 4.40k multi   .85 .85

Voyage Around Cape
Horn of the Hioma,
150th Anniv. — A173

2004, Feb. 18   *Perf. 13¾x14*
483 A173 8k multi   1.50 1.50

Spring Flowers Type of 2003
No. 484: a, Viola riviniana. b, Anemone nemorosa. c, Hepatica nobilis. d, Trollius europaeus.

2004, Mar. 17
484 A160 4.40k Sheet of 4, #a-d   3.25 3.25
e.   Booklet pane, like #484 without
        date in margin   3.25
        Complete booklet, #484e   3.25

Bird Type of 2003
2004, Apr. 6   *Perf. 12¾x13*
485 A159 4.40k Ciconia ciconia   .80 .80

Admission to
European
Union — A174

2004, May 1   *Perf. 13¼x13*
486 A174 6.50k multi   1.25 1.25

Europa
A175

2004, May 4   *Perf. 13*
487 A175 6.50k multi   1.25 1.25

Tallinn Town Hall,
600th
Anniv. — A176

**2004, May 13 Litho. *Perf. 12¾x13*
488 A176 4.40k multi   .80 .80

Consecration of
Estonian Flag, 120th
Anniv. — A177

2004, June 4   *Perf. 13¾x14*
489 A177 4.40k multi   .80 .80

Manor Type of 1999
2004, June 15   *Perf. 14x13¾*
490 A103 4.40k Vasalemma Hall   .80 .80

Admission to
NATO — A178

2004, June 28   *Perf. 13¾x14*
491 A178 6k multi   1.10 1.10

2004 Summer
Olympics,
Athens — A179

**2004, July 15 Litho. *Perf. 13¾x14*
492 A179 8k multi   1.40 1.40

Dragon Class
Yachting European
Championships
A180

2004, Aug. 17   *Perf. 14x13¾*
493 A180 6k multi   1.10 1.10

Taraxacum
Officinale — A181

Serpentine Die Cut 12½
2004, Sept. 14   Self-Adhesive
494 A181 30s multi   .40 .40
See Nos. 547, 560, 572.

County Arms — A182

2004, Sept. 28   Self-Adhesive
495 A182 4.40k Harjumaa   .80 .80
496 A182 4.40k Hiiumaa   .80 .80
See Nos. 506-507, 518-519, 532-533, 536, 552, 561, 573, 588, 594, 608.

Folk Costumes Type of 1994
Designs: 4.40k, Viru-Jaagupi boy and girl. 7.50k, Jõhvi woman and girl.

**2004, Oct. 5 Litho. *Perf. 13¾x14*
497-498 A57   Set of 2   2.10 2.10

A183

Christmas — A184

2004, Nov. 23   *Perf. 13¾x14*
499 A183 4.40k multi   .90 .90
                          Perf. 14x13¾
500 A184 6.50k multi   1.00 1.00

Lighthouse Type of 1995
Norrby Lighthouse with: 4.40k, White top, vert. 6.50k, Red top, vert.

**2005, Jan. 11 Litho. *Perf. 14*
501-502 A66   Set of 2   1.75 1.75

Castor
Fiber — A185

2005, Jan. 25   *Perf. 12¾x13*
503 A185 4.40k multi   .70 .70

Rotary International, Cent. — A186

2005, Feb. 11   *Perf. 13¾x14*
504 A186 8k multi   1.25 1.25

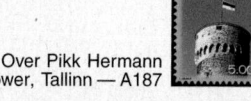

Flag Over Pikk Hermann Tower, Tallinn — A187

Serpentine Die Cut 12½
2005, Feb. 22   **Self-Adhesive**
505 A187 5k multi   .90 .90

See Nos. 530, 559, 574.

County Arms Type of 2004
2005   **Self-Adhesive**   **Litho.**
506 A182 4.40k Ida-Virumaa   .80 .80
507 A182 4.40k Järvamaa   .80 .80

Issued: No. 506, 3/8; No. 507, 3/15.

Souvenir Sheet

Spring A188

No. 508: a, Two swans, denomination at UL. b, One swan, denomination at UL. c, One swan, denomination at LL. d, Two swans, denomination at LR.

2005, Mar. 22 Litho.   *Perf. 14x13¾*
508 A188 4.40k Sheet of 4, #a-d 2.75 2.75

Bird Type of 2003
2005, Apr. 5   *Perf. 12¾x13*
509 A159 4.40k Accipiter gentilis   .80 .80

Mother's Day — A189

2005, Apr. 20   *Perf. 14x13¾*
510 A189 4.40k multi   .80 .80

Europa — A190

Designs: 6k, Vegetable wrap. 6.50k, Tomato, carrots, egg yolk, parsley, fish, onion, beet.

2005, May 3
511-512 A190   Set of 2   2.25 2.25

Eduard Tubin (1905-82), Composer — A191

2005, May 18
513 A191 6k multi   1.00 1.00

Intl. Children's Day — A192

No. 514: a, Birds. b, Butterflies.

2005, June 1   *Perf. 13¼x13¾*
514 A192 4.40k Horiz. pair, #a-b,
    + central label   1.50 1.50

Orchids — A193

Designs: 4.40k, Epipactis palustris. 8k, Epipogium aphyllum.

2005, June 16 Litho.   *Perf. 13¾x14*
515-516 A193   Set of 2   2.50 2.50

Restoration of St. John's Cathedral, Tartu — A194

2005, June 29
517 A194 4.40k multi   .80 .80

Tartu, 975th anniv.

County Arms Type of 2004
Serpentine Die Cut 12½
2005   **Self-Adhesive**   **Litho.**
518 A182 4.40k Jögevamaa   .75 .75
519 A182 4.40k Läänemaa   .75 .75

Issued: No. 518, 7/5; No. 519, 7/8.

Manor Type of 1999
2005, July 12   *Perf. 14x13¾*
520 A103 4.40k Kiltsi Hall   .75 .75

St. Catherine's Church, Karja — A195

2005, Sept. 20
521 A195 4.40k multi   .75 .75

Souvenir Sheet

Sculptures by Amandus Adamson (1855-1929) — A196

No. 522: a, Igavesti Voidutsev Armastus, 1889. b, Lüüriline Muusika, 1891. c, Memento Mori, 1907. d, Koit ja Hämarik, 1895.

2005, Oct. 12   *Perf. 13½*
522 A196 650s Sheet of 4, #a-d   4.00 4.00

Dogs A197

No. 523: a, Kazakh hound (Kasaahi hurt). b, Estonian hound (Eesti hagijas).

2005, Oct. 19   *Perf. 14x13¾*
523 A197 6.50k Horiz. pair, #a-b   2.10 2.10

See Kazakhstan No. 495.

Folk Costumes Type of 1994
Designs: 4.40k, Ambla man, woman and girl. 8k, Türi women.

2005, Oct. 28   *Perf. 13¾x14*
524-525 A57   Set of 2   2.25 2.25

New Year's Goat — A198

Adoration of the Magi — A199

2005, Nov. 22
526 A198 4.40k multi   .80 .80
527 A199   8k sil & red lil   1.45 1.45

Christmas and New Year's Day.

Due to the postponed conversion to the euro, originally scheduled for Jan. 1, 2007, Estonian stamps issued between 2006 and 2010 show denominations in kroons and the at-that-time-uncirculating euros.

Europa Stamps, 50th Anniv. — A200

CEPT emblem and: 6k, Superimposed letters. 6.50k, Map of Europe.

2006, Jan. 4 Litho.   *Perf. 14x13¾*
528 A200   6k multi   .95 .95

Souvenir Sheet
529 A200 6.50k multi   1.00 1.00

Flag Over Pikk Hermann Tower Type of 2005 With Euro Denominations Added
2006, Jan. 11   *Die Cut Perf. 12½*
Self-Adhesive
530 A187 11k multi   1.75 1.75

2006 Winter Olympics, Turin, Italy — A201

2006, Jan. 18   *Perf. 14x13¾*
531 A201 8k multi   1.25 1.25

County Arms Type of 2004 With Euro Denominations Added
2006   *Die Cut Perf. 12½*
Self-Adhesive
532 A182 4.40k Lääne-Virumaa   .70 .70
533 A182 4.40k Polvamaa   .70 .70

Issued: No. 532, 1/25; No. 533, 2/8.

Alces Alces — A202

2006, Feb. 1   *Perf. 12¾x13*
534 A202 4.40k multi   .75 .75

Opening of KUMU Art Museum — A203

2006, Feb. 17 Litho.   *Perf. 13¾x14*
535 A203 4.40k multi   .75 .75

County Arms Type of 2004 With Euro Denominations Added
2006, Mar. 8   *Die Cut Perf. 12½*
Self-Adhesive
536 A182 4.40k Pärnumaa   .85 .85

Souvenir Sheet

National Opera, Cent. A204

No. 537: a, Characters from Vikerlased, first opera staged in 1928. b, Ballerina.

2006, Mar. 27   *Perf. 13¾x14*
537 A204 6.50k Sheet of 2, #a-b,
    + central label   2.25 2.25

A205

Gold Medalists at 2006 Winter Olympics — A206

No. 539: a, Andrus Veerpalu. b, Kristina Smigun.

2006, Mar. 30   *Perf. 14x13¾*
538 A205 4.40k multi   .75 .75

Souvenir Sheet
539 A206   8k Sheet of 2, #a-b 2.50 2.50

Bird Type of 2003 With Euro Denominations Added
2006, Apr. 5   *Perf. 12¾x13*
540 A159 4.40k multi   .75 .75

Lighthouses — A207

Designs: 4.40k, Tallinn Bay lower lighthouse. 6.50k, Tallinn Bay upper lighthouse.

2006, Apr. 12   *Perf. 13¾x14*
541-542 A207   Set of 2   1.75 1.75

See Nos. 564, 587, 624.

Estonian Shooting Sport Federation, 75th Anniv. — A208

2006, Apr. 26
543 A208 4.40k car & sil   .75 .75

Europa — A209

2006, May 3
544 A209 6.50k multi   1.25 1.25

Confectionery Industry in Estonia, Bicent. — A210

2006, May 18   *Perf. 14x13¾*
545 A210 4.40k multi   .75 .75

Posthorns A211

2006, May 22   *Die Cut Perf. 10*
Self-Adhesive
546 A211 4.40k gray brn + label   .75 .75

Labels could be personalized.
See No. 563.

Flower Type of 2004 with Euro Denominations Added
2006, May 24   *Die Cut Perf. 12½*
Self-Adhesive
547 A181 30s Hepatica nobilis   .35   .35

Souvenir Sheet

Tori Stud Farm, 150th Anniv. A212

No. 548: a, Three horses, denomination at UL. b, Pony and three horses, denomination at UR.
2006, June 7   *Perf. 14x13¾*
548 A212 4.40k Sheet of 2, #a-b   1.40   1.40

Victory Day — A213

2006, June 23
549 A213 4.40k multi   .75   .75

20th Intl. Organ Music Festival, Tallinn — A214

2006, July 28   **Litho.**   *Perf. 14x13¾*
550 A214 4.40k multi   .75   .75

Manor Type of 1999 With Added Euro Denomination
2006, Aug. 16
551 A103 4.40k Taagepera Hall   .75   .75

County Arms Type of 2004 With Added Euro Denomination
2006, Sept. 6   *Die Cut Perf. 12½*
Self-Adhesive
552 A182 4.40k Raplamaa   .75   .75

St. Lawrence's Church, Noo — A215

2006, Sept. 20   *Perf. 13¾x14*
553 A215 4.40k multi   .75   .75

Betti Alver (1906-89), Writer — A216

2006, Oct. 11   *Perf. 13*
554 A216 4.40k multi   .75   .75

Antarctic Wildlife A217

No. 555 — Estonian and Chilean flags and: a, Aptenodytes forsteri. b, Balaenoptera acutorostrata.
2006, Oct. 25   *Perf. 13½*
555 A217 8k Pair, #a-b   2.50   2.50
    See Chile No. 1468.

A218

Christmas — A219

2006, Nov. 22   **Litho.**   *Perf. 13¾x14*
556 A218 4.40k multi   .70   .70
557 A219   6k multi   .95   .95

Lotte From Gadgetville — A220

2007, Jan. 4   *Perf. 14x13¾*
558 A220 4.40k multi   .85   .85

Flag Over Pikk Hermann Tower Type of 2005 With Euro Denomination Added
2007, Jan. 11   *Die Cut Perf. 12½*
Self-Adhesive
559 A187 5k tan & multi   .85   .85

Flower Type of 2004 With Euro Denomination Added
2007, Jan. 17   *Die Cut Perf. 12½*
Self-Adhesive
560 A181 30s Leucanthemum vulgare   .30   .30

County Arms Type of 2004 With Euro Denomination Added
2007, Jan. 25   *Die Cut Perf. 12½*
Self-Adhesive
561 A182 4.40k Saaremaa   .85   .85

Manor Type of 1999 With Euro Denomination Added
2007, Feb. 14   *Perf. 14x13¾*
562 A103 5.50k Sagadi Hall   .95   .95

Posthorns Type of 2006
2007, Feb. 22   *Die Cut Perf. 10*
Self-Adhesive
563 A211 5.50k bl grn + label   1.00   1.00
    Labels could be personalized.

Lighthouse Type of 2006
2007, Mar. 8   *Perf. 14x13¾*
564 A207 6k Juminda, horiz.   1.00   1.00

Meles Meles — A221

2007, Mar. 22   *Perf. 12¾x13*
565 A221 4.40k multi   .90   .90

Bird Type of 2003 With Euro Denomination Added
2007, Apr. 5   *Perf. 12¾x13*
566 A159 4.40k Cygnus bewickii   .90   .90

Miniature Sheet

Summer Flowers A222

No. 567: a, Paeonia officinalis. b, Lilium lancifolium. c, Rosa ecae Golden Chersonese. d, Iris latifolia.
2007, Apr. 19   *Perf. 13¾x14*
567 A222 4.40k Sheet of 4, #a-d   3.25   3.25

Europa A223

2007, May 3   *Perf. 12½*
568 A223 20.50k multi   3.50   3.50
    Scouting, cent.

Intl. Children's Day — A224

2007, June 1   **Litho.**   *Perf. 13½*
569 A224 10k multi   1.75   1.75

Souvenir Sheet

1941-51 Deportation of Estonians — A225

2007, June 14   *Perf. 13*
570 A225 8k multi   1.40   1.40

Pirita Convent, 600th Anniv. A226

2007, June 15   **Litho.**   *Perf. 12½*
571 A226 5.50k multi   1.00   1.00

Flower Type of 2004 With Euro Denominations Added
2007, July 2   *Die Cut Perf. 12½*
Self-Adhesive
572 A181 1.10k Centaurea phrygia   .30   .30

County Arms Type of 2004 With Euro Denominations Added
2007, July 2   **Self-Adhesive**
573 A182 5.50k Tartumaa   1.00   1.00

Flag Over Pikk Hermann Tower Type of 2005 With Euro Denominations Added
2007, Aug. 1   **Self-Adhesive**
574 A187 10k multi   1.75   1.75

Hellenurme Mill — A227

2007, Aug. 9   *Perf. 14x13¾*
575 A227 5.50k multi   1.00   1.00

Hirvepark Demonstration, 20th Anniv. — A228

2007, Aug. 23   *Perf. 14x14¼*
576 A228 5.50k multi   1.00   1.00

Souvenir Sheet

Matthias Johann Eisen (1857-1934), Folklorist A229

2007, Sept. 14   *Imperf.*
577 A229 10k multi   1.75   1.75
    No. 577 has simulated perforations.

Ragnar Nurkse (1907-59), Economist A230

2007, Oct. 5   *Perf. 13*
578 A230 10k multi   1.75   1.75

St. John's Church, Kanepi — A231

2007, Oct. 11   *Perf. 13¾x14*
579 A231 5.50k multi   1.00   1.00

Arms of Viljandi — A232

2007, Oct. 25   **Litho.**   *Perf. 13¾x14*
580 A232 5.50k multi   1.00   1.00

A233

Christmas — A234

Die Cut Perf. 11¼ Syncopated
2007, Nov. 22   **Self-Adhesive**
581 A233 5.50k multi   .90   .90
582 A234   8k multi   1.40   1.40

Post Horn — A235

**2008   Litho.   *Die Cut Perf. 12½*
Self-Adhesive**
583 A235 5.50k brt orange   1.00 1.00
584 A235 6.50k brt yel green   1.15 1.15
585 A235 9k blue   1.60 1.60
　　　Nos. 583-585 (3)   3.75 3.75
　Issued: 5.50k, 1/10; 6.50k, 3/6; 9k, 4/1.
　See Nos. 600, 638, 649, 658-662, 675-677,
682-684, 696-697, 708, 719-721.

Gustav Ernesaks
(1908-93),
Composer — A236

2008, Jan. 17   Litho.   Perf. 13
586 A236 5.50k multi   1.00 1.00

Lighthouse Type of 2006
2008, Jan. 24   Perf. 14x13¾
587 A207 5.50k Mehikoorma,
　　　　horiz.   1.00 1.00

**County Arms Type of 2004 With
Euro Denominations Added**
**2008, Feb. 7   Die Cut Perf. 12½
Self-Adhesive**
588 A182 5.50k Valgamaa   1.00 1.00

Plecotus
Auritus — A237

2008, Feb. 14   Perf. 12¾x13
589 A237 5.50k multi   1.00 1.00

Oak Tree — A238

2008, Feb. 23   Perf. 13
590 A238 5.50k multi   1.00 1.00
　Republic of Estonia, 90th anniv.

Kristjan Palusalu (1908-87), Olympic
Wrestling Gold Medalist
A239

2008, Mar. 10   Perf. 12½
591 A239 10k multi   1.75 1.75

State Awards of the
Baltic Countries — A240

　Designs: Nos. 592, 593a, Order of the
National Coat of Arms, Estonia. No. 593b,
Order of Three Stars, Latvia. No. 593c, Order
of Vytautas the Great, Lithuania.

2008, Mar. 15   Litho.   Perf. 13¾
592 A240 5.50k multi   1.00 1.00
Souvenir Sheet
593 A240 10k Sheet of 3, #a-c,
　　　　　+ label   5.25 5.25
　See Latvia Nos. 701-702, Lithuania Nos.
862-863.

**County Arms Type of 2004 With
Euro Denominations Added**
**2008, Mar. 27   Die Cut Perf. 12½
Self-Adhesive**
594 A182 5.50k Viljandimaa   1.00 1.00

**Bird Type of 2003 With Euro
Denomination Added**
2008, Apr. 3   Perf. 12¾x13
595 A159 5.50k Tetrao tetrix   1.10 1.10

Europa — A241

2008, Apr. 30   Perf. 14x14¼
596 A241 9k multi   1.60 1.60

Otto Strandman (1875-
1941),
Statesman — A242

2008, May 9   Litho.   Perf. 13¾x14
597 A242 5.50k brown   1.00 1.00

Wavy Lines
A243

**2008, May 22 *Serpentine Die Cut 10*
Self-Adhesive**
598 A243 9k multi + label   1.75 1.75
　The label shown is generic. Labels could be
personalized for a fee.

Peasant War at
Mahtra, 150th
Anniv. — A244

2008, May 31   Perf. 14x13¾
599 A244 5.50k multi   1.00 1.00

**Posthorn Type of 2008
*Die Cut Perf. 12½***
**2008, May 31   Litho.
Self-Adhesive**
600 A235 50s gray   .35 .35

2008 Summer
Olympics,
Beijing — A245

2008, Aug. 8   Litho.   Perf. 13¾x14
601 A245 9k multi   1.60 1.60

Polma
Windmill — A246

2008, Aug. 28   Perf. 14x13¾
602 A246 5.50k multi   1.00 1.00

**Manor Type of 1999 With Euro
Denomination Added**
2008, Sept. 18 Litho. Perf. 14x13¾
603 A103 5.50k Kalvi Hall   1.00 1.00

Gerd Kanter,
Olympic Discus
Champion — A247

2008. Sept. 25   Perf. 13½
604 A247 5.50k multi   1.00 1.00

Church of the Holy
Cross, Audru — A248

2008, Oct. 16   Litho. Perf. 13¾x14
605 A248 5.50k multi   1.00 1.00

**County Arms Type of 2004 With
Euro Denominations Added**
**2008, Oct. 30   Die Cut Perf. 12½
Self-Adhesive**
606 A182 5.50k Vorumaa   1.00 1.00

Estonia Post, 90th
Anniv. — A249

2008, Nov. 13   Perf. 13¾x14
607 A249 5.50k multi   1.00 1.00

Christmas — A250

　Designs: 5.50k, Gift on skis. 9k, Snowman
on gift.

Die Cut Perf. 11¼ Syncopated
**2008, Nov. 20   Litho.
Booklet Stamps Self-Adhesive**
608 A250 5.50k multi   .90 .90
　a.　Booklet pane of 10   8.25
609 A250 9k multi   1.60 1.60
　a.　Booklet pane of 10   13.50

Souvenir Sheet

International Polar Year — A251

　No. 610 — Antarctic glacier with snowflake
emblem in: a, White. b, Blue.

2009, Jan. 15 Litho. Perf. 13x12¾
610 A251 15k Sheet of 2, #a-b   5.50 5.50

Battle of Paju,
90th
Anniv. — A252

2009, Jan. 29   Perf. 12¾x13
611 A252 5.50k multi   1.00 1.00

Gen. Johan
Laidoner (1884-
1953)
A253

2009, Feb. 12   Litho.   Perf. 13
612 A253 5.50k multi   1.00 1.00

Ants Piip (1884-1942),
Prime Minister — A254

2009, Feb. 26   Perf. 14
613 A254 5.50k maroon   1.00 1.00

Pres. Lennart Meri
(1929-2006) — A255

2009, Mar. 26   Litho.   Perf. 14
614 A255 5.50k blue   1.00 1.00

Estonian
National
Museum,
Cent. — A256

2009, Apr. 14   Perf. 13
615 A256 5.50k multi   1.00 1.00

Estonian Parliament,
90th Anniv. — A257

2009, Apr. 23   Perf. 14
616 A257 5.50k multi   1.00 1.00

Europa
A258

　No. 617: a, Galaxies and hexagonal cells. b,
Galaxy and hexagonal cells at left.

2009, May 5   Litho.   Perf. 13¾x14
617 A258 9k Horiz. pair, #a-b   3.25 3.25
　Intl. Year of Astronomy.

Räpina Paper Mill,
275th Anniv. — A259

2009, May 14
618 A259 5.50k multi   1.00 1.00

Estonian Flag, 125th
Anniv. — A260

Die Cut Perf. 11¼ Syncopated
2009, June 5
Booklet Stamp Self-Adhesive
619 A260 9k multi   1.50 1.50
　a.　Booklet pane of 10   15.00

25th Song
Festival — A261

2009, June 18   Perf. 14x13¾
620 A261 5.50k multi   1.00 1.00

Alexander Church, Narva, 125th Anniv. — A262

2009, July 10   Litho.   Perf. 13¾x14
621 A262 5.50k multi   1.50 1.50

Ursus Arctos — A263

2009, Sept. 10   Perf. 12¾x13
622 A263 5.50k multi   1.00 1.00

First Track and Field Competition in Estonia, Cent. — A264

2009, Sept. 22   Perf. 14x13¾
623 A264 5.50k multi   1.10 1.10

Lighthouse Type of 2006
2009, Sept. 24   Perf. 14x13¾
624 A207 5.50k Hara Tuletorn, horiz.   1.10 1.10

Bird Type of 2003 With Euro Denomination Added
2009, Oct. 8   Litho.   Perf. 12¾x13
625 A159 5.50k Strix aluco   1.10 1.10

Windmill, Angla — A265

2009, Oct. 22   Perf. 13¾x14
626 A265 5.50k multi   1.10 1.10

Manor Type of 1999 With Euro Denomination Added
2009, Nov. 5   Perf. 14x13¾
627 A103 5.50k Saku Hall   1.10 1.10

A266

Christmas — A267

Die Cut Perf. 11¼ Syncopated
2009, Nov. 19
Booklet Stamps Self-Adhesive
628 A266 5.50k multi   .95   .95
  a.   Booklet pane of 10   9.50
629 A267 9k multi   1.60 1.60
  a.   Booklet pane of 10   16.00

Fabric Design — A268

Die Cut Perf. 11¼ Syncopated
2010, Jan. 7   Litho.
Booklet Stamp Self-Adhesive
630 A268 50k orange & multi   8.50 8.50
  a.   Booklet pane of 10   85.00
      See Nos. 646, 650.

Jüri Jaakson (1870-1942), Politician — A269

2010, Jan. 15   Perf. 14
631 A269 5.50k multi   .95   .95

2010 European Figure Skating Championships, Tallinn — A270

2010, Jan. 19   Perf. 12¾x13
632 A270 9k multi   1.50 1.50
  a.   Tete-beche pair   3.00 3.00

Tartu Peace Treaty, 90th Anniv. — A271

2010, Feb. 2   Perf. 13
633 A271 5.50k multi   1.00 1.00

Post Horn Type of 2008
2010, Feb. 4   Die Cut Perf. 12½
Self-Adhesive
634 A235 9k deep blue   1.50 1.50
      Dated 2010. Compare with No. 585.

2010 Winter Olympics, Vancouver — A272

2010, Feb. 4   Perf. 14
635 A272 9k multi   1.60 1.60

Platanthera Bifolia — A273

2010, Feb. 19
636 A273 5.50k multi   1.00 1.00

Estonia Pavilion, Expo 2010, Shanghai — A274

2010, Mar. 11
637 A274 9k multi   1.50 1.50

Posthorn Type of 2008
2010, Mar. 23   Die Cut Perf. 12½
Self-Adhesive
638 A235 5.50k bright pink   1.00 1.00

St. Catherine's Church, Pärnu — A275

2010, Mar. 23   Perf. 13¾x14
639 A275 6.50k multi   1.10 1.10

Juhan Kukk (1885-1942), State Elder — A276

2010, Apr. 13
640 A276 5.50k olive brown   1.00 1.00

Lighthouses Type of 2006
  Designs: 6.50k, Suurupi front lighthouse. 8k, Suurupi rear lighthouse.

2010, Apr. 22
641-642 A207 Set of 2   2.50 2.50

Europa — A277

  Children's book illustrations: No. 643, 9k, Family of mice, by Jüri Mildeberg. No. 644, 9k, Skaters in snow, by Viive Noor.

2010, May 6   Perf. 14x13¾
643-644 A277 Set of 2   2.50 2.50

Bird Type of 2003 With Euro Denominations Added
2010, May 13   Perf. 12¾x13
645 A159 5.50k Lanius collurio   1.00 1.00

Fabric Design Type of 2010
Die Cut Perf. 11¼ Syncopated
2010, June 1
Booklet Stamp Self-Adhesive
646 A268 26k brt yel grn & multi   4.50 4.50
  a.   Booklet pane of 10   45.00

Intl. Children's Day — A278

2010, June 1   Litho.
Booklet Stamp Self-Adhesive
647 A278 5.50k multi   1.00 1.00
  a.   Booklet pane of 10   10.00

Manor Type of 1999 With Euro Denominations Added
2010, Aug. 5   Litho.   Perf. 14x13¾
648 A103 5.50k Suuremõisa Hall   .95   .95

Posthorn Type of 2008
2010, Aug. 18   Die Cut Perf. 12
Self-Adhesive
649 A235 9k bright yellow   1.50 1.50

Fabric Design Type of 2010
Die Cut Perf. 11¼ Syncopated
2010, Aug. 18
Booklet Stamp Self-Adhesive
650 A268 26k lilac & multi   4.50 4.50
  a.   Booklet pane of 10   45.00

Tallinn, 2011 European Capital of Culture — A279

2010, Sept. 9   Litho.
Self-Adhesive
651 A279 5.50k multi   1.00 1.00

Eliomys Quercinus A280

2010, Sept. 23   Perf. 12¾x13
652 A280 5.50k multi   .75   .75

A281

A282

A283

Worldwide Fund for Nature (WWF) — A284

  Various views of Triturus cristatus.

2010, Oct. 14   Perf. 14x13¾
653   Horiz. strip of 4   6.50 6.50
  a.   A281 9k multi   1.60 1.60
  b.   A282 9k multi   1.60 1.60
  c.   A283 9k multi   1.60 1.60
  d.   A284 9k multi   1.60 1.60
  e.   Sheet of 8 stamps with two tete-
        beche strips   13.00 13.00

Lennuk, by Nikolai Triik — A285

2010, Nov. 17   Litho.   Perf. 14
654 A285 9k multi   1.60 1.60
      No. 654 was printed in sheets of 8.

A286

Christmas — A287

Die Cut Perf. 11¼ Syncopated
2010, Nov. 25
Booklet Stamps Self-Adhesive
655 A286 5.50k multi   .95   .95
  a.   Booklet pane of 10   9.50
656 A287 9k multi   1.60 1.60
  a.   Booklet pane of 10   16.00

  Stamps in No. 655a are tete-beche in relation to adjacent stamps. Vertical pairs of stamps in No. 656a are tete-beche.

100 Cents = 1 Euro

Introduction of Euro Currency — A288

Die Cut Perf. 11¼ Syncopated
2011, Jan. 1
Booklet Stamp Self-Adhesive
657 A288 €1 multi   2.75 2.75
  a.   Booklet pane of 10   27.50

Post Horn Type of 2008 with Euro Denominations Only

2011, Jan. 3   *Die Cut Perf. 12½*
Self-Adhesive

658	A235	1c orange	.25	.25
659	A235	5c salmon pink	.25	.25
660	A235	10c lilac	.25	.25
661	A235	50c blue	1.40	1.40
662	A235	65c green	1.75	1.75
		Nos. 658-662 (5)	3.90	3.90

New Year 2011
(Year of the
Rabbit) — A289

2011, Feb. 3   *Litho.*   *Perf. 12¾x13*
663   A289   58c multi   1.60   1.60

Friedebert Tuglas
(1886-1971),
Writer — A290

2011, Mar. 2   *Perf. 13¾x14*
664   A290   58c multi   1.60   1.60

Villem Reiman (1861-
1917),
Historian — A291

2011, Mar. 9
665   A291   35c multi   1.00   1.00

Peony — A292

2011, Mar. 24   *Perf. 13x12¾*
666   A292   58c multi   1.75   1.75

Printed in sheets of 4 having each stamp
rotated 90 degrees in relation to each other.

Folk Costumes — A293

Designs: 35c, Man and woman from Rapla.
58c, Two women from Joelähtme.

2011, Apr. 14   *Perf. 13¾x14*
667-668   A293   Set of 2   2.50   2.50

Hirundo
Rustica — A294

2011, Apr. 21   *Perf. 12¾x13*
669   A294   35c multi   1.00   1.00

Europa — A295

Designs: No. 670, 58c, Elk in forest. No.
671, 58c, Cut logs.

2011, Apr. 28   *Perf. 13*
670-671   A295   Set of 2   3.00   3.00

Intl. Year of Forests.

Souvenir Sheet

Struve
Geodetic
Arc
A296

No. 672 — Map of arc and: a, Friedrich
Georg Wilhelm Struve (1793-1864), astronomer. b, Tartu Observatory.

2011, May 6   *Perf. 14x13¾*
672   A296   58c Sheet of 2, #a-b   3.25   3.25

Lepus Europaeus
A297

2011, May 19   *Perf. 12¾x13*
673   A297   35c multi   1.00   1.00

Vergi
Lighthouse — A298

2011, June 2   *Perf. 14x13¾*
674   A298   35c multi   1.00   1.00

Posthorn Type of 2008 With Euro Denominations Only

2011   *Die Cut Perf. 12½*
Self-Adhesive

675	A235	35c brt yel grn	1.00	1.00
676	A235	58c lt purple	1.75	1.75
677	A235	58c green	1.60	1.60

Issued: 35c, No. 676, 6/2. No. 677, 8/25.

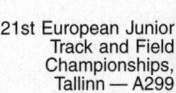

21st European Junior
Track and Field
Championships,
Tallinn — A299

2011, July 20   *Litho.*   *Perf. 14x13¾*
678   A299   35c multi   1.00   1.00

Restoration of
Independence, 20th
Anniv. — A300

2011, Aug. 20   *Perf. 13¾x14¼*
679   A300   35c multi   1.00   1.00

St. Margaret's
Church,
Karuse — A301

2011, Aug. 25   *Perf. 14x13¾*
680   A301   35c multi   1.00   1.00

Friedrich Karl Akel
(1871-1941), State
Elder — A302

2011, Sept. 5   *Perf. 13¾x14*
681   A302   35c brown   1.00   1.00

Posthorn Type of 2008 With Euro Denominations Only

2011   *Die Cut Perf. 12½*
Self-Adhesive

682	A235	10c sage green	.30	.30
683	A235	35c cerise	.95	.95
684	A235	45c rose	1.25	1.25
		Nos. 682-684 (3)	2.50	2.50

Issued: 10c, 45c, 11/1; 35c, 9/15.

Heinrich Mark (1911-
2004), Prime
Minister — A303

2011, Sept. 30   *Perf. 13¾x14*
685   A303   35c blue   .95   .95

Michael Andreas
Barclay de Tolly
(1761-1818), Military
Leader — A304

2011, Oct. 20   *Perf. 14x13¾*
686   A304   €1 multi   2.75   2.75

10-Cent and 2-Euro
Coins — A305

Die Cut Perf. 11¼ Syncopated
2011, Nov. 1
Booklet Stamp
Self-Adhesive
687   A305   €2.10 multi   5.50   5.50
  a.   Booklet pane of 10   55.00

Market, Painting by
Henn-Olavi Roode
(1924-74) — A306

2011, Nov. 17   *Perf. 14*
688   A306   €1 multi   2.75   2.75

Christmas — A307

Die Cut Perf. 11¼ Syncopated
2011, Nov. 24
Booklet Stamps
Self-Adhesive
689   A307   45c Angel   1.25   1.25
  a.   Booklet pane of 10   12.50
690   A307   €1 Ornament   2.75   2.75
  a.   Booklet pane of 10   27.50

Vertical pairs of stamps in Nos. 689a and
690a are tete-beche.

Oskar Luts
(1887-1953),
Writer — A308

2012, Jan. 7   *Litho.*   *Perf. 13*
691   A308   45c multi   1.25   1.25

Population and
Housing
Census — A309

Die Cut Perf. 11¼x11½ Syncopated
2012, Jan. 12   **Self-Adhesive**
692   A309   45c multi   1.25   1.25

New Year 2012
(Year of the
Dragon) — A310

2012, Jan. 23   *Perf. 12¾x13*
693   A310   €1.10 multi   3.00   3.00

Capreolus
Capreolus
A311

2012, Feb. 16   *Perf. 12¾x13*
694   A311   45c multi   1.25   1.25

Heino Eller (1887-
1970),
Composer — A312

2012, Mar. 7   *Perf. 14x13¾*
695   A312   45c multi   1.25   1.25

Posthorn Type of 2008 With Euro Denominations Only

2012, Mar. 29   *Die Cut Perf. 12½*
Self-Adhesive
Dated "2012"

696	A235	10c dull blue green	.25	.25
697	A235	50c pale yel grn	1.40	1.40

Compare Nos. 696 and 750.

Personalized
Stamp — A313

Die Cut Perf. 8¾ Syncopated
2012, Mar. 29   **Self-Adhesive**
698   A313   45c multi   1.25   1.25

The generic vignette shown, depicting a
map of Saaremaa, could be personalized for
an additional fee.
See Nos. 773, 901, 966.

Folk Costumes — A314

Designs: 45c, Woman and girl from Hageri. €1, Woman from Nissi.

2012, Apr. 14   **Litho.**   **Perf. 13¾x14**
699-700 A314   Set of 2   4.00 4.00

Charadrius
Dubius — A315

2012, Apr. 19   **Perf. 12¾x13**
701 A315 45c multi   1.25 1.25

Johannes
Pääsuke (1892-
1918), Creator of
First Estonian
Film in
1912 — A316

2012, Apr. 30
702 A316 45c multi   1.25 1.25

Europa — A317

Inscriptions: No. 703, €1, "wild est." No. 704, €1, "smart est."

2012, May 3   **Perf. 14x13¾**
703-704 A317   Set of 2   5.25 5.25

Church of St. Simeon
and the Prophet Anne,
Tallinn — A318

2012, May 17   **Perf. 13¾x14**
705 A318 45c multi   1.25 1.25

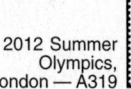

2012 Summer
Olympics,
London — A319

2012, June 1   **Perf. 14x13¾**
706 A319 €1.10 multi   2.75 2.75

Martin Klein
(1884-1947), First
Estonian Olympic
Medalist — A320

2012, July 13   **Perf. 14x14¼**
707 A320 €1 multi   2.50 2.50

**Posthorn Type of 2008 With Euro
Denominations Only**
2012, Aug. 10   **Die Cut Perf. 12½**
Self-Adhesive
708 A235 45c citron   1.25 1.25

One-Euro
Coin — A321

Die Cut Perf. 11¼ Syncopated
2012, Aug. 10   **Self-Adhesive**
709 A321 €1 multi   2.60 2.60

Amanita Virosa — A322

2012, Aug. 30   **Perf. 13¾x14**
710 A322 45c red & black   1.25 1.25

Käsmu
Lighthouse — A323

2012, Sept. 13   **Perf. 14x13¾**
711 A323 45c multi   1.25 1.25

Jaan Teemant (1872-
1941), State
Elder — A324

2012, Sept. 24   **Perf. 13¾x14**
712 A324 45c brown   1.25 1.25

Railway
Bridges — A325

Train and: Nos. 713, 714a, Narva Bridge, Estonia. No. 714b, Carnikava Bridge, Latvia. No. 714c, Lyduvenai Bridge, Lithuania.

2012, Oct. 25   **Perf. 13¼**
713 A325 45c multi   1.25 1.25
Souvenir Sheet
714 A325 €1 Sheet of 3, #a-c   8.00 8.00
See Latvia Nos. 815-816, Lithuania Nos. 985-986.

Scouting in Estonia,
Cent. — A326

2012, Nov. 7   **Perf. 14x13¾**
715 A326 45c multi   1.25 1.25

Still Life with Mandolin,
by Lepo Mikko — A327

2012, Nov. 16   **Perf. 14**
716 A327 €1.10 multi   3.00 3.00

Santa Claus
on Skis
A328   Poinsettia
A329

Die Cut Perf. 11¼ Syncopated
2012, Nov. 22   **Self-Adhesive**
717 A328 45c multi   1.25 1.25
718 A329 €1 multi   2.60 2.60

Christmas.

**Posthorn Type of 2008 With Euro
Denominations Only**
Self-Adhesive
2013, Jan. 10   **Die Cut Perf. 12½**
719 A235   5c light blue   .30 .30
720 A235   50c green   1.40 1.40
721 A235   65c red violet   1.75 1.75
    Nos. 719-721 (3)   3.45 3.45

Kiipsaare
Lighthouse — A330

2013, Jan. 31   **Perf. 14x13¾**
722 A330 45c multi   1.25 1.25

New Year 2013
(Year of the
Snake) — A331

2013, Feb. 8   **Perf. 12¾x13**
723 A331 €1.10 multi   3.00 3.00

Estonian
Flag — A332

Die Cut Perf. 11¼ Syncopated
2013, Feb. 22
Self-Adhesive
724 A332 €1 multi   2.60 2.60
a.   Dated "2014"   2.75 2.75
See Nos. 754, 929. Compare with illustration A449.
Issued No. 724a, 5/22/14.

Perdix
Perdix — A333

2013, Mar. 7   **Perf. 12¾x13**
725 A333 45c multi   1.25 1.25

Arms of Sindi — A333a

Die Cut Perf. 12½
2013, Mar. 28   **Litho.**
Self-Adhesive
725A A333a 45c multi   1.75 1.75

Folk Costumes — A334

Man and woman from: 45c, Kihelkonna. €1, Karja.

2013, Apr. 12   **Perf. 13¾x14**
726-727 A334   Set of 2   4.00 4.00

Icebreaker
"Tarmo" — A335

2013, Apr. 25   **Perf. 14x13¾**
728 A335 €1 multi   2.75 2.75

Europa
A336

No. 729 — Postal vehicles: a, Horse-drawn stagecoach, 1840s. b, Modern van.

2013, May 2   **Litho.**
729 A336 €1 Horiz. pair, #a-b   5.25 5.25

Souvenir Sheet

Estcube-1 Satellite — A337

2013, May 2
730 A337 €1.10 multi   3.00 3.00

Kuressaare, 450th
Anniv. — A338

2013, May 8   **Perf. 14x14¼**
731 A338 45c multi   1.40 1.40

Kaarel Eenpalu (1888-
1942), State Elder and
Prime Minister — A339

2013, May 28   **Perf. 13¾x14**
732 A339 45c dk brn violet   1.25 1.25

Mustela
Nivalis — A340

2013, June 6   **Perf. 12¾x13**
733 A340 45c multi   1.25 1.25

St. Catherine's Church,
Voru — A341

2013, July 24   **Perf. 13¾x14**
734 A341 45c multi   1.25 1.25

Souvenir Sheet

Cultural
Heritage
Year
A342

2013, Aug. 3   **Perf.**
735 A342 €1.10 multi   3.00 3.00

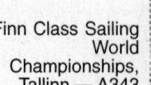

Finn Class Sailing
World
Championships,
Tallinn — A343

2013, Aug. 23   **Perf. 14¼x13¾**
736 A343 €1.10 multi   3.00 3.00

Estonia Theater and Concert House, Tallinn, Cent. A344

2013, Sept. 6   *Perf. 13*
737 A344 €1.10 multi   3.00 3.00

Amanita Phalloides — A345

2013, Sept. 12   *Perf. 13¾x14*
738 A345 45c multi   1.25 1.25

Raimond Valgre (1913-49), Composer A346

2013, Oct. 7   Litho.   *Perf. 13*
739 A346 45c multi   1.25 1.25

Arms of Moisaküla — A347

Die Cut Perf. 12½
2013, Oct. 31   Litho.
Self-Adhesive
740 A347 45c sil & black   1.50 1.50

Regular Postal Services in Estonia, 375th Anniv. — A348

Perf. 14¼x13¾
2013, Nov. 13   Litho.
741 A348 45c multi   1.50 1.50

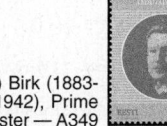

Aadu (Ado) Birk (1883-1942), Prime Minister — A349

2013, Nov. 14   Litho.   *Perf. 13¾x14*
742 A349 45c dull brown   1.25 1.25

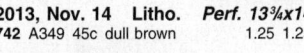

After Dinner, by Elmar Kits (1913-72) — A350

2013, Nov. 15   Litho.   *Perf. 14*
743 A350 €1.10 multi   2.50 2.50

A351

Christmas — A352

Serpentine Die Cut 11¼ Syncopated
2013, Nov. 22   Litho.
Self-Adhesive
744 A351 45c multi   1.25 1.25
745 A352 €1 multi   2.75 2.75

Estonian Olympic Committee, 90th Anniv. — A353

2013, Dec. 9   Litho.   *Perf. 13¾x14*
746 A353 45c multi   1.50 1.50

Jaan Tonisson (1888-c. 1941), Prime Minister — A354

2013, Dec. 20   Litho.   *Perf. 13¾x14*
747 A354 45c brown   1.25 1.25

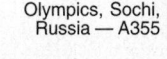

2014 Winter Olympics, Sochi, Russia — A355

2014, Jan. 16   Litho.   *Perf. 14x13¾*
748 A355 €1.10 multi   3.00 3.00

New Year 2014 (Year of the Horse) — A356

2014, Jan. 31   Litho.   *Perf. 12¾x13*
749 A356 €1.10 multi   3.00 3.00

Post Horn Type of 2008 With Euro Denomination Only
Die Cut Perf. 12½
2014, Feb. 19   Litho.
Self-Adhesive
Dated "2014"
750 A235 10c brt bl grn   .35 .35
   a.   Dated "2015"   .35 .35
    Issued: No. 750a, 10/16/15. Compare with No. 696.

Estonian History Museum. 150th Anniv. — A357

2014, Feb. 19   Litho.   *Perf. 12¾x13*
751 A357 45c multi   1.25 1.25

Pres. Konstantin Päts (1874-1956) — A358

2014, Feb. 21   Litho.   *Perf. 13¾x14*
752 A358 45c blue   1.25 1.25

Arms of Voru — A359

Die Cut Perf. 12½
2014, Mar. 5   Litho.
Self-Adhesive
753 A359 45c multi   1.25 1.25

Estonian Flag Type of 2013
Die Cut Perf. 11¼ Syncopated
2014, Mar. 5   Litho.
Self-Adhesive
754 A332 €2 multi   5.50 5.50
   a.   Dated "2018"   4.75 4.75
    Issued: No. 754a, 6/27/18.

Alcedo Atthis — A360

2014, Mar. 20   Litho.   *Perf. 12¾x13*
755 A360 45c multi   1.25 1.25

Folk Costumes — A361

Designs: 45c, Man and woman from Mihkli. €1, Women from Vigala.

2014, Apr. 12   Litho.   *Perf. 13¾x14*
756-757 A361   Set of 2   4.00 4.00

Juhan Liiv (1864-1913), Poet — A362

2014, Apr. 30   Litho.   *Perf. 13*
758 A362 45c multi   1.25 1.25

Inachis Io — A363

Serpentine Die Cut 12½
2014, May 2   Litho.
Booklet Stamp
Self-Adhesive
759 A363 45c multi   1.40 1.40
   a.   Booklet pane of 4   5.60

Europa — A364

Musical instruments: No. 760, €1, Väikekannel (zither). No. 761, €1, Lootspill (accordion).

2014, May 8   Litho.   *Perf. 14x13¾*
760-761 A364   Set of 2   5.00 5.00

Erinaceus Europaeus A365

2014, May 30   Litho.   *Perf. 12¾x13*
762 A365 45c multi   1.25 1.25

Estonian Herdbook, Cent. — A366

2014, July 19   Litho.   *Perf. 14x13½*
Textured and Flocked Granite Paper
763 A366 €1 multi   2.75 2.75

Baltic Chain Demonstration, 25th Anniv. — A367

Designs: 55c, Man and child.
No. 765: a, Five adults and one child. b, Three women. c, Like #764

2014, Aug. 23   Litho.   *Perf. 13¼*
764 A367 55c multi   1.50 1.50
Souvenir Sheet
765 A367 €1 Sheet of 3, #a-c   8.00 8.00
    See Latvia Nos. 883-884; Lithuania No. 1031.

Souvenir Sheet

Tallinn Zoo, 75th Anniv. — A368

No. 766: a, Gypaetus barbatus. b, Panthera pardus orientalis.

Perf. 14¼x13¾
2014, Aug. 25   Litho.
766 A368 55c Sheet of 2, #a-b   3.00 3.00

Estonian Academy of Arts, Cent. — A369

2014, Sept. 1   Litho.   *Perf. 14x13¾*
767 A369 55c multi   1.50 1.50

Inocybe Erubescens — A370

2014, Sept. 11   Litho.   *Perf. 13¾x14*
768 A370 55c red & black   1.40 1.40

Arms of Saue — A371

Die Cut Perf. 12½
2014, Sept. 11   Litho.
Self-Adhesive
769 A371 55c multi   1.40 1.40

1-Euro and 20-Cent Coins — A372

Die Cut Perf. 11¼ Syncopated
2014, Oct. 2   Litho.
Self-Adhesive
770 A372 €1.20 multi   3.00 3.00

Lighthouses — A373

Designs: 55c, Northern Soru Lighthouse. €1.30, Southern Soru Lighthouse.

2014, Oct. 17   Litho.   Perf. 13¾x14
771-772 A373   Set of 2   5.00 5.00

Personalized Stamp Type of 2012
Die Cut Perf. 8¾ Syncopated
2014, Nov. 17   Litho.
Self-Adhesive
773 A313   55c multi   1.40 1.40

The generic vignette, depicting a map of Hiiumaa, could be personalized for an additional fee.

Courtyard, by Herbert Lukk (1892-1919) — A374

2014, Nov. 17   Litho.   Perf. 14
774 A374   €1.30 multi   3.50 3.50

Christmas — A375

Christmas tree, ornaments and: 55c, Ribbon. €1.20, Pine cone.

Die Cut Perf. 11¼ Syncopated
2014, Nov. 20   Litho.
Self-Adhesive
775-776 A375   Set of 2   4.50 4.50

Jüri Uluots (1890-1945), Prime Minister — A376

2015, Jan. 13   Litho.   Perf. 13¾x14
777 A376   55c blue   1.25 1.25

Johannes Kotkas (1915-88), Wrestler A377

2015, Feb. 3   Litho.   Perf. 12½
778 A377   55c multi   1.25 1.25

New Year 2015 (Year of the Ram) — A378

2015, Feb. 19   Litho.   Perf. 12¾x13
779 A378   €1.30 multi   3.00 3.00

Eduard Vilde (1865-1933), Writer — A379

2015, Mar. 4   Litho.   Perf. 13
780 A379   55c multi   1.25 1.25

Arms of Elva — A380

Die Cut Perf. 12½
2015, Mar. 12   Litho.
Self-Adhesive
781 A380   55c multi   1.25 1.25

Souvenir Sheet

Seal and Map of Baltic Sea — A381

2015, Mar. 12   Litho.   Perf.
782 A381   €2.55 multi   6.25 6.25

Folk Costumes — A382

Designs: 55c, Man, woman and girl from Lihula. €1.20, Women from Kirbla.

2015, Apr. 14   Litho.   Perf. 13¾x14
783-784 A382   Set of 2   4.00 4.00

Europa — A383

Designs: No. 785, €1.20, Toy horses. No. 786, €1.20, Stuffed animals.

2015, May 6   Litho.   Perf. 14
785-786 A383   Set of 2   5.50 5.50

Pernis Apivorus — A384

2015, May 21   Litho.   Perf. 12¾x13
787 A384   55c multi   1.25 1.25

Characters From Animated Film *Lotte From Gadgetville* — A385

No. 788: a, Bruno the Kitten. b, Albert the Bunny. c, Bruno, Albert and Lotte. d, Lotte the Puppy.

Serpentine Die Cut 5x6
2015, May 30   Litho.
Self-Adhesive
788 A385   Booklet pane of 4
           + 6 stickers   5.50
a.-d.   55c Any single   1.35 1.35

Giraffe With Head Above Cloud — A386

Serpentine Die Cut 5x6
2015, June 4   Litho.
Booklet Stamp
Self-Adhesive
789 A386   €1.20 multi   2.75 2.75
a.   Booklet pane of 4   11.00

Aleksander Warma (1890-1970), Prime Minister — A387

2015, June 22   Litho.   Perf. 13¾x14
790 A387   55c Prus grn   1.25 1.25

European Under-23 Track and Field Championships, Tallinn — A388

2015, July 1   Litho.   Perf. 14x13¾
791 A388   55c multi   1.25 1.25

Estonian Business Innovations — A389

No. 792: a, Fortumo. b, GrabCAD. c, Skype. d, TransferWise.

Die Cut Perf. 12½
2015, July 6   Litho.
Self-Adhesive
792 A389   Booklet pane of 4   12.00
a.-d.   €1.30 Any single   3.00 3.00

Lutra Lutra — A390

2015, Aug. 25   Litho.   Perf. 12¾x13
793 A390   55c multi   1.35 1.35

Arms of Paide — A391

Die Cut Perf. 12½
2015, Sept. 10   Litho.
Self-Adhesive
794 A391   55c multi   1.25 1.25

Cortinarius Rubellus — A392

2015, Sept. 10   Litho.   Perf. 13¾x14
795 A392   55c multi   1.35 1.35

Tahkuna Lighthouse — A393

2015, Oct. 16   Litho.   Perf. 14x13¾
796 A393   55c multi   1.25 1.25

Penny Black, 175th Anniv. — A394

2015, Nov. 13   Litho.   Perf. 13½
797 A394   55c multi   1.25 1.25

A Girl and the Moon, by Karl Pärsimägi (1902-42) — A395

2015, Nov. 17   Litho.   Perf. 14
798 A395   55c multi   1.25 1.25

A396

Christmas — A397

Die Cut Perf. 11¼ Syncopated
2015, Nov. 19   Litho.
Self-Adhesive
799 A396   55c multi   1.25 1.25
800 A397   €1.20 multi   2.60 2.60

Arthur Joachim von Oettingen (1836-1920), Meteorologist, and Tartu University Meteorological Observatory A398

2015, Dec. 2   Litho.   Perf. 14¼x13¾
801 A398   65c multi   1.60 1.60

Tartu University Meteorological Observatory, 150th anniv.

Paul Keres (1916-75), Chess Player A399

2016, Jan. 7   Litho.   Perf. 12½
802 A399   65c multi   1.50 1.50

Souvenir Sheet

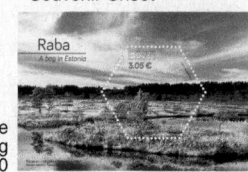

Tolkuse Bog A400

2016, Feb. 2   Litho.   Perf. 13
803 A400 €3.05 multi   7.25 7.25

New Year 2016 (Year of the Monkey) — A401

2016, Feb. 8   Litho.   Perf. 12¾x13
804 A401 €1.50 multi   3.25 3.25

Arms of Keila — A402

Die Cut Perf. 12½
2016, Feb. 10   Litho.
Self-Adhesive
805 A402 65c multi   1.40 1.40

Posthorn — A403

Die Cut Perf. 12½
2016, Feb. 10   Litho.
Self-Adhesive
806 A403 €1.40 multi   3.00 3.00
a.   Dated "2017"   3.00 3.00
Issued: No. 806a, 1/18/17.
See Nos. 816-818, 832-833, 926-928.

Parus Major — A404

2016, Feb. 17   Litho.   Perf. 12¾x13
807 A404 65c multi   1.40 1.40

Architecture — A405

No. 808: a, Tartu University Narva College, Narva (magenta background). b, Snail Tower, Tartu (green background). c, Estonian Embassy, Beijing (yellow brown background). d, Rotermann Quarter, Tallinn (turquoise green background).

2016, Mar. 17   Litho.   Perf. 14
808 A405 65c Block of 4, #a-d   6.00 6.00
e.   Booklet pane of 4, #808a-808d   6.00 —
    Complete booklet, #808e   6.00

August Rei (1886-1963), Chairman of Estonian National Council — A406

2016, Mar. 22   Litho.   Perf. 13¾x14
809 A406 65c brown   1.50 1.50

Otepää, 900th Anniv. — A407

2016, Apr. 1   Litho.   Perf. 13¼x12¾
810 A407 65c multi   1.50 1.50

Folk Costumes — A408

Designs: 65c, Man and woman from Audru. €1.50, Girl and woman from Tostamaa.

2016, Apr. 14   Litho.   Perf. 13¾x14
811-812 A408   Set of 2   5.00 5.00

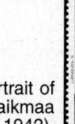

Self-Portrait of Ants Laikmaa (1866-1942), Painter — A409

2016, May 5   Litho.   Perf. 12¾x13
813 A409 65c multi   1.50 1.50

A410   Europa — A411

2016, May 9   Litho.   Perf. 14
814 A410 €1.40 multi   3.25 3.25
815 A411 €1.40 multi   3.25 3.25
Think Green Issue.

Posthorn Type of 2016
Die Cut Perf. 12½
2016, May 19   Litho.
Self-Adhesive
Background Colors
816 A403 5c yel & pale yel   .25 .25
817 A403 20c mag & pale mag   .45 .45
818 A403 40c brt grn & pale grn   .90 .90
    Nos. 816-818 (3)   1.60 1.60

2016 Summer Olympics, Rio de Janeiro — A412

2016, June 9   Litho.   Perf. 13¾x14¼
819 A412 €1.50 multi   3.50 3.50

Souvenir Sheet

Oil Shale Mining in Estonia, Cent. A413

Perf. 13¼x13½
2016, June 15   Litho.
820 A413 €2.95 multi   6.75 6.75

2016 Veterans' World Orienteering Championships, Tallinn and Harju County — A414

2016, Aug. 5   Litho.   Perf. 12¾x13
821 A414 €1.50 multi   3.50 3.50

Tonis Kint (1896-1991), Deputy Prime Minister of Exile Government — A415

2016, Aug. 17   Litho.   Perf. 13¾x14
822 A415 65c blue green   1.50 1.50

Sicista Betulina — A416

2016, Aug. 25   Litho.   Perf. 12¾x13
823 A416 65c multi   1.50 1.50

Amanita Muscaria — A417

2016, Sept. 8   Litho.   Perf. 13¾x14
824 A417 65c multi   1.50 1.50

National Museum A418

2016, Oct. 1   Litho.   Perf. 13
825 A418 €1.50 multi   3.50 3.50

Virtsu Lighthouse — A419

2016, Oct. 27   Litho.   Perf. 14x13¾
826 A419 65c multi   1.50 1.50

Baltic Assembly, 25th Anniv. — A420

2016, Nov. 8   Litho.   Perf. 13½
Stamp With White Frame
827 A420 65c multi   1.50 1.50
Souvenir Sheet
Stamp With Multicolored Frame
828 A420 €1.40 multi   3.25 3.25
See Latvia Nos. 948-949, Lithuania Nos. 1088-1089.

Fish Above Karlova, by Valve Janov (1921-2003) A421

2016, Nov. 17   Litho.   Perf. 14
829 A421 65c multi   1.50 1.50

Cookies — A422

Stylized Christmas Tree — A423

Die Cut Perf. 13½x14
2016, Nov. 18   Litho.
Self-Adhesive
830 A422 65c multi   1.50 1.50
831 A423 €1.40 multi   3.25 3.25
Christmas. No. 830 is impregnated with a gingerbread scent.

Posthorn Type of 2016
Die Cut Perf. 12½
2017, Jan. 18   Litho.
Self-Adhesive
Background Colors
832 A403 10c org & pale org   .30 .30
833 A403 65c bl grn & pale bl   1.50 1.50
a.   Dated "2019"   1.50 1.50
Issued: No. 833a, 11/19/19.

New Year 2017 (Year of the Rooster) — A424

2017, Jan. 28   Litho.   Perf. 12¾x13
834 A424 €1.50 multi   3.50 3.50

Streptopelia Turtur — A425

2017, Feb. 9   Litho.   Perf. 12¾x13
835 A425 65c multi   1.50 1.50

Baltic Herring A426

2017, Feb. 23   Litho.   Perf. 13
836 A426 65c multi   1.50 1.50

Ships Built in Estonia A427

No. 837: a, Patrol 4500 WP patrol vessel. b, AC600PVDB fish feeding barge. c, Saare 46 yacht. d, Koidula ferry.

2017, Mar. 30   Litho.   Perf. 14
837 A427 65c Block of 4, #a-d   6.00 6.00
  e. Booklet pane of 4, #837a-837d   6.00
    Complete booklet, #837e   6.00

No. 837 was printed in sheets containing two blocks that are tete-beche in relation to each other.

Souvenir Sheet

Figure Skating in Estonia, Cent. A428

2017, Apr. 15   Litho.   Perf. 13¼
838 A428 €3.05 multi + 2 labels   7.00 7.00

Lions Clubs International, Cent. — A429

2017, Apr. 29   Litho.   Perf. 13
839 A429 65c multi   1.50 1.50

Europa — A430

Designs: No. 840, €1.40, Keila-Joa Castle, lion. No. 841, €1.40, Maarjamäe Castle, eagle.

2017, May 8   Litho.   Perf. 12¾x13
840-841 A430   Set of 2   6.50 6.50

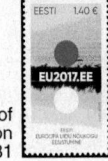

Estonian Presidency of the European Union Council in 2017 — A431

2017, May 13   Litho.   Perf. 14¼x14
842 A431 €1.40 multi   3.25 3.25

Statue of Martin Luther — A432

2017, May 27   Litho.   Perf. 13¾x14
843 A432 65c multi   1.50 1.50

Protestant Reformation, 500th anniv.

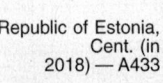

Republic of Estonia, Cent. (in 2018) — A433

Die Cut Perf. 11¼ Syncopated
2017, June 1   Litho.
Self-Adhesive
844 A433 €1.50 multi   3.50 3.50

Gustav Boesberg (1867-1922), Weight Lifter — A434

2017, June 19   Litho.   Perf. 12½
845 A434 65c multi   1.50 1.50

Constitution of Republic of Estonia, 25th Anniv. — A435

2017, June 28   Litho.   Perf. 14x13¾
846 A435 65c multi   1.50 1.50

World Orienteering Championships, Estonia — A436

2017, July 1   Litho.   Perf. 13¾x14
847 A436 €1.50 multi   3.50 3.50

Landscape with a Red Cloud, by Konrad Mägi (1878-1925) — A437

2017, Aug. 25   Litho.   Perf. 12¾x13
848 A437 €1.50 multi   3.75 3.75

Orjaku Lighthouses — A438

Designs: 65c, Lighthouse 26mm tall. €1.40, Lighthouse 29mm tall.

2017, Sept. 8   Litho.   Perf. 13¾x14
849-850 A438   Set of 2   5.00 5.00

Lynx Lynx — A439

2017, Sept. 11   Litho.   Perf. 12¾x13
851 A439 65c multi   1.60 1.60

Paxillus Involutus — A440

2017, Sept. 21   Litho.   Perf. 13¾x14
852 A440 65c multi   1.60 1.60

Pres. Kersti Kaljulaid — A441

2017, Oct. 10   Litho.   Perf. 13¾x14
853 A441 65c multi   1.50 1.50

Juniper Forest, Painting by Ulo Sooster (1924-70) — A442

2017, Nov. 17   Litho.   Perf. 14
854 A442 65c multi   1.60 1.60

Trees — A443

Designs: No. 855, Picea abies. No. 856, Sorbus aucuparia.

2017, Nov. 24   Litho.   Perf. 14
855 A443 €1.40 multi   3.50 3.50
  a. Tete-beche pair   7.00 7.00
856 A443 €1.40 multi   3.50 3.50
  a. Tete-beche pair   7.00 7.00

See Romania Nos. 6031-6032.

Miniature Sheet

Christmas — A444

No. 857: a, Bells and cinnamon sticks (43x34mm). b, Two Christmas ornaments on tree (27x31mm). c, Christmas tree with ornaments (33x47mm). d, Snowman and gifts (28x32mm).

2017, Nov. 24   Litho.   Die Cut
Self-Adhesive
857   A444   Sheet of 4 + 4 stickers, 2 etiquettes   7.00
  a.-d. 75c Any single   1.75 1.75

No. 857 is impregnated with a cinnamon scent.

2018 Winter Olympics, PyeongChang, South Korea — A445

2018, Jan. 12   Litho.   Perf. 13x12¾
858 A445 €1.50 multi   3.75 3.75

Estonian Defense League, Cent. — A446

2018, Jan. 26   Litho.   Perf. 14x14¼
859 A446 65c multi   1.60 1.60

New Year 2018 (Year of the Dog) — A447

2018, Feb. 16   Litho.   Perf. 12¾x13
860 A447 €1.50 multi   3.75 3.75

Republic of Estonia, Cent. — A448

Die Cut Perf. 12¾x12½
Etched on Silver Foil
2018, Feb. 22   Self-Adhesive
861 A448 €10 silver   25.00 25.00

No. 861 was sold as a single stamp in a protective plastic box.

Flag of Estonia and Centenary Emblem — A449

Die Cut Perf. 11¼ Syncopated
2018, Mar. 15   Litho.
Self-Adhesive
862 A449 €1.40 multi   3.50 3.50
  a. Dated "2020"   3.25 3.25

Issued: No. 862a, 1/6/20. Compare with Illustration A332.

Tetrao Urogallus — A450

2018, Mar. 29   Litho.   Perf. 12¾x13
863 A450 65c multi   1.60 1.60

Research Vessel Mare — A451

2018, Apr. 5   Litho.   Perf. 14x13¾
864 A451 65c multi   1.60 1.60

Estonian Maritime Museum, 50th anniv.

Estonian Ballet, Cent. — A452

2018, Apr. 29   Litho.   Perf. 12¾x13
865 A452 65c gold & blk   1.60 1.60

Europa — A453

Bridges in Tartu: No. 866, €1.40, Stone bridge. No. 867, €1.40, Arch bridge.

2018, May 3   Litho.   Perf. 14
866-867 A453   Set of 2   6.50 6.50

Pres. Arnold Rüütel — A454

2018, May 5   Litho.   Perf. 13¾x14
868 A454 65c cobalt & blue   1.50 1.50

Arms of Tallinn — A455

Die Cut Perf. 12½
2018, May 30   Litho.
Self-Adhesive
869 A455 65c multi   1.60 1.60

Manilaiu Lighthouse — A456

2018, June 7   Litho.   Perf. 14x13¾
870 A456 65c multi   1.50 1.50

Estonia No. 1 — A457

2018, July 13   Litho.   Perf. 13¾x14
871 A457 65c multi   1.60 1.60
First Estonian postage stamps, cent.

Kadriorg Palace, Tallinn, 300th Anniv. — A458

2018, July 22   Litho.   Perf. 13¾x14
872 A458 65c multi   1.60 1.60

Gyromitra Esculenta — A459

2018, Aug. 23   Litho.   Perf. 13¾x14
873 A459 65c multi   1.50 1.50

Litwinsky House, Tel Aviv — A460

2018, Aug. 28   Litho.   Perf. 14x13¾
874 A460 €1.50 multi   3.50 3.50
See Israel No. 2192.

Souvenir Sheet

Winning Art in Children's Stamp Design Contest — A461

No. 875: a, Map of Estonia, by Tartu kindergarten students. b, Barn swallow, by Emeli Matjusenko. c, Windmill, by Ann-Elisbeth Sang.

Serpentine Die Cut 5x6
2018, Sept. 1   Litho.
Self-Adhesive
875 A461 Sheet of 3   8.25
  a.   65c multi   1.50 1.50
  b.   €1.40 multi   3.25 3.25
  c.   €1.50 multi   3.50 3.50

Tallinn University of Technology, Cent. — A462

2018, Sept. 17   Litho.   Perf. 14x13¾
876 A462 €1.50 multi   3.50 3.50

Souvenir Sheet

Automobiles From 1933 Tallinn-Monte Carlo Rally — A463

No. 877: a, Hotchkiss AM 80S. b, GAZ-M20 Pobeda.

2018, Sept. 18   Litho.   Perf. 14x13¾
877 A463 €1.50 Sheet of 2, #a-
            b   7.00 7.00

Canis Aureus — A464

2018, Oct. 18   Litho.   Perf. 12¾x13
878 A464 65c multi   1.50 1.50

Estonian Postal Service, Cent. — A465

Perf. 13¾x14¼
2018, Nov. 12   Litho.
879 A465 65c multi   1.50 1.50

Estonian Paintings A466

No. 880: a, Truu Valvur, by Johann Köler (1826-99). b, Merikapsad, by Konrad Mägi (1878-1925). c, Pühapäev, by Felix Randel (1901-77). d, Comédie-Française, by Karin Luts (1904-93).

2018, Nov. 17   Litho.   Perf. 12¾x13
880 A466 €1.50 Block or
            horiz. strip
            of 4, #a-d   14.00 14.00

Estonian Spelling Dictionary, Cent. — A467

2018, Nov. 20   Litho.   Perf. 14x13¾
881 A467 65c multi   1.50 1.50

Christmas — A468

Die Cut Perf. 13½x14
2018, Nov. 23   Litho.
Self-Adhesive
882 A468 €1.50 multi   3.50 3.50
No. 882 is impregnated with a pine scent.

Toomas Hendrik Ilves, 4th President of Estonia — A469

2018, Dec. 20   Litho.   Perf. 13¾x14
883 A469 65c blue   1.50 1.50

Estonian Red Cross, Cent. — A470

2019, Jan. 24   Litho.   Perf. 14x13¾
884 A470 65c multi   1.50 1.50

Arms of Narva-Joesuu — A471

Die Cut Perf. 12½
2019, Jan. 31   Litho.
Self-Adhesive
885 A471 65c sil & multi   1.50 1.50

New Year 2019 (Year of the Pig) — A472

2019, Feb. 5   Litho.   Perf. 12¾x13
886 A472 €1.50 gold & multi   3.50 3.50

Tallinn Cathedral School, 700th Anniversary — A473

No. 887: a, St. Mary's Cathedral. b, St. Mary's Cathedral school house and crest.

2019, Feb. 11   Litho.   Perf. 13¼
887 A473 €1.50 Sheet of 2,
                  #a-b   7.00 7.00

Vello Agori (1894-1944), Cartoonist A474

Perf. 14¼x13¾
2019, Feb. 20   Litho.
888 A474 65c multi   1.50 1.50

Tallinn University, Cent. — A475

Perf. 14¼x13¾
2019, Feb. 22   Litho.
889 A475 65c multi   1.50 1.50

Osmussaare Lighthouse — A476

2019, Mar. 14   Litho.   Perf. 13¾x14
890 A476 65c multi   1.50 1.50

Hepatica Nobilis — A477

Serpentine Die Cut 6x7
2019, Mar. 28   Litho.
Self-Adhesive
891 A477 65c multi   1.50 1.50

Parliament of Estonia, Cent. — A478

2019, Apr. 24   Litho.   Perf. 13¾x14
892 A478 65c multi   1.50 1.50

Europa — A479

Map of Estonia and Hirundo rustica: No. 893, €1.40, Head. No. 894, €1.40, In flight.

2019, Apr. 25   Litho.   Perf. 14x13¾
893-894 A479 Set of 2   6.50 6.50

Estonian Bank, Cent. — A480

2019, May 3   Litho.   Perf. 14
895 A480 65c multi   1.50 1.50

Johann Voldemar Jannsen (1819-90), Journalist A481

2019, May 16   Litho.   Perf. 13
896 A481 65c multi   1.50 1.50

Metrosert (Central Office of Metrology), Cent. — A482

2019, May 20   Litho.   Perf. 14
897 A482 65c multi   1.50 1.50

Estonian Patent Office, Cent. — A483

2019, May 23   Litho.   Perf. 13¾
898 A483 65c multi   1.50 1.50

Battle of Lyndanisse, by Märt Bormeister (1916-91) — A484

2019, May 30   Litho.   Perf. 12¾x13
899 A484 €1.50 multi   3.50 3.50
First mention of Tallinn, 800th anniv.

Battle of Cesis, Cent. — A485

2019, June 21   Litho.   Perf. 14
900 A485 65c multi   1.50 1.50

Personalized Stamp Type of 2012
Die Cut Perf. 8¾ Syncopated
2019, July 5   Litho.
Self-Adhesive
901 A313 65c multi   1.50 1.50
The generic vignette depicting a map of Muhu could be personalized for an additional fee.

Souvenir Sheet

Estonian Song Festival, 150th Anniv. A486

2019, July 5   Litho.   Perf. 13½
On Cotton-faced Paper
902 A486 €10 multi   22.50 22.50

Galerina Marginata — A487

2019, Aug. 29   Litho.   Perf. 13¾x14
903 A487 65c multi   1.50 1.50

Souvenir Sheet

Fire Fighting in Estonia, Cent. A488

No. 904: a, Fire truck and female fire fighters, 1939. b, Fireman and helicopter fighting forest fire.

2019, Sept. 6   Litho.   Perf. 14
904   A488   Sheet of 2   6.50 6.50
a.-b.   €1.50 Either single   3.25 3.25

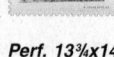

Talpa Europaea — A489

2019, Sept. 11   Litho.   Perf. 12¾x13
905 A489 65c multi   1.40 1.40

St. Peter's Church, Tartu, 150th Anniv. — A490

2019, Oct. 4   Litho.   Perf. 13¾x14
906 A490 65c multi   1.50 1.50

Caprimulgus Europaeus A491

2019, Oct. 17   Litho.   Perf. 12¾x13
907 A491 65c multi   1.50 1.50

Christmas — A492

Die Cut Perf. 13½x14
2019, Oct. 17   Litho.
Self-Adhesive
Flocked Paper
908 A492 65c multi   1.50 1.50

The Procession of the Bride, by Pieter Brueghel the Younger (1564-1638) A493

2019, Nov. 17   Litho.   Perf. 14x13¾
909 A493 65c multi   1.50 1.50

National University, Tartu, Cent. — A494

2019, Nov. 19   Litho.   Perf. 13
910 A494 65c multi   1.50 1.50

Ugala Theater, Viljandi, Cent. — A495

2020, Jan. 6   Litho.   Perf. 13¾x14
911 A495 65c multi   1.50 1.50

Estonian Supreme Court, Cent. — A496

2020, Jan. 14   Litho.   Perf. 13
912 A496 65c multi   1.50 1.50

New Year 2020 (Year of the Rat) — A497

2020, Jan. 25   Litho.   Perf. 12¾x13
913 A497 €1.50 sil & multi   3.50 3.50

Souvenir Sheet

Discovery of Antarctica, 200th Anniv. — A498

No. 914: a, Fabian von Bellingshausen (1778-1852), explorer. b, Mikhail P. Lazarev (1788-1851), explorer.

2020, Jan. 28   Litho.   Perf. 14x14¼
914 A498 €1.50 Sheet of 2, #a-
                 b   6.75 6.75
Joint issue between Estonia and Russia. See Russia No. 8114.

Jaan Poska (1866-1920) Signing Tartu Peace Treaty, Cent. — A499

2020, Jan. 29   Litho.   Perf. 13
915 A499 65c multi   1.50 1.50

Jaan Kross (1920-2007), Writer — A500

2020, Feb. 19   Litho.   Perf. 12¾x13
916 A500 65c multi   1.50 1.50

St. Nicholas' Church, Paldiski — A501

2020, Feb. 27   Litho.   Perf. 14x13¾
917 A501 65c multi   1.50 1.50

National Archives, Cent. — A502

2020, Mar. 3   Litho.   Perf. 12¾x13
918 A502 65c sil & multi   1.50 1.50

Souvenir Sheet

Georg Ots (1920-75), Singer — A503

2020, Mar. 21   Litho.   Perf. 13
919 A503 €5.50 multi   12.00 12.00

Estonian Internal Security Service, Cent. — A504

2020, Apr. 6   Litho.   Perf. 13
920 A504 65c multi   1.50 1.50

Estonian Students' Society, 150th Anniv. — A505

2020, Apr. 7   Litho.   Perf. 14x13½
921 A505 65c multi   1.50 1.50

Estonian Girl Guides, Cent. — A506

2020, Apr. 23   Litho.   Perf. 12½
922 A506 €1.50 multi   3.25 3.25

Podiceps Cristatus — A507

2020, Apr. 30   Litho.   Perf. 12¾x13
923 A507 65c multi   1.50 1.50

Tartu-Voru Post Road — A508

Estonian Road Museum, Varbuse — A509

2020, May 14   Litho.   Perf. 14x13¾
924 A508 €1.90 multi   4.25 4.25
925 A509 €1.90 multi   4.25 4.25
Ancient Postal Routes.
Europa.

Posthorn Type of 2016
Die Cut Perf. 12½
2020, May 26   Litho.
Self-Adhesive
Background Colors
926 A403 5c ol yel & pale grn   .25   .25
927 A403 25c purple & lilac   .55   .55
928 A403 90c brt org & pale org   2.00 2.00
     Nos. 926-928 (3)   2.80 2.80

Estonian Flag Type of 2013
Die Cut Perf. 11¼ Syncopated
2020, May 26   Litho.
Self-Adhesive
929 A332 €1.90 multi   4.25 4.25

Euphydryas Aurinia — A510

Serpentine Die Cut 5x6
2020, June 11   Litho.
Booklet Stamp
Self-Adhesive
930 A510 90c multi   2.00 2.00
a.   Booklet pane of 4   8.00

Amanita
Pantherina — A511

2020, Aug. 28 Litho. Perf. 13¾x14
931 A511 90c multi 2.25 2.25

Alfred Neuland (1895-
1966), First Estonian
Olympic Gold
Medalist — A512

**Etched on Silver Foil
2020, Aug. 28 Die Cut Perf. 13x12½
Self-Adhesive**
932 A512 €13 silver 31.00 31.00
No. 932 was sold individually inside a plastic case.

Souvenir Sheet

Toyota Yaris 2020 Rally Estonia Race
Car
A513

2020, Sept. 4 Litho. Perf. 12¾x13¼
933 A513 €5.90 multi 14.00 14.00

Souvenir Sheet

Estonian Railroads, 150th
Anniv. — A514

**Litho. With Foil Application
2020, Sept. 10 Perf. 13¼**
934 A514 €5.90 sil & multi 14.00 14.00

Rattus
Rattus — A515

2020, Sept. 11 Litho. Perf. 12¾x13
935 A515 90c multi 2.10 2.10

Christmas
A516

Designs: 90c, Bells. €1.90, Christmas tree.

**Die Cut Perf. 12¼x12¾
2020, Oct. 15 Litho.
Self-Adhesive**
936-937 A516 Set of 2 6.50 6.50

Kihnu
Lighthouse — A517

2020, Oct. 26 Litho. Perf. 14x13¾
938 A517 90c multi 2.10 2.10

River Seine, by Ado
Vabbe (1892-
1961) — A518

2020, Nov. 17 Litho. Perf. 14
939 A518 90c multi 2.25 2.25

Voldemar Panso
(1920-77), Actor
and
Director — A519

2020, Nov. 30 Litho. Perf. 14x13¾
940 A519 90c multi 2.25 2.25

Letipea
Lighthouse — A520

2021, Jan. 21 Litho. Perf. 14x13¾
941 A520 90c multi 2.25 2.25

Roses — A521

**Serpentine Die Cut
2021, Feb. 4 Litho.
Self-Adhesive**
942 A521 90c multi 2.25 2.25
Valentine's Day.

New Year 2021
(Year of the
Ox) — A522

2021, Feb. 12 Litho. Perf. 12¾x13
943 A522 €1.90 multi 4.75 4.75

Estonian
Medical
Association,
Cent. — A523

2021, Feb. 27 Litho. Perf. 12½
944 A523 90c multi 2.25 2.25

Centaurea
Cyanus — A524

**Die Cut Perf. 12½
2021, Mar. 1 Litho.
Self-Adhesive**
945 A524 90c multi 2.25 2.25

Statistics Estonia,
Cent. — A525

2021, Mar. 1 Litho. Perf. 14x13¾
946 A525 90c multi 2.25 2.25

Souvenir Sheet

King's
Pine,
Järvselja
Nature
Reserve
A526

**Serpentine Die Cut 6½ Syncopated
2021, Apr. 13 Litho.
On Wood Veneer
Self-Adhesive**
947 A526 €7.50 multi 18.00 18.00

Souvenir Sheet

Estonian Ornithological Society,
Cent. — A527

No. 948: a, Sturnus vulgaris. b, Society emblem, bird, binoculars and notebook.

2021, Apr. 29 Litho. Perf. 12¾x13
948 A527 €1.90 Sheet of 2, #a-b 9.25 9.25

Upupa
Epops — A528

Cypripedium
Calceolus
A529

2021, May 6 Litho. Perf. 13
949 A528 €1.90 multi 4.75 4.75
950 A529 €1.90 multi 4.75 4.75
Endangered species. Europa.

Papaver
Rhoeas — A530

2021, May 20 Litho. Perf. 13¼
951 A530 €4 multi 9.75 9.75
A poppy seed is under a gummed circle of plastic in the center of the stamp.

2020 Summer
Olympics,
Tokyo — A531

2021, May 26 Litho. Perf. 13¾x14¼
952 A531 €1.90 multi 4.75 4.75
The 2020 Summer Olympics were postponed until 2021 because of the COVID-19 pandemic.

Eighth World
Congress of
Finno-Ugric
Peoples,
Tartu — A532

Perf. 14¼x13¾
2021, June 16 Litho.
953 A532 90c multi 2.25 2.25

European Under-23 and Under-20
Track and Field Championships,
Tallinn — A533

2021, July 12 Litho. Perf. 12½
954 A533 €1.90 multi 4.50 4.50

People on Village
Swing — A534

Perf. 13¾x14¼
2021, Aug. 12 Litho.
955 A534 90c multi 2.25 2.25

Estonian Soccer
Federation,
Cent. — A535

**Silk-Screened
2021, Aug. 30 Die Cut
Self-Adhesive
Printed on Foam-backed Plastic**
956 A535 €5.90 blue & black 14.00 14.00

Mustela
Erminea — A536

2021, Sept. 10 Litho. Perf. 12¾x13
957 A536 90c multi 2.10 2.10

First Film Screening in Estonia, 125th
Anniv. — A537

2021, Sept. 16 Litho. Perf. 13
958 A537 90c multi 2.10 2.10

St. Michael's Church,
Keila — A538

2021, Sept. 17 Litho. Perf. 13¾x14
959 A538 90c multi 2.10 2.10

Estonian Civil
Aviation,
Cent. — A539

Perf. 14¼x13¾
2021, Sept. 20   Litho.
960   A539   €1.90 multi   4.50 4.50

Christmas — A540

Designs: 90c, Eurasian bullfinch. €1.90, Squirrel.

Die Cut Perf. 11¼ Syncopated
2021, Oct. 15   Litho.
Self-Adhesive
961-962 A540   Set of 2   6.50 6.50

Estonian Federation of the Blind, Cent. — A541

Litho. & Embossed
2021, Oct. 19   Perf. 14x13¾
963   A541   90c black & blue   2.10 2.10

Canis Lupus — A542

2021, Oct. 19   Litho.   Perf. 12¾x13
964   A542   90c multi   2.10 2.10

A543

Design: Ministry of Foreign Affairs, Tallinn, and Itamaraty Palace, Brasilia.

2021, Nov. 10   Litho.   Perf. 13
965   A543   €1.90 multi   4.50 4.50

Diplomatic relations between Estonia and Brazil, cent. See Brazil No. 3476.

Personalized Stamp Type of 2012
Die Cut Perf. 8¾ Syncopated
2021, Nov. 17   Litho.
Self-Adhesive
966   A313   90c multi   2.10 2.10

The generic vignette shown, depicting a map of Vormsi, could be personalized for an additional fee.

Estonian Bride, by Gustav Adolf Hippius (1792-1856) — A544

2021, Nov. 17   Litho.   Perf. 14
967   A544   90c multi   2.10 2.10

Souvenir Sheet

Estonian Women's Epee Team, Gold Medalists at 2020 Summer Olympics — A545

2021, Dec. 29 Litho.   Perf. 12¾x13
968   A545   €5.90 multi   13.50 13.50

The 2020 Summer Olympics were postponed until 2021 because of the COVID-19 pandemic.

St. Mary's Church, Tartu — A546

2022, Jan. 6   Litho.   Perf. 13¾x14
969   A546   90c multi   2.10 2.10

2022 Winter Olympics, Beijing — A547

2022, Jan. 6   Litho.   Perf. 13
970   A547   €1.90 multi   4.25 4.25

New Year 2022 (Year of the Tiger) — A548

2022, Feb. 1   Litho.   Perf. 12¾x13
971   A548   €1.90 multi   4.25 4.25

Rear Admiral Johan Pitka (1872-1944) A549

2022, Feb. 19   Litho.   Perf. 13
972   A549   90c multi   2.00 2.00

Society of Estonian Writers, 150th Anniv. — A550

2022, Mar. 9   Litho.   Perf. 13
973   A550   90c multi   2.00 2.00

Dove and Flag of Ukraine — A551

Die Cut Perf. 11¼ Syncopated
2022, Mar. 24   Litho.
Self-Adhesive
974   A551   €1.90 multi   4.25 4.25

Estonian solidarity with Ukraine after its invasion by Russia.

Scolopax Rusticola — A552

2022, Mar. 31 Litho.   Perf. 12¾x13
975   A552   90c multi   2.00 2.00

Town Hall Pharmacy, Tallinn, 600th Anniv. — A553

2022, Apr. 8   Litho.   Perf. 13¾x14¼
976   A553   €1.90 multi   4.00 4.00

Souvenir Sheet

Estonian Tennis Association, Cent. — A554

No. 977: a, Kaia Kanepi (blue background). b, Anett Kontaveit (green background).

2022, Apr. 11   Litho.   Perf. 13¾
977   A554   €1.90 Sheet of 2, #a-
             b   8.00 8.00

Betula Pendula Var. Carelica — A555

2022, Apr. 20 Litho.   Perf. 13¾x14¼
978   A555   90c multi   1.90 1.90

Tapestry of Siuru Bird, by Oskar Kallis — A556

Doing a Handstand, Painting by Kallis — A557

2022, May 5   Litho.   Perf. 14
979   A556   €1.90 multi   4.25 4.25
980   A557   €1.90 multi   4.25 4.25

Europa. Scenes from *Kalevipoeg*, Estonian national epic poem, by Friedrich Reinhold Kreutzwald (1803-82).

Miniature Sheet

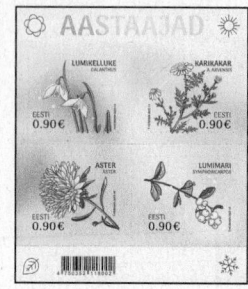

Flowers A558

No. 981: a, Galanthus. b, Anthemis arvensis. c, Aster. d, Symphoricarpos.

Die Cut Perf. 11¼ Syncopated
2022, May 19   Litho.
Self-Adhesive
981   A558   Sheet of 4   8.00
a.-d.   90c Any single   2.00 2.00

Cat Mailing Postcard — A559

2022, June 1   Litho.   Perf. 12¾x13
982   A559   90c multi   2.00 2.00

Motorized Sailboat Läänemaa — A560

2022, June 9   Litho.   Perf. 14x13¾
983   A560   90c multi   1.90 1.90

Diplomatic Relations Between Estonia and the United States, Cent. — A561

Perf. 14¼x13¾
2022, June 17   Litho.
984   A561   €1.90 multi   4.00 4.00

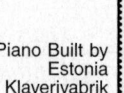

Tallinn Town Hall, 700th Anniv. — A562

Die Cut Perf. 11¼ Syncopated
2022, July 7   Litho.
Self-Adhesive
985   A562   90c multi   1.90 1.90

Piano Built by Estonia Klaverivabrik A563

2022, Aug. 25 Litho.   Perf. 12¾x13
986   A563   90c multi   1.90 1.90

Pteromys Volans — A564

2022, Sept. 9   Litho.   Perf. 12¾x13
987   A564   90c multi   1.75 1.75

Riigikogu
(Parliament)
Building, Tallinn,
Cent. — A565

2022, Sept. 12 Litho. *Perf. 14x14¼*
988 A565 90c multi   1.75 1.75

SEMI-POSTAL STAMPS

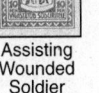

Assisting   Offering Aid
Wounded   to Wounded
Soldier   Hero
SP1   SP2

1920, June Unwmk. Litho. *Imperf.*
B1 SP1 35p + 10p red & ol grn   .50 2.00
B2 SP2 70p + 15p dp bl & brn   .50 2.00

Surcharged

1920
B3 SP1 1m on No. B1   .35 .30
B4 SP2 2m on No. B2   .35 .30

Nurse and Wounded
Soldier — SP3

1921, Aug. 1   *Imperf.*
B5 SP3 2½ (3½)m org, brn &
         car   2.00 8.00
B6 SP3 5 (7)m ultra, brn & car 2.00 8.00

1922, Apr. 26   *Perf. 13½x14*
B7 SP3 2½ (3½)m org, brn &
         car   2.00 8.00
  a.   Vert. pair, imperf. horiz. 30.00 95.00
B8 SP3 5 (7)m ultra, brn &
         car   2.00 8.00
  a.   Vert. pair, imperf. horiz. 30.00 95.00

Nos. B5-B8 Overprinted

1923, Oct. 8   *Imperf.*
B9   SP3 2½ (3½)m   60.00 160.00
B10 SP3 5 (7)m   60.00 160.00

**   *Perf. 13½x14***
B11 SP3 2½ (3½)m   60.00 160.00
  a.   Vert. pair, imperf. horiz. 300.00 1,000.
B12 SP3 5 (7)m   60.00 160.00
  a.   Vert. pair, imperf. horiz. 300.00 1,000.
     Nos. B9-B12 (4) 240.00 640.00
Set, never hinged   480.00

Excellent forgeries are plentiful.

Nos. B7 and B8
Surcharged

1926, June 15
B13 SP3 5 (6)m on #B7   3.75 9.50
  a.   Vert. pair, imperf. horiz. 32.50 120.00
B14 SP3 10 (12)m on #B8 4.50 9.50
  a.   Vert. pair, imperf. horiz. 32.50 120.00

Nos. B5-B14 had the franking value of the
lower figure. They were sold for the higher figure, the excess going to the Red Cross
Society.

Kuressaare
Castle
SP4

Tartu
Cathedral
SP5

Tallinn
Castle
SP6

Narva Fortress
SP7

View of
Tallinn — SP8

Laid Paper
Perf. 14½x14
1927, Nov. 19 Typo. *Wmk. 207*
B15 SP4 5m + 5m bl grn &
         ol, *grysh*   .60 9.50
B16 SP5 10m + 10m dp bl &
         brn, *cream*   .60 9.50
B17 SP6 12m + 12m rose red
         & ol grn, *bluish*   .60 9.50

Perf. 14x13½
B18 SP7 20m + 20m bl &
         choc, *gray*   .60 9.50
B19 SP8 40m + 40m org brn &
         slate, *buff*   .60 9.50
     Nos. B15-B19 (5) 3.00 47.50
Set, never hinged   10.00

The money derived from the surtax was
donated to the Committee for the commemoration of War for Liberation.

Red Cross Issue

Symbolical   Symbolical
of Succor   of "Light of
to Injured   Hope"
SP9   SP10

1931, Aug. 1 Unwmk. *Perf. 13½*
B20 SP9   2s + 3s grn & car   10.00 9.50
B21 SP10 5s + 3s red & car   10.00 9.50
B22 SP10 10s + 3s lt bl & car 10.00 9.50
B23 SP9   20s + 3s dk bl & car 12.00 20.00
     Nos. B20-B23 (4) 42.00 48.50
Set, never hinged   85.00

Nurse   Taagepera
and Child   Sanatorium
SP11   SP12

Lorraine Cross and
Flower — SP13

Paper with Network as in Parenthesis

1933, Oct. 1   *Perf. 14, 14½*
B24 SP11 5s + 3s ver (grn)   8.00 8.00
B25 SP12 10s + 3s lt bl & red
           (vio)   8.00 8.00
B26 SP13 12s + 3s rose & red
           (grn)   10.00 12.00
B27 SP12 20s + 3s dk bl & red
           (org)   12.00 16.00
     Nos. B24-B27 (4) 38.00 44.00
Set, never hinged   75.00

The surtax was for a fund to combat
tuberculosis.

Coats of Arms

Narva   Pärnu
SP14   SP15

Tartu   Tallinn
SP16   SP17

Paper with Network as in Parenthesis

1936, Feb. 1   *Perf. 13½*
B28 SP14 10s + 10s grn & ul-
           tra (gray)   2.50   8.00
B29 SP15 15s + 15s car & bl
           (gray)   4.00 12.00
B30 SP16 25s + 25s gray bl &
           red (brn)   4.50 16.00
B31 SP17 50s + 50s blk & dl
           org (ol)   18.00 52.50
     Nos. B28-B31 (4) 29.00 88.50
Set, never hinged   57.50

Paide   Rakvere
SP18   SP19

Valga   Viljandi
SP20   SP21

Paper with Network as in Parenthesis

1937, Jan. 2   *Perf. 13½x14*
B32 SP18 10s + 10s grn (gray) 2.50 9.50
B33 SP19 15s + 15s red brn
           (gray)   3.50 9.50
B34 SP20 25s + 25s dk bl (lil) 4.00 14.50
B35 SP21 50s + 50s dk vio
           (gray)   10.00 24.00
     Nos. B32-B35 (4) 20.00 57.50
Set, never hinged   40.00

Baltiski   Võru
SP22   SP23

Haapsalu   Kuressaare
SP24   SP25

Designs are the armorial bearings of various cities

1938, Jan. 21
Paper with Gray Network
B36 SP22 10s + 10s dk brn   2.00   8.00
B37 SP23 15s + 15s car & grn 2.00 12.00
B38 SP24 25s + 25s dk bl &
           car   4.00 20.00
B39 SP25 50s + 50s blk & org
           yel   12.00 40.00
  a.   Sheet of 4, #B36-B39   30.00 95.00
     Nos. B36-B39 (4) 20.00 80.00
Set, never hinged   40.00

Annual charity ball, Tallinn, Jan. 2, 1938.

Viljandimaa   Pärnumaa
SP27   SP28

Tartumaa   Harjumaa
SP29   SP30

Designs are the armorial bearings of various cities

1939, Jan. 10   *Perf. 13½*
Paper with Gray Network
B41 SP27 10s + 10s dk bl
           grn   2.00   8.00
B42 SP28 15s + 15s carmine   2.00   8.00
B43 SP29 25s + 25s dk blue   6.00 20.00
B44 SP30 50s + 50s brn lake 16.00 47.50
  a.   Sheet of 4, #B41-B44   45.00 175.00
     Nos. B41-B44 (4) 26.00 83.50
Set, never hinged   52.50

Võrumaa   Järvamaa
SP32   SP33

Läänemaa   Saaremaa
SP34   SP35

Designs are the armorial bearings of various cities

1940, Jan. 2 Typo. *Perf. 13½*
Paper with Gray Network
B46 SP32 10s + 10s dp grn &
           ultra   2.00 12.00
B47 SP33 15s + 15s dk car &
           ultra   2.00 16.00
B48 SP34 25s + 25s dk bl &
           scar   3.00 24.00
B49 SP35 50s + 50s ocher &
           ultra   8.00 32.50
     Nos. B46-B49 (4) 15.00 84.50
Set, never hinged   30.00

Catalogue values for unused
stamps in this section, from this
point to the end of the section, are
for Never Hinged items.

1992 Summer
Olympics,
Barcelona — SP40

1992, June 22 Litho. *Perf. 14*
B60 SP40 1r +50k red   .40   .40
B61 SP40 3r +1.50r green 1.75 1.75
B62 SP40 5r +2.50r blue & blk .80 .80
     Nos. B60-B62 (3) 2.95 2.95

While face values are shown in kopecks and
rubles, the stamps were sold in the new currency at the rate of 1 ruble = 10 sents.

No. 280 Surcharged

1994, Nov. 18 Litho. *Perf. 14*
B63 A51 2.50k +20k green 6.00 6.00

Surtax for benefit of survivors of sinking of
ferry "Estonia."

Haliaeetus
Albicilla — SP41

1995, Aug. 29   Litho.   Perf. 14
B64 SP41 2k +25k black & blue   .45   .45
Surtax for Keep the Estonian Sea Clean
Assoc.

UNICEF, 60th
Anniv. — SP42

2006, June 1   Litho.   Perf. 13½
B65 SP42 4.40k +1k multi   1.00 1.00

AIR POST STAMPS

Airplane — AP1

Unwmk.
1920, Mar. 13   Typo.   Imperf.
C1 AP1 5m yel, blk & lt grn   2.50   6.50
    Never hinged   7.00

No. C1 Overprinted "1923" in Red
1923, Oct. 1
C2 AP1 5m multicolored   8.00   32.50
    Never hinged   16.00

No. C1 Surcharged in Red

1923, Oct. 1
C3 AP1 15m on 5m multi   16.00   47.50
    Never hinged   32.50

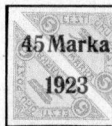

Pairs of No. C1
Surcharged in Black or
Red

1923, Oct.
C4 AP1 10m on 5m+5m
  (B)   10.00   35.00
C5 AP1 20m on 5m+5m   20.00   55.00
C6 AP1 45m on 5m+5m   60.00   200.00
Rough Perf. 11½
C7 AP1 10m on 5m+5m
  (B)   650.00   1,600.
C8 AP1 20m on 5m+5m   275.00   725.00
    Nos. C4-C8 (5)   1,015.   2,615.
    Set, never hinged   1,850.
The pairs comprising Nos. C7 and C8 are
imperforate between. Forged surcharges and
perforations abound. Authentication is
required.

Monoplane in
Flight — AP2

Designs: Various views of planes in flight.

1924, Feb. 12   Imperf.
C9 AP2 5m yellow & blk   1.60   8.00
C10 AP2 10m blue & blk   1.60   8.00
C11 AP2 15m red & blk   1.60   8.00
C12 AP2 20m green & blk   1.60   8.00
C13 AP2 45m violet & blk   1.60   16.00
    Nos. C9-C13 (5)   8.00   48.00
    Set, never hinged   16.00
The paper is covered with a faint network in
pale shades of the frame colors. There are
four varieties of the frames and five of the
pictures.

1925, July 15   Perf. 13½
C14 AP2 5m yellow & blk   1.25   8.00
C15 AP2 10m blue & blk   1.25   8.00
C16 AP2 15m red & blk   1.25   8.00
C17 AP2 20m green & blk   1.25   8.00
C18 AP2 45m violet & blk   1.25   16.00
    Nos. C14-C18 (5)   6.25   48.00
    Set, never hinged   12.00
Counterfeits of Nos. C1-C18 are plentiful.

REGISTRATION STAMP

> Catalogue values for unused
> stamps in this section are for
> Never Hinged items.

Arms Type of 1992
1992, Mar. 16   Litho.   Perf. 13x12½
F1 A42   R (10r) pink & red   .60   .60

OCCUPATION STAMPS

Issued under German Occupation
For Use in Tartu (Dorpat)

Russian Stamps of 1909-12
Surcharged

1918   Unwmk.   Perf. 14x14½
N1 A15 20pf on 10k dk bl   40.00   160.00
N2 A8   40pf on 20k bl &
    car   40.00   160.00
    Set, never hinged   250.00
Forged overprints exist.

Estonian Arms and
Swastika — OS1

Perf. 11½
1941, Aug.   Typo.   Unwmk.
N3 OS1 15k brown   8.00   16.00
N4 OS1 20k green   5.50   14.50
N5 OS1 30k dark blue   5.50   14.50
    Nos. N3-N5 (3)   19.00   45.00
    Set, never hinged   45.00
Exist imperf. Value, set $200.
Nos. N3-N5 were issued on both ordinary
paper with colorless gum and thick chalky
paper with yellow gum. Value, set on chalky
paper $22.50.

OCCUPATION SEMI-POSTAL STAMPS

Castle Tower,
Tallinn — OSP1

Designs: 20k+20k, Stone Bridge, Tartu,
horiz. 30k+30k, Narva Castle, horiz. 50k+50k,
Tallinn view, horiz. 60k+60k, Tartu University.
100k+100k, Narva Castle, close view.

Paper with Gray Network
Perf. 11½
1941, Sept. 29   Photo.   Unwmk.
NB1 OSP1 15k + 15k dk brn   .60   4.75
NB2 OSP1 20k + 20k red lil   .60   4.75
NB3 OSP1 30k + 30k dk bl   .60   4.75
NB4 OSP1 50k + 50k bluish
    grn   .70   9.50
NB5 OSP1 60k + 60k car   1.00   8.00
NB6 OSP1 100k + 100k gray   1.50   9.50
    Nos. NB1-NB6 (6)   5.00   41.25
    Set, never hinged   10.00
Nos. NB1-NB6 exist imperf. Value, set
unused $70, used $200.
A miniature sheet containing one each of
Nos. NB1-NB6, imperf., exists in various col-
ors. Value, mint $40, used $60. It was not pos-
tally valid. Reproductions are common.

ETHIOPIA
ē-thē-'ō-pē-ə

(Abyssinia)

LOCATION — Northeastern Africa
GOVT. — Republic (1988)
AREA — 426,260 sq. mi.
POP. — 59,680,383 (1999 est.)
CAPITAL — Addis Ababa

During the Italian occupation (1936-
1941) Nos. N1-N7 were used, also
stamps of Italian East Africa, Eritrea
and Somalia.
During the British administration
(1941-42) stamps of Great Britain and
Kenya were used when available.

16 Guerche = 1 Menelik Dollar or 1
Maria Theresa Dollar
100 Centimes = 1 Franc (1905)
40 Paras = 1 Piaster (1908)
16 Mehalek = 1 Thaler or Talari (1928)
100 Centimes = 1 Thaler (1936)
100 Cents = 1 Ethiopian Dollar (1946)
100 Cents = 1 Birr (1978)

> Catalogue values for unused
> stamps in this country are for
> Never Hinged items, beginning
> with Scott 247 in the regular post-
> age section, Scott B6 in the semi-
> postal section, Scott C18 in the
> airpost section, Scott E1 in the
> special delivery section, and Scott
> J57 in the postage due section.

Watermarks

Wmk. 140 — Crown

Wmk. 282 — Ethiopian Star and
Amharic Characters, Multiple

Excellent forgeries of Nos. 1-86 exist.

> Very Fine examples of Nos. 1-86
> and J1-J42 will have perforations
> touching the design on one or more
> sides due to the narrow spacing of
> the stamps on the plates and imper-
> fect perforating methods. Stamps
> with margins clear on all sides are
> scarce and command high
> premiums.

On March 9, 1894 Menelik II awarded
Alfred Ilg a concession to develop a railway, including postal service. Ilg's
stamps, Nos. 1-79, were valid locally
and to Djibouti. Mail to other countries
had to bear stamps of Obock, Somali
Coast, etc.
Ethiopia joined the UPU Nov. 1,
1908.

Menelik II
A1   Lion of
Judah
A2

Amharic numeral "8"

Perf. 14x13½
1895, Jan.   Unwmk.   Typo.
1 A1 ¼g green   4.00   6.00
2 A1 ½g red   3.50   5.00
3 A1 1g blue   3.50   5.00
4 A1 2g dark brown   3.00   6.00
5 A2 4g lilac brown   3.00   6.00
6 A2 8g violet   3.00   6.00
7 A2 16g black   4.00   6.00
    Nos. 1-7 (7)   24.00   40.00
For 4g, 8g and 16g stamps of type A1, see
Nos. J3a, J4a and J7a.
Earliest reported use is Jan. 29, 1895.
Forged cancellations are plentiful.
For overprints see Nos. 8-86, J8-J28, J36-
J42. For surcharges see Nos. 94-100, J29-
J35.

Nos. 1-7 Handstamped in
Violet or Blue

Overprint 9¼x2½mm, Serifs on "E"
1901, July 18
8 A1 ¼g green   27.50   27.50
9 A1 ½g red   27.50   27.50
10 A1 1g blue   27.50   27.50
11 A1 2g dark brown   27.50   27.50
12 A2 4g lilac brown   32.50   32.50
13 A2 8g violet   47.50   47.50
14 A2 16g black   60.00   60.00
    Nos. 8-14 (7)   250.00   250.00
Violet overprints were issued July 18, 1901,
for postal use, while the blue overprints were
issued in Jan. 5 1902 for philatelic purposes.
The blue overprints were not used in the mails.
Values for unused stamps are for examples
with blue overprints. The blue overprints
became valid for postage in 1908 only.
Unused stamps with violet overprints are
worth much more.
Overprints 8¼mm wide are unofficial
reproductions.

Nos. 1-7 Handstamped in
Violet, Blue or Black

Overprint 11x3mm, Low Colons
1902, Apr. 1
15 A1 ¼g green   14.00   14.00
16 A1 ½g red   14.00   14.00
17 A1 1g blue   14.00   14.00
18 A1 2g dark brown   14.00   14.00
19 A2 4g lilac brown   24.00   24.00
20 A2 8g violet   30.00   30.00
21 A2 16g black   55.00   55.00
    Nos. 15-21 (7)   165.00   165.00
The handstamp reads "Bosta" (Post).
Overprints 10¾mm and 11mm wide with
raised colons are unofficial reproductions.

Nos. 1-7 Handstamped in
Black

1903, Jan. 9   Overprint 16x3¾mm
22 A1 ¼g green   14.00   14.00
23 A1 ½g red   20.00   20.00
24 A1 1g blue   22.50   22.50
25 A1 2g dark brown   22.50   22.50
26 A2 4g lilac brown   35.00   35.00
27 A2 8g violet   50.00   50.00
28 A2 16g black   70.00   70.00
    Nos. 22-28 (7)   234.00   234.00
The handstamp reads "Malekt." (Also
"Melekt," message).
Original stamps have blurred colons. Unofficial reproductions have clean colons.
Nos. 22-28 have black overprints only. All
other colors are fakes.

Nos. 1-7 Handstamped in
Violet or Blue

Overprint 18¼mm Wide

1904, Dec.

36	A1	¼g green	30.00	30.00
37	A1	½g red	30.00	
38	A1	1g blue	40.00	
39	A1	2g dark brown	40.00	
40	A2	4g lilac brown	55.00	
41	A2	8g violet	100.00	
42	A2	16g black	140.00	
		Nos. 36-42 (7)	435.00	

The handstamp reads "Malekathe" (message). This set was never issued.

Preceding Issues Surcharged with New Values in French Currency in Blue, Violet, Rose or Black

a

b

On Nos. 1-7

1905, Jan. 1   Overprint 3mm High

43	A1 (a)	5c on ¼g	10.00	10.00
44	A1 (a)	10c on ½g	10.00	10.00
45	A1 (a)	20c on 1g	10.00	10.00
46	A1 (a)	40c on 2g	11.00	11.00
47	A2 (a)	80c on 4g	21.00	21.00
48	A2 (b)	1.60fr on 8g	22.50	22.50
49	A2 (b)	3.20fr on 16g	40.00	40.00
		Nos. 43-49 (7)	124.50	124.50

Nos. 48-49 exist with period or comma.

1905, Feb.
On No. 8, "Ethiopie" in Blue

50	A1 (a)	5c on ¼g	150.00	150.00

On No. 15, "Bosta" in Black

51	A1 (a)	5c on ¼g	100.00	100.00

On No. 22, "Malekt" in Black

52	A1 (a)	5c on ¼g	75.00	75.00

Unofficial reproductions exist of Nos. 50, 51, 52. The 5c on No. 36, 10c, 20c, 40c, 80c, and 1.60fr surcharges exist as unofficial reproductions only.

c

d

1905   On No. 2

54	A1 (c)	5c on half of ½g	10.00	10.00

On No. 21, "Bosta" in Black

55	A2 (d)	5c on 16g blk	200.00	100.00

On No. 55, "Bosta" is in black.

On No. 28, "Malekt" in Black

56	A2 (d)	5c on 16g blk	250.00	250.00
		Nos. 54-56 (3)	460.00	360.00

No. 54 issued in March. Nos. 55-56 issued Mar. 30.

The overprints and surcharges on Nos. 8 to 56 inclusive were handstamped, the work being very roughly done.

As is usual with handstamped overprints and surcharges there are many inverted and double, but most of them are fakes or unofficial reproductions.

Surcharged with New Values in Various Colors and in Violet

Overprint 14¾x3½mm

1906, Jan. 1

57	A1	5c on ¼g green	12.50	12.50
58	A1	10c on ½g red	15.00	15.00
59	A1	20c on 1g blue	15.00	15.00
60	A1	40c on 2g dk brn	15.00	15.00
61	A2	80c on 4g lilac brn	22.50	

62	A2	1.60fr on 8g violet	35.00	35.00
63	A2	3.20fr on 16g black	90.00	90.00
		Nos. 57-63 (7)	205.00	205.00

Two types of the 4-character overprint ("Menelik"): 14x¾x3½mm and 16x4mm.

Surcharged in Violet Brown

1906, July 1   Overprint 16x4¼mm

64	A1	5c on ¼g grn	12.50	12.50
	a.	Surcharged "20"	110.00	110.00
65	A1	10c on ½g red	12.50	12.50
66	A1	20c on 1g blue	22.50	22.50
67	A1	40c on 2g dk brn	22.50	22.50
68	A2	80c on 4g lil brn	35.00	35.00
69	A2	1.60fr on 8g vio	35.00	35.00
70	A2	3.20fr on 16g blk	75.00	75.00
		Nos. 64-70 (7)	215.00	215.00

The control overprint reads "Menelik."

Surcharged in Violet

e

f

1907, June 21

71	A1 (e)	¼ on ¼g grn	8.75	8.75
72	A1 (e)	½ on ½g red	8.75	8.75
73	A1 (f)	1 on 1g blue	11.00	11.00
74	A1 (f)	2 on 2g dk brn	12.00	12.00
	a.	Surcharged "40"	65.00	
75	A2 (f)	4 on 4g lil brn	13.00	13.00
	a.	Surcharged "80"	57.50	
76	A2 (f)	8 on 8g vio	25.00	25.00
77	A2 (f)	16 on 16g blk	30.00	30.00
		Nos. 71-77 (7)	108.50	108.50

Nos. 71-72 are also found with stars farther away from figures.

The control overprint reads "Dagmawi" ("Second"), meaning Emperor Menelik II.

On stamps with "1" in surcharge, genuine examples have straight serifs, forgeries have curved serifs.

Nos. 2, 23 Surcharged in
Bluish Green

1908, Aug. 14

78	A1	1pi on ½g red (#2)	15.00	15.00
79	A1	1pi on ½g red (#23)	*1,150.*	—

Official reproductions exist. Value, set $25.
Forgeries exist.
The surcharges on Nos. 57-78 are handstamped and are found double, inverted, etc.

Surcharged in Black

1908, Nov. 1

80	A1	¼p on ¼g grn	2.25	2.25
81	A1	½p on ½g red	2.25	2.25
82	A1	1p on 1g blue	2.75	2.75
83	A1	2p on 2g dk brn	5.00	5.00
84	A2	4p on 4g lil brn	7.50	7.50
85	A2	8p on 8g vio	14.00	14.00
86	A2	16p on 16g blk	18.00	18.00
		Nos. 80-86 (7)	51.75	51.75

Surcharges on Nos. 80-85 are found double, inverted, etc. Forgeries exist.
These are the 1st stamps valid for international mail.

King Solomon's Throne
A3

Menelik in Native Costume
A4

Menelik in Royal Dress — A5

1909, Jan. 29   Perf. 11½

87	A3	¼g blue green	.70	.60
88	A3	½g rose	.75	.75
89	A3	1g green & org	4.50	1.50
90	A4	2g blue	3.00	1.75
91	A4	4g green & car	5.00	4.00
92	A5	8g ver & dp grn	9.00	7.00
93	A5	16g ver & car	15.00	10.00
		Nos. 87-93 (7)	37.95	25.60

For overprints see Nos. 101-115, J43-J49, J55-J56. For surcharges see Nos. 116-119.

Nos. 1-7 Handstamped and
Surcharged in ms.

1911, Oct. 1   Perf. 14x13½

94	A1	¼g on ¼g grn	85.00	
95	A1	½g on ½g red	85.00	
96	A1	1g on 1g blue	85.00	
97	A1	2g on 2g dk brn	85.00	
98	A2	4g on 4g lil brn	85.00	
99	A2	8g on 8g violet	85.00	
100	A2	16g on 16g black	85.00	
		Nos. 94-100 (7)	595.00	

Nos. 94-100 were produced as a philatelic speculation by the postmaster at Dire-Dawa. The overprint is abbreviated from "Affranchissement Exceptionnel Faute Timbres" (Special Franking Lacking Stamps). The overprints and surcharges were applied to stamps on cover and then canceled. These covers were then sold to dealers in Europe. No. 98 is known postally used on a small number of commercial covers.

Nos. 94-100 without surcharge are forgeries.

Stamps of 1909 Handstamped in Violet or Black

Nos. 101-102

Nos. 104-107

1917, Mar. 30   Perf. 11½

101	A3	¼g blue grn (V)	7.50	9.00
102	A3	½g rose (V)	7.50	9.00
104	A4	2g blue (Bk)	10.00	9.50
105	A4	4g grn & car (Bk)	15.00	15.00
106	A5	8g ver & dp grn (Bk)	25.00	22.50
107	A5	16g ver & car (Bk)	40.00	45.00
		Nos. 101-107 (6)	105.00	110.00

Coronation of Empress Zauditu and appointment of Prince Tafari as Regent and Heir to the throne.
Exist with overprint inverted and double.

Stamps of 1909 Overprinted in Blue, Black or Red

Nos. 108-111

Nos. 112-115

1917, Apr. 5-Oct. 1

108	A3	¼g blue grn (Bl)	1.25	1.25
109	A3	½g rose (Bl)	1.25	1.25
110	A3	1g grn & org (Bl)	2.25	2.25
111	A4	2g blue (R)	82.50	87.25
112	A4	2g blue (Bk)	1.25	1.25
113	A4	4g grn & car (Bl)	1.25	1.25
	a.	Black overprint	11.00	11.00
114	A5	8g ver & dp grn (Bl)	1.25	1.25
115	A5	16g ver & car (Bl)	2.25	2.25
		Nos. 108-115 (8)	93.25	98.00

Coronation of Empress Zauditu.

Nos. 108-115 all exist with double overprint, inverted overprint, double overprint, one inverted, and various combinations.

Nos. 114-115 with Additional Surcharge

k

l

m

n

1917, May 28

116	A5 (k)	¼g on 8g	3.00	3.00
117	A5 (l)	½g on 8g	3.00	3.00
118	A5 (m)	1g on 16g	8.00	8.00
119	A5 (n)	2g on 16g	10.00	9.00
		Nos. 116-119 (4)	24.00	23.00

Nos. 116-119 all exist with the numerals double and inverted and No. 116 with the Amharic surcharge missing.

Sommering's Gazelle
A6

Prince Tafari
A9

Cathedral of St. George
A12

Empress Waizeri Zauditu
A18

¼g, Giraffes. ½g, Leopard. 2g, Prince Tafari, diff. 4g, Prince Tafari, diff. 8g, White rhinoceros. 12g, Somali ostriches. 1t, African elephant. 2t, Water buffalo. 3t, Lions. 5t, 10t, Empress Zauditu.

1919, June 16   Typo.   Perf. 11½

120	A6	¼g violet & brn	.25	.25
121	A6	¼g bl grn & drab	.25	.25
122	A6	½g scar & ol grn	.25	.25
123	A9	1g rose lil & gray grn	.25	.25
124	A9	2g dp ultra & fawn	.25	.25
125	A9	4g turq bl & org	.25	2.50
126	A12	6g lt blue & org	.25	.25
127	A12	8g ol grn & blk brn	.35	.25
128	A12	12g red vio & gray	.50	.30
129	A12	1t rose & gray blk	.90	.40
130	A12	2t black & brown	2.50	
131	A12	3t grn & dp org	2.50	1.90
132	A18	4t brn & lil rose	3.00	2.50
133	A18	5t carmine & gray	4.00	4.00
134	A18	10t gray grn & bis	8.00	5.25
		Nos. 120-134 (15)	23.50	
		Nos. 120-129,131-134 (14)		18.25

No. 130 was not issued.
For overprints see Nos. J50-J54. For surcharges see Nos. 135-154.
Reprints have brownish gum that is cracked diagonally. Originals have smooth, white gum. Reprints exist imperf. and some values with inverted centers. Value for set, unused or canceled, $5.

No. 132 Surcharged in Blue

1919, July
135	A18	4g on 4t brn & lil rose	3.00	3.00

Nos. 135-154

The Amharic surcharge indicates the new value and, therefore, varies on Nos. 135-154. There are numerous defective letters and figures, several types of the "2" of "¹⁄₂," the errors "guerhce," "gnerche," etc.

Many varieties of surcharge, such as double, inverted, lines transposed or omitted, and inverted "2" in "¹⁄₂," exist.

There are many irregularly produced settings in imitation of Nos. 136-154 which differ slightly from the originals. These may be essays or proofs.

Stamps of 1919 Surcharged

1921
136	A6	½g on ⅛g vio & brn	1.00	1.00
137	A6	1g on ¼g grn & db	2.50	1.00
138	A9	2g on 1g lil brn & gray grn	1.00	1.50
139	A18	2g on 4t brn & lil rose	35.00	30.00
140	A6	2½g on ½g scar & ol grn	1.00	1.50
141	A9	4g on 2g ultra & fawn	1.00	1.25
		Nos. 136-141 (6)	41.50	36.25

Forgeries of No. 139 exist.

Stamps and Type of 1919 Surcharged

1925-26
142	A12	½g on 1t rose & gray blk ('26)	1.25	1.25
a.		Without colon ('26)	12.50	12.50
143	A18	½g on 5t car & gray ('26)	1.50	1.50
144	A12	1g on 6g bl & org	1.25	1.25
145	A12	1g on 12g lil & gray	450.00	400.00
146	A12	1g on 3t grn & org ('26)	22.50	16.00
147	A18	1g on 10t gray grn & bis ('26)	1.50	1.50
		Nos. 142-147 (6)	478.00	421.50

On No. 142 the surcharge is at the left side of the stamp, reading upward. On No. 142a it is at the right, reading downward. The two surcharges are from different, though similar, settings. On No. 146 the surcharge is at the right, reading upward. See note following No. 154.

Type of 1919 Srchd.

1925, Oct.
147A	A12	1g on 12g lil & gray	400.00

Forgeries exist.

Nos. 126-128 Srchd.

1926
148	A12	½g on 8g	3.00	1.25
149	A12	1g on 6g	80.00	50.00
150	A12	1g on 12g	350.00	
		Nos. 148-150 (3)	433.00	51.25

The Amharic line has 7 (½g) or 6 characters (1g).

Nos. 126-128, 131 Srchd.

1925-27
151	A12	½g on 8g ('27)	1.50	1.50
152	A12	1g on 6g ('27)	60.00	40.00
153	A12	1g on 12g ('27)	5.00	1.50
154	A12	1g on 3t	375.00	
		Nos. 151-154 (4)	441.50	43.00

The Amharic line has 7 (½g) or 4 characters (1g). No. 152 has the lines closer together than do the others.

Forgeries of No. 154 exist.

Ras Tafari A22	Empress Zauditu A23

1928, Sept. 5   Typo.   Perf. 13½x14
155	A22	⅛m org & lt bl	.65	1.40
156	A23	¼m ind & red org	.40	1.40
157	A22	½m gray grn & blk	.65	1.40
158	A23	1m dk car & blk	.40	1.40
159	A22	2m dk bl & blk	.40	1.40
160	A22	4m yel & olive	.40	1.40
161	A22	8m vio & olive	1.00	1.40
162	A23	1t org brn & vio	1.10	1.40
163	A22	2t grn & bister	1.75	3.25
164	A23	3t choc & grn	2.75	3.75
		Nos. 155-164 (10)	9.50	18.20

For overprints and surcharges see Nos. 165-209, 217-230, C1-C10.

Preceding Issue Overprinted in Black, Violet or Red

1928, Sept. 1
165	A22	⅛m (Bk)	1.75	3.25
166	A23	¼m (V)	1.75	3.25
167	A22	½m (V)	1.75	3.25
168	A23	1m (V)	1.75	3.25
169	A22	2m (R)	1.75	3.25
170	A23	4m (Bk)	1.75	3.25
171	A22	8m (R)	1.75	3.25
172	A23	1t (Bk)	1.75	3.25
173	A22	2t (R)	2.75	3.25
174	A23	3t (R)	4.00	3.25
		Nos. 165-174 (10)	20.75	32.50

Opening of General Post Office, Addis Ababa.

Exist with overprint inverted, double, double, one inverted, etc.

Nos. 155, 157, 159, 161, 163 Handstamped in Violet, Red or Black

1928, Oct. 7
175	A22	⅛m (V)	2.10	8.00
176	A22	½m (R)	2.10	8.00
177	A22	2m (R)	2.10	10.00

178	A22	8m (Bk)	2.10	10.00
179	A22	2t (V)	2.10	10.00
		Nos. 175-179 (5)	10.50	46.00

Crowning of Prince Tafari as king (Negus) on Oct. 7, 1928.

Nos. 175-177 exist with overprint vertical, inverted, double, etc.

Forgeries exist.

Nos. 155-164 Overprinted in Red or Green

1930, Apr. 3
180	A22	⅛m org & lt bl (R)	.25	.25
181	A23	¼m ind & red org (G)	.50	.50
182	A22	½m gray grn & blk (R)	.25	.25
183	A23	1m dk car & blk (G)	.55	.55
184	A22	2m dk bl & blk (R)	.55	.55
185	A23	4m yel & ol (R)	.85	.85
186	A22	8m vio & ol (R)	1.60	1.60
187	A23	1t org brn & vio		
188	A22	2t grn & bis (R)	4.50	4.50
189	A23	3t choc & grn (R)	5.50	5.50
			8.00	8.00
		Nos. 180-189 (10)	22.55	22.55

Proclamation of King Tafari as King of Kings of Abyssinia under the name "Haile Selassie."

A similar overprint, set in four vertical lines, was printed on all denominations of the 1928 issue. It was not considered satisfactory and was rejected. The trial impressions were not placed on sale to the public, but some stamps reached private hands and have been passed through the post.

Nos. 155-164 Overprinted in Red or Olive Brown

1930, Apr. 3
190	A22	⅛m orange & lt bl	.50	.50
191	A23	¼m ind & red org (OB)	.55	.55
192	A22	½m gray grn & blk	1.40	1.40
193	A23	1m dk car & blk	.55	.55
194	A22	2m dk blue & blk	.55	.55
195	A23	4m yellow & ol	1.00	1.00
196	A22	8m violet & ol	1.60	1.60
197	A23	1t org brn & vio	4.50	4.50
198	A22	2t green & bister	5.50	5.50
199	A23	3t chocolate & grn	8.00	8.00
		Nos. 190-199 (10)	24.15	24.15

Proclamation of King Tafari as Emperor Haile Selassie.

All stamps of this series exist with "H" of "HAILE" omitted and with many other varieties.

Nos. 155-164 Handstamped in Violet or Red

1930, Nov. 2
200	A22	⅛m (V)	1.10	1.10
201	A23	¼m (V)	1.10	1.10
202	A22	½m (R)	1.10	1.10
203	A23	1m (R)	1.10	1.10
204	A22	2m (R)	1.10	1.10
205	A23	4m (V)	1.10	1.10
206	A22	8m (V or R)	1.90	1.90
207	A23	1t (V)	3.00	3.00
208	A22	2t (V or R)	4.50	4.50
209	A23	3t (V or R)	6.50	6.50
		Nos. 200-209 (10)	22.50	22.50

Coronation of Emperor Haile Selassie, Nov. 2, 1930.

Haile Selassie Coronation Monument, Symbols of Empire — A24

1930, Nov.   Engr.   Perf. 12½
210	A24	1g orange	1.00	1.00
211	A24	2g ultra	1.00	1.00
212	A24	4g violet	1.00	1.00
213	A24	8g dull green	1.00	1.00
214	A24	1t brown	1.25	1.25
215	A24	3t green	2.00	2.00
216	A24	5t red brown	2.00	2.00
		Nos. 210-216 (7)	9.25	9.25

Coronation of Emperor Haile Selassie. Issued: 4g, 11/2; others, 11/23.

Reprints of Nos. 210 to 216 exist. Colors are more yellow and the ink is thicker and slightly glossy. Ink on the originals is dull and granular. Value 50c each.

Nos. 158-160, 164 Surcharged in Green, Red or Blue

1/8 Mehalek

1/2 Mehalek	1/2 Mehalek
Type I	Type II

1931   Perf. 13½x14
217	A23	⅛m on 1m	.55	1.00
218	A23	⅛m on 2m (R)	.55	1.00
219	A23	⅛m on 4m	.55	1.00
220	A23	¼m on 1m (Bl)	.55	1.00
221	A22	¼m on 4m	1.60	2.10
222	A23	¼m on 4m	1.60	2.10
225	A23	½m on 1m (Bl)	1.60	2.10
226	A22	½m on 2m (R)	1.60	2.10
227	A23	½m on 4m, type II	1.60	2.10
a.		½m on 4m, type I	15.00	15.00
228	A23	½m on 3t (R)	13.00	16.00
230	A22	1m on 3m (R)	2.25	2.75
		Nos. 217-230 (11)	25.45	33.25

The ½m on ⅛m orange & light blue and ½m on ¼m indigo & red orange were clandestinely printed and never sold at the post office.

No. 230 with double surcharge in red and blue is a color trial.

Many varieties exist.

Issued: 1m, Apr.; others, 3/20.

Ras Makonnen A25	Empress Menen A27

View of Hawash River and Railroad Bridge — A26

Designs: 2g, 8g, Haile Selassie (profile). 4g, 1t, Statue of Menelik II. 3t, Empress Menen (full face). 5t, Haile Selassie (full face).

Perf. 12½, 12x12½, 12½x12

1931, June 27   Engr.
232	A25	⅛g red	.50	.80
233	A26	¼g olive green	.50	.80
234	A25	½g dark violet	.50	.80
235	A27	1g red orange	.50	.80
236	A27	2g ultra	.50	.80
237	A25	4g violet	.80	1.60
238	A27	8g blue green	2.50	3.00
239	A25	1t chocolate	24.00	10.00

240 A27 3t yellow green   7.00   7.00
241 A27 5t red brown   13.00 13.00
     Nos. 232-241 (10)   49.80 38.60

For overprints see Nos. B1-B5. For surcharges see Nos. 242-246.
Reprints of Nos. 232-236, 238-240 are on thinner and whiter paper than the originals. On originals the ink is dull and granular. On reprints, heavy, caked and shiny. Value 50c each.

Nos. 232-236 Surcharged in Blue or Carmine

1936, Jan. 29 *Perf. 12x12½, 12½x12*
242 A25   1c on ⅛g red   2.50   2.50
243 A26   2c on ¼g ol grn (C)   2.50   2.50
244 A25   3c on ½g dk vio   2.50   2.50
245 A27   5c on 1g red org   5.00   5.00
246 A27 10c on 2g ultra (C)   6.00   6.00
     Nos. 242-246 (5)   18.50 17.50

Catalogue values for unused stamps in this section, from this point to the end of the section, are for Never Hinged items.

Haile Selassie I — A32

1942, Mar. 23 Litho.   *Perf. 14x13½*
247 A32   4c lt bl grn, ind & blk   .80   .40
248 A32 10c rose, indigo & blk   2.50   .75
249 A32 20c dp ultra, ind & blk 5.00 1.25
     Nos. 247-249 (3)   8.30 2.40

Haile Selassie I — A33

1942-43   Unwmk.
250 A33   4c lt bl grn & indigo   .90   .25
251 A33   8c yel org & indigo   1.00   .25
252 A33 10c rose & indigo   1.25   .25
253 A33 15c dull vio & indigo   1.25   .30
254 A33 20c dp ultra & indigo   2.00   .50
255 A33 25c dull grn & indigo   2.50   .70
256 A33 50c dull brn & indigo   4.75 1.25
257 A33 60c lilac & indigo   7.25 1.50
     Nos. 250-257 (8)   20.90 5.00

Issued: 25c, 50c, 60c, 4/1/43; others, 6/22/42.
For surcharges see Nos. 258-262, 284, C18-C20.

Nos. 250-254 Surcharged in Black or Brown

1943, Nov. 3
258 A33   5c on 4c   65.00   —
259 A33 10c on 8c   65.00   —
260 A33 15c on 10c   65.00   —
261 A33 20c on 12c (Br)   65.00   —
262 A33 30c on 20c (Br)   65.00   —
     Nos. 258-262 (5)   325.00

Restoration of the Obelisk in Myazzia Place, Addis Ababa, and the 13th anniv. of the coronation of Emperor Haile Selassie.
Nos. 258-262 were almost entirely sold to collectors. Used examples are mostly CTO. Only 10 postally used examples are known.
No. 258 exists with inverted "5" in surcharge. Value $150. On No. 262, "3" is surcharged on "2" of "20" to make "30."

Approximately 40 sets exist with a somewhat different handstamped surcharge. Value, set $2,000. Forgeries exist.

Palace of Menelik II — A34

Menelik II
A35

Statue
A36

50c, Mausoleum. 65c, Menelik II (with scepter).

1944, Dec. 31   Litho.   *Perf. 10½*
263 A34   5c green   1.25   .65
264 A35 10c red lilac   2.25   1.10
265 A36 20c deep blue   4.00   2.25
266 A34 50c dull purple   5.25   2.25
267 A35 65c bister brown   9.25   3.50
     Nos. 263-267 (5)   22.00   9.75

Cent. of the birth of Menelik II, 8/18/44. Printed on gum-impregnated paper.

Unissued Semi-Postal Stamps Overprinted in Carmine

Nurse & Baby — A39

Various Designs Inscribed "Croix Rouge"

1945, Aug. 7   Photo.   *Perf. 11½*
268 A39   5c brt green   .90   1.50
269 A39 10c brt red   1.10   1.50
270 A39 25c brt blue   1.10   1.50
271 A39 50c dk yellow brn   5.00   7.00
272 A39   1t brt violet   7.50   9.00
     Nos. 268-272 (5)   15.60 20.50

Nos. 268-272 without overprint were ordered printed in Switzerland before Ethiopia fell to the invading Italians, so were not delivered to Addis Ababa. After the country's liberation, the set was overprinted "V" and issued for ordinary postage. These stamps exist without overprint, but were not issued. Value, set $17.50.
Some values exist inverted or double.
Forged overprints exist.
For surcharges see Nos. B11-B15, B36-B40.

Lion of Judah
A44

Menelik II
A45

Mail Transport, Old and New — A46

Designs: 50c, Old Post Office, Addis Ababa. 70c, Menelik II and Haile Selassie.

1947, Apr. 18   Engr.   *Perf. 13*
273 A44 10c yellow org   3.50   2.00
274 A45 20c deep blue   5.75   2.25
275 A46 30c orange brn   9.50   3.75
276 A46 50c dk slate grn   22.50   7.50
277 A46 70c red violet   37.50 14.00
     Nos. 273-277 (5)   78.75 29.50

50th anniv. of Ethiopia's postal system.

Haile Selassie and Franklin D. Roosevelt
A49

Design: 65c, Roosevelt and US Flags.

Engraved and Photogravure
1947, May 23   Unwmk.   *Perf. 12½*
278 A49 12c car lake & bl grn 1.60   2.25
279 A49 25c dk blue & rose   3.00   3.50
280 A49 65c blk, red & dp bl 6.00   7.50
     Nos. 278-280,C21-C22 (5) 45.60 51.25

King Sahle Selassie Reclining
A50

King Sahle Selassie
A52

Design: 30c, View of Ankober.

1947, May 1   Engr.   *Perf. 13*
281 A50 20c deep blue   2.00   2.40
282 A50 30c dark purple   4.00   4.00
283 A52 $1 deep green   10.00   8.00
     Nos. 281-283 (3)   16.00 14.40

150th anniversary of Selassie dynasty.

No. 255 Surcharged in Orange

1947, July 14   *Perf. 14x13½*
284 A33 12c on 25c   95.00 95.00

Amba Alaguie — A53

Designs: 2c, Trinity Church. 4c, Debra Sina. 5c, Mecan, near Achanguie. 8c, Lake Tana. 12c, 15c, Parliament Building, Addis Ababa. 20c, Aiba, near Mai Cheo. 30c, Bahr Bridge over Blue Nile. 60c, 70c, Canoe on Lake Tana. $1, Omo Falls. $3, Mt. Alamata. $5, Ras Dashan Mountains.

**   *Perf. 13x13½***
1947-53   Engr.   Wmk. 282
285 A53   1c rose violet   .25   .25
286 A53   2c blue violet   .25   .25
 a.   Unwatermarked ('51)   37.50 15.00
287 A53   4c green   .35   .25
288 A53   5c dark green   .35   .25
289 A53   8c deep orange   .65   .25
290 A53 12c red   .80   .25
290A A53 15c dk ol brn ('53)   .75   .25
291 A53 20c blue   1.10   .40
292 A53 30c orange brown   1.90   .55
292A A53 60c red ('51)   2.25   .95
293 A53 70c rose lilac   3.25   .70
294 A53 $1 dk carmine rose 5.25   .70
295 A53 $3 bright blue   14.00   2.75
296 A53 $5 olive   22.50   5.50
     Nos. 285-296 (14)   53.65 13.30

Issue dates: 15c, May 25, 1953; 60c, Feb. 10, 1951; others, Aug. 23, 1947.
Shades exist.
For overprints see Nos. 355-356. For surcharges see Nos. B6-B10, B16-B20.

Empress Waizero Menen and Emperor Haile Selassie — A54

1949, May 5   Wmk. 282   *Perf. 13*
297 A54 20c blue   1.75   .85
298 A54 30c yellow org   1.75   1.10
299 A54 50c purple   4.50   1.75
300 A54 80c green   4.50   2.75
301 A54 $1 red   9.00   4.50
     Nos. 297-301 (5)   21.50 10.95

Central ornaments differ on each denomination.
8th anniv. of Ethiopia's liberation from Italian occupation.

Dejach Balcha Hospital
A55

Abuna Petros
A56

Designs: 20c, Haile Selassie raising flag. 30c, Lion of Judah statue. 50c, Empress Waizero Menen, Haile Selassie and building.

**   *Perf. 13x13½, 13½x13***
1950, Nov. 2   Engr.   Wmk. 282
302 A55   5c purple   1.10   .65
303 A56 10c deep plum   3.50   1.60
304 A56 20c deep carmine   4.50   1.60
305 A56 30c green   9.50   3.25
306 A55 50c deep blue   13.50   6.50
     Nos. 302-306 (5)   32.10 13.60

20th anniv. of the coronation of Emperor Haile Selassie and Empress Menen.

Abbaye Bridge — A57

1951, Jan. 1   Unwmk.   *Perf. 14*
308 A57   5c dk green & dk
              brn   4.25   1.60
309 A57 10c dp orange & blk 6.50   2.75
310 A57 15c dp blue & org
              brn   11.00   4.50
311 A57 30c olive & lil rose 16.00   6.50
312 A57 60c brown & dp bl   22.50   8.50
313 A57 80c vio & green   32.50 12.50
     Nos. 308-313 (6)   92.75 36.35

Opening of the Abbaye Bridge over the Blue Nile.

Tomb of Ras Makonnen — A58

1951, Mar. 2   Center in Black
314 A58   5c dark green   3.25   1.10
315 A58 10c deep ultra   3.25   1.60
316 A58 15c blue   5.50   2.75
317 A58 30c dp claret   11.00   3.25
318 A58 80c rose carmine   17.00   5.50
319 A58 $1 orange brown   22.50   8.50
     Nos. 314-319 (6)   62.50 22.70

55th anniversary of the Battle of Adwa.

Emperor Haile Selassie — A59

1952, July 23   *Perf. 13½*
320 A59   5c dark green   .55   .55
321 A59 10c red orange   .85   .55
322 A59 15c black   1.10   .55
323 A59 25c ultra   1.75   .85
324 A59 30c violet   2.75   1.10
325 A59 50c rose red   3.50   1.10
326 A59 65c chocolate   9.00   2.75
     Nos. 320-326 (7)   19.50   7.45

60th birthday of Haile Selassie.

Open Road to Sea — A60

Designs: 25c, 50c, Road and broken chain. 65c, Map. 80c, Allegory: Reunion. $1, Haile Selassie raising flag. $2, Ethiopian flag and seascape. $3, Haile Selassie addressing League of Nations.

Wmk. 282

		1952, Sept. 11	**Engr.**	**Perf. 13**
327	A60	15c brown carmine	.85	.60
328	A60	25c red brown	1.10	1.00
329	A60	30c yellow brown	2.00	1.10
330	A60	50c purple	3.00	1.25
331	A60	65c gray	5.75	1.60
332	A60	80c blue green	6.50	2.25
333	A60	$1 rose carmine	13.00	3.00
334	A60	$2 deep blue	22.50	5.00
335	A60	$3 magenta	47.50	7.50
		Nos. 327-335 (9)	102.20	23.30

Issued to celebrate Ethiopia's federation with Eritrea, effected Sept. 11, 1952.

Haile Selassie and New Ethiopian Port — A61

15c, 30c, Haile Selassie on deck of ship.

1953, Oct. 4

337	A61	10c red & dk brn	4.75	2.75
338	A61	15c blue & dk brn	5.00	2.75
339	A61	25c orange & dk brn	9.00	5.00
340	A61	30c red brn & dk grn	16.00	8.00
341	A61	50c purple & dk brn	25.00	9.00
		Nos. 337-341 (5)	59.75	27.50

Federation of Ethiopia and Eritrea, 1st anniv.

Princess Tsahai at a Sickbed — A62

Perf. 13x13½

1955, July 8   **Engr.**   **Wmk. 282**
Cross Typo. in Red

342	A62	15c choc & ultra	2.50	1.25
343	A62	20c green & orange	3.75	1.50
344	A62	30c ultra & green	6.25	1.90
		Nos. 342-344 (3)	12.50	4.65

Ethiopian Red Cross, 20th anniv.
For surcharges see Nos. B33-B35.

Promulgating the Constitution A63   Bishops' Consecration by Archbishop A64

25c, Kagnew Battalion. 35c, Reunion with the Motherland. 50c, "Progress." 65c, Empress Waizero Menen & Emperor Haile Selassie.

Perf. 12½

1955, Nov. 3   **Unwmk.**   **Engr.**

345	A63	5c green & choc	1.25	.55
346	A64	20c carmine & slate grn	2.50	.90
347	A64	25c magenta & gray	3.50	1.40
348	A63	35c brown & red org	4.75	1.75
349	A64	50c dk brn & ultra	7.00	2.50
350	A64	65c violet & car	9.75	4.00
		Nos. 345-350 (6)	28.75	11.10

Silver jubilee of the coronation of Emperor Haile Selassie and Empress Waizero Menen.

Emperor Haile Selassie and Fair Emblem — A65

1955, Nov. 5   **Wmk. 282**

351	A65	5c green & ol grn	1.00	.35
352	A65	10c car & dp ultra	1.50	.40
353	A65	15c vio blk & grn	2.00	.60
354	A65	50c mag & red brn	3.00	2.00
		Nos. 351-354 (4)	7.50	3.35

Silver Jubilee Fair, Addis Ababa.

Nos. 291 and 292A Overprinted

1960, Apr. 7   **Perf. 13x13½**

355	A53	20c blue	1.75	1.25
356	A53	60c red	3.00	2.40

WRY, July 1, 1959-June 30, 1960.
The 60c without serifs is a trial printing.

Map of Africa, "Liberty" and Haile Selassie — A66

Perf. 13½

1960, June 14   **Engr.**   **Unwmk.**

357	A66	20c orange & green	.85	.85
358	A66	80c orange & violet	2.75	.85
359	A66	$1 orange & maroon	2.75	1.10
		Nos. 357-359 (3)	6.35	2.80

2nd Conf. of Independent African States at Addis Ababa. Issued in sheets of 10.

Emperor Haile Selassie — A67

1960, Nov. 2   **Wmk. 282**   **Perf. 14**

360	A67	10c brown & blue	.85	.85
361	A67	25c violet & emerald	1.10	1.10
362	A67	50c dk bl & org yel	2.75	2.75
363	A67	65c slate grn & sal pink	4.25	4.25
364	A67	$1 indigo & rose vio	5.00	5.00
		Nos. 360-364 (5)	13.95	13.95

30th anniv. of the coronation of Emperor Haile Selassie.

Africa Hall, UN Economic Commission for Africa — A68

1961, Apr. 15   **Wmk. 282**   **Perf. 14**

365	A68	80c ultra	2.75	1.40

Africa Freedom Day, Apr. 15. Sheets of 10.

Map of Ethiopia, Olive Branch — A69

1961, May 5   **Perf. 13x13½**

366	A69	20c green	.40	.40
367	A69	30c blue	.60	.45
368	A69	$1 brown	3.25	1.40
		Nos. 366-368 (3)	4.25	2.25

20th anniv. of Ethiopia's liberation from Italian occupation.

African Wild Ass — A70

1961, June 16   **Wmk. 282**   **Perf. 14**

369	A70	5c shown	1.10	.25
370	A70	15c Eland	1.10	.25
371	A70	25c Elephant	1.25	.40
372	A70	35c Giraffe	3.00	.50
373	A70	50c Beisa	3.00	.50
374	A70	$1 Lion	6.00	1.50
		Nos. 369-374 (6)	15.45	3.40

Issued in sheets of 10. Used values are for CTO's.

Emperor Haile Selassie and Empress Waizero Menen — A71

1961, July 27   **Unwmk.**   **Perf. 11**

375	A71	10c green	.85	.45
376	A71	50c violet blue	1.50	.80
377	A71	$1 carmine rose	3.25	1.60
		Nos. 375-377 (3)	5.60	2.85

Golden wedding anniv. of the Emperor and Empress.

Warlike Horsemanship (Guks) — A72

15c, Hockey. 20c, Bicycling. 30c, Soccer. 50c, 1960 Olympic marathon winner, Abebe Bikila.

Photogravure and Engraved

1962, Jan. 14   **Perf. 12x11½**

378	A72	10c yel grn & car	.50	.35
379	A72	15c pink & dk brn	.85	.60
380	A72	20c red & black	1.00	.70
381	A72	30c ultra & dl pur	1.10	.85
382	A72	50c yellow & green	1.75	1.00
		Nos. 378-382 (5)	5.20	3.50

Third Africa Football (soccer) Cup, Addis Ababa, Jan. 14-22.

Malaria Eradication Emblem, World Map and Mosquito — A73

Wmk. 282

1962, Apr. 7   **Engr.**   **Perf. 13½**

383	A73	15c black	.30	.25
384	A73	30c purple	.55	.25
385	A73	60c red brown	1.20	.65
		Nos. 383-385 (3)	2.05	1.15

WHO drive to eradicate malaria.

Abyssinian Ground Hornbill — A74

Birds: 15c, Abyssinian roller. 30c, Bateleur, vert. 50c, Double-toothed barbet, vert. $1, Didric cuckoo.

Perf. 11½

1962, May 5   **Unwmk.**   **Photo.**
Granite Paper

386	A74	5c multicolored	.85	.25
387	A74	15c emer, brn & ultra	1.10	.50
388	A74	30c lt brn, blk & red	2.25	.85
389	A74	50c multicolored	4.50	1.10
390	A74	$1 multicolored	9.00	2.50
		Nos. 386-390 (5)	17.70	5.20

See Nos. C77-C81, C97-C101, C107-C111.

Assab Hospital — A75

15c, School at Assab. 20c, Church at Massawa. 50c, Mosque at Massawa. 60c, Assab port.

Wmk. 282

1962, Sept. 11   **Engr.**   **Perf. 13½**

391	A75	3c purple	.25	.25
392	A75	15c dark blue	.25	.25
393	A75	20c green	.30	.25
394	A75	50c brown	.55	.30
395	A75	60c carmine rose	.85	.50
		Nos. 391-395 (5)	2.20	1.55

Federation of Ethiopia and Eritrea, 10th anniv.

King Bazen, Madonna and Stars over Bethlehem A76

15c, Ezana, obelisks & temple. 20c, Kaleb & sailing fleet. 50c, Lalibela, rock-church and frescoes, vert. 60c, King Yekuno Amlak & Abuna Tekle Haimanot preaching in Ankober. 75c, King Zara Yacob & Maskal celebration. $1, King Lebna Dengel & battle against Mohammed Gragn.

Perf. 14½

1962, Nov. 2   **Unwmk.**   **Photo.**

396	A76	10c multicolored	.30	.25
397	A76	15c multicolored	.50	.25
398	A76	20c multicolored	.50	.25
399	A76	50c multicolored	.85	.25
400	A76	60c multicolored	1.10	.50
401	A76	75c multicolored	1.75	.85
402	A76	$1 multicolored	2.25	1.25
		Nos. 396-402 (7)	7.25	3.60

32nd anniv. of the coronation of Emperor Haile Selassie and to commemorate ancient kings and saints.

Map of Ethiopian Telephone Network — A77

Designs: 50c, Radio mast and waves. 60c, Telegraph pole and rising sun.

Perf. 13½x14

1963, Jan. 1   **Engr.**   **Wmk. 282**

403	A77	10c dark red	.50	.25
404	A77	50c ultra	1.10	.50
405	A77	60c brown	1.75	.60
		Nos. 403-405 (3)	3.35	1.35

10th anniv. of the Imperial Board of Telecommunications.

Wheat Emblem — A78

1963, Mar. 21   **Unwmk.**   **Perf. 13½**

406	A78	5c deep rose	.25	.25
407	A78	10c rose carmine	.25	.25
408	A78	15c violet blue	.25	.25
409	A78	30c emerald	1.25	.25
		Nos. 406-409 (4)	2.00	1.00

FAO "Freedom from Hunger" campaign.

Abuna Salama — A79

Spiritual Leaders: 15c, Abuna Aregawi. 30c, Abuna Tekle Haimanot. 40c. Yared. 60c, Zara Yacob.

1964, Jan. 3		Unwmk.	Perf. 13½	
410	A79	10c blue	.55	.25
411	A79	15c dark green	.85	.25
412	A79	30c brown red	1.10	.50
413	A79	40c dark blue	1.60	.75
414	A79	60c brown	2.75	1.60
		Nos. 410-414 (5)	6.85	3.35

Queen of Sheba — A80

Ethiopian Empresses: 15c, Helen. 50c, Seble Wongel. 60c, Mentiwab. 80c, Taitu, consort of Menelik II.

Granite Paper

1964, Mar. 2		Photo.	Perf. 11½	
415	A80	10c multicolored	.85	.30
416	A80	15c multicolored	.85	.30
417	A80	50c multicolored	1.60	.85
418	A80	60c multicolored	2.75	1.10
419	A80	80c multicolored	4.50	1.60
		Nos. 415-419 (5)	10.55	4.15

Priest Teaching Alphabet to Children — A81

10c, Classroom. 15c, Woman learning to read. 40c, Students in chemistry laboratory. 60c, Graduation procession.

1964, June 1		Unwmk.	Perf. 11½	
		Granite Paper		
420	A81	5c brown	.25	.25
421	A81	10c emerald	.25	.25
422	A81	15c rose vio, vert.	.25	.25
423	A81	40c vio blue, vert.	1.00	.30
424	A81	60c dark pur, vert.	1.50	.55
		Nos. 420-424 (5)	3.25	1.60

Issued to publicize education.

Eleanor Roosevelt (1884-1962) — A82

1964, Oct. 11			Photo.	
		Granite Paper		
		Portrait in Slate Blue		
425	A82	10c yellow bister	.25	.25
426	A82	60c orange brown	1.10	.75
427	A82	80c green & gold	1.75	1.00
		Nos. 425-427 (3)	3.10	2.00

King Serse Dengel and View of Gondar, 1563 — A83

Ethiopian Leaders: 10c, King Fasiladas and Gondar in 1632. 20c, King Yassu the Great and Gondar in 1682. 25c, Emperor Theodore II and map of Ethiopia. 60c, Emperor John IV and Battle of Gura, 1876. 80c, Emperor Menelik II and Battle of Adwa, 1896.

1964, Dec. 12		Photo.	Perf. 14½x14	
428	A83	5c multicolored	.30	.25
429	A83	10c multicolored	.30	.25
430	A83	20c multicolored	.55	.25
431	A83	25c multicolored	.85	.25

432	A83	60c multicolored	1.60	1.10
433	A83	80c multicolored	1.60	1.10
		Nos. 428-433 (6)	5.20	3.20

Ethiopian Rose — A84

Flowers: 10c, Kosso tree. 25c, St.-John's-wort. 35c, Parrot's-beak. 60c, Maskal daisy.

1965, Mar. 30			Perf. 12x13½	
434	A84	5c multicolored	.30	.25
435	A84	10c multicolored	.30	.25
436	A84	25c multicolored	.85	.55
437	A84	35c multicolored	1.20	1.20
438	A84	60c green, yel & org	2.25	1.60
		Nos. 434-438 (5)	4.90	3.85

ITU Emblem, Old and New Communication Symbols — A85

			Perf. 13½x14½	
1965, May 17		Litho.	Unwmk.	
439	A85	5c blue, indigo & yel	.25	.25
440	A85	10c blue, indigo & org	.55	.25
441	A85	60c blue, indigo & lil rose	2.00	.95
		Nos. 439-441 (3)	2.80	1.45

Cent. of the ITU.

Laboratory — A86

Designs: 5c, Textile spinning mill. 10c, Sugar factory. 20c, Mountain road. 25c, Autobus. 30c, Diesel locomotive and bridge. 35c, Railroad station, Addis Ababa.

1965, July 19		Photo.	Perf. 11½	
		Granite Paper		
		Portrait in Black		
442	A86	3c sepia	.30	.25
443	A86	5c dull pur & buff	.30	.25
444	A86	10c black & gray	.30	.25
445	A86	20c green & pale yel	.30	.25
446	A86	25c dk brown & yel	.55	.30
447	A86	30c maroon & gray	.85	.30
448	A86	35c dk blue & gray	.85	.50
		Nos. 442-448 (7)	3.45	2.10

For overprints see Nos. 609-612.

ICY Emblem — A87

1965, Oct. 24		Unwmk.	Perf. 11½	
		Granite Paper		
449	A87	10c blue & red brn	.50	.25
450	A87	50c dp blue & red brn	1.40	.75
451	A87	80c vio blue & red brn	2.25	1.10
		Nos. 449-451 (3)	4.15	2.10

International Cooperation Year, 1965.

National Bank Emblem — A88

Designs: 10c, Commercial Bank emblem. 60c, Natl. and Commercial Bank buildings.

1965, Nov. 2		Photo.	Perf. 13	
452	A88	10c dp car, blk & indigo	.45	.25
453	A88	30c ultra, blk & indigo	1.00	.40
454	A88	60c black, yel & indigo	1.50	.65
		Nos. 452-454 (3)	2.95	1.30

Natl. and Commercial Banks of Ethiopia.

"Light and Peace" Press Building — A89

1966, Apr. 5		Engr.	Perf. 13	
455	A89	5c pink & black	.25	.25
456	A89	15c lt yel grn & blk	.60	.25
457	A89	30c orange yel & blk	1.10	.55
		Nos. 455-457 (3)	1.95	1.05

Opening of the "Light and Peace" Printing Press building.

Kabaro Drum — A90

Musical Instruments: 10c, Bagana harp. 35c, Messenko guitar. 50c, Krar lyre. 60c, Wachent flutes.

1966, Sept. 9		Photo.	Perf. 13½	
458	A90	5c brt green & blk	.30	.25
459	A90	10c dull blue & blk	.30	.25
460	A90	35c orange & blk	1.10	.85
461	A90	50c yellow & blk	1.75	1.10
462	A90	60c rose car & blk	2.75	1.60
		Nos. 458-462 (5)	6.20	4.05

Emperor Haile Selassie A91

1966, Nov. 1		Unwmk.	Perf. 12	
463	A91	10c black, gold & grn	.30	.25
464	A91	15c black, gold & dp car	.55	.25
465	A91	40c black & gold	1.10	.85
		Nos. 463-465 (3)	1.95	1.35

50 years of leadership of Emperor Haile Selassie.

UNESCO Emblem and Map of Africa — A92

Wmk. 282

1966, Nov. 30		Litho.	Perf. 13½	
466	A92	15c blue car & blk	.50	.25
467	A92	60c olive, brn & dk bl	1.10	.85

20th anniv. of UNESCO.

WHO Headquarters, Geneva — A93

1966, Nov. 30				
468	A93	5c olive, ultra & brn	.80	.25
469	A93	40c brown, pur & emer	1.25	.85

Opening of WHO Headquarters, Geneva.

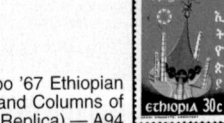

Expo '67 Ethiopian Pavilion and Columns of Axum (Replica) — A94

			Perf. 12x13½	
1967, May 2		Photo.	Unwmk.	
470	A94	30c brt blue & multi	.75	.30
471	A94	45c multicolored	1.00	.40
472	A94	80c gray & multi	1.25	.60
		Nos. 470-472 (3)	3.00	1.30

EXPO '67, Intl. Exhibition, Montreal, Apr. 28-Oct. 27, 1967.

Diesel Train and Map — A95

1967, June 7		Photo.	Perf. 12	
473	A95	15c multicolored	1.10	.55
474	A95	30c multicolored	2.75	1.50
475	A95	50c multicolored	4.25	2.25
		Nos. 473-475 (3)	8.10	4.30

Djibouti-Addis Ababa railroad, 50th anniv.

Papilionidae Aethiops — A96

Various Butterflies.

			Perf. 13½x13	
1967, June 30		Photo.	Unwmk.	
476	A96	5c buff & multi	.60	.25
477	A96	15c lilac & multi	2.00	.40
478	A96	20c multicolored	2.75	.75
479	A96	35c blue & multi	4.75	1.50
480	A96	40c multicolored	7.75	2.00
		Nos. 476-480 (5)	17.85	4.90

Emperor Haile Selassie and Lion of Judah — A97

1967, July 21			Perf. 11½	
		Granite Paper		
481	A97	10c dk brn, emer & gold	.45	.25
482	A97	15c dk brn, yel & gold	.80	.25
483	A97	$1 dk brn, red & gold	3.50	1.50
		Nos. 481-483 (3)	4.75	2.00

Souvenir Sheet

484	A97	$1 dk brn, pur & gold	16.00	22.50

75th birthday of Emperor Haile Selassie.

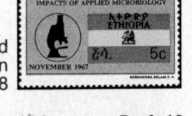

Microscope and Ethiopian Flag — A98

1967, Nov. 6		Litho.	Perf. 13	
		Flag in Grn, Yel, Red & Blk		
485	A98	5c blue	.25	.25
486	A98	30c ocher	.55	.30
487	A98	$1 violet	1.75	1.10
		Nos. 485-487 (3)	2.55	1.65

2nd Intl. Conf. on the Global Impact of Applied Microbiology, Addis Ababa, 11/6-12.

Wall Painting from Debre Berhan Selassie Church, Gondar, 17th Century — A99

ITY Emblem and: 25c, Votive throne from Atsbe Dera, 4th Cent. B.C., vert. 35c, Prehistoric cave painting, Harar Province. 50c, Prehistoric stone tools, Melke Kontoure, vert.

1967, Nov. 20		Photo.	Perf. 14½	
488	A99	15c multicolored	3.00	1.40
489	A99	25c yel grn, buff & blk	3.25	1.40
490	A99	35c green, brn & blk	3.00	1.75
491	A99	50c yellow & blk	5.50	2.75
		Nos. 488-491 (4)	14.75	7.30

International Tourist Year, 1967.

462

ETHIOPIA

A100

Crosses of Lalibela: 5c, Processional
Bronze Cross, Biet-Maryam Church. 10c, Processional copper cross. 15c, Copper cross,
Biet-Maryam church. 20c, Lalibela-style cross.
50c, Chiseled copper cross, Madhani Alem
church.

1967, Dec. 7   Photo.   Perf. 14½
Crosses in Silver
492 A100 5c yellow & blk   .30   .25
493 A100 10c red orange & blk   .30   .25
494 A100 15c violet & blk   .40   .25
495 A100 20c brt rose & blk   .65   .25
496 A100 50c orange yel & blk   2.00 .60
    Nos. 492-496 (5)   3.65 1.60

A101

Designs: 10c, Emperor Theodore (1818?-
1868). 20c, Emperor Theodore and lions,
horiz. 50c, Imperial crown.

Perf. 14x13½
1968, Apr. 18   Litho.   Unwmk.
497 A101 10c lt vio, ocher & brn   .50   .25
498 A101 20c lilac, brn & dk vio   .85   .50
499 A101 50c dk grn, org & rose
        cl   1.75 1.10
    Nos. 497-499 (3)   3.10 1.85

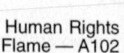

Human Rights
Flame — A102

1968, May 31   Unwmk.   Perf. 14½
500 A102 15c pink, red & blk   .55   .55
501 A102 $1 lt bl, brt bl & blk   2.40 2.40

International Human Rights Year, 1968.

Shah
Mohammed
Reza Pahlavi,
Emperor and
Flags — A103

1968, June 3   Litho.   Perf. 13½
502 A103 10c multicolored   .25   .25
503 A103 15c multicolored   .30   .30
504 A103 30c multicolored   1.25 1.25
    Nos. 502-504 (3)   1.80 1.80

Visit of Shah Mohammed Riza Pahlavi of
Iran.

Emperor Haile Selassie Appealing to
League of Nations, 1935
A104

35c, African Unity Building and map of
Africa. $1, World map, symbolizing intl.
relations.

1968, July 22   Photo.   Perf. 14x13½
505 A104 15c bl, red, blk & gold   .40   .25
506 A104 35c blk, emer, red &
        gold   .75   .75
507 A104 $1 dk bl, lil, blk & gold 2.50 2.75
    Nos. 505-507 (3)   3.65 3.75

Ethiopia's struggle for peace. Issued with
tabs on bottom row. Value, set $10.

WHO
Emblem — A105

Perf. 14x13½
1968, Aug. 30   Litho.   Unwmk.
508 A105 15c brt green & blk   .50   .35
509 A105 60c red lilac & blk   1.75 1.90

20th anniv. of the WHO.

Abebe Bikila,
Marathon
Runner — A106

1968, Oct. 12   Perf. 11½
510 A106 10c shown   .25   .25
511 A106 15c Soccer   .40   .40
512 A106 20c Boxing   .50   .50
513 A106 40c Basketball   1.25 1.25
514 A106 50c Bicycling   1.90 1.90
    Nos. 510-514 (5)   4.30 4.30

19th Olympic Games, Mexico City, 10/12-27.

Arrussi
Woman — A107

Regional Costumes: 15c, Man from Gemu
Gefa. 20c, Gojam man. 30c, Kefa man. 35c,
Harar woman. 50c, Ilubabor grass coat. 60c,
Woman from Eritrea.

Perf. 13½x13
1968, Dec. 10   Photo.   Unwmk.
515 A107 5c silver & multi   .65   .25
516 A107 10c silver & multi   .65   .25
517 A107 20c silver & multi   .65   .25
518 A107 30c silver & multi   .85   .55
519 A107 35c silver & multi   .85   .65
520 A107 50c silver & multi   1.75 1.10
521 A107 60c silver & multi   2.25 1.60
    Nos. 515-521 (7)   7.65 4.65

See Nos. 575-581.

Message Stick
and Amharic
Postal Emblem
A108

1969, Mar. 10   Litho.   Perf. 14
522 A108 10c emerald, blk & brn   .75   .75
523 A108 15c yellow, blk & brn   .75   .70
524 A108 35c multicolored   1.40 1.25
    Nos. 522-524 (3)   2.90 2.65

Ethiopian postal service, 75th anniv.

ILO
Emblem — A109

1969, Apr. 11   Litho.   Perf. 14½
525 A109 15c orange & blk   .50   .50
526 A109 60c emerald & blk   2.00 2.00

50th anniv. of the ILO.

Dove, Red
Cross, Crescent,
Lion and Sun
Emblems
A110

1969, May 8   Wmk. 282   Perf. 13
527 A110 5c lt ultra, blk & red   .25   .25
528 A110 15c lt ultra, grn & red   .65   .65
529 A110 30c lt ultra, vio bl & red 1.40 1.40
    Nos. 527-529 (3)   2.30 2.30

League of Red Cross Societies, 50th anniv.

Endybis Silver Coin, 3rd
Century — A111

Ancient Ethiopian Coins: 10c, Gold of
Ezana, 4th cent. 15c, Gold of Kaleb, 6th cent.
30c, Bronze of Armah, 7th cent. 40c, Bronze
of Wazena, 7th cent. 50c, Silver of Gersem,
8th cent.

1969, June 19   Photo.   Perf. 14½
530 A111 5c ultra, blk & sil   .30   .25
531 A111 10c brt red, blk & gold   .50   .45
532 A111 15c brown, blk & gold   .80   .70
533 A111 30c dp car, blk & brnz   1.10 1.25
534 A111 40c dk green, blk &
        brnz   1.60 1.10
535 A111 50c dp violet, blk & sil 1.75 1.75
    Nos. 530-535 (6)   6.05 5.50

Zebras and
Tourist Year
Emblem — A112

Designs: 10c, Camping. 15c, Fishing. 20c,
Water skiing. 25c, Mountaineering, vert.

Perf. 13x13½, 13½x13
1969, Aug. 29   Litho.   Unwmk.
536 A112 5c multicolored   .30   .30
537 A112 10c multicolored   .55   .30
538 A112 15c multicolored   .85   .55
539 A112 20c multicolored   .85   .85
540 A112 25c multicolored   1.75 1.10
    Nos. 536-540 (5)   4.30 3.10

International Year of African Tourism.

Stylized Bird and
UN
Emblem — A113

UN 25th anniv.: 30c, Stylized flowers, UN
and peace emblems, vert. 60c, Stylized bird,
UN emblem and plane.

1969, Oct. 24   Unwmk.   Perf. 11½
541 A113 10c lt blue & multi   .25   .25
542 A113 30c lt blue & multi   .80   .80
543 A113 60c lt blue & multi   2.00 2.00
    Nos. 541-543 (3)   3.05 3.05

Ancient Cross
and Holy
Family — A114

Designs: Various ancient crosses.

Perf. 14½x13½
1969, Dec. 10   Photo.
544 A114 5c black, yel & dk bl   .25   .25
545 A114 10c black & yellow   .25   .55
546 A114 25c black, yel & grn   1.10 1.10
547 A114 60c black & ocher   2.75 2.25
    Nos. 544-547 (4)   4.35 4.15

Ancient
Figurines
A115

Ancient Ethiopian Pottery: 20c, Vases, Yeha
period, 4th-3rd centuries B.C. 25c, Vases and
jugs, Axum, 4th-6th centuries A.D. 35c, Bird-
shaped jug and jugs, Matara, 4th-6th centuries
A.D. 60c, Decorated pottery, Adulis, 6th-7th
centuries A.D.

1970, Feb. 6   Photo.   Perf. 14½
548 A115 10c black & multi   .65   .55
549 A115 20c black & multi   .65   .55
550 A115 25c black & multi   .65   .55
551 A115 35c black & multi   1.40 1.25
552 A115 60c black & multi   2.50 2.25
    Nos. 548-552 (5)   5.85 5.15

Medhane
Alem Church
A116

Rock Churches of Lalibela, 12th-13th Centuries: 10c, Bieta Emmanuel. 15c, The four
Rock Churches of Lalibela. 20c, Bieta Mariam.
50c, Bieta Giorgis.

1970, Apr. 15   Unwmk.   Perf. 13
553 A116 5c brown & multi   .30   .25
554 A116 10c brown & multi   .30   .25
555 A116 15c brown & multi   .50   .40
556 A116 20c brown & multi   .75   .65
557 A116 50c brown & multi   1.80 1.50
    Nos. 553-557 (5)   3.65 3.05

Sailfish
Tang — A117

Tropical Fish: 10c, Undulate triggerfish. 15c,
Orange butterflyfish. 25c, Butterflyfish. 50c,
Imperial Angelfish.

1970, June 19   Photo.   Perf. 12½
558 A117 5c multicolored   .25   .25
559 A117 10c multicolored   .25   .25
560 A117 15c multicolored   .60   .60
561 A117 25c multicolored   1.50 1.50
562 A117 50c multicolored   3.00 3.00
    Nos. 558-562 (5)   5.60 5.60

Education Year
Emblem — A118

1970, Aug. 14   Unwmk.   Perf. 13½
563 A118 10c multicolored   .25   .25
564 A118 20c gold, ultra & emer   .45   .45
565 A118 50c gold, emer & org   1.40 1.40
    Nos. 563-565 (3)   2.10 2.10

Issued for International Education Year.

Map of
Africa
A119

30c, Flag of Organization of African Unity.
40c, OAU Headquarters, Addis Ababa.

1970, Sept. 21   Photo.   Perf. 13½
566 A119 20c multicolored   .30   .30
567 A119 30c multicolored   .60   .60
568 A119 40c green & multi   .85   .85
    Nos. 566-568 (3)   1.75 1.75

Africa Unity Day and Organization of African
Unity.

Emperor Haile
Selassie — A120

1970, Oct. 30   Unwmk.   Perf. 14½
569 A120 15c Prus bl & multi .30 .30
570 A120 50c multicolored 1.00 1.00
571 A120 60c multicolored 1.75 1.75
Nos. 569-571 (3) 3.05 3.05
Coronation, 40th anniv.

Buildings
A121

1970, Dec. 30   Litho.   Perf. 13½
572 A121 10c ver & multi .30 .30
573 A121 50c brown & multi 1.10 1.10
574 A121 80c multicolored 1.75 1.75
Nos. 572-574 (3) 3.15 3.15
Opening of new Posts, Telecommunications and General Post Office buildings.

Costume Type of 1968
Regional Costumes: 5c, Warrior from Begemdir and Semien. 10c, Woman from Bale. 15c, Warrior from Welega. 20c,Woman from Shoa. 25c, Man from Sidamo. 40c, Woman from Tigre. 50c, Man from Welo.

1971, Feb. 17   Photo.   Perf. 11½
Granite Paper
575 A107 5c gold & multi .30 .30
576 A107 10c gold & multi .30 .30
577 A107 15c gold & multi .55 .50
578 A107 20c gold & multi .60 .60
579 A107 25c gold & multi .85 .85
580 A107 40c gold & multi 1.10 1.10
581 A107 50c gold & multi 2.25 2.25
Nos. 575-581 (7) 5.95 5.90

Plane's Tail with Emblem — A122

Designs: 10c, Ethiopian scenes. 20c, Nose of Boeing 707. 60c, Pilots in cockpit, and engine. 80c, Globe with routes shown.

1971, Apr. 8   Perf. 14½x14
582 A122 5c multicolored .30 .30
583 A122 10c multicolored .30 .30
584 A122 20c multicolored .60 .60
585 A122 60c multicolored 1.25 1.25
586 A122 80c multicolored 2.00 2.00
Nos. 582-586 (5) 4.45 4.45
Ethiopian Airlines, 25th anniversary. Issued with tabs on bottom row. Value, set $11.

Fountain of Life, 15th Century Gospel Book — A123

Ethiopian Paintings: 10c, King David, 15th cent. manuscript. 25c, St. George, 17th cent. painting on canvas. 50c, King Lalibela, 18th cent. painting on wood. 60c, Yared singing before King Kaleb. Mural in Axum Cathedral.

1971, June 15   Photo.   Perf. 11½
Granite Paper
587 A123 5c tan & multi .25 .25
588 A123 10c pale sal & multi .25 .25
589 A123 25c lemon & multi .60 .60
590 A123 50c yellow & multi 1.60 1.60
591 A123 60c gray & multi 2.50 2.50
Nos. 587-591 (5) 5.20 5.20

Black and White Heads, Globes — A124

Designs: 60c, Black and white hand holding globe. 80c, Four races, globes.

1971, Aug. 31   Unwmk.
592 A124 10c org, red brn & blk .30 .30
593 A124 60c green, bl & blk 1.75 1.75
594 A124 80c bl, org, yel & blk 2.75 2.75
Nos. 592-594 (3) 4.80 4.80
Intl. Year Against Racial Discrimination.

Emperor Menelik II and Reading of Treaty of Ucciali — A125

Contemporary Paintings: 30c, Menelik II on horseback gathering the tribes. 50c, Ethiopians and Italians in Battle of Adwa. 60c, Menelik II and Taitu at head of their armies.

1971, Oct. 20   Litho.   Perf. 13½
595 A125 10c multicolored .35 .35
596 A125 30c multicolored .95 .95
597 A125 50c multicolored 1.40 1.40
598 A125 60c multicolored 2.40 2.40
Nos. 595-598 (4) 5.10 5.10
75th anniversary of victory of Adwa over the Italians, March 1, 1896.

Two telephones, 1897, Menelik II and Ras Makonnen A126

Designs: 10c, Haile Selassie Broadcasting and Map of Ethiopia. 30c, Ethiopians around television set. 40c, Telephone microwave circuits. 60c, Map of Africa on globe and telephone dial.

1971, Nov. 2
599 A126 5c brown & multi .30 .30
600 A126 10c yellow & multi .30 .30
601 A126 30c vio bl & multi .30 .30
602 A126 40c black & multi .85 .85
603 A126 60c vio bl & multi 2.25 2.25
Nos. 599-603 (5) 4.00 4.00
Telecommunications in Ethiopia, 75th anniv.

UNICEF Emblem, Mother and Child — A127

UNICEF Emblem and: 10c, Children drinking milk. 15c, Man holding sick child. 30c, Kindergarten class. 50c, Father and son.

1971, Dec. 15   Unwmk.
604 A127 5c yellow & multi .30 .30
605 A127 10c pale brn & multi .30 .30
606 A127 15c rose & multi .30 .30
607 A127 30c violet & multi .85 .85
608 A127 50c green & multi 1.60 1.60
Nos. 604-608 (5) 3.35 3.35
25th anniv. of UNICEF.

Nos. 445-448 Overprinted

1972, Jan. 28   Photo.   Perf. 11
Portrait in Black
609 A86 10c grn & pale yel .55 .55
610 A86 25c dk brn & yel .85 .85
611 A86 30c maroon & gray 3.50 3.50
612 A86 35c dk blue & gray 3.50 3.50
Nos. 609-612 (4) 8.40 8.40
1st meeting of UN Security Council in Africa.

River Boat on Lake Haik A128

1972, Feb. 7   Litho.   Perf. 11½
Granite Paper
613 A128 10c shown .30 .30
614 A128 20c Boats on Lake Abaya .55 .55
615 A128 30c on Lake Tana .85 .85
616 A128 60c on Baro River 1.75 1.75
Nos. 613-616 (4) 3.45 3.45

Proclamation of Cyrus the Great — A129

1972, Mar. 28   Photo.   Perf. 14x14½
617 A129 10c red & multi .50 .50
618 A129 60c emerald & multi 2.00 2.00
619 A129 80c gray & multi 3.00 3.00
Nos. 617-619 (3) 5.50 5.50
2500th anniversary of the founding of the Persian empire by Cyrus the Great.

Houses, Sidamo Province — A130

Ethiopian Architecture: 10c, Tigre Province. 20c, Eritrea Province. 40c, Addis Ababa. 80c, Shoa Province.

1972, Apr. 11   Litho.   Perf. 13½
620 A130 5c black & multi .30 .30
621 A130 10c black, gray & brn .30 .30
622 A130 20c black & multi .65 .65
623 A130 40c black, bl grn & brn 1.10 1.10
624 A130 80c black, brn & red brn 2.75 2.75
Nos. 620-624 (5) 5.10 5.10

Hands Holding Map of Ethiopia — A131

10c, Hands shielding Ethiopians. 25c, Map of Africa, hands reaching for African Unity emblem. 50c, Brown & white hands clasped, UN emblem. 60c, Hands protecting dove. Each denomination shows different portrait of the Emperor.

Perf. 14½x14
1972, July 21   Litho.   Unwmk.
625 A131 5c scarlet & multi .35 .35
626 A131 10c ultra & multi .35 .35
627 A131 25c vio bl & multi .60 .60
628 A131 50c lt blue & multi 1.25 1.25
629 A131 60c brown & multi 1.50 1.50
Nos. 625-629 (5) 4.05 4.05
80th birthday of Emperor Haile Selassie.

Running, Flags of Mexico, Japan, Italy — A132

1972, Aug. 25   Perf. 13½x13
630 A132 10c shown .35 .35
631 A132 30c Soccer .80 .80
632 A132 50c Bicycling 1.75 1.75
633 A132 60c Boxing 2.25 2.25
Nos. 630-633 (4) 5.15 5.15
20th Olympic Games, Munich, Germany, Aug. 26-Sept. 11.

Open Bible, Cross and Orbit — A133

Designs: 50c, First and 1972 headquarters of the British and Foreign Bible Society, vert. 80c, First Amharic Bible.

1972, Sept. 25   Photo.   Perf. 13½
634 A133 20c deep red & multi .60 .60
635 A133 50c deep red & multi 1.10 1.10
636 A133 80c deep red & multi 2.75 2.75
Nos. 634-636 (3) 4.45 4.45
United Bible Societies World Assembly, Addis Ababa, Sept. 1972.

Security Council Meeting — A134

Designs: 60c, Building where Security Council met. 80c, Map of Africa with flags of participating members.

1972, Nov. 1   Litho.   Perf. 13½
637 A134 10c lt bl & vio bl .25 .25
638 A134 60c multicolored 1.10 1.10
639 A134 80c multicolored 1.75 1.75
Nos. 637-639 (3) 3.10 3.10
First United Nations Security Council meeting, Addis Ababa, Jan. 28-Feb. 4, 1972.

Fish in Polluted Sea — A135

Designs: 30c, Fisherman, beacon, family. 80c, Polluted seashore.

1973, Feb. 23   Photo.   Perf. 13½
640 A135 20c gold & multi .75 .50
641 A135 30c gold & multi 1.00 .85
642 A135 80c gold & multi 2.25 2.00
Nos. 640-642 (3) 4.00 3.35
World message from the sea, Ethiopian anti-pollution campaign.

INTERPOL and Ethiopian Police Emblems A136

50c, INTERPOL emblem & General Secretariat, Paris. 60c, INTERPOL emblem.

1973, Mar. 20   Photo.   Perf. 13½
643 A136 40c dull orange & blk 1.25 1.25
644 A136 50c blue, blk & yel 1.75 1.75
645 A136 60c dk carmine & blk 2.00 2.00
Nos. 643-645 (3) 5.00 5.00
50th anniversary of International Criminal Police Organization (INTERPOL).

Virgin of Emperor Zara Yaqob — A137

Ethiopian Art: 15c, Crucifixion, Zara Yaqob period. 30c, Virgin and Child, from Entoto Mariam Church. 40c, Christ, contemporary mosaic. 80c, The Evangelists, contemporary bas-relief.

1973, May 15   Photo.   Perf. 11½
Granite Paper
646 A137 5c brown & multi .30 .30
647 A137 15c dp blue & multi .55 .55
648 A137 30c gray grn & multi .85 .85
649 A137 40c multicolored 1.10 1.10
650 A137 80c slate & multi 2.75 2.75
Nos. 646-650 (5) 5.55 5.55

Free African States in 1963 and 1973 — A138

Designs (Map of Africa and): 10c, Flags of OAU members. 20c, Symbols of progress. 40c, Dove and people. 80c, Emblems of various UN agencies.

1973 May 25   *Perf. 14½x14*
651	A138	5c red & multi	.25	.25
652	A138	10c ol gray & multi	.30	.30
653	A138	20c green & multi	.50	.50
654	A138	40c sepia & multi	1.10	1.10
655	A138	80c lt blue & multi	2.75	2.75
		Nos. 651-655 (5)	4.90	4.90

OAU, 10th anniv.

Scouts Saluting
Ethiopian and Scout
Flags — A139

Designs: 15c, Road and road sign. 30c, Girl Scout reading to old man. 40c, Scout and disabled people. 60c, Ethiopian Boy Scout.

1973, July 10   *Photo.*   *Perf. 11½*
Granite Paper
656	A139	5c blue & multi	.30	.30
657	A139	15c lt green & multi	.55	.55
658	A139	30c yellow & multi	.85	.85
659	A139	40c crimson & multi	1.10	1.10
660	A139	60c violet & multi	2.75	2.75
		Nos. 656-660 (5)	5.55	5.55

24th Boy Scout World Conference, Nairobi, Kenya, July 16-21.

WMO
Emblem — A140

50c, WMO emblem, anemometer. 60c, Weather satellite over earth, WMO emblem.

1973, Sept. 4   *Photo.*   *Perf. 13½*
661	A140	40c black, bl & dl bl	1.10	1.10
662	A140	50c dull blue & blk	1.25	1.25
663	A140	60c dull blue & multi	1.90	1.90
		Nos. 661-663 (3)	4.25	4.25

Cent. of intl. meteorological cooperation. Printed with tabs at top of sheet inscribed in Amharic and tabs at bottom with "ETHIOPIA."

Ras Makonnen, Duke of
Harar — A141

5c, Old wall of Harar. 20c, Operating room. 40c, Boy Scouts learning 1st aid & hospital. 80c, Prince Makonnen & hospital.

1973, Nov. 1   *Unwmk.*   *Perf. 14½*
664	A141	5c gray & multi	.30	.30
665	A141	10c red brn & multi	.30	.30
666	A141	20c green & multi	.60	.60
667	A141	40c brown red & multi	1.10	1.10
668	A141	80c ultra & multi	2.75	2.75
		Nos. 664-668 (5)	5.05	5.05

Opening of Ras Makonnen Memorial Hospital.

Human Rights
Flame — A142

Perf. 11½
1973, Nov. 16   *Photo.*   *Unwmk.*
Granite Paper
669	A142	40c yel, gold & dk grn	.70	.70
670	A142	50c lt grn, gold & dk grn	1.00	1.00
671	A142	60c org, gold & dk grn	1.25	1.25
		Nos. 669-671 (3)	2.95	2.95

25th anniversary of the Universal Declaration of Human Rights.

Emperor Haile
Selassie — A143

1973, Nov. 5   *Photo.*   *Perf. 11½*
672	A143	5c yellow & multi	.35	.30
673	A143	10c brt blue & multi	.35	.30
674	A143	15c green & multi	.45	.40
675	A143	20c dull yel & multi	.55	.40
676	A143	25c multicolored	.65	.40
677	A143	30c multicolored	.80	.40
678	A143	35c multicolored	.85	.40
679	A143	40c ultra & multi	.95	.40
680	A143	45c multicolored	1.10	.50
681	A143	50c orange & multi	1.25	.50
682	A143	55c magenta & multi	1.60	.85
683	A143	60c multicolored	1.75	1.10
684	A143	70c red org & multi	2.10	1.25
685	A143	90c brt vio & multi	2.75	1.40
686	A143	$1 multicolored	3.25	1.90
687	A143	$2 orange & multi	6.25	3.25
688	A143	$3 multicolored	10.50	5.00
689	A143	$5 multicolored	17.00	8.25
		Nos. 672-689 (18)	52.50	27.00

Wicker
Furniture — A144

Designs: Various wicker baskets, wall hangings, dinnerware.

1974, Jan. 31   *Photo.*   *Perf. 11½*
Granite Paper
690	A144	5c violet bl & multi	.25	.25
691	A144	10c violet bl & multi	.30	.30
692	A144	30c violet bl & multi	.60	.60
693	A144	50c violet bl & multi	.95	.95
694	A144	60c violet bl & multi	1.20	1.20
		Nos. 690-694 (5)	3.30	3.30

Cow, Calf,
Syringe — A145

Designs: 15c, Inoculation of cattle. 20c, Bullock and syringe. 50c, Laboratory technician, cow's head, syringe. 60c, Map of Ethiopia, cattle, syringe.

1974, Feb. 20   *Litho.*   *Perf. 13½x13*
695	A145	5c sepia & multi	.25	.25
696	A145	15c ultra & multi	.40	.40
697	A145	20c ultra & multi	.50	.50
698	A145	50c orange & multi	1.40	1.40
699	A145	60c gold & multi	1.75	1.75
		Nos. 695-699 (5)	4.30	4.30

Campaign against cattle plague.

Umbrella
Makers — A146

Designs: 30c, Weaving. 50c, Child care. 60c, Foundation headquarters.

1974, Apr. 17   *Photo.*   *Perf. 14½*
700	A146	10c lt lilac & multi	.30	.30
701	A146	30c multicolored	.50	.50
702	A146	50c multicolored	1.00	1.00
703	A146	60c blue & multi	1.25	1.25
		Nos. 700-703 (4)	3.05	3.05

20th anniv. of Haile Selassie Foundation.

Ceremonial
Robe — A147

Designs: Ceremonial robes.

1974, June 26   *Litho.*   *Perf. 13*
704	A147	15c multicolored	.40	.40
705	A147	25c ocher & multi	.60	.60
706	A147	35c green & multi	1.10	1.10
707	A147	40c lt brown & multi	1.25	1.25
708	A147	60c gray & multi	2.50	2.50
		Nos. 704-708 (5)	5.85	5.85

World Population
Statistics
A148

Designs: 50c, "Larger families-lower living standard." 60c, Rising population graph.

1974, Aug. 19   *Photo.*   *Perf. 14½*
709	A148	40c yellow & multi	.85	.85
710	A148	50c violet & multi	.85	.85
711	A148	60c green & multi	.85	.85
		Nos. 709-711 (3)	2.55	2.55

World Population Year 1974.

UPU Emblem, Letter
Carrier's Staff — A149

UPU Emblem and: 50c, Letters and flags. 60c, Globe. 70c, Headquarters, Bern.

1974, Oct. 9   *Photo.*   *Perf. 11½*
Granite Paper
712	A149	15c yellow & multi	.30	.30
713	A149	50c multicolored	.85	.85
714	A149	60c ultra & multi	1.25	1.10
715	A149	70c multicolored	1.25	1.25
		Nos. 712-715 (4)	3.65	3.50

Centenary of Universal Postal Union.

Celebration Around
"Damara" Pillar — A150

5c, Site of Gishen Mariam Monastery. 20c, Cross and festivities. 80c, Torch (Chibos) Parade.

1974, Dec. 17   *Photo.*   *Perf. 14x14½*
716	A150	5c yellow & multi	.30	.30
717	A150	10c yellow & multi	.30	.30
718	A150	20c yellow & multi	.30	.30
719	A150	80c yellow & multi	1.75	1.75
		Nos. 716-719 (4)	2.65	2.65

Meskel Festival, Sept. 26-27, commemorating the finding in the 4th century of the True Cross, of which a fragment is kept at Gishen Mariam Monastery in Welo Province.

Precis Clelia — A151

Butterflies: 25c, Charaxes achaemenes. 45c, Papilio dardanus. 50c, Charaxes druceanus. 60c, Papilio demodocus.

1975, Feb. 18   *Photo.*   *Perf. 12x12½*
720	A151	10c silver & multi	.60	.40
721	A151	25c gold & multi	.90	.75
722	A151	45c purple & multi	1.75	1.75

Adoration of the
Kings — A152

10c, Baptism of Jesus. 15c, Jesus teaching in the Temple. 30c, Jesus giving sight to the blind. 40c, Crucifixion. 80c, Resurrection.

Granite Paper
1975, Apr. 23   *Photo.*   *Perf. 11½*
725	A152	5c brown & multi	.30	.30
726	A152	10c black & multi	.30	.30
727	A152	15c dk brown & multi	.30	.30
728	A152	30c dk brown & multi	.60	.60
729	A152	40c black & multi	1.10	1.10
730	A152	80c slate & multi	2.25	2.25
		Nos. 725-730 (6)	4.85	4.85

Murals from Ethiopian churches.

Wild
Animals — A153

1975, May 27   *Photo.*   *Perf. 11½*
Granite Paper
731	A153	5c Warthog	.60	.60
732	A153	10c Aardvark	.60	.60
733	A153	20c Semien wolf	.85	.85
734	A153	40c Gelada baboon	1.75	1.75
735	A153	80c Civet	4.25	4.25
		Nos. 731-735 (5)	8.05	8.05

"Peace," Dove, Globe,
IWY Emblem — A154

50c, Symbols of development. 90c, Equality between men and women.

1975, June 30   *Litho.*   *Perf. 14x14½*
736	A154	40c blue & black	.60	.60
737	A154	50c salmon & multi	.85	.85
738	A154	90c multicolored	1.75	1.75
		Nos. 736-738 (3)	3.20	3.20

International Women's Year 1975.

Postal
Museum — A155

Various interior views of Postal Museum.

1975, Aug. 19   *Photo.*   *Perf. 13x12½*
739	A155	10c ocher & multi	.35	.30
740	A155	30c pink & multi	.65	.50
741	A155	60c multicolored	1.50	1.10
742	A155	70c lt green & multi	1.75	1.25
		Nos. 739-742 (4)	4.25	3.15

Ethiopian Natl. Postal Museum, opening.

Map of Ethiopia and
Sun — A156

1975, Sept. 11   *Photo.*   *Perf. 11½*
Granite Paper
743	A156	5c lilac & multi	.25	.25
744	A156	10c ultra & multi	.25	.25
745	A156	25c brown & multi	.35	.35
746	A156	50c yellow & multi	.90	.90
747	A156	90c brt green & multi	1.75	1.75
		Nos. 743-747 (5)	3.50	3.50

1st anniv. of Ethiopian revolution.

723 A151   50c green & multi   2.75   2.75
724 A151   60c brt blue & multi   3.50   3.00
Nos. 720-724 (5)   9.50   8.65

UN Emblem — A157

1975, Oct. 24   Photo.   Perf. 11½

748	A157	40c lilac & multi	.85	.85
749	A157	50c multicolored	.85	.85
750	A157	90c blue & multi	1.75	1.75
		Nos. 748-750 (3)	3.45	3.45

United Nations, 30th anniversary.

Regional Hair Styles — A158

1975, Dec. 15   Photo.   Perf. 11½

751	A158	5c Ilubabor	.30	.30
752	A158	15c Arusi	.40	.40
753	A158	20c Eritrea	.60	.60
754	A158	30c Bale	.85	.85
755	A158	35c Kefa	1.00	1.00
756	A158	50c Begemir	1.40	1.40
757	A158	60c Shoa	1.75	1.75
		Nos. 751-757 (7)	6.30	6.30

See Nos. 832-838.

Delphinium Wellbyi — A159

Flowers: 10c, Plectocephalus varians. 20c, Brachystelma asmarensis, horiz. 40c, Ceropegia inflata. 80c, Erythrina brucei.

1976, Jan. 15   Photo.   Perf. 11½

758	A159	5c multicolored	.35	.35
759	A159	10c multicolored	.40	.40
760	A159	20c multicolored	.60	.60
761	A159	40c multicolored	1.50	1.50
762	A159	80c multicolored	2.50	2.50
		Nos. 758-762 (5)	5.35	5.35

Goalkeeper, Map of Africa, Games' Emblem — A160

Designs: Various scenes from soccer, map of Africa and ball.

1976, Feb. 27   Photo.   Perf. 14½

763	A160	5c orange & multi	.30	.30
764	A160	10c yellow & multi	.30	.30
765	A160	25c lilac & multi	.60	.60
766	A160	50c green & multi	1.10	1.10
767	A160	90c brt grn & multi	2.25	2.25
		Nos. 763-767 (5)	4.55	4.55

10th African Cup of Nations, Addis Ababa and Dire Dawa, Feb. 29-Mar. 14.

Telephones, 1876 and 1976 — A161

Designs: 60c, Alexander Graham Bell. 90c, Transmission tower.

1976, Mar. 10   Litho.   Perf. 12x13½

768	A161	30c lt ocher & multi	.55	.55
769	A161	60c emerald & multi	1.10	1.10
770	A161	90c ver, blk & buff	1.75	1.75
		Nos. 768-770 (3)	3.40	3.40

Centenary of first telephone call by Alexander Graham Bell, Mar. 10, 1876.

Ethiopian Jewelry — A162

Designs: Women wearing various kinds of Ethiopian jewelry.

Granite Paper

1976, May 14   Photo.   Perf. 11½

771	A162	5c blue & multi	.30	.30
772	A162	10c plum & multi	.30	.30
773	A162	20c gray & multi	.60	.60
774	A162	40c green & multi	.90	.90
775	A162	80c orange & multi	1.75	1.75
		Nos. 771-775 (5)	3.85	3.85

Boxing — A163

Designs (Montreal Olympic Emblem and): 80c, Runner and maple leaf. 90c, Bicycling.

1976, July 15   Litho.   Perf. 12½x12

776	A163	10c multicolored	.30	.30
777	A163	80c brt red, blk & grn	1.75	1.75
778	A163	90c brt red & multi	1.75	1.75
		Nos. 776-778 (3)	3.80	3.80

21st Olympic Games, Montreal, Canada, July 17-Aug. 1.

Hands Holding Map of Ethiopia — A164

1976, Aug. 5   Photo.   Perf. 14½

779	A164	5c rose & multi	.25	.25
780	A164	10c olive & multi	.30	.30
781	A164	25c orange & multi	.40	.30
782	A164	50c multicolored	.95	.70
783	A164	90c dk blue & multi	1.75	1.40
		Nos. 779-783 (5)	3.65	2.90

Development through cooperation.

Revolution Emblem: Eye and Map — A165

1976, Sept. 9   Photo.   Perf. 13½

784	A165	5c multicolored	.30	.30
785	A165	10c multicolored	.30	.30
786	A165	25c multicolored	.30	.30
787	A165	50c yellow & multi	.90	.90
788	A165	90c green & multi	1.25	1.25
		Nos. 784-788 (5)	3.05	3.05

2nd anniversary of the revolution.

Sunburst Around Crest — A166

1976, Sept. 13   Photo.   Perf. 11½

789	A166	5c green, gold & blk	.25	.25
790	A166	10c org, gold & blk	.25	.25
791	A166	15c grnsh bl, gold & blk	.55	.25
792	A166	20c lilac, gold & blk	.55	.25
793	A166	25c brt grn, gold & blk	.55	.25
794	A166	30c car, gold & blk	.55	.55
795	A166	35c yel, gold & blk	.85	.55
796	A166	40c ol, gold & blk	.85	.55
797	A166	45c brt grn, gold & blk	.85	.55
798	A166	50c car rose, gold & blk	1.10	.85
799	A166	55c ultra, gold & blk	1.10	.85
800	A166	60c fawn, gold & blk	1.10	.85
801	A166	70c rose, gold & blk	1.75	.90
802	A166	90c blue, gold & blk	1.75	.90
803	A166	$1 dull grn, gold & blk	2.25	.90
804	A166	$2 gray, gold & blk	4.50	1.75
805	A166	$3 brn vio, gold & blk	7.00	2.75
806	A166	$5 slate bl, gold & blk	11.00	4.50
		Nos. 789-806 (18)	36.80	17.70

Denomination Expressed as "BIRR"

1983, June 16

806A	A166	1b dull grn, gold & blk	7.50	2.25
806B	A166	2b gray, gold & blk	20.00	4.50
806C	A166	3b brn vio, gold & blk	25.00	6.25

Plane Over Man with Donkey — A167

10c, Globe showing routes. 25c, Crew and passengers forming star. 50c, Propeller and jet engine. 90c, Airplanes surrounding map of Ethiopia.

1976, Oct. 28   Litho.   Perf. 12x12½

807	A167	5c dull bl & multi	.30	.30
808	A167	10c lilac & multi	.30	.30
809	A167	25c multicolored	.40	.40
810	A167	50c orange & multi	1.25	1.25
811	A167	90c olive & multi	2.00	2.00
		Nos. 807-811 (5)	4.25	4.25

Ethiopian Airlines, 30th anniversary.

Tortoises — A168

Reptiles: 20c, Chameleon. 30c, Python. 40c, Monitor lizard. 80c, Nile crocodiles.

1976, Dec. 15   Photo.   Perf. 14½

812	A168	10c multicolored	.40	.40
813	A168	20c multicolored	.60	.60
814	A168	30c multicolored	.90	.90
815	A168	50c multicolored	1.25	1.25
816	A168	80c multicolored	2.75	2.75
		Nos. 812-816 (5)	5.90	5.90

Hand Holding Makeshift Hammer — A169

Designs: 5c, Hands holding bowl and plane dropping food. 45c, Infant with empty bowl, and bank note. 60c, Map of affected area, footprints and tire tracks. 80c, Film strip, camera and Ethiopian sitting between eggshells.

1977, Jan. 20   Litho.   Perf. 12½

817	A169	5c multicolored	.40	.40
818	A169	10c multicolored	.40	.40
819	A169	45c multicolored	.85	.85
820	A169	60c multicolored	.85	.85
821	A169	80c multicolored	1.60	1.60
		Nos. 817-821 (5)	4.10	4.10

Ethiopian Relief and Rehabilitation Commission for drought and disaster areas.

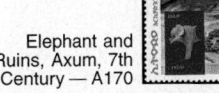

Elephant and Ruins, Axum, 7th Century — A170

Designs: 10c, Ibex and temple, 5th century, B.C., Yeha. 25c, Megalithic dolmen and pottery, Sourre Kabanawa. 50c, Awash Valley, stone axe, Acheulean period. 80c, Omo Valley, hominid jawbone.

1977, Mar. 15   Photo.   Perf. 13½

822	A170	5c gold & multi	.35	.35
823	A170	10c gold & multi	.35	.35
824	A170	25c gold & multi	.55	.55
825	A170	50c gold & multi	1.00	1.00
826	A170	80c gold & multi	1.40	1.40
		Nos. 822-826 (5)	3.65	3.65

Archaeological sites and finds in Ethiopia.

Map of Africa with Trans-East Highway — A171

1977, Mar. 30   Perf. 14

827	A171	10c gold & multi	.30	.30
828	A171	20c gold & multi	.30	.30
829	A171	40c gold & multi	.85	.85
830	A171	50c gold & multi	.85	.85
831	A171	60c gold & multi	1.10	1.10
		Nos. 827-831 (5)	3.40	3.40

Addis Ababa to Nairobi Highway and projected highways to Cairo, Egypt, and Gaborone, Botswana.

Hairstyle Type of 1975

1977, Apr. 28   Photo.   Perf. 11½

832	A158	5c Welega	.30	.30
833	A158	10c Gojam	.30	.30
834	A158	15c Tigre	.30	.30
835	A158	20c Harar	.60	.60
836	A158	25c Gemu Gefa	.60	.60
837	A158	40c Sidamo	1.10	1.10
838	A158	50c Welo	1.10	1.10
		Nos. 832-838 (7)	4.30	4.30

Addis Ababa — A172

Towns of Ethiopia: 10c, Asmara. 25c, Harar. 50c, Jima. 90c, Dese.

1977, June 20   Photo.   Perf. 14½

839	A172	5c silver & multi	.30	.30
840	A172	10c silver & multi	.30	.30
841	A172	25c silver & multi	.30	.30
842	A172	50c silver & multi	.85	.85
843	A172	90c silver & multi	1.25	1.25
		Nos. 839-843 (5)	3.00	3.00

Terebratula Abyssinica — A173

Fossil Shells: 10c, Terebratula subalata. 25c, Cuculloea lefeburiaua. 50c, Ostrea plicatissima. 90c, Trigonia cousobrina.

1977, Aug. 15   Photo.   Perf. 14x13½

844	A173	5c multicolored	.75	.30
845	A173	10c multicolored	1.25	.30
846	A173	25c multicolored	1.50	.60
847	A173	50c multicolored	2.50	1.10
848	A173	90c multicolored	4.00	1.75
		Nos. 844-848 (5)	10.00	4.05

Fractured Imperial Crown — A174

Designs: 10c, Symbol of the Revolution (spade, axe, torch). 25c, Warriors, hammer and sickle, map of Ethiopia. 60c, Soldier, farmer and map. 80c, Map and emblem of revolutionary government.

1977, Sept. 9   Litho.   Perf. 15

849	A174	5c multicolored	.30	.30
850	A174	10c multicolored	.30	.30
851	A174	25c multicolored	.55	.55
852	A174	60c multicolored	.85	.85
853	A174	80c multicolored	1.10	1.10
		Nos. 849-853 (5)	3.10	3.10

Third anniversary of the revolution.

Cicindela Petitii — A175

Insects: 10c, Heliocopris dillonii. 25c, Poekilocerus vignaudii. 50c, Pepsis heros. 90c, Pepsis dedjaz.

1977, Sept. 30 Photo. Perf. 14x13½
854	A175	5c multicolored	.40	.30
855	A175	10c multicolored	.50	.30
856	A175	25c multicolored	1.00	.60
857	A175	50c multicolored	2.50	1.75
858	A175	90c multicolored	3.75	2.90
	Nos. 854-858 (5)		8.15	5.85

Lenin, Globe, Map of Ethiopia and Emblem — A176

1977, Nov. 15 Litho. Perf. 12
859	A176	5c orange & multi	.40	.30
860	A176	10c multicolored	.40	.30
861	A176	25c salmon & multi	.40	.30
862	A176	50c lt blue & multi	1.00	.85
863	A176	90c yellow & multi	1.25	1.10
	Nos. 859-863 (5)		3.45	2.85

60th anniv. of Russian October Revolution.

Chondrostoma Dilloni — A177

Salt-water Fish: 10c, Ostracion cubicus. 25c, Serranus summana. 50c, Serranus luti. 90c, Tetraodon maculatus.

1978, Jan. 20 Litho. Perf. 15½
864	A177	5c multicolored	.65	.65
865	A177	10c multicolored	.75	.75
866	A177	25c multicolored	1.25	1.25
867	A177	50c multicolored	2.25	2.25
868	A177	90c multicolored	4.00	4.00
	Nos. 864-868 (5)		8.90	8.90

Domestic Animals — A178

1978, Mar. 27 Litho. Perf. 13½x14
869	A178	5c Cattle	.25	.25
870	A178	10c Mules	.25	.25
871	A178	25c Goats	.60	.55
872	A178	50c Dromedaries	1.25	1.25
873	A178	90c Horses	1.75	1.75
	Nos. 869-873 (5)		4.10	4.05

Weapons and Shield, Map of Ethiopia — A179

"Call of the Motherland." (Map of Ethiopia and): 10c, Civilian fighters. 25c, Map of Africa. 60c, Soldiers. 80c, Red Cross nurse and wounded man.

1978, May 13 Litho. Perf. 15½
874	A179	5c multicolored	.25	.25
875	A179	10c multicolored	.30	.30
876	A179	25c multicolored	.30	.30
877	A179	60c multicolored	.90	.90
878	A179	80c multicolored	1.25	1.25
	Nos. 874-878 (5)		3.00	3.00

Bronze Ibex, 5th Century B.C. — A180

Ancient Bronzes: 10c, Lion, Yeha, 5th cent. B.C., horiz. 25c, Lamp with ibex attacked by dog, Matara, 1st cent. B.C. 50c, Goat, Axum, 3rd cent. A.D., horiz. 90c, Ax, chisel and sickle, Yeha, 5th-4th centuries B.C.

1978, June 21 Litho. Perf. 15½
879	A180	5c multicolored	.25	.25
880	A180	10c multicolored	.30	.30
881	A180	25c multicolored	.60	.60
882	A180	50c multicolored	.90	.90
883	A180	90c multicolored	1.75	1.75
	Nos. 879-883 (5)		3.80	3.80

See Nos. 1024-1027.

Globe and Argentina '78 Emblem — A181

20c, Soccer player kicking ball. 30c, Two players embracing, net and ball. 55c, World map and ball. 70c, Soccer field, vert.

Perf. 14x13½, 13½x14
1978, July 19 Litho.
884	A181	5c multicolored	.30	.30
885	A181	20c multicolored	.60	.50
886	A181	30c multicolored	.60	.60
887	A181	55c multicolored	1.10	1.10
888	A181	70c multicolored	1.75	1.75
	Nos. 884-888 (5)		4.35	4.25

11th World Cup Soccer Championship, Argentina, June 1-25.

Map of Africa, Oppressed African — A182

Namibia Day: 10c, Policeman pointing gun. 25c, Sniper with gun. 60c, African caught in net. 80c, Head of free man.

1978, Aug. 25 Perf. 12½x13½
889	A182	5c multicolored	.25	.25
890	A182	10c multicolored	.30	.30
891	A182	25c multicolored	.60	.60
892	A182	60c multicolored	1.10	1.10
893	A182	80c multicolored	1.25	1.25
	Nos. 889-893 (5)		3.50	3.50

Soldiers, Guerrilla and Jets — A183

Design: 1b, People looking toward sun, crushing snake, flags.

1978, Sept. 8 Photo. Perf. 14
894	A183	80c multicolored	1.10	1.10
895	A183	1b multicolored	1.75	1.75

4th anniversary of revolution.

Hand and Globe with Tools — A184

Designs: 15c, Symbols of energy, communications, education, medicine, agriculture and industry. 25c, Cogwheels and world map. 60c, Globe and hands passing wrench. 70c, Flying geese and turtle over globe.

1978, Nov. 14 Litho. Perf. 12x12½
896	A184	10c multicolored	.25	.25
897	A184	15c multicolored	.30	.30
898	A184	25c multicolored	.60	.50
899	A184	60c multicolored	1.10	1.00
900	A184	70c multicolored	1.25	1.10
	Nos. 896-900 (5)		3.50	3.15

Technical Cooperation Among Developing Countries Conference, Buenos Aires, Argentina, Sept. 1978.

Human Rights Emblem — A185

1978, Dec. 7 Photo. Perf. 12½x13½
901	A185	5c multicolored	.25	.25
902	A185	15c multicolored	.30	.30
903	A185	25c multicolored	.30	.30
904	A185	35c multicolored	.60	.60
905	A185	1b multicolored	1.75	1.75
	Nos. 901-905 (5)		3.20	3.20

Declaration of Human Rights, 30th anniv.

Broken Chain, Anti-Apartheid Emblem — A186

1978, Dec. 28 Litho. Perf. 12½x12
906	A186	5c multicolored	.25	.25
907	A186	20c multicolored	.30	.30
908	A186	30c multicolored	.60	.60
909	A186	55c multicolored	.85	.85
910	A186	70c multicolored	1.25	1.25
	Nos. 906-910 (5)		3.25	3.25

Anti-Apartheid Year.

Stele from Osole — A187

Ancient Carved Stones, Soddo Region: 10c, Anthropomorphous stele, Gorashino. 25c, Leaning stone, Wado. 60c, Round stones, Ambeut. 80c, Bas-relief, Tiya.

1979, Jan. 25 Perf. 14
911	A187	5c multicolored	.25	.25
912	A187	10c multicolored	.30	.30
913	A187	25c multicolored	.30	.30
914	A187	60c multicolored	1.25	1.25
915	A187	80c multicolored	1.25	1.25
	Nos. 911-915 (5)		3.35	3.35

Cotton Plantation — A188

Shemma Industry: 10c, Women spinning cotton yarn. 20c, Man reeling cotton. 65c, Weaver. 80c, Shemma (Natl. dress).

1979, Mar. 15 Litho. Perf. 15½
916	A188	5c multicolored	.25	.25
917	A188	10c multicolored	.30	.30
918	A188	20c multicolored	.60	.60
919	A188	65c multicolored	1.25	1.25
920	A188	80c multicolored	1.75	1.75
	Nos. 916-920 (5)		4.15	4.15

Ethiopian Trees — A189

1979, Apr. 26 Photo. Perf. 13½x14
921	A189	5c Grar	.25	.25
922	A189	10c Weira	.30	.30
923	A189	25c Tidh	.60	.40
924	A189	50c Shola	.85	.85
925	A189	90c Zigba	1.75	1.50
	Nos. 921-925 (5)		3.75	3.30

Agricultural Development A190

Revolutionary Development Campaign: 15c, Industry. 25c, Transportation and communication. 60c, Education and health. 70c, Commerce.

1979, July 3 Litho. Perf. 12x12½
926	A190	10c multicolored	.25	.25
927	A190	15c multicolored	.30	.30
928	A190	25c multicolored	.30	.30

929	A190	60c multicolored	.85	.85
930	A190	70c multicolored	1.25	1.25
	Nos. 926-930 (5)		2.95	2.95

IYC Emblem — A191

Intl. Year of the Child: 15c, Adults leading children. 25c, Adult helping child. 60c, IYC emblem surrounded by children. 70c, Adult and children embracing.

1979, Aug. 16 Litho. Perf. 12x12½
931	A191	10c multicolored	.30	.30
932	A191	15c multicolored	.30	.30
933	A191	25c multicolored	.60	.60
934	A191	60c multicolored	1.10	1.10
935	A191	70c multicolored	1.75	1.75
	Nos. 931-935 (5)		4.05	4.05

Guerrilla Fighters A192

15c, Soldiers. 25c, Map of Africa within cogwheel, star. 60c, Students with book, torch. 70c, Family, hammer & sickle emblem.

1979, Sept. 11 Photo. Perf. 14
936	A192	10c multicolored	.30	.30
937	A192	15c multicolored	.30	.30
938	A192	25c multicolored	.60	.60
939	A192	60c multicolored	1.10	1.10
940	A192	70c multicolored	1.75	1.75
	Nos. 936-940 (5)		4.05	4.05

Fifth anniversary of revolution.

Telephone Receiver — A193

Telecom Emblem and: 5c, Symbolic waves. 35c, Satellite beaming to earth. 45c, Dish antenna. 65c, Television cameraman.

1979, Sept. 20 Photo. Perf. 11½
941	A193	5c multicolored	.30	.30
942	A193	30c multicolored	.60	.60
943	A193	35c multicolored	.60	.60
944	A193	45c multicolored	.85	.85
945	A193	65c multicolored	1.25	1.25
	Nos. 941-945 (5)		3.60	3.60

3rd World Telecommunications Exhibition, Geneva, Sept. 20-26.

Incense Container — A194

1979, Nov. 15 Litho. Perf. 15
946	A194	5c shown	.30	.30
947	A194	10c Vase	.60	.60
948	A194	25c Earthenware cover	.85	.85
949	A194	60c Milk container	1.25	1.25
950	A194	80c Storage container	1.75	1.75
	Nos. 946-950 (5)		4.75	4.75

Wooden Grain Bowl — A195

1980, Jan. 3 Litho. Perf. 13½x13
951	A195	5c shown	.30	.30
952	A195	30c Chair, stool	.85	.85
953	A195	35c Mortar, pestle	.85	.85
954	A195	45c Buckets	1.25	1.25
955	A195	65c Storage jars	1.75	1.75
	Nos. 951-955 (5)		5.00	5.00

Lappet-faced Vulture — A196

Birds of Prey: 15c, Long-crested hawk eagle. 25c, Secretary bird. 60c, Abyssinian long-eared owl. 70c, Lanner falcon.

1980, Feb. 12   *Perf. 13½x14*
956	A196	10c multicolored	.60	.60
957	A196	15c multicolored	.85	.85
958	A196	25c multicolored	1.25	1.25
959	A196	60c multicolored	2.90	2.90
960	A196	70c multicolored	4.50	4.50
		Nos. 956-960 (5)	10.10	10.10

Fight Against Cigarette Smoking — A197

1980, Apr. 7   Photo.   *Perf. 13x13½*
961	A197	20c shown	.60	.60
962	A197	60c Cigarette	1.25	1.25
963	A197	1b Respiratory system	1.75	1.75
		Nos. 961-963 (3)	3.60	3.60

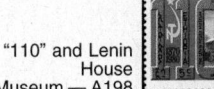

"110" and Lenin House Museum — A198

Lenin, 110th "Birthday" (Paintings): 15c, In hiding. 20c, As a young man. 40c, Returning to Russia. 1b, Speaking on the Goelro Plan.

1980, Apr. 22   Litho.   *Perf. 12x12½*
964	A198	5c multicolored	.30	.30
965	A198	15c multicolored	.30	.30
966	A198	20c multicolored	.30	.30
967	A198	40c multicolored	.85	.85
968	A198	1b multicolored	1.75	1.75
		Nos. 964-968 (5)	3.50	3.50

Grévy's Zebras — A199

Designs: 15c, Gazelles. 25c, Wild hunting dogs. 60c, Swayne's hartebeests. 70c, Cheetahs.

1980, June 10   Litho.   *Perf. 12½x12*
969	A199	10c shown	.30	.30
970	A199	15c multi	.60	.60
971	A199	25c multi	.85	.85
972	A199	60c multi	2.25	2.25
973	A199	70c multi	3.00	3.00
		Nos. 969-973 (5)	7.00	7.00

Runner, Moscow '80 Emblem — A200

1980, July 19   Photo.   *Perf. 11½x12*
974	A200	30c shown	.85	.85
975	A200	70c Cycling	1.25	1.25
976	A200	80c Boxing	1.75	1.75
		Nos. 974-976 (3)	3.85	3.85

22nd Summer Olympic Games, Moscow, July 19-Aug. 3.

Removing Blindfold — A201

40c, Revolutionary. 50c, Woman breaking chain. 70c, Russian & Ethiopian flags.

1980, Sept. 10   Photo.   *Perf. 14x13½*
977	A201	30c shown	.60	.50
978	A201	40c multicolored	.60	.60
979	A201	50c multicolored	.85	.85
980	A201	70c multicolored	1.25	1.25
		Nos. 977-980 (4)	3.30	3.20

6th anniversary of revolution.

Bamboo Folk Craft — A202

Designs: 5c, Bamboo food basket. 15c, Hand basket. 25c, Stool. 35c, Fruit basket. 1b, Lamp shade.

1980, Oct. 23   Litho.   *Perf. 14*
981	A202	5c multi	.30	.30
982	A202	15c multi	.30	.30
983	A202	25c multi	.60	.60
984	A202	35c multi	.85	.85
985	A202	1b multi	1.75	1.75
		Nos. 981-985 (5)	3.80	3.80

Mekotkocha (Used in Weeding) — A203

Traditional Harvesting Tools: 15c, Layda (grain separator). 40c, Mensh (fork). 45c, Mededekia (soil turner). 70c, Mofer & Kenber (plow and yoke).

1980, Dec. 18   Litho.   *Perf. 12½x12*
986	A203	10c multicolored	.30	.25
987	A203	15c multicolored	.30	.30
988	A203	40c multicolored	.60	.60
989	A203	45c multicolored	.85	.85
990	A203	70c multicolored	1.25	1.25
		Nos. 986-990 (5)	3.30	3.25

Baro River Bridge Opening — A204

1981, Feb. 28   Photo.   *Perf. 13½x13*
991	A204	15c Canoes and ferry	.30	.30
992	A204	65c Bridge construction	1.25	1.25
993	A204	1b shown	2.25	2.25
		Nos. 991-993 (3)	3.80	3.80

Semien National Park — A205

World Heritage Year: 5c, Wawel Castle, Poland. 15c, Quito Cathedral, Ecuador. 20c, Old Slave Quarters, Goree Island, Senegal. 30c, Mesa Verde Indian Village, US. 1b, L'Anse aux Meadows excavation, Canada.

Perf. 11x11½, 11½x11

1981, Mar. 10   Photo.
994	A205	5c multicolored	.30	.30
995	A205	15c multicolored	.30	.30
996	A205	20c multicolored	.55	.55
997	A205	30c multicolored	.60	.60
998	A205	80c multicolored	1.75	1.75
999	A205	1b multicolored	2.25	2.25
		Nos. 994-999 (6)	5.75	5.75

1981, June 16   Photo.

10c, Biet Medhanialem Church, Ethiopia. 15c, Nahanni Natl. Park, Canada. 20c, Yellowstone River Lower Falls, U.S. 30c, Aachen Cathedral, Germany. 80c, Kicker Rock, San Cristobal Island, Ecuador. 1b, The Lizak corridor, Holy Cross Chapel, Cracow, Poland.

1000	A205	10c multi	.30	.30
1001	A205	15c multi	.30	.30
1002	A205	20c multi	.60	.60
1003	A205	30c multi	.85	.80
1004	A205	80c multi	1.75	1.75
1005	A205	1b multi, vert.	2.25	2.25
		Nos. 1000-1005 (6)	6.05	6.00

Ancient Drinking Vessel — A206

Designs: 25c, Spice container. 35c, Jug. 40c, Cooking pot holder. 60c, Animal figurine.

1981, May 5   Litho.   *Perf. 12½x12*
1006	A206	20c shown	.30	.30
1007	A206	25c multicolored	.30	.30
1008	A206	35c multicolored	.60	.60
1009	A206	40c multicolored	.85	.85
1010	A206	60c multicolored	1.25	1.25
		Nos. 1006-1010 (5)	3.30	3.30

Intl. Year of the Disabled — A207

1981, July 16   Photo.   *Perf. 11½x12*
1011	A207	5c Prostheses	.25	.25
1012	A207	15c Boys writing	.30	.30
1013	A207	20c Activities	.60	.50
1014	A207	40c Knitting	.85	.85
1015	A207	1b Weaving	1.75	1.75
		Nos. 1011-1015 (5)	3.75	3.65

7th Anniv. of Revolution A208

1981, Sept. 10   *Perf. 14*
1016	A208	20c Children's Center	.30	.30
1017	A208	60c Heroes' Center	.85	.85
1018	A208	1b Serto Ader (state newspaper)	1.75	1.75
		Nos. 1016-1018 (3)	2.90	2.90

World Food Day — A209

Designs: 5c, Wheat airlift. 15c, Plowing. 20c, Malnutrition. 40c, Agriculture education. 1b, Cattle, corn.

1981, Oct. 15   Litho.   *Perf. 13½x12½*
1019	A209	5c multi	.25	.25
1020	A209	15c multi	.25	.25
1021	A209	20c multi	.30	.30
1022	A209	40c multi	.85	.85
1023	A209	1b multi	1.75	1.75
		Nos. 1019-1023 (5)	3.40	3.40

Ancient Bronze Type of 1978

Designs: 15c, Bird shaped pitcher. 45c, Tsenatsil (musical instrument). 50c, Pitcher with large handle on top. 70c, Pot.

1981, Dec. 15   Litho.   *Perf. 14x13½*
1024	A180	15c multi	.30	.30
1025	A180	45c multi	.85	.85
1026	A180	50c multi	.85	.85
1027	A180	70c multi	1.25	1.25
		Nos. 1024-1027 (4)	3.25	3.25

Horn Artifacts — A210

Designs: 10c, Tobacco containers. 15c, Horn cup. 40c, Tej container. 45c, Horn goblet. 70c, Horn spoons.

1982, Feb. 18   Photo.   *Perf. 12x12½*
1028	A210	10c multi	.25	.25
1029	A210	15c multi	.30	.30
1030	A210	40c multi	.85	.85
1031	A210	45c multi	.85	.85
1032	A210	70c multi	1.25	1.25
		Nos. 1028-1032 (5)	3.50	3.50

Coffee Cultivation A211

1982, May, 6   Photo.   *Perf. 13½*
1033	A211	5c Plants	.25	.25
1034	A211	15c Bushes	.30	.30
1035	A211	25c Mature bushes	.50	.45
1036	A211	35c Picking beans	.85	.80
1037	A211	1b Drinking coffee	2.00	1.75
		Nos. 1033-1037 (5)	3.90	3.55

1982 World Cup — A212

Various soccer plays.

Perf. 13½x12½

1982, June 10   Litho.
1038	A212	5c multicolored	.25	.25
1039	A212	15c multicolored	.30	.30
1040	A212	20c multicolored	.50	.50
1041	A212	40c multicolored	.85	.85
1042	A212	1b multicolored	1.75	1.75
		Nos. 1038-1042 (5)	3.65	3.65

TB Bacillus Centenary — A213

1982, July 12   Litho.   *Perf. 13½x12½*
1043	A213	15c Cow	.30	.30
1044	A213	20c Magnifying glass	.30	.30
1045	A213	30c Koch, microscope	.60	.60
1046	A213	35c Koch	.65	.65
1047	A213	80c Man coughing	1.75	1.75
		Nos. 1043-1047 (5)	3.60	3.60

8th Anniv. of Revolution — A214

Designs: Symbols of justice.

1982, Sept. 10   *Perf. 12½x13½*
1048	A214	80c multicolored	1.25	1.25
1049	A214	1b multicolored	1.75	1.75

World Standards Day — A215

1982, Oct. 14   Litho.   *Perf. 13½x12½*
1050	A215	5c Hand, foot, square	.30	.30
1051	A215	15c Scales	.30	.30
1052	A215	20c Rulers	.35	.35
1053	A215	30c Weights	.60	.60
1054	A215	1b Emblem	1.75	1.75
		Nos. 1050-1054 (5)	3.30	3.30

10th Anniv. of UN Conference on Human Environment A216

5c, Wildlife conservation. 15c, Environmental health and settlement. 20c, Forest protection. 40c, Natl. literacy campaign. 1b, Soil and water conservation.

1982, Dec. 13   Litho.   *Perf. 12*
1055	A216	5c multicolored	.25	.25
1056	A216	15c multicolored	.30	.30
1057	A216	20c multicolored	.40	.40
1058	A216	40c multicolored	.85	.85
1059	A216	1b multicolored	1.90	1.90
		Nos. 1055-1059 (5)	3.70	3.70

468 ETHIOPIA

Cave of Sof
Omar — A217

Various views.

1983, Feb. 10   Photo.   Perf. 13½
1060 A217 5c multicolored   .25 .25
1061 A217 10c multicolored   .30 .30
1062 A217 50c multicolored   .30 .30
1063 A217 70c multicolored   1.25 1.25
1064 A217 80c multicolored   1.25 1.25
   Nos. 1060-1064 (5)   3.35 3.35

A218

1983, Apr. 29   Photo.   Perf. 14
1065 A218 80c multicolored   1.25 1.25
1066 A218 1b multicolored   1.75 1.75
   25th Anniv. of Economic Commission for
Africa.

A219

Perf. 12½x11½
1983, June 3   Photo.
1067 A219 85c Emblem   1.25 1.25
1068 A219 1b Lighthouse, ship   2.25 2.25
   25th Anniv. of Intl. Maritime Org.

WCY — A220

Designs: 25c, UPU emblem. 55c, Dish
antenna, emblems. 1b, Bridge, tunnel.

1983, July 22   Litho.
1069 A220 25c multi   .55 .55
1070 A220 55c multi   .85 .85
1071 A220 1b multi   2.75 2.75
   Nos. 1069-1071 (3)   4.15 4.15

9th Anniv. of
Revolution — A221

1983, Sept. 10   Litho.   Perf. 14½
1072 A221 25c Dove   .30 .30
1073 A221 55c Star   .85 .85
1074 A221 1b Emblems   1.25 1.25
   Nos. 1072-1074 (3)   2.40 2.40

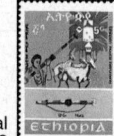

Musical
Instruments — A222

1983, Oct. 17 Litho. Perf. 12½x13½
1075 A222 5c Hura   .25 .25
1076 A222 15c Dinke   .30 .30
1077 A222 20c Meleket   .60 .60
1078 A222 40c Embilta   1.25 1.25
1079 A222 1b Tom   1.75 1.75
   Nos. 1075-1079 (5)   4.15 4.15

Charaxes
Galawadiwosi
A223

15c, Epiphora elianae. 55c, Batuana rouge-
oti. 1b, Achaea saboeareginae.

1983, Dec. 13   Photo.   Perf. 14
1080 A223 10c shown   .85 .85
1081 A223 15c multicolored   1.25 1.25
1082 A223 55c multicolored   2.75 2.75
1083 A223 1b multicolored   3.50 3.50
   Nos. 1080-1083 (4)   8.35 8.35

Intl. Anti-Apartheid
Year (1983) — A224

Perf. 13½x12½
1984, Feb. 10   Litho.
1084 A224 5c multicolored   .25 .25
1085 A224 15c multicolored   .30 .30
1086 A224 20c multicolored   .60 .60
1087 A224 40c multicolored   .85 .85
1088 A224 1b multicolored   2.25 2.25
   Nos. 1084-1088 (5)   4.25 4.25

Local Flowers — A225

5c, Protea gaguedi. 25c, Sedum epidendrum. 50c, Echinops amplexicaulis. 1b,
Canarina emini.

1984, Apr. 13   Litho.   Perf. 13½
1089 A225 5c multi   .30 .30
1090 A225 25c multi   .85 .85
1091 A225 50c multi   1.75 1.75
1092 A225 1b multi   3.00 3.00
   Nos. 1089-1092 (4)   5.90 5.90

Traditional
Houses — A226

1984, June 13   Photo.
1093 A226 15c Konso   .30 .30
1094 A226 65c Dorze   1.25 1.25
1095 A226 1b Harer   1.75 1.75
   Nos. 1093-1095 (3)   3.30 3.30

10th Anniv. of the
Revolution — A227

1984, Sept. 10   Photo.   Perf. 11½
1096 A227 5c Sept. 12, 1974   .40 .40
1097 A227 10c Mar. 4, 1975   .40 .40
1098 A227 15c Apr. 20, 1976   .40 .40
1099 A227 20c Feb. 11, 1977   .50 .50
1100 A227 25c Mar. 1978   .65 .65
1101 A227 40c July 8, 1980   1.20 1.20
1102 A227 45c Dec. 17, 1980   1.60 1.50
1103 A227 50c Sept. 15, 1980   1.75 1.75
1104 A227 70c Sept. 18, 1981   2.40 2.40
1105 A227 1b June 6, 1983   2.75 2.75
   Nos. 1096-1105 (10)   12.05 11.95

Traditional
Sports — A228

1984, Dec. 7   Photo.   Perf. 14
1106 A228 5c Gugs   .25 .25
1107 A228 25c Tigil   .40 .40
1108 A228 50c Genna   .95 .95
1109 A228 1b Gebeta   1.75 1.75
   Nos. 1106-1109 (4)   3.35 3.35

Birds — A229

Designs: 5c, Francolinus harwoodi. 15c,
Rallus rougetti. 80c, Merops pusillus. 85c,
Malimbus rubriceps.

1985, Jan. 4   Photo.   Perf. 14½
1110 A229 5c multi   .30 .30
1111 A229 15c multi   .85 .85
1112 A229 80c multi   3.00 3.00
1113 A229 85c multi   3.00 3.00
   Nos. 1110-1113 (4)   7.15 7.15

Indigenous
Fauna — A230

20c, Hippopotamus amphibius. 25c,
Litocranius walleri. 40c, Sylvicapra grimmia.
1b, Rhynchotragus guentheri.

1985, Feb. 4   Litho.   Perf. 12½x12
1114 A230 20c multicolored   .85 .85
1115 A230 25c multicolored   1.00 1.00
1116 A230 40c multicolored   2.00 2.00
1117 A230 1b multicolored   3.50 3.50
   Nos. 1114-1117 (4)   7.35 7.35

Freshwater
Fish — A231

10c, Barbus degeni. 20c, Labeo cylindricus.
55c, Protopterus annectens. 1b, Alestes
dentex.

1985, Apr. 3   Perf. 13½
1118 A231 10c multicolored   .50 .25
1119 A231 20c multicolored   .90 .50
1120 A231 55c multicolored   2.10 1.20
1121 A231 1b multicolored   3.25 2.50
   Nos. 1118-1121 (4)   6.75 4.45

Medicinal
Plants — A232

10c, Securidaca longepedunculata. 20c,
Plumbago zeylanicum. 55c, Brucea
antidysenteric. 1b, Dorstenia barminiana.

1985, May 23   Perf. 11½x12½
1122 A232 10c multicolored   .30 .30
1123 A232 20c multicolored   .30 .30
1124 A232 55c multicolored   .85 .85
1125 A232 1b multicolored   2.25 2.25
   Nos. 1122-1125 (4)   3.70 3.70

Ethiopian Red Cross
Soc., 50th
Anniv. — A233

1985, Aug. 6   Litho.   Perf. 13½x13
1126 A233 25c multicolored   .60 .60
1127 A233 35c multicolored   .85 .85
1128 A233 1b multicolored   2.25 2.25
   Nos. 1126-1128 (3)   3.70 3.70

Ethiopian
Revolution, 11th
Anniv. — A234

10c, Kombolcha Mills, Welo Region. 80c,
Muger Cement Factory, Mokoda, Shoa. 1b,
Relocating famine and drought victims.

1985, Sept. 10   Litho.   Perf. 13½
1129 A234 10c multicolored   .30 .30
1130 A234 80c multicolored   1.75 1.75
1131 A234 1b multicolored   2.25 2.25
   Nos. 1129-1131 (3)   4.30 4.30

UN 40th
Anniv. — A235

1985, Nov. 22 Litho. Perf. 13½x14
1132 A235 25c multicolored   .90 .75
1133 A235 55c multicolored   1.75 1.50
1134 A235 1b multicolored   3.25 2.50
   Nos. 1132-1134 (3)   5.90 4.75

Anti-Polio
Campaign — A236

Designs: 5c, Boy, prosthesis. 10c, Boy on
crutches. 20c, Nurse, boy. 55c, Man, sewing
machine. 1b, Nurse, mother, child.

1986, Jan. 10 Litho. Perf. 11½x12½
1135 A236 5c multi   .75 .25
1136 A236 10c multi   .30 .30
1137 A236 20c multi   .60 .50
1138 A236 55c multi   1.10 1.10
1139 A236 1b multi   2.75 2.75
   Nos. 1135-1139 (5)   5.50 4.90

Indigenous
Trees — A237

10c, Millettia ferruginea. 30c, Syzygium
guineense. 50c, Cordia africana. 1b, Hagenia
abyssinica.

1986, Feb. 10   Perf. 13½x14½
1140 A237 10c multicolored   .35 .35
1141 A237 30c multicolored   .60 .60
1142 A237 50c multicolored   .90 .90
1143 A237 1b multicolored   2.25 2.25
   Nos. 1140-1143 (4)   4.10 4.10

Spices — A238

10c, Zingiber officinale rosc. 15c, Ocimum
bacilicum. 55c, Sinapsis alba. 1b, Cuminum
cyminum.

1986, Mar. 10   Perf. 13½
1144 A238 10c multicolored   .60 .60
1145 A238 15c multicolored   .60 .60
1146 A238 55c multicolored   1.25 1.25
1147 A238 1b multicolored   2.75 2.75
   Nos. 1144-1147 (4)   5.20 5.20

Current Coins,
Obverse and
Reverse — A239

1986, May 9   Litho.   Perf. 13½x14
1148 A239 5c 1-cent   .30 .30
1149 A239 10c 25-cent   .30 .30
1150 A239 35c 5-cent   .85 .85
1151 A239 50c 50-cent   1.25 1.25
1152 A239 1b 10-cent   2.25 2.25
   Nos. 1148-1152 (5)   4.95 4.95

Discovery of 3.5
Million Year-old
Hominid Skeleton,
"Lucy" — A240

1986, July 4   **Perf. 13½**
1153 A240 2b multicolored   6.50 6.50

Ethiopian
Revolution, 12th
Anniv. — A241

Designs: 20c, Military service. 30c,
Tiglachin monument. 55c, Delachin Exhibition
emblem. 85c, Food processing plant, Merti.

1986, Sept. 10 Litho.   Perf. 14
1154 A241 20c multicolored   .40   .40
1155 A241 30c multicolored   .65   .65
1156 A241 55c multicolored   1.10 1.10
1157 A241 85c multicolored   1.40 1.40
      Nos. 1154-1157 (4)   3.55 3.55

Ethiopian Airlines, 40th
Anniv. — A242

1986, Oct. 14
1158 A242 10c DC-7   .30   .30
1159 A242 20c DC-3   .60   .60
1160 A242 30c Personnel, jet
            tail   .85   .85
1161 A242 40c Engine   .85   .85
1162 A242 1b DC-7, map   2.25 2.25
      Nos. 1158-1162 (5)   4.85 4.85

Intl. Peace
Year — A243

1986, Nov. 13   **Perf. 13½**
1163 A243 10c multicolored   .30   .30
1164 A243 80c multicolored   2.00 2.00
1165 A243 1b multicolored   2.25 2.25
      Nos. 1163-1165 (3)   4.55 4.55

UN Child
Survival
Campaign
A244

10c, Breast feeding. 35c, Immunization.
50c, Hygiene. 1b, Growth monitoring.

1986, Dec. 11   **Perf. 12½**
1166 A244 10c multi   .30   .30
1167 A244 35c multi   .85   .85
1168 A244 50c multi   1.25 1.10
1169 A244 1b multi   2.25 2.00
      Nos. 1166-1169 (4)   4.65 4.25

Umbrellas — A245

1987, Feb. 10   **Perf. 13½**
1170 A245 35c Axum   .85   .85
1171 A245 55c Negele-Borena   1.25 1.25
1172 A245 1b Jimma   1.75 1.75
      Nos. 1170-1172 (3)   3.85 3.85

Artwork by
Afewerk Tekle
(b. 1932) — A246

Designs: 50c, Defender of His Country —
Afar, stained glass window. 2b, Defender of
His Country — Adwa, painting.

1987, Mar. 19 Litho.   Perf. 13½
1173 A246 50c multicolored   1.50 1.00
1174 A246 2b multicolored   5.50 4.50

Stained
Glass
Windows by
Afewerk
Tekle
A247

1987, June 16 Photo.   Perf. 11½x12
Granite Paper
1175 A247 50c multicolored   4.00 2.00
            Size: 26x38mm
1176 A247 80c multicolored   5.00 2.75
1177 A247 1b multicolored   7.50   .40
      Nos. 1175-1177 (3)   16.50 5.15
Struggle of the African People.
Sold out in Addis Ababa on date of issue.

Simien
Fox — A248

1987, June 29 Litho.   Perf. 13½
1178 A248 5c multicolored   .25   .25
1179 A248 10c multicolored   .25   .25
1180 A248 15c multicolored   .35   .25
1181 A248 20c multicolored   .45   .30
1182 A248 25c multicolored   .60   .30
1183 A248 45c multicolored   1.00   .85
1184 A248 55c multicolored   1.25   .85
      Nos. 1178-1184 (7)   4.15 3.05
For overprints see Nos. 1234-1237. For similar design see A294a.

Ethiopian
Revolution, 13th
Anniv. — A249

Designs: 5c, Constitution, freedom of press.
10c, Popular elections. 80c, Referendum. 1b,
Bahir Dar Airport, map.

1987, Sept. 10   **Perf. 12½**
1185 A249 5c multi   .65   .65
1186 A249 10c multi   .65   .40
1187 A249 80c multi   1.75 1.75
1188 A249 1b multi   2.25 2.25
      Nos. 1185-1188 (4)   5.30 5.05

Addis Ababa,
Cent. — A251

"100" and views: 5c, Emperor Menelik II,
Empress Taitu and city. 10c, Traditional buildings. 80c, Central Addis Ababa. 1b, Aerial
view of city.

1987, Sept. 7   **Perf. 13½**
1193 A251 5c multicolored   .30   .30
1194 A251 10c multicolored   .30   .30
1195 A251 80c multicolored   1.75 1.75
1196 A251 1b multicolored   2.25 2.25
      Nos. 1193-1196 (4)   4.60 4.60

Wooden
Spoons — A252

1987, Nov. 30
1197 A252 85c Hurso, Harerge   1.25 1.25
1198 A252 1b Borena, Sidamo   1.75 1.75

Intl. Year of
Shelter for the
Homeless
A253

10c, Village revitalization program. 35c,
Resettlement program. 50c, Urban improve-
ment. 1b, Cooperative and government
housing.

1987, Dec. 12 Litho.   Perf. 13
1199 A253 10c multicolored   .30   .30
1200 A253 35c multicolored   .60   .60
1201 A253 50c multicolored   .85   .85
1202 A253 1b multicolored   1.25 1.25
      Nos. 1199-1202 (4)   3.00 3.00

October
Revolution,
Russia, 70th
Anniv. (in
1987) — A254

Painting: 1b, Lenin receiving Workers'
Council delegates in the Smolny Institute.

1988, Feb. 17   **Perf. 12½x12**
1203 A254 1b multicolored   2.25 2.00

Traditional Hunting
Methods and
Prey — A255

Designs: 85c, Bow and arrow. 1b, Double-
pronged spear.

1988, Mar. 30 Litho.   Perf. 13½
1204 A255 85c multi   1.75 1.75
1205 A255 1b multi   3.00 3.00

A256

1988, May 6
1206 A256 85c multicolored   1.25 1.25
1207 A256 1b multicolored   1.75 1.75
Intl. Red Cross and Red Crescent Organizations, 125th annivs.

A257

1988, June 7 Photo.   Perf. 11½x12
1208 A257 2b multicolored   3.00 2.75
Organizaton of African Unity, 25th anniv.

Ethiopian
Revolution, 14th
Anniv. — A258

Design: Various details of *The Victory of
Ethiopia*, six-panel mural by Afewerk Tekle (b.
1932) in the museum of the Heroes Center,
Debre Zeit — 10c, Jet over farm, vert. 20c,
Farm workers on road, vert. 35c, Allegory of
unity, vert. 55c, Jet over industry. 80c, Steel
works. 1b, Weaving.

1988, June 28 Litho.   Perf. 13½x13
1209 A258 10c multi   .30   .30
1210 A258 20c multi   .30   .30
1211 A258 35c multi   .60   .60
1212 A258 55c multi   .85   .85
1213 A258 80c multi   1.25 1.25
1214 A258 1b multi   1.25 1.25
      Nos. 1209-1214 (6)   4.55 4.55
      Nos. 1209-1211 vert.

Women, Bracelets
and
Maps — A259

1988, July 27 Litho.   Perf. 13x13½
1215 A259 15c Sidamo   .30   .30
1216 A259 85c Arsi   1.25 1.25
1217 A259 1b Harerge   1.75 1.75
      Nos. 1215-1217 (3)   3.30 3.30

Immunize Every
Child — A260

1988, June 14 Litho.   Perf. 13x13½
1218 A260 10c Measles   .30   .30
1219 A260 35c Tetanus   .60   .60
1220 A260 50c Whooping cough   .85   .85
1221 A260 1b Diphtheria   1.75 1.75
      Nos. 1218-1221 (4)   3.50 3.50

Intl. Fund for
Agricultural
Development
(IFAD), 10th
Anniv. — A261

1988, Aug. 16   **Perf. 13½**
1222 A261 15c Monetary aid   .30   .30
1223 A261 85c Farming activities 1.25 1.25
1224 A261 1b Harvest   1.75 1.75
      Nos. 1222-1224 (3)   3.30 3.30

People's
Democratic
Republic of
Ethiopia, 1st
Anniv. — A262

5c, 1st Session of the natl. Shengo (congress). 10c, Mengistu Haile-Mariam, 1st president of the republic. 80c, Natl. crest, flag &
crowd. 1b, State assembly building.

1988, Sept. 9   **Perf. 14**
1225 A262 5c multicolored   .30   .30
1226 A262 10c multicolored   .30   .30
1227 A262 80c multicolored   1.25 1.25
1228 A262 1b multicolored   1.75 1.75
      Nos. 1225-1228 (4)   3.60 3.60

Bank
Notes — A263

1988, Nov. 10 Photo.   Perf. 13
1229 A263 5c 1-Birr   .30   .30
1230 A263 10c 5-Birr   .30   .30
1231 A263 20c 10-Birr   .50   .50
1232 A263 75c 50-Birr   1.40 1.40
1233 A263 85c 100-Birr   1.75 1.75
      Nos. 1229-1233 (5)   4.25 4.25

Nos. 1181-1184
Ovptd. in Two
Languages

1988, Dec. 1 Litho.   Perf. 13½
1234 A248 20c multicolored   4.75 4.50
1235 A248 25c multicolored   6.25 5.50
1236 A248 45c multicolored   12.50 10.50
1237 A248 55c multicolored   13.00 11.00
      Nos. 1234-1237 (4)   36.50 31.50
Intl. Day for the Fight Against AIDS.

WHO, 40th Anniv. — A264

1988, Dec. 30　　Litho.　　Perf. 14
1238	A264	50c multicolored	.85	.85
1239	A264	65c multicolored	1.10	1.10
1240	A264	85c multicolored	1.25	1.25
		Nos. 1238-1240 (3)	3.20	3.20

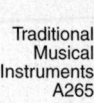

Traditional Musical Instruments A265

1989, Feb. 9　　　　Perf. 13x13½
1241	A265	30c Gere	.55	.55
1242	A265	40c Fanfa	.55	.55
1243	A265	50c Chancha	.85	.85
1244	A265	85c Negareet	1.25	1.25
		Nos. 1241-1244 (4)	3.20	3.20

Ethiopian Shipping Lines, 25th Anniv. — A266

1989, Mar. 27　　Litho.　　Perf. 14
1245	A266	15c Abyot	.30	.30
1246	A266	30c Wolwol	.60	.60
1247	A266	55c Queen of Sheba	1.25	1.25
1248	A266	1b Abbay Wonz	1.75	1.75
		Nos. 1245-1248 (4)	3.90	3.90

Birds — A267

10c, Yellow-fronted parrot. 35c, White-winged cliff chat. 50c, Yellow-throated seed eater. 1b, Black-headed forest oriole.

1989, May 18　　Litho.　　Perf. 13½x13
1249	A267	10c multicolored	.30	.30
1250	A267	35c multicolored	.85	.85
1251	A267	50c multicolored	1.25	1.25
1252	A267	1b multicolored	2.25	2.25
		Nos. 1249-1252 (4)	4.65	4.65

Production of Early Manuscripts A268

Designs: 5c, Preparing vellum. 10c, Ink horns, pens. 20c, Scribe. 75c, Book binding. 85c, Illuminated manuscript.

1989, June 16　　Litho.　　Perf. 13½
1253	A268	5c multi	.30	.30
1254	A268	10c multi	.30	.30
1255	A268	20c multi	.35	.35
1256	A268	75c multi	1.25	1.25
1257	A268	85c multi	1.50	1.50
		Nos. 1253-1257 (5)	3.70	3.70

Indigenous Wildlife — A269

1989, July 18
1258	A269	30c Greater kudu	.85	.85
1259	A269	40c Lesser kudu	.95	.95
1260	A269	50c Roan antelope	1.25	1.25
1261	A269	85c Nile lechwe	1.75	1.75
		Nos. 1258-1261 (4)	4.80	4.80

People's Democratic Republic of Ethiopia, 2nd Anniv. — A270

Designs: 15c, Melka Wakana Hydroelectric Power Station. 75c, Adea Berga Dairy Farm. 1b, Pawe Hospital.

1989, Sept. 8
1262	A270	15c multicolored	.30	.25
1263	A270	75c multicolored	1.25	1.25
1264	A270	1b multicolored	2.00	2.00
		Nos. 1262-1264 (3)	3.55	3.50

African Development Bank, 25th Anniv. — A271

1989, Nov. 10　　Litho.　　Perf. 13½x13
1265	A271	20c multicolored	.30	.30
1266	A271	80c multicolored	1.25	1.25
1267	A271	1b multicolored	1.75	2.00
		Nos. 1265-1267 (3)	3.30	3.55

Pan-African Postal Union, 10th Anniv. — A272

1990, Jan. 18　　Litho.　　Perf. 13½
1268	A272	50c multicolored	.75	.75
1269	A272	70c multicolored	1.25	1.25
1270	A272	80c multicolored	1.50	1.75
		Nos. 1268-1270 (3)	3.50	3.75

UNESCO World Literacy Year — A273

15c, Illiterate man holding newspaper upside down. 85c, Adults learning alphabet in school. 1b, Literate man holding newspaper upright.

1990, Mar. 13
1271	A273	15c multicolored	.40	.40
1272	A273	85c multicolored	1.40	1.40
1273	A273	1b multicolored	1.75	1.75
		Nos. 1271-1273 (3)	3.55	3.55

Abebe Bikila, Marathon Runner — A274

5c, Race. 10c, Flag bearer, Olympic team. 20c, Race, Rome Olympics. 75c, Race, Tokyo Olympics. 85c, Bikila, trophies, vert.

1990, Apr. 17
1274	A274	5c multicolored	.30	.30
1275	A274	10c multicolored	.30	.30
1276	A274	20c multicolored	.60	.60
1277	A274	75c multicolored	1.25	1.25
1278	A274	85c multicolored	1.75	1.75
		Nos. 1274-1278 (5)	4.20	4.20

Flag — A275

1990, Apr. 30　　Litho.　　Perf. 13½x13
1279	A275	5c multicolored	.30	.30
1280	A275	10c multicolored	.30	.30
1281	A275	15c multicolored	.30	.30
1282	A275	20c multicolored	.40	.30
1283	A275	25c multicolored	.50	.30
1284	A275	30c multicolored	.60	.30
1285	A275	35c multicolored	.70	.30

1286	A275	40c multicolored	.80	.30
1287	A275	45c multicolored	.85	.60
1288	A275	50c multicolored	1.00	.60
1289	A275	55c multicolored	1.00	.60
1290	A275	60c multicolored	1.25	.60
1291	A275	70c multicolored	1.25	.85
1292	A275	80c multicolored	1.25	.85
1293	A275	85c multicolored	1.25	.85
1294	A275	90c multicolored	1.25	.85
1295	A275	1b multicolored	1.75	1.25
1296	A275	2b multicolored	3.50	2.25
1297	A275	3b multicolored	5.50	4.50
		Nos. 1279-1297 (19)	23.75	16.20

Dated 1989.

Sowing of Teff — A276

Designs: 10c, Harvesting. 20c, Threshing. 75c, Storage, preparation. 85c, Consumption.

1990, May 18　　Litho.　　Perf. 13½
1298	A276	5c shown	.30	.30
1299	A276	10c multi	.30	.30
1300	A276	20c multi	.30	.30
1301	A276	75c multi	1.25	1.25
1302	A276	85c multi	1.75	1.75
		Nos. 1298-1302 (5)	3.90	3.90

Walia Ibex — A277

1990, June 18　　　　Perf. 14x13½
1303	A277	5c multi	.75	.35
1304	A277	15c multi	1.40	.75
1305	A277	20c multi	2.25	1.10
1306	A277	1b multi, horiz.	8.00	4.25
		Nos. 1303-1306 (4)	12.40	6.45

World AIDS Day — A278

Designs: 15c, Stages of disease. 85c, Education. 1b, Causes, preventatives.

1991, Jan. 31　　Litho.　　Perf. 14
1307	A278	15c multi	.30	.30
1308	A278	85c multi	1.50	1.50
1309	A278	1b multi	2.25	2.25
		Nos. 1307-1309 (3)	4.05	4.05

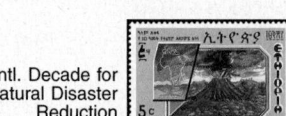

Intl. Decade for Natural Disaster Reduction A279

Map of disaster-prone African areas and: 5c, Volcano. 10c, Earthquake. 15c, Drought. 30c, Flood. 50c, Red Cross health education. 1b, Red Cross assisting fire victims.

1991, Apr. 9　　Litho.　　Perf. 14
1310	A279	5c multicolored	.30	.30
1311	A279	10c multicolored	.30	.30
1312	A279	15c multicolored	.30	.30
1313	A279	30c multicolored	.60	.60
1314	A279	50c multicolored	1.10	1.10
1315	A279	1b multicolored	2.25	2.25
		Nos. 1310-1315 (6)	4.85	4.85

The Cannon of Tewodros — A280

Designs: 15c, Villagers receiving cannon. 85c, Warriors leaving with cannon. 1b, Hauling cannon up mountainside.

1991, June 18　　Litho.　　Perf. 13½
1316	A280	15c multicolored	.40	.40
1317	A280	85c multicolored	1.50	1.50
1318	A280	1b multicolored	2.25	1.75
		Nos. 1316-1318 (3)	4.15	3.65

Fish — A281

5c, Lacepede. 15c, Black-finned butterflyfish. 80c, Regal angelfish. 1b, Bleeker.

1991, Sept. 6　　Litho.　　Perf. 13½
1319	A281	5c multi	.50	.50
1320	A281	15c multi	.50	.50
1321	A281	80c multi	2.25	2.25
1322	A281	1b multi	2.75	2.75
		Nos. 1319-1322 (4)	6.00	6.00

A282

Traditional Ceremonial Robes: Various robes.

1992, Jan. 1　　Litho.　　Perf. 13½x14
1323	A282	5c yellow & multi	.30	.30
1324	A282	15c orange & multi	.30	.30
1325	A282	80c yel green & multi	1.75	1.75
1326	A282	1b blue & multi	2.00	2.00
		Nos. 1323-1326 (4)	4.35	4.35

A283

Flowers: 5c, Cissus quadrangularis. 15c, Delphinium dasycaulon. 80c, Epilobium hirsutum. 1b, Kniphofia foliosa.

1992, Mar. 5　　Litho.　　Perf. 13½x14
1327	A283	5c multicolored	.30	.30
1328	A283	15c multicolored	.40	.40
1329	A283	80c multicolored	2.00	1.75
1330	A283	1b multicolored	2.50	2.00
		Nos. 1327-1330 (4)	5.20	4.45

Traditional Homes — A284

1992, May 14　　Litho.　　Perf. 12½x12
1331	A284	15c Afar	.30	.30
1332	A284	35c Anuak	.60	.60
1333	A284	50c Gimira	.90	.90
1334	A284	1b Oromo	2.25	1.75
		Nos. 1331-1334 (4)	4.05	3.55

A285

Pottery.

1992, July 7　　Litho.　　Perf. 13x13½
1335	A285	15c Cover	.30	.30
1336	A285	85c Jug	1.25	1.25
1337	A285	1b Tall jar	2.00	2.00
		Nos. 1335-1337 (3)	3.55	3.55

A286

1992, Sept. 29 — Perf. 14x13½
1338	A286	20c multicolored	.30	.30
1339	A286	80c multicolored	1.25	1.25
1340	A286	1b multicolored	2.00	1.75
		Nos. 1338-1340 (3)	3.55	3.30

Pan-African Rinderpest campaign.

Musical Instruments — A287

1993, Feb. 16 Litho. Perf. 14x13½
1341	A287	15c Catchel	.30	.30
1342	A287	35c Huludwa	.55	.55
1343	A287	50c Dita	.85	.85
1344	A287	1b Atamo	1.75	1.75
		Nos. 1341-1344 (4)	3.45	3.45

Birds — A288

Designs: 15c, Banded barbet. 35c, Ruppell's chat. 50c, Abyssinian catbird. 1b, White-billed starling.

1993, Apr. 22 Litho. Perf. 14x13½
1345	A288	15c multi	.30	.30
1346	A288	35c multi	.75	.75
1347	A288	50c multi	1.00	1.00
1348	A288	1b multi	2.00	2.00
		Nos. 1345-1348 (4)	4.05	4.05

Animals — A289

Designs: 15c, Honey badger. 35c, Spotted necked otter. 50c, Rock hyrax. 1b, White-tailed mongoose.

1993, May 14 — Perf. 13½x14
1349	A289	15c multi	.30	.30
1350	A289	35c multi	.60	.60
1351	A289	50c multi	1.00	1.00
1352	A289	1b multi	2.00	2.00
		Nos. 1349-1352 (4)	3.90	3.90

Herbs — A290

Designs: 5c, Caraway seed. 15c, Garlic. 80c, Turmeric. 1b, Capsicum peppers.

1993, June 10 Perf. 14x13½
1353	A290	5c multi	.60	.60
1354	A290	15c multi	.75	.75
1355	A290	80c multi	1.40	1.40
1356	A290	1b multi	1.50	1.50
		Nos. 1353-1356 (4)	4.25	4.25

Butterflies — A291

20c, Papilio echerioides. 30c, Papilio rex. 50c, Graphium policenes. 1b, Graphium leonidas.

1993, July 9 Litho. Perf. 14x13½
1357	A291	20c multicolored	1.00	.85
1358	A291	30c multicolored	.85	.85
1359	A291	50c multicolored	1.40	1.40
1360	A291	1b multicolored	2.50	2.50
		Nos. 1357-1360 (4)	5.75	5.60

Insects — A292

Designs: 15c, C. Variabilis. 35c, Lycus trabeatus. 50c, Malachius bifasciatus. 1b, Homoeogryllus xanthographus.

1993, Aug. 10
1361	A292	15c multi	.60	.60
1362	A292	35c multi	.60	.60
1363	A292	50c multi	.85	.85
1364	A292	1b multi	1.75	1.75
		Nos. 1361-1364 (4)	3.80	3.80

Trees — A293

15c, Euphorbia ampliphylla. 35c, Erythrina brucei. 50c, Dracaena steudneri. 1b, Allophylus abyssinicus.

1993, Oct. 12 Litho. Perf. 13½x14
1365	A293	15c multicolored	.30	.30
1366	A293	35c multicolored	.30	.30
1367	A293	50c multicolored	.30	.30
1368	A293	1b multicolored	1.00	1.00
		Nos. 1365-1368 (4)	1.90	1.90

Lakes — A294

1993, Dec. 14
1369	A294	15c Wonchi	.35	.30
1370	A294	35c Zuquala	.50	.30
1371	A294	50c Ashengi	.70	.50
1372	A294	1b Tana	1.25	1.00
		Nos. 1369-1372 (4)	2.80	2.10

Simien Fox A294a

Rough Perf. 13½
1994, Jan. 18 Litho.
Color of Border
1372A	A294a	5c violet	—	—
1372B	A294a	10c brown	—	—
1372C	A294a	15c lemon	—	—
1372D	A294a	20c salmon	—	—
1372E	A294a	40c pale rose	—	—
1372F	A294a	55c dull green	—	—
1372G	A294a	60c dark blue	—	—
1372H	A294a	80c bright blue	—	—
1372I	A294a	85c gray green	—	—
1372J	A294a	1b bright green	—	—
		Nos. 1372A-1372J (10)		3.65

Nos. 1372A-1372J have rough perforations and a poor quality printing impression. Dated "1991."
See Nos. 1393A-1393T.

A295

Transitional government: 15c, First anniversary of EPRDF's control of Addis Ababa. 35c, Transition Conference. 50c, National, regional elections. 1b, Coat of arms of Transitional Government.

1994, Mar. 31 Litho. Perf. 14
1373	A295	15c multicolored	.30	.30
1374	A295	35c multicolored	.30	.30
1375	A295	50c multicolored	.40	.40
1376	A295	1b multicolored	.75	.75
		Nos. 1373-1376 (4)	1.75	1.75

A296

1994, May 17 Perf. 13½
1377	A296	15c blue & multi	.30	.30
1378	A296	85c green & multi	.50	.50
1379	A296	1b violet & multi	.75	.75
		Nos. 1377-1379 (3)	1.55	1.55

Intl. Year of the Family.

Ethiopian Postal Service, Cent. — A297

Designs: 60c, Early, modern postal workers, Scott Type A1. 75c, Early letter carriers. 80c, Older building, methods of transportation. 85c, People, mail buses. 1b, Modern methods of transportation, modern high-rise building.

1994, July 4 Litho. Perf. 13½
1380	A297	60c multicolored	.75	.55
1381	A297	75c multicolored	.90	.60
1382	A297	80c multicolored	1.15	.70
1383	A297	85c multicolored	1.20	.75
1384	A297	1b multicolored	1.45	1.05
a.		Souvenir sheet, #1380-1384 + label	10.00	8.00
		Nos. 1380-1384 (5)	5.45	3.65

Enset Plant — A298

1994, Aug. 3
1385	A298	10c shown	.25	.25
1386	A298	15c Young plants, hut	.35	.30
1387	A298	25c Root, women processing leaves	.40	.35
1388	A298	50c Mature plants	.75	.40
1389	A298	1b Uses as food	1.50	.65
		Nos. 1385-1389 (5)	3.25	1.95

Hair Ornaments — A299

1994, Sept. 2
1390	A299	5c Gamo gofa	.40	.30
1391	A299	15c Sidamo	.50	.35
1392	A299	80c Gamo gofa, diff.	.80	.60
1393	A299	1b Wello	1.10	.85
		Nos. 1390-1393 (4)	2.80	2.10

Simien Fox Type of 1994
Size: 39x25mm
Color of Border
1994, Oct. 18 Litho. Perf. 14
1393A	A294a	5c dull lilac	—	.35
1393B	A294a	10c brown	—	.45
1393C	A294a	15c lemon	—	.55
1393D	A294a	20c salmon	—	.65
1393E	A294a	25c lemon	—	.75
1393F	A294a	30c yel brn	—	1.00
1393G	A294a	35c orange	—	1.25
1393H	A294a	40c pale rose	—	1.50
1393I	A294a	45c pale red org	—	1.75
1393J	A294a	50c rose lilac	—	2.00
1393K	A294a	55c pale grn	—	2.25
1393L	A294a	60c dark blue	—	2.50
1393M	A294a	65c pale lilac	—	2.75
1393N	A294a	70c brt grn	—	3.00
1393O	A294a	75c pale bl grn	—	3.25
1393P	A294a	80c bright blue	—	3.50
1393Q	A294a	85c dk grnsh blue	—	3.75
1393R	A294a	90c pale brn	—	4.00
1393S	A294a	1b grnsh blue	—	5.00
1393T	A294a	2b yel brn	—	9.00
		Nos. 1393A-1393T (20)		49.25

Nos. 1393A-1393T have sharp impressions, Questa imprint, clean perforations. Dated "1993."
For overprints see Nos. 1393U-1393X, 1396A-1396D.

Nos. 1393L, 1393P-1393Q, 1393S Ovptd. in Blue

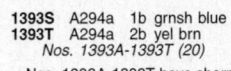

1994, Oct. 20 Litho. Perf. 14
1393U	A294a	60c on #1393L	—	—
1393V	A294a	80c on #1393P	—	—
1393W	A294a	85c on #1393Q	—	—
1393X	A294a	1b on #1393S	—	—

UNFPA, 50th anniv.

ICAO, 50th Anniv. — A300

1994, Dec. 7 Litho. Perf. 13½
1394	A300	20c mag, lt bl & yel	.40	.40
1395	A300	80c yel & lt bl	.60	.60
1396	A300	1b dk bl, lt bl & yel	.90	.90
		Nos. 1394-1396 (3)	1.90	1.90

Nos. 1393M-1393O, 1393R Ovptd.

1994, Dec. 20 Litho. Perf. 14
1396A	A294a	65c on #1393M	—	—
1396B	A294a	70c on #1393N	—	—
1396C	A294a	75c on #1393O	—	—
1396D	A294a	90c on #1393R	—	—

African Development Bank, 30th anniv.

Baskets for Serving Food — A301

1995, June 7 Litho. Perf. 13½
1397	A301	30c Erbo	.30	.25
1398	A301	70c Sedieka	.50	.50
1399	A301	1b Tirar	.85	.85
		Nos. 1397-1399 (3)	1.65	1.60

Traditional Hair Styles — A302

1995, July 5 Litho. Perf. 13½
1400	A302	25c Kuncho	.40	.40
1401	A302	75c Gamme	.60	.60
1402	A302	1b Sadulla	1.00	1.00
		Nos. 1400-1402 (3)	2.00	2.00

FAO, 50th Anniv. — A303

1995, Aug. 29 Litho. *Perf. 13½*
1403 A303 20c green & multi .75 .65
1404 A303 80c blue & multi 1.25 1.00
1405 A303 1b brown & multi 1.50 1.25
Nos. 1403-1405 (3) 3.50 2.90

Cultivating Tools — A304

1995, Sept. 7
1406 A304 15c Dangora .60 .60
1407 A304 35c Gheso .60 .60
1408 A304 50c Akafa .60 .60
1409 A304 1b Ankasse 1.10 1.10
Nos. 1406-1409 (4) 2.90 2.90

UN, 50th Anniv. — A305

1995, Oct. 18 Litho. *Perf. 13½*
Color of UN Emblem
1410 A305 20c black .40 .30
1411 A305 80c bister .85 .65
1412 A305 1b blue 1.00 .85
Nos. 1410-1412 (3) 2.25 1.80

Intergovernmental Authority on Drought and Development (IGADD), 10th Anniv. — A306

Flags of member nations and: 15c, Seedling being planted in arid region. 35c, People carrying supplies through desert. 50c, Person picking fruit. 1b, Map of member nations.

1995, Dec. 27 Litho. *Perf. 13½*
1413 A306 15c multicolored .45 .35
1414 A306 35c multicolored .55 .45
1415 A306 50c multicolored .70 .60
1416 A306 1b multicolored 1.10 1.00
Nos. 1413-1416 (4) 2.80 2.40

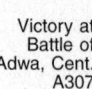

Victory at Battle of Adwa, Cent. — A307

Designs: 40c, Battle sites. 50c, Map of Africa focused at Ethiopia. 60c, Troops, ship. 70c, Warriors, soldiers in two battle scenes. 80c, Italians surrendering, Ethiopian troops, cannons. 1b, Emperor Menelik II, constitution, Empress Taitu.

1996, Mar. 2 Litho. *Perf. 13½x14½*
1417 A307 40c multicolored .35 .35
1418 A307 50c multicolored .40 .35
1419 A307 60c multicolored .60 .45
1420 A307 70c multicolored .75 .55
1421 A307 80c multicolored 1.00 .80
1422 A307 1b multicolored 1.40 1.10
  a. Souvenir sheet, #1417-1422 5.50 5.50
Nos. 1417-1422 (6) 4.50 3.60

UN Volunteers, 25th Anniv. — A308

Designs: 20c, People, temporary housing huts. 30c, Planting seedlings. 50c, Instructing students. 1b, Caring for infant.

1996, June 6 Litho. *Perf. 13½*
1423 A308 20c multicolored .25 .25
1424 A308 30c multicolored .35 .25
1425 A308 50c multicolored .50 .40
1426 A308 1b multicolored 1.40 1.25
Nos. 1423-1426 (4) 2.50 2.15

1996 Summer Olympic Games, Atlanta — A310

1996, Aug. 1 Litho. *Perf. 12½x12*
Overprint in Black
1427 A310 15c Boxing .30 .30
1428 A310 20c Swimming .30 .30
1429 A310 40c Cycling .30 .30
1430 A310 85c Athletics .60 .60
1431 A310 1b Soccer .90 .90
Nos. 1427-1431 (5) 2.40 2.40

Nos. 1427-1431 were originally prepared for the 1984 Summer Olympic Games in Los Angeles, but were not released due to the Soviet-led boycott. Nos. 1427-1431 exist without overprint. Value, set $100.

A311

UNICEF, 50th Anniv.: 10c, Emblems. 15c, Mother, child receiving vaccination. 25c, Woman carrying water, boy drinking from faucet. 50c, Children studying. 1b, Mother breastfeeding infant.

1996, Sept. 10 Litho. *Perf. 13½*
1432 A311 10c multicolored .35 .35
1433 A311 15c multicolored .40 .35
1434 A311 25c multicolored .50 .40
1435 A311 50c multicolored .85 .65
1436 A311 1b multicolored 1.40 1.05
Nos. 1432-1436 (5) 3.50 2.80

A312

Creation of Federal Democratic Republic of Ethiopia: 10c, People discussing new Constitution, approved Dec. 8, 1994. 20c, Ballot boxes, hand placing ballot in box. 30c, Marking ballot, placing into box, tower building, items from country's environment. 40c, Building, ballot, assembly hall. 1b, Natl. flag, transition of power.

1996, Dec. 26 Litho. *Perf. 13½*
1437 A312 10c multicolored .30 .30
1438 A312 20c multicolored .40 .30
1439 A312 30c multicolored .50 .30
1440 A312 40c multicolored .60 .30
1441 A312 1b multicolored .75 .60
Nos. 1437-1441 (5) 2.55 1.80

Traditional Baskets A313

1997, Feb. 20 Litho. *Perf. 13½*
1442 A313 5c Jimma .40 .40
1443 A313 15c Wello .40 .40
1444 A313 80c Welega 1.00 1.00
1445 A313 1b Shewa 1.25 1.25
Nos. 1442-1445 (4) 3.05 3.05

Traditional Baskets — A314

1997, May 22 Litho. *Perf. 13½*
1446 A314 35c Arssi .40 .40
1447 A314 65c Gojam .60 .50
1448 A314 1b Harer 1.25 1.00
Nos. 1446-1448 (3) 2.25 1.90

See Nos. 1464-1466.

UN Decade Against Drug Abuse & Illicit Trafficking — A315

1997, Sept. 9 Litho. *Perf. 14*
1449 A315 20c green & multi .60 .60
1450 A315 80c brown & multi .60 .60
1451 A315 1b blue & multi 1.00 .85
Nos. 1449-1451 (3) 2.20 2.05

Historic Buildings, Addis Ababa — A316

45c, Bitwoded Haile Giorgis' house. 55c, Alfred Ilg's house, vert. 3b, Menelik's Elfign.

Perf. 14½x14, 14x14½
1997, Dec. 23 Litho.
1452 A316 45c multicolored .30 .30
1453 A316 55c multicolored .45 .45
1454 A316 3b multicolored 1.50 1.50
Nos. 1452-1454 (3) 2.25 2.25

Addis Ababa's Oldest Historical Buildings — A317

Designs: 60c, Ras Biru W/Gabriel's house. 75c, Sheh Hojele Alhassen's house. 80c, Fitawrari H/Giorgis Dinegde's house. 85c, Etege Taitu Hotel. 1b, Dejazmach Wube Atnafseged's house.

1997, Dec. 30 Litho. *Perf. 14½x14*
1455 A317 60c multicolored .55 .45
1456 A317 75c multicolored .60 .55
1457 A317 80c multicolored .70 .60
1458 A317 85c multicolored .75 .70
1459 A317 1b multicolored 1.15 .90
Nos. 1455-1459 (5) 3.75 3.20

Pan African Postal Union, 18th Anniv. — A318

Union's emblem and wildlife: 45c, Deculla bushback. 55c, Soemmering's gazelle. 1b, Defassa waterbuck. 2b, Black buffalo.

1998, Mar. 25 Litho. *Perf. 14½x14*
1460 A318 45c multicolored .50 .35
1461 A318 55c multicolored .55 .45
1462 A318 1b multicolored 1.00 .65
1463 A318 2b multicolored 2.00 1.25
Nos. 1460-1463 (4) 4.05 2.70

Traditional Basket Type of 1997
1998, May 21 Litho. *Perf. 13½*
1464 A314 45c Gonder .45 .35
1465 A314 55c Harere .55 .35
1466 A314 3b Tigray 2.00 1.25
Nos. 1464-1466 (3) 3.00 1.95

Golden-Backed Woodpecker — A319

1998, Jan. 12 Photo. *Perf. 11½*
Granite Paper
Panel Color
1467 A319 5c green blue .45 .30
1468 A319 10c yellow .45 .30
1469 A319 15c blue .45 .30
1470 A319 20c light brown 15.00 .30
1471 A319 25c violet .45 .30
1472 A319 30c light blue .45 .30
1473 A319 35c salmon rose .45 .30
1474 A319 40c lilac .45 .30
1475 A319 45c green .45 .30
1476 A319 50c salmon .45 .35
1477 A319 55c blue .45 .35
1478 A319 60c brick red .45 .40
1479 A319 65c light gray .45 .45
1480 A319 70c bright yellow .45 .50
1481 A319 75c pale violet .70 .65
1482 A319 80c apple green .75 .70
1483 A319 85c gray .80 .75
1484 A319 90c orange .90 .80
1485 A319 1b yellow green 1.25 .95
1486 A319 2b pale rose 1.50 1.25
1487 A319 3b lilac rose 2.50 2.00
1488 A319 5b bister 3.50 3.00
1489 A319 10b orange yellow 7.00 6.00
Nos. 1467-1489 (23) 39.75 20.85

Agreement for Return of Axum Obelisk from Italy — A320

45c, Map of Italy, pieces of obelisk. 55c, Obelisk in Rome. 3b, Map of E. Africa, obelisk, ruins of Axum.

1998, Sept. 3 Litho. *Perf. 13½*
1490 A320 45c multicolored .50 .30
1491 A320 55c multicolored .60 .40
1492 A320 3b multicolored 2.50 1.50
Nos. 1490-1492 (3) 3.60 2.20

Ethiopia-Djibouti Railway, Cent. — A321

Designs: 45c, Men carrying rails during construction. 55c, Early steam train, CFE 404. 1b, Terminal building. 2b, Modern train, BB 1212.

1998, Nov. 24 Litho. *Perf. 11½*
Granite Paper
1493 A321 45c multicolored .55 .35
1494 A321 55c multicolored .70 .45
1495 A321 1b multicolored 1.20 .75
1496 A321 2b multicolored 2.50 1.25
Nos. 1493-1496 (4) 4.95 2.80

Universal Declaration of Human Rights, 50th Anniv. — A322

1998, Dec. 23 Litho. *Perf. 13x13½*
1497 A322 45c red & multi .45 .25
1498 A322 55c yellow & multi .45 .30
1499 A322 1b green & multi .75 .50
1500 A322 2b blue & multi 1.10 .75
Nos. 1497-1500 (4) 2.75 1.80

Mother Teresa (1910-97) — A323

Various portraits.

1999, Mar. 9 Litho. *Perf. 13½x13*
1501 A323 45c brown & multi .60 .60
1502 A323 55c green & multi .60 .60
1503 A323 1b yel org & multi 1.00 1.00
1504 A323 2b blue & multi 2.00 1.75
Nos. 1501-1504 (4) 4.20 3.70

Intl. Year of
the Ocean
A324

1999, May 6   Litho.   Perf. 13½x13¼

1505	A324	45c black & multi	.60	.30
1506	A324	55c red & multi	.75	.30
1507	A324	1b blue & multi	1.00	.60
1508	A324	2b green & multi	2.25	1.25
	Nos. 1505-1508 (4)		4.60	2.45

World Environment
Day — A325

1999, June 17   Litho.   Perf. 13½

1509	A325	45c pink & multi	.55	.30
1510	A325	55c vio & multi	.70	.40
1511	A325	1b yel org & multi	1.10	.70
1512	A325	2b grn & multi	1.90	1.00
	Nos. 1509-1512 (4)		4.25	2.40

National
Parks — A326

45c, Abijata, Shalla Lakes. 70c, Nechisar.
85c, Bale Mountains. 2b, Awash.

Perf. 13¾x13¼, 13¼x13¾

1999, Sept. 8   Litho.

1513	A326	45c multi, vert.	.50	.50
1514	A326	70c multi, vert.	.80	.70
1515	A326	85c multi, vert.	1.25	.90
1516	A326	2b multi	3.00	1.50
	Nos. 1513-1516 (4)		5.55	3.60

See Nos. 1521-1524.

UPU, 125th
Anniv. — A327

1999, Oct. 28   Perf. 13¼x13

1517	A327	20c multicolored	.50	.50
1518	A327	80c multicolored	.70	.35
1519	A327	1b multicolored	.75	.60
1520	A327	2b multicolored	1.50	.85
	Nos. 1517-1520 (4)		3.45	2.30

National Parks Type of 1999

Designs: 50c, Omo, vert. 70c, Mago, vert.
80c, Yangudi-Rassa, vert. 2b, Gambella.

1999, Nov. 30   Litho.   Perf. 13¼

1521-1524	A326	Set of 4	5.00 3.00

Intl. Year of Older
Persons — A328

45c, Woman attending to sick man. 70c,
Older people gardening. 85c, Four men,
bench. 2b, Older man, two young people.

1999, Dec. 30   Perf. 13¾x13¼

1525-1528	A328	Set of 4	4.50 3.50

Alexander Pushkin,
Writer, Birth Bicent.
(in 1999) — A329

Various portraits: 45c, 70c, 85c, 2b.

2000, Mar. 9   Litho.   Perf. 13¾x13¼

1529-1532	A329	Set of 4	3.25 2.25

Worldwide
Fund for
Nature
(WWF)
A330

Grevy's zebra: a, Grazing. b, Running. c,
Resting. d, Head.

2001, Jan. 30   Litho.   Perf. 13¼x13¾

1533		Strip of 4	4.25	3.50
a.	A330	45c multi	.40	.30
b.	A330	55c multi	.50	.40
c.	A330	1b multi	.80	.70
d.	A330	3b multi	2.50	2.25

Operation
Sunset — A331

Designs: 45c, President Meles Zenawi, Parliament. 55c, Soldiers, flag ceremony. 1b, People, house. 2b, Agriculture, construction.

2000, June 27   Perf. 13¾

1534-1537	A331	Set of 4	4.50 2.50

Flags — A332

Designs: 25c, Harar Region. 30c, Oromia
Region. 50c, Amhara Region. 60c, Tigre
Region. 70c, Benishangi Region. 80c, Somalia
Region. 90c, Peoples of the South Region.
95c, Gambella Region. 1b, Afar Region. 2b,
Ethiopia.

2000, Oct. 26   Perf. 13¼x13¾

1538-1547	A332	Set of 10	7.00 4.50

Afro Ayigeba, Cross
of St.
Lalibela — A333

2000, Apr. 27   Perf. 13¾x13¼

1548	A333	4b multi	2.50 2.25

Menelik's
Bushbuck — A334

Perf. 13¾x13¼

2000, June 19   Litho.

Frame Color

1548A	A334	5c dk Prus blue	2.00	.25
1549	A334	10c lilac	2.00	.25
1549A	A334	15c blue	2.00	.25
1549B	A334	20c yellow bister	2.00	.25
1549C	A334	25c purple	2.00	.25
1549D	A334	30c lt Prus blue	2.00	.25
1549E	A334	35c brt red	2.00	.25
1549F	A334	40c lilac	2.00	.25
1549G	A334	45c emerald	2.00	.25
1549H	A334	50c red	2.25	.25
1549I	A334	55c blue	2.50	.25
1549J	A334	60c yellow or-ange	2.50	.25
1549K	A334	65c deep blue	2.50	.25
1549L	A334	70c dull blue	2.50	.25
1549M	A334	75c orange yel-low	3.00	.35
1549N	A334	80c carmine	3.00	.35
1549O	A334	85c light blue	3.00	.40
1550	A334	90c ocher	3.00	.40
1551	A334	1b green	4.00	.50
1552	A334	2b red violet	9.00	.75
1553	A334	3b purple	16.00	.90
1554	A334	5b dark car-mine	27.50	1.75
1555	A334	10b light carmine	37.50	4.00
	Nos. 1548A-1555 (23)		136.25	12.90

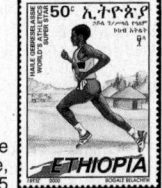

Haile
Gebreselassie,
Runner — A335

Gebreselassie: No. 1557, 50c, Running. No.
1557A, 60c, Running, diff. No. 1557B, 90c,
Running, diff. No. 1558, 2b, With arms raised.

2000, Nov. 9   Litho.   Perf. 13½

1557-1558	A335	Set of 4	3.50 2.00

World
Meteorological
Organization,
50th
Anniv. — A336

Color of inscriptions: 40c, Gray. 75c, Green.
85c, Brown. 2b, Blue.

2000, Oct. 10   Litho.   Perf. 13½

1559-1562	A336	Set of 4	3.00 2.00

Addis Ababa
University, 50th
Anniv. — A337

2000, Nov. 30   Perf. 13½x14¼

1563	A337	4b multi	3.25 2.75

UN High
Commissioner
for Refugees,
50th
Anniv. — A338

Frame color: 40c, Brown. 75c, Green. 85c,
Blue. 2b, Gold.

2000 Dec. 14   Perf. 13½x14

1564-1567	A338	Set of 4	4.00 2.50

Freshwater
Fish — A340

Designs: 45c, Catfish. 55c, Tilapia. 3b, Nile
perch.

2001, July 26   Litho.   Perf. 14¼

1572-1574	A340	Set of 3	3.50 1.75

Traditional
Means of
Transportation
A341

Designs: 40c, Man on horseback, horse-
drawn cart. 60c, Camel caravan. 1b, Man on
horseback, horse carrying load. 2b, Man on
donkey, donkeys carrying goods.

2001, Aug. 30   Perf. 13¼x13½

1575-1578	A341	Set of 4	4.25 2.25

Year of Dialogue
Among
Civilizations — A342

Color of country name: 25c, Light blue. 75c,
White. 1b, Light yellow. 2b, Pink.

2001, Oct. 9   Perf. 14

1579-1582	A342	Set of 4	3.50 2.25

Birds — A343

Designs: 50c, White-tailed swallow. 60c,
Spot-breasted plover. 90c, Abyssinian long-
claw. 2b, Prince Ruspoli's turaco.

2001, Nov. 29   Perf. 14¼

1583-1586	A343	Set of 4	5.00 3.00

Traditional
Beehives — A344

Various beehives: 40c, 70c, 90c, 2b.

2002, Jan. 24   Litho.   Perf. 14

1587-1590	A344	Set of 4	4.50 3.50

Traditional Grain
Storage — A345

Designs: 30c, Gota. 70c, Bekollo Gotera.
1b, Gotera. 2b, Gotera, diff.

2002, Mar. 28   Perf. 13½x14

1591-1594	A345	Set of 4	4.50 3.50

Lions Club
Intl. — A346

Lions Club Intl. emblem and: 45c, Quality
emblem. 55c, Woman at pump. 1b, Eye doctor
treating patient. 2b, Man in wheelchair.

2002, Apr. 26   Litho.   Perf. 13x13¼

1595-1598	A346	Set of 4	4.50 4.00

Trees — A347

Designs: 50c, Acacia abyssinica. 60c, Boswellia papyrifera, vert. 90c, Aningeria adolfi-freiderici, vert. 2b, Prunus africana, vert.

Perf. 13½x13¼, 13¼x13½
2002, June 27
1599-1602 A347   Set of 4   4.50 4.00

Traditional Beehives — A348

Various beehives with panel colors of: 45c, Pink. 55c, Yellow. 1b, Light blue. 2b, Light green.

2002, Sept. 19   Litho.   Perf. 13¼x13
1603-1606 A348   Set of 4   4.50 3.50

Granite — A349

Designs: 45c, Sidamo. 55c, Harrar. 1b, Tigray. 2b, Wollega.

2002, Oct. 24   Perf. 13x13¼
1607-1610 A349   Set of 4   4.50 4.00

Konso Waka — A350

Various wooden sculptures with background colors of: 40c, Green. 60c, Blue. 1b, Yellow. 2b, Red.

2002, Nov. 28   Perf. 14
1611-1614 A350   Set of 4   4.00 2.00

Menelik's Bushbuck — A351

2002, Dec. 12   Perf. 13½x13¾
Frame Color
1615	A351	5c	brt grn blue	.30	.25
1616	A351	10c	lilac	.30	.25
1617	A351	15c	bright blue	.30	.25
1618	A351	20c	brn orange	.30	.25
1619	A351	25c	purple	.30	.25
1620	A351	30c	bright blue	.30	.25
1621	A351	35c	carmine	.30	.25
1622	A351	40c	purple	.30	.25
1623	A351	45c	emerald	.30	.25
1624	A351	50c	red	.30	.25
1625	A351	55c	blue	.30	.25
1626	A351	60c	bright yel	.40	.25
1627	A351	65c	red	.40	.25
1628	A351	70c	light blue	.40	.25
1629	A351	75c	bright yel	.45	.35
1630	A351	80c	carmine	.45	.35
1631	A351	85c	bright blue	.60	.40
1632	A351	90c	orange brn	.60	.40
1633	A351	95c	green	.60	.40
1634	A351	1b	red violet	.70	.50
1635	A351	2b	purple	1.00	.75
1636	A351	3b	blue	1.25	.90
1637	A351	5b	dull red	2.25	1.50
1638	A351	10b	light green	6.50	3.00
1639	A351	20b	rose pink	11.00	6.00
		Nos. 1615-1639 (25)		29.90	18.05

Oil Crops — A352

Designs: 40c, Abyssinian mustard. 60c, Linseed. 3b, Niger seed.

2002, Dec. 31   Litho.   Perf. 13¼x13
1640-1642 A352   Set of 3   3.00 2.00

Pan-African Postal Union, 23rd Anniv. — A353

Background color: 20c, Green. 80c, Blue green. 1b, Orange brown. 2b, Purple.

2003, Feb. 18   Perf. 13x13¼
1643-1646 A353   Set of 4   3.00 2.00

Opals — A354

Designs: 45c, Milk opal. 60c, Brown precious opal. 95c, Fire opal. 2b, Yellow precious opal.

2003, May 8   Perf. 14
1647-1650 A354   Set of 4   4.00 2.00

Emperor Tewodros's Amulet — A355

Various views with frame color of: 40c, Green. 60c, Yellow orange. 3b, Red.

2003, Sept. 4   Litho.   Perf. 13x13¼
1651-1653 A355   Set of 3   4.50 2.50

Flowers — A356

Designs: 45c, Kniphofia isoetfolia. 55c, Kniphofia insignis. 1b, Crinum bambusetum. 2b, Crinum abyssinicum, horiz.

2003, Nov. 27   Litho.   Perf. 13x13¼
1654-1657 A356   Set of 4   3.00 2.00

Konso Terracing System — A357

Designs: 40c, Village, crops. 60c, Man and woman, ears of grains. 1b, Terraces, tool. 2b, Farmers working on terraces, crops.

2003, Dec. 30   Perf. 13¼x13¾
1658-1661 A357   Set of 4   3.00 2.00

Amaranths — A358

Designs: 20c, Seeds. 80c, White amaranth. 1b, Red amaranth. 2b, Amaranth bread.

2004, Mar. 11   Litho.   Perf. 13¼x14
1662-1665 A358   Set of 4   3.00 2.00

Marble — A359

Designs: 25c, Sabian multicolored marble. 75c, Eshet blue marble. 1b, Sabian rose green marble. 2b, Sabian purple marble.

2004, July 27   Perf. 14
1666-1669 A359   Set of 4   2.25 2.25

FIFA (Fédération Internationale de Football Association), Cent. — A360

Soccer field, "100" and: 5c, FIFA emblem. 95c, Old soccer ball. 1b, Cleats. 2b, Modern soccer ball.

2004, Sept. 7   Litho.   Perf. 14
1670-1673 A360   Set of 4   2.25 2.25

2004 Summer Olympics, Athens — A361

Designs: 20c, Track. 35c, Hammer throw. 45c, Boxing. 3b, Cycling.

2004, Dec. 7
1674-1677 A361   Set of 4   2.25 2.25

Gesho — A362

Designs: 40c, Chopped plant. 60c, Plants, horiz. 1b, Cut logs. 2b, Branch with berries.

2004, Dec. 28
1678-1681 A362   Set of 4   2.25 2.25

Black Rhinoceros A363

2005, June 20   Litho.   Perf. 14
Background Color
1682	A363	5c	bright blue	.25	.25
1683	A363	10c	lilac	.25	.25
1684	A363	15c	dark blue	.25	.25
1685	A363	20c	bister	1.00	1.00
1686	A363	25c	dark purple	1.00	1.00
1687	A363	30c	blue	1.00	1.00
1688	A363	35c	green	1.00	1.00
1689	A363	40c	purple	1.00	1.00
1690	A363	45c	green	1.00	1.00
1691	A363	4b	bright red	4.25	4.25
		Nos. 1682-1691 (10)		11.00	11.00

Sabean Inscriptions A364

Various inscriptions with background colors of: 15c, Green. 40c, Red, vert. 45c, Orange, vert. 3b, Blue, vert.

Perf. 13¾x14, 14x13¾
2005, Aug. 20   Litho.
1692-1695 A364   Set of 4   2.00 2.00

Surma Hairstyles — A365

Various hairstyles with background colors of: 15c, Red. 40c, Green. 45c, Blue. 3b, Lilac.

2005, Dec. 20   Perf. 14x13¾
1696-1699 A365   Set of 4   2.00 2.00

Flowers — A366

Designs: 45c, Chlorophytum neghellense. 55c, Aloe bertemariae, vert. 3b, Aloe schelpei, vert.

Perf. 13¾x14, 14x13¾
2006, June 6   Litho.
1700-1702 A366   Set of 3   2.00 2.00

Ethiopian Airlines, 60th Anniv. — A367

Designs: 15c, Douglas C-47A Dakota III. 40c, Douglas DC-6B Super Cloudmaster. 45c, Boeing 720-060B. 1b, Boeing 767-300ER. 2b, Boeing 787 Dreamliner.

2006, Sept. 28   Perf. 13x13¼
1703-1707 A367   Set of 5   2.00 2.00

Intl. Year of Deserts and Desertification A368

Emblem and: 15c, United Nations emblem. 40c, Map of Ethiopia showing desertification vulnerability. 45c, Map of Africa showing climate types. 3b, Map of world showing climate types.

2006, Oct. 31   Perf. 14x13½
1708-1711 A368   Set of 4   2.00 2.00

Ethiopian Millennium — A369

Panel color: 40c, Pink. 60c, Buff. 3b, Green.

2007, Nov. 15   Litho.   Perf. 13¾
1712-1714 A369   Set of 3   2.00 2.00

Minerals — A370

Designs: 40c, Gypsum. 60c, Quartz. 1b, Ambo sandstone. 2b, Feldspar.

2007, Dec. 25   Perf. 14
1715-1718 A370   Set of 4   2.00 2.00

Onslaught Martyrs Memorial — A371

Designs: 40c, Martyrs Memorial Center. 60c, Emblem of Association for the Erection of the Martyrs Memorial Monument, vert. 3b, Woman, jail cell, gun, vert.

2008, Aug. 26   Litho.   Perf. 14
1719-1721 A371 Set of 3   3.00 3.00

Catha Edulis — A372

Designs: 45c, Red leaves. 55c, Harvesting of plant. 3b, Plant.

2008, Sept. 8   Perf. 13¾
1722-1724 A372 Set of 3   3.00 3.00

Diplomatic Relations Between Ethiopia and India, 60th Anniv. — A373

"60" and: 30c, Ethiopian and Indian flowers. 70c, Rock church, Lalibela, and Taj Mahal, India. 3b, Symbols of India and Ethiopia.

2008, Dec. 30 Litho. Perf. 14x13¼
1725-1727 A373 Set of 3   3.00 3.00

Pan-African Tsetse and Trypanosomiasis Eradication Campaign — A374

Designs: 15c, Campaign emblem. 40c, Tsetse fly. 45c, Tsetse fly and blood drop, horiz. 3b, Tsetse fly, cow, silhouette of human, map of Africa, horiz.

Perf. 13½x14, 14x13½
2009, July 21   Litho.
1728-1731 A374 Set of 4   3.00 3.00

Addis Ababa Monuments A375

Designs: 45c, Arat Kilo, Miazia 27 Square Monument. 55c, Sidist Kilo, Yekatit 12 Square Monument. 3b, Abune Petros Monument, vert.

2009, Sept. 17   Litho.   Perf. 13¾
1732-1734 A375 Set of 3   3.00 3.00

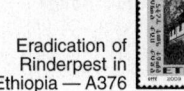

Eradication of Rinderpest in Ethiopia — A376

Designs: 15c, First laboratory in Addis Ababa where rinderpest vaccine was produced. 40c, Certificate from World Organization for Animal Health. 45c, Dead cattle. 3b, Dr. Alemework Beyene, monument to Dr. Engueda Johannes, veterinarians.

2009, Dec. 31   Perf. 14
1735-1738 A376   3.00 3.00

Pan-African Postal Union, 30th Anniv. — A377

Background color: 45c, Green. 55c, Yellow. 3b, Rose.

2010, Apr. 6   Litho.   Perf. 13¼x14
1739-1741 A377 Set of 3   3.00 3.00

Writers — A378

Designs: No. 1742, 1b, Tsegaye Gebremedhin (1936-2006). No. 1743, 1b, Dr. Sindehu Gebru (1915-2009). No. 1744, 1b, Dr. Haddis Alemayehu (1910-2003). No. 1745, 1b, Dr. Kebede Michael (1915-98).

2010, Aug. 6   Perf. 14
1742-1745 A378 Set of 4   3.25 3.25

Ethiopian Red Cross, 75th Anniv. — A379

75th anniversary emblem and: 45c, Ambulance, Red Cross workers and truck. 55c, Bags of blood, boy receiving transfusion. 1b, Amharic letters, vert. 2b, Red Cross building.

2010, Oct. 12   Litho.   Perf. 14
1746-1749 A379 Set of 4   3.00 3.00

Mosques — A380

Designs: 20c, Goze Mosque. 80c, Al-Nejashi Mosque. 3b, Sheh Hussein Mosque, Dire.

2011, May 24   Litho.   Perf. 14
1750-1752 A380 Set of 3   3.00 3.00

Monasteries and Churches A381

Designs: 35c, Zoz Amba St. George's Monastery, Gonder. 65c, Meskele Kiristonse Church, Wollo, vert. 3b, Debre Damo Abuna Aregawi Monastery, Tigrai, vert.

2011, June 9
1753-1755 A381 Set of 3   3.00 3.00

Bridges — A382

Designs: 20c, Tezeke Bridge No. 3. 80c, Hidassie Bridge. 1b, Beshela River Bridge. 2b, Blue Nile Bridge.

2011, Sept. 2   Litho.   Perf. 14x13¼
1756-1759 A382 Set of 4   3.00 3.00

Martyr's Monuments — A383

Designs: 40c, Amhara Region Martyr's Monument, Bahir Dar. 60c, Oromo Martyr's Monument, Adama. 3b, Tigrai Region Martyr's Monument, Mekelle, horiz.

2011, Sept. 9   Perf. 13¼x13, 13x13¼
1760-1762 A383 Set of 3   3.00 3.00

Coffee Ceremony — A384

Designs: 20c, Coffee pots. 80c, Preparation of coffee. 1b, Bean roasting. 2b, Pouring of coffee into cups.

2011, Dec. 20   Perf. 13¼x14
1763-1766 A384 Set of 4   3.00 3.00

Medicinal Plants — A385

Designs: 20c, Lippia adoensis. 35c, Artemisia absinthium. 45c, Thymus schimperi. 3b, Ocimum lamiifolium.

2012, Apr. 10   Perf. 14x13¼
1767-1770 A385 Set of 4   3.00 3.00

Addis Ababa Monuments A386

Designs: 40c, Lion of Judah Monument. 60c, Ras Mekonen Monument. 1b, Lion of Judah Monument, vert. 2b, Menelik II Monument, vert.

2012, July 5   Perf. 14x13¼, 13¼x14
1771-1774 A386 Set of 4   3.00 3.00

Writers — A387

Designs: 20c, Temesgen Gebre. 80c, Hiruy Woldeslassie. 1b, Yoftahe Nigussie. 2b, Afework Gebreyesus.

2012, Sept. 7   Perf. 13¼x14
1775-1778 A387 Set of 4   3.00 3.00

Addis Ababa, 125th Anniv. (in 2011) — A388

Various views of Addis Ababa: 15c, 35c, 2b, 4b.

Perf. 13¾x13½
2013, Aug. 20   Litho.
1779-1782 A388 Set of 4   4.00 4.00
Dated 2012.

African Union, 50th Anniv. — A389

African Union emblem, "50," and: 10c, Year of Pan-Africanism emblem, building. 40c, Building, diff. 2b, Assembly hall. 4b, Map of Africa, doves, airplane, road, farm field.

2013, Dec. 3   Litho.   Perf. 13¼x14
1783-1786 A389   4.00 4.00

Ethio Telecom — A390

Designs: 10c, Man holding wireless telephone console. 40c, Woman holding mobile telephone, woman using wall-mounted telephone, old dial telephone, vert. 2b, Man and woman using computer. 4b, Satellite, satellite dish, map, vert.

Perf. 14x13¼, 13¼x14
2014, May 13   Litho.
1787-1790 A390 Set of 4   4.00 4.00

Traditional Costumes of Southern Ethiopian People — A391

Map and costumes of the: 15c, Karo. 35c, Erbore. 2b, Hamer. 4b, Daasanach.

2014, May 27 Litho. Perf. 14x13¼
1791-1794 A391 Set of 4   4.00 4.00

Ethiopian Orthodox Tewahedo Churches and Monasteries A392

Designs: 50c, Orra Kidanemihiret Zege (monastery), Tana Island. 1b, Kibran Gebriel (monastery), Tana Island. 2b, Debrebirihan Silassie (church), Gonder, vert. 3b, Tsion Mariam Church, Axum.

Perf. 14x13¼, 13¼x14
2014, June 12   Litho.
1795-1798 A392 Set of 4   4.50 4.50

Rift Valley Sites — A393

Designs: 25c, Sulfur deposits, Dallol. 30c, Brine ponds, Dallol. 35c, Salt deposits, Dallol. 45c, Erta Ale Volcano erupting. 65c, Ash plume over Erta Ale Volcano. 4b, Erta Ale caldera.

2014, Aug. 26   Litho.   Perf. 14
1799-1804 A393 Set of 6   4.00 4.00

University of Gondar, 60th Anniv. A394

Designs: 5c, Millennium Steps, Referral Hospital, Health team training group on horses in 1964, new campus. 45c, President's office. 2b, Main gate. 4b, 60th anniv. emblem, vert.

2014, Dec. 2   Litho.   Perf. 13½
1805-1808 A394 Set of 4   3.50 3.50

Ethiopian Airlines — A395

Designs: 15c, Boeing 777-F6N cargo plane. 35c, Boeing 777-200R passenger plane. 2b, Ethiopian Airlines Star Alliance jet. 4b, Boeing 787 Dreamliner.

2014, Dec. 25   Litho.   Perf. 13x13¼
1809-1812 A395   Set of 4   3.50 3.50
1812a   Booklet pane of 16, 4
            each #1809-1812, perf.
            13x13¼ on 3 sides   15.00 —
            Complete booklet, #1812a 15.00

Ethiopian Visual Artists Association A396

Painters and their works: 10c, Yegezu Bisrat (1926-79). 40c, Emealaf Hiruy (1907-71). 2b, Belachew Yimer (1869-1957). 4b, Agegnehu Engida (1905-50).

2015, Nov. 10   Litho.   Perf. 13¼
1813-1816 A396   Set of 4   3.50 3.50

Ethiopian postal officials have declared as "illegal" sheets of 9 dated "2016" depicting Ferrari automobiles, Michael Schumacher, National Hockey League stars, Soccer stars, Cristiano Ronaldo, Crocodile, Fish, Tigers, Roses, and Nudes, sheets of 9 dated "2009" depicting Pandas, sheets of 6 dated "2009" depicting Chimpanzees, sheets of 5 dated "2015" depicting Netherlands 2018 World Cup soccer players, and sheets of 4 dated "2009" depicting Pandas and Chimpanzees.

Ethiopian National Archives and Libraries Agency, 70th Anniv. — A397

Designs: 10c, Sea of Computs. 15c, Ethiopian Cultural Medicine Book. 25c, Letter from Ethiopian King Theodros to Queen Victoria of Great Britain, 19th cent. 1b, Four Gospels Bible, 14th cent. 2b, Book of Enoch, 15th cent., horiz. 3b, National Archives, horiz.

Perf. 13¼x13½, 13½x13¼
2016, Jan. 28   Litho.
1817-1822 A397   Set of 6   3.50 3.50

Palaces — A398

Designs: 10c, Emperor Menelik Palace, Fit Ber Gate. 40c, Emperor Menelik Palace, Entoto. 2b, Guenete Leul Palace and gate, Addis Ababa. 4b, National Palace, Addis Ababa.

Perf. 13¼x13½
2016, Feb. 18   Litho.
1823-1826 A398   Set of 4   3.50 3.50

Haramaya University, 60th Anniv. — A399

Designs: 5c, Parking lot and Administration building. 45c, Agricultural research plot, dairy production. 2b, Main gate. 4b, 60th anniv. emblem, vert.

Perf. 13½x13¼, 13¼x13½
2016, Apr. 21   Litho.
1827-1830 A399   Set of 4   3.50 3.50

Waterfalls — A400

Designs: 10c, Habera River Falls, Bale. 40c, Sor Waterfalls, Ilu Abba Bora. 2b, Blue Nile Falls, Gojam. 4b, Ajora Falls, Wolaitta.

Perf. 13½x13¼
2016, June 14   Litho.
1831-1834 A400   Set of 4   3.50 3.50

Ministry of Urban Development and Housing — A401

Designs: 50c, Building under construction. 1b, Housing complexes and bricks. 2b, Main office. 3b, Emblem.

Perf. 13½x13¼
2016, Sept. 28   Litho.
1835-1838 A401   Set of 4   3.50 3.50

Snakes — A402

Designs: 50c, Ethiopian house snake. 1b, Abyssinian house snake. 2b, Ethiopian blind snake. 3b, Ethiopian mountain adder.

2016, Oct. 27   Litho.   Perf. 13½x13¼
1839-1842 A402   Set of 4   3.50 3.50

Defeat of Italy In East African Campaign, 75th Anniv. — A403

Designs: No. 1843, 1b, People on gallows, statue at left, monuments, four Ethiopians in foreground, green frame. No. 1844, 1b, Four Ethiopians, monument at center, green frame. No. 1845, 1b, Ethiopians planting flag in ground, monument, train, dam, tractor, red frame. No. 1846, 1b, Eight Ethiopians, monument at center, gray green frame. No. 1847, 1b, Six Ethiopians, monument at center, blue frame. 1.50b, Two Ethiopians, monument at center, blue frame.

2016, Nov. 6   Litho.   Perf. 13½x13¾
1843-1848 A403   Set of 6   4.00 4.00

Fish — A404

Map and: 5c, Labeobarbus marcophtalmus. 45c, Labeobarbus gorguari. 1b, Labeobarbus acutirostris. 5b, Labeobarbus osseensis.

Perf. 13½x13¼
2017, Mar. 21   Litho.
1849-1852 A404   Set of 4   3.50 3.50
            Dated 2016.

Gates of Harar — A405

Designs: 15c, Buda Gate. 35c, Fellana Gate. 1b, Senga Gate. 2b, Showa Gate. 3b, Erer Gate.

Perf. 13¾x13½
2017, Aug. 24   Litho.
1853-1857 A405   Set of 5   3.50 3.50

Commercial Bank of Ethiopia, 75th Anniv. — A406

75th anniversary emblem and: 40c, Tefera Degefe, first general manager of bank. 50c, State Bank of Ethiopia Building, horiz. 60c, Former headquarters, 1964, horiz. 2b, Bank builiding, automatic teller machine, mobile banking application on cell phone, computer and credit card reader. 3b, Bank emblem, train, ship, dam, wheat and factory.

Perf. 13¾x13¼, 13¼x13¾
2018, Apr. 26   Litho.
1858-1862 A406   Set of 5   3.50 3.50

Churches — A407

Designs: 5c, Narga Selassie Church, Bahar Dar. 45c, Adadi Maryam Church, Oromia. 2b, Medhane Alem Kesho Church, Tigray. 4b, Maryam Korkor Church, Tigray.

2018, June 5   Litho.   Perf. 13½x13¼
1863-1866 A407   Set of 4   3.50 3.50

Ethiopia-Djibouti Electrified Railway — A408

Designs: 50c, Train. 1b, Station. 2b, Trains on multiple tracks. 3b, Construction of railway.

Perf. 13¼x13½
2018, Aug. 31   Litho.
1867-1870 A408   Set of 4   3.50 3.50
1870a   Souvenir sheet of 4,
            #1867-1870   3.50 3.50

Diplomatic Relations Between Ethiopia and Russia, 120th Anniv. — A409

Designs: 50c, Balcha Safo (1863-1936), Ethiopian military commander, Nikolay S. Leontiev (1862-1910), Russian military officer, and Balcha Hospital. 1b, Musical instruments of Ethiopia and Russia. 2b, Castle of Fasilides, Ethiopia, and Castle of Nizhny Novgorod, Russia, horiz. 3b, Ethiopian jebena (coffee pot), and tagine and Russian Khokhloma bowls, horiz.

Perf. 14¼x14, 14x14¼
2018, Dec. 28   Litho.
1871-1874 A409   Set of 4   .45 .45

Birds — A410

Designs: 40c, White-bellied go-away bird. 50c, Long-tailed nightjar. 60c, Dusky turtle dove. 2b, Black-billed barbet. 3b, Red-fronted tinker bird.

2019, Jan. 24   Litho.   Perf. 13½
1875-1879 A410   Set of 5   .50 .50

Animals — A411

Designs: 50c, Aardwolves. 1b, Striped hyenas. 5b, Spotted hyenas.

2019, Feb. 14   Litho.   Perf. 14
1880-1882 A411   Set of 3   .45 .45

SEMI-POSTAL STAMPS

Types of 1931, Overprinted in Red at Upper Left

Perf. 12x12½, 12½x12
1936, Feb. 24   Unwmk.
B1 A27 1g light green   .60 1.00
B2 A27 2g rose   .60 1.00
B3 A27 4g blue   .60 1.00
B4 A25 8g brown   .85 1.50
B5 A25 1t purple   .85 1.50
    Nos. B1-B5 (5)   3.50 6.00

Nos. B1-B5 were sold at twice face value, the surtax going to the Red Cross.

> **Catalogue values for unused stamps in this section, from this point to the end of the section, are for Never Hinged items.**

Nos. 289, 290, 292-294 Surcharged in Blue

Perf. 13x13½
1949, June 13   Wmk. 282
B6   A53 8c + 8c deep org   2.50   2.50
B7   A53 12c + 5c red   2.50   2.50
B8   A53 30c + 15c org brn   4.00   4.00
B9   A53 70c + 70c rose lilac 25.00 25.00
B10 A53 $1 + 80c dk car rose 32.50 32.50
     Nos. B6-B10 (5)   66.50 66.50

No. B10 exists with "80+" error. See Nos. B16-B20.

Type A39 Surcharged in Red or Carmine

Perf. 11½
1950, May 8   Unwmk.   Photo.
Various Designs
Inscribed "Croix Rouge"

B11 A39 5c + 10c brt grn   .85   1.60
B12 A39 10c + 10c brt red   1.10   1.60
B13 A39 25c + 10c brt bl   2.25   3.25
B14 A39 50c + 10c dk yel brn 6.50 5.50
B15 A39 1t + 10c brt vio   11.00 13.50
     Nos. B11-B15 (5)   21.70 25.45

The surtax was for the Red Cross.
The surcharge includes two dots which invalidate the original surtax. The original surcharge with uneven cross was red, a 1951 printing with even cross was carmine. Forgeries exist.

Nos. B6-B10 Overprinted in Black

Perf. 13x13½

1951, Nov. 17   **Wmk. 282**

B16	A53	8c + 8c dp org	.70	.70
B17	A53	12c + 5c red	.70	.70
B18	A53	30c + 15c org brn	1.25	1.25
B19	A53	70c + 70c rose lilac	12.00	12.00
B20	A53	$1 + 80c dk car rose	20.00	20.00
		Nos. B16-B20 (5)	34.65	34.65

No. B20 exists with "80 +" error.

Tree, Staff and Snake — SP1

Wmk. 282

1951, Nov. 25   **Engr.**   **Perf. 13**

Lower Panel in Red

B21	SP1	5c + 2c dp bl grn	.50	.25
B22	SP1	10c + 3c orange	.55	.30
B23	SP1	15c + 3c dp bl	.85	.50
B24	SP1	30c + 5c red	1.60	1.10
B25	SP1	50c + 7c red brn	4.50	2.75
B26	SP1	$1 + 10c purple	9.00	4.50
		Nos. B21-B26 (6)	17.00	9.40

The surtax was for anti-tuberculosis work.

1958, Dec. 1

Lower Panel in Red

B27	SP1	20c + 3c dl pur	.75	.75
B28	SP1	25c + 4c emerald	1.10	1.10
B29	SP1	35c + 5c rose vio	1.50	1.50
B30	SP1	60c + 7c vio bl	2.75	2.75
B31	SP1	65c + 7c violet	5.00	5.00
B32	SP1	80c + 9c car rose	9.00	9.00
		Nos. B27-B32 (6)	20.10	20.10
		Nos. B21-B32 (12)	37.10	29.50

The surtax was for anti-tuberculosis work. Nos. B21-B32 were the only stamps on sale from Dec. 1-25, 1958.

Type of Regular Issue, 1955, Overprinted and Surcharged

Engr.; Cross Typo. in Red

1959, May 30   **Wmk. 282**

B33	A62	15c + 2c olive bister & rose red	.70	.70
B34	A62	20c + 3c vio & emer	.85	.85
B35	A62	30c + 5c rose car & grnsh bl	1.25	1.25
		Nos. B33-B35 (3)	2.80	2.80

Cent. of the Intl. Red Cross idea. Surtax for the Red Cross.

The overprint includes the cross, "RED CROSS CENTENARY" and date in two languages. The surcharge includes the date in Amharic and the new surtax. The surcharge was applied locally.

Design A39 Surcharged

Perf. 11½

1960, May 7   **Photo.**   **Unwmk.**

B36	A39	5c + 1c brt green	.85	.85
B37	A39	10c + 2c brt red	1.25	1.25
B38	A39	25c + 3c brt blue	1.60	1.60

B39	A39	50c + 4c dk yel brn	2.75	2.75
B40	A39	1t + 5c brt vio	6.50	6.50
		Nos. B36-B40 (5)	12.95	12.95

25th anniversary of Ethiopian Red Cross. Forgeries exist.

Crippled Boy on Crutches — SP2

Wmk. 282

1963, July 23   **Engr.**   **Perf. 13½**

B41	SP2	10c + 2c ultra	.30	.30
B42	SP2	15c + 3c red	.55	.55
B43	SP2	50c + 5c brt green	1.10	1.10
B44	SP2	60c + 5c red lilac	2.25	2.25
		Nos. B41-B44 (4)	4.20	4.20

The surtax was to aid the disabled.

AIR POST STAMPS

Regular Issue of 1928 Handstamped in Violet, Red, Black or Green

Perf. 13½x14

1929, Aug. 17   **Unwmk.**

C1	A22	⅛m orange & lt bl	1.50	2.00
C2	A23	¼m ind & red org	1.50	2.00
C3	A22	½m gray grn & blk	1.50	2.75
C4	A23	1m dk car & blk	1.50	2.75
C5	A22	2m dk blue & blk	1.50	2.75
C6	A23	4m yellow & olive	1.50	2.75
C7	A22	8m violet & olive	1.50	2.75
C8	A23	1t org brn & vio	2.75	4.25
C9	A22	2t green & bister	4.25	5.25
C10	A23	3t choc & grn	4.25	5.25
		Nos. C1-C10 (10)	21.75	32.50

The overprint signifies "17 August 1929-Airplane of the Ethiopian Government." The stamps commemorate the arrival at Addis Ababa of the 1st airplane of the Ethiopian Government.

There are 3 types of the overprint: (I) 19½mm high; "colon" at right of bottom word. (II) 20mm high; same "colon." (III) 19½mm high; no "colon." Many errors exist.

Symbols of Empire, Airplane and Map — AP1

1931, June 17   **Engr.**   **Perf. 12½**

C11	AP1	1g orange red	.25	.50
C12	AP1	2g ultra	.25	.50
C13	AP1	4g violet	.25	.80
C14	AP1	8g blue green	.80	1.40
C15	AP1	1t olive brown	1.60	2.10
C16	AP1	2t carmine	2.75	8.00
C17	AP1	3t yellow green	4.00	9.00
		Nos. C11-C17 (7)	9.90	22.30

Nos. C11 to C17 exist imperforate.

Reprints of C11 to C17 exist. Paper is thinner and gum whiter than the originals and the ink is heavy and shiny. Originals have ink that is dull and granular. Reprints usually sell at about one-third of above values.

> **Catalogue values for unused stamps in this section, from this point to the end of the section, are for Never Hinged items.**

Nos. 250, 255 and 257 Surcharged in Black

a   b

Perf. 14x13½

1947, Mar. 20   **Unwmk.**

C18	A33 (a)	12c on 4c	77.50	77.50
C19	A33 (b)	50c on 25c	72.50	72.50
a.		"26-12-46"	275.00	
C20	A33 (b)	$2 on 60c	125.00	125.00
a.		"26-12-46"	340.00	
		Nos. C18-C20 (3)	275.00	275.00
		Set, hinged	175.00	

Resumption of airmail service, 12/29/46.

Franklin D. Roosevelt — AP2

Design: $2, Haile Selassie.

Engraved and Photogravure

1947, May 23   **Perf. 12½**

C21	AP2	$1 dk purple & sepia	12.50	14.00
C22	AP2	$2 carmine & dp blue	22.50	24.00

Farmer Plowing — AP3

Designs: 10c, 25c, Zoquala, extinct volcano. 30c, 35c, Tesissat Falls, Abai River. 65c, 70c, Amba Alaguie. $1, Sacala, source of Nile. $3, Gorgora and Dembia, Lake Tana. $5, Magdala, former capital. $10, Ras Dashan, mountain peak.

Perf. 13x13½

1947-55   **Wmk. 282**   **Engr.**

C23	AP3	8c purple brown	.30	.30
C24	AP3	10c bright green	.30	.30
C25	AP3	25c dull pur ('52)	.45	.30
C26	AP3	30c orange yellow	.85	.30
C27	AP3	35c blue ('55)	.95	.45
C28	AP3	65c purple ('55)	1.10	.80
C29	AP3	70c red	1.25	.55
C30	AP3	$1 deep blue	1.60	.80
C31	AP3	$3 rose lilac	6.50	4.25
C32	AP3	$5 red brown	13.00	5.50
C33	AP3	$10 rose violet	27.50	13.50
		Nos. C23-C33 (11)	53.80	27.05

For overprints see Nos. C64-C70.

UPU Monument, Bern — AP4

1950, Apr. 3   **Unwmk.**   **Perf. 12½**

C34	AP4	5c green & red	1.00	.50
C35	AP4	15c dk sl grn & car	1.50	1.10
C36	AP4	25c org yel & grn	2.75	1.10
C37	AP4	50c carmine & ultra	4.50	3.25
		Nos. C34-C37 (4)	9.75	5.95

75th anniv. of the UPU.

No. C34 exists in the colors of Nos. C35-C37. These are considered to be trial color proofs.

Convair Plane over Mountains AP5

Engraved and Lithographed

1955, Dec. 30   **Unwmk.**   **Perf. 12½**

Center Multicolored

C38	AP5	10c gray green	1.25	.30
C39	AP5	15c carmine	1.60	.80
C40	AP5	20c violet	2.50	1.25
		Nos. C38-C40 (3)	5.35	2.35

10th anniversary of Ethiopian Airlines.

Promulgating the Constitution — AP6

Perf. 14x13½

1956, July 16   **Engr.**   **Wmk. 282**

C41	AP6	10c redsh brn & ultra	.60	.70
C42	AP6	15c dk car rose & ol grn	.95	1.00
C43	AP6	20c blue & org red	1.25	1.00
C44	AP6	25c purple & green	1.40	1.60
C45	AP6	30c dk grn & red brn	2.40	2.50
		Nos. C41-C45 (5)	6.60	6.80

25th anniversary of the constitution.

Aksum — AP7

Ancient Capitals: 10c, Lalibela. 15c, Gondar. 20c, Mekele. 25c, Ankober.

1957, Feb. 7   **Perf. 14**

Centers in Green

C46	AP7	5c red brown	.75	.40
C47	AP7	10c rose carmine	.75	.40
C48	AP7	15c red orange	.90	.50
C49	AP7	20c ultramarine	1.40	.70
C50	AP7	25c claret	2.10	1.00
		Nos. C46-C50 (5)	5.90	3.00

Amharic "A" — AP8

Designs: Various Amharic characters and views of Addis Ababa. The characters, arranged by values, spell Addis Ababa.

1957, Feb. 14   **Engr.**

Amharic Letters in Scarlet

C51	AP8	5c ultra, *sal pink*	.35	.35
C52	AP8	10c ol grn, *pink*	.35	.35
C53	AP8	15c dl pur, *yel*	.55	.35
C54	AP8	20c grn, *buff*	.90	.40
C55	AP8	25c plum, *pale bl*	2.50	.55
C56	AP8	30c red, *pale grn*	1.75	.60
		Nos. C51-C56 (6)	6.40	2.60

70th anniversary of Addis Ababa.

Map, Rock Church at Lalibela and Obelisk — AP9

1958, Apr. 15   **Wmk. 282**   **Perf. 13½**

C57	AP9	10c green	.50	.50
C58	AP9	20c rose red	1.10	1.10
C59	AP9	30c bright blue	1.75	1.10
		Nos. C57-C59 (3)	3.35	2.70

Conf. of Independent African States, Accra, Apr. 15-22.

Map of Africa and UN Emblem — AP10

1958, Dec. 29 — Perf. 13

C60	AP10	5c emerald	.25	.25
C61	AP10	20c carmine rose	.55	.55
C62	AP10	25c ultramarine	.75	.55
C63	AP10	50c pale purple	1.50	.75
		Nos. C60-C63 (4)	3.05	1.80

1st session of the UN Economic Conf. for Africa, opened in Addis Ababa Dec. 29.

Nos. C23-C29 Overprinted

Perf. 13x13½

1959, Aug. 16 — Engr. — Wmk. 282

C64	AP3	8c purple brown	.50	.30
C65	AP3	10c brt green	.70	.35
C66	AP3	25c dull purple	1.05	.40
C67	AP3	30c orange yellow	1.15	.60
C68	AP3	35c blue	1.40	.65
C69	AP3	65c purple	2.25	1.00
C70	AP3	70c red	2.75	1.25
		Nos. C64-C70 (7)	9.80	4.55

30th anniv. of Ethiopian airmail service.

Ethiopian Soldier and Map of Congo — AP11

Perf. 11½
1962, July 23 — Unwmk. — Photo. — Granite Paper

C71	AP11	15c org, bl, brn & grn	.30	.25
C72	AP11	50c pur, bl, brn & grn	.90	.50
C73	AP11	60c red, bl, brn & grn	1.60	.65
		Nos. C71-C73 (3)	2.80	1.40

2nd anniv. of the Ethiopian contingent of the UN forces in the Congo and in honor of the 70th birthday of Emperor Haile Selassie.

Globe with Map of Africa — AP12

1963, May 22 — Granite Paper

C74	AP12	10c magenta & blk	.60	.30
C75	AP12	40c emerald & blk	1.10	.55
C76	AP12	60c blue & blk	1.75	.85
		Nos. C74-C76 (3)	3.45	1.70

Conf. of African heads of state for African Unity, Addis Ababa.

Bird Type of Regular Issue

Birds: 10c, Black-headed forest oriole. 15c, Broad-tailed paradise whydah, vert. 20c, Lammergeier, vert. 50c, White-checked touraco. 80c, Purple indigo bird.

1963, Sept. 12 — Perf. 11½
Granite Paper

C77	A74	10c multicolored	.75	.25
C78	A74	15c multicolored	.90	.25
C79	A74	20c blue, blk & ocher	1.75	.60
C80	A74	50c lemon & multi	2.60	1.10
C81	A74	80c ultra, blk & brn	5.00	1.90
		Nos. C77-C81 (5)	11.00	4.10

Swimming AP13

Sport: 10c, Basketball, vert. 15c, Javelin. 80c, Soccer game in stadium.

Perf. 14x13½
1964, Sept. 15 — Litho. — Unwmk.

C82	AP13	5c multicolored	.30	.25
C83	AP13	10c multicolored	.40	.25
C84	AP13	15c multicolored	.85	.55
C85	AP13	80c multicolored	2.25	1.10
		Nos. C82-C85 (4)	3.80	2.15

18th Olympic Games, Tokyo, Oct. 10-25.

Queen Elizabeth II and Emperor Haile Selassie AP14

1965, Feb. 1 — Photo. — Perf. 11½
Granite Paper

C86	AP14	5c multicolored	.30	.30
C87	AP14	35c multicolored	.85	.55
C88	AP14	60c multicolored	1.10	.85
		Nos. C86-C88 (3)	2.25	1.70

Visit of Queen Elizabeth II, Feb. 1-8.

Koka Dam and Power Plant — AP15

Designs: 15c, Sugar cane field. 50c, Blue Nile Bridge. 60c, Gondar castles. 80c, Coffee tree. $1, Cattle at water hole. $3, Camels at well. $5, Ethiopian Air Lines jet plane.

1965, July 19 — Unwmk. — Perf. 11½
Granite Paper
Portrait in Black

C89	AP15	15c vio brn & buff	.30	.30
C90	AP15	40c vio bl & lt bl	.50	.40
C91	AP15	50c grn & lt bl	.80	.45
C92	AP15	60c claret & yel	1.30	.70
C93	AP15	80c grn, yel & red	1.75	.80
C94	AP15	$1 brn & lt bl	1.90	.95
C95	AP15	$3 claret & pink	6.50	2.40
C96	AP15	$5 ultra & lt bl	14.00	4.50
		Nos. C89-C96 (8)	27.05	10.50

Bird Type of Regular Issue

Birds: 10c, White-collared kingfisher. 15c, Blue-breasted bee-eater. 25c, African paradise flycatcher. 40c, Village weaver. 60c, White-collared pigeon.

1966, Feb. 15 — Photo. — Perf. 11½
Granite Paper

C97	A74	10c dull yel & multi	.85	.25
C98	A74	15c lt blue & multi	.85	.25
C99	A74	25c gray & multi	1.75	.55
C100	A74	40c pink & multi	3.50	.85
C101	A74	60c multicolored	4.50	1.10
		Nos. C97-C101 (5)	11.45	3.00

Black Rhinoceros AP16

Animals: 10c, Leopard. 20c, Black-and-white colobus (monkey). 30c, Mountain nyala. 60c, Nubian ibex.

1966, June 20 — Litho. — Perf. 13

C102	AP16	5c dp grn, blk & gray	.55	.30
C103	AP16	10c grn, blk & ocher	.55	.55
C104	AP16	20c cit, blk & grn	1.10	.55
C105	AP16	30c yel grn, blk & ocher	1.75	.85
C106	AP16	60c yel grn, blk & dk brn	4.50	1.60
		Nos. C102-C106 (5)	8.45	3.85

Bird Type of Regular Issue

Birds: 10c, Blue-winged goose, vert. 15c, Yellow-billed duck. 20c, Wattled ibis. 25c, Striped swallow. 40c, Black-winged lovebird, vert.

1967, Sept. 29 — Photo. — Perf. 11½
Granite Paper

C107	A74	10c lt ultra & multi	.55	.25
C108	A74	15c green & multi	.85	.25
C109	A74	20c yellow & multi	1.10	.55
C110	A74	25c salmon & multi	2.25	.55
C111	A74	40c pink & multi	4.50	1.10
		Nos. C107-C111 (5)	9.25	2.70

SPECIAL DELIVERY STAMPS

Catalogue values for unused stamps in this section are for Never Hinged items.

Motorcycle Messenger SD1

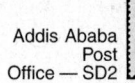

Addis Ababa Post Office — SD2

Unwmk.
1947, Apr. 24 — Engr. — Perf. 13

E1	SD1	30c orange brown	5.00	1.25
E2	SD2	50c blue	9.00	3.50

1954-62 — Wmk. 282

E3	SD1	30c org brown ('62)	4.50	1.25
E4	SD2	50c blue	5.50	1.25

POSTAGE DUE STAMPS

Very Fine examples of Nos. J1-J42 will have perforations touching the design on one or more sides.

Nos. 1-4 and unissued values Overprinted

Perf. 14x13½
1896, June 10 — Unwmk.
Black Overprint

J1	A1	¼g green	1.45
J2	A1	½g red	1.45
J3	A1	4g lilac brown	1.00
a.		Without overprint	1.00
J4	A1	8g violet	1.00
a.		Without overprint	1.00

Red Overprint

J5	A1	1g blue	1.45
J6	A1	2g dark brown	1.45
J7	A1	16g black	1.00
a.		Without overprint	1.00
		Nos. J1-J7 (7)	8.80

Nos. J1-J7 were not issued. Forgeries exist.

Nos. 1-7 Handstamped in Various Colors

a

1905, Apr.

J8	A1 (a)	¼g green	55.00	55.00
J9	A1 (a)	½g red	55.00	55.00
J10	A1 (a)	1g blue	55.00	55.00
J11	A1 (a)	2g dk brown	55.00	55.00
J12	A2 (a)	4g lilac brown	55.00	55.00
J13	A2 (a)	8g violet	55.00	55.00
J14	A2 (a)	16g black	55.00	55.00
		Nos. J8-J14 (7)	385.00	385.00

b

1905, Aug.

J15	A1 (b)	¼g green	55.00	55.00
J16	A1 (b)	½g red	55.00	55.00
J17	A1 (b)	1g blue	55.00	55.00
J18	A1 (b)	2g dark brown	55.00	55.00
J19	A2 (b)	4g lilac brown	55.00	55.00
J20	A2 (b)	8g violet	55.00	55.00
J21	A2 (b)	16g black	55.00	55.00
		Nos. J15-J21 (7)	385.00	385.00

Excellent forgeries of Nos. J8-J42 exist.

Nos. 1-7 Handstamped in Blue or Violet

1905, Sept.

J22	A1	¼g green	14.50	14.50
J23	A1	½g red	14.50	14.50
J24	A1	1g blue	14.50	14.50
J25	A1	2g dark brown	14.50	14.50
J26	A2	4g lilac brown	14.50	14.50
J27	A2	8g violet	21.00	21.00
J28	A2	16g black	25.00	25.00
		Nos. J22-J28 (7)	118.50	118.50

Nos. J22-J27 exist with inverted overprint, also No. J22 with double overprint.

Forgeries exist.

With Additional Surcharge of Value Handstamped as on Nos. 71-77

1907, July 1

J29	A1 (e)	¼ on ¼g grn	14.00	14.00
J30	A1 (e)	½ on ½g red	14.00	14.00
J31	A1 (f)	1 on 1g blue	14.00	14.00
J32	A1 (f)	2 on 2g dk brown	14.00	14.00
J33	A2 (f)	4 on 4g lilac brn	14.00	14.00
J34	A2 (f)	8 on 8g violet	14.00	14.00
J35	A2 (f)	16 on 16g blk	22.50	22.50
		Nos. J29-J35 (7)	106.50	106.50

Nos. J30-J35 exist with inverted surcharge. Nos. J30, J33-J35 exist with double surcharge.

Nos. 1-7 Handstamped in Black

1908, Dec. 1

J36	A1	¼g green	1.40	1.25
J37	A1	½g red	1.40	1.25
J38	A1	1g blue	1.40	1.25
J39	A1	2g dark brown	1.75	1.50
J40	A2	4g lilac brown	2.50	2.50
J41	A2	8g violet	5.50	6.25
J42	A2	16g black	17.50	20.00
		Nos. J36-J42 (7)	31.45	34.00

Nos. J36 to J42 exist with inverted overprint and Nos. J36, J37, J38 and J40 with double overprint.

Forgeries of Nos. J36-J56 exist.

Same Handstamp on Nos. 87-93

1912, Dec. 1 — Perf. 11½

J43	A3	¼g blue green	1.75	1.25
J44	A3	½g rose	1.75	1.50

1913, July 1

J45	A3	1g green & org	6.00	4.25
J46	A4	2g blue	7.00	6.00
J47	A4	4g green & car	11.00	7.00
J48	A5	8g ver & dp grn	14.00	11.00
J49	A5	16g ver & car	35.00	27.50
		Nos. J43-J49 (7)	76.50	58.50

Nos. J43-J49, all exist with inverted, double and double, one inverted overprint.

Same Handstamp on Nos. 120-124 in Blue Black

1925-27 — Perf. 11½

J50	A6	⅛g violet & brn	18.00	18.00
J51	A6	¼g bl grn & db	18.00	18.00
J52	A6	½g scar & ol grn	20.00	20.00
J53	A9	½g rose lil & gray grn	20.00	20.00
J54	A9	2g dp ultra & fawn	20.00	20.00
		Nos. J50-J54 (5)	96.00	96.00

Same Handstamp on Nos. 110, 112

1917 (?)

J55	A3 (i)	1g green & org	30.00	30.00
J56	A4 (j)	2g blue	30.00	30.00

The status of Nos. J55-J56 is questioned.

Catalogue values for unused stamps in this section, from this point to the end of the section, are for Never Hinged items.

D2

Perf. 11½

1951, Apr. 2 Unwmk. Litho.

J57	D2	1c emerald	.35	.25
J58	D2	5c rose red	.75	.25
J59	D2	10c violet	1.40	.55
J60	D2	20c ocher	2.00	1.25
J61	D2	50c bright ultra	3.75	2.75
J62	D2	$1 rose lilac	7.75	3.75
		Nos. J57-J62 (6)	16.00	8.80

Nos. J57-J62 were reissued in 1968 on slightly yellowish paper.

OCCUPATION STAMPS

Issued under Italian Occupation
100 Centesimi = 1 Lira

OS1

Emperor Victor Emmanuel III — OS2

1936 Wmk. 140 Perf. 14

N1	OS1	10c org brn	16.00	9.50
N2	OS1	20c purple	14.50	4.00
N3	OS2	25c dark green	9.50	.80
N4	OS2	30c dark brown	9.50	1.60
N5	OS2	50c rose car	4.00	.40
N6	OS1	75c deep orange	36.00	8.00
N7	OS1	1.25 l deep blue	36.00	12.00
		Nos. N1-N7 (7)	125.50	36.30
		Set, never hinged	300.00	

Issued: Nos. N3-N5, May 22; others Dec. 5. For later issues see Italian East Africa.

FALKLAND ISLANDS

ˈfȯl-klənd ˈī-ləndz

LOCATION — A group of islands about 300 miles east of the Straits of Magellan at the southern limit of South America
GOVT. — British Crown Colony
AREA — 4,700 sq. mi.
POP. — 2,607 (1996)
CAPITAL — Stanley

Dependencies of the Falklands are South Georgia and South Sandwich. In March 1962, three other dependencies — South Shetland Islands, South Orkneys and Graham Land—became the new separate colony of British Antarctic Territory. In 1985 South Georgia and the South Sandwich Islands became a separate colony.

12 Pence = 1 Shilling
20 Shillings = 1 Pound
100 Pence = 1 Pound (1971)

Catalogue values for unused stamps in this country are for Never Hinged items, beginning with Scott 97 in the regular postage section, Scott B1 in the semi-postal section, Scott J1 in the postage due section, Scott 1L1 in Falkland Island Dependencies regular issues, Scott 1LB1 in Falkland Island Dependencies semi-postals, and Scott 2L1, 3L1, 4L1, 5L1 in the Issues for Separate Islands.

Values for unused stamps are for examples with original gum as defined in the catalogue introduction.
Nos. 1-4, 7-8, and some printings of Nos. 5-6, exist with straight edges on one or two sides, being the imperforate margins of the sheets. This occurs in 24 out of 60 stamps. Catalogue values are for stamps with perforations on all sides.

Queen Victoria — A1

1878-79 Unwmk. Engr. Perf. 14

1	A1	1p claret	850.00	500.00
2	A1	4p dark gray ('79)	1,400.	200.00
3	A1	6p green	125.00	85.00
4	A1	1sh bister brown	85.00	80.00

1883-95 Wmk. 2

5	A1	1p brt claret ('94)	130.00	95.00
a.		1p claret	425.00	190.00
b.		Horiz. pair, imperf. vert.	90,000.	
c.		1p red brown ('91)	375.00	95.00
d.		Diag. half of #5c used as ½p on cover		4,600.
6	A1	4p ol gray ('95)	16.00	27.50
a.		4p gray black	875.00	100.00
b.		4p olive gray black ('89)	200.00	65.00
c.		4p brownish black ('94)	1,300.	400.00

No. 6c has watermark reversed. For surcharge see No. 19E.

1886 Wmk. 2 Sideways

7	A1	1p claret	95.00	65.00
a.		1p brownish claret	125.00	80.00
b.		Diagonal half of #7a used as ½p on cover		4,250.
8	A1	4p olive gray	525.00	60.00
a.		4p pale gray black	850.00	90.00

For surcharge see No. 19.

1891-1902 Wmk. 2

9	A1	½p green ('92)	19.00	18.00
a.		½p blue green	30.00	29.00
10	A1	½p yel green ('99)	3.75	3.50
11	A1	1p orange brown	130.00	85.00
a.		Diagonal half used as ½p on cover		4,250.
11B	A1	1p pale red ('99)	9.00	3.50
12	A1	1p org red ('02)	17.50	4.75
a.		1p Venetian red ('95)	32.50	20.00
13	A1	2p magenta ('96)	7.00	14.00
14	A1	2½p deep blue ('94)	275.00	160.00
15	A1	2½p ultra ('94)	50.00	14.00
a.		2½p pale ultra ('98)	70.00	20.00
b.		2½p dull blue	350.00	35.00
c.		2½p deep ultra ('01)	50.00	42.50
d.		2½p pale chalky ultra	275.00	60.00
16	A1	6p yellow ('96)	55.00	52.50
a.		6p orange ('92)	325.00	225.00
17	A1	9p ver ('95)	60.00	60.00
a.		9p salmon ('95)	65.00	65.00
18	A1	1sh gray brn ('95)	80.00	65.00
a.		1sh bis brn ('96)	75.00	55.00
		Nos. 9-18 (11)	706.25	480.25

Nos. 7 and 5a Surcharged in Black

1891 Wmk. 2 Sideways

19	A1	½p on half of 1p, #7	725.00	360.00
d.		Unsevered pair	4,000.	1,600.

Wmk. 2

19E	A1	½p on half of 1p, #5a	825.00	325.00
f.		Unsevered pair	5,000.	1,800.

Genuine used bisects should be canceled with a segmented circular cork cancel. Any other cancel must be linked by date to known mail ship departures. This surcharge exists on "souvenir" bisects, including examples of No. 11, and can be found inverted, double and sideways.

A3

A4

1898 Wmk. 1

20	A3	2sh6p dark blue	290.00	290.00
21	A4	5sh brown red	260.00	260.00

A5

A6

A7

A8

King Edward VII
1904-07 Wmk. 3 Perf. 14

22	A5	½p yellow green	9.00	1.75
23	A5	1p red, wmk. sideways ('07)	1.50	4.50
a.		Wmk. upright ('07)	17.00	1.75
24	A5	2p dull vio ('04)	25.00	24.00
25	A5	2½p ultramarine	35.00	10.00
a.		2½p deep blue	300.00	200.00
26	A6	6p orange ('05)	50.00	57.50
27	A5	1sh bis brn ('05)	50.00	40.00
28	A6	3sh gray green	180.00	160.00
29	A6	5sh dull red ('05)	240.00	160.00
		Nos. 22-29 (8)	590.50	457.75

King George V
1912-14 Perf. 13¾x14, 14 (#36-40)

30	A7	½p yel grn	3.00	3.75
31	A7	1p red	5.50	2.75
32	A7	2p brn vio	30.00	24.00
33	A7	2½p deep ultra	27.50	25.00
34	A7	6p orange	17.50	22.50
35	A7	1sh bis brn	40.00	37.50
36	A8	3sh dark green	100.00	100.00
37	A8	5sh brown red	120.00	120.00
38	A8	5sh plum ('14)	300.00	300.00
39	A8	10sh red, green	200.00	275.00
40	A8	£1 black, red	550.00	600.00
		Nos. 30-40 (11)	1,394.	1,511.

For overprints see Nos. MR1-MR3.

1921-29 Wmk. 4 Perf. 14

41	A7	½p yellow green	3.50	4.50
42	A7	1p red ('24)	6.00	2.10
43	A7	2p brown vio ('23)	26.00	8.50
44	A7	2½p dark blue	24.00	20.00
a.		2½p Prussian blue ('29)	375.00	550.00
45	A7	2½p vio, yel ('23)	6.00	42.50
46	A7	6p orange ('25)	11.00	45.00
47	A7	1sh bister brown	24.00	57.50
48	A8	3sh dk green ('23)	100.00	190.00
		Nos. 41-48 (8)	200.50	370.10

Some specialists call into question No. 44a. The editors would like to see authenticated evidence of its existence.

No. 43 Surcharged

1928

52	A7	2½p on 2p brn vio	1,300.	1,400.
a.		Double surcharge	60,000.	

Beware of forged surcharges.

King George V — A9

1929-31 Perf. 14

54	A9	½p green	1.40	4.25
55	A9	1p scarlet	4.50	.90
56	A9	2p gray	6.00	3.75
57	A9	2½p blue	6.00	2.50
58	A9	4p deep orange	23.00	15.00
59	A9	6p brown violet	24.00	19.00
60	A9	1sh black, green	32.50	37.50
a.		1sh black, emerald	27.50	37.50
61	A9	2sh6p red, green	70.00	70.00
62	A9	5sh green, yel	105.00	120.00
63	A9	10sh red, green	225.00	275.00

Wmk. 3

64	A9	£1 black, red	350.00	425.00
		Nos. 54-64 (11)	847.40	972.90

Issue dates: 4p, 1931, others, Sept. 2.

Romney Marsh Ram — A10

Iceberg — A11

Whaling Ship — A12

Port Louis — A13

Map of the Islands — A14

South Georgia — A15

Blue Whale — A16

Government House A17

Battle Memorial A18

King
Penguin
A19

Coat of
Arms
A20

King George V — A21

1933, Jan. 2   **Wmk. 4**   **Perf. 12**

65	A10	½p grn & blk	4.00	13.00
66	A11	1p dl red & blk	3.75	2.75
67	A12	1½p lt bl & blk	21.00	27.50
68	A13	2p ol brn & blk	17.50	32.50
69	A14	3p dl vio & blk	28.00	35.00
70	A15	4p org & blk	26.00	28.00
71	A16	6p gray & blk	75.00	95.00
72	A17	1sh ol grn & blk	75.00	100.00
73	A18	2sh6p dp vio & blk	250.00	400.00
74	A19	5sh yel & blk	950.00	1,500.
a.		5sh yel org & blk	3,250.	3,750.
75	A20	10sh lt brn & blk	850.00	1,500.
76	A21	£1 rose & blk	2,500.	3,500.
		Nos. 65-76 (12)	4,800.	7,234.

Cent. of the permanent occupation of the islands as a British colony.

Common Design Types
pictured following the introduction.

Silver Jubilee Issue
Common Design Type

1935, May 7   **Perf. 11x12**

77	CD301	1p car & blue	3.50	.50
78	CD301	2½p ultra & brn	22.50	2.25
79	CD301	4p indigo & grn	24.00	8.00
80	CD301	1sh brn vio & ind	15.00	4.00
		Nos. 77-80 (4)	55.00	14.75
		Set, never hinged	75.00	
		Set (4), Ovptd. "SPECIMEN"	500.00	

Coronation Issue
Common Design Type

1937, May 12   **Perf. 11x11½**

81	CD302	½p deep green	.25	.25
82	CD302	1p dark carmine	.75	.55
83	CD302	2½p deep ultra	1.90	1.50
		Nos. 81-83 (3)	2.90	2.30
		Set, never hinged	4.00	
		Set (3), Ovptd. "SPECIMEN"	450.00	

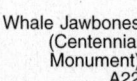

Whale Jawbones
(Centennial
Monument)
A22

Nos. 85, 86A, Black-necked swan. Nos. 85B, 86, Battle memorial. 2½p, 3p, Flock of sheep. 4p, Upland goose. 6p, R.R.S. "Discovery II." 9p, R.R.S. "William Scoresby." 1sh, Mt. Sugar Top. 1sh3p, Turkey vultures. 2sh6p, Gentoo penguins. 5sh, Sea lions. 10sh, Deception Island. £1, Arms of Colony.

1938-46   **Perf. 12**

84	A22	½p green & blk	.25	.75
85	A22	1p red & black	2.50	1.00
a.		1p rose carmine & black	22.50	1.00
85B	A22	1p dk vio & blk ('41)	2.00	2.00
86	A22	2p dk vio & blk	1.30	1.00
86A	A22	2p rose car & black ('41)	1.40	4.50
87	A22	2½p ultra & blk	1.00	.50
87A	A22	3p blue & blk ('41)	5.50	8.50
c.		3p dp blue & blk	12.50	4.50
88	A22	4p rose vio & black	2.75	2.00
89	A22	6p sepia & blk	7.50	4.25
90	A22	9p sl bl & blk	15.00	6.00
91	A22	1sh lt dl blue	30.00	19.00
92	A22	1sh3p car & blk	2.00	1.60
93	A22	2sh6p gray black	40.00	22.50

94	A22	5sh org brn & ultra	75.00	95.00
a.		5sh yel brown & indigo	650.00	150.00
95	A22	10sh org & blk	100.00	65.00
96	A22	£1 dk vio & blk	75.00	75.00
		Nos. 84-96 (16)	361.20	308.60
		Set, never hinged	600.00	
		Set (16), perf. "SPECIMEN"	2,500.	

Issued: Nos. 85B, 86A, 3p, 7/14/41; 1sh3p, 12/10/46; No. 94a, 1942; others, 1/3/38.
See Nos. 101-102. For overprints see Nos. 2L1-2L8, 3L1-3L8, 4L1-4L8.

Catalogue values for unused stamps in this section, from this point to the end of the section, are for Never Hinged items.

Peace Issue
Common Design Type

Perf. 13½x14

1946, Oct. 7   **Engr.**   **Wmk. 4**

97	CD303	1p purple	.35	.80
98	CD303	3p deep blue	.55	.55

Silver Wedding Issue
Common Design Types

1948, Nov. 1   **Photo.**   **Perf. 14x14½**

99	CD304	2½p bright ultra	2.10	1.10

Engr.; Name Typo.
Perf. 11½x11

100	CD305	£1 purple	110.00	75.00

Types of 1938-46

2½p, Upland goose. 6p, R.R.S. "Discovery II."

Perf. 12

1949, June 15   **Engr.**   **Wmk. 4**

101	A22	2½p dp blue & black	7.50	8.50
102	A22	6p gray black	6.75	5.50

UPU Issue
Common Design Types

Engr.; Name Typo. on 3p, 1sh3p

1949, Oct. 10   **Perf. 13½, 11x11½**

103	CD306	1p violet	1.75	1.10
104	CD307	3p indigo	5.00	5.00
105	CD308	1sh3p green	3.50	2.50
106	CD309	2sh blue	3.75	8.50
		Nos. 103-106 (4)	14.00	17.10

Sheep
A35

Arms of the
Colony
A36

Designs: 1p, R.M.S. Fitzroy. 2p Upland goose. 2½p, Map. 4p, Auster plane. 6p, M.S.S. John Biscoe. 9p, "Two Sisters" peaks. 1sh, Gentoo penguins. 1sh 3p, Kelp goose and gander. 2sh 6p, Sheep shearing. 5sh, Battle memorial. 10sh, Sea lion and clapmatch. £1, Hulk of "Great Britain."

Perf. 13½x13, 13x13½

1952, Jan. 2   **Engr.**   **Wmk. 4**

107	A35	½p green	1.25	1.00
108	A35	1p red	2.40	.55
109	A35	2p violet	4.50	3.00
110	A35	2½p ultra & blk	2.00	.70
111	A36	3p deep ultra	2.25	1.10
112	A35	4p claret	12.50	1.75
113	A35	6p yellow brn	12.00	1.10
114	A35	9p orange yel	9.00	2.25
115	A36	1sh black	24.00	1.10
116	A35	1sh3p red orange	18.00	7.00
117	A36	2sh6p olive	22.50	12.50
118	A36	5sh red violet	20.00	11.00
119	A35	10sh gray	30.00	20.00
120	A35	£1 black	40.00	22.50
		Nos. 107-120 (14)	200.40	90.05

Coronation Issue
Common Design Type

1953, June 4   **Perf. 13½x13**

121	CD312	1p car & black	.90	1.50

Types of 1952 with Portrait of Queen Elizabeth II

1955-57   **Perf. 13½x13, 13x13½**

122	A35	½p green ('57)	1.00	1.50
123	A35	1p red ('57)	1.25	1.25
124	A35	2p violet ('56)	3.25	4.75
125	A35	6p light brown	9.00	.70
126	A35	9p ocher ('57)	10.50	17.00
127	A36	1sh black	12.00	2.50
		Nos. 122-127 (6)	37.00	27.70

Marsh
Starling — A37

Birds: ½p, Falkland Islands Thrush. 1p, Dominican gull. 2p, Gentoo penguins. 3p, Upland geese. 4p, Steamer ducks. 5½p, Rock-hopper penguin. 6p, black-browed albatross. 9p, Silver grebe. 1sh, Pied oystercatchers. 1sh3p, Yellow-billed teal. 2sh, Kelp geese. 5sh, King shag. 10sh, Guadelupe caracara. £1, Black-necked swan.

Perf. 13½x13

1960, Feb. 10   **Engr.**   **Wmk. 314**
Center in Black

128	A37	½p green	5.00	2.25
a.		Wmk. sideways ('66)	.45	.40
129	A37	1p rose red	3.00	2.00
130	A37	2p blue	4.50	1.25
131	A37	2½p bister brn	2.50	1.00
132	A37	3p olive	1.25	.50
133	A37	4p rose car	1.50	1.25
134	A37	5½p violet	3.25	2.50
135	A37	6p sepia	3.50	.30
136	A37	9p orange	2.50	1.25
137	A37	1sh dull purple	1.25	.40
138	A37	1sh3p ultra	12.50	14.00
139	A37	2sh brown car	30.00	2.50
140	A37	5sh grnsh blue	27.50	11.00
141	A37	10sh rose lilac	42.60	22.00
142	A37	£1 yellow org	45.00	27.00
		Nos. 128-142 (15)	185.85	89.20

Morse Key — A38

1962, Oct. 5   **Photo.**   **Perf. 11½x11**

143	A38	6p dp org & dk red	.85	.50
144	A38	1sh brt ol grn & dp green	.95	.50
145	A38	2sh brt ultra & violet	1.25	1.75
		Nos. 143-145 (3)	3.05	2.75

Falkland Islands radio station, 50th anniv.

Freedom from Hunger Issue
Common Design Type

1963, June 4   **Perf. 14x14½**

146	CD314	1sh ultramarine	10.50	2.50

Red Cross Centenary Issue
Common Design Type
Wmk. 314

1963, Sept.2   **Litho.**   **Perf. 13**

147	CD315	1p black & red	2.00	.75
148	CD315	1sh ultra & red	16.00	4.75

Shakespeare Issue
Common Design Type

1964, Apr. 23   **Photo.**   **Perf. 14x14½**

149	CD316	6p black	1.60	.50

H.M.S.
Glasgow — A39

6p, H.M.S. Kent. 1sh, H.M.S. Invincible. 2sh, Falkland Islands Battle Memorial, vert.

1964, Dec. 8   **Engr.**   **Perf. 13**

150	A39	2½p ver & black	9.00	3.75
151	A39	6p blue & black	.55	.30
a.		"Glasgow" vignette	30,000.	
152	A39	1sh carmine & blk	.55	1.00

Perf. 13x14

153	A39	2sh dk blue & blk	.55	.75
		Nos. 150-153 (4)	10.65	5.80

Battle of the Falkland Islands between the British and German navies, 50th anniv.

ITU Issue
Common Design Type

Perf. 11x11½

1965, May 26   **Litho.**   **Wmk. 314**

154	CD317	1p blue & dl dk bl	.50	.40
155	CD317	2sh lilac & dl yel	6.25	2.75

Intl. Cooperation Year Issue
Common Design Type

1965, Oct. 25   **Perf. 14½**

156	CD318	1p blue grn & claret	1.25	.40
157	CD318	1sh lt violet & grn	4.75	1.25

Churchill Memorial Issue
Common Design Type

1966, Jan. 24   **Photo.**   **Perf. 14**
Design in Black, Gold and Carmine Rose

158	CD319	½p bright blue	.75	2.25
159	CD319	1p green	2.00	.30
160	CD319	1sh brown	5.50	3.00
161	CD319	2sh violet	4.50	4.00
		Nos. 158-161 (4)	12.75	9.55

Human Rights
Flame and
Globe — A40

Perf. 14x14½

1968, July 4   **Photo.**   **Wmk. 314**

162	A40	2p brt rose & multi	.40	.25
163	A40	6p brt green & multi	.45	.25
164	A40	1sh orange & multi	.55	.30
165	A40	2sh ultra & multi	.65	.35
		Nos. 162-165 (4)	2.05	1.15

International Human Rights Year.

Dusty Miller — A41

Falkland Islands flora: 1½p, Pig vine, horiz. 2p, Pale maiden. 3p, Dog orchid. 3½p, Sea cabbage, horiz. 4½p, Vanilla daisy. 5½p, Arrowleaf marigold, horiz. 6p, Diddle-dee, horiz. 1sh, Scurvy grass, horiz. 1sh6p, Prickly burr. 2sh, Fachine. 3sh, Lavender. 5sh, Felton's flower, horiz. £1, Yellow orchid.

1968, Oct. 9   **Photo.**   **Perf. 14**

166	A41	½p multicolored	.25	1.75
167	A41	1½p multicolored	.45	.25
168	A41	2p multicolored	.60	.25
169	A41	3p multicolored	6.00	1.00
170	A41	3½p multicolored	.35	1.00
171	A41	4½p multicolored	1.60	2.00
172	A41	5½p multicolored	1.60	2.00
173	A41	6p multicolored	.85	.30
174	A41	1sh multicolored	1.00	1.50
175	A41	1sh6p multicolored	5.00	15.00
176	A41	2sh multicolored	5.50	6.25
177	A41	3sh multicolored	7.75	8.00
178	A41	5sh multicolored	27.00	13.00
179	A41	£1 multicolored	11.50	3.25
		Nos. 166-179 (14)	69.45	55.55

See Nos. 210-222. For surcharges see Nos. 197-209.

Beaver DHC 2
Seaplane — A42

Designs: 6p, Norseman seaplane. 1sh, Auster plane. 2sh, Falkland Islands arms.

1969, Apr. 8   **Litho.**   **Perf. 14**

180	A42	1p multicolored	.45	.30
181	A42	2p multicolored	.65	.35
182	A42	1sh multicolored	.65	.40
183	A42	2sh multicolored	1.20	2.00
		Nos. 180-183 (4)	2.95	3.05

21st anniv. of Government Air Service.

Bishop
Stirling — A43

2p, Holy Trinity Church, 1869. 6p, Christ Church Cathedral, 1969. 2sh, Bishop's miter.

1969, Oct. 30			Perf. 14	
184	A43	2p emerald & black	.40	.60
185	A43	6p red orange & black	.50	.60
186	A43	1sh lilac & black	.50	.60
187	A43	2sh yellow & multi	.60	.75
		Nos. 184-187 (4)	2.00	2.55

Consecration of Waite Hocking Stirling (1829-1923), as first Bishop of the Bishopric of the Falkland Islands, cent.

Gun Emplacement A44

2p, Volunteer on horseback, vert. 1sh, Volunteer in dress uniform, vert. 2sh, Defense Force badge.

Perf. 13½x13, 13x13½

1970, Apr. 30		Litho.	Wmk. 314	
188	A44	2p ultra & multi	1.15	.70
189	A44	6p multicolored	1.40	.80
190	A44	1sh buff & multi	2.25	.80
191	A44	2sh yellow & multi	3.25	1.00
		Nos. 188-191 (4)	8.05	3.30

Falkland Islands Defense Force, 50th anniv.

The Great Britain, 1843 — A45

The Great Britain in: 4p, 1845. 9p, 1876. 1sh, 1886. 2sh, 1970.

1970, Oct. 30		Litho.	Perf. 14½	
192	A45	2p lemon & multi	1.00	.50
193	A45	4p lilac & multi	1.25	.90
194	A45	9p bister & multi	1.50	.90
195	A45	1sh org brn & multi	1.50	.90
196	A45	2sh multicolored	2.00	1.10
		Nos. 192-196 (5)	7.25	4.30

Nos. 166-178 Surcharged

1971, Feb. 15		Photo.	Perf. 14	
197	A41	½p on ½p multi	.40	.40
198	A41	1p on 1½p multi	.25	.25
a.		5p on 1½p (error)	750.00	
199	A41	1½p on 2p multi	.35	.35
200	A41	2p on 3p multi	.55	.55
201	A41	2½p on 3½p multi	.30	.30
202	A41	3p on 4p multi	.35	.35
203	A41	4p on 5½p multi	.40	.40
204	A41	5p on 6p multi	.70	.70
205	A41	6p on 1sh multi	6.00	7.00
206	A41	7½p on 1sh6p multi	8.00	8.00
207	A41	10p on 2sh multi	8.00	3.50
208	A41	15p on 3sh multi	3.50	2.75
209	A41	25p on 5sh multi	4.50	3.75
		Nos. 197-209 (13)	33.30	28.30

Flower Type of 1968
"p" instead of "d"

Designs as before. 1p, 2½p, 4p, 5p, 6p, 25p, horizontal.

Wmk. 314, Sideways on Vert. Stamps

1972, June 1			Perf. 14	
210	A41	½p Dusty miller	.75	4.75
a.		Wmk. upright ('74)	15.00	32.50
b.		Wmk. 373 ('75)	3.25	3.50
211	A41	1p Pig vine	.40	.40
212	A41	1½p Pale maiden	.55	4.50
213	A41	2p Dog orchid	6.00	1.50
a.		Wmk. upright ('74)	30.00	3.25
214	A41	2½p Sea cabbage	.70	4.50
215	A41	3p Vanilla daisy	.75	1.40
216	A41	4p Arrowleaf mari-gold	1.00	1.10
217	A41	5p Diddle-dee	1.10	.75
218	A41	6p Scurvy grass	18.00	9.50
a.		Wmk. sideways ('74)	2.10	2.50
219	A41	7½p Prickly burr	2.00	3.75
220	A41	10p Fachine	10.00	4.00
221	A41	15p Lavender	4.00	4.50
222	A41	25p Felton's flower	8.00	6.00
		Nos. 210-222 (13)	53.25	46.65

Silver Wedding Issue, 1972
Common Design Type

Design: Queen Elizabeth II, Prince Philip, Romney Marsh sheep and giant sea lions.

1972, Nov 20		Photo.	Perf. 14x14½	
223	CD324	1p sl grn & multi	.30	.30
224	CD324	10p ultra & multi	.70	.85

Princess Anne's Wedding Issue
Common Design Type

1973, Nov. 14		Litho.	Perf. 14	
225	CD325	5p lilac & multi	.25	.25
226	CD325	15p citron & multi	.45	.35

Fur Seals — A46

Tourist Publicity: 4p, Trout fishing. 5p, Rockhopper penguins. 15p, Military starling.

1974, Mar. 6		Litho.	Wmk. 314	
227	A46	2p lt ultra & multi	2.25	2.00
228	A46	4p brt blue & multi	3.25	1.50
229	A46	5p yellow & multi	10.50	2.50
230	A46	15p lt ultra & multi	12.00	5.00
		Nos. 227-230 (4)	28.00	11.00

Early 19th Cent. Mail Coach, UPU Emblem — A47

UPU Cent.: 5p, Packet, 1841. 8p, First British mail planes, 1911. 16p, Catapult mail, 1920's.

1974, July 31			Perf. 14	
231	A47	2p multicolored	.25	.25
232	A47	5p multicolored	.30	.45
233	A47	8p multicolored	.35	.55
234	A47	16p multicolored	.55	.75
		Nos. 231-234 (4)	1.45	2.00

Churchill, Parliament and Big Ben — A48

Design: 20p, Churchill and warships.

1974, Nov. 30			Perf. 13x13½	
235	A48	16p multicolored	1.00	1.00
236	A48	20p multicolored	1.50	1.50
a.		Souvenir sheet of 2, #235-236	8.00	8.00

Sir Winston Churchill (1874-1965).

HMS Exeter — A49

Battleships: 6p, HMNZS Achilles. 8p, Admiral Graf Spee. 16p, HMS Ajax.

1974, Dec. 13			Perf. 14	
237	A49	2p multicolored	2.50	1.75
238	A49	6p multicolored	4.25	3.50
239	A49	8p multicolored	5.25	4.50
240	A49	16p multicolored	10.00	14.00
		Nos. 237-240 (4)	22.00	23.75

35th anniv. of the Battle of the River Plate between British ships and the German battleship Graf Spee.

Seal and Flag Badge — A50

7½p, Coat of arms, 1925. 10p, Arms, 1948. 16p, Arms (Falkland Islands Dependencies), 1952.

1975, Oct. 28		Litho.	Wmk. 373	
241	A50	2p multicolored	1.00	.50
242	A50	7½p multicolored	1.60	1.50
243	A50	10p multicolored	1.75	1.75
244	A50	16p multicolored	2.50	3.25
		Nos. 241-244 (4)	6.85	7.00

Falkland Islands heraldic arms, 50th anniv.

½p-Coin and Trout — A51

New Coinage: 5½p, 1p-coin and gentoo penguins. 8p, 2p-coin and upland geese. 10p, 5p-coin and black-browed albatross. 16p, 10p-coin and sea lions.

1975, Dec. 31		Litho.	Wmk. 373	
245	A51	2p copper & multi	.75	.50
246	A51	5½p copper & multi	1.75	1.50
247	A51	8p copper & multi	2.00	1.75
248	A51	10p silver & multi	2.50	2.00
249	A51	16p silver & multi	3.00	3.00
		Nos. 245-249 (5)	10.00	8.75

Gathering Sheep — A52

Sheep Farming: 7½p, Shearing. 10p, Dipping sheep. 20p, Motor Vessel Monsunen collecting wool.

1976, Apr. 28		Litho.	Perf. 13½	
250	A52	2p multicolored	.90	.75
251	A52	7½p multicolored	1.25	1.25
252	A52	10p multicolored	1.60	1.60
253	A52	20p multicolored	2.50	3.50
		Nos. 250-253 (4)	6.25	7.10

Prince Philip, 1957 Visit — A53

11p, Queen, ampulla and spoon. 33p, Queen awaiting anointment, and Knights of the Garter.

1977, Feb. 7			Perf. 13½x14	
254	A53	6p multicolored	.35	.35
a.		Booklet pane of 4, wmk. 314	6.00	
b.		Single stamp from #254a	1.50	4.00
255	A53	11p multicolored	.60	.60
a.		Booklet pane of 4	2.40	
256	A53	33p multicolored	1.50	1.50
a.		Booklet pane of 4	6.00	
		Nos. 254-256 (3)	2.45	2.45

25th anniv. of the reign of Elizabeth II.

Map of West and East Falkland with Communications Centers — A54

Telecommunications: 11p, Ship to shore communications at Fox Bay. 40p, Globe with Telex tape and telephone.

1977, Oct. 24		Litho.	Perf. 14½x14	
257	A54	3p yel brown & multi	.90	.25
258	A54	11p lt ultra & multi	1.60	.60
259	A54	40p rose & multi	2.50	2.00
		Nos. 257-259 (3)	5.00	2.85

A.E.S., 1957-1974 A55

Designs: Mail ships.

1978, Jan. 25		Wmk. 373	Perf. 14	
		No Date Inscription		
260	A55	1p shown	.25	.25
261	A55	2p Darwin, 1957-75	.35	.25
262	A55	3p Merak-N 1951-53	.25	1.50
263	A55	4p Fitzroy, 1936-57	.25	1.50
264	A55	5p Lafonia 1936-41	.25	.30
265	A55	6p Fleurus, 1924-33	.30	.40
266	A55	7p S.S. Falkland, 1914-34	.40	2.75
267	A55	8p Oravia, 1900-12	.45	1.25
268	A55	9p Memphis, 1890-97	.45	1.00
269	A55	10p Black Hawk, 1873-80	.60	.50
270	A55	20p Foam, 1963-72	1.00	1.50
271	A55	25p Fairy, 1857-61	1.00	3.25
272	A55	50p Amelia, 1852-54	1.50	3.50
273	A55	£1 Nautilus, 1846-48	2.50	5.50
274	A55	£3 Hebe, 1842-46	9.00	13.00
		Nos. 260-274 (15)	18.55	36.45

The 1p, 3p, 5p, 6p and 10p were also issued in booklet panes of 4.
For overprints see Nos. 352-353.

1982, Dec. 1			Inscribed "1982"	
260a	A55	1p shown	.40	2.00
261a	A55	2p Darwin, 1957-75	.50	2.00
262a	A55	3p Merak-N 1951-53	.60	2.00
263a	A55	4p Fitzroy, 1936-57	.60	2.00
264a	A55	5p Lafonia 1936-41	.70	2.00
265a	A55	6p Fleurus, 1924-33	.70	2.00
266a	A55	7p S.S. Falkland, 1914-34	.75	2.00
267a	A55	8p Oravia, 1900-12	.75	2.00
268a	A55	9p Memphis, 1890-97	.80	2.00
269a	A55	10p Black Hawk, 1873-80	.85	2.00
270a	A55	20p Foam, 1963-72	1.50	3.25
271a	A55	25p Fairy, 1857-61	1.50	3.25
272a	A55	50p Amelia, 1852-54	1.75	4.00
273a	A55	£1 Nautilus, 1846-48	3.25	5.00
274a	A55	£3 Hebe, 1842-46	5.00	10.00
		Nos. 260a-274a (15)	19.65	45.50

Elizabeth II Coronation Anniversary Issue
Souvenir Sheet
Common Design Type

1978, June 2		Unwmk.	Perf. 15	
275		Sheet of 6	4.00	5.50
a.	CD326	25p Red Dragon of Wales	.60	.85
b.	CD327	25p Elizabeth II	.60	.85
c.	CD328	25p Hornless ram	.60	.85

No. 275 contains 2 se-tenant strips of Nos. 275a-275c, separated by horizontal gutter with commemorative and descriptive inscriptions.

Short Sunderland Mark III — A56

Design: 33p, Plane in flight and route Southampton to Stanley.

1978, Apr. 28		Wmk. 373	Perf. 14	
276	A56	11p multicolored	2.75	2.25
277	A56	33p multicolored	4.00	3.25

First direct flight Southampton, England to Stanley, Falkland Islands, 26th anniv.

First Fox Bay PO and No. 1 — A57

Designs: 11p, Second Stanley Post Office and #2. 15p, New Island Post Office and #3. 22p, 1st Stanley Post Office and #4.

1978, Aug. 8		Litho.	Perf. 13½x13	
278	A57	3p multicolored	.25	.25
279	A57	11p multicolored	.30	.40
280	A57	15p multicolored	.40	.50
281	A57	22p multicolored	.70	.85
		Nos. 278-281 (4)	1.65	2.00

Falkland Islands postage stamps, cent.

Macrocystis Pyrifera — A58

Kelp: 7p, Durvillea. 11p, Lessoniae, horiz. 15p, Callophyllis, horiz. 25p, Iridea.

1979, Feb. 19   Litho.   Perf. 14
282	A58	3p multicolored	.40	.40
283	A58	7p multicolored	.45	.45
284	A58	11p multicolored	.55	.55
285	A58	15p multicolored	.80	.80
286	A58	25p multicolored	.95	1.10
		Nos. 282-286 (5)	3.15	3.30

Britten-Norman Islander over Map — A59

Opening of Stanley Airport: 11p, Fokker F27 over map. 15p, Fokker F28 over Stanley. 25p, Cessna 172 Skyhawk, Islander and Fokkers F27, F28 over runway.

1979, May 1   Litho.   Perf. 13½
287	A59	3p multicolored	.45	.25
288	A59	11p multicolored	.85	.65
289	A59	15p multicolored	1.00	.65
290	A59	25p multicolored	1.50	1.00
		Nos. 287-290 (4)	3.80	2.55

Rowland Hill and No. 121 — A60

Sir Rowland Hill (1795-1879), originator of penny postage, and: 11p, Falkland Islands No. 1, vert. 25p, Penny Black. 33p, Falkland Islands No. 37, vert.

1979, Aug. 27   Perf. 14
291	A60	3p multicolored	.25	.25
292	A60	11p multicolored	.40	.40
293	A60	25p multicolored	.75	.75
		Nos. 291-293 (3)	1.40	1.40

Souvenir Sheet
294	A60	33p multicolored	1.50	1.50

Mail Delivery by Air, UPU Emblem — A61

UPU Membership Cent. (Modes of Mail Delivery): 11p, Horseback. 25p, Schooner Gwendolin.

1979, Nov. 26
295	A61	3p multicolored	.25	.25
296	A61	11p multicolored	.45	.55
297	A61	25p multicolored	.65	1.10
		Nos. 295-297 (3)	1.35	1.90

Commerson's Dolphin — A62

Designs: 3p, Peale's porpoise, vert. 7p, Hour-glass dolphin. 11p, Spectacled porpoise, vert. 15p, Dusky dolphin. 25p, Killer whale.

1980, Feb. 25   Wmk. 373   Perf. 14
298	A62	3p multicolored	.40	.40
299	A62	6p shown	.60	.60
300	A62	7p multicolored	.60	.60
301	A62	11p multicolored	.70	.70
302	A62	15p multicolored	.80	.80
303	A62	25p multicolored	.90	1.50
		Nos. 298-303 (6)	4.00	4.60

Miniature Sheet

A63

Designs: a, Falkland Islands Cancel, 1878. b, New Islds., 1915. c, Falklands Islds., 1901. d, Port Stanley, 1935. e, Port Stanley airmail, 1952. f, Fox Bay, 1934.

1980, May 6   Litho.   Perf. 14
304	A63	Sheet of 6	1.60	1.60
a.-f.		11p any single	.25	.25

London 1980 Intl. Stamp Exhib., May 6-14.

Queen Mother Elizabeth Birthday
Common Design Type

1980, Aug. 4   Litho.   Perf. 14
305	CD330	11p multicolored	.40	.40

Striated Caracara — A64

Designs: 11p, Red-backed buzzard. 15p, Crested caracara. 25p, Cassin's falcon.

1980, Aug. 11   Wmk. 373   Perf. 13½
306	A64	3p shown	.60	.30
307	A64	11p multicolored	.75	.55
308	A64	15p multicolored	.85	.65
309	A64	25p multicolored	1.00	1.00
		Nos. 306-309 (4)	3.20	2.50

Port Egmont, Early Settlement A65

1980, Dec. 22   Litho.   Perf. 14
310	A65	3p Stanley	.25	.25
311	A65	11p shown	.35	.35
312	A65	25p Port Louis	.75	.75
313	A65	33p Mission House, Keppel Island	.95	.95
		Nos. 310-313 (4)	2.30	2.30

Polwarth Sheep — A66

1981, Jan. 19   Litho.   Perf. 14
314	A66	3p shown	.25	.25
315	A66	11p Frisian cow and calf	.35	.30
316	A66	25p Horse	.70	1.00
317	A66	33p Welsh collies	.80	1.25
		Nos. 314-317 (4)	2.10	2.80

Map of Falkland Islands, Bowles and Carver, 1779 — A67

10p, Hawkin's Mainland, 1773. 13p, New Isles, 1747. 15p, French & British Islands. 25p, Falklands, 1771. 26p, Falklands, 1764.

1981, May 22   Litho.   Perf. 14
318	A67	3p shown	.25	.25
319	A67	10p multicolored	.30	.35
320	A67	13p multicolored	.35	.35
321	A67	15p multicolored	.45	.35
322	A67	25p multicolored	.60	.50
323	A67	26p multicolored	.65	.50
		Nos. 318-323 (6)	2.60	2.30

Royal Wedding Issue
Common Design Type

1981, July 22   Litho.   Perf. 13½x13
324	CD331	10p Bouquet	.25	.25
325	CD331	13p Charles	.40	.45
326	CD331	52p Couple	1.00	1.00
		Nos. 324-326 (3)	1.65	1.70

Duke of Edinburgh's Awards, 25th Anniv. — A68

1981, Sept. 28   Litho.   Perf. 14
327	A68	10p Spinning	.25	.25
328	A68	13p Camping	.25	.25
329	A68	15p Kayaking	.35	.35
330	A68	26p Duke of Edinburgh	.55	.55
		Nos. 327-330 (4)	1.40	1.40

The Holy Virgin, by Guido Reni (1575-1642) — A69

Christmas: 3p, Adoration of the Holy Child, 16th cent. Dutch. 13p, Holy Family in an Italian Landscape, 17th cent. Italian.

1981, Nov. 9   Litho.   Perf. 14
331	A69	3p multicolored	.25	.25
332	A69	13p multicolored	.50	.50
333	A69	26p multicolored	.75	.75
		Nos. 331-333 (3)	1.50	1.50

This set was issued Nov. 2 in London by the Crown Agents.

Rock Cod — A70

Designs: Shelf fish — 5p, Falkland herring, horiz. 15p, Patagonian hake, horiz. 25p, Southern blue whiting, horiz. 26p, Gray-tailed skate.

1981, Dec. 7
334	A70	5p multicolored	.25	.25
335	A70	13p shown	.30	.35
336	A70	15p multicolored	.35	.50
337	A70	25p multicolored	.55	.75
338	A70	26p multicolored	.55	.75
		Nos. 334-338 (5)	2.00	2.50

Shipwrecks A71

Designs: 5p, Lady Elizabeth, 1913. 13p, Capricorn, 1882. 15p, Jhelum, 1870. 25p, Snowsquall, 1864. 26p, St. Mary, 1890.

1982, Feb. 15   Wmk. 373   Perf. 14½
339	A71	5p multicolored	.35	.35
340	A71	13p multicolored	.45	.45
341	A71	15p multicolored	.50	.50
342	A71	25p multicolored	.70	.70
343	A71	26p multicolored	.70	.70
		Nos. 339-343 (5)	2.70	2.70

Sesquicentennial of Charles Darwin's Visit — A72

1982, Apr. 19   Litho.   Perf. 14
344	A72	5p Darwin	.45	.45
345	A72	17p Microscope	.55	.55
346	A72	25p Warrah	.85	.85
347	A72	34p Beagle	1.10	1.10
		Nos. 344-347 (4)	2.95	2.95

Princess Diana Issue
Common Design Type

1982, July 5   Wmk. 373   Perf. 13
348	CD333	5p Arms	.30	.30
349	CD333	17p Diana	.60	.60
350	CD333	37p Wedding	.90	.90
351	CD333	50p Portrait	1.15	1.15
		Nos. 348-351 (4)	2.95	2.95

Nos. 264, 271 Overprinted

1982, Oct. 7   Litho.   Perf. 14
352	A55	5p multicolored	.25	.30
353	A55	25p multicolored	.50	1.00

12th Commonwealth Games, Brisbane, Australia, Sept. 30-Oct. 9.

Tussock Bird — A73

Designs: 10p, Black-chinned siskin. 13p, Grass wren. 17p, Black-throated finch. 25p, Falkland-correndera pipit. 34p, Dark-faced ground-tyrant.

1982, Dec. 6   Perf. 15x14½
354	A73	5p shown	.40	.40
355	A73	10p multicolored	.50	.50
356	A73	13p multicolored	.50	.50
357	A73	17p multicolored	.50	.50
358	A73	25p multicolored	.60	.60
359	A73	34p multicolored	.70	.70
		Nos. 354-359 (6)	3.20	3.20

British Occupation Sesquicentennial — A74

1p, Raising the Standard, Port Louis, 1833. 2p, Chelsea pensioners & barracks, 1849. 5p, Wool trade, 1874. 10p, Ship repairing trade, 1850-90. 15p, Government House, early 20th cent. 20p, Battle of the Falkland Islands, 1914. 25p, Whalebone Arch centenary, 1933. 40p, Contribution to World War II effort, 1939-45. 50p, Visit of Duke of Edinburgh, 1957. £1, Royal Marines, 1933, 1983, vert. £2, Queen Elizabeth II.

1983, Jan. 1   Litho.   Perf. 14
360	A74	1p multi, vert.	.35	.35
361	A74	2p multi	.40	.40
362	A74	5p multi, vert.	.40	.40
363	A74	10p multi	.55	.70
364	A74	15p multi	.55	.80
365	A74	20p multi, vert.	.75	1.25
366	A74	25p multi	.75	1.25
367	A74	40p multi, vert.	.80	1.25
368	A74	50p multi	.95	1.25
369	A74	£1 multi	1.25	1.75
370	A74	£2 multi, vert.	2.50	3.00
		Nos. 360-370 (11)	9.25	12.40

For surcharges see Nos. 402-403.

A75

1983, Mar. 14
371	A75	5p No. 69	.25	.25
372	A75	17p No. 65	.45	.45
373	A75	25p No. 75, vert.	.70	1.00
374	A75	50p No. 370, vert.	.90	1.00
		Nos. 371-374 (4)	2.30	2.70

Commonwealth Day.

First Anniv. of Liberation — A76

1983, June 14   Wmk. 373   Perf. 14
375	A76	5p Army	.30	.30
376	A76	13p Merchant Navy	.40	.40
377	A76	17p Royal Air Force	.60	.60
378	A76	50p Royal Navy	1.20	1.75
a.		Souvenir sheet of 4, #375-378	2.50	2.75
		Nos. 375-378 (4)	2.50	3.05

Local Fruit — A77

1983, Oct. 10   Litho.   Perf. 14

379	A77	5p Diddle dee	.25	.25
380	A77	17p Tea berries	.35	.40
381	A77	25p Mountain berries	.50	.60
382	A77	34p Native strawberries	.70	.80
		Nos. 379-382 (4)	1.80	2.05

Britten-Norman Islander — A78

Designs: 13p, DHC-2 Beaver. 17p, Noorduyn Norseman. 50p, Auster.

1983, Nov. 14   Litho.   Perf. 14

383	A78	5p shown	.25	.25
384	A78	13p multicolored	.35	.40
385	A78	17p multicolored	.45	.50
386	A78	50p multicolored	1.00	1.25
		Nos. 383-386 (4)	2.05	2.40

Green Spider — A79

Insects and Spiders: 2p, 7p, Ichneumon-Fly. 3p, Brocade Moth. 4p, Black Beetle. 5p, Fritillary. 6p, Green Spider, diff. 8p, Ochre Shoulder. 9p, Clocker Weevil. 10p, Hover Fly. 20p, Weevil. 25p, Metallic Beetle. 50p, Camel Cricket. £1, Beauchene Spider. £3, Southern Painted Lady.

1984, Jan. 1   Litho.   Perf. 14

387	A79	1p shown	.30	.80
388	A79	2p multicolored	2.75	2.50
a.		Inscribed "1986"	4.00	3.25
389	A79	3p multicolored	.65	.85
390	A79	4p multicolored	.50	.85
391	A79	5p multicolored	.50	.85
392	A79	6p multicolored	.50	.85
393	A79	7p multicolored	.50	.70
394	A79	8p multicolored	.50	.70
395	A79	9p multicolored	.50	.70
396	A79	10p multicolored	.50	.70
397	A79	20p multicolored	2.75	1.10
398	A79	25p multicolored	.65	1.10
399	A79	50p multicolored	1.10	1.75
400	A79	£1 multicolored	1.40	2.50
401	A79	£3 multicolored	4.00	6.50
		Nos. 387-401 (15)	17.10	22.45

Nos. 364, 366 Surcharged

1984, Jan. 3   Litho.   Perf. 14

402	A74	17p on 15p multi	.65	.90
403	A74	22p on 25p multi	.35	.45

Lloyd's List Issue
Common Design Type

Designs: 6p, Wavertree. 17p, Port Stanley, 1910. 22p, Oravia. 52p, Cunard Countess.

1984, May 7   Wmk. 373   Perf. 14½

404	CD335	6p multi	.60	.50
405	CD335	17p multi	.90	.65
406	CD335	22p multi	.90	.75
407	CD335	52p multi	1.10	1.75
		Nos. 404-407 (4)	3.50	3.65

Great Grebe — A80

1984, Aug. 6   Perf. 14½x14

408	A80	17p shown	1.25	1.25
409	A80	22p Silver grebe	1.50	1.50
410	A80	52p Rolland's grebe	2.25	3.25
		Nos. 408-410 (3)	5.00	6.00

See Nos. 450-453.

1984 UPU Congress — A81

1984, June 25   Litho.   Perf. 14

411	A81	22p Emblem, jet, ship	.60	.75

Wildlife Conservation — A82

1984, Nov. 5   Litho.   Perf. 14½

412	A82	6p Birds	1.00	1.00
413	A82	17p Plants	.90	.70
414	A82	22p Mammals	1.00	.80
415	A82	52p Marine Life	1.60	2.25
a.		Souvenir sheet of 4, #412-415	7.00	7.75
		Nos. 412-415 (4)	4.50	4.75

Camber Railway, 1915-1927 — A83

1985, Feb. 18   Litho.   Perf. 14

416	A83	7p multicolored	.35	.35
417	A83	22p multicolored	.65	.65
418	A83	27p multicolored	.70	.85

Size: 77x26mm

419	A83	54p multicolored	1.40	1.75
		Nos. 416-419 (4)	3.10	3.60

Queen Mother 85th Birthday
Common Design Type

Designs: 7p, Commonwealth Visitor's Reception. 22p, With Prince Charles, Mark Phillips, Princess Anne. 27p, 80th birthday celebration. 54p, Holding Prince Henry. £1, In coach with Princess Diana.

Perf. 14½x14

1985, June 7   Litho.   Wmk. 384

420	CD336	7p multicolored	.35	.35
421	CD336	22p multicolored	.90	.70
422	CD336	27p multicolored	1.00	1.00
423	CD336	54p multicolored	1.10	1.60
		Nos. 420-423 (4)	3.35	3.65

Souvenir Sheet

424	CD336	£1 multicolored	4.00	3.00

Mount Pleasant Airport Opening — A84

Designs: 7p, Pioneer camp, docked ship. 22p, Construction site. 27p, Runway layout. 54p, Aircraft landing.

1985, May 12   Litho.   Perf. 14½

425	A84	7p multicolored	.75	.40
426	A84	22p multicolored	1.00	1.00
427	A84	27p multicolored	1.30	1.30
428	A84	54p multicolored	1.75	2.40
		Nos. 425-428 (4)	4.80	5.10

Captain J. McBride, HMS Jason, 1765 — A85

18th-19th century naval explorers: 22p, Commodore J. Byron, HMS Dolphin and Tamar, 1765. 27p, Vice-Adm. R. Fitzroy, HMS Beagle, 1831. 54p, Adm. Sir B.J. Sulivan, HMS Philomel, 1842.

1985, Sept. 23

429	A85	7p multicolored	.75	.45
430	A85	22p multicolored	1.25	.90
431	A85	27p multicolored	1.35	1.15
432	A85	54p multicolored	2.50	2.25
		Nos. 429-432 (4)	5.85	4.75

Philibert Commerson (1727-1773), Commerson's Dolphin — A86

Naturalists, endangered species: 22p, Rene Primevere Lesson (1794-1849), kelp. 27p, Joseph Paul Gaimard (1796-1858), diving petrel. 54p, Charles Darwin (1803-1882), Calceolaria darwinii.

1985, Nov. 4   Perf. 14½

433	A86	7p multicolored	.85	.30
434	A86	22p multicolored	1.10	1.10
435	A86	27p multicolored	2.00	2.00
436	A86	54p multicolored	2.25	2.25
		Nos. 433-436 (4)	6.20	5.65

Seashells — A87

Designs: 7p, Painted keyhole limpet. 22p, Magellanic volute. 27p, Falkland scallop. 54p, Rough thorn drupe.

1986, Feb. 10   Wmk. 384   Perf. 14½

437	A87	7p multicolored	.95	.95
438	A87	22p multicolored	1.50	1.50
439	A87	27p multicolored	1.60	1.90
440	A87	54p multicolored	2.75	3.25
		Nos. 437-440 (4)	6.80	7.60

Queen Elizabeth II 60th Birthday
Common Design Type

Designs: 10p, With Princess Margaret at St. Paul's, Waldenbury, 1932. 24p, Christmas broadcast from Sandringham, 1958. 29p, Order of the Thistle, St. Giles Cathedral, Edinburgh, 1962. 45p, Royal reception on the Britannia, US visit, 1976. 58p, Visiting Crown Agents' offices, 1983.

1986, Apr. 21   Litho.   Perf. 14x14½

441	CD337	10p scar, blk & sil	.30	.30
442	CD337	24p ultra, blk & sil	.55	.65
443	CD337	29p green & multi	.60	.85
444	CD337	45p violet & multi	1.25	1.40
445	CD337	58p rose vio & multi	1.25	1.75
		Nos. 441-445 (5)	3.95	4.95

AMERIPEX '86 A88

SS Great Britain's arrival in the Falkland Isls., Cent.: 10p, Maiden voyage, crossing the Atlantic, 1845. 24p, Wreck in Sparrow Cove, 1937. 29p, Refloating wreck, 1970. 58p, Restored vessel, Bristol, 1986.

1986, May 22

446	A88	10p multicolored	.50	.50
447	A88	24p multicolored	.60	.90
448	A88	29p multicolored	.75	1.10
449	A88	58p multicolored	1.10	2.25
a.		Souvenir sheet of 4, #446-449	3.75	3.75
		Nos. 446-449 (4)	2.95	4.75

Bird Type of 1984

Rockhopper Penguins.

1986, Aug. 25   Wmk. 373   Perf. 14½

450	A80	10p Adult	1.00	.75
451	A80	24p Adults swimming	1.90	1.90
452	A80	29p Adults, diff.	2.10	2.10
453	A80	58p Adult and young	3.25	4.25
		Nos. 450-453 (4)	8.25	9.00

Wedding of Prince Andrew and Sarah Ferguson — A90

Various photographs: 17p, Presenting Queen's Polo Cup, Windsor, 1986. 22p, Open carriage, wedding. 29p, Andrew wearing military fatigues.

1986, Nov. 10   Wmk. 384   Perf. 14½

454	A90	17p multicolored	.70	.70
455	A90	22p multicolored	.90	.90
456	A90	29p multicolored	1.25	1.25
		Nos. 454-456 (3)	2.85	2.85

Royal Engineers, 200th Anniv. — A91

10p, Surveying Sapper Hill. 24p, Explosives disposal. 29p, Boxer Bridge, Pt. Stanley. 58p, Postal services, Stanley Airport.

1987, Feb. 9   Litho.   Perf. 14½

457	A91	10p multicolored	1.35	.90
458	A91	24p multicolored	2.40	1.50
459	A91	29p multicolored	2.10	2.50
460	A91	58p multicolored	3.50	4.25
		Nos. 457-460 (4)	9.35	9.15

Seals — A92

Designs: 10p, Southern sea lion. 24p, Falkland fur seal. 29p, Southern elephant seal. 58p, Leopard seal.

1987, Apr. 27

461	A92	10p multicolored	1.25	1.25
462	A92	24p multicolored	2.00	2.00
463	A92	29p multicolored	2.25	2.25
464	A92	58p multicolored	3.00	4.50
		Nos. 461-464 (4)	8.50	10.00

Hospitals — A93

Designs: 10p, Victorian Cottage Home, c. 1912. 24p, King Edward VII Memorial Hospital, c. 1914. 29p, Churchill Wing, 1953. 58p, Prince Andrew Wing, 1987.

1987, Dec. 8   Perf. 14

465	A93	10p multicolored	.65	.50
466	A93	24p multicolored	1.10	.90
467	A93	29p multicolored	1.25	1.00
468	A93	58p multicolored	2.00	1.50
		Nos. 465-468 (4)	5.00	3.90

Fungi — A94

10p, Suillus luteus. 24p, Mycena. 29p, Camarophyllus adonis. 58p, Gerronema schusteri.

1987, Sept. 14   Litho.   Perf. 14½

469	A94	10p multicolored	2.50	1.75
470	A94	24p multicolored	3.50	3.00
471	A94	29p multicolored	4.00	3.50
472	A94	58p multicolored	5.00	5.50
		Nos. 469-472 (4)	15.00	13.75

1940 Morris Truck, Fitzroy — A95

Classic automobiles: 24p, 1929 Citroen Kegresse, San Carlos. 29p, 1933 Ford 1-Ton Truck, Port Stanley. 58p, 1935 Ford Model T Saloon, Darwin.

1988, Apr. 11   Litho.   Perf. 14

473	A95	10p multicolored	.65	.35
474	A95	24p multicolored	1.10	.65
475	A95	29p multicolored	1.25	.75
476	A95	58p multicolored	1.90	1.50
		Nos. 473-476 (4)	4.90	3.25

Geese — A96

1988, July 25

477	A96	10p Kelp	2.50	.60
478	A96	24p Upland	3.25	.90
479	A96	29p Ruddy-headed	3.50	1.10
480	A96	58p Ashy-headed	5.75	2.50
		Nos. 477-480 (4)	15.00	5.10

Lloyds of London, 300th Anniv.
Common Design Type

Designs: 10p, Lloyd's Nelson Collection silver service. 24p, Hydroponic Gardens, horiz. 29p, Supply ship A.E.S., horiz. 58p, Wreck of the Charles Cooper near the Falklands, 1866.

1988, Nov. 14   Litho.   Wmk. 373

481	CD341	10p multicolored	.45	.45
482	CD341	24p multicolored	.85	.85
483	CD341	29p multicolored	1.75	1.05
484	CD341	58p multicolored	2.40	1.50
		Nos. 481-484 (4)	5.45	3.85

Ships of Cape Horn — A97

Designs: 1p, Padua. 2p, Priwall, vert. 3p, Passat. 4p, Archibald Russell, vert. 5p, Pamir, vert. 6p, Mozart. 7p, Pommern. 8p, Preussen. 9p, Fennia. 10p, Cassard. 20p, Lawhill. 25p, Garthpool. 50p, Grace Harwar. £1, Criccieth Castle. £3, Cutty Sark, vert. £5, Flying Cloud.

1989, Feb. 28

485	A97	1p multicolored	1.75	.85
486	A97	2p multicolored	1.40	1.40
a.		Wmk. 384	1.20	1.20
487	A97	3p multicolored	1.40	1.40
a.		Wmk. 384	1.20	1.20
488	A97	4p multicolored	2.40	.85
489	A97	5p multicolored	2.40	.85
490	A97	6p multicolored	1.90	1.90
a.		Wmk. 384	1.90	1.90
491	A97	7p multicolored	2.40	.95
492	A97	8p multicolored	2.40	.95
493	A97	9p multicolored	1.90	1.90
a.		Wmk. 384	2.50	2.50
494	A97	10p multicolored	2.40	.95
495	A97	20p multicolored	3.50	1.90
496	A97	25p multicolored	3.75	1.90
497	A97	50p multicolored	4.25	3.00
498	A97	£1 multicolored	5.00	4.75
a.		Wmk. 384	6.00	6.00
499	A97	£3 multicolored	15.00	10.00
500	A97	£5 multicolored	27.50	11.50
		Nos. 485-500 (16)	79.35	45.05

Nos. 486a, 487a, 490a, 493a, 498a are dated "1991."

Whales A98

1989, May 15   Wmk. 384   Perf. 14

501	A98	10p Southern right	1.50	.85
502	A98	24p Minke	2.50	1.25
503	A98	29p Humpback	3.25	2.00
504	A98	58p Blue	4.75	3.00
		Nos. 501-504 (4)	12.00	7.10

Sports Assoc. Activities — A99

Children's drawings.

1989, Sept. 16

505	A99	5p Gymkhana	.30	.30
506	A99	10p Steer Riding	.35	.35
507	A99	17p Sheep shearing	.55	.55
508	A99	24p Dog trial	.70	.70
509	A99	29p Horse racing	.95	.95
510	A99	45p Sack race	1.25	1.25
		Nos. 505-510 (6)	4.10	4.10

Battles — A100

Commanders, ships and ship crests: 10p, Vice-Adm. Sturdee, HMS Invincible. 24p, Vice-Adm. Von Spee, SMS Scharnhorst. 29p, Commodore Harwood, HMS Ajax. 58p, Capt. Langsdorff, Admiral Graff Spee.

1989, Dec. 8   Perf. 14x13½

511	A100	10p multicolored	1.35	.35
512	A100	24p multicolored	2.25	.80
513	A100	29p multicolored	2.25	1.00
514	A100	58p multicolored	3.25	2.50
		Nos. 511-514 (4)	9.10	4.65

Battle of the Falklands, 75th anniv. (10p, 24p); Battle of the River Plate, 50th anniv. (29p, 58p).

Emblems and Presentation Spitfires, 1940 — A101

Designs: 12p, No. 92 Squadron, whole plane. 26p, No. 611 Squadron. 31p, No. 92 Squadron, close up of cockpit. 62p, Spitfires scramble. £1, Battle of Britain.

1990, May 3   Wmk. 373   Perf. 14

515	A101	12p multicolored	1.00	1.00
516	A101	26p multicolored	1.40	1.40
517	A101	31p multicolored	1.75	1.75
518	A101	62p multicolored	3.00	3.00
		Nos. 515-518 (4)	7.15	7.15

Souvenir Sheet

519	A101	£1 multicolored	7.00	7.00

Stamp World London '90.
For souvenir sheet similar to No. 519, see No. 530.

A102

1990, Apr. 1   Wmk. 384   Perf. 14½

520	A102	12p Kidney Is.	.80	.55
521	A102	26p Beauchene Is.	1.25	.55
522	A102	31p Bird Is.	1.50	1.25
523	A102	62p Elephant Jason Is.	2.25	2.75
		Nos. 520-523 (4)	5.80	5.10

Nature reserves and bird sanctuaries.

Queen Mother, 90th Birthday
Common Design Types

26p, Queen Mother in Dover. £1, Steering the "Queen Elizabeth," 1946.

1990, Aug. 4   Wmk. 384   Perf. 14x15

524	CD343	26p multicolored	1.00	1.00

Perf. 14½

525	CD344	£1 multicolored	3.75	3.75

A103

Designs: 12p, Black browed albatross. 26p, Adult bird. 31p, Adult, chick. 62p, Bird in flight.

Wmk. 384

1990, Oct. 3   Litho.   Perf. 14

526	A103	12p multicolored	1.00	.75
527	A103	26p multicolored	1.90	1.25
528	A103	31p multicolored	2.25	1.50
529	A103	62p multicolored	3.50	3.50
		Nos. 526-529 (4)	8.65	7.00

Battle of Britain Type of 1990
inscribed "SECOND VISIT OF / HRH
THE DUKE OF EDINBURGH"
Souvenir Sheet

1991, Mar. 7

530	A101	£1 multicolored	13.00	13.00

Orchids — A104

Designs: 12p, Gavilea australis. 26p, Codonorchis lessonii. 31p, Chlorea gaudichaudii. 62p, Gavilea littoralis.

1991, Mar. 18   Wmk. 373

531	A104	12p multi	1.60	1.00
532	A104	26p multi	1.90	1.50
533	A104	31p multi	2.25	1.75
534	A104	62p multi	3.50	4.00
		Nos. 531-534 (4)	9.25	8.25

King Penguin — A105

2p, Two adults crossing bills. 6p, Two adults, one brooding. 12p, Adult with two young. 20p, Adult swimming. 31p, Adult feeding young. 62p, Two adults, diff.

1991, Aug. 26   Wmk. 384

535	A105	2p multi	1.10	1.10
536	A105	6p multi	1.60	1.60
537	A105	12p multi	2.00	2.00
538	A105	20p multi	2.25	2.25
539	A105	31p multi	2.25	2.25
540	A105	62p multi	3.25	3.25
		Nos. 535-540 (6)	12.45	12.45

World Wildlife Fund.

Falkland Islands Bisects, Cent. — A106

1991, Sept. 10   Wmk. 384   Perf. 14½

541	A106	12p #9, #15	1.00	.90
542	A106	26p On cover	1.90	1.50
543	A106	31p Unsevered pair	1.50	1.50
544	A106	62p S.S. Isis	2.50	3.25
		Nos. 541-544 (4)	6.90	7.15

Discovery of America, 500th Anniv. (in 1992) — A107

Sailing ships: 14p, STV Eye of the Wind. 29p, STV Soren Larsen. 34p, Nina, Santa Maria, Pinta. 68p, Columbus and Santa Maria.

1991, Dec. 12   Wmk. 373   Perf. 14

545	A107	14p multicolored	.90	.90
546	A107	29p multicolored	2.00	1.75
547	A107	34p multicolored	2.25	2.00
548	A107	68p multicolored	3.50	4.25
		Nos. 545-548 (4)	8.65	8.90

World Columbian Stamp Expo '92, Chicago and Genoa '92 Intl. Philatelic Exhibitions.

Queen Elizabeth II's Accession to the Throne, 40th Anniv.
Common Design Type

1992, Feb. 6

549	CD349	7p multicolored	.65	.50
550	CD349	14p multicolored	.90	.90
551	CD349	29p multicolored	1.00	1.10
552	CD349	34p multicolored	1.40	1.40
553	CD349	68p multicolored	2.00	2.00
		Nos. 549-553 (5)	5.95	5.90

Christ Church Cathedral, Cent. — A108

Designs: 14p, Laying foundation stone. 29p, Interior, 1920. 34p, Bishop's chair. 68p, Without tower c. 1900, horiz.

1992, Feb. 21   Wmk. 384   Perf. 14½

554	A108	14p multicolored	1.00	.75
555	A108	29p multicolored	2.00	1.25
556	A108	34p multicolored	2.25	1.50
557	A108	68p multicolored	3.00	2.75
		Nos. 554-557 (4)	8.25	6.25

A109

Designs: 22p, Capt. John Davis using backstaff. 29p, Capt. Davis working on chart. 34p, Queen Elizabeth I, Queen Elizabeth II. 68p, The Desire sights Falkland Islands.

1992, Aug. 14   Wmk. 373

558	A109	22p multicolored	1.60	1.10
559	A109	29p multicolored	2.00	1.50
560	A109	34p multicolored	2.10	1.90
561	A109	68p multicolored	3.50	5.00
		Nos. 558-561 (4)	9.20	9.50

First sighting of Falkland Islands by Capt. John Davis, 400th anniv.

Falkland Islands Defense Force and West Yorkshire Regiment — A110

7p, Private, Falkland Islands Volunteers, 1892. 14p, Officer, Falkland Islands Defense Corps, 1914. 22p, Officer, Falkland Islands Defense Force, 1920. 29p, Private, Falkland Islands Defense Force, 1939-45. 34p, Officer, West Yorkshire Regiment, 1942. 68p, Private, West Yorkshire Regiment, 1942.

1992, Oct. 1   Perf. 14

562	A110	7p multicolored	.60	.60
563	A110	14p multicolored	.90	.90
564	A110	22p multicolored	1.25	.90
565	A110	29p multicolored	1.50	1.25
566	A110	34p multicolored	1.90	1.60
567	A110	68p multicolored	3.00	3.75
		Nos. 562-567 (6)	9.15	9.00

Gulls and Terns — A111

Designs: 15p, South American tern. 31p, Pink breasted gull. 36p, Dolphin gull. 72p, Dominican gull.

Perf. 14x14½

1993, Jan. 2   Litho.   Wmk. 384

568	A111	15p multicolored	1.40	1.00
569	A111	31p multicolored	1.90	1.50
570	A111	36p multicolored	2.50	2.25
571	A111	72p multicolored	3.50	5.50
		Nos. 568-571 (4)	9.30	10.25

Souvenir Sheet

Visit of Liner QE II to Falkland Islands A112

Wmk. 373

1993, Jan. 22   Litho.   Perf. 14

572	A112	£2 multicolored	10.00	10.00

Royal Air Force, 75th Anniv.
Common Designs Type

Designs: No. 573, Lockheed Tristar. No. 574, Lockheed Hercules. No. 575, Boeing Vertol Chinook. No. 576, Avro Vulcan. No. 577a, Hawker Siddeley Andover. b, Westland Wessex. c, Panavia Tornado F3. d, McDonnell Douglas Phantom.

Wmk. 373

1993, Apr. 3   **Perf. 14**

573	CD350	15p multicolored	1.15	1.15
574	CD350	15p multicolored	1.15	1.15
575	CD350	15p multicolored	1.15	1.15
576	CD350	15p multicolored	1.15	1.15
		Nos. 573-576 (4)	4.60	4.60

Souvenir Sheet of 4

577	CD350	36p #a.-d.	6.25	6.25

Fisheries A113

Designs: 15p, Short-finned squid. 31p, Stern haul of whiptailed hake. 36p, Fishery Patrol Vessel Falklands Protector. 72p, Aerial surveillance by Britten-Norman Islander.

Wmk. 384

1993, July 1   **Litho.**   **Perf. 14**

578	A113	15p multicolored	.85	.85
579	A113	31p multicolored	1.75	1.75
580	A113	36p multicolored	2.10	2.10
581	A113	72p multicolored	3.25	5.00
		Nos. 578-581 (4)	7.95	9.70

Launch of SS Great Britain, 150th Anniv. — A114

Perf. 14x13½

1993, July 19   **Litho.**   **Wmk. 384**

582	A114	8p In drydock, Bristol	.80	.50
583	A114	£1 At sea	4.25	5.50

Cruise Ships and Penguins A115

16p, Explorer. 34p, Rockhopper penguins. 39p, World Discoverer. 78p, Columbus Caravelle.

Wmk. 373

1993, Oct. 1   **Litho.**   **Perf. 14**

584	A115	16p multicolored	1.60	.80
585	A115	34p multicolored	2.50	1.60
586	A115	39p multicolored	2.75	2.00
587	A115	78p multicolored	3.75	7.50
		Nos. 584-587 (4)	10.60	11.90

Pets — A116

Perf. 14x14½

1993, Dec. 1   **Litho.**   **Wmk. 384**

588	A116	8p Pony	.90	.90
589	A116	16p Lamb	1.10	1.10
590	A116	34p Puppy, kitten	2.25	1.50

Perf. 14½x14

591	A116	39p Kitten, vert.	2.75	2.00
592	A116	78p Collie, vert.	3.75	5.75
		Nos. 588-592 (5)	10.75	11.25

Ovptd. with Hong Kong '94 Emblem

1994, Feb. 18

593	A116	8p on #588	1.00	1.25
594	A116	16p on #589	1.25	1.50
595	A116	34p on #590	2.75	3.00
596	A116	39p on #591	3.00	4.00
597	A116	78p on #592	4.00	6.50
		Nos. 593-597 (5)	12.00	16.25

Inshore Marine Life — A117

Designs: 1p, Goose barnacles, vert. 2p, Painted shrimp. 8p, Common limpet. 9p, Mullet. 10p, Sea anemones. 20p, Rock eel. 25p, Spider crab. 50p, Lobster krill, vert. 80p, Falkland skate. £1, Centollon crab. £3, Rock cod. £5, Octopus, vert.

Wmk. 384

1994, Apr. 4   **Litho.**   **Perf. 14**

598	A117	1p multicolored	1.00	.75
599	A117	2p multicolored	1.75	.75
600	A117	8p multicolored	2.00	1.00
601	A117	9p multicolored	2.00	1.00
602	A117	10p multicolored	2.00	.75
603	A117	20p multicolored	2.75	1.00
604	A117	25p multicolored	2.75	1.00
605	A117	50p multicolored	2.75	2.75
606	A117	80p multicolored	2.75	2.75
607	A117	£1 multicolored	2.75	3.00
a.		Souv. sheet of 1, wmk. 373	6.75	6.75
608	A117	£3 multicolored	12.00	8.00
609	A117	£5 multicolored	18.00	14.00
		Nos. 598-609 (12)	52.50	36.75

No. 607a for return of Hong Kong to China. Issued 7/1/97.
See No. 671.

Founding of Stanley, 150th Anniv. — A118

9p, Blacksmith's shop, dockyard, Sir James Clark Ross, explorer. 17p, James Leith Mody, 1st colonial chaplain, home at 21 Fitzroy Road. 30p, Stanley cottage, Dr. Henry J. Hamblin, 1st colonial surgeon. 35p, Pioneer row, Sergeant Major Henry Felton. 40p, Government House, Governor R. C. Moody R.E. 65p, View of Stanley, Edward Stanley, 14th Earl of Derby, Secretary of State for Colonies.

Wmk. 373

1994, July 1   **Litho.**   **Perf. 14**

610	A118	9p multicolored	.85	.75
611	A118	17p multicolored	1.25	1.00
612	A118	30p multicolored	2.00	1.25
613	A118	35p multicolored	2.25	1.75
614	A118	40p multicolored	2.50	2.00
615	A118	65p multicolored	3.00	3.50
		Nos. 610-615 (6)	11.85	10.25

Methods of Transportation A119

17p, Tristar over Gypsy Cove. 35p, Cruise ship, Sea Lion Island. 40p, FIGAS Islander, Pebble Island Beach. 65p, Land Rover, Volunteer Beach.

Wmk. 384

1994, Oct. 24   **Litho.**   **Perf. 14**

616	A119	17p multicolored	1.10	.75
617	A119	35p multicolored	2.10	1.50
618	A119	40p multicolored	2.75	2.75
619	A119	65p multicolored	3.25	4.25
		Nos. 616-619 (4)	9.20	9.25

South American Missionary Society, 150th Anniv. — A120

Designs: 5p, Mission House, Keppel Island. 17p, Thomas Bridges, compiler of Yahgan dictionary. 40p, Fuegian Indians. 65p, Schooner Allen Gardiner, Capt. Allen Gardiner.

1994, Dec. 1

620	A120	5p multicolored	.30	.30
621	A120	17p multicolored	.85	.85
622	A120	40p multicolored	1.75	1.75
623	A120	65p multicolored	2.75	3.50
		Nos. 620-623 (4)	5.65	6.40

Flowering Shrubs — A121

Designs: 9p, Lupinus arboreus. 17p, Boxwood. 30p, Fuchsia magellanica. 35p, Berberis ilicifolia. 40p, Gorse. 65p, Veronica.

Perf. 14½x14

1995, Jan. 3   **Litho.**   **Wmk. 384**

624	A121	9p multicolored	.90	.65
625	A121	17p multicolored	1.10	.80
626	A121	30p multicolored	1.45	1.45
627	A121	35p multicolored	1.75	1.45
628	A121	40p multicolored	1.90	1.60
629	A121	65p multicolored	3.25	4.25
		Nos. 624-629 (6)	10.35	10.20

Shore Birds — A122

Designs: 17p, Magellanic oystercatcher. 35p, Rufous chested dotterel. 40p, Black oystercatcher. 65p, Two banded plover.

Wmk. 373

1995, Mar. 1   **Litho.**   **Perf. 13½**

630	A122	17p multicolored	1.75	.90
631	A122	35p multicolored	2.50	1.50
632	A122	40p multicolored	2.75	1.75
633	A122	65p multicolored	4.00	7.00
		Nos. 630-633 (4)	11.00	11.15

End of World War II, 50th Anniv.
Common Design Types

17p, Falkland Islands Victory Parade contingent. 35p, Governor Sir Alan Wolsey Cardinall on Bren gun carrier. 40p, HMAS Esperance Bay, 1942. 65p, HMS Exeter, 1939. £1, Reverse of War Medal 1939-45.

Wmk. 373

1995, May 8   **Litho.**   **Perf. 14**

634	CD351	17p multicolored	1.50	.90
635	CD351	35p multicolored	2.40	1.50
636	CD351	40p multicolored	2.75	2.00
637	CD351	65p multicolored	4.75	5.50
		Nos. 634-637 (4)	11.40	9.90

Souvenir Sheet

638	CD352	£1 multicolored	7.25	7.25

Transporting Peat — A123

Wmk. 384

1995, Aug. 1   **Litho.**   **Perf. 14**

639	A123	17p Ox, cart	.80	.80
640	A123	35p Horse, cart	1.75	1.25
641	A123	40p Tractor, sledge	2.00	1.50
642	A123	65p Truck, peat bank	3.50	4.00
		Nos. 639-642 (4)	8.05	7.55

Miniature Sheet of 6

Wildlife — A124

Designs: a, Kelp geese. b, Albatross. c, Cormorants. d, Magellanic penguins. e, Fur seals. f, Rockhopper penguins.

1995, Sept. 11

643	A124	35p #a.-f.	19.00	19.00

No. 643 is a continuous design.

Wild Animals — A125

1995, Nov. 6   **Wmk. 373**

644	A125	9p Rabbit	1.00	.90
645	A125	17p Hare	1.60	1.10
646	A125	35p Guanaco	2.50	1.75
647	A125	40p Fox	3.00	2.00
648	A125	65p Otter	4.00	5.00
		Nos. 644-648 (5)	12.10	10.75

Visit by Princess Anne — A126

Princess Anne and: 9p, Government House. 19p, San Carlos Cemetery. 30p, Christ Church Cathedral. 73p, Goose Green.

1996, Jan. 30   **Perf. 14½**

649	A126	9p multicolored	1.00	.60
650	A126	19p multicolored	1.35	1.00
651	A126	30p multicolored	1.75	1.50
652	A126	73p multicolored	6.00	7.50
		Nos. 649-652 (4)	10.10	10.60

Queen Elizabeth II, 70th Birthday
Common Design Type

Various portraits of Queen, scenes from Falkland Islands: 17p, Steeple Jason. 40p, Ship, KV Tamar. 45p, New Island with shipwreck on beach. 65p, Community School. £1, Queen in formal dress at Sandringham Ball.

1996, Apr. 21   **Perf. 13½**

653	CD354	17p multicolored	.90	.70
654	CD354	40p multicolored	2.25	1.35
655	CD354	45p multicolored	2.40	1.90
656	CD354	65p multicolored	3.00	2.25
		Nos. 653-656 (4)	8.55	6.20

Souvenir Sheet

657	CD354	£1 multicolored	5.00	5.00

CAPEX '96 — A127

Mail delivery: 9p, Horseback, 1890. 40p, Norseman floatplane. 45p, Inter-island ship. 76p, Beaver floatplane. £1, LMS Jubilee Class 4-6-0 locomotive.

1996, June 8   **Wmk. 384**   **Perf. 14**

658	A127	9p multicolored	.90	.65
659	A127	40p multicolored	2.40	1.50
660	A127	45p multicolored	2.50	1.60
661	A127	76p multicolored	3.50	4.00
		Nos. 658-661 (4)	9.30	7.75

Souvenir Sheet

662	A127	£1 multicolored	4.25	4.25

No. 662 contains one 48x32mm stamp.

Beaked Whales A128

Designs: 9p, Southern bottlenose whale. 30p, Cuvier's beaked whale. 35p, Straptoothed beaked whale. 75p, Gray's beaked whale.

Wmk. 373

1996, Sept. 2   **Litho.**   **Perf. 14**

663	A128	9p multicolored	.80	.60
664	A128	30p multicolored	1.60	1.50
665	A128	35p multicolored	1.90	1.75
666	A128	75p multicolored	4.00	4.00
		Nos. 663-666 (4)	8.30	7.85

Magellanic Penguins A129

Designs: 17p, Two adults. 35p, Young in nest. 40p, Chick, adult. 65p, Swimming.

Wmk. 373

1997, Jan. 2		Litho.	Perf. 14	
667	A129	17p multicolored	2.00	.75
668	A129	35p multicolored	3.00	1.25
669	A129	40p multicolored	3.25	1.50
670	A129	65p multicolored	4.50	3.25
		Nos. 667-670 (4)	12.75	6.75

Fish Type of 1994
Souvenir Sheet
Wmk. 373

1997, Feb. 3		Litho.	Perf. 14	
671	A117	£1 Smelt	5.50	5.50

Hong Kong '97.

Ferns — A130

	Perf. 14½x14			
1997, Mar. 3		Litho.	Wmk. 373	
672	A130	17p Coral	1.75	.60
673	A130	35p Adder's tongue	2.50	1.25
674	A130	40p Fuegian tall	2.50	1.50
675	A130	65p Small fern	3.50	3.00
		Nos. 672-675 (4)	10.25	6.35

Lighthouses
A131

Designs: 9p, Bull Point. 30p, Cape Pembroke. £1, Cape Meredith.

Wmk. 373

1997, July 1		Litho.	Perf. 14	
676	A131	9p multi	3.25	1.00
677	A131	30p multi	4.50	2.00
678	A131	£1 multi	10.50	5.00
		Nos. 676-678 (3)	18.25	8.00

Queen Elizabeth II and Prince Philip,
50th Wedding Anniv.
A132

No. 679, Queen holding flowers. No. 680, Prince with horse. No. 681, Queen riding in open carriage. No. 682, Prince in uniform. No. 683, Queen in red coat & hat, Prince. No. 684, Princes William and Harry on horseback. £1.50, Queen, Prince riding in open carriage.

1997		Wmk. 384	Perf. 14½x14	
679		9p multicolored	1.00	.75
680		9p multicolored	1.00	.75
a.	A132	Pair, #679-680	2.75	2.75
681		17p multicolored	1.75	1.00
682		17p multicolored	1.75	1.00
a.	A132	Pair, #681-682	4.00	4.00
683		40p multicolored	3.00	1.50
684		40p multicolored	3.00	1.50
a.	A132	Pair, #683-684	8.00	8.00
		Nos. 679-684 (6)	11.50	6.50

Souvenir Sheet

685	A132	£1.50 multicolored	9.00	9.00

Endangered
Species
A133

Designs: 17p, Phalcoboenus australis. 19p, Otaria flavescens. 40p, Calandrinia feltonii. 73p, Aplochiton zebra.

Wmk. 373

1997, Oct. 16			Perf. 14½	
686	A133	17p multicolored	3.75	1.75
687	A133	19p multicolored	2.75	2.25
688	A133	40p multicolored	4.50	3.00
689	A133	73p multicolored	7.50	8.50
		Nos. 686-689 (4)	18.50	15.50

Fire Service in
Falkland Islands,
Cent. — A134

Equipment, manufacturer: 9p, Greenwich Gem, Merryweather & Son. 17p, Hatfield trailer pump, Merryweather & Son. 40p, Godiva trailer pump, Coventry Climax. 65p, Water tender type B, Carmichael Bedford.

Wmk. 384

1998, Feb. 26		Litho.	Perf. 14½	
690	A134	9p multicolored	3.25	1.50
691	A134	17p multicolored	3.75	1.50
692	A134	40p multicolored	6.00	3.00
693	A134	65p multicolored	8.00	9.25
		Nos. 690-693 (4)	21.00	15.25

Diana, Princess of Wales (1961-97)
Common Design Type

Portraits: a, Looking left. b, In red dress. c, Hand on cheek. d, Investigating land mines.

	Perf. 14½x14			
1998, Mar. 31			Wmk. 373	
694	CD355	30p Sheet of 4, #a-d	5.00	5.00

No. 694 sold for £1.20 + 20p, with surtax from international sales being donated to the Princess Diana Memorial Fund and surtax from national sales being donated to designated local charity.

Birds — A135

1p, Tawny-throated dotterel. 2p, Hudsonian godwit. 5p, Eared dove. No. 698, Great grebe. No. 699, Roseate spoonbill. 10p, Southern lapwing. 16p, Buff-necked ibis. 17p, Astral parakeet. 30p, Ashy-headed goose. 35p, American kestrel. 65p, Red-legged shag. 88p, Red shoveler. £1, Red-fronted coot. £3, Chilean flamingo. £5, Fork-tailed flycatcher.

1998, July 14			Perf. 14	
695	A135	1p multicolored	1.00	1.25
696	A135	2p multicolored	1.00	1.25
697	A135	5p multicolored	1.00	1.25
698	A135	9p multicolored	1.50	1.00
699	A135	9p multicolored	6.00	9.50
700	A135	10p multicolored	2.25	1.00
701	A135	16p multicolored	2.25	2.25
702	A135	17p multicolored	1.25	2.25
a.		Booklet pane, 2 #699, 8 #702 + 2 labels	22.00	
		Complete booklet, #702a	22.00	
703	A135	30p multicolored	2.50	1.75
704	A135	35p multicolored	3.00	4.00
		Complete booklet, 6 #704	18.00	
705	A135	65p multicolored	4.00	2.50
706	A135	88p multicolored	4.25	6.25
707	A135	£1 multicolored	4.50	4.50
708	A135	£3 multicolored	11.00	15.00
709	A135	£5 multicolored	15.00	22.50
		Nos. 695-709 (15)	60.50	76.25

Boats — A136

Boat, country flag, year: 17p, Penelope, Germany, 1926. 35p, Ilen, Italy, 1926. 40p, Weddell, Chile, 1940. 65p, Lively, Scotland, 1940.

Wmk. 373

1998, Sept. 30		Litho.	Perf. 14	
710	A136	17p multicolored	2.50	1.00
711	A136	35p multicolored	3.50	2.00
712	A136	40p multicolored	3.75	2.25

Size: 29x18mm

Wmk. 373

1998, Sept. 30		Litho.	Perf. 14	
713	A136	65p multicolored	5.50	6.00
		Nos. 710-713 (4)	15.25	11.25

FIGAS (First
Medivac Air
Ambulance
Service), 50th
Anniv. — A137

17p, Man carrying patient, airplane. £1, Airplane, map of Islands, float plane.

Wmk. 373

1998, Dec. 1		Litho.	Perf. 14	
714	A137	17p multicolored	3.00	1.25
715	A137	£1 multicolored	12.50	12.50

Military
Uniforms — A138

Uniform, background location: 17p, Marine Private, 1776, The Block House at Port Egmont, Saunders Island. 30p, Marine Officer, 1833, Port Louis, East Falkland. 35p, Royal Marine Corporal, 1914, HMS Kent. 65p, Royal Marine Bugler, 1976, Government House.

Wmk. 373

1998, Dec. 8		Litho.	Perf. 14½	
716	A138	17p multicolored	3.00	1.00
717	A138	30p multicolored	4.00	2.50
718	A138	35p multicolored	4.25	2.50
719	A138	65p multicolored	6.50	9.50
		Nos. 716-719 (4)	17.75	15.50

St. Mary's
Church,
Cent. — A139

Designs: 17p, Inside view. 40p, Outside view. 75p, Laying cornerstone, 1899.

Wmk. 373

1999, Feb. 12		Litho.	Perf. 14	
720	A139	17p multi	2.40	.90
721	A139	40p multi	3.75	3.00
722	A139	75p multi	7.75	2.75
		Nos. 720-722 (3)	13.90	6.65

Australia '99,
World Stamp
Expo — A140

25p, HMS Beagle. 35p, HMAS Australia. 40p, SS Canberra. No. 726, SS Great Britain. No. 727, All-England Eleven visit Australia, 1861-62.

1999, Mar. 5			Wmk. 384	
723	A140	25p multicolored	3.25	2.00
724	A140	35p multicolored	3.50	2.50
725	A140	40p multicolored	4.75	2.75
726	A140	50p multicolored	4.50	7.00
727	A140	50p multicolored	4.50	7.00
a.		Pair, #726-727	9.00	14.00
		Nos. 723-727 (5)	20.50	21.25

1999 Visit of HRH
Prince of
Wales — A141

	Perf. 14x13½			
1999, Mar. 13		Litho.	Wmk. 384	
728	A141	£2 multicolored	16.00	16.00

**Wedding of Prince Edward and
Sophie Rhys-Jones**
Common Design Type

	Perf. 13¾x14			
1999, June 15		Litho.	Wmk. 384	
729	CD356	80p Separate portraits	6.00	6.00
730	CD356	£1.20 Couple	8.00	8.00

PhilexFrance '99,
World Philatelic
Exhibition
A142

Designs: 35p, French cruiser, Jeanne d'Arc, Port Stanley, 1931. 40p, CAMS 37/11 Flying Boat's first flight. £1, CAMS 37 Flying Boat over Port Stanley, 1931.

1999, June 21		Wmk. 373	Perf. 14	
731	A142	35p multicolored	5.25	5.25
732	A142	40p multicolored	5.75	5.75

Souvenir Sheet

733	A142	£1 multicolored	13.00	14.00

No. 733 contains one 48x31mm stamp.

Queen Mother's Century
Common Design Type

Queen Mother: 9p, With King George VI at Port of London. 20p, With Queen Elizabeth at Women's Institute, Sandringham. 30p, With Princes Charles, William and Harry at Clarence House, 95th birthday. 67p, As Colonel-in-Chief of the Queen's Royal Hussars. £1.40, With Ernest Shackleton, Robert F. Scott and Edward A. Wilson.

Wmk. 384

1999, Aug. 18		Litho.	Perf. 13½	
734	CD358	9p multi	2.00	1.00
735	CD358	20p multi	3.00	1.50
736	CD358	30p multi	3.50	1.75
737	CD358	67p multi	5.50	8.00
		Nos. 734-737 (4)	14.00	12.25

Souvenir Sheet

738	CD358	£1.40 multi	16.00	16.00

For overprint see No. 767.

Waterfowl — A143

	Perf. 14¼x14½			
1999, Sept. 9		Litho.	Wmk. 384	
739	A143	9p Chiloe wigeon	2.50	1.75
740	A143	17p Crested duck	3.25	2.00
741	A143	30p Brown pintail	4.00	3.25
742	A143	35p Silver teal	4.25	3.50
743	A143	40p Yellow billed teal	4.75	4.00
744	A143	65p Flightless steamer duck	7.00	9.50
		Nos. 739-744 (6)	25.75	24.00

California Gold
Rush — A144

Designs: 9p, Vicar of Bray, 1999. 35p, Gold panning, 1849. 40p, Gold rocking cradle, 1849. 80p, Vicar of Bray, 1849. £1, Vicar of Bray in San Francisco Harbor, 1849.

Wmk. 373

1999, Nov. 3		Litho.	Perf. 14	
745	A144	9p multicolored	1.10	1.10
746	A144	35p multicolored	4.25	4.25
747	A144	40p multicolored	4.75	4.75
748	A144	80p multicolored	10.00	12.00
		Nos. 745-748 (4)	20.10	22.10

Souvenir Sheet
Perf. 13¾

749	A144	£1 multicolored	15.00	15.00

No. 749 contains one 48x31mm stamp.

Millennium — A145

Designs: No. 750, Kelp gull. No. 751, Upland goose. No. 752, Christchurch Cathedral. No. 753, Night heron. No. 754, King penguin. No. 755, Christmas at home.

1999, Dec. 6   **Perf. 14x14½**
750	A145	9p multicolored	2.75	2.75
751	A145	9p multicolored	2.75	2.75
752	A145	9p multicolored	2.75	2.75
753	A145	30p multicolored	4.75	4.75
754	A145	30p multicolored	4.75	4.75
755	A145	30p multicolored	4.75	4.75
	Nos. 750-755 (6)		22.50	22.50

Visit of Princess Alexandra A146

Designs: 9p, Princess in patterned dress, trees. £1, Princess in blue dress, trees.

Perf. 13¼x13¾
2000, Feb. 1   **Litho.**   **Wmk. 373**
756	A146	9p multicolored	2.00	2.00
757	A146	£1 multicolored	9.50	9.50

Sir Ernest Shackleton (1874-1922), Polar Explorer — A147

17p, Ship Endurance, discovery of the Caird Coast. 45p, Endurance trapped in pack ice. 75p, Shackleton, Chilean tugboat Yelcho.

2000, Feb. 10   **Wmk. 373**   **Perf. 14**
758	A147	17p multicolored	5.00	2.00
759	A147	45p multicolored	8.50	4.50
760	A147	75p multicolored	12.50	14.00
	Nos. 758-760 (3)		26.00	20.50

See British Antarctic Territory Nos. 285-287, South Georgia and South Sandwich Islands Nos. 254-256.

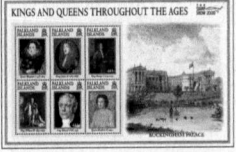

British Monarchs — A148

a, Elizabeth I. b, James II. c, George I. d, William IV. e, Edward VIII. f, Elizabeth II.

2000, Feb. 29   **Wmk. 373**   **Perf. 14**
761	A148	40p Sheet of 6, #a.-		
	f.		17.00	17.00

The Stamp Show 2000, London.

Prince William, 18th Birthday
Common Design Type

William: 10p, As toddler with fireman's helmet, vert. 20p, In checked suit and in navy suit, vert. 37p, With blue shirt. 43p, In gray suit and in navy suit holding flowers. 50p, As child with dog.

Perf. 13¾x14¼, 14¼x13¾
2000, June 21   **Litho.**   **Wmk. 373**
Stamps with White Border
762	CD359	10p multi	1.50	1.25
763	CD359	20p multi	2.10	1.90
764	CD359	37p multi	3.00	2.75
765	CD359	43p multi	4.00	3.00
	Nos. 762-765 (4)		10.60	8.50

Souvenir Sheet
Stamps Without White Border
Perf. 14¼
766		Sheet of 5	14.00	14.00
a.	CD359	10p multi	1.00	1.00
b.	CD359	20p multi	1.50	1.50
c.	CD359	37p multi	2.50	2.50
d.	CD359	43p multi	3.00	3.00
e.	CD359	50p multi	5.00	5.00

No. 738 Ovptd. in Gold

Wmk. 384
2000, Aug. 4   **Litho.**   **Perf. 13½**
767	CD358	£1.40 multi	17.00	17.00

Bridges — A149

Bridges over: 20p, Malo River. 37p, Bodie Creek. 43p, Fitzroy River.

2000, Oct. 16   **Perf. 14¼x14½**
768-770	A149	Set of 3	17.00	17.00

Christmas — A150

Designs: 10p, Shepherd, sheep. 20p, Shepherds, sheep, angel. 33p, Holy family, shepherds, Magus, donkey, sheep. 43p, Angel, two Magi. 78p, Camel.

2000, Nov. 1   **Wmk. 373**
771-775	A150	Set of 5	15.50	15.50
775a		Souvenir sheet, #771-775	17.50	17.50

Sunrises and Sunsets A151

Various photos: 10p, 20p, 37p, 43p.

2001, Jan. 10   **Perf. 14½x14¼**
776-779	A151	Set of 4	15.00	15.00

Souvenir Sheet

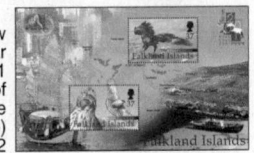

New Year 2001 (Year of the Snake) A152

Birds: a, Striated caracara. b, Mountain hawk eagle.

Perf. 14½x14¼
2001, Feb. 1   **Litho.**   **Wmk. 373**
780	A152	37p Sheet of 2, #a-b	10.50	12.00

Hong Kong 2001 Stamp Exhibition.

Age of Victoria — A153

Designs: 3p, Falkland Islands #1. 10p, S.S. Great Britain, horiz. 20p, Stanley Harbor, 1888, horiz. 43p, Cape Pembroke Lighthouse, telephones, 1897. 93p, Royal Marines, 1900. £1.50, Queen Victoria, by Franz Xavier Winterhalter, 1859. £1, Funeral procession for Queen Victoria.

2001, May 24   **Perf. 14**
781-786	A153	Set of 6	24.50	24.50

Souvenir Sheet
787	A153	£1 multi	10.50	10.50

Royal Navy Connections to Falkland Islands — A154

Designs: 10p, Welfare, ship that made first recorded landing, 1690. 17p, HMS Invincible, ship in Battle of the Falklands, 1914. 20p, HMS Exeter, ship in Battle of the River Plate, 1939. 37p, SN.R6 Hovercraft, 1967. 43p, Antarctic patrol ship HMS Protector and Wasp

helicopter, 1955. 68p, Desire, ship that made first sighting, 1592.

2001, July 24
788-793	A154	Set of 6	27.50	27.50

Carcass Island and its Flora and Fauna A155

No. 794, 37p: a, Yellow violet. b, Tussac bird.
No. 795, 43p: a, Carcass Island settlement. b, Black-crowned night heron.

Wmk. 373
2001, Sept. 28   **Perf. 13¾**
Pairs, #a-b
794-795	A155	Set of 2	19.00	19.00

Gentoo Penguins — A156

Designs: 10p, Birds flapping wings. 33p, Feeding young. 37p, Bird with beak open. 43p, Four birds walking.

2001, Oct. 26   **Perf. 14½x14¼**
796-799	A156	Set of 4	10.00	10.00

Falkland Islands Company, 150th Anniv. — A157

Designs: 10p, Company coat of arms, and gathering of cattle. 20p, Company flag, and ship Amelia. 43p, Manager F. E. Cobb, and company buildings. £1, Sheep farmer William Wickham Bertrand, sheep dip.

Wmk. 373
2002, Jan. 10   **Litho.**   **Perf. 14**
800-803	A157	Set of 4	16.00	16.00

Reign Of Queen Elizabeth II, 50th Anniv. Issue
Common Design Type

Designs: Nos. 804, 808a, 20p, Princess Elizabeth reading, 1945. Nos. 805, 808b, 37p, In 1977. Nos. 806, 808c, 43p, Holding Prince Charles, 1949. Nos. 807, 808d, 50p, At Garter ceremony, 1994. No. 808e, 50p, 1955 portrait by Annigoni (38x50mm).

Perf. 14¼x14½, 13¾ (#808e)
2002, Feb. 6   **Litho.**   **Wmk. 373**
With Gold Frames
804	CD360	20p multicolored	1.75	1.00
805	CD360	37p multicolored	2.25	2.00
806	CD360	43p multicolored	3.50	3.50
807	CD360	50p multicolored	4.00	4.00
	Nos. 804-807 (4)		11.50	10.50

Souvenir Sheet
Without Gold Frames
808	CD360	Sheet of 5, #a-e	11.50	11.50

Falkland Islands War, 20th Anniv. A158

No. 809, 22p: a, HMS Hermes, 1982. b, Fishery patrol vessel, 2002.
No. 810, 40p: a, Troops landing, 1982. b, Mine clearing, 2002.
No. 811, 45p: a, RAF Harrier on HMS Hermes, 1982. b, RAF Tristar, 2002.

Wmk. 373
2002, June 14   **Litho.**   **Perf. 14**
Horiz. pairs, #a-b
809-811	A158	Set of 3	20.00	20.00

Queen Mother Elizabeth (1900-2002)
Common Design Type

Designs: 22p, Wearing hat and scarf (black and white photograph). 25p, Wearing blue hat with polka dots. Nos. 814, 816a, 95p, Wearing feathered hat (black and white photograph). Nos. 815, 816b, £1.20, Wearing light blue hat.

Wmk. 373
2002, Aug. 5   **Litho.**   **Perf. 14¼**
With Purple Frames
812	CD361	22p multicolored	1.00	1.00
813	CD361	25p multicolored	1.25	1.25
814	CD361	95p multicolored	5.00	5.00
815	CD361	£1.20 multicolored	6.75	6.75
	Nos. 812-815 (4)		14.00	14.00

Souvenir Sheet
Without Purple Frames
Perf. 14½x14¼
816	CD361	Sheet of 2, #a-b	14.50	14.50

Worldwide Fund for Nature (WWF) — A159

Penguins: 36p, Rockhopper. 40p, Magellanic. 45p, Gentoo. 70p, Macaroni.

Wmk. 373
2002, Aug. 30   **Litho.**   **Perf. 14¼**
817-820	A159	Set of 4	11.50	11.50
a.	Horiz. strip of 4, #817-820		13.00	13.00

West Point Island and its Flora and Fauna A160

No. 821, 40p: a, Felton's flower. b, Black-browed albatross.
No. 822, 45p: a, Rockhopper penguin. b, Island settlement.

Perf. 14¼x14½
2002, Oct. 31   **Litho.**   **Wmk. 373**
Horiz. Pairs, #a-b
821-822	A160	Set of 2	15.00	15.00

Visit of Prince Andrew A161

No. 823: a, 22p, In uniform. b, £1.52, In suit and tie.

2002, Nov. 11   **Perf. 13¼x13½**
823	A161	Horiz. pair, #a-b	14.50	14.50

Shepherds' Houses — A162

Designs: 10p, Gun Hill shanty, Little Chartres. 22p, Paragon House, Lafonia. 45p, Dos Lomas, Lafonia. £1, Old House, Shallow Bay Farm.

Wmk. 373
2003, Mar. 31   **Perf. 14**
824-827	A162	Set of 4	12.00	12.00

Head of Queen Elizabeth II
Common Design Type

Wmk. 373
2003, June 2   **Litho.**   **Perf. 13¾**
828	CD362	£2 multi	9.00	9.00

Prince William, 21st Birthday
Common Design Type

Color photographs: a, In suit at right. b, With Prince Harry at left.

Wmk. 373
2003, June 21   **Litho.**   **Perf. 14¼**
829		Horiz. pair	13.50	13.50
a.-b.	CD364	95p Either single	5.50	5.50

Birds — A163

Designs: 1p, Chiloe widgeon. 2p, Dolphin gull, vert. 5p, Falkland flightless steamer duck. 10p, Black-throated finch, vert. 22p, White-tufted grebe. 25p, Rufous-chested dotterel, vert. 45p, Upland goose. 50p, Dark-faced ground-tyrant, vert. 95p, Black-crowned night heron. £1, Red-backed hawk, vert. £3, Black-necked swan. £5, Short-eared owl, vert.

Perf. 13x13¼, 13¼x13

2003, July 21		**Litho.**		**Wmk. 373**
830	A163	1p multi	.60	1.25
831	A163	2p multi	.90	1.50
832	A163	5p multi	1.25	1.50
833	A163	10p multi	1.50	1.50
834	A163	22p multi	1.75	1.25
835	A163	25p multi	2.00	1.25
836	A163	45p multi	2.50	2.00
837	A163	50p multi	3.00	3.00
838	A163	95p multi	4.25	5.25
839	A163	£1 multi	4.50	5.25
840	A163	£3 multi	12.00	13.00
841	A163	£5 multi	18.00	20.00
	Nos. 830-841,C1 (13)		54.75	59.25

See Nos. 917-919, C1.

Bird Life International — A164

Black-browed albatross: No. 842, Adult on nest, facing right. No. 843, Chick. 40p, Heads of two adults, vert. £1, Adult on nest, facing left, vert.
16p, In flight.

Perf. 14¼x13¾, 13¾x14¼

2003, Sept. 26				
842	A164	22p multi	1.75	1.75
a.		Perf. 14¼x14½	1.75	1.75
843	A164	22p multi	1.75	1.75
a.		Perf. 14¼x14½	1.75	1.75
844	A164	40p multi	2.75	2.75
a.		Perf. 14½x14¼	2.75	2.75
845	A164	£1 multi	7.25	7.25
a.		Perf. 14¼x14¼	7.25	7.25
	Nos. 842-845 (4)		13.50	13.50

Souvenir Sheet

846		Sheet, #842a-846a	16.50	16.50
a.	A164 16p multi, perf. 14¼x14½		1.40	1.40

New Island and its Flora and Fauna — A165

No. 847, 40p: a, Striated caracara. b, Lady's slipper.
No. 848, 45p: a, Stone Cottage. b, King penguin.

Wmk. 373

2003, Oct. 24		**Litho.**		**Perf. 13¾**
Pairs, #a-b				
847-848	A165	Set of 2	18.00	18.00

Christmas — A166

Various depictions of Pale maiden flower: 16p, 30p, 40p, 95p.

2003, Nov. 3				**Perf. 14x14¼**
849-852	A166	Set of 4	16.50	16.50

Sheep Farming A167

Designs: 19p, Traditional hand shearing. 22p, Driving the sheep. 45p, Big House, Hill Cove. 70p, The early years. £1, Wool collection, SS Fitzroy.

Unwmk.

2004, Apr. 30		**Litho.**		**Perf. 14**
853-857	A167	Set of 5	22.50	22.50

Wildlife Conservation in Falkland Islands, 25th Anniv. — A168

Designs: 20p, Man planting tussac grass. 24p, People cleaning beach. 50p, Satellite tracking of rockhopper penguins. £1, Weighing of albatross chick.

2004, June 17		**Litho.**		**Perf. 14**
858-861	A168	Set of 4	18.00	18.00

Sir Rowland Hill (1795-1879) and Falkland Islands Postage Stamps A169

Hill and: 24p, #20. 50p, #74. 75p, #94. £1, #151a.

2004, Aug. 31		**Litho.**		**Perf. 13¼**
862-865	A169	Set of 4	19.00	19.00

Sea Lion Island and its Flora and Fauna A170

No. 866, 42p: a, King cormorant. b, Dog orchid.
No. 867, 50p: a, Magellanic penguin. b, Sea Lion Lodge.

2004, Sept. 15				**Perf. 13¾**
Pairs, #a-b				
866-867	A170	Set of 2	19.50	19.50
866c	As #866a, dated "2005"		2.25	—
866d	As #866b, dated "2005"		2.25	—
866e	Pair, #866c-866d		7.00	—

Owls — A171

Designs: 18p, Head of short-eared owl. 45p, Short-eared owl. 50p, Barn owl in flight. £1.50, Barn owl.
£2, Barn owl in flight, horiz.

2004, Oct. 25				
868-871	A171	Set of 4	18.00	18.00

Souvenir Sheet

872	A171	£2 multi	12.00	12.00

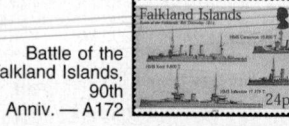

Battle of the Falkland Islands, 90th Anniv. — A172

No. 873: a, HMS Kent, HMS Inflexible, half of HMS Carnarvon, half of HMS Cornwall. b, British Navy flag, HMS Glasgow, half of HMS Carnarvon, half of HMS Cornwall, half of HMS Invincible. c, Medals, half of HMS Invincible.

No. 874: a, Medals, half of SMS Scharnhorst. b, German imperial war ensign, SMS Dresden, half of SMS Scharnhorst, half of SMS Leipzig. c, SMS Nürnberg, SMS Gneisenau, half of SMS Leipzig.

2004, Dec. 8			**Litho.**	**Perf. 14**
873		Horiz. strip of 3	9.50	9.50
a.-c.	A172 24p Any single		2.40	1.90
874		Horiz. strip of 3	17.50	17.50
a.-c.	A172 50p Any single		4.25	3.25

Camber Railway, 90th Anniv. — A173

Designs: 3p, Old track bed. 24p, Kerr Stuart Wren Class locomotive at Camber Depot, horiz. 50p, Kerr Stuart Wren Class locomotive Falkland Islands Express, horiz. £2, Camber sailing wagon.

2005, Feb. 28				**Perf. 13¾**
875-878	A173	Set of 4	17.00	17.00

Wedding of Prince Charles and Camilla Parker Bowles — A174

Designs: 24p, Couple. 50p, Couple in formal wear, vert.
£2, Couple, Windsor Castle.

2005, Apr. 29				**Perf. 14**
879-880	A174	Set of 2	5.00	5.00

Souvenir Sheet

881	A174	£2 multi	10.50	10.50

End of World War II, 60th Anniv. A175

No. 882, 24p: a, Walrus reconnaissance seaplane. b, Presentation Spitfire X4616.
No. 883, 80p: a, HMS Exeter at Port Stanley. b, Governor, King Edward Memorial Hospital staff, Rear Admiral Harwood and Capt. Bell.
No. 884, £1: a, Fitzroy. b, HMS William Scoresby.

Perf. 13¼x13½

2005, June 29				**Litho.**
Horiz. Pairs, #a-b				
882-884	A175	Set of 3	28.00	28.00

Maritime Heritage — A176

Designs: 24p, Snow Squall escaping CSS Tuscaloosa, 1863. No. 886, 55p, Jhelum, 1870. No. 887, 55p, Charles Cooper, 1866. £1.20, SS Imo colliding with the Mont Blanc, Halifax Harbor, 1917.

2005, Aug. 29		**Litho.**		**Perf. 14**
885-888	A176	Set of 4	13.00	13.00

Pebble Island and its Flora and Fauna A177

No. 889, 45p: a, Gentoo penguin. b, Falkland lavender.
No. 890, 55p: a, Pebble Island Lodge. b, Black-necked swan.

2005, Sept. 12				**Perf. 13¾**
Pairs, #a-b				
889-890	A177	Set of 2	14.00	14.00

Souvenir Sheet

The Fall of Nelson, Battle of Trafalgar, 21 October 1805, by Denis Dighton A178

2005, Oct. 21				
891	A178	£2 multi	12.00	12.00

Battle of Trafalgar, bicent.

Hans Christian Andersen (1805-75), Author — A179

Stories: 18p, The Little Mermaid. 30p, The Snowman. 45p, The Ugly Duckling. £1, Thumbelina.

2005, Oct. 28				**Perf. 14**
892-895	A179	Set of 4	11.50	11.50

Stanley Infant and Junior School, 50th anniv.

Black-crowned Night Heron — A180

Designs: 24p, Head. 55p, Bird on one leg. 80p, Juvenile standing. £1, Head of juvenile.

2006, Feb. 10		**Litho.**		**Perf. 13¾**
896-899	A180	Set of 4	13.00	13.00

Queen Elizabeth II, 80th Birthday — A181

Queen wearing: 24p, Yellow hat. 55p, Green hat. 80p, Blue hat. £1, Red hat.
£2, Tiara and white hat, horiz.

2006, Apr. 21				**Perf. 14**
900-903	A181	Set of 4	13.00	13.00

Souvenir Sheet

904	A181	£2 multi	11.00	11.00

SS Great Britain — A182

View of: 24p, Bow. 55p, Stern. £1.50, Deck and masts.

2006, May 19				**Perf. 13¾x13¼**
905-907	A182	Set of 3	13.00	13.00

Birds — A183

Designs: No. 908, 25p, Gentoo penguin chicks. No. 909, 25p, King cormorants. No. 910, 60p, King penguin. No. 911, 60p, Wandering albatross.

2006, Aug. 30		**Litho.**		**Perf. 14¼x14**
908-911	A183	Set of 4	11.00	11.00

Bleaker Island and its Flora and Fauna
A184

No. 912, 50p: a, Woolly Falkland ragwort. b, Macaroni penguin.
No. 913, 60p: a, The Outlook and sheep. b, Long-tailed meadowlark.

2006, Sept. 18   Perf. 13¼x13
Pairs, #a-b
912-913 A184   Set of 2   15.00 15.00

Victoria Cross, 150th Anniv. — A185

Designs: Nos. 914, 916a, 60p, Lt. Col. H. Jones. Nos. 915, 916b, 60p, Sgt. Ian McKay. No. 916c, £1, Victoria Cross.

2006, Nov. 11   Perf. 13¼
Stamps With White Frames
914-915 A185   Set of 2   7.00 7.00

Souvenir Sheet
Stamps Without White Frames
916 A185   Sheet of 3, #a-c   7.00 7.00

Bird Type of 2003
Designs: 20p, Black-browed albatross, vert. 25p, Rufous-chested dotterel, vert. £5, Short-eared owl, vert.

Perf. 13¼x13
2006, Nov. 15   Litho.   Unwmk.
917 A163 20p multi   2.50   2.00
918 A163 25p multi   2.75   2.50
919 A163 £5 multi   22.50 24.00
      Nos. 917-919 (3)   27.75 28.50

Nos. 918-919 differ from Nos. 835 and 841 by having less color around the Queen's head. Nos. 917-919 are dated "2006."

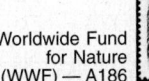

Worldwide Fund for Nature (WWF) — A186

Striated caracara: 25p, Heads of two birds. 50p, Bird in flight. 60p, Bird standing. 85p, Bird eating shellfish.

2006, Dec. 20   Litho.   Perf. 13¾
920-923 A186   Set of 4   10.00 10.00
923a   Miniature sheet, 4 each
         #920-923   47.50 47.50

Fisheries, 20th Anniv. — A187

Designs: 3p, Fishermen at sea. 11p, Fishing boat at night. 25p, Fishermen leaving boat. 30p, Japanese jigger. 60p, Fishery protection boat Dorada. £1.05, Trawler transferring fish to a freezer container ship.

2007, Feb. 24   Perf. 14¼
924-929 A187   Set of 6   13.50 13.50

HMS Plymouth A188

HMS Plymouth: 25p, Joining Falkland Islands Task Force. 40p, Supporting SBS. 60p, Under attack by Argentine fighters. £1.05, Docked at Port Stanley.

2007, Mar. 27
930-933 A188   Set of 4   17.50 17.50

Souvenir Sheet

Falkland Islands War, 25th Anniv. A189

No. 934: a, Avro Vulcan prototype VX770. b, Avro Vulcan XM597. c, Avro Vulcan XM607. d, Vulcan in the Sky Project.

2007, May 25   Litho.   Perf. 13¼
934 A189 60p Sheet of 4, #a-d 14.00 14.00

Miniature Sheets

British and Falkland Islander Casualties of the Falkland Islands War — A190

No. 935, 25p — Casualties beginning with: a, Doreen Bonner. b, G. W. J. Batt. c, J. R. Carlyle. d, S. J. Dixon. e, I. R. Farrell. f, G. C. Grace. g, R. R. Heath. h, A. S. James.
No. 936, 60p: a, D. Lee. b, P. B. McKay. c, G. T. Nelson. d, J. B. Pashley. e, M. Sambles. f, D. A. Strickland. g, R. G. Thomas. h, P. A. West.

2007, June 14   Litho.   Perf. 14¼
Sheets of 8, #a-h
935-936 A190   Set of 2   30.00 30.00

Scouting, Cent. — A191

Designs: 10p, Scouts on ladder of RRS Discovery. 20p, Dignitaries on ship's deck. 25p, Dignitaries, diff. £2, RRS Discovery.

2007, July 23   Litho.   Perf. 13½x13¼
937-940 A191   Set of 4   12.00 12.00
Voyage of RRS Discovery from Falkland Islands for presentation to British Scout Association, 70th anniv.

Princess Diana (1961-97) — A192

2007, Aug. 31   Perf. 14
941 A192 60p multi   3.75   3.75
Printed in sheets of 8 stamps + 2 labels.

Saunders Island and its Flora and Fauna — A193

No. 942, 50p: a, Rockhopper penguin. b, Dusty miller.
No. 943, 55p: a, Crested caracara. b, Earliest British settlement at Port Egmont.

2007, Sept. 28   Litho.   Perf. 13¾
Pairs, #a-b
942-943 A193   Set of 2   15.00 15.00

A194

2007, Nov. 20   Litho.   Perf. 14
944 A194 £1 multi   6.00   6.00
Wedding of Queen Elizabeth II and Prince Philip, 60th Anniv.

Polar Explorers and Their Ships — A195

Explorers and ships: 4p, James Weddell (1787-1834), and Jane. 25p, James Clark Ross (1800-62), and HMS Erebus. 85p, William Spiers Bruce (1867-1921), and Scotia. £1.61, James Marr (1902-65), and Discovery II.

2008, Apr. 7
945-948 A195   Set of 4   13.00 13.00

Southern Elephant Seals — A196

Designs: 27p, Seal pup. 55p, Male and female. 65p, Seals play fighting. £1.10, Seal and tussock bird.

2008, July 15   Litho.   Perf. 14
949-952 A196   Set of 4   14.00 14.00

Aircraft — A197

Designs: 1p, Taylorcraft Auster Mk 5. 2p, Boeing 747-300. 5p, De Havilland Canada DHC-6 Twin Otter. 10p, Lockheed C-130 Hercules. 27p, De Havilland Canada DHC-2 Beaver. 55p, Airbus A320. 65p, Lockheed L-1011-385-3 Tristar C2. 90p, Avro Vulcan B2. £1, Britten-Norman BN-2 Islander. £2, Panavia Tornado F3. £3, De Havilland Canada DHC-7-110 Dash 7. £5, BAE Sea Harrier.

2008, Aug. 1   Litho.   Perf. 14
953 A197 1p multi   .40   .75
954 A197 2p multi   .40   .75
955 A197 5p multi   .75   .85
956 A197 10p multi   .90   .90
957 A197 27p multi   1.75   1.75
958 A197 55p multi   2.25   2.25
959 A197 65p multi   2.75   2.75
960 A197 90p multi   3.50   3.50
961 A197 £1 multi   4.00   4.00
962 A197 £2 multi   7.25   8.00
963 A197 £3 multi   10.00 11.00
964 A197 £5 multi   16.00 18.00
      Nos. 953-964 (12)   49.95 54.50

Souvenir Sheet
Stamps With Royal Air Force 90th Anniv. Emblem Added
965   Sheet of 4   14.50 14.50
  a. A197 10p Like #956   .40   .40
  b. A197 65p Like #959   2.60   2.60
  c. A197 90p Like #960   3.50   3.50
  d. A197 £2 Like #962   8.00   8.00

Port Louis, 175th Anniv. — A198

Designs: 27p, Sailor raising British flag. 65p, Royal Marines, British flag. £2, Capt. Onslow of HMS Clio, British flag.

2008, Sept. 22   Litho.   Perf. 14
966-967 A198   Set of 2   4.75   4.75
Souvenir Sheet
968 A198 £2 multi   9.00   9.00

Islands and Rocks — A199

Designs: 22p, The Slipper. 40p, Kidney Island. 60p, Stephens Bluff and Castle Rock. £1, The Colliers.

2008, Oct. 1   Litho.   Perf. 13¾
969-972 A199   Set of 4   10.00 10.00
See Nos. 986-989, 1025-1028.

Retirement of Queen Elizabeth 2 as Ocean Liner — A200

Designs: 23p, Launch of Queen Elizabeth 2. 27p, Service of Queen Elizabeth 2 as troop ship in Falkland Islands War. 65p, Queen Elizabeth 2, Palm Jumeirah, Dubai. £2, Queen Elizabeth 2 (70x34mm).

2008, Nov. 21   Litho.   Perf. 13¼
973-976 A200   Set of 4   13.00 13.00

Charles Darwin (1809-82), Naturalist A201

Designs: 4p, Darwin seated. 27p, Warrah. 65p, HMS Beagle in Berkeley Sound, 1834. £1.10, Darwin encountering a Magellanic penguin.

2009, Apr. 23   Litho.   Perf. 14
977-980 A201   Set of 4   8.00   8.00

Naval Aviation, Cent. — A202

Royal Navy aircraft and ships: 30p, Westland/Aerospatiale Gazelle AH1 helicopter. 50p, Westland Lynx HAS2 helicopter. 65p, Westland Wessex HU5 helicopter. £1.10, Westland Sea King HAS5 helicopter. £2, BAe Sea Harrier, HMS Hermes.

2009, May 7   Litho.   Perf. 14
981-984 A202   Set of 4   11.00 11.00
Souvenir Sheet
985 A202 £2 multi   7.50   7.50

Islands and Rocks Type of 2008
Designs: 27p, Seal Rocks. 40p, Beauchene Island. 65p, Jason East Cay, Steeple Jason. £1.50, Horse Block.

2009, Aug. 14   Litho.   Perf. 13¾
986-989 A199   Set of 4   11.50 11.50

Albatrosses A203

Designs: 22p, Black-browed albatross. 27p, Gray-headed albatross. 60p, Light-mantled sooty albatross. 90p, Wandering albatross.

2009, Oct. 19   Litho.   Perf. 13¾
990-993 A203   Set of 4   8.50   8.50

Cobb's Wren — A204

Designs: Nos. 994, 998a, 27p, Wren on seaweed. Nos. 995, 998b, 65p, Wrens at nest.

Nos. 996, 998c, 90p, Wren on rock. Nos. 997, 998d, £1.10, Two wrens.

2009, Nov. 10   *Perf. 13¾*
Stamps With WWF Emblem
994-997 A204   Set of 4   10.00 10.00
997a   Sheet of 16, 4 each   52.50 52.50
   #994-997

Souvenir Sheet
Stamps With Falklands Conservation Emblem
998 A204   Sheet of 4, #a-d   10.00 10.00

Ships Named HMS Exeter — A205

Ship used from: 4p, 1931-42. 20p, 1931-42, with helicopter. 30p, 1980-2009, with helicopter. £1.66, 1980-2009, with helicopter, diff.

2009, Dec. 8   Litho.   *Perf. 14*
999-1002 A205   Set of 4   7.50 7.50

Skies in Four Seasons — A206

Designs: 27p, Carcass Island in spring. 55p, Beach on New Island in summer. 65p, Rainbow over Stanley in autumn. £1.10, Islands in winter.

2010, Jan. 25   Litho.   *Perf. 13*
1003-1006 A206   Set of 4   8.00 8.00

Restoration of the SS Great Britain — A207

SS Great Britain: 27p, On pontoon near jetty in Stanley. 50p, Beached at Sparrow Cove. 65p, Bow. £1.10, Mast and rigging.

2010, Apr. 12   *Perf. 13¼*
1007-1010 A207   Set of 4   8.00 8.00

Miniature Sheet

Battle of Britain, 70th Anniv. A208

No. 1011 — Airplanes: a, Hawker Hurricane P2961. b, Supermarine Spitfire P9398. c, Hawker Hurricane P3854. d, Supermarine Spitfire P7350. e, Hawker Hurricane V6665. f, Supermarine Spitfire L1035. g, Hawker Hurricane P3576. h, Supermarine Spitfire X4620.

2010, May 7   Litho.   *Perf. 14x14¼*
1011 A208 65p Sheet of 8, #a-h   15.00 15.00
London 2010 Festival of Stamps.

Birds — A209

Designs: Nos. 1012, 1016a, 27p, Sooty shearwater. Nos. 1013, 1016b, 70p, White-

chinned petrel. Nos. 1014, 1016c, 95p, Southern giant petrel. Nos. 1015, 1016d, £1.15, Greater shearwater.

2010, July 8   Litho.   *Perf. 13¾*
Stamps With White Frames
1012-1015 A209   Set of 4   9.50 9.50
Souvenir Sheet
Stamps Without White Frames
1016 A209   Sheet of 4, #a-d   11.50 11.50

Flowering Shrubs — A210

Designs: 27p, Fuchsia. 70p, Boxwood. 95p, Gorse. £1.15, Honeysuckle.

2010, Oct. 27   Litho.   *Perf. 13¼x13*
1017-1020 A210   Set of 4   10.00 10.00

Royal Air Force Search and Rescue Force, 70th Anniv. A211

Anniversary emblem and: 27p, Helicopter on ground. 70p, Helicopter in flight. 95p, Crew in helicopter cockpit. £1.15, Helicopter in flight with open door.

2011, Mar. 9   *Perf. 13¼*
1021-1024 A211   Set of 4   10.00 10.00

Islands and Rocks Type of 2008

Designs: 3p, Bird Island. 27p, Eddystone Rock. 70p, Round Island and Sail Rock. £1.71, Direction Island.

2011, Apr. 11   *Perf. 13¼x13*
1025-1028 A199   Set of 4   8.50 8.50

Wedding of Prince William and Catherine Middleton A212

2011, Apr. 29   *Perf. 13¼*
1029 A212   £2 multi   6.75 6.75

Worldwide Fund for Nature (WWF) — A213

Southern sea lions: 27p, Males and females on beach. 40p, Pod in water. 70p, Males on beach. £1.15, Head.

2011, May 30   *Perf. 13¾*
1030-1033 A213   Set of 4   8.75 8.75
1033a   Miniature sheet of 16, 4 each #1030-1033   35.00 35.00

Queen Elizabeth II, 85th Birthday — A214

Queen Elizabeth II wearing: 27p, Red violet hat with flower. 30p, Fur hat. 70p, White hat with pink and white ribbons. £1.50, White hat with feather.

2011, June 11   *Perf. 13¾*
1034-1037 A214   Set of 4   8.50 8.50

Souvenir Sheet

Queen Elizabeth II A215

2011, Aug. 8   Litho.   *Perf. 14¼x15*
1038 A215   £2 multi   6.75 6.75
Commonwealth Parliamentary Association, cent.

Wildlife — A216

Designs: 27p, Gentoo penguins. 70p, Leopard seal. 95p, Gonatus squid. £1.15, Gentoo penguins, diff.

2011, Nov. 16   *Perf. 13¾*
1039-1042 A216   Set of 4   10.00 10.00

Marine Life — A217

Designs: 27p, Sea anemone. 50p, Jellyfish. 70p, Starfish. £1.15, Nudibranch.

2012, Apr. 11   *Perf. 13¼x13½*
1043-1046 A217   Set of 4   8.00 8.00

Reign of Queen Elizabeth II, 60th Anniv. — A218

Photograph of Queen Elizabeth II in: 27p, 1952. 30p, 1977. 70p, 2002. £1.71, 2012. £3, Queen Elizabeth II wearing tiara, 1955.

2012, May 10   *Perf. 13½x13¼*
1047-1050 A218   Set of 4   9.00 9.00
Souvenir Sheet
Perf. 13¼
1051 A218   £3 multi   9.00 9.00
No. 1051 contains one 30x48mm stamp.

Liberation of the Falkland Islands, 30th Anniv. — A219

Designs: No. 1052, 30p, Ferry MV Concordia Bay. No. 1053, 30p, Liberation Monument, Stanley. No. 1054, 75p, School, Stanley. No. 1055, 75p, Wind turbines. £1, Sign and houses near Stanley Harbor. £1.20, Children and penguins.

2012, June 14   *Perf. 14*
1052-1057 A219   Set of 6   12.50 12.50

Coastal Landscapes A220

Designs: 30p, Surf Bay, East Falkland Island. 75p, Cliffs, New Island. £1, Mountain, Steeple Jason Island. £1.20, Deaths Head and Grave Cove, West Falkland Island.

2012, July 12   *Perf. 13*
1058-1061 A220   Set of 4   9.25 9.25

Sinking of the P.S.N.C. Oravia, Cent. — A221

Designs: 30p, Oravia at sea. 75p, Passengers and crew wearing life vests. £1, Passengers filling lifeboats. £1.20 Oravia and the Samson.

2012, Aug. 28   *Perf. 14*
1062-1065 A221   Set of 4   12.00 12.00

Souvenir Sheet

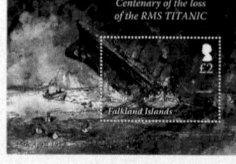

Sinking of the Titanic, Cent. A222

2012, Aug. 28   *Perf. 14x14¾*
1066 A222   £2 multi   9.00 9.00

Dolphins and Whales A223

Designs: 1p, Southern right whale dolphins. 2p, Minke whale. 5p, Peale's dolphin. 10p, Dusky dolphin. 30p, Southern right whale. 50p, Fin whale. 75p, Hourglass dolphin. £1, Long-finned pilot whale. £1.20, Killer whales. £2, Sperm whale. £3.50, Commerson's dolphin. £5, Sei whale.

2012, Nov. 9   *Perf. 13¼*

1067	A223	1p multi	.25	.25
1068	A223	2p multi	.25	.25
1069	A223	5p multi	.25	.25
1070	A223	10p multi	.30	.30
1071	A223	30p multi	.95	.95
1072	A223	50p multi	1.60	1.60
1073	A223	75p multi	2.40	2.40
1074	A223	£1 multi	3.25	3.25
1075	A223	£1.20 multi	4.00	4.00
1076	A223	£2 multi	6.50	6.50
1077	A223	£3.50 multi	11.00	11.00
1078	A223	£5 multi	14.00	14.00

Nos. 1067-1078 (12)   44.75 44.75
See No. 1172.

Color in Nature A224

No. 1079: a, Night heron. b, Diddle-dee berries.
No. 1080: a, Short-eared owl. b, Scurvy grass flowers.

2012, Dec. 14   *Perf. 13*
1079   Pair   2.00 2.00
a.-b.   A224 30p Either single   1.00 1.00
1080   Pair   4.50 4.50
a.-b.   A224 75p Either single   2.25 2.25
See Nos. 1108-1109, 1122-1123, 1136-1137.

2013 Referendum on Political Status — A225

Map, of Falkland Island, hand and ballot box with denomination color of: 3p, Deep blue. 40p, Red violet. 75p, Green. £1.76, Red brown. £3, Purple.

2013, Feb. 15
1081-1084 A225   Set of 4   8.75 8.75
Souvenir Sheet
Perf. 13½x13¼
1085 A225   £3 multi   9.00 9.00
No. 1085 contains one 56x45mm stamp.

Wildlife — A226

Designs: 30p, Johnny rook. 75p, Rockhopper penguins. £1, Rockhopper penguin swimming. £1.20, Lobster krill.

2013, Mar. 28   *Perf. 13¾*
1086-1089 A226   Set of 4   10.00 10.00

Lady Margaret Thatcher (1925-2013), British Prime Minister — A227

Lady Thatcher: 30p, And husband, Denis arriving at 10 Downing Street, 1979. 75p, Inspecting Falkland Islands minefield, 1983. £1, With flag at celebration of 10th anniversary of Falkland Islands liberation, 1992. £1.20, Holding Falkland Islands coin commemorating 25th anniversary of the liberation, 2007.

2013, May 16   *Perf. 13¾*
1090-1093 A227   Set of 4   10.00 10.00

Sir Rex Hunt (1926-2012), Governor of Falkland Islands — A228

Falkland Islands coat of arms and Hunt: 30p, As Civil Commissioner, 1982. 75p, In uniform next to Governor's car. £1, With flag of Falkland Islands, 1992. £1.20, Talking to Queen Elizabeth II, 2000.

2013, June 11   *Perf. 14*
1094-1097 A228   Set of 4   10.00 10.00

Coronation of Queen Elizabeth II, 60th Anniv. — A229

Queen Elizabeth II: 30p, Wearing coronation gown. 75p, With crown and orb. £1, Waving. £1.20, With Prince Philip.

2013, July 22   *Perf. 13½x13¼*
1098-1101 A229   Set of 4   10.00 10.00

Shallow Marine Surveys Group — A230

Marine life: Nos. 1102, 1106a, 30p, Saffron sea cucumber. Nos. 1103, 1106b, 75p, Stalked jellyfish. Nos. 1104, 1106c, £1, Scythe-edged serolis. Nos. 1105, 1106d, £1.20, Naked sea urchin.
No. 1107a, £1, Painted shrimp, vert.

2013, Aug. 29   *Perf. 13¼x13½*
Stamps With White Frames
1102-1105 A230   Set of 4   10.50 10.50
Stamps Without White Frames
1106 A230   Strip of 4, #a-d   10.50 10.50
Souvenir Sheet
Perf. 13¼x13¼
1107 A230   Sheet of 3 (see
       footnote)   9.75 9.75
  a.   A230 £1 multi   3.25 3.25
No. 1107 contains No. 1107a, Ascension No. 1104a and South Georgia and South Sandwich Islands No. 485a. This sheet was sold in Ascension, Falkland Islands and South Georgia and South Sandwich Islands.

Color in Nature Type of 2012
No. 1108: a, Macaroni penguin. b, Purple cap fungi.

No. 1109: a, Crested duck. b, Southern painted lady butterfly.

2013, Oct. 3   *Perf. 13¼*
1108   Pair   1.90 1.90
  a.-b.   A224 30p Either single   .95 .95
1109   Pair   4.80 4.80
  a.-b.   A224 75p Either single   2.40 2.40

Wildlife — A231

Designs: 30p, King penguin and chick. 75p, Gaptooth lanternfish. £1, Southern sea lion. £1.20, King penguins, diff.

2014, Mar. 25   *Litho.*   *Perf. 13¼*
1110-1113 A231   Set of 4   11.00 11.00

Mushrooms A232

Designs: 30p, False chanterelle. 75p, Red wax cap. £1, Clustered domecap. £1.20, Shaggy inkcap.

2014, Apr. 15   *Litho.*   *Perf. 13¼*
1114-1117 A232   Set of 4   10.00 10.00

Royal Christenings — A233

Photograph from christening of: 30p, Queen Elizabeth II. 75p, Prince Charles. £1, Prince William. £1.20, Prince George.

2014, May 21   *Litho.*   *Perf. 13¼*
1118-1121 A233   Set of 4   10.00 10.00

Color in Nature Type of 2012
No. 1122: a, King penguins. b, Marsh marigolds.
No. 1123: a, Black oystercatcher. b, Vanilla daisies.

2014, Sept. 16   *Litho.*   *Perf. 13¼*
1122   Pair   2.00 2.00
  a.-b.   A224 30p Either single   1.00 1.00
1123   Pair   5.00 5.00
  a.-b.   A224 75p Either single   2.50 2.50

Battle of the Falkland Islands, Cent. — A234

Designs: 30p, SMS Scharnhorst. 75p, HMS Invincible. £1, British and German flags, poppies. £1.20, Sailor, Battle of the Falkland Islands Monument.

2014, Dec. 8   *Litho.*   *Perf. 13¾*
1124-1127 A234   Set of 4   10.00 10.00

Type 42 Destroyers — A235

Designs: 30p, HMS Sheffield. 75p, HMS Exeter. £1, HMS Liverpool. £1.20, HMS Edinburgh.

2014, Dec. 22   *Litho.*   *Perf. 14*
1128-1131 A235   Set of 4   9.00 9.00

Birds — A236

Adult and chicks: 30p, Pied oystercatchers. 75p, Gentoo penguins. £1, Black-browed albatrosses. £1.20, Falkland skuas.

2015, Feb. 11   *Litho.*   *Perf. 13¾*
1132-1135 A236   Set of 4   10.00 10.00

Color in Nature Type of 2012
No. 1136: a, Black-throated finch. b, Fuegian ferns.
No. 1137: a, Dolphin gulls. b, Yellow daisies.

2015, May 12   *Litho.*   *Perf. 13¼*
1136   Pair   1.90 1.90
  a.-b.   A224 30p Either single   .95 .95
1137   Pair   4.50 4.50
  a.-b.   A224 75p Either single   2.25 2.25

Magna Carta, 800th Anniv. — A237

Designs: 30p, King John, Magna Carta and barons. 75p, Courtroom. £1, Gilbert House, Stanley. £1.20, King John, arms of Falkland Islands.

2015, June 15   *Litho.*   *Perf. 14*
1138-1141 A237   Set of 4   10.50 10.50

Wildlife — A238

Designs: 30p, Magellanic penguin. 75p, Falkland sprats. £1, Falkland skua. £1.20, Heads of two magellanic penguins.

2015, Aug. 21   *Litho.*   *Perf. 13¾*
1142-1145 A238   Set of 4   10.00 10.00

Queen Elizabeth II, Longest-Reigning British Monarch — A239

Queen Elizabeth II and events during her reign: 30p, Publications reporting on her coronation, 1953. 75p, Arrival of first Land Rovers in the Falkland Islands, 1950s. £1, Coach used for Golden Jubilee, 2012. £1.25, Falkland Islands referendum, 2013.

2015, Sept. 9   *Litho.*   *Perf. 14*
1146-1149 A239   Set of 4   10.00 10.00

Elephant Seal Research Group, 20th Anniv. — A240

No. 1150, 30p: a, Seal in water. b, Researcher with equipment near seal.
No. 1151, 75p: a, Pod of seals on beach. b, Researcher approaching seal.
No. 1152, £1: a, Seal and penguins. b, Researcher holding measuring stick above seal.

2015, Nov. 30   *Litho.*   *Perf. 13*
Horiz. Pairs, #a-b
1150-1152 A240   Set of 3   12.50 12.50

Clouds A241

Designs: 31p, Asperitas. 76p, Altocumulus. £1.01, Altocumulus lenticularis. £1.22, Cumulonimbus and Stratocumulus.

2015, Dec. 9   *Litho.*   *Perf. 13¼*
1153-1156 A241   Set of 4   9.75 9.75

Birds of Prey — A242

Designs: No. 1157, 31p, Barn owl. No. 1158, 31p, Short-eared owl. No. 1159, 76p, Red-backed buzzard. No. 1160, 76p, Crested caracara. £1.01, Peregrine falcon. £1.22, Striated caracara.

2016, Jan. 13   *Litho.*   *Perf. 13¾*
1157-1162 A242   Set of 6   13.00 13.00

Items at Historic Dockyard Museum — A243

Designs: 31p, Traditional horse gear. 76p, Peat-burning stove. £1.01, Warrah skull. £1.22, Antarctic exploration hut.

2016, Mar. 30   *Litho.*   *Perf. 13¾*
1163-1166 A243   Set of 4   9.50 9.50

Queen Elizabeth II, 90th Birthday — A244

Photographs of Queen Elizabeth from: 31p, 1977. 76p, 1982. £1.01, 1953. £1.22, 2014. £3, Queen Elizabeth II in 1962.

2016, Apr. 21   *Litho.*   *Perf. 14*
1167-1170 A244   Set of 4   9.75 9.75
Souvenir Sheet
1171 A244 £3 multi   9.00 9.00

Dolphins and Whales Type of 2012
2016, Aug. 1   *Litho.*   *Perf. 13¼*
1172 A223 31p Southern right whale   .85 .85

Endemic Plants — A245

Designs: No. 1173, 31p, Falkland rockcress. No. 1174, 31p, Lady's slipper. No. 1175, 76p, False-plantain. No. 1176, 76p, Silvery buttercup. No. 1177, £1.01, Snakeplant. No. 1178, £1.01, Falkland nassauvia.
No. 1179, 66p: a, Like No. 1173. b, Like No. 1174. c, Like No. 1175. d, Like No. 1176. e, Like No. 1177. f, Like No. 1178.

2016, Nov. 21   *Litho.*   *Perf. 13¾*
1173-1178 A245   Set of 6   11.00 11.00
Miniature Sheet
1179 A245 66p Sheet of 6, #a-f   10.00 10.00
No. 1179 has cream colored margins around the stamps.

Shipwrecks A246

Designs: 31p, Acteon. 76p, Charles Cooper. £1.01, Afterglow. £1.22, Capricorn.

2017, Mar. 27　Litho.　Perf. 13
1180-1183 A246　Set of 4　8.25 8.25
See Nos. 1213-1216, 1244-1247, 1264-1267.

Falkland Islands Journal, 50th Anniv. — A247

Journal cover from: 31p, 2010. 76p, 2013r. £1.01, 2014. £1.22, 2016.

2017, July 5　Litho.　Perf. 13½x13¼
1184-1187 A247　Set of 4　8.50 8.50

A248　　　　Birds — A249

Designs: 1p, Tussacbird. 2p, Long-tailed meadowlark. 5p, Black-chinned siskin. 10p, Falkland pipit, above white flowers. 20p, Cobb's wren. 50p, White-bridled finch. 76p, Falkland thrush. £1, Two-banded plover. £1.20, Falkland grass wren. £2, Dark-faced ground tyrant. £3.50, Rufous-chested dotterel. £5, Magellanic snipe.
(31p), Falkland pipit, above red flowers.

2017, Aug. 14　Litho.　Perf. 13
1188	A248	1p multi	.25	.25
1189	A248	2p multi	.25	.25
1190	A248	5p multi	.25	.25
1191	A248	10p multi	.30	.30
1192	A248	20p multi	.55	.55
1193	A248	50p multi	1.40	1.40
1194	A248	76p multi	2.00	2.00
1195	A248	£1 multi	2.75	2.75
1196	A248	£1.20 multi	3.25	3.25
1197	A248	£2 multi	5.25	5.25
1198	A248	£3.50 multi	9.25	9.25
1199	A248	£5 multi	13.50	13.50
		Nos. 1188-1199 (12)	39.00	39.00

Booklet Stamp
Self-Adhesive
Serpentine Die Cut 13
1200	A249	(31p) multi	.85	.85
a.	Booklet pane of 10		8.50	
b.	Dated "2019"		.80	.80
c.	Booklet pane of 10 #1200b		8.00	

Issued: No. 1200b, 8/6/19. No. 1200b sold for 32p on day of issue.

Falkland Islands Fisheries, 30th Anniv. — A250

Designs: 31p, Toothfish and CFL Hunter. 76p, FPV Protegat and fishery RIB. £1.01, Argos Vigo and Frank Wild. £1.22, Robin M. Lee and Falkland calamari.

2017, Oct. 23　Litho.　Perf. 13½x13¼
1201-1204 A250　Set of 4　8.75 8.75

70th Wedding Anniversary of Queen Elizabeth II and Prince Philip — A251

Photograph of Queen Elizabeth II and Prince Philip from: 31p, 1952. 76p, 1961. £1.22, 1972. £1.78, 2016.

2017, Nov. 20　Litho.　Perf. 13¼x13
1205-1208 A251　Set of 4　11.00 11.00

Christ Church Cathedral, Stanley, 125th Anniv. — A252

Various views of Cathedral: 31p, 76p, £1.01, £1.22.

2017, Dec. 18　Litho.　Perf. 13¼x13
1209-1212 A252　Set of 4　9.00 9.00

Shipwrecks Type of 2017

Designs: 31p, Glengowan. 76p, Jhelum. £1.01, Golden Chance. £1.22, Lady Elizabeth.

2018, Mar. 2　Litho.　Perf. 13
1213-1216 A246　Set of 4　9.25 9.25

Wildlife — A253

Designs: 31p, Macaroni penguin on nest. 76p, Euphausiid krill. £1.01, Southern sea lion. £1.22, Two Macaroni penguins.

2018, Apr. 18　Litho.　Perf. 13
1217-1220 A253　Set of 4　9.00 9.00

Royal Air Force, Cent. — A254

Designs: 31p, Hawker Siddeley Nimrod MR2. 76p, McDonnell Douglas F-4 Phantom. £1.22, Hawker Siddeley Harrier GR.3. £1.92, Eurofigher Typhoon.

2018, July 2　Litho.　Perf. 13¼x13½
1221-1224 A254　Set of 4　11.00 11.00

Wedding of Prince Harry and Meghan Markle — A255

Designs: 31p, Engagement photograph. 75p, Couple at ANZAC Day service. £1.10, Couple at altar on wedding day. £1.22, Couple leaving wedding. £3, Couple kissing, vert.

Perf. 13¼x13½
2018, Aug. 14　　　　Litho.
1225-1228 A255　Set of 4　8.25 8.25
Souvenir Sheet
Perf. 13½x13¼
1229 A255　£3 multi　7.75 7.75

Migratory Birds — A256

No. 1230 — Southern rockhopper penguin and map of: a, 31p, South America and Northern Patagonian Shelf. b, 76p, Southern tip of South America and the Falkland Islands.
No. 1231 — Sooty shearwater and map of: a, £1.01, North America, Europe and Northern Africa. b, £1.22, South America, Falkland Islands and Southern Africa.

2018, Oct. 18　Litho.　Perf. 13¼x13½
1230	A256	Vert. pair, #a-b	2.75	2.75
1231	A256	Vert. pair, #a-b	5.75	5.75

Old Fox Bay Post Office, Cent. — A257

Fox Bay cancel and: 31p, 1940s photograph of Post Office. 76p, Old post office scales. £1.01, Princess Anne mailing postcard, old postmark box. £1.22, Old Post Office and Museum.

Perf. 13¼x13½
2018, Nov. 28　　　　Litho.
1232-1235 A257　Set of 4　8.50 8.50

Falkland Islands Government Air Service, 70th Anniv. — A258

Airplanes: 31p, Auster 4. 76p, Norseman V. £1.01, DHC-2 Beaver. £1.22, BN-2B-26 Islander.

Perf. 13¼x13½
2018, Dec. 19　　　　Litho.
1236-1239 A258　Set of 4　8.50 8.50

Landscapes — A259

Photographs: 31p, Quarry Point, Fox Bay, by Carli Sudder. 76p, New Island, by Georgina Strange. £1.01, Road to Nowhere, Port Howard, by Maria Forman. £1.22, Towards Albemarle, by Ben Cockwell.

2018, Dec. 28　Litho.　Perf. 13¼
1240-1243 A259　Set of 4　8.50 8.50

Shipwrecks Type of 2017

Designs: 31p, Lily. 76p, Plym. £1.01, Philomel. £1.22, Protector.

2019, Mar. 4　Litho.　Perf. 13
1244-1247 A246　Set of 4　8.75 8.75

D-Day, 75th Anniv. — A260

Designs: 32p, Troops looking at graffiti on side of their glider. 78p, Airplanes for invasion on runway in England. £1.04, Soldiers landing on Utah Beach. £1.26, Tank in water after leaving landing craft.

2019, June 6　Litho.　Perf. 13¼x13½
1248-1251 A260　Set of 4　8.75 8.75

Feathers — A261

Feathers of: No. 1252, 32p, Striated caracara. No. 1253, 32p, Black-browed albatross. No. 1254, 78p, Yellow-billed teal. No. 1255, 78p, Barn owl. No. 1256, £1.26, Black-crowned night heron. No. 1257, £1.26, King penguin.

2019, Aug. 5　Litho.　Perf. 13¼x13½
1252-1257 A261　Set of 6　11.50 11.50

Cancer Support and Awareness Fund Emblem and Peter Collins A262

Stephen Jaffray Memorial Medical Emergency Assistance Fund Emblem and Stephen Jaffray (1970-92) A263

2019, Dec. 6　Litho.　Perf. 13
1258	A262	78p multi	2.10	2.10
1259	A263	78p multi	2.10	2.10

Land Rovers — A264

Designs: 32p, Series I 88-inch. 78p, Series I hard top. £1.26, Series IIA roadless traction forest rover. £1.96, Series IIB forward control.

2019, Dec. 20　Litho.　Perf. 13
1260-1263 A264　Set of 4　11.50 11.50

Shipwrecks Type of 2017

Designs: 32p, Samson. 78p, St. Mary. £1.04, Weddell. £1.26, Garland.

2020, Mar. 16　Litho.　Perf. 13
1264-1267 A246　Set of 4　8.50 8.50

Penguins Depicted on Falkland Islands 50-Pence Coins — A265

Designs: 32p, Rockhopper penguin. 68p, King penguin. 78p, Magellanic penguin. £1.04, Gentoo penguin. £1.26, Macaroni penguin.

Perf. 13¼x13½
2020, Aug. 10　　　　Litho.
1268-1272 A265　Set of 5　11.00 11.00

Falkland Islands Philatelic Study Group, 50th Anniv. — A266

Designs: 32p, Falkland Islands #21, Stanley Post Office and Philatelic Bureau. 78p, Falkland Islands #74, Jane Cameron National Archives. £1.04, Falkland Islands #94a, publications of Falkland Islands Philatelic Study Group. £1.26, Falkland Islands #151a, 1875 cover sent from Falkland Islands to Tobago.

2020, Sept. 7　Litho.　Perf. 13¼x13½
1273-1276 A266　Set of 4　8.75 8.75

Paintings of Birds by Mike Peake (1939-2005) — A267

Painting of: 32p, Black-necked swan. 40p, Black-crowned night heron. 78p, Upland geese. £1.04, Belcher's gull. £1.26, Variable hawk. £1.35, Upland geese and seal.

2020, Oct. 1　Litho.　Perf. 13
1277-1282 A267　Set of 6　13.50 13.50

Falkland Islands Mine Clearance Program — A268

Designs: 32p, Discovered mines. 49p, Manual demining. £1.10, Penguin watchers. £1.96, Mechanical demining.

Perf. 13¼x13½
2020, Nov. 14　　　　Litho.
1283-1286 A268　Set of 4　10.50 10.50

Christmas — A269

Children's art by: 32p, Rylee Molkernbuhr. 78p, Tessa Blake. £1.04, Laura Blake. £1.26, Neve Stanworth.

2020, Nov. 20   Litho.   Perf. 13¼x13
1287-1290 A269   Set of 4   9.25 9.25

Queen Elizabeth II, 95th Birthday — A270

Designs: 32p, Princess Elizabeth as child in ballet costume. 49p, Queen Elizabeth II at her coronation. 78p, Queen Elizabeth II with Prince Philip, 2007. £1.04, Queen Elizabeth II holding camera, 1982. £1.10, Queen Elizabeth II at Trooping the Color ceremony. £1.26, Queen Elizabeth II, 2017.

2021, Apr. 21   Litho.   Perf. 13¼
1291-1296 A270   Set of 6   14.00 14.00

See Isle of Man No. 2150a.

Paintings of Settlements by Mike Peake (1939-2005) A271

Painting of: 27p, Port Howard. 32p, Stanley. 68p, Goose Green. 78p, Port Louis. £1.82, Egg Harbour. £1.96, Horseshoe Bay.

2021, July 14   Litho.   Perf. 13
1297-1302 A271   Set of 6   16.50 16.50

Prince Philip (1921-2021) A272

Designs: 32p, Prince Philip reviewing troops in Falkland Islands, 1957. 78p, Prince Philip on horse. £1.04, Prince Philip facing right, £1.26, Prince Philip, cabinet with glass door in background.

2021, Aug. 30   Litho.   Perf. 13¼x13
1303-1306 A272   Set of 4   9.50 9.50

Winning Photographs in Tourism Recovery Incentive Program Stamp Design Contest — A273

Photograph of: 32p, Sea Lion Island cliff, by Adam Yould. 68p, Southern elephant seal, by Yould. 78p, Steamer duck and ducklings, by Chris Gilbert. £1.04, Falkland Islands Government Air Service plane and Sea Lion Island Lodge, by Gilbert. £1.26, Magellanic snipe, by Jesse Ross. £1.35, Wreck of the Protector 2, by Jody Aldridge.

2021, Oct. 22   Litho.   Perf. 13
1307-1312 A273   Set of 6   15.00 15.00

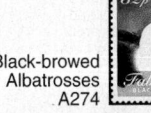

Black-browed Albatrosses A274

Designs: 32p, Heads of two albatrosses. 78p, Adult albatross feeding chicks. £1.04, Albatross in flight. £1.26, Head of albatross.

2021, Nov. 17   Litho.   Perf. 13
1313-1316 A274   Set of 4   9.50 9.50

Souvenir Sheet

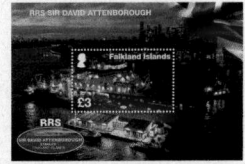

Arrival of RRS Sir David Attenborough in the Falkland Islands — A275

2021, Dec. 11   Litho.   Perf. 13¼x13
1317 A275   £3 multi   8.25 8.25

Sir Ernest Shackleton (1874-1922), Antarctic Explorer — A276

Designs: 32p, Shackleton as child. 78p, Shackleton, Tom Crean, Captain Ingvar Thom, and Capt. Frank Worsley in Stanley, 1916. £1.10, Shackleton and his ice-bound ship, Nimrod. £1.26, Shackleton's Cairn, Grytviken, South Georgia.

2022, Jan. 5   Litho.   Perf. 13¼x13
1318-1321 A276   Set of 4   9.50 9.50

Reign of Queen Elizabeth II, 70th Anniv. — A277

Photograph of Queen Elizabeth II wearing: No. 1322, £2, Diadem, 1957. No. 1323, £2, Hat, 2021.

£3.50, Queen Elizabeth II wearing diadem, vert.

2022, Mar. 24   Litho.   Perf. 13¼x13
1322-1323 A277   Set of 2   10.50 10.50
Souvenir Sheet
Perf. 13x13¼
1324 A277   £3.50 multi   9.25 9.25

No. 1324 contains one 29x48mm stamp.

A278

Designs: £1.30, Royal Mail Aircraft Hudson. £2.05, A330 Voyager.

2022, June 2   Litho.   Perf. 13¼x13¾
1325-1326 A278   Set of 2   8.50 8.50

First direct airmail flight from Great Britain to the Falkland Islands, 70th anniv.

Liberation of the Falkland Islands, 40th Anniv. — A279

Designs: 33p, Stylized "40" with flag of Great Britain. 80p, Fishing boat CFA Hunter. £1.07, Tourist ship and penguins. £1.30, Sheep at pasture.

Perf. 13¼x13¾
2022, June 14   Litho.
1327-1330 A279   Set of 4   8.50 8.50

Designation of Stanley as a Jubilee City — A280

Designs: 33p, Christ Church Cathedral and Centennial Monument. 80p, Secretariat Building and 1982 Liberation Memorial. £1.13, Government House. £1.30, Residential houses.

2022, Aug. 5   Litho.   Perf. 13¼x13½
1331-1334 A280   Set of 4   8.75 8.75

Lighthouse Seafarer's Mission, 25th Anniv. — A281

Designs: 33p, Mission building. 80p, Mission building, anchor, dog and car. £1.10, Mission building and dog. £1.45, Aerial view of Mission building and boats in harbor.

Perf. 13¼x13½
2022, Sept. 20   Litho.
1335-1338 A281   Set of 4   8.25 8.25

A282

Rural Heritage — A283

Designs: 1p, Vehicle crossing San Carlos River at Rudd's Pass. 2p, Shipwreck of the St. Mary. 5p, Hillside House. 10p, Ferguson's Lookout. 54p, Mission station, Keppel Island. 77p, Farm caravan. 80p, Little Chartres Bridge. £1, Bull's House. £2, Whaling station, New Island. £2.05, Stone corral. £3.60, Sheep dip. £5, Standing man (stone cairn), Weddell Island.
(33p), Farm cart.

2022, Oct. 10   Litho.   Perf. 11½
1339 A282   1p multi   .30   .30
1340 A282   2p multi   .30   .30
1341 A282   5p multi   .30   .30
1342 A282   10p multi   .30   .30
1343 A282   54p multi   1.25   1.25
1344 A282   77p multi   1.75   1.75
1345 A282   80p multi   1.90   1.90
1346 A282   £1 multi   2.25   2.25
1347 A282   £2 multi   4.50   4.50
1348 A282   £2.05 multi   4.75   4.75
1349 A282   £3.60 multi   8.00   8.00
1350 A282   £5 multi   11.00   11.00
Nos. 1339-1350 (12)   36.60   36.60

Booklet Stamp
Self-Adhesive
Serpentine Die Cut 12¾
1351 A283   (33p) multi   .75   .75
a.   Booklet pane of 10   7.50

SEMI-POSTAL STAMPS

Catalogue values for unused stamps in this section are for Never Hinged items.

Rebuilding after Conflict with Argentina — SP1

Wmk. 373
1982, Sept. 13   Litho.   Perf. 11
B1   SP1   £1 + £1 Battle sites   3.00 3.00

Liberation of Falkland Islands, 10th Anniv. — SP2

Designs: 14p+6p, San Carlos Cemetery. 29p+11p, 1982 War Memorial, Port Stanley. 34p+16p, South Atlantic Medal. 68p+32p, Government House, Port Stanley.

Wmk. 373
1992, June 14   Litho.   Perf. 14
B2   SP2   14p + 6p multicolored   1.00 1.60
B3   SP2   29p + 11p multicolored   1.75 2.00
B4   SP2   34p + 16p multicolored   2.00 2.25
B5   SP2   68p + 32p multicolored   2.75 3.50
a.   Souvenir sheet of 4, #B2-B5   8.50 8.50
Nos. B2-B5 (4)   7.50 9.35

Surtax for Soldiers', Sailors' and Airmen's Families Association.

AIR POST STAMPS

Bird Type of 2003

Design: Rockhopper penguins, vert.

Booklet Stamp
Serpentine Die Cut 6x6½ Syncopated
2003, Sept. 19   Litho.
Self-Adhesive
C1   A163   (40p) multi   2.50 2.50
a.   Booklet pane of 8   20.00

Penguins — AP1

Designs: No. C2, (55p), King penguin. No. C3, (55p), Macaroni penguin. No. C4, (55p), Magellanic penguin. No. C5, (55p), Rockhopper penguin. No. C6, (55p), Gentoo penguin. No. C7, (55p), Albino rockhopper penguin.

2008, Dec. 1   Litho.   Perf. 13¼
C2-C7   AP1   Set of 6   19.00 19.00
C7a   Souvenir sheet, #C2-C7   19.00 19.00

Penguins — AP2

Designs: Nos. C8, C14a, (70p), King penguin. Nos. C9, C14b, (70p), Macaroni penguin. Nos. C10, C14c, (70p), Rockhopper penguins. Nos. C11, C14d, (70p), Albino and normal rockhopper penguins. Nos. C12, C14e, (70p), Magellanic penguin. Nos. C13, C14f, (70p), Gentoo penguins.

2010, Sept. 29   Litho.   Perf. 13¾
Stamps With White Frames
C8-C13   AP2   Set of 6   13.50 13.50
Stamps Without White Frames
C14   AP2   (70p)   Sheet of 6, #a-f   13.50 13.50

Albino and Normal Rockhopper Penguins AP3

Gentoo Penguins AP4

Magellanic Penguin AP5

Rockhopper Penguins AP6

King Penguins AP7

Macaroni Penguins AP8

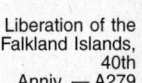

2013, Nov. 21   Litho.   Perf. 13¼
Stamps With White Frames

C15	AP3	(65p) multi	2.10	2.10
C16	AP4	(65p) multi	2.10	2.10
C17	AP5	(65p) multi	2.10	2.10
C18	AP6	(65p) multi	2.10	2.10
C19	AP7	(65p) multi	2.10	2.10
C20	AP8	(65p) multi	2.10	2.10
		Nos. C15-C20 (6)	12.60	12.60

Souvenir Sheet
Stamps Without White Frames

C21		Sheet of 6	14.00	16.00
a.	AP3	(65p) multi	2.25	2.60
b.	AP4	(65p) multi	2.25	2.60
c.	AP5	(65p) multi	2.25	2.60
d.	AP6	(65p) multi	2.25	2.60
e.	AP7	(65p) multi	2.25	2.60
f.	AP8	(65p) multi	2.25	2.60

POSTAGE DUE STAMPS

> Catalogue values for unused stamps in this section are for never hinged items.

Penguin — D1

Perf. 14½x14
1991, Jan. 7   Litho.   Wmk. 373

J1	D1	1p lilac rose & lake	.25	.60
J2	D1	2p buff & brown org	.25	.60
J3	D1	3p yel & orange yel	.25	.60
J4	D1	4p lt bl grn & dk bl grn	.25	.60
J5	D1	5p sky blue & Prus bl	.25	.60
J6	D1	10p lt blue & dk blue	.35	.70
J7	D1	20p lt violet & dk vio	.90	1.50
J8	D1	50p brt yel grn & dk yel green	2.00	3.00
		Nos. J1-J8 (8)	4.50	8.20

Penguins — D2

Various penguins.

2005, Dec. 2   Litho.   Perf. 13¾

J9	D2	1p multi	.25	.25
J10	D2	3p multi	.25	.25
J11	D2	5p multi	.25	.25
J12	D2	10p multi	.45	.45
J13	D2	20p multi	.85	.85
J14	D2	50p multi	1.90	1.90
J15	D2	£1 multi	3.75	3.75
J16	D2	£2 multi	7.50	7.50
J17	D2	£3 multi	11.00	11.00
J18	D2	£5 multi	17.00	17.00
		Nos. J9-J18 (10)	43.20	43.20

WAR TAX STAMPS

Regular Issue of 1912-14 Overprinted

1918-20   Wmk. 3   Perf. 14

MR1	A7	½p dp ol grn	.55	7.25
MR2	A7	1p org ver ('19)	.55	4.00
a.		Double overprint	4,250.	
MR3	A7	1sh bis brn	6.50	52.50
a.		Pair, one without overprint	18,000.	
b.		Double ovpt., one albino	2,250.	
c.		1sh brn, thick grayish paper ('20)	6.00	50.00
d.		As "c," double ovpt., one albino	2,000.	
		Nos. MR1-MR3 (3)	7.60	63.75

No. MR3a probably is caused by a foldover and is not constant.

FALKLAND ISLANDS DEPENDENCIES

> Catalogue values for unused stamps in this section are for Never Hinged items.

Map of Falkland Islands — A1

Engr., Center Litho. in Black
1946, Feb. 1   Wmk. 4   Perf. 12

1L1	A1	½p yellow green	1.10	3.50
1L2	A1	1p blue violet	1.30	2.00
1L3	A1	2p deep carmine	1.30	2.60
1L4	A1	3p ultramarine	1.90	5.25
1L5	A1	4p deep plum	2.40	5.00
1L6	A1	6p orange yellow	3.75	5.25
1L7	A1	9p brown	2.25	4.00
1L8	A1	1sh rose violet	3.00	4.50
		Nos. 1L1-1L8 (8)	17.00	32.10

Nos. 1L1-1L8 were reissued in 1948, printed on more opaque paper with the lines of the map finer and clearer. Value for set, unused or used $130.
See No. 1L13.

Common Design Types pictured following the introduction.

Peace Issue
Common Design Type
1946, Oct. 4   Perf. 13½x14

1L9	CD303	1p purple	.50	.50
1L10	CD303	3p deep blue	.80	.50

Silver Wedding Issue
Common Design Types
1948, Dec. 6   Photo.   Perf. 14x14½

1L11	CD304	2½p brt ultra	1.75	3.25

Perf. 11½x11
Engr.

1L12	CD305	1sh blue violet	2.50	2.75

Type of 1946
1949, Mar. 6   Perf. 12
Center Litho. in Black

1L13	A1	2½p deep blue	9.00	4.25

UPU Issue
Common Design Types
Engr.; Name Typo. on 2p, 3p
1949, Oct. 10   Perf. 13½, 11x11½

1L14	CD306	1p violet	1.10	4.00
1L15	CD307	2p deep carmine	5.00	4.00
1L16	CD308	3p indigo	3.75	2.25
1L17	CD309	6p red orange	4.75	4.25
		Nos. 1L14-1L17 (4)	14.60	14.50

Coronation Issue
Common Design Type
1953, June 4   Perf. 13½x13

1L18	CD312	1p purple & black	1.80	1.40

John Biscoe — A2   Trepassey — A3

Ships: 1½p, Wyatt Earp. 2p, Eagle. 2½p, Penola. 3p, Discovery II. 4p, William Scoresby. 6p, Discovery. 9p, Endurance. 1sh, Deutschland. 2sh, Pourquoi-pas? 2sh6p, Français. 5sh, Scotia. 10sh, Antarctic. £1, Belgica.

1954, Feb. 1   Engr.   Perf. 12½
Center in Black

1L19	A2	½p blue green	.25	2.00
1L20	A3	1p sepia	1.75	1.50
1L21	A3	1½p olive	2.00	1.75
1L22	A3	2p rose red	1.25	2.50
1L23	A3	2½p yellow	1.25	.35
1L24	A3	3p ultra	1.25	.35
1L25	A3	4p red violet	3.00	1.75
1L26	A2	6p rose violet	3.50	1.75

1L27	A2	9p black	3.50	2.00
1L28	A3	1sh org brown	3.50	2.00
1L29	A3	2sh lilac rose	18.00	10.00
1L30	A2	2sh6p blue gray	19.00	7.00
1L31	A2	5sh violet	40.00	7.50
1L32	A3	10sh brt blue	55.00	18.00
1L33	A2	£1 black	85.00	47.50
		Nos. 1L19-1L33 (15)	238.25	105.95

Nos. 20, 23-24, 26 Ovptd. in Black

1956, Jan. 30   Center in Black

1L34	A3	1p sepia	.30	.30
1L35	A3	2½p yellow	.55	.55
1L36	A3	3p ultramarine	.65	.65
1L37	A2	6p rose violet	.75	.75
		Nos. 1L34-1L37 (4)	2.25	2.25

Trans-Antarctic Expedition, 1955-1958.

A4

1p, Map of Dependencies. 2p, Shag Rocks. 3p, Bird and Willis Islands. 4p, Gulbrandsen Lake. 5p, King Edward Point. 6p, Shackleton's Memorial Cross. 7p, Shackleton's grave. 8p, Grytviken Church. 9p, Coaling Hulk "Louise". 10p, Clerke Rocks. 20p, Candlemas Island. 25p, Twitcher Rock, Cook Island. 50p, "John Biscoe". £1, "Bransfield". £3, "Endurance".

1980, May 5   Wmk. 373   Litho.   Perf. 13½

1L38	A4	1p multicolored	.25	.25
1L39	A4	2p multicolored	.25	.25
1L40	A4	3p multicolored	.25	.25
1L41	A4	4p multicolored	.25	.25
1L42	A4	5p multicolored	.25	.25
1L43	A4	6p multicolored	.25	.25
1L44	A4	7p multicolored	.25	.25
1L45	A4	8p multicolored	.25	.25
1L46	A4	9p multicolored	.25	.30
1L47	A4	10p multicolored	.25	.30
1L48	A4	20p multicolored	.45	.55
1L49	A4	25p multicolored	.60	.70
1L50	A4	50p multicolored	1.10	1.25
1L51	A4	£1 multicolored	2.25	2.75
1L52	A4	£3 multicolored	5.50	7.00
		Nos. 1L38-1L52 (15)	12.40	14.85

Nos. 38-50 exist dated 1984; issued May 3, 1984. Value, set $16.

1985, Nov. 18   Wmk. 384

1L48a	A4	20p	3.25	4.50
1L49a	A4	25p	3.25	4.50
1L50a	A4	50p	3.25	4.50
1L51a	A4	£1	3.25	4.50
1L52a	A4	£3	7.50	6.50
		Nos. 1L48a-1L52a (5)	20.50	24.50

Magellanic Clubmoss — A5

Designs: 6p, Alpine cat's-tail. 7p, Greater burnet. 11p, Antarctic bedstraw. 15p, Brown rush. 25p, Antarctic hair grass.

1981, Feb. 5   Wmk. 373   Litho.   Perf. 14

1L53	A5	3p shown	.25	.25
1L54	A5	6p multicolored	.25	.25
1L55	A5	7p multicolored	.25	.25
1L56	A5	11p multicolored	.35	.35
1L57	A5	15p multicolored	.45	.45
a.		Brown missing	3,750.	
1L58	A5	25p multicolored	.65	.65
		Nos. 1L53-1L58 (6)	2.20	2.20

Royal Wedding Issue
Common Design Type
Wmk. 373
1981, July 22   Litho.   Perf. 14

1L59	CD331	10p Bouquet	.25	.25
1L60	CD331	13p Charles	.35	.35
1L61	CD331	52p Couple	.85	.85
		Nos. 1L59-1L61 (3)	1.45	1.45

Reindeer in Spring — A6

Wmk. 373
1982, Jan. 29   Litho.   Perf. 14

1L62	A6	5p shown	.25	.60
1L63	A6	13p Autumn	.35	.75
1L64	A6	25p Winter	.45	1.00
1L65	A6	26p Late winter	.50	1.00
		Nos. 1L62-1L65 (4)	1.55	3.35

Gamasellus Racovitzai — A7

10p, Alaskozetes antarcticus. 13p, Cryptopygus antarcticus. 15p, Notiomaso australis. 25p, Hydromedion sparsutum. 26p, Parochlus steinenii.

Wmk. 373
1982, Mar. 16   Litho.   Perf. 14

1L66	A7	5p shown	.25	.25
1L67	A7	10p multicolored	.25	.35
1L68	A7	13p multicolored	.30	.40
1L69	A7	15p multicolored	.35	.40
1L70	A7	25p multicolored	.40	.50
1L71	A7	26p multicolored	.45	.50
		Nos. 1L66-1L71 (6)	2.00	2.40

Princess Diana Issue
Common Design Type
Perf. 13½x14
1982, July 1   Litho.   Wmk. 373

1L72	CD333	5p Arms	.25	.25
1L73	CD333	17p Diana	.35	.45
a.		Perf. 13.5	2.50	2.75
1L74	CD333	37p Wedding	.90	.90
1L75	CD333	50p Portrait	1.00	1.00
		Nos. 1L72-1L75 (4)	2.50	2.60

Crustacea — A8

5p, Euphausia superba. 17p, Glyptonotus antarcticus. 25p, Epimeria monodon. 34p, Serolis pagenstecheri.

Perf. 14½x14
1984, Mar. 23   Wmk. 373

1L76	A8	5p multicolored	.30	.30
1L77	A8	17p multicolored	.40	.40
1L78	A8	25p multicolored	.70	.70
1L79	A8	34p multicolored	1.10	1.10
		Nos. 1L76-1L79 (4)	2.50	2.50

Manned Flight Bicentenary — A9

Designs: 5p, Westland Whirlwind. 13p, Westland Wasp. 17p, Saunders-Roe Walrus. 50p, Auster.

Wmk. 373
1983, Dec. 23   Litho.   Perf. 14

1L80	A9	5p multicolored	.25	.25
1L81	A9	13p multicolored	.45	.45
1L82	A9	17p multicolored	.55	.55
1L83	A9	50p multicolored	1.75	1.75
		Nos. 1L80-1L83 (4)	3.00	3.00

South Sandwich Islds. Volcanoes — A10

6p, Zavodovski Island. 17p, Mt. Michael, Saunders Island. 22p, Bellingshausen Island. 52p, Bristol Island.

1984, Nov. 8   **Wmk. 373**   *Perf. 14½*

1L84	A10	6p multicolored	.60	.60
1L85	A10	17p multicolored	1.40	1.40
1L86	A10	22p multicolored	2.00	2.00
1L87	A10	52p multicolored	3.50	3.50
		Nos. 1L84-1L87 (4)	7.50	7.50

Albatrosses —
A11

7p, Diomedea chrysostoma. 22p, Diomedea melanophris. 27p, Diomedea exulans. 54p, Phoebetria palpebrata.

1985, May 5   **Wmk. 384**   *Perf. 14½*

1L88	A11	7p multicolored	.80	.80
1L89	A11	22p multicolored	2.25	2.25
1L90	A11	27p multicolored	2.50	2.50
1L91	A11	54p multicolored	4.75	4.75
		Nos. 1L88-1L91 (4)	10.30	10.30

Queen Mother 85th Birthday
Common Design Type

Designs: 7p, 14th birthday celebration. 22p, With Princess Anne, Lady Sarah Armstrong-Jones, Prince Edward. 27p, Queen Mother. 54p, Holding Prince Henry. £1, On the Britannia.

Perf. 14½x14

1985, June 23   **Wmk. 384**

1L92	CD336	7p multicolored	.25	.25
1L93	CD336	22p multicolored	.75	.75
1L94	CD336	27p multicolored	1.00	1.00
1L95	CD336	54p multicolored	2.00	2.00
		Nos. 1L92-1L95 (4)	4.00	4.00

Souvenir Sheet

1L96	CD336	£1 multicolored	4.00	4.00

Falkland Islands Naturalists Type of 1985

Naturalists, endangered species: 7p, Dumont d'Urville (1790-1842), kelp. 22p, Johann Reinhold Forster (1729-1798), king penguin. 27p, Johann Georg Adam Forster (1754-1794), tussock grass. 54p, Sir Joseph Banks (1743-1820), dove prion.

Perf. 13½x14

1985, Nov. 4   **Wmk. 373**

1L97	A86	7p multicolored	.75	.75
1L98	A86	22p multicolored	1.60	1.60
1L99	A86	27p multicolored	2.00	2.00
1L100	A86	54p multicolored	3.75	3.75
		Nos. 1L97-1L100 (4)	8.10	8.10

SEMI-POSTAL STAMP

Rebuilding Type of Falkland Islands
Wmk. 373

1982, Sept. 13   **Litho.**   *Perf. 11*

1LB1	SP1	£1 Map of So. Georgia	2.75	2.75

ISSUES FOR THE SEPARATE ISLANDS

Graham Land

Nos. 84, 85B, 86A, 87A, 88-91
Overprinted in Red

1944, Feb. 12   **Wmk. 4**   *Perf. 12*

2L1	A22	½p green & black	.45	2.25
2L2	A22	1p dk vio & black	.45	1.10
2L3	A22	2p rose car & blk	.55	1.10
2L4	A22	3p deep bl & blk	.55	1.10
2L5	A22	4p rose vio & blk	1.90	1.75
2L6	A22	6p brown & black	19.00	2.75
2L7	A22	9p slate bl & blk	1.25	1.50
2L8	A22	1sh dull blue	1.25	1.50
		Nos. 2L1-2L8 (8)	25.40	13.05

South Georgia

1944, Apr. 3   **Wmk. 4**   *Perf. 12*

3L1	A22	½p green & black	.35	2.25
3L2	A22	1p dark vio & blk	.35	1.10
3L3	A22	2p rose car & blk	.55	1.10
3L4	A22	3p deep bl & blk	.55	1.10
3L5	A22	4p rose vio & blk	1.90	1.75
3L6	A22	6p brown & black	19.00	2.50
3L7	A22	9p slate bl & blk	1.25	1.50
3L8	A22	1sh dull blue	1.25	1.50
		Nos. 3L1-3L8 (8)	25.20	12.80

South Orkneys

1944, Feb. 21   **Wmk. 4**   *Perf. 12*

4L1	A22	½p green & black	.45	2.25
4L2	A22	1p dark vio & blk	.45	1.10
4L3	A22	2p rose car & blk	.75	1.10
4L4	A22	3p deep bl & blk	.75	1.10
4L5	A22	4p rose vio & blk	1.75	1.75
4L6	A22	6p brown & black	19.00	2.50
4L7	A22	9p slate bl & blk	1.25	1.50
4L8	A22	1sh dull blue	1.25	1.50
		Nos. 4L1-4L8 (8)	25.65	12.80

South Shetlands

1944   **Wmk. 4**   *Perf. 12*

5L1	A22	½p green & black	.45	2.25
5L2	A22	1p dark vio & blk	.45	1.10
5L3	A22	2p rose car & blk	.55	1.10
5L4	A22	3p deep bl & blk	.55	1.10
5L5	A22	4p rose vio & blk	1.25	1.75
5L6	A22	6p brown & black	19.00	2.50
5L7	A22	9p slate bl & blk	1.25	1.50
5L8	A22	1sh dull blue	1.25	1.50
		Nos. 5L1-5L8 (8)	24.75	12.80

FAR EASTERN REPUBLIC

'fär 'ē-stərn ri-'pə-blik

LOCATION — In Siberia east of Lake Baikal
GOVT. — Republic
AREA — 900,745 sq. mi.
POP. — 1,560,000 (approx. 1920)
CAPITAL — Chita

A short-lived independent government was established here in 1920.

100 Kopecks = 1 Ruble

Watermark

Wmk. 171 —
Diamonds

Vladivostok Issue
Russian Stamps Surcharged or Overprinted

a   b

c

On Stamps of 1909-17
Perf. 14, 14½x15, 13½

1920   **Unwmk.**

2	A14(a)	2k green	10.00	15.00
3	A14(a)	3k red	10.00	10.00
4	A11(b)	3k on 35k red brn & grn	40.00	50.00
5	A15(a)	4k carmine	10.00	12.00
6	A11(b)	4k on 70k brn & org	10.00	15.00
8	A11(b)	7k on 15k red brn & bl	2.00	2.00
a.		Inverted surcharge	100.00	
b.		Pair, one ovptd. "DBP" only	100.00	
9	A15(a)	10k dark blue	100.00	75.00
a.		Overprint on back	125.00	
10	A12(c)	10k on 3½r mar & lt grn	25.00	25.00
11	A11(a)	14k blue & rose	50.00	35.00
12	A11(a)	15k red brn & bl	35.00	25.00
13	A8(a)	20k blue & car	150.00	100.00
14	A11(b)	20k on 14k bl & rose	10.00	8.00
a.		Surcharge on back	30.00	
15	A11(a)	25k green & vio	25.00	20.00
16	A11(a)	35k red brn & grn	75.00	50.00
17	A8(a)	50k brn vio & grn	10.00	12.00
18	A9(a)	1r pale brn, dk brn & org	700.00	700.00

On Stamps of 1917
Imperf

21	A14(a)	1k orange	25.00	10.00
22	A14(a)	2k gray grn	20.00	10.00
23	A14(a)	3k red	20.00	10.00
25	A11(b)	7k on 15k red brn & dp bl	2.00	5.00
a.		Pair, one without surcharge	100.00	
b.		Pair, one ovptd. "DBP" only	100.00	
26	A12(c)	10k on 3½r mar & lt grn	30.00	15.00
27	A9(a)	1r pale brn, brn & red org	50.00	20.00

On Stamps of Siberia 1919
Perf. 14, 14½x15

30	A14(a)	35k on 2k green	5.00	8.00
a.		"DBP" on back	25.00	50.00

Imperf

31	A14(a)	35k on 2k green	35.00	25.00
32	A14(a)	70k on 1k orange	6.00	6.00

Counterfeit surcharges and overprints abound, including digital forgeries.

On Russia Nos. AR2, AR3

Perf. 14½x15
Wmk. 171

35	PF1	1k on 5k green, *buff*	30.00	25.00
36	PF1	2k on 10k brown, *buff*	40.00	30.00

The letters on these stamps resembling "DBP," are the Russian initials of "Dalne Vostochnaya Respublika" (Far Eastern Republic).

Chita Issue

A2   A2a

1921   **Unwmk.**   **Typo.**   *Imperf.*

38	A2	2k gray green	1.50	1.50
39	A2a	4k rose	3.00	3.00
40	A2	5k claret	3.00	3.00
41	A2a	10k blue	2.50	2.50
		Nos. 38-41 (4)	10.00	10.00

For overprints see Nos. 62-65.

Blagoveshchensk Issue

A3

1921   **Litho.**   *Imperf.*

42	A3	2r red	3.00	2.00
43	A3	3r dark green	3.00	2.00
44	A3	5r dark blue	3.00	2.00
a.		Tête bêche pair	50.00	15.00
45	A3	15r dark brown	3.00	2.00
46	A3	30r dark violet	3.00	2.00
a.		Tête bêche pair	35.00	15.00
		Nos. 42-46 (5)	15.00	10.00

Remainders of Nos. 42-46 were canceled in colored crayon or by typographed bars. These sell for half of foregoing values.

Chita Issue

A4   A5

1922   **Litho.**   *Imperf.*

49	A4	1k orange	1.00	.85
50	A4	3k dull red	.40	.45
51	A5	4k dp rose & buff	.40	.45
52	A4	5k orange brown	.80	.45
53	A4	7k light blue	1.50	1.50
a.		Perf. 11½	2.00	2.50
b.		Rouletted 9	3.00	3.00
c.		Perf. 11½x rouletted	6.50	6.50
54	A5	10k dk blue & red	.60	.65
55	A4	15k dull rose	.80	1.10
56	A5	20k blue & red	.80	1.10
57	A5	30k green & red org	1.25	1.10
58	A5	50k black & red org	3.00	2.25
		Nos. 49-58 (10)	10.55	9.90

The 4k exists with "4" omitted. Value $100.

Vladivostok Issue

Stamps of 1921 Overprinted in Red

1922				*Imperf.*
62	A2	2k gray green	35.00	25.00
a.		Inverted overprint	250.00	
63	A2a	4k rose	35.00	25.00
a.		Inverted overprint	250.00	
b.		Double overprint	250.00	
64	A2	5k claret	35.00	35.00
a.		Inverted overprint	100.00	
b.		Double overprint	350.00	
65	A2a	10k blue	35.00	35.00
a.		Inverted overprint	250.00	
		Nos. 62-65 (4)	140.00	120.00

Russian revolution of Nov. 1917, 5th anniv.

Once in the setting the figures "22" of 1922 have the bottom stroke curved instead of straight. Value, each $75.

No. 63 exists in a block with overprints missing on some stamps.

Vladivostok Issue

Russian Stamps of 1922-23 Surcharged in Black or Red

1923   *Imperf.*

66	A50	1k on 100r red	.40	1.00
a.		Inverted surcharge	60.00	
67	A50	2k on 70r violet	.40	.75
68	A49	5k on 10r blue (R)	.40	.75
69	A50	10k on 50r brown	.90	1.25
a.		Inverted surcharge	250.00	
		Perf. 14½x15		
70	A50	1k on 100r red	.90	1.25
		Nos. 66-70 (5)	3.00	5.00

OCCUPATION STAMPS

Issued under Occupation of General Semenov
Chita Issue
Russian Stamps of 1909-12
Surcharged

a

b

c

		1920 Unwmk. Perf. 14, 14x15½		
N1	A15 (a)	1r on 4k car	150.00	100.00
N2	A8 (b)	2r50k on 20k bl & car	40.00	30.00
N3	A14 (c)	5r on 5k clar	25.00	50.00
a.		Double surcharge	200.00	
N4	A11 (a)	10r on 70k brn & org	20.00	25.00
		Nos. N1-N4 (4)	235.00	205.00

FAROE ISLANDS

ˈfar-ˌü ˈī-lənds

(The Faroes)

LOCATION — North Atlantic Ocean
GOVT. — Self-governing part of Kingdom of Denmark
AREA — 540 sq. mi.
POP. — 41,059 (1999 est.)
CAPITAL — Thorshavn

100 Ore = 1 Krone

Catalogue values for unused stamps in this country are for Never Hinged items, beginning with Scott 7.

Denmark No. 97
Handstamp Surcharged

1919, Jan.   Typo.   Perf. 14x14½

| 1 | A16 | 2o on 5o green | 1,400. | 475.00 |

Counterfeits of surcharge exist.
Denmark No. 88a, the bisect, was used with Denmark No. 97 in Faroe Islands Jan. 3-23, 1919.

Denmark Nos. 220, 224, 238A, 224C Surcharged in Blue or Black

Nos. 2, 5-6   No. 3

No. 4

1940-41   Engr.   Perf. 13

2	A32	20o on 1o ('41)	40.00	110.00
3	A32	20o on 5o ('41)	40.00	35.00
4	A30	20o on 15o (Bk)	60.00	22.50
5	A32	50o on 5o (Bk)	275.00	90.00
6	A32	60o on 6o (Bk)	125.00	250.00
		Nos. 2-6 (5)	540.00	507.50
		Set, never hinged	1,150.	

Issued during British administration.

Catalogue values for unused stamps in this section, from this point to the end of the section, are for Never Hinged items.

Map of Islands, 1673 — A1   Map of North Atlantic, 1573 — A2

West Coast, Sandoy — A3   Vidoy and Svinoy, by Eyvindur Mohr — A4

Designs: 200o, like 70o. 250o, 300o, View of Streymoy and Vagar. 450o, Houses, Nes, by Ruth Smith. 500o, View of Hvitanes and Skalafjordur, by S. Joensen-Mikines.

Unwmk.

1975, Jan. 30   Engr.   Perf. 13

7	A1	5o sepia	.25	.25
8	A2	10o emer & dark blue	.25	.25
9	A1	50o graysh green	.25	.25
10	A2	60o brown & dark blue	.80	.80
11	A2	70o vio bl & slate grn	.80	.80
12	A2	80o ocher & dark blue	.45	.45
13	A1	90o red brown	.80	.80
14	A2	120o brt bl & dark bl	.60	.40
15	A3	200o vio bl & slate grn	.60	.60
16	A3	250o multicolored	.60	.60
17	A3	300o multicolored	5.00	1.60

Photo.
Perf. 12½x13

18	A4	350o multicolored	.80	.80
19	A4	450o multicolored	.80	.80
20	A4	500o multicolored	1.00	1.00
		Nos. 7-20 (14)	13.00	9.40

Faroe Boat — A5

Faroe Flag — A6

Faroe Mailman — A7

Perf. 12½x13, 12 (A6)

1976, Apr. 1   Engr.; Litho. (A6)

21	A5	125o copper red	1.60	1.25
22	A6	160o multicolored	.45	.45
23	A7	800o olive	1.75	1.25
		Nos. 21-23 (3)	3.80	2.95

Faroe Islands independent postal service, Apr. 1, 1976.

Motor Fishing Boat — A8

Faroese Fishing Vessels and Map of Islands: 125o, Inland fishing cutter. 160o, Modern seine fishing vessel. 600o, Deep-sea fishing trawler.

1977, Apr. 28   Photo.   Perf. 14½x14

24	A8	100o green & black	4.50	3.75
25	A8	125o carmine & black	.65	.65
26	A8	160o blue & black	.90	.65
27	A8	600o brown & black	1.60	1.10
		Nos. 24-27 (4)	7.65	6.15

Common Snipe — A9

Photogravure & Engraved

1977, Sept. 29   Perf. 14½x14

28	A9	70o shown	.25	.25
29	A9	180o Oystercatcher	.55	.55
30	A9	250o Whimbrel	.65	.65
		Nos. 28-30 (3)	1.45	1.45

North Coast, Puffins A10   Mykines Village A11

Mykines Island: 140o, Coast. 150o, Aerial view. 180o, Map.

Perf. 13x13½, 13½x13

1978, Jan. 26   Photo.
Size: 21x28mm, 28x21mm

31	A10	100o multicolored	.25	.25
32	A11	130o multicolored	.45	.45
33	A11	140o multicolored	.55	.55

| 34 | A10 | 150o multicolored | .55 | .55 |

Size: 37x26mm
Perf. 14½x14

| 35 | A11 | 180o multicolored | .55 | .55 |
| | | *Nos. 31-35 (5)* | 2.35 | 2.35 |

Sea Birds — A12

Lithographed and Engraved

1978, Apr. 13   Perf. 12x12½

36	A12	140o Gannets	.45	.45
37	A12	180o Puffins	.55	.55
38	A12	400o Guillemots	1.40	1.10
		Nos. 36-38 (3)	2.40	2.10

Old Library — A13

1978, Dec. 7   Perf. 13

| 39 | A13 | 140o shown | .45 | .45 |
| 40 | A13 | 180o New library | .55 | .55 |

Completion of New Library Building.

Girl Guide, Tent and Fire — A14

1978, Dec. 7   Photo.   Perf. 13½

| 41 | A14 | 140o multicolored | .45 | .45 |

Faroese Girl Guides, 50th anniversary.

Ram — A15

Lithographed and Engraved

1979, Mar. 19   Perf. 12

| 42 | A15 | 25k multicolored | 6.00 | 6.00 |

Denmark No. 88a — A16

Europa: 180o, Faroe Islands No. 1.

1979, May 7   Perf. 12½

| 43 | A16 | 140o yellow & blue | .45 | .45 |
| 44 | A16 | 180o rose, grn & blk | .55 | .55 |

Girl Wearing Festive Costume — A17

Children's Drawings and IYC Emblem: 150o, Fisherman. 200o, Two friends.

1979, Oct. 1   Perf. 12

45	A17	110o multicolored	.45	.45
46	A17	150o multicolored	.45	.45
47	A17	200o multicolored	.55	.55
		Nos. 45-47 (3)	1.45	1.45

International Year of the Child.

Sea Plantain — A18

1980, Mar. 17 Photo. Perf. 12x11½

48	A18	90o shown	.25	.25
49	A18	110o Glacier buttercup	.45	.45
50	A18	150o Purple saxifrage	.55	.55
51	A18	200o Starry saxifrage	.55	.55
52	A18	400o Lady's mantle	.90	.90
		Nos. 48-52 (5)	2.70	2.70

Europa — A19

Europa: 150o, Jakob Jakobsen (1864-1918), linguist. 200o, Venceslas Ulricus Hammershaimb (1819-1909), theologian, linguist and folklorist.

1980, Oct. 6   Engr.   Perf. 11½

| 53 | A19 | 150o dull green | .40 | .40 |
| 54 | A19 | 200o dull red brown | .60 | .60 |

Perf. 13 bicolored examples of Nos. 53-54 are rejected stamps never put on sale that were to have been burned, but which escaped destruction.

Coat of Arms, Virgin and Child, Gothic Pew Gable — A20

Kirkjubour Pew Gables, 15th Century: 140o, Norwegian coat of arms, John the Baptist. 150o, Christ's head, St. Peter. 200o, Hand in halo, Apostle Paul.

Photo. & Engr.

1980, Oct. 6   Perf. 13½

55	A20	110o multicolored	.45	.45
56	A20	140o multicolored	.45	.45
57	A20	150o multicolored	.45	.45
58	A20	200o multicolored	.55	.55
		Nos. 55-58 (4)	1.90	1.90

See Nos. 102-105, 389-392.

A21

Sketches of Old Torshavn by Ingalzur Reyni.

1981, Mar. 2   Engr.

59	A21	110o dark green	.45	.45
60	A21	140o black	.45	.45
61	A21	150o dark brown	.45	.45
62	A21	200o dark blue	.55	.55
		Nos. 59-62 (4)	1.90	1.90

The Ring Dance — A22

Europa: 200o, The garter dance.

1981, June 1   Engr.   Perf. 13x14

| 63 | A22 | 150o pale rose & grn | .35 | .35 |
| 64 | A22 | 200o pale yel grn & dk brn | .55 | .55 |

Rune Stones, 800-1000 AD — A23

Historic Writings: 1k, Folksong, 1846. 3k, Sheep Letter excerpt, 1298. 6k, Seal and text,

1533. 10k, Titlepage from Faeroae et Faeroa, by Lucas Jacobson Debes, library.

Photo. & Engr.

1981, Oct. 19   *Perf. 11½*
65	A23	10o	multicolored	.25 .25
66	A23	1k	multicolored	.25 .25
67	A23	3k	multicolored	1.00 .65
68	A23	6k	multicolored	1.60 1.25
69	A23	10k	multicolored	2.75 2.75
		Nos. 65-69 (5)		5.85 5.15

Nos. 70-80 not assigned.

Europa 1982 — A24

1.50k, Viking North Atlantic routes. 2k, Viking house foundation.

1982, Mar. 15   **Engr.**   *Perf. 13½*
81	A24	1.50k	dk blue & blue	.45 .45
82	A24	2k	gray & blk	.55 .55

View of Gjogv, by Ingalvur av Reyni — A25

1982, June 7   **Litho.**   *Perf. 12½x13*
83	A25	180o	shown	.45 .45
84	A25	220o	Hvalvik	1.00 .75
85	A25	250o	Kvivik	.65 .65
		Nos. 83-85 (3)		2.10 1.85

Ballad of Harra Paetur and Elinborg — A26

Scenes from the medieval ballad of chivalry.

1982, Sept. 27   **Litho.**
86	A26	220o	multicolored	.65 .65
87	A26	250o	multicolored	.75 .75
88	A26	350o	multicolored	1.00 1.00
89	A26	450o	multicolored	1.20 1.20
		Nos. 86-89 (4)		3.60 3.60

Cargo Ships — A27

1983, Feb. 21   **Litho.**   *Perf. 14x14½*
90	A27	220o	Arcturus, 1856	.65 .65
91	A27	250o	Laura, 1882	.90 .90
92	A27	700o	Thyra, 1866	2.00 2.00
		Nos. 90-92 (3)		3.55 3.55

Chessmen, by Pol i Buo (1791-1857) A28

1983, May 2   **Engr.**   *Perf. 13 Vert.*
Booklet Stamps
93		250o	King	2.25 2.25
94		250o	Queen	2.25 2.25
a.		Bklt. pane of 6, 3 each #93-94		16.00
b.		A28 Pair, #93-94		5.50 5.50

Europa 1983 — A29

Nobel Prizewinners in Medicine: 250o, Niels R. Finsen (1860-1903), ultraviolet radiation pioneer. 400o, Alexander Fleming (1881-1955), discoverer of penicillin.

1983, June 6   **Engr.**   *Perf. 12x11½*
95	A29	250o	dark blue	.65 .65
96	A29	400o	red brown	1.10 1.10

A30

1983, Sept. 19   **Litho.**   *Perf. 12½x13*
97	A30	250o	Tusk	.65 .65
98	A30	280o	Haddock	.85 .85
99	A30	500o	Halibut	1.60 1.60
100	A30	900o	Catfish	2.50 2.50
		Nos. 97-100 (4)		5.60 5.60

Souvenir Sheet

Traditional Costumes — A31

Various national costumes.

1983, Nov. 4   **Litho.**   *Perf. 12*
101	A31	Sheet of 3		10.00 11.00
a.-c.		250o multicolored		2.75 2.75

Nordic House Cultural Center opening. Margin shows Scandinavian flags.

Pew Gables Type of 1980

Designs: 250o, John, shield with three crowns. 300o, St. Jacob, shield with crossed keys. 350o, Thomas, shield with crossbeam. 400o, Judas Taddeus, Toulouse cross halo.

Photo. & Engr.

1984, Jan. 30   *Perf. 14x13½*
102	A20	250o	lil, pur & dk brn	.75 .75
103	A20	300o	red brn, dk buff & dk brn	.85 .85
104	A20	350o	blk, lt gray & dk brn	1.00 1.00
105	A20	400o	ol grn, pale yel & dk brn	1.10 1.10
		Nos. 102-105 (4)		3.70 3.70

Europa (1959-84) — A33

1984, Apr. 2   **Engr.**   *Perf. 13½*
106	A33	250o	red	.60 .60
107	A33	500o	dark blue	1.40 1.40

Sverri Patursson (1871-1960), Writer — A34

Poets: 2.50k, Joannes Patursson (1866-1946). 3k, J. H. O. Djurhuus (1881-1948). 4.50k, H.A. Djurhuus (1883-1951).

1984, May 28   **Engr.**   *Perf. 13½*
108	A34	2k	olive green	.55 .55
109	A34	2.50k	red	.65 .65
110	A34	3k	dark blue	.85 .85
111	A34	4.50k	violet	1.25 1.25
		Nos. 108-111 (4)		3.30 3.30

Faroese Smack (Fishing Boat) — A35

Designs: 300o, Fishermen, vert. 12k, Helmsman, vert.

Perf. 12½x13, 13x12½
1984, Sept. 10   **Engr.**
112	A35	280o	dark blue	.75 .75
113	A35	300o	brown	.85 .85
114	A35	12k	deep grn	3.75 3.75
		Nos. 112-114 (3)		5.35 5.35

Fairytale Illustrations by Elinborg Lutzen — A36

Designs: No. 115, Beauty of the Veils. No. 116, Veils, diff. No. 117, Girl Shy Prince. No. 118, The Glass Sword. No. 119, Little Elin. No. 120, The Boy and the Ox.

1984, Oct. 29   **Litho.**   *Perf. 13 Vert.*
Booklet Stamps
115	A36	140o	multicolored	5.00 5.00
116	A36	280o	multicolored	5.00 5.00
117	A36	280o	multicolored	5.00 5.00
118	A36	280o	multicolored	5.00 5.00
119	A36	280o	multicolored	5.00 5.00
120	A36	280o	multicolored	5.00 5.00
a.		Booklet pane of 6, #115-120		30.00

View of Torshavn and the Forts, by Edward Dayes — A37

Dayes' Landscapes, 1789: 280o, Skaeling. 550o, View Towards the North Seen from the Hills Near Torshavn in Stremoy, Faroes. 800o, The Moving Stones in Eysturoy, Faroes.

Litho. & Engr.

1985, Feb. 4   *Perf. 13*
121	A37	250o	multicolored	.65 .65
122	A37	280o	multicolored	.85 .85
123	A37	550o	multicolored	2.00 2.00
124	A37	800o	multicolored	2.50 2.50
		Nos. 121-124 (4)		6.00 6.00

Europa 1985 — A38

Children taking music lessons.

1985, Apr. 1   **Litho.**   *Perf. 13½x14½*
125	A38	280o	multicolored	.85 .85
126	A38	550o	multicolored	1.90 1.90

Paintings, Faroese Museum of Art — A39

Designs: 280o, The Garden, Hoyvik, 1973, by Thomas Arge (1942-78). 450o, Self-Portrait, 1952, by Ruth Smith (1913-58), vert. 550o, Winter's Day in Nolsoy, 1959, by Steffan Danielsen (1922-76).

Litho. & Engr.

1985, June 3   *Perf. 12½*
127	A39	280o	multicolored	1.25 1.25
128	A39	450o	multicolored	1.75 1.75
129	A39	550o	multicolored	2.50 2.50
		Nos. 127-129 (3)		5.50 5.50

Lighthouses — A40

1985, Sept. 23   **Litho.**   *Perf. 13½x14*
130	A40	270o	Nolsoy, 1893	.85 .85
131	A40	320o	Thorshavn, 1909	1.25 1.25
132	A40	350o	Mykines, 1909	1.25 1.25
133	A40	470o	Map of locations	1.60 1.60
		Nos. 130-133 (4)		4.95 4.95

Passenger Aviation in the Faroes, 22nd Anniv. — A41

Designs: No. 134, Douglas DC-3. No. 135, Fokker Friendship. No. 136, Boeing 737. No.

137, Interisland LM-IKB. No. 138, Helicopter Snipan.

Perf. 13½ Horiz.
1985, Oct. 28   **Photo.**
Booklet Stamps
134	A41	300o	multicolored	2.75 2.75
135	A41	300o	multicolored	2.75 2.75
136	A41	300o	multicolored	2.75 2.75
137	A41	300o	multicolored	2.75 2.75
138	A41	300o	multicolored	2.75 2.75
a.		Booklet pane of 5, #134-138		14.00 14.00

Skrimsla, Ancient Folk Ballad — A42

Designs: No. 139, Peasant in woods. No. 140, Meets Giant. No. 141, Giant loses game. No. 142, Giant grants Peasant's wish.

1986, Feb. 3   **Litho.**   *Perf. 12½x13*
139	A42	300o	multicolored	.80 .80
140	A42	420o	multicolored	1.20 1.20
141	A42	550o	multicolored	1.40 1.40
142	A42	650o	multicolored	1.60 1.60
		Nos. 139-142 (4)		5.00 5.00

Europa 1986 — A43

1986, Apr. 7   **Litho.**   *Perf. 13½*
143	A43	3k	shown	1.60 1.60
144	A43	5.50k	Sea pollution	2.25 2.25

Amnesty Intl., 25th Anniv. — A44

Winning design competition artwork.

1986, June 2   *Perf. 14x13½*
145	A44	3k	Olivur vid Neyst	1.25 1.25
146	A44	4.70k	Eli Smith	1.90 1.90
147	A44	5.50k	Ranna Kunoy	2.40 2.40
		Nos. 145-147 (3)		5.55 5.55

Nos. 145-146 horiz.

Souvenir Sheet

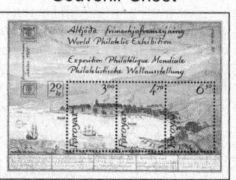

HAFNIA '87, Copenhagen — A45

Design: East Bay of Torshavn, watercolor, 1782, by Christian Rosenmeyer (1728-1802).

1986, Aug. 29   *Perf. 13x13½*
148	A45	Sheet of 3		8.75 8.75
a.		3k multicolored		2.75 2.75
b.		4.70k multicolored		2.75 2.75
c.		6.50k multicolored		2.75 2.75

Sold for 20k.

Old Stone Bridges — A46

2.70k, Glyvrar on Eysturoy. 3k, Leypanagjogv on Vagar, vert. 13k, Skaelingon on Streymoy.

Perf. 13½x14½, 14½x13½
1986, Oct. 13   **Engr.**
149	A46	2.70k	dp brown vio	1.75 1.75
150	A46	3k	bluish blk	1.40 1.40
151	A46	13k	gray green	3.00 3.00
		Nos. 149-151 (3)		6.15 6.15

Farmhouses A47

Traditional architecture: 300o, Depil on Borooy, 1814. 420o, Depil, diff. 470o, Frammi vio Gjonna on Streymoy, c. 1814. 650o, Frammi, diff.

1987, Feb. 9   Engr.   Perf. 13x14½
152	A47	300o pale blue & blue	.90	.90
153	A47	420o buff & brown	1.40	1.40
154	A47	470o pale grn & dp grn	1.75	1.75
155	A47	650o pale gray & black	2.25	2.25
		Nos. 152-155 (4)	6.30	6.30

Europa 1987 — A48

Nordic House.

1987, Apr. 6   Perf. 13x14
156	A48	300o Exterior	.85	.85
157	A48	550o Interior	1.90	1.60

Fishing Trawlers — A49

Designs: 3k, Joannes Patursson. 5.50k, Magnus Heinason. 8k, Sjurdarberg.

1987, June 1   Litho.   Perf. 14x13½
158	A49	3k multi	.90	.90
159	A49	5.50k multi	1.90	1.90
160	A49	8k multi	4.00	4.00
		Nos. 158-160 (3)	6.80	6.80

Hestur (Horse) Island — A50

Litho. & Engr.
1987, Sept. 7   Perf. 13
161	A50	270o Map	.80	.80
162	A50	300o Seaport	.75	.75
163	A50	420o Bird cliff	1.60	1.60
164	A50	470o Pasture, sheep	1.75	1.75
165	A50	550o Seashore	1.75	1.75
		Nos. 161-165 (5)	6.65	6.65

Nos. 161, 163 and 165 vert.

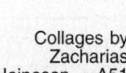

Collages by Zacharias Heinesen — A51

West Bay of Torshavn, Watercolor by Rosenmeyer — A52

1987, Oct. 16   Litho.   Perf. 13½x14
166	A51	4.70k Eystaravag	1.25	1.25
167	A51	6.50k Vestarvag	1.75	1.75

Souvenir Sheet
Perf. 13½x13
168	A52	3k multicolored	3.50	3.50

HAFNIA '87. Sold for 4k.

Flowers — A53

Designs: 2.70k, Bellis perennis. 3k, Dactylorchis maculata. 4.70k, Potentilla erecta. 9k, Pinguicula vulgaris.

1988, Feb. 8   Litho.   Perf. 11½
Granite Paper
169	A53	2.70k multicolored	1.10	1.10
170	A53	3k multicolored	.65	.65
171	A53	4.70k multicolored	1.75	1.75
172	A53	9k multicolored	2.50	2.50
		Nos. 169-172 (4)	6.00	6.00

Europa — A54

Communication and transport: 3k, Satellite dish, satellite. 5.50k, Fork lift, crane, ship.

1988, Apr. 11   Photo.   Perf. 11½
173	A54	3k multicolored	.90	.90
174	A54	5.50k multicolored	1.50	1.50

A55

Writers: 270o, Jorgen-Frantz Jacobsen (1900-38). 300o, Christian Matras (b. 1900). 470o, William Heinesen (b. 1900). 650o, Hedin Bru (1901-87).

1988, June 6   Engr.   Perf. 13½
175	A55	270o myrtle green	1.40	1.40
176	A55	300o rose lake	.85	.85
177	A55	470o dark blue	2.00	2.00
178	A55	650o brown black	2.25	2.25
		Nos. 175-178 (4)	6.50	6.50

A56

Text, illustrations and cameo portraits of organizers: 3k, Announcement and Djoni Geil, Enok Baerentsen and H.H. Jacobsen. 3.20k, Meeting, Rasmus Effersoe, C.L. Johannesen and Samal Krakusteini. 12k, Oystercatcher and lyrics of Now the Hour Has Come, by poet Sverri Patursson (1871-1960), Just A. Husum, Joannes Patursson and Jens Olsen.

Granite Paper
1988, Sept. 5   Photo.   Perf. 12
179	A56	3k multicolored	.80	.80
180	A56	3.20k multicolored	1.20	1.20
181	A56	12k multicolored	4.50	4.50
		Nos. 179-181 (3)	6.50	6.50

1888 Christmas meeting to preserve cultural traditions and the natl. language, cent.

Kirkjubour Cathedral Ruins — A57

270o, Exterior. 300o, Arch. 470o, Crucifixion, bas-relief. 550o, Interior.

1988, Oct. 17   Engr.   Perf. 13
182	A57	270o dark green	1.40	1.40
183	A57	300o dark bl, vert.	1.10	1.10
184	A57	470o dark brn, vert.	1.60	1.60
185	A57	550o dark violet	1.60	1.60
		Nos. 182-185 (4)	5.70	5.70

Havnar Church, Torshavn, 200th Anniv. — A58

Designs: 350o, Church exterior. 500o, Crypt, vert. 15k, Bell, vert.

1989, Feb. 6   Engr.   Perf. 13
186	A58	350o dark green	1.00	1.00
187	A58	500o dark brown	1.75	1.75
188	A58	15k deep blue	3.50	3.50
		Nos. 186-188 (3)	6.25	6.25

Folk Costumes — A59

Photo. & Engr.
1989, Apr. 10   Perf. 13½
189	A59	350o Man	1.00	1.00
190	A59	600o Woman	2.00	2.00

Europa 1989 — A60

Wooden children's toys.

1989, Apr. 10   Photo.   Perf. 12x11½
Granite Paper
191	A60	3.50k Boat	1.00	1.00
192	A60	6k Horse	1.50	1.50

Island Games, July 5-13 — A61

1989, June 5   Photo.   Perf. 12½
Granite Paper
193	A61	200o Rowing	.75	.75
194	A61	350o Handball	1.25	1.25
195	A61	600o Soccer	1.75	1.75
196	A61	700o Swimming	2.25	2.25
		Nos. 193-196 (4)	6.00	6.00

A62

Bird cliffs of Suduroy.

1989, Oct. 2   Engr.   Perf. 14x13½
197	A62	320o Tvoran	1.00	1.00
198	A62	350o Skuvanes	1.40	1.40
199	A62	500o Beinisvord	1.75	1.75
200	A62	600o Asmundarstakkur	2.00	2.00
		Nos. 197-200 (4)	6.15	6.15

A63

Modern fish factory (filleting station): 3.50k, Unloading fish. 3.70k, Cleaning and sorting. 5k, Filleting. 7k, Packaged frozen fish.

1990, Feb. 5   Litho.   Perf. 14x13½
201	A63	3.50k multi	1.00	1.00
202	A63	3.70k multi	1.00	1.00
203	A63	5k multi	1.25	1.25
204	A63	7k multi	2.00	2.00
		Nos. 201-204 (4)	5.25	5.25

Europa 1990 — A64

Post offices.

1990, Apr. 9   Litho.   Perf. 13½x14
205	A64	3.50k Gjogv	1.00	1.00
206	A64	6k Klaksvik	1.75	1.75

Souvenir Sheet

Recognition of the Merkid, Flag of the Faroes, by the British, 50th Anniv. — A65

Designs: a, Flag. b, Fishing trawler Nyggjaberg, disappeared, 1942. c, Sloop Saana, sunk by the Germans, 1942.

1990, Apr. 9   Photo.   Perf. 12
Granite Paper
207	A65	Sheet of 3	4.50	4.50
a.-c.		3.50k any single	1.60	1.60

Whales — A66

Designs: 320o, Mesoplodon bidens. 350o, Balaena mysticetus. 600o, Eubalaena glacialis. 700o, Hyperoodon ampullatus.

1990, June 6   Photo.   Perf. 11½
Granite Paper
208	A66	320o multi	1.25	1.25
209	A66	350o multi	1.50	1.50
210	A66	600o multi	2.25	2.25
211	A66	700o multi	2.50	2.50
		Nos. 208-211 (4)	7.50	7.50

Nolsoy Island by Steffan Danielsen — A67

1990, Oct. 8   Photo.   Perf. 11½
Granite Paper
212	A67	50o shown	.25	.25
213	A67	350o Coastline	1.10	1.10
214	A67	500o Town	1.50	1.50
215	A67	1000o Coastline, cliffs	3.00	3.00
		Nos. 212-215 (4)	5.85	5.85

Flora and Fauna — A68

3.70k, Plantago lanceolata. 4k, Rumex longifolius. 4.50k, Amara aulica. 6.50k, Lumbricus terrestris.

1991, Feb. 4   Litho.   Perf. 13
216	A68	3.70k multi	1.00	1.00
217	A68	4k multi	1.20	1.20
218	A68	4.50k multi	1.50	1.50
219	A68	6.50k multi	2.00	2.00
		Nos. 216-219 (4)	5.70	5.70

Europa — A69

Designs: 3.70k, Weather satellite. 6.50k, Celestial navigation.

1991, Apr. 4   Litho.   Perf. 13
220 A69 3.70k multicolored   1.00 1.00
221 A69 6.50k multicolored   1.75 1.75

Town of Torshavn, 125th Anniv. — A70

1991, Apr. 4   Perf. 14x13½
222 A70 3.70k Town Hall   1.25 1.25
223 A70 3.70k View of town   1.25 1.25

Birds — A71

1991, June 3   Litho.   Perf. 13½
224 A71 3.70k Rissa tridactyla   1.20 1.20
225 A71 3.70k Sterna paradisaea   1.20 1.20
  a.   Bklt. pane, 3 each #224-225   9.00

Village of Saksun — A72

Design: 650o, Cliffs of Vestmanna.

1991, June 3
226 A72 370o shown   1.00 1.00
227 A72 650o multicolored   1.75 1.75

Samal Joensen-Mikines (1906-1979), Painter — A73

Designs: 340o, Funeral Procession. 370o, The Farewell. 550o, Handanagarthur. 1300o, Winter morning.

1991, Oct. 7   Litho.   Perf. 13½
228 A73 340o multi   1.00 1.00
229 A73 370o multi   1.10 1.10
230 A73 550o multi   1.60 1.60
231 A73 1300o multi   3.75 3.75
    Nos. 228-231 (4)   7.45 7.45

Mail Boats — A74

1992, Feb. 10   Litho.   Perf. 13½x14
232 A74 200o Ruth   .70 .70
233 A74 370o Ritan   1.00 1.00
234 A74 550o Sigmundur   1.50 1.50
235 A74 800o Masin   2.50 2.50
    Nos. 232-235 (4)   5.70 5.70

Europa — A75

Designs: 3.70k, Map of North Atlantic, Viking ship. 6.50k, Map of Central Atlantic region, one of Columbus' ships.

1992, Apr. 6   Litho.   Perf. 13½x14
236 A75 3.70k multicolored   1.10 1.10
237 A75 6.50k multicolored   2.00 2.00

Souvenir Sheet
238 A75 Sheet of 2, #236-237   8.50 8.50

First landing in the Americas by Leif Erikson (No. 236). Discovery of America by Christopher Columbus, 500th anniv. (No. 237).
See Iceland Nos. 749-751.

Seals — A76

Designs: No. 239, Halichoerus grypus. No. 240, Phoca vitulina.

1992, June 9   Litho.   Perf. 14x13½
239 A76 3.70k multi   1.40 1.40
240 A76 3.70k multi   1.40 1.40
  a.   Bklt. pane, 3 #239, 3 #240   17.50

Minerals — A77

1992, June 9   Photo.   Perf. 12
Granite Paper
241 A77 370o Stilbite   1.25 1.25
242 A77 650o Mesolite   2.25 2.25

Traditional Houses — A78

1992, Oct. 5   Litho.   Perf. 13½
243 A78 3.40k Hja Glyvra Hanusi   1.00 1.00
244 A78 3.70k I Nordragotu   1.10 1.10
245 A78 6.50k Blasastova   2.00 2.00
246 A78 8k Jakupsstova   2.40 2.40
    Nos. 243-246 (4)   6.50 6.50

Nordic House Entertainers A79

1993, Feb. 8   Litho.   Perf. 13½
247 A79 400o Dancers   1.10 1.10
248 A79 400o Pianist   1.10 1.10
249 A79 400o Trio   1.10 1.10
  a.   Souv. sheet, #247-249, perf 12½   4.00 4.00
    Nos. 247-249 (3)   3.30 3.30

Village of Gjogv — A80

1993, Apr. 5
250 A80 4k View toward sea   1.50 1.50
251 A80 4k Ravine, village   1.50 1.50
  a.   Booklet pane, 3 each #250-251   9.00

Europa — A81

Sculptures by Hans Pauli Olsen: 4k, Movement. 7k, Reflection.

1993, Apr. 5
252 A81 4k multicolored   1.50 1.50
253 A81 7k multicolored   2.00 2.00

Horses — A82

Perf. 13½x13, 13x13½
1993, June 7   Engr.
254 A82 400o shown   1.10 1.10
255 A82 20k Mare, foal, horiz.   5.50 5.50

Butterflies — A83

1993, Oct. 4   Litho.   Perf. 14½
256 A83 350o Apamea zeta   1.10 1.10
257 A83 400o Hepialus humuli   1.25 1.25
258 A83 700o Vanessa atalanta   2.10 2.10
259 A83 900o Perizoma albulata   2.75 2.75
    Nos. 256-259 (4)   7.20 7.20

Fish — A84

Designs: 1Oo, Gasterosteus aculeatus. 4k, Neocyttus helgae. 7k, Salmo trutta fario. 10k, Hoplostethus atlanticus.

1994, Feb. 7   Litho.   Perf. 14½
260 A84 10o multi   .25 .25
261 A84 4k multi   1.25 1.25
262 A84 7k multi   2.25 2.25
263 A84 10k multi   3.00 3.00
    Nos. 260-263 (4)   6.75 6.75

Voyages of St. Brendan (484-577) — A85

Europa: 4k, St. Brendan on island with sheep, Irish monks in boat. 7k, St. Brendan, monks sailing past volcano.

1994, Apr. 18   Litho.   Perf. 14½x14
264 A85 4k multicolored   1.25 1.25
265 A85 7k multicolored   2.40 2.00
  a.   Miniature sheet of 2, #264-265   4.50 4.50

Nos. 264-265 have designers name below the design. Stamps in No. 265a do not.
See Iceland Nos. 780-781; Ireland Nos. 923-924.

Sheepdogs — A86

Design: No. 267, Dog watching over sheep.

1994, June 6   Litho.   Perf. 13½
266 A86 4k multicolored   1.40 1.40

Size: 39x25mm
267 A86 4k multicolored   1.40 1.40
  a.   Booklet pane, 3 each #266-267   8.50
    Complete booklet, #267a   9.50

School of Navigation — A87

Designs: 3.50k, Man using sextant, schooner. 7k, Ship, man at computer.

1994, June 6
268 A87 3.50k multicolored   1.00 1.00
269 A87 7k multicolored   2.50 2.50

Brusajokil's Lay — A88

Scenes, verses of the ballad: 1k, Ship at sea. 4k, Asbjorn entering Brusajokil's cave.

6k, Ormar with cat, trolls. 7k, Ormar pulling Brusajokil's beard.

1994, Sept. 19   Litho.   Perf. 14
270 A88 1k multicolored   .35 .35
271 A88 4k multicolored   1.40 1.40
272 A88 6k multicolored   1.75 1.75
273 A88 7k multicolored   2.25 2.25
    Nos. 270-273 (4)   5.75 5.75

Twelve Days of Christmas — A89

No. 274, Goats, men, deer, hides. No. 275, Ducks, cattle, sheep, horses, banners, barrels.

1994, Oct. 31   Litho.   Perf. 14x13
274 A89 4k multicolored   1.10 1.10
275 A89 4k multicolored   1.10 1.10
  a.   Bklt. pane, 3 each #274-275   7.00
    Complete booklet, #275a   7.00

Leafhoppers — A90

Designs: 50o, Ulopa reticulata. 4k, Streptanus sordidus. 5k, Anoscopus flavostriatus. 13k, Macrosteles alpinus.

1995, Feb. 6   Litho.   Perf. 14
276 A90 50o multicolored   .25 .25
277 A90 4k multicolored   1.60 1.60
278 A90 5k multicolored   1.60 1.60
279 A90 13k multicolored   4.50 4.50
    Nos. 276-279 (4)   7.95 7.95

Tourism — A91

1995, Apr. 10   Litho.   Perf. 13½x14
280 A91 4k Village of Famjin   1.50 1.50
281 A91 4k Vatnsdalur valley   1.50 1.50

Peace & Freedom — A92

Europa: 4k, Island couple, "Vidar, vali og baldur." 7k, Couple looking toward sun, "Liv og livtrasir."

1995, Apr. 10   Perf. 13x14
282 A92 4k multicolored   1.20 1.20
283 A92 7k multicolored   2.50 2.50

Nordic Art — A93

Designs: 2k, Museum of Art, Torshavn. 4k, Woman, by Frimod Joensen, vert. 5.50k, Self-portrait, by Joensen, vert.

Perf. 13½x14, 14x13½
1995, June 12   Litho.
284 A93 2k multicolored   .65 .65
285 A93 4k multicolored   1.40 1.40
286 A93 5.50k multicolored   1.90 1.90
    Nos. 284-286 (3)   3.95 3.95

Corvus Corax — A94

Designs: No. 287, Black raven. No. 288, White-speckled raven.

1995, June 12 Perf. 13½x14
287 A94 4k multicolored 1.40 1.40
288 A94 4k multicolored 1.40 1.40
a. Booklet pane, 5 each #287-288 14.00
Complete booklet, #288a 14.00

Saint Olaf (955?-1030), Patron Saint of Faroe Islands — A95

Litho. & Engr.
1995, Sept. 12 Perf. 13½x13
289 A95 4k multicolored 1.60 1.60

See Aland Islands No. 119.

Early Folk Life — A95a

4k, Dairy maids carrying buckets. 6k, Peasants fleecing sheep. 15k, Schooners, saltfish being brought ashore, vert.

1995, Sept. 12 Engr. Perf. 12½
290 A95a 4k dark green 1.50 1.50
291 A95a 6k pur brn, vert. 2.25 2.25
292 A95a 15k ultra 5.00 5.00
Nos. 290-292 (3) 8.75 8.75

Church of Mary Catholic Church — A96

Designs: No. 293, Stained glass window. No. 294, Exterior view of church.

1995, Nov. 9 Litho. Perf. 13½
293 A96 4k multicolored 1.40 1.40
294 A96 4k multicolored 1.40 1.40
a. Booklet pane, 5 ea #293-294 14.00
Complete booklet, #294a 14.00

Rocky Coastline — A97

1996, Jan. 1 Litho. Perf. 14
295 A97 4.50k multicolored 1.40 1.40

Seaweed — A98

4k, Ptilota plumosa. 5.50k, Fucus spiralis. 6k, Ascophyllum nodosum. 9k, Laminaria hyperborea.

1996, Feb. 12 Perf. 15
296 A98 4k multicolored 1.10 1.10
297 A98 5.50k multicolored 1.40 1.40
298 A98 6k multicolored 1.60 1.60
299 A98 9k multicolored 2.75 2.75
Nos. 296-299 (4) 6.85 6.85

Birds — A99

Designs: No. 300, Laxia curvirostra. No. 301, Bombycilla garrulus.

1996, Apr. 15 Litho. Perf. 14x15
300 A99 4.50k multicolored 1.40 1.40
301 A99 4.50k multicolored 1.40 1.40
a. Booklet pane, 5 each #300-301 14.00
Complete booklet, #301a 14.00

See Nos. 313-314.

A100

Europa (Wives of Faroese Seamen): 4.50k, Woman standing beside sea coast. 7.50k, Portrait of a woman, vert.

1996, Apr. 15 Perf. 15x14½, 14½x15
302 A100 4.50k multicolored 1.50 1.50
303 A100 7.50k multicolored 2.00 2.00

A101

Nordatlantex '96 (Children's drawings): a, Boy playing with hoop, stick, by Bugvi. b, Two girls on steet, road sign, by Gudrid. c, Girl on bicycle, car on street, by Herborg.

1996, June 7 Litho. Perf. 14½
Souvenir Sheet of 3
304 A101 4.50k #a.-c. 3.50 3.50

A102

Sea bed off the Faroes.

Litho. & Engr.
1996, June 7 Perf. 13
305 A102 10k violet & multi 2.50 2.50
306 A102 16k green & multi 4.00 4.00

See Nos. 319-320, 343, 377-378.

Janus Kamban (b. 1913), Sculptor, Graphic Artist — A103

Works of art: 4.50k, Flock of Sheep. 6.50k, Fisherman on the Way Home. 7.50k, View from Tórshavn's Old Quarter.

1996, Sept. 16 Litho. Perf. 14
307 A103 4.50k multicolored 1.40 1.40
308 A103 6.50k multicolored 1.60 1.60
309 A103 7.50k multicolored 2.25 2.25
Nos. 307-309 (3) 5.25 5.25

A104

Christian's Church, Klaksvík — A105

Designs: No. 310, Exterior. No. 311, Interior, altar fresco.

1996, Nov. 4 Litho. Perf. 14x15
310 A104 4.50k multi 1.40 1.40
311 A105 4.50k multi 1.40 1.40
a. Booklet pane, 6 #310, 4 #311 14.00
Complete booklet, #311a 14.00

Christmas.

Souvenir Sheet

Reign of Queen Margaret II, 25th Anniv. — A106

1997, Jan. 14 Litho. Perf. 14½
312 A106 4.50k multicolored 1.25 1.25

Bird Type of 1996

Designs: No. 313, Pyrrhula pyrrhula. No. 314, Carduelis flammea.

1997, Feb. 17 Litho. Perf. 14x15
313 A99 4.50k multi 1.25 1.25
314 A99 4.50k multi 1.25 1.25
a. Booklet pane, 5 each #313-314 12.50 —
Complete booklet, #314a 12.50

Mushrooms — A107

Designs: 4.50k, Hygrocybe helobia. 6k, Hygrocybe chlorophana. 6.50k, Hygrocybe virginea. 7.50k, Hygrocybe psittacina.

1997, Feb. 17 Perf. 14½
315 A107 4.50k multicolored 1.10 1.10
316 A107 6k multicolored 1.60 1.60
317 A107 6.50k multicolored 1.60 1.60
318 A107 7.50k multicolored 2.00 2.00
Nos. 315-318 (4) 6.30 6.30

Map Type of 1996
Litho. & Engr.
1997, May 20 Perf. 13
319 A102 11k red & multi 2.90 2.90
320 A102 18k claret & multi 4.50 4.50

Europa — A108

Legends illustrated by William Heinesen: 4.50k, The Temptations of Saint Anthony. 7.50k, The Merman sitting at bottom of sea eating fish bait.

1997, May 20 Litho. Perf. 14½
321 A108 4.50k multicolored 1.40 1.40
322 A108 7.50k multicolored 2.25 2.25

Kalmar Union, 600th Anniv. — A109

1997, May 20 Engr. Perf. 12½
323 A109 4.50k deep blue violet 1.50 1.50

A110

Barbara, Film Shot in Faroe Islands (Scenes from film): 4.50k, Danish theologian Poul Aggerso arriving at Faroe Islands. 6.50k, Barbara and Poul. 7.50k, Barbara with men on boat. 9k, Barbara in row boat, sailing ship.

1997, Sept. 15 Litho. Perf. 14
324 A110 4.50k multicolored 1.25 1.25
325 A110 6.50k multicolored 1.60 1.60
326 A110 7.50k multicolored 2.00 2.00
327 A110 9k multicolored 2.25 2.25
Nos. 324-327 (4) 7.10 7.10

A111

Hvalvik church.

1997, Sept. 15
328 A111 4.50k Interior 1.25 1.25
329 A111 4.50k Exterior 1.25 1.25
a. Booklet pane, 5 each #328-329 12.50 —
Complete booklet, #329a 12.50

Birds — A112

1998, Feb. 23 Litho. Perf. 14x14½
330 A112 4.50k Sturnus vulgaris 1.25 1.25
331 A112 4.50k Turdus merula 1.25 1.25
a. Bkt. pane, 5 each #330-331 12.50 —
Complete booklet, #331a 12.50

A113

Scenes from the Sigurd poem "Brynhild's Ballad": 4.50k, King Buole, daughter Brynhild. 6.50k, Sigurd riding through wall of fire on horseback. 7.50k, Sigurd, Brynhild together. 10k, Guthrun alone leading horse.

1998, Feb. 23 Perf. 14
332 A113 4.50k multicolored 1.25 1.25
333 A113 6.50k multicolored 1.60 1.60
334 A113 7.50k multicolored 1.90 1.90
335 A113 10k multicolored 2.50 2.50
Nos. 332-335 (4) 7.25 7.25

Europa — A114

1998, May 18 Litho. Perf. 14
336 A114 4.50k Parade 1.25 1.25
337 A114 7.50k Processional 1.25 1.25

Olavsoka, Natl. Festival of Faroe Islands.

A115

1998, May 18 Perf. 14½
338 A115 7.50k multicolored 1.90 1.90

UN Declaration of Human Rights, 50th anniv.

Intl. Year of the Ocean — A116

Toothed whales: 4k, Lagenorhynchus acutus. 4.50k, Orcinus orca. 7k, Tursiops truncatus. 9k, Delphinapterus leucas.

1998, May 18 Perf. 14½x14
339 A116 4k multicolored 1.00 1.00
340 A116 4.50k multicolored 1.10 1.10
341 A116 7k multicolored 1.75 1.75
342 A116 9k multicolored 2.25 2.25
Nos. 339-342 (4) 6.10 6.10

Map Type of 1996
Litho. & Engr.
1998, Sept. 14   *Perf. 13*
343 A102 14k multicolored   3.75 3.75

Frederickschurch
A117

Designs: No. 344, Exterior, coastline. No. 345, Interior.

1998, Sept. 14   **Litho.**   *Perf. 14*
344 A117 4.50k multi   1.25 1.25
345 A117 4.50k multi   1.25 1.25
  a.   Bkt. pane, 5 each #344-345   12.50
     Complete booklet, #345a   12.50

A118

Paintings by Hans Hansen (1920-70): 4.50k, Fell-field, 1966. 5.50k, Village Interior, 1965. 6.50k, Portrait of Farmer Ólavur í Utistovu from Mikladalur, 1968. 8k, Self-portrait, 1968.

Perf. 13½x14, 14x13½
1998, Sept. 14
346 A118 4.50k multi   1.25 1.25
347 A118 5.50k multi   1.50 1.50
348 A118 6.50k multi, vert.   1.60 1.60
349 A118   8k multi, vert.   2.25 2.25
  Nos. 346-349 (4)   6.60 6.60

Birds — A119

Designs: No. 350, Passer domesticus. No. 351, Troglodytes troglodytes.

1999, Feb. 22   **Litho.**   *Perf. 13½*
350 A119 4.50k multi   1.25 1.25
351 A119 4.50k multi   1.25 1.25
  a.   Bkt. pane, 5 each #350-351   12.50
     Complete booklet, #351a   12.50

Ships Named "Smyril" — A120

1999, Feb. 22   *Perf. 14½x14*
352 A120 4.50k 1895   1.25 1.25
353 A120   5k 1932   1.40 1.40
354 A120   8k 1967   2.25 2.25
355 A120 13k 1975   3.50 3.50
  Nos. 352-355 (4)   8.40 8.40

Northern Islands — A121

1999, May 25   **Litho.**   *Perf. 13½*
356 A121   50o Kalsoy   .25 .25
357 A121 100o Vithoy   .25 .25
358 A121 400o Svinoy   1.10 1.10
359 A121 450o Fugloy   1.25 1.25
360 A121 600o Kunoy   1.60 1.60
361 A121 800o Borthoy   2.10 2.10
  Nos. 356-361 (6)   6.55 6.55

See Nos. 383-386.

Waterfalls — A122

Europa: 6k, Svartifossur. 8k, Foldarafossur.

1999, May 25   *Perf. 14x14½*
362 A122 6k multicolored   1.60 1.60
363 A122 8k multicolored   2.25 2.25

Abstract Paintings of Ingálvur av Reyni — A123

1999, Sept. 27   **Litho.**   *Perf. 12½*
364 A123 4.50k Bygd   1.25 1.25
365 A123   6k Húsavik   1.60 1.60
366 A123   8k Reytt regn   2.10 2.10
367 A123 20k Genta   5.25 5.25
  Nos. 364-367 (4)   10.20 10.20

Bible Stories — A124

1999, Sept. 27   *Perf. 14½x14*
368 A124 450o John 1:1-5   1.25 1.25
  a.   Booklet pane of 6   7.50
     Complete booklet, #368a   7.50
369 A124 600o Luke 1:26-28   1.60 1.60
  a.   Booklet pane of 6   10.00
     Complete booklet, #369a   10.00

See Nos. 387-388, 407-408.

A125

Christianity in the Faroes, 1000th Anniv.: 4.50k, Man on rocks in ocean. 5.50k, Monk with cross, man with sword. 8k, People, flags. 16k, Cross in sky.

Perf. 13½x13¼
2000, Feb. 21   **Litho.**
370 A125 4.50k multi   1.25 1.25
371 A125 5.50k multi   1.40 1.40
372 A125   8k multi   2.10 2.10
373 A125 16k multi   4.25 4.25
  Nos. 370-373 (4)   9.00 9.00

A126

School and: No. 374, Sanna av Skarthi, Anna Suffia Rasmussen, wives of founders. No. 375, Rasmus Rasmussen (1871-1962), Símun av Skarthi (1872-1942), school founders.

2000, Feb. 21
374 A126 4.50k multi   1.25 1.25
375 A126 4.50k multi   1.25 1.25
  a.   Bkt. pane, 4 ea #374-375   10.00
     Complete booklet, #375a   10.00

Faroese Folk High School, cent.

Europa, 2000
Common Design Type
2000, May 9   **Litho.**   *Perf. 13¼x13*
376 CD17 8k multi   2.40 2.40

Map Type of 1996
Litho. & Engr.
2000, May 22   *Perf. 13¼x13*
377 A102 15k multi   3.75 3.75
378 A102 22k multi   5.75 5.75

Stampin' The Future Children's Stamp Design Contest Winners — A127

Art by: 4k, Katrin Mortensen. 4.50k, Sigga Andreassen. 6k, Steingrímur Joensen. 8k, Dion Dam Frandsen.

2000, May 22   **Litho.**   *Perf. 13x13¼*
379 A127   4k multi   1.10 1.10
380 A127 4.50k multi   1.25 1.25
381 A127   6k multi   1.60 1.60
382 A127   8k multi   2.25 2.25
  Nos. 379-382 (4)   6.20 6.20

Island Type of 1999
2000, Sept. 18   **Litho.**   *Perf. 13½*
383 A121   200o Skúvoy   .65 .65
384 A121   650o Hestoy   1.60 1.60
385 A121   750o Koltur   1.90 1.90
386 A121 1000o Nólsoy   2.50 2.50
  Nos. 383-386 (4)   6.65 6.65

Bible Story Type of 1999
2000, Sept. 18   **Litho.**   *Perf. 13x13¼*
387 A124 4.50k Micah 5:1   1.25 1.25
  a.   Booklet pane of 6   7.50
     Booklet, #387a   7.50
388 A124   6k John 1:14   1.60 1.60
  a.   Booklet pane of 6   10.00
     Booklet, #388a   10.00

Pew Gables Type of 1980
Kirkjubour pew gables: 430o, St. Andrew with cross. 650o, St. Bartholomew. 800o, Unknown apostle. 18k, Unknown apostle, diff.

Photo. & Engr.
2001, Feb. 12   *Perf. 12¾x12½*
389 A20 450o multi   1.25 1.25
390 A20 650o multi   1.60 1.60
391 A20 800o multi   2.10 2.10
392 A20   18k multi   4.50 4.50
  Nos. 389-392 (4)   9.45 9.45

Faroese Red Cross, 75th Anniv. — A128

Designs: 4.50k, Old person. 6k, Relief worker.

2001, Feb. 12   **Litho.**   *Perf. 14½x14*
393 A128 4.50k multi   1.25 1.25
  a.   Booklet pane of 6   7.50
     Booklet, #393a   7.50
394 A128   6k multi   1.60 1.60
  a.   Booklet pane of 6   10.00
     Booklet, #394a   10.00

Souvenir Sheet

Faroe Islands Postal Service, 25th Anniv. A129

No. 395: a, Boat for interisland mail transport, 19th cent. b, Tórshavn post office, 1906. c, Simon Pauli Poulsen (Morkabóndin), mail carrier.

Photo. & Engr.
2001, Apr. 1   *Perf. 13x13¼*
395 A129 4.50k Sheet of 3, #a-c   5.00 5.00

Nordic Myths and Legends About Light and Darkness — A130

No. 396: a, The Death of Hogni. b, The Tree of the Year. c, The Harp. d, Gram and Grane. e, The Ballad of Nornagest. f, Gudrun's Evil Magic.

Litho. with Foil Application
2001, Apr. 1   *Perf. 13½x13¼*
396 A130 6k Sheet of 6, #a-f   10.00 10.00

Hafnia 2001 Philatelic Exhibition, Copenhagen.

Paintings by Zacharias Heinesen — A131

Designs: 4k, The Artist's Mother, 1992. 4.50k, Uti á Reyni, 1974. 10k, Ur Vágunum, 2000. 15k, Sunrise, 1975.

2001, June 11   **Litho.**   *Perf. 13¼x13*
397 A131   4k multi   1.10 1.10
398 A131 4.50k multi   1.25 1.25
399 A131 10k multi   2.75 2.75
400 A131 15k multi   4.00 4.00
  Nos. 397-400 (4)   9.10 9.10

Europa — A132

Hydroelectric power stations: 6k, Fossáverkith. 8k, Eithisverkith.

2001, June 11   *Perf. 13x13½*
401 A132 6k multi   1.60 1.60
402 A132 8k multi   2.25 2.25

Whales — A133

Designs: 4.50k, Physeter macrocephalus. 6.50k, Balaenoptera physalus. 9k, Balaenoptera musculus. 20k, Balaenoptera borealis.

Perf. 13¾x13¼
2001, Sept. 17   **Litho.**
403 A133 4.50k multi   1.25 1.25
404 A133 6.50k multi   1.60 1.60
405 A133   9k multi   2.25 2.25
406 A133 20k multi   5.50 5.50
  Nos. 403-406 (4)   10.60 10.60

Bible Stories Type of 1999
2001, Sept. 17   *Perf. 13*
407 A124   5k Luke 2:34-35   1.40 1.40
  a.   Booklet pane of 6   8.50
     Booklet, #407a   8.50
408 A124 6.50k Matthew 2:18   1.60 1.60
  a.   Booklet pane of 6   10.00
     Booklet, #408a   10.00

Mollusks — A134

Designs: 5k, Sepiola atlantica. 7k, Modiolus modiolus. 7.50k, Polycera faeroensis. 18k, Buccinum undatum.

2002, Feb. 11   **Litho.**   *Perf. 13*
409 A134   5k multi   1.40 1.40
410 A134   7k multi   1.75 1.75
411 A134 7.50k multi   1.90 1.90
412 A134 18k multi   4.50 4.50
  Nos. 409-412 (4)   9.55 9.55

Portions of the designs were applied by a thermographic process producing a shiny, raised effect.

Souvenir Sheet

Viking Voyages A135

No. 413: a, Navigation tool. b, Viking sailor on boat. c, Viking boat.

Litho. & Engr.

2002, Feb. 11   *Perf. 13*
413 A135 6.50k Sheet of 3, #a-c   5.00 5.00

Europa — A136

Designs: 6.50k, Clowns. 8k, Various circus performers.

2002, Apr. 8   **Litho.**   *Perf. 13¼x13½*
414 A136 6.50k multi   1.60 1.60
415 A136 8k multi   2.10 2.10

Art by Tróndur Patursson A137

Designs: 5k, Bládypi. 6.50k, Kosmiska Rúmith.

2002, Apr. 8
416 A137 5k multi   1.40 1.40
417 A137 6.50k multi   1.60 1.60
   a.   Booklet pane of 8, 4 each
     #416-417   13.00 —
     Booklet, #417a   13.00

Eggs and Chicks — A138

Designs: 5k, Numenius phaeopus. 7.50k, Gallinago gallinago. 12k, Haematopus ostralegus. 20k, Pluvialis apricaria.

2002, June 17   *Perf. 14x14½*
418 A138 5k multi   1.40 1.40
419 A138 7.50k multi   1.90 1.90
420 A138 12k multi   3.00 3.00
421 A138 20k multi   5.25 5.25
    Nos. 418-421 (4)   11.55 11.55

Souvenir Sheet

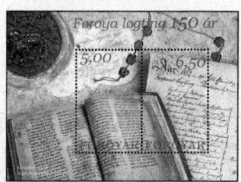

Faroese Representative Council, 150th Anniv. — A139

Designs: 5k, Royal book and seal. 6.50k, Royal book, Protocol of 1852.

2002, June 17   *Perf. 14*
422 A139 Sheet of 2, #a-b   4.00 4.00

Falco Columbarius Subaesalon A140

Litho. & Embossed

2002, Sept. 23   *Perf. 13¼*
423 A140 30k multi   8.25 8.25

Gota Church — A141

2002, Sept. 23   **Litho.**   *Perf. 12½*
424 A141 5k Exterior   1.40 1.40
425 A141 6.50k Interior   1.60 1.60
   a.   Booklet pane, 5 each #424-425   15.00
     Booklet, #425a   15.00

Souvenir Sheet

Intl. Council for the Exploration of the Sea, Cent. — A142

No. 426: a, Micromesistius poutassou and island. b, Exploration ship Magnus Heinason and fish.

Litho. & Engr.

2002, Sept. 23   *Perf. 13*
426 A142 8k Sheet of 2, #a-b   4.50 4.50

See Denmark Nos. 1237-1238, Greenland Nos. 401-402.

Opening of Vagár-Streymoy Tunnel, Nov. 2002 — A143

Designs: No. 427, Wheeled tunneling machine at right. No. 428, Workers in red uniforms at left.

2003, Feb. 24   **Litho.**   *Perf. 13¼x13*
427 A143 5k multi   1.40 1.40
428 A143 5k multi   1.40 1.40
   a.   Booklet pane, 5 each #427-428   14.00 —
     Complete booklet, #428a   14.00

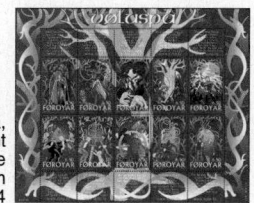

Voluspá, Ancient Norse Poem A144

No. 429: a, Seeress Heid holding staff. b, Heid sees animal and man in vision. c, Nude man and woman. d, Scribe and horseman. e, Battle between group with swords and man with hammer. f, Horseman and warriors. g, Men, large sword. h, Longboat. i, Attack on man holding spear, fire. j, Two figures with staffs, winged serpent.

2003, Feb. 24   *Perf. 14*
429 A144 Sheet of 10   17.50 17.50
   a.-j.   6.50k Any single   1.60 1.60

Europa — A145

Poster art for Nordic House: 6.50k, Fish Tree, by Astrid Andreasen, 1991. 8k, Ceramics by Guthrith Poulsen, 1997.

2003, Apr. 14   *Perf. 13½x13¼*
430 A145 6.50k multi   1.60 1.60
431 A145 8k multi   2.10 2.10

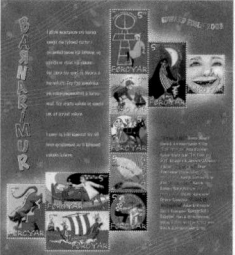

Children's Songs — A146

No. 432: a, Woman playing hopscotch (26x44mm). b, Boy on rocks, moon (26x44mm). c, Girl with missing teeth (26x26mm). d, Boy with toy sailboat (26x26mm). e, Cat, horse and girl (26x26mm). f, Butterfly and fly (26x26mm). g, Girl in bed, boy with stars (44x26mm). h, Cat on stairs, mouse (26x36mm). i, Man playing drums

---

(26x26mm). j, King and queen in longboat (44x26mm).

Perf. 13¼, 13¼x13¼x13¼x14 (#432g, 432j), 13¼x14 (#432h)

2003, Apr. 14
432 A146 Sheet of 10   14.00 14.00
   a.-j.   5k Any single   1.25 1.25

Small Towns — A147

2003, June 10   **Litho.**   *Perf. 13x13¼*
433 A147 5k Bour   1.40 1.40
434 A147 5k Gásadalur   1.40 1.40

Communities With Post Offices 100 Years Old — A148

No. 435: a, Fuglafjorthur. b, Strendur. c, Sandur. d, Eithi. e, Vestmanna. f, Vágur. g, Mithvágur. h, Hvalba.

2003, June 10   *Perf. 13¼x13*
435 A148 Sheet of 8   11.00 11.00
   a.-h.   5k Any single   1.25 1.25

Theologians — A149

Designs: 5k, Jesper Rasmussen Brochmand (1585-1652). 6.50k, Thomas Kingo (1634-1703).

2003, Sept. 22   *Perf. 13x13¼*
436 A149 5k multi   1.40 1.40
437 A149 6.50k multi   1.60 1.60
   a.   Booklet pane, 5 each #436-437   15.00
     Complete booklet, #437a   15.00

Souvenir Sheet

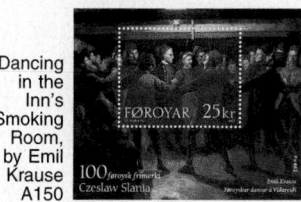

Dancing in the Inn's Smoking Room, by Emil Krause A150

Litho. & Engr.

2003, Sept. 22   *Perf. 12¼*
438 A150 25k multi   7.50 7.50

100th Faroese stamp engraved by Czeslaw Slania.

Islands Type of 1999

2004, Jan. 26   **Litho.**   *Perf. 13½*
439 A121 550o Stóra Dímun   1.40 1.40
440 A121 700o Lítla Dímun   1.90 1.90

Suthuroy Island A151

No. 441: a, Sigmundargjogv, Sandvik. b, Fiskieithi, Hvalba. c, A Hamri, Frothba. d, Tjaldavíkshólmur, Oravík. e, Fossurin Stóri, Fámjin. f, Hovsfjorthur, Hov. g, I Eystrum, Porkeri. h, A Okrum. i, I Horg, Sumba. j, I Akrabergi.

2004, Jan. 26   *Perf. 13x13¼*
441 A151 5k Sheet of 10, #a-j   14.00 14.00

1854 Cruise of Yacht "Maria" A152

No. 442: a, Gáshólmur and Tindhólmur. b, Framvith "Diamantunum." c, Hús av tí betra slagnum. d, Mylingur sunnanífrá. e, Mylingur northanífrá. f, Kalsoyggin northanífrá. g, Raetha teir infoddu. h, Sunnari endi av Kunoynni.

2004, Mar. 26   **Litho.**   *Perf. 13*
442 A152 6.50k Sheet of 8, #a.-h.   14.00 14.00

Souvenir Sheet

Norse Gods A153

No. 443: a, Thor, in boat, fighting Midgard serpent. b, Ran in fishing net.

2004, Mar. 26
443 A153 6.50k Sheet of 2, #a.-b.   4.50 4.50

Souvenir Sheet

Wedding of Crown Prince Frederik and Mary Donaldson — A154

Litho. & Photo.

2004, May 14   *Perf. 13¼*
444 A154 Sheet of 2 + central label   4.00 4.00
   a.   5k Couple facing right   1.60 1.60
   b.   6.50k Couple facing left   2.25 2.25

See Denmark No. 1275 and Greenland Nos. 429-430.

Soccer Organization Centenaries — A155

Soccer players and emblems of: 5k, Klaksvík and Tórshavn teams. 6.50k, FIFA (Fédération Internationale de Football Association).

2004, May 24　Litho.　Perf. 13¼x13
445	A155	5k multi	1.40	1.40
446	A155	6.50k multi	1.60	1.60
a.		Booklet pane, 4 each #445-446	12.00	
		Complete booklet, #446a	12.00	

Europa — A156

Designs: 6.50k, Tourists in gorge, Hestur. 8k, Tourists at shore, Stóra Dímun.

2004, May 24　　Perf. 13x13¼
447	A156	6.50k multi	1.60	1.60
448	A156	8k multi	2.25	2.25

Churches — A157

2004, Sept. 20　Litho.　Perf. 13¼x13
449	A157	5.50k Vágur	1.40	1.40
450	A157	7.50k Tvoroyri	2.00	2.00
a.		Booklet pane, 4 each #449-450	14.00	
		Complete booklet, #450a	14.00	

Poems by Janus Djurhuus (1881-1948) — A158

No. 451: a, Atlantis. b, Grímur Kamban. c, Gandkvaethi Tróndar. d, Til Foroya I-III. e, Mín sorg. f, Loki. g, I búri og Slatur. h, Heimferth Nólsoyar Páls. i, Móses á Sinai fjalli. j, Cello.

2004, Sept. 20　　Perf. 13
451	A158	Sheet of 10	20.00	20.00
a.-j.		7.50k Any single	2.00	2.00

Souvenir Sheet

Life of the Vikings A159

No. 452: a, Men tending sheep. b, Men with farm implements. c, Women weaving and woman milking cow.

Litho. & Engr.
2005, Feb. 7　　Perf. 13
452	A159	Sheet of 3	6.00	6.00
a.-c.		7.50k Any single	2.00	2.00

Miniature Sheet

Vágar Island A160

No. 453: a, Víkar. b, Gásadalur. c, Bour. d, Slaettanes. e, Kvígandalsá. f, Sorvágur. g,

Sandavágur. h, Vatnsoyrar. i, Fjallavatn. j, Mithvágur.

2005, Feb. 7　Litho.　Perf. 13x13¼
453	A160	Sheet of 10	15.00	15.00
a.-j.		5.50k Any single	1.50	1.50

Lepus Timidus — A161

2005, Apr. 18　　Perf. 13¼x13½
454	A161	5.50k shown	1.60	1.60
455	A161	5.50k Brown fur	1.60	1.60
a.		Booklet pane, 4 each #454-455	13.00	—
		Complete booklet, #455a	13.00	

Europa A162

Various traditional foods with: 7.50k, Brown panel. 10k, Green panel.

2005, Apr. 18　　Perf. 13¼x13
456	A162	7.50k multi	2.00	2.00
457	A162	10k multi	2.75	2.75

Worldwide Fund for Nature (WWF) — A163

Petrels: 8.50k, Oceanodroma leucorhoa. 9k, Hydrobates pelagicus. 12k, Oceanodroma leucorhoa on ground. 20k, Hydrobates pelagicus on ground.

2005, June 6　　Perf. 13
458	A163	8.50k multi	1.60	1.60
459	A163	9k multi	2.75	2.75
460	A163	12k multi	3.25	3.25
461	A163	20k multi	5.50	5.50
		Nos. 458-461 (4)	13.10	13.10

Miniature Sheet

Landscapes by Jógvan Waagstein (1879-1949) — A164

No. 462: a, Path and wall at LL, denomination in red, year date in black in grass. b, Path and wall at LL, denomination in white, year date in black on wall. c, Stone hut at left, denomination in red, year date in black. d, Path at right, denomination in red, year date in black. e, Two large rocks at right, denomination in red, year date in black. f, Rocks at LL, denomination in red, year date in white. g, Path at center, denomination in white, year date in black on path. h, Buildings at LL, denomination in red, year date in black in path. i, Churches, denomination in white, year date in black in water.

2005, Sept. 19　Litho.　Perf. 14x14¼
462	A164	Sheet of 9	17.00	17.00
a.-i.		7.50k Any single	1.90	1.90

End of British Occupation In World War II, 60th Anniv. — A165

Soldiers with: 5.50k, Arms. 9k, Children.

2005, Sept. 19　　Perf. 14
463	A165	5.50k pale blue & blk	1.40	1.40
464	A165	9k pale yel & blk	2.40	2.40

Christmas — A166

Ballads: 5.50k, Jólavísan. 7.50k, Rudisar Vísa.

2005, Nov. 7　　Perf. 13½x13¼
465	A166	5.50k multi	1.40	1.40
466	A166	7.50k multi	2.00	2.00
a.		Booklet pane, 5 each #465-466	17.00	
		Complete booklet, #466a	17.00	

Villages — A167

2006, Feb. 13　Litho.　Perf. 13¾
467	A167	7k Sythrugota	1.90	1.90
468	A167	12k Fuglafjorthur	2.50	2.50
469	A167	20k Leirvík	5.00	5.00
		Nos. 467-469 (3)	9.40	9.40

Miniature Sheet

Fish A168

No. 470: a, Himantolophus groenlandicus. b, Gonostoma elongatum. c, Sebastes mentella. d, Neoraja caerulea. e, Rhinochimaera atlantica. f, Linophryne lucifer. g, Ceratias holboelli. h, Lampris guttatus. i, Argyropelecus olfersi. j, Lophius piscatorius.

2006, Feb. 13　　Perf. 14
470	A168	Sheet of 10	15.00	15.00
a.-j.		5.50k Any single	1.40	1.40

Souvenir Sheet

Norse Folklore A169

No. 471: a, Norns surrounding sleeping child. b, Sea ghost.

2006, Mar. 29　　Perf. 13
471	A169	7.50k Sheet of 2, #a-b	4.00	4.00

Miniature Sheet

Ballad of the Long Serpent, by Jens Christian Djurhuus A170

No. 472: a, Building of ship. b, Launch of ship. c, King on throne. d, King's fleet at sea (brown ship at LL, blue ship at LR). e, King and sailors on shore. f, King pointing. g, Ship with red sail at R. h, Battle scene (injured men falling into water). i, Battle scene (men with shields jumping from ship to ship). j, Dead men on ship's deck.

2006, Mar. 29　　Perf. 13¼x13
472	A170	Sheet of 10	15.00	15.00
a.-j.		5.50k Any single	1.40	1.40

Opening of Northoy Tunnel — A171

Tunnel and: No. 473, Fish. No. 474, Canoe.

2006, June 12　　Perf. 13¼
473	A171	5.50k multi	1.40	1.40
474	A171	5.50k multi	1.40	1.40
a.		Booklet pane, 4 each #473-474	11.00	
		Complete booklet, #474a	11.00	

Europa — A172

2006, June 12　　Perf. 13¾
475	A172	7.50k shown	2.00	2.00
476	A172	10k Hands, diff.	2.75	2.75

Miniature Sheet

Sandoy Island A173

No. 477: a, Sunnan fyri Skopun. b, Dalur. c, Soltuvík. d, Skálavík. e, Skopun. f, Sandur. g, Skarvanes. h, Húsavík.

2006, Sept. 18　Litho.　Perf. 13x13¼
477	A173	Sheet of 8	16.00	16.00
a.-h.		7.50k Any single	2.00	2.00

Sandur Church — A174

Designs: 5.50k, Building exterior, steeple cross. 7.50k, Interior.

2006, Sept. 18　　Perf. 14
478	A174	5.50k multi	1.40	1.40
479	A174	7.50k multi	2.00	2.00
a.		Booklet pane, 4 each #478-479	14.00	
		Complete booklet, #479a	14.00	

Wave
Energy — A175

2007, Feb. 12   Litho.   Perf. 12½x13
480 A175 7.50k multi   2.00 2.00

Art From 1838 La
Recherche
Expedition
A176

Art by Barthélemy Lauvergne: 5.50k, La
Recherche off Nólsoy. 7.50k, Skaelingsfjall.

2007, Feb. 12
481 A176 5.50k multi   1.40 1.40
482 A176 7.50k multi   2.00 2.00
a.   Booklet pane, 4 each #481-482   12.00 —
      Complete booklet, #482a   12.00

Miniature Sheet

Legend
of the
Seal
Woman
A177

No. 483: a, Man, head of white seal. b,
Woman and seals in ring. c, Man, nude
woman, seals. d, Man and nude woman
seated on chest. e, Ship and two seals. f, Children, seal woman nursing child. g, Seal
woman and man. h, Sleeping man and seal
woman with hands open. i, Man and dead
seals. j, Seal woman.

2007, Feb. 12   Perf. 14
483 A177 Sheet of 10   15.00 15.00
a.-j.   5.50k Any single   1.50 1.50

Miniature Sheet

The Old
Man and
His
Sons,
Novel by
Hethin
Brú
A178

No. 484: a, Ketil cutting whale's throat. b,
Men carrying injured Klávus on log. c, Kálvur
and fiancee, Klávusardóttir with pot and kettle.
d, Ketil and Kálvur in fishing boat. e, Ketil's
wife arguing with daughter-in-law. f, Ketil
catching flying northern fulmars. g, Kálvur and
stone fence. h, Ketil, Kálvur and cow.

2007, Apr. 10   Litho.   Perf. 13x12½
484 A178 Sheet of 8   16.00 16.00
a.-h.   7.50k Any single   2.00 2.00

Europa — A179

Design: 5.50k, Scout holding bird. 10k, Tent.

2007, Apr. 10
485 A179 5.50k multi   1.40 1.40
486 A179 10k multi   2.75 2.75

Scouting, cent.

Souvenir Sheet

Bible Translators — A180

No. 487: a, Jákup Dahl (1878-1944). b, Kristian O. Videro (1906-91). c, Victor Danielsen
(1894-1961).

2007, June 11   Litho.   Perf. 13x12½
487 A180 Sheet of 3   5.00 5.00
a.-c.   5.50k Any single   1.60 1.60

Domesticated
Birds — A181

Designs: 9k, Chickens and rooster. 20k,
Ducks. 25k, Geese.

2007, June 11   Perf. 12½x13
488 A181 9k multi   2.40 2.40
489 A181 20k multi   5.00 5.00
490 A181 25k multi   6.50 6.50
        Nos. 488-490 (3)   13.90 13.90

Hoyvík
A182

2007, Oct. 1   Perf. 13½
491 A182 7.50k multi   2.00 2.00

Wooden Religious
Statues of Kirkjubour
Cathedral — A183

2007, Oct. 1   Perf. 13x12½
492 A183 5.50k Jesus   1.40 1.40
493 A183 7.50k Mary   2.00 2.00
a.   Booklet pane, 4 each #492-493   14.00 —
      Complete booklet, #493a   14.00

Miniature Sheet

Stone
Fence
and
Wildlife
A184

No. 494: a, Bird, worm. b, Two red beetles,
fern. c, Mouse, purple flowers. d, Mosquito,
pink flowers. e, Large black and white bird,
dandelions. f, Bird with black wings, butter-
cups. g, Earwigs, grass. h, Bird and eggs.

2007, Oct. 1   Perf. 13½x14¼
494 A184 Sheet of 8   12.00 12.00
a.-h.   5.50k Any single   1.40 1.40

Klaksvík,
Cent. — A185

Litho. & Embossed

2008, Feb. 11   Perf. 14
495 A185 5.50k multi   1.40 1.40

Tinganes — A186

2008, Feb. 11   Litho.   Perf. 13¼
496 A186 14k multi   3.50 3.50

Hoydalar
Tuberculosis
Sanatorium,
Cent. — A187

Lungs and: 5.50k, Patients, buildings. 9k,
Dr. Vilhelm Magnussen examining patient,
child.

2007, Feb. 11   Perf. 12½x13
497 A187 5.50k multi   1.40 1.40
498 A187 9k multi   2.50 2.50
a.   Booklet pane, 4 each #497-
      498   16.00
      Complete booklet, #498a   16.00

Miniature Sheet

Prints by
Elinborg
Lützens
A188

No. 499: a, Houses below mountain. b, Milk
maids (30x30mm). c, Houses. d, Underwater
scene. e, Chicken (30x30mm). f, Person and
bird near wooden bucket.

2008, Feb. 11   Perf. 13¼
499 A188 Sheet of 6   16.00 16.00
a.-f.   10k Any single   2.60 2.60

Souvenir Sheet

Mythical
Places
A189

No. 500: a, Alvheyggur. b, Klovningasteinur.

2008, Mar. 27   Litho.   Perf. 12½x13
500 A189 Sheet of 2   4.00 4.00
a.-b.   7.50k Either single   2.00 2.00

Caltha
Palustris — A190

2008, May 19   Perf. 13¼
501 A190 30k multi   8.00 8.00

Europa — A191

Designs: 550o, Heart and "Teg." 750o, Posthorn with "@" symbol and "Hey."

2008, May 19   Perf. 13¼x13
502 A191 550o multi   1.40 1.40
503 A191 750o multi   2.00 2.00

Miniature Sheet

Famous
People
A192

No. 504: a, Niels Winther (1822-92), politician and newspaper publisher. b, Súsanna
Helena Patursson (1864-1916), writer and
newspaper publisher. c, Rasmus C. Effersoe
(1857-1916), writer and newspaper editor. d,
Jógvan Poulsen (1854-1941), religious and
school book writer. e, Frithrikur Petersen
(1853-1917), poet. f, Andreas Christian
Evensen (1874-1917), magazine publisher
and school book writer.

2008, May 19   Perf. 13½x13¼
504 A192 Sheet of 6   9.00 9.00
a.-f.   5.50k Any single   1.40 1.40

Miniature Sheet

Ferns
A193

No. 505: a, Gymnocarpium dryopteris. b,
Polypodium vulgare. c, Dryopteris dilatata. d,
Asplenium adiantum-nigrum. e, Athyrium filix-
femina. f, Dryopteris filix-mas. g, Cystopteris
fragilis. h, Phegopteris connectilis. i, Polys-
tichum lonchitis. j, Asplenium trichomanes.

2008, Sept. 22   Litho.   Perf. 13x13½
505 A193 Sheet of 10   25.00 25.00
a.-j.   800o Any single   2.40 2.40

Christmas — A194

2008, Sept. 22   Perf. 13x12½
506 A194 6k shown   1.60 1.60
507 A194 10k Wooden cross   2.75 2.75
a.   Booklet pane of 8, 4 each
      #506-507   17.00 —
      Complete booklet, #507a   17.00

Global
Warming — A195

Designs: 6k, Earth and "No entry" sign. 8k,
Earth in shape of water droplet.

2009, Feb. 23   Litho.   Perf. 13¾x14
508 A195 6k multi   1.60 1.60
509 A195 8k multi   2.10 2.10
a.   Souvenir sheet, #508-509   3.75 3.75

Portions of the designs were applied by a
thermographic process producing a shiny
raised effect.

Miniature Sheet

Scenes From *The Lost Musicians,* by
William Heinesen — A196

No. 510: a, People, stylized harp. b, Ring of
silhouetted dancers. c, Woman on roof of
house, kneeling people and standing woman
near house. d, Silhouetted man approaching
woman on park bench. e, Women and seated
cellist. f, Violinist and two silhoutted men. g,
Man in bed. h, People in rowboat.

2009, Feb. 23			**Perf. 13½**	
510	A196	Sheet of 8	19.00	19.00
a.-h.		8k Any single	2.25	2.25

Europa — A197

Designs: 10k, Trollhovdi Island and Saturn.
12k, Heygadrangur Island, Jupiter and one of
its moons, Europa.

2009, May 25		**Litho.**	**Perf. 13x12½**	
511	A197	10k multi	2.75	2.75
512	A197	12k multi	3.25	3.25

Intl. Year of Astronomy.

Miniature Sheet

Geological Formation of the Faroe
Islands — A198

No. 513: a, Large volcano spewing lava,
trees. b, Smaller volcano spewing ash, dead
tree, lava on landscape. c, Map of area 60
million years ago. d, Map of area 15 million
years ago. e, Map of Faroe Isands, map of
Faroe Islands and area nearby. f, Glacier, rock
pinnacles.

2009, May 25			**Perf. 12½x13**	
513	A198	Sheet of 6	18.00	18.00
a.-f.		10k Any single	3.00	3.00

Thorshavn
Gymnastics Club,
Cent. — A199

Gymnasts: 6k, Male lifting female. 10k,
Female doing handstand. 26k, Male on rings.

2009, May 25			**Perf. 14**	
514	A199	6k multi	1.75	1.75
515	A199	10k multi	3.00	3.00
516	A199	26k multi	7.75	7.75
		Nos. 514-516 (3)	12.50	12.50

Serpentine Die Cut 14
Booklet Stamps
Self-Adhesive

517	A199	6k multi	2.00	2.00
518	A199	10k multi	3.00	3.00
a.		Booklet pane of 8, 4 each		
		#517-518	20.00	

Leynar
A200

2009, Sept. 16			**Perf. 12¾**	
519	A200	10k multi	3.00	3.00

Rock
Pigeons — A201

Designs: 14k, Two pigeons on rocks. 36k,
Head of pigeon, two pigeons in flight.

2009. Sept. 16			**Perf. 13**	
520	A201	14k multi	4.00	4.00
521	A201	36k multi	11.00	11.00

Altarpiece at
Vestmanna
Church
A202

Altarpiece at
Hattarvik Church
A203

2009, Sept. 16			**Perf. 13¾x13¼**	
522	A202	6k multi	1.75	1.75
a.		Perf. 13¾ vert.	1.75	1.75
523	A203	10k multi	3.25	3.25
a.		Perf. 14¼x13¾ on 3 sides	3.25	3.25
b.		Booklet pane of 8, 4 each		
		#522a, 523a	20.00	—
		Complete booklet, #523b	20.00	

Christmas.

Globicephala
Melas — A204

2010, Feb. 22		**Litho.**	**Perf. 14¾**	
524	A204	50k multi	15.00	15.00

Marine Flora and
Fauna — A205

Various photographs.

2010, Feb. 22			**Perf. 13¼x13½**	
525	A205	1k multi	.35	.35
526	A205	6k multi	1.75	1.75
527	A205	8k multi	2.50	2.50
528	A205	12k multi	3.50	3.50
		Nos. 525-528 (4)	8.10	8.10

Butterflies and
Moths — A206

Designs: 6k, Inachis io. 8k, Vanessa cardui.
14k, Agrius convolvuli. 16k, Acherontia
atropos.

2010, Feb. 22			**Perf. 13x12¾**	
529	A206	6k multicolored	1.75	1.75
530	A206	8k multicolored	2.50	2.50
531	A206	14k multicolored	4.25	4.25
532	A206	16k multicolored	5.00	5.00
		Nos. 529-532 (4)	13.50	13.50

Souvenir Sheet

Aquaculture — A207

No. 533: a, Fish, net. b, Fisherman holding
net.

			Perf. 14¼x14½	
2010, Mar. 24			**Litho.**	
533	A207	Sheet of 2	6.00	6.00
a.-b.		10k Either single	3.00	3.00

Paintings by Eli
Smith — A208

Various paintings.

2010, Apr. 26			**Perf. 14½**	
534	A208	18k multicolored	5.50	5.50
535	A208	24k multicolored	7.50	7.50

Europa — A209

Scenes from children's books: 10k, A Dog,
A Cat and A Mouse, by Bárthur Oskarsson.
12k, Moss Mollis's Journey, by Janus á
Húsagarthi.

2010, Apr. 26			**Perf. 13¾**	
536	A209	10k multicolored	3.00	3.00
537	A209	12k multicolored	3.50	3.50

Booklet Stamps
Self-Adhesive
Serpentine Die Cut 14

538	A209	10k multicolored	3.00	3.00
539	A209	12k multicolored	3.50	3.50
a.		Booklet pane of 8, 4 each		
		#538-539	26.00	26.00

Jens Christian
Svabo (1746-
1824), Writer and
Lexicographer
A210

Writings of Svabo and Svabo: 6k, Holding
walking stick. 12k, At desk. 14k, Holding book.
22k, With sheaf of papers, pen and inkwell.

			Perf. 13¼x13¾	
2010, Sept. 20			**Litho. & Engr.**	
540	A210	6k multicolored	1.75	1.75
541	A210	12k multicolored	3.75	3.75
542	A210	14k multicolored	4.50	4.50
543	A210	22k multicolored	7.00	7.00
		Nos. 540-543 (4)	17.00	17.00

Vegetables — A211

2010, Sept. 20		**Litho.**	**Perf. 13x13¼**	
544	A211	6k Potatoes	1.75	1.75
545	A211	8k Turnips	2.50	2.50

Christmas — A212

Carols: 6k, My Little Sweet Brownie (Lítla
Fitta Nissa Mín). 10k, In My Early Childhood
(A Barnaárum Ungu).

2010, Sept. 20			**Perf. 13x12½**	
546	A212	6k multicolored	1.75	1.75
547	A212	10k multicolored	3.25	3.25
a.		Booklet pane of 8, 4 each		
		#546-547	20.00	—
		Complete booklet, #547a	20.00	

See Nos. 570-571, 592-593.

Intl. Women's
Day,
Cent. — A213

2011, Feb. 21		**Litho.**	**Perf. 14**	
548	A213	10k multicolored	3.00	3.00

Traditional
Women's
Professions
A214

Designs: 6k, Nurses with patient and child.
16k, Midwives holding babies.

2011, Feb. 21			**Perf. 13x13¼**	
549	A214	6k multicolored	1.75	1.75
550	A214	16k multicolored	5.00	5.00

Cats — A215

Color of cat: 6k, Black and white. 10k,
Brown and white.

2011, Feb. 21			**Perf. 13¾**	
551	A215	6k multicolored	1.75	1.75
552	A215	10k multicolored	3.25	3.25

Booklet Stamps
Self-Adhesive
Serpentine Die Cut 14

553	A215	6k multicolored	1.75	1.75
554	A215	10k multicolored	3.25	3.25
a.		Booklet pane of 8, 4 each		
		#553-554	20.00	

Souvenir Sheet

Legend
of
Annika
od
Dímun
A216

No. 555 — Annika: a, With chalice. b, With
guards. c, With bound hands in water.

2011, Feb. 21			**Perf. 14¾**	
555	A216	Sheet of 3	9.00	9.00
a.-c.		10k Any single	3.00	3.00

Paintings by
Bergithe
Johannessen
(1905-95)
A217

Designs: 2k, Skerjut Strond (Glowing
Beach). 24k, Ur Nólsoy (From Nólsoy).

2011, Apr. 26   *Perf. 12½x13*
556 A217 2k multicolored   .65 .65
557 A217 24k multicolored   7.50 7.50

6 KR
FØROYAR

Paintings by Frida Zachariassen (1912-92) — A218

Designs: 6k, Urtagardhur (The Garden). 26k, Kona (Woman).

2011, Apr. 26   *Perf. 13*
558 A218 6k multicolored   1.75 1.75
559 A218 26k multicolored   7.50 7.50

10 KR

Europa — A219

Tree plantations on: 10k, Tórshavn. 12k, Kunoy, vert.

2011, Apr. 26   *Perf. 12½*
560 A219 10k multicolored   3.25 3.25
561 A219 12k multicolored   3.75 3.75

Intl. Year of Forests.

FØROYAR
14 KR

Flowers — A220

Designs: 14k, Silene dioica. 20k, Geranium sylvaticum.

2011, Apr. 26   *Perf. 13¼*
562 A220 14k multicolored   4.50 4.50
563 A220 20k multicolored   6.00 6.00

FØROYAR
0,50 KR

Berries — A221

Designs: 50o, Juniperus communis subsp. alpina. 6.50k, Empetrum nigrum. subsp. hermaphroditum.

2011, Sept. 1   Litho.   *Perf. 12¾x13½*
564 A221 50o multicolored   .25 .25
565 A221 6.50k multicolored   2.00 2.00

FØROYAR
10,50KR

Stóridrangur — A222

2011, Sept. 28   *Perf. 12½x13*
566 A222 10.50k multicolored   3.25 3.25

FØROYAR

Old Motor Vehicles — A223

Designs: No. 567, Black Ford TT truck, first vehicle on Faroe Islands. No. 568, Red Morris bus. No. 569, White De Luxe Model, automobile built on Faroe Islands.

2011, Sept. 28   *Perf. 13½x12¾*
567 A223 13k multicolored   4.00 4.00
568 A223 13k multicolored   4.00 4.00
569 A223 13k multicolored   4.00 4.00
   a.   Souvenir sheet of 3, #567-569   12.50 12.50
     Nos. 567-569 (3)   12.00 12.00

Christmas Type of 2010

Carols: 6.50k, I Can't Wait for Christmas to Come (Eg Eri So Spent Til Jóla). 10.50k, I Rejoice Every Christmas Eve (Eg Gledist So Hvort Jólakvold).

2011, Sept. 28   *Perf. 13x12½*
570 A212 6.50k multi   2.00 2.00
571 A212 10.50k multi   3.25 3.25
   a.   Booklet pane of 8, 4 each
     #570-571   21.00 —
     Complete booklet, #571a   21.00

10.50
FØROYAR 1972 2012

Reign of Queen Margrethe II, 40th Anniv. — A224

Litho. & Engr.
2012, Jan. 4   *Perf. 13¼*
572 A224 10.50k multicolored   3.00 3.00
   a.   Souvenir sheet of 1   3.00 3.00

FØROYAR 13KR

Extinct Animals — A225

Designs: 13k, Pinguinis impennis. 21k, Dímun sheep (Ovis aries), horiz.

2012, Feb. 20   Litho.   *Perf. 13¼x13*
573 A225 13k multicolored   4.00 4.00
     Perf. 13x13¼
574 A225 21k multicolored   6.00 6.00

FØROYAR
3 KR

Sea Anemones — A226

Various sea anemones.

2012, Feb. 20   *Perf. 14*
575 A226 3k multi   .90 .90
576 A226 6.50k multi   2.00 2.00
577 A226 8.50k multi   2.40 2.40
578 A226 10.50k multi   3.00 3.00
     Nos. 575-578 (4)   8.30 8.30

Booklet Stamps
Self-Adhesive
Serpentine Die Cut 14
579 A226 6.50k multi   2.00 2.00
580 A226 10.50k multi   3.00 3.00
   a.   Booklet pane of 8, 4 each
     #579-580   20.00

Sea Rescue A227

No. 581: a, Helicopter. b, Life raft.

2012, Mar. 21   *Perf. 14¼x13½*
581 A227 Sheet of 2   6.00 6.00
   a.-b.   10.50k Either single   3.00 3.00

FØROYAR
6,50KR

Europa A228

Designs: 6.50k, Tourists on boat near Suthuroy Island cliffs. 10.50k, Hikers on rocks.

2012, Apr. 30   *Perf. 12½x13*
582 A228 6.50k multi   2.00 2.00
583 A228 10.50k multi

6,50 KR
FØROYAR

Monsters — A229

Designs: 6.50k, Gryla. 11k, Marra. 17k, Nithagrísur. 19k, Fjorutroll.

2012, Apr. 30   *Perf. 13*
584 A229 6.50k multi   2.00 2.00
585 A229 11k multi   3.25 3.25
586 A229 17k multi   4.75 4.75
587 A229 19k multi   5.50 5.50
     Nos. 584-587 (4)   15.50 15.50

FØROYAR
8.50

Old Pharmacy, Klaksvík — A230

2012, Sept. 24   *Perf. 12½x13*
588 A230 8.50k multi   2.40 2.40

FØROYAR 13KR

Contemporary Art — A231

Designs: 13k, Mr. Walker on the Faroes, by Jan Hafström. 21k, Egg Procession, by Edward Fuglo.

2012, Sept. 24   *Perf. 13*
589 A231 13k multicolored   3.50 3.50
590 A231 21k multicolored   5.75 5.75

Miniature Sheet

REGIN SMIÐUR

Legend of Regin the Blacksmith — A232

No. 591: a, Hjordis attends to dying husband, Sigmund, on battlefield. b, Sigurd on horse. c, Regin hammering sword. d, Sigurd on horseback encounters Odin. e, Sigurd attacks serpent. f, Birds watching Sigurd cooking serpent's heart.

Litho., Litho & Embossed (#591e)
2012, Sept. 24   *Perf. 13¼x13*
591 A232 Sheet of 6   20.00 20.00
   a.-f.   11k Any single   3.25 3.25

Christmas Type of 2010

Carols: 6.50k, Why is Everything So Cozy Tonight? (Hví Man Tadh Vera?) 12.50k, Silent Night (Gledhilig Jól).

2012, Sept. 24   Litho.   *Perf. 13x12½*
592 A212 6.50k multi   2.00 2.00
593 A212 12.50k multi   4.00 4.00
   a.   Booklet pane of 8, 4 each
     #592-593   24.00 24.00
     Complete booklet, #593a   24.00 24.00

FØROYAR
12,50KR

Lambs A233

2013, Feb. 25   *Perf. 13¼x13¾*
594 A233 12.50k multi   4.00 4.00

FØROYAR
7 KR

Crustaceans A234

Designs: 7k, Cancer pagurus. 9k, Chaceon affinis. 23k, Pandalus borealis. 34k, Nephrops norvegicus.

2013, Feb. 25   *Perf. 12½x13*
595 A234 7k multi   2.50 2.50
596 A234 9k multi   3.25 3.25
597 A234 23k multi   8.00 8.00
598 A234 34k multi   12.00 12.00
     Nos. 595-598 (4)   25.75 25.75

Miniature Sheet

FØROYSKI BÁTURIN

Traditional Faroese Rowboat — A235

No. 599: a, Tollur og homluband (oarlock and strap, 26x23mm). b, Arar (oars, 66x23mm). c, Rodhur og rodhurarmur (rudder, 26x23mm). d, Kumpass (compass, 26x23mm). e, Seksmannafar (hull of six-man boat, 66x23mm). f, Kaggi (barrel, 26x23mm). g, Eyskar (bailing scoop, 26x23mm). h, Mastur og vrá vidh segli (mast and sail, 66x23mm). i, Nogla og togendi (bung and rope, 26x23mm).

Litho. & Engr.
2013, Feb. 25   *Perf. 13¼*
599 A235 Sheet of 9   20.00 20.00
   a.-i.   7k Any single   2.00 2.00

35,00
SØREN AABYE KIERKE GAARD
FØROYAR

Soren Kierkegaard (1813-55), Philosopher A266

2013, Mar. 4   *Perf. 12¼*
600 A266 35k multi   11.00 11.00

FØROYAR
7 KR

Europa — A267

Designs: 7k, Postal van. 12.50k, Postal truck.

2013, Apr. 29   Litho.   *Perf. 14*
601 A267 7k multi   2.25 2.25
602 A267 12.50k multi   4.00 4.00

Booklet Stamps
Self-Adhesive
Serpentine Die Cut 14
603 A267 7k multi   2.25 2.25
604 A267 12.50k multi   4.00 4.00
   a.   Booklet pane of 8, 4 each
     #603-604   27.00

FØROYAR 11,00 KR

Rodents — A268

Designs: 11k, Rattus norvegicus. 12.50k, Mus domesticus.

2013, Apr. 29   *Perf. 13¾x13¼*
605 A268 11k multi   3.50 3.50
606 A268 12.50k multi   4.00 4.00

FØROYAR 19KR

Paintings by Olivur Vith Neyst — A269

Designs: 19k, Sólskin (Sunshine). 38k, Vestaravág (West Harbor).

2013, Sept. 23   *Perf. 12½*
607 A269 19k multi   5.50 5.50
608 A269 38k multi   11.00 11.00

Souvenir Sheet

Nordafar Fishery, Foroyinghavn,
Greenland — A270

No. 609: a, Fishing boat, white building in
background. b, Fishermen on dock. c, Fishing
boats, red buildings in background.

Perf. 13¼x13¾

2013, Sept. 23		**Litho. & Engr.**		
609	A270	Sheet of 3	8.50	8.50
a.-c.		9k Any single	2.75	2.75

See Greenland No. 652.

Christmas — A271

Designs: 7k, Manger. 12.50k, Holy Family.

2013, Sept. 23		**Litho.**	**Perf. 12¾**	
610	A271	7k multi	2.25	2.25
611	A271	12.50k multi	3.75	3.75
a.		Booklet pane of 8, 4 each		
		#610-611	24.00	
		Complete booklet, #611a	24.00	

See Nos. 632-633, 651-652.

Rosa
Mollis
A272

2014, Feb. 26		**Litho.**	**Perf. 12½x13**	
612	A272	14.50k multi	4.75	4.75

Jellyfish — A273

Designs: 8k, Aurelia aurita. 15.50k, Cyanea
capillata. 18.50k, Pelagia noctiluca. 26k,
Beroe cucumis.

2014, Feb. 26		**Litho.**	**Perf. 13**	
613	A273	8k multi	2.50	2.50
614	A273	15.50k multi	4.75	4.75
615	A273	18.50k multi	5.75	5.75
616	A273	26k multi	7.50	7.50
		Nos. 613-616 (4)	20.50	20.50

Souvenir Sheet

Legend
of the
Lady of
Húsavík
A274

No. 617: a, Woman holding horn of Viking
chief. b, Woman and nykur (mythical beast). c,
Woman on throne.

2014, Feb. 26		**Litho.**	**Perf. 13x13½**	
617	A274	Sheet of 3	10.00	10.00
a.-c.		10k Any single	3.25	3.25

Souvenir Sheet

Ferry MS
Norröna
A275

No. 618: a, Ship's stern. b, Ship's bow.

2014, Mar. 17		**Litho.**	**Perf. 13x13¼**	
618	A275	Sheet of 2	9.00	9.00
a.-b.		14.50k Either single	4.25	4.25

Europa — A276

Designs: 14.50k, Faroese Symphony
Orchestra. 19.50k, Bass players, vert.

2014, Apr. 28		**Litho.**	**Perf. 13x13¼**	
619	A276	14.50k multi	4.50	4.50
		Perf. 13¼x13		
620	A276	19.50k multi	6.00	6.00

Lighthouses
A277

Designs: 14.50k, Akraberg Lighthouse.
15.50k, Dímun Lighthouse. 17k, Toftir
Lighthouse.

2014, Apr. 28		**Litho.**	**Perf. 14**	
621	A277	14.50k multi	4.50	4.50
622	A277	15.50k multi	4.75	4.75
623	A277	17k multi	5.25	5.25
		Nos. 621-623 (3)	14.50	14.50

Booklet Stamps
Self-Adhesive
Serpentine Die Cut 14

624	A277	14.50k multi	4.50	4.50
625	A277	15.50k multi	4.75	4.75
626	A277	17k multi	5.25	5.25
a.		Booklet pane of 6, 2 each		
		#624-626	29.00	
		Nos. 624-626 (3)	14.50	14.50

Prince Henrik,
80th
Birthday — A278

Perf. 13½x13¼

2014, June 11		**Litho.**		
627	A278	14.50k multi	4.50	4.50

Booklet Stamp
Self-Adhesive
Die Cut Perf. 13½x13¼

628	A278	14.50k multi	4.50	4.50
a.		Booklet pane of 4	18.00	

Roger Casement, Boats, Congolese
Natives, and Daniel J. Danielsen
A279

Perf. 13¼x13½

2014, Sept. 24			**Litho.**	
629	A279	25k multi	7.50	7.50

Danielsen (1871-1916), missionary to the
Congo, and documenter of human rights
abuses reported on in Casement's 1904
report to the British Government.

Captain Vilhelm Reinert-Joensen
(1891-1949), Ships Used in D-Day
Invasion — A280

Perf. 13¼x13½

2014, Sept. 24			**Litho.**	
630	A280	26k multi	7.50	7.50

D-Day, 70th anniv.

Miniature Sheet

World
War I,
Cent.
A281

No. 631: a, Newspaper headlines, map of
Europe, man in rowboat. b, Children, ration
coupons, national leaders of the World War I
combatants. c, Faroese boat attacked by German submarine, map of Faroe islands and
British Isles. d, Map of Vimy Ridge, Faroese-
Canadian soldier Christian L. Petersen,
soldiers.

Perf. 13¼x13½

2014, Sept. 24			**Litho.**	
631	A281	Sheet of 4	10.00	10.00
a.-d.		8k Any single	2.50	2.50
e.		Like #631, with "In		
		Memoriam" and poppies		
		added in red in sheet		
		margin	9.00	9.00

Issued: No. 631e, 5/13/15.

Christmas Type of 2013

Designs: 8k, Angels. 14.50k, Shepherds.

2014, Sept. 24		**Litho.**	**Perf. 12¾**	
632	A271	8k multi	2.50	2.50
633	A271	14.50k multi	4.50	4.50
a.		Booklet pane of 8, 4 each		
		#632-633	28.00	
		Complete booklet, #633a	28.00	

Magna Carta, 800th
Anniv. — A282

2015, Feb. 23		**Litho.**	**Perf. 13½**	
634	A282	24k multi	7.00	7.00

Woman Suffrage,
Cent. — A283

2015, Feb. 23		**Litho.**	**Perf. 13x13¼**	
635	A283	36k multi	11.00	11.00

Opening of New
Terminal at Vagar
Airport — A284

Designs: 8.50k, Airplanes on ground. 15k,
New terminal.

2015, Feb. 23		**Litho.**	**Perf. 13x13¼**	
636	A284	8.50k multi	2.60	2.60
637	A284	15k multi	4.50	4.50
a.		Booklet pane of 8, 4 each		
		#636-637	28.50	—
		Complete booklet, #637a	28.50	

Miniature Sheet

1833 Expedition of George Clayton
Atkinson to Faroe Islands — A285

No. 638 — Paintings by Thomas Miles
Richarson of: a, Vatnmylla (watermill). b, Tórshavn. c, Waterfall on Vágar, Koltur and Hestur Islands. d, Trollkonufingur.

2015, Feb. 23		**Litho.**	**Perf. 13x13¼**	
638	A285	Sheet of 4	10.50	10.50
a.-d.		8.50k Any single	2.60	2.60

March 20, 2015
Total Solar
Eclipse — A286

Eclipse at: 17k, Right. 19k, Left.

2015, Mar. 11		**Litho.**	**Perf. 12**	
639	A286	17k multi	5.00	5.00
640	A286	19k multi	5.75	5.75
a.		Souvenir sheet of 2, #639-640	11.00	11.00

Booklet Stamps
Self-Adhesive
Die Cut Perf. 11½

641	A286	17k multi	5.00	5.00
a.		Booklet pane of 4	20.00	
642	A286	19k multi	5.75	5.75
a.		Booklet pane of 4	23.00	

Faroe Islands Flag,
75th Anniv. — A287

Designs: 11k, Arne Vatnhamar holding
Faroe Islands flag on Mt. Everest. 12k, Map
and flag of Faroe Islands.

2015, Apr. 14		**Litho.**	**Perf. 13½**	
643	A287	11k multi	3.50	3.50
644	A287	12k multi	3.75	3.75

Europa — A288

Old toys: 17k, Rag doll. 22k, Hoop made of
ram's horn.

2015, Apr. 14		**Litho.**	**Perf. 13½**	
645	A288	17k multi	5.25	5.25
646	A288	22k multi	6.75	6.75

Knitted Art by
Randi
Samsonsen
A289

2015, Sept. 28		**Litho.**	**Perf. 13x12¾**	
647	A289	17k multi	5.25	5.25

H. N. Jacobsen's
Bookstore, 150th
Anniv. — A290

Designs: 17k, Bookstore exterior. 26k,
Bookstore interior, book covers, bindery
machinery.

2015, Sept. 28		**Litho.**	**Perf. 12½**	
648	A290	17k multi	5.25	5.25
649	A290	26k multi	8.00	8.00

Souvenir Sheet

Christian Artifacts of the Viking Era
A291

No. 650 — Inscriptions: a, Krossteinur úr Olansgardhi í Skúvoy (stone with crucifix from Olansgardhi). b, Botnur úr laggadhum traeílati (cross on wooden bucket bottom). c, Vadh-steinur vidh ihogdum St. Hanskrossi (stone fishing sinkers with St. Hans crucifix).

Litho. & Engr.

2015, Sept. 28   Perf. 12¾x13
650 A291 Sheet of 3   11.50 11.50
a.-c.   12k Any single   3.75 3.75

Christmas Type of 2013

Designs: 8.50k, Magi on camels. 17k, Holy Family fleeing to Egypt.

2015, Sept. 28   Litho.   Perf. 12¾
651 A271 8.50k multi   2.60 2.60
652 A271 17k multi   5.25 5.25
a.   Booklet pane of 8, 4 each #651-
     652   32.00   —
     Complete booklet, #652a   32.00

Oystercatchers in Flight — A292

Perf. 13¼x13¾
2016, Feb. 22   Litho.
653 A292 17k multi   5.25 5.25

Grounding of the Westerbeek off Lopra, 274th Anniv. — A293

Designs: 17k, Chest and the Westerbeek. 19k, Grounding of the Westerbeek.

Perf. 13¾x13½
2016, Feb. 22   Litho.
654 A293 17k multi   5.25 5.25
655 A293 19k multi   5.75 5.75
a.   Souvenir sheet of 2, #654-
     655   11.00 11.00

Fire Fighting Equipment A294

Designs: 1k, Fire pump, 1776. 15k, 1948 Bedford K fire truck. 19k, 1937 Triangle fire truck.

2016, Feb. 22   Litho.   Perf. 13
656 A294 1k multi   .30   .30
657 A294 15k multi   4.75 4.75
658 A294 19k multi   5.75 5.75
     Nos. 656-658 (3)   10.80 10.80

Booklet Stamps
Self-Adhesive
Serpentine Die Cut 13¼
659 A294 1k multi   .30   .30
660 A294 15k multi   4.75 4.75
661 A294 19k multi   5.75 5.75
a.   Booklet pane of 6, 2 each
     #659-661   22.00
     Nos. 659-661 (3)   10.80 10.80

Faroe Islands Mailboxes — A295

Designs: 9k, Blue Postverk Foroya mailbox used 1976-present. 17k, Red Danish Postal Service mailbox used until 1976.

2016, Apr. 1   Litho.   Perf. 14¼
662 A295 9k multi   2.75 2.75

Souvenir Sheet
663   Sheet of 2, #662, 663a   8.00 8.00
a.   A295 17k multi   5.25 5.25

Postverk Foroya (Faroe Islands Postal Service), 40th anniv.

Foods in Faroese Drying Shed A296

2016, Apr. 26   Litho.   Perf. 13½
664 A296 9k multi   2.75 2.75

Nólsoyar Páll (1766-1808 or 1809), National Hero — A297

Litho. & Engr.
2016, Apr. 26   Perf. 13
665 A297 24k blk & brn lake   7.50 7.50

A298

Europa — A299

2016, May 9   Litho.   Perf. 13½x13
666 A298 9k green   2.75 2.75
667 A299 17k multi   5.25 5.25

Booklet Stamps
Self-Adhesive
Serpentine Die Cut 13¾
667A A298 9k green   2.75 2.75
667B A299 17k multi   5.25 5.25
c.   Booklet pane of 6, 3 each
     #667A-667B   24.00

Think Green Issue.

Cod — A300

Litho. & Engr.
2016, Sept. 26   Perf. 13x13¼
668 A300 50k multi   15.00 15.00

A square of tanned cod skin with engraved text is affixed to No. 668. The square of cod skin has a fish odor and may detach from the stamp if soaked.

Traditional Woman's Blouse A301

Traditional Men's Waistcoat A302

2016, Sept. 26   Litho.   Perf. 13x13½
669 A301 17k multi   5.25 5.25
670 A302 20k multi   6.00 6.00

Booklet Stamps
Self-Adhesive
Serpentine Die Cut 14x13¾
670A A301 17k multi   5.25 5.25
670B A302 20k multi   6.00 6.00
c.   Booklet pane of 6, 3 each
     #670A-670B   34.00

Miniature Sheet

Life of Jesus A303

No. 671 — Wood carvings by Edward Fuglo depicting: a, Annunciation. b, Adoration of the Shepherds. c, Jesus as child in temple. d, Baptism of Jesus. e, Jesus feeding the multitude. f, Jesus healing lepers. g, Jesus calming storm at sea. h, Entry into Jerusalem. i, Jesus carrying cross. j, Resurrection.

2016, Sept. 26   Litho.   Perf. 13x12½
671 A303 Sheet of 10   27.50 27.50
a.-j.   9k Any single   2.75 2.75

House Near Skorá River Waterfall — A304

2017, Feb. 27   Litho.   Perf. 13
672 A304 9.50k multi   2.75 2.75

Leitisvatn Lake A305

Lakeside: 17k, Cliffs. 19k, Buildings.

Perf. 13½x13¼
2017, Feb. 27   Litho.
673 A305 17k multi   5.00 5.00
674 A305 19k multi   5.50 5.50

Booklet Stamps
Self-Adhesive
Serpentine Die Cut 9
674A A305 17k multi   5.00 5.00
674B A305 19k multi   5.50 5.50
c.   Booklet pane of 6, 3 each
     #674A-674B   32.00

Somateria Mollissima Faeroensis A306

Eider facing: 18k, Right. 27k, Left.

Perf. 13½x13¾
2017, Feb. 27   Litho.
675 A306 18k multi   5.25 5.25
676 A306 27k multi   7.75 7.75

Miniature Sheet

Natural Dyes A307

No. 677: a, Trifolium repens. b, Erica cinerea. c, Ochrolechia tartarea. d, Parmelia saxatilis. e, Narthecium ossifragum. f, Filipendula ulmaria.

2017, Feb. 27   Litho.   Perf. 13x12½
677 A307 Sheet of 6   16.50 16.50
a.-f.   9.50k Any single   2.75 2.75

Europa — A308

Legend of the Princess of Nólsoy: 9.50k, Ship and castle. 17k, Ship, Princess and her husband.

2017, May 15   Litho.   Perf. 14
678 A308 9.50k multi   3.00 3.00
679 A308 17k multi   5.25 5.25

Booklet Stamps
Self-Adhesive
Serpentine Die Cut 13½
680 A308 9.50k multi   3.00 3.00
681 A308 17k multi   5.25 5.25
a.   Booklet pane of 6, 3 each
     #680-681   25.00

Items From 1817 Visit to Faroe Islands of Hans Christian Lyngbye (1782-1837), Botanist — A309

Designs: 9.50k, Carex lyngbyei. 13k, Illustrations of seaweeds from Lyngbye's book, Tentamen Hydrophytologiae Danicae, horiz. 19k, Illustrations by Lyngbye of Faroese baptismal fonts and rocking stones, horiz. 22k, Seaweed from Lyngbye's herbarium, horiz.

2017, May 15   Litho.   Perf. 13¼x13
682 A309 9.50k multi   3.00 3.00

Perf. 13x13¼
683 A309 13k multi   4.00 4.00
684 A309 19k multi   5.75 5.75
685 A309 22k multi   6.75 6.75
     Nos. 682-685 (4)   19.50 19.50

Souvenir Sheet

Queen Margrethe II and Prince Henrik, 50th Wedding Anniversary — A310

2017, May 15   Litho.   Perf. 13½
686 A310 50k gold & multi   15.00 15.00
See Denmark No. 1777, Greenland No. 754.

Legend of the Seven Swans — A311

Designs: 9.50k, Men turning into swans. 19k, Woman near stake.

Perf. 13¾x13¼
2017, Sept. 8   Litho. & Engr.
687 A311 9.50k multi   3.00 3.00
688 A311 19k multi   6.00 6.00
a.   Souvenir sheet of 2, #687-688   9.00 9.00

Traditional Clothing — A312

Designs: 9.50k, Women's dress, apron and shoes. 17k, Men's breeches, stockings and shoes.

2017, Oct. 2   Litho.   Perf. 12¾x13½
689 A312 9.50k multi   3.00 3.00
690 A312 17k multi   5.50 5.50

Booklet Stamps
Self-Adhesive
Serpentine Die Cut 13¾
691 A312 9.50k multi   3.00 3.00
692 A312 17k multi   5.50 5.50
a.   Booklet pane of 6, 3 each #691-
     692   26.00

Martin Luther Nailing 95 Theses to Church Door — A313

2017, Oct. 2   Litho.   Perf. 13¼x13
693 A313 18k multi   5.75 5.75
a.   Souvenir sheet of 1   5.75 5.75
Protestant Reformation, 500th anniv.

Faroese Knives and Sheaths A314

Litho. & Embossed With Foil Application
2017, Oct. 2   Perf. 13¼x13
Inscribed "sepac"
694 A314 19k gold & multi   6.00 6.00
Souvenir Sheet
Without "sepac" Inscription
695 A314 19k gold & multi   6.00 6.00

Hans C. Müller (1818-97), First Postal Agent for Denmark in the Faroe Islands — A315

2018, Feb. 26   Litho.   Perf. 13½
696 A315 18k multi   6.00 6.00

Seabird Fowling — A316

Designs: 10k, Man carrying fowling net. 44k, Men fowling in boat.

2018, Feb. 26   Engr.   Perf. 12¾x13
697 A316 10k deep claret   3.25 3.25
698 A316 44k dp vio blue   14.50 14.50

Lakes A317

Designs: 10k, Sandsvatn Lake. 20k, Toftavatn Lake.

Perf. 13½x13¾
2018, Feb. 26   Litho.
699 A317 10k multi   3.25 3.25
700 A317 20k multi   6.50 6.50
Booklet Stamps
Self-Adhesive
Serpentine Die Cut 9
701 A317 10k multi   3.25 3.25
702 A317 20k multi   6.50 6.50
a.   Booklet pane of 6, 3 each
        #701-702   29.50

Miniature Sheet

Flies A318

No. 703: a, Protophormia terraenovae. b, Bibio pomonae. c, Scatophaga stercoraria. d, Musca domestica.

Perf. 13½x13¼
2018, Feb. 26   Litho.
703 A318 Sheet of 4   16.00 16.00
a.-d.   12k Any single   4.00 4.00

Scomber Scombrus A319

2018, Apr. 23   Litho.   Perf. 13¾x13¼
704 A319 18k multi   6.00 6.00

Recreational Vehicles and Large Wave Near Torshavn — A320

2018, Apr. 23   Litho.   Perf. 13½x13¼
705 A320 20k multi   6.50 6.50

Celtic Quaternary Knot — A321

Gate to the World, Sculpture by 7-9-13 Art Group — A322

2018, Apr. 23   Litho.   Perf. 13¼x13
706 A321 14k multi   4.50 4.50
Perf. 13x13¼
707 A322 22k multi   7.25 7.25
Town of Fuglafjordhur, cent.

Europa — A323

Designs: 10k, Streymin Bridge. 18k, Sandá River Bridge.

2018, Apr. 23   Litho.   Perf. 13x13¼
708 A323 10k multi   3.25 3.25
709 A323 18k multi   6.00 6.00
Booklet Stamps
Self-Adhesive
Die Cut Perf. 13x12½
710 A323 10k multi   3.25 3.25
711 A323 18k multi   6.00 6.00
a.   Booklet pane of 6, 3 each
        #710-711   28.00

Souvenir Sheet

Tórshavn Actors' Association, Cent. — A324

No. 712 — Masks and: a, Three actors. b, Five actors.

2018, Apr. 23   Litho.   Perf. 14
712 A324 Sheet of 2   12.50 12.50
a.-b.   19k Either single   6.25 6.25

Miniature Sheet

End of World War I, Cent. A325

No. 713: a, Soldiers and map of battle lines of 100 Day Offensive in France. b, Airplanes, ambulance, wounded soldier and Red Cross nurses. c, Dove and soldiers. d, Dove, soldier, woman at cemetery.

Perf. 13¼x13¾
2018, Sept. 24   Litho.
713 A325 Sheet of 4   13.00 13.00
a.-d.   10k Any single   3.25 3.25

Regin Dahl (1918-2007), Poet and Musician A326

2018, Sept. 24   Litho.   Perf. 13x12¾
714 A326 28k multi   8.75 8.75

Traditional Clothing — A327

Designs: 18k, Woman wearing bonnet. 20k, Man wearing hat.

Perf. 12¾x13½
2018, Sept. 24   Litho.
715 A327 18k multi   5.75 5.75
716 A327 20k multi   6.25 6.25
Booklet Stamps
Self-Adhesive
Serpentine Die Cut 14x13¾
717 A327 18k multi   5.75 5.75
718 A327 20k multi   6.25 6.25
a.   Booklet pane of 6, 2 each #717-
        718   36.00

Christmas — A328

Icon of: 10k, Angel and gannet. 18k, Madonna and Child.

Litho. & Embossed
2018, Sept. 24   Perf. 13
719 A328 10k gold & multi   3.25 3.25
720 A328 18k gold & multi   5.75 5.75

Souvenir Sheet

1919 Provisional Stamp, Cent. — A329

No. 721: a, Surcharging device (21x28mm). b, Essays of handwritten surcharge (63x28mm).

2019, Jan. 11 Litho. Perf. 13¼x13½
721 A329 Sheet of 2   7.00 7.00
a.-b.   11k Either single   3.50 3.50

Old Farmhouse, Kirkjubøur — A330

Litho. & Silk-Screened
2019, Feb. 25   Perf. 13
722 A330 19k multi   5.75 5.75

Detail From 1539 Nautical Map by Olaus Magnus (1490-1557) — A331

Various map details.

2019, Feb. 25   Litho.   Perf. 13
723 A331 11k multi   3.50 3.50
724 A331 17k multi   5.25 5.25
725 A331 27k multi   8.25 8.25
a.   Souvenir sheet of 3, #723-
        725, perf. 13 on 3 sides   17.00 17.00
        Nos. 723-725 (3)   17.00 17.00

Lakes A332

Designs: Nos. 726, 728, Lake Leynar. No. 727, 729, Lake Eidhi.

Perf. 13½x13¼
2019, Feb. 25   Litho.
726 A332 19k multi   5.75 5.75
727 A332 19k multi   5.75 5.75
Booklet Stamp
Self-Adhesive
Serpentine Die Cut 9
728 A332 19k multi   5.75 5.75
729 A332 19k multi   5.75 5.75
a.   Booklet pane of 6, 3 each #728-
        729   34.50

First Man on the Moon, 50th Anniv. — A333

2019, Apr. 29   Litho.   Perf. 13¾
730 A333 17k multi   5.25 5.25

1896 Drawings of Water Mills by Daniel Bruun (1856-1931) — A334

Mill in: 11k, Sandágerdhi. 35k, Frodhba.

Perf. 13½x13¾
2019, Apr. 29   Litho. & Engr.
731 A334 11k multi   3.50 3.50
732 A334 35k multi   10.50 10.50

Europa — A335

Cepphus grylle faeroeensis: 19k, Two on rock. 26k, One in water.

2019, Apr. 29   Litho.   Perf. 13
733 A335 19k multi   5.75 5.75
734 A335 26k multi   7.75 7.75
Booklet Stamp
Self-Adhesive
Die Cut Perf. 13x12¾
735 A335 19k multi   5.75 5.75
a.   Booklet pane of 6   34.50

Souvenir Sheet

Venceslaus Ulricus Hammershaimb (1819-1909), Theologian, Linguist, and Folklorist — A336

No. 736: a, Faroese Anthology, by Hammershaimb. b, Hammershaimb. c, The Native Tongue, sculpture by Janus Karnban, and alphabet of Hammershaimb's orthography.

2019, Apr. 29	Litho.	Perf. 13x13¼	
736 A336	Sheet of 3	14.50	14.50
a.	11k multi	3.50	3.50
b.	17k multi	5.25	5.25
c.	19k multi	5.75	5.75

Souvenir Sheet

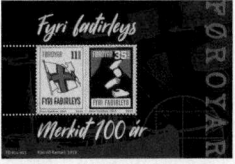

Labels Created for Fatherless Children's Fund — A337

No. 737: a, Flag of Faroe Islands. b, Mother and child.

2019, June 3	Litho.	Perf. 13¼	
737 A337	Sheet of 2	14.00	14.00
a.	11k multi	3.50	3.50
b.	35k multi	10.50	10.50

Children's Aid Foundation, 77th anniv.; flag of the Faroe Islands, cent.

Smacks Johanna and Westward Ho A338

2019, Sept. 23	Litho.	Perf. 13¼	
738 A338	11k multi	3.25	3.25

Sculpture of Elinborg Lützen, by Pauli Olsen — A339

2019, Sept. 23	Litho.	Perf. 13¼x13	
739 A339	55k multi	16.00	16.00

Lützen (1919-95), graphic artist.

Chasubles — A340

Chasuble from church in: 11k, Sandvík. 19k, Funning.

2019, Sept. 23	Litho.	Perf. 13¼x13	
740 A340	11k multi	3.25	3.25
741 A340	19k multi	5.50	5.50

Booklet Stamps
Self-Adhesive
Die Cut Perf. 12¾x13

742 A340	11k multi	3.25	3.25
743 A340	19k multi	5.50	5.50
a.	Booklet pane of 6, 3 each #742-743	36.00	

See Nos. 765-766.

Vatndalsvatn Lake — A341

No. 744: a, Aerial view of lake. b, Aerial view of lake, text and location marker.

2020, Feb. 14	Litho.	Perf. 14½	
744 A341	Horiz. pair, #a-b	6.00	6.00
a.	8k multi	2.40	2.40
b.	12k multi	3.50	3.50

St. Valentine's Day.

Seal Pup — A342

2020, Feb. 24	Litho.	Perf. 13x13¼	
745 A342	20k multi	6.00	6.00

Booklet Stamp
Self-Adhesive
Die Cut Perf. 13x12¾

746 A342	20k multi	6.00	6.00
a.	Booklet pane of 6	36.00	

Volleyball, 125th Anniv. — A343

Designs: 12k, Male player. 17k, Female player.

2020, Feb. 24	Litho.	Perf. 13¼	
747 A343	12k multi	3.50	3.50
748 A343	17k multi	5.25	5.25

Mother Teresa at Eidhi A344 — Bread Which Satiates Hunger A345

2020, Feb. 24	Litho.	Perf. 13¼	
749 A344	12k multi	3.50	3.50
750 A345	27k multi	8.00	8.00

Paintings by Sigrun Gunnarsdóttir.

Souvenir Sheet

Mikkjal Dánjalsson á Ryggi (1879-1956), Writer — A346

No. 751: a, Profile portrait. b, Full-face portrait.

2020, Feb. 24	Litho.	Perf. 13	
751 A346	Sheet of 2	13.00	13.00
a.	17k multi	5.25	5.25
b.	26k multi	7.75	7.75

Souvenir Sheet

Bird Song and Animal Language She Was Able to Understand, by Edward Fuglo — A347

Litho. With Foil Application

2020, Apr. 16		Perf. 13	
752 A347	50k multi	15.00	15.00

Queen Margrethe II, 80th birthday.

Moon Pigeons, by Díthrikur á Skarvanesi (1802-65) — A348

2020, Apr. 27	Litho.	Perf. 13x13¼	
753 A348	20k multi	6.00	6.00

British World War II Field Post Offices in the Faroe Islands — A349

Military Post Office in: 20k, Midvágur. 35k, Tórshavn.

2020, Apr. 27	Litho.	Perf. 13¼x13	
754 A349	20k multi	6.00	6.00
a.	Souvenir sheet of 1	6.00	6.00
755 A349	35k multi	10.50	10.50

Europa A350

Map of postal route and: 17k, Postmen in snowstorm on mountain. 20k, Mailboat Olavur and dinghy.

2020, Apr. 27	Litho.	Perf. 13¼	
756 A350	17k multi	5.00	5.00
757 A350	20k multi	6.00	6.00

Booklet Stamps
Self-Adhesive
Die Cut Perf. 11¾

758 A350	17k multi	5.00	5.00
759 A350	20k multi	6.00	6.00
a.	Booklet pane of 6, 3 each #758-759	33.00	

Souvenir Sheet

Ludwig van Beethoven (1770-1827), Composer — A351

2020, Sept. 21	Litho.	Perf. 13¼x13	
760 A351	44k multi	14.00	14.00

A352

Scenes from Faroese motion pictures: 12k, Bye Bye Blue Bird, 1999. 26k, Ludo, 2014.

2020, Sept. 21	Litho.	Perf. 13	
761 A352	12k multi	3.75	3.75
762 A352	26k multi	8.25	8.25

First screening of motion pictures to audience, 125th anniv.

Chess — A353

Designs: 17k, Standard chessboard, rook, silhouettes of other pieces. 27k, Four-player chessboard, king, queen, bishop and knight.

2020, Sept. 21	Litho.	Perf. 13¼	
763 A353	17k multi	5.50	5.50
764 A353	27k multi	8.50	8.50

Chasubles Type of 2019

Chasuble from church in: 12k, Vithareithi. 20k, Kvívík, horiz.

2020, Sept. 21	Litho.	Perf. 13¼x13	
765 A340	12k multi	3.75	3.75
		Perf. 13x13¼	
766 A340	20k multi	6.50	6.50

Booklet Stamps
Self-Adhesive
Die Cut Perf. 12¾x13

767 A340	12k multi	3.75	3.75
		Die Cut Perf. 13x12¾	
768 A340	20k multi	6.50	6.50
a.	Booklet pane of 6, 3 each #767-768	39.00	

Souvenir Sheet

Postal History of the Faroe Islands, 150th Anniv. A354

No. 769: a, Postal knapsack. b, Postmen carrying mail. c, Sketch of boat drawn by Czeslaw Slania (1921-2005), stamp engraver.

2021, Jan. 7	Litho.	Perf. 13¼x13¾	
769 A354	Sheet of 3	16.50	16.50
a.-c.	17k Any single	5.50	5.50

Postal Services Act of 1871, 150th anniv., and establishment of Postverk Faroya (Faroe Islands Postal Service), 45th anniv.

Miniature Sheet

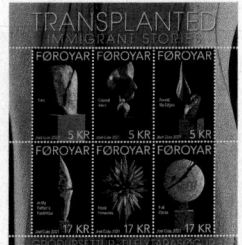

Wood Sculptures by Joel Cole — A355

No. 770: a, Torn. b, Casual Alien. c, Round My Edges. d, In My Father's Footsteps. e, Floral Fireworks. f, Full Circle.

		Perf. 13¾x13¼	
2021, Feb. 19		Litho.	
770 A355	Sheet of 6	21.50	21.50
a.-c.	5k Any single	1.60	1.60
d.-f.	17k Any single	5.50	5.50

Car and Eysturoy Tunnel Traffic Circle — A356

Eysturoy Tunnel — A357

2021, Feb. 19   Litho.   *Perf. 13x13¼*
771	A356	10k multi	3.25 3.25
772	A357	17k multi	5.50 5.50

Opening of the Eysturoy Tunnel.

Kirkja — A358

Hattarvík — A359

2021, Feb. 19   Litho.   *Perf. 13x13½*
773	A358	17k multi	5.50 5.50
774	A359	27k multi	8.75 8.75

Booklet Stamps
Self-Adhesive
Die Cut Perf. 13x12¾
775	A358	17k multi	5.50 5.50
776	A359	27k multi	8.75 8.75
a.		Booklet pane of 6, 4 #775, 2 #776	40.00

Andrea Arting (1891-1988), Trade Union Leader — A360

2021, Mar. 8   Litho.   *Perf. 13½x13*
777	A360	39k multi	12.50 12.50

Souvenir Sheet

1578 Map of the Faroe Islands by Sebastian Münster (1488-1552) — A361

Perf. 14¼x14½ on 3 Sides
2021, Apr. 26   Litho.
778	A361	27k multi	8.75 8.75

Cattle Farming in the Faroe Islands — A362

Designs: 7k, Head of cow, manure, pail of milk, hay bale and grain. 10k, Woman milking cow. 17k, Cows in field.

2021, Apr. 26   Litho.   *Perf. 13x13¼*
779	A362	7k multi	2.25 2.25
780	A362	10k multi	3.25 3.25
781	A362	17k multi	5.50 5.50
		Nos. 779-781 (3)	11.00 11.00

Visit of King Christian X to Faroe Islands, Cent. — A363

Designs: 17k, King Christian X and Queen Alexandrine and sailors in rowboat. 27k, Tórshavn dignitaries welcoming King on his arrival.

2021, Apr. 26   Litho.   *Perf. 13*
782	A363	17k multi	5.50 5.50
783	A363	27k multi	8.75 8.75

Fratercula Arctica — A364

Endangerd animals: 17k, Head of puffin. 27k, Three puffins on rock.

2021, Apr. 26   Litho.   *Perf. 13¼x13*
784	A364	17k multi	5.50 5.50
785	A364	27k multi	8.75 8.75

Booklet Stamps
Self-Adhesive
Die Cut Perf. 12¾x13
786	A364	17k multi	5.50 5.50
787	A364	27k multi	8.75 8.75
a.		Booklet pane of 6, $ #787, 2 #787	39.50

Europa.

Souvenir Sheet

Czeslaw Slania (1921-2005), Engraver of Postage Stamps — A365

Litho. & Engr.
2021, Aug. 12   *Perf. 13¼x13*
788	A365	39k multi	12.50 12.50

See Denmark No. 1879, Greenland No. 874.

Souvenir Sheet

Diseases A366

No. 789: a, Salmon, infectious salmon anemia virus. b, COVID-19 viruses, Petri dish and cotton swab.

2021, Sept. 20   Litho.   *Perf. 12½*
789	A366	Sheet of 2	14.00 14.00
a.		20k multi	6.25 6.25
b.		25k multi	7.75 7.75

Tinganes, Painting by Ingálvur av Reyni (1920-2005) A367

Through Tima and Spaces, Painting by Reyni A368

2021, Sept. 20   Litho.   *Perf. 14½*
790	A367	17k multi	5.50 5.50
791	A368	39k multi	12.50 12.50

Bishop's Cope — A369

Designs: 17k, White cope with cross. 27k, Gold cope with floral trim.

2021, Sept. 20   Litho.   *Perf. 13¼x13*
792	A369	17k multi	5.50 5.50
793	A369	27k multi	8.50 8.50

Booklet Stamps
Self-Adhesive
Die Cut Perf. 12¾x13
794	A369	17k multi	5.50 5.50
795	A369	27k multi	8.50 8.50
a.		Booklet pane of 6, 3 each #794-795	42.00

Souvenir Sheet

Reign of Queen Margrethe II, 50th Anniv. — A370

Litho. & Engr. With Foil Application
2022, Jan. 14   *Perf. 13*
796	A370	50k multi	15.00 15.00

A371

Kalsoy Island, Filming Location for 2021 Movie, *No Time to Die* A372

Perf. 13½x13¼
2022, Feb. 28   Litho.
797	A371	19k multi	5.75 5.75
798	A372	29k multi	8.75 8.75

Booklet Stamps
Self-Adhesive
Die Cut Perf. 11¾
799	A371	19k multi	5.75 5.75
800	A372	29k multi	8.75 8.75
a.		Booklet pane of 6, 3 each #799-800	43.50

A373

Aurora Borealis — A374

2022, Feb. 28   Litho.   *Perf. 13x13¼*
801	A373	19k multi	5.75 5.75
802	A374	43k multi	13.00 13.00

Souvenir Sheet

Map of Voyage from Scotland to Faroe Islands and Iceland A375

2022, Feb. 28   Litho.   *Perf. 12*
803	A375	61k multi	18.50 18.50

Trip to Faroe Islands by William Morris (1834-96), fabric designer, 150th anniv.

Simon Hansen (1863-1935), Founder of Föroya Bjór Brewery, Glass of Beer and Ram Emblem — A376

2022, May 16   Litho.   *Perf. 12*
804	A376	29k multi	8.50 8.50

Babyboom, Fabric Art by Astrid Andreasen A377

Embroidery by Jórunn D. Poulsen A378

Roots, Rope and Fabric Art by Tita Vinther (1941-2019) A379

A Year's Work, Art by Andreasen A380

Fabric Art by Poulsen A381

Sea Anemones, Horsehair and Fabric Art by Vinther A382

2022, May 16   Litho.   *Perf. 13¾x13½*
805	A377	19k multi	5.50 5.50
806	A378	19k multi	5.50 5.50
807	A379	19k multi	5.50 5.50

808	A380	29k multi	8.50	8.50
809	A381	29k multi	8.50	8.50
810	A382	29k multi	8.50	8.50
	Nos. 805-810 (6)		42.00	42.00

Europa — A383

Designs: 19k, Legend of Svinoy, Island of pigs. 29k, Legend of floating islands.

2022, May 16   Litho.   Perf. 12

811	A383	19k multi	5.50	5.50
812	A383	29k multi	8.50	8.50

Booklet Stamps
Self-Adhesive
Die Cut Perf. 10½x10¾

813	A383	19k multi	5.50	5.50
814	A383	29k multi	8.50	8.50
a.	Booklet pane of 6, 3 each			
	#813-814		42.00	

Souvenir Sheet

Printing of First Book in the Faroe Islands, 200th Anniv. A384

No. 815: a, Dragon, dancers and sheet music. b, Title page of *Faroese Heroic Ballads of Sigurd, the Slayer of the Dragon Fafnir and His Kindred*, by H. C. Lyngbe.

2022, May 16   Litho.   Perf. 12½

815	A384	Sheet of 2	21.00	21.00
a.		29k multi	8.50	8.50
b.		43k multi	12.50	12.50

Souvenir Sheet

Minerals A385

No. 816: a, Calcite. b, Copper.

2022, Oct. 24   Litho.   Perf. 12

816	A385	Sheet of 2	19.50	19.50
a.		29k multi	7.75	7.75
b.		43k multi	11.50	11.50

Christmas — A386

Candles on: 19k, Wreath. 29k, Christmas tree.

2022, Oct. 24   Litho.   Perf. 12

817	A386	19k multi	5.25	5.25
818	A386	29k multi	7.75	7.75

Booklet Stamps
Self-Adhesive
Die Cut Perf. 10¾x10½

819	A386	19k multi	5.25	5.25
820	A386	29k multi	7.75	7.75
a.	Booklet pane of 6, 3 each			
	#819-820		39.00	

FERNANDO PO

fər-'nan-ᵈō 'pō

LOCATION — An island in the Gulf of Guinea off west Africa.
GOVT. — Former province of Spain
AREA — 800 sq. mi.
POP. — 62,612 (1960)

CAPITAL — Santa Isabel

Together with the islands of Elobey, Annobon and Corisco, Fernando Po came under the administration of Spanish Guinea. Postage stamps of Spanish Guinea were used until 1960.

The provinces of Fernando Po and Rio Muni united Oct. 12, 1968, to form the Republic of Equatorial Guinea.

100 Centimos = 1 Escudo = 2.50 Pesetas
100 Centimos = 1 Peseta
1000 Milesimas = 100 Centavos = 1 Peso (1882)

> **Catalogue values for unused stamps in this country are for Never Hinged items, beginning with Scott 181 in the regular postage section and Scott B1 in the semi-postal section.**

Isabella II — A1

1868   Unwmk.   Typo.   Perf. 14

1	A1	20c brown	350.00	140.00
a.		20c red brown	525.00	140.00

No. 1 is valued in the grade of fine, as illustrated. Examples with very fine centering are uncommon and sell for more.
Forgeries exist.

Alfonso XII — A2

1879   Centimos de Peseta

2	A2	5c green	52.50	15.00
3	A2	10c rose	40.00	15.00
4	A2	50c blue	90.00	15.00
	Nos. 2-4 (3)		182.50	45.00

1882-89   Centavos de Peso

5	A2	1c green	9.50	5.00
6	A2	2c rose	18.00	8.75
7	A2	5c gray blue	60.00	12.00
8	A2	10c dk brown ('89)	82.50	6.75
	Nos. 5-8 (4)		170.00	33.00

Nos. 5-7 Handstamp Surcharged in Blue, Black or Violet — a

1884-95

9	A2	50c on 1c green ('95)	120.00	19.00
11	A2	50c on 2c rose	32.00	6.00
12	A2	50c on 5c blue ('87)	150.00	25.00
	Nos. 9-12 (3)		302.00	50.00

Values above are for examples surcharged in black. Stamps surcharged in violet or blue are worth about 25% more.
Inverted and double surcharges exist. No. 12 exists overprinted in carmine. Value $100.

King Alfonso XIII — A4

1894-97   Perf. 14

13	A4	⅛c slate ('96)	22.00	3.00
14	A4	2c rose ('96)	15.50	2.50
15	A4	5c blue grn ('97)	16.00	2.50
16	A4	6c dk violet ('96)	13.00	3.00
17	A4	10c blk vio ('94)	450.00	115.00
17A	A4	10c dark brown ('94)	30.00	5.00
18	A4	10c lake ('95)	50.00	8.75
19	A4	10c org brn ('96)	10.50	2.50
20	A4	12½c dk brown ('96)	11.50	3.00
21	A4	20c slate bl ('96)	11.50	3.00
22	A4	25c claret ('96)	23.00	3.00
	Nos. 13-22 (11)		653.00	151.25

Most exist imperf. Value, set, pairs Nos. 13-16 and Nos. 18-22, $2,500.

Stamps of 1894-97 Handstamped in Blue, Black or Red

b   c

Type "b" Surcharge

1896-98

22A	A4	5c on ⅛c slate (Bl)	100.00	27.50
23	A4	5c on 2c rose (Bl)	50.00	16.50
23A	A4	5c on 6c dk vio (Bl)	180.00	45.00
24	A4	5c on 10c brn vio (Bl)	180.00	45.00
24A	A4	5c on 10c org brn (Bl)	180.00	45.00
24B	A4	5c on 10c dk brn (Bk)	67.50	27.50
25	A4	5c on 12½c brn (Bl)	37.50	13.00
a.		Black surcharge	37.50	13.00
25B	A4	5c on 20c sl bl (R)	180.00	45.00
25C	A4	5c on 25c claret (Bk)	180.00	35.00
	Nos. 22A-25C (9)		1,155.	299.50

Type "c" Surcharge

26	A4	5c on ⅛c slate (Bk)	32.50	6.75
27	A4	5c on 2c rose (Bl)	32.50	6.75
a.		Black surcharge	32.50	6.75
28	A4	5c on 5c green (R)	160.00	22.00
29	A4	5c on 6c dk vio (R)	23.00	14.00
a.		Violet surcharge	24.00	15.50
30	A4	5c on 10c org brn (Bk)	210.00	27.50
30A	A4	5c on 10c dk brn (Bk)	160.00	26.00
30B	A4	5c on 10c lake (Bl)	400.00	110.00
31	A4	5c on 12½c brn (R)	70.00	11.00
32	A4	5c on 20c sl bl (R)	40.00	10.50
33	A4	5c on 25c claret (Bk)	37.50	11.00
a.		Blue surcharge	37.50	13.50
	Nos. 26-33 (10)		1,166.	245.50

Exist surcharged in other colors.

Type "a" Srch. in Blue or Black

1898-99

34	A4	50c on 2c rose	92.50	11.50
35	A4	50c on 10c brn vio	220.00	33.00
36	A4	50c on 10c lake	230.00	33.00
37	A4	50c on 10c org brn	220.00	33.00
38	A4	50c on 12½c brn (Bk)	190.00	22.00

The "a" surch. also exists on ⅛c, 5c & 25c. Values, $325, $225 and $210, respectively.

Revenue Stamps Privately Handstamped in Blue

Arms
A5   A6

1897-98   Imperf.

39	A5	5c on 10c rose	28.00	12.50
40	A6	10c rose	24.00	11.00

Revenue Stamps Handstamped in Black or Red

A7

A8

A9

Arms — A9a

1899   Imperf.

41	A7	15c on 10c grn	45.00	23.00
a.		Blue surcharge, vert.	39.00	21.00
42	A8	10c on 25c grn	120.00	65.00
43	A9	15c on 25c grn	190.00	120.00
43A	A9a	15c on 25c grn (R)	1,800.	1,100.
b.		Black surcharge	1,800.	1,100.

Surcharge on No. 41 is either horizontal, inverted or vertical.
On No. 42 "CORREOS" is ovptd. in red.
On Nos. 43A and 43Ab, the signature is always in black.

King Alfonso XIII — A10

Double-lined shaded letters at sides.

1899   Perf. 14

44	A10	1m orange brn	2.40	.45
45	A10	2m orange brn	2.40	.45
46	A10	3m orange brn	2.40	.45
47	A10	4m orange brn	2.40	.45
48	A10	5m orange brn	2.40	.45
49	A10	1c black vio	2.40	.45
50	A10	2c dk blue grn	2.40	.45
51	A10	3c dk brown	2.40	.45
52	A10	4c orange	13.00	1.10
53	A10	5c carmine rose	2.50	.45
54	A10	6c dark blue	2.50	.45
55	A10	8c gray brn	8.00	.45
56	A10	10c vermilion	5.25	.45
57	A10	15c slate grn	5.25	.45
58	A10	20c maroon	14.50	1.10
59	A10	40c violet	100.00	19.00
60	A10	60c black	100.00	19.00
61	A10	80c red brown	100.00	19.00
62	A10	1p yellow grn	325.00	92.50
63	A10	2p slate blue	325.00	95.00
	Nos. 44-63 (20)		1,020.	252.55

Nos. 44-63 exist imperf. Value for set, $3,500.
See Nos. 66-85. For surcharges see Nos. 64-65, 88-88B.

1900   Surcharged type "a"

64	A10	50c on 20c maroon	16.00	2.50
a.		Blue surcharge	32.00	4.75

Surcharged type "b"

64B	A10	5c on 20c maroon	300.00	40.00

Surcharged type "c"

65	A10	5c on 20c maroon	9.50	2.40
	Nos. 64-65 (3)		325.50	44.90

1900   Dated "1900"

Solid letters at sides.

66	A10	1m black	3.00	.50
67	A10	2m black	3.00	.50
68	A10	3m black	3.00	.50
69	A10	4m black	3.00	.50
70	A10	5m black	3.00	.50
71	A10	1c green	3.00	.50
72	A10	2c violet	3.00	.50
73	A10	3c rose	3.00	.50
74	A10	4c black brn	3.00	.50
75	A10	5c blue	3.00	.50
76	A10	6c orange	3.00	.50
77	A10	8c bronze grn	3.00	.50
78	A10	10c claret	3.00	.50
79	A10	15c dk violet	3.00	.50
80	A10	20c olive brn	3.00	.50
81	A10	40c brown	7.75	2.25
82	A10	60c green	16.50	2.50
83	A10	80c dark blue	17.50	3.75
84	A10	1p red brown	110.00	30.00
85	A10	2p orange	190.00	62.50
	Nos. 66-85 (20)		386.75	108.50
	Set, never hinged		750.00	

Nos. 66-85 exist imperf. Value, set $3,500.

Revenue Stamps Overprinted or Surcharged with Handstamp in Red or Black

A11   A12

1900   *Imperf.*

86	A11	10c blue (R)	37.50	17.50
87	A12	5c on 10c blue	100.00	40.00
	Set, never hinged		175.00	

Nos. 52 and 80 Surcharged type "a" in Violet or Black

1900

88	A10	50c on 4c orange (V)	14.00	4.00
a.		Green surcharge	22.50	12.00
88B	A10	50c on 20c ol brn	14.00	3.50
	Set, never hinged		37.50	

A13

1901   *Perf. 14*

89	A13	1c black	2.60	.90
90	A13	2c orange brn	2.60	.90
91	A13	3c dk violet	2.60	.90
92	A13	4c lt violet	2.60	.90
93	A13	5c orange red	1.60	.90
94	A13	10c violet brn	1.60	.90
95	A13	25c dp blue	1.75	.90
96	A13	50c claret	2.60	.90
97	A13	75c dk brown	2.00	.90
98	A13	1p blue grn	60.00	7.50
99	A13	2p red brown	40.00	10.00
100	A13	3p olive grn	400.00	14.00
101	A13	4p dull red	40.00	14.00
102	A13	5p dk green	47.50	14.00
103	A13	10p buff	115.00	40.00
	Nos. 89-103 (15)		722.45	107.60
	Set, never hinged		850.00	

Dated "1902"

1902   **Control Numbers on Back**

104	A13	5c dk green	2.60	.45
105	A13	10c slate	2.90	.50
106	A13	25c claret	6.25	1.00
107	A13	50c violet brn	15.00	3.25
108	A13	75c lt violet	15.00	3.25
109	A13	1p car rose	18.50	4.00
110	A13	2p olive grn	40.00	9.50
111	A13	5p orange red	57.50	20.00
	Nos. 104-111 (8)		157.75	41.95
	Set, never hinged		250.00	

Exist imperf. Value for set, $1,500.

A14

Dated "1903"

1903   *Perf. 14*
Control Numbers on Back

112	A14	¼c dk violet	.45	.25
113	A14	½c black	.45	.25
114	A14	1c scarlet	.45	.25
115	A14	2c dk green	.45	.30
116	A14	3c blue grn	.45	.30
117	A14	4c violet	.45	.30
118	A14	5c rose lake	.50	.30
119	A14	10c orange buff	.60	.45
120	A14	15c blue green	2.50	1.00
121	A14	25c red brown	2.75	1.25
122	A14	50c black brn	4.50	2.00
123	A14	75c carmine	16.50	3.50
124	A14	1p dk brown	25.00	6.00
125	A14	2p dk olive grn	32.50	7.50
126	A14	3p claret	32.50	7.50
127	A14	4p dark blue	40.00	12.50
128	A14	5p dp dull blue	60.00	16.00
129	A14	10p dull red	130.00	27.50
	Nos. 112-129 (18)		350.05	87.15
	Set, never hinged		600.00	

Dated "1905"

1905   **Control Numbers on Back**

136	A14	1c dp violet	.40	.30
137	A14	2c black	.40	.30
138	A14	3c vermilion	.40	.30
139	A14	4c dp green	.40	.30
140	A14	5c blue grn	.45	.35
141	A14	10c violet	1.60	.75
142	A14	15c car lake	1.60	.75
143	A14	25c orange buff	12.50	2.25

144	A14	50c green	8.00	2.75
145	A14	75c red brown	11.00	7.50
146	A14	1p dp gray brn	12.50	7.50
147	A14	2p carmine	20.00	14.00
148	A14	3p deep brown	32.50	14.00
149	A14	4p bronze grn	40.00	18.00
150	A14	5p claret	62.50	25.00
151	A14	10p deep blue	90.00	35.00
	Nos. 136-151 (16)		294.25	127.55
	Set, never hinged		600.00	

King Alfonso XIII — A15

1907   **Control Numbers on Back**

152	A15	1c blue black	.30	.25
153	A15	2c car rose	.30	.25
154	A15	3c dp violet	.40	.25
155	A15	4c black	.40	.25
156	A15	5c orange buff	.40	.25
157	A15	10c maroon	2.00	.80
158	A15	15c bronze grn	.55	.35
159	A15	25c dk brown	65.00	15.00
160	A15	50c blue green	.45	.30
161	A15	75c vermilion	.45	.30
162	A15	1p dull blue	3.00	.60
163	A15	2p brown	11.00	4.00
164	A15	3p lake	11.00	4.00
165	A15	4p violet	11.00	4.00
166	A15	5p black brn	11.00	4.00
167	A15	10p orange brn	11.00	4.00
	Nos. 152-167 (16)		128.25	38.60
	Set, never hinged		350.00	

No. 157 Handstamp Surcharged in Black, Blue or Red

1908

168	A15	5c on 10c mar (Bk)	2.75	2.00
a.		Blue surcharge	10.00	5.50
b.		Red surcharge	30.00	10.00
169	A15	25c on 10c mar (Bk)	60.00	20.00
	Set, never hinged		77.50	

The surcharge on Nos. 168-169 exist inverted, double, etc. The surcharge also exists on other stamps.

Seville-Barcelona Issue of Spain, 1929, Overprinted in Blue or Red

1929   *Perf. 11*

170	A52	5c rose lake	.25	.25
171	A53	10c green (R)	.25	.25
a.		Perf. 14	.65	.65
172	A50	15c Prus bl (R)	.25	.25
173	A51	20c purple (R)	.25	.25
174	A52	25c brt rose	.25	.25
175	A52	30c black brn	.25	.25
176	A53	40c dk blue (R)	.45	.45
177	A51	50c dp orange	1.00	1.00
178	A52	1p blue blk (R)	3.75	3.75
179	A53	4p deep rose	20.00	20.00
180	A53	10p brown	25.00	25.00
	Nos. 170-180 (11)		51.70	51.70
	Set, never hinged		100.00	

> **Catalogue values for unused stamps in this section, from this point to the end of the section, are for Never Hinged items.**

Virgin Mary — A16

1960   Unwmk.   Photo.   *Perf. 13x12½*

181	A16	25c dull gray vio	.40	.25
182	A16	50c brown olive	.40	.25
183	A16	75c violet brn	.40	.25
184	A16	1p orange ver	.40	.25
185	A16	1.50p lt blue grn	.40	.25
186	A16	2p red lilac	.40	.25
187	A16	3p dark blue	4.00	.80
188	A16	5p lt red brn	.65	.25
189	A16	10p lt olive grn	.80	.30
	Nos. 181-189 (9)		7.85	2.85

Tricorn and Windmill from "The Three-Cornered Hat" by Falla — A17

Manuel de Falla — A18

1960   *Perf. 13x12½, 12½x13*

190	A17	35c slate green	.60	.60
191	A18	80c Prus green	.70	.70

Issued to honor Manuel de Falla (1876-1946), Spanish composer. See Nos. B1-B2.

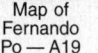

Map of Fernando Po — A19   General Franco — A20

Designs: 70c, Santa Isabel Cathedral.

1961, Oct. 1   Photo.   Unwmk.
Perf. 13x12½, 12½x13

192	A19	25c gray violet	.35	.35
193	A19	50c olive brown	.35	.35
194	A19	70c brt green	.40	.40
195	A20	1p red orange	.45	.45
	Nos. 192-195 (4)		1.55	1.55

25th anniv. of the nomination of Gen. Francisco Franco as Chief of State.

Ocean Liner — A21

Design: 50c, S.S. San Francisco.

1962, July 10   *Perf. 12½x13*

196	A21	25c dull violet	.30	.30
197	A21	50c gray olive	.35	.35
198	A21	1p orange brn	.35	.35
	Nos. 196-198 (3)		1.00	1.00

Mailman A22   Mail Transport Symbols A23

Perf. 13x12½, 12½x13
1962, Nov. 23   **Unwmk.**

199	A22	15c dark green	.30	.30
200	A23	35c lilac rose	.35	.35
201	A22	1p brown	.35	.35
	Nos. 199-201 (3)		1.00	1.00

Issued for Stamp Day.

Fetish — A24

1963, Jan. 29   *Perf. 13x12½*

202	A24	50c olive gray	.30	.30
203	A24	1p deep magenta	.35	.35

Issued to help victims of the Seville flood.

Nuns — A25

Design: 50c, Nun and child, vert.

Perf. 12½x13, 13x12½
1963, July 6   Photo.   Unwmk.

204	A25	25c bright lilac	.30	.30
205	A25	50c dull green	.35	.35
206	A25	1p red orange	.35	.35
	Nos. 204-206 (3)		1.00	1.00

Issued for child welfare.

Child and Arms — A26

1963, July 12   *Perf. 12½x13*

207	A26	50c brown olive	.30	.30
208	A26	1p carmine rose	.35	.35

Issued for Barcelona flood relief.

Governor Chacon A27   Orange Blossoms A28

1964, Mar. 6   *Perf. 12½x13, 13x12½*

209	A27	25c violet black	.30	.30
210	A28	50c dark olive	.35	.35
211	A27	1p brown red	.35	.35
	Nos. 209-211 (3)		1.00	1.00

Issued for Stamp Day 1963.

Men in Dugout Canoe — A29

Design: 50c, Pineapple.

1964, June 1   Photo.   *Perf. 13x12½*

212	A29	25c purple	.30	.30
213	A28	50c dull olive	.35	.35
214	A29	1p deep claret	.35	.35
	Nos. 212-214 (3)		1.00	1.00

Issued for child welfare.

Ring-necked Francolin — A30

Designs: 15c, 70c, 3p, Ring-necked francolin. 25c, 1p, 5p, Two mallards. 50c, 1.50p, 10p, Head of great blue touraco.

1964, July 1

215	A30	15c chestnut	.30	.30
216	A30	25c dull violet	.30	.30
217	A30	50c dk olive grn	.30	.30
218	A30	70c green	.30	.30
219	A30	1p brown orange	.35	.30
220	A30	1.50p grnsh blue	.40	.35
221	A30	3p violet blue	.65	.35
222	A30	5p dull purple	1.60	.40
223	A30	10p bright green	2.40	1.00
	Nos. 215-223 (9)		6.60	3.60

The Three Kings — A31

Designs: 50c, 1.50p, Caspar, vert.

Perf. 13x12½, 12½x13

1964, Nov. 23		Unwmk.	
224	A31	50c green	.35 .35
225	A31	1p orange ver	.40 .35
226	A31	1.50p deep green	.45 .35
227	A31	3p ultra	1.75 1.40
	Nos. 224-227 (4)		2.95 2.45

Issued for Stamp Day, 1964.

Boy
A32

Woman
Fruit Picker
A33

1.50p, Girl learning to write, and church.

1964, Mar. 1	Photo.	Perf. 13x12½	
228	A32	50c indigo	.30 .30
229	A33	1p dark red	.35 .30
230	A33	1.50p grnsh blue	.40 .35
	Nos. 228-230 (3)		1.05 .95

Issued to commemorate 25 years of peace.

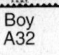

Plectrocnemia
Cruciata — A34

Design: 1p, Metopodontus savagei, horiz.

Perf. 13x12½, 12½x13

1965, June 1	Photo.	Unwmk.	
231	A34	50c slate green	.45 .35
232	A34	1p rose red	.45 .35
233	A34	1.50p Prus blue	.45 .35
	Nos. 231-233 (3)		1.35 1.05

Issued for child welfare.

Pole Vault — A35

Arms of
Fernando
Po — A36

Perf. 12½x13, 13x12½

1965, Nov. 23	Photo.	Unwmk.	
234	A35	50c yellow green	.30 .30
235	A36	1p brt org brn	.35 .30
236	A35	1.50p brt blue	.40 .35
	Nos. 234-236 (3)		1.05 .95

Issued for Stamp Day, 1965.

Children
Reading — A37

1.50p, St. Elizabeth of Hungary, vert.

Perf. 12½x13, 13x12½

1966, Nov. 23	Photo.	Unwmk.	
237	A37	50c dark green	.30 .30
238	A37	1p brown red	.35 .35
239	A37	1.50p dark blue	.35 .35
	Nos. 237-239 (3)		1.00 .95

Issued for child welfare.

White-nosed
Monkey — A38

Stamp Day: 40c, 4p, Head of moustached
monkey, vert.

1966, Nov. 23		Photo.	Perf. 13
240	A38	10c dk blue & yel	.35 .30
241	A38	40c lt brn, bl & blk	.40 .30
242	A38	1.50p ol bis, brn org & blk	.45 .40
243	A38	4p sl grn, brn org & blk	.55 .45
	Nos. 240-243 (4)		1.75 1.45

Flowers — A39

Designs: 40c, 4p, Six flowers.

1967, June 1		Photo.	Perf. 13
244	A39	10c brt car & pale grn	.30 .30
245	A39	40c red brn & org	.35 .30
246	A39	1.50p red lil & lt red brn	.40 .35
247	A39	4p dk blue & lt grn	.45 .40
	Nos. 244-247 (4)		1.50 1.35

Issued for child welfare.

Linsang — A40

Stamp Day: 1.50p, Needle-clawed galago,
vert. 3.50p, Fraser's scaly-tailed flying squirrel.

1967, Nov. 23		Photo.	Perf. 13
248	A40	1p black & bister	.35 .30
249	A40	1.50p brown & olive	.40 .30
250	A40	3.50p rose lake & dl grn	.50 .40
	Nos. 248-250 (3)		1.25 1.05

Stamp of 1868,
No. 1, and Arms
of San
Carlos — A41

Fernando Po No. 1 and: 1.50p, Arms of
Santa Isabel. 2.50p, Arms of Fernando Po.

1968, Feb. 4		Photo.	Perf. 13
251	A41	1p brt plum & brn org	.30 .30
252	A41	1.50p dp blue & brn org	.40 .30
253	A41	2.50p brn & brn org	.50 .40
	Nos. 251-253 (3)		1.20 1.00

Centenary of the first postage stamp.

Signs of the
Zodiac — A42

1968, Apr. 25		Photo.	Perf. 13
254	A42	1p Libra	.30 .30
255	A42	1.50p Leo	.40 .35
256	A42	2.50p Aquarius	.50 .40
	Nos. 254-256 (3)		1.20 1.05

Issued for child welfare.

SEMI-POSTAL STAMPS

Catalogue values for unused
stamps in this section are for
Never Hinged items.

Types of Regular Issue, 1960

Designs: 10c+5c, Manuel de Falla. 15c+5c,
Dancers from "Love, the Magician."

Perf. 12½x13, 13x12½

1960		Photo.	Unwmk.
B1	A18	10c + 5c maroon	.35 .30
B2	A17	15c + 5c dk brn & bister	.35 .35

The surtax was for child welfare.

Whale — SP1

Design: Nos. B4, B6, Harpooning whale.

1961		Perf. 12½x13	
B3	SP1	10c + 5c rose brown	.35 .30
B4	SP1	20c + 5c dk slate grn	.35 .30
B5	SP1	30c + 10c olive brn	.40 .30
B6	SP1	50c + 20c dark brn	.45 .30
	Nos. B3-B6 (4)		1.55 1.20

Issued for Stamp Day, 1960.

Hand Blessing
Woman — SP2

Design: 25c+10c, Boy making sign of the
cross, and crucifix.

1961, June 21		Perf. 13x12½	
B7	SP2	10c + 5c rose brn	.40 .30
B8	SP2	25c + 10c gray vio	.40 .30
B9	SP2	80c + 20c dk grn	.50 .35
	Nos. B7-B9 (3)		1.30 .95

The surtax was for child welfare.

Ethiopian
Tortoise — SP3

Stamp Day: 25c+10c, 1p+10c, Native carriers, palms and shore.

1961, Nov. 23		Perf. 12½x13	
B10	SP3	10c + 5c rose red	.35 .30
B11	SP3	25c + 10c dk pur	.40 .30
B12	SP3	30c + 10c vio brn	.40 .30
B13	SP3	1p + 10c red org	.50 .40
	Nos. B10-B13 (4)		1.65 1.30

FIJI

'fē-ˌjē

LOCATION — Group of 332 islands
(106 inhabited) in the South Pacific
Ocean east of Vanuatu
GOVT. — Independent nation in British
Commonwealth
AREA — 7,078 sq. mi.
POP. — 812,918 (1999 est.)
CAPITAL — Suva

A British colony since 1874, Fiji
became fully independent in 1970.

12 Pence = 1 Shilling

20 Shillings = 1 Pound

100 Cents = 1 Dollar (1872-74, 1969)

Syncopated Perforations
Type A (1st stamp #873): On
shorter sides, the seventh hole from the
larger side is an oval hole equal in width
to three holes.

Catalogue values for unused
stamps in this country are for
Never Hinged items, beginning
with Scott 137 in the regular postage section and Scott B1 in the
semi-postal section.

Values for unused stamps are for
examples with original gum as defined
in the catalogue introduction except for
Nos. 1-10 which are valued without
gum. Additionally, Nos. 1-10 are valued
with roulettes showing on two or more
sides, but expect small faults that do not
detract from the appearance of the
stamps. Very few examples of Nos. 1-
10 will be found free of faults, and these
will command substantial premiums.

Watermark

A1

Wmk. 17 — FIJI POSTAGE Across
Center Row of Sheet

1870		Unwmk. Typeset Rouletted Thin Quadrille Paper	
1	A1	1p black, pink	4,500. 4,750.
2	A1	3p black, pink	5,500. 5,000.
a.		Comma after "EXPRESS"	8,000. 8,000.
3	A1	6p black, pink	3,000. 3,000.
5	A1	1sh black, pink	2,250. 2,500.

1871		Thin Vertically Laid Paper	
6	A1	1p black, pink	1,250. 2,100.
7	A1	3p black, pink	1,900. 3,400.
8	A1	6p black, pink	1,600. 2,100.
9	A1	9p black, pink	3,400. 4,000.
10	A1	1sh black, pink	1,900. 1,900.

This service was established by the Fiji
Times, a weekly newspaper, for the delivery of
the newspaper. Since there was no postal service to the other islands, delivery of letters to
agents of the newspaper on the islands was
offered to the public.

Nos. 1-5 were printed in the same sheet,
one horizontal row of 6 of each (6p, 1sh, 1p,
3p). Nos. 6-10 were printed from the same
plate with three 9p replacing three 3p.

Most used examples have pen cancels.

Up to three sets of imitations exist. One on
pink laid paper, pin-perforated, measuring
22½x16mm. Originals measure 22½x18½mm.
A later printing was made on pink wove paper.
Forgeries also exist plus fake cancellations.

Crown and "CR"
(Cakobau Rex)
A2   A3

A4

1871		Typo. Wmk. 17 Perf. 12½ Wove Paper	
15	A2	1p blue	62.50 140.00
16	A3	3p green	125.00 400.00
17	A4	6p rose	170.00 325.00
	Nos. 15-17 (3)		357.50 865.00

Sheets of 50 (10x5).
For overprints and surcharges see Nos. 18-
39.
Forgeries exist.

Stamps of 1871
Surcharged in Black

1872, Jan. 13			
18	A2	2c on 1p blue	60.00 65.00
19	A3	6c on 3p green	90.00 90.00
20	A4	12c on 6p rose	125.00 90.00
	Nos. 18-20 (3)		275.00 245.00

Nos. 18-20 with Additional Overprint in Black

b   c

1874, Oct. 10			
21	A2(b)	2c on 1p blue	1,250. 340.00
a.		No period after "R"	3,250. 1,150.
22	A2(c)	2c on 1p blue	1,150. 300.00
a.		Invtd. "A" instead of "V"	3,250. 1,500.

```
b.   Period after "R" is a
        Maltese Cross        3,250.   1,500.
c.   No period after "R"     3,250.   1,500.
d.   Round raised period
        after "V"            3,250.   1,500.
e.   Round raised period
        after "V" and "R"    3,250.   1,500.
23  A3(b) 6c on 3p
        green                3,250.   1,000.
a.   No period after "R"     5,500.   2,000.
24  A3(c) 6c on 3p
        green                2,750.   750.00
a.   Inverted "A"            5,500.   1,900.
b.   Period after "R" is a
        Maltese Cross        5,250.   2,000.
c.   No period after "R"     5,500.   2,000.
d.   Round raised period
        after "V"            5,500.   2,000.
e.   Round raised period
        after "V" and "R"    5,500.   2,000.
25  A4(b) 12c on 6p
        rose                 1,050.   275.00
a.   "V.R." inverted         7,500.
b.   No period after "R"     3,000.   1,150.
26  A4(c) 12c on 6p
        rose                 1,000.   250.00
a.   Inverted "A"            3,000.   1,200.
b.   Period after "R" is a
        Maltese Cross        3,000.   1,200.
c.   "V.R." inverted           —      6,250.
d.   No period after "R"     3,000.   1,225.
e.   Round raised period
        after "V"            3,000.   1,225.
f.   Round raised period
        after "V" and "R"    3,000.   1,225.
```

Forged overprints exist on both forged stamps and on genuine stamps. Types "b" and "c" were in the same sheet.

Nos. 23-26 with Additional Surcharge in Black or Red

1875
```
27  A3(b) 2p on 6c on
        3p                   2,750.   800.00
a.   Period btwn. "2" and
        "d"                  4,750.   1,600.
b.   "V.R." double           5,500.   4,500.
c.   No period after "R"     4,750.   1,600.
28  A3(b) 2p on 6c on
        3p (R)               900.00   325.00
a.   Period btwn. "2" and
        "d"                  2,250.   850.00
b.   No period after "R"     2,250.   900.00
29  A3(c) 2p on 6c on
        3p                   1,900.   600.00
a.   Inverted "A"            4,750.   1,600.
b.   Period after "R" is a
        Maltese Cross        4,750.   1,600.
c.   No period after "2d"    4,750.   1,600.
d.   No period after "R"     4,750.   1,600.
e.   Round raised period
        after "V"            4,750.   1,600.
f.   Round raised period
        after "V" and "R"    4,750.   1,600.
30  A3(c) 2p on 6c on
        3p (R)               750.00   250.00
a.   Inverted "A"            2,400.   850.00
b.   Period after "R" is a
        Maltese Cross        2,400.   875.00
c.   No period after "2d"    2,400.   875.00
d.   No period after "R"     2,400.   875.00
e.   Round raised period
        after "V"            2,400.   875.00
f.   Round raised period
        after "V" and "R"    2,400.   875.00
31  A4(b) 2p on 12c on
        6p                   3,250.   1,000.
a.   Period btwn. "2" and
        "d"
b.   No period after "2d"
c.   "2d, VR" double                  5,500.
32  A4(c) 2p on 12c on
        6p                   3,000.   900.00
a.   Inverted "A"            4,500.   1,400.
b.   No period after "2d"      —      2,250.
c.   "2d, VR" double                  5,500.
d.   Round raised period
        after "R"              —      1,250.
f.   As "a," with raised pe-
        riod after "V"       3,000.   1,000.
```

Forged overprints exist on both forged stamps and on genuine stamps.

Types of 1871 Overprinted or Surcharged in Black

   e   f

1876, Jan. 31   Unwmk.
Wove Paper
```
33  A2(e) 1p ultramarine     60.00   60.00
a.   Inverted surcharge
b.   Dbl. impression of
        stamp                1,000.
c.   Horiz. pair, imperf. vert. 1,000.
34  A3(e+f) 2p on 3p dk
        grn                  60.00   65.00
a.   Dbl. surch. "Two
        Pence"
35  A4(e) 6p rose            70.00   65.00
b.   Surcharge inverted
c.   Dbl. impression of
        stamp                2,750.
Nos. 33-35 (3)               190.00  190.00
```

1877   Laid Paper
```
36  A2(e) 1p ultramarine     32.50   50.00
a.   Horiz. pair, imperf. vert. 1,000.
37  A3(e+f) 2p on 3p dk grn  80.00   85.00
b.   Perf 10                 400.00
c.   Perf 11                 375.00
d.   Horiz. pair, imperf. vert. 1,100.
e.   Horiz. pair, imperf. be-
        tween                1,000.
38  A3(e+f) 4p on 3p lilac   110.00  27.50
a.   Horiz. pair, imperf. vert. 1,000.
39  A4(e) 6p rose            60.00   40.00
a.   Horiz. pair, imperf. vert. 800.00
Nos. 36-39 (4)               282.50  202.50
```

Many of the preceding stamps are known imperforate. They are printer's waste and were never issued.

A12   A13

Queen Victoria
A14   A15

Perf. 10-13½ & Compound
1878-90   Wove Paper   Typo.
```
40  A12 1p ultra ('79)       20.00   20.00
a.   1p blue                 65.00   6.50
41  A12 2p green             45.00   1.75
b.   2p ultramarine (error)  40,000.
42  A12 4p brt vio ('90)     16.00   9.00
a.   4p mauve                40.00   12.00
43  A13 6p brt rose ('80)    16.00   4.75
b.   Printed on both sides   2,500.  2,000.
44  A14 1sh yel brn ('81)    60.00   12.50
a.   1sh deep brown          100.00  32.50
```

Litho. & Typo.
```
45  A15 5sh blk & red
        brn ('82)            75.00   50.00
Nos. 40-45 (6)               232.00  98.00
```

No. 41b was not put on sale. All examples were supposed to be destroyed.

A quantity of No. 45 was sold as remainders, canceled-to-order with the following Suva dates: 15.DEC.00; 22.DE.1900; 28.DEC.1900; 12.DEC.01; 15.DEC.01; 16.DE.1901; 21.JUN.02; 15.DEC.02; 15. DE. 1902; and 21.DE.1902. Examples so canceled are worth less than postally used examples.

No. 45 imperf was sold only as a remainder, canceled "Suva, 15.DEC.00."

A late printing of the 5sh, made from an electrotyped plate, exists in gray black and red orange, perf 10, differing from No. 45 in many details. It was also sold only as a remainder, canceled "Suva, 15.DEC.00." It is scarce.

For surcharges see Nos. 46-52.

Nos. 40-45 exist with sheetmaker's watermark. Watermarked stamps are scarcer than unwatermarked.

1881-90   Perf. 10
```
40d  A12 1p ultramarine      32.50   3.00
40e  A12 1p blue             65.00   3.25
41d  A12 2p yellow green     45.00   1.00
41e  A12 2p blue green       55.00   6.00
42d  A12 4p mauve            85.00   75.00
43d  A13 6p bright rose      30.00   32.50
43e  A13 6p pale rose        75.00   32.50
44d  A14 1sh pale yel brown  100.00  32.50
44e  A14 1sh deep brown      100.00  32.50
```

Surcharged type "f" in Black
1878-90   Typo.
```
46  A12 2p on 3p green       12.00   42.50
47  A12 4p on 1p vio ('90)   75.00   60.00
48  A12 4p on 2p lilac ('83) 100.00  16.00
Nos. 46-48 (3)               187.00  118.50
```

Nos. 40-43 Surcharged in Black

   g   h

   j   k

1891-92   Perf. 10
```
49  A12(g) ½p on 1p ultra ('92) 62.50  80.00
50  A12(h) 2½p on 2p         52.50   55.00
a.   Wider space (2mm) be-
        tween "2" and "½"    140.00  150.00
51  A12(j) 5p on 4p ('92)    62.50   80.00
52  A13(k) 5p on 6p ('92)    67.50   75.00
a.   "FIVE" and "PENCE"
        3mm apart            75.00   85.00
Nos. 49-52 (4)               245.00  290.00
```

No. 50a resulted from loose type, sometimes printing narrow, sometimes wide. Intermediate spacing is known.

A18   A20

Fijian Canoe — A19

1891-96   Perf. 10-12 & Compound
```
53  A18 ½p grnsh blk ('92)   2.75   7.00
a.   ½p gray                 3.75   7.00
54  A19 1p black ('93)       22.50   7.50
55  A19 1p lilac rose ('96)  22.50   1.10
56  A19 2p green ('93)       9.00   .85
57  A20 2½ red brown ('94)   8.75   5.50
a.   Perf. 10x12 ('94)       800.00  425.00
58  A19 5p ultra ('93)       25.00   8.00
Nos. 53-58 (6)               90.50   29.95
```

Perf. 10
```
53d  A18 ½p slate gray       6.75   10.00
54d  A19 1p black            30.00   6.00
56d  A19 2p green            145.00  22.50
57d  A20 2½p brown           60.00   30.00
58d  A19 5p ultramarine      125.00  65.00
```

Edward VII — A22

1903, Feb. 1   Wmk. 2   Perf. 14
```
59  A22 ½p gray grn &
        pale grn             3.25   2.25
60  A22 1p vio & blk, red    20.00   .65
61  A22 2p vio & orange      4.50   1.40
62  A22 2½p vio & ultra, bl  15.00   1.75
63  A22 3p vio & red vio     1.60   4.00
64  A22 4p violet & blk      1.60   2.75
65  A22 5p vio & green       1.60   2.50
66  A22 6p vio & car rose    1.60   2.00
67  A22 1sh grn & car rose   18.50   85.00
68  A22 5sh green & blk      85.00   170.00
69  A22 £1 gray & ultra      400.00  500.00
     Revenue cancel          75.00
Nos. 59-68 (10)              152.65  272.30
```

Numerals of 2p, 4p, 6p and 5sh of type A22 are in color on plain tablet.

1904-12   Ordinary Paper   Wmk. 3
```
70  A22 ½p grn & pale grn
        ('04)                18.50   3.25
70A A22 ½p green ('08)       15.00   3.50
71  A22 1p vio & blk, red
        ('04)                40.00   .25
72  A22 1p carmine ('06)     25.00   .25
73  A22 2½p ultra ('10)      7.50   10.00
```

Chalky Paper
```
74  A22 6p violet ('10)      30.00   50.00
75  A22 1sh grn & car rose
        ('09)                32.50   42.50
76  A22 1sh blk, grn ('11)   11.00   16.00
77  A22 5sh grn & scar, yel
        ('11)                75.00   105.00
78  A22 £1 vio & blk, red
        ('12)                360.00  300.00
Nos. 70-77 (9)               254.50  230.75
```

George V — A23

Die I

For description of Dies I and II see "Dies of British Colonial Stamps" in Table of Contents.

1912-23   Ordinary Paper
```
79  A23 ¼p brown ('16)       2.75   .40
80  A23 ½p green             4.50   1.10
81  A23 1p scarlet           3.75   .50
a.   1p carmine ('16)        2.25   .75
82  A23 2p gray ('14)        2.00   .25
83  A23 2½p ultra ('14)      3.50   3.75
84  A23 3p violet, yel       4.50   12.50
a.   Die II ('21)            3.25   30.00
```

```
85  A23 4p blk & red, lem
        ('21)                24.00   22.50
a.   Die II ('23)            3.25   35.00
```
Chalky Paper
```
86  A23 5p dl vio & ol grn
        ('14)                5.50   12.50
87  A23 6p dl vio & red
        vio ('14)            2.40   6.00
88  A23 1sh black, green     1.30   14.50
a.   1sh black, blue green, ol
        back                 3.25   11.00
b.   1sh black, emerald ('21) 5.50  67.50
c.   Die II ('22)            3.25   37.50
89  A23 2sh 6p blk & red,
        blue                 37.50   35.00
90  A23 5sh grn & scar,
        yellow               37.50   45.00
91  A23 £1 vio & blk, red    300.00  325.00
a.   Die II ('21)            300.00  325.00
     Revenue cancel          52.50
```
Surface-colored Paper
```
92  A23 1sh black, green     1.25   14.50
Nos. 79-90,92 (13)           130.45  168.50
```

Numerals of ¼p, 1½p, 2p, 4p, 6p, 2sh, 2sh6p and 5sh of type A23 are in color on plain tablet.

For overprints see Nos. MR1-MR2.

Die II
1922-27   Wmk. 4   Ordinary Paper
```
93  A23 ¼p dl vio & dl brn   3.75   27.50
94  A23 ½p green             1.10   1.50
95  A23 1p rose red          6.00   1.00
96  A23 1p violet ('27)      1.40   .25
97  A23 1½p rose red
        ('27)                4.50   1.50
98  A23 2p gray              1.40   .25
a.   "2d" and value tablet omit-
        ted                  27,500.
99  A23 3p ultra ('23)       3.00   1.20
100 A23 4p blk & red,
        yel                  16.00   7.00
101 A23 5p dl vio & ol
        grn                  1.75   2.25
102 A23 6p dl vio & red
        violet               2.40   1.50
```
Chalky Paper
```
103 A23 1sh blk, emerald     14.00   2.75
104 A23 2sh vio & ultra,
        bl ('27)             30.00   72.50
105 A23 2sh6p blk & red, bl  12.50   35.00
106 A23 5sh grn & scar,
        yellow               55.00   90.00
Nos. 93-106 (14)             152.80  244.20
```

The only known example of No. 98a is the center stamp of an unused block of nine.

Common Design Types pictured following the introduction.

Silver Jubilee Issue
Common Design Type
1935, May 6   Perf. 13½x14
```
110 CD301 1½p car & blue     1.00   10.00
111 CD301 2p gray blk & ul-
        tra                  1.50   .50
112 CD301 3p blue & brown    2.75   5.50
113 CD301 1sh brt vio & indi-
        go                   15.00   18.00
Nos. 110-113 (4)             20.25   34.00
Set, never hinged            30.00
```

Coronation Issue
Common Design Type
1937, May 12   Perf. 11x11½
```
114 CD302 2p dark violet     .45   1.25
115 CD302 2p gray black      .45   2.25
116 CD302 3p indigo          .45   2.25
Nos. 114-116 (3)             1.35   5.75
Set, never hinged            2.00
```

Outrigger Canoe A24   Fijian Village A25

Outrigger Canoe — A26   Map of Fiji Islands — A27

Government
Buildings — A27a

Canoe and
Arms of
Fiji — A28

Sugar
Cane — A29

Spear Fishing
at
Night — A30

Arms of
Fiji — A31

Suva
Harbor — A32

River
Scene — A33

Fijian
House — A34

Papaya
Tree — A35

Bugler — A36

8p, 1sh5p, 1sh6p, Arms of Fiji.

Perf. 13½, 12½ (1p)

1938-55			Engr.	Wmk. 4
117	A24	½p green	.25	1.00
c.		Perf. 14 ('41)	16.00	6.75
d.		Perf. 12 ('48)	.80	3.00
118	A25	1p blue & brn	.40	.25
119	A26	1½p rose car (empty canoe)	12.00	.50
120	A27	2p grn & org brn (no "180 degree")	40.00	.50
121	A27a	2p mag & grn	.45	.80
a.		Perf. 12 ('46)	1.25	.90

Perf. 12½, 13x12 (6p), 13¾x14 (8p)

122	A28	3p dp ultra	.80	.40
123	A29	5p rose red & blue	32.50	13.00
124	A29	5p rose red & yel grn	.25	.40
125	A27	6p blk (no "180 degree")	45.00	16.00
126	A31	8p rose car	1.40	3.50
a.		Perf. 13x13¼ ('50)	1.25	3.50
127	A30	1sh black & yel	1.50	.90

Perf. 14

128	A31	1sh5p car & blk	.25	.25
128A	A31	1sh6p ultra	2.75	3.50
b.		Perf. 13 ('55)	1.10	20.00

Perf. 12½

129	A32	2sh vio & org	2.25	.55
130	A33	2sh6p brn & grn	4.00	2.00
131	A34	5sh dk vio & grn	4.00	2.50
131A	A35	10sh emer & brn org	27.50	52.50
131B	A36	£1 car & ultra	37.50	65.00
		Nos. 117-131B (18)	212.80	163.55

Issued: 1sh5p, 6/13/40; 5p, 10/1/40; No. 121, 5/19/42; 8p, 11/15/48; 10sh, £1, 3/13/50; 1sh6p, 8/1/50; others, 4/5/38.

Types of 1938-40 Redrawn

Man in Canoe —
A36a

**180 Degree
Added to the
Lower Right Hand
Corner of the
Design — A36b**

Perf. 13½ (1½p, 2p, 6p), 14 (2½p)

1940-49				Wmk. 4
132	A36a	1½p rose carmine	1.00	3.00
a.		Perf. 12 ('49)	.80	1.60
b.		Perf. 14 ('42)	14.50	22.50
133	A36b	2p grn & org brn ("180 degree")	12.50	17.50
134	A36b	2½p grn & org brn	.50	1.25
a.		Perf. 12 ('48)	.80	.60
b.		Perf. 13½ ('42)	.55	1.00
135	A36b	6p blk ("180 degree")	2.50	2.00
a.		Perf. 12 ('47)	1.40	1.50
		Nos. 132-135 (4)	16.50	23.75

Issued: 2½p, Jan. 6, 1942; others Oct. 1, 1940.

**No. 133
Surcharged in
Black**

2⅓d.

1941, Feb. 10   **Perf. 13½**

136	A27	2½p on 2p grn & org brn	1.50	1.00
		Never hinged		2.50

> Catalogue values for unused stamps in this section, from this point to the end of the section, are for Never Hinged items.

**Peace Issue
Common Design Type**

1946, Aug. 17   **Perf. 13½**

137	CD303	2½p bright green	.25	1.50
138	CD303	3p deep blue	.50	.25

**Silver Wedding Issue
Common Design Types**

1948, Dec. 17 Photo. Perf. 14x14½

139	CD304	2½p dark green	.70	2.50

**Engr.; Name Typo.
Perf. 11½x11**

140	CD305	5sh blue violet	17.50	9.00

**UPU Issue
Common Design Types
Engr.; Name Typo. on 3p, 8p
Perf. 13½, 11x11½**

1949, Oct. 10				Wmk. 4
141	CD306	2p red violet	.35	.75
142	CD307	3p indigo	2.25	7.50
143	CD308	8p dp carmine	.35	4.50
144	CD309	1sh6p blue	.40	3.00
		Nos. 141-144 (4)	3.35	15.75

**Coronation Issue
Common Design Type**

1953, June 2   **Perf. 13½x13**

145	CD312	2½p dk green & blk	1.00	.60
		Nos. 145 (1)	1.00	.60

**Type of 1938-40 with Portrait of
Queen Elizabeth II Inscribed: "Royal
Visit 1953"**

1953, Dec. 16   **Perf. 13**

146	A31	8p carmine lake	.65	.35

Visit of Queen Elizabeth II and the Duke of Edinburgh, 1953.

**Types of 1938-50 with Portrait of
Queen Elizabeth II, and**

A39

Loading
Copra — A40

Designs: 1sh6p, Sugar cane train. 2sh, Bananas for export. 5sh, Gold industry.

**Perf. 11½ (A24, A27, A39); 11½x11
(A40); 12 (A27, 2p); 12½ (A30, A33,
A35, A36); 13 (A31)**

1954-56				Engr.
147	A24	½p green	1.00	1.60
148	A39	1p grnsh blue	1.90	.25
149	A39	1½p brown	3.00	.70
150	A27a	2p mag & green	1.35	.40
151	A39	2½p blue vio	3.25	.25
152	A40	3p purple & brn	5.00	.25
154	A27	6p black	2.75	.90
155	A31	8p carmine lake	8.50	1.90
156	A30	1sh black & yel	3.25	.25
157	A40	1sh6p grn & dp ultra	17.00	1.05
158	A40	2sh brt car & blk	5.00	.65
159	A33	2sh6p brn & bl grn	1.90	.25
160	A40	5sh dp ultra & yel	8.50	1.30
161	A35	10sh emer & brn org	8.00	15.00
162	A36	£1 car & ultra	35.00	11.00
		Nos. 147-162 (15)	105.40	35.75

Issued: 2p, 1sh, 2sh6p, 2/1/54; ½p, 6p, 8p, 10sh, £1, 7/1/54; 1p, 6/1/56; 1½p, 2½p, 3p, 1sh6p, 2sh, 5sh, 10/1/56.

Types of 1954-56 and

Nautilus
Shells
A41

Hibiscus
A42

Kandavu
Parrot — A43

½p, 2p, 2½p, Queen Elizabeth II (A39). 1p, Queen, turtles in bottom panels. 6p, Fijian beating drum (lali). 10p, Yaqona ceremony. 1sh, South Pacific map. 2sh6p, Nadi Airport. 10sh, Cutting sugar cane. £1, Arms of Fiji.

**Perf. 11½ (A39, A41); 11½x11 (A40);
14½x14 (A42); 14x14½ (A43)
Engr. (A39, A40, A41); others Photo.**

1959-63				Wmk. 4
163	A39	½p green ('61)	.25	2.60
164	A41	1p dk blue ('62)	3.75	2.60
165	A41	1½p dk brown ('62)	3.75	2.60
166	A39	2p crim rose ('61)	1.60	.25
167	A39	2½p brown org ('62)	3.25	5.00
168	A40	6p blk & car rose ('61)	1.90	.25
169	A42	8p gray, red, yel & grn ('61)	.55	.30
170	A40	10p car & brn ('63)	2.60	.65
171	A40	1sh dk bl & bl ('61)	1.60	.25
172	A40	2sh6p pur & blk ('61)	9.50	.25
173	A43	4sh dk grn, red, bl & emer	3.00	1.30
174	A40	10sh sep & emer ('61)	2.75	1.30
175	A40	£1 org & blk ('61)	5.75	3.75
		Nos. 163-175 (13)	40.25	21.10

Issued: 4sh, 7/13; 8p, 8/1; ½p, 2p, 6p, 1sh, 2sh6p, 10sh, £1, 11/14; 1p, 1½p, 2½p, 12/3; 10p, 4/1.
For type overprinted see No. 205.

Types of 1954-63 and

Elizabeth II — A44

1sh6p, 180th meridian and Intl. Date Line. 2sh, White orchids. 5sh, Orange dove.

**Perf. 11½ (A41); 12½ (A44); 11½x11
(A40); 14x14½ (A43)
Engr. (A39, A40, A41); others Photo.**

1962-67				Wmk. 314
176	A41	1p dark blue ('64)	1.00	3.75
177	A39	2p crim rose ('65)	.50	.25
178	A44	3p rose cl & multi	.25	.25
179	A40	6p blk & car rose ('64)	1.50	.25
180	A42	9p ultra, red, yel & grn ('63)	.90	.65
181	A40	10p car & brn ('64)	.60	.50
182	A40	1sh dk bl & bl ('66)	2.25	.45
183	A43	1sh6p dk bl & multi	1.50	.60

184	A42	2sh gold, yel grn & grn	10.00	3.50
185	A40	2sh6p pur & blk ('65)	5.50	1.25
186	A43	4sh grn & multi, wmk. sideways ('67)	4.25	1.00
a.		As #186, wmk. upright ('64)	7.50	2.00
b.		4sh dark green & multi ('66)	6.00	2.50
187	A43	5sh dk gray, yel & red	10.00	.35
188	A40	10sh sep & emer ('64)	7.50	2.30
189	A40	£1 org & blk ('64)	14.00	7.00
		Nos. 176-189 (14)	59.75	22.30

Issued: 3p, 1sh6p, 2sh, 5sh, 12/3; 9p, No. 186a, 4/1; 1p, 10p, 10sh, 1/14; 6p, £1, 6/9; 2p, 2sh6p, 8/3; No. 186b, 3/1; No. 186, 2/16.

Nos. 178 and 171 Overprinted

**ROYAL VISIT
1963**

ROYAL VISIT 1963

1963, Feb. 1

196	A44	3p multicolored	.50	.35
197	A40	1sh dark blue & blue	.65	.65

Visit of Elizabeth II & Prince Philip, Feb. 3.

**Freedom from Hunger Issue
Common Design Type**

1963, June 4 Photo. Perf. 14x14½

198	CD314	2sh ultramarine	3.50	2.25

Running — A45

9p, Throwing the discus, vert. 1sh, Field hockey, vert. 2sh6p, Women's high jump.

Perf. 14½x14, 14x14½

1963, Aug. 6				Wmk. 314
199	A45	3p yel, blk & brn	.45	.25
200	A45	9p violet, blk & brn	.45	1.00
201	A45	1sh green, blk & brn	.45	.45
202	A45	2sh6p blue, blk & brn	1.10	.95
		Nos. 199-202 (4)	2.45	2.45

1st So. Pacific Games, Suva, 8/29-9/7.

**Red Cross Centenary Issue
Common Design Type**

1963, Sept. 2 Litho. Perf. 13

203	CD315	2p black & red	1.00	.30
204	CD315	2sh ultra & red	2.25	2.50

Type of 1959-63
Overprinted

1963, Dec. 2 Engr. Perf. 11½x11

205	A40	1sh dark blue & blue	1.00	.35

Opening of the Commonwealth Pacific (telephone) Cable service, COMPAC.

Fiji Scout
Badge
A46

Scouts of
India, Fiji
and Europe
Tying Knot
A47

518   FIJI

1964, Aug. 3   **Photo.**   **Perf. 12½**
206	A46	3p multicolored	.50	.50
207	A47	1sh ocher & purple	.65	.65

50th anniv. of the founding of the Fiji Boy Scouts.

Amphibian "Aotearoa," 1939 — A48   Map of Fiji and Tonga Islands and Plane — A49

Design: 6p, Heron plane.

1964, Oct. 24   **Perf. 12½, 14½**
208	A48	3p brt red & black	.50	.35
209	A48	6p ultra & red	.85	.85
210	A49	1sh grnsh blue & black	.85	.85
		Nos. 208-210 (3)	2.20	2.05

Fiji-Tonga airmail service, 25th anniv.

ITU Issue
Common Design Type
Perf. 11x11½

1965, May 17   **Litho.**   **Wmk. 314**
211	CD317	3p blue & rose red	.50	.30
212	CD317	1sh yel & bister	1.50	.75

Intl. Cooperation Year Issue
Common Design Type

1965, Oct. 25   **Perf. 14½**
213	CD318	2p blue grn & claret	.35	.25
214	CD318	2sh6p lt vio & grn	1.60	1.00

Churchill Memorial Issue
Common Design Type

1966, Jan. 24   **Photo.**   **Perf. 14**
Design in Black, Gold and Carmine Rose
215	CD319	3p brt blue	.75	.25
216	CD319	9p green	1.10	1.25
217	CD319	1sh brown	1.10	1.25
218	CD319	2sh6p violet	1.45	1.25
		Nos. 215-218 (4)	4.40	3.00

World Cup Soccer Issue
Common Design Type

1966, July 1   **Litho.**   **Perf. 14**
219	CD321	2p multicolored	.30	.25
220	CD321	2sh multicolored	1.40	.35

H.M.S. Pandora and Split Island, Rotuma — A50

Designs: 10p, Rotuma chiefs, Pandora, and Rotuma's position in Pacific. 1sh6p, Rotuma islanders welcoming Pandora.

1966, Aug. 29   **Photo.**   **Perf. 14x13**
221	A50	3p multicolored	.40	.25
222	A50	10p multicolored	.40	.25
223	A50	1sh6p multicolored	.65	.95
		Nos. 221-223 (3)	1.45	1.45

175th anniv. of the discovery of Rotuma, a group of eight islands forming part of the colony of Fiji.

WHO Headquarters Issue
Common Design Type

1966, Sept. 20   **Litho.**   **Perf. 14**
224	CD322	6p multicolored	1.45	.30
225	CD322	2sh6p multicolored	3.25	3.00
		Nos. 224-225 (2)	4.70	3.30

Woman Runner — A51

Designs: 9p, Shot put, vert. 1sh, Diver.

1966, Dec. 8   **Photo.**   **Perf. 14x14½**
226	A51	3p ol, black & lt brn	.25	.25
227	A51	9p brt blue, blk & brn	.35	.35
228	A51	1sh blue green & multi	.40	.40
		Nos. 226-228 (3)	1.00	1.00

2nd South Pacific Games, Noumea, New Caledonia, Dec. 8-18.

Military Band — A52

Intl. Tourist Year: 9p, Reef diving. 1sh, Beqa fire walkers. 2sh, Liner Oriana and Mt. Rama volcano.

1967, Oct. 20   **Perf. 14x13**
229	A52	3p multi & gold	.60	.25
230	A52	9p multi & silver	.30	.25
231	A52	1sh multi & gold	.30	.25
232	A52	2sh multi & silver	.60	.30
		Nos. 229-232 (4)	1.80	1.05

Admiral Bligh, H.M.S. Providence and Old Map of "Feejee" — A53

Designs: 1sh, Bligh's longboat being chased by double canoe and map of Fiji Islands. 2sh6p, Bligh's tomb, St. Mary's Cemetery, Lambeth, London.

Perf. 15x14, 12½x13 (1sh)
1967, Dec. 7   **Photo.**   **Wmk. 314**
     Size: 35x21mm
233	A53	4p emer, blk & yel	.25	.25

     Size: 54x20mm
234	A53	1sh brt bl, brn org & blk	.40	.25

     Size: 35x21mm
235	A53	2sh6p sepia & multi	.40	.30
		Nos. 233-235 (3)	1.05	.80

150th anniv. of the death of Adm. William Bligh (1754-1817), captain of the Bounty and principal discoverer of the Fiji Islands.

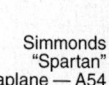

Simmonds "Spartan" Seaplane — A54

Designs: 6p, Fiji Airways Hawker-Siddeley H748 and emblems of various airlines. 1sh, Fokker "Southern Cross," Capt. Charles Kingsford-Smith, his crew and Southern Cross constellation. 2sh, Lockheed Altair "Lady Southern Cross."

Perf. 14x14½
1968, June 5   **Wmk. 314**
236	A54	2p green & black	.25	.25
237	A54	6p brt blue, car & blk	.25	.25
238	A54	1sh dp violet & green	.30	.25
239	A54	2sh org brn & dk blue	.50	.25
		Nos. 236-239 (4)	1.30	1.00

40th anniv. of the first Trans-Pacific Flight through Fiji under Capt. Charles Kingsford-Smith.

Fijian Bures A55   Eastern Reef Heron A56

1p, Passion fruit flowers. 2p, Nautilus pompilius shell. 4p, Hawk moth. 6p, Reef butterflyfish. 9p, Bamboo raft (bilibili). 10p, Tiger moth. 1sh, Black marlin. 1sh6p, Orange-breasted honey eaters. 2sh, Ringed sea snake, horiz. 2sh6p, Outrigger canoes (takia), horiz. 3sh, Golden cowrie shell. 4sh, Emperor gold mine and gold ore. 5sh, Bamboo orchids, horiz. 10sh, Tabua (ceremonial whale's tooth). £1, Coat of Arms and Queen Elizabeth II, horiz.

Perf. 13½ (A55), 14 (A56)
1968, July 15   **Photo.**   **Wmk. 314**
240	A55	½p multicolored	.25	.25
241	A55	1p multicolored	.25	.25
242	A55	2p multicolored	.25	.25
243	A56	3p multicolored	.45	.25
244	A55	4p multicolored	.95	1.60
245	A55	6p multicolored	.30	.25
246	A55	9p multicolored	.25	1.60
247	A55	10p multicolored	1.50	.25
248	A56	1sh multicolored	.25	.25
249	A56	1sh6p multicolored	5.50	4.50
250	A56	2sh multicolored	.90	1.60
251	A56	2sh6p multicolored	.90	.30
252	A56	3sh multicolored	1.90	4.75
253	A56	4sh multicolored	4.25	2.25
254	A56	5sh multicolored	2.40	1.25
255	A56	10sh multicolored	1.25	2.40
256	A56	£1 red & multi	2.40	2.40
		Nos. 240-256 (17)	23.05	24.40

See Nos. 260-276.

WHO Emblem, Map of Fiji and Nurses — A57

WHO Emblem and: 9p, Medical team loading patient on stretcher on dinghy and medical ship "Vuniwai." 3sh, People playing on beach.

1968, Dec. 9   **Litho.**   **Perf. 14**
257	A57	3p blue green & multi	.25	.25
258	A57	9p brt blue & multi	.40	.40
259	A57	3sh dk blue & multi	.60	.60
		Nos. 257-259 (3)	1.25	1.25

WHO, 20th anniv.

Types of 1968
Values in Cents and Dollars

Designs: 1c, Passion fruit flowers. 2c, Nautilus pompilius shell. 3c, Reef heron. 4c, Hawk moth. 5c, Reef butterflyfish. 6c, Fijian bures. 8c, Bamboo raft. 9c, Tiger moth. 10c, Black marlin. 15c, Orange-breasted honey-eater. 20c, Ringed sea snake, horiz. 25c, Outrigger canoes (takia), horiz. 30c, Golden cowrie shell. 40c Emperor gold mine and gold ore. 50c, Bamboo orchids, horiz. $1, Tabua (ceremonial whale's tooth). $2, Coat of Arms and Queen Elizabeth II, horiz.

Perf. 13½ (A55), 14 (A56)
1969, Jan. 13   **Photo.**   **Wmk. 314**
260	A55	1c multicolored	.25	.25
261	A55	2c multicolored	.25	.25
262	A56	3c multicolored	1.25	1.00
263	A55	4c multicolored	1.50	1.00
264	A55	5c multicolored	.25	.25
265	A55	6c multicolored	.25	.25
266	A55	8c multicolored	.25	.25
267	A55	9c multicolored	1.50	2.25
268	A56	10c multicolored	.25	.25
269	A56	15c multicolored	6.50	6.00
270	A56	20c multicolored	1.25	.80
271	A55	25c multicolored	1.00	.25
272	A55	30c multicolored	3.50	1.50
273	A56	40c multicolored	7.50	4.00
274	A56	50c multicolored	2.00	.25
275	A56	$1 multicolored	1.50	.40
276	A56	$2 red & multi	3.00	1.50
		Nos. 260-276 (17)	32.00	20.45

For overprints & surcharges see Nos. 286-288, B5-B6.

Nos. 274 and 275 exist on glazed paper. Values, set: $15 unused, $5 used.

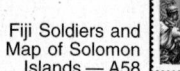

Fiji Soldiers and Map of Solomon Islands — A58

Designs: 10c, Flags of Fiji Military Force, soldiers in full and battle dress. 25c, Cpl. Sefanaia Sukanaivalu and Victoria Cross.

1969, June 23   **Wmk. 314**   **Perf. 14**
277	A58	3c emerald & multi	.50	.25
278	A58	10c red & multi	.55	.25
279	A58	25c black & multi	.85	.45
		Nos. 277-279 (3)	1.90	.95

25th anniv. of the Fiji Military Forces campaign in the Solomon Islands and of the posthumous award of the Victoria Cross to Cpl. Sefanaia Sukanaivalu.

Yachting — A59

Designs: 4c, Javelin. 20c, Winners and South Pacific Games medal.

1969, Aug. 18   **Photo.**   **Perf. 14½x14**
280	A59	4c red, brown & blk	.30	.30
281	A59	8c blue & black	.40	.40
282	A59	20c ol grn, blk & ocher	.50	.50
		Nos. 280-282 (3)	1.20	1.20

3rd South Pacific Games, Port Moresby, Papua New Guinea, Aug. 13-23.

Students in Laboratory A60

2c, Map of South Pacific and mortarboard. 8c, Site of University at Royal New Zealand Air Force Seaplane Station, Laucala Bay, RNZAF badge and Sunderland flying boat.

1969, Nov. 10   **Perf. 14x14½**
283	A60	2c multicolored	.25	.25
284	A60	8c red & multi	.35	.35
285	A60	25c dk green & multi	.80	.75
		Nos. 283-285 (3)	1.40	1.35

Inauguration of the University of the South Pacific, Laucala Bay, Suva.

Nos. 261, 268 and 271 Overprinted

1970, Mar. 4   **Perf. 13½, 14**
286	A55	2c multicolored	.30	.40
287	A56	10c multicolored	.40	.30
288	A55	25c multicolored	.80	.80
		Nos. 286-288 (3)	1.50	1.50

Visit of Queen Elizabeth II, Prince Philip and Princess Anne, Mar. 4-5.

Nuns Sitting under Chaulmoogra Tree, and Chaulmoogra Fruit — A61

Designs: 10c, Paintings by Semisi Maya (former patient). No. 290, Cascade, vert. No. 291, Sea urchins, vert. 30c, Aerial view of Makogai Hospital.

Perf. 14x14½, 14½x14
1970, May 25   **Photo.**   **Wmk. 314**
289	A61	2c brt pink & multi	.25	.55
290	A61	10c gray green & blk	.50	.55
291	A61	10c blue, car & blk	.50	.55
a.		Pair, #290-291	1.00	1.10
292	A61	30c orange & multi	1.00	.60
		Nos. 289-292 (4)	2.25	2.25

Closing of the Leprosy Hospital on Makogai Island in 1969.

Abel Tasman and Ship's Log, 1643 — A62

3c, Capt. James Cook & "Endeavour." 8c, Capt. William Bligh & longboat, 1789. 25c, Man of Fiji & Fijian ocean-going canoe.

1970, Aug. 18   **Litho.**   **Perf. 13x12½**
293	A62	2c blue green & multi	.75	.55
294	A62	3c gray green & multi	1.25	.55
295	A62	8c multicolored	1.25	.45
296	A62	25c dull lilac & multi	.75	.45
		Nos. 293-296 (4)	4.00	2.00

Discoverers and explorers of Fiji Islands.

King Cakobau and Cession Stone at Lavuka — A63

Designs: 3c, Chinese, Fijian, Indian and European children. 10c, Prime Minister Ratu Sir Kamisese Mara and flag of Fiji. 25c, Fijian male dancer and Indian female dancer.

1970, Oct. 10   Wmk. 314   Perf. 14

297	A63	2c multicolored	.25	.25
298	A63	3c multicolored	.25	.25
299	A63	10c multicolored	1.10	.25
300	A63	25c multicolored	.30	.30
		Nos. 297-300 (4)	1.90	1.05

Fijian independence.

Fiji Nos. 1 and 3 — A64

15c, Fiji #15, 44, 59, 81, 127, 166. 20c, Fiji Times Office, Levuka, & G. P. O., Suva.

1970, Nov. 2   Photo.   Perf. 14½x14

Size: 35x21mm

301	A64	4c multicolored	.30	.25

Size: 60x21½mm

302	A64	15c multicolored	.75	.30

Size: 35x21mm

303	A64	20c multicolored	.75	.30
		Nos. 301-303 (3)	1.80	.85

Centenary of first postage stamps of Fiji.

Gray-backed White Eyes — A65

Yellow-breasted Musk Parrots — A66

Designs: 1c, Cirrhopetalum umbellatum. 2c, Cardinal honey eaters. 3c, Calanthe furcata. 4c, Bulbophyllum. 6c, Phaius tancarviliae. 8c, Blue-crested broadbills. 10c, Acanthephippiumvitiense. 15c, Dendrobium tokai. 20c, Slaty flycatchers. 25c, Kandavu honey eaters. 30c, Dendrobium gordonii. 50c, White-throated pigeon. $1, Collared lories (kula). $2, Dendrobium platygastrium. (Orchids shown on 1c, 3c, 4c, 6c, 10c, 15c, 30c, $2.)

Wmk. 314 Upright

1971-72   Litho.   Perf. 13½x14

305	A65	1c blk & multi	.25	.30
306	A65	2c carmine & multi	.45	.25
307	A65	3c multi ('72)	.85	.25
308	A65	4c blk & multi ('72)	.65	1.75
309	A65	5c brown & multi	.35	.25
310	A65	6c lt bl & multi ('72)	4.75	6.00
311	A65	8c black & multi	.35	.25
312	A65	10c multi ('72)	.35	.25
313	A65	15c multi ('72)	4.75	1.00
314	A65	20c gray & multi	1.35	.30

Perf. 14

315	A66	25c sepia & multi	3.75	.25
316	A66	30c grn & multi ('72)	8.75	.85
317	A66	40c blue & multi	4.00	.45
318	A66	50c gray & multi	2.60	.45
319	A66	$1 red & multi	3.50	.85
320	A66	$2 multi ('72)	2.75	8.00
		Nos. 305-320 (16)	39.45	21.45

Issued: 5c, 20c, 40c, 50c, 8/6; 2c, 8c, 25c, $1, 11/22; 1c, 10c, 30c, $2, 1/4; 3c, 4c, 6c, 15c, 6/23.

1972-74   Wmk. 314 Sideways

306c	A65	2c ('73)	.40	9.00
307a	A65	3c ('73)	2.25	.50
308a	A65	4c ('73)	5.50	.85
309a	A65	5c ('73)	7.75	3.75
310a	A65	6c ('73)	9.75	1.40
311a	A65	8c ('73)	3.50	.80
313a	A65	15c ('73)	5.00	2.50
314a	A65	20c	13.50	2.10
315a	A66	25c ('73)	1.75	.95
317a	A66	40c ('74)	2.75	9.50
318a	A66	50c ('74)	2.75	4.00

319a	A66	$1	2.75	4.50
320a	A66	$2	2.75	4.50
		Nos. 306c-320a (13)	60.40	44.35

Issued: 20c, $1, $2, 11/17; 3c, 5c, 3/8; 4c, 6c, 8c, 15c, 25c, 4/11; 2c, 12/12; 40c, 50c, 3/15.

1975-77   Wmk. 373

305b	A65	1c	1.00	4.50
306d	A65	2c	.80	4.50
307b	A65	3c	.45	4.50
308b	A65	4c ('76)	3.50	.25
309b	A65	5c ('76)	1.30	4.75
310b	A65	6c ('76)	2.90	.25
311b	A65	8c ('76)	.35	.25
312b	A65	10c	.40	2.50
313b	A65	15c ('76)	2.60	.50
314b	A65	20c ('77)	3.75	.60
316b	A66	30c ('76)	5.00	1.10
317b	A66	40c ('76)	4.50	.65
318b	A66	50c ('76)	3.00	1.05
319b	A66	$1 ('76)	3.00	1.05
320b	A66	$2 ('76)	1.45	1.05
		Nos. 305b-320b (15)	34.00	27.10

Issued: 1c, 2c, 3c, 5c, 10c, 4/9; 20c, 7/15; others, 9/3.

Women's Basketball — A67

1971, Sept. 6   Wmk. 314   Perf. 14

321	A67	8c shown	.25	.25
322	A67	10c Running	.50	.50
323	A67	25c Weight lifting	1.00	.95
		Nos. 321-323 (3)	1.75	1.70

4th South Pacific Games, Papeete, French Polynesia, Sept. 8-19.

Community Education — A68

Designs: 4c, Public health. 50c, Economic growth (farm scenes).

1972, Feb. 7

324	A68	2c bright rose & multi	.25	.25
325	A68	4c gray & multi	.25	.25
326	A68	50c bright blue & multi	1.05	1.05
		Nos. 324-326 (3)	1.55	1.55

South Pacific Commission, 25th anniv.

Arts Festival Emblem — A69

1972, Apr. 10

327	A69	10c blue, org & black	.40	.40

South Pacific Festival of Arts, May 6-20.

Silver Wedding Issue, 1972
Common Design Type

Queen Elizabeth II, Prince Philip, flowers, shells.

1972, Nov. 20   Photo.   Perf. 14x14½

328	CD324	10c slate grn & multi	.25	.25
329	CD324	25c red lilac & multi	.45	.45
a.		Blue omitted	550.00	

On No. 329a, Prince Philip's coat is brown instead of blue.

Rugby — A70

Forestry Development A71

Development projects: 8c, Irrigation of rice field. 10c, Low income housing. 25c, Highway construction.

1973, July 23   Perf. 14

333	A71	5c multicolored	.25	.45
334	A71	8c multicolored	.35	.25
335	A71	10c multicolored	.40	.25
336	A71	25c multicolored	.70	.75
		Nos. 333-336 (4)	1.70	1.70

1973, Mar. 9   Litho.   Perf. 14

330	A70	2c shown	.40	.40
331	A70	8c Tackle	.80	.80
332	A70	25c Kicking ball	1.05	1.05
		Nos. 330-332 (3)	2.25	2.25

60th anniversary of Fiji Rugby Union.

Holy Family — A72

Festivals: 10c, Diwali (Candles; Indian New Year). 20c, Id-Ul-Fitar (Friendly greeting and mosque; Moslem, Ramadan). 25c, Chinese New Year (dragon dance).

1973, Oct. 26   Perf. 14x14½

337	A72	3c blue & multi	.30	.25
338	A72	10c purple & multi	.30	.25
339	A72	20c emerald & multi	.55	.60
340	A72	25c red & multi	.55	.60
		Nos. 337-340 (4)	1.70	1.70

Festivals celebrated by various groups in Fiji.

Runners — A73

1974, Jan. 7

341	A73	3c shown	.40	.25
342	A73	8c Boxing	.40	.25
343	A73	50c Lawn bowling	1.20	1.50
		Nos. 341-343 (3)	2.00	2.00

10th British Commonwealth Games, Christchurch, N.Z., Jan. 24-Feb. 2.

Centenary of Cricket in Fiji — A74

Designs: 3c, Bowler. 25c, Batsman and wicketkeeper. 40c, Fielder, horiz.

Perf. 14x14½, 14½x14

1974, Feb. 21   Litho.

344	A74	3c multicolored	1.10	.25
345	A74	25c multicolored	1.35	.25
346	A74	40c multicolored	1.60	2.25
		Nos. 344-346 (3)	4.05	2.75

Mailman and UPU Emblem — A75

UPU Emblem and: 8c, Loading mail on ship. 30c, Post office and truck. 50c, Jet.

1974, May 22   Wmk. 314   Perf. 14

347	A75	3c orange & multi	.25	.25
348	A75	8c multicolored	.30	.25
349	A75	30c lt blue & multi	.45	.40
350	A75	50c multicolored	.90	1.00
		Nos. 347-350 (4)	1.90	1.90

Centenary of the Universal Postal Union.

Cub Scouts — A76

Designs: 10c, Boy Scouts reading map. 40c, Scouts and Fiji flag, vert.

1974, Aug. 30

351	A76	3c multicolored	.25	.25
352	A76	10c multicolored	.50	.25
353	A76	40c multicolored	1.25	1.80
		Nos. 351-353 (3)	2.00	2.30

First National Boy Scout Jamboree, Lautoka, Viti Levu Island.

Cakobau Club and Flag — A77

King Cakobau, Queen Victoria — A78

Design: 50c, Signing ceremony at Levuka.

1974, Oct. 9   Litho.   Perf. 13½x13

354	A77	3c multicolored	.25	.25
355	A78	8c multicolored	.25	.25
356	A78	50c multicolored	.60	.60
		Nos. 354-356 (3)	1.10	1.10

Deed of Cession, cent. and 4th anniv. of independence.

Diwali, Hindu Festival of Lights — A79

Designs: 15c, Id-Ul-Fitar (women exchanging greetings under moon). 25c, Chinese New Year (girl twirling streamer, and fireworks). 30c, Christmas (man and woman singing hymns, and star).

1975, Oct. 31   Wmk. 373   Perf. 14

357	A79	3c black & multi	.25	.25
358	A79	15c black & multi	.45	.25
359	A79	25c black & multi	.85	.25
360	A79	30c black & multi	1.10	1.90
a.		Souvenir sheet of 4, #357-360	4.50	4.50
		Nos. 357-360 (4)	2.65	2.65

Festivals celebrated by various groups in Fiji.

Steam Locomotive No. 21 — A80

Sugar mill trains: 15c, Diesel locomotive No. 8. 20c, Diesel locomotive No. 1. 30c, Free passenger train.

1976, Jan. 26   Litho.   Perf. 14½

361	A80	4c yellow & multi	.45	.25
362	A80	15c salmon & multi	.85	.25
363	A80	20c multicolored	.95	1.00
364	A80	30c blue & multi	1.20	1.80
		Nos. 361-364 (4)	3.45	3.45

Fiji Blind Society and Rotary Emblems — A81

Rotary Intl. of Fiji, 40th Anniv.: 25c, Ambulance and Rotary emblems.

Perf. 13x13½

1976, Mar. 26   **Wmk. 373**

365	A81	10c lt green, brn, ultra	.25	.25
366	A81	25c multicolored	.65	.65

De Havilland Drover A82

Planes: 15c, BAC One-Eleven. 25c, Hawker-Siddeley 748. 30c, Britten Norman Trislander.

1976, Sept. 1   **Litho.**   **Perf. 14**

367	A82	4c multicolored	.60	.25
368	A82	15c multicolored	1.10	1.10
369	A82	25c multicolored	1.25	1.25
370	A82	30c multicolored	1.40	1.75
		Nos. 367-370 (4)	4.35	4.35

Fiji air service, 25th anniversary.

Queen's Visit, 1970 — A83

Designs: 25c, King Edward's Chair. 30c, Queen wearing cloth-of-gold supertunica.

1977, Feb. 7   **Litho.**   **Perf. 14x13½**

371	A83	10c silver & multi	.25	.25
372	A83	25c silver & multi	.30	.25
373	A83	30c silver & multi	.40	.30
		Nos. 371-373 (3)	.95	.80

25th anniv. of reign of Elizabeth II.

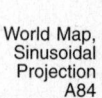

World Map, Sinusoidal Projection A84

Design: 30c, Map showing Fiji Islands.

Wmk. 373

1977, Apr. 12   **Litho.**   **Perf. 14½**

374	A84	4c multicolored	.25	.25
375	A84	30c multicolored	.60	.60

First Joint Council of Ministers Conference of the European Economic Community (EEC) and of African, Caribbean and Pacific States (ACP).

Hibiscus — A85

1977, Aug. 27   **Wmk. 373**   **Perf. 14**

376	A85	4c red	.25	.25
377	A85	15c orange	.25	.25
378	A85	30c pink	.45	.30
379	A85	35c yellow	.75	.90
		Nos. 376-379 (4)	1.70	1.70

Fiji Hibiscus Festival, 21st anniversary.

Drua, Double Canoe — A86

Canoes: 15c, Tabilai. 25c, Takia, dugout outrigger canoe. 40c, Camakau.

1977, Nov. 7   **Litho.**   **Perf. 14½**

380	A86	4c multicolored	.25	.25
381	A86	15c multicolored	.35	.30
382	A86	25c multicolored	.50	.45
383	A86	40c multicolored	.60	.70
		Nos. 380-383 (4)	1.70	1.70

Elizabeth II Coronation Anniversary Issue
Common Design Types
Souvenir Sheet
Unwmk.

1978, Apr. 21   **Litho.**   **Perf. 15**

384		Sheet of 6	1.75	1.75
a.	CD326	25c White hart of Richard II	.25	.25
b.	CD327	25c Elizabeth II	.25	.25
c.	CD328	25c Banded iguana	.25	.25

No. 384 contains 2 se-tenant strips of Nos. 348a-348c, separated by horizontal gutter.

Southern Cross on Naselai Beach — A87

4c, Fiji Defence Force surrounding Southern Cross. 25c, Wright Flyer. 30c, Bristol F2B.

1978, June 26   **Wmk. 373**   **Perf. 14½**

385	A87	4c multicolored	.25	.25
386	A87	15c multicolored	.40	.30
387	A87	25c multicolored	.75	.60
388	A87	30c multicolored	1.10	.75
		Nos. 385-388 (4)	2.50	1.90

50th anniv. of Kingsford-Smith's Trans-Pacific flight, May 31-June 10, 1928 (4c, 15c); 75th anniv. of Wright brothers' first powered flight, Dec. 17, 1903 (25c); 60th anniv. of Royal Air Force, Apr. 1, 1918 (30c).

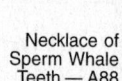

Necklace of Sperm Whale Teeth — A88

Fiji artifacts: 4c, Wooden oil dish in shape of man, vert. 25c, Twin water bottles. 30c, Carved throwing club (Ula), vert.

1978, Aug. 14   **Litho.**   **Perf. 14**

389	A88	4c multicolored	.25	.25
390	A88	15c multicolored	.25	.25
391	A88	25c multicolored	.30	.30
392	A88	30c multicolored	.45	.45
		Nos. 389-392 (4)	1.25	1.25

Christmas Wreath and Candles — A89

Festivals: 15c, Diwali (oil lamps). 25c, Id-Ul-Fitr (fruit, coffeepot and cups). 40c, Chinese New Year (paper dragon).

1978, Oct. 30   **Perf. 14**

393	A89	4c multicolored	.25	.25
394	A89	15c multicolored	.25	.25
395	A89	25c multicolored	.35	.35
396	A89	40c multicolored	.55	.55
		Nos. 393-396 (4)	1.40	1.40

Banded Iguana — A90

Endangered species and Wildlife Fund emblem: 15c, Tree frog. 25c, Long-legged warbler. 30c, Pink-billed parrot finch.

1979, Mar. 19   **Litho.**   **Wmk. 373**

397	A90	4c multicolored	1.25	.50
398	A90	15c multicolored	2.00	1.00
399	A90	25c multicolored	8.75	1.50
400	A90	30c multicolored	8.75	5.00
		Nos. 397-400 (4)	20.75	8.00

Indian Women Making Music — A91

15c, Indian men sitting around kava bowl. 30c, Indian sugar cane, houses. 40c, Sailing ship Leonidas, map of South Pacific.

1979, May 11   **Wmk. 373**   **Perf. 14**

401	A91	4c multicolored	.25	.25
402	A91	15c multicolored	.25	.25
403	A91	30c multicolored	.35	.35
404	A91	40c multicolored	.50	.50
		Nos. 401-404 (4)	1.35	1.35

Arrival of Indians as indentured laborers, cent.

Soccer — A92

Games Emblem and: 15c, Rugby. 30c, Tennis. 40c, Weight lifting.

1979, July 2   **Litho.**   **Perf. 14**

405	A92	4c multicolored	.30	.25
406	A92	15c multicolored	.40	.30
407	A92	30c multicolored	.80	.65
408	A92	40c multicolored	.95	1.25
		Nos. 405-408 (4)	2.45	2.45

6th South Pacific Games.

Old Town Hall, Suva — A93

2c, Dudley Church, Suva. 3c, Telecommunications building, Suva. 4c, 5c, Lautoka Mosque. 6c, GPO, Suva. 8c, 12c, Levuka Public School. 10c, Visitors' Bureau, Suva. 15c, Colonial War Memorial Hospital Suva. 18c, Labasa Sugar Mill. 20c, Rewa Bridge, Nausori. 35c Sacred Heart Cathedral, Suva. 35c Grand Pacific Hotel, Suva. 45c, Shiva Temple, Suva. 50c Serua Island Village. $1, Solo Lighthouse. $2, Baker memorial Hall, Nausori. $5, Government House.

Without Inscribed Date, except #411B (1991)
Chalky Paper (#409-411, 414, 416, 418-419, 425)
Ordinary Paper (#412-413, 415, 417, 420-424)

1979-94   **Wmk. 373**   **Perf. 14**

409	A93	1c multicolored	.30	.60
a.		Ordinary paper	1.75	2.00
b.		Inscribed "1994"	2.00	3.00
410	A93	2c multicolored	.90	.75
a.		Ordinary paper	1.75	2.00
b.		Inscribed "1983"	1.00	.30
c.		Inscribed "1986"	1.50	.25
d.		Inscribed "1991"	.75	.75
e.		Ordinary paper	3.50	3.50
f.		Inscribed "1994"	1.00	1.50
411	A93	3c multicolored	.75	.75
a.		Ordinary paper	2.00	2.00
b.		Inscribed "1993"	4.50	4.50
411B	A93	4c multicolored	1.50	1.50
a.		Inscribed "1993"	6.00	6.00
b.		Inscribed "1994"	3.50	5.50
412	A93	5c multicolored	.25	.25
a.		Inscribed "1983"	.60	.25
413	A93	6c multicolored	.25	.75
a.		Inscribed "1983"	.30	.25
414	A93	10c multicolored	.40	.25
a.		Ordinary paper	2.00	1.75
b.		Inscribed "1991"	2.75	3.00
415	A93	12c multicolored	.40	2.75
a.		Inscribed "1993"	3.50	4.00
b.		Inscribed "1994"	2.00	3.50
416	A93	15c multicolored	.75	.60
a.		Ordinary paper	1.75	1.75
b.		Inscribed "1991"	3.50	3.00
417	A93	18c multicolored	.30	.25
418	A93	20c multicolored	1.00	.30
a.		Ordinary paper	2.50	2.00
b.		Inscribed "1993"	3.75	3.75
c.		Inscribed "1994"	3.50	3.50
419	A93	30c multi, vert.	1.25	.50
a.		Ordinary paper	.60	1.75
420	A93	35c multicolored	.60	1.50
421	A93	45c multicolored	.45	.45
422	A93	50c multicolored	.60	.40
a.		Inscribed "1994"	3.50	4.00

Perf. 14x13½, 13½x14
Size: 45x29mm, 29x45mm (#423)

423	A93	$1 multi, vert.	1.50	2.50
424	A93	$2 multicolored	1.50	1.75
425	A93	$5 multicolored	2.50	2.75
		Nos. 409-425 (18)	15.20	18.60

Issued: 5c, 6c, 12c, 18c, 35c-$2, 12/22/80; No. 411B, 11/1991; others, 11/11/79.

1986-92   **Wmk. 384**
With Date Inscription
1986

410g	A93	2c multicolored	1.25	1.25
413B	A93	8c multicolored	4.50	4.50

1988

410h	A93	2c multicolored	1.00	1.00
411h	A93	3c multicolored	1.00	1.00
411Bh	A93	4c multicolored	1.00	1.00
418h	A93	20c multicolored	2.00	2.00

1990

414i	A93	10c multicolored	1.50	1.50
418i	A93	20c multicolored	2.00	2.00

1991

409j	A93	1c multicolored	1.75	3.50
410j	A93	2c multicolored	1.00	2.00
411j	A93	3c multicolored	1.75	1.75
411Bj	A93	4c multicolored	1.00	1.00
414j	A93	10c multicolored	2.00	2.00
416j	A93	15c multicolored	1.00	1.00
420j	A93	35c multicolored	2.75	2.75
422j	A93	50c multicolored	3.75	3.75
423j	A93	$1 multi, vert.	9.00	9.00

1992

409k	A93	1c multicolored	2.00	2.00
411k	A93	3c multicolored	3.75	3.75
411Bk	A93	4c multicolored	3.75	3.75
416k	A93	15c multicolored	2.75	2.75
418k	A93	20c multicolored	5.50	5.50
420k	A93	35c multicolored	5.50	5.50
422k	A93	50c multicolored	5.50	5.50
423k	A93	$1 multi, vert.	11.00	11.00

Southern Cross, 1873, London 1980 Emblem — A94

1980, Apr. 28   **Wmk. 373**   **Perf. 13½**

426	A94	6c shown	.25	.25
427	A94	20c Levuka, 1910	.35	.25
428	A94	45c Matua, 1936	.70	.50
429	A94	50c Oronsay, 1951	.70	1.00
		Nos. 426-429 (4)	2.00	2.00

London 80 Intl. Stamp Exhib., May 6-14.

Sovi Bay — A95

Designs: 20c, Yanuca Island, evening scene. 45c, Dravuni Beach. 50c, Wakaya Island.

1980, Aug. 18   **Perf. 13½x14**

430	A95	6c shown	.25	.25
431	A95	20c multicolored	.25	.25
432	A95	45c multicolored	.40	.40
433	A95	50c multicolored	.40	.40
		Nos. 430-433 (4)	1.30	1.30

Opening of Parliament, 1979 — A96

1980, Oct. 6   **Litho.**   **Perf. 13**

434	A96	6c shown	.25	.25
435	A96	20c Coat of arms, vert.	.35	.25
436	A96	45c Fiji flag	.50	.50
437	A96	50c Elizabeth II, vert.	.60	.65
		Nos. 434-437 (4)	1.70	1.65

Independence, 10th anniversary.

Coastal Scene, by Semisi Maya — A97

Intl. Year of the Disabled: Paintings and portrait of disabled artist Semisi Maya.

1981, Apr. 21   **Wmk. 373**   **Perf. 14**

438	A97	6c shown	.25	.25
439	A97	35c Underwater Scene	.35	.35
440	A97	50c Maya Painting, vert.	.45	.45
441	A97	50c Peacock, vert.	.50	.50
		Nos. 438-441 (4)	1.55	1.55

Royal Wedding Issue
Common Design Type

1981, July 22   **Wmk. 373**   **Perf. 14**

442	CD331	6c Bouquet	.25	.25
443	CD331	45c Charles	.40	.25
444	CD331	$1 Couple	.70	.85
		Nos. 442-444 (3)	1.35	1.35

Operator
Assistance
Center — A98

35c, Microwave station, map. 50c, Satellite
earth station. 60c, Cableship Retriever.

1981, Aug. 7   Litho.   *Perf. 14*

445	A98	6c shown	.25 .25
446	A98	35c multicolored	.50 .50
447	A98	50c multicolored	.60 .60
448	A98	75c multicolored	.75 .75
		Nos. 445-448 (4)	2.10 2.10

World Food
Day — A99

1981, Sept. 21   Litho.   *Perf. 14½x14*

449	A99	20c multicolored	.45 .25

Ratu Sir Lala
Sukuna, First
Legislative
Council
Speaker — A100

Designs: 35c, Mace, flag. 50c, Suva Civic
Center.

60c, Emblem, participants' flags.

1981, Oct. 19   Litho.   *Perf. 14*

450	A100	6c shown	.25 .25
451	A100	35c multicolored	.40 .40
452	A100	50c multicolored	.60 .60
		Nos. 450-452 (3)	1.25 1.25

Souvenir Sheet

453	A100	60c multicolored	1.10 1.10

27th Commonwealth Parliamentary Assoc.
Conf., Suva.

World War II
Aircraft — A101

6c, Bell P-39 Aircobra. 18c, Consolidated
PBY-5 Catalina. 35c, Curtiss P-40 Warhawk.
60c, Short Singapore.

1981, Dec. 7   Litho.   *Perf. 14*

454	A101	6c multi	1.50 .25
455	A101	18c multi	2.40 .30
456	A101	35c multi	3.25 .65
457	A101	60c multi	3.50 5.00
		Nos. 454-457 (4)	10.65 6.20

Scouting
Year — A102

1982, Feb. 22   Litho.   *Perf. 14½*

458	A102	6c Building	.35 .25
459	A102	20c Sailing, vert.	.60 .35
460	A102	45c Campfire	.75 .50
461	A102	60c Baden-Powell, vert.	1.00 1.00
		Nos. 458-461 (4)	2.70 2.10

Disciplined
Forces — A103

Designs: 12c, UN checkpoint. 30c, Construction project. 40c, Police, car. 70c, Navy
ship.

1982, May 10   Wmk. 373   *Perf. 14*

462	A103	12c multicolored	.60 .25
463	A103	30c multicolored	.70 .55
464	A103	40c multicolored	2.00 1.00
465	A103	70c multicolored	2.00 3.50
		Nos. 462-465 (4)	5.30 5.30

1982 World
Cup — A104

Designs: 6c, Fiji Soccer Assoc. emblem.
18c, Flag, ball. 50c, Stadium. 90c, Emblem.

1982, June 15   Litho.   *Perf. 14*

466	A104	6c multicolored	.25 .25
467	A104	18c multicolored	.35 .25
468	A104	50c multicolored	.85 .50
469	A104	90c multicolored	1.25 1.60
		Nos. 466-469 (4)	2.70 2.60

Princess Diana Issue
Common Design Type

1982, July 1   *Perf. 14½x14*

470	CD333	20c Arms	.35 .35
471	CD333	35c Diana	.50 .35
472	CD333	45c Wedding	.65 .50
473	CD333	$1 Portrait	1.75 1.75
		Nos. 470-473 (4)	3.25 2.95

October Royal
Visit — A105

1982, Nov. 1   Litho.   *Perf. 14*

474	A105	6c Duke of Edinburgh	.30 .30
475	A105	45c Elizabeth II	1.10 1.10

Souvenir Sheet

476		Sheet of 3	3.50 3.50
c.		A105 $1 Britannia	1.00 1.00

No. 476 contains Nos. 474-475 and 476c.

Christmas — A106

Designs: 6c, Holy Family. 20c, Adoration of
the Kings. 35c, Carolers.

$1, Faith, from The Three Virtues, by
Raphael.

1982, Nov. 22   *Perf. 14x14½*

477	A106	6c multi	.25 .25
478	A106	20c multi	.40 .40
479	A106	35c multi	.70 .70
		Nos. 477-479 (3)	1.35 1.35

Souvenir Sheet

480	A106	$1 multi	2.00 2.00

Red-throated
Lory — A107

Parrots: 40c, Blue-crowned lory. 55c,
Sulphur-breasted musk parrot. 70c, Red-
breasted musk parrot.

1983, Feb. 14   Litho.   *Perf. 14*

481	A107	20c shown	2.00 .30
482	A107	40c multicolored	2.50 .60
483	A107	55c multicolored	3.00 1.75
484	A107	70c multicolored	3.25 5.25
		Nos. 481-484 (4)	10.75 7.90

A108

Designs: 8c, Traditional house. 25c, Barefoot firewalkers. 50c, Sugar cane crop. 80c,
Kava Yagona ceremony.

1983, Mar. 14

485	A108	8c multicolored	.25 .25
486	A108	25c multicolored	.30 .30
487	A108	50c multicolored	.50 .50
488	A108	80c multicolored	.65 .65
		Nos. 485-488 (4)	1.70 1.70

Commonwealth Day.

Manned Flight
Bicentenary
A109

1983, July 18   Wmk. 373   *Perf. 14*

489	A109	8c Montgolfiere, 1783	.45 .25
490	A109	20c Wright Flyer	.55 .35
491	A109	25c DC-3	.65 .40
492	A109	40c DeHavilland Comet	1.00 .70
493	A109	50c Boeing 747	1.15 .85
494	A109	58c Columbia space shuttle	1.35 1.00
		Nos. 489-494 (6)	5.15 3.55

Cordia
Subcordata — A110

Flowers: 25c, Gmelina vitiensis. 40c, Car-
ruthersia scandens. $1, Amylotheca
insularum.

1983, Sept. 26   Litho.   *Perf. 14*

495	A110	8c shown	.25 .25
496	A110	25c multicolored	.45 .30
497	A110	40c multicolored	.55 .45
498	A110	$1 multicolored	.90 1.15
		Nos. 495-498 (4)	2.15 2.15

See Nos. 505-508.

Earth Satellite
Station, Fijian Playing
Lali — A111

Perf. 14x13½

1983, Nov. 7   Wmk. 373

499	A111	50c multicolored	.75 .75

Dacryopinax
Spathularia — A112

Various fungi: 15c, Podoscypha involuta.
40c, Lentinus squarrosulus. 50c, Scleroderma
flavidum. $1, Phillipsia domingensis.

1984, Jan. 9   *Perf. 14x13½, 13½x14*

500	A112	8c shown	1.25 .25
501	A112	15c multicolored	1.50 .45
502	A112	40c multicolored	2.50 1.10
503	A112	50c multicolored	2.50 1.50
504	A112	$1 multicolored	3.75 3.50
		Nos. 500-504 (5)	11.50 6.80

Flower Type of 1983

Designs: 15c, Pseuderanthemum lax-
iflorum. 20c, Storkiella vitiensis. 50c, Paphia
vitiensis. 70c, Elaeocarpus storkii.

1984   Litho.   *Perf. 14x14½*

505	A110	15c multicolored	.40 .25
506	A110	20c multicolored	.50 .30
507	A110	50c multicolored	.70 .80
508	A110	70c multicolored	.80 1.05
		Nos. 505-508 (4)	2.40 2.40

Lloyd's List Issue
Common Design Type
Perf. 14½x14

1984, May 7   Wmk. 373

509	CD335	8c Tui Lau on reef	.80 .25
510	CD335	40c Tofua	1.50 .90
511	CD335	55c Canberra	1.50 1.50
512	CD335	60c Suva Wharf	1.50 2.25
		Nos. 509-512 (4)	5.30 4.90

Souvenir Sheet

1984 UPU Congress — A113

1984, June 14   Litho.   *Perf. 14½*

513	A113	25c Map	2.50 2.50

Ausipex
'84 — A114

Designs: 8c, Yalavou cattle. 25c, Wailoa
Power Station, vert. 40c, Boeing 737. $1,
Cargo ship Fua Kavenga.

Perf. 14x14½

1984, Sept. 17   Wmk. 373

514	A114	8c multicolored	.25 .25
515	A114	25c multicolored	.50 .55
516	A114	40c multicolored	1.90 .95
517	A114	$1 multicolored	1.50 2.40
		Nos. 514-517 (4)	4.15 4.15

No. 515 is perf. 14½x14

Christmas
A115

Designs: 8c, Church on hill. 20c, Sailing.
25c, Santa, children, tree. 40c, Going to
church. $1, Family, tree, vert.

1984, Nov. 5   Litho.   *Perf. 14*

518	A115	8c multicolored	.25 .25
519	A115	20c multicolored	.50 .25
520	A115	25c multicolored	.50 .25
521	A115	40c multicolored	.50 .60
522	A115	$1 multicolored	.95 1.35
		Nos. 518-522 (5)	2.70 2.70

Butterflies
A116

Designs: 8c, Monarch. 25c, Common
eggfly. 40c, Long-tailed blue, vert. $1,
Meadow argus, vert.

1985, Feb. 4   *Perf. 14*

523	A116	8c multicolored	2.00 .25
524	A116	25c multicolored	3.25 .80
525	A116	40c multicolored	4.00 1.40
526	A116	$1 multicolored	5.75 6.50
		Nos. 523-526 (4)	15.00 8.95

EXPO '85, Tsukuba,
Japan — A117

Designs: 20c, Outrigger canoe, Toberua
Island. 25c, Wainivula Falls. 50c, Mana Island.
$1, Sawa-I-Lau Caves.

1985, Mar. 18   Litho.   *Perf. 14*
527	A117	20c multi	.90	.40
528	A117	25c multicolored	1.20	.50
529	A117	35c multicolored	1.35	1.25
530	A117	$1 multicolored	1.60	2.50
		Nos. 527-530 (4)	5.05	4.65

Queen Mother 85th Birthday Issue
Common Design Type

Designs: 8c, Holding Prince Andrew. 25c, With Prince Charles. 40c, On Oaks Day, Epsom Races. 50c, Holding Prince Henry. $1, In Royal Wedding Cavalcade, 1981.

Perf. 14½x14

1985, June 7   Wmk. 384
531	CD336	8c multicolored	.25	.25
532	CD336	25c multicolored	.40	.40
533	CD336	40c multicolored	1.00	.80
534	CD336	50c multicolored	1.00	1.20
		Nos. 531-534 (4)	2.65	2.65

Souvenir Sheet
535	CD336	$1 multicolored	3.50	3.50

Shallow Water Fish — A118

Designs: 40c, Horned squirrel fish. 50c, Yellow-banded goatfish. 55c, Fairy cod. $1, Peacock rock cod.

1985, Sept. 23   *Perf. 14½*
536	A118	40c multicolored	1.50	.75
537	A118	50c multicolored	1.75	1.00
538	A118	55c multicolored	2.00	1.50
539	A118	$1 multicolored	2.75	4.50
		Nos. 536-539 (4)	8.00	7.75

Sea Birds — A119

Designs: 15c, Collared petrel. 20c, Lesser frigate bird. 50c, Brown booby. $1, Crested tern.

1985, Nov. 4   *Perf. 14*
540	A119	15c multi	2.50	.45
541	A119	20c multi	2.50	.50
542	A119	50c multi	4.75	4.00
543	A119	$1 multi	7.25	8.00
		Nos. 540-543 (4)	17.00	12.95

Queen Elizabeth II 60th Birthday Issue
Common Design Type

20c, With the Duke of York at the Royal Tournament, 1936. 25c, On Buckingham Palace balcony, wedding of Princess Margaret and Anthony Armstrong-Jones, 1960. 40c, Inspecting the Guard of Honor, Suva, 1982. 50c, State visit to Luxembourg, 1976. $1, Visiting Crown Agents' offices, 1983.

Perf. 14x14½

1986, Apr. 21   Wmk. 384
544	CD337	20c scar, blk & sil	.40	.30
545	CD337	25c ultra & multi	.40	.30
546	CD337	40c green & multi	.65	.50
547	CD337	50c violet & multi	.75	.75
548	CD337	$1 rose vio & multi	.80	1.15
		Nos. 544-548 (5)	3.00	3.00

Intl. Peace Year — A120

1986, June 23   Wmk. 373   *Perf. 14½*
549	A120	8c shown	.50	.25
550	A120	40c Dove	.85	1.10

Halley's Comet — A121

Designs: 25c, Newton's reflector telescope. 40c, Comet over Lomaiviti. $1, Comet nucleus, Giotto probe.

1986, July 7   *Perf. 13½*
551	A121	25c multicolored	2.00	.55
552	A121	40c multicolored	2.25	.95
553	A121	$1 multicolored	2.75	5.50
		Nos. 551-553 (3)	7.00	7.00

Reptiles and Amphibians A122

1986, Aug. 1   *Perf. 14½*
554	A122	8c Ground frog	1.05	.25
555	A122	20c Burrowing snake	1.50	.30
556	A122	25c Spotted gecko	1.50	.35
557	A122	40c Crested iguana	1.60	.85
558	A122	50c Blotched skink	1.60	2.50
559	A122	$1 Speckled skink	2.00	5.50
		Nos. 554-559 (6)	9.25	9.75

Ancient War Clubs — A123

1986, Nov. 10   Wmk. 384   *Perf. 14*
560	A123	25c Gatawaka	.95	.35
561	A123	40c Siriti	1.25	.60
562	A123	50c Bulibuli	1.40	1.60
563	A123	$1 Culacula	2.50	3.00
		Nos. 560-563 (4)	6.10	5.55

Cone Shells — A124

1987, Feb. 26   Litho.   *Perf. 14x14½*
564	A124	15c Weasel	1.25	.25
565	A124	20c Pertusus	1.25	.30
566	A124	25c Admiral	1.40	.30
567	A124	40c Leaden	1.50	1.00
568	A124	50c Imperial	1.75	2.25
569	A124	$1 Geography	2.00	5.00
		Nos. 564-569 (6)	9.15	9.10

Souvenir Sheet

Tagimoucia Flower — A125

1987, Apr. 23   Wmk. 373   *Perf. 14½*
570	A125	$1 multicolored	4.75	3.75

No. 570 Overprinted

1987, June 13
571	A125	$1 multicolored	40.00 40.00

Intl. Year of Shelter for the Homeless A126

Designs: 55c, Hut. 70c, Government housing.

1987, July 20   *Perf. 14*
572	A126	55c multicolored	.65	.65
573	A126	70c multicolored	.85	.85

Beetles A127

Designs: 20c, Bulbogaster ctenostomoides. 25c, Paracupta flaviventris. 40c, Cerambyrhynchus schoenherri. 50c, Rhinoscapha lagopyga. $1, Xixuthrus heros.

1987, Sept. 7   Wmk. 384
574	A127	20c multicolored	2.50	.45
575	A127	25c multicolored	2.50	.55
576	A127	40c multicolored	3.00	1.75
577	A127	50c multicolored	3.25	3.50
578	A127	$1 multicolored	4.00	8.50
		Nos. 574-578 (5)	15.25	14.75

Christmas A128

Designs: 8c, Holy Family, vert. 40c, Shepherds see star. 50c, Three Kings follow star. $1, Adoration of the Magi.

1987, Nov. 19
579	A128	8c multicolored	1.00	.25
580	A128	40c multicolored	2.25	.65
581	A128	50c multicolored	2.75	1.50
582	A128	$1 multicolored	3.75	5.00
		Nos. 579-582 (4)	9.75	7.40

World Expo '88, Apr. 30-Oct. 30, Brisbane, Australia — A129

1988, Apr. 27   Litho.   *Perf. 14*
583	A129	30c Windsurfing	1.60 1.60

Intl. Council of Women, Cent. — A130

1988, June 14
584	A130	45c Fiji Nouna	1.30 1.30

Pottery — A131

Designs: 9c, Lapita (bowl). 23c, Kuro (cooking pot). 58c, Saqa (Priest drinking vessel).

63c, Saqa, diff. 69c, Ramarama (oil lamp). 75c, Tall Kuro, vert.

Wmk. 384, 373 (69c)
1988, Aug. 29   Litho.   *Perf. 13½*
585	A131	9c multicolored	.25	.25
586	A131	23c multicolored	.40	.25
587	A131	58c multicolored	.80	.80
588	A131	63c multicolored	.90	.90
589	A131	69c multicolored	.95	1.00
590	A131	75c multicolored	1.10	1.20
		Nos. 585-590 (6)	4.40	4.40

Fiji Tree Frog — A132

1988, Oct. 3   Wmk. 384   *Perf. 14*
591	A132	18c multicolored	4.50	3.00
592	A132	23c multi, diff.	5.00	3.00
593	A132	30c multi, diff.	5.75	5.75
594	A132	45c multi, diff.	6.50	10.00
		Nos. 591-594 (4)	21.75	21.75

World Wildlife Fund.

Indigenous Flowering Plants — A133

Designs: 9c, Dendrobium mohlianum. 30c, Dendrobium cattilare. 45c, Degeneria vitiensis. $1, Degeneria roseiflora.

1988, Nov. 21   Wmk. 373
595	A133	9c multicolored	.85	.25
596	A133	30c multicolored	1.25	.45
597	A133	45c multicolored	.95	1.35
598	A133	$1 multicolored	1.75	2.75
		Nos. 595-598 (4)	4.80	4.80

Intl. Red Cross and Red Crescent Orgs., 125th Anniv. — A134

Designs: 58c, Battle of Solferino, 1859. 63c, Jean-Henri Dunant, vert. 69c, Medicine. $1, Anniv. emblem, vert.

1989, Feb. 6   Wmk. 384
599	A134	58c multicolored	1.75	1.00
600	A134	63c multicolored	1.75	1.10
601	A134	69c multicolored	2.25	1.40
602	A134	$1 multicolored	2.75	1.90
		Nos. 599-602 (4)	8.50	5.40

Epic Voyage of William Bligh — A135

Designs: 45c, Plans (line drawing) of the Bounty's launch. 58c, Diary and inscription on artifacts "The cup I eat my miserable allowance out of." 80c, Silhouette, lightning, quote "O Almighty God, relieve us. . ." $1, Map of Bligh's Islands, launch and compass rose.

1989, Apr. 28   *Perf. 14½*
603	A135	45c multicolored	2.10	.70
604	A135	58c multicolored	2.25	1.50
605	A135	80c multicolored	3.50	3.25
606	A135	$1 multicolored	4.75	3.50
		Nos. 603-606 (4)	12.60	8.95

Coral — A136

Designs: 46c, Platygyra daedalea. 60c, Caulastrea furcata. 75c, Acropora echinata. 90c, Acropora humilis.

1989, Aug. 21   Wmk. 373   Perf. 14
607	A136	46c multicolored	2.00	1.00
608	A136	60c multicolored	2.50	2.00
609	A136	75c multicolored	3.00	2.50
610	A136	90c multicolored	3.75	3.00
		Nos. 607-610 (4)	11.25	8.50

Nos. 609-610 vert.

1990 World Cup Soccer Championships, Italy — A137

Various Fijian soccer players.

1989, Sept. 25   Wmk. 384   Perf. 14½
611	A137	35c shown	1.35	.75
612	A137	63c multi, diff.	2.40	2.40
613	A137	70c multi, diff.	2.60	2.60
614	A137	85c multi, diff.	2.90	3.00
		Nos. 611-614 (4)	9.25	8.75

Christmas — A138

Designs: 9c, Church service. 45c, *Delonix regia* tree. $1, Holy family. $1.40, Tree, Fijian children.

1989, Nov. 1   Wmk. 373
615	A138	9c multicolored	.40	.25
616	A138	45c multicolored	1.00	.25
617	A138	$1 multicolored	2.00	2.10
618	A138	$1.40 multicolored	2.25	3.00
		Nos. 615-618 (4)	5.65	5.60

Fish — A139

Designs: 50c, Mangrove jack. 70c, Orange-spotted therapon perch. 85c, Spotted scat. $1, Flagtail.

1990, Apr. 23   Litho.   Wmk. 384
619	A139	50c multicolored	2.60	1.00
620	A139	70c multicolored	3.50	3.50
621	A139	85c multicolored	3.75	3.75
622	A139	$1 multicolored	4.25	4.25
		Nos. 619-622 (4)	14.10	12.50

Souvenir Sheet

Stamp World London '90 A140

1990, May 1
623	A140	Sheet of 2	12.50	9.50
a.		$1 No. 243	3.75	2.60
b.		$2 No. 249	8.00	6.00

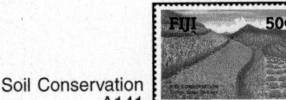

Soil Conservation A141

50c, Vertiver grass contours. 70c, Mulching. 90c, Contour cultivation. $1, Proper land use.

1990, July 23   Litho.   Wmk. 373
625	A141	50c multi	1.25	.65
626	A141	70c multi	1.75	1.75
627	A141	90c multi	1.90	2.25
628	A141	$1 multi, vert.	2.00	2.50
		Nos. 625-628 (4)	6.90	7.15

Trees — A142

25c, Dacrydium nidulum. 35c, Decussocarpus vitiensis. $1, Agathis vitiensis. $1.55, Santalum yasi.

1990, Oct. 2
629	A142	25c multi	.90	.25
630	A142	35c multi	1.00	.35
631	A142	$1 multi	3.00	3.00
632	A142	$1.55 multi	4.25	5.50
		Nos. 629-632 (4)	9.15	9.10

Christmas A143

Christmas carols: 10c, Hark! The Herald Angels Sing. 35c, Silent Night. 65c, Joy to the World! $1, The Race that Long in Darkness Pined.

1990, Nov. 26   Wmk. 373   Perf. 14
633	A143	10c multicolored	.40	.25
634	A143	35c multicolored	1.00	.35
635	A143	65c multicolored	1.60	1.75
636	A143	$1 multicolored	2.50	2.75
		Nos. 633-636 (4)	5.50	5.10

Scenic Views — A144

Designs: 35c, Sigatoka sand dunes. 50c, Monu, Monuriki Islands. 65c, Ravilevu Nature Reserve. $1, Colo-I-Suva Forest Park.

1991, Feb. 25   Wmk. 384
637	A144	35c multicolored	1.35	.35
638	A144	50c multicolored	2.25	1.25
639	A144	65c multicolored	2.60	2.75
640	A144	$1 multicolored	4.00	4.50
		Nos. 637-640 (4)	10.20	8.85

Discovery of Rotuma Island, Bicent. — A145

Designs: 54c, HMS Pandora. 70c, Map of Rotuma Island. 75c, Natives. $1, Mt. Solroroa, Uea Island.

1991, Aug. 8   Wmk. 373   Perf. 14
641	A145	54c multicolored	2.75	1.25
642	A145	70c multicolored	3.00	3.00
643	A145	75c multicolored	3.00	3.00
644	A145	$1 multicolored	4.75	4.75
		Nos. 641-644 (4)	13.50	12.00

Crabs — A146

Designs: 38c, Scylla serrata. 54c, Metopograpsus messor. 96c, Parasesarma erythrodactyla. $1.65, Cardisoma carnifex.

1991, Sept. 26   Perf. 14½x14
645	A146	38c multicolored	1.15	.45
646	A146	54c multicolored	1.75	.75
647	A146	96c multicolored	2.90	2.75
648	A146	$1.65 multicolored	4.00	5.50
		Nos. 645-648 (4)	9.80	9.45

Christmas — A147

Designs: 11c, Mary, Joseph travelling to Bethlehem. 75c, Manger scene. 96c, Jesus being blessed at temple in Jerusalem. $1, Baby Jesus.

1991, Oct. 31   Wmk. 384   Perf. 14
649	A147	11c multicolored	.65	.25
650	A147	75c multicoloed	2.00	.75
651	A147	96c multicolored	2.10	2.50
652	A147	$1 multicolored	2.25	2.50
		Nos. 649-652 (4)	7.00	6.00

No. 649 exists with wmk. 373.

Air Pacific, 40th Anniv. — A148

Airplanes: 54c, Dragon Rapide, Harold Gatty, founder. 75c, Douglas DC3. 96c, ATR 42. $1.40, Boeing 767.

1991, Nov. 18   Perf. 14½
653	A148	54c multicolored	2.40	1.25
654	A148	75c multicolored	3.25	2.50
655	A148	96c multicolored	3.50	3.50
656	A148	$1.40 multicolored	4.75	5.00
		Nos. 653-656 (4)	13.90	12.25

Expo '92, Seville A149

Designs: 27c, Traditional dance and costumes. 75c, Faces of people. 96c, Train and gold bars. $1.40, Cruise ship in port.

1992, Mar. 23   Litho.   Wmk. 373
657	A149	27c multicolored	.75	.50
658	A149	75c multicolored	1.75	1.75
659	A149	96c multicolored	8.25	5.50
660	A149	$1.40 multicolored	8.75	8.25
		Nos. 657-660 (4)	19.50	16.00

Inter-Islands Shipping A150

1992, June 22   Perf. 14
661	A150	38c Tabusoro	2.75	.75
662	A150	54c Degei II	3.25	1.50
663	A150	$1.40 Dausoko	5.50	4.50
664	A150	$1.65 Nivanga	5.50	4.50
		Nos. 661-664 (4)	17.00	11.25

1992 Summer Olympics, Barcelona — A151

1992, July 30   Perf. 13½
665	A151	20c Running	1.00	.25
666	A151	86c Yachting	3.00	2.50
667	A151	$1.34 Swimming	3.50	4.00
668	A151	$1.50 Judo	3.50	4.00
		Nos. 665-668 (4)	11.00	10.75

Levuka — A152

30c, European War Memorial. 42c, Map. 59c, Beach Street. 77c, Sacred Heart Church, vert. $2, Deed of Cession Site, vert.

1992, Sept. 21   Perf. 14½
669	A152	30c multicolored	.45	.30
670	A152	42c multicolored	.65	.50
671	A152	59c multicolored	.95	.95
672	A152	77c multicolored	1.20	1.25
673	A152	$2 multicolored	2.50	2.75
		Nos. 669-673 (5)	5.75	5.75

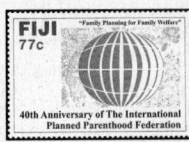

Intl. Planned Parenthood Federation, 40th Anniv. — A153

1992, Nov. 2   Perf. 15x14½
674	A153	77c Globe	1.35	1.00
675	A153	$2 Family	3.50	3.50

Christmas A154

Bible interpretations: 12c, "God so loved the world..." 77c, "We love because God first loved us." 83c, "It is more blessed to give..." $2, "Every good gift..."

1992, Nov. 17
676	A154	12c multicolored	.75	.25
677	A154	77c multicolored	2.25	1.75
678	A154	83c multicolored	2.50	2.00
679	A154	$2 multicolored	4.00	5.50
		Nos. 676-679 (4)	9.50	9.50

Peace Corps in Fiji, 25th Anniv. — A155

Designs: 59c, Voluntary service. 77c, Fiji/US friendship. $1, Education. $2, Income generating business through volunteer help.

Wmk. 373

1993, Feb. 22   Litho.   Perf. 14½
680	A155	59c multicolored	1.40	.75
681	A155	77c multicolored	1.90	1.00
682	A155	$1 multicolored	2.00	1.50
683	A155	$2 multicolored	3.50	5.00
		Nos. 680-683 (4)	8.80	8.25

Hong Kong Rugby Sevens — A156

Designs: 77c, Players performing traditional Cibi Dance. $1.06, Two players, map of Fiji, Hong Kong, and Australia. $2, Stadium, players in scrum.

Perf. 14x15

1993, Mar. 26   Litho.   Wmk. 384
684	A156	77c multicolored	1.75	1.50
685	A156	$1.06 multicolored	4.00	2.50
686	A156	$2 multicolored	4.25	5.50
		Nos. 684-686 (3)	10.00	9.50

Royal Air Force, 75th Anniv.
Common Design Type

Designs: 59c, Gloster Gauntlet. 77c, Armstrong Whitworth Whitley. 83c, Bristol F2b. $2, Hawker Tempest.
No. 691: a, Vickers Vildebeest. b, Handley Page Hampden. c, Vickers Vimy. d, British Aerospace Hawk.

1993, Apr. 1   Perf. 14
687	CD350	59c multicolored	1.50	.75
688	CD350	77c multicolored	1.75	1.40
689	CD350	83c multicolored	2.25	1.75
690	CD350	$2 multicolored	3.50	4.75
		Nos. 687-690 (4)	9.00	8.65

Souvenir Sheet of 4
691	CD350	$1 #a.-d.	8.75	8.75
e.		Overprinted in sheet margin	9.75	9.75

Overprint on No. 691e is exhibition emblem for Hong Kong '94.

Nudibranchs A157

12c, Chromodoris fidelis. 42c, Halgerda carlsoni. 53c, Chromodoris lochi. 83c,

Glaucus atlanticus. $1, Phyllidia bourguini. $2, Hexabranchus sanguineus.

Wmk. 373

1993, July 27		**Litho.**	**Perf. 14**	
692	A157	12c multicolored	.80	.25
693	A157	42c multicolored	1.60	.50
694	A157	53c multicolored	1.75	1.00
695	A157	83c multicolored	2.50	2.25
696	A157	$1 multicolored	2.90	2.25
697	A157	$2 multicolored	4.00	6.50
	Nos. 692-697 (6)		13.55	12.75

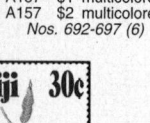

Tropical Fruit — A158

Wmk. 373

1993, Oct. 25		**Litho.**	**Perf. 13½**	
698	A158	30c Mango	1.90	.50
699	A158	42c Guava	2.10	1.00
700	A158	$1 Lemon	3.75	3.00
701	A158	$2 Soursop	6.00	8.00
	Nos. 698-701 (4)		13.75	12.50

Souvenir Sheet

Hong Kong '94 A159

Butterflies: a, Caper white. b, Blue branded king crow. c, Vagrant. d, Glasswing.

Perf. 14½x13

1994, Feb. 18		**Litho.**	**Wmk. 373**	
702	A159	$1 Sheet of 4, #a.-d.	9.00	9.00

Easter A160

59c, The Last Supper. 77c, The Crucifixion. $1, The Resurrection. $2, Jesus showing his wounds to his disciples.

Perf. 14x15, 15x14

1994, Mar. 31		**Litho.**	**Wmk. 373**	
703	A160	59c multi	1.35	.50
704	A160	77c multi, vert.	1.75	.75
705	A160	$1 multi	2.00	1.75
706	A160	$2 multi, vert.	3.75	5.25
	Nos. 703-706 (4)		8.85	8.25

Edible Seaweeds — A161

42c, Codium bulbopilum. 83c, Coulerpa racemosa. $1, Hypnea pannosa. $2, Gracilaria.

Wmk. 384

1994, June 6		**Litho.**	**Perf. 14**	
707	A161	42c multicolored	1.10	.40
708	A161	83c multicolored	2.25	1.60
709	A161	$1 multicolored	2.75	1.90
710	A161	$2 multicolored	4.00	6.25
	Nos. 707-710 (4)		10.10	10.15

Souvenir Sheet

White-Collared Kingfisher — A162

Designs: a, On branch. b, In flight.

Wmk. 373

1994, Aug.		**Litho.**	**Perf. 13½**	
711	A162	$1.50 Sheet of 2, #a.-b.	11.50	11.50
	c.	Overprinted in sheet margin	11.50	11.50

Overprint on No. 711c consists of exhibition emblem and "JAKARTA '95."
Issued: #711, 8/16; #711c, 8/19.

Souvenir Sheet

Singpex '94 A163

Neoveitchia storckii: a, Complete tree. b, Fruits, inflorescence.

1994, Aug. 31		**Wmk. 384**	**Perf. 14**	
712	A163	$1.50 Sheet of 2, #a.-b.	9.00	9.00

First Catholic Missionaries in Fiji, 150th Anniv. — A164

Designs: 23c, Father Ioane Batita. 31c, Local catechist. 44c, Sacred Heart Cathedral. 63c, Lomary Church. 81c, Pope Gregory XVI. $2, Pope John Paul II.

Wmk. 373

1994, Dec. 16		**Litho.**	**Perf. 14**	
713	A164	23c multicolored	.50	.25
714	A164	31c multicolored	.60	.25
715	A164	44c multicolored	.80	.60
716	A164	63c multicolored	1.10	1.00
717	A164	81c multicolored	1.50	1.50
718	A164	$2 multicolored	4.00	4.75
	Nos. 713-718 (6)		8.50	8.35

Souvenir Sheet

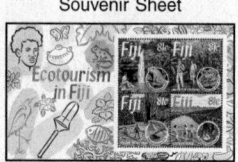

Ecotourism in Fiji — A165

Designs: a, Waterfalls, banded iguana. b, Mountain trekking, Fiji tree frog. c, Bilibili River trip, kingfisher. d, Historic sites, flying fox.

Wmk. 373

1995, Mar. 27		**Litho.**	**Perf. 14**	
719	A165	81c Sheet of 4, #a.-d.	8.25	8.25

End of World War II, 50th Anniv.
Common Design Types

Designs: 13c, Fijian regiment guarding crashed Japanese Zero Fighter. 63c, Kameli Airstrip, Solomon Islands, built by Fijian regiment. 87c, Corp. Sukanaivalu VC, Victoria Cross. $1.12, HMS Fiji. $2, Reverse side of War Medal 1939-45.

Wmk. 373

1995, May 8		**Litho.**	**Perf. 13½**	
720	CD351	13c multicolored	1.25	.25
721	CD351	63c multicolored	2.75	1.75
722	CD351	87c multicolored	3.25	2.75
723	CD351	$1.12 multicolored	3.75	3.25
	Nos. 720-723 (4)		11.00	8.00

Souvenir Sheet
Perf. 14

724	CD352	$2 multicolored	6.50	6.50

Birds — A166

1c, Red-headed parrotfinch. 2c, Golden whistler. 3c, Ogea flycatcher. 4c, Peale's pigeon. 6c, Blue-crested broadbill. 13c, Island thrush. 23c, Many-colored fruit dove. 31c, Mangrove heron. 44c, Purple swamphen. 63c, Fiji goshawk. 81c, Kadavu fantail. 87c, Collared lory. $1, Scarlet robin. $2, Peregrine falcon. $3, Barn owl. $5, Yellow-breasted musk parrot.

1995	**Litho.**	**Wmk. 373**	**Perf. 13**	
725	A166	1c multi	1.00	1.75
726	A166	2c multi	1.00	1.75
727	A166	3c multi	1.00	1.75
728	A166	4c multi	1.00	1.75
729	A166	6c multi	1.00	1.75
730	A166	13c multi	.75	.25
731	A166	23c multi	.75	.30
732	A166	31c multi	.85	.35
733	A166	44c multi	1.00	.40
734	A166	63c multi	1.50	.50
735	A166	81c multi	1.75	.65
736	A166	87c multi	2.00	.75
737	A166	$1 multi	2.00	.85
738	A166	$2 multi	3.00	1.75
739	A166	$3 multi	4.25	3.75
739A	A166	$5 multi	4.50	5.50
	Nos. 725-739A (16)		27.35	23.80

Issued: 13c, 23c, 31c, 44c, 63c, 81c, $2, $3, 7/25; 1c, 2c, 3c, 4c, 6c, 87c, $1, $5, 11/7.
See No. 1011.
For surcharges, see Nos. 1149-1160, 1191-1197C, 1214-1223A, 1249-1254G, 1314-1317, 1346-1347, 1353-1356, 1370-1371, 1407A-1407B.

Souvenir Sheet

Singapore '95 — A167

Orchids: a, Arundina graminifolia. b, Phaius tankervilliae.

Wmk. 373

1995, Sept. 1		**Litho.**	**Perf. 14**	
740	A167	$1 Sheet of 2, #a.-b.	7.50	7.50

Independence, 25th Anniv. — A168

Designs: 81c, Pres. Kamisese Mara, Parliament Building. 87c, Fijian youth. $1.06, Playing rugby. $2, Air Pacific Boeing 747.

Wmk. 373

1995, Oct. 4		**Litho.**	**Perf. 14**	
741	A168	81c multicolored	1.50	1.10
742	A168	87c multicolored	1.35	1.35
743	A168	$1.06 multicolored	2.10	2.25
744	A168	$2 multicolored	4.25	4.50
	Nos. 741-744 (4)		9.20	9.20

Christmas — A169

Paintings: 10c, Praying Madonna with the Crown of Stars, from Correggio Workshop. 63c, Madonna and Child with Crowns on porcelain. 87c, The Holy Virgin with the Holy Child and St. John, after Titian. $2, The Holy Family and St. John, from Rubens Workshop.

Wmk. 373

1995, Nov. 22		**Litho.**	**Perf. 13**	
745	A169	10c multicolored	.30	.25
746	A169	63c multicolored	1.20	1.00
747	A169	87c multicolored	1.60	1.50
748	A169	$2 multicolored	3.50	3.75
	Nos. 745-748 (4)		6.60	6.50

Arrival of Banabans in Fiji, 50th Anniv. — A170

Perf. 14x14½, 14½x14

1996, Jan. 24		**Litho.**	**Wmk. 373**	
749	A170	81c Trolling lure	2.25	1.25
750	A170	87c Canoes	2.50	1.25
751	A170	$1.12 Warrior, vert.	2.75	2.00
752	A170	$2 Frigate bird, vert.	5.25	7.00
	Nos. 749-752 (4)		12.75	11.50

A171

Radio, Cent.: 44c, L2B portable tape recorder. 63c, Fiji Broadcasting Center. 81c, Communications satellite in orbit. $3, Marconi.

Wmk. 373

1996, Mar. 11		**Litho.**	**Perf. 14½**	
753	A171	44c multicolored	.90	.75
754	A171	63c multicolored	1.25	.75
755	A171	81c multicolored	1.60	1.25
756	A171	$3 multicolored	5.25	6.50
	Nos. 753-756 (4)		9.00	9.00

A172

Ancient Chinese artifacts: 63c, Bronze monster mask and ring, c. 450 BC. 81c, Archer, 210 BC. $1, Plate, Hsuan Te Period, 1426-35. $2, Central Asian horseman, dated 706. 30c, Yan Deng Mountain.

Wmk. 384

1996, Apr. 25		**Litho.**	**Perf. 13½**	
757	A172	63c multicolored	1.25	.90
758	A172	81c multicolored	1.60	1.00
759	A172	$1 multicolored	2.00	1.50
760	A172	$2 multicolored	3.50	4.25
	Nos. 757-760 (4)		8.35	7.25

Souvenir Sheet
Perf. 13½x13

761	A172	30c multicolored	2.50	2.50

No. 761 contains one 48x76mm stamp.
CHINA '96, 9th Asian Intl. Philatelic Exhibition.

A173

Wmk. 373

1996, June 18		**Litho.**	**Perf. 14**	
762	A173	31c Hurdling	.65	.25
763	A173	63c Judo	1.50	1.00
764	A173	87c Sailboarding	2.10	1.75
765	A173	$1.12 Swimming	2.40	2.50
	Nos. 762-765 (4)		6.65	5.50

Souvenir Sheet

766	A173	$2 Athlete, 1896	3.75	3.75

Modern Olympic Games, cent.

A174

31c, Computerized telephone exchange, horiz. 44c, Mail being unloaded, horiz. 81c, Manual switchboard operator. $1, Mail delivery.
No. 771: a, #117. b, #527.

1996, July 1
767	A174	31c multicolored	.60	.35
768	A174	44c multicolored	.85	.75
769	A174	81c multicolored	1.20	1.50
770	A174	$1 multicolored	2.10	2.10
		Nos. 767-770 (4)	4.75	4.70

Souvenir Sheet of 2
771	A174	$1.50 #a.-b.	8.25	8.25

Creation of independent Postal, Telecommunications Companies.

UNICEF, 50th Anniv. — A175

Designs: 81c, "Our children, our future." 87c, Village scene. $1, "Living in harmony the world over." $2, "Their future."

Wmk. 384
1996, Aug. 13   Litho.   Perf. 14
772	A175	81c multicolored	2.00	1.50
773	A175	87c multicolored	2.00	1.50
774	A175	$1 multicolored	2.10	1.60
775	A175	$2 multicolored	3.25	4.75
		Nos. 772-775 (4)	9.35	9.35

Nadi Intl. Airport, 50th Anniv. — A176

Designs: 31c, First airplane in Fiji, 1921. 44c, Nadi Airport commences Commercial Operations, 1946. 63c, First jet in Fiji, 1959. 87c, Airport entrance. $1, Control tower, 1996. $2, Global positioning system, first commercial use, 1994.

Wmk. 373
1996, Oct. 1   Litho.   Perf. 14
776	A176	31c multicolored	.80	.35
777	A176	44c multicolored	1.00	.50
778	A176	63c multicolored	1.60	1.15
779	A176	87c multicolored	1.75	1.60
780	A176	$1 multicolored	2.10	1.90
781	A176	$2 multicolored	3.50	5.00
		Nos. 776-781 (6)	10.75	10.50

Christmas A177

Scene from the Christmas story and native story or scene: 13c, Angel Gabriel & Mary, beating of Lali. 81c, Shepherds with sheep, Fijian canoe. $1, Wise men on camels, multiracial Fiji. $3, Mary, Christ Child in stable, blowing of conch shell.

1996, Nov. 20   Wmk. 373
782	A177	13c multicolored	.50	.25
783	A177	81c multicolored	1.90	1.00
784	A177	$1 multicolored	2.10	1.50
785	A177	$3 multicolored	6.25	7.25
		Nos. 782-785 (4)	10.75	10.00

Hong Kong '97 — A178

Cattle: a, Brahman. b, Freisian (Holstein). c, Hereford. d, Fiji draught bullock.

1997, Feb. 12
786	A178	$1 Sheet of 4, #a.-d.	8.50	8.50

Souvenir Sheet

Black-Faced Shrikebill — A179

1997, Feb. 21   Perf. 14x15
787	A179	$2 multicolored	4.25	4.25

Singpex '97.

Orchids — A180

Designs: 81c, Dendrobium biflorum. 87c, Dendrobium dactylodes. $1.06, Spathoglottis pacifica. $2, Dendrobium macropus.

Wmk. 384
1997, Apr. 22   Litho.   Perf. 14
788	A180	81c multicolored	2.40	1.50
789	A180	87c multicolored	2.40	1.50

Wmk. 373
790	A180	$1.06 multicolored	2.75	2.50
791	A180	$2 multicolored	4.50	4.50
		Nos. 788-791 (4)	12.05	10.00

Souvenir Sheet

Hawksbill Turtle — A181

Designs: a, 63c, Female laying eggs. b, 81c, Baby turtles emerging from nest. c, $1.06 Young turtles in water. d, $2, One adult in water, coral.

1997, May 26   Wmk. 373
792	A181	Sheet of 4, #a.-d.	10.00	10.00

Coral — A182

Designs: 63c, Branching hard coral 87c, Massive hard coral. $1, Soft coral, sinularia. $3, Soft coral, dendronephthya.

Wmk. 373
1997, July 16   Litho.   Perf. 14
793	A182	63c multicolored	1.25	.50
794	A182	87c multicolored	1.90	1.00
795	A182	$1 multicolored	2.10	1.50
796	A182	$3 multicolored	5.25	7.50
		Nos. 793-796 (4)	10.50	10.50

Fijian Monkey-faced Bat — A183

63c, With nose pointed downward. 81c, Hanging below flower. $2, Between leaves on tree branch.

Perf. 13½
1997, Oct. 15   Litho.   Unwmk.
797	A183	44c multicolored	1.00	.50
798	A183	63c multicolored	1.40	.75
799	A183	81c multicolored	1.75	1.15
800	A183	$2 multicolored	3.50	4.50
a.		Sheet, 2 each #797-800	15.50	15.50
		Nos. 797-800 (4)	7.65	6.90

World Wildlife Fund.

Christmas — A184

Designs: 13c, Angel, shepherd. 31c, Birth of Jesus. 87c, Magi. $3, Madonna and Child.

Perf. 14x14½
1997, Nov. 18   Wmk. 373
801	A184	13c multicolored	.35	.25
802	A184	31c multicolored	.75	.25
803	A184	87c multicolored	1.75	.85
804	A184	$3 multicolored	4.25	5.75
		Nos. 801-804 (4)	7.10	7.10

A185

1997 Rugby World Cup Sevens Champions: a, 50c, Waisale Serevi, captain, highest point scorer. b, 50c, Taniela Qauqau. c, 50c, Jope Tuikabe. d, 50c, Leveni Duvuduvukula. e, 50c, Inoke Maraiwai. f, 50c, Aminiasi Naituyaga. g, 50c, Lemeki Koroi. h, 50c, Marika Vunibaka, highest try scorer. i, 50c, Luke Erenavula. j, 50c, Manasa Bari. k, $1, Entire team.

Wmk. 373
1997, Oct. 30   Litho.   Perf. 14
805	A185	Sheet of 11, #a.-k.	14.50	14.50

No. 805k is 53x39mm.

A186

Chief's Traditional Costumes: 81c, War dress. 87c, Formal dress. $1.12, Presentation dress. $2, Highland war dress.

Wmk. 373
1998, Jan. 20   Litho.   Perf. 14
806	A186	81c multicolored	1.25	.75
807	A186	87c multicolored	1.25	1.00
808	A186	$1.12 multicolored	1.50	1.50
809	A186	$2 multicolored	2.75	3.50
		Nos. 806-809 (4)	6.75	6.75

Asian and Pacific Decade of Disabled Persons, 1993-2000 A187

63c, Mastering modern technology. 87c, Assisting the will to overcome. $1, Using natural born skills. $2, Competing to win.

Wmk. 373
1998, Mar. 18   Litho.   Perf. 13
810	A187	63c multicolored	1.25	.60
811	A187	87c multicolored	1.50	.75
812	A187	$1 multicolored	1.50	1.40
813	A187	$2 multicolored	2.75	4.25
		Nos. 810-813 (4)	7.00	7.00

Royal Air Force, 80th Anniv.
Common Design Type of 1993 Re-Inscribed

Designs: 44c, R34 Airship. 63c, Handley Page Heyford. 87c, Supermarine Swift FR.5. $2, Westland Whirlwind.
No. 818: a, Sopwith Dolphin. b, Avro 504K. c, Vickers Warwick V. d, Shorts Belfast.

1998, Apr. 1   Perf. 13½x14
814	CD350	44c multicolored	1.00	.50
815	CD350	63c multicolored	1.25	.75
816	CD350	87c multicolored	1.75	1.50
817	CD350	$2 multicolored	3.00	3.00
		Nos. 814-817 (4)	7.00	5.75

Souvenir Sheet of 4
818	CD350	$1 #a.-d.	7.00	7.00

Diana, Princess of Wales (1961-97)
Common Design Type

Design: No. 819, Wearing plaid jacket.
No. 820: a, Wearing blue jacket. b, In high-collared blouse. c, Holding flowers.

1998, Mar. 31   Litho.   Perf. 14x14½
819	CD355	81c multicolored	1.00	1.00
820	CD355	81c Sheet of 4, #819,		
		a.-c.	4.25	4.25

No. 820 sold for $3.24 + 50c, with surtax from international sales being donated to the Princess Diana Memorial Fund and surtax from national sales being donated to designated local charity.

Sperm Whale A188

Designs: 81c, Adult, calf. 87c, Breaching. $2, Sperm whale tooth.

Wmk. 373
1998, June 22   Litho.   Perf. 14
821	A188	63c shown	1.75	.75
822	A188	81c multi	1.90	1.00
823	A188	87c multi	2.25	1.25
824	A188	$2 multi	3.00	4.00
a.		Souvenir sheet	5.50	5.50
		Nos. 821-824 (4)	8.90	7.00

16th Commonwealth Games, Kuala Lumpur, Malaysia — A189

Designs: 44c, Athletics. 63c, Lawn bowls. 81c, Javelin. $1.12, Weight lifting. $2, Waisale Serevi, rugby sevens.

Wmk. 384
1998, Sept. 11   Litho.   Perf. 14
825	A189	44c multi	.85	.75
826	A189	63c multi	1.00	.50
827	A189	81c multi	1.40	1.15
828	A189	$1.12 multi	1.75	2.50
		Nos. 825-828 (4)	5.00	4.50

Souvenir Sheet
829	A189	$2 multi	4.25	4.25

Maritime Heritage A190

Designs: 13c, Takia, hollowed-out log with outrigger. 44c, Camakau, sailing canoe. 87c, Drua, twin-hulled sailing canoe. $3, MV Pioneer motor yacht. $1.50, Camakau, map of Fiji.

Wmk. 384
1998, Oct. 26   Litho.   Perf. 13½
830	A190	13c multicolored	.45	.25
831	A190	44c multicolored	.75	.35
832	A190	87c multicolored	1.40	1.00
833	A190	$3 multicolored	5.00	6.00
		Nos. 830-833 (4)	7.60	7.60

Souvenir Sheet
834	A190	$1.50 multicolored	3.75	3.75

Australia '99, World Stamp Expo (#834). See Nos. 843-847.

Christmas A191

Children's drawings: 13c, "Jesus in a Manger." 50c, "A Time for Family and Friends." $1, "What Christmas Means to Me," vert. $2, "The Joy of Christmas," vert.

1998, Nov. 23   **Wmk. 373**

835 A191	13c multicolored	.50	.25
836 A191	50c multicolored	1.20	.45
837 A191	$1 multicolored	2.00	1.10
838 A191	$2 multicolored	2.60	4.50
	Nos. 835-838 (4)	6.30	6.30

Traditional Dances — A192

Designs: 13c, Vakamalolo (women's sitting dance). 81c, Mekeiwau (club dance). 87c, Seasea (women's fan dance). $3, Meke ni yaqona (Kava serving dance).

1999, Jan. 20   **Wmk. 373**
Litho.   **Perf. 14½**

839 A192	13c multicolored	.75	.25
840 A192	81c multicolored	1.75	1.25
841 A192	87c multicolored	1.75	1.25
842 A192	$3 multicolored	5.25	6.75
	Nos. 839-842 (4)	9.50	9.50

Maritime Heritage Type of 1998

Designs: 63c, SS Toufua, 1920-30's. 81c, MF Adi Beti, 1920-30's. $1, SS Niagara, 1920-30's. $2, MV Royal Viking Sun, 1990's. $1.50, SS. Makatea, 1920's.

1999, Mar. 19   **Wmk. 384**   **Perf. 13½**

843 A190	63c multicolored	1.60	.50
844 A190	81c multicolored	1.75	.75
845 A190	$1 multicolored	1.90	1.50
846 A190	$2 multicolored	3.00	4.00
	Nos. 843-846 (4)	8.25	6.75

Souvenir Sheet

847 A190	$1.50 multicolored	4.00	4.00

Australia '99, World Stamp Exhibition (#847).

Souvenir Sheet

Ducks A193

a, Wandering whistling. b, Pacific black.

1999, Apr. 27   **Wmk. 373**

848 A193	$2 Sheet of 2, #a.-b.	6.25	6.25

IBRA '99, Intl. Philatelic Exhibition, Nuremberg.

Orchids — A194

Designs: 44c, Calanthe ventilabrum. 63c, Dendrobium prasinum. 81c, Dendrobium macrophyllum. $3, Dendrobium tokai.

1999, June 28

849 A194	44c multicolored	1.00	.50
850 A194	63c multicolored	1.25	.90
851 A194	81c multicolored	1.75	1.00
852 A194	$3 multicolored	4.00	5.00
	Nos. 849-852 (4)	8.00	7.40

1st Manned Moon Landing, 30th Anniv.
Common Design Type

13c, Astronaut waves goodbye. 87c, Stage 3 fires towards moon. $1, Aldrin walks on lunar surface. $2, Command module fires towards earth.

$2, Looking at earth from moon.

Perf. 14x13¾

1999, July 20   **Wmk. 384**

853 CD357	13c multicolored	.60	.25
854 CD357	87c multicolored	1.35	1.10
855 CD357	$1 multicolored	1.45	1.45
856 CD357	$2 multicolored	2.60	2.60
	Nos. 853-856 (4)	6.00	5.20

Souvenir Sheet
Perf. 14

857 CD357	$2 multicolored	3.25	3.25

No. 857 contains one circular stamp 40mm in diameter.

Queen Mother's Century
Common Design Type

Queen Mother: 13c, Visiting Hull to see bomb damage. 63c, With Prince Charles. 81c, As Colonel-in-Chief of Light Infantry. $3, With Prince Charles at Clarence House. $2, With crowd on Armistice Day.

Wmk. 384

1999, Aug. 18   **Litho.**   **Perf. 13½**

858 CD358	13c multicolored	.80	.75
859 CD358	63c multicolored	1.25	.75
860 CD358	81c multicolored	2.00	1.75
861 CD358	$3 multicolored	4.00	5.50
	Nos. 858-861 (4)	8.05	8.50

Souvenir Sheet

862 CD358	$2 multicolored	4.75	4.75

UPU, 125th Anniv. A195

Sugar Mills rolling stock: 50c, Diesel locomotive. 87c, Steam locomotive. $1, Diesel locomotive, diff. $2, Free passenger train.

Wmk. 373

1999, Oct. 26   **Litho.**   **Perf. 13¾**

863 A195	50c multicolored	.85	.40
864 A195	87c multicolored	1.25	.75
865 A195	$1 multicolored	1.40	1.10
866 A195	$2 multicolored	2.50	3.75
	Nos. 863-866 (4)	6.00	6.00

Christmas A196

Designs: 13c, Giving gifts. 31c, Angels and star. 63c, Bible, Magi, Holy family. 87c, Joseph, mary, donkey, vert. $1, Mary, Jesus, animals, vert. $2, Children, Santa, vert.

Perf. 13¼x13

1999, Nov. 29   **Litho.**   **Wmk. 373**

867 A196	13c multicolored	.25	.25
868 A196	31c multicolored	.60	.35
869 A196	63c multicolored	.95	.50
870 A196	87c multicolored	1.15	.75
871 A196	$1 multicolored	1.30	.85
872 A196	$2 multicolored	2.25	3.50
	Nos. 867-872 (6)	6.50	6.20

Millennium — A197

Designs: No. 873, Outstretched hands, islands (arch at top). No. 874, Map, flag (arch at right). No. 875, Globe, warrior beating lali, temple (arch at bottom). No. 876, Globe, drua, red line (arch at left).

No. 877: a, Fiji petrel (arch at top). b, Crested iguana, islands (arch at top). c, Red prawns (arch at bottom). d, Tagimaucia (arch at bottom).

Perf. 13¼ Syncopated Type A
Litho. with Foil Application

2000, Jan. 1   **Unwmk.**

873 A197	$5 gold & multi	7.00	7.00
874 A197	$5 gold & multi	7.00	7.00
875 A197	$5 gold & multi	7.00	7.00
876 A197	$5 gold & multi	7.00	7.00
	Nos. 873-876 (4)	28.00	28.00

Souvenir Sheet

877 A197	$10 Sheet of 4, #a-d	60.00	60.00

Beetles A198

Designs: 15c, Paracupta sulcata. 87c, Agrilus sp. $1.06, Cyphogastra abdominalis. $2, Paracupta sp.

Perf. 13¾x14

2000, Mar. 14   **Litho.**   **Wmk. 373**

878 A198	15c multi	.40	.25
879 A198	87c multi	1.20	.75
880 A198	$1.06 multi	1.45	1.50
881 A198	$2 multi	2.40	3.00
	Nos. 878-881 (4)	5.45	5.50

Sesame Street A199

No. 882: a, Big Bird. b, Oscar the Grouch. c, Cookie Monster. d, Grover. e, Elmo. f, Ernie. g, Zoe. h, The Count. i, Bert.

No. 883, Big Bird, Elmo and Ernie, horiz. No. 884, Cookie Monster, Bert and Ernie, horiz.

Perf. 14½x14¾

2000, Apr. 20   **Litho.**   **Wmk. 373**

882 A199	50c Sheet of 9, #a-i	7.75	7.75

Souvenir Sheets
Perf. 14¾x14½

883 A199	$2 multi	3.25	3.25
884 A199	$2 multi	3.25	3.25

The Stamp Show 2000, London (#882).

Pres. Ratu Sir Kamisese Mara, 80th Birthday — A200

President with: 15c, Lumberjack, timber truck. 81c, Women. $1, Workers in cane field. $3, Ships.

2000, May 13   **Perf. 14x13¾**

885 A200	15c multi	.35	.25
886 A200	81c multi	.95	.65
887 A200	$1 multi	1.05	.75
888 A200	$3 multi	4.50	5.00
	Nos. 885-888 (4)	6.85	6.65

Prince William, 18th Birthday
Common Design Type

William: Nos. 889, 893a, As child, wearing fireman's helmet, vert. Nos. 890, 893b, Wearing navy suit, vert. Nos. 891, 893c, Wearing scarf. Nos. 892, 893d, Wearing suit and wearing blue shirt. No. 893e, As child, wearing camouflage and beret.

Perf. 13¾x14¼, 14¼x13¾

2000, June 21   **Wmk. 373**
Stamps With White Border

889 CD359	$1 multi	1.35	1.35
890 CD359	$1 multi	1.35	1.35
891 CD359	$1 multi	1.35	1.35
892 CD359	$1 multi	1.35	1.35
	Nos. 889-892 (4)	5.40	5.40

Souvenir Sheet
Stamps Without White Border
Perf. 14¼

893 CD359	$1 Sheet of 5, #a-e	7.50	7.50

2000 Summer Olympics, Sydney A201

Wmk. 373

2000, Aug. 8   **Litho.**   **Perf. 13¾**

894 A201	44c Swimming, vert.	.75	.50
895 A201	87c Judo, vert.	1.15	.75
896 A201	$1 Running	1.25	1.25
897 A201	$2 Windsurfing	2.25	2.90
	Nos. 894-897 (4)	5.40	5.40

Souvenir Sheet

Alsmithia Longipes A202

No. 898: a, Red frond at R. b, Red frond at L. c, Yellow frond. d, Fruit.

Wmk. 373

2000, Sept. 12   **Litho.**   **Perf. 13½**

898 A202	$1 Sheet of 4, #a-d	6.50	6.50

Lapita Pottery Shards and Discovery Sites — A203

44c, Yanuca Island. 63c, Mago Island. $1, Ugaga Island. $2, Sigatoka sand dunes.

2000, Oct. 24   **Perf. 13¾**

899-902 A203	Set of 4	5.75	5.75

Christmas — A204

Designs: 15c, Jungle. 81c, Cliffside trail. 87c, Coastal village. $3, Outrigger canoe.

2000, Nov. 21

903-906 A204	Set of 4	6.25	6.25

Souvenir Sheet

Taveuni Rain Forest A205

Designs: a, Orange dove. b, Xixuthrus heyrovskyi.

Perf. 13¾x13½

2001, Feb. 1   **Litho.**   **Unwmk.**

907 A205	$2 Sheet of 2, #a-b	6.00	6.00

Moths — A206

Designs: 17c, Macroglossum hirundo vitiensis. 48c, Hippotion celerio. 69c, Gnathothlibus erotus eras. 89c, Theretra pinastrina intersecta. $1.17, Deilephila placida torenia. $2, Psilogramma jordana.

2001, Mar. 20   **Perf. 13¼x13**

908-913 A206	Set of 6	6.75	6.75

Souvenir Sheet

Gallus Gallus A207

Designs: a, Hen. b, Rooster.

2001, May 22   **Perf. 13¾x14**
914 A207 $2 Sheet of 2, #a-b   7.00 7.00

Society for Prevention of Cruelty — A208

Designs: 34c, Girl, cat. 96c, Boy, dogs. $1.23, Girl, cat, diff. $2, Boy, dog.

    Perf. 14x13¾
2001, June 26   **Litho.**   **Unwmk.**
915-918 A208 Set of 4   6.50 6.50

Pigeons A209

Designs: 69c, White-throated. 89c, Pacific, vert. $1.23, Peal's, vert. $2, Rock.

2001, July 20   **Perf. 14x13¾, 14¾x14**
919-922 A209 Set of 4   7.25 7.25

Westpac Pacific Bank, 100th Anniv. in Fiji — A210

Bank office in: 48c, 1901. 96c, 1916. $1, 1934. $2, 2001.

2001, Aug. 10   **Perf. 13¼x13¾**
923-926 A210 Set of 4   5.00 5.00

Fish — A211

Designs: 50c, Yellowfin tuna. 96c, Wahoo. $1.17, Dolphin fish. $2, Pacific blue marlin.

2001, Aug. 23
927-930 A211 Set of 4   5.50 5.50

Christmas — A212

Designs: 17c, Angel appears to Mary. 34c, Nativity. 48c, Adoration of the shepherds. 69c, Adoration of the Magi. 89c, Flight to Egypt. $2, Fijian Chirst child.

2001, Oct. 29   **Litho.**   **Perf. 13¾x13¼**
931-936 A212 Set of 6   6.75 6.75

Colonial Financial Services Group, 125th Anniv. in Fiji — A213

Designs: 17c, Bank office. 48c, Women using automatic teller machine. $1, Suva Private Hospital. $3, Hoisting of British flag.

2001, Nov. 16   **Litho.**   **Perf. 13¼**
937-940 A213 Set of 4   6.75 6.75

Air Pacific, 50th Anniv. — A214

No. 941: a, De Havilland Drover. b, Hawker Siddley HS-748. c, Douglas DC-10-30. d, Boeing 747-200.

2001, Nov. 30   **Litho.**   **Perf. 13**
941   Horiz. strip of 4   7.50 7.50
   a.   A214 89c multi   1.50 1.50
   b.   A214 96c multi   1.75 1.75
   c.   A214 $1 multi   1.75 1.75
   d.   A214 $2 multi   2.25 2.25

Spices — A215

Designs: 69c, Pepper. 89c, Nutmeg. $1, Vanilla. $2, Cinnamon.

2002, Mar. 12   **Litho.**   **Perf. 13¼**
942-945 A215 Set of 4   6.25 6.25

Souvenir Sheet

Balaka Palm A216

Palm and: a, Bird, butterfly, beetle. b, Lizard, butterfly

2002, Apr. 29
946 A216 $2 Sheet of 2, #a-b   6.75 6.75

Freshwater Fish — A217

Designs: 48c, Redigobius sp. 96c, Spotted flagtail. $1.23, Silverstripe mudskipper. $2, Snakehead gudgeon.

2002, May 13
947-950 A217 Set of 4   6.50 6.50

Fruit — A218

Designs: 25c, Breadfruit. 34c, Wi. $1, Jakfruit. $3, Avocado.

2002, July 25   **Litho.**   **Perf. 13¾x13¼**
951-954 A218 Set of 4   6.25 6.25

Murex Shells — A219

Designs: 69c, Saul's murex. 96c, Caltrop murex. $1, Purple Pacific drupe. $2, Ramose murex.

2002, Aug. 20   **Perf. 13¾**
955-958 A219 Set of 4   7.00 7.00

Fiji Goshawk — A220

Designs: 48c, Goshawk and eggs. 89c, Chicks in nest. $1, Juvenile on branch. $3, Adult.

2002, Sept. 10
959-962 A220 Set of 4   8.25 8.25

2002 Operation Open Heart Visit to Fiji — A221

Designs: 34c, Doctors performing operation, vert. 69c, Doctor listening to patient's heart with stethoscope. $1.17, Technician administering echocardiogram. $2, Administration of anesthesia to patient, vert.

2002, Oct. 30   **Perf. 13¼**
963-966 A221 Set of 4   7.25 7.25

Fiji Natural Artesian Water — A222

Designs: 25c, Bottle of water, flowers, vert. 48c, Bottling plant. $1, Delivery truck. $3, Children with bottled water, vert.

2002, Nov. 5
967-970 A222 Set of 4   7.50 7.50

Christmas — A223

Designs: 17c, Christian church. 89c, Mosque. $1, Hindu temple. $3, Christian church, diff.

2002, Nov. 20
971-974 A223 Set of 4   7.50 7.50

Post Fiji, Ltd. Improvements A224

Designs: 48c, General Post Office. 96c, Post Fiji Mail Center. $1, Post Fiji Logistics Center. $2, Smart Mail.

2003, Mar. 19   **Litho.**   **Perf. 13¼**
975-978 A224 Set of 4   6.75 6.75

Souvenir Sheet

Intl. Year of Fresh Water A225

No. 979: a, Top of waterfall, flowers. b, Base of waterfall, butterfly.

2003, Apr. 22
979 A225 $2 Sheet of 2, #a-b   7.25 7.25

2003 South Pacific Games, Suva — A226

Designs: 10c, Track athlete with arms raised. 14c, Baseball. 20c, Netball. No. 983, $5, Shot put.
No. 984, $5, Flags of participating nations, venues, volleyball players.

2003   **Perf. 13¼**
980-983 A226 Set of 4   7.25 7.25
      Size: 120x85mm
      Imperf
984 A226 $5 multi   6.75 6.75
  Issued: Nos. 980-983, 5/26; No. 984, 6/28.

Fish — A227

Siganus uspi: 58c, Fish, crab and coral. 83c, Two fish and coral. $1.15, Two fish, coral, and other fish species. $3, Fish and coral.

2003, Aug. 12   **Perf. 13¼**
985-988 A227 Set of 4   8.50 8.50

Bird Life International — A228

Designs: 41c, Long-legged warbler. 60c, Silktail. $1.07, Red-throated lorikeet. $3, Pink-billed parrot finch.

2003, Sept. 16
989-992 A228 Set of 4   13.00 13.00

Geckos A229

Designs: 83c, Pacific slender-toed gecko. $1.07, Indopacific tree gecko. $1.15, Mann's gecko. $2, Voracious gecko.

2003, Oct. 21   **Litho.**   **Perf. 13¼**
993-996 A229 Set of 4   9.75 9.75

Christmas
A230

Children's art: 18c, Children, Christmas tree. 41c, Children, flag of Fiji. 58c, Children, Santa Claus, reindeer pulling sleighs, vert. 83c, Santa Claus on chimney, gifts, children, Christmas tree, vert. $1.07, Children with candles, Christmas tree, vert. $1.15, Santa Claus, children, bell, rainbow, vert. $1.41, Handshake.

2003, Nov. 26   Litho.   *Perf. 13¼*
997-1002 A230   Set of 6   7.25 7.25

Souvenir Sheet
1003 A230 $1.41 multi   3.50 3.50

Tagimoucia
A231

2003, Dec. 1   Litho.   *Perf. 14½x14*
1004 A231 50c multi + label   5.00 5.00

Sold in sheets of 10 stamps + 10 labels that could be personalized for $15 per sheet.

Xixuthrus Heyrovskyi, Longest Beetle in the World — A232

2003, Feb. 27   *Imperf.*
1005 A232 $5 multi   7.50 7.50

Miniature Sheet

Worldwide Fund for Nature (WWF) — A233

No. 1006: a, 58c, Skipjack tuna. b, 83c, Albacore tuna. c, $1.07, Yellowfin tuna. d, $3, Bigeye tuna.

2004, Apr. 7   *Perf. 13¼*
1006 A233   Sheet of 4, #a-d   8.50 8.50
   e.   Like #1006, with artist's name
      at LL of each stamp   8.50 8.50

Land Snails
A234

Designs: 18c, Malleated placostyle. 41c, Kandavu placostyle. $1.15, Fragile orpiella. $3, Thin Fijian placostyle.

2004, May 28
1007-1010 A234   Set of 4   7.25 7.25

Bird Type of 1995 and

No. 1011A

Perf. 13¼x13
2004, June 26   *Unwmk.*
1011   A166 18c Island
         thrush   1.90 1.90
1011A A166 4c on 18c
        #1011   250.00 250.00

No. 1011A issued Aug. 2008. Surcharge on No. 1011A exists only inverted. Values are for stamps with surcharge at top, as shown. Value, with surcharge centered $400.

Coral Reef
Shrimp
A235

Designs: 58c, Boxer shrimp. 83c, Bumblebee shrimp. $1.07, Mantis shrimp. $3, Anemone shrimp.

2004, June 30   *Perf. 13¼*
1012-1015 A235   Set of 4   7.25 7.25

Birds — A236

Designs: 41c, Wandering tattler. 58c, Whimbrel. $1.15, Pacific golden plover. $3, Bristle-thighed curlew.

2004, July 28
1016-1019 A236   Set of 4   10.00 10.00

2004 Summer
Olympics,
Athens — A237

Designs: 41c, Swimming. 58c, Judo, vert. $1.40, Weight lifting, vert. $2, Makelesi Bulikiobo, runner.

2004, Aug. 12
1020-1023 A237   Set of 4   7.25 7.25

Musket Cove
to Port Vila
Yacht Race,
25th Anniv.
A238

Various yachts: 83c, $1.07, $1.15, $2. $1.07 and $2 are vert.

2004, Sept. 18   *Perf. 14¼*
1024-1027 A238   Set of 4   8.00 8.00
1027a   Souvenir sheet of 1   4.25 4.25

Joint issue between Fiji and Vanuatu. See Vanuatu Nos. 858-861.

Souvenir Sheet

Coconut
Crab
A239

2004, Oct. 20   Litho.   *Perf. 14*
1028 A239 $5 multi   7.50 7.50

Papilio
Schmeltzii
A240

Designs: 58c, Newly-emerged adult, vert. 83c, Larva. $1.41, Adult. $3, Pupa, vert.

Perf. 14x14½, 14½x14
2004, Nov. 10
1029-1032 A240   Set of 4   9.50 9.50

Christmas — A241

Designs: 18c, Annunciation. 58c, Infant in manger. $1.07, Madonna and child. $3, Adoration of the Shepherds.

2004, Dec. 1   Litho.   *Perf. 13¼*
1033-1036 A241   Set of 4   9.00 9.00

Birds — A242

No. 1037: a, Little heron. b, Great white egret. c, White-faced heron. d, Pacific reef heron.

2005, Jan. 26
1037   Horiz. strip of 4   9.25 9.25
  a.-d.   A242 $1 Any single   2.25 2.25

Flowers For
Perfume — A243

Designs: 58c, Cananga odorata. $1.15, Euodia hortensis. $1.41, Pandanus tecorius. $2, Santalum yasi.

2005, Feb. 20   *Perf. 14x14½*
1038-1041 A243   Set of 4   7.50 7.50

Peregrine
Falcons
A244

Designs: 41c, Head of falcon. 83c, Adult at nest. $1.07, Chicks. $3, Adult on rock.

2005, Mar. 14   Litho.   *Perf. 14½x14*
1042-1045 A244   Set of 4   9.50 9.50

Triggerfish
A245

Designs: 58c, Whitebanded triggerfish. 83c, Yellow-spotted triggerfish. $1.15, Orange-lined triggerfish. $2, Clown triggerfish.

2005, Apr. 27
1046-1049 A245   Set of 4   8.00 8.00

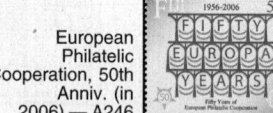

European
Philatelic
Cooperation, 50th
Anniv. (in
2006) — A246

Color of arches: 58c, Red. 83c, Blue green. $1.41, Purple. $4, Yellow bister.

2005, June 1   *Perf. 13¾*
1050-1053 A246   Set of 4   10.00 10.00
  1053a   Souvenir sheet, #1050-
        1053   10.00 10.00

Europa stamps, 50th anniv. (in 2006).

Miniature Sheet

End of World War II, 60th Anniv.
A247

No. 1054: a, HMNZS Achilles. b, Japanese Yokosuka E14Y "Glen" over Suva Harbor. c, Fijian South Pacific Scouts in Solomon Islands. d, USS Chicago. e, Patrol vessel HMS Viti. f, British Prime Minister Winston Churchill. g, HMS Hood. h, Dambusters Raid. i, German King Tiger tank in Ardennes. j, Gen. Dwight D. Eisenhower.

2005, June 27   Litho.   *Perf. 13¾*
1054 A247 83c Sheet of 10,
      #a-j   12.75 12.75

Game
Fish — A248

Designs: 41c, Great barracuda. 58c, Narrow-barred Spanish mackerel. $1.07, Giant trevally. $3, Indo-Pacific sailfish.

2005, July 27   Litho.   *Perf. 14½x14*
1055-1058 A248   Set of 4   8.75 8.75

Pope John Paul II
(1920-2005) — A249

2005, Aug. 18   *Perf. 14*
1059 A249 $1 multi   2.50 2.50

Dragonflies
A250

Designs: 83c, Yellow-striped flutterer. $1.07, Agrionoptera insignis. $1.15, Green skimmer. $2, Common percher.

2005, Aug. 30   Litho.   *Perf. 13¼*
1060-1063 A250   Set of 4   7.50 7.50

Albert Einstein (1879-
1955),
Physicist — A251

Einstein: 83c, As a child. $1.07, In 1905. $1.15, And blackboard. $2, And galaxies.

2005, Sept. 27   Litho.   *Perf. 14¼x14*
1064-1067 A251   Set of 4   9.25 9.25
     Intl. Year of Physics.

Root Crops — A252

Designs: 41c, Manihot utilissima. 83c, Ipomoea satatas. $1.41, Colocasia esculenta. $2, Dioscorea sativa.

2005, Oct. 13   *Perf. 13¼*
1068-1071 A252   Set of 4   7.25 7.25

Tall Ships — A253

Designs: 83c, Eliza of Province. $1.15, Elbe. $1.41, HMS Rosario. $2, L'Astrolabe.

2005, Nov. 21   **Litho.**   *Perf. 14x14¼*
1072-1075 A253   Set of 4   9.00 9.00

Barn Owls — A254

Owl: 18c, And eggs. $1.15, Juvenile. $1.41, With prey. $2, Perched.

2006, Jan. 10   **Litho.**   *Perf. 14¼x14*
1076-1079 A254   Set of 4   9.75 9.75

Platymantis Vitianus A255

Various depictions: 50c, 83c, $1.15, $2.

2006, Feb. 8   **Litho.**   *Perf. 14x14¼*
1080-1083 A255   Set of 4   8.00 8.00

Skinks — A256

Designs: 18c, Pygmy snake-eyed skink. 58c, Brown-tailed copper striped skink. $1.15, Pacific black skink. $3, Pacific blue-tailed skink.

2006, Mar. 22
1084-1087 A256   Set of 4   7.50 7.50

Queen Elizabeth II, 80th Birthday — A257

Designs: 50c, As child. 65c, Wearing tiara. 90c, Wearing blue hat. $3, Wearing blue hat, diff.
No. 1092: a, Like 65c. b, Like 90c.

2006, Apr. 21   **Litho.**   *Perf. 14*
With White Frames
1088-1091 A257   Set of 4   7.00 7.00
Souvenir Sheet
Without White Frames
1092 A257 $2 Sheet of 2, #a-b   5.75 5.75

Miniature Sheet

Vijay Singh, Golfer A258

No. 1097 — Singh: a, Head. b, With arm raised. c, Leaning on golf club. d, Hitting ball from sand trap. e, Holding trophy (60x87mm).

Perf. 14x14¼
2006, May 26   **Litho.**   **Unwmk.**
1097 A258 $1 Sheet of 5, #a-e   8.50 8.50

2006 World Cup Soccer Championships, Germany — A259

Various players: 65c, 90c, $1.20, $2.

2006, June 9
1098-1101 A259   Set of 4   7.50 7.50

Souvenir Sheet

Purple Swamphen — A260

No. 1102: a, Swamphen and flowers. b, Swamphen on nest.

2006, July 20   *Perf. 14½x14*
1102 A260 $2 Sheet of 2, #a-b   6.50 6.50

Extinct Species A261

Designs: 50c, Brachylophus vitiensis. $1.10, Natunaornis gigoura, vert. $1.20, Vitirallus watlingi, vert. $1.50, Platymantis megabotoniviti.

Perf. 14x14¼, 14¼x14
2006, Aug. 15   **Litho.**
1103-1106 A261   Set of 4   7.00 7.00

Phasmids A262

Designs: 10c, Hermarchus apollonius. $1.10, Cotylosoma dipneusticum. $1.20, Chitoniscus feejeeanus. $2, Graeffea crouanii.

2006, Sept. 7   *Perf. 14½x14*
1107-1110 A262   Set of 4   7.00 7.00

Honey Production — A263

Designs: 18c, Bees and honeycomb. 40c, Apiarist examining honeycomb, horiz. $1, Woman and beehives, horiz. $3, Man and bottle of honey.

2006, Oct. 16   *Perf. 14x14½, 14½x14*
1111-1114 A263   Set of 4   7.50 7.50

Christmas — A264

Flowering plants: 18c, Decaspermum vitiense. 65c, Quisqualis indica. 90c, Mussaendra raiateensis. $3, Delonix regia.

2006, Dec. 5   *Perf. 14x14½*
1115-1118 A264   Set of 4   7.50 7.50

Anemonefish A265

Designs: 18c, Spine-cheek anemonefish. 60c, Pink anemonefish. 90c, Orange-fin anemonefish. $3, Dusky anemonefish.

Perf. 14½x14, 14x14½
2006, Nov. 7   **Litho.**
1119-1122 A265   Set of 4   7.50 7.50

Souvenir Sheet

Thalassina Anomala — A266

2007, Jan. 24   *Perf. 13½*
1123 A266 $4 multi   5.50 5.50

Traditional Architecture A267

Designs: 20c, Coastal dwelling. 65c, Inland dwelling. $1.10, Temple, Bau. $3, Lauan-style house.

2007, Mar. 20   **Litho.**   *Perf. 13¼*
1124-1127 A267   Set of 4   7.25 7.25

Freshwater Gobies A268

Designs: 20c, Sicyopterus lagocephalus. $1.10, Stiphodon rutilaureus. $1.20, Sicyopus zosterophorum. $2, Stiphodon sp.

2007, Apr. 5   **Litho.**   *Perf. 13¼*
1128-1131 A268   Set of 4   6.25 6.25

Birds Introduced to Fiji — A269

Designs: 50c, Red-vented bulbul. 65c, Spotted dove, horiz. $1.50, Australian magpie, horiz. $2, Java sparrow.

2007, May 22
1132-1135 A269   Set of 4   7.50 7.50

Scouting, Cent. — A270

Designs: 50c, Scout in kayak, hand holding compass. 90c, Three Scouts wearing helmets, hands tying knot. No. 1138, $1.50, Scout in harness climbing, Scout saluting. $2, Scout writing observation notes, hands tying neckerchief.
No. 1140, $1.50, vert.: a, Scout emblem. b, Lord Robert Baden-Powell.

2007, July 9   *Perf. 13¾*
1136-1139 A270   Set of 4   7.00 7.00
Souvenir Sheet
1140 A270 $1.50 Sheet of 2, #a-b   4.75 4.75

Snails — A271

Designs: 40c, Clithon diadema. 90c, Neritina variegata. $1.20, Fijidoma maculata. $2, Neritina squamaepicta.

2007, Aug. 18   *Perf. 14x14¼*
1141-1144 A271   Set of 4   6.50 6.50

Orchids — A272

Designs: 20c, Liparis layardii. 65c, Dendrobium catillare, horiz. $1.10, Dendrobium mohlianum, horiz. $3, Glomera montana.

Perf. 14¼x14, 14x14¼
2007, Aug. 21
1145-1148 A272   Set of 4   7.25 7.25

Nos. 725 and 729 Surcharged

 No. 1149   No. 1150

Methods, Types and Watermarks As Before
2006-08
1149 A166 1c on 6c #729   1.50 1.50
1150 A166 1c on 6c #729   7.00 7.00

No. 1149 exists with inverted surcharge. Value, $90. No. 1149 also exists with double surcharge, one inverted. Value, $150. No. 1149 also exists with normal surcharge shifted 75% upward. Value, $50. No. 1149 exists with "c" omitted from surcharge.

 No. 1151   No. 1152

 No. 1152c

1151 A166 2c on 1c #725   4.50 4.50
1152 A166 2c on 1c #725, larger font   2.50 2.50
   c.   1½mm gap between "2" and "c" (position 67)   60.00 60.00

No. 1152 exists with normal surcharge shifted 50% upward. Value, $50.

2c XX

No.
1152A

2c XX

No.
1152Ab

2c XX

No. 1152Ac

1152A A166 2c on 1c #725,
4mm be-
tween "c"
and obliter-
ator
b. 5mm between "c" and
obliterator　　　　　　200.00 200.00
c. 3mm between "c" and
obliterator　　　　　　—

No. 1152Ab exists with inverted surcharge.
Value, $375.

2c XX

No. 1153

2c XX

No.
1153a

2c XX No. 1153c

1153 A166 2c on 6c #729,
4mm between
"c" and obliter-
ator
a. 5mm between "c" and obliterator　　　　　　　　1.25 1.25
c. 1½mm gap between "2" and
"c" (position 57)　　　　60.00 60.00

No. 1153a exists with inverted surcharge.
Value, $110. No. 1153a also exists with double
surcharge, one inverted. Value, $150.

2c xx

No.
1153B

3c xx

No.
1154

3c XX

No. 1154A

1153B A166 2c on 6c #729　550.00 550.00
1154 A166 3c on 1c #725　　1.25 1.25
1154A A166 3c on 1c #725,
larger font　　　　650.00 650.00

No. 1154 exists with inverted surcharge.
Value, $275. No. 1154 exists with double
surcharge, one inverted. Value, $225.

4c xx

No.
1155

4c xx

No.
1155a

1155 A166 4c on 1c #725　　1.50 1.50
a. 1½mm gap between "4" and
"c" (position 57)　　　60.00 60.00

4c XX

No.
1156

4c XX

No.
1156a

1156 A166 4c on 6c #729, 4mm
between "c" an
obliterator　　　　1.25 1.25
a. 5mm between "c" and obliterator　　　　　　　1.25 1.25

No. 1156a exists with inverted surcharge.
Value, $110. No. 1156a also exists with double
surcharge, one inverted. Value, $150. No.
1156a also exists with normal surcharge
shifted 75% upward and 50% upward. Values,
each $50.

6c xx

No.
1156B

18c xx

No.
1157

1156B A166 6c on 6c #729　650.00 650.00
1157 A166 18c on 6c
#729,
4mm be-
tween "c"
and oblit-
erator　　　　6.50 6.50

No. 1157 exists with double surcharge, one
with normal 4mm between "c" and obliterator
and the other with 2½mm between "c" and
obliterator. One surcharge is shifted 75%
upward. Half of the errors have the normal
separation between "c" and obliterator at top
and half have it at bottom. Each error variety is
equally scarce. Value, each $130. No. 1157
exists with double surcharge, both with 4mm
between "c" and obliterator. Value, $150.
No. 1157 also exists with normal surcharge
shifted 75% upward but with no second
surcharge. Value, $50.

18c XX

No.
1158

18c XX

No.
1158a

1158 A166 18c on 6c #729,
2½mm be-
tween "c" and
obliterator　　　11.00 11.00
a. 4mm between "c" and obliterator　　　　　22.00 22.00

No. 1158 exists with double surcharge.
Value, $150. No. 1158 also exists with double
surcharge, both inverted. Value, $225.

20c xx

No.
1159

20c xx

No.
1159a

1159 A166 20c on 6c #729,
2½mm be-
tween "c" and
obliterator　　　6.50 6.50
a. 4mm between "c" and obliterator　　　　　14.50 14.50

No. 1159 exists with inverted surcharge.
Value, $110.

20c XX

No. 1160

20c XX

No.
1160a

20cXX No. 1160b

1160 A166 20c on 6c #729,
4mm be-
tween "c"
and obliter-
ator　　　　30.00 30.00
a. 1½mm between "c" and
obliterator　　　　60.00 60.00
b. No gap between "c" and
obliterator　　　475.00 475.00
Nos. 1149-1160 (16)　2,125. 2,125.

No. 1160a exists with double surcharge.
Value, $150.
Issued: No. 1149, 5/30/07; No. 1150,
9/19/07; No. 1151, 4/3; No. 1152, 11/13; No.
1152A, July 2007, No. 1152Ab, 8/20/08; Nos.
1153, 1153B 2/19/07; No. 1153a, 2/27/07; No.
1154, 3/13; No. 1155, 6/27; No. 1156, 6/6/07;
No. 1156a, 2/19/08; No. 1156B, Feb. 2007;
No. 1157, 6/8; No. 1158, 9/8; No. 1158a, Aug.
2007; No. 1159, 1/19/07; No. 1159a, Jan.
2007; No. 1160, 3/8/07; No. 1160a, 4/12/08.

FIJI Coronation Trout

Variola louti

50c

Fish — A273

Designs: 50c, Coronation trout. 90c, Roving
coral trout. $1.50, Squaretail coral trout. $2,
Chinese footballer.

2007, Oct. 15　Litho.　Perf. 13¼
1161-1164 A273　Set of 4　7.75 7.75

20c

Butterflies — A274

Designs: 20c, Polyura caphontis. $1.10,
Hypolimnas bolina, horiz. $1.20, Doleschallia
bisaltide, horiz. $2, Danaus hamata.

2007, Nov. 20　Litho.　Perf. 13¼
1165-1168 A274　Set of 4　6.00 6.00

Souvenir Sheet

Barred-winged Rail — A275

No. 1169: a, Head of adult. b, Chick.

2007, Dec. 3
1169 A275 $2 Sheet of 2, #a-b　5.50 5.50

FIJI 50c

National
Medals — A276

Designs: 50c, Medal of the Order of Fiji.
65c, Member of the Order of Fiji. $1.20, Officer
of the Order of Fiji. $2, Companion of the
Order of Fiji.

2008, Feb. 20　Litho.　Perf. 13¼
1170-1173 A276　Set of 4　6.25 6.25

Souvenir Sheet

Spiny
Lobster
A277

2008, Apr. 22　Litho.　Perf. 14x14½
1174 A277 $4 multi　5.25 5.25

20c

First Trans-Pacific Flight of the
Southern Cross, 80th Anniv.
A278

Southern Cross: 20c, Over Fiji. 90c, In
Albert Park, Suva. $1.50, Surrounded by
police guard. $2, With crew.

2008, June 13　　　Perf. 13½
1175-1178 A278　Set of 4　5.75 5.75

2008 Summer
Olympics,
Beijing — A279

Designs: 20c, Bamboo, Running. 65c,
Dragon, Judo. 90c, Lanterns, Shooting. $1.50,
Carp, Swimming.

2008, May 5　Litho.　Perf. 13¼
1179-1182 A279　Set of 4　4.25 4.25

65c

Red-breasted Musk
Parrot
Varieties — A280

Prosopeia tabuensis: 65c, Koroensis. 90c,
Atrogularis, horiz. $1.50, Taviunensis, horiz.
$2, Splendens.

2008, Mar. 25　Litho.　Perf. 13½
1183-1186 A280　Set of 4　6.75 6.75

FIJI

20c

Humpback
Whales
A281

Humpback whale: 20c, Pair underwater.
50c, Breaching water's surface. $1.10, Reen-
tering water. $3, Flukes.

2008, July 17　Litho.　Perf. 14½x14
1187-1190 A281　Set of 4　6.00 6.00

**Nos. 729-731 Surcharged Like Nos.
1149-1160**

1c XX

No.
1191

1c XX

No.
1191A

1c XX

No. 1191Ab

Methods, Perfs and Watermarks As Before

2007-09

1191	A166	1c on 13c #730, 5mm between "c" and obliterator		
			1.50	1.50
b.		4mm between "c" and obliterator (positions 3 and 89)	50.00	50.00
1191A	A166	1c on 23c #731, 4mm between "c" and obliterator	1.00	1.00
b.		5mm between "c" and obliterator	1.00	1.00
c.		Pair, Nos. 1191Ab and 1191A (positions 3 and 89)	50.00	50.00

No. 1191 exists with double surcharge, one inverted. Value, $150. No. 1191 exists with double surcharge: one upright with "XX" obliterator, the other inverted with "xxx" obliterator. Value, $175. No. 1191A exists with inverted surcharge. Value, $160. No. 1191A exists with a "2c" surcharge having a 1½mm gap between the "2" and the "c" (position 57). Value, $100. No. 1191Ab exists with inverted surcharge. Value, $160. No. 1191Ab also exists with double surcharge, one inverted. Value, $175.

No. 1191C | No. 1192

1191C	A166	2c on 6c #729	175.00	175.00
d.		1½mm gap between "2" and "c" (position 57)	—	
1192	A166	2c on 6c #729	175.00	175.00
c.		2½mm gap between pair of double bars of obliterator	400.00	400.00
d.		4mm between "c" and obliterator	325.00	325.00

No. 1192 exists with obliterator of three double bars and with obliterator of four double bars. Value, each $500. No. 1192 exists with obliterator of two double bars and a single bar. Value, $400. No. 1192 exists with obliterator omitted. Value, $750.

No. 1192A | No. 1192Ab

No. 1193 | No. 1193a

No. 1193B | No. 1193C

1192A	A166	2c on 6c #729	175.00	175.00
b.		Short obliterator	250.00	250.00
e.		4½mm obliterator	250.00	250.00
f.		12½mm obliterator	250.00	250.00
1193	A166	2c on 13c #730, 5 mm between "c" and obliterator	1.50	1.50
a.		4mm between "c" and obliterator (positions 3 and 89)	50.00	50.00
1193B	A166	2c on 23c #731, 5 mm between "c" and obliterator	125.00	125.00
a.		4mm between "c" and obliterator (positions 3 and 89)	200.00	200.00
1193C	A166	3c on 13c #730	175.00	175.00

No. 1192A has an 8mm obliterator. Two lines comprise the obliterator on No. 1192Ab: one long, one short. The obliterator on No. 1192Af extends into the right margin and must be collected with right selvage attached to show the entire obliterator.

No. 1193 exists with double surcharge, one inverted. Value, $150. No. 1193 exists with double surcharge: one upright with "XX" obliterator, the other inverted with "xxx" obliterator. Value, $175. No. 1193 exists with a period after the "2c." Value, $500.

No. 1194 | No. 1194a

No. 1195 | No. 1195b

1194	A166	4c on 13c #730, 5mm between "c" and obliterator	1.50	1.50
a.		4mm between "c" and obliterator (positions 3 and 89)	50.00	50.00
b.		1½mm gap between "4" and "c"	225.00	225.00
1195	A166	20c on 6c #729	100.00	100.00
b.		No gap between "c" and obliterator	550.00	550.00

No. 1194 exists with double surcharge, one inverted at top of stamp. Value, $200. No. 1194 exists with double surcharge, one inverted in center of stamp. Value, $200.

 No. 1195A

1195A	A166	20c on 23c #731	400.00	400.00
c.		3½mm between "c" and obliterator	400.00	400.00

No. 1195A exists with normal surcharge shifted 75% upward. Value, $300. No. 1195A also exists with inverted surcharge. Value, $350. No. 1195A also exists with "c" of surcharge omitted. Value, $400.

No. 1196 | No. 1196a

1196	A166	20c on 23c #731	2.00	2.00
a.		No gap between "c" and obliterator (position 70)	35.00	35.00

No. 1196 exists with inverted surcharge. Value, $90. No. 1196 also exists with double surcharge and with double surcharge, one inverted. Value, each $150. No. 1196 also exists surcharged on gum side only; the surcharge is always inverted. Value, $200. No. 1196 also exists surcharged on both sides. Value, $180.

No. 1197 | No. 1197a

No. 1197d | No. 1197e

No. 1197f

1197	A166	20c on 23c #731, 1½mm between "c" and obliterator	200.00	200.00
a.		2½mm between "c" and obliterator	90.00	90.00
d.		3mm between "c" and obliterator	100.00	100.00
e.		4mm between "c" and obliterator	90.00	90.00
f.		5mm between "c" and obliterator	175.00	175.00
g.		Pair, #1191A, 1197	—	—

No. 1197 exists with surcharge shifted 75% upward. Value, $175. No. 1197d exists with inverted surcharge. Value, $150.

No. 1197B | No. 1197C

1197B	A166	20c on 23c #731	35.00	35.00
a.		No gap between "c" and obliterator (positions 70 and 79)	100.00	100.00
c.		3mm between "c" and obliterator	70.00	70.00
1197C	A166	20c on 23c #731	175.00	175.00
a.		No gap between "c" and obliterator	450.00	450.00
		Nos. 1191-1197C (15)	1,743.	1,743.

No. 1197B exists with inverted surcharge. Value, $150. No. 1197C exists with inverted surcharge. Value, $350. No 1197C exists with obliterator of two double bars with a dash between them. Value, $450.

Issued: No. 1191, 8/22/08; No. 1191A, 12/18/08; No. 1191Ab, 1/23/09; No. 1191C, 1192, 1192A, 2/19/07; Nos. 1193, 1194, 8/20/08; No. 1195, 4/28/08; No. 1195A, Apr. 2008; Nos. 1196, 4/12/08; Nos. 1197, 1197a, 1197d, 1197e, 1197f. Apr. 2008; 1197B, 4/12/08; 1197C, Apr. 2008.

Bananas — A282

Various banana varieties: 65c, $1.10, $1.20, $2.

2008, Sept. 23   Litho.   Perf. 14x14½
1198-1201 A282   Set of 4   5.50 5.50

Eels — A283

Designs: 50c, Anguilla obscura. 90c, Anguilla marmorata. $1.50, Anguilla obscura, diff. $2, Gymnothorax potyuranodon.

2008, Oct. 15   Perf. 14½x14
1202-1205 A283   Set of 4   5.50 5.50

Christmas A284

Various choirs: 20c, 50c, 65c, $3.

2008, Dec. 10   Litho.   Perf. 14½x14
1206-1209 A284   Set of 4   4.50 4.50

Fruit Doves — A285

Designs: 50c, Many-colored fruit dove. 65c, Crimson-crowned fruit dove. 90c, Whistling dove. $3, Orange dove.

2009, Feb. 17   Litho.   Perf. 14x14½
1210-1213 A285   Set of 4   5.50 5.50

Nos. 729-731 Surcharged Like Nos. 1149-1160

No. 1214 | No. 1214B

No. 1215 | No. 1215A

1214	A166	1c on 13c #730	45.00	45.00
a.		2½mm gap between "c" and obliterator (positions 3 and 89)	120.00	120.00
1214B	A166	1c on 13c #730, small font	90.00	90.00
1215	A166	1c on 23c #731	1.25	1.25
b.		2½mm gap between "c" and obliterator (positions 3 and 89)	50.00	50.00
1215A	A166	1c on 23c #731, small font	1.00	1.00

No. 1215 exists with inverted surcharge. Value, $90. No. 1215A exists with inverted surcharge. Value, $90. No. 1215A also exists with "xx" obliterator (position 70). Value, $300.

No. 1216 | No. 1216A

No. 1216B | No. 1216D

1216	A166	2c on 6c #729	100.00	100.00
e.		2½mm gap between "c" and obliterator (positions 3 and 89)	175.00	175.00
1216A	A166	2c on 13c #730	45.00	45.00
c.		2½mm gap between "c" and obliterator (positions 3 and 89)	120.00	120.00
1216B	A166	2c on 23c #731	175.00	175.00
1216D	A166	2c on 13c #730, small font	175.00	175.00

No. 1216D has a 2½mm gap between "c" and obliterator.

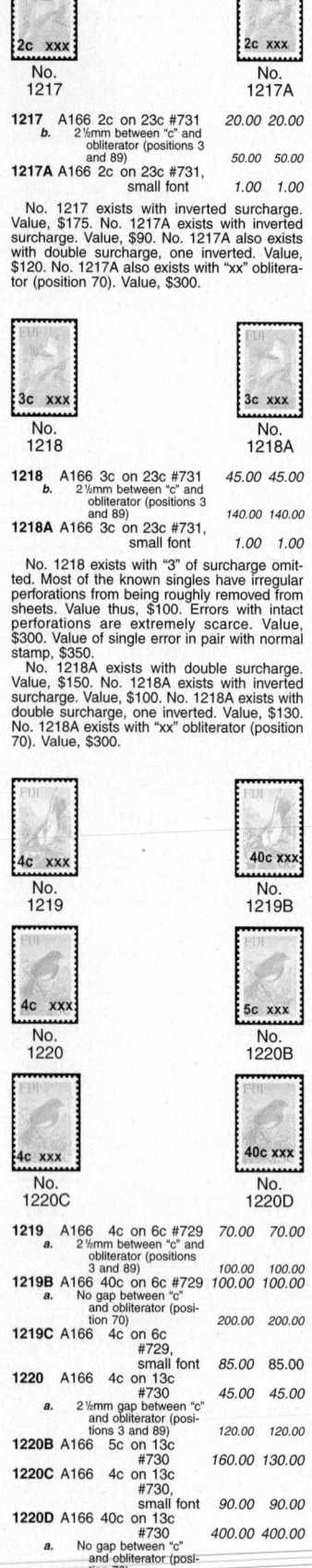

No. 1217 — 2c xxx

No. 1217A — 2c xxx

1217 A166 2c on 23c #731   20.00   20.00
   b.   2½mm between "c" and obliterator (positions 3 and 89)   50.00   50.00
1217A A166 2c on 23c #731, small font   1.00   1.00

No. 1217 exists with inverted surcharge. Value, $175. No. 1217A exists with inverted surcharge. Value, $90. No. 1217A also exists with double surcharge. Value, $120. No. 1217A also exists with "xx" obliterator (position 70). Value, $300.

No. 1218 — 3c xxx

No. 1218A — 3c xxx

1218 A166 3c on 23c #731   45.00   45.00
   b.   2½mm between "c" and obliterator (positions 3 and 89)   140.00   140.00
1218A A166 3c on 23c #731, small font   1.00   1.00

No. 1218 exists with "3" of surcharge omitted. Most of the known singles have irregular perforations from being roughly removed from sheets. Value thus, $100. Errors with intact perforations are extremely scarce. Value, $300. Value of single error in pair with normal stamp, $350.

No. 1218A exists with double surcharge. Value, $150. No. 1218A exists with inverted surcharge. Value, $100. No. 1218A exists with double surcharge, one inverted. Value, $130. No. 1218A exists with "xx" obliterator (position 70). Value, $300.

No. 1219 — 4c xxx

No. 1219B — 40c xxx

No. 1220 — 4c xxx

No. 1220B — 5c xxx

No. 1220C — 4c xxx

No. 1220D — 40c xxx

1219 A166 4c on 6c #729   70.00   70.00
   a.   2½mm between "c" and obliterator (positions 3 and 89)   100.00   100.00
1219B A166 40c on 6c #729   100.00   100.00
   a.   No gap between "c" and obliterator (position 70)   200.00   200.00
1219C A166 4c on 6c #729, small font   85.00   85.00
1220 A166 4c on 13c #730   45.00   45.00
   a.   2½mm gap between "c" and obliterator (positions 3 and 89)   120.00   120.00
1220B A166 5c on 13c #730   160.00   130.00
1220C A166 4c on 13c #730, small font   90.00   90.00
1220D A166 40c on 13c #730   400.00   400.00
   a.   No gap between "c" and obliterator (position 70)

Nos. 1219 and 1219a exist with inverted surcharge. Value, each $200. No. 1219C exists with inverted surcharge. Value, $175. No. 1219C also exists with double surcharge, one inverted. Value, $225. No. 1220C exists with inverted surcharge. Value, $100.

No. 1221 — 4c XX

No. 1222 — 4c xxx

No. 1221 — 4c XX

No. 1222A — 4c xxx

No. 1222C — 50c xxx

1221 A166 4c on 23c #731   90.00   90.00
   a.   4mm between "c" and obliterator (positions 3 and 89)   250.00   250.00
1222 A166 4c on 23c #731   1.50   1.50
   b.   2½mm between "c" and obliterator (positions 3 and 89)   50.00   50.00
1222A A166 4c on 23c #731, small font   1.00   1.00
1222C A166 50c on 23c #731   300.00   300.00
   a.   No gap between "c" and obliterator (position 70)   1,000.

No. 1221 exists with inverted surcharge. Value, $150.

No. 1222 exists with inverted surcharge. Value, $90. No. 1222 exists with double surcharge, one inverted. Value, $130. No. 1222 exists with double surcharge, one with normal 4mm between "c" and obliterator and the other with 2½mm between "c" and obliterator. Value, $150.

No. 1222A exists with inverted surcharge. Value, $100. No. 1222A exists with double surcharge, one inverted. Value, $120. No. 1222A exists with double surcharge. Value, $150.

No. 1223 — 5c xxx

No. 1223b — 5c xxx

No. 1223c — 5c

No. 1223A — 5c xxx

1223 A166 5c on 23c #731, 4mm between "c" and obliterator   1.50   1.50
   b.   2½mm between "c" and obliterator (positions 3 and 89)   50.00   50.00
   c.   No obliterator   325.00   325.00
1223A A166 5c on 23c #731, small font   1.00   1.00
   Nos. 1214-1223A (23)   1,644.   1,614.

No. 1223 exists with surcharge shifted 50% upward. Value, $60. No. 1223 also exists with inverted surcharge and with double surcharge, one inverted. Values, $100 and $150, respectively. No. 1223A exists with inverted surcharge. Value, $90.

On Nos. 1215, 1217, 1218, 1219, 1222 and 1223, the "c" and obliterator are 4mm apart.

Issued: Nos. 1214, 1215, 1215b, Mar. 10; Nos. 1215A, 1217A, 1218A, 8/5/10; No. 1216A, Mar. 30; Nos. 1216, 1216B, Mar.; Nos. 1217, 1217b, Mar. 30; No. 1218, Aug. 27; No. 1219, 1220, 1221, 1222, Mar. 10; No. 1222A, 8/3/10; No. 1223, July 8; No. 1223A, 8/6/10.

Weddings in Fiji — A286

Designs: 20c, Chinese wedding. 40c, Muslim wedding. $1.50, Indian wedding. $3, Fijian wedding, vert.

Perf. 14½x14, 14x14½

2009, Aug. 17   **Litho.**   **Unwmk.**
1224-1227 A286   Set of 4   6.00   6.00

Passion Fruit — A287

Designs: 20c, Passiflora foetida. 65c, Passiflora edulis (yellow green). $1.20, Passiflora maliformis. $2, Passiflora edulis (purple).

2009, Sept. 29   **Perf. 14x14¼**
1228-1231 A287   Set of 4   6.00   6.00

Souvenir Sheet

People's Republic of China, 60th Anniv. A288

2009, Oct. 1   **Perf. 13¼**
1232 A288 $5 multi   6.00   6.00

Ferns — A289

Designs: 20c, Cyathea lunulata. 40c, Asplenium australasicum. $1.50, Diplazium proliferum. $3, Nephrolepsis biserrata.

2009, Dec. 15   **Perf. 14x14½**
1233-1236 A289   Set of 4   6.00   6.00

Snakes A290

Designs: 20c, Yellow-bellied sea snake. 90c, Fiji burrowing snake. $1.10, Banded sea krait. $2, Pacific boa.

2010, Mar. 30   **Litho.**   **Perf. 14½x14**
1237-1240 A290   Set of 4   4.50   4.50

Peonies A291

No. 1241: a, 20c, Pink peony. b, 40c, Red peony.

2010, Apr. 8   **Litho.**   **Perf. 13¼**
1241 A291   Horiz. pair, #a-b   13.00   13.00

Raiateana Knowlesi — A292

No. 1242: a, 20c, Newly-emerged insect. b, $1.50, Mature insect.

Perf. 14x14½

2010, June 30   **Unwmk.**
1242 A292   Vert. pair, #a-b   2.00   2.00

A293

A294

A295

Worldwide Fund for Nature (WWF) — A296

2010, Oct. 27   **Perf. 14¼x14**
1243   Horiz. strip of 4   9.00   9.00
   a.   A293 $2 multi   2.25   2.25
   b.   A294 $2 multi   2.25   2.25
   c.   A295 $2 multi   2.25   2.25
   d.   A296 $2 multi   2.25   2.25

Fruit — A297

Designs: 20c, Citrus maxima. 40c, Barringtinia edulis. 65c, Pometia pinnata. $1.20, Musa troglogytarum. $10, Syzygium malacensis.

2010, Dec. 2   **Perf. 14¼**
1244-1248 A297   Set of 5   14.50   14.50

No. 1249 — 1c xxx

No. 1249A — 1c XX

1c XX
No. 1249Ab

3c xxx
No. 1251

4c xxx
No. 1252

5c xxx
No. 1253

20c xxx
No. 1254

20c xxx
No. 1254a

20c XX
No. 1254C

20c XXX
No. 1254G

Methods, Perfs and Watermarks As Before

2011-14

1249	A166	1c on 31c #732	1.00	1.00
c.		3½mm between "c" and obliterator	75.00	75.00
d.		1½mm between "c" and obliterator	125.00	125.00
e.		4mm between "c" and obliterator, larger font	50.00	50.00
f.		2½mm between "c" and obliterator	100.00	100.00
g.		2½mm between "c" and obliterator	75.00	75.00
1249A	A166	1c on 31c #732	80.00	80.00
b.		Extra large "XX" (position 51)	275.00	275.00
1250	A166	2c on 31c #732	1.00	1.00
a.		4mm between "c" and obliterator	95.00	95.00
b.		3mm between "c" and obliterator (positions 3 and 89)	185.00	185.00
1251	A166	3c on 31c #732	1.00	1.00
1252	A166	4c on 31c #732	1.00	1.00
a.		4mm between "c" and obliterator	95.00	95.00
b.		3mm between "c" and obliterator (positions 3 and 89)	185.00	185.00
1253	A166	5c on 31c #732	1.00	1.00
a.		3½mm between "c" and obliterator	75.00	75.00
b.		1½mm between "c" and obliterator	100.00	100.00
c.		2¼mm between "c" and obliterator	100.00	100.00
1254	A166	20c on 31c #732	2.00	2.00
a.		Larger font	50.00	50.00
b.		As "a," 2½mm between "c" and obliterator	100.00	100.00
d.		As No. 1254, no gap between "c" and obliterator (position 70)	35.00	35.00
f.		As "a," no gap between "c" and obliterator	250.00	300.00
h.		3 ¾mm btwn "c" and obliterator	180.00	180.00
1254C	A166	20c on 31c #732	125.00	125.00
1254E	A166	40c on 31c #732	3.00	3.00
a.		No gap between "c" and obliterator	50.00	50.00
1254G	A166	20c on 31c #732	180.00	180.00
a.		No gap between "c" and obliterator	225.00	225.00
		Nos. 1249A-1254G (10)	395.00	395.00

Nos. 1249-1253 have 2½mm between "c" and obliterator. No. 1249A has 3½mm spacing. Nos. 1249Ab, 1254, 1254a, 1254E and 1254G have 1½mm spacing.

No. 1249 exists with inverted surcharge. Value, $90. No. 1249 exists with double surcharge. Value, $120; and with double surcharge, one inverted, value, $130. No. 1249A exists with denomination omitted (position 77). Value, $500.

No. 1250 exists with inverted surcharge. Value, $90. No. 1250 exists with double surcharge. Value, $120. No. 1250 exists with double surcharge, one inverted. Value, $130. No. 1250a exists with double surcharge. Value, $200.

No. 1251 exists with inverted surcharge. Value, $100. No. 1251 exists with double surcharge. Value, $120. No. 1251 exists with

double surcharge, one inverted. Value, $130. No. 1251 exists with surcharge shifted 50% upward. Value, $50. No. 1252 exists with inverted surcharge. Value, $90. No. 1252 exists with double surcharge. Value, $120. No. 1252 with double surcharge, one inverted. Value, $130.

No. 1253 exists with inverted surcharge. Value, $90. No. 1253 exists with double surcharge, with double surcharge, one shifted 50% upward, and with double surcharge, one inverted, value, each $130. No. 1253 exists with surcharge shifted 50% upward. Value, $50.

No. 1254 exists with inverted surcharge. Value, $100. No. 1254 exists with double surcharge. Value, $65. No. 1254 exists with double surcharge, one with large "20," the other with small "20." Value, $175. No. 1254 exists with double surcharge, one inverted: one with large "20," the other with small "20." Value, $175. No. 1254 exists with double surcharge, one inverted (top surcharge inverted, bottom shifted 50% upward). Value, $110. No. 1254 exists with surcharge shifted 50% upward. Value, $50. No. 1254 exists with double surcharge, one shifted 50% upward. Value, $100. No. 1254 exists with double surcharge, one shifted 50% upward; both with no gap between "c" and obliterator. Value, $300. No. 1254a exists with surcharge shifted 50% upward. Value, $80. No. 1254a exists with surcharge inverted and shifted 50% upward. Value, $130. No. 1254f exists with surcharge shifted 50% upward. Value, $250.

No. 1254E exists with inverted surcharge. Value, $90. No. 1254E exists with double surcharge. Value, $120. No. 1254E exists with double surcharge, one inverted. Value, $130. No. 1254E exists with surcharge shifted 45% upward. Value, $50.

No. 1254G exists with inverted surcharge. Value, $225. No. 1254G also exists with "c" of "20c" omitted. Value, $325.

Issued: No. 1249, 6/6; No. 1249A, 7/30/14; Nos. 1250, 1253, 3/24; No. 1250a, 3/2014; No. 1251, 7/8; No. 1252, 5/20; No. 1252a, 2/2014; No. 1254, 5/4; Nos. 1254a, 1254b, 2011; No. 1254d, 5/4; Nos. 1254E, 1254Ea, 12/7/12.

Souvenir Sheet

Wedding of Prince William and Catherine Middleton — A298

Perf. 14¾x14¼

2011, Apr. 29		**Litho.**		**Wmk. 406**
1255	A298	$10 multi	11.50	11.50

Campaign Against AIDS — A299

People, UNAIDS emblem and slogan: 20c, Protect youth from HIV infection. 40c, Zero new HIV infections, vert. 65c, Stop mothers & babies from being infected with HIV, vert. $5, Zero discrimination.

Perf. 14½x14, 14x14½

2011, June 22				**Unwmk.**
1256-1259	A299	Set of 4	7.25	7.25

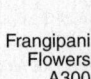

Frangipani Flowers A300

Designs: 50c, Plumeria rubra bud. 90c, Plumeria rubra f. rubra flower. $1.50, Plumeria rubra f. lutea. $3, Plumeria obtusa.

2011, July 12			**Perf. 14½x14**	
1260-1263	A300	Set of 4	6.75	6.75

Pomegranate Tree Branches and Birds — A301

No. 1264: a, 65c, Bird on branch. b, $1.20, Bird in flight near branch.

2011, Aug. 15			**Perf. 13¼x13¾**	
1264	A301	Horiz. pair, #a-b	2.25	2.25

No. 1264 was printed in sheets containing three pairs.

War Clubs A302

Designs: 20c, Saulaki vividrasa. 65c, Cali. $1.20, Totokia. $10, I ula tavatava.

2011, Aug. 15			**Perf. 14½x14**	
1265-1268	A302	Set of 4	14.00	14.00

Intl. Year of Volunteers A303

Volunteers for: 40c, St. John Ambulance Association. 90c, Suva City Council, vert. $1.10, Red Cross, vert. $10, National Blood Bank.

Perf. 14½x14, 14x14½

2011, Nov. 25				
1269-1272	A303	Set of 4	14.50	14.50

Christmas A304

Designs: 20c, Fijian with gift box. 65c, Fijian with pottery. $1.20, Fijian with necklace. $2, Holy Family.

2011, Dec. 16			**Perf. 14½x14**	
1273-1276	A304	Set of 4	4.50	4.50

New Year 2012 (Year of the Dragon) — A305

2012, Jan. 23			**Perf. 14¼**	
1277	A305	$3 multi	3.50	3.50

No. 1277 was printed in sheets of 4.

Endangered Flora — A306

Designs: 20c, Fijian acmopyle. 65c, Lau fan palm. $1.20, Cycad. $2, Fiji magnolia.

2012, Apr. 26			**Perf. 14½x14**	
1278-1281	A306	Set of 4	4.50	4.50

Intl. Year of Sustainable Energy For All — A307

Designs: 20c, Water power. 50c, Biomass. $1.20, Wind energy. $3, Solar power.

2012, June 25				
1282-1285	A307	Set of 4	5.50	5.50

A308

A309

A310

Worldwide Fund for Nature (WWF) — A311

2012, July 11			**Perf. 14¼x14**	
1286		Horiz. strip of 4	9.00	9.00
a.	A308	$2 multi	2.25	2.25
b.	A309	$2 multi	2.25	2.25
c.	A310	$2 multi	2.25	2.25
d.	A311	$2 multi	2.25	2.25

Christmas A312

Designs: 20c, Journey to Bethlehem. 40c, Holy Family. 65c, Adoration of the Shepherds. $1.20, Adoration of the Shepherds, diff. $5, Adoration of the Magi.

2012, Dec. 14		**Litho.**	**Perf. 14½x14**	
1287-1291	A312	Set of 5	8.50	8.50

Birth of Prince George of Cambridge — A313

Prince George and: 40c, Duke and Duchess of Cambridge. 65c, Duchess of Cambridge. $1.20, Duke and Duchess of Cambridge, diff. $5, Duke of Cambridge.

2013, Aug. 28		**Litho.**	**Perf. 13½**	
1292-1295	A313	Set of 4	7.75	7.75

Mangrove Protection A314

Designs: 50c, Mangroves. 65c, Mangrove, jellyfish, starfish. $1.20, Fish and underwater root system of mangrove. $10, People planting mangroves.

2013, Oct. 30		**Litho.**	**Perf. 13½**	
1296-1299	A314	Set of 4	13.50	13.50

Christmas — A315

Bell-shaped Christmas ornament with: 40c, Cathedral. 65c, Flowers. $1.20, Fijian family walking on beach. $3, Fijian children with Christmas gifts.

2013, Dec. 2   Litho.   Perf. 13½
1300-1303 A315 Set of 4   5.75 5.75

Submarine Cable Between Fiji and Vanuatu — A316

No. 1304: a, Workers, ship and cable with floats. b, Diver examining cable. c, Electronic cables plugged into machine.

Litho. With Foil Application
2014, Jan. 15   Perf. 14½x14

1304	Horiz. strip of 6 + central label, #1304a-1304c, Vanuatu #1070a-1070c	14.50	14.50
a.	A316 65c multi	.70	.70
b.	A316 $1.20 multi	1.25	1.25
c.	A316 $6 multi	6.50	6.50

No. 1304 sold for $13.30 in Fiji and 750v in Vanuatu. See Vanuatu No. 1070.

Sharks — A317

Designs: 50c, Blacktip reef shark. 90c, Silky shark. $1.20, Oceanic whitetip shark. $5, Big-eye thresher shark.

2014, July 28   Litho.   Perf. 13¾x13¼
1305-1308 A317 Set of 4   8.25 8.25

Grand Pacific Hotel, Cent. — A318

Designs: 40c, Hotel driveway and entrance. 65c, Sofas and tables. 90c, Swimming pool. $1.20, Dining area. $5, Entrance, diff.

2014, Aug. 8   Litho.   Perf. 13¾x13¼
1309-1313 A318 Set of 5   8.75 8.75

Nos. 732-733 Surcharged

No. 1313A

No. 1314

No. 1314b

No. 1313D

No. 1313E

No. 1315

No. 1315B

No. 1316

No. 1317

50c xxx

Methods, Perfs and Watermarks As Before
2014-15

1313A	A166	1c on 44c #733	4.00	4.00
b.		2¼mm between "c" and obliterator	50.00	50.00
c.		4¼mm between "c" and obliterator	40.00	40.00
1314	A166	20c on 44c #733	1.50	1.50
a.		No gap between "c" and obliterator (position 70)	50.00	50.00
b.		Large "20"	30.00	30.00
c.		As "b," no gap between "c" and obliterator (positions 70 and 79)	75.00	75.00
d.		As "b," 3mm between "c" and obliterator (positions 31, 41, 61, 71, 81 and 91)	50.00	50.00
e.		3¾mm between "c" and obliterator (position 3)	175.00	175.00
1313D	A166	1c on 44c #733, Capital "XX"	—	—
1313E	A166	1c on 44c #733, Lower case "xx"	—	—
1315	A166	40c on 44c #733	2.00	2.00
a.		No gap between "c" and obliterator (position 70)	60.00	60.00
1315B	A166	50c on 3c #727	450.00	450.00
c.		No gap between "c" and obliterator (position 70)	—	—
1316	A166	50c on 31c #732	6.00	6.00
a.		No gap between "c" and obliterator (position 70)	50.00	50.00
1317	A166	50c on 44c #733	3.00	3.00
a.		No gap between "c" and obliterator (position 70)	65.00	65.00
		Nos. 1313A-1317 (6)	466.50	466.50

No. 1313A exists with double surcharge. Value, $120. No. 1313A also exists with inverted surcharge. Value, $110.

No. 1314 exists with surcharge shifted 50% upward. Value, $25. No. 1314 exists with surcharge inverted. Value, $60. No. 1314a exists with surcharge shifted 50% upward. Value, $75. No. 1314b exists with surcharge inverted. Value, $100. No. 1314b exists with double surcharge. Value, $120.

No. 1315 exists with surcharge shifted 50% upward. Value, $25. No. 1315a exists with surcharge shifted 50% upward. Value, $80.

No. 1316 exists with double surcharge. Value, $70. Nos. 1316 and 1316a exist with inverted surcharge. Value, both $120.

No. 1317 exists with surcharge shifted 50% upward. Value, $30. No. 1317a exists with surcharge shifted 50% upward. Value, $90.

Issued: No. 1313A, 8/28/15; No. 1314, 6/11; No. 1314b, 7/31; Nos. 1315, 1317, 6/10. No. 1316, 3/5.

Christmas — A319

Houses of worship: 40c, The Church of Jesus Christ of Latter-day Saints, Suva. 65c, Holy Redeemer Anglican Church, Levuka. $3, Baker Memorial Methodist Church, Nausori. $10, St. Francis Xavier Church, Navunibitu.

Perf. 13½
2014, Dec. 4   Litho.   Unwmk.
1320-1323 A319 Set of 4   14.00 14.00

Souvenir Sheet

Blue Coral A320

No. 1324 — Heliopora coerulea: a, 65c. b, $5.

Perf. 13½x13¼
2015, Feb. 23   Litho.
1324 A320 Sheet of 2, #a-b   5.50 5.50

Fiji Flying Fox — A321

Fiji flying fox: 40c, Head. 65c, In flight, horiz. 90c, Head, horiz. $10, Hanging from tree.

Perf. 13¼x13¾, 13¾x13¼
2015, Apr. 30   Litho.
1325-1328 A321 Set of 4   13.50 13.50

Levuka UNESCO World Heritage Site — A322

Designs: 50c, Fiji Times Building, Beach Street, c. 1894. 65c, Sacred Heart Church, c. 1902, vert. 90c, Levuka Public School, c. 1884, vert. $5, Public Office, Nasova, c. 1877-82.

2015, June 16   Litho.   Perf. 13½
1329-1332 A322 Set of 4   6.75 6.75

Voyages of Uto Ni Yalo Outrigger Canoe — A323

Uto Ni Yalo: 40c, Near shore with white and black sails. 65c, Near Sydney Harbour Bridge and Sydney Opera House. $1.50, Near Golden Gate Bridge. $10, Near shore with red and black sails.

Perf. 13¾x13¼
2015, Aug. 31   Litho.
1333-1336 A323 Set of 4   11.50 11.50

Medicinal Plants — A324

Designs: 40c, Scaevola sericea. 65c, Vigna marina. 90c, Ipomoea pes-caprae subsp. brasiliensis. $1.20, Clerodendrum inerme. $5, Morinda citrifolia.

2015, Oct. 21   Litho.   Perf. 13¾x13¼
1337-1341 A324 Set of 5   7.75 7.75

Christmas — A325

Archangels: 40c, St. Uriel. 65c, St. Gabriel. 90c, St. Raphael. $10, St. Michael.

2015, Dec. 7   Litho.   Perf. 13¼x13¾
1342-1345 A325 Set of 4   11.50 11.50

Nos. 735 Surcharged

Nos. 734 Surcharged

Methods, Perfs. and Watermarks As Before
2015-16

1346	A166	1c on 81c #735	7.50	10.00
a.		2¼mm between and obliterator (positions 1 and 2)	125.00	125.00
b.		4¼mm between "c" and obliterator (position 51)	175.00	175.00
1347	A166	20c on 63c #734	20.00	20.00
a.		No gap between "c" and obliterator (position 70)	120.00	120.00
b.		3¼mm between "c" and obliterator (position 3)	120.00	120.00
c.		Large "20"	120.00	120.00

No. 1346 has 3¼mm between "c" and obliterator. No. 1347 has 1½mm between "c" and obliterator.

Issued: No. 1346, 1/29/16; No. 1347, 12/31.

New Year 2016 (Year of the Monkey) — A326

No. 1348: a, Macaca arctoides, bananas. b, Rhinopithecus, peonies. c, Rhesus macaque, coconut palm trees. d, White-headed langur, hibiscus flowers.

Perf. 13½x13¼
2016, Mar. 30   Litho.   Unwmk.

1348	Horiz. strip of 4 + central label	11.50	11.50
a.	A326 38c multi	.40	.40
b.	A326 47c multi	.45	.45
c.	A326 85c multi	.85	.85
d.	A326 $10 multi	9.75	9.75

Rotary International in Fiji, 80th Anniv. — A327

Designs: 38c, Medical incinerator for Wainibokasi Hospital. 62c, Dialysis machine for Kidney Foundation of Fiji, vert. $1.04, Emergency Response Kit label, vert. $5, Braille machine for Fiji Society for the Blind.

Perf. 13½x13¼, 13¼x13½
2016, May 19   Litho.   Unwmk.
1349-1352 A327 Set of 4   6.75 6.75

No. 733 Surcharged

No. 1353

3c xxx

No. 1354

4c xxx

No. 1355

5c xxx

No. 1356

23c xx

No. 1356A

23c xxx

Methods, Perfs. and Watermarks As Before
2016-21 ?

1353	A166	3c on 44c #733	3.00	3.00
1354	A166	4c on 44c #733	3.00	3.00
1355	A166	5c on 44c #733	3.00	3.00
1356	A166	23c on 44c #733	4.50	4.50
1356A	A166	23c on 44c #733, "xxx" obliterator	—	—
b.		"xxxx" obliterator	—	—
		Nos. 1353-1356 (4)	13.50	13.50

No. 1355 exists with double surcharge. Value, $800.

Issued: No. 1353, 6/13; No. 1354, 6/15; No. 1355, 8/26; No. 1356, 10/25.

Thatched Structures at Navala Village — A328

Designs: 38c, Dwelling. 47c, Home for the elderly. 85c, Meeting house. $10, Chief's home.

Perf. 13½x13¼

2016, July 27	Litho.	Unwmk.
1357-1360 A328 Set of 4	11.50	11.50

Flowers — A329

Designs: 47c, Pink Hibiscus rosa-sinensis. 58c, Abelmoschus esculentus (okra). 85c, Red Hibiscus rosa-sinensis. $1.04, Thespesia populnea. $15, Hibiscus tiliaceus.

Perf. 13¼x13½

2016, Aug. 12	Litho.	Unwmk.
1361-1365 A329 Set of 5	17.50	17.50

Christmas — A330

Designs: 40c, Carolers. 90c, People preparing lovo for feast. $1.20, Family going to church. $10, Exchanging gifts.

Perf. 13½x13¼

2016, Dec. 5	Litho.	Unwmk.
1366-1369 A330 Set of 4	12.00	12.00

No. 733 Surcharged

No. 1370

No. 1371

Methods, Perfs. and Watermarks As Before

2016-17

1370 A166	2c on 44c #733	3.00	3.00
a.	1½mm btwn "c" and obliterator	75.00	75.00
1371 A166	50c on 44c #733	24.00	24.00

Issued: No. 1370, 2016; No. 1371, 2017. Compare No. 1371 with No. 1317.

No. 1370 has a standard gap of 2¼mm between the "c" and the obliterator.

New Year 2017 (Year of the Rooster) — A331

Designs: 85c, Rooster and red hibiscus flower. $1.20, Hen and yellow frangipani flower. $3, Rooster and palm trees. $15, Rooster and tree blossoms.

Perf. 13¼x13½

2017, Feb. 10	Litho.	Unwmk.
1372-1375 A331 Set of 4	19.50	19.50

Great Sea Reef — A332

Designs: 62c, Branching coral. 85c, Boulders. $1.04, Soft coral. $15, Plate coral.

Perf. 13½x13¼

2017, May 19	Litho.	Unwmk.
1376-1379 A332 Set of 4	17.00	17.00

National Women's Expo — A333

Women and: 40c, Pottery. 62c, Boxes, baskets and handbags. $1.14, Pottery, baskets and textiles. $10, Textiles, bowls and kitchen utensils.

Perf. 13½x13¼

2017, June 14	Litho.	Unwmk.
1380-1383 A333 Set of 4	12.00	12.00

Sigatoka Sand Dunes — A334

Designs: 40c, Vegetation surrounding the dunes. 85c, People trekking through the dunes. $1.14, Dunes overlooking the Pacific Ocean. $5, Team training at the dunes.

Perf. 13½x13¼

2017, Sept. 28	Litho.	Unwmk.
1384-1387 A334 Set of 4	7.25	7.25

2017 United Nations Climate Change Conference, Bonn — A335

Designs: 40c, Drua. 62c, People planting mangroves. $1.40, Traditional Fijian houses. $10, Workers in sugar cane field.

Perf. 13½

2018, Feb. 5	Litho.	Unwmk.
1388-1391 A335 Set of 4	12.50	12.50

New Year 2018 (Year of the Dog) — A336

Various dogs: 38c, 50c, $1.04, $10.

2018, Feb. 28	Litho.	Perf. 14½
1392-1395 A336 Set of 4	12.00	12.00

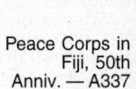

Peace Corps in Fiji, 50th Anniv. — A337

Various Peace Corps workers and Fijians: 40c, $1.14, $2, $10.

2018, Mar. 28	Litho.	Perf. 14½
1396-1399 A337 Set of 4	13.50	13.50

Reptiles — A338

Designs: 38c, Giant forest gecko. 40c, Fiji barred tree skink. $1.63, Gau banded iguana. $5, Ono I Lau skink.

2018, July 13	Litho.	Perf. 13½
1400-1403 A338 Set of 4	7.25	7.25

Mohandas K. Gandhi (1869-1948), Indian Nationalist Leader — A339

Gandhi and: 38c, Manilal Doctor (1881-1956), Indian barrister assisting Indians in Fiji, Charles Freer Andrews (1871-1940), social reformer in India, and Totaram Sanadhya (1876-1947), indentured Indian laborer working in Fiji. 50c, Devanagari script and pencil. 90c, Doves. $15, Drua.

Perf. 13½

2018, Dec. 20	Litho.	Unwmk.
1404-1407 A339 Set of 4	16.00	16.00

Nos. 729 and 733 Surcharged

No. 1407A

No. 1407B

Methods, Perfs. and Watermarks As Before

2018-19 ?

1407A A166	3c on 6c #729	425.00	425.00
1407B A166	40c on 44c #733	30.00	30.00
c.	1¼mm btwn "c" and "XX."	125.00	125.00

Issued: No. 1407A, 2019 ?; No. 1407B, Sept. 2018. Compare No. 1407B with No. 1315.

The issue date of No. 1407A is uncertain and may have been as early as 2007.

New Year 2019 (Year of the Pig) — A340

Designs: 38c, Flower, bananas and orange and red pig. 40c, Flowers and blue pig. $1.20, Dove, trees and red pig. $10, Trees and green pig.

Perf. 14½

2019, Feb. 2	Litho.	Unwmk.
1408-1411 A340 Set of 4	11.50	11.50

International Labor Organization, Cent. A341

Designs: 40c, Five workers. 90c, Worker wearing face mask. $1.15, Child playing with blocks. $10, People on arrows surrounding globe.

Perf. 14¼

2019, May	Litho.	Unwmk.
1412-1415 A341 Set of 4	11.50	11.50

Morris Hedstrom Ltd., 150th Anniv. in Fiji — A342

Designs: Inscribed: 50c, The Voyage — MH Copra Boat. 65c, They Way We Were. 85c, Steeped in History. $1.50, Way Back When. $5, The Birth of a Legacy.

Perf. 14x13½

2019, July	Litho.	Unwmk.
1416-1420 A342 Set of 5	8.00	8.00

No. 733 Surcharged

No. 733 Surcharged

Method, Perf. and Watermark As Before

2020, Aug.

1421 A166 6c on 44c #733	—	—

Fish — A343

Designs: 40c, Brown marbled grouper. 90c, Squaretail coral grouper. $1.10, Leopard coral grouper. $15, Camouflage grouper.

2019, Sept. 16	Litho.	Perf. 14½x14
1422-1425 A343 Set of 4	16.00	16.00

Religious Festivals — A344

Designs: 38c, Chinese New Year. $1.20, Eid ul-Fitr. $3, Diwali. $5, Christmas.

2019, Dec. 4	Litho.	Perf. 14½x14
1426-1429 A344 Set of 4	9.00	9.00

New Year 2020 (Year of the Rat) — A345

Designs: 40c, Rat and split pineapple. 90c, Rats and mangos. $1.10, Rats and split coconut. $15, Rats on bamboo.

2020, Jan. 17	Litho.	Perf. 14½
1430-1433 A345 Set of 4	16.00	16.00

Independence, 50th Anniv. — A346

Perf. 13½x13¼

2020, Sept. 29		Litho.
1434 A346 38c multi	—	—

Diplomatic Relations Between Fiji and People's Republic of China, 45th Anniv. A347

Designs: 38c, Rugby players. $1.38, Table tennis players. $2.38, Fijian woman. $5, Chinese woman.

2020, Nov. 5	Litho.	Perf. 14½x14
1435-1438 A347 Set of 4	—	—

Dorje Chang Buddha III, Religious Leader — A348

2021, Feb. 26	Litho.	Perf. 12x11½
1439 A348 $3 multi	3.00	3.00

New Year 2021 (Year of the Ox) — A349

Designs: 38c, Ox and palm trees. $1.04, Ox and mountains. $2.38, Ox and Fijian houses. $10, Ox plowing field.

2021, Feb. 9   **Litho.**   *Perf. 14x14½*
1440-1443   A349   Set of 4   —   —

Swami Pranavanandaji Maharaj (1896-1941), Founder of Bharat Sevashram Sangha — A350

Designs: 38c, Girl at summer camp. $1.38, Members of Nar-Narayan Seva walking in water. $2, Nationwide Ganesh Utsav. $5, Swami Pranavanandaji Mahara.

2021, Mar. 1   **Litho.**   *Perf. 13½x13¼*
1444-1447   A350   Set of 4

SEMI-POSTAL STAMPS

> Catalogue values for unused stamps in this section are for Never Hinged items.

Children at Play SP1	Rugby Player SP2

Perf. 13x13½
1951, Sept. 17   **Engr.**   **Wmk. 4**
B1   SP1   1p + 1p brown   .30   1.60
B2   SP2   2p + 1p deep green   .55   1.10

Bamboo River Raft — SP3

Design: 2½p+½p, Cross of Lorraine.

1954, Apr. 1   *Perf. 11x11½*
B3   SP3   1½p + ½p green & brn   .25   1.10
B4   SP3   2½p + ½p black & org   .30   .30

Nos. 269 and 272 Surcharged

1972, Dec. 4   **Photo.**   *Perf. 14, 13½*
B5   A56   15c + 5c multi   .40   .35
B6   A55   30c + 10c multi   1.10   .35

Indian Boy, Map of Fiji — SP4

Map of Fiji and: 15c+2c, European girl. 30c+3c, Chinese girl. 40c+4c, Fijian boy.

Wmk. 373
1979, Sept. 17   **Litho.**   *Perf. 14½*
B7   SP4   4c + 1c multicolored   .25   .25
B8   SP4   15c + 2c multicolored   .25   .25
B9   SP4   30c + 3c multicolored   .40   .40
B10   SP4   40c + 4c multicolored   .60   .60
Nos. B7-B10 (4)   1.50   1.50

The surtax was for IYC fund.

Iliesa Delana, Gold Medalist at 2012 Paralympic Games — SP5

Delana: 40c+10c, High jumping. 65c+10c, Standing and waving flag of Fiji, vert. $1.20+10c, Wearing gold medal, vert. $2+10c, Going around track waving flag of Fiji.

2013, Mar. 7   *Perf. 14½x14, 14x14½*
B11-B14   SP5   Set of 4   5.25   5.25

Surtax for Fiji Paralympic Committee.

POSTAGE DUE STAMPS

D1   D2

POSTAGE DUE **1d.** FIJI

D3

1917   **Unwmk.**   **Typeset**   *Perf. 11*
Laid Papers; Without Gum

J1	D1	½p black	1,450.	500.00
J2	D2	½p black	550.00	300.00
a.		Narrow setting	500.00	150.00
J3	D3	1p black	575.00	150.00
a.		Narrow setting	350.00	150.00
J4	D3	2p black	325.00	80.00
a.		Narrow setting	1,350.	650.00
J5	D3	3p black	675.00	125.00
J6	D3	4p black	1,600.	575.00
a.		Strip of 8, 3 #J3, 1 ea. #J1 and #J6, and 3 #J5	19,000.	
		Nos. J1-J6 (6)	5,175.	1,730.

There were two printings of this issue. In the first printing, the 2d was printed in sheets of 84 (7x12), and the other four values were printed together in sheets of 96 (8x12), with each row consisting of three 1p, one ½p, one 4p and three 3p values. Setenant multiples exist. Sheets were not perforated on the margins, so that marginal stamps were not perforated on the outer edge. Examples from the first printing are 25mm wide (including margins).

In the second printing, the ½p, 1p and 2p were printed in separate sheets of 84 (7x12). The clichés were set a little closer, so that examples of this printing are 23mm wide.

 D4

Perf. 14
1918, June 1   **Typo.**   **Wmk. 3**

J7	D4	½p black	3.25	30.00
J8	D4	1p black	3.75	5.50
J9	D4	2p black	3.50	8.00
J10	D4	3p black	3.50	60.00
J11	D4	4p black	6.50	30.00
		Nos. J7-J11 (5)	20.50	133.50

 D5

1940   **Wmk. 4**   *Perf. 12½*

J12	D5	1p bright green	9.00	72.50
J13	D5	2p bright green	17.50	72.50
J14	D5	3p bright green	20.00	80.00
J15	D5	4p bright green	20.00	85.00
J16	D5	5p bright green	24.00	90.00
J17	D5	6p bright green	25.00	90.00
J18	D5	1sh dk carmine	25.00	115.00
J19	D5	1sh6p dk carmine	25.00	175.00
		Nos. J12-J19 (8)	165.50	780.00
		Set, never hinged	295.00	

WAR TAX STAMPS

Regular Issue of 1912-16 Overprinted

Die I
1916   **Wmk. 3**   *Perf. 14*

MR1	A23	½p green	1.90	7.50
a.		Inverted overprint	700.00	
b.		Double overprint		
MR2	A23	1p scarlet	4.00	.80
a.		1p carmine	42.50	27.50
b.		Pair, one without ovpt.	8,000.	
c.		Inverted overprint	800.00	

Most examples of No. MR2b are within horiz. strips of 12.

FINLAND

'fin-lənd

(Suomi)

LOCATION — Northern Europe bordering on the Gulfs of Bothnia and Finland
GOVT. — Republic
AREA — 130,119 sq. mi.
POP. — 5,147,349 (1997)
CAPITAL — Helsinki

Finland was a Grand Duchy of the Russian Empire from 1809 until December 1917, when it declared its independence.

100 Kopecks = 1 Ruble
100 Pennia = 1 Markka (1866)
100 Cents = 1 Euro (2002)

> Catalogue values for unused stamps in this country are for Never Hinged items, beginning with Scott 220 in the regular postage section, Scott B39 in the semipostal section, Scott C2 in the airpost section, Scott M1 in the military stamp section, and Scott Q6 in the parcel post section.

Unused stamps are valued with original gum as defined in the catalogue introduction except for Nos. 1-3B which are valued without gum. Used values for Nos. 1-3B are for pen-canceled examples. Very fine examples of the serpentine rouletted issues, Nos. 4-13c, will have roulettes cutting the design slightly on one or more sides and will have all "teeth" complete and intact. Stamps with roulettes clear of the design on all four sides are extremely scarce and sell for substantial premiums. Stamps with teeth entirely missing or with several short roulettes are worth much less. See *Scott Classic Specialized Catalogue* for values for used stamps with one or two short roulettes.

Watermarks

Wmk. 121 — Multiple Swastika   Wmk. 208 — Post Horn

Wmk. 168 — Wavy Lines and Letters

Wmk. 273 — Roses   Wmk. 363 — Tree Stump

Syncopated Perforations

Type A (1st stamp #1065): On one longer side, groups of five holes are separated by an oval hole equal in width to eight holes.

Type B (1st stamp, #1142): On the top groups of 3 holes at left and right and a middle group of 4 holes separated by rectangular perforations equal in width to 4 holes.

Issues under Russian Empire

Coat of Arms — A1

1856-58   **Unwmk.**   **Typo.**   *Imperf.*
Small Pearls in Post Horns
Wove Paper

1	A1	5k blue	5,000.	1,200.
		Pen and town cancellation		1,580.
		Town cancellation		2,500.
a.		Tête bêche pair	55,000.	50,000.
		Pen and town cancellation		75,000.
2	A1	10k rose	7,500.	350.
		Pen and town cancellation		450.
		On cover		1,850.
		Town cancellation		700.
		On cover		2,850.
a.		Tête bêche pair	60,000.	50,000.
		Pen and town cancellation		55,000.

Cut to shape

1	A1	5k blue		150.
		Pen and town cancellation		200.
		Town cancellation		250.
2	A1	10k rose		65.
		Pen and town cancellation		60.
		Town cancellation		100.

Wide Vertically Laid Paper

2C	A1	10k rose ('58)	—	1,200.
		Pen and town cancellation		1,600.
		Town cancellation		2,000.
d.		Tête bêche pair		

Cut to shape

2C	A1	10k rose		500.
		Pen and town cancellation		650.
		Town cancellation		300.

Narrow Vertically Laid Paper

2C	A1	10k carmine		625.
		Pen and town cancellation		800.
		Town cancellation		900.

The wide vertically laid paper has 13-14 distinct lines per 2 centimeters. The narrow laid paper has lines that sometimes are indistinct.

A 5k blue with small pearls exists on narrow vertically laid paper. It is rare. Value $16,250 used.

Stamps on diagonally laid paper are envelope cut squares. Envelope cut squares also exist on unwatermarked wove paper.

Large Pearls in Post Horns

1858   **Wove Paper**

3	A1	5k blue	7,500.	1,200.
		Pen and town cancellation		1,400.
		Town cancellation		2,000.
a.		Tête bêche pair		45,000.

Pen and town cancella-tion		50,000.

Cut to shape

3	A1	5k blue		90.00
		Pen and town cancella-tion		120.00
		Town cancellation		150.00

1859 Wide Vertically Laid Paper

3B	A1	5k blue	—	15,000.
		Pen and town cancellation		20,000.

Cut to shape

3B	A1	5k blue	2,000.	
		Pen and town cancellation	2,500.	

Reprints of Nos. 2 and 3, made in 1862, are on brownish paper, on vertically laid paper, and in tête bêche pairs on normal and verti-cally laid paper. Reprints of 1871, 1881 and 1893 are on yellowish or white paper. Value for least costly of each, $40.

In 1956, Nos. 2 and 3 were reprinted for the Centenary with post horn watermark and gum. Value, $50 each.

Values for rouletted stamps with one or two short teeth are considera-bly less than the values shown, which are for stamps with all teeth full and intact. See the *Scott Classic Specialized Catalogue* for greater detail. Stamps with several short teeth or teeth entirely missing sell for very small percentages of the values shown.

Coat of Arms — A2

I —	II — Depth
Depth 1-1 ¼mm	1 ½-1 ¾mm

III — Depth 2-2 ¼mm

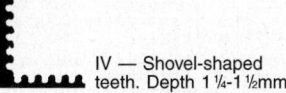

IV — Shovel-shaped teeth. Depth 1 ¼-1 ½mm

Wove Paper

1860 Serpentine Roulette 7½, 8

4	A2	5k blue, *bluish*, I	800.00	175.00
a.		Roulette II	800.00	190.00
b.		Perf. vert.		
5	A2	10k rose, *pale rose*, I	550.00	47.50
a.		Roulette II	1,100.	140.00

A3　　　　A4

1866-74 Serpentine Roulette

6	A3	5p pur brn, *lil*, I ('73)	300.00	150.00
a.		Roulette II		3,500.
b.		5p red brn, *lil*, III ('71)	275.00	160.00
7	A3	8p blk, *grn*, III ('67)	275.00	160.00
a.		Ribbed paper, III ('72)	1,000.	750.00
b.		Roulette II ('74)	300.00	240.00
c.		As "b," ribbed paper ('74)	340.00	200.00
d.		Roulette I ('73)	450.00	280.00
e.		As "d," ribbed paper	900.00	350.00

f.		Serpentine roulette 10 ½ ('67)		12,500.
8	A3	10p blk, *yel*, III ('70)	600.00	300.00
a.		10p blk, *buff*, II	700.00	400.00
b.		10p blk, *buff*, I ('73)	650.00	325.00
9	A3	20p bl, *bl*, III	500.00	50.00
a.		Roulette II	550.00	90.00
b.		Roulette I ('73)	600.00	100.00
c.		Roulette IV ('74)		1,000.
d.		Perf. horiz.		
e.		Printed on both sides (40p blue on back)		10,500.
10	A3	40p rose, *lil rose*, III	450.00	60.00
a.		Ribbed paper, III ('73)	500.00	140.00
b.		Roulette II	450.00	75.00
c.		As "b," ribbed paper ('73)	500.00	125.00
d.		Roulette I	650.00	150.00
e.		As "d," ribbed paper	600.00	100.00
f.		Roulette IV	—	2,000.
g.		As "f," ribbed paper		
h.		Serpentine roulette 10 ½	—	
11	A4	1m yel brn, III ('67)	2,000.	750.00
a.		Roulette II	2,500.	1,500.

Nos. 7f and 10h are private roulettes and are also known in compound serpentine rou-lette 10 ½ and 7 ½.

Nos. 4-11 were reprinted in 1893 on thick wove paper. Colors differ from originals. Rou-lette type IV. Value for Nos. 4-5, each $40, Nos. 6-10, each $50. Value for No. 11, $55.

Thin or Thick Laid Paper

12	A3	5p red brn, *lil*, III	290.00	130.00
a.		Roulette II	350.00	275.00
b.		Roulette I	290.00	275.00
d.		5p blk, *buff*, roul. III (error)		20,000.
e.		Tête bêche pair		17,500.
13	A3	10p black, *buff*, III	600.00	250.00
a.		10p black, *yel*, II	750.00	250.00
b.		10p black, *yel*, I	1,000.	650.00
c.		10p red brown, *lil*, III (error)	7,000.	6,250.

Forgeries of No. 13c exist.

A5

1875 Perf. 14x13½

16	A5	32p lake	2,000.	400.00

Forgeries exist of No. 16 that have been created by perforating cut squares.

1875-82 Perf. 11

17	A5	2p gray	45.00	50.00
18	A5	5p orange	100.00	10.00
a.		5p yellow org	100.00	10.00
19	A5	8p blue green	225.00	65.00
a.		8p yellow green	200.00	50.00
20	A5	10p brown ('81)	500.00	50.00
21	A5	20p ultra	125.00	3.00
a.		20p blue	125.00	4.50
b.		20p Prussian blue	300.00	32.50
c.		Tête bêche pair		2,500.
22	A5	25p car ('79)	200.00	15.00
a.		25p rose ('82)	275.00	65.00
23	A5	32p carmine	300.00	30.00
a.		32p rose	325.00	32.50
24	A5	1m violet ('77)	750.00	120.00
		Nos. 17-24 (8)	2,245.	343.00

A souvenir card issued in 1974 for NORDIA 1975 reproduced a block of four of the unis-sued "1 MARKKAA" design.

Nos. 19, 23 were reprinted in 1892-93, perf. 12½. Value $20 each. They exist imperf.

1881-83 Perf. 12½

25	A5	2p gray	15.00	14.00
a.		Imperf., pair	425.00	350.00
26	A5	5p orange	45.00	5.00
a.		Tête bêche pair	6,250.	3,500.
b.		Imperf. vert., pair		600.00
c.		Imperf. horiz., pair		800.00
27	A5	10p brown	75.00	17.50
28	A5	20p ultra	75.00	15.00
a.		20p blue	47.50	1.50
b.		Tête bêche pair	—	1,750.
c.		Imperf., pair		
29	A5	25p rose ('82)	40.00	8.50
a.		25p carmine	40.00	15.00
b.		Tête bêche pair	15,000.	
30	A5	1m violet ('82)	350.00	40.00
		Nos. 25-30 (6)	600.00	100.00

Nos. 27-29 were reprinted in 1893 in deeper shades, perf. 12½. Value $30 each.

Most examples of No. 28c are from printer's waste.

1881 Perf. 11x12½

26d	A5	5p orange	400.00	80.00
27a	A5	10p brown	800.00	200.00
28d	A5	20p ultra	550.00	40.00
28e	A5	20p blue	500.00	37.50
29c	A5	25p rose	600.00	160.00
29d	A5	25p carmine	500.00	100.00
30a	A5	1m violet		1,250.

1881 Perf. 12½x11

26e	A5	5p orange	400.00	80.00
27b	A5	10p brown	—	275.00
28f	A5	20p ultra	500.00	37.50
28g	A5	20p blue	500.00	37.50
29e	A5	25p rose	—	250.00
29f	A5	25p carmine	500.00	100.00

1885 Perf. 12½

31	A5	5p emerald	15.00	.50
a.		5p yellow green	17.50	1.00
b.		Tête bêche pair	10,000.	8,000.
32	A5	10p carmine	22.50	2.50
a.		10p rose	35.00	4.00
33	A5	20p yellow	25.00	.40
a.		20p yellow	32.50	5.00
b.		Tête bêche pair	—	2,500.
34	A5	25p ultra	55.00	3.00
a.		25p blue	50.00	2.50
35	A5	1m gray & rose	27.50	18.00
36	A5	5m grn & rose	350.00	350.00
37	A5	10m brn & rose	450.00	550.00

Denomination on No. 35 is spelled "MARKKA". Denomination on Nos. 36-37 is spelled "MARKKAA",

A6

1889-92 Perf. 12½

38	A6	2p slate ('90)	.50	.80
39	A6	5p green ('90)	25.00	.40
40	A6	10p carmine ('90)	50.00	.40
a.		10p rose ('90)	75.00	.40
b.		Imperf.	80.00	
41	A6	20p orange ('92)	60.00	.30
a.		20p yellow ('89)	60.00	.90
42	A6	25p ultra ('91)	60.00	.70
b.		25p blue	60.00	.70
43	A6	1m slate & rose ('92)	3.50	3.00
a.		1m brnsh gray & rose ('90)	20.00	3.00
44	A6	5m grn & rose ('90)	20.00	60.00
45	A6	10m brn & rose ('90)	30.00	80.00
		Nos. 38-45 (8)	249.00	145.60

The 2p slate, perf. 14x13, is believed to be an essay.

See Nos. 60-63.

See Russia for types similar to A7-A18.

Finnish stamps have "dot in circle" devices or are inscribed "Markka," "Markkaa," "Pen." or "Pennia."

Imperial Arms of Russia
A7　　A8　　A9

A10　　　　　A11

Laid Paper

1891-92 Wmk. 168 Perf. 14½x15

46	A7	1k org yel	5.00	9.00
47	A7	2k green	5.00	9.00
48	A7	3k carmine	11.00	18.00
49	A8	4k rose	10.00	14.00
50	A7	7k dark blue	6.00	2.25
51	A8	10k dark blue	13.00	14.00
52	A9	14k blue & rose	16.00	22.50
53	A8	20k blue & car	15.00	18.00
54	A9	35k vio & grn	20.00	45.00
55	A8	50k vio & grn	25.00	32.50

Perf. 13½

56	A10	1r brn & org	70.00	70.00
57	A11	3 ½ blk & gray	240.00	400.00
a.		3½ black & yellow (error)	11,000.	13,500.
58	A11	7r blk & yel	180.00	250.00
		Nos. 46-58 (13)	616.00	904.25

Forgeries of Nos. 57, 57a, 58 exist.

Type of 1889-90 Wove Paper

1895-96 Unwmk. Perf. 14x13

60	A6	5p green	.60	.40
61	A6	10p carmine	.60	.50
62	A6	20p orange	.60	.40
b.		Imperf.	120.00	
63	A6	25p ultra	.70	.60
a.		25p blue	1.75	.60
b.		Imperf.	90.00	
		Nos. 60-63 (4)	2.50	1.90

A12　　　　　A13

A14　　　　　A15

1901 Litho. Perf. 14½x15
Chalky Paper

64	A12	2p yellow	4.50	6.00
65	A12	5p green	9.00	1.20
66	A13	10p carmine	20.00	2.00
67	A12	20p dark blue	50.00	1.00
68	A14	1m violet & grn	250.00	7.50

Perf. 13½

69	A15	10m black & gray	240.00	260.00
		Nos. 64-69 (6)	573.50	277.70

Imperf sheets of 10p and 20p, stolen during production, were privately perforated 11½ to defraud the P.O. Uncanceled imperfs. of Nos. 65-68 are believed to be proofs.
See Nos. 70-75, 82.

Types of 1901 Redrawn

No. 64   No. 70

2p. On No. 64, the "2" below "II" is shifted slightly leftward. On No. 70, the "2" is centered below "II."

No. 65   No. 71

5p. On No. 65, the frame lines are very close. On No. 71, a clear white space separates them.

Nos. 66, 67   Nos. 72, 73

10p, 20p. On Nos. 66-67, the horizontal central background lines are faint and broken. On Nos. 72-73, they are clear and solid, though still thin.

20p. On No. 67, "H" close to "2" with period midway. On No. 73 they are slightly separated with period close to "H."

No. 68   Nos. 74, 74a

1m. On No. 68, the "1" following "MARKKA" lacks serif at base. On Nos. 74-74a, this "1" has serif.

No. 69   No. 75

10m. On No. 69, the serifs of "M" and "A" in top and bottom panels do not touch. On No. 75, the serifs join.

Perf. 14¼x14¾, 14¼x14
1901-14 Typo. Ordinary Paper

70	A12	2p orange	.50	1.20
		Never hinged	1.50	
71	A12	5p green	1.50	.60
a.		Perf 14¼x14 ('06)	1.50	.75
		Never hinged	3.50	
72	A13	10p carmine	10.00	.50
a.		Perf 14¼x14 ('07)	65.00	.70
		Never hinged	110.00	
b.		Background inverted, perf 14¼x14¾	12.50	2.00
c.		Background inverted, perf 14¼x14	70.00	2.00
73	A12	20p dark blue	7.50	.50
a.		Perf 14¼x14 ('06)	60.00	.80
		Never hinged	100.00	
74	A14	1m lil & grn, perf. 14¼x14 ('14)	1.20	.80
a.		1m violet & blue green, perf. 14¼x14¾ ('02)	7.50	.80
		Never hinged	25.00	
		Nos. 70-74 (5)	20.70	3.60
		Set, never hinged	90.00	

Perf. 13½

75	A15	10m blk & drab ('03)	120.00	45.00
		Never hinged	240.00	

Imperf Pairs

70a	A12	2p	280.00	400.00
71b	A12	5p	75.00	150.00
72d	A13	10p	85.00	180.00
73b	A12	20p	150.00	180.00
74b	A14	1m	140.00	160.00
		Nos. 70a-74b (5)	730.00	1,070.

A16   A17   A18

1911-16 Perf. 14, 14¼x14¾

77	A16	2p orange	.25	.80
78	A16	5p green	.25	.40
a.		Imperf.	—	
b.		Perf. 14¼x14¾	1,000.	100.00
		Never hinged	2,200.	
79	A17	10p rose ('15)	.25	.50
a.		Imperf. pair	80.00	120.00
b.		Perf. 14¼x14¾ ('16)	2.50	9.00
		Never hinged	6.50	
80	A16	20p deep blue	.25	.50
a.		Imperf.	140.00	110.00
b.		Perf. 14¼x14¾	20.00	2.50
		Never hinged	45.00	
81	A18	40p violet & blue	.30	.40
a.		Perf. 14¼x14¾	4,500.	3,000.
		Nos. 77-81 (5)	1.30	2.60
		Set, never hinged	2.70	

There are three minor types of No. 79. Values are for the least expensive type.

Perf. 14½

82	A15	10m blk & grnsh gray ('16)	120.00	160.00
		Never hinged	270.00	
a.		Horiz. pair, imperf. vert.	2,800.	

Republic
Helsinki Issue

Arms of the Republic — A19

Type I

Type II

Two types of the 40p.
Type I — Thin figures of value.
Type II — Thick figures of value.

Perf. 14, 14¼x14¾
1917-30 Unwmk.

83	A19	5p green	.30	.25
84	A19	5p gray ('19)	.30	.30
85	A19	10p rose	.30	.40
a.		Imperf., pair	180.00	300.00
86	A19	10p green ('19)	1.10	.80
a.		Perf. 14¼x14¾		2,200.
87	A19	10p brt blue ('21)	.30	.40
88	A19	20p buff	.30	.40
89	A19	20p rose ('20)	.30	.40
90	A19	20p brown ('24)	.60	.70
a.		Perf.14¼x14¾	.50	22.50
		Never hinged	1.20	
91	A19	25p blue	.30	.40
92	A19	25p lt brn ('19)	.30	.25
93	A19	30p green ('23)	.40	.50
94	A19	40p violet (I)	.30	.25
a.		Perf. 14¼x14¾	300.00	20.00
		Never hinged	650.00	
95	A19	40p bl grn (II) ('29)	.40	2.50
a.		Type I ('24)	10.00	4.50
		Never hinged	25.00	
b.		Perf. 14¼x14¾	1.00	18.00
		Never hinged	2.00	
96	A19	50p orange brn	.40	.40
97	A19	50p dp blue ('19)	3.00	.50
				1,600.
98	A19	50p green ('21)	3.50	.40
a.		Perf. 14¼x14¾	.30	1.20
		Never hinged	1.00	
99	A19	60p red vio ('21)	.70	.40
a.		Imperf., pair	—	
100	A19	75p yellow ('21)	.30	.60
101	A19	1m dull rose & blk	10.00	.25
102	A19	1m red org ('25)	6.50	20.00
a.		Perf. 14 ('30)	.30	450.00
		Never hinged	.80	
103	A19	1½m bl grn & red vio ('29)	.30	1.50
a.		Perf. 14¼x14¾	.40	1.00
		Never hinged	.90	
104	A19	2m green & blk ('21)	2.50	.70
105	A19	2m dk blue & ind ('22)	2.00	.40
a.		Perf. 14¼x14¾	.50	3.50
		Never hinged	1.20	
106	A19	3m blue & blk ('21)	50.00	.90
107	A19	5m red vio & blk	12.50	.40

108	A19	10m brn & gray blk, perf. 14	.80	1.00
a.		10m light brown & black, perf. 14¼x14¾ ('29)	3.00	380.00
		Never hinged	5.50	
110	A19	25m dull red & yel ('21)	.80	24.00
		Nos. 83-108,110 (27)	98.50	59.00
		Set, never hinged	205.90	

Examples of a 2½p gray of this type exist. They are proofs from the original die which were distributed through the UPU. No plate was made for this denomination.
See Nos. 127-140, 143-152. For surcharge and overprints see Nos. 119-126, 153-154.

Vasa Issue

Arms of the Republic — A20

1918 Litho. Perf. 11½

111	A20	5p green	.40	1.00
112	A20	10p red	.40	1.00
113	A20	30p slate	.70	2.50
114	A20	40p brown vio	.40	1.00
115	A20	50p orange brn	.40	4.00
116	A20	70p gray brown	1.50	18.00
117	A20	1m red & gray	.40	1.40
118	A20	5m red violet & gray	35.00	85.00
		Nos. 111-118 (8)	39.20	113.90
		Set, never hinged	80.00	

Nos. 111-118 exist imperforate but were not regularly issued in that condition.
Sheet margin examples, perf. on 3 sides, imperf. on margin side, were sold by post office.

Stamps and Type of 1917-29 Surcharged

1919 Perf. 14

119	A19	10p on 5p green	.40	.70
120	A19	20p on 10p rose	.40	.70
121	A19	50p on 25p blue	.80	.70
122	A19	75p on 20p orange	.40	.70
		Nos. 119-122 (4)	2.00	2.80
		Set, never hinged	4.95	

Stamps and Type of 1917-29 Surcharged

Nos. 123-125   No. 126

1921

123	A19	30p on 10p green	.70	.90
124	A19	60p on 40p red violet	3.00	1.20
125	A19	90p on 20p rose	.30	.40
126	A19	1m on 50p blue	1.10	.60
a.		Thin "2" in "½"	9.00	6.00
b.		Imperf., pair	200.00	350.00
		Nos. 123-126 (4)	5.10	3.10
		Set, never hinged	12.40	

Arms Type of 1917-29
Perf. 14, 14¼x14¾

1925-29 Wmk. 121

127	A19	10p ultra ('27)	.40	2.00
128	A19	20p brown	.40	1.50
129	A19	25p brn org ('29)	.70	75.00
130	A19	30p yel green	.30	.70
a.		Perf. 14¼x14¾	.30	—
		Never hinged	.50	
131	A19	40p blue grn (I) ('26)	2.50	1.20
a.		Perf. 14¼x14¾ ('26)	5.00	1.00
		Never hinged	15.00	
b.		Type II ('28)	100.00	60.00
		Never hinged	240.00	
c.		As "b," perf. 14¼x14¾ ('28)	7.00	1.00
		Never hinged	20.00	
132	A19	50p gray grn ('26)	.90	.60
a.		Perf. 14¼x14¾ ('26)	.40	.40
		Never hinged	1.20	
133	A19	60p red violet	.30	.70
134	A19	1m dp orange	5.00	.40
a.		Perf. 14¼x14¾	80.00	.90

		Never hinged	200.00	

Perf. 14¼x14¾

135	A19	1½m blue grn & red vio ('26)	4.00	.40
a.		Perf. 14 ('26)	60.00	.50
		Never hinged	130.00	
136	A19	2m dk blue & indigo ('27)	.70	.40
a.		Perf. 14	.80	.40
		Never hinged	2.00	
137	A19	3m chlky blue & blk ('26)	.80	.40
138	A19	5m red violet & blk ('27)	.40	.40
a.		Perf. 14	1.00	.40
		Never hinged	2.50	
139	A19	10m lt brn & blk ('27)	3.00	25.00
140	A19	25m dp org & yel ('27)	15.00	300.00
		Nos. 127-140 (14)	34.40	408.70
		Set, never hinged	95.55	

No. 130a is not known cancelled during the period in which it was valid for postal use.

A21

Wmk. 208
1927, Dec. 6 Typo. Perf. 14

141	A21	1½m deep violet	.30	.40
142	A21	2m deep blue	.30	1.80

10th anniv. of Finnish independence.

Arms Type of 1917-29
Perf. 14, 14¼x14¾

1927-29 Wmk. 208

143	A19	20p lt brown ('29)	1.50	3.00
144	A19	40p bl grn (II) ('28)	.40	1.00
145	A19	50p gray grn ('28)	.40	.75
146	A19	1m dp orange	.40	1.00
a.		Imperf., pair	100.00	180.00
b.		Perf. 14	.90	.90
147	A19	1½m bl grn & red vio ('28)	3.00	1.00
a.		Perf. 14	800.00	20.00
148	A19	2m dk bl & ind ('28)	.40	1.00
149	A19	3m chlky bl & blk	.40	1.00
a.		Perf. 14	4.00	10.00
150	A19	5m red vio & blk ('28)	.40	1.60
151	A19	10m lt brown & blk	1.10	35.00
152	A19	25m brown org & yel	1.50	180.00
		Nos. 143-152 (10)	9.50	225.35
		Set, never hinged	23.75	

Nos. 146-147 Overprinted

1928, Nov. 10 Litho. Wmk. 208

153	A19	1m deep orange	6.00	16.00
154	A19	1½m bl grn & red vio	6.00	16.00
		Set, never hinged	28.00	

Nos. 153 and 154 were sold exclusively at the Helsinki Philatelic Exhibition, Nov. 10-18, 1928, and were valid only during that period.

S. S. "Bore" Leaving Turku A23   Turku Cathedral A24

Turku Castle — A25

Wmk. 208
1929, May 22 Typo. Perf. 14

155	A23	1m olive green	1.50	4.50
156	A24	1½m chocolate	4.00	4.50
157	A25	2m dark gray	1.50	4.50
		Nos. 155-157 (3)	7.00	13.50
		Set, never hinged	20.00	

Founding of the city of Turku (Åbo), 700th anniv.

A26

1930-46   Unwmk.   Perf. 14

158	A26	5p chocolate	.30	.40
159	A26	10p dull violet	.30	.30
160	A26	20p yel grn	.30	.40
161	A26	25p yel brn	.30	.30
162	A26	40p blue grn	1.50	.25
163	A26	50p yellow	.40	.25
164	A26	50p blue grn ('32)	.30	.30
b.		Imperf., pair	110.00	150.00
165	A26	60p dark gray	.40	.60
165A	A26	75p dp org ('42)	.30	.40
166	A26	1m red org	.40	.25
166B	A26	1m yel grn ('42)	.30	.25
167	A26	1.20m crimson	.40	1.00
168	A26	1.25m yel ('32)	.30	.25
169	A26	1½m red vio	1.60	.25
170	A26	1½m car ('32)	.30	.25
170A	A26	1½m sl ('40)	.30	.25
170B	A26	1.75m org yel ('40)	.50	.50
171	A26	2m indigo	.30	.25
172	A26	2m dp vio	4.50	.40
173	A26	2m car ('36)	.30	.25

Complete booklet, panes of 4 #161, 164, 166, 168, 173   5.00

173B	A26	2m yel org ('42)	.30	.25
173C	A26	2m blue grn ('45)	.30	.25
174	A26	2½m brt blue ('32)	2.50	.40
174A	A26	2½m car ('42)	.30	.25
174B	A26	2.75m rose vio ('40)	.30	.25
175	A26	3m olive blk	20.00	.40
175B	A26	3m car ('45)	.30	.25
175C	A26	3m yel ('45)	.30	.60
176	A26	3½m brt bl ('36)	7.00	.25
176A	A26	3½m olive ('42)	.30	.25
176B	A26	4m olive ('45)	.40	.25
176C	A26	4½m saph ('42)	.30	.25
176D	A26	5m saph ('45)	.40	.25
176E	A26	5m pur ('45)	.40	.40
j.		Imperf., pair	120.00	150.00
176F	A26	5m yel ('46)	.50	.25
k.		Imperf., pair	120.00	150.00
176G	A26	6m car ('45)	.40	.40
m.		Imperf., pair	150.00	200.00
176H	A26	8m pur ('46)	.30	.25
176I	A26	10m saph ('45)	.80	.25

Nos. 158-176I (38)   48.40   12.55

See Nos. 257-262, 270-274, 291-296, 302-304. For surcharges and overprints see Nos. 195-196, 212, 221-222, 243, 250, 275, M2-M3.

Stamps of types A26-A29 overprinted "ITA KARJALA" are listed under Karelia, Nos. N1-N15.

Castle in Savonlinna
A27

Lake Saima
A28

Woodchopper — A29

1930   Engr.

177	A27	5m blue	.50	.40
178	A28	10m gray lilac	40.00	4.00
179	A29	25m black brown	.80	.40

Nos. 177-179 (3)   41.30   4.80
Set, never hinged   113.70

See Nos. 205, 305. For overprint see No. C1.

Elias Lönnrot
A30

Seal of Finnish Literary Society
A31

1931, Jan. 1   Typo.

180	A30	1m olive brown	2.00	5.00
181	A31	1½m dull blue	10.00	5.00
		Never hinged	30.00	

Centenary of Finnish Literary Society.

A32

1931, Feb. 28

182	A32	1½m red	2.20	8.00
		Never hinged	5.00	
183	A32	2m blue	2.20	10.00
		Never hinged	5.00	

1st use of postage stamps in Finland, 75th anniv.

Nos. 162-163 Surcharged

1931, Dec.

195	A26	50p on 40p blue grn	1.20	1.00
		Never hinged	4.00	
196	A26	1.25m on 50p yellow	3.00	1.80
		Never hinged	10.00	

Svinhufvud — A33

1931, Dec. 15

197	A33	2m gray blue & blk	1.00	3.00
		Never hinged	3.00	

Pres. Pehr Eyvind Svinhufvud, 70th birthday.

Lake Saima Type of 1930

1932-43   Re-engraved

205	A28	10m red violet ('43)	.50	.40
		Never hinged	1.20	
a.		10m dark violet	15.00	.60
		Never hinged	30.00	

On Nos. 205 and 205a the lines of the islands, the clouds and the foliage are much deeper and stronger than on No. 178.

Alexis Kivi — A34

1934, Oct. 10   Typo.

206	A34	2m red violet	1.20	4.00
		Never hinged	4.00	

Alexis Kivi, Finnish poet (1834-1872).

Bards Reciting the "Kalevala"
A35

Goddess Louhi, As Eagle Seizing Magic Mill
A36

Kullervo — A37

1935, Feb. 28   Engr.

207	A35	1¼m brown lake	1.00	1.80
		Never hinged	3.00	
208	A36	2m black	2.50	1.80
		Never hinged	9.00	
209	A37	2½m blue	2.20	1.80
		Never hinged	7.00	

Nos. 207-209 (3)   5.70   5.40
Set, never hinged   19.00

Cent. of the publication of the "Kalevala" (Finnish National Epic).

No. 170 Surcharged in Black

1937, Feb.

212	A26	2m on 1½m car	4.00	1.20
		Never hinged	11.00	

Gustaf Mannerheim — A38

1937, June 4   Photo.   Perf. 14

213	A38	2m ultra	.50	1.80
		Never hinged	2.00	

70th birthday of Field Marshal Baron Carl Gustaf Mannerheim, June 4th, 1937.

Swede-Finn Co-operation in Colonization — A39

1938, June 1

214	A39	3½m dark brown	.80	2.50
		Never hinged	3.50	

Tercentenary of the colonization of Delaware by Swedes and Finns.

Early Post Office — A40

Designs: 1¼m, Mail delivery in 1700. 2m, Modern mail plane. 3½m, Helsinki post office.

1938, Sept. 6   Photo.   Perf. 14

215	A40	50p green	.30	.80
		Never hinged	.80	
216	A40	1¼m dk blue	1.00	2.50
		Never hinged	3.50	
217	A40	2m scarlet	1.00	1.50
		Never hinged	5.00	
218	A40	3½m slate black	3.00	8.00
		Never hinged	9.00	

Nos. 215-218 (4)   5.30   12.80
Set, never hinged   18.30

300th anniv. of the Finnish Postal System. Margin strips of each denomination (3 of No. 215, 2 each of Nos. 216, 217, 218) were pasted on to advertising sheets and stapled into a booklet. Value, $90.

Post Office, Helsinki — A44

1939-42   Photo.

219	A44	4m brown black	.40	.40
		Never hinged	.80	

Engr.

219A	A44	7m black brn ('42)	.50	.40
		Never hinged	1.20	
219B	A44	9m rose lake ('42)	.50	.40
		Never hinged	1.20	

Nos. 219-219B (3)   1.40   1.20
Set, never hinged   3.20

See No. 248.

Catalogue values for unused stamps in this section, from this point to the end of the section, are for Never Hinged items.

University of Helsinki — A45

1940, May 1   Photo.

220	A45	2m dp blue & blue	.80	.80

300th anniv. of the founding of the University of Helsinki.

Nos. 168 and 173 Surcharged in Black

1940, June 16   Typo.

221	A26	1.75m on 1.25m yel	2.20	3.00
222	A26	2.75m on 2m carmine	6.50	1.00

President Kallio Reviewing Military Band — A46

1941, May 24   Engr.

223	A46	2.75m black	.80	.90

Pres. Kyösti Kallio (1873-1940).

Castle at Viborg — A47

1941, Aug. 30   Typo.

224	A47	1.75m yellow orange	.80	.80
225	A47	2.75m rose violet	.80	.80
226	A47	3.50m blue	1.80	1.80

Field Marshal Mannerheim — A48

1941, Dec. 31   Engr.   Wmk. 273

227	A48	50p dull green	.90	1.50
228	A48	1.75m deep brown	.90	1.50
229	A48	2m dark red	.90	1.50
230	A48	2.75m dull vio brn	.90	2.00
231	A48	3.50m deep blue	.90	1.50
232	A48	5m slate blue	1.20	1.50

Nos. 227-232 (6)   5.70   9.50

Pres. Risto Ryti — A49

233	A49	50p dull green	1.00	2.00
234	A49	1.75m deep brown	1.00	2.00
235	A49	2m dark red	2.00	2.00
236	A49	2.75m dull vio brn	2.00	2.00
237	A49	3.50m deep blue	1.00	1.50
238	A49	5m slate blue	1.00	1.50

Nos. 233-238 (6)   8.00   11.00

Types A48-A49 overprinted "ITA KARJALA" are listed under Karelia, Nos. N16-N27.

Häme Bridge, Tampere — A50

South Harbor, Helsinki — A51

1942   Unwmk.

239	A50	50m dull brown vio	2.50	.40
240	A51	100m indigo	4.00	.40

See No. 350.

Altar and Open Bible
A52

17th Century Printer
A53

1942, Oct. 10
241 A52 2.75m dk brown .50 *1.00*
242 A53 3.50m violet blue .80 *2.50*
   300th anniv. of the printing of the 1st Bible in Finnish.

No. 174B Surcharged in Black

1943, Feb. 1
243 A26 3.50m on 2.75m rose vio .40 .40

Minna Canth (1844-96), Author and Playwright — A54

1944, Mar. 20
244 A54 3.50m dk olive grn .25 *.80*

Pres. P. E. Svinhufvud — A55

1944, Aug. 1
245 A55 3.50m black .40 *1.20*
   Death of President Svinhufvud (1861-1944).

K. J. Stahlberg — A56

1945, May 16   Engr.   Perf. 14
246 A56 3.50m brown vio .40 *.50*
   80th birthday of Dr. K. J. Stahlberg.

Castle in Savonlinna — A57

1945, Sept. 4
247 A57 15m lilac rose 2.00 .40
248 A44 20m sepia 2.00 .40
   See Nos. 219-219B. For a 35m of type A57, see No. 280.

Jean Sibelius — A58

1945, Dec. 8
249 A58 5m dk slate green .50 .50
   Jean Sibelius (1865-1957), composer.

No. 176E Surcharged in Black

1946, Mar. 16
250 A26 8(m) on 5m purple .50 .40

Victorious Athletes — A59

1946, June 1   Engr.   Perf. 13½
251 A59 8m brown violet .40 .50
   3rd Sports Festival, Helsinki, June 27-30, 1946.

Lighthouse at Uto — A60

1946, Sept. 19
252 A60 8m deep violet .40 .50
   250th anniv. of the Finnish Department of Pilots and Lighthouses.

Post Bus — A61

1946-47   Unwmk.   Perf. 14
253 A61 16m gray black .60 .80
253A A61 30m gray black ('47) 2.00 .40
   Issue dates: 16m, Oct. 16, 30m, Feb. 10.

Old Town Hall, Porvoo A62

Cathedral, Porvoo A63

1946, Dec. 3
254 A62 5m gray black .40 .50
255 A63 8m deep claret .40 .50
   600th anniv. of the founding of the city of Porvoo (Borga).

Waterfront, Tammisaari — A64

1946, Dec. 14
256 A64 8m grnsh black .60 .75
   400th anniv. of the founding of the town of Tammisaari (Ekenas).

Lion Type of 1930
1947   Typo.   Perf. 14
257 A26 2½m dark green .50 .40
258 A26 3m slate gray .40 .25
259 A26 6m deep orange 1.50 .40
260 A26 7m carmine .80 .25
261 A26 10m purple 2.50 .25
262 A26 12m deep blue 2.20 .25
   Nos. 257-262 (6) 7.90 1.80
   Issued: 3m, 6/9; 7m, 12m, 2/10; others, 1/20.

Pres. Juho K. Paasikivi — A65

1947, Mar. 15   Engr.
263 A65 10m gray black .50 .40

Postal Savings Emblem — A66

1947, Apr. 1
264 A66 10m brown violet .40 .40
   60th anniv. of the foundation of the Finnish Postal Savings Bank.

Ilmarinen, the Plowman — A67

1947, June 2
265 A67 10m gray black .40 .40
   2nd year of peace following WW II.

Girl and Boy Athletes — A68

1947, June 2
266 A68 10m bright blue .40 .50
   Finnish Athletic Festival, Helsinki, June 29-July 3, 1947.

Wheat and Savings Bank Assoc. Emblem — A69

1947, Aug. 21
267 A69 10m red brown .40 .60
   Finnish Savings Bank Assoc., 125th anniv.

Sower — A70

1947, Nov. 1
268 A70 10m gray black .50 .50
   150th anniv. of Finnish Agricultural Societies.

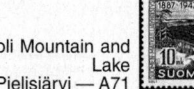

Koli Mountain and Lake Pielisjärvi — A71

1947, Nov. 1
269 A71 10m indigo .50 .60
   60th anniv. of the Finnish Touring Assoc.

Lion Type of 1930
1948   Typo.   Perf. 14
270 A26 3m dark green 2.50 .25
271 A26 6m yellow green 1.00 .50
272 A26 9m carmine 1.00 .25
273 A26 15m dark blue 4.00 .40
274 A26 24m brown lake 1.50 .25
   Nos. 270-274 (5) 10.00 1.65
   Issued: 3m, 2/9; 24m, 4/26; others, 9/13.

No. 261 Surcharged in Black

1948, Feb. 9
275 A26 12(m) on 10m purple 1.20 .40

Statue of Michael Agricola — A72

   12m, Agricola translating New Testament.

1948, Oct. 2   Engr.   Perf. 14
276 A72 7m rose violet 1.00 *1.70*
277 A72 12m gray blue 1.00 *1.70*
   400th anniv. of publication of the Finnish translation of the New Testament, by Michael Agricola.

Sveaborg Fortress — A73

1948, Oct. 15
278 A73 12m deep green 1.50 *2.00*
   200th anniv. of the construction of Sveaborg Fortress on the Gulf of Finland.

Post Rider — A74

1948, Oct. 27
279 A74 12m green 7.00 *18.00*
   Helsinki Philatelic Exhibition. Sold only at exhibition for 62m, of which 50m was entrance fee.

Castle Type of 1945
1949
280 A57 35m violet 7.00 .40
   See Nos. 219-219B, 248-249.

Sawmill and Cellulose Plant — A75

Pine Tree and Globe — A76

1949, June 15
281 A75 9m brown 2.00 *3.00*
282 A76 15m dull green 2.50 *3.00*
   Issued to publicize the Third World Forestry Congress, Helsinki, July 10-20, 1949.

Woman with Torch — A77

1949, July 16   Engr.   Perf. 14
283 A77 5m dull green 4.00 *7.50*
284 A77 15m red *(Worker)* 4.50 *8.00*
   50th anniv. of the Finnish labor movement.

Harbor of Lappeenranta (Willmanstrand) A78

Raahe (Brahestad) A79

1949

285	A78	5m dk blue grn	1.50	1.00
286	A79	9m brown carmine	1.50	1.50
287	A78	15m brt blue (Kristi-inan-kaupunki)	2.00	3.00
		Nos. 285-287 (3)	5.00	5.50

300th anniv. of the founding of Willman-strand, Brahestad and Kristinestad (Kristiinan-kaupunki).
Issued: 5m, 8/6; 9m, 8/13; 15m, 7/30.

Technical High School Badge — A80

1949, Sept. 13

288	A80	15m ultra	1.00	1.20

Founding of the technical school, cent.

Hannes Gebhard — A81

1949, Oct. 2

289	A81	15m dull green	1.00	1.20

Establishment of Finnish cooperatives, 50th anniv.

Finnish Lake Country — A82

1949, Oct. 8

290	A82	15m blue	1.20	1.50

75th anniv. of the UPU.

Lion Type of 1930

1950, Jan. 9   Typo.   Perf. 14

291	A26	8m brt green	1.50	1.00
292	A26	9m red orange	1.80	.40
293	A26	10m violet brown	5.00	.25
294	A26	12m scarlet	1.00	.40
295	A26	15m plum	13.00	.25
296	A26	20m deep blue	6.00	.25
		Nos. 291-296 (6)	28.30	2.55

Forsell's Map of Old Helsinki — A83

J. A. Ehrenstrom and C. L. Engel — A84

City Hall — A85

1950, June 11   Engr.

297	A83	5m emerald	.50	.70
298	A84	9m green	1.00	1.20
299	A85	15m deep blue	.80	.80
		Nos. 297-299 (3)	2.30	2.70

400th anniv. of the founding of Helsinki.

J. K. Paasikivi — A86

1950, Nov. 27

300	A86	20m deep ultra	.80	.40

80th birthday of Pres. J. K. Paasikivi.

View of Kajaani — A87

1951, July 7   Unwmk.   Perf. 14

301	A87	20m red brown	.80	.70

Tercentenary of Kajaani.

Lion and Chopper Types of 1930

1952, Jan. 18   Typo.

302	A26	10m emerald	3.00	.25
303	A26	15m red	3.00	.25
304	A26	25m blue	4.00	.25

Engr.

305	A29	40m black brown	3.50	.40
		Nos. 302-305 (4)	13.50	1.15

Arms of Pietarsaari — A88

1952, June 19   Unwmk.   Perf. 14

306	A88	25m blue	1.00	1.00

300th anniv. of the founding of Pietarsaari (Jacobstad).

Rooftops of Vaasa — A89

1952, Aug. 3

307	A89	25m brown	1.00	1.00

Centenary of the burning of Vaasa.

Chess Symbols — A90

1952, Aug. 10

308	A90	25m gray	2.00	2.50

10th Chess Olympics, Helsinki, 8/10-31/52.

Torch Bearers — A91

1953, Jan. 27

309	A91	25m blue	1.20	1.00

Temperance movement in Finland, cent.

Air View of Hamina (Fredrikshamn) A92

1953, June 20

310	A92	25m dk gray green	.90	.90

Tercentenary of Hamina.

Ivar Wilskman — A93

1954, Feb. 26

311	A93	25m blue	.80	.80

Centenary of the birth of Prof. Ivar Wilskman, "father of gymnastics in Finland."

Arms of Finland — A94

1954-59   Perf. 11½

312	A94	1m red brown ('55)	.25	.25
313	A94	2m green ('55)	.25	.25
314	A94	3m deep orange	.25	.25
314A	A94	4m gray ('58)	.60	.50
315	A94	5m violet blue	.70	.25
316	A94	10m blue green	1.20	.25
a.		Bkt. pane of 5 (vert. strip)	15.00	15.00
		Complete booklet, #316a	17.50	
317	A94	15m rose red	3.50	.25
318	A94	15m yellow org ('57)	7.00	.25
319	A94	20m rose lilac	12.00	.25
320	A94	20m rose red ('56)	2.50	.25
321	A94	25m deep blue	4.50	.25
322	A94	25m rose lilac ('59)	10.00	.25
323	A94	30m lt ultra ('56)	2.50	.25
		Nos. 312-323 (13)	45.25	3.50

See Nos. 398, 400-405A, 457-459A, 461A-462, 464-464B.

"In the Outer Archipelago" — A95

1954, July 21   Perf. 14

324	A95	25m black	.80	.80

Cent. of the birth of Albert Edelfelt, painter.

J. J. Nervander — A96

1955, Feb. 23

325	A96	25m blue	1.00	1.00

150th anniv. of the birth of J. J. Nervander, astronomer and poet.

Composite of Finnish Public Buildings — A97

1955, Mar. 30   Engr.   Perf. 14

326	A97	25m gray	9.00	18.00

Sold for 125m, which included the price of admission to the Natl. Postage Stamp Exhibition, Helsinki, Mar. 30-Apr. 3, 1955.

Bishop Henrik with Foot on Lalli, his Murderer — A98

25m, Arrival of Bishop Henrik and monks.

1955, May 19

327	A98	15m rose brown	1.20	.80
328	A98	25m green	1.50	.80

Adoption of Christianity in Finland, 800th anniv.

Conference Hall, Helsinki — A99

1955, Aug. 25

329	A99	25m bluish green	1.50	1.80

44th conf. of the Interparliamentarian Union, Helsinki, Aug. 25-31, 1955.

Sailing Vessel and Merchant — A100

1955, Sept. 2

330	A100	25m sepia	1.50	1.80

350th anniv. of founding of Oulu.

Town Hall, Lahti — A101

1955, Nov. 1   Perf. 14x13½

331	A101	25m violet blue	1.50	2.00

50th anniversary of founding of Lahti.

Radio Sender, Map of Finland — A102

Designs: 15m, Otto Nyberg. 25m, Telegraph wires and pines under snow.

Inscribed: Lennatin 1855-1955 Telegrafen

1955, Dec. 10   Perf. 14

332	A102	10m green	1.50	1.50
333	A102	15m dull violet	1.50	.80
334	A102	25m lt ultra	1.80	1.20
		Nos. 332-334 (3)	4.80	3.50

Cent. of the telegraph in Finland.

A103

1956, Jan. 26   Unwmk.   Perf. 14

335	A103	25m Lighthouse, Pork-kala Peninsula	.80	1.00

Return of the Porkkala Region to Finland by Russia, Jan. 1956.

A104

30m, 50m, Church at Lammi. 40m, House of Parliament. 60m, Fortress of Olavinlinna (Olofsborg).

1956-57   Perf. 11½

336	A104	30m gray olive	1.00	.40
337	A104	40m dull purple	3.50	.25
338	A104	50m gray ol ('57)	7.00	.25
338A	A104	60m pale pur ('57)	13.00	.25
		Nos. 336-338A (4)	24.50	1.15

Issued: 30m, 3/4; 40m, 3/11; 50m, 3/3; 60m, 4/7. See Nos. 406-408A.

Johan V. Snellman — A105

1956, May 12   Engr.   Perf. 14
339 A105 25m dk violet brn   .90   .90
Johan V. Snellman (1806-81), statesman.

Gymnast and Athletes — A106

1956, June 28
340 A106 30m violet blue   1.20 1.00
Finnish Gymnastic and Sports Games, Helsinki, June 28-July 1, 1956.

A107

Wmk. 208
1956, July 7   Typo.   Rouletted
341 A107 30m deep ultra   3.50   *6.50*
  a.   Tête bêche pair   7.00   *12.00*
  b.   Pane of 10   42.50 *75.00*

Issued to publicize the FINLANDIA Philatelic Exhibition, Helsinki, July 7-15, 1956.
Printed in sheets containing four 2x5 panes, with white margins around each group. The stamps in each double row are printed tete-beche, making the position of the watermark differ in the vertical row of each pane of ten.
Sold for 155m, price including entrance ticket to exhibition.

Town Hall at Vasa — A108

Unwmk.
1956, Oct. 2   Engr.   Perf. 14
342 A108 30m bright blue   1.20 1.00
350th anniversary of Vasa.

Northern Countries Issue

Whooper Swans — A108a

1956, Oct. 30   Perf. 12½
343 A108a 20m rose red   2.00 1.50
344 A108a 30m ultra   6.00 1.20
See footnote after Denmark No. 362.

University Clinic, Helsinki — A109

1956, Dec. 17   Perf. 11½
345 A109 30m dull green   1.50 1.00
Public health service in Finland, bicent.

Scout Sign, Emblem and Globe — A110

1957, Feb. 22   Perf. 14
346 A110 30m ultra   1.90 1.20
50th anniversary of Boy Scouts.

Arms Holding Hammers and Laurel — A111

Design: 20m, Factories and cogwheel.

1957   Engr.   Perf. 13½
347 A111 20m dark blue   .80   .80
348 A111 30m carmine   1.00 1.00
50th anniv.: Central Fed. of Finnish Employers (20m, issued 9/27); Finnish Trade Union Movement (30m, issued 4/15).

"Lex" from Seal of Parliament — A112

1957, May 23   Perf. 14
349 A112 30m olive gray   1.20 1.20
50th anniv. of the Finnish parliament.

Harbor Type of 1942
1957   Unwmk.   Perf. 14
350 A51 100m grnsh blue   10.00   .25

Ida Aalberg — A114

1957, Dec. 4   Perf. 14
351 A114 30m vio gray & mar   .90 *1.00*
Birth cent. of Ida Aalberg, Finnish actress.

Arms of Finland — A115

1957, Dec. 6   Perf. 11½
352 A115 30m blue   1.00 *1.20*
40th anniv. of Finland's independence.

Jean Sibelius — A116

1957, Dec. 8   Perf. 14
353 A116 30m black   1.50 1.00
Jean Sibelius (1865-1957), composer.

Ski Jump — A117

Design: 30m, Skier, vert.

1958, Feb. 1   Engr.   Perf. 11½
354 A117 20m slate green   1.20 1.00
355 A117 30m blue   1.20   .80
Nordic championships of the Intl. Ski Federation, Lahti.

"March of the Bjorneborgienses," by Edelfelt — A118

1958, Mar. 8
356 A118 30m violet gray   .90   .90
400th anniv. of the founding of Pori (Bjorneborg).

South Harbor, Helsinki — A119

1958, June 2   Unwmk.   Perf. 11½
357 A119 100m bluish green   20.00   .25
See No. 410.

Seal of Jyväskylä Lyceum — A120

1958, Oct. 1   Perf. 11½
358 A120 30m rose carmine   1.50 1.20
Cent. of the founding of the 1st Finnish secondary school.

Chrismon and Globe — A121

1959, Jan. 19   Perf. 11½
359 A121 30m dull violet   .70   .60
Finnish Missionary Society, cent.

Diet at Porvoo, 1809 — A122

1959, Mar. 22   Perf. 11½
360 A122 30m dk blue gray   .70   .60
150th anniv. of the inauguration of the Diet at Porvoo.

Saw Cutting Log — A123

1959, May 13   Engr.
361 A123 10m shown   .70   .70
362 A123 30m Forest   .70   .70
No. 361 for the cent. of the establishment of the 1st steam saw-mill in Finland; No. 362, the cent. of the Dept. of Forestry.

Pyhakoski Power Station — A124

1959, May 24
363 A124 75m gray   4.50   .40
See No. 409.

Oil Lamp — A125

1959, Dec. 19
364 A125 30m blue   .80   .70
Cent. of the liberation of the country trade.

Woman Gymnast — A126

1959, Nov. 14   Unwmk.
365 A126 30m rose lilac   1.00   .80
Finnish women's gymnastics and the cent. of the birth of Elin Oihonna Kallio, pioneer of Finnish women's physical education.

Arms of Six New Towns — A127

1960, Jan. 2   Perf. 14
366 A127 30m light violet   .90   .90
Issued to commemorate the founding of new towns in Finland: Hyvinkaa, Kouvola, Riihimaki, Rovaniemi, Salo and Seinajoki.

Type of 1860 Issue — A128

1960, Mar. 25   Typo.   Rouletted 4½
367 A128 30m blue & gray   4.00 7.00
Cent. of Finland's serpentine roulette stamps, and in connection with HELSINKI 1960, 40th anniv. exhib. of the Federation of Philatelic Societies of Finland, Mar. 25-31. Sold only at the exhibition for 150m including entrance ticket.

Mother and Child, Waiting Crowd and Uprooted Oak Emblem — A129

1960, Apr. 7   Engr.   Perf. 11½
368 A129 30m rose claret   .80   .60
369 A129 40m dark blue   1.00   .60
World Refugee Year, 7/1/59-6/30/60.

Johan Gadolin — A130

1960, June 4   Perf. 11½
370 A130 30m dark brown   .80   .70
Bicent. of the birth of Gadolin, chemist.

Hj. Nortamo — A131

1960, June 13   Unwmk.
371 A131 30m gray green   .80   .70
Cent. of the birth of Hj. Nortamo (Hjalmar Nordberg), writer.

Symbolic Tree and Cuckoo — A132

1960, June 18
372 A132 30m vermilion   .80   .70
Karelian Natl. Festival, Helsinki, June 18-19.

Geodetic Instrument — A133

Design: 30m, Aurora borealis and globe.

1960, July 26   Unwmk.   Perf. 13½
373 A133 10m blue & pale brn   .80 .60
374 A133 30m ver & rose car   1.00 .60

12th General Assembly of the Intl. Union of Geodesy and Geophysics, Helsinki.

Urho Kekkonen — A134

1960, Sept. 3   Engr.   Perf. 11½
375 A134 30m violet blue   .90 .40

Issued to honor President Urho Kekkonen on his 60th birthday.

Common Design Types pictured following the introduction.

Europa Issue, 1960
Common Design Type

1960, Sept. 19   Perf. 13½
Size: 30½x21mm.
376 CD3 30m dk bl & Prus bl   .80 .70
377 CD3 40m dk brn & plum   1.00 .70

A 30m gray similar to No. 376 was printed with simulated perforations in a non-valid souvenir sheet privately released in London for STAMPEX 1961.

Uno Cygnaeus — A135

1960, Oct. 13   Perf. 11½
378 A135 30m dull violet   .70 .70

150th anniv. of the birth of Pastor Uno Cygnaeus, founder of elementary schools.

"Pommern" and Arms of Mariehamn — A136

1961, Feb. 21   Perf. 11½
379 A136 30m grnsh blue   2.50 1.80

Centenary of the founding of Mariehamn.

Lake and Rowboat A137   Turku Castle A138

1961   Engr.   Unwmk.
380 A137 5m green   .25 .25
381 A138 125m slate green   20.00 .35

See Nos. 399, 411.

Postal Savings Bank Emblem — A139

1961, May 24
382 A139 30m Prus green   .70 .40

75th anniv. of Finland's Postal Savings Bank.

Symbol of Standardization A140

1961, June 5   Litho.   Perf. 14x13½
383 A140 30m dk sl grn & org   .70 .50

Meeting of the Intl. Organization for Standardization (ISO), Helsinki, June 5.

Juhani Aho — A141

Perf. 11½
1961, Sept. 11   Unwmk.   Engr.
384 A141 30m red brown   .70 .70

Juhani Aho (1861-1921), writer.

Various Buildings — A142

1961, Oct. 16   Perf. 11½
385 A142 30m slate   .70 .70

150 years of the Central Board of Buildings.

Arvid Jarnefelt — A143

1961, Nov. 16
386 A143 30m deep claret   .70 .60

Cent. of the birth of Arvid Jarnefelt, writer.

Bank of Finland — A144

1961, Dec. 12   Engr.   Perf. 11½
387 A144 30m brown violet   .70 .70

150th anniversary of Bank of Finland.

First Finnish Locomotive — A145

30m, Steam locomotive & timber car. 40m, Diesel locomotive & passenger train.

1962, Jan. 31   Unwmk.   Perf. 11½
388 A145 10m gray green   1.00 .60
389 A145 30m violet blue   1.50 .60
390 A145 40m dull red brown   4.00 .60
   Nos. 388-390 (3)   6.50 1.80

Centenary of the Finnish State Railways.

Mora Stone — A146

1962, Feb. 15
391 A146 30m gray brown   .70 .80

Issued to commemorate 600 years of political rights of the Finnish people.

Senate Place, Helsinki — A147

1962, Apr. 8   Unwmk.   Perf. 11½
392 A147 30m violet brown   .70 .80

Sesquicentennial of the proclamation of Helsinki as capital of Finland.

Customs Emblem — A148

1962, Apr. 11
393 A148 30m red   .70 .80

Finnish Board of Customs, sesquicentennial.

Staff of Mercury — A149

1962, May 21   Engr.
394 A149 30m bluish green   .70 .70

Cent. of the 1st commercial bank in Finland.

Santeri Alkio — A150

1962, June 17   Unwmk.   Perf. 11½
395 A150 30m brown carmine   .80 .80

Cent. of the birth of Santeri Alkio, writer and pioneer of the young people's societies in Finland.

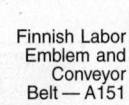
Finnish Labor Emblem and Conveyor Belt — A151

1962, Oct. 19
396 A151 30m chocolate   .70 .40

National production progress.

Survey Plane and Compass — A152

1962, Nov. 14
397 A152 30m yellow green   .90 .70

Finnish Land Survey Board, 150th anniv.

Types of 1954-61 and

House of Parliament — A152a   Church at Lammi — A152b

Fortress of Olavinlinna — A152c   Log Floating — A153

Parainen Bridge — A154

Farm on Lake Shore — A155

Aerial View of Punkaharju — A155a

A155b

Ristikallio in Kuusamo — A156

1963-67   Engr.   Perf. 11½
398 A94 5p vio blue   .80 .25
 a.   Booklet pane of 2 (vert. pair)   22.50 20.00
 b.   Bklt. pane of 2 (horiz. pair)   12.00 10.00
399 A137 5p green   .25 .25
400 A94 10p blue grn   2.50 .25
 a.   Booklet pane of 2 (vert. pair)   22.50 20.00
401 A94 15p yel org   1.50 .25
402 A94 20p rose red   2.50 .25
 a.   Complete booklet, #398a, 400a, 402a   24.00
 b.   Bklt. pane, 2 #400, 1 #402 + label; horiz. strip   45.00 35.00
      Complete booklet, #398b, 402b   100.00
 c.   Bklt. pane, 2 #398, 2 #400, 1 #402; horiz. strip   3.50 3.50
      Complete booklet, #402c   5.00
403 A94 25p rose lilac   2.50 .25
404 A94 30p lt ultra   4.00 .25
404A A94 30p blue gray ('65)   7.00 .25
405 A94 35p blue   1.50 .25
405A A94 40p ultra ('67)   1.50 .40
406 A152a 40p dull pur   7.00 .40
407 A152b 50p gray olive   4.50 .40
408 A152c 60p pale pur   12.00 .40
408A A152c 65p pale pur ('67)   1.50 .25
409 A124 75p gray   2.50 .40
410 A119 1m bluish grn   1.50 .25
411 A138 1.25m slate grn   2.50 .40
412 A153 1.50m dk grnsh gray   1.50 .40
413 A154 1.75m blue   2.00 .40
414 A155 2m grn ('64)   18.00 .25
414A A155a 2.50m ultra & yel grn ('67)   15.00 .50
414B A155b 2.50m ultra, dk grn & yel grn ('69)   2.50 .40
415 A156 5m dk slate grn ('64)   20.00 .40
   Nos. 398-415 (23)   114.55 7.50

Pennia denominations expressed: "0.05," "0.10," etc.

Four stamps of type A94 (5p, 10p, 20p, 25p) come in two types: I. Four vertical lines in "O" of SUOMI. II. Three lines in "O."

For similar designs see Nos. 457-470A.

Mother and Child — A157

1963, Mar. 21   Unwmk.   Perf. 11½
416 A157 40p red brown   .55 .40

FAO "Freedom from Hunger" campaign.

"Christ Today" — A158

Design: 10p, Crown of thorns and medieval cross of consecration.

1963, July 30   Engr.   Perf. 11½
417 A158 10p maroon   .50 .45
418 A158 30p dark green   .50 .45

4th assembly of the Lutheran World Federation, Helsinki, July 30-Aug. 8.

Europa Issue, 1963
Common Design Type

1963, Sept. 16 Size: 30x20mm
419 CD6 40p red lilac 1.25 .55

Assembly Building, Helsinki — A159

1963, Sept. 18
420 A159 30p violet blue .70 .40

Representative Assembly of Finland, cent.

Convair Metropolitan — A160

Design: 40p, Caravelle jetliner.

1963, Nov. 1
421 A160 35p slate green 1.00 .60
422 A160 40p brt ultra 1.10 .50

40th anniversary of Finnish air traffic.

M. A. Castrén — A161

1963, Dec. 2 Unwmk.
423 A161 35p violet blue .70 .45

Matthias Alexander Castrén (1813-52), ethnologist and philologist.

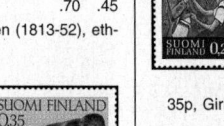

Stone Elk's Head, 2000 B.C. — A162

1964, Feb. 5 Litho. Perf. 14
424 A162 35p ocher & slate grn .70 .45

Cent. of the Finnish Artists' Association. The soapstone sculpture was found at Huittinen.

Emil Nestor Setälä — A163

1964, Feb. 27 Engr. Perf. 11½
425 A163 35p dk red brown .80 .50

Emil Nestor Setälä (1864-1946), philologist, minister of education and foreign affairs and chancellor of Abo University.

Staff of Aesculapius — A164

1964, June 13 Unwmk. Perf. 11½
426 A164 40p slate green 1.10 .45

18th General Assembly of the World Medical Association, Helsinki, June 13-19, 1964.

Ice Hockey — A165

1965, Jan. 4 Engr.
427 A165 35p dark blue 1.10 .60

World Ice Hockey Championships, Finland, March 3-14, 1965.

Design from Centenary Medal — A166

1965, Feb. 6 Unwmk. Perf. 11½
428 A166 35p olive gray .70 .40

Centenary of communal self-government in Finland.

K. J. Stahlberg and "Lex" by W. Runeberg — A167

1965, Mar. 22 Engr.
429 A167 35p brown .70 .40

Kaarlo Juho Stahlberg (1865-1952), 1st Pres. of Finland.

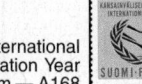

International Cooperation Year Emblem — A168

1965, Apr. 2 Litho. Perf. 14
430 A168 40p bis, dull red, blk & grn .70 .40

UN International Cooperation Year.

"Fratricide" by Gallen-Kallela — A169

35p, Girl's Head by Akseli Gallen-Kallela.

1965, Apr. 26 Perf. 13½x14
431 A169 25p multicolored 1.20 .65
432 A169 35p multicolored 1.20 .65

Centenary of the birth of the painter Aksell Gallen-Kallela.

Sibelius, Piano and Score — A170

Design: 35p, Musical score and bird.

1965, May 15 Engr. Perf. 11½
433 A170 25p violet 1.00 .60
434 A170 35p dull green 1.00 .40

Jean Sibelius (1865-1957), composer.

Antenna for Satellite Telecommunication A171

1965, May 17
435 A171 35p blue .70 .50

Cent. of the ITU.

"Winter Day" by Pekka Halonen — A172

Perf. 14x13½
1965, Sept. 23 Litho. Unwmk.
436 A172 35p gold & multi .70 .40

Centenary of the birth of the painter Pekka Halonen.

Europa Issue, 1965
Common Design Type
Engraved and Lithographed
1965, Sept. 27 Perf. 13½x14
437 CD8 40p bister, red brn, dk bl & grn 1.25 .55

"Growth" — A173

1966, May 11 Litho. Perf. 14
438 A173 35p vio blue & blue .70 .40

Centenary of the promulgation of the Elementary School Decree.

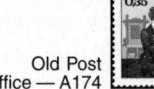

Old Post Office — A174

1966, June 11 Litho. Perf. 14
439 A174 35p ocher, yel, dk bl & blk 4.00 7.00

Cent. of the 1st postage stamps in Finnish currency, and in connection with the NORDIA Stamp Exhibition, Helsinki, June 11-15. The stamp was sold only to buyers of a 1.25m exhibition entrance ticket.

UNESCO Emblem and World Map — A175

Lithographed and Engraved
1966, Oct. 9 Perf. 14
440 A175 40p grn, yel, blk & brn org .65 .30

20th anniv. of UNESCO.

Finnish Police Emblem — A176

1966, Oct. 15
441 A176 35p dp ultra, blk & sil .65 .30

Issued to honor the Finnish police.

Insurance Sesquicentennial Medal — A177

1966, Oct. 28 Engr. & Photo.
442 A177 35p mar, ol & blk .65 .30

150th anniv. of the Finnish insurance system.

UNICEF Emblem — A178

1966, Nov. 14
443 A178 15p lt ultra, pur & grn .50 .40

Activities of UNICEF.

"FINEFTA," Finnish Flag and Circle — A179

1967, Feb. 15 Engr. Perf. 14
444 A179 40p ultra .65 .30

European Free Trade Association, EFTA. See note after Denmark No. 431.

Windmill and Arms of Uusikaupunki — A180

Lithographed and Engraved
1967, Apr. 19 Perf. 14
445 A180 40p multicolored .65 .30

350th anniv. of Uusikaupunki (Nystad).

Mannerheim Monument by Aimo Tukiainen — A181

1967, June 4 Perf. 14
446 A181 40p violet & multi .65 .30

Cent. of the birth of Field Marshal Carl Gustav Emil Mannerheim.

Double Mortise Corner — A182

1967, June 16 Litho. & Photo.
447 A182 40p multicolored .65 .30

Issued to honor Finnish settlers in Sweden.

Watermark of Thomasböle Paper Mill — A183

1967, Sept. 6 Perf. 14
448 A183 40p olive & black .65 .30

300th anniv. of the Finnish paper industry.

Martin Luther, by Lucas Cranach — A184

Photogravure and Engraved
1967, Nov. 4 Perf. 14
449 A184 40p bister & brown .65 .30

450th anniversary of the Reformation.

"Wood and Water" Globe and Flag — A185

Designs (Globe, Flag and): 25p, Flying swan. 40p, Ear of wheat.

1967, Dec. 5 Perf. 11½
450 A185 20p green & blue .80 .30
451 A185 25p ultra & blue .80 .30
452 A185 40p magenta & bl .80 .30
 Nos. 450-452 (3) 2.40 .90

50th anniv. of Finland's independence.

Zachris Topelius and Blue Bird — A186

1968, Jan. 14 Litho. Perf. 14
453 A186 25p blue & multi 1.10 .50

Topelius (1818-98), writer and educator.

Skiers and Ski Lift — A187

1968, Feb. 19   Photo.   Perf. 14
454 A187 25p multicolored   .85   .70
Winter Tourism in Finland.

Paper Making, by Hannes Autere — A188

1968, Mar. 12   Litho.   Wmk. 363
455 A188 45p dk red, brn & org   .70   .45
Finnish paper industry and 150th anniv. of the oldest Finnish paper mill, Tervakoski, whose own watermark was used for this stamp.

World Health Organization Emblem — A189

Lithographed and Photogravure
1968, Apr. 6   Unwmk.   Perf. 14
456 A189 40p red org, dk blue & gold   .65   .30
To honor World Health Organization.

Lion Type of 1954-58 and

Market Place and Mermaid Fountain, Helsinki A190

Keuru Wooden Church, 1758 A191

Häme Bridge, Tampere A192

Finnish Arms from Grave of King Gustav Vasa, 1581 A194

A194a

25p, Post bus. 30p, Aquarium-Planetarium, Tampere. No. 463, P.O., Tampere. No. 465, National Museum, Helsinki, vert. No. 467A, like 70p. 1.30m, Helsinki railroad station.

Engr. (type A94, except #459A);
Litho. (#459A, 465 & type A190);
Engr. & Litho. (others)
Perf. 11½; 12½ (#466, 467A); 13 (#465); 13½ (#470); 14 (#463, 470A)
1968-78

457	A94	1p lt red brn	.25	.40
458	A94	2p gray green	.25	.40
459	A94	4p gray	.60	.50
459A	A94	5p violet blue	1.80	2.50
460	A192	25p multi ('71)	.80	.25
461	A191	30p multi ('71)	2.00	.25
461A	A94	35p dull org ('74)	.60	.40
b.		Bklt. pane of 4, #459A, 461A, 400, 464A + label	2.50	2.50
		Complete booklet, #461b	3.50	

462	A94	40p org ('73)	.80	.50
a.		Bklt. pane of 3, #462, 2 #404A + 2 labels	6.00	8.00
		Complete booklet, #462a	8.00	
463	A192	40p multi ('73)	1.20	.25
464	A94	50p lt ultra ('70)	2.50	.25
c.		Bklt. pane of 5, #401, 403, 464, 2 #459A + 5 labels	13.00	14.50
		Complete booklet, #464c	14.00	
464A	A94	50p rose lake	1.00	.25
d.		Bklt. pane of 4, #400, 464A, 2 #402 + label	1.75	1.75
		Complete booklet, #464Ad	2.00	
464B	A94	60p blue ('73)	.80	.25
465	A191	60p multi ('73)	1.20	.25
466	A190	70p multi ('73)	2.00	.40
467	A191	80p multi ('70)	6.00	.40
467A	A190	80p multi ('76)	1.00	.40
468	A192	90p multi	1.50	.40
469	A191	1.30m multi ('71)	.80	.40
470	A194	10m multi ('74)	6.00	.25
470A	A194a	20m multi ('78)	10.00	1.00
		Nos. 457-470A (20)	41.10	9.70

Issued: 5p, 6/72.

Infantry Monument, Vaasa — A195

Designs: 25p, War Memorial (cross), Hietaniemi Cemetery. 40p, Soldier, 1968.

1968, June 4   Photo.   Perf. 14
471 A195 20p lt violet & multi   1.00   .40
472 A195 25p lt blue & multi   1.00   .40
473 A195 40p orange & multi   1.00   .40
        Nos. 471-473 (3)   3.00 1.20
To honor Finnish national defense.

Camping Ground — A196

1968, June 10   Litho.
474 A196 25p multicolored   .80   .70
Issued to publicize Finland for summer vacations.

Paper, Pulp and Pine — A197

Lithographed and Embossed
1968, July 2   Unwmk.   Perf. 14
475 A197 40p multicolored   .70   .40
Finnish wood industry.

Mustola Lock, Saima Canal — A198

1968, Aug. 5   Litho.   Perf. 14
476 A198 40p multicolored   .70   .40
Opening of the Saima Canal.

Oskar Merikanto and Pipe Organ — A199

1968, Aug. 5   Unwmk.
477 A199 40p vio, silver & lt brn   1.10   .40
Centenary of the birth of Oskar Merikanto, composer.

Ships in Harbor and Emblem of Central Chamber of Commerce — A200

1968, Sept. 13   Litho.   Perf. 14
478 A200 40p lt bl, brt bl & blk   .70   .40
Publicizing economic development and for the 50th anniv. of the Central Chamber of Commerce of Finland.

Welder — A201

1968, Oct. 11   Litho.   Perf. 14
479 A201 40p blue & multi   .70   .40
Finnish metal industry.

Lyre, Students' Emblem — A202

Lithographed and Engraved
1968, Nov. 24   Perf. 14
480 A202 40p ultra, vio bl & gold   .70   .40
Issued to publicize the work of the student unions in Finnish social life.

Nordic Cooperation Issue

Five Ancient Ships — A203

1969, Feb. 28   Engr.   Perf. 11½
481 A203 40p lt ultra   2.00   .40
50th anniv. of the Nordic Society and centenary of postal cooperation among the northern countries. The design is taken from a coin found at the site of Birka, an ancient Swedish town. See also Denmark Nos. 454-455, Iceland Nos. 404-405, Norway Nos. 523-524 and Sweden Nos. 808-810.

Town Hall and Arms of Kemi — A203a

1969, Mar. 5   Photo.   Perf. 14
482 A203a 40p multicolored   .70   .40
Centenary of the town of Kemi.

Europa Issue, 1969
Common Design Type
1969, Apr. 28   Photo.   Perf. 14
Size: 30x20mm
483 CD12 40p dl rose, vio bl & dk bl   2.50   .60

ILO Emblem — A204

Lithographed and Engraved
1969, June 2   Perf. 11½
484 A204 40p dp rose & vio blue   .70   .40
50th anniv. of the ILO.

Armas Järnefelt — A205

1969, Aug. 14   Photo.   Perf. 14
485 A205 40p multicolored   1.00   .40
Järnefelt (1869-1958), composer and conductor. Portrait on stamp by Vilho Sjöström.

Emblems and Flag — A206

1969, Sept. 19   Photo.   Perf. 14
486 A206 40p lt bl, blk, grn & lil   .70   .40
Publicizing the importance of National and International Fairs in Finnish economy.

Johannes Linnankoski — A207

1969, Oct. 18   Litho.
487 A207 40p dk brn red & multi   .70   .40
Linnankoski (1869-1913), writer.

Educational Symbols — A208

Lithographed and Engraved
1969, Nov. 24   Perf. 11½
488 A208 40p gray, vio & grn   .70   .40
Centenary of the Central School Board.

DC-8-62 CF Plane and Helsinki Airport — A209

1969, Dec. 22   Photo.   Perf. 14
489 A209 25p sky blue & multi   1.10   .75

Golden Eagle — A210

1970, Feb. 10   Litho.   Perf. 14
490 A210 30p multicolored   2.00   .50
Year of Nature Conservation, 1970.

Swatches in Shape of Factories — A211

1970, Mar. 9   Litho.   Perf. 14
491 A211 50p multicolored   .85   .40
Finnish textile industry.

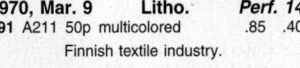

Molecule Diagram and Factories — A212

1970, Mar. 26   Photo.   Perf. 14
492 A212 50p multicolored   .85   .40
Finnish chemical industry.

UNESCO Emblem and Lenin A213

Atom Diagram and Laurel A214

UN Emblem and Globe — A215

1970   **Litho. and Engr.**
493 A213 30p gold & multi   .70   .40
494 A214 30p red & multi   .70   .40

Photogravure and Gold Embossed
495 A215 50p bl, vio bl & gold   .70   .40
    Nos. 493-495 (3)   2.10 1.20

25th anniv. of the UN. No. 493 also publicizes the UNESCO-sponsored Lenin Symposium, Tampere, Apr. 6-10. No. 494 also publicizes the Nuclear Data Conf. of the Atomic Energy Commission, Otaniemi (Helsinki), June 15-19.
Issued: No. 493, 4/6; No. 494, 6/15; No. 495, 10/24.

Handicapped Volleyball Player — A216

1970, June 27   **Litho.**   **Perf. 14**
496 A216 50p orange, red & blk   1.00   .40

Issued to publicize the position of handicapped civilians and war veterans in society and their potential contributions to it.

Meeting of Auroraseura Society — A217

1970, Aug. 15   **Photo.**   **Perf. 14**
497 A217 50p multicolored   .70   .40

200th anniv. of the Auroraseura Soc., dedicated to the study of Finnish history, geography, economy and language. The design of the stamp is after a painting by Eero Jarnefelt.

Uusikaarlepyy Arms, Church and 17th Cent. Building — A218

Design: No. 499, Arms of Kokkola, harbor, Sports Palace and 17th century building.

1970   **Perf. 14**
498 A218 50p multicolored   .70   .40
499 A218 50p multicolored   .70   .40

Towns of Uusikaarlepyy and Kokkola, 350th anniv.
Issued: No. 498, Aug. 21; No. 499, Sept. 17.

Urho Kekkonen, Medal by Aimo Tukiainen — A219

1970, Sept. 3   **Litho. & Engr.**
500 A219 50p ultra, sil & blk   .70   .40

70th birthday of Pres. Urho Kekkonen.

Globe, Maps of US, Finland, USSR — A220

Lithographed and Gold Embossed
1970, Nov. 2
501 A220 50p blk, bl, pink & gold   .70   .40

Strategic Arms Limitation Talks (SALT) between the US & USSR, Helsinki, 11/2-12/18.

Pres. Paasikivi by Essi Renavall — A221

1970, Nov. 27   **Photo.**   **Perf. 14**
502 A221 50p gold, brt bl & slate   .70   .40

Centenary of the birth of Juho Kusti Paasikivi (1870-1956), President of Finland.

Cogwheels — A222

1971, Jan. 28   **Litho.**   **Perf. 14**
503 A222 50p multicolored   .70   .40

Finnish industry.

Europa Issue, 1971
Common Design Type
1971, May 3   **Litho.**   **Perf. 14**
    Size: 30x20mm
504 CD14 50p dp rose, yel & blk   2.50   .50

Tornio Church — A223

1971, May 12   **Litho.**   **Perf. 14**
505 A223 50p multicolored   1.00   .40

350th anniversary of the town of Tornio.

Front Page, January 15, 1771 — A224

1971, June 1   **Litho.**   **Perf. 14**
506 A224 50p multicolored   .70   .40

Bicentenary of the Finnish press.

Athletes in Helsinki Stadium — A225

50p, Running & javelin in Helsinki Stadium.

1971, July 5   **Litho.**   **Perf. 14**
507 A225 30p multicolored   1.00   .50
508 A225 50p multicolored   2.00   .50

European Athletic Championships.

Sailboats — A226

1971, July 14
509 A226 50p multicolored   1.25   .60

International Lightning Class Championships, Helsinki, July 14-Aug. 1.

Silver Tea Pot, Guild's Emblem, Tools — A227

1971, Aug. 6
510 A227 50p lilac & multi   .70   .40

600th anniv. of Finnish goldsmiths' art.

"Plastic Buttons and Houses" — A228

Photogravure and Embossed
1971, Oct. 20   **Perf. 14**
511 A228 50p multicolored   .70   .40

Finnish plastics industry.

Europa Issue 1972
Common Design Type
1972, May 2   **Litho.**   **Perf. 14**
    Size: 20x30mm
512 CD15 30p dk red & multi   1.50   .50
513 CD15 50p lt brn & multi   2.50   .50

Finnish National Theater — A229

1972, May 22   **Litho.**   **Perf. 14**
514 A229 50p lt violet & multi   .70   .40

Centenary of the Finnish National Theater, founded by Kaarlo and Emilie Bergbom.

Globe, US and USSR Flags — A230

1972, June 2
515 A230 50p multicolored   1.00   .40

Strategic Arms Limitation Talks (SALT), final meeting, Helsinki, Mar. 28-May 26; treaty signed, Moscow, May 26.

Map and Arms of Aland — A231

1972, June 9
516 A231 50p multicolored   1.50   .50

1st Provincial Meeting of Aland, 50th anniv.

Training Ship Suomen Joutsen — A232

1972, June 19
517 A232 50p orange & multi   1.00   .40

Tall Ships' Race 1972, Helsinki, Aug. 20.

Costume from Perni, 12th Cent. — A233

No. 519, Couple, Tenhola, 18th cent. No. 520, Girl, Nastola, 19th cent. No. 521, Man, Voyni, 19th cent. No. 522, Lapps, Inari, 19th cent.

1972, Nov. 19   **Litho.**   **Perf. 13**
518 A233 50p shown   2.00   .40
519 A233 50p multicolored   2.00   .40
520 A233 50p multicolored   2.00   .40

---

521 A233 50p multicolored   2.00   .40
522 A233 50p multicolored   2.00   .40
   a.   Strip of 5, #518-522   10.00 14.50
     Complete booklet, 2 each
     #518-522   20.00
     Regional costumes.
     See Nos. 533-537.

Circle Surrounding Map of Europe — A234

1972, Dec. 11   **Perf. 14x13½**
523 A234 50p multicolored   2.00   .50

Preparatory Conference on European Security and Cooperation.

Book, Finnish and Soviet Colors — A235

Litho.; Gold Embossed
1973, Apr. 6   **Perf. 14**
524 A235 60p gold & multi   .70   .40

Soviet-Finnish Treaty of Friendship, 25th anniv.

Kyösti Kallio (1873-1940), Pres. of Finland — A236

1973, Apr. 10   **Litho.**   **Perf. 13**
525 A236 60p multicolored   .70   .40

Europa Issue 1973
Common Design Type
1973, Apr. 30   **Photo.**   **Perf. 14**
    Size: 31x21mm
526 CD16 60p bl, brt bl & emer   1.25   .55

Nordic Cooperation Issue

Nordic House, Reykjavik A236a

1973, June 26   **Engr.**   **Perf. 12½**
527 A236a 60p multicolored   1.00   .40
528 A236a 70p multicolored   1.00   .40

A century of postal cooperation among Denmark, Finland, Iceland, Norway and Sweden, and in connection with the Nordic Postal Conference, Reykjavik.

Map of Europe, "EUROPA" as a Maze — A237

Litho. & Embossed
1973, July 3   **Perf. 13**
529 A237 70p multicolored   .75   .40

Conference for European Security and Cooperation, Helsinki, July 1973.

Paddling — A238

1973, July 18   **Litho.**   **Perf. 14**
530 A238 60p multicolored   .75   .40

Canoeing World Championships, Tampere, July 26-29.

Radiosonde, WMO
Emblem — A239

1973, Aug. 6   Litho.   *Perf. 14*
531 A239 60p multicolored   .70   .40
Cent. of intl. meteorological cooperation.

Eliel Saarinen
and Design for
Parliament,
Helsinki — A240

1973, Aug. 20   *Perf. 12½x13*
532 A240 60p multicolored   .70   .40
Eliel Saarinen (1873-1950), architect.

Costume Type of 1972

Designs: No. 533, Woman, Kaukola. 534, Woman, Jaaski. No. 535, Married couple, Koivisto. No. 536, Mother and son, Sakyla. No. 537, Girl, Hainavesi.

1973, Oct. 10   Litho.   *Perf. 13*
533 A233 60p multicolored   2.50   .40
534 A233 60p multicolored   2.50   .40
535 A233 60p multicolored   2.50   .40
536 A233 60p multicolored   2.50   .40
537 A233 60p multicolored   2.50   .40
   a.   Strip of 5, #533-537   12.50   19.00
Regional costumes.

DC10-30
Jet — A241

1973, Nov. 1   Litho.   *Perf. 14*
538 A241 60p multicolored   .80   .40
50th anniv. of regular air service, Finnair.

Santa Claus in
Reindeer
Sleigh — A242

1973, Nov. 15   Litho.   *Perf. 14*
539 A242 30p multicolored   .95   .40
Christmas 1973.

"The Barber of
Seville" — A243

1973, Nov. 21
540 A243 60p multicolored   .70   .40
Centenary of opera in Finland.

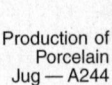

Production of
Porcelain
Jug — A244

1973, Nov. 23
541 A244 60p blue & multi   .70   .40
Finnish porcelain.

Nurmi, by Waino
Aaltonen — A245

1973, Dec. 11
542 A245 60p multicolored   .85   .40
Paavo Nurmi (1897-1973), runner, Olympic winner, 1920-1924-1928.

Arms, Map and
Harbor of
Hanko — A246

1974, Jan. 10   Litho.   *Perf. 14*
543 A246 60p blue & multi   .75   .40
Centenary of the town of Hanko.

Ice Hockey — A247

1974, Mar. 5   Litho.   *Perf. 14*
544 A247 60p multicolored   .70   .40
European and World Ice Hockey Championships, held in Finland.

Seagulls (7 Baltic
States) — A248

1974, Mar. 18   *Perf. 12½*
545 A248 60p multicolored   1.00   .40
Protection of marine environment of the Baltic Sea.

Goddess of Freedom,
by Waino
Aaltonen — A249

1974, Apr. 29   Litho.   *Perf. 13x12½*
546 A249 70p sil & multi   1.50   .50
Europa.

Ilmari Kianto and Old
Pine — A250

1974, May 7   *Perf. 13*
547 A250 60p multicolored   .70   .40
Ilmari Kianto (1874-1970), writer.

Society Emblem,
Symbol — A251

Lithographed and Embossed
1974, June 12   *Perf. 13½x14*
548 A251 60p gold & multi   .70   .40
Centenary of Adult Education.

Grid — A252

1974, June 14   Litho.   *Perf. 14x13½*
549 A252 60p multicolored   .70   .40
Rationalization Year in Finland, dedicated to economic and business improvements.

UPU Emblem — A253

1974, Oct. 10   Litho.   *Perf. 13½x14*
550 A253 60p multicolored   .70   .40
551 A253 70p multicolored   .70   .40
Centenary of Universal Postal Union.

Elves Distributing
Gifts — A254

1974, Nov. 16   Litho.   *Perf. 14x13½*
552 A254 35p multicolored   1.00   .25
Christmas 1974.

Concrete Bridge and
Granite Bridge,
Aunessilta — A255

Litho. & Engr.
1974, Dec. 17   *Perf. 14*
553 A255 60p multicolored   .70   .50
Royal Finnish Directorate of Roads and Waterways, 175th anniversary.

Coat of
Arms,
1581
A256

Chimneyless
Log Sauna
A256a

Cheese Frames
A257

Carved
Wooden
Distaffs
A258

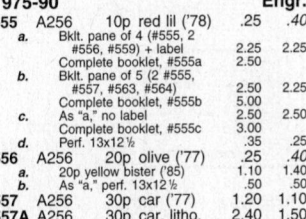

Kirvu Weather
Vane — A258a

1.50m, Wood-carved high drinking bowl, 1542.

Perf. 11½; 14 (2m, 5m)

				Engr.
1975-90				
555	A256	10p red lil ('78)	.25	.40
a.		Bklt. pane of 4 (#555, 2 #556, #559) + label	2.25	2.25
		Complete booklet, #555a	2.50	
b.		Bklt. pane of 5 (2 #555, #557, #563, #564)	2.50	2.25
		Complete booklet, #555b	5.00	
c.		As "a," no label	2.50	2.50
		Complete booklet, #555c	3.00	
d.		Perf. 13x12½	.35	.25
556	A256	20p olive ('77)	.25	.40
a.		20p yellow bister ('85)	1.10	1.40
b.		As "a," perf. 13x12½	.50	.50
557	A256	30p car ('77)	1.20	1.10
557A	A256	30p car, litho.	2.40	1.50
558	A256	40p orange	.25	.25
a.		Perf. 13x12½	.70	.70
559	A256	50p green ('76)	.25	.25
a.		Perf. 13x12½	.80	.80
560	A256	60p blue	.40	.25
a.		Perf. 13x12½	.60	.60
561	A256	70p sepia	.40	.25
562	A256	80p dl red & bl grn ('76)	.40	.40
a.		Perf. 13x12½	3.25	3.25
563	A256	90p vio bl ('77)	.40	.40
564	A256	1.10m yellow ('79)	.40	.40
565	A256	1.20m dk blue ('79)	.40	.50
566	A258	1.50m multi ('76)	.80	.25

		Litho.		
567	A256a	2m multi ('77)	1.00	.25
		Lithographed and Engraved		
568	A257	2.50m multi ('76)	.90	.40
a.		Perf. 14	1.20	.80
569	A258	4.50m multi ('76)	1.60	.40
a.		Perf. 14	2.00	2.00
570	A258a	5m multi ('77)	6.00	.25
		Nos. 555-570 (17)	17.30	7.65

Some denominations of design A256 exist in up to three engraving types.
Nos. 560a and 562a was only issued within the booklet panes Nos. 713a and 715a.
Issued: No. 557A, 6/3/80; No. 560a, 7/25/88; No. 555d, 7/25/89; No. 562a, 3/1/90; No. 558a, 8/18/94; No. 568a, 12/28/88; No. 569a, 9/26/88; No. 556b, 4/3/98.
See Nos. 629, 631-633, 711-715, 861.

Finland No. 16 — A259

Lithographed and Typographed
1975, Apr. 26   *Perf. 13*
571 A259 70p multicolored   3.00   4.00
Nordia 75 Philatelic Exhibition, Helsinki, Apr. 26-May 1. Sold only at exhibition for 3m including entrance ticket.

Girl Combing Hair, by
Magnus
Enckell — A260

Europa: 90p, The Washerwomen, by Tyko Sallinen (1879-1955).

1975, Apr. 28   Litho.   *Perf. 13x12½*
572 A260 70p gray & multi   1.00   .40
573 A260 90p tan & multi   1.50   .40

Balance of Justice,
Sword of Legality — A261

1975, May 7   *Perf. 14*
574 A261 70p vio blue & multi   .70   .40
Sesquicentennial of State Economy Comptroller's Office.

Rescue Boat and
Sinking Ship — A262

1975, June 2   Litho.   *Perf. 14*
575 A262 70p multicolored   .85   .40
12th Intl. Salvage Conf., Finland, stressing importance of coordinating sea, air and communications resources in salvage operations.

Safe and Unsafe
Levels of
Drugs — A263

1975, July 21   Litho.   *Perf. 14*
576 A263 70p multicolored   .70   .40
Importance of pharmacological studies and for the 6th Intl. Pharmacology Cong., Helsinki.

Olavinlinna Castle — A264

1975, July 29 *Perf. 13*
577 A264 70p multicolored .70 .40
500th anniversary of Olavinlinna Castle.

Swallows over Finlandia Hall — A265

1975, July 30
578 A265 90p multicolored .70 .40
European Security and Cooperation Conference, Helsinki, July 30-Aug. 1. (The swallows of the design represent freedom, mobility and continuity.) See No. 709.

"Men and Women Working for Peace" — A266

1975, Oct. 24 Litho. *Perf. 13x12½*
579 A266 70p multicolored .70 .40
International Women's Year 1975.

"Continuity and Growth" — A267

1975, Oct. 29 *Perf. 13*
580 A267 70p brown & multi .70 .40
Industrial Art and for the centenary of the Finnish Society of Industrial Art.

Boys as Three Kings and Herod — A268

1975, Nov. 8 *Perf. 14*
581 A268 40p blue & multi 1.10 .35
Christmas 1975.

Top Border of State Debenture — A269

Lithographed and Engraved
1976, Jan. 9 *Perf. 11½*
582 A269 80p multicolored .70 .40
Centenary of State Treasury.

Glider over Lake Region — A270

1976, Jan. 13 Litho. *Perf. 14*
583 A270 80p multicolored .90 .40
15th World Glider Championships, Rayskala, June 13-27.

Prof. Heikki Klemetti (1876-1953), Musician & Writer — A271

1976, Feb. 14 Litho. *Perf. 13*
584 A271 80p green & multi .70 .40

Map with Areas of Different Dialects — A272

1976, Mar. 10 Litho. *Perf. 13*
585 A272 80p multicolored .70 .40
Finnish Language Society, centenary.

Aino Ackté, by Albert Edelfelt — A273

1976, Apr. 23
586 A273 70p yellow & multi .70 .40
Aino Ackté (1876-1944), opera singer.

Europa Issue

Knife from Voyri, Sheath and Belt — A274

1976, May 3 Litho. *Perf. 13*
587 A274 80p violet bl & multi 1.50 .50

Radio and Television — A275

1976, Sept. 9 Litho. *Perf. 13*
588 A275 80p multicolored .70 .40
Radio broadcasting in Finland, 50th anniv.

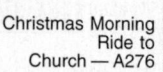

Christmas Morning Ride to Church — A276

1976, Oct. 23 Litho. *Perf. 14*
589 A276 50p multicolored .90 .40
Christmas 1976.

Turku Chapter Seal (Virgin and Child) — A277

1976, Nov. 1 Litho. *Perf. 12½*
590 A277 80p buff, brn & red .70 .40
Cathedral Chapter of Turku, 700th anniv.

Alvar Aalto, Finlandia Hall, Helsinki — A278

1976, Nov. 4
591 A278 80p multicolored .70 .40
Hugo Alvar Henrik Aalto (1898-1976), architect.

Ice Dancers — A280

1977, Jan. 25 Litho. *Perf. 13*
592 A280 90p multicolored .70 .40
European Figure Skating Championships, Finland, Jan. 25-29.

Five Water Lilies — A281

Photogravure and Engraved
1977, Feb. 2 *Perf. 12½*
593 A281 90p brt green & multi .70 .40
594 A281 1m ultra & multi .70 .40
Nordic countries cooperation for protection of the environment and 25th Session of Nordic Council, Helsinki, Feb. 19.

Icebreaker Rescuing Merchantman A282

1977, Mar. 2 Litho. *Perf. 13*
595 A282 90p multicolored .80 .40
Winter navigation between Finland and Sweden, centenary.

Nuclear Reactor — A283

1977, Mar. 3 *Perf. 12½x13*
596 A283 90p multicolored .70 .40
Opening of nuclear power station on Hästholmen Island.

Europa Issue

Autumn Landscape, Northern Finland — A284

1977, May 2 Litho. *Perf. 12½x13*
597 A284 90p multicolored 1.50 .45

Tree, Birds and Nest — A285

1977, May 4 *Perf. 13x12½*
598 A285 90p multicolored .70 .40
75th anniversary of cooperative banks.

Orthodox Church, Valamo Cloister — A286

1977, May 31 Litho. *Perf. 14*
599 A286 90p multicolored .70 .40
Consecration festival of new Orthodox Church at Valamo Cloister, Heinävesi; 800th anniversary of introduction of orthodoxy in Karelia and of founding of Valamo Cloister.

Paavo Ruotsalainen (1777-1852), Lay Leader of Pietists in Finland — A287

1977, July 8 Litho. *Perf. 13*
600 A287 90p multicolored .70 .40

People Fleeing Fire and Water — A288

1977, Sept. 14 Litho. *Perf. 14*
601 A288 90p multicolored .70 .40
Civil defense for security.

Volleyball — A289

1977, Sept. 15
602 A289 90p multicolored .70 .40
European Women's Volleyball Championships, Finland, Sept. 29-Oct. 2.

Children Bringing Water for Sauna — A290

1977, Oct. 25
603 A290 50p multicolored 1.10 .40
Christmas 1977.

Finnish Flag — A291

1977, Dec. 5 Litho. *Perf. 14*
Size: 31x21mm
604 A291 80p multicolored .70 .40
Size: 37x25mm
Perf. 13
605 A291 1m multicolored 1.20 .40
Finland's declaration of independence, 60th anniv.

Wall Telephone, 1880, New Telephone — A292

1977, Dec. 9 *Perf. 14*
606 A292 1m multicolored .70 .40
Centenary of first telephone in Finland.

Harbor, Sunila Factory, Kotka Arms — A293

1978, Jan. 2   **Litho.**   *Perf. 14*
607 A293 1m multicolored   .70   .40
Centenary of founding of Kotka.

Paimio Sanitarium by Alvar Aalto — A294

Europa: 1.20m, Hvittrask studio house, 1902, horiz.

1978, May 2   **Litho.**   *Perf. 13*
608 A294   1m multicolored   4.00   .50
609 A294   1.20m multicolored   5.00   6.00

Rural Bus Service — A295

1978, June 8   **Litho.**   *Perf. 14*
610 A295 1m multicolored   .70   .40

Eino Leino and Eagle — A296

1978, July 6   **Litho.**   *Perf. 13*
611 A296 1m multicolored   .70   .40
Eino Leino (1878-1926), poet.

Function Theory and Rhythmical Lines — A297

1978, Aug. 15   **Litho.**   *Perf. 14*
612 A297 1m multicolored   .70   .40
ICM 78, International Congress of Mathematicians, Helsinki, Aug. 15-23.

Child Feeding Birds — A298

1978, Oct. 23   **Litho.**   *Perf. 14*
613 A298 50p multicolored   .90   .40
Christmas 1978.

A299

1979, Jan. 2   **Litho.**   *Perf. 13*
614 A299 1.10m multicolored   .75   .40
International Year of the Child.

Runner — A300

1979, Feb. 7   **Litho.**   *Perf. 14*
615 A300 1.10m multicolored   .70   .40
8th Orienteering World Championships, Finland, Sept. 1-4.

Old School, Hamina, Academy Flag — A301

1979, Mar. 20   **Litho.**   *Perf. 14*
616 A301 1.10m multicolored   .70   .40
200th anniv. of Finnish Military Academy.

A302

Design: Turku Cathedral and Castle, Prinkkala house, Brahe statue.

1979, Mar. 31
617 A302 1.10m multicolored   .70   .40

Streetcar, Helsinki — A303

1979, May 2   **Litho.**   *Perf. 14*
618 A303 1.10m multi   .70   .30
Non-polluting urban transportation.

View of Tampere, 1779 — A304

1979, May 2
619 A304 90p multicolored   .70   .40

View of Tampere, 1979 — A305

1979, Oct. 1   *Perf. 13*
620 A305 1.10m multicolored   .70   .40
Bicentenary of founding of Tampere.

Optical Telegraph, 1796, Map of Islands — A306

Europa: 1.10m, Letter of Queen Christina to Per Brahe, 1638, establishing postal service.

1979, May 2   *Perf. 13*
621 A306 1.10m multi   1.50   .40
622 A306 1.30m multi, horiz.   2.50   1.00

Shops and Merchants' Signs — A307

1979, Sept. 26   *Perf. 14*
623 A307 1.10m multicolored   .70   .40
Business and industry regulation centenary.

Old and New Cars, Street Crossing — A308

1979, Oct. 1
624 A308 1.10m multicolored   .70   .40
Road safety.

Elves Feeding Horse — A309

1979, Oct. 24
625 A309 60p multicolored   .90   .40
Christmas 1979.

Korppi House, Lapinjarvi — A310

Farm houses, First Row: Syrjala House, Tammela, 2 stamps in continuous design; Murtovaara House, Valtimo; Antila House, Lapua. Second row: Lofts, Pohjanmaa; Courtyard gate, Kanajarvi House, Kalvola; Main door, Havuselka House, Kauhajoki; Maki-Rasinpera House and dinner bell tower; Gable and eaves, Rasula Kuortane granary.

1979, Oct. 27   **Litho.**   *Perf. 13*
626   Booklet pane of 10   6.00   4.00
a.-j. A310 1.10m single stamp   .60   .35
     Complete booklet, #626   6.00
See design A349a.

Type of 1975 and

Kauhaneva Swamp A315

Hame Castle, Hameenlinna A316

Windmill, Harrstrom A318

Shuttle, Raanu Designs A322

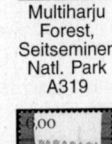

Multiharju Forest, Seitseminen Natl. Park A319

Kaspaikka Towel Design A323

Bridal Rug, Teisko, 1815 A324

Iron-forged Door, Hollola Church A325

Iron Fish Spear c. 1100 — A326

Design: 1.80m, Eastern Gulf natl. park.

Litho. & Engr., Litho., Engr.
1979-98   *Perf. 14, 11½ (A256, A318)*

627	A315	70p multicolored	.40	.40
628	A316	90p brown red	.40	.40
629	A256	1m red brown	.40	.40
a.		Perf. 13x12½ ('98)	1.25	1.25
630	A318	1m bl & red brn	.40	.40
631	A256	1.30m dk green	.60	.60
631A	A256	1.30m dk green, litho.	.50	.60
b.		Booklet pane, #555-556, 557A, 560, 631A	3.00	3.00
		Complete booklet, #631Ab	6.00	
632	A256	1.40m purple	.50	.60
633	A256	1.50m grnsh blue	.60	.60
634	A319	1.60m multicolored	.50	.40
635	A318	1.80m multicolored	1.00	.40
636	A322	3m multicolored	1.50	.40
637	A323	6m multicolored	2.50	.25
638	A324	7m multicolored	2.50	.40
639	A325	8m multicolored	3.50	.50
640	A326	9m blk & dk bl	3.00	.70
		Nos. 627-640 (15)	18.30	7.05

Coil Stamps
Perf. 11½ Vert.
641 A316 90p brown red   .40   .40
Perf. 12½ Horiz.
642 A318 1m blue & red brn   .40   .60

Issued: 3m, 10/27/79; 6m, 4/9/80; No. 629, 1/2/81; 70p, 1/12/81; 90p, 9/1/82; 1.60m, 2/8/82; 7m, 2/15/82; No. 631, 1/3/83; Nos. 630, 642, 1/12/83; 1.80m, 8m, 2/10/83; 1.40m, 9m, 1/2/84; 1.50m, 1/2/85; No. 631A, 11/1/85.

Maria Jotuni (1880-1943), Writer — A327

1980, Apr. 9   **Litho.**
643 A327 1.10m multicolored   .55   .40

Frans Eemil Sillanpaa (1888-1964), Writer — A328

Europa: 1.30m, Artturi Ilmari Virtanen (1895-1973), chemist, vert.

1980, Apr. 28   *Perf. 13*
644 A328 1.10m multicolored   1.00   .40
645 A328 1.30m multicolored   1.50   1.00

Pres. Urho Kekkonen, 80th Birthday — A329

1980, Sept. 3   **Litho.**   *Perf. 13*
646 A329 1.10m multicolored   .55   .40

Nordic Cooperation Issue

Back-piece Harness, 19th century — A330

1980, Sept. 9   *Perf. 14*
647 A330 1.10m shown   .55 .40
648 A330 1.30m Collar harness, vert.   .55 .40

Biathlon — A331

1980, Oct. 17   Litho.   *Perf. 14*
649 A331 1.10m multicolored   .55 .40

World Biathlon Championship, Lahti, Feb. 10-15, 1981.

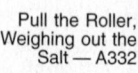

Pull the Roller, Weighing out the Salt — A332

Christmas 1980 (Traditional Games): 1.10m, Putting out the shoemaker's eye.

1980, Oct. 27
650 A332 60p multicolored   .60 .40
651 A332 1.10m multicolored   .60 .40

Boxing Match — A333

1981, Feb. 28   Litho.   *Perf. 14*
652 A333 1.10m multicolored   .60 .40

European Boxing Championships, Tampere, May 2-10.

Glass Blowing — A334

1981, Mar. 12
653 A334 1.10m multicolored   .60 .40

Glass industry, 300th anniversary.

Mail Boat Furst Menschikoff, 1836 — A335

Litho. & Engr.
1981, May 6   *Perf. 13*
654 A335 1.10m brown & tan   2.50 3.00

Nordia '81 Stamp Exhibition, Helsinki, May 6-10. Sold only at exhibition for 3m including entrance ticket.

Europa Issue

Rowing to Church — A336

Design: 1.50m, Midsummer's Eve dance.

1981, May 18   Litho.   *Perf. 13*
655 A336 1.10m shown   .80 .40
656 A336 1.50m multicolored   1.20 .60

Traffic Conference Emblem — A337

1981, May 26   Litho.   *Perf. 14*
657 A337 1.10m multicolored   .60 .40

European Conference of Ministers of Transport, May 25-28.

Boy and Girl Riding Pegasus — A338

1981, June 11
658 A338 1m multicolored   .60 .40

Youth associations centenary.

Intl. Year of the Disabled — A339

1981, Sept. 2   Litho.   *Perf. 13*
659 A339 1.10m multicolored   .60 .40

Christmas 1981 — A340

70p, Children, Christmas tree. 1.10m, Decorating tree, vert.

1981, Oct. 27   Litho.   *Perf. 14*
660 A340 70p multicolored   .60 .40
661 A340 1.10m multicolored   .80 .40

"Om Konsten att Ratt Behaga" First Issue (Periodicals Bicentenary) — A341

1982, Jan. 15
662 A341 1.20m multicolored   .60 .40

Kuopio Bicentenary — A343

1982, Mar. 4   Litho.   *Perf. 14*
664 A343 1.20m multicolored   .60 .40

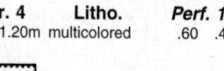

Score, String Instrument Neck — A344

1982, Mar. 11   *Perf. 13*
665 A344 1.20m multicolored   .80 .45

Centenaries of Sibelius Academy of Music and Helsinki Orchestra.

Electric Power Plant Centenary — A345

1982, Mar. 15   *Perf. 14*
666 A345 1.20m multicolored   .60 .40

Gardening — A346

1982, Apr. 16   Litho.   *Perf. 14*
667 A346 1.10m multicolored   .60 .40

Europa — A347

1.20m, Publication of Abckiria (1st Finnish book), 1543 (Sculpture of Mikael Agricola, translator, by Oskari Jauhiainen, 1951). 1.50m, Turku Academy, 1st Finnish university (Turku Academy Inaugural Procession, 1640, after Albert Edelfelt).

1982, Apr. 29   Litho.   *Perf. 13x12½*
668 A347 1.20m multicolored   1.00 .40
     Size: 47x31mm
     Perf. 12½
669 A347 1.50m multicolored   1.50 .60

Intl. Monetary Fund and World Bank Emblems — A348

1982, May 12   *Perf. 14*
670 A348 1.60m multicolored   .60 .40

IMF Interim Committee and IMF-WB Joint Development Committee Meeting, Helsinki, May 12-14.

75th Anniv. of Unicameral Parliament — A349

2.40m, Future, by Waino Aaltonen, Parliament.

1982, May 25
671 A349 2.40m ultra & blk   .85 .50

Manor Houses — A349a

1st Row: a, Kuitia, Parainen, 1490. b, Louhisaari, Askainen, 1655. c, Frugard, Joroinen, 1780. d, Jokioinen, 1798. e, Moisio, Elimaki, 1820.
2nd Row: f, Sjundby, Siuntio, 1560. g, Fagervik, Inkoo, 1773. h, Mustio, Karjaa, 1792. i, Fiskars, Pohja, 1818. j, Kotkaniemi, Vihti, 1836.

1982, June 14   Litho.   *Perf. 13x13½*
672   Booklet pane of 10   8.00 8.00
   a.-j. A349a 1.20m single stamp   .80 .40
    Complete booklet, #672   8.00 8.00

See design A310.

Christmas 1982 — A350

Designs: 90p, Feeding forest animals. 1.20m, Children eating porridge.

1982, Oct. 25
673 A350 90p multi   .70 .40
674 A350 1.20m multi   .70 .40

Nordic Cooperation — A351

1.20m, Panning for gold. 1.30m, Kitkajoki River rapids.

1983, Mar. 24   Litho.   *Perf. 14*
675 A351 1.20m multi   .55 .40
676 A351 1.30m multi   .55 .40

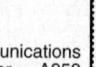

World Communications Year — A352

1.30m, Postal services. 1.70m, Sound waves, optical cables.

1983, Apr. 9   Litho.   *Perf. 13*
677 A352 1.30m multi   .55 .40
678 A352 1.70m multi   .65 .45

Europa 1983 — A353

1.30m, Flash smelting method. 1.70m, Temppeliaukio Church.

1983, May 2   Litho.   *Perf. 12½x13*
679 A353 1.30m multicolored   1.00 .45
680 A353 1.70m multicolored   3.00 .90

Pres. Lauri Kristian Relander (1883-1942) — A354

1983, May 31   Litho.   *Perf. 14*
681 A354 1.30m multicolored   .60 .40

Running — A355

1983, June 6
682 A355 1.20m Javelin, horiz.   .60 .40
683 A355 1.30m shown   .60 .40

First World Athletic Championships, Helsinki, Aug. 7-14.

Toivo Kuula (1883-1918), Composer — A356

1983, July 7   *Perf. 14*
684 A356 1.30m multicolored   .55 .40

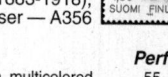

Christmas 1983 — A357

Childrens drawings: 1m, Santa, reindeer, sled and gifts by Eija Myllyviita. 1.30m, Two candles by Camilla Lindberg.

Engr., Litho.
1983, Nov. 4   *Perf. 12, 14*
685 A357 1m dark blue   .85 .40
686 A357 1.30m multi, vert.   .85 .40

A358

1983, Nov. 25   Litho.   *Perf. 14*
687 A358 1.30m brt blue & blk   .60 .40

President Mauno Henrik Koivisto, 60th birthday.

A360

1.10m, Letters (2nd class rate). 1.40m, Automated sorting (1st class rate), vert.

1984, Mar. 1   **Engr.**   **Perf. 12**
689 A360 1.10m multicolored   .60   .40

Photo. & Engr.
690 A360 1.40m multicolored   .60   .40

Inauguration of Nordic postal rates.

Museum Pieces A361   Work and Skill A362

Designs: No. 691, Pottery, 3200 B.C.; Silver chalice, 1416; Crossbow, 16th cent. No. 692, Kaplan hydraulic turbine.

1984, Apr. 30   **Litho.**   **Perf. 13½**
691 A361 1.40m multicolored   .50   .40
692 A362 1.40m multicolored   .50   .40

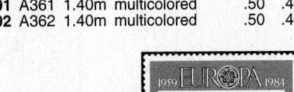

Europa (1959-84) A363

1984, May 7   **Perf. 12½x13**
693 A363 1.40m multicolored   1.50   .40
694 A363 2m multicolored   3.00   1.00

Dentistry — A364

1984, Aug. 27   **Litho.**   **Perf. 14**
695 A364 1.40m Dentist, teeth   .80   .50

Astronomy — A365

Design: Observatory, planets, sun.

1984, Sept. 12
696 A365 1.10m multicolored   1.00   .55

Aleksis Kivi (1934-72), Writer — A366

Design: Song of my Heart.

1984, Oct. 10   **Litho.**   **Perf. 14**
697 A366 1.40m blk & dull mauve   .50   .40

Christmas 1984 — A367

Design: Father Christmas, brownie.

Litho. & Engr.

1984, Nov. 30   **Perf. 12**
698 A367 1.10m multicolored   .80   .40

Common Law of 1734 — A368

1984, Dec. 6   **Perf. 14**
699 A368 2m Statute Book   .70   .70

25th Anniv. of EFTA — A369

1985, Feb. 2   **Litho.**
700 A369 1.20m multicolored   .50   .40

100th Anniv. of Society of Swedish Literature in Finland — A370

Design: Johan Ludvig Runeberg.

1985, Feb. 5   **Litho.**
701 A370 1.50m multicolored   .50   .35

Icon — A371

1985, Feb. 18   **Litho.**   **Perf. 11½x12**
702 A371 1.50m multicolored   .50   .40

Order of St. Sergei and St. Herman, 100th anniv.

150th Anniv. of Kalevala — A372

Designs: 1.50m, Pedri Shemeikka. 2.10m, Larin Paraske.

Litho. & Engr.

1985, Feb. 28   **Perf. 13x12½**
703 A372 1.50m multicolored   .50   .40
704 A372 2.10m multicolored   .70   .60

Mermaid and Sea Lions — A373

Litho. & Engr.

1985, May 15   **Perf. 13**
705 A373 1.50m multicolored   3.00   4.00

NORDIA 1985 philatelic exhibition, May 15-19. Sold for 10m, which included admission ticket.

A374

Finnish Banknote Cent.: banknotes of 1886, 1909, 1922, 1945 and 1955.

Photo. & Engr.

1985, May 18   **Perf. 11½**
706 A374   Booklet pane of 8   6.00   6.00
a.-   1.50m any single   .80   .60
h.
   Complete booklet, #706   6.00

A375

Europa: 1.50m, Children playing the recorder. 2.10m, Excerpt "Ramus Virens Olivarum" from the "Piae Cantiones," 1582.

1985, June 17   **Litho.**   **Perf. 13**
707 A375 1.50m multicolored   1.50   .40
708 A375 2.10m multicolored   4.00   1.00

Security Conference Type of 1975

1985, June 19   **Litho.**
709 A265 2.10m multicolored   .75   .60

European Security and Cooperation Conference, 10th Anniv.

Provincial Arms, Count's Seal — A376

1985, Sept. 5   **Litho.**   **Perf. 14**
710 A376 1.50m multicolored   .80   .35

Provincial Administration Established by Count Per Brahe, 350th Anniv.

Arms Type of 1975 and

Kerimaki Church A376a   Urho Kekkonen Natl. Park A376b

Tulip Damask Table Cloth, 18th Cent. A377   Postal Service A377a

Brown Bear — A377b

Perf. 11½, 13x12½ (2m)

1985-90   **Engr.**
711 A256 1.60m vermilion   .60   .60
712 A256 1.70m black   .60   .60
   a.   Bkt. pane, #558, 560, 2
      each #555, 556a, 712 + 2
      labels   9.00   11.00
      Complete booklet, #712a   10.00
713 A256 1.80m ol grn   .70   .60
   a.   Bkt. pane, 2 ea #555d,
      560a, 713b   3.50   3.00
      Complete booklet, #713a   3.50
   b.   Perf. 13x12½   1.00   .90
714 A256 1.90m brt orange   .70   .25
715 A256 2m blue grn,
      bklt. stamp   1.50   .70
   a.   Bkt. pane, #562a, 2 ea
      #715, 555d   7.00   7.00
      Complete booklet, #715a   7.00

Litho.   **Perf. 14**
716 A376a 2.20m multi   .80   .25
717 A376b 2.40m multi   .90   .40
718 A377 12m multi   4.00   .50

Litho. & Engr.
Perf. 13x12½
719 A377b 50m blk, grn & lt
      red brn   15.00   5.50
    Nos. 711-719 (9)   24.80   9.40

No. 712a contains two labels inscribed to publicize FINLANDIA '88.

Issued: 12m, 9/13/85; 1.60m, 1/2/86; 1.70m, 1/2/87; No. 712a, 8/10/87; 1.80m, 1/4/88; 2.20m, 2.40m, 1/20/88; No. 713b, 7/25/88; 1.90m, 1/2/89; 2m, 1/19/90; 50m, 8/30/89.

Booklet Stamps

No. 720, Telephone, mailbox. No. 721, Postal truck, transport plane. No. 722, Transport plane, fork lift. No. 723, Postman delivering letter. No. 724, Woman accepting letter.

Perf. 12½ on 3 Sides

1988, Feb. 1   **Litho.**
720 A377a 1.80m multi   .80   .40
721 A377a 1.80m multi   .60   .40
722 A377a 1.80m multi   .60   .40
723 A377a 1.80m multi   .60   .40
724 A377a 1.80m multi   .60   .40
   a.   Bkt. pane, 2 each #720-
      724   7.00   7.00
      Complete booklet, #724a   7.00
    Nos. 720-724 (5)   3.20   2.00

Nos. 721-722 and 723-724 printed se-tenant in continuous designs. No. 724c sold for 14m to households on mainland Finland. Each household entitled to buy 2 booklets at discount price from Feb. 1 to May 31, with coupon.

Miniature Sheet

Postal Map, 1698 — A378

Designs: a, Postman on foot. b, Postal Map, 1698. c, Sailing vessel, diff. d, Postrider, vert.

Litho. & Engr.

1985, Oct. 16   *Perf. 14*
728 A378   Sheet of 4   10.00   12.00
a.-d.   1.50m any single   2.50   3.00

FINLANDIA '88, 350th anniv. of Finnish Postal Service, founded in 1638 by Gov.-Gen. Per Brahe. Sheet sold for 8m.

Intl. Youth Year — A379

1985, Nov. 1   Litho.   *Perf. 13*
729 A379 1.50m multicolored   .50   .35

Christmas — A380

No. 730, Bird, tulips. No. 731, Cross of St. Thomas, hyacinths.

1985, Nov. 29   *Perf. 14*
730 A380 1.20m multicolored   1.10   .40
731 A380 1.20m multicolored   1.10   .40

Natl. Geological Society, Cent. — A390

1986, Feb. 8   Litho.   *Perf. 14*
732 A390 1.30m Orbicular granite   .60   .40
733 A390 1.60m Rapaviki   .70   .40
734 A390 2.10m Veined gneiss   .90   .60
   Nos. 732-734 (3)   2.20   1.40

Europa 1986 — A391

1.60m, Saimaa ringed seal. 2.20m, Environmental conservation.

1986, Apr. 10   *Perf. 12½x13*
735 A391 1.60m multicolored   1.50   .40
736 A391 2.20m multicolored   4.00   .80

Natl. Construction Year — A392

a, Conference Palace, Baghdad, 1982. b, Lahti Theater, 1983. c, Kuusamo Municipal Offices, 1978. d, Hamina Court Building, 1983. e, Finnish Embassy, New Delhi, 1986. f, Western Sakyla Daycare Center, 1980.

1986, Apr. 19   *Perf. 14*
737 A392   Booklet pane of 6   4.00   4.00
a.-f.   1.60m, any single   .70   .60
   Complete booklet, #737   4.00

Nordic Cooperation Issue 1986 — A393

Sister towns.

1986, May 27   Litho.   *Perf. 14*
738 A393 1.60m Joensuu   .50   .40
739 A393 2.20m Jyvaskyla   .70   .75

Souvenir Sheet

FINLANDIA '88 — A394

Postal ships: a, Iron paddle steamer Aura, Stockholm-St. Petersburg, 1858. b, Screw vessel Alexander, Helsinki-Tallinn-Lubeck, 1859. c, Steamship Nicolai, Helsinki-Tallinn-St. Petersburg, 1858. d, 1st Ice steamship Express II, Helsinki-Stockholm, 1877-98, vert.

Litho. & Engr.

1986, Aug. 29   *Perf. 13*
740 A394   Sheet of 4   10.00   10.00
a.-b.   1.60m, any single   2.50   2.50
c.-d.   2.20m, any single   2.50   2.50
   Sold for 10k.

Pierre-Louis Moreau de Maupertuis (1698-1759) A395

1986, Sept. 5   Litho.   *Perf. 12½x13*
741 A395 1.60m multicolored   .70   .40

Lapland Expedition, 250th anniv., proved Earth's poles are flattened. See France No. 2016.

Urho Kaleva Kekkonen (1900-86), Pres. — A396

1986, Sept. 30   Engr.   *Perf. 14*
742 A396 5m black   1.60   1.00

Intl. Peace Year — A397

1986, Oct. 13   Litho.   *Perf. 13*
743 A397 1.60m multicolored   .50   .40

A398

Christmas — A399

Photo. & Engr.

1986, Oct. 31   *Perf. 12*
744   1.30m Denomination at L   .70   .45
745   1.30m Denomination at R   1.20   .40
a.   A398 Pair, #744-745   2.00   2.00
746 A399 1.60m Elves   .80   .40
   Nos. 744-746 (3)   2.70   1.25

No. 745a has a continuous design.

Postal Savings Bank, Cent. — A400

1987, Jan. 2   Litho.   *Perf. 14*
747 A400 1.70m multicolored   .50   .40

Natl. Tourism, Cent. — A401

1987, Feb. 4   Litho.   *Perf. 14*
748 A401 1.70m Winter   .50   .40
749 A401 2.30m Summer   .70   .70

A402

1987, Feb. 4   *Perf. 14*
750 A402 1.40m multicolored   .50   .40

Metric system in Finland, cent.

A403

1987, Feb. 17   Litho.   *Perf. 14*
751 A403 2.10m multicolored   1.10   .50

Leevi Madetoja (1887-1947), composer.

European Wrestling Championships — A404

1987, Feb. 17
752 A404 1.70m multicolored   .60   .40

1987 World Bowling Championships — A405

1987, Apr. 13
753 A405 1.70m multicolored   .60   .40

Mental Health — A406

1987, Apr. 13
754 A406 1.70m multicolored   .50   .40

Souvenir Sheet

FINLANDIA '88 — A407

Locomotives and mail cars: a, Steam locomotive, 6-wheeled tender. b, 4-window mail car. c, 7-window mail car.

Litho. & Engr.

1987, May 8   *Perf. 12½x13*
755 A407   Sheet of 4   10.00   12.00
a.-c.   1.70m any single   2.50   3.00
d.   2.30m multicolored   2.50   3.00
   Sold for 10m.

Europa 1987 — A408

Modern architecture: 1.70m, Tampere Main Library, 1986, designed by Raili and Reima Pietila. 2.30m, Stoa Monument, Helsinki, c. 1981, by sculptor Hannu Siren.

1987, May 15   Litho.   *Perf. 13*
756 A408 1.70m multicolored   *1.50*   .40
757 A408 2.30m multicolored   *4.00*   1.00

Natl. Art Museum, Ateneum, Cent. — A409

Paintings: a, Strawberry Girl, by Nils Schillmark (1745-1804). b, Still-life on a Lady's Work Table, by Ferdinand von Wright (1822-1906). c, Old Woman with Basket, by Albert Edelfelt (1854-1906). d, Boy and Crow, by Akseli Gallen-Kallela (1865-1931). e, Late Winter, by Tyko Sallinen (1879-1955).

1987, May 15
758   Booklet pane of 5   6.00   6.00
a.-e.   A409 1.70m any single   1.20   .70
   Complete booklet, #758   6.00

A410

1987, Aug. 12   *Perf. 14*
759 A410 1.70m multicolored   .50   .40

European Physics Soc. 7th gen. conf., Helsinki, Aug. 10-14.

A411

1987, Oct. 12
760 A411 1.70m ultra, sil & pale
   lt gray   .60   .40

Size: 30x41mm
761 A411   10m dark ultra, lt
   blue & sil   3.50   1.20

Natl. independence, 70th anniv.

Ylppo, Child and Lastenlinna Children's Hospital — A412

1987, Oct. 27
762 A412 1.70m multicolored   .50   .40

Arvo Ylppo (b. 1887), pediatrics pioneer.

Christmas — A413

Design: 1.40m, Santa Claus, youths, horiz.

1987, Oct. 30
763 A413 1.40m multi   1.00   .40
764 A413 1.70m shown   1.00   .40

Finnish News Agency (STT), Cent. — A414

1987, Nov. 1
765 A414 2.30m multicolored   .80   .80

A415

1988, Jan. 5   Litho.   Perf. 14
766 A415 1.80m blk, chalky blue
& brt blue   .70 .40

Lauri "Tahko" Pihkala (1888-1981), promulgator of sports and physical education.

A416

1988, Mar. 14   Litho.
767 A416 1.40m multicolored   .50 .40

Meteorological Institute, 150th anniv.

Settlement of New Sweden in
America, 350th Anniv. — A417

Design: 17th Century European settlers
negotiating with 3 American Indians, map of
New Sweden, the Swedish ships Kalmar
Nyckel and Fogel Grip, based on an 18th cent.
illustration from a Swedish book about the
American Colonies.

Litho. & Engr.
1988, Mar. 29   Perf. 13
768 A417   3m multicolored   1.25 .80

See US No. C117 and Sweden No. 1672.

FINLANDIA '88, June 1-12, Helsinki
Fair Center — A418

Agathon Faberge (1876-1951), famed philatelist, & rarities from his collection.

Booklet Stamp
1988, May 2   Litho.   Perf. 13
769 A418 5m Pane of 1+2 labels   10.00 12.00
Complete booklet, #769   10.00

350th Anniv. of the Finnish Postal Service.
No. 769 sold for 30m to include the price of
adult admission to the exhibition.

Achievements of
Finnish Athletes at
the 1988 Winter
Olympics,
Calgary — A419

Design: Matti Nykanen, gold medalist in all 3
ski jumping events at the '88 Games.

1988, Apr. 6   Perf. 14
770 A419 1.80m multicolored   .60 .40

Europa
1988 — A420

Communication and transport: 2.40m,
Horse-drawn tram, 1890.

1988, May 23   Litho.   Perf. 13
771 A420 1.80m shown   1.50 .40
772 A420 2.40m multicolored   4.00 1.00

Souvenir Sheet

FINLANDIA '88 — A421

1st airmail flights: a, Finnish air force
Breguet 14 biplane transporting mail from Helsinki to Tallinn, Feb. 12, 1920. b, AERO
Junkers F-13 making 1st airmail night flight
from Helsinki to Copenhagen, May 15, 1930.
c, AERO Douglas DC-3, 1st intl. route, Helsinki-Norrkoping-Copenhagen-Amsterdam,
1947. d, Douglas DC 10-30, 1975-88, inauguration of Helsinki-Beijing route, June 2, 1988.

Litho. & Engr.
1988, June 2   Perf. 13½
773 A421 Sheet of 4   10.00 12.00
a.-c.   1.80m any single   2.50 3.00
d.   2.40m multicolored   2.50 3.00
Sold for 11m.

Turku Fire Brigade,
150th Anniv. — A422

Design: 1902 Horse-drawn, steam-driven
fire pump, preserved at the brigade.

1988, Aug. 15   Litho.   Perf. 14
774 A422 2.20m multicolored   .70 .55

A423

Missale Aboense, the 1st printed book in
Finland, 500th anniv.

1988, Aug. 17
775 A423 1.80m multicolored   .60 .40

A424

Finnish Postal Service, 350th Anniv.: No.
776, Postal tariff issued by Queen Christina of
Sweden, Sept. 6, 1638. No. 777, Postal cart,
c. 1880. #778, Leyland Sherpa 185 mail van,
1976. No. 779, Malmi P.O. interior. #780,
Skier using mobile telephone, c. 1970. No.
781, Telecommunications satellite in orbit.

Booklet Stamps
1988, Sept. 6   Litho.   Perf. 13
776 A424 1.80m multicolored   .80 .60
777 A424 1.80m multicolored   .80 .60
778 A424 1.80m multicolored   .80 .60
779 A424 1.80m multicolored   .80 .60
780 A424 1.80m multicolored   .80 .60
781 A424 1.80m multicolored   .80 .60
a.   Booklet pane of 6, #776-781   4.50 4.50
Complete booklet, #781a   4.50

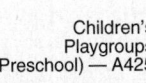

Children's
Playgroups
(Preschool) — A425

1988, Oct. 10   Perf. 14
782 A425 1.80m multicolored   .60 .40

Christmas — A426

1988, Nov. 4   Litho.
783 A426 1.40m multicolored   .80 .40
784 A426 1.80m multicolored   1.00 .40

Hameenlinna
Township, 350th
Anniv. — A427

Design: Market square, coat of arms and
17th century plan of the town.

1989, Jan. 19   Litho.
785 A427 1.90m multicolored   .80 .40

1989 Nordic Ski
Championships, Lahti,
Feb. 17-26 — A428

1989, Jan. 25
786 A428 1.90m multicolored   .80 .40

Salvation Army in
Finland, Cent. — A429

1989, Feb. 6   Litho.
787 A429 1.90m multicolored   .80 .40

Photography, 150th
Anniv. — A430

1.50m, Photographer, box camera, c.1900.

1989, Feb. 6
788 A430 1.50m brn, buff, cream   .60 .55

31st Intl. Physiology
Congress, Basel,
July 9-14 — A431

Design: Congress emblem, silhouettes of
Robert Tigerstedt and Ragnar Granit, eye,
flowmeter measuring flow of blood through
heart, color-sensitive retinal cells and
microelectrode.

1989, Mar. 2
789 A431 1.90m multicolored   .80 .40

Sports — A432

1989, Mar. 10   Booklet Stamps
790 A432 1.90m Skiing   .80 .40
791 A432 1.90m Jogging   .80 .40
792 A432 1.90m Cycling   .80 .40
793 A432 1.90m Canoeing   .80 .40
a.   Booklet pane of 4, #790-793   3.20 3.20
Complete booklet, #793a   3.20

Souvenir Sheet

Finnish
Kennel
Club,
Cent. —
A433

Dogs: a, Lapponian herder. b, Finnish spitz.
c, Karelian bear dog. d, Finnish hound.

1989, Mar. 17   Litho.   Perf. 14
794 A433 Sheet of 4   3.50 3.50
a.-d.   1.90m any single   .90 .60

Europa — A434

1989, Mar. 31   Perf. 13
795 A434 1.90m Hopscotch   1.50 .40
796 A434 2.50m Sledding   2.50 .65

A435

Nordic Cooperation Year: Folk Costumes.

1989, Apr. 20   Perf. 14
797 A435 1.90m Sakyla (man)   1.10 .45
798 A435 2.50m Veteli (woman)   1.10 .65

Finnish Pharmacies,
300th Anniv. — A436

Foxglove, distilling apparatus, mortar, flask.

1989, June 2   Litho.
799 A436 1.90m multicolored   .70 .35

A437

1989, June 2
800 A437 1.90m multicolored   .70 .35

Savonlinna Municipal Charter, 350th anniv.

Helsinki Zoo,
Cent. — A438

No. 801, Panthera uncia. No. 802, Capra
falconeri

1989, June 12
801 A438 1.90m multi   .70 .45
802 A438 2.50m multi   .80 .70

Vocational Training,
150th Anniv. — A439

Interparliamentary
Union, Cent. — A440

Council of Europe,
40th Anniv. — A441

1989, Sept. 4   Litho.   Perf. 14
803 A439 1.50m multicolored   .60 .70
804 A440 1.90m multicolored   .70 .35
805 A441 2.50m multicolored   .90 .70
Nos. 803-805 (3)   2.20 1.75

Admission of Finland to the Council of
Europe (2.50m).

A442

1989, Oct. 9 **Litho.**
806 A442 1.90m multicolored   .70 .35

Hannes Kolehmainen (1889-1966) winning the 5000-meter race at the Stockholm Olympics, 1912.

A443

1989, Oct. 20
807 A443 1.90m multicolored   .70 .35

Continuing Education in Finland, cent.

A444

Christmas: 1.90m, Sodankyla Church, Siberian jays in snow.

1989, Nov. 3
808 A444 1.50m shown   1.10 .40
809 A444 1.90m multicolored   1.10 .40

A445

1990, Jan. 19 Litho. Perf. 13x13½
810 A445 1.90m multicolored   .80 .80
811 A445 2.50m multicolored   .90 .90

Incorporation of the State Posts and Telecommunications Services.
Emblem of the corporation was produced by holography. Soaking may affect the design.

Musical Soc. of Turku and Finnish Orchestras, 200th Annivs. — A446

1990, Jan. 26   **Perf. 14**
812 A446 1.90m multicolored   1.10 .40

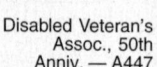

Disabled Veteran's Assoc., 50th Anniv. — A447

1990, Mar. 13   **Litho.**
813 A447 2m multicolored   .70 .35

End of the Winter (Russo-Finnish) War, 50th Anniv. — A448

1990, Mar. 13
814 A448 2m blue   .70 .35

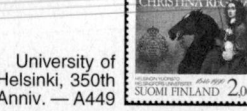

University of Helsinki, 350th Anniv. — A449

University crest and: 2m, Queen Christina on horseback. 3.20m, Degree ceremony procession in front of the main university building.

1990, Mar. 26   Litho.   Perf. 13
815 A449 2m multicolored   .70 .40
816 A449 3.20m multicolored   1.00 .70

Europa 1990 — A450

Post Offices: 2m, Lapp man, P.O. at Nuvvus, Mt. Nuvvus Ailigas. 2.70m, Turku main P.O.

1990, Mar. 26   **Perf. 12½x13**
817 A450 2m multicolored   2.00 .40
818 A450 2.70m multicolored   4.00 1.00

Rural Postal Service and Address Reform, Cent. — A451

1990, Apr. 19   Litho.   Perf. 13
819 A451 2m multicolored   .70 .35

"Ali Baba and the Forty Thieves" A452

"Story of the Great Musician" A453

"Story of the Giants, the Witches and the Daughter of the Sun" A454

"The Golden Bird, the Golden Horse and the Princess" A455

"Lamb Brother" A456

"The Snow Queen" A457

Fairy tale illustrations by Rudolf Koivu.

Booklet Stamps
Perf. 14 on 3 sides

1990, Aug. 29   **Litho.**
820 A452 2m multicolored   1.60 .65
821 A453 2m multicolored   1.60 .65
822 A454 2m multicolored   1.60 .65
823 A455 2m multicolored   1.60 .65
824 A456 2m multicolored   1.60 .65
825 A457 2m multicolored   1.60 .65
  a. Booklet pane of 6, #820-825   10.00 8.00
    Complete booklet, #825a   10.00

Souvenir Sheet

Horse Care A458

a, Feeding. b, Riding. c, Watering. d, Currying.

1990, Oct. 10   Litho.   Perf. 14
826 A458 Sheet of 4   3.50 3.50
  a.-d. 2m any single   .90 .60

Christmas — A459

1990, Nov. 2
827 A459 1.70m Santa's elves   1.00 .40
828 A459 2m Santa, reindeer   1.00 .40

Provincial Flowers

A460

A460a

A460b

A460c

A460d

A460e

A460f

A460g

A460h

A460i

A460j

A460k

2m, Wood anemone. 2.10m, Rowan. 2.70m, Heather. 2.90m, Sea buckthorn. 3.50m, Oak. No. 834, Globeflower. No. 835, Hepatica. No. 836, Iris. No. 838, Rosebay willowherb. No. 839, Labrador tea. No. 840, Karelian rose. No. 841, Daisy. No. 842, Water lily. No. 843, Bird cherry. No. 844, Harebell. No. 845, Cowslip.

1990-99   **Perf. 13x12½**
829 A460 2m multi   1.10 .25
830 A460 2.10m multi   .80 .25
831 A460 2.70m multi   1.40 .40
832 A460 2.90m multi   1.00 .40
833 A460 3.50m multi   1.20 .40
834 A460a 2 multi   2.50 .50
835 A460b 1 multi   3.00 .25
  Nos. 829-835 (7)   11.00 2.45

Self-Adhesive
Die Cut

836 A460c 2 multi   2.50 .50
  a. Booklet pane of 20   25.00 25.00
837 A460 2.10m like #830   .80 .40
838 A460d 1 multi   2.50 .35
839 A460e 1 multi   3.00 .25
  a. Booklet pane of 10   30.00 15.00
840 A460f 1 multi   3.00 .25
841 A460g 1 multi   3.00 .25
842 A460h 1 multi   3.00 .25
843 A460i 1 multi   3.00 .25
844 A460j 1 multi   3.00 .25
845 A460k 1 multi   3.00 .40
  Nos. 836-845 (10)   26.80 3.30

Issued: 2m, 2.70m, 1/19/90; No. 830, 2.90m, 3.50m, 2/5/90; 2.10m, 1991; Nos. 834-835, 3/2/92; No. 838, 10/9/92; No. 836, 3/1/93; No. 839, 6/14/93; No. 840, 5/5/94; No. 841, 3/15/95; No. 842, 6/3/96; No. 843, 3/18/97; No. 844, 3/12/98; No. 845, 4/28/99.
No. 834 sold for 1.60m, No. 836 sold for 1.90m, Nos. 835, 838 for 2.10m, Nos. 839-840 for 2.30m, Nos. 841-844 sold for 2.80m, No. 845 sold for 3m at time of release.
Nos. 837-838, 840-845 issued in sheets of 10. Nos. 836a and 839a were issued as complete booklets. The peelable backing serves as a booklet cover.
The numbers on the stamps represent the class of mail for which each was intended at time of release.

A461

1991, Mar. 1   **Perf. 14**
846 A461 2.10m multicolored   .70 .40

World Hockey Championships, Turku.

A462

1991, Mar. 1
847 A462 2.10m Cooking class   .60 .40

Home economics teacher education, cent.

Sauna Type of 1977 and

Birds — A463

No. 848, Great tit. No. 849, Wagtail. No. 850, Aegolius funereus. No. 850A, Phoenicurus phoenicurus. No. 851, Chaffinches. No. 852, Robin. No. 856, Bullfinch. No. 857, Waxwing. No. 859, Dendrocopos leucotos.

Perf. 13x12½, 14 (#861)
1991-99   **Litho.**
Booklet Stamps (#848-859)
848 A463 10p multi   .40 .25
849 A463 10p multi   .25 .25
850 A463 10p multi   .90 .40
850A A463 20p multi   3.00 2.00
851 A463 60p multi   3.00 .50
852 A463 60p multi   2.50 1.00
856 A463 2.10m multi   .70 .25
  a. Bklt. pane, #851, 2 each #848, 856   4.00 4.00
    Complete booklet, #856a   4.00
857 A463 2.10m multi   .80 .25
  a. Bklt. pane, #852, 2 each #849, 857   4.00 4.00
    Complete booklet, #857a   4.00
859 A463 2.30m multi   .80 .40
  a. Booklet pane of #850A, 2 each #850, #859 + 1 label   6.00 6.00
    Complete booklet, #859a   6.00

Sheet Stamp

861 A256a 4.80m multi   2.50 1.00
  Nos. 848-861 (10)   14.85 6.30

Issued: Nos. 848, 851, 856, 3/20/91; Nos. 849, 852, 857, 4/22/92; Nos. 850, 850A, 859, 6/4/93. 861, 7/1/99.
"SUOMI" is in upper left on Nos. 849, 852, 857.

Fishing — A464

Designs: a, Fly fisherman, trout. b, Perch, bobber. c, Crayfish, trap. d, Trawling for herring. e, Stocking powan.

1991, Mar. 20   **Perf. 14**
863 Booklet pane of 5   5.00 5.00
  a.-e. A464 2.10m any single   1.00 .40
    Complete booklet, #863   5.00

Tourism — A465

2.10m, Seurasaari Island. 2.90m, Steamship, Lake Saimaa.

1991, June 4   **Litho.**   **Perf. 14**
864 A465 2.10m multi   .80 .25
865 A465 2.90m multi   1.10 .70

Europa — A466

European map and: 2.10m, Human figures. 2.90m, Satellites, dish antennae.

1991, June 7   Litho.   Perf. 12½x13
866 A466 2.10m multicolored   2.00 .40
867 A466 2.90m multicolored   4.00 1.00

Alfred W. Finch (1854-1930) — A467

Designs: 2.10m, Iris, ceramic vase. 2.90m, Painting, The English Coast at Dover.

1991, Sept. 7   Litho.   Perf. 13
868 A467 2.10m multicolored   1.10 .40
869 A467 2.90m multicolored   2.00 1.20

See Belgium No. 1410.

Finnish Candy Industry, Cent. — A468

1991, Sept. 17   Photo.   Perf. 11½
870 A468 2.10m multicolored   .70 .50

Souvenir Sheets

Children's Stamp Designs — A469

a, Sun. b, Rainbow. c, Cows grazing.

1991, Sept. 17   Litho.   Perf. 13½
871 A469 Sheet of 3   2.40 2.40
a.-c.   2.10m any single   .80 .60

Skiing — A470

Color of skisuit: a, red. b, green. c, yellow. d, blue.

1991, Oct. 4   Perf. 14
872 A470 Sheet of 4   2.80 2.80
a.-d.   2.10m any single   .70 .50

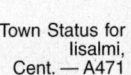

Town Status for Iisalmi, Cent. — A471

1991, Oct. 18   Litho.   Perf. 14
873 A471 2.10m multicolored   .70 .50

Christmas — A472

1.80m, Santa, animals carrying candles. 2.10m, Reindeer pulling Santa's sleigh.

1991, Nov. 1   Litho.   Perf. 14
874 A472 1.80m multi   1.00 .45
875 A472 2.10m multi, vert.   1.00 .45

Chemists' Club, Finnish Chemists' Society, Cent. — A473

1991, Nov. 1
876 A473 2.10m multi   .70 .40
877 A473 2.10m multi, diff.   .70 .40
a.   Pair, #876-877 + label   2.00 2.00

Second and third vertical branches merge while second and third branches below almost touch in the upper left part of camphor molecular structure on No. 877. Nos. 876-877 are designed to produce a three dimensional effect when viewed together.

1992 Olympic Games — A474

Designs: No. 878, Skier, Albertville. No. 879, Swimmer, Barcelona.

1992, Feb. 4   Litho.   Perf. 14
878 A474 2.10m multicolored   1.00 .40
879 A474 2.90m multicolored   1.20 .50

Expo '92, Seville — A475

1992, Mar. 20   Litho.   Perf. 14
880 A475 3.40m multicolored   1.20 .75

Conference on Security and Cooperation in Europe, Helsinki — A476

1992, Mar. 20   Perf. 14½x15
881 A476 16m multicolored   5.00 3.50

Town of Rauma, 550th Anniv. — A477

1992, Mar. 27   Perf. 14
882 A477 2.10m multicolored   1.20 .40

Healthy Brains — A478

1992, Mar. 27
883 A478 3.50m multicolored   1.10 .80

Discovery of America, 500th Anniv. — A479

Designs: No. 884, Santa Maria, map. No. 885, Map, Columbus.

1992, May 8   Litho.   Perf. 12½x13
884 A479 2.10m multicolored   1.50 .40
885 A479 2.10m multicolored   1.50 .40
a.   Pair, #884-885   3.50 3.50

Europa.

Finnish Technology — A480

Hologram of trees and: 2.10m, Drawing of blowing machine. 2.90m, Schematic of electronic circuits. 3.40m, Triangles and grid.

1992, May 8   Perf. 13x12½
886 A480 2.10m multicolored   1.10 .60
887 A480 2.90m multicolored   1.20 .75
888 A480 3.40m multicolored   1.50 1.00
Nos. 886-888 (3)   3.80 2.35

First Finnish patent granted, sesqui. (No. 886), Finnish chairmanship of Eureka (No. 887), Government Technology Research Center, 50th anniv. (No. 888).
Nos. 886-888 have holographic images. Soaking in water may affect the hologram.

Natl. Board of Agriculture, Cent. — A481

Design: Currant harvesting.

1992, June 4   Litho.   Perf. 14
889 A481 2.10m multicolored   .70 .40

Finnish Women — A482

No. 890, Aurora Karamzin (1808-1902), founder of Deaconesses' Institution of Helsinki. No. 891, Baroness Sophie Mannerheim (1863-1928), reformer of nursing education. No. 892, Laimi Leidenius (1877-1938), physician and educator. No. 893, Miina Sillanpaa (1866-1952), Minister for social affairs. No. 894, Edith Sodergran (1892-1923), poet. No. 895, Kreeta Haapasalo (1813-1893), folk singer.

Litho. & Engr.
1992, June 8   Perf. 14
Booklet Stamps
890 A482 2.10m multicolored   .80 .50
891 A482 2.10m multicolored   .80 .50
892 A482 2.10m multicolored   .80 .50
893 A482 2.10m multicolored   .80 .50
894 A482 2.10m multicolored   .80 .50
895 A482 2.10m multicolored   .80 .50
a.   Booklet pane of 6, #890-895   4.50 4.50
     Complete booklet, #895a   4.50

Child's Painting — A483

Independence, 75th Anniv. — A484

1992, Oct. 5   Litho.   Perf. 13
896 A483 2.10m multicolored   .70 .40

Souvenir Sheet
Perf. 13½
897 A484 2.10m multicolored   .70 .50

Nordia '93 — A485

Illustrations depicting "Moomin" characters, by Tove Jansson: No. 898, Winter scene, ice covered bridges. No. 899, Winter scene in forest. No. 900, Boats in water. No. 901, Characters on beach.

Perf. 13 on 3 Sides
1992, Oct. 9   Litho.
Booklet Stamps
898 A485 2.10m multicolored   2.00 .50
899 A485 2.10m multicolored   2.00 .50
900 A485 2.10m multicolored   2.00 .50
901 A485 2.10m multicolored   2.00 .50
a.   Booklet pane of 4, #898-901   8.00 8.00
     Complete booklet, #901a   8.00

A486

1992, Oct. 20   Litho.   Perf. 13
902 A486 2.10m multicolored   .70 .40

Printing in Finland, 350th anniv.

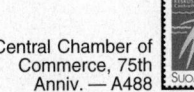

Christmas — A487

Designs: 1.80m, Church of St. Lawrence, Vantaa. 2.10m, Stained glass window of nativity scene, Karkkila Church, vert.

1992, Oct. 30   Litho.   Perf. 14
903 A487 1.80m multicolored   1.00 .45
904 A487 2.10m multicolored   1.00 .45

Central Chamber of Commerce, 75th Anniv. — A488

1993, Feb. 8   Litho.   Perf. 14
905 A488 1.60m multicolored   .50 .40

Friendship — A489

1993, Feb. 8   Litho.   Perf. 14
906 A489 1 multicolored   3.00 .40
a.   Booklet pane of 5 + label   14.00 7.50
     Complete booklet, 2 #906a   30.00

No. 906 sold for 2m at time of release. See note following No. 845.
See Estonia No. 237.

Alopex Lagopus — A490

a, Adult with winter white coat. b, Face, full view, winter white coat. c, Mother, kits, summer coat. d, Two on rock, summer coat.

1993, Mar. 19   Litho.   Perf. 12½x13
907 A490 Block of 4   4.00 4.00
a.-d.   2.30m Any single   1.00 .40

World Wildlife Fund.

Sculptures — A491

Europa: 2m, Rumba, by Martti Aiha. 2.90m, Complete Works, by Kari Caven.

1993, Apr. 26   Perf. 13
908 A491 2m multicolored   1.00 .40
909 A491 2.90m multicolored   2.50 1.00

Organized Philately in Finland, Cent. — A492

Design: Rosa pimpinellifolia.

1993, May 6   Perf. 13x12½
910 A492 2.30m multicolored   1.10 .70

Vyborg Castle, 700th Anniv. — A493

1993, May 6   **Perf. 13½**
911 A493 2.30m multicolored   .70 .25

Tourism — A494

1993, May 7   **Perf. 13x12½**
912 A494 2.30m Naantali   .80 .25
913 A494 2.90m Imatra   1.00 .50

550th anniv. of Naantali (No. 912).

A495

Independent Finland Defense Forces, 75th Anniv.: 2.30m, Finnish landscape in form of soldier's silhouette. 3.40m, UN checkpoint of Finnish battalion, Middle East.

1993, June 4   Litho.   Perf. 14
914 A495 2.30m multicolored   .70 .25
915 A495 3.40m multicolored   1.10 .80

A496

Art by Martta Wendelin (1893-1986): No. 916, Boy on skis, 1936. No. 917, Mother, daughter knitting, 1931. No. 918, Children building snowman, 1931. No. 919, Mother, children at fence, 1935. #920, Girl with lamb, 1936.

Booklet Stamps

1993, June 14   Litho.   Perf. 12½x13
916 A496 2.30m multicolored   1.30 .40
917 A496 2.30m multicolored   1.30 .40
918 A496 2.30m multicolored   1.30 .40
919 A496 2.30m multicolored   1.30 .40
920 A496 2.30m multicolored   1.30 .40
a.   Booklet pane of 5, #916-920   6.50 6.50
      Complete booklet, #920a   6.50

Water Birds A497

No. 921, Flock of gavia arctica. No. 922, Pair of gavia arctica. No. 923, Mergus merganser. No. 924, Anas platyrhynchos. No. 925, Mergus serrator.

Perf. 12½x13 on 3 or 4 Sides
1993, Sept. 20   Litho.
Booklet Stamps
921 A497 2.30m multicolored   1.00 .70
922 A497 2.30m multicolored   1.00 .70
      Size: 26x40mm
923 A497 2.30m multicolored   1.00 .70
924 A497 2.30m multicolored   1.00 .70
925 A497 2.30m multicolored   1.00 .70
a.   Booklet pane of 5, #921-925   5.00 5.00
      Complete booklet, #925a   5.00

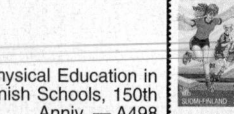

Physical Education in Finnish Schools, 150th Anniv. — A498

1993, Oct. 8   Perf. 14
926 A498 2.30m multicolored   .80 .25

New Opera House, Helsinki — A499

Operas and ballet: a, 2.30m, Ostrobothnians, by Leevi Madetoja. b, 2.30m, The Faun (four dancers), by Claude Debussy. c, 2.90m, Giselle, by Adolphe Adam. d, 3.40m, The Magic Flute, by Wolfgang Amadeus Mozart.

1993, Oct. 8   Perf. 13
927 A499   Sheet of 4   5.00 5.00
a.-b.   2.30m Either single   1.00 .80
c.   2.90m multi   1.50 1.50
d.   3.40m multi   1.50 2.00

Christmas — A500

Designs: 1.80m, Christmas tree, elves. 2.30m, Three angels.

1993, Nov. 5   Litho.   Perf. 14
928 A500 1.80m multi   1.00 .40
a.   Booklet pane of 10   12.00 12.00
      Complete booklet, #928a   12.00
929 A500 2.30m multi   1.00 .40

Pres. Mauno Koivisto, 70th Birthday — A501

1993, Nov. 25
930 A501 2.30m multicolored   .70 .40

Friendship — A502

Moomin characters: No. 931, Two standing. No. 932, Seven running.

1994, Jan. 27   Litho.   Perf. 12½x13
Booklet Stamps
931 A502 1 multicolored   3.00 .25
932 A502 1 multicolored   3.00 .25
a.   Bklt. pane, 4 each #931-932 24.00 12.00
      Complete booklet, #932a   24.00

Nos. 931-932 each sold for 2.30m at time of release. See note following No. 845.

Intl. Olympic Committee, Cent. — A503

Winter Olympics medalists from Finland: a, Marja-Liisa Kirvesniemi, Marjo Matikainen, cross-country skiing. b, Clas Thunberg, speed skating. c, Veikko Kankkonen, ski jumping. d, Veikko Hakulinen, cross-country skiing.

1994, Jan. 27   Perf. 13
933 A503 4.20m Sheet of 4, #a-d   6.00 6.00
      See No. 939.

A504

Waino Aaltonen (1894-1966), Sculptor — A505

1994, Mar. 8
934 A504 2m "Peace"   .80 .40
935 A505 2m "Muse"   .80 .40
a.   Pair, #934-935   1.60 1.60

Postal Service Civil Servants' Federation, Cent. — A506

1994, Mar. 11
936 A506 2.30m multicolored   .70 .45

Finnish Technology A507

Europa: 2.30m, Paper roll, nitrogen fixation, safety lock, ice breaker MS Fennica. 4.20m, Radiosonde, fishing lure, mobile phone, wind power plant.

1994, Mar. 18
937 A507 2.30m multicolored   2.00 .40
938 A507 4.20m multicolored   2.50 1.20

Olympic Athlete Type of 1994
Souvenir Sheet

Finnish athletes: a, Riitta Salin, Pirjo Haggman, runners. b, Lasse Viren, runner. c, Tiina Lillak, javelin thrower. d, Pentti Nikula, pole vaulter.

1994, May 5   Litho.   Perf. 13
939 A503 4.20m Sheet of 4, #a-d   6.00 6.00

European Track & Field Championships, Finlandia '95.

Finlandia '95, Helsinki A508

Coccinella septempunctata.

1994, May 10   Perf. 13½x13
940 A508 16m multicolored   8.00 8.00
      See Nos. 962, 1009.

Wildflowers — A509

Designs: a, Hypericum perforatum (b). b, Lychnis viscaria. c, Campanula rotundifolia. d, Campanula glomerata. e, Geranium sanguineum (d). f, Fragaria vesca. g, Veronica chamaedrys (f, h). h, Saxifraga granulata (c, i). i, Viola tricolor (j). j, Potentilla anserina.

1994, June 1   Perf. 12
941 A509 1 Sheet of 10   30.00 15.00
a.-j.   Any single   3.00 .40

No. 941 sold for 23m at time of release. See note following No. 845.

Finland-Sweden Track and Field Meet — A510

No. 942, Seppo Raty, Finland, javelin. No. 943, Patrick Sjoberg, Sweden, high jump.

1994, Aug. 26   Litho.   Perf. 12½
Booklet Stamps
942 A510 2.40m multicolored   1.50 .50
943 A510 2.40m multicolored   1.50 .50
a.   Booklet pane, 2 each #942-943 6.00 6.00
      Complete booklet, #943a   6.00

See Sweden Nos. 2091-2092.

Population Registers, 450th Anniv. — A511

1994, Sept. 1
944 A511 2.40m multicolored   1.20 .80

Intl. Year of the Family — A512

1994, Sept. 1
945 A512 3.40m multicolored   1.20 .80

Letter Writing Day A513

Dog Hill Kids in the Post Office: a, At Post Office window. b, Standing in doorway, mail cart. c, Blowing horn, pig. d, Putting letters in mailbox.

1994, Oct. 7   Litho.   Perf. 14
946 A513 2.80m Sheet of 4, #a-d   6.00 6.00

Christmas — A514

2.10m, Reindeer, bullfinches on antlers. 2.80m, Elves among snow-covered trees.

1994, Nov. 4
947 A514 2.10m multi   .80 .25
a.   Booklet pane of 10   15.00 15.00
      Complete booklet, #947a   15.00
948 A514 2.80m multi, vert.   1.00 .40

Greetings — A515

"Dog Hill Kids," sending/receiving greetings: No. 949, Delivering mail to Moon, spaceman. No. 950, Cat writing letter, clown. No. 951, Receiving mail from postman, baby. No. 952, Writing in bed, friend. No. 953, Winter scene at mailbox, characters at beach. No. 954, On bus, girl friend. No. 955, Standing at microphone with guitar, fan. No. 956, Baby in play pen, teddy bear.

Perf. 13 on 3 Sides
1995, Jan. 30   Litho.
Booklet Stamps
949 A515 2.80m multicolored   1.50 .60
950 A515 2.80m multicolored   1.50 .60
951 A515 2.80m multicolored   1.50 .60
952 A515 2.80m multicolored   1.50 .60
953 A515 2.80m multicolored   1.50 .60

954	A515	2.80m multicolored	1.50	.60
955	A515	2.80m multicolored	1.50	.60
956	A515	2.80m multicolored	1.50	.60
a.		Booklet pane, #949-956	12.00	12.00
		Complete booklet, 956a	12.00	

Nos. 949-952 are printed tete beche with Nos. 953-956. Soaking in water may affect the holographic images on Nos. 949-956.

Souvenir Sheet

Team Sports A516

a, Paivi Ikola, pesapallo. b. Jari Kurri, ice hockey. c, Jari Litmanen, soccer. d, Lea Hakala, basketball.

1995, Jan. 30 — Perf. 13

957	A516	3.40m Sheet of 4, #a-d	6.00	6.00

See No. 961.

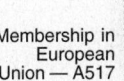

Membership in European Union — A517

1995, Jan. 30 — Perf. 14

958	A517	3.50m multicolored	1.20	.70

Peace & Liberty — A518

Europa: 2.90m, Stylized parachutists.

1995, Mar. 1 — Litho. — Perf. 14

959	A518	2.90m multicolored	2.50	.60

Endangered Species — A519

Designs: a, Felis lynx. b, Lake, forest. c, Rocks, lake. d, Pusa hispida.

1995, Mar. 1 — Perf. 13

960		Block of 4	4.75	4.75
a.-d.		A519 2.90m Any single	1.20	.90

Nos. 960a-960b, 960c-960d are continuous designs. See Russia No. 6249.

Athlete Type of 1995
Souvenir Sheet

Motor sports drivers in cars, on motorcycles: a, Timo Makinen. b, Juha Kankkunen. c, Tommi Ahvala. d, Heikki Mikkola.

1995, May 10 — Litho. — Perf. 13

961	A516	3.50m Sheet of 4, #a.-d.	8.00	8.00

Insect Type of 1994
1995, May 11

962	A508	19m Geotrupes stercorarius	9.00	9.00

Tourism — A520

Designs: 2.80m, Linnanmaki amusement park, Helsinki. 2.90m, Town of Mantyharju.

1995, May 12

963	A520	2.80m multicolored	1.00	.50
964	A520	2.90m multicolored	1.20	.70

Town of Loviisa, 250th Anniv. — A521

1995, June 30 — Litho. — Perf. 14

965	A521	3.20m multicolored	1.20	1.00

Intl. Union of Forestry Research Organizations, 20th World Congress, Tampere — A522

Designs: No. 966, Betula pendula. No. 967, Pinus sylvestris. No. 968, Picea abies. No. 969, Research, tree grown from needle.

Perf. 14 on 2 or 3 Sides
1995, Aug. 8 — Litho.
Booklet Stamps

966	A522	2.80m multicolored	2.50	.50
967	A522	2.80m multicolored	2.50	.50
968	A522	2.80m multicolored	2.50	.50
969	A522	2.80m multicolored	1.25	.50
a.		Booklet pane of 4, #966-969	10.00	10.00
		Complete booklet, #969a	10.00	

Wilhelm Roentgen (1845-1923), Discovery of the X-Ray, Cent. — A523

1995, Aug. 8 — Perf. 14

970	A523	4.30m multicolored	1.50	1.00

Cats — A525

Designs: No. 972, Somali. No. 973, Siamese. No. 974, Norwegian forest. No. 975, Persian. No. 976, European domestic female. No. 977, Three kittens, frog.

1995, Oct. 9 — Litho. — Perf. 13½

972	A525	2.80m multi	1.50	.60
973	A525	2.80m multi	1.50	.60
974	A525	2.80m multi	1.50	.60
975	A525	2.80m multi	1.50	.60

Size: 59x35mm

976	A525	2.80m multi	1.50	.60
977	A525	2.80m multi	1.50	.60
a.		Booklet pane of 6, #972-977	9.00	
		Complete booklet, #977a	9.00	

UN, 50th Anniv. — A526

1995, Oct. 20 — Perf. 14

978	A526	3.40m multicolored	1.20	.60

A527

Christmas — A528

1995, Nov. 3 — Litho. — Perf. 14

979	A527	2m Santa on skates	1.10	.25
980	A528	2.80m Poinsettias	1.10	.60

Letter Stamps — A529

1996, Feb 2 — Litho. — Perf. 13½x14
Booklet Stamps

981	A529	1m "M"	.50	.50
982	A529	1m "O"	.50	.50
983	A529	1m "I"	.50	.50
984	A529	1m "H"	.50	.50
985	A529	1m "E"	.50	.50
986	A529	1m "J"	.50	.50
987	A529	1m "A"	.50	.50
988	A529	1m "N"	.50	.50
989	A529	1m "T"	.50	.50
990	A529	1m "P"	.50	.50
991	A529	1m "U"	.50	.50
992	A529	1m "S"	.50	.50
a.		Booklet pane of 12, #981-992	6.00	6.00
		Complete booklet, No. 992a	6.00	

UNICEF, 50th Anniv. — A530

1996, Feb. 2 — Perf. 14

993	A530	2.80m multicolored	.90	.55

Women's Gymnastics in Finland, Cent. — A531

1996, Feb. 26 — Litho. — Perf. 13

994	A531	2.80m multicolored	.90	.55

Woman Suffrage, 90th Anniv. — A532

Litho. & Engr.
1996, Mar. 8 — Perf. 13

995	A532	3.20m multicolored	2.50	.75

Europa.

Cinema, Cent. — A533

Finnish films: No. 996, "Juha," 1937. No. 997, "Laveata Tieta," 1931. No. 998, "Tuntematon Sotilas," 1935. No. 999, Oldest known photo of a motion picture show, 1896. No. 1000, "Jäniksen Vuosi," 1977. No. 1001, "Valkoinen Peura," 1952. No. 1002, "Kaikki Rakastavat," 1935. No. 1003, "Varjoja Paratiisissa," 1986.

1996, Apr. 1 — Litho. — Perf. 14x13½
Booklet Stamps

996	A533	2.80m multicolored	1.50	.60
997	A533	2.80m multicolored	1.50	.60
998	A533	2.80m multicolored	1.50	.60
999	A533	2.80m multicolored	1.50	.60
1000	A533	2.80m multicolored	1.50	.60
1001	A533	2.80m multicolored	1.50	.60
1002	A533	2.80m multicolored	1.50	.60
1003	A533	2.80m multicolored	1.50	.60
a.		Bkt. pane of 8, #996-1003	12.00	10.00
		Complete booklet, #1003a	12.00	

Radio, Cent. — A534

1996, Apr. 25 — Perf. 14

1004	A534	4.30m multicolored	1.40	1.10

1996 Summer Olympic Games, Atlanta — A535

1996, June 3 — Litho. — Perf. 12 Vert.
Booklet Stamps

1005	A535	3.40m Kayaking	1.50	1.00
1006	A535	3.40m Sailing	1.50	1.00
1007	A535	3.40m Rowing	1.50	1.00
1008	A535	3.40m Swimming	1.50	1.00
a.		Booklet pane of 4, #1005-1008	6.00	6.00
		Complete booklet, #1008a	6.00	

Insect Type of 1994

1996, July 1 — Litho. — Perf. 13

1009	A508	19m Dytiscus marginalis	9.00	9.00

Shore Birds — A536

No. 1010, Gallinago gallinago. No. 1011, Haematopus ostralegus. No. 1012, Scolopax rusticola. No. 1013, Vanellus vanellus. No. 1014, Numenius arquata.

Perf. 13½ on 3 Sides
1996, Sept. 6 — Litho. & Engr.

1010	A536	2.80m multicolored	1.50	.80
1011	A536	2.80m multicolored	1.50	.80
1012	A536	2.80m multicolored	1.50	.80
1013	A536	2.80m multicolored	1.50	.80

Size: 30x52mm

1014	A536	2.80m multicolored	1.50	.80
a.		Sheet of 5, #1010-1014	6.00	6.00

Finnish Comic Strips — A537

No. 1015, "Professor Itikainen" examining plant with magnifying glass, by Ilmari Vainio. No. 1016, "Pekka Puupää (Peter Blockhead)" taking letter from mailbox, by Ola Fogelberg. No. 1017, "Joonas" holding drawing pencil, by Veikko Savolainen. No. 1018, "Mämmilä" wearing helmet, by Tarmo Koivisto. No. 1019, "Rymy-Eetu" smoking pipe, by Erkki Tanttu. No. 1020, "Kieku" writing letter, by Asmo Alho. No. 1021, "Pikku Risunen" with animal, by Riitta Uusitalo. No. 1022, "Kiti" holding up pencil, by Kati Kovács.

1996, Oct. 9 — Litho. — Perf. 13½
Booklet Stamps

1015	A537	2.80m black & red	1.50	1.00
1016	A537	2.80m black & red	1.50	1.00
1017	A537	2.80m red & black	1.50	1.00
1018	A537	2.80m black & red	1.50	1.00
1019	A537	2.80m black & red	1.50	1.00
1020	A537	2.80m red & black	1.50	1.00
1021	A537	2.80m red & black	1.50	1.00
1022	A537	2.80m red & black	1.50	1.00
a.		Bkt. pane of 8, #1015-1022	12.00	12.00
		Complete booklet, #1022a	12.00	

Christmas — A538

2m, Snowman, Santa, gnome playing musical instruments. 2.80m, Rabbit, reindeer watching northern lights. 3.20m, Santa reading letters.

1996, Nov. 1 — Litho. — Perf. 14

1023	A538	2m multi	1.00	.40
1024	A538	2.80m multi	1.00	.40
1025	A538	3.20m multi, vert.	1.50	1.00
		Nos. 1023-1025 (3)	3.50	1.80

Greetings
Stamps — A539

Sticker designs from end of 19th cent.: No. 1026, Two angels. No. 1027, Flowers in basket. No. 1028, Hand reaching through garland, bluebird. No. 1029, Boy, girl dancing. No. 1030, Boy, envelope, shamrocks. No. 1031, Clasping hands through heart-shaped garlands. No. 1032, Roses. No. 1033, Angel.

Perf. 13x12½ on 3 Sides
1997, Jan. 30   Litho.
Booklet Stamps

1026	A539	1 multicolored	3.00	1.00
1027	A539	1 multicolored	3.00	1.00
1028	A539	1 multicolored	3.00	1.00
1029	A539	1 multicolored	3.00	1.00
1030	A539	1 multicolored	3.00	1.00
1031	A539	1 multicolored	3.00	1.00
1032	A539	1 multicolored	3.00	1.00
1033	A539	1 multicolored	3.00	1.00
a.		Bkt. pane of 8, #1026-1033	24.00	12.00
		Complete booklet, #1033a	24.00	

Nos. 1026-1033 sold for 2.80m on day of issue.
Number on stamp represents class of mail.

Mail Order Sales in
Finland,
Cent. — A540

1997, Jan. 30   **Perf. 13½x14**
1034 A540 2.80m multicolored   .90 .40

1997 Ice Hockey World
Championships,
Helsinki — A541

1997, Jan. 30
1035 A541 2.80m multicolored   .90 .40

On each stamp from the right vertical row of the sheet, No. 1035 exists without the thin, curved black line at the center right edge of the stamp. Value, single stamp $3.00.

Lepus
Timidus — A542

1997, Mar. 4   **Litho.**   **Perf. 14**
1036 A542 2.80m multicolored   .90 .40

Saami Folktale,
"Girl Who Turned
into a Golden
Merganser"
A543

Europa: 3.20m, Duck, girl, prince. 3.40m, Girl falling into crevice.

1997, Mar. 4   **Perf. 13**
1037 A543 3.20m multicolored   2.00 .50
1038 A543 3.40m multicolored   3.00 1.00

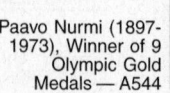

Paavo Nurmi (1897-
1973), Winner of 9
Olympic Gold
Medals — A544

1997, Mar. 18   **Perf. 14**
1039 A544 3.40m multicolored   1.20 .60

Southwest
Archipelago Natl.
Park — A545

Litho. & Engr.
1997, Apr. 25   **Perf. 14**
1040 A545 4.30m multicolored   1.75 .70

Tango — A546

1997, May 19   **Litho.**
1041 A546 1 multicolored   3.00 .40
     Complete booklet of 5   12.50

No. 1041 sold for 2.80m on day of release. Number on stamp represents class of mail.

A547

Sailing Ships: No. 1042, Astrid. No. 1043, Jacobstads Wapen. No. 1044, Tradewind. No. 1045, Merikokko. No. 1046, Suomen Joutsen. No. 1047, Sigyn.

Booklet Stamps
1997, May 19   **Perf. 13½**
1042 A547 2.80m multicolored   1.50 1.00
1043 A547 2.80m multicolored   1.50 1.00
1044 A547 2.80m multicolored   1.50 1.00
1045 A547 2.80m multicolored   1.50 1.00
     Size: 48x25½mm
1046 A547 2.80m multicolored   1.50 1.00
1047 A547 2.80m multicolored   1.50 1.00
a.   Booklet pane of 6, #1042-1047   9.00
     Complete booklet, #1047a   9.00

Pres. Martti
Ahtisaari, 60th
Birthday — A548

1997, June 23   **Litho.**   **Perf. 14**
1048 A548 2.80m multicolored   .90 .40

Independence, 80th
Anniv. — A549

Four seasons: No. 1049, Spring, lily-of-the-valley (natl. flower). No. 1050, Summer, white clouds. No. 1051, Fall, colorful leaves. No. 1052, Winter, snow crystals.

Perf. 13x12½ on 2 or 3 Sides
1997, June 23   **Booklet Stamps**
1049 A549 2.80m multicolored   1.50 1.00
1050 A549 2.80m multicolored   1.50 1.00
1051 A549 2.80m multicolored   1.50 1.00
1052 A549 2.80m multicolored   1.50 1.00
a.   Booklet pane, #1049-1052   6.00 6.00
     Complete booklet, #1052a   6.00

Souvenir Sheet

A550

Grus Grus (Cranes): a, With young. b, With frog. c, Performing mating dance. d, In flight.

1997, Aug. 19   **Litho.**   **Perf. 14**
1053 A550 2.80m Sheet of 4,
         #a.-d.   6.00 6.00

A551

Finnish Writers Assoc. (Covers from books): No. 1054, "Seven Brothers," by Aleksis Kivi. No. 1055, "Sinuhe the Egyptian," by Mika Waltari. No. 1056, "Täällä Pohjantähden alla

---

I," by Väinö Linna. No. 1057, "Hyvästi lijoki," by Kalle Päätalo. No. 1058, "Haukka, minum rakkaani," by Kaari Utrio. No. 1059, "Juhannustanssit," by Hannu Salama. No. 1060, "Manillaköysi," by Veijo Meri. No. 1061, "Uppo-Nalle ja Kumma," by Elina Karjalainen.

Booklet Stamps
1997, Oct. 9   **Litho.**   **Perf. 14¼, 14½**
1054 A551 2.80m multicolored   1.50 .60
1055 A551 2.80m multicolored   1.50 .60
1056 A551 2.80m multicolored   1.50 .60
1057 A551 2.80m multicolored   1.50 .60
1058 A551 2.80m multicolored   1.50 .60
1059 A551 2.80m multicolored   1.50 .60
1060 A551 2.80m multicolored   1.50 .60
1061 A551 2.80m multicolored   1.50 .60
a.   Booklet pane, #1054-1061   12.00 8.00
     Complete booklet, #1061a   12.00

No. 1056 exists perf 14½x14¼. The other values also should exist thus. The editors would like to examine such stamps.

Christmas — A552

Designs: 2m, Village. 2.80m, Candelabra, vert. 3.20m, Church, vert.

1997, Oct. 31
1062 A552   2m multi   1.00 .40
1063 A552 2.80m multi   1.00 1.00
1064 A552 3.20m multi   1.25 1.80
     Nos. 1062-1064 (3)   3.25 3.20

Wildlife — A553

2nd, Stizostedion lucioperca. 1st, Turdus merula.

Die Cut Perf. 10 Horiz. Syncopated
1998, Jan. 15   **Litho.**
     Self-Adhesive
     Coil Stamps
1065 A553 2 multicolored   2.50 .60
1066 A553 1 multicolored   3.00 1.00

Nos. 1065-1066 were valued at 2.40m and 2.80m, respectively, on date of issue. Number on stamp represents class of mail.
See Nos. 1099-1100.

A554

Moomin Cartoon Characters, by Tove Jansson: No. 1067, Boy Moomin drawing with pad and pencil. No. 1068, Girl Moomin in sunshine. No. 1069, Organ grinder. No. 1070, Boy Moomin giving flower to girl Moomin.

1998, Jan. 15   **Perf. 13 on 3 Sides**
     Booklet Stamps
1067 A554 1 multicolored   2.90 .60
1068 A554 1 multicolored   2.90 .60
1069 A554 1 multicolored   2.90 .60
1070 A554 1 multicolored   2.90 .60
a.   Booklet pane, #1067-1070   12.00 8.00
     Complete booklet, #1070a   12.00

Nos. 1067-1070 each sold for 2.80m on day of issue. Number on stamp represents class of mail.
See No. 1127.

A555

1998, Feb. 3   **Perf. 14**
1071 A555 2.80m multicolored   .90 .40
   Finnish Federation of Nurses, cent.

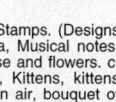

A556

Valentine's Day Surprise Stamps. (Designs beneath scratch-off heart): a, Musical notes, two dogs. b, Elephant, mouse and flowers. c, Puppy, sealed envelope. d, Kittens, kittens hugging. e, Dog with nose in air, bouquet of flowers. f, Flowers, two rodents.

1998, Feb. 3   **Perf. 12**
1072   1 Sheet of 6   18.00 9.00
a.-f.   A556 Any single, un-
       scratched   3.00 .70

Nos. 1072a-1072f were each valued at 2.80m on day of issue. Number on stamp represents class of mail. Unused values are for singles with attached selvage. Inscriptions are shown in selvage above or below each stamp. Each stamp bears a heart-shaped, golden scratch-off overlay. Values are for unscratched examples. Scratched stamps, with hearts partially or fully removed, sell for about 20 percent less.

Tussilago Farfara — A557

1998, Mar. 27   **Litho.**   **Perf. 14**
1073 A557 2.80m multi   .90 .40

National
Festivals — A558

Europa: 3.20m, Boy and girl, balloons, "Vappu" (May Day). 3.40m, Boy and girl in a dream floating over water, Midsummer Festival.

1998, Mar. 27   **Perf. 14x14½**
1074 A558 3.20m multicolored   1.50 .80
1075 A558 3.40m multicolored   2.00 1.50

Finnish Marine
Research Institute,
80th Anniv. — A559

Designs: 2.80m, Research vessel, "Aranda." 3.20m, "Vega," chart showing route of Nils Adolf Erik Nordenskjold's expedition.

Litho. & Engr.
1998, May 7   **Perf. 14x13**
1076 A559 2.80m multicolored   1.00 .70
1077 A559 3.20m multicolored   1.50 1.00

First Performance
of National
Anthem, 150th
Anniv. — A560

1998, May 7   **Perf. 13**
1078 A560 5m multicolored   2.00 1.00

Puppies — A561

No. 1079, Bernese Mountain dog. No. 1080, Puli. No. 1081, Boxer. No. 1082, Bichon Frisé. No. 1083, Finnish lapphound. No. 1084, Wire-haired dachshund. No. 1085, Scottish cairn terrier. No. 1086, Labrador retriever.

Perf. 13½x13 on 2 or 3 Sides
1998, June 4 Litho.
Booklet Stamps
1079	A561	1 multicolored	3.00	.50
1080	A561	1 multicolored	3.00	.50
1081	A561	1 multicolored	3.00	.50
1082	A561	1 multicolored	3.00	.50
1083	A561	1 multicolored	3.00	.50
1084	A561	1 multicolored	3.00	.50
1085	A561	1 multicolored	3.00	.50
1086	A561	1 multicolored	3.00	.50
a.		Booklet pane, #1079-1086	24.00	12.00
		Complete booklet, #1086a	24.00	

Nos. 1079-1086 each sold for 2.80m on day of issue. Number on stamp represents class of mail.

Owls
A562

Designs: a, Bubo bubo. b, Wing of bubo bubo. c, Bubo bubo, aegolius funereus. d, Strix nebulosa. e, Nyctea scandiaca.

1998, Sept. 4 Litho. *Perf. 13½*
1087	A562	Sheet of 5 + label	7.50	7.50
a.-e.		3m any single	1.50	.80

No. 1087b is 52x27mm; Nos. 1087c-1087d, 26x44mm; No. 1087e, 30x44mm.
See No. 1113.

Cycling — A563

1998, Sept. 4 *Perf. 14*
1088	A563	3m multicolored	1.00	.40

Finnish Design A564

No. 1089, Savoy vases, by Alvar Aalto. No. 1090, Karuselli chair, by Yrjö Kukkapuro. No. 1091, Tasaraita knitwear, designed by Annika Rimala for Marimekko. No. 1092, Kilta tableware set, by Kaj Franck. No. 1093, Cast iron pot, by Timo Sarpaneva. No. 1094, Carelia cutlery set, by Bertel Gardberg.

Perf. 13½ on 3 Sides
1998, Oct. 9 Litho.
Booklet Stamps
1089	A564	3m multicolored	1.50	.80
1090	A564	3m multicolored	1.50	.80
1091	A564	3m multicolored	1.50	.80
1092	A564	3m multicolored	1.50	.80
1093	A564	3m multicolored	1.50	.80
1094	A564	3m multicolored	1.50	.80
a.		Booklet pane, #1089-1094	7.50	7.50
		Complete booklet, #1094a	7.50	

Nos. 1090-1091, 1093-1094 are 29x34mm.

Christmas — A565

Designs: 2m, Christmas tree, children, vert. 3m, Children, dog riding sled. 3.20m, Winter scene of cottage in center of island.

1998, Oct. 30 *Perf. 14*
1095	A565	2m multicolored	1.00	.40
1096	A565	3m multicolored	1.00	.50
1097	A565	3.20m multicolored	1.20	.70
		Nos. 1095-1097 (3)	3.20	1.60

Souvenir Sheet

Mika Häkkinen, Formula 1 Driving Champion — A566

1999, Jan. 15 *Perf. 13½*
1098	A566	3m multicolored	1.50	1.50

Native Wildlife Type of 1998

2, Salmo salar. 1, Luscinia svecica.

Coil Stamps
Die Cut Perf. 10 Horiz. Syncopated
1999, Jan. 27 Litho.
Self-Adhesive
1099	A553	2 multi	2.50	.40

Die Cut Perf. 10 Vert. Syncopated
1100	A553	1 multi, vert.	3.00	.40

Nos. 1099-1100 were valued at 2.40m and 3m, respectively, on day of issue. Number on stamp represents class of mail.

Friendship — A567

Animals' tails: No. 1101, Zebra, lion. No. 1102, Dog, cat.

Booklet Stamps
Serpentine Die Cut Perf. 13 Horiz.
1999, Jan. 27 Self-Adhesive
1101	A567	3m multicolored	1.20	.50
1102	A567	3m multicolored	1.20	.50
a.		Bklt. pane, 3 each #1101-1102	7.25	7.25

No. 1102a is a complete booklet.

Finnish Labor Movement, Cent. — A568

1999, Jan. 27 *Perf. 13½*
1103	A568	4.50m multicolored	1.50	1.00

Finland's Roads — A569

No. 1104, Snow-covered landscape, Arctic Ocean Road. No. 1105, Freeway interchanges, Jyväsjtkä Lakeshore Road. No. 1106, Raippaluoto Bridge. No. 1107, Wooded drive, Kitee.

1999, Feb. 15 Litho. *Perf. 14 Horiz.*
Booklet Stamps
1104	A569	3m multicolored	1.50	1.00
a.		Perf. 12¾ horiz.	50.00	10.00
1105	A569	3m multicolored	1.50	1.00
a.		Perf. 12¾ horiz.	50.00	10.00
1106	A569	3m multicolored	1.50	1.00
a.		Perf. 12¾ horiz.	50.00	10.00
1107	A569	3m multicolored	1.50	1.00
a.		Booklet pane, #1104-1107	6.00	
		Complete booklet, #1107a	6.00	
b.		Perf. 12¾ horiz.	50.00	10.00
c.		Booklet pane, #1104a, 1105a, 1106a, 1107b	200.00	200.00
		Complete booklet, #1107c	200.00	

A570

Women's Kalevala-style brooches: a, Horse clasp. b, Bird clasp. c, Virusmäki clasp.

1999, Feb. 15 *Perf. 13½x14*
1108		Sheet of 3	4.50	4.50
a.-c.		A570 3m any single	1.50	.80

1st Publication of Legend of the Kalevala, 150th Anniv.

Crocus Vernus — A571

1999, Mar. 15 *Perf. 13x13½*
1109	A571	3m multi	.90	.50

Martha Organization, Cent. — A572

1999, Mar. 15 *Perf. 13½x13*
1110	A572	3m multicolored	1.00	.50

Europa — A573

Designs: 2.70m, Esplanade Park. 3.20m, Ruissalo Park.

1999, Mar. 15 *Perf. 13½x14*
1111	A573	2.70m multi	1.50	1.20
1112	A573	3.20m multi	2.50	1.50

Bird Type of 1998

Designs: a, Luscinia luscinia. b, Cuculus canorus. c, Botaurus stellaris. d, Caprimulgus europaeus. e, Crex crex.

1999, May 18 *Perf. 13½*
1113		Sheet of 5 + label	6.00	6.00
a.-e.		A562 3m any single	1.20	.75

No. 1113b is 25x43mm. No. 1113c is 45x30mm. No. 1113d-1113e are 26x37mm.

Finland's Presidency of European Union — A574

1999, July 1 Litho. *Perf. 13¾x13½*
1114	A574	3.50m multicolored	1.10	.60

Finnish Entertainers — A575

a, Harmony Sisters, Vera (1914-97), Maire (1916-95) & Raija (1918-97) Valtonen. b, Olavi Virta (1915-72), singer. c, Georg Malmstén (1902-81), composer, conductor. d, Topi Kärki (1915-22), composer, and Reino (Repe) Helismaa (1913-65), lyricist. e, Tapio Rautavaara (1915-79), singer. f, Esa Parkarinen (1911-89), musician, actor.

Perf. 13¼ on 3 Sides
1999, Sept. 6 Litho.
1115	A575	Booklet pane of 6		9.00
a.-f.		3.50m any single	1.50	1.00
		Complete booklet, #1115		9.00

Nos. 1115a, 1115d are each 60x34mm.

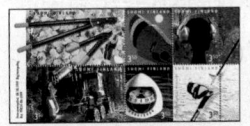
Finnish Commercial Product Design — A576

a, Fiskars cutting tools. b, Zoel/Versoul guitars. c, Ergo II/Silenta hearing protectors. d,

Ponsse Cobra HS 10 tree harvester. e, Suunto compass. f, Exel Avanti QLS ski pole.

Perf. 13¼ on 3 Sides
1999, Oct 8 Litho.
1116	A576	Booklet pane of 6		7.00
a.-f.		3.50m any single	1.20	1.00
		Complete booklet, #1116		7.00

Size of b, c, e, f: 30x35mm.

"The Nativity," by Giorgio di Chirico (1888-1978) A577
Rabbits, Birds A578

Design: 2.50m, Santa Claus, vert.

1999, Nov. 5 *Perf. 14*
1117	A578	2.50m multicolored	.90	.40
1118	A577	3m multicolored	1.20	1.20
1119	A578	3.50m multicolored	1.60	1.20
		Nos. 1117-1119 (3)	3.70	2.20

Christmas. See Italy Nos. 2314-2315.

Sveaborg Fortress — A579

2000, Jan. 12 Litho. *Perf. 13¾x13½*
1120	A579	7.20m multi	3.00	1.50

Helsinki, 450th Anniv. — A580

Designs: No. 1121, Baltic herring market (designer's name at UL).
No. 1122: a, Museum of Contemporary Art (blue building), vert. b, Cathedral, Senate Square (green building). c, Finlandia Hall (orange building). d, Glass Palace Film and Media Center (red building), vert.
No. 1123: a, Quest for the Lost Crown, Sveaborg Fortress (children and arch), vert. b, Like No. 1121, no designer's name. c, Forces of Light City Festival. d, Cellist at outdoor concert, Kaivopuisto Park.

2000, Jan. 12 *Perf. 14*
1121	A580	3.50m multi	1.10	.60

Perf. 14½x14¾ (vert. stamps), 14¾x14½
1122		Booklet pane of 4	8.00	8.00
a.-d.		A580 3.50m any single	2.00	2.00
1123		Booklet pane of 4	8.00	8.00
a.-d.		A580 3.50m Any single	2.00	2.00
		Complete booklet, #1122-1123	16.00	

Valentine's Day — A581

Designs: a, Earth as backpack. b, Painters on ladder. c, Birds in balloon. d, Alien with magnet. e, Boy with heart-shaped balloon. f, Polar bear and igloo.

Perf. 13x12¾ on 3 sides
2000, Jan. 12
1124		Bklt. pane of 6 + 4 labels		9.00
a.-f.		A581 3.50m Any single	1.50	1.00
		Complete booklet, #1124		9.00

Souvenir Sheet of 2

Tommi Mäkinen, 1999 Rally World Champion — A582

a, Mäkinen behind wheel. b, Race car.

2000, Mar. 3   **Perf. 13x13¼**
1125 A582 3.50m #a.-b.   3.00   3.00

Caltha Palustris — A583

2000, Mar. 15   **Perf. 13¾x13¼**
1126 A583 3.50m multi   1.10   .60

Easter.

Moomin Type of 1998

a, Rat with broom looking at Moomins. b, Moomin with uniform, figures sprouting from ground. c, Moomin with hat in forest. d, Moomin with hat, children, in front of stove.

Perf. 13x12¾ on 3 Sides
2000, Mar. 15
1127   Booklet pane of 4   24.00 24.00
  a.-d. A554 1 Any single   6.00   1.00
    Complete booklet, #1127   30.00 12.00
  e.   As #1127, perf. 13¼ on 3
    sides   12.00
  f.-i.   As #a-d, perf. 13¼ on 3 sides   3.00   .70
    Booklet, #1127e   12.50

Nos. 1127a-1127d sold for 3.50m on day of issue. Number on stamp represents class of mail.

Issued: No. 1127e, 7/10/00.

Jubilee Year — A584

Turku Cathedral: a, Nave. b, Woman, votive candles. c, Christ on the Mount of Transfiguration, alterpiece. d, Infant baptism.

2000, Mar. 15   **Litho.**   **Perf. 14 Vert.**
1128   Booklet pane of 4   6.00 3.50
  a.-d. A584 3.50m Any single   1.50   .60
    Complete booklet, #1128   6.00

Europa, 2000
Common Design Type

2000, May 9   **Perf. 13¼x13**
1129 CD17 3.50m multi   2.00   .60

Provincial Flowers

 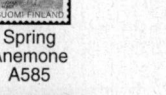

Spring   Blue
Anemone   Cornflower
A585   A586

Pulsatilla Patens — A587

Die Cut Perf. 13x12½
2000-01   **Litho.**
Booklet Stamps
Self-Adhesive
1130 A585 1 multi   3.00   .40
  a.   Booklet pane of 10   16.00

Die Cut Perf. 14¾x13½
1131 A586 1 multi   3.00   .40
1132 A587 1 multi   3.00   .40
  a.   Booklet pane, 5 each #1131-
    1132   30.00

Number on stamp represents class of mail. No. 1130 sold for 3.50m at time of release. Nos. 1131-1132 each sold for 3.60m on day of issue. No. 1132a was issued in two printings. The white box containing the stamps on the original printing is 114mm wide and on the 2003 printing, the box is 110mm wide.

Issued: No. 1130, 5/9. Nos. 1131-1132, 5/16/01.

Souvenir Sheet

Science
A595

Designs: a, Children, molecuar model (triangular stamp). b, Man's face, DNA strand (rhomboid stamp). c, Man's face, Sierpinski triangles (square stamp).

2000, May 30   **Perf. 14¼**
1140 A595 3.50m Sheet of 3,
    #a.-c.   4.50 3.60

No. 1140 has holographic image. Soaking in water may affect the hologram.

Finnish
Design
A596

No. 1141: a, Rug, by Akseli Gallen-Kallela (1865-1931). b, Pearl Bird, by Birger Kaipiainen (1915-88). c, Pot, by Kyllikki Salmenhaara (1915-81). d, Leaf, by Tapio Wirkkala (1915-85). e, Detail from damask, by Dora Jung (1906-80). f, Glass vase, by Valter Jung (1879-1946).

Perf. 13¼ on 3 Sides
2000, Sept. 5   **Litho.**
1141   Booklet pane of 6   9.00 6.00
  a.-f. A596 3.50m Any single   1.50 1.00
    Booklet, #1141   9.00

Size of b, c, e, f: 30x35mm.

Coregonus   Lagopus
Lavaretus   Lagopus
A597   A598

Coil Stamps

Die Cut Perf. 10 Horiz. Syncopated
2000, Sept. 5   **Self-Adhesive**
1142 A597 2 multi   2.50   .40
1143 A598 1 multi   3.00   .40

Nos. 1142-1143 sold for 3m and 3.50m respectively on day of sale.

> On modern stamps bearing the "denominations" "1" or "2," the number represents the class of mail.

Christmas — A599

2.50m, Costumed Tiernapojat carol singers. 3.50m, Bullfinch on door ornament, vert.

Serpentine Die Cut 14¼
2000, Nov. 3   **Photo.**
Self-Adhesive
1144-1145 A599 Set of 2   2.20 1.00
Litho.
Serpentine Die Cut 13¾
1146 A599 3.50m multi + label   8.00 8.00

No. 1146 issued in sheets of 20 that sold for 120m, together with a separate sheet of stickers that could be affixed on the label. The labels attached to the stamps are separated by a row of interrupted serpentine die cutting. Labels could be personalized with photographs taken at some sale sites.

European Year of
Languages — A600

2001, Jan. 17   **Litho.**   **Perf. 13¼**
1147 A600 1 multi   3.00   .60

No. 1147 sold for 3.50m on day of sale.

World Ski Championships,
Lahti — A601

No. 1148: a, Ski jumper Janne Ahonen (yellow helmet). b, Skier Mika Myllylä.

2001, Jan. 17
1148 A601 3.50m Horiz. pair,
    #a-b   3.00 1.40

Valentine's
Day — A602

No. 1149: a, Oval wreath. b, Basket of flowers, letter. c, Heart-shaped wreath. d, Bouquet of flowers, letter. e, Flowers, tea set. f, Flowers, heart-shaped pastry.

Serpentine Die Cut 11½x11¾ on 3 Sides
2001, Jan. 17   **Photo.**
Self-Adhesive
1149   Booklet pane of 6   18.00 4.20
  a.-f. A602 1 Any single   3.00 1.00
    Booklet, #1149   18.00

Nos. 1149a-1149f each sold for 3.50m on day of issue.

Souvenir Sheet

Donald
Duck
Comics
in
Finland,
50th
Anniv.
A603

No. 1150: a, Mickey Mouse, Donald Duck, Santa Claus, Goofy. b, First comics, silhouette of boy. c, Tin soldier with Finnish flag, Chip and Dale (25x30mm). d, Finnish epic hero Väinämöinen, silhouette of Donald Duck. e, Helsinki Cathedral, Donald Duck.

Perf. 7¾ on 3 or 4 Sides
2001, Mar. 13   **Litho.**
1150 A603 1 Sheet of 5, #a-e   10.00 7.50

Nos. 1150a-1150e sold for 3.50m each on day of issue.

Santa Claus and
Sleigh — A604

2001-04   **Serpentine Die Cut 14½x14**
Self-Adhesive
1151 A604 1 multi   3.00   .60
  a.   Serpentine die cut 13¾x13¼
    ('04)   3.00 1.20

No. 1151 sold for 3.60m on day of issue. No. 1151a sold for 65c on day of issue.
No. 1151, 4/2/01. No. 1151a, 12/04.

Europa — A605

2001, Apr. 2   **Perf. 13x13½**
1152 A605 5.40m multi   3.50 1.00

Easter
A606

No. 1153: a, Chick. b. Decorated egg.

2001, Apr. 2   **Perf. 13¼**
1153 A606 3.60m Horiz. pair,
    #a-b   5.00 5.00

Souvenir Sheet

Verla Mill, UNESCO World Heritage
Site — A607

Denominations in: a, UL. b, UR. c, LL. d, LR.

2001, Apr. 2
1154 A607 3.60m Sheet of 4,
    #a-d   6.00 6.00

Orienteering World
Championships,
Tampere — A608

2001, May 16
1155 A608 3.60m multi   1.40   .60

Values are for stamps with surrounding selvage.

Souvenir Sheet

Woodpeckers — A609

No. 1156: a, Dendrocopos minor (32x36mm). b, Picoides tridactylus (29x36mm). c, Dendrocopos leucotos (32x42mm). d, Dendrocopos major (29x42mm). e, Picus canus (32x41mm). f, Dryocopus martius (29x41mm).

Perf. 14½x14¼ on 2, 3 or 4 Sides
2001, May 16
1156 A609 3.60m Sheet of 6,
    #a-f   9.00 9.00

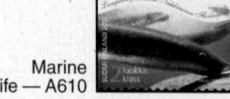

Marine
Life — A610

No. 1157: a, Lampetra fluviatilis. b, Aspius aspius. c, Coregonus albula.

Die Cut Perf. 10 Horiz. Syncopated
2001, Sept. 6   **Photo.**

Self-Adhesive
Coil Stamps

1157	Horiz. strip of 3	7.50	4.50
a.-c.	A610 2 Any single	2.50	1.50

Nos. 1157a-1157c were sold in boxes of 100 stamps that sold at a discount price of 270m on day of sale. The franking value on the day of sale for each stamp was 3m.

Birds — A611

No. 1158: a, Parus caeruleus. b, Motacilla alba. c, Oriolus oriolus.

Die Cut Perf. 10 Horiz. Syncopated
2001, Sept. 6   **Photo.**

Self-Adhesive
Coil Stamps

1158	Horiz. strip of 3	9.00	1.20
a.-c.	A611 1 Any single	3.00	.40

Nos. 1158a-1158c were sold in boxes of 100 stamps that sold at a discount price of 330m on day of sale. The franking value on the day of sale for each stamp was 3.60m.

History of Gulf of Finland — A612

No. 1159: a, Utö Lighthouse. b, Wreck of the St. Mikael. c, Diver exploring St. Mikael. d, Opossum shrimp, isopod. e, Ship's cabin and nautical chart (32x55mm).

Perf. 13¼x13¾ on 2 or 3 Sides
2001, Sept. 6   **Litho.**

1159	Booklet pane of 5	15.00	5.00
a.-e.	A612 1 Any single	3.00	1.00
	Booklet, #1159	15.00	

Nos. 1159a-1159e each sold for 3.60m on day of sale.
See No. 1177.

Christmas — A613

Designs: 2.50m, Elf reading Santa's book, candle. 3.60m, Elf delivering package on sled, horiz.

Serpentine Die Cut 14¼
2001, Oct. 26   **Photo.**

Self-Adhesive

1160	A613 2.50m multi	1.10	.40
1161	A613 3.60m multi	1.20	.65

Slightly larger examples of Nos. 1160-1161 serpentine die cut 14 are known on first day and other covers produced by the postal service. They were not sold unused to the public.

100 Cents = 1 Euro (€)

Flowers A614   National Symbols A615

Heraldic Lion — A616

Type A614 — No. 1162, Myosotis scorpioides: a, Forty-one flowers. b, Four flowers, five buds. c, One flower, four buds. d, Entire plant. e, Five flowers.
No. 1163, Convallaria majallis: a, Leaf, stem with five flowers. b, Two leaves, stem

---

with eight flowers. c, Two flowers. d, Two leaves, stem with five flowers. e, Entire plants.
Type A615: 50c, Swan, vert. 60c, Birch. 1, Flag and bird. 90c, Kymintehtaalta, by Victor Westerholm. €1.30, Granite cliff. €2.50, Spruce. €3.50, Pine.

Die Cut Perf. 15
2002, Jan. 1   **Photo.**

1162	Vert. strip of 5	.90	.40
a.-e.	A614 5c Any single	.25	.25
f.	As #1162, die cut perf 14	.80	
g.-k.	A614 5c Any single, die cut perf 14	.25	.25

Die Cut Perf. 14

1163	Vert. strip of 5	1.00	1.20
a.-e.	A614 10c Any single	.35	.25
1164	A615 50c multi	.90	.40
1165	A615 60c multi	1.70	.40

Die Cut Perf. 13¾

1166	A615 1 multi	3.00	.40
a.	Booklet pane of 10	30.00	
	Booklet, #1166a	30.00	

Die Cut Perf. 14¾x15

1167	A615 90c multi	1.80	.65

Die Cut Perf. 12 Syncopated

1168	A616 €1 blue & multi	1.80	1.00

Die Cut Perf. 14¾x15

1169	A615 €1.30 multi	2.40	1.00
a.	Die cut perf 14 ('04)	2.40	1.00

Die Cut Perf. 14

1170	A615 €2.50 multi	5.00	1.00
1171	A615 €3.50 multi	7.00	1.50

Die Cut Perf. 12 Syncopated

1172	A616 €5 red & multi	10.00	3.00
	Nos. 1162-1172 (11)	35.50	10.95

No. 1166 sold for 60c on day of issue.
Die cut perf 14 examples of No. 1167 exist on first day and other covers produced by the postal service. They were not sold unused to the public.
No. 1169a issued 7/04. No. 1169a has a duller blue panel and a duller black denomination than that found on No. 1169, and a die cut perf. 14 version of No. 1169 that was available only on first day covers with 1/1/02 cancels, and which was not made available to the public unused. Nos. 1169 and 1169a were produced by different printers.
Nos. 1162f-1162k were printed and put on first day and other covers in 2002 but were not sold to the public until 2006.
See Nos. 1179-1180, 1383-1384.

Easter — A617

Die Cut Perf. 14
2002, Mar. 6   **Photo.**

Self-Adhesive

1173	A617 60c multi	1.20	.50

Souvenir Sheet

Elias Lönnrot (1802-84), Botanist, Linguist — A618

No. 1174: a, Plantain. b, Opening lines of "Kalevala" (denomination at UL). c, Closing lines of "Kalevala" (denomination at UR). d, Portrait.

Perf. 13¼ on 3 or 4 Sides
2002, Mar. 6   **Litho.**

1174	A618 60c Sheet of 4, #a-d	4.75	4.75

Souvenir Sheet

Old Rauma, UNESCO World Heritage Site — A619

Denominations at: a, UL. b, UR. c, LL. d, LR.

2002, Mar. 6   **Perf. 13½**

1175	A619 60c Sheet of 4, #a-d	4.75	4.75

Europa — A620

2002, Apr. 15   **Perf. 13**

1176	A620 60c multi	1.00	.50

Gulf of Finland Type of 2001

No. 1177: a, Birds, fish. b, Sailboat, plankton. c, Flounder on sea bed. d, Shrimp, herring. e, Tvärminne Zoological Station, ship, isopod, oceanographic equipment, mussels (32x55mm).

Perf. 13¼x13¾ on 2 or 3 Sides
2002, Apr. 15

1177	Booklet pane of 5	15.00	5.00
a.-e.	A612 1 Any single	3.00	1.00
	Booklet, #1177	15.00	

Nos. 1177a-1177e each sold for 60c on day of issue.

Sibelius Monument, Helsinki, by Eila Hiltunen — A621

2002, May 3   **Perf. 13**

1178	A621 60c multi	1.20	.50

National Symbols Type of 2002 Without Finland Post Emblem

Designs: 60c, Juniperus communis. 1, Reindeer in Lapland.

Die Cut Perf. 14
2002, Oct. 9   **Photo.**

Self-Adhesive

1179	A615 60c multicolored	1.20	.50
1180	A615 1 multicolored	3.00	1.00

No. 1180 sold for 60c on day of issue.

Christmas — A622

Designs: 45c, Horse-drawn sleigh. 60c, Angel with trumpet, vert.

Serpentine Die Cut 14¼
2002, Nov. 1   **Self-Adhesive**

1181-1182	A622 Set of 2	2.20	1.20

Fish — A623

No. 1183: a, Abramis brama. b, Salmo trutta lacustris. c, Esox lucius.

Syncopated Die Cut Perf. 10 Horiz.
2003, Jan. 15   **Self-Adhesive**

Coil Stamps

1183	Horiz. strip of 3	7.50	4.50
a.-c.	A623 2 Any single	2.50	1.50

Nos. 1183a-1183c were sold in boxes of 100 that sold at a discount price of €47 on day of issue. The franking value on the day of issue for each stamp was 50c.

Birds — A624

No. 1184: a, Cuculus canorus. b, Alauda arvensis. c, Perisoreus infaustus.

Syncopated Die Cut Perf. 10 Horiz.
2003, Jan. 15   **Self-Adhesive**

Coil Stamps

1184	Horiz. strip of 3	3.00	1.50
a.-c.	A624 1 Any single	3.00	.50

Nos. 1184a-1184c were sold in boxes of 100 that sold at a discount price of €57 on day of issue. The franking value on the day of issue for each stamp was 60c.

Viivi and Wagner, by Jussi Tuomola — A625

No. 1185: a, Viivi and Wagner running. b, Viivi and Wagner dancing. c, Viivi writing love letter. d, Wagner and Viivi in bed. e, Viivi and Wagner kissing. f, Wagner reading love letter.

Serpentine Die Cut 11½x11¾ on 3 Sides
2003, Jan. 15   **Self-Adhesive**

1185	Booklet pane of 6	18.00	
a.-f.	A625 1 Any single	3.00	1.00
	Booklet, #1185	18.00	

Nos. 1185a-1185f each sold for 60c on day of issue.

Ice Hockey World Championships A626

2003, Mar. 3   **Litho.**   **Perf. 13¼x13¾**

1186	A626 65c multi	1.20	.75

St. Bridget (1303-73) — A627

2003, Mar. 3   **Perf. 13**

1187	A627 65c multi	1.20	.75

Viola Wittrockiana — A628

Die Cut Perf. 13¾x14
2003, Mar. 3   **Photo.**

Self-Adhesive

1188	A628 65c multi	1.20	.60

Fighting Wood Grouses, by Ferdinand von Wright — A629

2003, Mar. 3   **Die Cut Perf. 13¾**

Self-Adhesive

1189	A629 90c multi	1.50	1.00

Airplanes — A630

No. 1190: a, Super Caravelle. b, Airbus 320. c, Junkers Ju 52/3m. d, Douglas DC-3.

Perf. 14x14½ on 3 Sides
2003, Mar. 3
1190   Booklet pane of 4 + 4
     etiquettes   4.80 —
a.-d.   A630 65c Any single   1.20 .80
     Complete booklet, #1190   4.80

Finnair, 80th anniv.; Powered flight, cent.

Europa — A631

No. 1191 — Posters by Lasse Hietala: a, Woman with newspaper. b, Hearts.

2003, May 7   **Litho.**   **Perf. 13¾x13¼**
1191   A631   Pair   3.00 3.00
a.-b.   65c Either single   1.50 1.20

Souvenir Sheet

Flora
and
Fauna
Seen in
Summer
A632

No. 1192: a, Moth, flowers (35x29mm). b, Dragonfly, grasshopper (44x35mm). c, Grasshopper, caterpillar, thistle (35x25mm). d, Frog, flowers, butterfly, insects (44x36mm). e, Magpie, snail, flowers (35x46mm). f, Hedgehog, bee, ant, spider, flowers (44x29mm).

Perf. 14½ on 2 or 3 Sides
2003, May 7
1192   Sheet of 6   7.00 7.00
a.-f.   65c Any single   1.20 1.00

Moomins — A633

No. 1193: a, Moomin ancestors. b, Moomins around stove. c, Moomin standing on hands in water. d, Moomin and fox. e, Moomin looking at film negative. f, Moomin with hat, flowers.

Serpentine Die Cut 11½x11¾ on 3 Sides
2003, May 7
Self-Adhesive   **Photo.**
1193   Booklet pane of 6   18.00 —
a.-f.   A633 1 Any single   3.00 .70
     Complete booklet, #1193   18.00

Nos. 1193a-1193f each sold for 65c on day of issue.

Cupid — A634

Serpentine Die Cut 11½ Syncopated
2003, May 14   **Litho.**
Self-Adhesive
1194   A634 1 multi   3.00 1.20

No. 1194 could be personalized. It sold for 65c on day of issue.

Lingonberries — A635

Serpentine Die Cut 14
2003, Sept. 10   **Photo.**
Self-Adhesive
1195   A635 65c multi   1.20 .60

Philanthropists
A636

No. 1196: a, Juho (1852-1913) and Maria (1858-1923) Lallukka. b, Emil Aaltonen (1869-1949), vert. c, Heikki Huhtamäki (1900-70), vert. d, Antti (1883-1962) and Jenny Wihuri. e, Alfred Kordelin (1868-1917), vert. f, Amos Anderson (1878-1961), vert.

Perf. 13¼x13¾, 13¾x13¼ on 3 Sides
2003, Sept. 10   **Litho.**
1196   Booklet pane of 6   7.25 7.25
a.-f.   A636 65c Any single   1.20 1.20
     Complete booklet, #1196   7.50

Lighthouses — A637

No. 1197: a, Bengtskär. b, Russarö. c, Rönnskär. d, Harmaja Grahara. e, Söderskär.

2003, Sept. 10   **Perf. 13¼x13¾**
1197   A637   Sheet of 5   15.00 7.50
a.-e.   1 Any single   3.00 .70

Nos. 1197a-1197e sold for 65c on day of issue. Size of No. 1197a, 28x45mm; Nos. 1197b-1197e, 21x36mm.

Christmas — A638

Designs: 45c, Elf mailing letter. 65c, Elf with ginger biscuit on baking pan, vert.

Serpentine Die Cut 14x14¼, 14¼x14
2003, Oct. 31   **Photo.**
Self-Adhesive
1198-1199   A638   Set of 2   1.90 1.30

Slightly larger versions of No. 1198 with a serpentine die cutting of 13¼x13¾ and of No. 1199 with a serpentine die cutting of 13¾x13¼ exist only on first day and other covers produced by the postal service. They were not sold unused to the public.

Apples — A639

Serpentine Die Cut 11½ Syncopated
2003, Oct. 31   **Litho.**
Self-Adhesive
1200   A639 1 multi   3.00 1.20

No. 1200 could be personalized. It sold for 65c on day of issue.

Pres. Tarja Halonen, 60th
Birthday — A640

2003, Dec. 1   **Litho.**   **Perf. 13**
1201   A640 65c multi   1.20 .60

Linnaea Borealis — A641

Die Cut Perf. 14
2004, Jan. 14   **Photo.**
Self-Adhesive
1202   A641 30c multi   .70 .70

Souvenir Sheet

Johan Ludvig Runeberg (1804-77),
Poet — A642

No. 1203: a, Title page of *Tales of Ensign Stahl.* b, Sven Dufva with gun. c, Illustration for "Our Country." d, Sculpture of Runeberg.

Perf. 13½x13¼ on 3 or 4 Sides
2004, Jan. 14   **Litho.**
1203   A642 65c Sheet of 4, #a-d   4.80 4.80

Jean Sibelius
(1865-1957),
Composer — A643

No. 1204: a, Satu, and Sibelius, paintings by Akseli Gallen-Kallela. b, Hands of Sibelius on piano keyboard. c, Swans, musical score by Sibelius.
No. 1205: a, Sibelius' house, Ainola. b, Sibelius and wife, Aino. c, Score of "Voces Intimae."

Die Cut Perf. 10 Horiz. Syncopated
2004, Jan. 14   **Photo.**
Coil Stamps
Self-Adhesive
1204   Horiz. strip of 3   7.50
a.-c.   A643 2 Any single   2.50 .50
1205   Horiz. strip of 3   9.00
a.-c.   A643 1 Any single   3.00 .50

Nos. 1204a-1204c each sold for 55c on day of issue and have two short syncopations; Nos. 1205a-1205c each sold for 65c on day of issue, and have one large syncopation.

Love — A644

Text and: a, Rose. b, Man kissing. c, Woman's eye. d, Man and woman embracing. e, Elderly woman. f, Hand pulling petal from daisy.

Serpentine Die Cut 11½x11¾ on 3 Sides
2004, Jan. 14   **Self-Adhesive**
1206   Booklet pane of 6   18.00 —
a.-f.   A644 1 Any single   3.00 .75

Nos. 1206a-1206f each sold for 65c on day of issue.

Ursus Arctos — A645

2004, Mar. 1   **Die Cut Perf. 14**
Self-Adhesive
1207   A645 2 multi   2.50 .80
a.   Pale yellow background, animal
     name 8mm long   2.50 .80

No. 1207 sold for 55c on day of issue. No. 1207 has a pale pink background and animal name is 6mm long.
Issued: No. 1207a, 2009.

Rose — A646

2004, Mar. 1   **Booklet Stamp**
Self-Adhesive
1208   A646 1 multi   3.00 .40
a.   Booklet pane of 10   30.00

No. 1208 sold for 65c on day of issue. Booklet pane was sold folded.

Easter Flowers — A647

Die Cut Perf. 14
2004, Mar. 1   **Self-Adhesive**   **Litho.**
1209   A647 65c multi   1.20 .60

Heraldic Lion Type of 2002
Die Cut Perf. 12 Syncopated
2004, Mar. 1   **Self-Adhesive**
1210   A616   €3 multi   6.50 2.50

Swallows — A648

Orchid — A649

Serpentine Die Cut 11½ Syncopated
2004, Mar. 26   **Self-Adhesive**
1211   A648 1 multi   3.00 1.50
1212   A649 1 multi   3.00 1.50

Nos. 1211-1212 each sold for 65c on day of issue, and they could be personalized.

Souvenir Sheet

Norse
Gods
A650

No. 1213: a, Head of Luonnotar (33x30mm). b, Luonnotar with arms extended (22x42mm).

Perf. 14¼x14½ (#1213a), 14½x14 (#1213b)
2004, Mar. 26
1213   A650 65c Sheet of 2, #a-b   3.00 3.00

Forest Animals A651

No. 1214: a, Red squirrel (40x40mm). b, Raven (40x31mm). c, Variable hare (40x34mm). d, Stoat (40x37mm). e, Lizard (40x34mm). f, Red fox (40x40mm).

Perf. 13¼x14 on 2 or 3 Sides
2004, Apr. 28
1214 A651 Sheet of 6   7.00   7.00
a.-f.   65c Any single   1.20   1.00

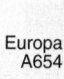

Fragaria Vesca — A652

Die Cut Perf. 14
2004, Apr. 28   Photo.
Self-Adhesive
1215 A652 65c multi   1.20   .60

Luxembourg Gardens, by Albert Edelfelt (1854-1905) A653

2004, Apr. 28   Self-Adhesive
1216 A653 1 multi   3.00   .50
No. 1216 sold for 65c on day of issue.

Europa A654

No. 1217: a, People around campfire. b, Family in rowboat.

2004, Apr. 28   Litho.   Perf. 13
1217 A654 65c Horiz. pair, #a-b   4.00   3.00

Snufkin and Moomintroll A655

Litho. & Embossed
2004, Sept. 8   Perf. 13
Flocked Paper
1218 A655 1 multi   5.00   1.00
No. 1218 sold for 65c on day of issue.

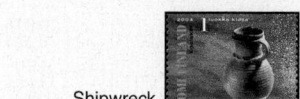

Shipwreck Treasures — A656

No. 1219: a, Tankard. b, Fabric seal. c, Gold watch. d, Powder keg. e, Figurehead (23x40mm).

Perf. 14¼x13 on 3 or 4 Sides
2004, Sept. 8
1219   Booklet pane of 5   15.00   6.00
a.-e.   A656 1 Any single   3.00   1.20
  Complete booklet, #1219   15.00
Stamps sold for 65c each on day of issue.

Souvenir Sheet

Sammallahdenmäki, UNESCO World Heritage Site — A657

No. 1220: a, Stone wall and trees. b, Lichen-covered rocks.

2004, Sept. 8   Litho.   Perf. 14¾x14¼
1220 A657 65c Sheet of 2, #a-b   3.00   3.00

Rights of the Child A658

No. 1221: a, Two girls. b, Boy painting.

2004, Oct. 29   Perf. 13
1221 A658 65c Horiz. pair, #a-b   3.00   2.40

Christmas — A659

Designs: 45c, Boy writing Santa Claus. 65c, Christmas tree branch, candle, ornaments, vert.

Serpentine Die Cut 13¼x13¾, 13¾x13¼
2004, Oct. 29   Photo.
Self-Adhesive
1222-1223 A659   Set of 2   2.20   1.20

Rotary International, Cent. — A660

2005, Jan. 14   Litho.   Perf. 13
1224 A660 65c blue & gold   1.50   .80

Lahti, Cent. A661

No. 1225: a, Sibelius Concert Hall. b, Illuminated radio towers.

2005, Jan. 14
1225 A661 65c Pair, #a-b   3.00   2.40

Oulo, 400th Anniv. A662

No. 1226: a, Child with pail and shovel. b, Woman riding bicycle.

2005, Jan. 14
1226 A662 65c Horiz. pair, #a-b   3.00   2.40

Publishing of First Finnish Almanac, 300th Anniv. — A663

Die Cut Perf. 14
2005, Jan. 14   Photo.
Self-Adhesive
1227 A663 65c multi   1.50   .60

Children's Toys — A664

No. 1228: a, Stuffed lion and tiger. b, Stuffed elephant and dog. c, Airplane, train and car. d, Stuffed bear and rabbit.

Serpentine Die Cut 9¼x8½ on 3 Sides
2005, Jan. 14   Self-Adhesive
1228   Booklet pane of 4   12.00   —
a.-d.   A664 1 Any single   3.00   1.00
Stamps sold for 65c each on day of issue.

End of Winter War, 65th Anniv. — A665

2005, Mar. 2   Litho.   Perf. 13
1229 A665 65c multi   1.50   .80

Easter — A666

2005, Mar. 2   Serpentine Die Cut 14
Self-Adhesive
1230 A666 65c multi   1.50   .70

Apple Blossom — A667

Die Cut Perf. 14
2005, Mar. 2   Photo.
Booklet Stamp
Self-Adhesive
1231 A667 1 multi   3.00   .50
a.   Booklet pane of 10   30.00
No. 1231 sold for 65c on day of issue.

Door Decoration, by Eliel Saarinen — A668   Copper Stove Door — A669

Chair Back A670   Stained Glass Window, by Olga Gummerus-Ehrström A671

Dining Room — A672   Exterior of Hvitträsk — A673

Die Cut Perf. 10 Horiz. Syncopated
2005, Mar. 2   Litho.
Self-Adhesive
Coil Stamps
1232   Horiz. strip of 3   7.50
a.   A668 2 multi   2.50   .50
b.   A669 2 multi   2.50   .50
c.   A670 2 multi   2.50   .50
1233   Horiz. strip of 3   9.00
a.   A671 1 multi   3.00   .50
b.   A672 1 multi   3.00   .50
c.   A673 1 multi   3.00   .50

Hvitträsk, home and studio of architects Eliel Saarinen, Armas Lindgren and Herman Gesellius. Nos. 1232a-1232c each sold for 55c on day of issue and have two short syncopations. Nos. 1233a-1233c each sold for 65c on day of issue and have one large syncopation.

Miniature Schnauzer — A674

Serpentine Die Cut 11½ Syncopated
2005, Apr. 6
1234 A674 1 multi   3.00   1.50
Sold for 65c on day of issue. Sheets could be personalized.

Europa A675

No. 1235 — Plates with: a, Whitefish and beetroot tartare on lettuce. b, Sauteed reindeer and grouse breast.

2005, May 11   Perf. 13
1235 A675 65c Pair, #a-b   3.00   2.40

Souvenir Sheet

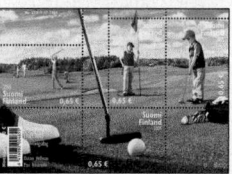

Golf A676

No. 1236: a, Man driving ball (44x31mm). b, Boy holding flag, vert. (30x44mm). c, Boy putting, vert. (33x44mm). d, Putter and golf ball (44x32mm).

Perf. 13¼ on 3 or 4 Sides
2005, May 11
1236 A676 65c Sheet of 4, #a-d   6.00   6.00

World Track Championships, Helsinki — A677

Serpentine Die Cut 12½
2005, May 11   Self-Adhesive
1237 A677 65c multi   1.50   .70

Buses in Finland, Cent. — A678

Die Cut Perf. 14
2005, May 11   Photo.
Self-Adhesive
1238 A678 65c brown & black   1.50   .60

Horses — A679

No. 1239: a, Icelandic horse with saddle. b, White Welsh Mountain pony. c, New Forest pony with blanket. d, Shetland Pony.

Serpentine Die Cut 9¼x8½ on 3 Sides

2005, May 11　　　**Self-Adhesive**
1239　　Booklet pane of 4　　12.00
a.-d.　A679 1 Any single　　3.00　.80

Stamps sold for 65c each on day of issue.

Cloudberries — A680

Die Cut Perf. 14

2005, Sept. 7　　　**Photo.**
　　　　Self-Adhesive
1240　A680 1 multi　　　3.00　.50

Sold for 65c on day of issue.

Fruits I, by Kari Huhtamo — A681

Die Cut Perf. 11½ Syncopated

2005, Sept. 7　　　**Litho.**
　　　　Self-Adhesive
1241　A681 90c multi　　　3.50 2.50

Sheets could be personalized.

Souvenir Sheet

Petäjävesi Church, UNESCO World Heritage Site — A682

No. 1242: a, Bell tower (26x47mm). b, Church (34x39mm). c, Angel (26x39mm). d, Chandelier (27x39mm).

2005, Sept. 7　**Litho.**　**Perf. 13**
1242　A682 65c Sheet of 4, #a-d　6.00 6.00

Icebreakers — A683

No. 1243: a, Urho, 1975. b, Otso, 1986. c, Fennica, 1993. d, Botnica, 1998.

2005, Sept. 7　　**Perf. 13¼ Horiz.**
1243　　Booklet pane of 4　　12.00
a.-d.　A683 1 Any single　　3.00　1.20

Each stamp sold for 65c on day of issue.

Souvenir Sheet

Imperial Winter Egg, by Carl Fabergé A684

No. 684: a, Flowers in egg. b, Frost detail of egg.

Litho. & Embossed with Foil Application

2005, Oct. 28　　　**Perf. 13**
1244　A684　€3.50 Sheet of 2,
　　　　#a-b　　15.00 15.00

A limited quantity of 2,500 numbered sheets, which sold for €30, exist. Value, $100.

Christmas — A685

Designs: 50c, Santa Claus reading letters. 1, Santa Claus and wife dancing, horiz.

Serpentine Die Cut 13¾x13¼, 13¼x13¾

2005, Oct. 28　　　**Photo.**
　　　　Self-Adhesive
1245-1246　A685　Set of 2　　4.00 1.00

No. 1246 sold for 65c on day of issue.

Postal Employees Union, Cent. — A686

2006, Jan. 11　**Litho.**　**Perf. 13**
1247　A686 65c multi　　　1.50　.75

Heart — A687

2006, Jan. 11　　　**Die Cut**
　　　　Self-Adhesive
1248　A687 65c bright pink　　1.50　.60

Renaming of Helsinki University Library as National Library of Finland — A688

2006, Jan. 11　**Die Cut Perf. 14x13¾**
　　　　Self-Adhesive
1249　A688 1 multi　　　3.00　.50

Sold for 65c on day of issue.

Forest in Winter — A689

2006, Jan. 11　　　**Photo.**
　　　　Self-Adhesive
1250　A689 1 multi　　　3.00　.50

Sold for 65c on day of issue.

Taxis, Cent. — A690

No. 1251: a, Women passengers in taxi, 1906. b, Driver standing in front of 1929 Chevrolet taxi. c, Driver leaning on 1957 Pobeda taxi. d, Driver on phone at taxi stand next to Mercedes-Benz taxi.

Serpentine Die Cut 11¼ Vert.

2006, Jan. 11　　　**Litho.**
　　　　Self-Adhesive
1251　　Booklet pane of 4　　6.00　—
a.-d.　A690 65c Any single　　1.50 1.00

Souvenir Sheet

Johan Vilhelm Snellman (1806-81), Philosopher — A691

No. 1252: a, Caricature of Snellman, masthead of his newspaper "Saima." b, Snellman's portrait on 1940 five thousand mark note. c, Snellman and European railway map. d, Ilmarinen, first Finnish locomotive, and European railway map.

2006, Jan. 11　　**Perf. 13¼x13¾**
1252　A691 65c Sheet of 4, #a-d　4.75 4.75

Parliament, Cent. — A692

Serpentine Die Cut 14

2006, Feb. 3　　　**Litho.**
　　　　Self-Adhesive
1253　A692 1 multi　　　3.00　.70

Sold for 65c on day of sale.

Flag — A693

2006, Mar. 1　　　**Self-Adhesive**
1254　A693 1 multi　　　3.00　.50

Sold for 65c on day of sale.

Lilacs — A694

Die Cut Perf. 13¾x14

2006, Mar. 1　　　**Photo.**
　　　　Self-Adhesive
1255　A694 1 multi　　　3.00　.50

Sold for 65c on day of sale.

Easter — A695

2006, Mar. 1　**Litho.**　**Die Cut**
　　　　Self-Adhesive
1256　A695 65c multi　　　1.50　.70

Fortune Teller, by Helene Schjerfbeck — A696

Die Cut Perf. 13¾x14

2006, Mar. 1　　　**Photo.**
　　　　Self-Adhesive
1257　A696 95c multi　　　2.00 1.50

Bil-Bol Poster — A697

Errotaja 2 Poster — A698

Concert Finnois Poster A699

Madonna A700

Self-Portrait A701

Home of Artist Akseli Gallen-Kallela, Tarvaspää A702

Die Cut Perf. 10 Horiz. Syncopated

2006, Mar. 1　　　**Self-Adhesive**
　　　　Coil Stamps
1258　　Horiz. strip of 3　　7.50
a.　A697 2 multi　　2.50 1.50
b.　A698 2 multi　　2.50 1.50
c.　A699 2 multi　　2.50 1.50

Die Cut Perf. 10 Vert. Syncopated

1259　　Vert. strip of 3　　9.00
a.　A700 1 multi　　3.00　.50
b.　A701 1 multi　　3.00　.50
c.　A702 1 multi　　3.00　.50

Akseli Gallen-Kallela (1865-1931), artist. Nos. 1258a-1258c each sold for 55c and Nos. 1259a-1259c each sold for 65c on day of issue.

Souvenir Sheet

Norse Mythology — A703

No. 1260 — Fairy tale book cover illustrations by Rudolf Koivu: a, Fairy. b, Fairy dancing with Santa Claus, vert.

Perf. 13½x13¼, 13¼x13½ (#1260b)

2006, Mar. 29　　　**Litho.**
1260　A703 65c Sheet of 2, #a-b　3.00 3.00

Europa — A704

2006, May 4　　　**Perf. 13**
1261　A704 65c multi　　　1.50　.80

Vaasa, 400th Anniv. — A705

2006, May 4
1262 A705 1 multi   3.00   .80
Sold for 65c on day of issue.

A706

Serpentine Die Cut 10 Syncopated
2006, May 4   **Booklet Stamp**
Self-Adhesive
1263 A706 1 multi   3.00 1.50
   a.   Booklet pane of 8   24.00
No. 1263 sold for 65c on day of issue. Design portion of stamp could be personalized.

Summer Activities — A707

No. 1264: a, Woman fishing. b, Children making flower garlands. c, Man making sauna whisk. d, Woman weeding flower garden.

Serpentine Die Cut 11¼ Vert.
2006, May 4   **Self-Adhesive**
1264   Booklet pane of 4   12.00
   a.-d.   A707 1 Any single   3.00   .80
Nos. 1264a-1264d each sold for 65c on day of issue.

Cats — A708

No. 1265: a, Striped house cat. b, British shorthair (gray cat). c, Ragdoll cat (brown and white). d, Chocolate Persian cat.

2006, May 4   **Self-Adhesive**
1265   Booklet pane of 4   12.00
   a.-d.   A708 1 Any single   3.00 1.00
Nos. 1265a-1265d each sold for 65c on day of issue.

Suomenlinna (Sveaborg) Fortress, Helsinki — A709

No. 1266: a, Ship without oars. b, Ship with oars facing fortress. c, Ship with oars, windmill.

Litho. & Engr.
2006, May 4   **Perf. 13x12¾**
1266 A709   Booklet pane of 3   9.00
   a.-c.   1 Any single   3.00 1.20
    Complete booklet, #1266   9.00
Nos. 1266a-1266c each sold for 65c on day of issue. See Sweden No. 2530.

Blueberries and Blueberry Pie — A710

Die Cut Perf. 14
2006, Aug. 24   **Photo.**
Self-Adhesive
1267 A710 1 multi   3.00   .70
Sold for 70c on day of issue.

Miniature Sheet

Family Life A711

No. 1268: a, Family watching television. b, Woman writing letter to husband.

2006, Aug. 24   **Die Cut**
Self-Adhesive
1268 A711 1 Sheet of 2, #a-b   6.00 2.00
Nos. 1268a-1268b each sold for 70c on day of issue.

Newspaper Journalism — A712

Die Cut Perf. 14
2006, Sept. 22   **Litho.**
Self-Adhesive
1269 A712 70c multi   1.50   .80

Points, Textile Art by Ritva Puotila — A713

Serpentine Die Cut 11½ Syncopated
2006, Sept. 22   **Self-Adhesive**
1270 A713 1 multi   3.00 1.50
Sold for 70c on day of issue.

Dryas Octopetala — A714

Serpentine Die Cut 14
2006, Sept. 22   **Photo.**
Self-Adhesive
1271 A714 1 multi   3.00   .60
Sold for 70c on day of issue.

Art of Snow and Ice — A715

No. 1272: a, Horse. b, Kemi Snow Castle. c, Wall of ice tiles. d, Snowball lantern.

Serpentine Die Cut 11¾ Vert.
2006, Sept. 22   **Self-Adhesive**
1272   Booklet pane of 4   12.00
   a.-d.   A715 1 Any single   3.00 1.00
Nos. 1272a-1272d each sold for 70c on day of issue. Denominations are printed in thermographic ink that changes color when warmed.

Miniature Sheet

Finnish Postage Stamps, 150th Anniv. A716

No. 1273: a, 70c, Heraldic lion and fleurons in white. b, 95c, Part of vignette of type A1. c, €1.40, Heraldic lion in gold, fleurons in red.

Litho. & Embossed With Foil Application
2006, Oct. 27   **Perf. 13½x13**
1273 A716   Sheet of 3, #a-c   6.00 6.00

A717

Christmas — A718

Serpentine Die Cut 13¼x13¾
2006, Oct. 27   **Photo.**
Self-Adhesive
1274 A717 50c multi   .70   .70
Serpentine Die Cut 13¾x13¼
1275 A718 1 multi   3.00   .70
No. 1275 sold for 70c on day of issue.

Television Broadcasting in Finland, 50th Anniv. — A719

Die Cut Perf. 14
2007, Jan. 24   **Litho.**
Self-Adhesive
1276 A719 70c multi   1.50   .60

Faces — A720

2007, Jan. 24   **Self-Adhesive**
1277 A720 70c multi   1.50   .60

Winter Landscape, Haminalahti, by Ferdinand von Wright — A721

2007, Jan. 24   **Photo.**
Booklet Stamp
Self-Adhesive
1278 A721 1 multi   3.00   .80
   a.   Booklet pane of 10   30.00
Sold for 70c on day of issue.

Sun Setting Over Flower Field — A722

2007, Jan. 24   **Litho.**
Self-Adhesive
1279 A722 €1.40 multi   2.00 1.00

Souvenir Sheet

Intl. Polar Year A723

No. 1280: a, Snowflake. b, Aurora borealis.

Perf. 13 Syncopated (#1280a), 13 (#1280b)
Litho. With Hologram Affixed
2007, Jan. 24
1280 A723 70c Sheet of 2, #a-b + label   3.00 3.00

Truck Transport A724

No. 1281: a, Log truck. b, Milk truck. c, Dump truck. d, Tractor trailer.

Serpentine Die Cut 12¼ Horiz.
2007, Jan. 24   **Litho.**
Self-Adhesive
1281   Booklet pane of 4   6.00 4.00
   a.-d.   A724 70c Any single   1.50 1.00

Central Organization of Finnish Trade Unions — A725

2007, Mar. 7   **Perf. 13**
1282 A725 70c multi   1.50   .60

Soccer Association of Finland, Cent. — A726

2007, Mar. 7   **Die Cut**
Self-Adhesive
1283 A726 70c multi   1.50   .60

Easter — A727

2007, Mar. 7   **Die Cut Perf. 14**
Self-Adhesive
1284 A727 1 multi   3.00   .80
Sold for 70c on day of issue. Portions of design were applied by a thermographic process producing a shiny, raised effect.

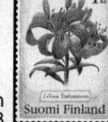

Lilium Enchantment — A728

2007, Mar. 7   *Litho.*
Booklet Stamp
Self-Adhesive
1285	A728 1 multi	3.00	.80
a.	Booklet pane of 10	30.00	

No. 1285 sold for 70c on day of issue.

Souvenir Sheet

Bishop Michael Agricola (1509-57) — A729

No. 1286: a, Text and open book. b, Agricola preaching.

2007, Mar. 7   *Perf. 13½*
1286	A729 70c Sheet of 2, #a-b	3.00	3.00

Tampere Cathedral, Cent. — A730

2007, May 9   *Perf. 13¼*
1287	A730 70c multi	1.50	.80

Europa A731

No. 1288: a, Scouts on sailboat. b, Scouts around campfire.

2007, May 9   *Perf. 12½x13*
1288	A731 Horiz. pair	2.40	2.40
a.-b.	70c Either single	1.20	1.20

Scouting, cent.

Helsinki Public Transportation — A732

No. 1289: a, Commuter train in station. b, Tram on street. c, Subway train on bridge. d, People in Kamppi Bus Station.

Serpentine Die Cut 12¼ Horiz.
2007, May 9   **Self-Adhesive**
1289	Booklet pane of 4	8.00	4.75
a.-d.	A732 1 Any single	2.00	1.25

Nos. 1289a-1289d each sold for 70c on day of issue.

Moomins — A733

No. 1290: a, Little My in water. b, Moomintroll running across rocks. c, Moominpappa at typewriter. d, Snork Maiden picking flowers. e, Moominmamma making pancakes. f, Snufkin amid flowers.

Serpentine Die Cut 11¾ Vert.
2007, May 9   *Photo.*
Self-Adhesive
1290	Booklet pane of 6	12.00	
a.-f.	A733 1 Any single	2.00	1.00

Nos. 1290a-1290f each sold for 70c on day of issue.

Souvenir Sheet

2007 Eurovision Song Contest, Helsinki — A734

No. 1291: a, Eurovision Song Contest emblem. b, Finnish singers Laila Kinnunen, Marion Rung, Kirka Babitzin and Katri Helena. c, 2006 Finnish contest-winning band, Lordi. d, Lead singer of Lordi.

Litho. With Foil Application
2007, May 9   *Die Cut*
Self-Adhesive
1291	A734 70c Sheet of 4, #a-d	4.75	4.75

A735

Serpentine Die Cut 11½ Syncopated
2007, Aug. 24   *Litho.*
Self-Adhesive
1292	A735 1 multi	3.00	1.00

No. 1292 sold for 70c on day of issue. Design portion of stamp could be personalized.

Home Furnishings — A736

No. 1293 — Picture frame and: a, Empire-style chair, "Porvoo Garland" wallpaper, 19th cent. (country name at LR). b, Paimio chair, "2+3" wallpaper, 20th cent. (country name at LL).

Die Cut Perf. 14
2007, Aug. 24   *Litho.*
Self-Adhesive
1293	Pair	6.00	1.20
a.-b.	A736 1 Either single	3.00	.60

Nos. 1293a-1293b each sold for 70c on day of issue.

Raspberries and Raspberry Cake — A737

Die Cut Perf. 14
2007, Aug. 24   *Photo.*
Self-Adhesive
Booklet Stamp
1294	A737 1 multi	3.00	.60

No. 1294 sold for 70c on day of issue.

Finnish Olympic Committee, Cent. — A738

2007, Aug. 24   *Litho.*
Self-Adhesive
Booklet Stamp
1295	A738 1 multi	3.00	.60

No. 1295 sold for 70c on day of issue.

Butterflies — A739

No. 1296: a, Apatura iris. b, Scolitantides orion. c, Colias palaeno.

Die Cut Perf. 10 Vert., Syncopated at Right
2007, Aug. 24   **Self-Adhesive**
Coil Stamps
1296	Vert. strip of 3	9.00	
a.-c.	A739 1 Any single	3.00	.60

Nos. 1296a-1296c had a franking value of 70c on day of issue. A roll of 100 stamps sold for €68.

Miniature Sheet

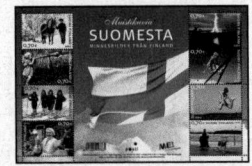

Independence, 90th Anniv. — A740

No. 1297 — Photographs of people at work and play: a, Man and horse hauling wood. b, Girl blowing horn. c, Four boys with skis. d, People at coffee break. e, People near bonfire. f, Boy ski jumping. g, Boy diving. h, Ice fisherman. Nos. 1297a-1297d are black and white photos.

2007, Nov. 2   *Perf. 13¼*
1297	A740 Sheet of 8	11.00	11.00
a.-h.	70c Any single	1.30	1.00

Souvenir Sheet

Woodwork — A741

No. 1298: a, Zitan armchair with dragon design, China (denomination at left). b, Modern Finnish bowls (denomination at right).

2007, Nov. 2   *Perf. 13¼x14¼*
1298	A741 Sheet of 2	2.50	2.50
a.-b.	70c Either single	1.30	1.00

See Hong Kong Nos. 1298-1299.

A742

Christmas — A743

Serpentine Die Cut 13¼x13¾
2007, Nov. 2   *Photo.*
Self-Adhesive
1299	A742 55c multi	.70	.25

Serpentine Die Cut 13¾x13¼
1300	A743 1 multi	3.00	.50

No. 1300 sold for 70c on day of issue.

A744   A745

Water — A746

A747   A748

Islands — A749

2008, Jan. 24   *Photo.*   *Die Cut*
Self-Adhesive
1301	Horiz. strip of 3	.45	
a.	A744 5c multi	.25	.25
b.	A745 5c multi	.25	.25
c.	A746 5c multi	.25	.25
1302	Horiz. strip of 3	.90	
a.	A747 10c multi	.30	.30
b.	A748 10c multi	.30	.30
c.	A749 10c multi	.30	.30

Souvenir Sheet

Helsinki University of Technology, Cent. — A750

No. 1303: a, Robot. b, University building.

2008, Jan. 24   *Litho.*   *Perf. 13½x13¼*
1303	A750 Sheet of 2	6.00	2.50
a.-b.	1 Any single	3.00	1.00

Nos. 1303a-1303b each sold for 70c on day of issue.

Miniature Sheet

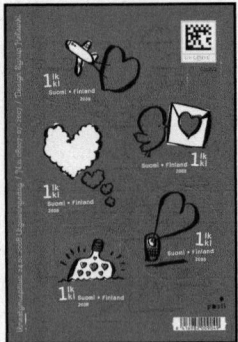

Love A751

No. 1304: a, Airplane pulling heart banner. b, Carrier pigeon with envelope. c, Heart-shaped smoke signals. d, Heart and cell phone. e, Bottle with hearts.

2008, Jan. 24   *Die Cut*
Self-Adhesive
1304	A751 Sheet of 5	15.00	6.00
a.-e.	1 Any single	3.00	1.00

Nos. 1304a-1304e each sold for 70c on day of issue.

Miniature Sheet

Snow Sports A752

No. 1305: a, Matti Räty in yellow ski suit. b, Antti Autti (snowboarder) in air in red ski suit. c, Tapio Saarimaki in red ski suit. d, Tanja Poutiainen in white and green ski suit.

Litho. With Three-Dimensional Plastic Affixed
Serpentine Die Cut 9 Syncopated

2008, Jan. 24		Self-Adhesive	
1305	A752 Sheet of 4	12.00	4.75
a.-d.	1 Any single	3.00	1.00

Nos. 1305a-1305d each sold for 70c on day of issue.

Clock and Lamp on Desk — A753

Die Cut Perf. 13¾

2008, Feb. 27			Litho.
Booklet Stamp			
Self-Adhesive			
1306	A753 €1.05 multi	2.25	1.50
a.	Booklet pane of 10	22.50	

Finnish Book Publishers Association, 150th Anniv. — A754

Serpentine Die Cut 13¼

2008, Feb. 27		Self-Adhesive	
1307	A754 1 multi	3.00	.60

No. 1307 sold for 70c on day of issue.

Lathyrus Odoratus — A755

Die Cut Perf. 13¾

2008, Feb. 27			Photo.
Self-Adhesive			
1308	A755 1 multi	3.00	.60

No. 1308 sold for 70c on the day of issue and has Braille dots applied by a thermographic process.

Easter — A756

Litho. With Foil Application
Serpentine Die Cut 13¾

2008, Feb. 27		Self-Adhesive	
1309	A756 1 multi	3.00	.60

No. 1309 sold for 70c on day of issue.

Fauna Associated With Weather Forecasting Folk Beliefs — A757

No. 1310: a, Perch. b, Lambs. c, Frogs. d, Swallows. e, Snail.

Serpentine Die Cut 12¼ Horiz.

2008, Feb. 27			Litho.
Self-Adhesive			
1310	Booklet pane of 5	15.00	5.00
a.-e.	A757 1 Any single	3.00	1.00

Nos. 1310a-1310e each sold for 70c on day of issue.

Souvenir Sheet

Mythical Places A758

No. 1311: a, Cliff resembling human face, Astuvansalmi. b, Amber carving of head found at Astuvansalmi.

2008, Mar. 27			Perf. 13½
1311	A758 Sheet of 2	2.50	2.50
a.-b.	70c Either single	1.25	1.00

Europa A759

No. 1312 — Handwritten letters and portraits by Pekka Halonen of: a, Himself. b, His wife, Maija.

2008, May 9			Perf. 13
1312	A759 Horiz. pair	2.40	2.40
a.-b.	70c Either single	1.20	1.00

Kvarken Archipelago UNESCO World Heritage Site — A760

Serpentine Die Cut 13¾

2008, May 9		Self-Adhesive	
1313	A760 €1.50 blk & red	3.00	1.80

Moths — A761

No. 1314: a, Arctia caja. b, Aglia tau. c, Deilephila elpenor.

Die Cut Perf. 10 Syncopated

2008, May 9			Photo.
Coil Stamps			
Self-Adhesive			
1314	Vert. strip of 3	9.00	3.00
a.-c.	A761 1 Any single	3.00	1.00

Nos. 1314a-1314c each sold for 70c on day of issue.

Psychedelic Art — A762

No. 1315: a, Melting mushrooms and teardrops. b, Guitars. c, Flying fish. d, Flowers and woman's legs in high heels. e, Six balloons.

Serpentine Die Cut 12½ Horiz.

2008, May 9			Litho.
Self-Adhesive			
1315	Booklet pane of 5	15.00	
a.-e.	A762 1 Any single	3.00	1.00

Nos. 1315a-1315e each sold for 70c on day of issue.

Modern Art — A763

No. 1316: a, Sinistä ja Punaista, by Sam Vanni. b, Merirosvolaiva, by Kimmo Kaivanto. c, Hiljaisuuden Kuuntelija, by Juhani Linnovaara. d, Odotan Kevään Tuloa, by Göran Augustson. e, Minä, by Carolus Enckell. f, Pöytä, by Reino Hietanen.

Serpentine Die Cut 11¾ Vert.

2008, May 9		Self-Adhesive	
1316	Booklet pane of 6	18.00	4.75
a.-f.	A763 1 Any single	3.00	.75

Nos. 1316a-1316f each sold for 70c on day of issue.

Personalized Stamp — A764

Serpentine Die Cut 10

2008, Sept. 5			Litho.
Self-Adhesive			
1317	A764 1 multi	3.00	1.00

No. 1317 sold for 80c on day of issue. The generic design portion of the stamp shown could be personalized.

Dogs — A765

No. 1318: a, Spitz with open mouth, facing forward. b, Rough collie, with open mouth, facing right. c, Boxer, facing left. d, Finnish hound, facing left. e, Cavalier King Charles spaniel, facing right. f, Jack Russell terrier, looking over shoulder.

Serpentine Die Cut 11¾ Vert.

2008, Sept. 5		Self-Adhesive	
1318	Booklet pane of 6	18.00	6.00
a.-f.	A765 1 Any single	3.00	1.00

Nos. 1318a-1318f each sold for 80c on day of issue.

Souvenir Sheet

Mika Waltari (1908-79), Writer — A766

No. 1319: a, Waltari. b, Cover of Waltari's book, *Komisario Palmun Erehdys.*

2008, Sept. 5			Perf. 14x13½
1319	A766 Sheet of 2	3.00	3.00
a.-b.	80c Either single	1.50	1.20

Souvenir Sheet

Kimi Räikkönen, 2007 Formula 1 Racing Champion — A767

No. 1320: a, Räikkönen (24x30mm). b, Räikkönen's Ferrari Formula 1 race car (74x30mm).

Die Cut Perf. 11x11½ on 2 Sides (#1320a), 11½ Vert. (#1320b)

2008, Sept. 5		Self-Adhesive	
1320	A767 Sheet of 2	6.00	3.00
a.-b.	1 Either single	3.00	1.00

Nos. 1320a-1320b each sold for 80c on day of issue.

Souvenir Sheet

Adolf Erik Nordenskiöld (1832-1901), Arctic Explorer — A768

No. 1321: a, Nordenskiöld (29x34mm). b, Ship Sofia (58x34mm).

Litho. & Engr.

2008, Oct. 20			Perf. 13x13¼
1321	A768 Sheet of 2	6.00	3.00
a.-b.	1 Either single	3.00	1.20

Nos. 1321a-1321b each sold for 80c on day of issue. See Greenland Nos. 527-528.

A769   A770

Christmas — A771

Die Cut Perf. 14

2008, Nov. 6			Litho.
Self-Adhesive			
1322	A769 60c multi	.70	.25

Serpentine Die Cut 13¼x13¾

		Photo.	
1323	A770 1 multi	2.00	.50

Printed On Plastic
Die Cut Perf. 13¾

1324	A771 1 multi	3.00	1.00
	Nos. 1322-1324 (3)	5.70	1.75

On day of issue, Nos. 1323 and 1324 each sold for 80c.

Pres. Martti Ahtisaari, 2008 Nobel Peace Laureate — A772

2008, Dec. 10		Litho.	Perf. 13
1325	A772 80c light blue	1.50	1.25

Hospital Work — A773

2009, Jan. 22		Litho.	Perf. 13
1326	A773 80c multi	1.50	1.20

Pallas-Yllästunturi National Park — A774

2009, Jan. 22		Die Cut Perf. 14	
Self-Adhesive			
1327	A774 1 multi	3.00	1.20

No. 1327 sold for 80c on day of issue and has Braille dots applied in varnish.

Peony — A775

Die Cut Perf. 14
2009, Jan. 22   **Photo.**
Self-Adhesive

1328	A775	€1.10 multi	2.50 1.75

Children's Dream Occupations — A776

No. 1329 — Child dressed as: a, Policeman. b, Doctor. c, Firefighter. d, Skier. e, Construction worker.

Serpentine Die Cut 12¼ Vert.
2009, Jan. 22   **Litho.**
Self-Adhesive

1329		Booklet pane of 5	15.00 6.00
a.-e.	A776	1 Any single	3.00 1.20

Nos. 1329a-1329e each sold for 80c on day of issue.

Miniature Sheet

Finland as Grand Duchy of Russia, 200th Anniv. A777

No. 1330: a, Tsar Alexander I (1777-1825), facing left with blue sash. b, Count Georg Magnus Sprengtporten (1740-1819), with red sash and gold epaulets. c, Count Carl Erik Mannerheim (1759-1837), without epaulets. d, Count Gustaf Mauritz Armfelt (1757-1814), facing right, with blue sash. Names are on sheet margin.

Litho. & Embossed With Foil Application
2009, Jan. 22   **Perf. 13¾**

1330	A777	80c Sheet of 4, #a-d	6.00 6.00

Miniature Sheet

St. Valentine's Day — A778

No. 1331: a, Birthday cake and candle. b, Cupid. c, Three people, flower. d, Swans. e, Teddy bear hugging heart.

2009, Jan. 22   **Litho.**   *Die Cut*
Self-Adhesive

1331	A778	1 Sheet of 5, #a-e	15.00 7.50

Nos. 1331a-1331e each sold for 80c on day of issue.

Rose — A779

Die Cut Perf. 14
2009, Mar. 18   **Litho.**
Self-Adhesive

1332	A779	1 multi	2.00 1.20

No. 1332 sold for 80c on day of issue.

Easter — A780

2009, Mar. 18   **Self-Adhesive**

1333	A780	1 multi	3.00 1.00

No. 1333 sold for 80c on day of issue.

Souvenir Sheet

Preservation of Polar Regions and Glaciers — A781

No. 1334: a, Sky, blue emblem. b, Sea and ice, silver emblem.

Litho. With Foil Application
2009, Mar. 18   **Perf.**

1334	A781	Sheet of 2	6.00 3.00
a.-b.		1 Either single	3.00 1.50

Nos. 1334a-1334b each sold for 80c on day of issue.

Greetings — A782

No. 1335: a, Gift and tulips. b, Chocolate-covered strawberries, cake. c, Flowers. d, Coffee cup, letter and rose. e, Dove and apples.

Serpentine Die Cut 10¼ Horiz.
2009, Mar. 18   **Litho.**
Self-Adhesive

1335		Booklet pane of 5 + 5 labels	15.00 5.00
a.-e.	A782	1 Any single	3.00 1.00

Nos. 1335a-1335e each sold for 80c on day of issue.

Europa A783

No. 1336: a, Lake, birds, Moon, stars and other heavenly bodies. b, Lake, comet, Saturn, stars and other heavenly bodies.

2009, May 6   **Perf. 13**

1336	A783	Horiz. pair	3.00 3.00
a.-b.		80c Either single	1.50 1.00

Intl. Year of Astronomy.

Sauna A784

No. 1337: a, Towels, scrubber, bucket of birch branches (55x23mm). b, People in sauna (55x23mm). c, Waterside sauna (55x23mm). d, Birch whisk (27x45mm). e, Water tubs and window (27x45mm).

Serpentine Die Cut 11¾ Horiz.
2009, May 6   **Self-Adhesive**

1337		Booklet pane of 5	15.00 6.00
a.-e.	A784	1 Any single	3.00 1.20

Nos. 1337a-1337e each sold for 80c on day of issue. No. 1337d is impregnated with a birch scent.

Moomins — A785

No. 1338: a, Moomin carrying purse. b, Moominpappa with hat holding paper. c, Little My holding large pair of glasses. d, Moomin at mirror. e, Moomin and Snufkin fishing. f, Moominpappa slipping down hill.

Serpentine Die Cut 11¾ Horiz.
2009, May 6   **Self-Adhesive**

1338		Booklet pane of 6	18.00 6.00
a.-f.	A785	1 Any single	3.00 1.00

Nos. 1338a-1338f each sold for 80c on day of issue.

Miniature Sheet

Women's Fashion A786

No. 1339: a, Dress by Anna and Tuomas Laitinen (30x45mm). b, Dress by Jasmin Santanen (30x45mm). c, Handbag by Lumi (30x35mm). d, Red shoes by Minna Parikka (30x25mm). e, Shoes by Julia Lundsten (30x30mm).

Serpentine Die Cut 14¼x13¾
2009, May 6   **Self-Adhesive**

1339	A786	Sheet of 5	15.00 7.50
a.-e.		1 Any single	3.00 1.00

Nos. 1339a-1339e each sold for 80c on day of issue.

Gustavian Style Clock, Table and Candle Holder — A787

Die Cut Perf. 13¾
2009, Sept. 9   **Litho.**
Self-Adhesive

1340	A787	1 multi	3.00 1.00
a.		Booklet pane of 10	30.00

No. 1340 sold for 80c on day of issue.

Aurora Borealis — A788

No. 1341 — Various pictures of Aurora Borealis taken at: a, 65 degrees, 1 minute, 17.03 seconds north; 25 degrees, 39 minutes, 31.26 seconds east. b, 65 degrees, 57.16 seconds north; 25 degrees, 39 minutes, 41.01 seconds east. c, 67 degrees, 45 minutes, 2.44 seconds north; 23 degrees, 36 minutes, 41.53 seconds east.

Die Cut Perf. 10 Vert., Syncopated at Right
2009, Sept. 9   **Self-Adhesive**
Coil Stamps

1341		Vert. strip of 3	9.00 3.00
a.-c.	A788	1 Any single	3.00 1.00

Nos. 1341a-1341c each sold for 80c on day of issue.

Paintings of Flowers — A789

No. 1342: a, Snapdragons, by Helene Schjerfbeck. b, Blooming Irises, by Wäinö Aaltonen. c, Burnet Roses, by Eero Järnefelt. d, Lone Calla, by Ester Helenius. e, Amaryllis, by Birger Carlstedt. f, Still Life with Carnations, by Tuomas von Boehm.

Serpentine Die Cut 11¾ Horiz.
2009, Sept. 9   **Self-Adhesive**

1342		Booklet pane of 6	18.00 6.00
a.-f.	A789	1 Any single	3.00 1.00

Nos. 1342a-1342f each sold for 80c on day of issue.

Wreath A790

Girl and Basket of Apples A791

Amaryllis — A792

Personalized Stamp — A793

Die Cut Perf. 14
2009, Nov. 6   **Litho.**
Self-Adhesive

1343		Horiz. pair	1.40
a.	A790	60c multi	.70 .25
b.	A791	60c multi	.70 .25
1344	A792	1 multi	3.00 1.20

Serpentine Die Cut 11½x11¾ Syncopated

1345	A793	1 multi	3.00 1.00

Nos. 1344 and 1345 each sold for 80c on day of issue. The generic design portion of No. 1345, shown, could be personalized.

Antennaria Dioica — A794

Die Cut Perf. 11 Syncopated
2010, Jan. 25   **Litho.**
Self-Adhesive

1346	A794	1 multi	3.00 1.00

No. 1346 sold for 80c on day of issue.

Miniature Sheet

Fairies A795

No. 1347 — Fairy: a, Holding flowers. b, Holding heart. c, On swing. d, Holding violin. e, With stars.

Serpentine Die Cut 14½x14
Litho. & Silk-screened
2010, Jan. 25   **Self-Adhesive**

1347	A795	Sheet of 5	15.00 7.50
a.-e.		1 Any single	3.00 1.00

Nos. 1347a-1347e each sold for 80c on day of issue.

Rock Stars — A796

No. 1348: a, Eppu Normaali (45x33mm). b, Yö (41x31mm). c, Popeda (40x28mm). d, Dingo (44x33mm). e, Maarit (34x41mm). f, Mamba (38x36mm).

Die Cut Perf. 8½
2010, Jan. 25   **Litho.**
Self-Adhesive
1348   Booklet pane of 6   18.00   6.00
a.-f.   A796 1 Any single   3.00   1.20
Nos. 1348a-1348f each sold for 80c on day of issue.

A797   Easter — A798

Serpentine Die Cut 12½
2010, Mar. 8   **Litho. & Embossed**
Self-Adhesive
1349   A797 1 multi   3.00   1.00
Litho.
Die Cut Perf. 14
1350   A798 1 multi   3.00   1.00
Nos. 1349 and 1350 each sold for 80c on day of issue.

Rural Life A799

No. 1351: a, Mussels, children lifting caught fish. b, Children on swing, strawberries, flowers, horse in meadow. c, Farmer on tractor, farmhouses. d, Milk cans, girl milking cow. e, Musicians and dancers.

Serpentine Die Cut 10¼ Horiz.
2010, Mar. 8   **Litho.**
Self-Adhesive
1351   Booklet pane of 5   15.00   5.00
a.-e.   A799 1 Any single   3.00   1.00
Nos. 1351a-1351e each sold for 80c on day of issue.

Famous Women A800

No. 1352: a, Ritva-Liisa Pohjalainen, jewelry and clothing designer. b, Elina Haavio-Mannila, sociologist. c, Aira Samulin, dance instructor. d, Maria-Liisa Nevala, director of National Theater. e, Laila Hirvisaari, writer. f, Leena Palotie (1952-2010), geneticist.

Serpentine Die Cut 11 Horiz. Syncopated
Litho. & Silk-screened
2010, Mar. 8   **Self-Adhesive**
1352   Booklet pane of 6   18.00   6.00
a.-f.   A800 1 Any single   3.00   1.00
Nos. 1352a-1352f each sold for 80c on day of issue.

Vegetables A801

No. 1353: a, Tomato (38x33mm). b, Onions (47x34mm). c, Pumpkin (34x36mm). d, Cucumber (27x43mm). e, Eggplant (42x41mm). f, Carrot (29x44mm). g, Broccoli (43x35mm). h, Potato (40x30mm).

2010, Mar. 8   **Litho.**   *Die Cut*
Self-Adhesive
1353   Booklet pane of 8   24.00   8.00
a.-h.   A801 1 Any single   3.00   1.00
Nos. 1353a-1353h each sold for 80c on day of issue.

Souvenir Sheet

Kotka Harbor A802

No. 1354: a, Vellamo Maritime Center, museum ship Tarmo, crane. b, Sailboat, Wooden Boat Center, vert.

2010, Mar. 24   *Perf. 13¾*
1354   A802   Sheet of 2   6.00   3.00
a.-b.   1 Either single   3.00   1.50
Nos. 1354a-1354b each sold for 80c on day of issue.

Europa A803

No. 1355 — Children, books, characters and background in: a, Orange. b, Blue green.

2010, May 4   *Perf. 14x13¼*
1355   A803   Horiz. pair   3.00   3.00
a.-b.   80c Either single   1.50   1.00

Personalized Stamp — A804

Serpentine Die Cut 11¾ Syncopated
2010, May 4   **Self-Adhesive**
1356   A804 1 multi   3.00   1.00
No. 1356 sold for 80c on day of issue. The generic design part of the stamp shown could be personalized.

Sculpture — A805

No. 1357: a, Hymy, by Kain Tapper (28x33mm). b, Hefaistos, by Laila Pullinen (28x33mm). c, Cyclist, by Pekka Aarnio (28x33mm). d, Construction, by Kari Huhtamo (28x33mm). e, Salvos, by Mauno Hartman, horiz. (56x29mm). f, Joy, by Miina Akkijyrkka, horiz. (56x29mm).

Serpentine Die Cut 11¾ Horiz.
2010, May 4   **Self-Adhesive**
1357   Booklet pane of 6   18.00   6.00
a.-f.   A805 1 Any single   3.00   1.00
Nos. 1357a-1357f each sold for 80c on day of issue.

Souvenir Sheet

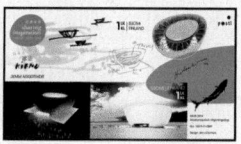

Finnish Pavilion, Expo 2010, Shanghai — A806

No. 1358: a, Aerial view of model and drawing. b, Side view of model.

Serpentine Die Cut 4½ At Bottom
2010, May 4   **Self-Adhesive**
1358   A806   Sheet of 2   6.00   3.00
a.-b.   1 Either single   3.00   1.50
Nos. 1358a-1358b each sold for 80c on day of issue.

Miniature Sheet

People Jumping A807

No. 1359 — Jumpers in: a, Purple. b, Red. c, Yellow. d, Blue. e, Green.

2010, May 4   *Serpentine Die Cut 5*
Self-Adhesive
1359   A807   Sheet of 5   15.00   5.00
a.-e.   1 Any single   3.00   1.00
Nos. 1359a-1359e each sold for 80c on day of issue.

Torronsuo National Park — A808

Die Cut Perf. 14
2010, Sept. 13   **Litho.**
Self-Adhesive
1360   A808 1 multi   3.00   1.20
No. 1360 sold for 75c on day of issue.

1960s-1970s Era Room Furnishings — A809

2010, Sept. 13   **Booklet Stamp**
Self-Adhesive
1361   A809 1 multi   3.00   1.20
a.   Booklet pane of 10   30.00
No. 1361 sold fo 75c on day of issue.

Souvenir Sheet

Autumn A810

No. 1362 — Forest and: a, Crayfish. b, Ducks. c, Elk.

Serpentine Die Cut 12¾x13¼ Syncopated
Litho. & Silk-screened
2010, Sept. 13   **Self-Adhesive**
1362   A810   Sheet of 3   9.00   4.50
a.-c.   1 Any single   3.00   1.20
On day of issue, Nos. 1362a-1362c each sold for 75c.

Santa Claus A811   Reindeer and Moon A812

Sleigh of Santa Claus Over Lapland — A813

No. 1365: a, Star and Santa Claus with sack. b, Poinsettias, ribbon and bell. c, Sleigh of Santa Claus over church. d, Heart-shaped wreath. e, Reindeer and Aurora Borealis.

Die Cut Perf. 14
2010, Nov. 5   **Litho.**
Self-Adhesive
1363   Horiz. pair   2.00   1.00
a.   A811 55c multi   1.00   .50
b.   A812 55c multi   1.00   .50
1364   A813 1 multi   3.00   1.20
Souvenir Sheet
1365   Sheet of 5   5.00   5.00
a.   A811 55c multi   1.00   .80
b.   A811 55c multi   1.00   .80
c.   A813 55c multi   1.00   .80
d.   A811 55c multi   1.00   .80
e.   A811 55c multi   1.00   .80
Christmas. No. 1364 sold for 75c on day of issue. See Japan No. 3269.

Birch Bud A814   Birch Leaves A815

2011, Jan. 24   **Litho.**   *Die Cut*
Self-Adhesive
1366   A814 20c multi   .40   .25
1367   A815 30c multi   .50   .25

Flag of Finland — A816

2011, Jan. 24   **Litho. & Embossed**
Self-Adhesive
1368   A816 2 gray & blue   2.50   .50
No. 1368 sold for 60c on day of issue.

Birds and Flowers A817

No. 1369: a, Bird on branch, country name in red circle. b, Bird in flight, country name in blue circle. c, Flowers, country name in red circle. d, Bird on branch, country name in blue circle. e, Bird in flight, country name in red circle.

Serpentine Die Cut 10¼ Horiz.
2011, Jan. 24   **Litho.**
Self-Adhesive
1369   Booklet pane of 5   12.50   6.00
a.-e.   A817 2 Any single   2.50   1.00
Nos. 1369a-1369e each sold for 60c on day of issue.

Mailboxes — A818

No. 1370: a, Mailbox mounted on tire. b, Snow-covered mailbox. c, Child opening mailbox. d, Mailbox next to sauna. e, Mailbox with posthorn and Finnish lion.

Die Cut Perf. 10 Vert. Syncopated at Right

2011, Jan. 24   **Self-Adhesive**
Coil Stamps

1370		Strip of 5	12.50	4.00
a.-e.	A818	2 Any single	2.50	.80

Nos. 1370a-1370e each sold for 60c on day of issue.

Miniature Sheet

Finnish National Opera, Cent. A819

No. 1371: a, Male and female performers dancing, men in helmets. b, Man with hat and red ribbon, vert. c, Male and female performers in embrace. d, Woman in red dress in water, vert.

Serpentine Die Cut 15½ Horiz.

2011, Jan. 24   **Self-Adhesive**

1371	A819	Sheet of 4	10.00	4.75
a.-d.		2 Any single	2.50	1.00

Nos. 1371a-1371d each sold for 60c on day of issue.

Miniature Sheet

Birds in Trees A820

No. 1372 — Various stylized birds with tree leaves in: a, Green (53x24mm). b, Blue (64x32mm). c, Orange (70x20mm). d, Yellow brown (89x39mm). e, Red violet (78x31mm).

2011, Jan. 24   **Die Cut**
Self-Adhesive

1372	A820	Sheet of 5	12.50	6.00
a.-e.		2 Any single	2.50	1.00

Nos. 1372a-1372e each sold for 60c on day of issue.

Tulips — A821

2011, Apr. 1   **Die Cut Perf. 13¾**
Self-Adhesive

1373	A821	2 multi	2.50	.80

No. 1373 sold for 60c on day of issue.

Dahlias — A822

2011, Apr. 1   **Die Cut**
Self-Adhesive
Color of Country Name

1374	A822	1 red violet	3.00	.50
1375	A822	1 gray green	3.00	.50
a.		Horiz. pair, #1374-1375	6.00	

Nos. 1374-1375 each sold for 75c on day of issue.

Miniature Sheet

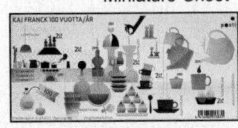

Kitchen A823

No. 1376: a, Lamp, counter, pitcher, stove with pots (32x22mm, serpentine die cut 10x10¾). b, Bottles with stoppers (19x46mm, serpentine die cut 9¾x10). c, Hand dropping seasonings into bowl (24x32mm, serpentine die cut 10x10¼). d, Cup, saucer, bowl with lid (22x32mm, serpentine die cut 9½x10¼). e, Cup, eggs in bowl (24x32mm, serpentine die cut 9¾x10).

2011, Apr. 1   **Serpentine Die Cut**
Self-Adhesive

1376	A823	Sheet of 5	12.50	6.00
a.-e.		2 Any single	2.50	1.00

Nos. 1376a-1376e each sold for 60c on day of issue.

Government Buildings — A824

No. 1377: a, House of the Estates, Helsinki, 1890. b, Finnish Embassy, New Delhi, India, 1985. c, Helsinki Music Center, 2011. d, Government Palace, Helsinki, 1828. e, Malmi Airport, Helsinki, 1938. f, Finnish Forest Research Institute Research Center, Joensuu, 2004.

2011, Apr. 1   **Die Cut Perf. 13¼**
Self-Adhesive

1377		Booklet pane of 6	15.00	6.00
a.-f.	A824	2 Any single	2.50	1.00

Nos. 1377a-1377f each sold for 60c on day of issue.

National Council of Women, Cent. — A825

No. 1378 — Comic strip characters Maisa and Kaarina, by Tiina Paju and Sari Luhtanen: a, Holding star-tipped wands. b, Knitting blanket with stars. c, Playing tennis. d, Posing and taking picture. e, Wearing stars on dresses. f, Placing star on cake.

2011, Apr. 1   **Serpentine Die Cut 11**
Self-Adhesive

1378		Booklet pane of 6	15.00	6.00
a.-f.	A825	2 Any single	2.50	1.00

Nos. 1378a-1378f each sold for 60c on day of issue.

Europa A826

No. 1379 — Trees in: a, Spring and summer. b, Autumn and winter.

2011, May 6   **Perf. 12¾x13¼**
Self-Adhesive

1379	A826	Horiz. pair	5.00	2.40
a.-b.		2 Either single		

Intl. Year of Forests. Nos. 1379a-1379b each sold for 60c on day of issue.

Moomin A827

Mymble A828

Little My A829

Moominmamma and Moomin A830

Hemulen A831

Hattifatteners A832

2011, May 6   **Die Cut**
Self-Adhesive

1380		Booklet pane of 6	15.00	6.00
a.		A827 2 multi	2.50	1.00
b.		A828 2 multi	2.50	1.00
c.		A829 2 multi	2.50	1.00
d.		A830 2 multi	2.50	1.00
e.		A831 2 multi	2.50	1.00
f.		A832 2 multi	2.50	1.00

Nos. 1380a-1380f each sold for 60c on day of issue.

Souvenir Sheet

Struve Geodetic Arc A833

No. 1381: a, Land, water, geodetic arc triangulations. b, Map of Finland with path of triangulations.

2011, May 6   **Die Cut**
Self-Adhesive

1381	A833	Sheet of 2	5.00	2.40
a.-b.		2 Either single	2.50	1.20

Nos. 1381a-1381b each sold for 60c on day of issue.

Miniature Sheet

Tree of Happiness — A834

No. 1382: a, Balloons and gifts (32mm diameter). b, Birds on branch (32mm diameter). c, Cake with Finnish flags (34x29mm

oval). d, Bird in birdhouse (34x29mm oval). e, Boy and girl on branch (32mm diameter).

2011, May 6   **Die Cut**
Self-Adhesive

1382	A834	Sheet of 5	12.50	5.00
a.-e.		2 Any single	2.50	1.00

Nos. 1382a-1382e each sold for 60c on day of issue.

Heraldic Lion Type of 2002
Die Cut Perf. 12 Syncopated

2011, Sept. 5   **Litho.**
Self-Adhesive

1383	A616	€2 green & multi	4.00	2.00
1384	A616	€4 pur & multi	8.00	4.00

Souvenir Sheet

Juhani Aho (1861-1921), Writer — A835

No. 1385: a, Stack of paper, trees. b, Aho on skis.

Litho. & Embossed

2011, Sept. 5   **Perf. 13½**
Self-Adhesive

1385	A835	Sheet of 2	5.00	2.40
a.-b.		2 Either single	2.50	1.20

Nos. 1385a-1385b each sold for 60c on day of issue.

Miniature Sheet

Finnish Comics, Cent. A836

No. 1386: a, Kili ja Possu, by Olavi Vikainen, 1950s. b, Unto Uneksija, by Joonas (Veikko Savolainen), 1960s. c, Herra Kerhonen, by Gösta Thilén, 1930s. d, Antti Puuhaara, by Aarne Nopsanen, 1940s. e, Janne Ankkanen, by Ola Fogelberg, 1910s. f, Olli Pirteä, by Hjalmar Löfving, 1920s.

2011, Sept. 5   **Die Cut Perf. 8½**
Self-Adhesive   **Litho.**

1386	A836	Sheet of 6	15.00	6.00
a.-f.		2 Any single	2.50	1.00

Nos. 1386a-1386f each sold for 60c on day of issue.

Houses with Snow-covered Roofs — A837

2011, Nov. 7   **Die Cut Perf. 14**
Booklet Stamp
Self-Adhesive

1387	A837	1 multi	3.00	1.00
a.		Booklet pane of 10 + 10 etiquettes	30.00	

No. 1387 sold for 75c on day of issue.

Personalized Stamp — A838

Serpentine Die Cut 11¾ Syncopated

2011, Nov. 7   **Self-Adhesive**
1388   A838   2 multi   2.50   1.00

No. 1388 sold for 60c on day of issue. The generic design part of the stamp shown could be personalized.

A839

Christmas — A840

Die Cut Perf. 14

2011, Nov. 7   **Self-Adhesive**
1389	A839	55c multi	1.00	.50
1390	A840	2 multi	2.50	.50

No. 1390 sold for 60c on day of issue.

Miniature Sheet

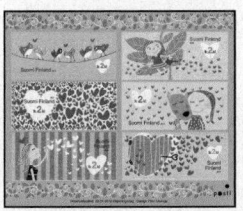

A841

No. 1391: a, Birds on wire. b, Girl with watering can. c, Hearts. d, Girl and dog. e, Woman blowing heart-shaped bubbles. f, Heart-shaped door and key.

2012, Jan. 23   **Die Cut Perf. 13¼x13**
     Self-Adhesive
1391	A841	Sheet of 6	15.00	6.00
a.-f.		2 Any single	2.50	1.00

Nos. 1391a-1391f each sold for 60c on day of issue.

Miniature Sheet

Sami Culture
A842

No. 1392: a, Stick-figure man holding forked stick. b, Stick figure of woman. c, Reindeer at sides of rectangle. d, Three daughters of Sami's mother god and reindeer. Stamps are of various sizes.

2012, Jan. 23   **Die Cut**
     Self-Adhesive
1392	A842	Sheet of 4	12.00	4.75
a.-d.		1 Any single	3.00	1.20

Nos. 1392a-1392d each sold for 75c on day of issue.

The School Girl II — A843   Green Apples and Champagne Glass — A844

Self-Portrait on Black — A845   Silk Shoes — A846

Die Cut Perf. 13, 12¾x13¼ (#1393b), 13¼ (#1393c)

2012, Jan. 23   **Self-Adhesive**
1393		Booklet pane of 4	12.00	3.25
a.	A843	1 multi	3.00	.75
b.	A844	1 multi	3.00	.75
c.	A845	1 multi	3.00	.75
d.	A846	1 multi	3.00	.75

Paintings by Helene Schjerfbeck (1862-1946). Nos. 1393a-1393d each sold for 75c on day of issue.

Winning Designs in Future City Stamp Design Contest
A847

Designs: No. 1394, Hands, by Varpu Kangas. No. 1395, Shapes and dots, by Kangas. No. 1396, Future City is Diversity, by Chloé Chapeaublanc. No. 1397, Buildings, balloons, and inverted umbrella on tree branch, by Sini Henttonen. No. 1398, Children's drawing in red, blue, and black, by Daniel Kallström, vert. No. 1399, Children's drawing of animal under sun, by Elias Ollila, vert. No. 1400, Rabbits, by Katja Hynninen. No. 1401, Cat's head and heavy man on bicycle, by Ville Korhonen.

Booklet Stamps

Serpentine Die Cut 8¾x9 (#1394, 1400), Rectangle and Arc Die Cut (#1395-1396), Arc Die Cut 12¾ (#1397, 1401), Sawtooth Die Cut 15½x15¼ (#1398-1399)

2012, Jan. 23   **Self-Adhesive**
1394	A847	1 multi	3.00	1.50
1395	A847	1 multi	3.00	1.50
a.		Booklet pane of 2, #1394-1395	6.00	3.00
1396	A847	1 multi	3.00	1.50
1397	A847	1 multi	3.00	1.50
a.		Booklet pane of 2, #1396-1397	6.00	3.00
1398	A847	1 multi	3.00	1.50
1399	A847	1 multi	3.00	1.50
a.		Booklet pane of 2, #1398-1399	6.00	3.00
1400	A847	1 multi	3.00	1.50
1401	A847	1 multi	3.00	1.50
a.		Booklet pane of 2, #1400-1401	6.00	3.00
		Complete booklet, #1395a, 1397a, 1399a, 1401a	24.00	16.00
		Nos. 1394-1401 (8)	24.00	12.00

Nos. 1394-1401 each sold for 75c on day of issue.

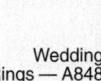

Wedding Rings — A848

Die Cut Perf. 14

2012, Mar. 5   **Litho. & Engr.**
     Self-Adhesive
1402   A848   1 multi   3.00   1.00

No. 1402 sold for 75c on day of issue.

Easter — A849

Serpentine Die Cut 8¼ Vert.

2012, Mar. 5   **Litho.**
     Self-Adhesive
1403   A849   1 multi   3.00   1.00

No. 1403 sold for 75c on day of issue.

Souvenir Sheet

Flowers
A850

No. 1404: a, Hepatica triloba (three small yellow flowers at L, large yellow flower at R, denomination al LL). b, Orobus virnus (six yellow and white flowers on stem, denomination at UR), vert. c, Gagea minima (two partially opened buds, denomination at UL). d, Pulmonaria officinalis (four purple flowers, denomination at LR), vert. e, Caltha palastris (yellow flowers, denoimination at UR). f, Corydalis solida (cluster of purple flowers, denomination at LL), vert.

2012, Mar. 5   **Die Cut Perf. 10**
     Self-Adhesive
1404	A850	Sheet of 6	18.00	6.00
a.-f.		1 Any single	3.00	1.00

Nos. 1404a-1404f each sold for 75c on day of issue.

Intl. Women's Day — A851

No. 1405: a, Woman and hearts. b, Women's hands with glasses of fruit, vert. c, Women's legs and shoes, vert. d, Women and musical notes.

2012, Mar. 5   **Die Cut Perf. 12½**
     Self-Adhesive
1405		Booklet pane of 4	10.00	3.25
a.-d.	A851	1 Any single	2.50	.75

Nos. 1405a-1405d each sold for 75c on day of issue.

Railroads in Finland, 150th Anniv.
A852

No. 1406: a, Train engineer, steam locomotive. b, Train, ticket. c, Railroad warning sign, train in snow. d, Passenger car and passengers at platform, clock. e, Railway worker, modern train. f, Train, lake, statue.

Serpentine Die Cut 9½ Horiz.

2012, Mar. 5   **Self-Adhesive**
1406		Booklet pane of 6	15.00	6.00
a.-f.	A852	1 Any single	2.50	1.00

Nos. 1406a-1406f each sold for 75c on day of issue.

2012 Men's Ice Hockey World Cup Tournament, Finland and Sweden — A853

2012, Mar. 21   **Die Cut Perf. 14**
     Self-Adhesive
1407   A853   1 multi   3.00   1.00

No. 1407 sold for 75c on day of issue.

Souvenir Sheet

Rescue Boats
A854

No. 1408: a, Jenny Wihuri (red and white boat). b, Merikarhu (green, orange and white boat).

2012, Mar. 21   **Perf. 13½x13**
     Self-Adhesive
1408	A854	Sheet of 2	6.00	3.00
a.-b.		1 Either single	3.00	1.50

Nos. 1408a-1408b each sold for 75c on day of issue.

Europa — A855

No. 1409: a, Ship on lake. b, People at beach.

2012, May 7   **Perf. 13¼x12¾**
     Self-Adhesive
1409   A855   1 Vert. pair, #a-b   6.00   2.00

Nos. 1409a-1409b each sold for 75c on day of issue.

Bothnian Sea National Park — A856

2012, May 7   **Die Cut Perf. 14**
     Self-Adhesive
1410   A856   1 multi   3.00   1.00

No. 1410 sold for 75c on day of issue.

A857

Sunflowers — A858

2012, May 7   **Die Cut Perf. 17**
     Self-Adhesive
1411	A857	1 multi	2.50	1.00
1412	A858	1 multi	2.50	1.00

Nos. 1411-142 each sold for 75c on day of issue.

A859   A860

Clouds — A861

Die Cut Perf. 10 Horiz., Syncopated at Bottom

2012, May 7   **Self-Adhesive**

Coil Stamps

1413	Horiz. strip of 3	7.50	7.00
a.	A859 1 multi	2.50	1.00
b.	A860 1 multi	2.50	1.00
c.	A861 1 multi	2.50	1.00

Nos. 1413a-1413c each sold for 75c on day of issue.

Souvenir Sheet

Disabled Athletes A862

No. 1414: a, Leo-Pekka Tahti, cyclist. b, Saana-Maria Sinisalo, archer.

Die Cut Perf. 11¼x11½

Litho. & Silk-screened

2012, May 7   **Self-Adhesive**

1414	A862 1 Sheet of 2, #a-b	6.00	3.00

Nos. 1414a-1414b each sold for 75c on day of issue.

Miniature Sheet

Autumn Dreams — A863

No. 1415: a, Hot-air balloon (36x46mm). b, Moon, lanterns in tree (37x39mm). c, Flying geese (28x36mm). d, Scarecrow and hay rolls (29x46mm). e, Girl feeding carrots to horse (44x34mm).

Serpentine Die Cut 4 to 7

2012, Sept. 3   **Litho.**

Self-Adhesive

1415	A863 Sheet of 5	12.50	5.00
a.-e.	1 Any single	2.50	1.00

On day of issue, Nos. 1415a-1415e each sold for 80c.

Recording Stars of the 1990s — A864

No. 1416: a, Kaija Koo. b, Jari Sillanpää. c, Laura Voutilainen. d, Yölintu. e, Agents. f, Anna Eriksson.

2012, Sept. 3   **Die Cut Perf. 8½**

Self-Adhesive

1416	Booklet pane of 6	15.00	6.00
a.-f.	A864 1 Any single	2.50	1.00

On day of issue, Nos. 1416a-1416f each sold for 80c.

Pets — A865

No. 1417: a, Cat, inscriptions in red. b, White rabbit facing left. c, Gray rabbit facing right. d, Dachshund puppy, year date at LR. e, Jack Russell terrier puppy, year date at LL. f, Kitten, inscriptions in green.

Serpentine Die Cut 11¾ Horiz.

2012, Sept. 3   **Self-Adhesive**

1417	Booklet pane of 6	15.00	6.00
a.-f.	A865 1 Any single	2.50	1.00

On day of issue, Nos. 1417a-1417f each sold for 80c.

Christmas Tree A866   Stable Lantern A867

2012, Nov. 5   **Serpentine Die Cut 9½**

Self-Adhesive

1418	A866 60c multi	1.00	.50

Serpentine Die Cut 10

1419	A867 1 multi	3.00	.50

Christmas. No. 1419 sold for 80c on day of issue.

Sledders — A868

Self-Adhesive

2013, Jan. 21   **Die Cut Perf. 14**

1420	A868 1 multi	3.00	1.00

No. 1420 sold for 80c on day of issue.

Coilostylis Parkinsoniana A869

Self-Adhesive

2013, Jan. 21   **Die Cut Perf. 14**

1421	A869 €1.10 multi	2.00	1.00

See No. 1442.

Miniature Sheet

St. Valentine's Day — A870

No. 1422: a, Polar bears. b, Whale. c, Parrots. d, Elephants. e, Chameleon. f, Monkey.

2013, Jan. 21   **Die Cut**

Self-Adhesive

1422	A870 Sheet of 6 + 4 labels	18.00	6.00
a.-f.	1 Any single	3.00	1.00

Nos. 1422a-1422f each sold for 80c on day of issue.

Actors and Actresses A871

No. 1427: a, Ritva Valkama. b, Esko Salminen. c, Outi Mäenpää. d, Martti Suosalo. e, Krista Kosonen. f, Aku Hirviniemi.

Die Cut Perf. 6¾ Vert. Syncopated

2013, Mar. 4   **Self-Adhesive**

1423	Booklet pane of 6	18.00	6.00
a.-f.	A871 1 Any single	3.00	1.00

Finnish Actors Federation, cent. On day of issue, Nos. 1423a-1423f each sold for 80c.

Easter Rooster — A872

2013, Mar. 8   **Die Cut Perf. 14**

Self-Adhesive

1424	A872 1 multi	3.00	1.00

No. 1424 sold for 80c on day of issue.

Roses — A873

2013, Mar. 8   **Self-Adhesive**

1425	A873 1 multi	3.00	1.00

No. 1425 sold for 80c on day of issue.

Blackberries A874   Gooseberry A875

Red Currants — A876

Die Cut Perf. 10 Horiz. Syncopated

2013, Mar. 8   **Self-Adhesive**

Coil Stamps

1426	Horiz. strip of 3	9.00	3.00
a.	A874 1 multi	3.00	1.00
b.	A875 1 multi	3.00	1.00
c.	A876 1 multi	3.00	1.00

On day of issue, Nos. 1426a-1426c each sold for 80c.

A877   A878

A879   Outhouses — A880

2013, Mar. 8   **Die Cut Perf. 12**

Self-Adhesive

1427	Booklet pane of 4	10.00	4.00
a.	A877 2 multi	2.50	1.00
b.	A878 2 multi	2.50	1.00
c.	A879 2 multi	2.50	1.00
d.	A880 2 multi	2.50	1.00

On day of issue, Nos. 1527a-1527d each sold for 70c.

Flower Bouquet — A881

2013, May 6   **Die Cut Perf. 14**

Self-Adhesive

1428	A881 1 multi	3.00	1.00

No. 1428 sold for 80c on day of issue.

Nuuksio Natl. Park — A882

2013, May 6   **Litho.**

Self-Adhesive

1429	A882 1 multi	3.00	1.00

No. 1429 sold for 80c on day of issue.

2012 Ford Transit Connect Mail Van — A883

1933 Volvo LV-70 Mail Truck — A884

2013, May 6   **Die Cut Perf. 12½x13¼**

Self-Adhesive

1430	Horiz. pair	6.00	2.00
a.	A883 1 multi	3.00	1.00
b.	A884 1 multi	3.00	1.00

Europa. On day of issue, Nos. 1430a-1430b each sold for 80c.

Miniature Sheet

Odd Finnish Sports and Activities A885

No. 1431: a, Man carrying wife. b, Boot throwing. c, Air guitarist. d, Woman pushing man in milk cart. e, Man sitting on ant hill. f, Swamp soccer.

2013, May 6   **Die Cut Perf. 10**

Self-Adhesive

1431	A885 Sheet of 6 + 6 etiquettes	18.00	6.00
a.-f.	1 Any single	3.00	1.00

On day of issue, Nos. 1431a-1431f each sold for 80c.

Moomins — A886

No. 1432: a, Moominpappa holding drink (red background, 30x34mm). b, Moomintroll jumping (blue background, 33x31mm). c, Moominmamma with purse (green background, 33x34mm). d, Little My with basket on head (yellow orange background, 32x33mm). e, Snorkmaiden and piece of paper (red violet background, 30x35mm). f, Snufkin (brown orange background, 32x36mm).

2013, May 6   **Die Cut**

Self-Adhesive

1432	Booklet pane of 6 + 6 etiquettes	18.00	6.00
a.-f.	A886 1 Any single	3.00	1.00

On day of issue, Nos. 1432a-1432f each sold for 80c.

Personalized Stamp — A891

Serpentine Die Cut 11¾ Syncopated

2013, Aug. 12   **Litho.**
Self-Adhesive
1437	A891	1 black	4.50	4.50

No. 1437 had a franking value of 85c on the day of issue. The vignette shown for No. 1437 is a generic image depicting a Volvo PV 444 police vehicle and is one of ten different police vehicles depicted in the image portion of stamps in a sheet of ten stamps having the same common "frame" that sold for €16.50. Customers purchasing sheets of No. 1437 could also download vignette images from an online library of images on the stamp creation website or use their own downloaded images.

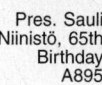

Pres. Sauli
Niinistö, 65th
Birthday
A895

Die Cut Perf. 12 Syncopated

2013, Aug. 23   **Litho.**
Self-Adhesive
1441	A895	1 blk & gray	2.75	1.40

No. 1441 sold for 85c on day of issue.

Coilostylis Parkinsoniana Type of 2013

Die Cut Perf. 14

2013, Aug. 23   **Litho.**
Self-Adhesive
1442	A869	€1.20 multi	2.00	1.00

Souvenir Sheet

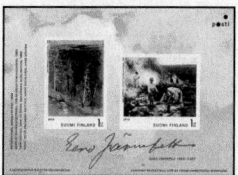

Paintings by Eero Järnefelt (1863-1937) — A896

No. 1443: a, Metsämaisema (Forest Scene) (34x49mm). b, Raatajat Rahanalaiset (Under the Yoke - Burning the Brushwood) (44x40mm).

Serpentine Die Cut 14½

2013, Sept. 9   **Litho.**
Self-Adhesive
1443	A896	Sheet of 2	6.00	3.00
a.-b.		1 Either single	3.00	1.50

On day of issue, Nos. 1443a-1443b each sold for 85c.

Postcrossing
A897

No. 1444 — Stylized postal card and: a, Hand holding pencil. b, Blackboard. c, Heart-shaped Earth. d, Open mouth.

Serpentine Die Cut 12¼

2013, Sept. 9   **Litho.**
Self-Adhesive
1444	Booklet pane of 4 + 4 etiquettes		12.00	
a.-d.	A897 1 Any single		3.00	.75

On day of issue Nos. 1444a-1444d each sold for 85c.

Miniature Sheet

Autumn
Scenes
A898

No. 1445: a, Boy with umbrella, falling leaves. b, Lakeside sauna, geese in flight, buoy, horiz. c, Rowboat and ducks, horiz. d, Apples in basket, house, falling leaves. e, Park bench, falling leaves, horiz.

Serpentine Die Cut 14x14¼, 14¼x14

2013, Sept. 9   **Litho.**
Self-Adhesive
1445	A898	Sheet of 5	15.00	5.00
a.-e.		1 Any single	3.00	1.00

On day of issue, Nos. 1445a-1445e each sold for 85c.

Miniature Sheet

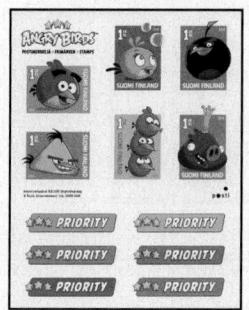

Angry Birds Characters — A899

No. 1446: a, Red Bird. b, Pink Bird, vert. c, Black Bird, vert. d, Yellow Bird. e, Blue Birds, vert. f, King Pig, vert.

Die Cut Perf. 8¼

2013, Sept. 9   **Litho.**
Self-Adhesive
1446	A899	Sheet of 6 + 6 etiquettes	18.00	4.75
a.-f.		1 Any single	3.00	.75

On day of issue, Nos. 1446a-1446f each sold for 85c.

Finnish Parliament, 150th
Anniv. — A900

Die Cut Perf. 14

2013, Sept. 17   **Litho.**
Self-Adhesive
1447	A900	1 multi	3.00	1.00

No. 1447 sold for 85c on day of issue.

Finnish School
System — A901

No. 1448: a, Girl receiving school lunch, apple, lettuce, pitcher and plate. b, Boy receiving medical examination, posture diagrams. c, Girl practicing writing on blackboard, letters in Finnish alphabet. d, Uno Cygnaeus (1810-88), founder of Finnish school system, map of Finland. e, Children in physical education class, children skiing. f, Teacher watching boys writing at desk, orrery, sun and planet.

Die Cut Perf. 6¾ Horiz. At Top

2013, Nov. 14   **Litho.**
Self-Adhesive
1448	Booklet pane of 6		18.00	4.75
a.-f.	A901 1 Any single		3.00	.75

On day of issue, Nos. 1448a-1448f each sold for 85c.

Children
Hugging
A902

Angel
A903

Boy with Christmas
Trees — A904

Die Cut Perf. 14

2013, Nov. 4   **Litho.**
Self-Adhesive
1449	A902	65c multi	1.00	.75
1450	A903	2 multi	2.50	1.00
1451	A904	1 multi	3.00	.75
		Nos. 1449-1451 (3)	6.50	2.50

Christmas. On day of issue, No. 1450 sold for 75c; No. 1451, 85c.

Snowmen — A905

Serpentine Die Cut 10¼

2014, Jan. 20   **Litho.**
Self-Adhesive
1452	A905	1 multi	3.00	1.00

No. 1452 sold for €1 on day of issue.

Miniature Sheet

Teddy
Bears
A906

No. 1453: a, Teddy bear writing with quill pen. b, Teddy bear pushing another on sled, horiz. c, Two Teddy bears and flower. d, Two Teddy bears dancing. e, Teddy bear sleeping in slipper, horiz. f, Two Teddy bears playing musical instruments.

Serpentine Die Cut 16

2014, Jan. 20   **Litho.**
Self-Adhesive
1453	A906	Sheet of 6 + 4 stickers	18.00	6.00
a.-f.		1 Any single	3.00	1.00

Nos. 1453a-1453f each sold for €1 on day of issue.

Castles — A907

No. 1454: a, Turun Linna (Turku Castle) (34x50mm). b, Hämeen Linna (Häme Castle) (34x50mm). c, Raaseporin Linna (Raseborg Castle) (34x50mm). d, Suomenlinna (Sveaborg Fortress) (34x58mm). e, Olavinlinna (Olavinlinna Castle) (34x50mm). f, Kastelholma (Kastelholma Castle) (50x34mm).

Die Cut Perf. 7½

2014, Jan. 20   **Litho.**
Self-Adhesive
1454	Booklet pane of 6		18.00	4.75
a.-f.	A907 1 Any single		3.00	.75

Nos. 1454a-1454f each sold for €1 on day of issue.

Souvenir Sheet

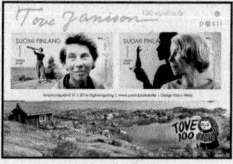

Tove Jansson (1914-2001), Creator of
Moomins Characters — A908

No. 1456: a, Jansson with telescope. b, Silhouette of Jansson and Moomin character, Sniff.

Die Cut Perf. 12½

2014, Jan. 31   **Litho.**
Self-Adhesive
1455	A908	Sheet of 2	6.00	3.00
a.-b.		1 Either single	3.00	1.50

Nos. 1455a-1455b each sold for €1 on day of issue.

Easter — A909

Die Cut Perf. 9¾ Horiz.

2014, Mar. 3   **Litho.**
Self-Adhesive
1456	A909	1 multi	3.00	1.00

No. 1456 sold for €1 on day of issue.

Sami Jauhojärvi and Iivo Niskanen,
2014 Winter Olympic Cross-Country
Team Sprint Gold Medalists — A909a

Serpentine Die Cut 11¾ Syncopated

2014, Mar. 3   **Litho.**
Self-Adhesive
1456A	A909a	1 multi	3.50	3.00

No. 1456A was printed in sheets of 10 that sold for €18. No. 1456 had a franking value of €1 on day of issue.

Fruits and
Blossoms — A910

No. 1457: a, Pears (light green background). b, Apples (yellow background). c, Cherries (pink background).

Die Cut Perf. 10 Vert. Syncopated

2014, Mar. 3   **Litho.**
Coil Stamps
Self-Adhesive
1457	Vert. strip of 3		7.50	
a.-c.	A910 2 Any single		2.50	1.00

Nos. 1457a-1457c each sold for 90c on day of issue.

A911

Congratulations
A912

No. 1458: a, Cat, cake with strawberries. b, Butterflies and flower. c, Squirrel and flowers. d, Strrawberries, blueberries and flower. e, Basket of flowers.

Serpentine Die Cut 13¾x13½ (A911), 14½x15¼ (A912)

2014, Mar. 3		Self-Adhesive		Litho.
1458		Booklet pane of 5	15.00	5.00
a.-b.	A911	1 Either single	3.00	1.00
c.-e.	A912	1 Any single	3.00	1.00

Nos. 1458a-1458e each sold for €1 on day of issue.

Souvenir Sheet

Finnjet Ferry
A913

No. 1459 — Ferry with posthorn at: a, Left. b, Right.

Serpentine Die Cut 13½

2014, Mar. 17		Self-Adhesive		Litho.
1459	A913	Sheet of 2	6.00	3.00
a.-b.		1 Either single	3.00	1.50

Nos. 1459a-1459b each sold for €1 on day of issue.

Violas — A914

2014, May 5	Litho.	Die Cut Perf. 14
	Self-Adhesive	
1460	A914 1 multi	3.00 1.00

No. 1460 sold for €1 on day of issue.

Linnansaari National Park — A915

2014, May 5	Litho.	Die Cut Perf. 14
	Self-Adhesive	
1461	A915 1 multi	3.00 1.00

No. 1461 sold for €1 on day of issue.

Europa — A916

No. 1462: a, Man playing accordion. b, Woman playing kantele.

Irregular Serpentine Die Cut

2014, May 5		Self-Adhesive		Litho.
1462		Horiz. pair	6.00	2.00
a.-b.	A916	1 Either single	3.00	1.00

Nos. 1462a-1462b each sold for €1 on day of issue.

A917

A918

A919

A920

A921

A922

Die Cut Perf. 13½

2014, May 5		Self-Adhesive		Litho.
1463		Booklet pane of 6	18.00	4.75
a.	A917	1 multi	3.00	.75
b.	A918	1 multi	3.00	.75
c.	A919	1 multi	3.00	.75
d.	A920	1 multi	3.00	.75
e.	A921	1 multi	3.00	.75
f.	A922	1 multi	3.00	.75

Nos. 1463a-1463f each sold for €1 on day of issue.

Miniature Sheet

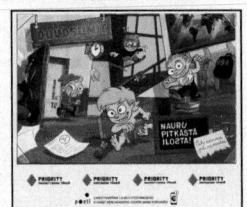

Caricatures of Dudesons Television Show Cast Members — A923

No. 1464 — Dudeson: a, On snowboard. b, With red cap. c, Wearing shirt with target. d, Running naked, holding book.

Crenellated Die Cut 5

2014, Sept. 1		Self-Adhesive		Litho.
1464	A923	Sheet of 4	12.00	3.25
a.-d.		1 Any single	3.00	.75

Nos. 1464a-1464d each sold for €1 on day of issue.

A924

A925

A926

A927

Watercolors of Yards and Gardens by Urpo Martikainen
A927

Die Cut Perf. 13

2014, Sept. 8		Self-Adhesive		Litho.
1465		Booklet pane of 4	12.00	3.25
a.	A924	1 multi	3.00	.75
b.	A925	1 multi	3.00	.75
c.	A926	1 multi	3.00	.75
d.	A927	1 multi	3.00	.75

Nos. 1465a-1465d each sold for €1 on day of issue.

Celestial and Meteorological Objects — A928

No. 1466: a, Saturn (45x40mm). b, Moon (36x36mm). c, Sun (40x38mm). d, Cloud and lightning bolt (40x51mm). e, Earth and Moon (35x41mm). f, Comet (40x45mm). g, Cloud (48x42mm). h, Rainbow (40x38mm).

Serpentine Die Cut 9¼ on 1 or 2 Sides

2014, Sept. 8		Self-Adhesive		Litho.
1466		Booklet pane of 8	24.00	.50
a.-h.	A928	1 Any single	3.00	.80

Nos. 1466a-1466h each sold for €1 on day of issue.

Souvenir Sheet

Art by Tom of Finland (Touko Laaksonen) (1920-91)
A929

No. 1467: a, Man wearing police cap smoking cigarette (43x32mm). b, Man's head between legs of another man (45x33mm). c, Man's head and buttocks (36x33mm).

Die Cut Perf. 5½

2014, Sept. 8		Self-Adhesive		Litho.
1467		Sheet of 3	9.00	3.00
a.-c.	A929	1 Any single	3.00	1.00

Nos. 1467a-1467c each sold for €1 on day of issue.

A930

A931

A932

A933

A934

A935

A936

A937

A938

Bridges — A939

Die Cut Perf. 8½ Horiz.

2014, Oct. 23				Litho.
		Coil Stamps		
		Self-Adhesive		
1468	A930	1 multi + etiquette	3.00	.80
1469	A931	1 multi + etiquette	3.00	.80
1470	A932	1 multi + etiquette	3.00	.80
1471	A933	1 multi + etiquette	3.00	.80
1472	A934	1 multi + etiquette	3.00	.80
1473	A935	1 multi + etiquette	3.00	.80
1474	A936	1 multi + etiquette	3.00	.80
1475	A937	1 multi + etiquette	3.00	.80
1476	A938	1 multi + etiquette	3.00	.80
1477	A939	1 multi + etiquette	3.00	.80
a.		Horiz. strip of 10, #1468-1477, + 10 etiquettes	30.00	
		Nos. 1468-1477 (10)	30.00	8.00

On day of issue, Nos. 1468-1477 had a franking value of €1. A complete roll of 100 stamps sold for €97.50 on the day of issue,

Changes in Everyday Items
A940

No. 1478: a, Computer keyboard, computer storage disks, computer, dial telephone, computer chip, television, computer mouse, compact disk and video cassette tapes (54x30mm). b, Potatoes, olives, cookies, cracker, sushi, shrimp, fish, pizza slice (54x30mm). c, Satellite, vacuum cleaner, chest freezer, coffee maker, stove, refrigerator, toaster, washing machine (54x30mm). d, Hay bales, cattle, tractor, storage shed, boarded windows, apartment house, automobiles, house (54x30mm). e, Radio, phonograph record, cassette tape player and headphones, mirrored ball, aerosol cans, electronic piano, dresses, make-up (54x30mm). f, Automobiles, rowboat, bus, scooter, sled, bicycle, cart, train (44x35mm).

2014, Oct. 23		Litho.		Die Cut
		Self-Adhesive		
1478		Booklet pane of 6	18.00	4.75
a.-f.	A940	1 Any single	3.00	.75

Nos. 1478a-1478f each sold for €1 on day of issue.

A941

Christmas — A942

Die Cut Perf. 13

2014, Oct. 23		Self-Adhesive		Litho.
1479	A941	75c multi	2.00	.75
1480	A942	1 multi	3.00	.75

No. 1480 sold for €1 on day of issue.

Christmas — A942a

Serpentine Die Cut 11½ Syncopated
2014, Nov. 17 *Litho.*
Self-Adhesive
1480A A942a 1 multi   3.00 2.50

No. 1480A had a franking value of €1 on day of issue and was printed in sheets of 10 that sold for €18.

Marigold IceUnity Synchronized Skating Team — A943

Die Cut Perf. 14
2015, Jan. 19 *Litho.*
Self-Adhesive
Textured Paper
1481 A943 1 multi   3.00 .75

No. 1481 sold for €1 on day of issue.

Miniature Sheet

St. Valentine's Day — A944

No. 1482 — Smiling: a, Snowflakes. b, Trees, snowflakes and bird. c, Mouse and snow angel. d, Birds in nest. e, Berry plants. f, Fox and rabbit.

Serpentine Die Cut 7
2015, Jan. 19 *Litho.*
Self-Adhesive
1482 A944   Sheet of 6 + 6 eti-
     quettes   18.00 4.75
a.-f.   1 Any single   3.00 .75

Nos. 1482a-1482f each sold for €1 on day of issue.

Artists' Association of Finland, 150th Anniv. — A945

No. 1483: a, Line Form, by Anneli Hilli (36x36mm). b, Point, by Mika Natri (36x36mm). c, Artist's Rollercoaster, by Marjo Suikkanen (36x40mm). d, Dance from the Bride, by Mayumi Niiranen-Hisatomi (32x40mm oval). e, Flight, by Laura Konttinen (36x30mm). f, You Will Know Them By Their Fruits, by Kalevi Karlsson (36x30mm).

Serpentine Die Cut 10¼
2015, Jan. 19 *Litho.*
Self-Adhesive
1483   Booklet pane of 6 + 6
     etiquettes   18.00 4.75
a.-f. A945 1 Any single   3.00 .75

Nos. 1483a-1483f each sold for €1 on day of issue.

Flowers — A946

Die Cut Perf. 13¾
2015, Mar. 2 *Litho.*
Self-Adhesive
1484 A946 1 multi   3.00 .75

No. 1484 sold for €1.10 on day of issue.

Easter — A947

Serpentine Die Cut 8¾
2015, Mar. 2 *Litho.*
Self-Adhesive
1485 A947 1 multi   3.00 .75

No. 1485 sold for €1.10 on day of issue.

Student's Cap — A948

Die Cut Perf. 14¼
2015, Mar. 2 *Litho.*
Self-Adhesive
1486 A948 1 multi   3.00 .75

No. 1486 sold for €1.10 on day of issue.

A949

A950

A951

International Women's Day — A952

2015, Mar. 2 *Litho.*   **Die Cut**
Self-Adhesive
1487   Booklet pane of 4   12.00 3.25
a. A949 1 multi   3.00 .75
b. A950 1 multi   3.00 .75
c. A951 1 multi   3.00 .75
d. A952 1 multi   3.00 .75

Nos. 1487a-1487d each sold for €1.10 on day of issue.

Souvenir Sheet

Toivo Kärki (1915-92), Composer — A953

No. 1488 — Kärki and: a, Record album (44mm diameter). b, Score (45x32mm). c, Accordion, silhouette of man and woman (45x32mm).

Die Cut (#1488a), Die Cut Perf. 5¼
2015, Mar. 2 *Litho.*
Self-Adhesive
1488 A953   Sheet of 3   9.00 2.50
a.-c.   1 Any single   3.00 .75

Nos. 1488a-1488c each sold for €1.10 on day of issue.

Rugosa Roses — A954

Orchids — A955

Die Cut Perf. 13¾
2015, May 8 *Litho.*
Self-Adhesive
1489   Horiz. pair   5.00 2.00
a. A954 2 multi   2.50 1.00
b. A955 2 multi   2.50 1.00

Nos. 1489a-1489b each sold for €1 on day of issue.

Swan — A956

Litho. With Foil Application
2015, May 8   **Die Cut Perf. 13½**
Self-Adhesive
1490 A956 1 multi   3.00 .75

A957

Moomin Toys — A958

Serpentine Die Cut 9¾
2015, May 8   **Self-Adhesive**   *Litho.*
1491   Horiz. pair   6.00 2.00
a. A957 1 multi   3.00 1.00
b. A958 1 multi   3.00 1.00

Europa. Nos. 1491a-1491b each sold for €1.10 on day of issue.

Miniature Sheet

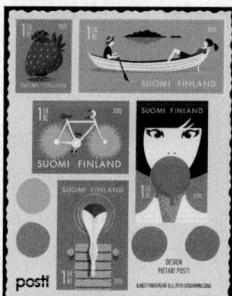

Sights of Summer A959

No. 1492: a, Strawberry, ladybug and ant (22x30mm). b, Man and woman in rowboat (62x30mm). c, Bicycle (41x30mm). d, Woman with ice cream cone (30x50mm). e, Woman diving into water (30x45mm).

Serpentine Die Cut 9¼x11 (#1492a), 7½x6¼ (#1492b), 8x8¼ (#1492c), 7x6½ (#1492d), 7x7¼ (#1492e)
2015, May 8   **Self-Adhesive**   *Litho.*
1492 A959   Sheet of 5   15.00 7.50
a.-e.   1 Any single   3.00 1.00

Nos. 1492a-1492e each sold for €1.10 on day of issue.

Man Pushing Lawnmower — A959a

Serpentine Die Cut 11½ Syncopated
2016, Mar. 30 *Litho.*
Self-Adhesive
1492F A959a 1 multi   — —

No. 1492F had a franking value of €1.20 on day of issue and was printed in sheets of 10 that sold for €15.

Miniature Sheet

Scenes From Imaginary Town — A960

No. 1493: a, Woman riding giraffe (20x33mm). b, Woman with shopping bag (38x21mm). c, Sailboat and swan (30mm diameter). d, House and horse (41x24mm). e, Rabbits in front of building with clock (34x21mm). f, Birds and flowers in pots (18x35mm).

Serpentine Die Cut 7¾ on 2 Opposite Sides, Die Cut (#1493c, 1493d)
2015, Sept. 11 *Litho.*
Self-Adhesive
1493 A960   Sheet of 6   15.00
a.-f.   1 Any single   2.50 2.50

Nos. 1493a-1493f each sold for €1.10 on day of issue.

Miniature Sheet

Art A961

No. 1494: a, Horse running. b, Head and arm of woman. c, Woman unzipping dress. d, Woman's legs with high-heeled shoes.

Litho. With Foil Application
Serpentine Die Cut 6¾
2015, Sept. 11   **Self-Adhesive**
1494 A961   Sheet of 4   10.00
a.-d.   1 Any single   2.50 2.50

Nos. 1494a-1494d each sold for €1.10 on day of issue.

A962

A963

Jean Sibelius (1865-1957), Composer — A964

Serpentine Die Cut 10¼
2015, Sept. 11 *Litho.*
Self-Adhesive
1495   Booklet pane of 3 + 3
     etiquettes   7.50
a. A962 1 multi   2.50 2.50
b. A963 1 multi   2.50 2.50
c. A964 1 multi   2.50 2.50

Nos. 1495a-1495c each sold for €1.10 on day of issue.

The Rasmus
A965

HIM
A966

Apocalyptica
A967

Children of Bodom
A968

Hanoi Rocks
A969

Nightwish
A970

Serpentine Die Cut 10¼x10 (#1496b-1496b), 9¾x10 (#1496c), 10¼x9½ (#1496d), 9½x10 (#1496e), 10¼x9¼ (#1496f)

2015, Sept. 11   Litho.
Self-Adhesive

1496	Booklet pane of 6 + 6 etiquettes	15.00		
a.	A965 1 multi		2.50	2.50
b.	A966 1 multi		2.50	2.50
c.	A967 1 multi		2.50	2.50
d.	A968 1 multi		2.50	2.50
e.	A969 1 multi		2.50	2.50
f.	A970 1 multi		2.50	2.50

Rock bands. Nos. 1496a-1496f each sold for €1.10 on day of issue.

Finnish Design — A971

No. 1497: a, Marimekko Kukkuluuruu fabric design, by Sanna Annukka (28x45mm). b, Ultima Thule drinking glass, by Tapio Wirkkala (27x27mm). c, Block lamp, by Harri Koskinen (32x27mm). d, Paratiisi plate, by Birger Kaipiainen (27x33mm). e, Mademoiselle lounge chair, by Ilmari Tapiovaara (28x45mm). f, Solifer moped, by Richard Lindh (36x27mm).

Die Cut Perf. 13¼

2015, Sept. 11   Litho.

1497	Booklet pane of 6	15.00		
a.-f.	A971 1 Any single		2.50	2.50

Nos. 1497a-1497f each sold for €1.10 on day of issue.

Pertti Kurikan Nimipälvät
A972

Die Cut Perf. 11½ Syncopated

2015, Apr. 28   Litho.
Self-Adhesive

1498	A972 1 multi		2.50	2.50

Eurovision Song Contest. No. 1498 sold for €1.10 on day of issue.

Peppers — A975

Die Cut Perf. 9¾ Vert. Syncopated

2015, Nov. 6   Litho.
Coil Stamps
Self-Adhesive

1499	A973 1 multi + etiquette		2.50	2.50
1500	A974 1 multi + etiquette		2.50	2.50
1501	A975 1 multi + etiquette		2.50	2.50
a.	Vert. strip of 3, #1499-1501, + 3 etiquettes		7.50	
	Nos. 1499-1501 (3)		7.50	7.50

Nos. 1499-1501 each sold for €1.10 on day of issue.

Miniature Sheet

Craft Items
A976

No. 1502: a, Purse made of tree bark (40x36mm). b, Crocheted square (35x35mm). c, Socks (32x50mm). d, Dancing shoes (38x35mm). e, Mushroom-shaped wooden stool (37x34mm).

Various Die Cuts

2015, Nov. 6   Litho.
Self-Adhesive

1502	A976	Sheet of 5	12.50	
a.-e.	1 Any single		2.50	2.50

On day of issue, Nos. 1502a-1502e each sold for €1.10.

Father and Son Dragging Christmas Tree Past Church
A977

Child Looking at Christmas Ornament
A978

Die Cut Perf. 11 Syncopated

2015, Nov. 6   Litho.
Self-Adhesive

1503	A977 1 multi		2.50	2.50

Booklet Stamp

1504	A978 80c multi		1.90	1.90
a.	Booklet pane of 20		38.00	

No. 1503 sold for €1.10 on day of issue and was printed in sheets of 10 + 10 etiquettes.

Victory of Finnish Team in World Junior Ice Hockey Championships
A979

Die Cut Perf. 11½ Syncopated

2016, Jan. 15   Litho.
Self-Adhesive

1505	A979 1 multi		2.40	2.40

No. 1505 sold for €1.10 on day of issue.

Litho. With Holographic Foil
Die Cut Perf. 9¾ Horiz.

2016, Jan. 22   Self-Adhesive

1506	A980 1 multi + etiquette		2.40	2.40

No. 1506 sold for €1.10 on day of issue.

Karelian Pasties
A981

Serpentine Die Cut 8 Syncopated

2016, Jan. 22   Litho.
Self-Adhesive

1507	A981 1 multi + etiquette		2.40	2.40

No. 1507 sold for €1.10 on day of issue.

Deer and Bird — A982

Birds — A983

Horse and Dog — A984

Bird and Butterfly
A985

Cat and Dog — A986

Serpentine Die Cut 6½

2016, Jan. 22   Litho.
Self-Adhesive

1508	Booklet pane of 5 + 5 etiquettes	12.00		
a.	A982 1 multi		2.40	2.40
b.	A983 1 multi		2.40	2.40
c.	A984 1 multi		2.40	2.40
d.	A985 1 multi		2.40	2.40
e.	A986 1 multi		2.40	2.40

On day of issue, Nos. 1508a-1508e each sold for €1.10.

Rabbit and Easter Basket — A987

Die Cut Perf. 13¾

2016, Feb. 26   Litho.
Self-Adhesive

1509	A987 1 multi + etiquette		2.60	2.60

No. 1509 sold for €1.20 on day of issue.

Siberian Iris — A988

Die Cut Perf. 13¾

2016, Feb. 26   Litho.
Self-Adhesive

1510	A988 1 multi		2.60	2.60

No. 1510 sold for €1.20 on day of issue.

Nuuksio National Park — A989

Birch Tree — A990

Die Cut Perf. 11 Horiz.

2016, Feb. 26   Litho.
Self-Adhesive

1511	A989 €1.30 multi + etiquette		3.00	3.00
1512	A990 €1.30 multi + etiquette		3.00	3.00
a.	Horiz. pair, #1511-1512, + 2 etiquettes		6.00	

Wings of Thoughts — A991

Die Cut Perf. 13¾

2016, Feb. 26   Litho.
Self-Adhesive

1513	A991 €1.80 multi		4.00	4.00

See Nos. 1537, 1554.

Package With Legs — A992

Bird Carrying Letter — A993

Angel Blowing Trumpet — A994

Birthday Cake — A995

Boot and Flowers — A996

2016, Feb. 26   Litho.   Die Cut
Self-Adhesive

1514	Booklet pane of 5 + 5 etiquettes and 5 stickers	13.00		
a.	A992 1 multi		2.60	2.60
b.	A993 1 multi		2.60	2.60
c.	A994 1 multi		2.60	2.60
d.	A995 1 multi		2.60	2.60
e.	A996 1 multi		2.60	2.60

On day of issue, Nos. 1514a-1514e each sold for €1.20.

Tomatoes
A973

Basil
A974

Snowflake
A980

This stamp and many other stamps having the same gray panel at bottom were released on Apr. 8, 2016. The stamps, each with a coat of arms of a region or city of Finland, were printed using the Finland Post apparatus used to create personalized stamps. Apparently only coats of arms were printed in the vignette area and no personalized stamps could be created by customers using other vignette images and this gray panel. Even though Finland Post sold these items as "regional stamps," there is no indication that the stamps were sold only in the region of the coat of arms on each stamp, or that the stamps were valid only in those regions. Each stamp was printed in sheets of ten that sold for €15. The coat of arms of the city of Vaasa is shown in the image above.

Feather — A997

Die Cut Perf. 13¾
2016, May 6   **Litho.**
Self-Adhesive
1515   A997   50c multi   1.10 1.10

Europa — A998

Serpentine Die Cut 12¼ Syncopated
2016, May 6   **Litho.**
Self-Adhesive
1516   A998   1 multi + etiquette   2.75 2.75
Think Green Issue.
No. 1516 sold for €1.20 on day of issue.

Vacation Scenes — A999

No. 1517: a, Woman's crossed feet in sandals, women in park. b, Feet of skateboarder, buildings and cranes. c, Men and women, umbrella and bicycle. d, People at beach. e, Woman at market stall.

2016, May 6 Litho. Die Cut Perf. 13
Self-Adhesive
1517   Booklet pane of 5 + 5 etiquettes   14.00
a.-e. A999 1 Any single   2.75 2.75
Nos. 1517a-1517e each sold for €1.20 on day of issue.

A1000

A1001

A1002

A1003

Barns — A1004

Die Cut Perf. 9¼ Syncopated
2016, May 6   **Litho.**
Self-Adhesive
1518   Booklet pane of 5 + 5 etiquettes   14.00
a. A1000 1 multi   2.75 2.75
b. A1001 1 multi   2.75 2.75
c. A1002 1 multi   2.75 2.75
d. A1003 1 multi   2.75 2.75
e. A1004 1 multi   2.75 2.75
Nos. 1518a-1518e each sold for €1.20 on day of issue.

Worldwide Fund for Nature (WWF) — A1005

No. 1519: a, Pusa hispida saimensis. b, Nehalennia speciosa. c, Anser erythropus.

Serpentine Die Cut 4¼ at Top
2016, Sept. 9   **Litho.**
Self-Adhesive
1519   Vert. strip of 3 + 3 etiquettes   8.25
a.-c. A1005 1 Any single + etiquette   2.75 2.75
Nos. 1519a-1519c each sold for €1.20 on day of issue.

Mushrooms — A1006

No. 1520: a, Russula paludosa. b, Tricholoma matsutake. c, Craterellus cornucopioides. d, Cantharellus cibarius. e, Lactarius deterrimus.

Serpentine Die Cut 14¼x13¾
2016, Sept. 9   **Litho.**
Self-Adhesive
1520   Booklet pane of 5 + 5   14.00
a.-e. A1006 1 Any single   2.75 2.75
Nos. 1520a-1520e each sold for €1.20 on day of issue.

People Enjoying Nature — A1007

No. 1521: a, Flower picking. b, Ice fishing. c, Berry harvesting. d, Boating. e, Camping. f, Skiing.

Die Cut Perf. 8¾ on 1 Side
2016, Sept. 9   **Litho.**
Self-Adhesive
1521   Booklet pane of 6 + 6 etiquettes   16.50
a.-f. A1007 1 Any single   2.75 2.75
Nos. 1521a-1521f each sold for €1.20 on day of issue.

Miniature Sheet

Art by Ville Andersson and Eeva-Riitta Eerola — A1008

Various unnamed works, as shown.

Serpentine Die Cut 6¾
2016, Sept. 9   **Litho.**
Self-Adhesive
1522   A1008   Sheet of 4   11.00
a.-d.   1 Any single   2.75 2.75
Nos. 1522a-1522d each sold for €1.20 on day of issue.

Kirkonvarkaus Bridge — A1009

Serpentine Die Cut 11½ Syncopated
2016, Sept. 19   **Litho.**
Self-Adhesive
1523   A1009 1 multi   —   —
No. 1523 had a franking value of €1.20 and was printed in sheets of 10 that sold for €20.

Flag of Finland and Candles — A1010

Serpentine Die Cut 11½ Syncopated
2016, Nov. 4   **Litho.**
Self-Adhesive
1524   A1010   (€1.20) multi   —   —
No. 1524 was printed in sheets of 10 that sold for €15.

Church, Soini A1011

Wooden Pauper Statue, Soini A1012

Wooden Pauper Statue, Alajärvi — A1013

Church, Alajärvi A1014

Church, Hauho — A1015

Wooden Pauper Statue, Hauho — A1016

Sawtooth Die Cut 6
2016, Nov. 10   **Litho.**
Self-Adhesive
1525   Booklet pane of 6   16.00
a. A1011 (€1.20) multi   2.60 2.60
b. A1012 (€1.20) multi   2.60 2.60
c. A1013 (€1.20) multi   2.60 2.60
d. A1014 (€1.20) multi   2.60 2.60
e. A1015 (€1.20) multi   2.60 2.60
f. A1016 (€1.20) multi   2.60 2.60

Reindeer A1017

Girl and Squirrel With Cookies A1018

Snow-covered House — A1019

Die Cut Perf. 7¾
2016, Nov. 10   **Litho.**
Self-Adhesive
1526   A1017   (90c) multi   1.90 1.90
Die Cut Perf. 7¾x7½
1527   A1018   (€1.20) multi   2.60 2.60
Die Cut Perf. 14
1528   A1019   (€1.30) multi   2.75 2.75
Nos. 1526-1528 (3)   7.25 7.25
Etiquettes are found to the sides of No. 1528 in the sheet margin.

Flag of Finland — A1020

Die Cut Perf. 5¾ Horiz.
2017, Jan. 20   **Litho.**
Self-Adhesive
1529   A1020   (€1.20) multi   2.60 2.60

Snow Castle — A1021

Die Cut Perf. 8¾ Horiz.
2017, Jan. 20   **Litho.**
Self-Adhesive
1530   A1021   (€1.20) multi   2.60 2.60
Europa.

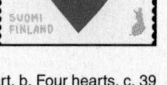

Hearts — A1022

No. 1531: a, One heart. b, Four hearts. c, 39 hearts. d, Two hearts upright. e, Two hearts sideways.

Die Cut Perf. 9½ Vert.
2017, Jan. 20   Litho.
Self-Adhesive

1531	Booklet pane of 5	13.00	
a.-e.	A1022 (€1.20) Any single	2.60	2.60

Souvenir Sheet

Lions Clubs International,
Cent. — A1023

No. 1532 — Various Lions pins and Lions International emblem, with map of Finland at: a, LL. b, UL.

Die Cut Perf. 12¾x12¼
2017, Jan. 20   Litho.
Self-Adhesive

1532	A1023 Sheet of 2	5.25	
a.-b.	(€1.20) Either single	2.60	2.60

Flowers in
Cup — A1024

Die Cut Perf. 12½
2017, Feb. 24   Litho.
Self-Adhesive

1533	A1024 (€1.20) multi	2.60	2.60

Pussy
Willows — A1025

Die Cut Perf. 8½x8¼
2017, Feb. 24   Litho.
Self-Adhesive

1534	A1025 (€1.20) multi	2.60	2.60

Carousel — A1026

Die Cut Perf. 8½x8¼
2017, Feb. 24   Litho.
Self-Adhesive

1535	A1026 (€1.20) multi	2.60	2.60

Fishermen in
Boat — A1027

Reflection of
Clouds in
Lake — A1028

Swans — A1029

Die Cut Perf. Horiz.
2017, Feb. 24   Litho.
Self-Adhesive

1536	Vert. strip of 3 + 3 etiquettes	8.25	
a.	A1027 (€1.30) multi + etiquette	2.75	2.75
b.	A1028 (€1.30) multi + etiquette	2.75	2.75
c.	A1029 (€1.30) multi + etiquette	2.75	2.75

Wings of Thoughts Type of 2016
Die Cut Perf. 13¾
2017, Mar. 11   Litho.
Self-Adhesive

1537	A991 €2 multi		

Miniature Sheet

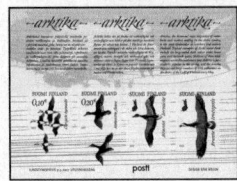

Arctic
Birds
A1030

No. 1538: a, Clangula hyemalis (27x27mm). b, Melanitta fusca (27x27mm). c, Branta bernicla (27x39mm). d, Branta leucopsis (27x39mm).

Die Cut Perf. 13¼
2017, May 9   Litho.
Self-Adhesive

1538	A1030 Sheet of 4	6.75	
a.	10c multi	.25	.25
b.	20c multi	.45	.45
c.-d.	(€1.30) Either single	3.00	3.00

Nos. 1538a and 1538b were each printed in sheets of 15.

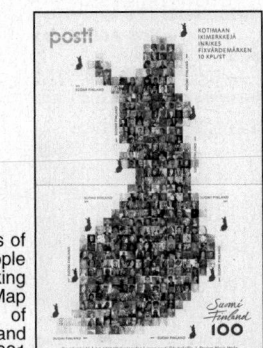

Faces of
People
Making
Up Map
of
Finland
A1031

No. 1539 — Approximate areas of map of Finland: a, Northwestern Lappi Province. b, Northeastern Lappi Province, vert. c, Southwestern Lappi Province and upper Gulf of Bothnia, vert. d, Southeastern Lappi Province and northeastern Oulu Province, vert. e, Southwestern Oulu Province and northern Vaasa Province. f, Eastern Oulu Province. g, Southern Vaasa Province and northern Turku ja Pori Province. h, Mikkeli Province and southern Kuopio and Pohjois-Karjala Provinces. i, Aland Islands and Southern Turku ja Pori Province. j, Uusimaa and Kymi Provinces.

2017, May 9   Litho.   Die Cut Perf. 13
Self-Adhesive

1539	A1031 Booklet pane of 10	30.00	
a.-j.	(€1.30) Any single	3.00	3.00

Independence, cent.

Sauna
A1032

Sauna
A1033

Sauna
A1034

Sauna
A1035

Sauna
Bucket and
Birch Branch
Whisk
A1036

Die Cut Perf. 6 Horiz.
2017, May 24   Litho.
Self-Adhesive

1540	Booklet pane of 5	15.00	
a.	A1032 (€1.30) multi	3.00	3.00
b.	A1033 (€1.30) multi	3.00	3.00
c.	A1034 (€1.30) multi	3.00	3.00
d.	A1035 (€1.30) multi	3.00	3.00
e.	A1036 (€1.30) multi	3.00	3.00

See Aland Islands Nos. 396-397.

A1037

A1038

A1039

A1040

Moomin
Characters
A1041

Die Cut Perf. 7 Horiz.
2017, May 24   Litho.
Self-Adhesive

1541	Booklet pane of 5 + 5 etiquettes	16.50	
a.	A1037 (€1.40) multi	3.25	3.25
b.	A1038 (€1.40) multi	3.25	3.25
c.	A1039 (€1.40) multi	3.25	3.25
d.	A1040 (€1.40) multi	3.25	3.25
e.	A1041 (€1.40) multi	3.25	3.25

Souvenir Sheets

A1042

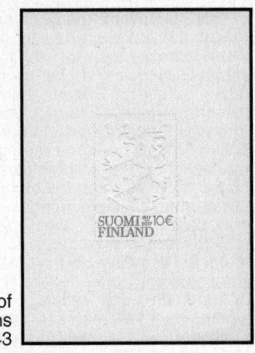

Coat of
Arms
A1043

Die Cut Perf. 10
2017, May 24   Litho.
Self-Adhesive

1542	A1042 Sheet of 2	6.00	
a.	(€1.30) green	3.00	3.00
b.	(€1.30) blue	3.00	3.00

Souvenir Sheet
Embossed With Foil Application
Die Cut Perf. 13¼

1543	A1043 €10 gold	22.50	22.50

Independence, cent. Finlandia 2017 Stamp Exhibition, Tampere (No. 1542).

Children's
Art — A1044

Serpentine Die Cut 11½ Syncopated
2017, May 24   Litho.
Self-Adhesive

1544	A1044 (€1.30) multi		

Pres. Mauno Koivisto
(1923-2017)
A1045

Die Cut Perf. 13¾
2017, June 9   Litho.
Self-Adhesive

1545	A1045 (€1.30) multi	3.00	3.00

2017 Tall Ship
Races,
Turku — A1046

Serpentine Die Cut 11½ Syncopated
2017, July 20   Litho.
Self-Adhesive

1546	A1046 (€1.30) multi	—	—

A1047

A1048

Figurines
A1049

Die Cut Perf. 8½
2017, Sept. 6   Litho.
Self-Adhesive

1547	Strip of 3	9.75	
a.	A1047 (€1.30) multi	3.25	3.25
b.	A1048 (€1.30) multi	3.25	3.25
c.	A1049 (€1.30) multi	3.25	3.25

City Parks — A1050

No. 1548 — Park in: a, Porvoo. b, Hämeen-linna. c, Turku.

Die Cut Perf. 10¼

2017, Sept. 6			Litho.
	Self-Adhesive		
1548	Strip of 3	9.75	
a.-c.	A1050 (€1.30) Any single	3.25	3.25

Flower in Spring A1051

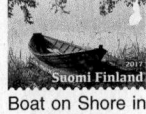

Boat on Shore in Summer A1052

Lake in Autumn A1053

Ice in Winter A1054

Die Cut Perf. 9½ Horiz.

2017, Sept. 6			Litho.
	Coil Stamps		
	Self-Adhesive		
1549	A1051 (€1.30) multi	3.25	3.25
1550	A1052 (€1.30) multi	3.25	3.25
1551	A1053 (€1.30) multi	3.25	3.25
1552	A1054 (€1.30) multi	3.25	3.25
a.	Horiz. strip of 4, #1549-1552	13.00	
	Nos. 1549-1552 (4)	13.00	13.00

Baron Carl Gustaf Emil Mannerheim (1867-1951), President of Finland — A1055

Serpentine Die Cut 11½ Syncopated

2017, Sept. 6			Litho.
	Self-Adhesive		
1553	A1055 (€1.30) multi	2.00	1.00

Wings of ThoughtsType of 2016

Die Cut Perf. 13¾

2017, Oct. 2			Litho.
	Self-Adhesive		
1554	A991 €2.10 multi	—	—

Presidential Palace, Helsinki A1056

President Sauli Niinistö, His Three Predecessors and Their Spouses A1057

Woman in Dressing Room — A1058

Pres. Niinistö Shaking Hands A1059

Formal Ball — A1060

Children Watching Pres. Niinistö Shaking Hands A1061

Serpentine Die Cut 9 Syncopated

2017, Nov. 3			Litho.
	Self-Adhesive		
1555	Booklet pane of 6	21.00	
a.	A1056 (€1.40) multi	3.50	3.50
b.	A1057 (€1.40) multi	3.50	3.50
c.	A1058 (€1.40) multi	3.50	3.50
d.	A1059 (€1.40) multi	3.50	3.50
e.	A1060 (€1.40) multi	3.50	3.50
f.	A1061 (€1.40) multi	3.50	3.50

Independence of Finland, cent.

Snow Queen — A1062

Die Cut Perf. 14¾x14

2017, Nov. 3			Litho.
	Self-Adhesive		
1556	A1062 (€1.40) multi	3.50	3.50

Candles in Christmas Tree A1063

Man and Squirrels Holding Candles A1064

Die Cut Perf. 14½x14¾

2017, Nov. 3			Litho.
	Self-Adhesive		
1557	A1063 (95c) multi	2.25	2.25

Die Cut Perf. 14¾x14

1558	A1064 (€1.40) multi	3.50	3.50

Christmas.

Souvenir Sheet

Zacharias Topelius (1818-98), Writer — A1065

No. 1559: a, Portrait of Topelius by Albert Edelfelt (39x36mm). b, Cradle and Angel Guardians, painting by Rudolf Koivu (39x29mm).

Die Cut Perf. 6½

2018, Jan. 24			Litho.
	Self-Adhesive		
1559	A1065 Sheet of 2	7.00	
a.-b.	(€1.40) Either single	3.50	3.50

A1066

A1067

A1068

A1069

St. Valentine's Day — A1070

Die Cut Perf. 13x12¾

2018, Jan. 24			Litho.
	Self-Adhesive		
1560	Booklet pane of 5	17.50	
a.	A1066 (€1.40) multi	3.50	3.50
b.	A1067 (€1.40) multi	3.50	3.50
c.	A1068 (€1.40) multi	3.50	3.50
d.	A1069 (€1.40) multi	3.50	3.50
e.	A1070 (€1.40) multi	3.50	3.50

Aurora Borealis A1071

Reindeer A1072

Die Cut Perf. 8½ Horiz.

2018, Jan. 24			Litho.
	Self-Adhesive		
1561	Horiz. pair	7.50	
a.	A1071 (€1.50) multi + etiquette	3.75	3.75
b.	A1072 (€1.50) multi + etiquette	3.75	3.75

Worldwide Fund for Nature (WWF) — A1073

No. 1562: a, Vulpes lagopus. b, Bubo scandiacus. c, Salmo salar.

Die Cut Perf. 8½ Horiz.

2018, Feb. 28			Litho.
	Self-Adhesive		
1562	Vert. strip of 3	10.50	
a.-c.	A1073 (€1.40) Any single	3.50	3.50

A1074

A1075

Easter — A1076

Die Cut Perf. 12½

2018, Feb. 28			Litho.
	Self-Adhesive		
1563	Vert. strip of 3	10.50	
a.	A1074 (€1.40) multi	3.50	3.50
b.	A1075 (€1.40) multi	3.50	3.50
c.	A1076 (€1.40) multi	3.50	3.50

Wooden Bridge, Humppila A1077

Wooden Bridge, Suomussalmi A1078

Serpentine Die Cut 7 Horiz.

2018, May 9			Litho.
	Self-Adhesive		
1564	Horiz. pair	7.00	
a.	A1077 (€1.50) multi	3.50	3.50
b.	A1078 (€1.50) multi	3.50	3.50

Europa.

Gerbera Daisies — A1079

Daisies and Harebells A1080

Peonies — A1081

Hydrangeas A1082

Poppies — A1083

Die Cut Perf. 15¼x14¾

2018, May 9			Litho.
	Self-Adhesive		
1565	Horiz. strip of 5	17.50	
a.	A1079 (€1.50) multi	3.50	3.50
b.	A1080 (€1.50) multi	3.50	3.50
c.	A1081 (€1.50) multi	3.50	3.50
d.	A1082 (€1.50) multi	3.50	3.50
e.	A1083 (€1.50) multi	3.50	3.50

1918 Airplane A1084

2018 Airplane A1085

1918 Soldier A1086

2018 Soldier A1087

1918 Ship A1088

2018 Ship A1089

Die Cut Perf. 8¼ Horiz.
2018, June 4   Litho.
Self-Adhesive

1566	Booklet pane of 6	21.00	
a.	A1084 (€1.50) multi	3.50	3.50
b.	A1085 (€1.50) multi	3.50	3.50
c.	A1086 (€1.50) multi	3.50	3.50
d.	A1087 (€1.50) multi	3.50	3.50
e.	A1088 (€1.50) multi	3.50	3.50
f.	A1089 (€1.50) multi	3.50	3.50

Finnish Defense Forces, cent.

Fish — A1090

No. 1567: a, Sander lucioperca. b, Coregonus albula.

Die Cut Perf. 12½ Horiz. at Bottom
2018, June 6   Litho.
Self-Adhesive

1567	Horiz. pair	7.00	
a.-b.	A1090 (€1.50) Either single	3.50	3.50

A1091

A1092

A1093

A1094

A1095

Popular Foods and Beverages A1096

Sawtooth Die Cut 9¾
2018, June 6   Litho.
Self-Adhesive

1568	Booklet pane of 6	21.00	
a.	A1091 (€1.50) multi	3.50	3.50
b.	A1092 (€1.50) multi	3.50	3.50
c.	A1093 (€1.50) multi	3.50	3.50
d.	A1094 (€1.50) multi	3.50	3.50
e.	A1095 (€1.50) multi	3.50	3.50
f.	A1096 (€1.50) multi	3.50	3.50

Miniature Sheet

Traditional Costumes — A1097

No. 1569: a, Woman wearing bonnet (37x25mm). b, Brooch (25x30mm). c, Tasseled scarf and jacket (25x30mm). d, Skirt with horizontal stripes (37x25mm). e, Skirt with vertical stripes (37x25mm). f, Bottom of skirt, stockings and shoes (25x30mm).

Sawtooth Die Cut 5⅜x6, 6x6½
2018, June 6   Litho.
Self-Adhesive

1569	A1097	Sheet of 6	21.00	
a.-f.		(€1.50) Any single	3.50	3.50

Grafitti by EGS on Building, Melbourne, Australia A1098

Grafitti by EGS on Truck, St. Petersburg, Russia A1099

Serpentine Die Cut 6¾ Horiz.
2018, Sept. 12   Litho.
Self-Adhesive

1570	Horiz. pair	7.00	
a.	A1098 (€1.50) multi	3.50	3.50
b.	A1099 (€1.50) multi	3.50	3.50

Seven-spot Ladybug A1100

Whooper Swans A1101

Brown Bears — A1102

Lily of the Valley — A1103

Finnish Spitz — A1104

Die Cut Perf. 9½ Horiz.
2018, Sept. 12   Litho.
Coil Stamps
Self-Adhesive

1571	Horiz. strip of 5	17.50	
a.	A1100 (€1.50) multi	3.50	3.50
b.	A1101 (€1.50) multi	3.50	3.50
c.	A1102 (€1.50) multi	3.50	3.50
d.	A1103 (€1.50) multi	3.50	3.50
e.	A1104 (€1.50) multi	3.50	3.50

Finnish national flora and fauna.

Park in Pori — A1105

Park in Hanko — A1106

Park in Kotka — A1107

Die Cut Perf. 10¼
2018, Sept. 12   Litho.

1572	Vert. strip of 3	10.50	
a.	A1105 (€1.50) multi	3.50	3.50
b.	A1106 (€1.50) multi	3.50	3.50
c.	A1107 (€1.50) multi	3.50	3.50

Souvenir Sheet

Climate Change A1108

No. 1573 — Silhouette of: a, Cloud and snowflakes. b, Arrows and map of Finalnd. c, Bird.

Litho. & Silk-Screened
2018, Sept. 12   **Sawtooth Die Cut 4**
Self-Adhesive

1573	A1108	Sheet of 3	10.50	
a.-c.		(€1.50) Any single	3.50	3.50

Parts of the designs of Nos. 1573a-1573c were printed with thermographic ink, which changes color when warmed.

Rowanberries in Snow A1109

Die Cut Perf. 8½ Horiz.
2018, Nov. 7   Litho.
Self-Adhesive

1574	A1109 (€1.50) multi	3.50	3.50

Ice Skates — A1110

Die Cut Perf. 13x13½
2018, Nov. 7   Litho.
Self-Adhesive

1575	A1110 (€1.60) multi	3.75	3.75

Ornament on Christmas Tree Branch A1111

Candles A1112

Die Cut Perf. 13½x13¼
2018, Nov. 7   Litho.
Self-Adhesive

1576	A1111 (€1.05) multi	2.40	2.40

Die Cut Perf. 13¼x13½

1577	A1112 (€1.50) multi	3.50	3.50

Christmas.

Ice Fishing A1113

Swimming in Ice Water — A1114

Die Cut Perf. 8¾ Horiz.
2019, Jan. 23   Litho.
Self-Adhesive

1578	Horiz. pair	7.00	
a.	A1113 (€1.50) multi	3.50	3.50
b.	A1114 (€1.50) multi	3.50	3.50

Sharing of Joy — A1115

No. 1579: a, Woman writing post card, white cat. b, Two women walking dogs. c, Two women swimming. d, Two women having tea. e, Woman and child on sled. f, Man giving flower to woman.

2019, Jan. 23   Litho.   **Die Cut**
Self-Adhesive

1579	Booklet pane of 6	21.00	
a.-f.	A1115 (€1.50) Any single	3.50	3.50

Miniature Sheet

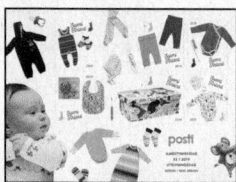

Layette Items A1116

No. 1580: a, Striped baby onesie with snaps, socks. b, Two pairs of pants. c, Long sleeve baby onesie, hair brush. d, Children's book, bib. e, Storage box. f, Long sleeve baby onesie with animal print, bonnet.

Sawtooth Die Cut 17½
2019, Jan. 23   Litho.
Self-Adhesive

1580	A1116	Sheet of 6	21.00	
a.-f.		(€1.50) Any single	3.50	3.50

A1117

Easter — A1118

Reversed Die Cut Perf. 4¾ Horiz.
2019, Mar. 13   Litho.
Self-Adhesive

1581	Horiz. pair	7.00	
a.	A1117 (€1.50) multi	3.50	3.50
b.	A1118 (€1.50) multi	3.50	3.50

Girl Singing Karaoke A1119

Boy Eating Sushi — A1120

Die Cut Perf. 11x11¼
2019, Mar. 13   Litho.
Self-Adhesive

1582	Horiz. pair	7.50	
a.	A1119 (€1.60) multi	3.75	3.75
b.	A1120 (€1.60) multi	3.75	3.75

Dog With Floral Headdress A1121

Jewelry With Flowers — A1122

Floral Wreath — A1123

Die Cut Perf. 11½ Horiz.
2019, Mar. 13   Litho.
Self-Adhesive

1583	Vert. strip of 3	10.50	
a.	A1121 (€1.50) multi	3.50	3.50
b.	A1122 (€1.50) multi	3.50	3.50
c.	A1123 (€1.50) multi	3.50	3.50
d.	Booklet pane of 15, 5 each #1583a-1583c	52.50	

Miniature Sheet

Helsinki Central Railroad Station A1124

No. 1584: a, Lamps on statues on exterior wall. b, Main entrance, horiz. c, Aerial view of station, horiz. d, Clock tower.

Die Cut Perf. 7 Syncopated
2019, Mar. 13   Litho.
Self-Adhesive

1584	A1124	Sheet of 4	14.00
a.-d.		(€1.50) Any single	3.50 3.50

Cygnus Cygnus
A1125   A1126

Die Cut Perf. 13¼
2019, May 8   Litho.
Self-Adhesive

1585	Vert. pair	7.50	
a.	A1125 (€1.50) multi	3.50	3.50
b.	A1126 (€1.50) multi	3.50	3.50

Europa.

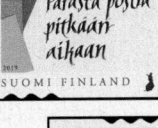

Calligraphy by Marja-Liisa Neuvonen A1127

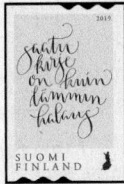

Calligraphy by Taru Tarvainen A1128

Calligraphy by Taru Tarvainen A1129

Calligraphy by Maarit Ali-Marttila-Olkkola A1130

Calligraphy by Iiris Lyra — A1131

Serpentine Die Cut 4 Horiz.
2019, May 8   Litho.
Self-Adhesive

1586	Booklet pane of 5	17.50	
a.	A1127 (€1.50) multi	3.50	3.50
b.	A1128 (€1.50) multi	3.50	3.50
c.	A1129 (€1.50) multi	3.50	3.50
d.	A1130 (€1.50) multi	3.50	3.50
e.	A1131 (€1.50) multi	3.50	3.50

Rose on Letter — A1132

Flowers in Wagon — A1133

Sunflower on Typewriter A1134

Tulips in Watering Can — A1135

Roses in Tea Cup — A1136

Rose on Books — A1137

Die Cut Perf. 12¼
2019, May 8   Litho.
Self-Adhesive

1587	Booklet pane of 6	21.00	
a.	A1132 (€1.50) multi	3.50	3.50
b.	A1133 (€1.50) multi	3.50	3.50
c.	A1134 (€1.50) multi	3.50	3.50
d.	A1135 (€1.50) multi	3.50	3.50
e.	A1136 (€1.50) multi	3.50	3.50
f.	A1137 (€1.50) multi	3.50	3.50

Rantapuisto Park and Siltasaari Island, Heinola A1138

Park Along Loimijoki River, Forssa A1139

Kuopio Cathedral — A1140

Die Cut Perf. 10¼
2019, June 5   Litho.
Self-Adhesive

1588	Vert. strip of 3	10.50	
a.	A1138 (€1.50) multi	3.50	3.50
b.	A1139 (€1.50) multi	3.50	3.50
c.	A1140 (€1.50) multi	3.50	3.50
d.	Booklet pane of 15, 5 each #1588a-1588c	52.50	

A1141

A1142

A1143

A1144

A1145

Moomin Characters A1146

Die Cut Perf. 5¼ Horiz.
2019, June 5   Litho.
Self-Adhesive

1589	Booklet pane of 6	21.00	
a.	A1141 (€1.50) multi	3.50	3.50
b.	A1142 (€1.50) multi	3.50	3.50
c.	A1143 (€1.50) multi	3.50	3.50
d.	A1144 (€1.50) multi	3.50	3.50
e.	A1145 (€1.50) multi	3.50	3.50
f.	A1146 (€1.50) multi	3.50	3.50

Holly Blue Butterfly A1147

Finnhorse A1148

European Perch — A1149

Silver Birch Trees — A1150

Granite Stones — A1151

Die Cut Perf. 9½ Horiz. (horiz. stamps), Die Cut Perf. 9½ Vert. (vert. stamps)
2019, June 5   Litho.
Coil Stamps
Self-Adhesive

1590	A1147	(€1.50) multi	3.50	3.50
1591	A1148	(€1.50) multi	3.50	3.50
1592	A1149	(€1.50) multi	3.50	3.50
1593	A1150	(€1.50) multi	3.50	3.50
1594	A1151	(€1.50) multi	3.50	3.50
a.		Coil strip of 5, #1590-1594	17.50	
		Nos. 1590-1594 (5)	17.50	17.50

House of Kalle Päätalo (1919-2000), Writer A1152

Die Cut Perf. 8½ Horiz.
2019, Sept. 11   Litho.
Self-Adhesive

1595	A1152	(€1.60) multi	3.50	3.50

Calla Lily — A1153

Die Cut Perf. 14
2019, Sept. 11   Litho.
Self-Adhesive

1596	A1153	(€1.60) multi	3.50	3.50

A1154

Women's Clothing Designed by Mert Otsamo — A1155

Litho. With Foil Application
Die Cut Perf. 13x13½
2019, Sept. 11   **Self-Adhesive**

1597	Vert. pair	7.00	
a.	A1154 (€1.60) multi	3.50	3.50
b.	A1155 (€1.60) multi	3.50	3.50

Boy and Puppies — A1156

Girl and Puppy — A1157

Serpentine Die Cut 9½ Horiz.
2019, Sept. 11   Litho.
Self-Adhesive

1598	Pair	7.00	
a.	A1156 (€1.60) multi	3.50	3.50
b.	A1157 (€1.60) multi	3.50	3.50
c.	Booklet pane of 2, #1598a-1598b	7.00	

Snowflakes and Trees — A1158

Litho. With Foil Application
2019, Nov. 6   **Die Cut Perf. 4 Horiz.**
Self-Adhesive

1599	A1158	(€1.60) multi	3.50	3.50

Elves A1159

Carolers, Dog and Cat A1160

Snowman and Rabbits — A1161

Die Cut Perf. 13½x13¼
2019, Nov. 6   **Litho.**
Self-Adhesive
1600	A1159	(€1.10) multi	2.50	2.50

Die Cut Perf. 13
1601	A1160	(€1.60) multi	3.50	3.50
a.		Booklet pane of 5	17.50	

Die Cut Perf. 13¼
1602	A1161	(€1.70) multi	3.75	3.75
		Nos. 1600-1602 (3)	9.75	9.75

A1162

Children's Art — A1163

Litho. With Foil Application
Die Cut Perf. 13¼x13½
2020, Jan. 22   **Self-Adhesive**
1603		Pair	7.00	
a.	A1162	(€1.60) silver & multi	3.50	3.50
b.	A1163	(€1.60) silver & multi	3.50	3.50

Mannerheim League for Child Welfare, cent.

People Near Campfire A1164

Women With Ice Cream Cones A1165

Woman Blowing Bubbles A1166

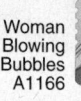

People at Rock Concert A1167

Men on Carousel Horses A1168

Woman and Child on Swings A1169

Die Cut Perf. 7½ Syncopated
2020, Jan. 22   **Litho.**
Self-Adhesive
1604		Booklet pane of 6	21.00	
a.	A1164	(€1.60) multi	3.50	3.50
b.	A1165	(€1.60) multi	3.50	3.50
c.	A1166	(€1.60) multi	3.50	3.50
d.	A1167	(€1.60) multi	3.50	3.50
e.	A1168	(€1.60) multi	3.50	3.50
f.	A1169	(€1.60) multi	3.50	3.50

Moomin in Rowboat A1170

Moomin and Seahorse in Water — A1171

Snufkin Fishing — A1172

Moomin, Pearl and Shell — A1173

Whale Lifting Moomin's Rowboat A1174

Mymble in Pot Floating in Water — A1175

Serpentine Die Cut 5¼ Horiz.
2020, Jan. 22   **Litho.**
Self-Adhesive
1605		Booklet pane of 6	21.00	
a.	A1170	(€1.60) multi	3.50	3.50
b.	A1171	(€1.60) multi	3.50	3.50
c.	A1172	(€1.60) multi	3.50	3.50
d.	A1173	(€1.60) multi	3.50	3.50
e.	A1174	(€1.60) multi	3.50	3.50
f.	A1175	(€1.60) multi	3.50	3.50

Two Hearts A1176

Serpentine Die Cut 5
2020, Mar. 11   **Litho.**
Self-Adhesive
1606	A1176	(€1.60) gold & red	3.50	3.50

Chicken, Chicks and Chick in Egg — A1177

Birds on Tree — A1178

2020, Mar. 11   **Litho.**   **Die Cut**
Self-Adhesive
1607		Pair	7.00	
a.	A1177	(€1.60) multi	3.50	3.50
b.	A1178	(€1.60) multi	3.50	3.50

Easter.

Souvenir Sheet

Birds A1179

No. 1608: a, Bird on branch. b, Birds in flight. c, Bird on ground facing right. d, Bird on ground facing left.

Serpentine Die Cut 11½x11¾
2020, Mar. 11   **Litho.**
Self-Adhesive
1608	A1179	Sheet of 4	14.00	
a.-d.		(€1.60) Any single	3.50	3.50

Flag of Finland and Reflection A1180

Die Cut Perf. 8 Vert. Syncopated
2020, May 6   **Litho.**
Self-Adhesive
1609	A1180	(€1.60) multi	3.75	3.75

Owl — A1181

Stylized Tree — A1182

Die Cut Perf. 13½x13
2020, May 6   **Litho.**
Self-Adhesive
1610		Horiz. pair	7.50	
a.	A1181	(€1.60) gold & multi	3.75	3.75
b.	A1182	(€1.60) silver & multi	3.75	3.75

Sleigh of Santa Claus in Flight A1183

Serpentine Die Cut 7¼ Horiz.
Litho. With Foil Application
2020, May 6
Self-Adhesive
1611	A1183	(€1.70) multi	3.75	3.75

Europa.

Squirrel A1184

Hedgehog A1185

Die Cut Perf. 8¾ Horiz.
2020, June 3   **Litho.**
Self-Adhesive
1612		Horiz. pair	7.50	
a.	A1184	(€1.60) multi	3.75	3.75
b.	A1185	(€1.60) multi	3.75	3.75

Heart Rate Monitor, 1975 A1186

Xylitol, 1974 A1187

Wobbler Fishing Lure, 1936 A1188

Abloy Parking Meter Locks, 1907 A1189

Reflex Pedestrian Reflector, 1965 A1190

Snow Tire, 1934 A1191

Die Cut Perf. 11¾ Horiz.
2020, June 3   **Litho.**
Self-Adhesive
1613		Booklet pane of 6	22.50	
a.	A1186	(€1.60) multi	3.75	3.75
b.	A1187	(€1.60) multi	3.75	3.75
c.	A1188	(€1.60) multi	3.75	3.75
d.	A1189	(€1.60) multi	3.75	3.75
e.	A1190	(€1.60) multi	3.75	3.75
f.	A1191	(€1.60) multi	3.75	3.75

Items created in Finland.

A1192

A1193

A1194

A1195

A1196

A1197

A1198

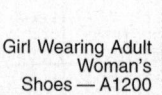

Flowers — A1199

Serpentine Die Cut 7½ Horiz.
2020, June 3   **Litho.**
Coil Stamps
Self-Adhesive
1614	A1192	(€1.60) multi	3.75	3.75
1615	A1193	(€1.60) multi	3.75	3.75
1616	A1194	(€1.60) multi	3.75	3.75
1617	A1195	(€1.60) multi	3.75	3.75
1618	A1196	(€1.60) multi	3.75	3.75
1619	A1197	(€1.60) multi	3.75	3.75
1620	A1198	(€1.60) multi	3.75	3.75
1621	A1199	(€1.60) multi	3.75	3.75
a.		Horiz. coil strip of 8, #1614-1621	30.00	
		Nos. 1614-1621 (8)	30.00	30.00

Girl Wearing Adult Woman's Shoes — A1200

Die Cut Perf. 10¾ Vert.
2020, Sept. 2   **Litho.**
Self-Adhesive
1622	A1200	(€1.75) multi	4.25	4.25

In the Duet, Art by Janne Laine — A1201

The Afterglow,
Art by
Laine — A1202

Die Cut Perf. 13½
2020, Sept. 2   Litho.
Self-Adhesive
1623   Horiz. pair   8.50
 a. A1201 (€1.75) multi   4.25 4.25
 b. A1202 (€1.75) multi   4.25 4.25

Miniature Sheet

International Literacy Day — A1203

No. 1624 — Various faces made from letters
and symbols with background colors of: a,
Light green. b, Pink. c, Pale yellow green. d,
Light blue.

Sawtooth Die Cut 11¼ Horiz.
2020, Sept. 2   Litho.
Self-Adhesive
1624 A1203 Sheet of 4   17.00
 a.-d.   (€1.75) Any single   4.25 4.25

Children's Book Characters Tatu and
Patu — A1204

No. 1625: a, Patu repairing rip with tape
(40x31mm). b, Tatu with pencil (40x31mm). c,
Patu peeling back edge of stamp design
(40x33mm). d, Tatu and Patu shaking hands
(51x37mm). e, Tatu looking through circle
(38x33mm). f, Tatu using scissors (40x31mm).

2020, Sept. 2 Litho. *Die Cut Perf. 7*
Self-Adhesive
1625 A1204 Booklet pane of 6 25.50
 a.-f.   (€1.75) Any single   4.25 4.25

In the vignettes of Nos. 1625a, 1625e and
1625f, small areas enclosed by die cutting
may adhere to the backing when the stamps
are removed.

Christmas — A1205

A1206

A1207

Christmas — A1208

Die Cut Perf. 12¼x13
2020, Nov. 4   Litho.
Self-Adhesive
1626 A1205 (€1.20) multi   3.00 3.00

Die Cut Perf. 13x12¼
1627 A1206 (€1.75) multi   4.25 4.25
Die Cut Perf. 8¾ Horiz.
1628 A1207 (€1.75) multi   4.25 4.25
Die Cut
1629 A1208 (€1.85) multi +   4.50 4.50
            etiquette
 Nos. 1626-1629 (4)   16.00 16.00

Union of Journalists in
Finland, Cent. — A1209

Die Cut Perf. 14½
2021, Jan. 20   Litho.
Self-Adhesive
1630 A1209 (€1.75) black &   4.25 4.25
            multi

Columbines
A1210

Day Lily
A1211

Die Cut Perf. 13x12½
2021, Jan. 20   Litho.
Self-Adhesive
1631   Horiz. pair   8.50
 a. A1210 (€1.75) multi   4.25 4.25
 b. A1211 (€1.75) multi   4.25 4.25
 c. Souvenir sheet of 2, #1631a- 8.50
      1631b

A1212

A1213

A1214

A1215

A1216

Flora and
Fauna — A1217

Serpentine Die Cut 9¾ Horiz.
2021, Jan. 20   Litho.
Self-Adhesive
1632   Booklet pane of 6   25.50
 a. A1212 (€1.75) multi   4.25 4.25
 b. A1213 (€1.75) multi   4.25 4.25
 c. A1214 (€1.75) multi   4.25 4.25
 d. A1215 (€1.75) multi   4.25 4.25
 e. A1216 (€1.75) multi   4.25 4.25
 f. A1217 (€1.75) multi   4.25 4.25

A1218

Flowers — A1219

Die Cut Perf. 9½ Horiz.
2021, Jan. 20   Litho.
Self-Adhesive
1633   Horiz. pair   8.50
 a. A1218 (€1.75) pink & multi   4.25 4.25
 b. A1219 (€1.75) yellow & multi 4.25 4.25

Champagne
Flutes — A1220

Serpentine Die Cut 5 Syncopated
2021, Apr. 28   Litho.
Self-Adhesive
1634 A1220 (€1.75) multi   4.25 4.25

Health Care
Volunteer of
Lotta Svärd
Foundation
A1221

Food Supply
Volunteers of
Lotta Svärd
Foundation
A1222

Die Cut Perf. 7¼ Horiz.
2021, Apr. 28   Litho.
Self-Adhesive
1635   Horiz. pair   8.50
 a. A1221 (€1.75) multi   4.25 4.25
 b. A1222 (€1.75) multi   4.25 4.25

Endangered
Animals — A1223

No. 1636: a, Alcedo atthis. b, Parnassius
apollo. c, Pteromys volans.

Die Cut Perf. 8½ Horiz. Syncopated
2021, Apr. 28   Litho.
Self-Adhesive
1636   Vert. strip of 3   13.00
 a.-c.   A1223 (€1.75) Any single   4.25 4.25

Europa and Worldwide Fund for Nature
(WWF).

First Finnish
Post Card,
1871
A1224

Post Card
Depicting
Farmer and Flag
of
Finland — A1225

Post Card
Depicting Soldier
Writing
Home — A1226

Post Card
Depicting Elf
and
Princess
A1227

Post Card
Depicting Porvoo
A1228

Post Card
With
Sender's
Photograph
A1229

Die Cut Perf. 8¾x8½ Syncopated
2021, Apr. 28   Litho.
Self-Adhesive
1637   Booklet pane of 6   25.50
 a. A1224 (€1.75) multi   4.25 4.25
 b. A1225 (€1.75) multi   4.25 4.25
 c. A1226 (€1.75) multi   4.25 4.25
 d. A1227 (€1.75) multi   4.25 4.25
 e. A1228 (€1.75) multi   4.25 4.25
 f. A1229 (€1.75) multi   4.25 4.25
Finnish post cards, 150th anniv.

Cactus
Pigga,
Blown Glass
by Alma
Jantunen
A1230

Fruit Bottles,
Blown Glass
by Alma
Jantunen
A1231

Die Cut Perf. 13x13½
2021, Sept. 8   Litho.
Self-Adhesive
1638   Vert. pair   8.50
 a. A1230 (€1.85) multi   4.25 4.25
 b. A1231 (€1.85) multi   4.25 4.25

Dinner Plate,
Fork and
Knife — A1232

Running
Legs — A1233

Sleeping
Snowman
A1234

Stylized
Recycling
Emblem
A1235

Shower Head
and
Water — A1236

Earth — A1237

Die Cut Perf. 9¾ Horiz.
2021, Sept. 8   Litho.
Self-Adhesive
1639   Booklet pane of 6   25.50
 a. A1232 (€1.85) multi   4.25 4.25
 b. A1233 (€1.85) multi   4.25 4.25
 c. A1234 (€1.85) multi   4.25 4.25
 d. A1235 (€1.85) multi   4.25 4.25
 e. A1236 (€1.85) multi   4.25 4.25
 f. A1237 (€1.85) multi   4.25 4.25
Sustainable living.

Miniature Sheet

Autumnal Landscapes — A1238

No. 1640: a, Sun over wheat field (60x26mm). b, Moon over red house (60x26mm). c, Birch trees along dirt road (60x26mm). d, Lake and boat ramp (26x43mm). e, Forest with sun near horizon (26x43mm).

Die Cut Perf. 10¾

2021, Sept. 8   Litho.

Self-Adhesive

1640	A1238	Sheet of 5	21.50	
a.-e.		(€1.85) Any single	4.25	4.25

Echo, Painting by Ellen Thesleff (1869-1954) A1239

Boys Playing on the Shore, Painting by Albert Edelfelt (1854-1905) A1240

Skaters Near the Shore of Kalela, Painting by Akseli Gallen-Kallela (1865-1931) A1241

The Convalescent, Painting by Helene Schjerfbeck (1862-1946) A1242

Landscape from Koli, Painting by Eero Järnefelt (1863-1937) A1243

Winter Fishing, Painting by Juho Rissanen (1873-1950) A1244

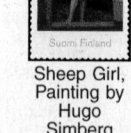

Sheep Girl, Painting by Hugo Simberg (1873-1917) A1245

The Fighting Capercaillies, Painting by Ferdinand von Wright (1822-1906) A1246

Die Cut Perf. 13¼x13½ (#1641, 1643, 1647), Die Cut Perf. 13½x13¼ (others)

2021, Sept. 8   Litho.

Coil Stamps
Self-Adhesive

1641	A1239	(€1.85) multi	4.25	4.25
1642	A1240	(€1.85) multi	4.25	4.25
1643	A1241	(€1.85) multi	4.25	4.25
1644	A1242	(€1.85) multi	4.25	4.25
1645	A1243	(€1.85) multi	4.25	4.25
1646	A1244	(€1.85) multi	4.25	4.25
1647	A1245	(€1.85) multi	4.25	4.25
1648	A1246	(€1.85) multi	4.25	4.25
a.		Strip of 8, #1641-1648	34.00	
		Nos. 1641-1648 (8)	34.00	34.00

Eurasian Bullfinch A1247

Christmas Tree A1248

Dog Catching Snow on Tongue A1249

Snowman A1250

Aurora Borealis — A1251

Serpentine Die Cut 6½

2021, Nov. 3   Litho.

Self-Adhesive

1649	A1247	(€1.30) sil & multi	3.00	3.00
1650	A1248	(€1.85) multi	4.25	4.25

Die Cut

1651		Horiz. pair	8.50	
a.	A1249	(€1.85) multi	4.25	4.25
b.	A1250	(€1.85) multi	4.25	4.25

Serpentine Die Cut 6½

1652	A1251	(€1.95) multi	4.50	4.50

Christmas.

Fazer Blue Chocolate Bar, Cent. — A1252

Serpentine Die Cut 4½ at Bottom

2022, Jan. 19   Litho.

Self-Adhesive

1653	A1252	(€1.85) multi	4.25	4.25

Cat and Bird on Swing — A1253

Clothesline and Trees — A1254

Serpentine Die Cut 13½ Horiz.

2022, Jan. 19   Litho.

Self-Adhesive

1654		Horiz. pair	8.50	
a.	A1253	(€1.85) multi	4.25	4.25
b.	A1254	(€1.85) multi	4.25	4.25

Women and Floor Lamp — A1255

Hand Touching Heart — A1256

Rollerskaters A1257

Perfume Bottle — A1258

Women Holding Coffee Cups — A1259

Serpentine Die Cut 7¼ Horiz.

2022, Jan. 19   Litho.

Booklet Stamps
Self-Adhesive

1655	A1255	(€1.85) multi	4.25	4.25
1656	A1256	(€1.85) multi	4.25	4.25
1657	A1257	(€1.85) multi	4.25	4.25
1658	A1258	(€1.85) multi	4.25	4.25
1659	A1259	(€1.85) multi	4.25	4.25
a.		Booklet pane of 10, 2 each #1655-1659	42.50	
		Nos. 1655-1659 (5)	21.25	21.25

Goddess Päivätär A1260

Goddess Kuutar A1261

Serpentine Die Cut 7 Syncopated

2022, Apr. 27   Litho.

Self-Adhesive

1660		Vert. pair	9.00	
a.	A1260	(€2.05) sil & multi	4.50	4.50
b.	A1261	(€2.05) multi	4.50	4.50

Europa.

Women Outside the Church at Ruokolahti, Painting by Albert Edelfelt (1854-1905) A1262

The Washerwomen, Painting by Tyko Sallinen (1879-1955) A1263

Dancing Shoes, Painting by Helene Schjerfbeck (1862-1946) A1264

The Luxembourg Gardens, Paris, Painting by Edelfelt A1265

Boy and a Crow, Painting by Akseli Gallen-Kallela (1865-1931) A1266

Maidens at the Headlands, Painting by Pekka Halonen (1865-1933) A1267

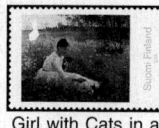

Girl with Cats in a Summer Landscape, Painting by Elin Danielson (1861-1919) A1268

Reading Time, Painting by Ellen Thesleff (1869-1954) A1269

Die Cut Perf. 13x13½, 13½x13

2022, Apr. 27   Litho.

Coil Stamps
Self-Adhesive

1661	A1262	(€1.95) multi	4.25	4.25
1662	A1263	(€1.95) multi	4.25	4.25
1663	A1264	(€1.95) multi	4.25	4.25
1664	A1265	(€1.95) multi	4.25	4.25
1665	A1266	(€1.95) multi	4.25	4.25
1666	A1267	(€1.95) multi	4.25	4.25
1667	A1268	(€1.95) multi	4.25	4.25
1668	A1269	(€1.95) multi	4.25	4.25
a.		Coil strip of 8, #1661-1668	34.00	
		Nos. 1661-1668 (8)	34.00	34.00

Together, by Jenni Tuominen and Jukka Pylväs — A1270

Just Add Water, by Nelli Ahosola A1271

A Bouquet for You, by Anna Kesäniemi A1272

Coffee and Cake, by Tuomas Ikonen A1273

Flower Delivery, by Noora Katto — A1274

Die Cut Perf. 8½x9

2022, Apr. 27   Litho.

Booklet Stamps
Self-Adhesive

1669	A1270	(€1.95) multi	4.25	4.25

Serpentine Die Cut 5 Horiz.

1670	A1271	(€1.95) multi	4.25	4.25
1671	A1272	(€1.95) multi	4.25	4.25

Serpentine Die Cut 6

1672	A1273	(€1.95) multi	4.25	4.25

Die Cut

1673	A1274	(€1.95) multi	4.25	4.25
a.		Booklet pane of 10, 2 each #1669-1673	42.50	
		Nos. 1669-1673 (5)	21.25	21.25

Winning entries in stamp design contest.

Miniature Sheet

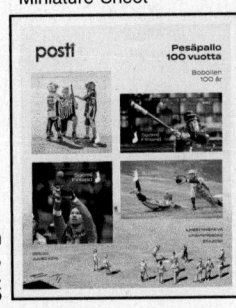

Finnish Baseball, Cent. A1275

No. 1674: a, Players and umpire with bat (30x30mm). b, Batter (40x20mm). c, Pitcher throwing ball (30x30mm). d, Fielder catching ball and runner sliding into base (40x20mm).

Serpentine Die Cut 6 Vert.
2022, Apr. 27   Litho.
Self-Adhesive

1674	A1275	Sheet of 4	17.00	
a.-d.		(€1.95) Any single	4.25	4.25

Bubblegum Girl, Sculpture by Kim Simonsson A1276

Sleeping Reading Moss Girl, Sculpture by Simonsson A1277

Die Cut Perf. 8¼ Vert.
2022, Sept. 7   Litho.
Self-Adhesive

1675	Vert. pair	8.00	
a.	A1276 (€1.95) multi	4.00	4.00
b.	A1277 (€1.95) multi	4.00	4.00

Moomin Characters and Letters of the Alphabet A1278

No. 1676 — Various Moomin characters and: a, "A." b, "B." c, "C." d, "D." e, "E." f, "F."

Die Cut Perf. 5¼ Horiz.
2022, Sept. 7   Litho.
Self-Adhesive

1676	Booklet pane of 6	24.00	
a.-f.	A1278 (€1.95) Any single	4.00	4.00

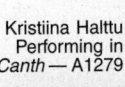 Kristiina Halttu Performing in *Canth* — A1279

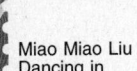 Miao Miao Liu Dancing in *COW* — A1280

 Various Actors in Lifeboat in Performance of *The Eleventh Moment* — A1281

 Michal Krcmár and Zhiyao Chen Dancing in *The Nutcracker and the Mouse King* — A1282

 Hannu-Pekka Björkman Performing in *Death of a Salesman* A1283

 Xiaoyu He Dancing in *The Sleeping Beauty* — A1284

 Minka Kuustonen, Jukka Puotila and Paula Simes Performing in *Exit the King* — A1285

 Hanako Matsune Dancing in *Swan Lake* — A1286

 Finnish National Theater — A1287

 Sergei Popov and Tiina Myllymäki Dancing in *The Little Mermaid* A1288

Die Cut Perf. 3¾ Vert.
2022, Sept. 7   Litho.
Self-Adhesive

1677	Booklet pane of 10	40.00	
a.	A1279 (€1.95) multi	4.00	4.00
b.	A1280 (€1.95) multi	4.00	4.00
c.	A1281 (€1.95) multi	4.00	4.00
d.	A1282 (€1.95) multi	4.00	4.00
e.	A1283 (€1.95) multi	4.00	4.00
f.	A1284 (€1.95) multi	4.00	4.00
g.	A1285 (€1.95) multi	4.00	4.00
h.	A1286 (€1.95) multi	4.00	4.00
i.	A1287 (€1.95) multi	4.00	4.00
j.	A1288 (€1.95) multi	4.00	4.00

Finnish National Theater, 150th anniv.; Finnish National Ballet, cent.

A1290

A1291

A1292

A1293

Christmas — A1293

Reversed Serpentine Die Cut 10¾x10¼ (#1679, 1681), Die Cut Perf. 10¾ (#1680)
2022, Nov. 9   Litho.
Self-Adhesive

1679	A1290 (€2.10) multi	4.50	4.50
1680	Horiz. pair	9.00	
a.	A1291 (€2.10) multi	4.50	4.50
b.	A1292 (€2.10) multi	4.50	4.50

Litho. With Foil Application

1681	A1293 (€2.25) multi + eti-quette	4.75	4.75

SEMI-POSTAL STAMPS

Arms — SP1

Unwmk.
1922, May 15   **Typo.**   **Perf. 14**

B1	SP1 1m + 50p gray & red		.90	10.00
	Never hinged		2.00	
a.	Perf. 13x13½		9.00	
	Never hinged		18.00	

Red Cross Standard SP2

Symbolic SP3

 Ship of Mercy — SP4

1930, Feb. 6

B2	SP2 1m + 10p red org & red	1.50	10.00
	Never hinged	3.50	
B3	SP3 1½m + 15p grysh grn & red	1.00	10.00
	Never hinged	2.50	
B4	SP4 2m + 20p dk bl & red	2.50	45.00
	Never hinged	5.50	
	Nos. B2-B4 (3)	5.00	65.00
	Set, never hinged	11.50	

The surtax on this and subsequent similar issues was for the benefit of the Red Cross Society of Finland.

Church in Hattula — SP5

Designs: 1½m+15p, Castle of Hameenlinna. 2m+20p, Fortress of Viipuri.

1931, Jan. 1   **Cross in Red**   **Engr.**

B5	SP5 1m + 10p gray grn	1.50	11.00
	Never hinged	4.00	
B6	SP5 1½m + 15p lil brn	9.00	13.00
	Never hinged	27.50	
B7	SP5 2m + 20p dull bl	1.50	30.00
	Never hinged	4.00	
	Nos. B5-B7 (3)	12.00	54.00
	Set, never hinged	35.50	

 SP8

1931, Oct. 15 Typo.   **Rouletted 4, 5**

B8	SP8 1m + 4m black	8.00	45.00
	Never hinged	22.50	

The surtax was to assist the Postal Museum of Finland in purchasing the Richard Granberg collection of entire envelopes.

Helsinki University Library SP9

Nikolai Church at Helsinki SP10

2½m+25p, Parliament Building, Helsinki.

1932, Jan. 1   **Perf. 14**

B9	SP9 1¼m + 10p ol bis & red	1.50	12.50
	Never hinged	4.00	
B10	SP10 2m + 20p dp vio & red	1.00	8.00
	Never hinged	4.00	
B11	SP9 2½m + 25p lt blue & red	1.80	30.00
	Never hinged	4.50	
	Nos. B9-B11 (3)	4.30	50.50
	Set, never hinged	11.50	

Bishop Magnus Tawast SP12

Michael Agricola SP13

Design: 2½m+25p, Isacus Rothovius.

1933, Jan. 20   **Engr.**

B12	SP12 1¼m + 10p blk brn & red	3.25	9.00
	Never hinged	9.00	
B13	SP13 2m + 20p brn vio & red	.70	4.00
	Never hinged	2.50	
B14	SP13 2½m + 25p indigo & red	.70	7.00
	Never hinged	2.50	
	Nos. B12-B14 (3)	4.65	20.00
	Set, never hinged	14.00	

Evert Horn — SP15

Designs: 2m+20p, Torsten Stalhandske. 2½m+25p, Jakob (Lazy Jake) de la Gardie.

1934, Jan. 20   **Cross in Red**

B15	SP15 1¼m + 10p brown	.80	3.00
	Never hinged	2.50	
B16	SP15 2m + 20p gray lil	1.20	5.50
	Never hinged	6.50	
B17	SP15 2½m + 25p gray	.90	4.50
	Never hinged	3.00	
	Nos. B15-B17 (3)	2.90	13.00
	Set, never hinged	12.00	

Mathias Calonius — SP18

Designs: 2m+20p, Henrik C. Porthan. 2½m+25p, Anders Chydenius.

1935, Jan. 1   **Cross in Red**

B18	SP18 1¼m + 15p brown	.80	2.50
	Never hinged	2.50	
B19	SP18 2m + 20p gray lil	2.00	4.50
	Never hinged	6.00	
B20	SP18 2½m + 25p gray bl	1.00	3.00
	Never hinged	3.00	
	Nos. B18-B20 (3)	3.80	10.00
	Set, never hinged	11.50	

Robert Henrik Rehbinder — SP21

2m+20p, Count Gustaf Mauritz Armfelt. 2½m+25p, Count Arvid Bernard Horn.

1936, Jan. 1   **Cross in Red**

B21	SP21 1¼m + 15p dk brn	.75	3.50
	Never hinged	2.50	
B22	SP21 2m + 20p vio brn	2.50	5.00
	Never hinged	7.00	
B23	SP21 2½m + 25p blue	.75	3.50
	Never hinged	2.50	
	Nos. B21-B23 (3)	4.00	12.00
	Set, never hinged	12.00	

Type "Uusimaa"
SP24

Type
"Turunmaa"
SP25

Design: 3½m+35p, Type "Hameenmaa."

1937, Jan. 1　　　Cross in Red
B24	SP24	1¼m + 15p brown	.60	3.00
		Never hinged	1.75	
B25	SP25	2m + 20p brn lake	11.00	7.50
		Never hinged	37.50	
B26	SP24	3½m + 35p indigo	.75	3.00
		Never hinged	2.00	
		Nos. B24-B26 (3)	12.35	13.50
		Set, never hinged	41.25	

Aukuste
Makipeska — SP27

Designs: 1¼m+15p, Robert Isidor Orn.
2m+20p, Edward Bergenheim. 3½m+35p,
Johan Mauritz Nordenstam.

1938, Jan. 5　Cross in Red　Engr.
B27	SP27	50p + 5p dk grn	.40	1.80
		Never hinged	.95	
B28	SP27	1¼m + 15p dk brn	.70	3.00
		Never hinged	2.00	
B29	SP27	2m + 20p rose		
		lake	6.00	7.00
		Never hinged	14.00	
B30	SP27	3½m + 35p dk blue	.55	3.00
		Never hinged	2.00	
		Nos. B27-B30 (4)	7.65	14.80
		Set, never hinged	18.95	

Skiing — SP31

Designs:　2m+1m,　Ski　jumper.
3.50m+1.50m, Skier.

1938, Jan. 18
B31	SP31	1.25m + 75p sl grn	2.50	11.50
		Never hinged	6.50	
B32	SP31	2m + 1m dk car	2.50	11.50
		Never hinged	6.50	
B33	SP31	3.50m + 1.50m dk		
		blue	2.50	11.50
		Never hinged	6.50	
		Nos. B31-B33 (3)	7.50	34.50
		Set, never hinged	19.50	

Ski championships held at Lahti.

Soldier — SP34

1938, May 16
B34	SP34	2m + ½m blue	1.20	4.00
		Never hinged	3.50	

Victory of the White Army over the Red
Guards. The surtax was for the benefit of the
members of the Union of the Finnish Front.

Battlefield at
Solferino — SP35

1939, Jan. 2　　　Cross in Scarlet
B35	SP35	50p + 5p dk grn	.60	1.50
		Never hinged	1.25	
B36	SP35	1¼m + 15p dk brn	.70	2.50
		Never hinged	1.25	
B37	SP35	2m + 20p lake	10.00	4.00
		Never hinged	27.50	

B38	SP35	3½m + 35p dk bl	.60	2.50
		Never hinged	1.00	
		Nos. B35-B38 (4)	11.90	10.50
		Set, never hinged	31.00	

Intl. Red Cross Soc., 75th anniv.

> **Catalogue values for unused
> stamps in this section, from this
> point to the end of the section, are
> for Never Hinged items.**

Soldiers with
Crossbows — SP36

1¼m+15p, Cavalryman. 2m+20p, Soldier of
Charles XII of Sweden. 3½m+35p, Officer and
soldier of War with Russia, 1808-1809.

1940, Jan. 26　　　Cross in Red
B39	SP36	50p + 5p dk grn	1.80	1.75
B40	SP36	1¼m + 15p dk brn	2.50	2.50
B41	SP36	2m + 20p lake	4.00	3.50
B42	SP36	3½m + 35p dp ultra	1.75	3.50
		Nos. B39-B42 (4)	10.05	11.25

The surtax aided the Finnish Red Cross.

Arms of Finland — SP40

1940, Feb. 15　　　Litho.
B43	SP40	2m +2m indigo	.80	1.50

The surtax was given to a fund for the preservation of neutrality.

Mason — SP41

1.75m+15p, Farmer plowing. 2.75m+25p,
Mother and child. 3.50m+35p, Finnish flag.

1941, Jan. 1　　Cross in Red　Engr.
B44	SP40	50p + 5p green	.80	.80
B45	SP41	1.75m + 15p brown	1.75	2.40
B46	SP41	2.75m + 25p brn car	11.00	8.00
B47	SP41	3.50m + 35p dp ul-		
		tra	1.75	2.50
		Nos. B44-B47 (4)	15.30	13.70

See Nos. B65-B68.

Soldier's
Emblem — SP45

1941, May 24　　　Unwmk.
B48	SP45	2.75m + 25p brt ultra	.80	1.00

The surtax was for the aid of the soldiers
who fought in the Russo-Finnish War.

Aland Arms — SP46

Coats of Arms: 1.75m+15p, Nyland.
2.75m+25p, Finland's first arms. 3.50m+35p,
Karelia. 4.75m+45p, Satakunta.

1942, Jan. 2　　　Perf. 14
Cross in Red
B49	SP46	50p + 5p green	1.00	1.00
B50	SP46	1.75m + 15p brown	1.50	2.50
B51	SP46	2.75m + 25p dark		
		red	2.00	2.50

B52	SP46	3.50m + 35p deep		
		ultra	1.50	4.00
B53	SP46	4.75m + 45p dk sl		
		grn	1.00	3.00
		Nos. B49-B53 (5)	7.00	13.00

The surtax aided the Finnish Red Cross.

Lapland Arms — SP51

Coats　of　Arms:　2m+20p,　Hame.
3.50m+35p, Eastern Bothnia. 4.50m+45p,
Savo.

Cross in Red
1943, Jan. 2　　　Inscribed "1943"
B54	SP51	50p + 5p green	.80	1.20
B55	SP51	2m + 20p brown	1.20	2.00
B56	SP51	3.50m + 35p dark red	1.20	2.00
B57	SP51	4.50m + 45p brt ultra	3.00	11.00
		Nos. B54-B57 (4)	6.20	16.20

The surtax aided the Finnish Red Cross.

Soldier's Helmet
and Sword
SP55

Mother and
Children
SP56

1943, Feb. 1　　　Perf. 13
B58	SP55	2m + 50p dk brown	.50	1.00
B59	SP56	3.50m + 1m brown red	.80	1.00

The surtax was for national welfare.

Red Cross
Train — SP57

2m+50p, Ambulance. 3.50m+75p, Red
Cross Hospital, Helsinki. 4.50m+1m, Hospital
plane.

1944, Jan. 2　Cross in Red　Perf. 14
B60	SP57	50p + 25p green	.25	.40
B61	SP57	2m + 50p sepia	.50	1.20
B62	SP57	3.50m + 75p ver	.50	1.00
B63	SP57	4.50m + 1m brt ultra	1.00	5.00
		Nos. B60-B63 (4)	2.25	7.60

The surtax aided the Finnish Red Cross.

Symbols of
Peace — SP61

1944, Dec. 1
B64	SP61	3.50m + 1.50m dk red		
		brn	.40	.80

The surtax was for national welfare.

Type of 1941 Inscribed "1945"
1945, May 2　　　Photo. & Engr.
Cross in Red
B65	SP41	1m + 25p green	.25	.40
B66	SP41	2m + 50p brown	.25	.80
B67	SP41	3.50m + 75p brn car	.25	.60
B68	SP41	4.50m + 1m dp ultra	.60	2.40
		Nos. B65-B68 (4)	1.35	4.20

The surtax was for the Finnish Red Cross.

Wrestling — SP62

2m+1m, Gymnast. 3.50m+1.75m, Runner.
4.50m+2.25m, Skier. 7m+3.50m, Javelin
thrower.

1945, Apr. 16　　Engr.　　Perf. 13½
B69	SP62	1m + 50p bluish		
		grn	.25	.90
B70	SP62	2m + 1m dp red	.25	.90
B71	SP62	3.50m + 1.75m dull vio	.25	.90
B72	SP62	4.50m + 2.25m ultra	.50	1.20
B73	SP62	7m + 3.50m dull		
		brn	.80	2.00
		Nos. B69-B73 (5)	2.05	5.90

Fishing — SP67

Designs: 3m+75p, Churning. 5m+1.25m,
Reaping. 10m+2.50m, Logging.

Engraved; Cross Typo. in Red
1946, Jan. 7
B74	SP67	1m + 25p dull		
		grn	.40	.50
B75	SP67	3m + 75p lil brn	.25	.40
B76	SP67	5m + 1.25m		
		rose red	.40	.50
a.		Red cross omitted	650.00	650.00
B77	SP67	10m + 2.50m ul-		
		tra	1.00	1.00
		Nos. B74-B77 (4)	1.55	2.40

The surtax was for the Finnish Red Cross.

Nurse and
Children — SP71

Design: 8m+2m, Doctor examining infant.

1946, Sept. 2　　　Engr.
B78	SP71	5m + 1m green	.25	.60
B79	SP71	8m + 2m brown vio	.25	.60

The surtax was for the prevention of
tuberculosis.

**Nos. B78 and B79 Surcharged with
New Values in Black**
1947, Apr. 1
B80	SP71	6m + 1m on 5m + 1m	.40	.70
B81	SP71	10m + 2m on 8m + 2m	.40	.70

The surtax was for the prevention of
tuberculosis.

SP73

Medical Examination of
Infants — SP74

Designs: 10m+2.50m, Infant held by the
feet. 12m+3m, Mme. Alli Paasikivi and a child.
20m+5m, Infant standing.

1947, Sept. 15　　　Engr.
B82	SP73	2.50m + 1m green	.80	1.00
B83	SP74	6m + 1.50m dk		
		red	.80	1.50
B84	SP74	10m + 2.50m red		
		brn	.80	1.50
B85	SP73	12m + 3m dp blue	1.50	2.00
B86	SP74	20m + 5m dk red		
		vio	1.50	3.50
		Nos. B82-B86 (5)	5.40	9.50

The surtax was for the prevention of
tuberculosis.
For surcharges see Nos. B91-B93.

Zachris Topelius — SP78

7m+2m, Fredrik Pacius. 12m+3m, Johan L. Runeberg. 20m+5m, Fredrik Cygnaeus.

Engraved; Cross Typo. in Red
1948, May 10   Unwmk.   Perf. 14

B87	SP78	3m + 1m green	.80	1.00
B88	SP78	7m + 2m rose red	.80	1.50
B89	SP78	12m + 3m brt blue	.75	1.50
B90	SP78	20m + 5m dk vio	1.50	2.50
		Nos. B87-B90 (4)	3.85	6.50

The surtax was for the Finnish Red Cross.

Nos. B83, B84 and B86 Surcharged with New Values and Bars in Black
1948, Sept. 13   Engr.   Perf. 13½

B91	SP74	7m + 2m on #B83	1.50	3.00
B92	SP74	15m + 3m on #B84	1.50	3.00
B93	SP74	24m + 6m on #B86	2.50	4.50
		Nos. B91-B93 (3)	5.50	10.50

The surtax was for the prevention of tuberculosis.

Tying Birch Boughs — SP79

9m+3m, Bathers in Sauna house. 15m+5m, Rural bath house. 30m+10m, Cold plunge in lake.

Engraved; Cross Typo. in Red
1949, May 5   Perf. 13½x14

B94	SP79	5m + 2m dull grn	.90	1.20
B95	SP79	9m + 3m dk car	.90	1.20
B96	SP79	15m + 5m dp blue	.90	4.00
B97	SP79	30m + 10m dk vio brn	2.00	7.20
		Nos. B94-B97 (4)	4.70	13.60

The surtax was for the Finnish Red Cross.

Wood Anemone — SP83

1949, June 2   Engr.
Inscribed: "1949"

B98	SP83	5m + 2m shown	.90	1.00
B99	SP83	9m + 3m Wild rose	1.20	1.50
B100	SP83	15m + 5m Coltsfoot	1.20	1.50
		Nos. B98-B100 (3)	3.30	4.00

The surtax was for the prevention of tuberculosis.

Similar to Type of 1949

Designs: 5m+2m, Water lily. 9m+3m, Pasqueflower. 15m+5m, Bell flower cluster.

1950, Apr. 1   Inscribed: "1950"

B101	SP83	5m + 2m emer	2.70	2.20
B102	SP83	9m + 3m rose car	2.20	1.50
B103	SP83	15m + 5m blue	2.20	1.50
		Nos. B101-B103 (3)	7.10	5.20

The surtax was for the prevention of tuberculosis.

Hospital Entrance, Helsinki SP84

Blood Donor's Medal SP86

Design: 12m+3m, Giving blood.

Engraved; Cross Typo. in Red
1951, Mar. 17   Unwmk.   Perf. 14

B104	SP84	7m + 2m chocolate	2.50	2.00
B105	SP84	12m + 3m bl vio	2.50	2.00
B106	SP84	20m + 5m car	2.50	3.00
		Nos. B104-B106 (3)	7.50	7.00

The surtax was for the Finnish Red Cross.

Capercaillie — SP87

Designs: 12m+3m, European cranes. 20m+5m, Caspian terns.

1951, Oct. 26   Engr.

B107	SP87	7m + 2m dk grn	2.75	2.75
B108	SP87	12m + 3m rose brn	2.75	2.75
B109	SP87	20m + 5m blue	2.75	2.75
		Nos. B107-B109 (3)	8.25	8.25

The surtax was for the prevention of tuberculosis.

Diver SP88

Soccer Players SP89

No. B112, Stadium, Helsinki. No. B113, Runners.

1951-52

B110	SP88	12m + 2m rose car	1.50	1.50
B111	SP89	15m + 2m grn ('52)	1.75	1.75
B112	SP88	20m + 3m deep blue	1.50	1.50
B113	SP89	25m + 4m brn ('52)	2.00	2.25
		Nos. B110-B113 (4)	6.75	7.00

XV Olympic Games, Helsinki, 1952. The surtax was to help finance the games.
Issued: B110, B112, 11/16; B111, B113, 2/15/52.
Margin blocks of four of each denomination were cut from regular or perf-through-margin sheets and pasted by the selvage, overlapping, in a printed folder to create a kind of souvenir booklet. Value $45.

Field Marshal Mannerheim — SP90

Engraved; Cross Typo. in Red
1952, Mar. 4

B114	SP90	10m + 2m gray	2.50	2.00
B115	SP90	15m + 3m rose vio	2.50	2.00
B116	SP90	25m + 5m blue	2.50	2.00
		Nos. B114-B116 (3)	7.50	6.00

The surtax was for the Red Cross.

Great Titmouse — SP91

Designs: 15m+3m, Spotted flycatchers and nest. 25m+5m, Swift.

1952, Dec. 4   Engr.

B117	SP91	10m + 2m green	2.50	2.50
B118	SP91	15m + 3m plum	2.50	2.50
B119	SP91	25m + 5m dp blue	2.50	2.50
		Nos. B117-B119 (3)	7.50	7.50

The surtax was for the prevention of tuberculosis.
See Nos. B148-B150.

European Red Squirrel — SP92

No. B121, Brown bear. No. B122, European elk.

Unwmk.
1953, Nov. 16   Engr.   Perf. 14

B120	SP92	10m + 2m red brn	2.75	3.00
B121	SP92	15m + 3m violet	2.75	3.00
B122	SP92	25m + 5m dk grn	2.75	3.00
		Nos. B120-B122 (3)	8.25	9.00

Surtax for the prevention of tuberculosis.

Children Receiving Parcel from Welfare Worker — SP93

Designs: 15m+3m, Aged woman knitting. 25m+5m, Blind basket-maker and dog.

Engraved; Cross Typo. in Red
1954, Mar. 8   Perf. 11½

B123	SP93	10m + 2m dk ol grn	2.50	1.75
B124	SP93	15m + 3m dk blue	2.50	1.75
B125	SP93	25m + 5m dk brown	2.50	1.75
		Nos. B123-B125 (3)	7.50	5.25

The surtax was for the Finnish Red Cross.

Bumblebees, Dandelions — SP94

15m+3m, Butterfly. 25m+5m, Dragonfly.

Engraved; Cross Typo. in Red
1954, Dec. 7   Perf. 14

B126	SP94	10m + 2m brown	2.00	1.50
B127	SP94	15m + 3m carmine	2.50	2.00
B128	SP94	25m + 5m blue	2.50	2.00
		Nos. B126-B128 (3)	7.00	5.50

The surtax was for the prevention of tuberculosis.

European Perch — SP95

Designs: 15m+3m, Northern pike. 25m+5m, Atlantic salmon.

Engraved; Cross Typo. in Red
1955, Sept. 26   Perf. 14

B129	SP95	10m + 2m dl grn	1.50	1.75
B130	SP95	15m + 3m vio brn	2.00	1.75
B131	SP95	25m + 5m dk bl	2.50	1.75
		Nos. B129-B131 (3)	6.00	5.25

Surtax for the Anti-Tuberculosis Society.

Gen. von Dobeln in Battle of Juthas, 1808 — SP96

Illustrations by Albert Edelfelter from J. L. Runeberg's "Tales of Ensign Stal": 15m+3m, Col. J. Z. Duncker holding flag. 25m+5m, Son of fallen Soldier.

Engraved; Cross Typo. in Red
1955, Nov. 24

B132	SP96	10m + 2m dp ultra	2.00	1.75
B133	SP96	15m + 3m dk red brn	2.00	1.75
B134	SP96	25m + 5m green	2.00	1.75
		Nos. B132-B134 (3)	6.00	5.25

The surtax was for the Red Cross.

Waxwing — SP97

Birds: 20m+3m, Eagle owl. 30m+5m, Mute swan.

Engraved; Cross Typo. in Red
1956, Sept. 25   Perf. 11½

B135	SP97	10m + 2m dl red brn	1.60	1.25
B136	SP97	20m + 3m bl grn	2.25	1.75
B137	SP97	30m + 5m blue	2.75	1.75
		Nos. B135-B137 (3)	6.60	4.75

Surtax for the Anti-Tuberculosis Society.

Pekka Aulin — SP98

Portraits: 10m+2m, Leonard von Pfaler. 20m+3m, Gustaf Johansson. 30m+5m, Viktor Magnus von Born.

Engraved; Cross Typo. in Red
1956, Nov. 26   Unwmk.

B138	SP98	5m + 1m grysh grn	1.50	1.00
B139	SP98	10m + 2m brown	1.50	1.25
B140	SP98	20m + 3m mag	1.75	1.75
B141	SP98	30m + 5m lt blue	1.75	1.75
		Nos. B138-B141 (4)	6.50	5.75

The surtax was for the Red Cross.

Wolverine (Glutton) — SP99

20m+3m, Lynx. 30m+5m, Reindeer.

Engraved; Cross Typo. in Red
1957, Sept. 5   Perf. 11½

B142	SP99	10m + 2m dull purple	1.50	1.25
B143	SP99	20m + 3m sepia	2.40	1.75
B144	SP99	30m + 5m dark blue	2.40	1.75
		Nos. B142-B144 (3)	6.30	4.75

The surtax was for the Anti-Tuberculosis Society. See Nos. B160-B165.

Red Cross Flag — SP100

1957, Nov. 25   Engr.   Perf. 14
Cross in Red

B145	SP100	10m + 2m ol grn	1.75	1.75
B146	SP100	20m + 3m maroon	1.75	2.50
B147	SP100	30m + 5m dull blue	2.25	2.50
		Nos. B145-B147 (3)	5.75	6.75

80th anniv. of the Finnish Red Cross.

Type of 1952

Flowers: 10m+2m, Lily of the Valley. 20m+3m, Red clover. 30m+5m, Hepatica.

Engraved; Cross Typo. in Red
1958, May 5   Unwmk.   Perf. 14

B148	SP91	10m + 2m green	1.75	1.25
B149	SP91	20m + 3m lilac rose	2.00	2.00
B150	SP91	30m + 5m ultra	2.25	2.00
		Nos. B148-B150 (3)	6.00	5.25

Surtax for the Anti-Tuberculosis Society.

Raspberry — SP101

20m+3m, Cowberry. 30m+5m, Blueberry.

Engraved; Cross Typo. in Red
1958, Nov. 20   Perf. 11½

B151	SP101	10m + 2m orange	1.75	1.40
B152	SP101	20m + 3m red	2.25	1.75
B153	SP101	30m + 5m dk blue	2.25	1.75
		Nos. B151-B153 (3)	6.25	4.90

The surtax was for the Red Cross.

Daisy — SP102

20m+5m, Primrose. 30m+5m, Cornflower.

Engraved; Cross Typo. in Red
1959, Sept. 7   Unwmk.

B154	SP102 10m + 2m green	2.00	1.50
B155	SP102 20m + 3m lt brown	3.00	2.50
B156	SP102 30m + 5m blue	3.00	2.50
	Nos. B154-B156 (3)	8.00	6.50

Surtax for the Anti-Tuberculosis Society.

Reindeer — SP103

No. B158, Lapp & lasso. No. B159, Mountains.

Engraved; Cross Typo. in Red
1960, Nov. 24   Perf. 11½

B157	SP103 10m + 2m dk gray	1.25	1.25
B158	SP103 20m + 3m gray vio	1.75	1.75
B159	SP103 30m + 5m rose vio	1.75	1.75
	Nos. B157-B159 (3)	4.75	4.75

The surtax was for the Red Cross.

Animal Type of 1957

Designs: 10m+2m, Muskrat. 20m+3m, Otter. 30m+5m, Seal.

Engr.; Cross at right, Typo. in Red
1961, Sept. 4

B160	SP99 10m + 2m brn car	1.40	1.00
B161	SP99 20m + 3m slate bl	2.00	1.50
B162	SP99 30m + 5m bl grn	2.00	1.50
	Nos. B160-B162 (3)	5.40	4.00

Surtax for the Anti-Tuberculosis Society.

Animal Type of 1957

Designs: 10m+2m, Hare. 20m+3m, Pine marten. 30m+5m, Ermine.

Engraved; Cross Typo. in Red
1962, Oct. 1

B163	SP99 10m + 2m gray	1.50	1.50
B164	SP99 20m + 3m dl red brn	2.00	1.75
B165	SP99 30m + 5m vio bl	2.00	1.75
	Nos. B163-B165 (3)	5.50	5.00

The surtax was for the Anti-Tuberculosis Society.

Cross and Outstretched Hands — SP104

Engraved; Cross Typo. in Red
1963, May 8   Unwmk.   Perf. 11½

B166	SP104 10p + 2p red brn	.50	.75
B167	SP104 20p + 3p violet	1.00	1.20
B168	SP104 30p + 5p green	1.00	1.20
	Nos. B166-B168 (3)	2.50	3.15

The surtax was for the Red Cross.

Attending the Wounded — SP105

Red Cross Activities: 25p+4p, Hospital ship. 35p+5p, Prisoner-of-war health examination. 40p+7p, Gift parcel distribution.

Engraved; Cross Typo. in Red
1964, May 26   Perf. 11½

B169	SP105 15p + 3p vio bl	1.00	.60
B170	SP105 25p + 4p green	1.25	.90
B171	SP105 35p + 5p vio brn	1.25	.90
B172	SP105 40p + 7p dk ol grn	1.25	.90
	Nos. B169-B172 (4)	4.75	3.30

The surtax was for the Red Cross.

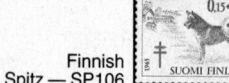

Finnish Spitz — SP106

Designs: 25p+4p, Karelian bear dog. 35p+5p, Finnish hunting dog.

Engraved; Cross Typo. in Red
1965, May 10   Perf. 11½

B173	SP106 15p + 3p org brn	1.00	1.00
B174	SP106 25p + 4p black	1.50	1.50
B175	SP106 35p + 5p gray brn	1.50	1.50
	Nos. B173-B175 (3)	4.00	4.00

Surtax for Anti-Tuberculosis Society.

Artificial Respiration — SP107

First Aid: 25p+4p, Skin diver rescuing occupants of submerged car. 35p+5p, Helicopter rescue in winter.

1966, May 7   Litho.   Perf. 14

B176	SP107 15p + 3p multi	1.10	1.00
B177	SP107 25p + 4p multi	1.25	1.25
B178	SP107 35p + 5p multi	1.25	1.25
	Nos. B176-B178 (3)	3.60	3.50

The surtax was for the Red Cross.

Birch — SP108

Trees: 25p+4p, Pine. 40p+7p, Spruce.

1967, May 12   Litho.   Perf. 14

B179	SP108 20p + 3p multi	.75	.75
B180	SP108 25p + 4p multi	1.00	1.00
B181	SP108 40p + 7p multi	1.00	1.00
	Nos. B179-B181 (3)	2.75	2.75

Surtax for Anti-Tuberculosis Society.
See Nos. B185-B187.

Horse-drawn Ambulance — SP109

25p+4p, Ambulance, 1967. 40p+7p, Red Cross.

Cross in Red
1967, Nov. 24   Litho.   Perf. 14

B182	SP109 20p + 3p dl yel, grn & blk	.90	.90
B183	SP109 25p + 4p vio & blk	1.25	1.25
B184	SP109 40p + 7p dk grn, blk & dk ol	1.25	1.25
	Nos. B182-B184 (3)	3.40	3.40

The surtax was for the Red Cross.

Tree Type of 1967

Trees: 20p+3p, Juniper. 25+4p, Aspen. 40p+7p, Chokecherry.

1969, May 12   Litho.   Perf. 14

B185	SP108 20p + 3p multi	.80	.80
B186	SP108 25p + 4p multi	1.20	1.20
B187	SP108 40p + 7p multi	1.20	1.20
	Nos. B185-B187 (3)	3.20	3.20

Surtax for Anti-Tuberculosis Society.

"On the Lapp's Magic Rock" — SP110

Designs: 30p+6p, Juhani blowing horn on Impivaara Rock, vert. 50p+10p, The Pale Maiden. The designs are from illustrations by Askeli Gallen-Kallelas for "The Seven Brothers" by Aleksis Kivi.

1970, May 8   Litho.   Perf. 14

B188	SP110 25p + 5p multi	.70	.70
B189	SP110 30p + 6p multi	1.20	1.20
B190	SP110 50p + 10p multi	1.20	1.20
	Nos. B188-B190 (3)	3.10	3.10

The surtax was for the Red Cross.

Cutting and Loading Timber — SP111

Designs: 30p+6p, Floating logs downstream. 50p+10p, Sorting logs at sawmill.

1971, Apr. 25   Litho.   Perf. 14

B191	SP111 25p + 5p multi	.90	.80
B192	SP111 30p + 6p multi	.90	.80
B193	SP111 50p + 10p multi	1.20	.80
	Nos. B191-B193 (3)	3.00	2.40

Surtax for Anti-Tuberculosis Society.

Blood Donor and Nurse — SP112

30p+6p, Blood research (microscope, slides), vert. 50p+10p, Blood transfusion.

1972, Oct. 25

B194	SP112 25p + 5p multi	.70	.85
B195	SP112 30p + 6p multi	1.10	.90
B196	SP112 50p + 10p multi	1.10	.90
	Nos. B194-B196 (3)	2.90	2.65

Surtax was for the Red Cross.

Girl with Lamb, by Hugo Simberg — SP113

Paintings: 40p+10p, Summer Evening, by Vilho Sjöström. 60p+15p, Woman at Mountain Fountain, by Juho Rissanen.

1973, Sept. 12   Litho.   Perf. 13x12½

B197	SP113 30p + 5p multi	1.00	1.00
B198	SP113 40p + 10p multi	1.40	1.40
B199	SP113 60p + 15p multi	1.40	1.40
	Nos. B197-B199 (3)	3.80	3.80

Surtax for the Finnish Anti-Tuberculosis Assoc. Birth centenaries of featured artists.

Morel — SP114

Mushrooms: 50p+10p, Chanterelle. 60p+15p, Boletus edulis.

1974, Sept. 24   Litho.   Perf. 12½x13

B200	SP114 35p + 5p multi	1.00	1.00
B201	SP114 50p + 10p multi	1.50	1.50
B202	SP114 60p + 15p multi	1.50	1.50
	Nos. B200-B202 (3)	4.00	4.00

Finnish Red Cross.

Echo, by Ellen Thesleff (1869-1954) — SP115

Paintings: 60p+15p, Hilda Wiik, by Maria Wiik (1853-1928). 70p+20p, At Home (old woman in chair), by Helene Schjerfbeck (1862-1946).

1975, Sept. 30   Litho.   Perf. 13x12½

B203	SP115 40p + 10p multi	.90	.90
B204	SP115 60p + 15p multi	1.25	1.00
B205	SP115 70p + 20p multi	1.25	1.25
	Nos. B203-B205 (3)	3.40	3.15

Finnish Red Cross. In honor of International Women's Year paintings by women artists were chosen.

Disabled Veterans' Emblem — SP116

Lithographed and Photogravure
1976, Jan. 15   Perf. 14

B206	SP116 70p + 30p multi	.80	.60

The surtax was for hospitals for disabled war veterans.

Wedding Procession SP117

Designs: 70p+15p, Wedding dance, vert. 80p+20p, Bride, groom, matron and pastor at wedding dinner.

1976, Sept. 15   Litho.   Perf. 13

B207	SP117 50p + 10p multi	.85	.85
B208	SP117 70p + 15p multi	1.10	.90
B209	SP117 80p + 20p multi	1.10	1.10
	Nos. B207-B209 (3)	3.05	2.85

Surtax for Anti-Tuberculosis Society.

Disaster Relief — SP118

Designs: 80p+15p, Community work. 90p+20p, Blood transfusion service.

1977, Jan. 19   Litho.   Perf. 14

B210	SP118 50p + 10p multi	.80	.80
B211	SP118 80p + 15p multi	1.20	.80
B212	SP118 90p + 20p multi	1.20	1.20
	Nos. B210-B212 (3)	3.20	2.80

Finnish Red Cross centenary.

Long-distance Skiing — SP119

Design: 1m+50p, Ski jump.

1977, Oct. 5   Litho.   Perf. 13

B213	SP119 80p + 40p multi	2.00	2.00
B214	SP119 1m + 50p multi	1.50	1.50

Surtax was for World Ski Championships, Lahti, Feb. 17-26, 1978.

Saffron Milkcap — SP120

Edible Mushrooms: 80p+15p, Parasol, vert. 1m+20p, Gypsy.

1978, Sept. 13   Litho.   Perf. 13

B215	SP120 50p + 10p multi	1.00	1.00
B216	SP120 80p + 15p multi	1.50	1.20
B217	SP120 1m + 20p multi	1.50	1.50
	Nos. B215-B217 (3)	4.00	3.70

Surtax was for Red Cross. See Nos. B221-B223.

Pehr Kalm, 1716-1779 SP121

Finnish Scientists: 90p+15p, Title page of Pehr Adrian Gadd's (1727-97) book, vert. 1.10m+20p, Petter Forsskal (1732-63).

Perf. 12½x13, 13x12½

1979, Sept. 26		Litho.	
B218	SP121	60p + 10p multi	.80	.80
B219	SP121	90p + 15p multi	1.20	.80
B220	SP121	1.10m + 20p multi	1.20	1.20
	Nos. B218-B220 (3)		3.20	2.80

Surtax for Finnish Anti-Tuberculosis Assoc.

Mushroom Type of 1978

Edible Mushrooms: 60p+10p, Woolly milk-cap. 90p+15p, Orange-cap boletus, vert. 1.10m+20p, Russula paludosa.

1980, Apr. 19		Litho.	Perf. 13	
B221	SP120	60p + 10p multi	.80	.80
B222	SP120	90p + 15p multi	1.00	1.50
B223	SP120	1.10m + 20p multi	1.50	1.50
	Nos. B221-B223 (3)		3.30	3.80

Surtax was for Red Cross.

Fuchsia — SP122

No. B225, African violet. No. B226, Geranium.

1981, Aug. 24		Litho.	Perf. 13	
B224	SP122	70p + 10p shown	.80	.80
B225	SP122	1m + 15p multi	.90	1.00
B226	SP122	1.10m + 20p multi	1.20	1.20
	Nos. B224-B226 (3)		2.90	3.00

Surtax for Finnish Anti-Tuberculosis Assoc.

Garden Dormouse SP123

No. B228, Flying squirrels. No. B229, European minks.

1982, Aug. 16		Litho.	Perf. 13	
B227	SP123	90p + 10p shown	.90	.80
B228	SP123	1.10m + 15p multi	.90	1.20
B229	SP123	1.20m + 20p multi	1.20	1.20
	Nos. B227-B229 (3)		3.00	3.20

Surtax was for Red Cross. No. B228 vert.

Forest and Wetland Plants — SP124

1m+20p, Chickweed wintergreen. 1.20m+25p, Marsh violet. 1.30m+30p, Marsh marigold.

1983, July 7		Litho.	Perf. 13	
B230	SP124	1m + 20p multi	.80	.80
B231	SP124	1.20m + 25p multi	.80	1.20
B232	SP124	1.30m + 30p multi	1.20	1.20
	Nos. B230-B232 (3)		2.80	3.20

Surtax for Finnish Anti-Tuberculosis Assoc.

Globe Puzzle — SP125

2m+40p, Symbolic world communication.

1984, May 28		Litho.	Perf. 13	
B233	SP125	1.40m + 35p multi	.60	.60
B234	SP125	2m + 40p multi	1.00	1.00

Surtax for Red Cross.

Butterflies — SP126

No. B235, Anthocharis cardamines. No. B236, Nymphalis antiopa. No. B237, Parnassius apollo.

1986, May 22		Litho.	Perf. 13	
B235	SP126	1.60m + 40p multi	1.00	.60
B236	SP126	2.10m + 45p multi	1.50	1.20
B237	SP126	5m + 50p multi	3.00	3.00
	Nos. B235-B237 (3)		5.50	4.80

Surtax for Red Cross.

Festivals — SP127

Designs: No. B238, Christmas. No. B239, Easter. No. B240, Midsummer.

1988, Mar. 14		Litho.	Perf. 13	
B238	SP127	1.40m + 40p multi	.90	.60
B239	SP127	1.80m + 45p multi	1.25	1.20
B240	SP127	2.40m + 50p multi	1.25	1.50
	Nos. B238-B240 (3)		3.40	3.30

Surtax for the Red Cross.

Heodes virgaureae on Goldrod Plant — SP128

Butterflies and plants: No. B242, Agrodiaetus amandus on meadow vetchling. No. B243, Inachis io on tufted vetch.

1990, Apr. 6		Photo.	Perf. 12x11½	
B241	SP128	1.50m + 40p multi	.70	.70
B242	SP128	2m + 50p multi	1.25	1.25
B243	SP128	2.70m + 60p multi	1.50	1.50
	Nos. B241-B243 (3)		3.45	3.45

Surtax for the natl. Red Cross Soc.

Paintings by Helene Schjerfbeck — SP129

Designs: No. B244a, The Little Convalescent, No. B244b, Green Still-Life.

1991, Mar. 8		Litho.	Perf. 13	
B244	SP129	Pair	2.00	2.00
a.-b.		2.10m +50p any single	1.00	1.00

Surtax for philately.

Butterflies — SP130

No. B245, Xestia brunneopicta. No. B246, Acerbia alpina. No. B247, Baptria tibiale.

Litho. & Embossed

1992, Apr. 22			Perf. 13	
B245	SP130	1.60m + 40p multi	.70	.70
B246	SP130	2.10m + 50p multi	.90	1.20
B247	SP130	5m + 60p multi	2.00	2.00
	Nos. B245-B247 (3)		3.60	3.60

Surtax for Finnish Red Cross. Embossed "Arla 100" in braille for Arla Institute, training center for the blind, cent.

Autumn Landscape of Lake Pielisjarvi, by Eero Jarnefelt — SP131

a, Tree-covered hill. b, Lake shoreline.

1993, Mar. 19		Litho.	Perf. 13	
B248	SP131	2.30m + 70p Pair,		
		#a.-b.	2.00	2.00

Surtax for philately.

Finnhorses SP132

Designs: No. B249, Draft horses. No. B250, Trotter. No. B251, War horses, vert.

1994, Mar. 11		Litho.	Perf. 13	
B249	SP132	2m +40p multi	.80	.80
B250	SP132	2.30m +50p multi	1.20	1.20
B251	SP132	4.20m +60p multi	1.75	1.75
	Nos. B249-B251 (3)		3.75	3.75

Surtax for Finnish Red Cross.

Paintings, by Albert Edelfelt (1854-1905) — SP133

No. B252, Playing Boys on the Shore. No. B253, Queen Blanche.

1995, Mar. 1		Litho.	Perf. 13½	
B252		2.40m +60p multi	1.50	1.00

Size: 22x31mm

B253		2.40m +60p multi	1.50	1.00
a.		SP133 Pair, #B252-B253	3.00	3.00

Surtax for philately.

Chickens — SP134

Designs: No. B254, Chicks. No. B255, Hens. No. B256, Rooster, vert.

1996, Mar. 18		Litho.	Perf. 13	
B254	SP134	2.80m +60p multi	1.50	1.20
B255	SP134	3.20m +70p multi	2.00	2.00
B256	SP134	3.40m +70p multi	4.00	3.00
	Nos. B254-B256 (3)		7.50	6.20

Surtax for Finnish Red Cross.

The Aino Myth, by Akseli Gallen-Kallela (1865-1931) — SP135

Designs: No. B257, Väinämöinen proposing marriage to Aino in forest. No. B258, Aino jumping into water to escape Väinämöinen. No. B259, Aino at shore for bath.

1997, Sept. 5   Litho.   Perf. 13½x13

Booklet Stamps

B257	SP135	2.80m +60p multi	1.50	1.50
B258	SP135	2.80m +60p multi	1.50	1.50
B259	SP135	2.80m +60p multi	1.50	1.50
a.		Booklet pane, #B257-B259	4.50	4.50
		Complete booklet, #B259a	4.50	

No. B258 is 33x46mm.

Surtax for philately.

Pigs — SP136

2.80m+60p, Sow, piglets. 3.20m+70p, Three piglets. 3.40m+70p, Pig's head.

1998, Mar. 12		Litho.	Perf. 13	
B260	SP136	2.80m +60p multi	1.50	1.50
B261	SP136	3.20m +70p multi	2.00	1.50
B262	SP136	3.40m +70p multi	3.50	2.50
	Nos. B260-B262 (3)		7.00	5.50

Surtax for Finnish Red Cross.

Paintings by Hugo Simberg (1873-1917) SP137

a, Garden of Death. b, Wounded Angel.

Perf. 13¼x13¾

1999, Sept. 24			Litho.	
B263		Booklet pane of 2	4.00	3.00
a.-b.		SP137 3.50m +50p any single	2.00	1.50
		Complete booklet, #B263	4.00	

Surtax for philately.

Cow and Calf — SP138

Perf. 13¾x13¼

2000, Mar. 15			Litho.	
B264	SP138	3.50m +70p Bull,		
		vert.	2.00	1.50

Perf. 13¼x13¾

B265	SP138	4.80m +80p shown	3.00	2.50

Surtax for Finnish Red Cross.

Post Horn — SP139

2010, May 4	Litho.	Perf. 14½x14¼	
B266	SP139	1 +5c multi	3.00	1.20

No. B266 had a franking value of 80c on day of issue. Surtax for construction of Finland's first solar energy plant.

No. 769 Surcharged in Silver and Black

Methods and Perfs. As Before

2017, May 24				
B267	A418	(€1.30) on 5m +		
		(€28.70)		
		booklet		
		pane of		
		1 + 2 la-		
		bels	60.00	60.00
		Complete booklet, #B267	60.00	

No. B267 had a franking value of €1.30. The surtax was for Finlandia 2017 International Philatelic Exhibition, as it does not appear that the purchase of the booklet for €30 included the price of admission to the exhibition, as was the case with No. 789 in 1988. The booklet was sold in a numbered envelope that included a postcard.

AIR POST STAMPS

No. 178 Overprinted
in Red

1930, Sept. 24   Unwmk.   *Perf. 14*
C1   A28   10m gray lilac   100.00   *220.00*
   a.   1830 for 1930   1,800.   *8,500.*

Overprinted expressly for use on mail carried in "Graf Zeppelin" on return flight from Finland to Germany on Sept. 24, 1930, after which trip the stamps ceased to be valid for postage. Forgeries are almost always on No. 205, rather than No. 178.

> **Catalogue values for unused stamps in this section, from this point to the end of the section, are for Never Hinged items.**

Douglas DC-
2 — AP1

1944   Engr.
C2   AP1   3.50m dark brown   .50   *1.00*

Air Transport Service anniv., 1923-43.

Douglas DC-6 Over
Winter Landscape — AP2

1950, Feb. 13
C3   AP2   300m blue   18.00   7.50

Available also for ordinary postage.

Redrawn
1958, Jan. 20   *Perf. 11½*
C4   AP2   300(m) blue   30.00   1.00

On No. C4 "mk" is omitted.
See Nos. C9-C9a.

Convair 440 over
Lakes — AP3

1958, Oct. 31   Unwmk.   *Perf. 11½*
C5   AP3   34m blue   1.80   .90

No. C5 Surcharged

1959, Apr. 5
C6   AP3   45m on 34m blue   2.50   2.25

C7   C8

1959, Nov. 2
C7   AP3   45m blue   2.50   1.50

1963, Feb. 15
C8   AP3   45p blue   1.80   .40

On No. C7 the denomination is "45." On No. C8 it is "0.45."

DC-6 Type, Comma After
"3" — AP5

Type I — 16 lines in numeral "0"
Type II — 13 lines in numeral "0"

1963, Oct. 10
C9   AP5   3m blue, Type II ('73)   2.50   .50
   a.   Type I   25.00   .40

Convair Type of 1958
1970, July 15
C10   AP3   57p ultra   2.50   1.25

MILITARY STAMPS

> **Catalogue values for unused stamps in this section are for Never Hinged items.**

M1

Unwmk.
1941, Nov. 1   Typo.   *Imperf.*
M1   M1   (4m) blk, *dk org*   .40   *.70*

#M1 has simulated roulette printed in black.

Type of 1930-46
Overprinted in Black

1943, Oct. 16   *Perf. 14*
M2   A26   2m deep orange   .25   *.70*
M3   A26   3½m greenish blue   .25   *.70*

Post Horn and
Sword — M2

1943, July 1   Size: 29½x19½mm
M4   M2   (2m) green   .50   .50
M5   M2   (3m) rose violet   .70   .50

1944, Feb. 16   Size: 20x16mm
M6   M2   (2m) green   .50   .40
M7   M2   (3m) rose violet   .40   .40

Post Horns and
Arms of
Finland — M3

1963, Sept. 26   Litho.   *Perf. 14*
M8   M3   violet blue   80.00   80.00

Used during maneuvers Sept. 30-Oct. 5, 1963. Valid from Sept. 26.

No. M8 Overprinted "1983"
1983, Apr. 20
M9   M3   violet blue   180.00   100.00

Used during maneuvers Apr. 24-30.

PARCEL POST STAMPS

PP1

Wmk. Rose & Triangles Multiple
Rouletted 6 on 2 or 3 Sides
1949-50   Typo.
Q1   PP1   1m brt grn & blk   .50   3.50
Q2   PP1   5m red & blk   7.50   17.50
Q3   PP1   20m org & blk   15.00   30.00
Q4   PP1   50m bl & blk ('50)   6.00   12.00

Q5   PP1   100m brn & blk
       ('50)   6.00   12.00
   Nos. Q1-Q5 (5)   35.00   75.00
   Set, never hinged   75.00

> **Catalogue values for unused stamps in this section, from this point to the end of the section, are for Never Hinged items.**

Mail Bus — PP2

1952-58   Unwmk.   Engr.   *Perf. 14*
Q6   PP2   5m car rose   3.00   3.00
Q7   PP2   20m orange   10.00   5.50
Q8   PP2   50m blue ('54)   15.00   12.00
Q9   PP2   100m brn ('58)   25.00   20.00
   Nos. Q6-Q9 (4)   53.00   40.50

Mail Bus — PP3

1963   *Perf. 12*
Q10   PP3   5p red & blk   2.00   2.50
Q11   PP3   20p org & blk   2.00   2.50
Q12   PP3   50p blue & blk   3.00   3.00
Q13   PP3   1m brn & blk   1.50   1.50
   Nos. Q10-Q13 (4)   8.50   9.50

Nos. Q1-Q13 were issued only in booklets: panes of 6 for Nos. Q1-Q5, 10 for Nos. Q6-Q9 and 5 for Nos. Q10-Q13.

Used values are for regular postal or mail-bus cancels. Pen strokes, cutting or other cancels sell for half as much.

1981 SISU
Bus — PP4

Photo. & Engr.
1981, Dec. 7   *Perf. 12 Horiz.*
Q14   PP4   50p dk bl & blk   1.00   4.50
Q15   PP4   1m dk brn & blk   1.50   4.50
Q16   PP4   5m grn & blk   3.50   8.00
Q17   PP4   10m red & blk   5.50   18.00
   Nos. Q14-Q17 (4)   11.50   35.00

Parcel post stamps invalid after Jan. 9, 1985.

ALAND ISLANDS

LOCATION — A group of 6,554 islands at the mouth of the Gulf of Bothnia, between Finland and Sweden.
GOVT. — Province of Finland
AREA — 590 sq. mi.
POP. — 23,761
CAPITAL — Mariehamn

The province of Aland was awarded to Finland in 1921 by the League of Nations. The Swedish language is spoken and the province has a considerable amount of self-determination.

> **Catalogue values for unused stamps in this country are for Never Hinged items.**
> **Most Aland Island issues exist favor canceled, and used values are for such cancellations. Postally used examples are worth 30 to 40% more than the values shown.**

Gaff-
rigged
Sloop
A1

Aland Flag
A2

Midsummer Pole — A3

Landscapes
A4

Map of
Scandinavia
A5

Seal of St. Olaf
and Aland
Province,
1326 — A6

Artifacts — A7

Sea
Birds — A8

Gothic
Tower,
Jomala
Church,
12th
Cent. — A9

Mariehamn Town
Hall, Designed by
Architect Lars
Sonck — A9a

Designs: 1.50m, Statue of Frans Petter von Knorring, vicar from 1834 to 1875, and St. Michael's Church, Finstrom, 12th cent. 1.60m, Burial site, clay hands. 1.70m, Somateria mollissima. 2.20m, Bronze Staff of Finby, apostolic decoration. 2.30m, Aythya fuligula. 5m, Outer Aland Archipelago. 8m, Farm and windmill. 12m, Melantha fusca. 20m, Ancient court site, contemporary monument.

1984-90   Engr.   Unwmk.   *Perf. 12*
1   A1   10p magenta   .25   .25
2   A1   20p brown olive   .25   .25
3   A1   50p bright green   .25   .25
4   A1   1.10m deep blue   .40   .40
5   A1   1.20m black   .40   .40
6   A1   1.30m dark green   .40   .50

Litho.
Perf. 14, 13x14 (#8)
7   A2   1.40m multi   .40   .40
8   A9   1.40m multi   1.00   1.20
9   A3   1.50m multi, I   1.00   1.00
9A   A3   1.50m multi, II   .70   .90
10   A9   1.50m multi   1.00   1.25

Perf. 13, 14 (#13)
11   A7   1.60m multi, vert.   1.00   1.00
12   A8   1.70m multi   4.00   6.00
13   A9a   1.90m multi   .80   1.00
14   A4   2m multi   1.00   1.00
15   A7   2.20m multi, vert.   1.00   .80
16   A8   2.30m multi   2.00   2.00
17   A5   3m multi   .90   .80
18   A4   5m multi, horiz.   1.50   1.40
19   A4   8m multi, horiz.   2.50   2.50

Litho. & Engr.
20   A6   10m multi   3.00   2.50

Litho.
21   A8   10m multi   4.00   4.00
22   A7   20m multi   6.00   6.00
   Nos. 1-22 (23)   33.75   35.80

On No. 9A (type II) "Aland" is 10½mm long, figure support is 2mm wide, pole supports are thinner, diagonal black highlighting lines in pole greenery and horizontal black line on support under the man removed.

Issued: Nos. 2-4, 7, 17, 20, 3/1/84; Nos. 1, 5, 6, 9, 1/2/85; Nos. 14, 18-19, 9/16/85; Nos. 11, 15, 22, 4/4/86; Nos. 12, 16, 21, 1/2/87; No. 8, 8/26/88; No. 13, 1/2/89; No. 10, 9/4/89; No. 9A, 5/21/90.
See Nos. 39-42, 87-92, 178-179, 195-196.

A10

Bark Pommern and car ferries, Mariehamn West Harbor

1984, Mar. 1   Litho.   Perf. 14
23   A10   2m multicolored   1.00   1.20

A11

1986, Jan. 2   Litho.   Perf. 14
24   A11   1.60m multicolored   1.00   1.20

1986 Nordic Orienteering Championships, Aug. 30-31.

Onningeby Artists' Colony, Cent. — A12

Design: Pallette, pen and ink drawing of Onningeby landscape, 1891, by Victor Westerholm (1860-1919), founder.

1986, Sept. 1   Litho.
25   A12   3.70m multicolored   1.00   *1.50*

Mariehamn Volunteer Fire Brigade, Cent. — A13

1987, Apr. 27   Litho.   Perf. 14
26   A13   7m multicolored   5.00   7.00

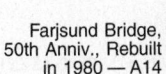

Farjsund Bridge, 50th Anniv., Rebuilt in 1980 — A14

1987, Apr. 27   Engr.   Perf. 13x13½
27   A14   1m greenish black   .40   .40

Municipal Meeting, Finstrom, 1917 — A15

1987, Aug. 20   Litho.   Perf. 14
28   A15   1.70m multicolored   1.00   1.20

Movement for reunification with Sweden, 70th anniv.

Loading of Mail Barrels on Sailboat, Post Office, Eckero — A16

1988, Jan. 4   Litho.   Perf. 14
29   A16   1.80m multicolored   1.00   1.20

Postal Service, 350th anniv. From Feb. 1 to May 31, Alanders were entitled to buy 20 stamps for 28m with a discount coupon.

New Aland Farm School, Horse-Drawn Plow — A17

1988, Mar. 29   Litho.   Perf. 14
30   A17   2.20m multicolored   1.20   *1.50*

Haga Farm School, cent.; Aland Farm School, 75th anniv.; 50th anniv. of experimental farming on Aland.

Sailing Ships — A18

Designs: 1.80m, Albanus, 1904, vert. 2.40m, Ingrid, c. 1900. 11m, Pamir, c. 1900.

1988, June 4   Litho.   Perf. 13
31   A18   1.80m multi   1.00   1.50
32   A18   2.40m multi   2.00   2.50
33   A18   11m multi   5.00   7.00
    Nos. 31-33 (3)   8.00   11.00

Type of 1988 and

Orchids A19

Fish A20

Handicrafts A21

Fresco, St. Anna's Church of Kumlinge A22

Mammals — A23

Geological Formations
A24   A25

Designs: 10p, Boulder field, Geta. No. 35, *Dactylorhiza sambucina*. No. 36, *Clupea harengus membras*. No. 37, *Erinaceus europauus*. No. 38, Drumlin, Finstrom. 1.70m, St. Andrew Church, Lumparland. No. 40, Vardo Church. No. 41, Hammarland Church. No. 42, Sottunga Church. No. 43, *Esox lucius*. No. 45, Diabase dike, Sottunga, Basskar. 2.10m, *Sciurus vulgaris*. 2.50m, *Cephalanthera longifolia*. No. 48, *Platichthys flesus*. No. 49, Pillow lava, Kumlinge, western Varpskar. No. 50, *Capreolus capreolus*. No. 51, Rouche Moutonne, Roda Kon, Lumparn. 6m, Folded gneiss, Sottunga, Gloskar. 13m, Tapestry, 1793. 14m, *Cypripedium calceolus*.

Perf. 13, 14 (Nos. 39-42, 44, 53),
15x14½ (10p, Nos. 38, 45, 49, 51-52)
1989-94   Litho.
34   A25   10p multicolored   .25   .25
35   A19   1.50m multicolored   1.00   1.50
36   A20   1.50m multicolored   1.00   1.20
37   A23   1.60m multicolored   1.00   1.20
38   A25   1.60m multicolored   .60   .70
39   A9   1.70m multicolored   1.00   1.20
40   A9   1.80m multicolored   1.00   1.00
41   A9   1.80m multicolored   1.00   1.25
42   A9   1.80m multicolored   1.00   1.25
43   A20   2m multicolored   1.00   1.20
44   A22   2m multicolored   .70   1.00
45   A24   2m multicolored   .70   .60
46   A23   2.10m multicolored   1.00   1.20
47   A19   2.50m multicolored   1.50   1.50
48   A20   2.70m multicolored   1.00   1.20
49   A24   2.70m multicolored   .90   .80
50   A9   2.90m multicolored   1.20   1.40
51   A25   2.90m multicolored   1.00   1.00
52   A24   6m multicolored   1.50   2.00
53   A21   13m multicolored   3.00   4.00
54   A19   14m multicolored   7.00   8.00
    Nos. 34-54 (21)   28.35   33.45

Issued: 2.50m, 14m, No. 35, 4/10/89; 2.70m, No. 36, 43, 3/1/90; 13m, 4/19/90; 1.70m, No. 44, 9/10/90; 1.60m, 2.10m, No. 50, 3/3/91; No. 40, 10/9/91; No. 41 10/5/92; Nos.

45, 49, 52, 9/3/93; No. 42, 10/8/93; 10p, Nos. 38, 51, 2/1/94.
   See Nos. 96, 102, 105.

Educational System of the Province, 350th Anniv. — A33

1989, May 31   Litho.   Perf. 14
57   A33   1.90m multicolored   1.00   1.20

Souvenir Sheet

1991 Aland Island Games A34

a, Volleyball. b, Shooting. c, Soccer. d, Running.

1991, Apr. 5   Litho.   Perf. 13x12½
58   A34   2.10m Sheet of 4, #a.-d.   4.00   4.00

Autonomy of Aland, 70th Anniv. — A35

1991, June 4   Perf. 13
59   A35   16m multicolored   4.00   5.00

Kayaking — A36

1991, June 4   Perf. 14
60   A36   2.10m shown   .70   1.00
61   A36   2.90m Cycling   1.00   1.25

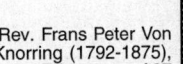

Rev. Frans Peter Von Knorring (1792-1875), Educator — A37

Cape Horn Congress, Mariehamn, June 8-11 — A38

1992, Mar. 2   Litho.   Perf. 13
62   A37   2 multicolored   1.20   1.10
    Litho. & Engr.
      Perf. 13½x14
63   A38   1 multicolored   1.00   1.40

No. 62 sold for 1.60m, No. 63 for 2.10m.

> On stamps bearing the "denominations" "1" or "2," the number represents the class of mail.

Lighthouses — A39

1992, May 8   Litho.   Perf. 13
      Booklet Stamps
64   A39   2.10m Ranno   5.00   5.00
65   A39   2.10m Salskar   5.00   5.00
66   A39   2.10m Lagskar   5.00   5.00
67   A39   2.10m Market   5.00   5.00
a.   Booklet pane of 4, #64-67   20.00   20.00

First Aland Provincial Parliament, 70th Anniv. — A40

1992, June 8   Litho.   Perf. 13
68   A40   3.40m multicolored   1.20   1.40

Joel Pettersson (1892-1937), Painter — A41

Designs: 2.90m, Landscape from Lemland. 16m, Self-Portrait.

1992, June 8
69   A41   2.90m multicolored   1.00   1.40
70   A41   16m multicolored   5.50   5.50

Arms of
Aland—A42

1993, Mar. 1　Litho.　Perf. 14
71　A42　1.60m gray, sepia & blue　　.80　1.00
　　Autonomy Act, Jan. 1.

Souvenir Sheet

Autonomous Postal
Administration — A43

Designs: a, Inscriptions from old letter canceled in Kastelholm, vert. b, Mariehamn post office. c, Ferry, mail truck. d, New post office emblem, vert.

Perf. 12½x13, 14 (#b.-c.)
1993, Mar. 1　Litho., Engr. (#b.-c.)
72　A43　1.90m Sheet of 4, #a.-d.　3.25　4.00

Fiddler, Jan
Karlsgarden
Museum — A44

2.30m, Boat Shed, Jan Karlsgarden Museum.

Perf. 13x12½, 12½x13
1993, May 7　　　　　　Litho.
73　A44　2m multicolored　　　.80　1.00
74　A44　2.30m multi, horiz.　　.80　1.00

Folk Dresses — A45

Clothing from: 1.90m, Saltvik. 3.50m, Brando, Eckero, Mariehamn. 17m, Finstrom.

1993, June 1　　　　　　Perf. 12½
75　A45　1.90m multicolored　　1.00　1.20
76　A45　3.50m multicolored　　1.20　1.50
77　A45　17m multicolored　　　5.00　6.50
　　　Nos. 75-77 (3)　　　　　7.20　9.20

Butterflies — A46

No. 78, Melitaea cinxia. No. 79, Quercusia querqus. No. 80, Parnassius mnemosyne. No. 81, Hesperia comma.

Perf. 14 on 3 Sides
1994, Mar. 1　　　　　　Litho.
Booklet Stamps
78　A46　2.30m multicolored　　1.00　1.00
79　A46　2.30m multicolored　　1.00　1.00
80　A46　2.30m multicolored　　1.00　1.00
81　A46　2.30m multicolored　　1.00　1.00
a.　Booklet pane, 2 each #78-81　8.00　—
　　　Nos. 78-81 (4)　　　　　4.00　4.00

A47

Europa, Inventions and Discoveries: 2.30m, Diagram showing transmission of von Willebrand's Disease, discovered by E. A. von Willebrand. 2.90m, Purification of heparin, by Erik Jorpes.

1994, May 5　　Litho.　　Perf. 13
82　A47　2.30m multicolored　　2.00　2.00
83　A47　2.90m multicolored　　2.00　2.00

Types of 1989-93 and

Ice Age
Survivors
A48　　　　　Fossils
　　　　　　　A49

Sea Birds — A50　　Bronze
　　　　　　　　Age — A51

Stone
Age — A52　　　Ships — A53

Lichens
A54　　　　　Primula
　　　　　　　Veris
　　　　　　　A55

30p, Saduria entomon, mysis relicta. 40p, Trilobita asaphus. 1.80m, Sterna paradisaea. No. 87, Church of Mariehamn. No. 88, Church of Eckerö. No. 89, St. Bridget's Church, Lemland. No. 90, Church of St. John the Baptist, Sund. No. 91, St. George Church, Geta. No. 92, Church of Brando. No. 93, Bronze sword, bronze dagger. No. 94, Ship tumulus grave. No. 95, Larus canus. 2.30m, Pitcher of Kallskar. No. 97, Pottery. No. 98, Myoxocephalus quadricornis. 2.60m, Larus marinus. No. 100, Stone tools. No. 101, SS Thornbury. 3.40m, Erratic boulders. 3.50m, SS Osmo. 4.30m, Phoca hispida. 7m, Potholes. 9m, Gastropoda euomophalus. 18m, Settlement. 2, Hypogmnia physodes. 1, Xanthoria parietina.

Perf. 13 (A48, A50, A52, A54),
15x14½ (No. 89), 14½x15 (Nos. 101-
103, 105), 14½ (40p, Nos. 88, 93-94,
96), 14 (Nos. 87, 90-92), 15 (No. 106)
1994-2000　　　　　　　Engr.
84　A48　30p multi　　　　.25　.25
85　A49　40p multi　　　　.25　.40
86　A50　1.80m multi　　　.60　.70
87　A9　1.90m multi　　　1.00　1.00
88　A9　1.90m multi　　　1.00　1.20
89　A9　1.90m multi　　　1.00　1.00
90　A9　2m multi　　　　1.00　1.00
91　A9　2m multi　　　　1.00　1.00
92　A9　2m multi　　　　1.00　.80
93　A51　2m multi　　　　.70　.90
94　A51　2.20m multi, vert.　.80　1.00
95　A50　2.20m multi, vert.　.70　.70
96　A24　2.30m multi　　　.70　.80
97　A52　2.40m vio brn, vert.　1.20　1.50
98　A48　2.40m multi　　　1.00　.90
99　A50　2.60m multi　　　.90　.90
100　A52　2.80m bluish blk,
　　　　　vert.　　　　1.00　1.20
101　A53　2.80m multi　　1.00　1.20
102　A24　3.40m multi, horiz.　1.10　1.20
103　A53　3.50m multi　　1.40　1.50
104　A48　4.30m multi　　1.40　1.40
105　A24　7m multi, horiz.　2.20　2.20
106　A49　9m multi　　　2.70　3.00
107　A52　18m dk grn　　6.00　6.00
Perf. 13
107A　A54　2 multi　　　1.50　1.20
107B　A54　1 multi　　　2.00　1.40

Self-Adhesive
Serpentine Die Cut Perf. 10
108　A55　2.40m multicolored　.90　.90
　　　Nos. 84-108 (27)　　34.30　35.25

No. 108 was issued in sheets of 10.
Nos. 107A-107B sold for 2m and 2.40m, respectively, on day of issue.
Issued: Nos. 97, 100, 18m, 8/16/94; No. 90, 10/7/94; 2.30m, 3.40m, 7m, 1/2/95; No. 91, 9/15/95; 40p, No. 92, 9m, 10/9/96; 30p, No. 98, 4.30m, 2/3/97; Nos. 101, 103, 9/8/97; No.

87, 10/9/97; No. 88, 10/9/98; Nos. 93-94, 2/1/99; No. 108, 4/28/99; Nos. 107A-107B, 9/25/99; No. 89, 10/8/99; 1.80m, No. 95, 2.60m, 1/3/00.

Cargo
Vessels — A58

Perf. 14 on 3 Sides
1995, Mar. 1　　　　　　Litho.
Booklet Stamps
109　A58　2.30m Skuta　　　.80　.70
110　A58　2.30m Sump　　　.80　.70
111　A58　2.30m Storbat　　.80　.70
112　A58　2.30m Jakt　　　.80　.70
a.　Booklet pane, 2 each #109-112　8.00　11.00
　　Complete booklet, #112a　　8.00
　　　Nos. 109-112 (4)　　　3.20　2.80

Entry into European
Union — A59

1995, Mar. 1　Litho.　Perf. 13x14
113　A59　2.90m multicolored　1.00　1.40

Europa — A60

Design: 2.90m, Dove, island in sea.

1995, May 5　Litho.　Perf. 13x14
114　A60　2.80m shown　　1.20　1.50
115　A60　2.90m multicolored　1.20　1.50

Tourism — A61

1995, May 12
116　A61　2 Golf　　　　1.50　1.50
117　A61　1 Fishing　　　2.00　1.00

Nos. 116-117 sold for value 2m and 2.30m, respectively.

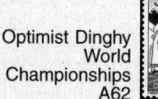

Optimist Dinghy
World
Championships
A62

1995, June 2　Litho.　Perf. 13½x14
118　A62　3.40m multicolored　1.10　1.50

St. Olaf (995?-1030),
Patron Saint of
Aland — A63

Litho. & Engr.
1995, Sept. 15　　Perf. 13½x13
119　A63　4.30m multicolored　1.50　1.70

See Faroe Islands No. 289

A64

Greeting Stamps (stylized designs): No. 120, Fish with natl. flag, "Hälsningar fran

---

Aland." No. 121, Yellow bird with flower, "Grattis."

1996, Feb. 14　Litho.　Perf. 13x14
120　A64　1 multicolored　　2.00　1.00
121　A64　1 multicolored　　2.00　.80

Nos. 120-121 had a face value of 2.30m on day of issue.

A65

Eagle owl (bubo bubo): No. 122, Landing on tree branch over lake. No. 123, Perched on branch over lake. No. 124, Male, darker feathers. No. 125, Female, lighter feathers.

Booklet Stamps
1996, Mar. 1　　Perf. 14 on 3 Sides
122　A65　2.40m multicolored　.80　1.00
123　A65　2.40m multicolored　.80　1.00
124　A65　2.40m multicolored　.80　1.00
125　A65　2.40m multicolored　.80　1.00
a.　Booklet pane, 2 ea #122-125　8.00　10.00
　　Complete booklet, No. 125a　8.00
　　　Nos. 122-125 (4)　　　3.20　4.00

World Wildlife Fund.

Famous
Women — A66

Europa: 2.80m, Sally Salminen (1906-76), writer. 2.90m, Fanny Sundström (1883-1944), politician.

1996, May 6　Litho.　Perf. 14x13
126　A66　2.80m multicolored　1.00　1.50
127　A66　2.90m multicolored　1.00　1.50

A67

1996, June 7　Litho.　Perf. 13½x14
128　A67　2.40m multicolored　.80　1.00

Aland '96 Song and Music Festival.

A68

"Haircut," by Karl Emanuel Jansson (1846-74).

1996, June 7　　　　　Perf. 13
129　A68　18m multicolored　　4.50　5.00

Spring
Flowers — A69

Designs: No. 130, Tussilago farfara. No. 131, Hepatica nobilis. No. 132, Anemone nemorosa. No. 133, Anemone ranunculoides.

1997, Feb. 3　Litho.　Perf. 14
Booklet Stamps
130　A69　2.40m multicolored　.80　1.00
131　A69　2.40m multicolored　.80　1.00
132　A69　2.40m multicolored　.80　1.00
133　A69　2.40m multicolored　.80　1.00
a.　Booklet pane, 2 each #130-133　8.00　10.00
　　Complete booklet, #133a　　8.00

A64

A70

1997, May 3   Litho.   Perf. 14x13½
134 A70 3.40m multicolored   1.00 1.00
1st Floorball World Championships, Aland.

Europa — A71

Devil's Dance with Clergyman's Wife.

1997, May 9   Perf. 13x14
135 A71 2.90m multicolored   1.40 1.00

Kalmar Union,
600th Anniv. — A72

Design: Kastelholm Castle, arms of Lord
High Chancellor Bo Jonsson Grip.

1997, May 30   Litho.   Perf. 14x13
136 A72 2.40m multicolored   .90 1.10

Souvenir Sheet

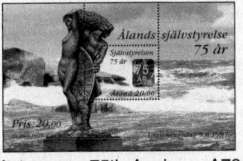

Autonomy, 75th Anniv. — A73

1997, June 9   Perf. 13
137 A73 20m multicolored   7.50 8.00
No. 137 contains a holographic image.
Soaking in water may affect the hologram.

Horticulture — A74

1998, Feb. 2   Litho.   Perf. 14½x15
138 A74   2m Apples   .60 .90
139 A74 2.40m Cucumbers   1.00 1.00

Youth
Activities — A75

No. 140, Riding moped. No. 141, Computer.
No. 142, Listening to music. No. 143,
Aerobics.

1998, Mar. 28   Perf. 14 on 3 Sides
Booklet Stamps
140 A75 2.40m multicolored   .80 1.00
141 A75 2.40m multicolored   .80 1.00
142 A75 2.40m multicolored   .80 1.00
143 A75 2.40m multicolored   .80 1.00
a. Booklet pane, 2 each #140-143 7.50 10.00
    Complete booklet, #143a   8.00

Midsummer
Celebration in
Aland — A76

1998, Apr. 27   Litho.   Perf. 14
144 A76 4.20m multicolored   1.50 1.50
Europa.

Passenger
Ferry — A77

1998, May 8   Perf. 14½
145 A77 2.40m multicolored   1.00 1.20

Intl. Year of the
Ocean — A78

1998, May 8
146 A78 6.30m multicolored   1.50 2.00

ATP Senior Tour of
Champions Tennis
Tournament,
Mariehamn — A79

Serpentine Die Cut
1998, June 25   Litho.
Self-Adhesive
147 A79 2.40m multicolored   .80 .90
Issued in sheets of 10.

Scouting — A80

1998, Aug. 1   Perf. 14
148 A80 2.80m multicolored   1.00 1.20

Foyers — A81

Homesteads: 1.60m, Seffers. 2m, Labbas.
2.90m, Abras.

1998, Sept. 11   Litho.   Perf. 14½
149 A81 1.60m multicolored   .70 1.00
150 A81   2m multicolored   .70 1.00
151 A81 2.90m multicolored   1.00 1.20
Nos. 149-151 (3)   2.40 3.20

18th Century
Furniture
Ornamentation
A82

Perf. 14 on 3 Sides
1999, Feb. 1   Litho.
Booklet Stamps
152 A82 2.40m Wardrobe   .80 1.00
153 A82 2.40m Distaff   .80 1.00
154 A82 2.40m Chest   .80 1.00
155 A82 2.40m Spinning wheel   .80 1.00
a. Booklet pane, 2 each #152-
    155   7.50
    Complete booklet, #155a   8.00

Passage of Cape
Horn by Grain
Ships Pamir &
Passat, 50th
Anniv. — A83

1999, Mar. 19   Litho.   Perf. 14½
156 A83 3.40m multicolored   1.20 1.20

Beginning with No. 157, denominations are indicated on many stamps in both Markkas and Euros. The value shown is in Markkas.

Nature Reserve,
Kökar — A84

1999, Apr. 28   Litho.   Perf. 13
157 A84 2.90m multicolored   1.25 1.20
Europa.

Match Sailboat
Racing — A85

1999, Aug. 5   Litho.   Perf. 14½x15
158 A85 2.70m multicolored   1.20 1.20

UPU, 125th
Anniv. — A86

1999, Sept. 25
159 A86 2.90m multicolored   1.20 1.20

Finnish Cross-Country
Championships,
Mariehamn — A87

1999, Oct. 9   Litho.   Perf. 14¾x14½
160 A87 3.50m multicolored   1.00 1.20

Souvenir Sheet

Peace
Symbol,
Aland
Flag
A88

Background colors: a, Yellow. b, Red. c,
Blue. d, White.

Litho. & Embossed
2000, Jan. 3   Perf. 13
161 A88 3.40m Sheet of 4, #a.-d. 4.50 4.75

Elk — A89

Elk in: No. 162, Spring. No. 163, Summer.
No. 164, Autumn. No. 165, Winter.

Perf. 11¾on 3 sides
2000, Mar. 1   Litho.
Booklet Stamps
162 A89 2.60m multicolored   .90 1.00
163 A89 2.60m multicolored   .90 1.00
164 A89 2.60m multicolored   .90 1.00
165 A89 2.60m multicolored   .90 1.00
a. Block of 4, #162-165   3.60 4.00
b. Booklet pane, 2 #165a   6.75 10.50
    Complete booklet, #165b   7.25

Europa, 2000
Common Design Type
2000, May 9   Perf. 13
166 CD17 3m multicolored   1.10 1.20

A90

Self-Adhesive
Coil Stamp
2000, June 9   Die Cut Perf. 13x13¼
167 A90 2.60m multicolored   .90 1.00
Gymnastics Festival, Mariehamn.

A91

2000, July 21   Litho.   Perf. 13½x13¼
168 A91 3.40m multicolored   1.00 1.20
Cutty Sark Tall Ships race to Mariehamn.

Vikings From
Aland — A92

2000, July 28
169 A92 4.50m multicolored   1.00 1.20
Recreation of Viking market, Saltvik.

Architecture by
Hilda Hongell
(1867-1952) — A93

2000, Aug. 25   Perf. 13¼x13¾
170 A93 3.80m shown   1.00 1.00
171 A93 10m House, diff.   2.50 3.00

Christianity, 2000th
Anniv. — A94

2000, Oct. 9   Perf. 13
172 A94 3m multicolored   1.00 1.20

Church Type of 1984-90 and

Swamp Plants — A95

Swamp plants: 1.90m, Equisetum fluviatile.
2.80m, Lycopodium annotinum. 3.50m, Polypodium vulgare.
Churches: No. 179, Föglö Church, Föglö.
2m, Kökar Church, Kökar.

Perf. 13x13¼, 13 (#178)
2000-01   Litho.
177 A95 1.90m multicolored   .70 .80
178 A9   2m multicolored   .80 .80
179 A9   2m multicolored   .70 .80
180 A95 2.80m multicolored   .90 1.00
182 A95 3.50m multicolored   1.20 1.30
Nos. 177-182 (5)   4.30 4.70

These stamps are part of an ongoing definitive set. Numbers have been reserved for additional stamps.
Issued: 2m, 10/9; 1.90m, 2.80m, 3.50m, 1/2/01; No. 179, 10/9/01.

Worldwide
Fund for
Nature
(WWF)
A100

Polysticta stelleri: a, Pair in flight. b, Pair on rock. c, Pair in water. d, Male in water.

Perf. 13¼ on 3 sides
2001, Jan. 2   **Litho.**
Booklet Stamps
185 A100 Block of 4   3.60 3.60
a.-d.   2.70m any single   .90   .90
e.   Booklet pane, 2 #185   7.00 11.00
         Booklet, #185e   8.00

Valentine's
Day — A101

2001, Feb. 14   **Perf. 14½x14¾**
186 A101 3.20m multicolored   1.00 1.20

Europa — A102

2001, May 9   **Litho.**   **Perf. 14½x14¾**
187 A102 3.20m multi   1.00 1.20

Windmills — A103

Windmill types: 3m, Archipelago. 7m, Timbered, horiz. 20m, Nest, horiz.

Perf. 13¾x14¼, 14¼x13¾
2001, June 8
188-190 A103 Set of 3   7.50 7.50

Puppies — A104

Designs: 2, Golden retriever. 1, Wire-haired dachshund.

2001, Sept. 3   **Perf. 13¼**
191-192 A104 Set of 2   5.50 2.00
Nos. 191-192 sold for 2.30m and 2.70m respectively on day of issue.

100 Cents = 1 Euro (€)
Church Type of 1998 with Euro Denominations and

Fauna — A105

Post
Terminal
A106

Mushrooms — A107

Designs: 5c, Coronella austriaca. 10c, Chanterelle mushroom. 35c, Saltviks Church. 40c, Kumlinge Church. 50c, King Bolete mushroom. 70c, Triturus cristatus. €1, Post Terminal. €2.50, Parasol mushroom.

Perf. 12½, 13 (#193, 196), 13¼ (#198), 14¾x14 (#195)
2002-03   **Litho.**
193 A105   5c multi   .25   .25
194 A107   10c multi   .25   .25
195 A9   35c multi   .70   .80
196 A9   40c multi   .80   .80
197 A107   50c multi   1.00 1.00
198 A105   70c multi   1.20 1.20

---

199 A106   €1 multi   2.00 2.20
200 A107   €2.50 multi   4.50 4.00
    Nos. 193-200 (8)   10.70 10.50

Issue dates: 5c, 70c, 1/2/02; €1, 2/28/02; 35c, 10/9/02; 10c, 50c, €2.50, 1/2/03. No. 196, 10/9/03.

Introduction of the
Euro — A108

2002, Jan. 2   **Litho.**   **Perf. 12½**
201 A108 60c multi   1.20 1.20

St. Canute's
Day — A109

2002, Jan. 2
202 A109 €2 multi   4.00 3.50

Cuisine
A110

Flowers and: a, Gravlax, boiled potatoes. b, Fried herring, beets, mashed potatoes. c, Black bread, cheese, butter. d, Pancake with prune sauce and whipped cream, coffee.

Perf. 13½x13¼ on 3 Sides
2002, Feb. 28   **Litho.**
203 A110 Block of 4   12.00 4.00
a.-d.   1 Any single   3.00 1.00
e.   Booklet pane, 2 #203   12.00
        Booklet, #203e   24.00
Nos. 203a-203d each sold for 55c on day of issue.

Europa — A111

2002, May 3   **Perf. 13¼**
204 A111 40c multi   .80   .80

Radar II, Sculpture
by Stefan
Lindfors — A112

2002, May 3   **Perf. 13**
205 A112 €3 multi   6.00 5.00

"My Aland," by Lill
Lindfors — A113

2002, Aug. 12   **Litho.**   **Perf. 13¼**
206 A113 90c multi   2.00 1.50

Iron Age
Artifacts — A114

Designs: No. 207, 2, Buckle found in Persby. No. 208, 1, Ornamental pin found in Syllöda.

2002, Sept. 2   **Perf. 13x13¼**
207-208 A114 Set of 2   5.50 2.00
Nos. 207-208 sold for 45c and 55c respectively on day of issue.

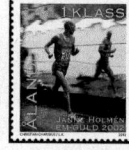

Janne Holmén,
Marathon Gold
Medalist in European
Track and Field
Championships
A115

2002, Nov. 1   **Perf. 12½**
209 A115 1 multi   3.00 1.20
Sold for 55c on day of issue.

House Cats — A116

2003, Mar. 14   **Litho.**   **Perf. 13¼**
210 A116 2 Tovis   2.50 1.00
211 A116 1 Randi, horiz.   3.00 1.10
Nos. 210-211 sold for 45c and 55c respectively on day of issue.

Landscape in Summer, by Elin
Danielson-Gambogi (1861-
1919) — A117

No. 212: a, Woman at fence. b, Tree without leaves. c, Sun. d, Boat.

2003, Mar. 28   **Perf. 14 Vert.**
Booklet Stamps
212 A117 Horiz. strip of 4 12.00 4.75
a.-d.   1 Any single   3.00 1.00
e.   Booklet pane, 2 #212 12.50 12.50
        Complete booklet, #212e 24.00
Nos. 212a-212d each sold for 55c on day of issue.

Europa — A118

2003, May 9   **Perf. 13¼**
213 A118 45c multi   1.00 1.00

Museum Ship
"Pommern,"
Cent. — A119

2003, June 6   **Die Cut Perf. 9¼x9½**
Booklet Stamp
Self-Adhesive
214 A119 55c multi   1.20 1.20
a.   Booklet pane of 4   5.00 5.00
        Complete booklet, 2 #214a 9.75

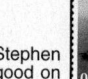

Mark and Stephen
Levengood on
Beach — A120

2003, June 18   **Perf. 12½**
215 A120 55c multi   1.00 1.00

Aland Folk Music
Association, 50th
Anniv. — A121

2003, Aug. 1   **Perf. 14¼**
216 A121 €1.10 buff & black 2.00 1.50

St. Lucia's Day
Celebrations
A122

2003, Oct. 9   **Litho.**   **Perf. 12½**
217 A122 60c multi   1.20 1.00

Mammals — A123

Designs: 20c, Mustela erminea. 60c, Vulpes vulpes. €3, Martes martes.

2004, Feb. 2   **Litho.**   **Perf. 14½x14¼**
218 A123 20c multi   .40   .40
219 A123 60c multi   1.20 1.00
220 A123 €3 multi   5.50 5.00
    Nos. 218-220 (3)   7.10 6.40

Souvenir Sheet

Norse
Gods
Fenja
and
Menja
A124

2004, Mar. 26   **Perf. 14¼x14¾**
221 A124 55c multi   2.50 2.50

Aland Flag, 50th
Anniv. — A125

Serpentine Die Cut 12½
2004, Apr. 23   **Booklet Stamp**
Self-Adhesive
222 A125 1 multi   3.00 1.00
a.   Booklet pane of 4   12.00 10.00
        Complete booklet, 2 #222a 24.00
No. 222a was reprinted in 2007 with a hole for a pegboard hook. See No. 296.

Finnish Pres. Mauno
Koivisto and Guests
on Boat — A126

2004, Apr. 23   **Perf. 12½**
223 A126 90c multi   1.80 2.00

Europa — A127

2004, May 10   **Perf. 13¾x14¼**
224 A127 75c multi   1.50 1.20

Destruction of
Bomarsund Fortress,
150th Anniv. — A128

No. 225: a, Fortress, six ships in harbor. b,
Fortress, three ships in harbor. c, Three
soldiers in foreground. d, Six soldiers in
foreground.

2004, June 9   **Perf. 13**
225   Booklet pane of 4   6.00 4.00
   a.-d.   A128 75c Any single   1.50 1.00
   Complete booklet, 2 #225   12.00

2004 Summer
Olympics,
Athens — A183

2004, Aug. 13   **Litho.**   **Perf. 14¼**
226 A183 80c multi   1.50 1.50

Landscapes
A184

Designs: 2, Storklynkan, Brändö. 1, Präst-
gardsnäset Nature Reserve, Finström.

2004, Aug. 13   **Perf. 12½**
227-228 A184   Set of 2   5.50 2.20

Nos. 227-228 sold for 50c and 60c respectively on day of issue.
See Nos. 252-253, 260.

Christmas — A185

2004, Oct. 8   **Perf. 14½x14¾**
229 A185 45c multi   1.00 .75

Birds — A186

Designs: 15c, Phalacrocorax carbo sinensis. 65c, Cygnus cygnus. €4, Ardea cinerea,
vert.

2005, Jan. 14   **Litho.**   **Perf. 13¼**
230 A186 15c multi   .40 .40
231 A186 65c multi   1.25 1.00
232 A186 €4 multi   8.00 5.00
   Nos. 230-232 (3)   9.65 6.40

Automobiles
A187

No. 233: a, 1928 Oakland Sport Cabriolet.
b, 1939 Ford V8. c, 1957 Buick Super 4D HT.
d, 1964 Volkswagen 1200.

2005, Mar. 4   **Perf. 13¼ Horiz.**
Booklet Stamps
233   Vert. strip of 4   12.00 4.75
   a.-d.   A187 1 Any single   3.00 1.20
   e.   Booklet pane, 2 #233   24.00
   Complete booklet, #233e   24.00

Stamps sold for 60c each on day of issue.

Europa — A188

2005, Apr. 29   **Perf. 13¼**
234 A188 90c multi   1.20 1.50

Walpurgis Night
Bonfire — A189

Serpentine Die Cut 12½
2005, Apr. 29   **Booklet Stamp**
Self-Adhesive
235 A189 2 multi   2.50 1.00
   a.   Booklet pane of 4   9.00
   Complete booklet, 2 #235a   20.00

Stamp sold for 50c on day of issue.

Tennis Player Bjorn
Borg — A190

2005, May 26   **Perf. 12½**
236 A190 55c multi   1.10 1.00

Mr. Black and Mr.
Smith at
Bomarsund, by
Fritz von
Dardel — A191

2005, Aug. 12   **Litho.**   **Perf. 13¾**
237 A191 €1.30 multi   2.50 2.00

Schooner
Linden — A192

2005, Aug. 26   **Perf. 13¼**
238 A192 60c multi   1.30 1.00

Landscapes Type of 2004

Designs: 70c, Pine tree on Sandö Island.
80c, Cliffs, Gröndal.

2005, Aug. 26   **Perf. 12½**
239-240 A184   Set of 2   3.40 2.20

Christmas — A193

Litho. with Hologram Applied
2005, Oct. 10   **Perf. 13**
241 A193 45c multi   .90 .90

Stars in hologram differ on each stamp.

Beetles — A194

Designs: 40c, Potosia cuprea. 65c, Coccinella septempunctata. €2, Oryctes
nasicornis.

Litho. & Embossed
2006, Jan. 2   **Perf. 13½**
242 A194 40c multi   .80 .80
243 A194 65c multi   1.30 1.00
244 A194 €2 multi   4.00 3.00
   Nos. 242-244 (3)   6.10 4.80

Woman Suffrage in
Finland,
Cent. — A195

2006, Mar. 8   **Litho.**   **Perf. 12½**
245 A195 85c multi   1.90 1.20

Demilitarization of
Aland, 150th
Anniv. — A196

2006, Mar. 29   **Perf. 13¾**
246 A196 €1.50 multi   3.00 2.00

Souvenir Sheet

Lettesgubbe, Mythological
Being — A197

2006, Mar. 29   **Perf. 12½x13**
247 A197 85c multi   2.50 2.50

Europa — A198

2006, May 4
248 A198 €1.30 multi   2.50 1.50

A199

Serpentine Die Cut 10 Syncopated
2006, May 26
249 A199 1 multi   2.00 1.40
   a.   Booklet pane of 8   11.25 11.25

No. 249 sold for 65c on day of issue. Design
portion of stamp could be personalized at
€10.40 per booklet with a minimum purchase
of three booklets. The label design shown is a
generic vignette. Other generic vignettes were
created for sale at stamp shows beginning in
2008.

Tattoos — A200

No. 250: a, Tribal tattoo on man's biceps. b,
Sailor's tattoo on man's forearm. c, Flower tattoo, on woman's torso.

2006, Sept. 7   **Perf. 14 Vert.**
Booklet Stamps
250   Horiz. strip of 3   3.50 3.50
   a.-c.   A200 65c Any single   1.25 1.25
   d.   Booklet pane, 3 #250   10.75
   Complete booklet, #250d   10.75

Fishing Boat From
Television Film
Directed by Ake
Lindman — A201

2006, Aug. 4   **Litho.**   **Perf. 12½**
251 A201 75c multi   1.60 1.20

Landscapes Type of 2004

Designs: 55c, Foggy grove, windmill and
houses, Söderby, Lemland. €1.20, Rocks,
Norra Essvik, Sottunga.

2006, Aug. 4
252-253 A184   Set of 2   3.75 2.50

Christmas — A202

Litho. With Holograms Affixed
2006, Oct. 9   **Perf. 13**
254 A202 (50c) multi   .90 .60

Flowers — A203

Designs: 80c, Tripolium vulgare. 90c,
Lythrum salicaria. €5, Angelica archangelica.

2007, Feb. 1   **Litho.**   **Perf. 12½x13**
255 A203 80c multi   1.75 1.75
256 A203 90c multi   2.00 1.25
257 A203 €5 multi   9.50 8.00
   Nos. 255-257 (3)   13.25 11.00

Mail
Planes — A204

Designs: 2, Junkers F13. 1, Saab 340.

2007, Mar. 1   **Perf. 12½**
258-259 A204   Set of 2   5.50 2.25

No. 258 sold for 55c, and No. 259 sold for
70c on day of issue.

Landscapes Type of 2004
2007, Mar. 13
260 A184 2 Skaftö, Kumlinge   2.50 1.00

Sold for 55c on day of issue.

Untitled Painting
by Tove
Jansson — A205

2007, Apr. 18   **Perf. 13¼x13¾**
261 A205 85c multi   1.75 1.25

Europa — A206

2007, May 9   *Perf. 12½x13¼*
262 A206 70c multi   1.40 1.25

Scouting, cent.

Contemporary Crafts — A207

Designs: No. 263, Bridal crown, by Titti Sundblom. No. 264, Floral textile design, by Maria Korpi-Gordon and Adam Gordon. No. 265, Cups, bowl and plate, by Judy Kuyitunen.

2007, May 18   *Perf. 13 Horiz.*
Booklet Stamps
263 A207 1 multi   3.00 1.20
264 A207 1 multi   3.00 1.20
265 A207 1 multi   3.00 1.20
  a.   Booklet pane, 3 each #263-265   27.00 27.50
     Complete booklet, #265a   27.00

Nos. 263-265 each sold for 70c on day of issue.

A208

Serpentine Die Cut 10 Syncopated
2007, June 7   **Booklet Stamp**
Self-Adhesive
266 A208 1 multi   3.00 1.25
  a.   Booklet pane of 8   24.00 20.00
     Complete booklet, #266a   24.00

No. 266 sold for 70c on day of issue. Design portion of stamp could be personalized at €10.40 per booklet with a minimum purchase of three booklets.

Emigration to America — A209

2007, Aug. 9   Litho.   *Perf. 13¼x12½*
267 A209 75c multi   1.40 1.20

Kjusan, Hammarland A210

2007, Oct. 1   *Perf. 12½*
268 A210 1 multi   3.00 .80

No. 268 sold for 70c on day of issue.

Christmas — A211

2007, Oct. 9   *Perf. 14*
269 A211 (50c) multi   .90 .50

Fish — A212

Designs: 45c, Perca fluviatilis. €4.50, Sander lucioperca.

2008, Feb. 1   Litho.   *Perf. 13¼x13*
270 A212   45c multi   1.00 .70
271 A212   €4.50 multi   8.50 6.50

Souvenir Sheet

Mythical Princess Signhild at Drottningkleven — A213

Perf. 12½x13¼
2008, Mar. 27   Litho.
272 A213 (85c) multi   3.00 2.50

Badhusberget, Mariehamn A214   Langvikshagen, Lumparland A215

2008, Apr. 15   *Perf. 13x12½*
273 A214 (70c) multi   2.00 1.00
274 A215 (70c) multi   2.00 1.00

2008 Summer Olympics, Beijing — A216

2008, May 9   *Perf. 13¾*
275 A216 (90c) multi   1.80 1.20

Europa — A217

2008, May 9   *Perf. 13¼x13*
276 A217 €1 multi   2.00 1.20

Lighthouses — A218

No. 277: a, Marhällan Lighthouse. b, Gustaf Dalén Lighthouse. c, Kökarsören Lighthouse. d, Bogskär Lighthouse.

Litho., Litho & Engr (#277c-277d)
2008, June 6   *Perf. 12¾ on 3 Sides*
Booklet Stamps
277   Block or strip of 4   8.00 4.75
  a.-d. A218 (75c) Any single   2.00 1.25
  e.   Booklet pane, 2 #277   16.00
     Complete booklet, #277e   16.00

Within the booklet pane, stamps in one row are tete-beche in relation to stamps in the adjacent row.

Gravel Road and Profiles of Marcus Grönholm, Rally Driver, and Christoph Treier, Trainer — A219

2008, July 26   Litho.   *Perf. 13½*
278 A219 (90c) multi   2.00 1.20

Particles of granite were applied to portions of the design using a thermographic process.

Aland Peasant Bride, by Karl Emanuel Jansson — A220

2008, Aug. 15   *Perf. 13x13¼*
279 A220   €1.50 multi   2.50 2.00

Christmas — A221

Litho. With Hologram Applied
2008, Oct. 9   *Perf. 13¾x13¼*
280 A221 (55c) multi   .90 .70

Personalized Stamp — A222

Serpentine Die Cut 10 Syncopated
2008, Oct. 9   Litho.
Booklet Stamp
Self-Adhesive
281 A222 (75c) multi   1.50 1.25
  a.   Booklet pane of 8   12.00 10.50
     Complete booklet, #281a   12.00

The generic design portion of the stamp shown could be personalized. Other generic vignettes were created for sale at stamp shows in 2009 and 2010.

1810 Boundary Post — A223

Litho. & Embossed With Foil Application
2009, Jan. 22   *Perf. 14¼*
282 A223 (80c) multi   2.00 1.20

Souvenir Sheet

Electricity on Aland Islands, Cent. — A224

Litho. & Embossed
2009, Jan. 22   *Perf. 12½x13¼*
283 A224 €2 black   4.00 4.00

Writers — A225

No. 284: a, Ulla-Lena Lundberg and ship. b, Anni Blomqvist (1909-90), sailboat and dock-side shack. c, Valdemar Nyman (1904-98), flowers, cattle.

2009, Mar. 21   Litho.   *Perf. 13 Horiz.*
Booklet Stamps
284   Vert. strip of 3   6.00 3.50
  a.-c. A225 (80c) Any single   2.00 1.25
  d.   Booklet pane, 3 #284   18.00 —
     Complete booklet, #284d   18.00

Movie Theaters in Aland, Cent. — A226

2009, Apr. 6   *Perf. 12½x13¼*
285 A226 €1.60 multi   3.50 2.50

Divers at Plus Shipwreck — A227

2009, May 8
286 A227 (75c) multi   2.00 1.20

Europa — A228

2009, May 8   *Perf. 13*
287 A228 (80c) multi   2.00 1.20

Intl. Year of Astronomy. Star-shaped holes are die cut in stamp.

Passenger Ferries — A229

Designs: (75c), SS Viking. (80c), New Viking Line ferry, 2009.

2009, June 1   Litho.   *Perf. 13*
288-289 A229   Set of 2   4.00 2.25

See Nos. 301-302, 311-312, 325-326, 339, 347, 351-352.

Personalized Stamp — A230

Booklet Stamp
Serpentine Die Cut 10 Syncopated
2009, June 27   **Self-Adhesive**
290 A230 (90c) multi   2.00 2.00
  a.   Booklet pane of 8   16.00
     Complete booklet, #290a   16.00

The generic design portion of the stamp shown could be personalized.

Cliffs, Föglö — A231   Islets, Saltvik — A232

2009, Sept. 16   *Perf. 12½*
291 A231 (75c) multi   2.00 1.00
292 A232 (80c) multi   2.00 1.00

Honeymoon Cabin
of Finland
President Martti
Ahtisaari — A233

2009, Sept. 29   *Perf. 13x12½*
293   A233 (90c) multi   2.00 1.50

Christmas — A234

Poinsettia and: (60c), Man and woman.
(90c), Woman with scroll.

2009, Oct. 9   *Perf. 13¾*
294-295 A234   Set of 2   3.00 2.25

**Flag Type of 2004 Inscribed
"Inrikes"**
Serpentine Die Cut 12½
2009, July 1   **Litho.**
**Booklet Stamp
Self-Adhesive**
296   A125 (75c) multi   2.00 1.50
   a.   Booklet pane of 4   8.00
     Complete booklet, 2 #296a   16.00

Mail Jetty at
Eckerö, Painting
by Victor
Westerholm
A235

2010, Jan. 4   *Perf. 13*
297   A235 (80c) multi   2.00 1.20

Jesus Christ, Painting
by Warner
Sallman — A236

Litho. With Foil Application
2010, Mar. 24   *Perf. 14x14¼*
298   A236 (90c) multi   2.00 1.20

Souvenir Sheet

Kobba
Klintar
Pilot
Station
A237

2010, Mar. 24   **Litho.**   *Perf. 12½*
299   A237 (90c) multi   2.00 2.00

Europa — A238

2010, Apr. 19   *Perf. 12½x13*
300   A238 (85c) multi   2.50 1.50

Ferries Type of 2009
Designs: 75c, MS Skandia. €3.50, MS
Prinsessan.

2010, May 3   **Litho.**   *Perf. 13*
301-302 A229   Set of 2   9.50 3.25

Plastic Toys
Made By
Plasto
A239

No. 303: a, Scooter. b, Dump truck. c,
Ducks.

2010, May 10   *Perf. 13¾ Horiz.*
Booklet Stamps
303   Vert. strip of 3   6.00 3.50
  a.-c.   A239 (85c) Any single   2.00 1.20
  d.   Booklet pane, 3 #303   18.00 18.00
    Complete booklet, #303d   18.00

Farmhand Delivering
Mail — A240

2010, June 12   *Perf. 12½x13¼*
304   A240 (75c) multi   2.00 1.00

Personalized
Stamp — A241

2010, June 12   *Perf. 12½*
305   A241 (85c) black   2.00 2.00

No. 305 was printed in sheets of 8. The
generic design portion of the stamp shown
could be personalized for an extra fee.

Stained-Glass
Windows — A242

Stained-glass window from church in
Jomala: 80c, St. Olaf. €1.60, St. Olaf and
other figures, horiz.

2010, Aug. 30   **Litho.**   *Perf. 13*
306   A242   80c multi   3.00 3.00
Souvenir Sheet
307   A242   €1.60 multi   3.00 3.00

See Macao Nos. 1317-1318.

Shoreline,   Cliffs,
Eckerö — A243   Sund — A244

2010, Sept. 16   *Perf. 12½*
308   A243   80c multi   2.00 1.50
309   A244   85c multi   2.00 1.30

Christmas — A245

2010, Oct. 8   *Perf. 13*
310   A245 (65c) multi   2.00 1.20

Ferries Type of 2009
Designs: 80c, MS Alandia. €1.50, MS
Apollo.

2011, Feb. 1   **Litho.**   *Perf. 13*
311-312 A229   Set of 2   5.00 2.50

Souvenir Sheet

Princess Maria Alexandrovna of
Russia (1824-80) — A246

2011, Feb. 21   *Perf.*
313   A246   €1 multi   2.00 1.50

City of Mariehamn, 150th anniv. A limited
edition of No. 313 with gold embossing sold for
€15. Value, $30. See Russia No. 7255.

Georg August Wallin
(1811-52), Explorer of
Arabia — A247

2011, Apr. 1   *Perf. 14x14¼*
314   A247 (90c) multi   2.00 1.20

Europa — A248

2011, May 9   *Perf. 13*
315   A248 (85c) multi   2.00 1.20

Intl. Year of Forests.

Comic Book
Superheroes Created
by Paul Gustafson
(1916-77) — A249

No. 316: a, The Arrow. b, Fantom of the
Fair. c, Alias the Spider.

2011, May 9   *Perf. 13*
Booklet Stamps
316   Horiz. strip of 3   6.00 3.50
  a.-c.   A249 (90c) Any single   2.00 1.20
  d.   Tete-beche block of 6   15.00 15.00
  e.   Booklet pane of 3 #316   18.00 17.50
    Complete booklet, #316e   18.00

Champagne Bottles
From 1840s
Shipwreck — A250

2011, June 3   **Litho.**   *Perf. 13½*
317   A250 (90c) multi   1.75 1.00

Chips Ab Potato
Chips — A251

2011, June 7   *Perf. 13¾*
318   A251 85c multi   1.75 1.20

Strömma
Apples — A252

2011, June 7   **Litho.**
319   A252   5c shown   .25 .25
320   A252   €4 Apples, diff.   7.50 1.50

Personalized
Stamp — A253

2011, Aug. 16   *Perf. 13¾x14¼*
321   A253 (95c) blk & grn   2.00 1.50

No. 321 was printed in sheets of 8. The
generic design portion of the stamp shown
could be personalized for an extra fee.

Kökar — A254   Jomala — A255

2011, Sept. 28   **Litho.**   *Perf. 12½*
322   A254 (85c) multi   2.00 1.00
323   A255 (90c) multi   2.00 1.20

Christmas — A256

2011, Oct. 7   *Perf. 14½*
324   A256 (55c) multi   1.20 .80

Ferries Type of 2009
Designs: 55c, SS Birger Jarl. (75c), MS
Sally Albatross.

2012, Feb. 1   *Perf. 13¼*
325-326 A229   Set of 2   3.00 2.00

No. 326 is inscribed "Lokalpost."

Souvenir Sheet

Fishermen at Sea — A257

2012, Mar. 21   *Perf. 13¼x13*
327   A257 (€1) multi   2.00 2.00

Sinking of the Titanic,
Cent. — A258

2012, Apr. 16   *Perf. 12¾x13¼*
328   A258 €1.80 multi   3.50 1.50

See Belgium No. 2562.

The Man at the Wheel,
Sculpture by Emil
Cedercreutz — A259

Litho. & Engr.
2012, Apr. 26   *Perf. 13¼x13*
329   A259 €3 multi   6.00 3.00

Europa — A260

2012, May 9   Litho.   Perf. 13¾
330 A260 (95c) multi   2.00 1.20

Personalized Stamp — A261

2012, June 4   Perf. 14¼x13¾
331 A261 (95c) multi   2.00 1.00

Printed in sheets of 8. The design portion of this stamp could be personalized. The design shown is a generic vignette. Other generic vignettes were created for sale at stamp shows beginning in 2013.

Dragonflies A262

Designs: (75c), Aeshna cyanea. (95c), Sympetrum sanguineum.

2012, June 4   Perf. 14¼
332-333 A262 Set of 2   4.00 2.25

No. 332 is inscribed "Lokalpost;" No. 333, "Europa."

Architecture A263

No. 334: a, Miramar. b, Societetshusen. c, Badhotellet.

2012, Aug. 23   Perf. 13¾ Horiz.
Booklet Stamps
334   Vert. strip of 3   6.00 3.50
a.-c.   A263 (€1) Any single   2.00 1.20
d.   Booklet pane of 9, 3 each
         #334a-334c   18.00
         Complete booklet, #334d   18.00

Nos. 334a-334c are each inscribed "Värlüen."

Public Transportation A264

Designs: No. 335, (95c), 1954 Volvo L224 bus. No. 336, (95c), 1924 Ford TT bus.

2012, Sept. 19   Perf. 13¾x13½
335-336 A264 Set of 2   4.00 2.25

No. 335 is inscribed "Inrikes." No. 336 is inscribed "Europa."

Christmas — A265

2012, Oct. 9   Perf. 13
337 A265 (60c) multi   1.20 .80

Yearning, Painting by Guy Frisk — A266

2013, Jan. 15   Perf. 13¾x13¼
338 A266 (€1.10) multi   2.00 1.20

Aland Art Museum, 50th anniv.

Ferries Type of 2009
Design: (80c), SS Alandsfärjan.

2013, Feb. 19   Perf. 13
339 A229 (80c) multi   2.00 1.00

Worldwide Fund for Nature (WWF) — A267

No. 340: a, Gavia arctica. b, Gavia stellata. c, Podiceps auritus. d, Podiceps cristatus.

2013, Apr. 5   Perf. 12½x12¾
Booklet Stamps
340   A267 Block of 4   8.00 4.75
a.-d.   (€1) Any single   2.00 1.20
e.   Booklet pane of 8, 2 each
           #340a-340d   16.00 17.50
           Complete booklet, #340e   16.00

Europa — A268

2013, May 6   Perf. 13¾x13¼
341 A268 (€1) multi   2.00 1.20

Personalized Stamp — A269

2013, May 6   Perf. 12½
342 A269 (€1.10) ol grn & blk   2.00 1.50

No. 342 was printed in sheets of 8. The generic design portion of the stamp shown could be personalized for an extra fee. Other generic vignettes were created for sale at stamp shows beginning in 2014.

Water Lilies — A270

Designs: (€1), Nymphaea alba. €2.50, Nuphar lutea.

2013, June 4   Perf. 13x13¼
343-344 A270 Set of 2   6.50 3.00

Crowd at Rockoff Music Festival A271

Woman at Island in the Sun Music Festival A272

2013, July 12   Litho.   Perf. 13¾
345 A271 (80c) multi   2.00 1.00
346 A272 (€1.10) multi   2.00 1.20

Ferries Type of 2009
Design: €2, MS Princess Anastasia.

2013, Aug. 5   Litho.   Perf. 13
347 A229 €2 multi   4.00 1.75

See Russia No. 7468.

Inachis Io — A273

2013, Aug. 20   Litho.   Perf. 13¾
348 A273 (€1.10) multi   2.00 1.20

Christmas — A274

Paintings by Pinturicchio: No. 349, Adoration of the Magi. No. 350, Nativity.

2013, Nov. 8   Litho.   Perf. 13¼x13¾
349 A274 (€1) multi   1.40 1.00
350 A274 65c multi   1.40 1.00

No. 350 was printed in sheets of 8 + central label. Value, $11. See Vatican City Nos. 1549-1550.

Ferries Type of 2009
Designs: No. 351, MS Birka Princess. No. 352, MS Viking Grace.

2014, Feb. 7   Litho.   Perf. 13¾
351 A229 (€1.10) multi   2.00 1.00
352 A229 (€1.10) multi   2.00 1.20

No. 351 is inscribed "Inrikes"; No. 352, "Europa."

Mariehamn Theater Society, Cent. — A275

2014, Feb. 7   Litho.   Perf. 13¼
353 A275 €1.50 multi   3.00 2.00

Souvenir Sheet

Bridge of a Freighter and Horizon A276

2014, Mar. 17   Litho.   Perf. 13¼
354 A276 €3 multi   5.50 3.50

Grand Piano of Alie Lindberg (1849-1933), Concert Pianist — A277

2014, May 8   Litho.   Perf. 13¼x13
355 A277 (€1.10) multi   2.00 1.50

Europa.

Campanula Trachelium — A278

2014, May 8   Litho.   Perf. 12½
356 A278 (€1.10) multi   2.00 1.50

Kenta Sandvik, Weight Lifter — A279

2014, May 31   Litho.   Perf. 13x13¼
357 A279 (90c) multi   1.40 1.00

Personalized Stamp — A280

2014, May 31   Litho.   Perf. 12½
358 A280 (€1.10) multi   2.00 2.00

No. 358 was printed in sheets of 8. The generic design portion of the stamp shown could be personalized for an extra fee. Other generic vignettes were created for sale at stamp shows beginning in 2015.

Robert Helenius, Professional Boxer, and Family on Aland Island — A281

2014, June 9   Litho.   Perf. 13x13¼
359 A281 €2.30 multi   4.00 2.00

Musical Groups of the 1960s A282

No. 360: a, Hitch Hikers. b, Stockdoves. c, Anacondas.

2014, Aug. 25   Litho.   Perf. 13x12¼
Booklet Stamps
360   Vert. strip of 3   4.25 3.00
a.-c.   A282 (90c) Any single   1.40 1.00
d.   Booklet pane of 9, 3 each
         #360a-360c   16.00
         Complete booklet, #360d   16.00

Christmas — A283

Litho. With Foil Application
2014, Oct. 9   Perf. 13¾x13¼
361 A283 (70c) multi   1.20 .60

New Year 2015 (Year of the Ram) — A284

No. 362: a, Ram, ewe and lamb. b, Ram's head.

Litho. & Engr.
2014, Nov. 5   Perf. 13x12¾
362   A284 Pair   6.25 6.25
a.-b.   80c Either single   1.50 1.50

Printed in sheets containing two pairs.

Ships — A285

Designs: 85c, Schooner Lemland. (€1.20), Barquentine Leo.

2015, Feb. 2   Litho.   Perf. 13x13¼
363-364 A285   Set of 2   3.50 3.50
See Nos. 377-378.

Campanula Persicifolia — A286

2015, Apr. 10   Litho.   Perf. 14¼
365 A286   85c multi   1.70 1.70

Midvinterblot, Painting by Carl Larsson (1853-1919) — A287

2015, Apr. 10   Litho.   Perf. 14x14¼
366 A287   €3 multi   6.00 6.00

Race Horse Indian Silver — A288

2015, May 1   Litho.   Perf. 14
367 A288   (95c) multi   1.40 1.00

Europa — A289

2015, May 8   Litho.   Perf. 14¼
368 A289   (€1.20) multi   2.00 2.00

Personalized Stamp — A290

2015, May 8   Litho.   Perf. 12½
369 A290   (€1.20) multi   2.00 2.00
Printed in sheets of 8. The design portion of this stamp could be personalized. The design shown is a generic vignette.

Julius Sundblom (1865-1945), Politician A291

2015, June 22   Litho.   Perf. 13
370 A291   (€1.20) multi   2.00 2.00

Silver Jewelry A292

Designs: (€1.20), Buckle from Aland Islands. €2, Brooch from Bern, Switzerland.

Litho. & Embossed
2015, Sept. 3   Perf. 13
371 A292   (€1.20) multi   2.50 2.00
372 A292   €2 multi   3.50 1.50
See Switzerland Nos. 1568-1569.

Dogs — A293

No. 373: a, Finnish hound (Finsk stövare). b, Gray Norwegian elkhound (Norsk ålghund gra). c, Wire-haired dachshund (Strävharig tax).

2015, Sept. 3   Litho.   Perf. 13
Booklet Stamps
373   Horiz. strip of 3   6.00 4.50
a.-c.   A293 (€1.20) Any single   2.00 1.50
d.   Booklet pane of 9, 3 each   20.00 —
      #373a-373c
      Complete booklet, #373d   20.00

A294

Christmas — A295

2015, Oct. 9   Litho.   Perf. 13
374 A294   (70c) multi   2.00 1.00
375 A295   (€1.20) multi   2.50 2.00

Aland Sea Rescue Society, 50th Anniv. — A296

2015, Oct. 30   Litho.   Perf. 13
376 A296   (95c) multi   2.00 1.00

Ships Type of 2015
Designs: 10c, Brig Altai. €10, Barque Pehr Brahe.

2016, Feb. 2   Litho.   Perf. 13x13¼
377-378 A285   Set of 2   18.00 7.50

Buckthorn Dessert Made by Chef Michael Björklund — A297

2016, Mar. 18   Litho.   Perf. 14¼
379 A297   (€1.30) multi   3.00 3.00

Witch Trials, 350th Anniv. — A298

2016, Apr. 8   Litho.   Perf. 13
380 A298   (€1.30) multi   3.00 3.00

A299

Europa — A300

2016, May 9   Litho.   Perf. 13
381 A299   (€1.30) multi   3.00 3.00
382 A300   (€1.30) multi   3.00 3.00
Think Green Issue.

Medicinal Plants A301

No. 383: a, Hyoscyamus niger. b, Digitalis purpurea. c, Tanacetum vulgare.

2016, May 9   Litho.   Perf. 12 Horiz.
Booklet Stamps
383   Vert. strip of 3   9.00 9.00
a.-c.   A301 (€1.30) Any single   3.00 3.00
d.   Booklet pane of 9, 3 each   27.00 —
      #383a-383c
      Complete booklet, #383d   27.00

Lilla Aland Chair Designed by Carl Malmsten — A302

2016, May 27   Litho.   Perf. 11½
384 A302   €2.50 multi   5.75 5.75

House and Brudhäll Harbor, by Björn Ulvaeus — A303

2016, July 8   Litho.   Perf. 11½
385 A303   (€1.30) multi   3.00 3.00

Apple and Blossom — A304

2016, Aug. 12   Litho.   Perf. 12½
386 A304   (€1.30) multi   3.00 3.00

Elves Decorating Christmas Tree A305

Elf, Reindeer and Gifts A306

2016, Oct. 10   Litho.   Perf. 13
387 A305   (70c) multi   1.60 1.60
388 A306   (€1.30) multi   3.00 3.00
Christmas.

Souvenir Sheet

New Year 2017 (Year of the Rooster) A307

No. 389 — Rooster and: a, Flower. b, Rowboat.

2016, Nov. 11   Litho.   Perf. 13
389 A307   Sheet of 2   9.00 9.00
a.-b.   €2 Either single   4.50 4.50

Mermerus A308

Mariehamn A309

2017, Feb. 2   Litho.   Perf. 13x13¼
390 A308   20c multi   .45 .45
391 A309   (€1.10) multi   2.40 2.40

Personalized Stamp — A310

2017, Mar. 14   Litho.   Perf. 12½
392 A310   (€1.30) multi   3.00 3.00
No. 392 was printed in sheets of 8. The generic design portion of the stamp shown could be personalized for an extra fee.

Pinus Sylvestris and Salvadora Oleoides — A311

2017, Mar. 14   Litho.   Perf. 13x13¼
393 A311   (€1.30) multi   3.00 3.00
Cultural Diversity.

Kastelholm Castle — A312

2017, May 9   Litho.   Perf. 13x13¼
394 A312   (€1.40) multi   3.25 3.25
Europa.

Independence of Finland, Cent. — A313

Litho. & Embossed With Foil Application
2017, May 24   Perf. 13x13¼
395 A313   €5 multi   11.50 11.50

Sauna Bench, Bucket and Whisk — A314

Exterior of Sauna — A315

2017, May 24   Litho.   Perf. 13¼x13½
396 A314   (€1.40) multi   3.25 3.25
397 A315   (€1.40) multi   3.25 3.25
a.   Souvenir sheet of 2, #396-397   6.50 6.50
See Finland No. 1540.

Handcrafted Jewelry Made From Recycled Items — A316

2017, Aug. 17   Litho.   *Perf. 13x13¼*
398   A316   €1 multi   2.40   2.40

Mammals — A317

No. 399: a, Lepus timidus. b, Mustela nivalis. c, Nyctereutes procyonoides.

Perf. 14¼x14½
2017, Sept. 15   Litho.
Booklet Stamps
399   Horiz. strip of 3   8.00   8.00
a.-c.   A317 (€1.10) Any single   2.60   2.60
  d.   Booklet pane of 9, 3 each
    #399a-399c   24.00   —
    Complete booklet, #399d   24.00

A318   Gingerbread Houses — A319

2017, Oct. 9   Litho.   *Perf. 13¼*
400   A318   (70c) multi   1.60   1.60
401   A319   (€1.40) multi   3.25   3.25
Christmas.

Souvenir Sheet

New Year 2018 (Year of the Dog) A320

No. 402 — China dog at: a, Right. b, Left.

2017, Nov. 10   Litho.   *Perf. 13¼x13*
402   A320   €1 Sheet of 2, #a-b   4.75   4.75

Clipper Ship Albania — A321

Schooner Atlas — A322

2018, Feb. 1   Litho.   *Perf. 12*
403   A321   (€1.30) multi   3.25   3.25
404   A322   €3 multi   7.50   7.50

Salmo Salar — A323

2018, Mar. 13   Litho.   *Perf. 11½*
405   A323   (€1.50) sil & multi   3.75   3.75

Bomarsund Bridge A324

2018, May 9   Litho.   *Perf. 12*
406   A324   (€1.50) multi   3.50   3.50
Europa.

Spray of Wave Hitting Rocks — A325

2018, May 9   Litho.   *Perf. 12*
407   A325   (€1.50) multi   3.50   3.50

Apis Mellifera — A326

2018, May 28   Litho.   *Perf. 13¼*
408   A326   (€1.50) gold & multi   3.50   3.50

Motorcycles — A327

No. 409: a, 2011 Victory Cross Country. b, 1919 Harley-Davidson F1000CC. c, 1944 Indian Chief. d, 1980 Harley-Davidson Chopper.

2018, May 28   Litho.   *Perf. 13¼*
Booklet Stamps
409   A327   Block of 4   14.00   14.00
a.-d.   (€1.50) Any single   3.50   3.50
  e.   Booklet pane of 8, 2 each
    #409a-409d   28.00
    Complete booklet, #409e   28.00

A328   Fireworks — A329

2018, Sept. 18   Litho.   *Perf. 13*
410   A328   (€1.50) multi   3.50   3.50
411   A329   €4 multi   9.25   9.25

Christmas
A330   A331
Litho. With Hologram Affixed
2018, Oct. 9   *Perf. 13¼*
412   A330   (80c) red & multi   1.90   1.90
413   A331   (€1.50) gold & multi   3.50   3.50

Souvenir Sheet

New Year 2019 (Year of the Pig) A332

No. 414 — Apples and: a, Entire pig. b, Head of sow.

2018, Nov. 1   Litho.   *Perf. 12*
414   A332   Sheet of 2   9.00   9.00
a.-b.   €2 Either single   4.50   4.50

Ships — A333

Designs: €1.40, Schooner Vineta. €1.60, Barque Parma.

2019, Feb. 1   Litho.   *Perf. 12*
415-416   A333   Set of 2   7.00   7.00

Ice Skaters A334

2019, Mar. 8   Litho.   *Perf. 12*
417   A334   €1.20 multi   2.75   2.75

Small Boat Transatlantic Voyage Captained by Uno Ekblom (1905-55), 80th Anniv. — A335

2019, Mar. 8   Litho.   *Perf. 12*
418   A335   €1.60 multi   3.75   3.75

Aurora Borealis and Notvik Tower — A336

2019, Mar. 8   Litho.   *Perf. 14*
419   A336   €1.70 multi   4.00   4.00

Haliaeetus Albicilla — A337

2019, May 9   Litho.   *Perf. 13*
420   A337   (€1.40) multi   3.25   3.25
Europa.

Jonesas Farmhouse, Onningeby A338

2019, May 9   Litho.   *Perf. 14x14¼*
421   A338   (€1.70) multi   4.00   4.00

Postcrossing A339

2019, June 7   Litho.   *Perf. 13¾*
422   A339   (€1.80) multi   4.25   4.25
Values are for stamps with surrounding selvage.

House, Sailboat and Signature of Lasse Holm, Composer — A340

2019, June 7   Litho.   *Perf. 13*
423   A340   €6 multi   14.00   14.00

Harvest Festival A341

No. 424: a, Two girls in hay. b, Person feeding apple to cow. c, Apple in woman's hands.

Perf. 13. Horiz.
2019, Sept. 20   Litho.
Booklet Stamps
424   Vert. strip of 3   10.50   10.50
a.-c.   A341 (€1.60) Any single   3.50   3.50
  d.   Booklet pane of 9, 3 each
    #424a-424c   31.50   —
    Complete booklet, #424d   31.50

Nos. 424a-424c are each inscribed "Inrikes."

Christmas
A342   A343

2019, Oct. 24   Litho.   *Perf. 13¼*
425   A342   (90c) multi   2.00   4.00
426   A343   (€1.80) multi   4.00   4.00

Souvenir Sheet

New Year 2020 (Year fo the Rat) A344

No. 427: a, Two mice. b, Three mice.

2019, Oct. 24   Litho.   *Perf. 13*
427   A344   Sheet of 2   2.80   2.80
a.-b.   60c Either single   1.40   1.40

Ships — A345

Designs: €1.30, Barquentine Mozart. €1.80, Four-masted barque Viking.

2020, Feb. 3   Litho.   *Perf. 13x13¼*
428-429   A345   Set of 2   7.00   7.00

Sabina Triptych, by Henrik Nylund (1945-82) — A346

2020, Mar. 5   Litho.   *Perf. 13¼x13*
430   A346   €1.40 multi   3.00   3.00

Europa A347

2020, May 8   Litho.   *Perf. 14½x14*
431   A347   (€2) multi   4.50   4.50
Ancient postal routes.

Personalized Stamp — A348

2020, May 8   Litho.   *Perf. 12½*
432   A348   (€1.80) multi   4.00   4.00
No. 432 was printed in sheets of 8. The generic design portion of the stamp shown could be personalized for an extra fee.

Bats and Library Clock — A349

2020, June 5   Litho.   *Perf. 13*
433   A349   €1 multi   2.25   2.25

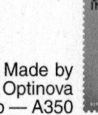

Tubing Made by Optinova Group — A350

2020, June 5 Litho. Perf. 13¼
434 A350 (€1.70) multi 4.00 4.00

Aland Police Van — A351

2020, Sept. 4 Litho. Perf. 14x14¼
435 A351 €1.50 multi 3.50 3.50

Mariehamn Esplanade in Autumn A352

Mariehamn Esplanade in Winter A353

Mariehamn Esplanade in Spring A354

Mariehamn Esplanade in Summer A355

2020, Sept. 4 Litho. Perf. 13
Booklet Stamps
436 Block of 4 14.00 14.00
a. A352 (€1.50) multi 3.50 3.50
b. A353 (€1.50) multi 3.50 3.50
c. A354 (€1.50) multi 3.50 3.50
d. A355 (€1.50) multi 3.50 3.50
e. Booklet pane of 8, 2 each
#436a-436d 28.00
Complete booklet, #436e 28.00

Glogg, Cookie and Nuts — A356

Toffee — A357

2020, Oct. 23 Litho. Perf. 13¼x12¾
437 A356 (€1) multi 2.40 2.40
438 A357 (€2) multi 4.75 4.75

Christmas.

Souvenir Sheet

New Year 2021 (Year of the Ox) A358

No. 439: a, Team of oxen. b, Team of oxen, farmers and plow, horiz.

2020, Oct. 23 Litho. Perf. 13
439 A358 Sheet of 2 4.80 4.80
a.-b. €1 Either single 2.40 2.40

Tractors — A359

Designs: €1.60, 1924 Fordson F tractor. €3, Cletrac tractor, c. 1919.

2021, Feb. 2 Litho. Perf. 13x13¼
440-441 A359 Set of 2 11.00 11.00

Verner E. Suomi NPP Weather Satellite — A360

Perf. 14¼x13¾
2021, Mar. 25 Litho.
442 A360 (€2.20) multi 5.25 5.25

1747 Nautical Chart of Rödhamn — A361

2021, Mar. 25 Litho. Perf. 13
443 A361 €4 multi 9.50 9.50

Great Northern War, 300th Anniv. — A362

2021, May 7 Litho. Perf. 13
444 A362 (€1.80) multi 4.50 4.50

Rana Arvalis — A363

2021, May 7 Litho. Perf. 14
445 A363 €2 multi 5.00 5.00

Europa.

Autonomy of Aland Islands, Cent. — A364

2021, June 9 Litho. Perf. 14
446 A364 (€1.70) multi 4.00 4.00

Female Premiers of Aland A365

No. 447: a, Veronica Thörnroos. b, Camilla Gunell. c, Viveka Eriksson. d, Katrin Sjögren.

2021, June 9 Litho. Perf. 13¾
Booklet Stamps
447 A365 Block of 4 19.00 19.00
a.-d. €2 Any single 4.75 4.75
e. Booklet pane of 8, 2 each
#447a-447d 38.00
Complete booklet, #447e 38.00

A366

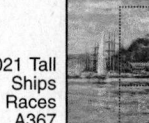

2021 Tall Ships Races A367

2021, July 23 Litho. Perf. 13
448 A366 (€2.20) multi 5.25 5.25

Souvenir Sheet
Litho. With Foil Application
449 A367 €5 multi 12.00 12.00

The 2021 Tall Ships Races were canceled because of the COVID-19 pandemic.

Christmas
A368 A369

2021, Oct. 20 Litho. Perf. 13¼
450 A368 (€1) multi 2.40 2.40
451 A369 (€2.20) multi 5.25 5.25

Souvenir Sheet

New Year 2022 (Year of the Tiger) A370

2021, Oct. 20 Litho. Perf. 13¼
452 A370 €3 multi 7.00 7.00

Early 1940s Ford Tractor — A371

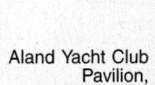

1956 Valmet 20 Tractor — A372

2022, Feb. 1 Litho. Perf. 13x13¼
453 A371 (€1.90) multi 4.25 4.25
454 A372 €3.50 multi 8.00 8.00

Aland Yacht Club Pavilion, Cent. — A373

2022, Mar. 25 Litho. Perf. 13x13¼
455 A373 €2.10 multi 4.75 4.75

Disc Golf — A374

2022, Mar. 25 Litho. Perf. 13
456 A374 (€2.40) multi 5.50 5.50

Sjöra (Water Sprite) — A375

2022, May 9 Litho. Perf. 13¼
457 A375 €2.30 multi 5.00 5.00

Europa.

Contemporary Art — A376

No. 458: a, Aland Originals, photograph by Tiina Tahvanainen (62x41mm). b, Japanese Lantern, engraving by Gunnar Sjöblom (31x29mm). c, Augur I, painting by Kurt Simons (31x29mm). d, #sniffigaround3, painting by Minna Oberg (31x40mm). e, Sacrificial Cardigan, fabric art by Barbro Eriksson (31x40mm). f, All Over the Place, painting by Erica Signell (31x40mm). g, Rooster, sculpture by Johan Karlsson (31x40mm).

Perf. 13¼ on 2 or 3 Sides
2022, June 9 Litho.
458 A376 Booklet pane of 7 47.50 —
a.-g. €3.20 Any single 6.75 6.75
Complete booklet, #458 47.50

Souvenir Sheet

Autonomy of Aland Islands, Cent. — A377

2022, June 9 Litho. Perf. 14½
459 A377 €5 multi 10.50 10.50

Sea Buckthorn Berries and Bottles of Sea Buckthorn Juice — A378

2022, Sept. 6 Litho. Perf. 14½x14¼
460 A378 €1.90 multi 3.75 3.75

Ixodes Ricinus, Borrelia Burgdorferi, and Tick-Borne Disease Researcher — A379

2022, Sept. 6 Litho. Perf. 13¼x13
461 A379 €2.70 multi 5.25 5.25

A380

Christmas — A381

2022, Oct. 20   **Litho.**   **Perf. 13¼**
462 A380   (€1.20) multi   2.40   2.40
463 A381   (€2.60) multi   5.25   5.25

Souvenir Sheet

New Year 2023 (Year of the Rabbit) A382

2022, Oct. 20   **Litho.**   **Perf. 14**
464 A382   €3.60 multi   7.25   7.25

SEMI-POSTAL STAMPS

Campaign Against Breast Cancer — SP1

2012, Oct. 1   **Litho.**   **Perf. 13½x13¾**
B1 SP1   €1+20c multi   2.25   1.50
Surtax for Aland Cancer Society.

Sculpture of Gnome by Hakan Sandberg — SP2

2013, Sept. 2   **Litho.**   **Perf. 13¾x13½**
B2 SP2   €1+20c multi   2.00   1.50
Surtax for Aland Cancer Society.

Zero Tolerance Program Against Drug Abuse SP3

Litho. & Embossed
2014, Apr. 11   **Perf. 14¾**
B3 SP3   €1.10 +20c black   2.50   1.50

FIUME

'fyü-ˌmā

LOCATION — A city and surrounding territory on the Adriatic Sea
GOVT. — Formerly a part of Italy
AREA — 8 sq. mi.
POP. — 44,956 (estimated 1924)

Fiume was under Hapsburg rule after 1466 and was transferred to Hungarian control after 1870. Of mixed Italian and Croatian population and strategically important, it was Hungary's only international seaport. Following World War I, Fiume was disputed between Italy and the newly created Kingdom of the Serbs, Croats and Slovenes (later Yugoslavia). A force of Allied troops occupied the city in Nov. 1918, while its future status was negotiated at the Paris Peace Conference.

In Sept. 1919, the Italian nationalist poet Gabriele d'Annunzio organized his legionnaires and seized Fiume, together with the islands of Arbe, Carnaro and Veglia, in the name of Italy. D'Annunzio established an autonomous administration, which soon

came into conflict with the Italian government. There followed several years of instability, with three Italian interventions after 1920. In Jan. 1924, the Treaty of Rome between Italy and Yugoslavia established formal Italian sovereignty over Fiume, and Fiume stamps were replaced by those of Italy after March 31, 1924.

100 Filler = 1 Korona
100 Centesimi = 1 Corona (1919)
100 Centesimi = 1 Lira

See note on FIUME-KUPA Zone, Italian Occupation, after Yugoslavia No. NJ22.

The overprints on Nos. 1-23a have been extensively forged. Even the inexpensive values are difficult to find with genuine overprints. Forgeries of many later issues also exist, most created for the packet trade in the 1920s. Values are for genuine stamps. Collectors should be aware that stamps sold "as is" are likely to be forgeries, and unexpertized collections should be assumed to consist of mostly forged stamps. Education plus working with knowledgeable dealers is mandatory in this collecting area. More valuable stamps should be expertized.

Hungarian Stamps of 1916-18 Typograph Overprinted, Bold Sans Serif Letters

1918, Dec. 2   **Wmk. 137**   **Perf. 15**
On Stamps of 1916
Colored Numerals
1A A9   20f gray brown   5,500.   3,000.

Hungarian Stamps of 1916-18 Typograph Overprinted

On Stamps of 1916
White Numerals
1   A8   10f rose   7,250.   7,250.
  b.   Handstamped overprint   75.00   35.00
2   A8   15f violet   40.00   30.00
Value for No. 1a is for handstamped overprint. Value for No. 2 is for typographed overprint.

On Stamps of 1916-18
Colored Numerals
3   A9   2f brown orange   4.00   2.40
4   A9   3f red violet   4.00   2.40
5   A9   5f green   4.00   2.40
6   A9   6f grnsh blue   4.00   2.40
7a   A9   10f rose red, from   50.00   20.00
8   A9   15f violet   4.00   2.40
9   A9   20f gray brown   3.00   1.50
10   A9   25f deep blue   12.00   3.00
11   A9   35f brown   7.50   4.00
12a   A9   40f olive green,
       from   30.00   17.50

White Numerals
13   A10   50f red vio & lil   5.00   3.00
14   A10   75f brt bl & pale bl   10.00   4.00
15   A10   80f grn & pale grn   10.00   3.00
16   A10   1k red brn & claret   30.00   7.50
17   A10   2k ol brn & bis   5.00   3.00
18   A10   3k dk vio & ind   40.00   20.00
19   A10   5k dk brn & lt brn   145.00   40.00
20a   A10   10k vio brn & vio,
       from   400.00   175.00
Inverted or double overprints exist on most of Nos. 4-15.

On Stamps of 1918
21   A11   10f scarlet   3.00   3.00
22   A11   20f dark brown   2.50   2.00
23a   A12   40f olive green   17.50   17.50
The overprint on Nos. 3-23a was applied by 2 printing plates and 6 handstamps. Values are for the less costly. Values of Nos. 7a, 12a, 20a and 23a are for handstamps. See the *Scott Specialized Catalogue of Stamps and Covers* for detailed listings.

Postage Due Stamps of Hungary, 1915-20 Ovptd. & Surcharged in Black

1919, Jan.
24   D1   45f on 6f green & red   15.00   10.00
25   D1   45f on 20f green & red   40.00   10.00
Set, never hinged   138.00

Hungarian Savings Bank Stamp Surcharged in Black

A2

1919, Jan. 29
26   A2   15f on 10f dk violet   22.00   17.00
   Never hinged   55.00
Overprints on Nos. 24-26 are typographed. No. 26 also exists with double surcharge, one black and one red, and with one violet and one black.

"Italy" — A3   Italian Flag on Clock-Tower in Fiume — A4

"Revolution" A5   Sailor Raising Italian Flag at Fiume (1918) A6

Nos. 30-43 exist on three types of paper: (A) grayish, porous paper, printed in sheets of 70 stamps (Jan, Feb. printings); (B) translucent or semi-translucent good quality white paper, printed in sheets of 70 stamps (March printing); and (C) good quality medium white paper, plain and opaque, sometimes grayish or yellowish, printed in sheets of 100 (April printing). Values are for the least expensive variety. See the *Scott Specialized Catalogue of Stamps and Covers* for detailed listings.

Perf. 11½
1919, April   **Unwmk.**   **Litho.**
27   A3   2c dull blue   1.50   1.50
28   A3   3c gray brown   1.50   1.50
29   A3   5c yellow green   1.50   1.50
30a   A4   10c rose   17.50   9.00
31   A4   15c violet   1.50   1.50
32a   A4   20c emerald green   2.50   *3.00*
33   A5   25c dark blue   2.25   1.50
34   A5   30c deep violet   2.25   1.50
35   A5   40c brown   2.25   2.25
36   A5   45c orange   2.25   2.25
37   A6   50c yellow green   2.25   1.50
38   A6   60c claret   2.25   1.50
39   A6   1cor brown orange   3.75   2.25
40   A6   2cor brt blue   3.75   2.25
41   A6   3cor orange red   4.50   2.25
42   A6   5cor deep brown   22.00   22.00
43a   A6   10cor olive green   45.00   *75.00*
   Nos. 27-43a (17)   118.50   132.25
The earlier printings of Jan. and Feb. are on thin grayish paper, the Mar. printing is on semi-transparent white paper, all in sheets of 70. An Apr. printing is on white paper of medium thickness in sheets of 100. Part-perf. examples of most of this series are known.
For surcharges see Nos. 58, 60, 64, 66-69.

A7   A8

A9   A10

1919, July 28   **Perf. 11½**
46   A7   5c yellow green   2.00   2.00
47   A8   10c rose   2.00   2.00
48   A9   30c violet   7.75   2.50
49   A10   40c yellow brown   8.00   *2.00*
50   A10   45c orange   8.00   5.50
51   A9   50c yellow green   8.00   5.50
52   A9   60c claret   7.75   5.40
  a.   Perf. 13x12½   140.00
    Never hinged   200.00
  b.   Perf. 10½   320.00
    Never hinged   825.00
53   A9   10cor olive green   8.00   *15.00*
  a.   Perf. 13x12½   50.00   *72.50*
    Never hinged   125.00
  b.   Perf. 10½   320.00   *225.00*
    Never hinged   825.00
   Nos. 46-53 (8)   45.50   39.90
Set, never hinged   115.00

Five other denominations (25c, 1cor, 2cor, 3cor and 5cor) were not officially issued. Some examples of the 25c are known canceled.
For surcharges see Nos. 59, 61-63, 65, 70.

Stamps and Types of 1919 Handstamp Surcharged

1919-20
58   A4   5c on 20c grn ('20)   2.00   2.00
59   A9   5c on 25c blue   2.00   2.00
60   A5   10c on 45c orange   2.50   2.00
61   A9   15c on 30c vio ('20)   2.00   2.00
62   A10   15c on 45c orange   2.00   2.00
63   A9   15c on 60c cl ('20)   2.00   2.00
64   A6   25c on 50c yel grn ('20)   9.75   *24.00*
65   A9   25c on 50c yel grn ('20)   2.00   2.00
66   A6   55c on 1cor brn org   30.00   30.00
67   A6   55c on 2cor brt bl   5.00   *7.00*
68   A6   55c on 3cor org red   5.00   6.00
69   A6   55c on 5cor dp brn   5.00   6.00
70   A9   55c on 10cor ol grn   24.00   27.50
   Nos. 58-70 (13)   93.25   *114.50*
Set, never hinged   235.00

Semi-Postal Stamps of 1919 Surcharged

a   b

First Setting
Surcharge letters thin and small.
1919-20
73   SP6(a)   5c on 5c grn   2.00   2.00
74   SP6(a)   10c on 10c rose   2.00   2.00
75   SP6(a)   15c on 15c gray   2.00   2.00
76   SP6(a)   20c on 20c org   2.00   2.00
78   SP7(a)   45c on 45c ol grn   2.50   2.50
79   SP7(b)   60c on 60c rose   2.50   2.50
80   SP7(b)   80c on 80c vio   4.00   4.00
81   SP7(b)   1cor on 1cor sl   4.00   4.00
82   SP8(a)   2cor on 2cor red brn   4.00   4.00
83   SP8(a)   3cor on 3cor blk brn   5.00   5.00
84   SP8(a)   5cor on 5cor yel brn   6.00   6.00

Second Setting
Surcharge letters bold, 2.5mm between "Cent." and figures of value, 5c-25c; overprint larger, 45c-10cor.
1920, Feb.5
73A   SP6(a)   5c on 5c grn   2.00   2.00
74A   SP6(a)   10c on 10c rose   24.00   5.00
75A   SP6(a)   15c on 15c gray   2.00   2.00

76A	SP6(a)	20c on 20c org	2.00	2.00
77	SP9(a)	25c on 25c bl ('20)	2.00	2.00
78A	SP7(b)	45c on 45c ol grn	2.50	2.50
79A	SP7(b)	60c on 60c rose	2.50	2.50
80A	SP7(b)	80c on 80c lil	2.00	2.00
81A	SP7(b)	1cor on 1cor sl	2.50	2.50
82A	SP8(a)	2cor on 2cor red brn	17.00	20.00
83A	SP8(a)	3cor on 3cor blk brn	35.00	22.00
84A	SP8(a)	5cor on 5cor yel brn	24.00	50.00
85	SP8(a)	10cor on 10cor dk vio ('20)	2.50	2.50

Third Setting, Milano Printing (new plates)
5c and 10c: 2mm spacing between "Cent." and denominations; 15c: new color; 45c: surcharge with bold letters.

1920, Apr. 5

73B	SP6(a)	5c on 5c grn	2.00	2.00
74B	SP6(a)	10c on 10c rose	2.00	2.00
75B	SP6(a)	15c on 15c brown gray	4.00	4.00

Gabriele d'Annunzio — A11

1920, Sept. 12   Typo.   Perf. 11½
Pale Buff Background

86	A11	5c green	3.00	3.00
87	A11	10c carmine	3.00	3.00
88	A11	15c dark gray	3.00	3.00
89	A11	20c orange	3.00	3.00
90	A11	25c dark blue	3.00	3.00
91	A11	30c red brown	3.00	3.00
92	A11	45c olive gray	5.00	5.00
93	A11	50c lilac	5.00	5.00
94	A11	55c bister	5.00	5.00
95	A11	1 l black	17.50	25.00
96	A11	2 l red violet	17.50	25.00
97	A11	3 l dark green	17.50	25.00
98	A11	5 l brown	65.00	45.00
99	A11	10 l gray violet	17.50	25.00
		Nos. 86-99 (14)	168.00	178.00
		Set, never hinged	415.00	

The background print, pale buff, also exists doubly printed or shifted on several denominations.
Counterfeits of Nos. 86 to 99 are plentiful. For overprints see Nos. 134-148.

Severing the Gordian Knot — A12

Designs: 10c, Ancient emblem of Fiume. 20c, Head of "Fiume." 25c, Hands holding daggers.

1920, Sept. 12

100	A12	5c green	35.00	25.00
a.		Imperf.	135.00	
b.		Horiz. pair, imperf. between	400.00	—
101	A12	10c deep red	22.50	22.50
a.		Imperf.	87.50	
102	A12	20c brown orange	35.00	22.50
103	A12	25c blue	22.50	47.50
a.		Imperf.	155.00	
b.		Double impression, imperf.	1,225.	
c.		Horiz. pair, imperf. between	550.00	
d.		25c blue	80.00	80.00
e.		As "d," imperf.	340.00	
f.		As "d," horiz. pair, imperf. between	1,200.	
		Nos. 100-103 (4)	115.00	117.50
		Set, never hinged	280.00	

Anniv. of the occupation of Fiume by d'Annunzio. They were available for franking the correspondence of the legionnaires on the day of issue only, Sept. 12, 1920.
Counterfeits of Nos. 100-103 are plentiful. Genuine stamps have a slight projection on the right side of the second vertical stroke of the "U" of "FIUME", and the basal serif of the "I" of "FIUME" projects more on the left than the right.
For overprints and surcharges see Nos. 104-133, E4-E9.

Nos. 100-103 Overprinted or Surcharged in Black or Red

1920, Nov. 20

104	A12	1c on 5c green	2.40	2.40
a.		Inverted overprint	55.00	55.00
b.		Double overprint	200.00	
105	A12	2c on 25c indigo (R)	2.40	2.40
a.		Inverted overprint	55.00	55.00
b.		Double overprint	72.50	72.50
c.		2c on 25c blue (R)	80.00	80.00
106	A12	5c green	20.00	2.40
a.		Inverted overprint	47.50	47.50
b.		Double overprint	72.50	72.50
107	A12	10c rose	20.00	2.40
a.		Inverted overprint	55.00	55.00
b.		Double overprint	72.50	72.50
108	A12	15c on 10c rose	2.40	2.40
a.		Inverted overprint	65.00	65.00
b.		Double overprint	72.50	72.50
109	A12	15c on 20c brn org	2.40	2.40
a.		Inverted overprint	65.00	65.00
b.		Double overprint	72.50	72.50
110	A12	15c on 25c indigo (R)	2.40	2.40
a.		Inverted overprint	65.00	65.00
b.		Double overprint	72.50	72.50
c.		15c on 25c blue (R)	225.00	225.00
111	A12	20c brn org	2.40	2.40
a.		Inverted overprint	27.50	27.50
b.		Double overprint	125.00	125.00
112	A12	25c indigo (R)	2.40	2.40
a.		Inverted overprint	24.00	24.00
b.		25c blue (R)	8.00	8.00
113	A12	25c indigo (Bk)	175.00	175.00
a.		Inverted overprint	450.00	350.00
b.		25c blue (Bk)	240.00	240.00
c.		As "b," inverted overprint	725.00	
114	A12	25c on 10c rose	2.40	4.75
a.		Double overprint	72.50	72.50
115	A12	50c on 20c brn org	5.00	2.40
a.		Double overprint	72.50	72.50
116	A12	55c on 5c green	21.00	4.75
a.		Inverted overprint	95.00	95.00
b.		Double overprint	72.50	72.50
117	A12	1 l on 10c rose	47.50	40.00
a.		Inverted overprint	275.00	275.00
b.		Double overprint	275.00	
118	A12	1 l on 25c indigo (R)	100.00	100.00
a.		1 l on 25c blue (R)	600.00	600.00
b.		As "a," inverted overprint	875.00	725.00
119	A12	2 l on 5c green	47.50	40.00
a.		Inverted overprint	325.00	
b.		Double overprint	200.00	
120	A12	5 l on 10c rose	225.00	240.00
a.		Inverted overprint	725.00	725.00
b.		Double overprint	725.00	
121	A12	10 l on 20c brn org	700.00	550.00
a.		Inverted overprint	1,600.	800.00
b.		Double overprint	1,600.	800.00
		Nos. 104-121 (18)	1,380.	1,179.
		Set, never hinged	3,850.	

The Fiume Legionnaires of d'Annunzio occupied the islands of Arbe and Veglia in the Gulf of Carnaro Nov. 13, 1920-Jan. 5, 1921.
Varieties of overprint or surcharge exist for most of Nos. 104-121.
Nos. 113, 117-121, 125, 131 have a backprint.

Nos. 106-107, 111, 113, 115-116 Overprinted or Surcharged at top

1920, Nov. 28

122	A12	5c green	35.00	24.00
123	A12	10c rose	45.00	52.50
124	A12	20c brown org	87.50	52.50
125	A12	25c deep blue	52.50	52.50
126	A12	50c on 20c brn org	95.00	52.50
127	A12	55c on 5c green	95.00	52.50
		Nos. 122-127 (6)	410.00	286.50
		Set, never hinged	1,000.	

The overprint on Nos. 122-125 comes in two widths: 11mm and 14mm. Values are for the 11mm width.

Nos. 106-107, 111, 113, 115-116 Overprinted or Surcharged at top

1920, Nov. 28

128	A12	5c green	35.00	24.00
129	A12	10c rose	45.00	52.50
130	A12	20c brown orange	87.50	52.50
131	A12	25c deep blue	52.50	52.50
132	A12	50c on 20c brn org	95.00	52.50
133	A12	55c on 5c green	95.00	52.50
		Nos. 128-133 (6)	410.00	286.50
		Set, never hinged	1,000.	

Nos. 86-99 Overprinted

1921, Feb. 2
"Provvisorio" 20mm wide
Space between lines 3mm
Pale Buff Background

134	A11	5c green	2.40	2.40
a.		Inverted overprint	27.50	27.50
b.		Double overprint	52.50	52.50
135	A11	10c carmine	2.40	2.40
a.		Inverted overprint	27.50	27.50
b.		Double overprint	52.50	52.50
136	A11	15c dark gray	2.40	2.40
a.		Inverted overprint	27.50	27.50
b.		Double overprint	52.50	52.50
137	A11	20c orange	4.00	4.00
a.		Inverted overprint	27.50	27.50
b.		Double overprint	27.50	27.50
138	A11	25c dark blue	4.00	4.00
a.		Inverted overprint	27.50	27.50
b.		Double overprint	52.50	52.50
139	A11	30c red brown	4.00	4.00
a.		Inverted overprint	27.50	27.50
b.		Double overprint	27.50	27.50
140	A11	45c olive gray	2.40	2.40
a.		Inverted overprint	55.00	55.00
b.		Double overprint	40.00	40.00
141	A11	50c lilac	4.00	4.00
a.		Inverted overprint	27.50	27.50
142	A11	55c bister	4.00	4.00
a.		Inverted overprint	16.00	16.00
143	A11	1 l black	145.00	180.00
a.		Inverted overprint	350.00	350.00
144	A11	2 l red violet	95.00	95.00
145	A11	3 l dark green	95.00	95.00
146	A11	5 l brown	95.00	95.00
147	A11	10 l gray violet	95.00	95.00

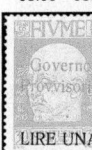

With Additional Surcharge

148	A11	1 l on 30c red brown	2.50	2.50
a.		Inverted overprint	27.50	27.50
b.		Double overprint	55.00	55.00
		Nos. 134-148 (15)	557.10	592.10
		Set, never hinged	1,400.	

Most of Nos. 134-143, 148 and E10-E11 exist with inverted or double overprint.
See Nos. E10-E11.

Second Printing, Milan
"Provvisorio" 21mm wide
Space between overprint lines 4mm
1921, Dec. 18

148A	A11	5c yellow green	50.00	57.50
		Never hinged	125.00	
		On cover		300.00
148B	A11	10c carmine	135.00	40.00
		Never hinged	340.00	
		On cover		300.00
c.		Vert. pair, imperf. between	650.00	

First Constituent Assembly

Nos. B4-B15 Overprinted

1921, Apr. 24

149	SP6	5c blue green	6.50	4.75
150	SP6	10c rose	6.50	4.75
a.		Inverted overprint	65.00	65.00
151	SP6	15c gray	6.50	4.75
152	SP6	20c orange	6.50	4.75
153	SP7	45c olive green	17.50	12.00
154	SP7	60c car rose	17.50	12.00
155	SP7	80c brt violet	27.50	24.00
a.		Inverted overprint	47.50	47.50

With Additional Overprint "L"

156	SP7	1 l on 1cor dk slate	32.50	35.00
a.		Inverted overprint	80.00	80.00

157	SP8	2 l on 2cor red brn	120.00	4.25
a.		Inverted overprint	325.00	160.00
158	SP8	3 l on 3cor black brn	120.00	130.00
159	SP8	5 l on 5cor yel brn	120.00	4.25
160	SP8	10 l on 10cor dk vio	175.00	175.00
a.		Inverted overprint	400.00	400.00
		Nos. 149-160 (12)	656.00	415.50
		Set, never hinged	1,625.	

The overprint exists inverted on several denominations.

Second Constituent Assembly
"Constitution" Issue of 1921 With Additional Overprint "1922"

1922

161	SP6	5c blue green	4.75	3.25
a.		Inverted overprint	24.00	24.00
162	SP6	10c rose	2.40	2.40
a.		Inverted overprint	24.00	24.00
b.		Double overprint, one inverted	40.00	40.00
163	SP6	15c gray	20.00	12.00
164	SP6	20c orange	2.40	2.40
a.		Inverted overprint	32.50	32.50
b.		Double overprint	40.00	40.00
c.		Double overprint, one inverted	—	
165	SP7	45c olive grn	13.00	12.00
a.		Inverted overprint	40.00	40.00
166	SP7	60c car rose	2.40	3.25
167	SP7	80c brt violet	2.40	3.25
168	SP7	1 l on 1cor dk slate	2.40	2.40
a.		Inverted overprint	55.00	55.00
b.		Double overprint	40.00	40.00
169	SP8	2 l on 2cor red brn	20.00	16.00
170	SP8	3 l on 3cor blk brn	2.50	3.25
171	SP8	5 l on 5cor yel brn	2.50	3.25
		Nos. 161-171 (11)	74.75	63.45
		Set, never hinged	170.00	

Nos. 161-171 have the overprint in heavier type than Nos. 149-160 and "IV" in Roman instead of sans-serif numerals.
The overprint exists inverted or double on almost all values.

Venetian Ship — A16

Roman Arch — A17

St. Vitus A18

Rostral Column A19

1923, Mar. 23   Perf. 11½
Pale Buff Background

172	A16	5c blue green	2.40	2.40
173	A16	10c violet	2.40	2.40
174	A16	15c brown	2.40	2.40
175	A17	20c orange red	2.40	2.40
176	A17	25c dark gray	2.40	2.40
177	A17	30c dark green	2.40	2.40
178	A18	50c dull blue	2.40	2.40
179	A18	60c rose	4.00	4.00
180	A18	1 l dark blue	4.00	4.00
181	A19	2 l violet brown	65.00	20.00
182	A19	3 l olive bister	55.00	45.00
183	A19	5 l yellow brown	55.00	52.50
		Nos. 172-183 (12)	199.80	142.30
		Set, never hinged	465.00	

Nos. 172-183 Overprinted

1924, Feb. 22
Pale Buff Background

184	A16	5c blue green	2.40	12.00
a.		Inverted overprint	20.00	40.00
b.		Double overprint	130.00	
185	A16	10c violet	2.40	12.00
a.		Inverted overprint	16.00	40.00
186	A16	15c brown	2.40	12.00
a.		Inverted overprint	17.00	40.00
187	A17	20c orange red	2.40	12.00
a.		Inverted overprint	21.00	40.00
b.		Double overprint	260.00	

188	A17	25c dk gray	2.40	12.00
189	A17	30c dk green	2.40	12.00
a.		Inverted overprint	42.50	
190	A18	50c dull blue	2.40	12.00
a.		Inverted overprint	42.50	42.50
191	A18	60c red	2.40	12.00
a.		Inverted overprint	87.50	
192	A18	1 l dark blue	2.40	12.00
a.		Inverted overprint	21.00	40.00
193	A19	2 l violet brown	4.00	32.50
a.		Inverted overprint	130.00	160.00
194	A19	3 l olive	6.00	40.00
195	A19	5 l yellow brown	6.00	40.00
		Nos. 184-195 (12)	37.60	220.50
		Set, never hinged	80.00	

The overprint exists inverted on almost all values.

Nos. 172-183
Overprinted

1924, Mar. 1
Pale Buff Background

196	A16	5c blue green	2.40	20.00
197	A16	10c violet	2.40	20.00
198	A16	15c brown	2.40	20.00
199	A17	20c orange red	2.40	20.00
200	A17	25c dark gray	2.40	20.00
201	A17	30c dark green	2.40	20.00
202	A18	50c dull blue	2.40	20.00
203	A18	60c red	2.40	20.00
204	A18	1 l dark blue	2.40	20.00
205	A19	2 l violet brown	4.00	27.50
206	A19	3 l olive	4.00	27.50
207	A19	5 l yellow brown	4.00	27.50
		Nos. 196-207 (12)	33.60	262.50
		Set, never hinged	62.50	

Postage stamps of Fiume were superseded by stamps of Italy.

SEMI-POSTAL STAMPS

Semi-Postal Stamps of
Hungary, 1916-17
Overprinted

1918, Dec. 2   Wmk. 137   Perf. 15

B1	SP3	10f +2f rose	8.00	8.00
a.		Inverted overprint	72.50	40.00
b.		Double overprint	240.00	120.00
B2	SP4	15f +2f dl vio	8.00	8.00
a.		Inverted overprint	145.00	40.00
b.		Double overprint	145.00	47.50
B3	SP5	40f +2f brn car	14.50	8.00
a.		Inverted overprint	87.50	37.50
		Nos. B1-B3 (3)	30.50	24.00
		Set, never hinged	72.50	

Examples of Nos. B1-B3 with overprint handstamped sell for higher prices.

Statue of Romulus and
Remus Being Suckled
by Wolf — SP6

Venetian Galley
SP7

Church of St.
Mark's,
Venice
SP8

Perf. 11½
1919, May 18   Unwmk.   Typo.

B4	SP6	5c +5 l bl grn	47.50	32.50
B5	SP6	10c +5 l rose	47.50	32.50
B6	SP6	15c +5 l dk gray	47.50	32.50
B7	SP6	20c +5 l orange	47.50	32.50
B8	SP7	45c +5 l ol grn	47.50	32.50
B9	SP7	60c +5 l car rose	47.50	32.50
B10	SP7	80c +5 l lilac	47.50	32.50
B11	SP7	1cor +5 l dk slate	47.50	32.50

B12	SP8	2cor +5 l red brn	47.50	32.50
B13	SP8	3cor +5 l blk brn	47.50	32.50
B14	SP8	5cor +5 l yel brn	47.50	32.50
B15	SP8	10cor +5 l dk vio	47.50	32.50
		Nos. B4-B15 (12)	570.00	390.00
		Set, never hinged	1,450.	

200th day of peace. The surtax aided Fiume students in Italy. "Posta di Fiume" is printed on the back of Nos. B4-B16.

The surtax is shown on the stamps as "LIRE 5" but actually was 5cor.

For surcharges and overprints see Nos. 73-76, 78-85, 149-171, J15-J26.

Dr. Antonio
Grossich — SP9

1919, Sept. 20

B16	SP9	25c +2 l blue	3.25	3.25
		Set, never hinged	8.00	

Surtax for the Dr. Grossich Foundation. For overprint and surcharge, see No. 77.

SPECIAL DELIVERY STAMPS

1916 Special Delivery
Stamp of Hungary
Overprinted

1918, Dec. 2   Wmk. 137   Perf. 15
Typographed Overprint

E1	SD1	2f gray green & red	4.75	4.75
		Never hinged	12.00	
a.		Double overprint	190.00	175.00

Handstamped overprints sell for more.

SD3

Perf. 11½
1920, Sept. 12   Unwmk.   Typo.

E2	SD3	30c slate blue	25.00	25.00
E3	SD3	50c rose	25.00	25.00
		Set, never hinged	125.00	

For overprints see Nos. E10-E11.

Nos. 102 and 100
Surcharged

1920, Nov.

E4	A12	30c on 20c brn org	190.00	175.00
a.		Inverted overprint	625.00	
b.		Double overprint	625.00	
E5	A12	50c on 5c green	290.00	125.00
a.		Inverted overprint	1,000.	
b.		Double overprint	1,000.	
c.		Double overprint, one inverted	1,100.	

Nos. E4-E5 have a backprint.

Same Surcharge as on Nos. 124, 122

E6	A12	30c on 20c brn org	275.00	180.00
E7	A12	50c on 5c green	210.00	180.00
a.		Double overprint	950.00	

Overprint on Nos. E6-E7 is 11mm wide.

Same Surcharge as on Nos. 130, 128

E8	A12	30c on 20c brn org	275.00	180.00
E9	A12	50c on 5c green	210.00	180.00
a.		Double overprint	950.00	950.00
		Nos. E4-E9 (6)	1,450.	1,020.
		Set, never hinged	2,900.	

Overprint on Nos. E8-E9 is 17mm wide.

Nos. E2 and E3 Overprinted

1921, Feb. 2

E10	SD3	30c slate blue	11.00	12.00
a.		Inverted overprint	120.00	120.00
b.		Double overprint	40.00	40.00
E11	SD3	50c rose	15.00	12.00
a.		Inverted overprint	27.50	27.50
b.		Double overprint	105.00	105.00
		Set, never hinged	62.50	

Fiume in 16th
Century — SD4

1923, Mar. 23   Perf. 11, 11½

E12	SD4	60c rose & buff	24.00	24.00
E13	SD4	2 l dk bl & buff	24.00	24.00
		Set, never hinged	120.00	

Nos. E12-E13 Overprinted

1924, Feb. 22

E14	SD4	60c car & buff	3.25	20.00
E15	SD4	2 l dk bl & buff	3.25	20.00
a.		Inverted overprint	130.00	160.00
		Set, never hinged	16.00	

Nos. E12-E13 Overprinted

1924, Mar. 1

E16	SD4	60c car & buff	4.00	80.00
E17	SD4	2 l dk bl & buff	4.00	80.00
		Set, never hinged	20.00	

POSTAGE DUE STAMPS

Postage Due Stamps of
Hungary, 1915-1916,
Overprinted

1918, Dec.   Wmk. 137   Perf. 15

J1c	D1	6f green & black	190.00	105.00
d.		Double overprint	—	1,450.
J2c	D1	12f green & black	180.00	72.50
d.		Double overprint		1,450.
J3c	D1	50c green & black	65.00	35.00
d.		Double overprint		1,450.
J4c	D1	1f green & red	40.00	24.00
d.		Double overprint		425.00
e.		Inverted overprint	525.00	190.00
J5	D1	2f green & red	6.50	6.50
a.		Inverted overprint	52.50	45.00
b.		Double overprint	175.00	
J6c	D1	5f green & red	40.00	47.50
d.		Inverted overprint	320.00	440.00
e.		Double overprint	525.00	525.00
J7	D1	6f green & red	6.50	6.50
a.		Inverted overprint	25.00	25.00
b.		Double overprint	27.50	
J8c	D1	10f green & red	32.50	32.50
d.		Inverted overprint	475.00	475.00
J9	D1	12f green & red	6.50	6.50
J10c	D1	15f green & red	32.50	32.50
d.		Inverted overprint		800.00
e.		Double overprint	440.00	440.00
J11	D1	20f green & red	6.50	6.50
d.		Inverted overprint	45.00	32.50
J12c	D1	30f green & red	32.50	32.50
d.		Inverted overprint		900.00
e.		Double overprint	950.00	950.00
		Nos. J1c-J12c (12)	638.50	407.50
		Set, never hinged	1,275.	

Overprint was applied by press or handstamp. Six minor varieties of the handstamp exist. Some are sought by specialists at much higher prices. Excellent forgeries exist. For more detailed listings, see Scott Classic Specialized Catalogue of Stamps and Covers 1840-1940.

Eagle — D2

Perf. 11½
1919, July 28   Unwmk.   Typo.

J13	D2	2c brown	2.40	2.40
J14	D2	5c brown	2.40	2.40
		Set, never hinged	12.00	

Semi-Postal Stamps of
1919 Overprinted and
Surcharged

1921, Mar. 21

J15	SP6	2c on 15c gray	6.50	6.50
J16	SP6	4c on 10c rose	4.75	4.75
J17	SP9	5c on 25c blue	4.75	4.75
J18	SP6	6c on 20c orange	4.75	4.75
J19	SP6	10c on 20c orange	6.50	6.50

Nos. B8-B11
Surcharged

J20	SP7	20c on 45c ol grn	2.40	4.75
J21	SP7	30c on 1cor dk slate	12.00	12.00
J22	SP7	40c on 80c violet	4.75	6.50
J23	SP7	50c on 60c car	4.75	6.50
J24	SP7	60c on 45c ol grn	2.40	4.75
J25	SP7	80c on 45c ol grn	2.40	4.75

Surcharged like Nos. J15-J19

J26	SP8	1 l on 2cor red brown	24.00	24.00
		Nos. J15-J26 (12)	79.95	90.50
		Set, never hinged	190.00	

See note below No. 85 regarding settings of "Valore Globale" overprint.

NEWSPAPER STAMPS

Newspaper Stamp of Hungary, 1914,
Overprinted like Nos. 1-23

1918, Dec. 2   Wmk. 137   Imperf.

P1	N5	(2f) orange	4.75	3.25
		Never hinged	15.00	
a.		Inverted overprint	55.00	52.50
b.		Double overprint	210.00	190.00

Handstamped overprints sell for more.

Eagle — N1

1919   Unwmk.   Perf. 11½

P2	N1	2c deep buff	9.50	14.50

Re-engraved

P3	N1	2c deep buff	9.50	14.50
		Set, never hinged	48.00	

In the re-engraved stamp the top of the "2" is rounder and broader, the feet of the eagle show clearly and the diamond at bottom has six lines instead of five.

Steamer
N2

1920, Sept. 12

P4	N2	1c gray green	4.00	3.25
		Never hinged	10.00	
a.		Imperf	24.00	24.00

FRANCE

'fran̩t̩s

LOCATION — Western Europe
GOVT. — Republic
AREA — 210,033 sq. mi.
POP. — 58,978,172 (1999 est.)
CAPITAL — Paris

100 Centimes = 1 Franc
100 Cents = 1 Euro (2002)

Catalogue values for unused stamps in this country are for Never Hinged items, beginning with Scott 299 in the regular postage section, Scott B42 in the semipostal section, Scott C18 in the airpost section, Scott CB1 in the airpost semi-postal section, Scott J69 in the postage due section, Scott M10 in the military stamps section, Scott 1O1 in the section for official stamps for the Council of Europe, Scott 2O1 for the section for UNESCO, Scott S1 for franchise stamps, Scott N27 for occupation stamps, and Scott 2N1 for AMG stamps.

Watermarks

Wmk. 407

Ceres — A1

FORTY CENTIMES

Type I   Type II

			Unwmk.	Imperf.
1849-50		**Typo.**		
1	A1	10c bis, *yelsh* ('50)	*1,500.*	210.00
a.		10c dark bister, *yelsh*	*1,825.*	240.00
		10c greenish bister	*2,350.*	600.00
d.		As #1, tête beche pair	*85,000.*	18,000.
2	A1	15c grn, *grnsh*	*21,500.*	800.00
a.		15c yellow green, *grnsh*	*20,000.*	700.00
c.		Tête beche pair	—	
3	A1	20c blk, *yelsh*	340.00	34.00
a.		20c black	375.00	50.00
b.		20c black, *buff*	1,100.	135.00
c.		Tête beche pair	9,250.	6,500.
4	A1	20c dark blue	2,400.	
a.		20c blue, *bluish*	2,050.	
b.		20c blue, *yelsh*	2,750.	
c.		Tête beche pair	60,000.	
6	A1	25c lt bl, *bluish*	5,400.	30.00
a.		25c blue, *bluish* ('50)	5,400.	30.00
b.		25c blue, *yelsh*	6,250.	40.00
c.		Tête beche pair	155,000.	12,500.
7	A1	40c org, *yelsh* (I) ('50)	*2,950.*	360.00
a.		40c org ver, *yelsh* (I)	*3,500.*	475.00
b.		40c orange, *yelsh* (II)	20,750.	5,250.
c.		Pair, types I and II	31,000.	12,500.
g.		Vertical half used as 20c on cover		260,000.
8	A1	1fr ver, *yelsh*	92,500.	13,750.
a.		1fr dull orange red	95,000.	17,000.
c.		1fr pale ver ("Vervelle")	20,000.	
d.		As "c," tête beche pair	450,000.	
9	A1	1fr lt car	8,750.	650.00
a.		Tête beche pair	200,000.	23,250.
b.		1fr brown carmine	10,000.	800.00
c.		1fr dark carmine, *yelsh*	12,250.	1,075.

No. 4 was printed but not yet gummed when the rate change to 25c made them unnecessary. An essay with a red "25" surcharge on No. 4 was rejected.

An ungummed sheet of No. 8c was found in 1895 among the effects of Anatole A. Hulot, the printer. It was sold to Ernest Vervelle, a Parisian dealer, by whose name the stamps are known.

See Nos. 329-329e, 612-613, 624.

Nos. 1, 4a, 6a, 7 and 13 are of similar designs and colors to French Colonies Nos. 9, 11, 12, 14, and 8. There are numerous shades of each. Identification by those who are not experts can be difficult, though cancellations can be used as a guide for used stamps.

Because of the date of issue the Colonies stamps are similar in shades and papers to the perforated French stamps, Nos. 23a, 54, 57-59, and are not as clearly printed. Except for No. 13, unused, the French Colonies stamps sell for much less than the values shown here for properly identified French versions.

Expertization of these stamps is recommended.

				Re-issue
1862				
1g	A1	10c bister		435.
2d	A1	15c yellow green		560.
3d	A1	20c black, *yellowish*		375.
4d	A1	20c blue		340.
6d	A1	25c blue		400.
7d	A1	40c orange (I)		575.
7e	A1	40c orange (II)		11,000.
h.		Pair, types I and II		15,000.
9d	A1	1fr pale lake		600.

The re-issues are fine impressions in lighter colors and on whiter paper than the originals. An official imitation of the essay, 25c on 20c blue, also in a lighter shade and on whiter paper, was made at the same time as the re-issues.

President Louis Napoleon — A2

Inscribed: "REPUB FRANC"

1852				
10	A2	10c pale bister, *yelsh*	30,000.	450.00
a.		10c dark bister, *yelsh*	30,000.	525.00
11	A2	25c blue, *bluish*	2,450.	32.50
b.		25c dark blue, *bluish*	2,900.	50.00

			Re-issue
1862			
10b	A2	10c bister	525.00
11a	A2	25c blue	350.00

The re-issues are in lighter colors and on whiter paper than the originals.

Emperor Napoleon III — A3

Die I. The curl above the forehead directly below "R" of "EMPIRE" is made up of two lines very close together, often appearing to form a single thick line. There is no shading across the neck.

Die II. The curl is made of two distinct, more widely separated lines. There are lines of shading across the upper neck.

Inscribed: "EMPIRE FRANC"

				Imperf.
1853-60				
12	A3	1c ol grn, *pale bl* ('60)	165.00	62.50
a.		1c bronze grn, *pale bluish*	155.00	67.50
13	A3	5c grn, *grnsh* (I) ('54)	630.00	62.50
14	A3	10c bis, *yelsh* (I)	360.00	6.50
a.		10c yellow, *yelsh* (I)	1,200.	27.50
b.		10c bister brn, *yelsh* (I)	450.00	18.50
c.		10c bister, *yelsh* (II) ('60)	450.00	19.00
15	A3	20c bl, *bluish* (I) ('54)	150.00	1.35
a.		20c dark bl, *bluish* (I)	220.00	1.35
b.		20c milky blue (I)	225.00	10.00
c.		20c blue, *lilac* (I)	4,250.	62.50
d.		20c blue, *bluish* (I) ('60)	285.00	4.00
e.		Half used as 10c on cover		16,000.
f.		Tête beche pair	155,000.	
16	A3	20c bl, *grnsh* (II)	5,250.	150.00
a.		20c blue, *greenish* (II)	4,250.	100.00
17	A3	25c bl, *bluish* (I)	2,050.	165.00
18	A3	40c org, *yelsh* (I)	2,000.	10.00
a.		40c org ver, *yellowish*	2,850.	16.00
b.		Half used as 20c on cover		110,000.

19	A3	80c lake, *yelsh* (I) ('54)	2,800.	40.00
a.		Tête beche pair	340,000.	22,000.
b.		Half used as 40c on cover		50,000.
20	A3	80c rose, *pnksh* (I) ('60)	1,875.	42.50
a.		Tête-beche pair	49,500.	10,000.
21	A3	1fr lake, *yelsh* (I)	7,450.	2,475.
a.		Tête beche pair	300,000.	135,000.

Most values of the 1853-60 issue are known privately rouletted, pin-perf., perf. 7 and percé en scie.

			Re-issue
1862			
17c	A3	25c blue (I)	450.
19c	A3	80c lake (I)	1,800.
21c	A3	1fr lake (I)	1,500.
d.		Tête beche pair	27,500.

The re-issues are in lighter colors and on whiter paper than the originals.

		Perf. 14x13½		
1862-71				
22	A3	1c ol grn, *pale bl* (II)	140.00	30.00
a.		1c bronze grn, *pale bl* (II)	140.00	35.00
		On cover		175.00
		On cover, single franking		325.00
23	A3	5c yel grn, *grnsh* (I)	190.00	10.00
a.		5c deep green, *grnsh* (I)	225.00	12.50
24	A3	5c grn, *pale bl* ('71) (I)	1,800.	110.00
25	A3	10c bis, *yelsh* (II)	1,350.	3.75
a.		10c yel brn, *yelsh* (II)	1,750.	8.50
26	A3	20c bl, *bluish* (II)	200.00	1.25
a.		Tête beche pair (II)	4,000.	1,000.
27	A3	40c org, *yelsh* (I)	1,200.	6.50
28	A3	80c rose, *pnksh* (I)	1,100.	30.00
a.		80c bright rose, *pink-ish* (I)	1,300.	35.00
c.		Tête beche pair (I)	17,500.	7,750.

No. 26a imperf is from a trial printing.

A4   A5

Napoleon III — A6

		Perf. 14x13½		
1863-70				
29	A4	1c brnz grn, *pale bl* ('70)	37.50	16.00
a.		1c olive green, *pale blue*	37.50	16.00
30	A4	2c red brn, *yelsh*	105.00	25.00
b.		Half used as 1c on cover		36,000.
31	A4	4c gray	165.00	37.50
a.		Tete beche pair	17,500.	11,000.
d.		Half used as 2c on cover		50,000.
32	A5	10c bis, *yelsh* ('67)	215.00	5.00
c.		Half used as 5c on cover with other stamps		3,750.
33	A5	20c bl, *bluish* ('67)	175.00	1.55
c.		Half used as 10c on cover		62,500.
e.		20c dark blue ('67)	275.00	3.25
		No gum	140.00	
		On cover, single franking		4.00
34	A5	30c brn ('67)	625.00	12.50
a.		30c dk brn, *yellowish*	1,000.	30.00
35	A5	40c pale org, *yelsh*	700.00	8.00
a.		40c org, *yelsh* ('68)	700.00	8.00
c.		Half used as 20c on cover		35,000.
36	A5	80c rose, *pnksh* ('68)	800.00	20.00
d.		80c carmine, *yellowish*	950.00	24.00
c.		Half used as 40c on cover		42,500.
e.		Quarter used as 20c on cover		50,000.
37	A6	5fr vio gray, *pnksh* ('69)	6,000.	750.00

Values for blocks of 4
Original Issue Imperfs

31c	A4	4c gray	270.00	—
32b	A5	10c bis, *yelsh*	360.00	—
33b	A5	20c bl, *bluish*	270.00	—
36c	A5	80c rose, *pnksh*	250.00	—
37b	A6	5fr gray lil, *lav*	7,800.	—

Imperfs, "Rothschild" Re-issue
Paper Colors are the Same

29b	A4	1c olive green	1,050.
30a	A4	2c pale red brown	200.00
31b	A4	4c pale gray	185.00

32a	A5	10c pale bister	160.00
33a	A5	20c pale blue	250.00
34c	A5	30c pale brown	190.00
35b	A5	40c pale orange	225.00
36b	A5	80c rose	400.00

The re-issues constitute the "Rothschild Issue." These stamps were authorized exclusively for the banker to use on his correspondence. Used examples exist.

Ceres
A7   A8

A9   A10

A11

Bordeaux Issue

On the lithographed stamps, except for type I of the 20c, the shading on the cheek and neck is in lines or dashes, not in dots. On the typographed stamps the shading is in dots. The 2c, 5c, 10c and 20c (types II and III) occur in two or more types. The most easily distinguishable are:

2c — Type A. To the left of and within the top of the left "2" are lines of shading composed of dots.

2c — Type B. These lines of dots are replaced by solid lines.

5c — Type A. The head and hairline merge with the background of the medallion, without a distinct separation.

5c — Type B. A white line separates the contour of the head and hairline from the background of the medallion.

10c — Type A. The inner frame lines are of the same thickness as all other frame lines.

10c — Type B. The inner frame lines are much thicker than the others.

Three Types of the 20c.

A9 — The inscriptions in the upper and lower labels are small and there is quite a space between the upper label and the circle containing the head. There is also very little shading under the eye and in the neck.

A10 — The inscriptions in the labels are similar to those of the first type, the shading under the eye and in the neck is heavier and the upper label and circle almost touch.

A11 — The inscriptions in the labels are much larger than those of the two preceding types, and are similar to those of the other values of the same type in the set.

1870-71		Litho.		Imperf.
38	A7	1c ol grn, *pale bl*	125.00	100.00
a.		1c bronze green, *pale blue*	160.00	155.00
39	A7	2c red brn, *yelsh* (B)	225.00	225.00
a.		2c brick red, *yelsh* (B)	800.00	700.00
b.		2c chestnut, *yelsh* (B)	1,350.	700.00
c.		2c chocolate, *yelsh* (A)	750.00	700.00
40	A7	4c gray	250.00	200.00
41	A8	5c yel grn, *grnsh* (B)	250.00	160.00
a.		5c grn, *grnsh* (B)	325.00	175.00
b.		5c emerald, *greenish* (B)	3,500.	1,250.
c.		5c yellowish green, *greenish* (A)	2,400.	3,250.
42	A8	10c bis, *yelsh* (A)	825.00	60.00
a.		10c bister, *yellowish* (A)	825.00	90.00
43	A9	20c bl, *bluish*	21,500.	550.00
a.		20c dark blue, *bluish*	25,000.	725.00
44	A10	20c bl, *bluish*	950.00	45.00
a.		20c dark blue, *bluish*	1,150.	85.00
b.		20c ultra, *bluish*	20,000.	3,100.
45	A11	20c bl, *bluish* ('71)	825.00	16.00
a.		20c ultra, *bluish*	2,200.	675.00
46	A8	30c brn, *yelsh*	325.00	200.00
a.		30c blk brn, *yelsh*	1,750.	675.00
47	A8	40c org, *yelsh*	425.00	100.00
a.		40c yel orange, *yelsh*	1,250.	225.00
b.		40c red orange, *yelsh*	625.00	190.00
c.		40c scarlet, *yelsh*	1,250.	675.00
48	A8	80c rose, *pinkish*	600.00	250.00
a.		80c dull rose, *pinkish*	600.00	275.00

All values of the 1870 issue are known privately rouletted, pin-perf and perf. 14. See Nos. 50-53.

A12

Dark Blue Surcharge

1871		Typo.	Perf. 14x13½
49	A12	10c on 10c bister	1,400.
a.		Pale blue surcharge	1,900.

No. 49 was never placed in use. Counterfeits exist.

A13

Two types of the 40c as in the 1849-50 issue.

1870-73		Typo.	Perf. 14x13½
50	A7	1c ol grn, *pale bl*	40.00	11.50
a.		1c bronze green, *pale bl* ('72)	47.50	14.00
51	A7	2c red brn, *yelsh* ('70)	80.00	13.50
52	A7	4c gray ('70)	250.00	40.00
53	A7	5c yel grn, *pale bl* ('72)	150.00	7.50
a.		5c green	150.00	7.50
54	A13	10c bis, *yelsh*	540.00	55.00
a.		Tête beche pair	5,500.	2,250.
b.		Half used as 5c on cover		4,500.
55	A13	10c bis, *rose* ('73)	265.00	9.50
a.		Tête bêche pair	3,750.	1,750.
56	A13	15c bis, *yelsh* ('71)	300.00	4.50
a.		Tête bêche pair	37,500.	12,000.
57	A13	20c dl bl, *bluish*	225.00	6.75
a.		20c bright blue, *bluish*	350.00	8.00
b.		Tête bêche pair	3,750.	1,450.
c.		Half used as 10c on cover		55,000.
d.		Quarter used as 5c on cover		52,500.
58	A13	25c bl, *bluish* ('71)	110.00	1.10
a.		25c dk bl, *bluish*	135.00	1.10
b.		Tête bêche pair	6,750.	3,000.
59	A13	40c org, *yelsh* (I)	475.00	6.00
a.		40c orange, *yelsh* (I)	575.00	9.00
b.		40c orange, *yelsh* (II)	3,150.	130.00
c.		40c orange yel, *yelsh* (II)	3,150.	130.00
d.		Pair, types I and II	6,500.	525.00
f.		Half used as 20c on circular		20,000.
g.		Half used as 20c on cover		40,000.

No. 58 exists in three main plate varieties, differing in one or another of the flower-like corner ornaments.

Margins on this issue are extremely small.
Nos. 54, 57 and 58 were reprinted imperf. in 1887. See note after No. 37.

Imperf.

50b	A7	1c	270.00	
51a	A7	2c	350.00	
52a	A7	4c	450.00	
53b	A7	5c yel grn, *pale bl*	260.00	
55b	A13	10c	350.00	
56b	A13	15c	375.00	

A14

1872-75			**Larger Numerals**	Perf. 14x13½
60	A14	10c bis, *rose* ('75)	325.00	11.00
a.		Cliché of 15c in plate of 10c	3,750.	4,250.
b.		Pair, #60, 60a	6,750.	8,500.
61	A14	15c bister ('73)	320.00	3.25
62	A14	30c brn, *yelsh*	550.00	5.25
63	A14	80c rose, *pnksh*	640.00	11.50

Imperf.

62a	A14	30c	475.00	
63a	A14	80c	650.00	

Peace and Commerce ("Type Sage") — A15

Type I. The "N" of "INV" is under the "B" of "REPUBLIQUE."
Type II. The "N" of "INV" is under the "U" of "REPUBLIQUE."

Type I

1876-78			Perf. 14x13½
64	A15	1c grn, *grnsh*	125.00	70.00
65	A15	2c grn, *grnsh*	1,425.	240.00
66	A15	4c grn, *grnsh*	145.00	55.00
67	A15	5c grn, *grnsh*	650.00	45.00
68	A15	10c grn, *grnsh*	800.00	21.00
69	A15	15c gray lil, *grysh*	800.00	17.50
70	A15	20c red brn, *straw*	575.00	17.50
71	A15	20c bl, *bluish*	27,500.	
72	A15	25c ultra, *bluish*	7,750.	55.00
73	A15	30c brn, *yelsh*	425.00	8.25
74	A15	40c red, *straw* ('78)	600.00	35.00
75	A15	75c car, *rose*	950.00	12.50
76	A15	1fr brnz grn, *straw*	925.00	10.00

No. 71 was never put into use.
The reprints of No. 71 are type II. They are imperforate or with forged perforation.

For overprints and surcharges see Offices in China Nos. 1-17, J7-J10, J20-J22, Offices in Egypt, Alexandria 1-15, Port Said 1-17, Offices in Turkish Empire 1-7, Cavalle 1-8, Dedeagh 1-8, Port Lagos 1-5, Vathy 1-9, Offices in Zanzibar 1-33, 50-54, French Morocco 1-8, and Madagascar 14-27.

Imperf.

64a	A15	1c	150.00	
65a	A15	2c	1,000.	
66a	A15	4c	160.00	
67a	A15	5c	525.00	
68a	A15	10c	575.00	
69a	A15	15c	575.00	
70a	A15	20c	375.00	
73a	A15	30c	275.00	
74a	A15	40c	250.00	
75a	A15	75c	550.00	
76a	A15	1fr	400.00	

Beware of French Colonies Nos. 24-29.

Type II

1876-77			Perf. 14x13½
77	A15	2c grn, *grnsh*	115.00	19.00
78	A15	5c grn, *grnsh*	25.00	.60
a.		Imperf.	175.00	
79	A15	10c grn, *grnsh*	1,100.	240.00
80	A15	15c gray lil, *grysh*	675.00	1.90
81	A15	25c ultra, *bluish*	425.00	1.00
a.		25c blue, *bluish*	475.00	1.50
b.		Pair, types I & II	60,000.	17,500.
c.		Imperf.	325.00	
82	A15	30c yel brn, *yelsh*	82.50	1.40
a.		30c brown, *yellowish*	90.00	1.40
b.		Imperf.	325.00	
83	A15	75c car, *rose* ('77)	1,775.	110.00
84	A15	1fr brnz grn, *straw* ('77)	145.00	7.50
a.		Imperf.	1,100.	

Beware of French Colonies Nos. 31, 35.

1877-80

86	A15	1c blk, *lil bl*	3.75	1.65
a.		1c black, *gray blue*	3.75	1.65
b.		Imperf.	75.00	
87	A15	1c blk, *Prus bl* ('80)	11,000.	4,350.

Values for No. 87 are for examples with the perfs touching the design on at least one side.

88	A15	2c brn, *straw*	4.50	1.90
a.		2c brown, *yellow*	4.50	1.90
b.		Imperf.	210.00	

89	A15	3c yel, *straw* ('78)	200.00	42.50
a.		Imperf.	150.00	
90	A15	4c claret, *lav*	5.00	1.90
a.		4c vio brown, *lavender*	8.25	4.50
b.		Imperf.	60.00	
91	A15	10c blk, *lavender*	35.00	1.00
a.		10c black, *rose lilac*	37.50	1.00
b.		10c black, *lilac*	37.50	1.00
c.		Imperf.	70.00	
92	A15	15c blue ('78)	22.50	.60
a.		Imperf.	95.00	
b.		15c blue, *bluish*	435.00	15.00
93	A15	25c blk, *red* ('78)	1,075.	25.00
a.		Imperf.	675.00	
94	A15	35c blk, *yel* ('78)	525.00	35.00
a.		35c blk, *yel org*	525.00	35.00
b.		Imperf.	250.00	
95	A15	40c red, *straw*	90.00	2.10
a.		Imperf.	240.00	
96	A15	5fr vio, *lav*	440.00	70.00
a.		As #96, imperf.	750.00	
b.		5fr red lilac, *lavender*	650.00	100.00

Beware of French Colonies Nos. 38-40, 42, 44.

1879-90

97	A15	3c gray, *grysh* ('80)	3.00	1.65
a.		Imperf.	67.50	
98	A15	20c red, *yel grn*	37.50	4.25
a.		20c red, *deep green* ('84)	72.50	6.00
b.		Imperf.	100.00	
99	A15	25c yel, *straw*	340.00	5.00
a.		Imperf.	250.00	
100	A15	25c blk, *pale rose* ('86)	72.50	1.00
a.		Imperf.	155.00	
101	A15	50c rose, *rose* ('90)	210.00	2.65
a.		50c carmine, *rose*	225.00	3.50
102	A15	75c dp vio, *org* ('90)	215.00	35.00
a.		75c deep violet, *yellow*	265.00	45.00
		Nos. 97-102 (6)	878.00	49.55

Beware of French Colonies No. 43.

1892 — Quadrille Paper

103	A15	15c blue	12.50	.35
a.		Imperf.	175.00	

1898-1900 — Ordinary Paper

104	A15	5c yel grn	16.00	1.30
a.		Imperf.	82.50	

Type I

105	A15	5c yel grn	14.00	1.30
a.		Imperf.	575.00	
106	A15	10c blk, *lavender*	21.00	2.50
a.		Imperf.	275.00	
107	A15	50c car, *rose*	200.00	30.00
108	A15	2fr brn, *azure* ('00)	110.00	40.00
b.		Imperf.	2,250.	
		Nos. 104-108 (5)	361.00	75.10

See No. 226.
Reprints of A15, type II, were made in 1887 and left imperf. See note after No. 37. Value for set of 27, $4,000.

> Stamps of types A16, A18, A20, A22 and D2 were printed in 1916-20 on paper of poor quality, usually grayish and containing bits of fiber. This is called G. C. (Grande Consommation) paper. These wartime printings are noted (GC) in the descriptions above.

Liberty, Equality, Fraternity A16

"The Rights of Man" A17

Liberty and Peace — A18

1900-29			Perf. 14x13½
109	A16	1c gray	.55	.40
b.		Grayish paper (GC) ('16)	.65	.55
110	A16	2c violet brn	.70	.25
b.		Grayish (GC) paper ('17)	1.60	.25
111	A16	3c orange	.45	.45
a.		3c red	19.00	7.50
b.		Grayish (GC) paper ('17)	.55	.55
112	A16	4c yellow brn	3.00	1.60
113	A16	5c green	2.00	.35
b.		Booklet pane of 10	330.00	
114	A16	7½c lilac ('26)	.60	.45
115	A16	10c lilac ('29)	4.00	.60

116	A17	10c carmine	25.00	1.50
a.		Numerals printed separately	24.00	10.00
117	A17	15c orange	8.00	.60
118	A17	20c brown vio	55.00	9.25
119	A17	25c blue	125.00	1.65
a.		Numerals printed separately	115.00	9.25
120	A17	30c violet	70.00	6.00
121	A18	40c red & pale bl	15.00	.85
b.		Grayish (GC) paper ('16)	25.00	1.20
122	A18	45c grn & bl ('06)	29.00	2.10
b.		Grayish (GC) paper ('16)	45.00	4.00
123	A18	50c bis brn & gray	100.00	1.65
b.		Grayish paper (GC) ('16)	200.00	2.00
124	A18	60c vio & ultra ('20)	1.00	1.15
125	A18	1fr claret & ol grn	26.50	.85
b.		Grayish paper (GC) ('16)	52.50	.95
126	A18	2fr gray vio & yel	625.00	75.00
127	A18	2fr org & pale bl ('20)	42.50	.60
128	A18	3fr vio & bl ('25)	27.50	7.50
129	A18	3fr brt vio & rose ('27)	55.00	2.80
130	A18	5fr dk bl & buff	85.00	5.00
131	A18	10fr grn & red ('26)	125.00	17.00
132	A18	20fr mag & grn ('26)	200.00	37.50
		Nos. 109-132 (24)	1,626.	175.10

In the 10c and 25c values, the first printings show the numerals to have been impressed by a second operation, whereas, in later printings, the numerals were inserted in the plates. Two operations were used for all 20c and 30c, and one operation for the 15c.

No. 114 was issued precanceled only. Values for precanceled stamps in first column are for those which have not been through the post and have original gum. Values in the second column are for postally used, gumless stamps.

See Offices in China Nos. 34, 40-44, Offices in Crete 1-5, 10-15, Offices in Egypt, Alexandria 16-20, 26-30, 77, 84-86, Port Said 18-22, 28-32, 83, 90-92, Offices in Turkish Empire 21-26, 31-33, Cavalle 9, Dedeagh 9.

For overprints and surcharge see Nos. 197, 246, C1-C2, M1, P7. Offices in China 57, 62-65, 71, 73, 75, 83-85, J14, J27, Offices in Crete 17-20, Offices in Egypt, Alexandria 31-32, 34-35, 40-48, 57-64, 66, 71-73, Port Said 33, 35-40, 43, 46-57, 59, 65-71, 73, 78-80, Offices in Turkish Empire 35-38, 47-49, Cavalle 13-15, Dedeagh 16-18, Offices in Zanzibar 39, 45-49, 55, Offices in Morocco 11-15, 20-22, 26-29, 35-41, 49-54, 72-76, 84-85, 87-89, B6.

Imperf.

109a	A16	1c	55.00	
110a	A16	2c	67.50	60.00
111b	A16	3c	55.00	
112a	A16	4c	150.00	
113a	A16	5c	75.00	
116b	A17	10c #116 or 116a	235.00	135.00
117a	A17	15c	190.00	165.00
119b	A17	25c #119 or 119a	500.00	
121a	A18	40c	190.00	155.00
122a	A18	45c	260.00	
123a	A18	50c	375.00	375.00
124a	A18	60c	525.00	
125a	A18	1fr	250.00	225.00
126a	A18	2fr No gum	1,300.	
127a	A18	2fr	475.00	
128a	A18	3fr	725.00	500.00
129a	A18	3fr	425.00	
130a	A18	5fr	950.00	

Flat Plate & Rotary Press

The following stamps were printed by both flat plate and rotary press: Nos. 109-113, 144-146, 163, 166, 168, 170, 175, 177-178, 185, 192 and P7.

"Rights of Man" — A19

1902			Perf. 14x13½
133	A19	10c rose red	32.50	.90
134	A19	15c pale red	11.00	.60
135	A19	20c brown violet	82.50	14.00
136	A19	25c blue	100.00	2.25
137	A19	30c lilac	250.00	14.50
		Nos. 133-137 (5)	476.00	32.25

Imperf.

133a	A19	10c rose red	450.00	275.00
134a	A19	15c pale red	450.00	325.00
135a	A19	20c brown violet	800.00	475.00
136a	A19	25c blue	950.00	625.00
137a	A19	30c lilac	1,100.	675.00

See Offices in China Nos. 35-39, Offices in Crete 6-10, Offices in Egypt, Alexandria 21-25, 81-82, Port Said 23-27, 87-88, Offices in Turkish Empire 26-30, Cavalle 10-11, Dedeagh 10-11.

For overprints and surcharges see Nos. M2, Offices in China 45, 58-61, 66-70, 76-82, J15-J16, J28-J30, Offices in Crete 16, Offices in Egypt, Alexandria 33, 36-39, 49-50, 52-56, 65, 67-70, B1-B4, Port Said 34, 41-42, 44-45, 57, 60-64, 77, 74-77, B1-B4, Offices in Turkish Empire 34, 39, Cavalle 12, Dedeagh 15,

Offices in Zanzibar 40-44, 56-59, Offices in Morocco 16-19, 30-34, 42-48, 77-83, 86, B1-B5, B7, B9.

Sower — A20

1903-38 — Perf. 14x13½

138	A20	10c rose	8.00	.40
139	A20	15c slate grn	4.00	.25
b.		Booklet pane of 10	450.00	
c.		Grayish (GC) paper ('16)	4.50	.25
140	A20	20c violet brn	67.50	1.90
141	A20	25c dull blue	75.00	1.40
142	A20	30c violet	175.00	5.25
143	A20	45c lt violet ('26)	6.00	1.90
144	A20	50c dull blue ('21)	27.50	1.40
145	A20	50c gray grn ('26)	6.25	1.25
146	A20	50c vermilion ('26)	1.25	.25
a.		Booklet pane of 10	40.00	
147	A20	50c grnsh bl ('38)	1.00	.35
148	A20	60c lt vio ('24)	6.25	2.10
149	A20	65c rose ('24)	3.00	1.75
150	A20	65c gray grn ('27)	6.50	2.10
151	A20	75c rose lil ('26)	5.25	.60
152	A20	80c ver ('25)	26.50	9.50
153	A20	85c ver ('24)	13.50	3.25
154	A20	1fr dull blue ('26)	6.00	.75
		Nos. 138-154 (17)	438.50	34.40
		Set, never hinged	940.00	

See Nos. 941, 942A. For surcharges and overprints see Nos. 229-230, 232-233, 236, 256, B25, B29, B32, B36, B40, M3-M4, M6, Offices in Turkish Empire 46, 54.

Imperf.

138a	A20	10c	175.00	
139a	A20	15c	140.00	55.00
140a	A20	20c	300.00	160.00
141a	A20	25c	350.00	
142a	A20	30c	625.00	
144a	A20	50c	140.00	
145b	A20	50c	125.00	
		No gum	70.00	
147a	A20	50c	67.50	
149a	A20	65c	300.00	
151a	A20	75c	450.00	
154a	A20	1fr	*1,000.*	

Ground — A21

1906, Apr. 13 — Perf. 14x13½
With Ground Under Feet of Figure

155	A21	10c red	2.50	1.75
a.		Imperf, pair, no gum	275.00	225.00
		As "a," with gum	450.00	

No Ground — A22

TEN AND THIRTY-FIVE CENTIMES
Type I — Numerals and letters of the inscriptions thin.
Type II — Numerals and letters thicker.

No Ground Under the Feet

1906-37 — Perf. 14x13½

156	A22	1c olive bis ('33)	.25	.30
157	A22	2c dk grn ('33)	.25	.30
158	A22	3c ver ('33)	.25	.30
159	A22	5c green ('07)	1.50	.25
a.		Imperf., pair	40.00	30.00
b.		Booklet pane of 10	100.00	
c.		Grayish (GC) paper ('16)	2.75	.35
160	A22	5c orange ('21)	1.25	.30
a.		Booklet pane of 10	72.50	
161	A22	5c cerise ('34)	.25	.25
162	A22	10c red (II) ('07)	1.50	.25
a.		Imperf., pair	37.50	115.00
b.		10c red (I) ('06)	8.25	1.00
c.		As #162b, imperf., pair	37.50	115.00
d.		Booklet pane of 10 (I)	125.00	
e.		Booklet pane of 10 (II)	75.00	
f.		Booklet pane of 6 (II)	240.00	
g.		Grayish (GC) paper ('16)	12.00	2.10
163	A22	10c grn (II) ('21)	1.00	.55
a.		10c green (I) ('27)	32.50	37.50
b.		Booklet pane of 10 (I, "Phena")	350.00	
c.		Booklet pane of 10 (I, "Mineraline")	3,200.	
164	A22	10c ultra ('32)	1.40	.25
165	A22	15c red brn ('26)	.25	.25
a.		Booklet pane of 10	27.50	
166	A22	20c brown	3.00	.65
a.		Imperf., pair	82.50	100.00
b.		20c black brown	6.00	2.00
167	A22	20c red vio ('26)	.25	.25
a.		Booklet pane of 10	7.50	
168	A22	25c blue	2.40	.25
a.		Booklet pane of 10	37.50	
b.		Imperf, pair (dark blue)	45.00	60.00
d.		Grayish (GC) paper ('17)	4.00	1.20

169	A22	25c yel brn ('27)	.25	.25
a.		25c red brown	.30	
170	A22	30c orange	13.50	1.40
a.		Imperf, pair	200.00	175.00
b.		Grayish (GC) paper ('16)	15.00	1.75
171	A22	30c red ('21)	6.50	2.25
172	A22	30c cerise ('25)	1.25	.80
a.		Booklet pane of 10	13.50	
b.		Imperf, pair	575.00	
173	A22	30c lt blue ('25)	3.75	.60
a.		Booklet pane of 10	35.00	
b.		Imperf, pair	2,200.	
174	A22	30c cop red ('37)	.25	.30
a.		Booklet pane of 10	9.00	
175	A22	35c vio (II) ('07)	8.25	.90
a.		Imperf, pair	150.00	120.00
b.		35c violet (I) ('06)	150.00	7.50
c.		As "b," Imperf, pair, no gum	*575.00*	
176	A22	35c grn ('37)	.50	.55
a.		Imperf, pair	750.00	
177	A22	40c olive ('25)	1.40	.55
b.		Booklet pane of 10	30.00	
178	A22	40c ver ('26)	2.50	.80
a.		Booklet pane of 10	25.00	
179	A22	40c violet ('27)	2.00	.90
180	A22	40c lt ultra ('28)	1.25	.50
181	A22	1.05fr ver ('25)	9.50	5.25
182	A22	1.10fr cerise ('27)	11.50	2.50
183	A22	1.40fr cerise ('26)	20.00	22.50
184	A22	2fr Prus grn ('31)	14.00	1.75
		Nos. 156-184 (29)	109.95	45.95
		Set, never hinged	225.00	

The 10c and 35c, type I, were slightly retouched by adding thin white outlines to the sack of grain, the underside of the right arm and the back of the skirt. It is difficult to distinguish the retouches except on clearly-printed copies. The white outlines were made stronger on the stamps of type II.

Stamps of types A16, A18, A20 and A22 were printed in 1916-20 on paper of poor quality, usually grayish and containing bits of fiber. This is called G. C. (Grande Consommation) paper.

Nos. 160, 162b, 163, 175b and 176 also exist imperf.

See Nos. 241-241b. For surcharges and overprint see Nos. 227-228, 234, 238, 240, 400, B1, B24, B28, B31, B35, B37, B39, B41, M5, P8, Offices in Turkish Empire 40-45, 52, 55.

Louis Pasteur — A23

1923-26

185	A23	10c green	.55	.30
a.		Booklet pane of 10	15.00	
186	A23	15c green ('24)	1.40	.30
187	A23	20c green ('26)	2.75	.90
188	A23	30c red	.90	*1.50*
189	A23	30c green ('26)	.55	.50
190	A23	45c red ('24)	1.90	2.10
191	A23	50c blue	4.50	.50
192	A23	75c blue ('24)	3.75	1.00
a.		Imperf., pair	250.00	
193	A23	90c red ('26)	11.00	3.50
194	A23	1fr blue ('25)	21.00	.50
195	A23	1.25fr blue ('26)	25.00	8.00
196	A23	1.50fr blue ('26)	5.25	.50
		Nos. 185-196 (12)	78.55	19.60
		Set, never hinged	150.00	

Nos. 185, 188 and 191 were issued to commemorate the cent. of the birth of Pasteur.
For surcharges and overprint see Nos. 231, 235, 257, B26, B30, B33, C4.

No. 125 Overprinted in Blue

1923, June 15

197	A18	1fr claret & ol grn	440.00	500.00
		Never hinged	825.00	

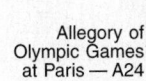

Allegory of Olympic Games at Paris — A24

The Trophy
A25

Milo of Crotona
A26

Victorious Athlete — A27

1924, Apr. 1 — Perf. 14x13½, 13½x14

198	A24	10c gray grn & yel grn	2.25	1.25
199	A25	25c rose & dk rose	3.00	.80
200	A26	30c brn red & blk	9.50	11.00
201	A27	50c ultra & dk bl	26.00	5.75
		Nos. 198-201 (4)	40.75	18.80
		Set, never hinged	125.00	

Imperf Singles

198a	A24	10c	1,000.	
199a	A25	25c	1,000.	*725.*
200a	A26	30c	1,000.	
201a	A27	50c	1,000.	1,000.

8th Olympic Games, Paris.

Pierre de Ronsard (1524-85), Poet — A28

1924, Oct. 6 — Perf. 14x13½

219	A28	75c blue, *bluish*	1.90	1.40
		Never hinged	2.75	

"Light and Liberty" Allegory A29

Majolica Vase A30

Potter Decorating Vase — A31

Terrace of Château — A32

1924-25 — Perf. 14x13½, 13½x14

220	A29	10c dk grn & yel ('25)	.55	.75
221	A30	15c ind & grn ('25)	.55	.85
a.		Imperf.	400.00	
		Never hinged	640.00	
222	A31	25c vio brn & garnet	.80	.50

223	A32	25c gray bl & vio ('25)	1.60	.65
a.		Imperf.	450.00	150.00
		Never hinged	700.00	
224	A31	75c indigo & ultra	3.50	2.25
225	A29	75c dk bl & lt bl ('25)	18.00	6.50
a.		Imperf.	375.00	
		Never hinged	650.00	
		Nos. 220-225 (6)	25.00	11.50
		Set, never hinged	52.50	

Intl. Exhibition of Decorative Modern Arts at Paris, 1925.

Philatelic Exhibition Issue
Souvenir Sheet

A32a

1925, May 2 — Perf. 14x13½

226	A32a	Sheet of 4, A15 II	1,100.	1,100.
		Never hinged	3,750.	
a.		Imperf. sheet	5,000.	1,750.
		Never hinged	7,750.	
b.		5fr carmine, perf.	125.00	140.00
		Never hinged	225.00	
c.		5fr carmine, imperf.	900.00	
		Never hinged	1,325.	

These were on sale only at the Intl. Phil. Exhib., Paris, May, 1925. Size: 140x220mm.

Nos. 148-149, 152-153,
173, 175, 181, 183, 192,
195 Surcharged

1926-27

227 A22	25c on 30c lt bl		.25	.50
a.	Pair, one without surcharge		1,050.	925.00
228 A22	25c on 35c vio		.25	.50
a.	Double surcharge		525.00	350.00
b.	Pair, one without surcharge		550.00	925.00
229 A20	50c on 60c lt vio ('27)		1.40	1.10
a.	Pair, one without surcharge		525.00	925.00
230 A20	50c on 65c rose ('27)		.75	.55
a.	Inverted surcharge		1,225.	1,400.
b.	Pair, one without surcharge		675.00	925.00
231 A23	50c on 75c blue		3.25	1.50
232 A20	50c on 80c ver ('27)		1.25	1.10
a.	Pair, one without surcharge		475.00	925.00
233 A20	50c on 85c ver ('27)		2.25	1.00
a.	Pair, one without surcharge		475.00	925.00
234 A22	50c on 1.05fr ver		1.25	.75
a.	Pair, one without surcharge		475.00	925.00
235 A23	50c on 1.25fr blue		2.75	2.25
a.	Pair, one without surcharge		525.00	925.00
236 A20	55c on 60c lt vio		125.00	52.50
238 A22	90c on 1.05fr ver ('27)		2.25	2.75
a.	Pair, one without surcharge		1,000.	925.00
240 A22	1.10fr on 1.40fr cer		1.00	1.10
a.	Pair, one without surcharge		575.00	925.00
	Nos. 227-240 (12)		141.65	65.60
	Set, never hinged		275.00	

Issue dates: Nos. 229-230, 232-234, 1927.
No. 236 is known only precanceled. See second note after No. 132.

Nos. 229, 230, 234, 238 and 240 have three bars instead of two. The 55c surcharge has thinner, larger numerals and a rounded "c." Width, including bars, is 17mm. instead of 13mm.

The 55c was used only precanceled at the Magasins du Louvre department store in Paris, August 1926.

Strasbourg Exhibition Issue
Souvenir Sheet

A32b

1927, June 4

241 A32b	Sheet of 2		1,000.	1,000.
	Never hinged		2,300.	
a.	5fr light ultra (A22)		250.00	250.00
	Never hinged		400.00	
b.	10fr carmine rose (A22)		250.00	250.00
	Never hinged		400.00	

Sold at the Strasbourg Philatelic Exhibition as souvenirs. Size: 111x140mm.

Marcelin Berthelot (1827-1907), Chemist and Statesman — A33

1927, Sept. 7

242 A33	90c dull rose		1.90	.60
	Never hinged		3.00	

For surcharge see No. C3.

Lafayette, Washington, S. S. Paris and Airplane "Spirit of St. Louis" — A34

1927, Sept. 15

243 A34	90c dull red		1.25	1.75
a.	Value omitted		2,000.	1,725.
244 A34	1.50fr deep blue		4.00	2.50
a.	Value omitted		1,450.	
	Set, never hinged		10.00	

Visit of American Legionnaires to France, September, 1927. Exist imperf.

Joan of Arc — A35

1929, Mar.

245 A35	50c dull blue		1.90	.25
	Never hinged		2.75	
a.	Booklet pane of 10		50.00	
b.	Imperf.		140.00	

500th anniv. of the relief of Orleans by the French forces led by Joan of Arc.

No. 127 Overprinted in Blue

EXPOSITION
LE HAVRE
1929
PHILATÉLIQUE

1929, May 18

246 A18	2fr org & pale bl		600.00	600.00
	Never hinged		1,325.	

Sold exclusively at the Intl. Phil. Exhib., Le Havre, May, 1929, for 7fr, which included a 5fr admission ticket.
Excellent counterfeits of No. 246 exist.

Reims Cathedral — A37

Die I, II, III   Die IV

Die I   Die II   Die III

Die I — The window of the 1st turret on the left is made of 2 lines. The horizontal line of the frame surrounding 3F is continuous.
Die II — Same as Die I but the line under 3F is not continuous.
Die III — Same as Die II but there is a deeply cut line separating 3 and F.
Die IV — Same as Die III but the window of the first turret on the left is made of three lines.

Mont-Saint-Michel — A38

Die I   Die II

Die I — The line at the top of the spire is broken.
Die II — The line is unbroken.

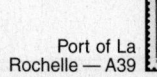

Port of La Rochelle — A39

Dies I & II   Die III

Die I — The top of the "E" of "POSTES" has a serif. The oval of shading inside the "0" of "10 fr" and the outer oval are broken at their bases.
Die II — The same top has no serif. Interior and exterior of "0" broken as in Die I.
Die III — Top of "E" has no serif. Interior and exterior of "0" complete.

Pont du Gard, Nimes — A40

Dies I & II

Die III

Die I — Shading of the first complete arch in the left middle tier is made of horizontal lines. Size 36x20¾mm. Perf. 13½.
Die II — Same, size 35½x21mm. Perf. 11.
Die III — Shading of same arch is made of three diagonal lines. Thin paper. Perf. 13.

1929-33   Engr.   Perf. 11, 13, 13½

247 A37	3fr dk gray ('30) (I)		62.50	2.40
	Never hinged		115.00	
247A A37	3fr dk gray ('30) (II)		125.00	3.50
	Never hinged		200.00	
247B A37	3fr dk gray ('30) (III)		375.00	24.00
	Never hinged		600.00	
248 A37	3fr bluish sl ('31) (IV)		60.00	2.40
	Never hinged		115.00	
249 A38	5fr brn ('30) (I)		24.00	4.25
	Never hinged		40.00	
250 A38	5fr brn ('31) (II)		21.00	.75
	Never hinged		32.50	
251 A39	10fr lt ultra (I)		95.00	15.00
	Never hinged		160.00	
251A A39	10fr ultra (II)		140.00	26.00
	Never hinged		225.00	
252 A39	10fr dk ultra ('31) (III)		70.00	6.50
	Never hinged		140.00	
253 A40	20fr red brn (I)		275.00	40.00
	Never hinged		500.00	
254 A40	20fr brt red brn ('30) (II)		1,000.	350.00
	Never hinged		1,650.	
254A A40	20fr org brn ('31) (III)		250.00	35.00
	Never hinged		450.00	
	Nos. 247-254A (12)		2,498.	509.80

View of Algiers — A41

1929, Jan. 1   Typo.

255 A41	50c blue & rose red		2.40	.50
	Never hinged		5.50	

Cent. of the 1st French settlement in Algeria.

Nos. 146 and 196 Overprinted

CONGRÈS DU B. I. T. 1930

1930, Apr. 23   Perf. 14x13½

256 A20	50c vermilion		3.00	3.25
257 A23	1.50fr blue		20.00	14.50
	Set, never hinged		47.50	

Intl. Labor Bureau, 48th Congress, Paris.

Colonial Exposition Issue

Fachi Woman A42   French Colonials A43

1930-31   Typo.   Perf. 14x13½

258 A42	15c gray black		1.10	.30
259 A42	40c dark brown		2.40	.30
260 A42	50c dark red		.65	.25
a.	Booklet pane of 10		12.50	
261 A42	1.50fr deep blue		9.00	.65

Perf. 13½
Photo.

262 A43	1.50fr dp blue ('31)		45.00	2.75
	Nos. 258-262 (5)		58.15	4.25
	Set, never hinged		125.00	

No. 260 has two types: type 1 shows four short downward hairlines near top of head, type 2 has no lines. Booklet stamps are type 2.

Arc de Triomphe — A44

1931   Engr.   Perf. 13

263 A44	2fr red brown		40.00	1.25
	Never hinged		80.00	

Peace with Olive Branch — A45

1932-39   Typo.   Perf. 14x13½

264 A45	30c dp green		1.00	.55
265 A45	40c brt violet		.30	.30
266 A45	45c yellow brown		1.75	1.00
267 A45	50c rose red		.25	.25
a.	Imperf., pair		140.00	
b.	Booklet pane of 10		5.50	
268 A45	55c dull vio ('37)		.60	.25
269 A45	60c ocher ('37)		.30	.25
270 A45	65c violet brown		.50	.50
271 A45	65c brt ultra ('37)		.25	.25
a.	Booklet pane of 10		7.00	
272 A45	75c olive green		.25	.30
273 A45	80c orange ('38)		.25	.25
274 A45	90c dk red		32.50	2.00
275 A45	90c brt green ('38)		.25	.25
276 A45	90c ultra ('38)		.90	.25
a.	Booklet pane of 10		8.50	
277 A45	1fr orange		3.25	.25
278 A45	1fr rose pink ('38)		3.25	.50
279 A45	1.25fr brown ol		75.00	4.75
280 A45	1.25fr rose car ('39)		1.90	2.25
281 A45	1.40fr brt red vio ('39)		5.75	5.25
282 A45	1.50fr deep blue		.30	.30
283 A45	1.75fr magenta		4.00	.50
	Nos. 264-283 (20)		132.55	20.20
	Set, never hinged		275.00	

The 50c is found in 4 types, differing in the lines below belt and size of "c."
For surcharges and overprints see Nos. 298, 333, 401-403, 405-409, M7-M9, S1.

Le Puy-en-Velay A46

1933   Engr.   Perf. 13

290 A46	90c rose		3.00	1.10
	Never hinged		5.75	

Aristide Briand A47   Paul Doumer A48

Victor Hugo — A49

1933, Dec. 11   Typo.   Perf. 14x13½
291	A47	30c blue green	17.00	8.00
292	A48	75c red violet	27.50	1.90
293	A49	1.25fr claret	6.00	2.25
	Nos. 291-293 (3)		50.50	12.15
	Set, never hinged		110.00	

Dove and Olive Branch — A50

1934, Feb. 20
294	A50	1.50fr ultra	50.00	15.00
	Never hinged		95.00	

Joseph Marie Jacquard — A51

1934, Mar. 14   Engr.   Perf. 14x13
295	A51	40c blue	3.00	1.10
	Never hinged		4.50	

Jacquard (1752-1834), inventor of an improved loom for figured weaving.

Jacques Cartier — A52

1934, July 18   Perf. 13
296	A52	75c rose lilac	30.00	2.25
297	A52	1.50fr blue	50.00	4.25
	Set, never hinged		210.00	

Cartier's discovery of Canada, 400th anniv.

No. 279 Surcharged

1934, Nov.   Perf. 14x13½
298	A45	50c on 1.25fr brn ol	3.75	.65
	Never hinged		7.00	

> **Catalogue values for unused stamps in this section, from this point to the end of the section, are for Never Hinged items.**

Breton River Scene — A53

1935, Feb.   Engr.   Perf. 13
299	A53	2fr blue green	70.00	1.00
	Hinged		32.50	

S. S. Normandie — A54

1935, Apr.
300	A54	1.50fr dark blue	29.00	2.00
	Hinged		14.00	
a.	1.50fr pale blue ('36)		145.00	19.00
	Hinged		55.00	
b.	1.50fr blue green ('36)		30,000.	12,500.
	Hinged		19,000.	
c.	1.50fr turquoise ('36)		400.00	40.00
	Hinged		275.00	

Maiden voyage of the transatlantic steamship, the "Normandie."

Benjamin Delessert — A55

1935, May 20
301	A55	75c blue green	47.50	1.75
	Hinged		17.50	

Opening of the International Savings Bank Congress, May 20, 1935.

View of St. Trophime at Arles — A56

1935, May 3
302	A56	3.50fr dark brown	70.00	4.25
	Hinged		27.50	

Victor Hugo (1802-85) — A57

1935, May 30   Perf. 14x13
303	A57	1.25fr magenta	8.25	2.00
	Hinged		4.00	

Cardinal Richelieu — A58

1935, June 12   Perf. 13
304	A58	1.50fr deep rose	70.00	1.75
	Hinged		20.00	

Tercentenary of the founding of the French Academy by Cardinal Richelieu.

Jacques Callot — A59

1935, Nov.   Perf. 14x13
305	A59	75c red	19.00	.75
	Hinged		10.00	

300th anniv. of the death of Jacques Callot, engraver.

André Marie Ampère (1775-1836), Scientist, by Louis Boilly — A60

1936, Feb. 27   Perf. 13
306	A60	75c brown	37.50	2.00
	Hinged		17.50	

Windmill at Fontvielle, Immortalized by Daudet — A61

1936, Apr. 27
307	A61	2fr ultra	5.75	.40
	Hinged		3.00	

Publication, in 1866, of Alphonse Daudet's "Lettres de mon Moulin," 75th anniv.

Pilâtre de Rozier and his Balloon — A62

1936, June 4
308	A62	75c Prus blue	37.50	2.75
			19.00	

150th anniversary of the death of Jean Francois Pilâtre de Rozier, balloonist.

Rouget de Lisle A63   "La Marseillaise" A64

1936, June 27
309	A63	20c Prus green	5.75	2.00
	Hinged		3.25	
310	A64	40c dark brown	11.50	3.25
	Hinged		5.50	

Cent. of the death of Claude Joseph Rouget de Lisle, composer of "La Marseillaise."

Canadian War Memorial at Vimy Ridge — A65

1936, July 26
311	A65	75c henna brown	25.00	2.00
	Hinged		9.50	
312	A65	1.50fr dull blue	32.50	9.50
	Hinged		16.00	

Unveiling of the Canadian War Memorial at Vimy Ridge, July 26, 1936.

A66

Jean Léon Jaurès — A67

1936, July 30
313	A66	40c red brown	5.75	1.40
	Hinged		4.00	
314	A67	1.50fr ultra	32.50	3.75
	Hinged		13.00	

Assassination of Jean Léon Jaurès (1859-1914), socialist and politician.

Herald A68   Allegory of Exposition A69

1936, Sept. 15   Typo.   Perf. 14x13½
315	A68	20c brt violet	1.00	.50
	Hinged		.30	

316	A68	30c Prus green	4.00	1.75
	Hinged		2.40	
317	A68	40c ultra	2.50	.50
	Hinged		1.00	
318	A68	50c red orange	2.25	.25
	Hinged		1.00	
319	A69	90c carmine	25.00	7.50
	Hinged		11.00	
320	A69	1.50fr ultra	67.50	4.00
	Hinged		30.00	
	Nos. 315-320 (6)		102.25	14.50

Publicity for the 1937 Paris Exposition.

"Peace" — A70

1936, Oct. 1   Engr.   Perf. 13
321	A70	1.50fr blue	27.50	4.00
	Hinged		12.50	

Skiing — A71

1937, Jan. 18
322	A71	1.50fr dark blue	14.00	1.75
	Hinged		7.00	

Intl. Ski Meet at Chamonix-Mont Blanc.

Pierre Corneille, Portrait by Charles Le Brun — A72

1937, Feb. 15
323	A72	75c brown carmine	3.75	1.40
	Hinged		1.90	

300th anniv. of the publication of "Le Cid."

Paris Exposition Issue

Exposition Allegory — A73

1937, Mar. 15
324 A73 1.50fr turq blue   4.00   1.25
   Hinged   2.25

Jean Mermoz (1901-36), Aviator A74

Memorial to Mermoz A75

1937, Apr. 22
325 A74 30c dk slate green   1.00   .55
   Hinged   .50
326 A75 3fr dark violet   13.50   3.75
   Hinged   6.25
   a.   3fr violet   15.00   4.50
   Hinged   6.75

Electric Train — A76

Streamlined Locomotive A77

1937, May 31
327 A76 30c dk green   1.40   1.75
   Hinged   1.00
328 A77 1.50fr dk ultra   15.00   8.25
   Hinged   7.25

13th International Railroad Congress.

Intl. Philatelic Exhibition Issue
Souvenir Sheet

Ceres Type A1 of 1849-50 A77a

1937, June 18   Typo.   Perf. 14x13½
329 A77a Sheet of 4   700.00   300.00
   Lightly hinged in margins   360.00
   a.   5c ultra & dark brown   90.00   47.50
   b.   15c red & rose red   90.00   47.50
   c.   30c ultra & rose red   90.00   47.50
   d.   50c red & dark brown   90.00   47.50
   e.   Sheet of 4, imperf   3,000.
   Lightly hinged in margins   2,350.

Issued in sheets measuring 150x220mm. The sheets were sold only at the exhibition in Paris, a ticket of admission being required for each sheet purchased.

René Descartes, by Frans Hals — A78

1937, June   Engr.   Perf. 13
Inscribed "Discours sur la Méthode"
330 A78 90c copper red   3.25   1.40
      1.90

Inscribed "Discours de la Méthode"
331 A78 90c copper red   11.00   1.75
      5.50

3rd centenary of the publication of "Discours de la Méthode" by René Descartes.

France Congratulating USA — A79

1937, Sept. 17
332 A79 1.75fr ultra   4.50   2.00
   Hinged   2.50

150th anniv. of the US Constitution.

No. 277 Surcharged in Red

1937, Oct.   Perf. 14x13½
333 A45 80c on 1fr orange   1.90   .85
   Hinged   .80
   a.   Inverted surcharge   1,225.
   Hinged   825.00

Mountain Road at Iseran — A80

1937, Oct. 4   Engr.   Perf. 13
334 A80 90c dark green   3.75   .30
   Hinged   1.90

Issued in commemoration of the opening of the mountain road at Iseran, Savoy.

Ceres — A81

1938-40   Typo.   Perf. 14x13½
335 A81 1.75fr dk ultra   1.40   .55
   Hinged   .55
336 A81 2fr car rose ('39)   .30   .30
   Hinged   .25
337 A81 2.25fr ultra ('39)   15.00   1.10
   Hinged   8.00
338 A81 2.50fr green ('39)   3.00   .50
   Hinged   1.25
339 A81 2.50fr vio blue ('40)   1.25   .75
   Hinged   .65
340 A81 3fr rose lilac ('39)   1.25   .50
   Hinged   .55
   Nos. 335-340 (6)   22.20   3.70

For surcharges see Nos. 397-399.

Léon Gambetta (1838-82), Lawyer and Statesman — A82

1938, Apr. 2   Engr.   Perf. 13
341 A82 55c dark violet   .55   .40
   Hinged   .35

Arc de Triomphe of Orange A82a

Miners A83

Keep and Gate of Vincennes A86

Palace of the Popes, Avignon A84

Medieval Walls of Carcassonne A85

Port of St. Malo — A87

1938
342 A82a 2fr brown black   1.75   1.25
   Hinged   .55
343 A83 2.15fr violet brn   9.50   1.00
      4.75
344 A84 3fr car brown   26.50   5.00
      12.50
345 A85 5fr deep ultra   1.50   .40
      .75
346 A86 10fr brown, *blue*   3.25   1.90
      1.50
347 A87 20fr dk blue grn   80.00   19.00
      37.50
   Nos. 342-347 (6)   122.50   28.55

For surcharges see Nos. 410-413.

Clément Ader, Air Pioneer — A88

1938, June 16
348 A88 50fr ultra (thin paper)   150.00   65.00
   Hinged   95.00
   a.   50fr dark ultra (thick paper)   175.00   77.50
   Hinged   100.00

For surcharge, see No. 414.

Soccer Players — A89

1938, June 1
349 A89 1.75fr dark ultra   29.00   13.50
   Hinged   13.50

World Cup Soccer Championship.

Costume of Champagne Region — A90

1938, June 13
350 A90 1.75fr dark ultra   7.50   4.50
   Hinged   3.75

Tercentenary of the birth of Dom Pierre Pérignon, discoverer of the champagne process.

Jean de La Fontaine — A91

1938, July 8
351 A91 55c dk blue green   1.00   .80
   Hinged   .65

Jean de La Fontaine (1621-1695) the fabulist.

Seal of Friendship and Peace, Victoria Tower and Arc de Triomphe — A92

1938, July 19
352 A92 1.75fr ultra   1.25   .80
      .65

Visit of King George VI and Queen Elizabeth of Great Britain to France.

Mercury — A93

1938-42   Typo.   Perf. 14x13½
353 A93 1c dark brn ('39)   .25   .25
   Hinged   .25
354 A93 2c slate grn ('39)   .25   .25
   Hinged   .25
355 A93 5c rose   .25   .25
   Hinged   .25
356 A93 10c ultra   .25   .25
   Hinged   .25
357 A93 15c red orange   .25   .25
   Hinged   .25
358 A93 15c org brn ('39)   1.00   .50
   Hinged   .55
359 A93 20c red violet   .25   .25
   Hinged   .25
360 A93 25c blue green   .25   .25
   Hinged   .25
361 A93 30c rose red ('39)   .25   .25
   Hinged   .25
362 A93 40c dk violet ('39)   .25   .25
   Hinged   .25
363 A93 45c lt green ('39)   .80   .50
   Hinged   .50
364 A93 50c deep blue ('39)   4.00   .40
   Hinged   2.25
365 A93 50c dk green ('41)   .55   .35
   Hinged   .30
366 A93 50c grnsh blue ('42)   .25   .25
   Hinged   .25
367 A93 60c red org ('39)   .25   .25
   Hinged   .25
368 A93 70c magenta ('39)   .25   .25
   Hinged   .25
369 A93 75c dk org brn ('39)   7.50   2.50
   Hinged   3.75
   Nos. 353-369 (17)   16.85   7.25

No. 366 exists imperforate. See Nos. 455-458. For overprints and surcharge see Nos. 404, 499-502.

Self-portrait — A95

1939, Mar. 15   Engr.   Perf. 13
370 A95 2.25fr Prussian blue   8.25   3.50
   Hinged   3.50

Paul Cézanne (1839-1906), painter.

Georges Clemenceau and Battleship Clemenceau A96

1939, Apr. 18
371 A96 90c ultra   1.00   .75
   Hinged   .50

Laying of the keel of the warship "Clemenceau," Jan. 17, 1939.

Statue of Liberty, French Pavilion, Trylon and Perisphere — A97

1939-40
372 A97 2.25fr ultra   17.00   6.50
   Hinged   8.00
373 A97 2.50fr ultra ('40)   22.50   9.50
   Hinged   8.50

New York World's Fair.

A98

Design: Joseph Nicéphore Niepce and Louis Jacques Mandé Daguerre.

1939, Apr. 24

374 A98 2.25fr dark blue   16.00   7.00
   Hinged   7.00

     Centenary of photography.

Iris — A99

1939-44	**Typo.**	**Perf. 14x13½**		
375 A99	80c red brown ('40)	.25	.25
	Hinged		.25
376 A99	80c yellow grn ('44)	.25	.25
	Hinged		.55
377 A99	1fr green	1.00	.25
	Hinged		.25
378 A99	1fr crimson ('40)	.40	.35
	Hinged		.25
a.	Booklet pane of 10	7.50
379 A99	1fr grnsh blue ('44)	.25	.25
	Hinged		.25
380 A99	1.20fr violet ('44)	.25	.25
	Hinged		.25
381 A99	1.30fr ultra ('40)	.25	.25
	Hinged		.25
382 A99	1.50fr red org ('41)	.25	.25
	Hinged		.25
383 A99	1.50fr henna brn ('44)	.25	.25
	Hinged		.25
384 A99	2fr violet brn ('44)	.25	.25
	Hinged		.25
385 A99	2.40fr car rose ('44)	.25	.25
	Hinged		.25
386 A99	3fr orange ('44)	.25	.25
	Hinged		.25
387 A99	4fr ultra ('44)	.25	.25
	Hinged		.25
	Nos. 375-387 (13)	4.15	3.35

Pumping Station at Marly — A100

1939   **Engr.**   **Perf. 13**

388 A100 2.25fr brt ultra   25.00   5.00
   Hinged   11.00

     France's participation in the International Water Exposition at Liège.

St. Gregory of Tours — A101

1939, June 10

389 A101 90c red   .90   .55
   Hinged   .50

     14th centenary of the birth of St. Gregory of Tours, historian and bishop.

"The Oath of the Tennis Court" by Jacques David — A102

1939, June 20

390 A102 90c deep slate green   3.50   1.90
   Hinged   1.90

     150th anniversary of French Revolution.

Cathedral of Strasbourg — A103

1939, June 23

391 A103 70c brown carmine   1.50   1.00
   Hinged   .75

     500th anniv. of the completion of Strasbourg Cathedral.

Porte Chaussée, Verdun — A104

1939, June 23

392 A104 90c black brown   1.00   .80
   Hinged   .80

     23rd anniv. of the Battle of Verdun.

View of Pau — A105

1939, Aug. 25

393 A105 90c brt rose, gray bl   1.25   1.25
   Hinged   .80

Maid of Languedoc A106

Bridge at Lyons — A107

1939

394 A106 70c black, *blue*   .50   .40
   Hinged   .40
395 A107 90c dull brown vio   1.00   *1.25*
   Hinged   .90

     Imperforates

     Nearly all French stamps issued from 1940 onward exist imperforate. Officially 20 sheets, ranging from 25 to 100 subjects, were left imperforate.

Georges Guynemer (1894-1917), World War I Ace — A108

1940, Nov. 7

396 A108 50fr ultra   16.00   9.00
   Hinged   8.00

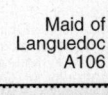

Stamps of 1938-39 Surcharged in Carmine

1940-41   **Perf. 14x13½**

397 A81 1fr on 1.75fr dk ultra   .30   .30
   Hinged   .25
398 A81 1fr on 2.25fr ultra ('41)   .30   .30
   Hinged   .25
399 A81 1fr on 2.50fr grn ('41)   1.40   1.40
   Hinged   .65
     Nos. 397-399 (3)   2.00   2.00

Stamps of 1932-39 Surcharged in Carmine, Red (#408) or Black (#407)

1940-41   **Perf. 13, 14x13½**

400 A22 30c on 35c grn ('41)   .30   .30
   Hinged   .25
401 A45 50c on 55c dl vio ('41)   .30   .30
   Hinged   .25
   a.   Inverted surcharge   1,000.
402 A45 50c on 65c brt ultra ('41)   .30   .30
   Hinged   .25

---

403 A45 50c on 75c ol grn ('41)   .30   .30
   Hinged   .25
404 A93 50c on 75c dk org brn ('41)   .30   .30
   Hinged   .25
405 A45 50c on 80c org ('41)   .30   .30
   Hinged   .25
406 A45 50c on 90c ultra ('41)   .30   .30
   Hinged   .25
   a.   Inverted surcharge   550.00
   b.   "05" instead of "50"   9,000.   6,400.
407 A45 1fr on 1.25fr rose car (Bk) ('41)   .30   .30
   Hinged   .25
408 A45 1fr on 1.40fr brt red vio (R) ('41)   .40   .40
   Hinged   .25
   a.   Double surcharge   1,600.
409 A45 1fr on 1.50fr dk bl ('41)   1.40   1.40
   Hinged   .25
410 A83 1fr on 2.15fr vio brn   .40   .40
   Hinged   .25
411 A85 2.50fr on 5fr dp ultra ('41)   .40   .40
   Hinged   .25
   a.   Double surcharge   350.00   190.00
412 A86 5fr on 10fr brn, *bl* ('41)   1.90   1.90
   Hinged   1.00
413 A87 10fr on 20fr dk grn ('41)   1.60   1.60
   Hinged   1.00
414 A88 20fr on 50fr dk ultra (#348a) ('41)   70.00   37.50
   Hinged   29.00
   a.   20fr on 50fr ultra, thin paper (#348)   75.00   50.00
     Nos. 400-414 (15)   78.50   46.00

     Issued: No. 410, 1940; others, 1941

Marshal Pétain — A109

1941   **Perf. 13**

415 A109 40c red brown   .40   .25
416 A109 80c turq blue   .45   .40
417 A109 1fr red   .25   .25
418 A109 2.50fr deep ultra   1.40   1.10
     Nos. 415-418 (4)   2.50   2.00

     For No. 417 with surcharge, see No. B111.

Frédéric Mistral — A110

1941, Feb. 20   **Perf. 14x13**

419 A110 1fr brown lake   .25   .25

     Issued in honor of Frédéric Mistral, poet and Nobel prize winner for literature in 1904.

Beaune Hospital — A111

View of Angers — A112

Ramparts of St. Louis, Aiguesmortes A113

1941

420 A111 5fr brown black   .35   .25
421 A112 10fr dark violet   .60   .45
422 A113 20fr brown black   1.10   .80
     Nos. 420-422 (3)   2.05   1.50

Inscribed "Postes Francaises"

1942

     Imprint: "FELTESSE" at right

423 A111 15fr brown lake   .60   .40

A114   A115

A116   A117

Marshal Pétain — A118

1941-42   **Typo.**   **Perf. 14x13½**

427	A114	20c lilac ('42)	.25	.25
428	A114	30c rose red	.25	.25
429	A114	40c ultra	.25	.25
431	A115	50c dp green	.25	.25
432	A115	60c violet ('42)	.25	.25
433	A115	70c saph ('42)	.25	.25
434	A115	70c orange ('42)	.25	.25
435	A115	80c brown	.25	.25
436	A115	80c emerald ('42)	.25	.25
437	A115	1fr rose red	.25	.25
438	A115	1.20fr red brn ('42)	.25	.25
439	A115	1.50fr rose	.25	.25
440	A116	1.50fr dl red brn ('42)	.25	.25
a.		Booklet pane of 10	2.75	
441	A116	2fr blue grn ('42)	.25	.25
443	A116	2.40fr rose red ('42)	.25	.25
444	A116	2.50fr ultra	.25	.55
445	A116	3fr orange	.25	.25
446	A115	4fr ultra ('42)	.25	.25
447	A115	4.50fr dk green ('42)	.25	.25

Engr.

Perf. 14x13

448	A115	4fr brt ultra ('42)	.25	.25
449	A115	4.50fr dark green ('42)	.25	.25
450	A117	5fr Prus green ('42)	.25	.25

Perf. 13

451	A118	50fr black ('42)	3.00	3.00
		Nos. 427-451 (23)	8.50	8.80

Nos. 431 to 438 measure 16½x20½mm. Nos. 448 and 449 measure 18x21½mm.

No. 440 was forged by the French Underground ("Défense de la France") and used to frank clandestine journals, etc., from Feb. to June, 1944. The forgeries were ungummed, both perf. 11½ and imperf., with a back handstamp covering six stamps and including the words: "Atelier des Faux."
For surcharge see No. B134.

Jules Massenet — A119

1942, June 22   **Perf. 14x13**
452   A119   4fr Prus green   .25   .25
Jules Massenet (1842-1912), composer.

Stendhal (Marie Henri Beyle) — A120

1942, Sept. 14   **Perf. 13**
453   A120   4fr blk brn & org red   .40   .40
Stendhal (1783-1842), writer.

André Blondel — A121

1942, Sept. 14
454   A121   4fr dull blue   .40   .40
André Eugène Blondel (1863-1938), physicist.

Mercury Type of 1938-42
Inscribed "Postes Françaises"

1942   **Perf. 14x13½**

455	A93	10c ultra	.25	.25
456	A93	30c rose red	.25	.25
457	A93	40c dark violet	.25	.25
458	A93	50c turq blue	.25	.25
		Nos. 455-458 (4)	1.00	1.00

Town-Hall Belfry, Arras — A122

1942, Dec. 8   **Engr.**   **Perf. 13**
459   A122   10fr green   .25   .25

Coats of Arms

Lyon — A123

1943   **Typo.**   **Perf. 14x13½**

460	A123	5fr shown	.30	.30
461	A123	10fr Brittany	.40	.40
462	A123	15fr Provence	1.75	1.10
463	A123	20fr Ile de France	1.40	1.20
		Nos. 460-463 (4)	3.85	3.00

Antoine Lavoisier (1743-94), French Scientist — A127

1943, July 5   **Engr.**   **Perf. 14x13**
464   A127   4fr ultra   .25   .25

Lake Lerie and Meije Dauphiné Alps — A128

1943, July 5   **Perf. 13**
465   A128   20fr dull gray grn   .75   .75

Nicolas Rolin, Guigone de Salins and Hospital of Beaune — A129

1943, July 21
466   A129   4fr blue   .25   .25
500th anniv. of the founding of the Hospital of Beaune.

Arms of Flanders — A130

1944, Mar. 27   **Typo.**   **Perf. 14x13½**

467	A130	5fr shown	.25	.25
468	A130	10fr Languedoc	.25	.25
469	A130	15fr Orleans	.60	.55
470	A130	20fr Normandy	1.00	.85
		Nos. 467-470 (4)	2.10	1.90

Edouard Branly — A134

1944, Feb. 21   **Engr.**   **Perf. 14x13**
471   A134   4fr ultra   .25   .25
Cent. of the birth of Edouard Branly, electrical inventor.

Early Postal Car — A135

1944, June 10   **Perf. 13**
472   A135   1.50fr dark blue green   .55   .45
Cent. of France's traveling postal service.

Chateau de Chenonceaux A136

1944, June 10

473	A136	15fr lilac brown	.60	.45
a.		15fr black brown	10.50	3.00
b.		15fr black	100.00	55.00

See No. 496.

Claude Chappe — A137

1944, Aug. 14   **Perf. 14x13**
474   A137   4fr dark ultra   .25   .25
150th anniv. of the invention of an optical telegraph by Claude Chappe (1763-1805).

Arc de Triomphe — OS2

1944, Oct. 9   **Unwmk.**   **Litho.**   **Perf. 11**

475	OS2	5c brt red violet	.25	.25
476	OS2	10c lt gray	.25	.25
476A	OS2	25c brown	.25	.25
476B	OS2	50c olive bis	.25	.25
476C	OS2	1fr pck green	.25	.25
476D	OS2	1.50fr rose pink	.25	.25
476E	OS2	2.50fr purple	.25	.25
476F	OS2	4fr ultra	.25	.25
476G	OS2	5fr black	.25	.25
476H	OS2	10fr yellow org	27.50	21.00
		Nos. 475-476H (10)	29.75	23.25

Nos 475-476H were printed by the U.S. Bureau of Engaving and Printing and were intended to be used by an Allied Military government, which was expected to administer the liberated areas of France. Instead, the Allies recognized the authority of Gen. de Gaulle's Provisional Government over these territories, and these stamps were transferred to the Free French in July, 1944. They were put on sale in liberated areas as the Allied armies advanced, and on Oct. 9, they were officially issued in Paris.
See Nos. 523A-523J.

Gallic Cock A138

Marianne A139

1944   **Litho.**   **Perf. 12**

477	A138	10c yellow grn	.25	.25
478	A138	30c dk rose vio	.30	.35
479	A138	40c blue	.25	.25
480	A138	50c dark red	.25	.25
481	A139	60c olive brown	.25	.25
482	A139	70c rose lilac	.25	.25
483	A139	80c yellow grn	.90	.90
484	A139	1fr violet	.25	.25
485	A139	1.20fr dp carmine	.25	.25
486	A139	1.50fr deep blue	.25	.25
487	A138	2fr indigo	.25	.25
488	A139	2.40fr red orange	1.10	1.10
489	A139	3fr dp blue grn	.25	.25
490	A139	4fr grnsh blue	.25	.25
491	A139	4.50fr black	.25	.25
492	A138	5fr violet blue	3.75	3.75
493	A138	10fr violet	4.50	4.25
494	A138	15fr olive brown	4.25	4.25
495	A138	20fr dk slate grn	3.75	3.75
		Nos. 477-495 (19)	21.55	21.35

Nos. 477-495 were issued first in Corsica after the Allied landing, and released in Paris Nov. 15, 1944.

Chateau Type Inscribed "RF"
1944, Oct. 30   **Engr.**   **Perf. 13**
496   A136   25fr black   .75   .55

Thomas Robert Bugeaud — A141

1944, Nov. 20
497   A141   4fr dp blue grn   .25   .25
Battle of Isly, Aug. 14th, 1844.

Church of St. Denis — A142

1944, Nov. 20
498   A142   2.40fr brown carmine   .30   .30
800th anniv. of the Church of St. Denis.

Type of 1938-42, Overprinted in Black

Inscribed "Postes Francaises"

1944   **Perf. 14x13½**

499	A93	10c ultra	.25	.25
500	A93	30c rose red	.25	.25
501	A93	40c dark violet	.25	.25
502	A93	50c grnsh blue	.25	.25
		Nos. 499-502 (4)	1.00	1.00

The overprint "RF" in various forms, with or without Lorraine Cross, was also applied to stamps of the French State at Lyon and fourteen other cities.

French Forces of the Interior and Symbol of Liberation — A143

1945, Jan.
503   A143   4fr dark ultra   .30   .30
Issued to commemorate the Liberation.

Stamps of the above design, and of one incorporating "FRANCE" in the top panel, were printed by photo. in England during WW II upon order of the Free French Government. They were not issued. There are 3 values in each design; 25c green, 1fr red, 2.50fr blue. Value: set, above design, $100; set inscribed "FRANCE," $600.

Marianne — A144

Perf. 11½x12½

1944-45   **Engr.**   **Unwmk.**

504	A144	10c ultra	.25	.25
505	A144	30c bister	.25	.25
506	A144	40c indigo	.25	.25
507	A144	50c red orange	.25	.25
508	A144	60c chalky blue	.25	.25
509	A144	70c sepia	.25	.25
510	A144	80c deep green	.25	.25
511	A144	1fr lilac	.25	.25
512	A144	1.20fr dk ol grn	.25	.25
513	A144	1.50fr rose ('44)	.25	.25
514	A144	2fr dk brown	.25	.25
515	A144	2.40fr red	.25	.25
516	A144	3fr brt ol grn	.25	.25
517	A144	4fr brt ultra	.25	.25
518	A144	4.50fr slate gray	.25	.25
519	A144	5fr brt orange	.25	.25
520	A144	10fr yellow grn	.25	.25
521	A144	15fr lake	.25	.25
522	A144	20fr brown org	1.10	1.10
523	A144	50fr deep purple	2.90	2.40
		Nos. 504-523 (20)	8.50	8.00

The 2.40fr exists imperf. in a miniature sheet of 4 which was not issued. Value: never hinged $6,500; unused $4,500.
Compare with type A1759. See Nos. 4905, 4909.

Arc de Triomphe Type of 1944

1945, Feb. 12   **Litho.**   **Perf. 11**

Denominations in Black

523A	OS2	30c orange	.25	.25
523B	OS2	40c pale gray	.25	.25
523C	OS2	50c olive bis	.25	.25
523D	OS2	60c violet	.25	.25
523E	OS2	80c emerald	.25	.25
523F	OS2	1.20fr brown	.25	.25
523G	OS2	1.50fr vermilion	.25	.25
523H	OS2	2fr yellow	.25	.25
523I	OS2	2.40fr dark rose	.25	.25
523J	OS2	3fr brt red violet	.25	.25
		Nos. 523A-523J (10)	2.50	2.50

Coat of Arms
A145

Ceres
A146

Marianne — A147

1945-47   **Typo.**   **Perf. 14x13½**

524	A145	10c brown black	.25	.25
525	A145	30c dk blue grn	.25	.25
526	A145	40c lilac rose	.25	.25
527	A145	50c violet blue	.25	.25
528	A146	60c bis	.25	.25
530	A146	80c brt green	.25	.25
531	A146	90c dull grn ('46)	.65	.55
532	A146	1fr rose red	.25	.25
533	A146	1.20fr brown black	.25	.25
534	A146	1.50fr rose lilac	.25	.25
535	A147	1.50fr rose pink	.25	.25
536	A147	2fr myrtle green	.25	.25
536A	A146	2fr lt bl grn ('46)	.25	.25
537	A147	2.40fr scarlet	.30	.30
538	A146	2.50fr brown ('46)	.25	.25
539	A147	3fr sepia	.25	.25
540	A147	3fr dp rose ('46)	.25	.25
541	A147	4fr ultra	.25	.25
541A	A147	4fr violet ('46)	.25	.25
541B	A147	4.50fr ultra ('47)	.25	.25
542	A147	5fr lt green	.25	.25
542A	A147	5fr rose pink ('47)	.25	.25
543	A147	6fr brt ultra	.35	.25
544	A147	6fr crim rose ('46)	1.60	.90
545	A147	10fr red orange	.45	.30
546	A147	10fr ultra ('46)	1.20	.75
547	A147	15fr brt red vio	3.00	1.60
		Nos. 524-547 (27)	12.55	9.65

No. 531 is known only precanceled. See second note after No. 132.

Due to a reduction of the domestic postage rate, No. 542A was sold for 4.50fr.

Compare with types A1814 and A3213. See Nos. 576-580, 594-602, 614, 615, 650-654, 4906, 4908. For surcharges see Nos. 589, 610, 706, Reunion 270-276, 278, 285, 290-291, 293, 295.

1945-46   **Engr.**   **Perf. 14x13**

548	A147	4fr dark blue	.25	.25
549	A147	10fr dp blue ('46)	1.10	.55
550	A147	15fr brt red vio ('46)	6.75	1.75
551	A147	20fr blue grn ('46)	1.00	.55
552	A147	25fr red ('46)	6.75	1.50
		Nos. 548-552 (5)	15.85	4.60

Nos. 548-552 have "GANDON" at lower right in design, and no inscription below design.

Marianne — A148

1945   **Engr.**   **Perf. 13**

553	A148	20fr dark green	1.00	.90
554	A148	25fr violet	1.10	1.10
555	A148	50fr red brown	1.50	1.50
556	A148	100fr brt rose car	10.00	5.50
		Nos. 553-556 (4)	13.60	9.00

CFA

French stamps inscribed or surcharged "CFA" and new value are listed under Réunion at the end of the French listings.

Arms of Metz
A149

Arms of Strasbourg
A150

1945, Mar. 3   **Perf. 14x13**

557	A149	2.40fr dull blue	.25	.25
558	A150	4fr black brown	.25	.25

Liberation of Metz and Strasbourg.

A151

Design: Costumes of Alsace and Lorraine and Cathedrals of Strasbourg and Metz.

1945, May 16   **Perf. 13**

559   A151   4fr henna brown   .25   .25

Liberation of Alsace and Lorraine. See No. 4907.

World Map Showing French Possessions
A152

1945, Sept. 17

560   A152   2fr Prussian blue   .25   .25

No. B193 Surcharged in Black

1946   **Perf. 14x13½**

561   SP147   3fr on 2fr+1fr red org   .25   .25

Arms of Corsica — A153

1946   **Unwmk.**   **Typo.**   **Perf. 14x13½**

562	A153	10c shown	.25	.25
563	A153	30c Alsace	.25	.25
564	A153	50c Lorraine	.25	.25
565	A153	60c County of Nice	.25	.25
		Nos. 562-565 (4)	1.00	1.00

For surcharges see Reunion Nos. 268-269.

Reaching for "Peace"
A157

Holding the Dove of Peace
A158

1946, July 29   **Engr.**   **Perf. 13**

566	A157	3fr Prussian green	.25	.25
567	A158	10fr blue	.25	.25

Peace Conference of Paris, 1946.

Vézelay — A159

Luxembourg Palace
A160

Rocamadour
A161

Pointe du Raz, Finistère — A162

1946   **Unwmk.**   **Perf. 13**

568	A159	5fr rose violet	.25	.25
569	A160	10fr dark blue	.25	.25
570	A161	15fr dk violet brn	3.50	.55
571	A162	20fr slate gray	1.00	.25
		Nos. 568-571 (4)	5.00	1.30

See Nos. 591-592. For surcharges see Reunion Nos. 277, 279.

Globe and Wreath — A163

1946, Nov.

572   A163   10fr dark blue   .25   .25

Gen. conf. of UNESCO, Paris, 1946.

Cannes — A164

Stanislas Square, Nancy — A165

1946-48   **Engr.**   **Perf. 13**

573	A164	6fr rose red	1.10	.40
574	A165	25fr black brown	3.00	.25
575	A165	25fr dark blue ('48)	10.00	.90
		Nos. 573-575 (3)	14.10	1.55

For surcharges see Reunion Nos. 280-281.

Ceres & Marianne Types of 1945

1947   **Unwmk.**   **Typo.**   **Perf. 14x13½**

576	A146	1.30fr dull blue	.25	.25
577	A147	3fr green	1.50	.25
578	A147	3.50fr brown red	.60	.30
579	A147	5fr blue	.25	.25
580	A147	6fr carmine	.25	.25
		Nos. 576-580 (5)	2.85	1.30

Colonnade of the Louvre — A166

La Conciergerie, Paris Prison — A167

La Cité, Oldest Section of Paris — A168

Place de la Concorde — A169

Auguste Pavie — A170

1947, May 7   **Engr.**   **Perf. 13**

581	A166	3.50fr chocolate	.30	.30
582	A167	4.50fr dk slate gray	.30	.30
583	A168	6fr red	.85	.85
584	A169	10fr bright ultra	.85	.85
		Nos. 581-584 (4)	2.30	2.30

12th UPU Cong., Paris, May 7-July 7. See No. 5035a.

1947, May 30

585   A170   4.50fr sepia   .30   .25

Cent. of the birth of Auguste Pavie, French pioneer in Laos.

Francois Fénelon — A171

1947, July 12

586   A171   4.50fr chocolate   .30   .25

Issued to honor Francois de Salignac de la Mothe-Fénelon, prelate and writer.

Fleur-de-Lis and Double Carrick Bend — A172

1947, Aug. 2   **Unwmk.**

587   A172   5fr brown   .30   .25

6th World Boy Scout Jamboree held at Moisson, Aug. 9th-18th, 1947.

Captured Patriot — A173

1947, Nov. 10   **Engr.**   **Perf. 13**

588   A173   5fr sepia   .40   .35

No. 576 Surcharged in Carmine

1947, Nov.   **Typo.**   **Perf. 14x13½**

589   A146   1fr on 1.30fr dull blue   .25   .25

View of Conques — A174

1947, Dec. 18   **Engr.**   **Perf. 13**

590   A174   15fr henna brown   3.50   .70

For surcharge see Reunion No. 282.

Types of 1946-47

1948   **Re-engraved**
591 A160 12fr rose carmine   2.50 .45
592 A160 15fr bright red   .60 .40
593 A174 18fr dark blue   3.50 .40
     Nos. 591-593 (3)   6.60 1.25

"FRANCE" substituted for inscriptions "RF" and "REPUBLIQUE FRANCAISE."

Marianne Type of 1945

1948-49   **Typo.**   **Perf. 14x13½**
594 A147 2.50fr brown   2.75 1.25
595 A147 3fr lilac rose   .25 .25
596 A147 4fr lt blue grn   .25 .25
597 A147 4fr brown org   2.50 .90
598 A147 5fr lt blue grn   .60 .25
599 A147 8fr blue   .30 .25
600 A147 10fr brt violet   .25 .25
601 A147 12fr ultra ('49)   2.50 .25
602 A147 15fr crim rose ('49)   .85 .25
  a.   Booklet pane of 10   150.00
     Nos. 594-602 (9)   10.25 3.90

No. 594 known only precanceled. See second note after No. 132.

François René de Chateaubriand A175

1948, July 3   **Engr.**   **Perf. 13**
603 A175 18fr dark blue   .30 .25

Vicomte de Chateaubriand (1768-1848).

Philippe François M. de Hautecloque (Gen. Jacques Leclerc) — A176

1948, July 3
604 A176 6fr gray black   .30 .25

See Nos. 692-692A.

Chaillot Palace — A177

A178

1948, Sept. 21
605 A177 12fr carmine rose   .35 .30
606 A178 18fr indigo   .35 .30

Meeting of the UN General Assembly, Paris, 1948.

Genissiat Dam — A179

1948, Sept. 21
607 A179 12fr carmine rose   .85 .75

Paul Langevin — A180

1948, Nov. 17   **Perf. 14x13**
608 A180 5fr shown   .50 .25
609 A180 8fr Jean Perrin   .50 .25

Placing of the ashes of physicists Langevin (1872-1946) and Perrin (1870-1942) in the Pantheon.

No. 580 Surcharged with New Value and Bars in Black

1949, Jan.   **Perf. 14x13½**
610 A147 5fr on 6fr carmine   .25 .25

Arctic Scene — A181

1949, May 2   **Perf. 13**
611 A181 15fr indigo   .30 .25

French polar explorations.

Types of 1849 and 1945

1949, May 9   **Engr.**   **Imperf.**
612 A1 15fr red   3.00 3.00
613 A1 25fr deep blue   3.00 3.00
     Perf. 14x13
614 A147 15fr red   3.00 3.00
615 A147 25fr deep blue   3.00 3.00
  a.   Strip of 4, #612-615 + label   14.00 12.00
     Nos. 612-615 (4)   12.00 12.00

Cent. of the 1st French postage stamps.

Arms of Burgundy — A182

Arms: 50c, Guyenne (Aquitania). 1fr, Savoy. 2fr, Auvergne. 4fr, Anjou.

1949, May 11   **Typo.**   **Perf. 14x13½**
616 A182 10c blue, red & yel   .25 .25
617 A182 50c blue, red & yel   .25 .25
618 A182 1fr brown & red   .40 .25
619 A182 2fr green, yel & red   .40 .25
620 A182 4fr blue, red & yel   .30 .25
     Nos. 616-620 (5)   1.60 1.25

See Nos. 659-663, 694-699, 733-739, 782-785. For surcharges see Reunion Nos. 283-284, 288-289, 297, 301, 305, 311.

Collegiate Church of St. Barnard and Dauphiné Arms — A183

1949, May 14   **Engr.**   **Perf. 13**
621 A183 12fr red brown   .30 .25

600th anniv. of France's acquisition of the Dauphiné region.

US and French Flags, Plane and Steamship A184

1949, May 14
622 A184 25fr blue & carmine   .45 .35

Franco-American friendship.

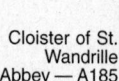

Cloister of St. Wandrille Abbey — A185

1949, May 18
623 A185 25fr deep ultra   .30 .25

See No. 649. For surcharge see Reunion No. 287.

Type of 1849 Inscribed "1849-1949" in Lower Margin

1949, June 1
624 A1 10fr brown orange   55.00 40.00
  a.   Sheet of 10   700.00 450.00

Cent. of the 1st French postage stamp. No. 624 has wide margins, 40x52mm from perforation to perforation. Sold for 110fr, which included cost of admission to the Centenary Intl. Exhib., Paris, June 1949.

Claude Chappe — A186

15fr, François Arago & André M. Ampère. 25fr, Emile Baudot. 50fr, Gen. Gustave A. Ferrié.

Inscribed: "C.I.T.T. PARIS 1949"

1949, June 13   **Unwmk.**   **Perf. 13**
625 A186 10fr vermilion   .75 .70
626 A186 15fr sepia   .75 .70
627 A186 25fr deep claret   1.90 1.90
628 A186 50fr deep blue   3.75 2.75
     Nos. 625-628 (4)   7.15 6.05

International Telegraph and Telephone Conference, Paris, May-July 1949.

Jean Racine — A187

1949
629 A187 12fr sepia   .30 .25

Death of Jean Racine, dramatist, 250th anniv.

Abbey of St. Bertrand de Comminges A188

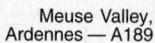

Meuse Valley, Ardennes — A189

Mt. Gerbier de Jonc, Vivarais — A190

1949   **Engr.**
630 A188 20fr dark red   .25 .25
631 A189 40fr Prus green   12.50 .25
632 A190 50fr sepia   2.10 .25
     Nos. 630-632 (3)   14.85 .75

For surcharge see Reunion No. 286.

A191

1949, Oct. 18
633 A191 15fr deep carmine   .25 .25

50th anniv. of the Assembly of Presidents of Chambers of Commerce of the French Union.

UPU Allegory — A192

1949, Nov. 7
634 A192 5fr dark green   .25 .25
635 A192 15fr deep carmine   .30 .25
636 A192 25fr deep blue   1.00 .90
     Nos. 634-636 (3)   1.55 1.40

UPU, 75th anniversary.

Raymond Poincaré — A193

1950, May 27   **Unwmk.**   **Perf. 13**
637 A193 15fr indigo   .30 .25

Charles Péguy and Cathedral at Chartres A194

François Rabelais A195

1950, June
638 A194 12fr dk brown   .30 .25
639 A195 12fr red brown   .60 .45

Chateau of Chateaudun A196

1950, Nov. 25
640 A196 8fr choc & bis brn   .55 .40

Madame Récamier A197

Marie de Sévigné A198

1950
641 A197 12fr dark green   .45 .40
642 A198 15fr ultra   .45 .40

See footnote after No. 4642.

Palace of Fontainbleau A199

1951, Jan. 20
643 A199 12fr dark brown   .75 .60

Jules Ferry — A200

1951, Mar. 17
644 A200 15fr bright red   .40 .40

Hands Holding Shuttle — A201

1951, Apr. 9
645 A201 25fr deep ultra   .75 .45

Intl. Textile Exposition, Lille, April-May, 1951.

Jean-Baptiste de la Salle — A202

1951, Apr. 28
646 A202 15fr chocolate .45 .35
300th anniv. of the birth of Jean-Baptiste de la Salle, educator and saint.

Map and Anchor — A203

1951, May 12
647 A203 15fr deep ultra .60 .30
50th anniv. of the creation of the French colonial troops.

Vincent d'Indy — A204

1951, May 15
648 A204 25fr deep green 1.50 1.50
Vincent d'Indy, composer, birth cent.

Abbey Type of 1949
1951
649 A185 30fr bright blue 4.00 3.25

Marianne Type of 1945-47

1951	**Typo.**		**Perf. 14x13½**
650 A147	5fr dull violet	.30	.25
651 A147	6fr green	4.75	.45
652 A147	12fr red orange	.70	.25
653 A147	15fr ultra	.25	.25
a.	Booklet pane of 10	60.00	
654 A147	18fr cerise	15.00	1.20
	Nos. 650-654 (5)	21.00	2.40

A205

Design: Professors Nocard, Bouley and Chauveau; gate at Lyons school.

1951, June 8 **Engr.** **Perf. 13**
655 A205 12fr red violet .60 .40
Issued to honor Veterinary Medicine.

A206

Design: Gen. Picqué, Cols. Roussin and Villemin; Val de Grace Dome.

1951, June 17 **Unwmk.**
656 A206 15fr red brown .75 .40
Issued to honor Military Medicine.

St. Nicholas, by Jean Didier — A207

1951, June 23
657 A207 15fr ind, dp claret & org 1.00 .75

Chateau Bontemps, Arbois — A208

1951, June 23
658 A208 30fr indigo .75 .25
For surcharge see Reunion No. 296.

Arms Type of 1949

Arms of: 10c, Artois. 50c, Limousin. 1fr, Béarn. 2fr, Touraine. 3fr, Franche-Comté.

1951, June	**Typo.**		**Perf. 14x13½**
659 A182	10c red, vio bl & yel	.25	.25
660 A182	50c green, red & blk	.25	.25
661 A182	1fr blue, red & yel	.25	.25
662 A182	2fr vio bl, red & yel	.60	.25
663 A182	3fr red, vio bl & yel	.45	.30
	Nos. 659-663 (5)	1.80	1.30

Seal of Paris — A209

Unwmk.
1951, July 7 **Engr.** **Perf. 13**
664 A209 15fr dp bl, dk brn & red .55 .30
2,000th anniv. of the founding of Paris.

Maurice Noguès and Globe — A210

1951, Oct. 13
665 A210 12fr indigo & blue .70 .60
Maurice Nogues, aviation pioneer.

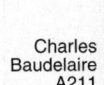

Charles Baudelaire A211

Poets: 12fr, Paul Verlaine. 15fr, Arthur Rimbaud.

1951, Oct. 27
666 A211 8fr purple .70 .45
667 A211 12fr gray .70 .45
668 A211 15fr dp green .70 .45
Nos. 666-668 (3) 2.10 1.35

Georges Clemenceau, Birth Cent. — A212

1951, Nov. 11
669 A212 15fr black brown .55 .35

Chateau du Clos, Vougeot — A213

1951, Nov. 17
670 A213 30fr blk brn & brn 5.25 1.75

Chaillot Palace and Eiffel Tower — A214

1951, Nov. 6
671 A214 18fr red .90 .60
672 A214 30fr deep ultra 1.50 1.50
Opening of the Geneva Assembly of the United Nations, Paris, Nov. 6, 1951.

Observatory, Pic du Midi — A215

Abbaye aux Hommes, Caen — A216

1951, Dec. 22
673 A215 40fr violet 4.50 .25
674 A216 50fr black brown 4.00 .25
For surcharge see Reunion No. 294.

Marshal Jean de Lattre de Tassigny, 1890-1952 A217

1952, May 8 **Unwmk.** **Perf. 13**
675 A217 15fr violet brown .75 .45
See No. 717.

Gate of France, Vaucouleurs — A218

1952, May 11
676 A218 12fr brown black 1.00 .75

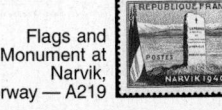

Flags and Monument at Narvik, Norway — A219

1952, May 28
677 A219 30fr violet blue 2.50 1.75
Battle of Narvik, May 27, 1940.

Chateau de Chambord A220

1952, May 30
678 A220 20fr dark purple .45 .25
For surcharge see Reunion No. 292.

Assembly Hall, Strasbourg A221

1952, May 31
679 A221 30fr dark green 6.50 4.50
Issued to honor the Council of Europe.

Monument, Bir-Hacheim Cemetery — A222

1952, June 14
680 A222 30fr rose lake 3.00 1.75
10th anniv. of the defense of Bir-Hacheim.

Abbey of the Holy Cross, Poitiers — A223

1952, June 21
681 A223 15fr bright red .40 .40
14th cent. of the foundation of the Abbey of the Holy Cross at Poitiers.

A224

Design: Leonardo da Vinci, Amboise Chateau and La Signoria, Florence.

1952, July 9
682 A224 30fr deep ultra 7.00 5.25
Leonardo da Vinci, 500th birth anniv.

Garabit Viaduct — A225

1952, July 5
683 A225 15fr dark blue .45 .45

Sword and Military Medals, 1852-1952 — A226

1952, July 5
684 A226 15fr choc, grn & yel .45 .40
Cent. of the creation of the Military Medal.

Dr. René Laennec — A227

1952, Nov. 7
685 A227 12fr dark green .60 .45

Versailles Gate, Painted by Utrillo — A228

1952, Dec. 20
686 A228 18fr violet brown 2.25 1.50
Publicity for the restoration of Versailles Palace. See No. 728.

Mannequin — A229

1953, Apr. 24 **Unwmk.** **Perf. 13**
687 A229 30fr blue blk & rose vio .75 .30
Dressmaking industry of France.

Gargantua
of François
Rabelais
A230

Figaro, from
the Barber
of Seville
A232

Célimène
from The
Misanthrope
A231

Hernani of
Victor Hugo
A233

1953

688	A230	6fr dp plum & car	.25	.25
689	A231	8fr indigo & ultra	.25	.25
690	A232	12fr vio brn & dk grn	.25	.25
691	A233	18fr vio brn & blk brn	.50	.25
		Nos. 688-691 (4)	1.25	1.00

For surcharge see Reunion No. 298.

Type of 1948
Inscribed "Général Leclerc Maréchal
de France"

1953-54

692	A176	8fr red brown	.75	.60
692A	A176	12fr dk grn & gray grn ('54)	2.25	1.50

Issued to honor the memory of General Jacques Leclerc.

Map and Cyclists,
1903-1953
A234

1953, July 26

693	A234	12fr red brn, ultra & blk	1.75	1.10

50th anniv. of the Bicycle Tour de France.

Arms Type of 1949
50c, Picardy. 70c, Gascony. 80c, Berri. 1fr,
Poitou. 2fr, Champagne. 3fr, Dauphiné.

1953   Typo.   Perf. 14x13½

694	A182	50c blue, yel & red	.25	.25
695	A182	70c red, blue & yel	.25	.25
696	A182	80c blue, red & yel	.25	.25
697	A182	1fr black, red & yel	.25	.25
698	A182	2fr brown, bl & yel	.30	.25
699	A182	3fr red, blue & yel	.45	.25
		Nos. 694-699 (6)	1.75	1.50

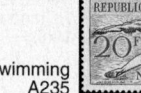

Swimming
A235

1953, Nov. 28   Engr.   Perf. 13

700	A235	20fr shown	1.90	.25
701	A235	25fr Track	10.50	.25
702	A235	30fr Fencing	1.90	.25
703	A235	40fr Canoe racing	11.00	.25
704	A235	50fr Rowing	6.00	.25
705	A235	75fr Equestrian	30.00	11.00
		Nos. 700-705 (6)	61.30	12.25

For surcharges see Reunion Nos. 299-300.

No. 654 Surcharged with New Value and Bars in Black

1954   Perf. 14x13½

706	A147	15fr on 18fr cerise	.40	.25

Farm
Woman
A236

Gallic
Cock
A237

1954   Typo.

707	A236	4fr blue	.25	.25
708	A236	8fr brown red	4.75	1.00
709	A237	12fr cerise	3.00	.55
710	A237	24fr blue green	16.00	3.25
		Nos. 707-710 (4)	24.00	5.05

Nos. 707-710 are known only precanceled.
See second note after No. 132.
See Nos. 833-834, 840-844, 910-913, 939,
952-955. For surcharges see Reunion Nos.
324, 326-327.

Tapestry and Gobelin
Workshop — A238

Designs: 30fr, Book manufacture. 40fr, Porcelain and glassware. 50fr, Jewelry and metalsmith's work. 75fr, Flowers and perfumes.

1954, May 6   Engr.   Perf. 13

711	A238	25fr red brn car & blk brn	9.50	.45
712	A238	30fr dk grn & lil gray	1.10	.25
713	A238	40fr dk brn, vio brn & org brn	3.50	.25
714	A238	50fr brt ultra, dl grn & org brn	1.10	.25
715	A238	75fr dp car & magenta	11.00	1.10
		Nos. 711-715 (5)	26.20	2.30

For surcharges see Reunion Nos. 303-304.

Entrance to Exhibition
Park — A239

1954, May 22

716	A239	15fr blue & dk car	.30	.25

Founding of the Fair of Paris, 50th anniv.

De Lattre Type of 1952

1954, June 5

717	A217	12fr vio bl & indigo	1.50	.75

Allied
Landings — A240

1954, June 5

718	A240	15fr scarlet & ultra	1.75	.90

The 10th anniversary of the liberation.

View of Lourdes
A241

Street
Corner,
Quimper
A242

Views: 8fr, Seine valley, Les Andelys. 10fr,
Beach at Royan. 18fr, Cheverny Chateau.
20fr, Beach, Gulf of Ajaccio.

1954

719	A241	6fr ultra, ind & dk grn	.30	.25
720	A241	8fr brt blue & dk grn	.30	.25
721	A241	10fr aqua & org brn	.25	.25
722	A242	12fr rose vio & dk vio	.30	.25
723	A241	18fr bl, dk grn & ind	2.50	.50
724	A241	20fr blk brn, bl grn & red brn	2.25	.25
		Nos. 719-724 (6)	5.90	1.75

See No. 873. For surcharges see Reunion
Nos. 302, 306-310. See footnote after No.
4642.

Abbey Ruins,
Jumièges — A243

1954, June 13

725	A243	12fr vio bl, ind & dk grn	1.50	.75

13th centenary of Abbey of Jumièges.

St. Philibert Abbey,
Tournus — A244

1954, June 18

726	A244	30fr indigo & blue	4.00	3.00

1st conf. of the Intl. Center of Romance
Studies.

View of
Stenay — A245

1954, June 26

727	A245	15fr dk brn & org brn	.70	.30

Acquisition of Stenay by France, 300th anniv.

Versailles Type of 1952

1954, July 10

728	A228	18fr dp bl, ind & vio brn	7.50	4.50

Villandry
Chateau — A246

1954, July 17

729	A246	18fr dk bl & dk bl grn	4.00	3.00

Napoleon
Awarding Legion
of Honor
Decoration
A247

1954, Aug. 14

730	A247	12fr scarlet	1.20	.75

150th anniv. of the 1st Legion of Honor
awards at Camp de Boulogne.

Cadets Marching
Through
Gateway — A248

1954, Aug. 1

731	A248	15fr vio gray, dk bl & car	1.00	1.00

150th anniversary of the founding of the Military School of Saint-Cyr.

Allegory — A249

1954, Oct. 4

732	A249	30fr indigo & choc	4.00	3.00

Issued to publicize the fact that the metric
system was first introduced in France.

Arms Type of 1949
Arms: 50c, Maine. 70c, Navarre. 80c, Nivernais. 1fr, Bourbonnais. 2fr, Angoumois. 3fr,
Aunis. 5fr, Saintonge.

1954   Typo.   Perf. 14x13½

733	A182	50c multicolored	.25	.25
734	A182	70c green, red & yel	.25	.25
735	A182	80c blue, red & yel	.25	.25
736	A182	1fr red, blue & yel	.25	.25
737	A182	2fr black, red & yel	.25	.25
738	A182	3fr brown, red & yel	.25	.25
739	A182	5fr blue & yellow	.25	.25
		Nos. 733-739 (7)	1.75	1.75

Duke de Saint-
Simon — A250

1955, Feb. 5   Engr.   Perf. 13

740	A250	12fr dk brn & vio brn	.45	.25

Louis de Rouvroy, Duke de Saint-Simon
(1675-1755).

Allegory and
Rotary
Emblem — A251

1955, Feb. 23

741	A251	30fr vio bl, bl & org	2.00	.75

50th anniv. of Rotary International.

Marianne — A252

1955-59   Typo.   Perf. 14x13½

751	A252	6fr fawn	2.00	1.40
752	A252	12fr green	2.40	1.10
a.		Bklt. pane of 10 + 2 labels	30.00	
753	A252	15fr carmine	.25	.25
a.		Booklet pane of 10	10.00	
754	A252	18fr green ('58)	.25	.25
755	A252	20fr ultra ('57)	.30	.25
756	A252	25fr rose red ('59)	1.00	.25
a.		Booklet pane of 8	40.00	
b.		Booklet pane of 10	30.00	
		Nos. 751-756 (6)	6.20	3.50

No. 751 was issued in coils of 1,000.
No. 752 was issued in panes of 10 stamps
and two labels with marginal instructions for
folding to form a booklet.
Nos. 754-755 are found in two types, distinguished by the numerals. On the 18fr there is
no serif at left of base of the "1" on the 1st
type. The 2nd type has a shorter "1" with no
serifs at base. On the 20fr the 2nd type has a
well formed "2" and the horiz. lines of the "F"
of the denomination are longer and of equal
length.
No. 756 also in two types, distinguished by
border width. On the 1st type, the border is
thicker than the width of the letters. On the 2nd
type, the border is thinner than the width of the
letters.
For surcharges see Reunion Nos. 330-331.

Philippe Lebon,
Inventor of
Illuminating
Gas — A253

Inventors: 10fr, Barthélemy Thimonnier,
sewing machine. 12fr, Nicolas Appert, canned

foods. 18fr, Dr. E. H. St. Claire Deville, aluminum. 25fr, Pierre Martin, steel making. 30fr, Bernigaud de Chardonnet, rayon.

1955, Mar. 5   Engr.   Perf. 13
757	A253	5fr dk vio bl & bl	.70	.60
758	A253	10fr dk brn & org brn	.70	.60
759	A253	12fr dk green	.90	.70
760	A253	18fr dk vio bl & ind	2.25	1.40
761	A253	25fr dk brnsh pur & vio	2.50	1.50
762	A253	30fr rose car & scar	2.50	1.50
		Nos. 757-762 (6)	9.55	6.30

St. Stephen Bridge, Limoges — A254

1955, Mar. 26   Unwmk.   Perf. 13
763	A254	12fr yel brn & dk vio brn	1.20	1.00

Gloved Model in Place de la Concorde — A255

1955, Mar. 26
764	A255	25fr blk brn, vio bl & blk	.75	.25

French glove manufacturing. See footnote after No. 4642.

Jean Pierre Claris de Florian — A256

1955, Apr. 2
765	A256	12fr blue green	.60	.40

200th anniv. of the birth of Jean Pierre Claris de Florian, fabulist.

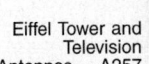

Eiffel Tower and Television Antennas — A257

1955, Apr. 16
766	A257	15fr indigo & ultra	.75	.70

French advancement in television.

Wire Fence and Guard Tower — A258

1955, Apr. 23
767	A258	12fr dk gray bl & brn blk	.75	.60

10th anniv. of the liberation of concentration camps.

Electric Train — A259

1955, May 11
768	A259	12fr blk brn & slate bl	1.60	1.10

Issued to publicize the electrification of the Valenciennes-Thionville railroad line.

Jacquemart of Moulins — A260

1955, May 28
769	A260	12fr black brown	1.40	1.00

Jules Verne and Nautilus — A261

1955, June 3
770	A261	30fr indigo	6.00	3.75

50th anniv. of the death of Jules Verne.

Auguste and Louis Lumière and Motion Picture Projector — A262

1955, June 12
771	A262	30fr rose brown	5.25	3.25

Invention of motion pictures, 60th anniv.

Jacques Coeur and His Mansion at Bourges — A263

1955, June 18
772	A263	12fr violet	1.90	1.20

5th centenary of the death of Jacques Coeur (1395?-1456), French merchant.

Corvette "La Capricieuse" A264

1955, July 9
773	A264	30fr aqua & dk blue	3.75	3.25

Centenary of the voyage of La Capricieuse to Canada.

Bordeaux — A265

Designs: 8fr, Marseille. 10fr, Nice. 12fr, Valentre bridge, Cahors. 18fr, Uzerche. 25fr, Fortifications, Brouage.

1955, Oct. 15
774	A265	6fr carmine lake	.25	.25
775	A265	8fr indigo	.45	.25
776	A265	10fr dp ultra	.25	.25
777	A265	12fr violet & brn	.25	.25
778	A265	18fr bluish grn & ind	.60	.25
779	A265	25fr org brn & red brn	.75	.25
		Nos. 774-779 (6)	2.55	1.50

See Nos. 838-839. For surcharges see Reunion Nos. 312-317, 323.

Mount Pelée, Martinique A266

1955, Nov. 1
780	A266	20fr dk & lt purple	2.40	.25

Gérard de Nerval — A267

1955, Nov. 11
781	A267	12fr lake & sepia	.40	.25

Centenary of the death of Gérard de Nerval (Labrunie), author.

Arms Type of 1949

Arms of: 50c, County of Foix. 70c, Marche. 80c, Roussillon. 1fr, Comtat Venaissin.

1955, Nov. 19   Typo.   Perf. 14x13½   Unwmk.
782	A182	50c multicolored	.25	.25
783	A182	70c red, blue & yel	.25	.25
784	A182	80c brown, yel & red	.25	.25
785	A182	1fr blue, red & yel	.25	.25
		Nos. 782-785 (4)	1.00	1.00

Concentration Camp Victim and Monument — A268

1956, Jan. 14   Engr.   Perf. 13
786	A268	15fr brn blk & red brn	.45	.40

Natl. memorial for Nazi deportation victims erected at the Natzwiller Struthof concentration camp in Alsace.

Belfry at Douai — A269

1956, Feb. 11
787	A269	15fr ultra & indigo	.40	.40

Col. Emil Driant — A270

1956, Feb. 21
788	A270	15fr dark blue	.30	.25

40th anniv. of the death of Col. Emil Driant during the battle of Verdun.

Trench Fighting — A271

1956, Mar. 3
789	A271	30fr indigo & dk olive	1.50	1.25

40th anniversary of Battle of Verdun.

A272

A272a

A272b

A272c

Scientists: 12fr, Jean Henri Fabre, Entomology. 15fr, Charles Tellier, Refrigeration. 18fr, Camille Flammarion, Popular Astronomy. 30fr, Paul Sabatier, Catalytic Chemistry.

1956, Apr. 7
790	A272	12fr vio brn & org brn	.75	.40
791	A272a	15fr vio bl & int blk	.75	.40
792	A272b	18fr brt ultra	1.40	1.25
793	A272c	30fr Prus grn & dk grn	3.50	2.00
		Nos. 790-793 (4)	6.40	4.05

Grand Trianon, Versailles — A273

1956, Apr. 14
794	A273	12fr vio brn & gray grn	1.10	.75

For similar stamp with euro denominations, see No. 5449a.

Symbols of Latin American and French Culture — A274

1956, Apr. 21
795	A274	30fr brown & red brn	1.60	1.40

Issued in recognition of the friendship between France and Latin America.

"The Smile of Reims" and Botticelli's "Spring" — A275

1956, May 5
796	A275	12fr black & green	.60	.40

Issued to emphasize the cultural and artistic kinship of Reims and Florence.

Leprosarium and Maltese Cross — A276

1956, May 12
797	A276	12fr sepia, red brn & red	.40	.35

Issued in honor of the Knights of Malta.

St. Yves de Treguier — A277

1956, May 19
798	A277	15fr bluish gray & blk	.35	.25

St. Yves, patron saint of lawyers.

Marshal Franchet
d'Esperey — A278

1956, May 26
799 A278 30fr deep claret　　2.25　1.40
Centenary of the birth of Marshal Louis
Franchet d'Esperey.

Miners
Monument — A279

1956, June 2
800 A279 12fr violet brown　　　.45　.40
Town Montceau-les-Mines, 100th anniv.

Basketball — A280

Sports: 40fr, Pelota (Jai alai). 50fr, Rugby.
75fr, Mountain climbing.

1956, July 7
801 A280 30fr gray vio & blk　　1.10　.25
802 A280 40fr brown & vio brn　4.00　.25
803 A280 50fr rose vio & vio　　1.50　.25
804 A280 75fr indigo, grn & bl　9.00　1.75
　　　Nos. 801-804 (4)　　　15.60　2.50
For surcharges see Reunion Nos. 318-321.

Europa Issue

"Rebuilding
Europe" — A281

1956, Sept. 15　Typo.　Unwmk.
Perf. 13½x14
805 A281 15fr rose & rose lake　.75　.25
Perf. 13
Engr.
806 A281 30fr lt blue & vio bl　4.50　.75

Issued to symbolize the cooperation among
the six countries comprising the Coal and
Steel Community.
No. 805 measures 21x35½mm, No. 806
measures 22x35½mm.

Dam at Donzère-
Mondragon
A282

Cable
Railway to
Pic du Midi
A283

Rhine Port of
Strasbourg
A284

1956, Oct. 6　Engr.　Perf. 13
807 A282 12fr gray vio & vio brn　1.10　.90
808 A283 18fr indigo　　　　2.25　1.50
809 A284 30fr indigo & dk blue　9.50　4.50
　　　Nos. 807-809 (3)　　　12.85　6.90
French technical achievements.

Antoine-Augustin
Parmentier
A285

1956, Oct. 27
810 A285 12fr brn red & brn　　.65　.45
Parmentier, nutrition chemist, who popular-
ized the potato in France.

Petrarch — A286

Portraits: 12fr, J. B. Lully. 15fr, J. J. Rousseau. 18fr, Benjamin Franklin. 20fr, Frederic
Chopin. 30fr, Vincent van Gogh.

1956, Nov. 10
811 A286 8fr green　　　　.60　.45
812 A286 12fr claret　　　　.60　.45
813 A286 15fr dark red　　　.90　.45
814 A286 18fr ultra　　　　1.90　1.50
815 A286 20fr brt violet　　2.40　1.50
816 A286 30fr brt grnsh blue　4.75　2.25
　　　Nos. 811-816 (6)　　　11.15　6.60
Famous men who lived in France.

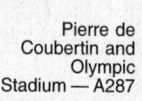

Pierre de
Coubertin and
Olympic
Stadium — A287

1956, Nov. 24
817 A287 30fr dk blue gray & pur 1.50　.90
Issued in honor of Baron Pierre de Coubertin, founder of the modern Olympic Games.

Homing
Pigeon — A288

1957, Jan. 12
818 A288 15fr dp ultra, ind & red
　　　brn　　　　　　.40　.25

Victor
Schoelcher — A289

1957, Feb. 16　Engr.
819 A289 18fr lilac rose　　.45　.40
Issued in honor of Victor Schoelcher, who
freed the slaves in the French Colonies.

Sèvres
Porcelain — A290

1957, Mar. 23　Unwmk.　Perf. 13
820 A290 30fr ultra & vio blue　.60　.40
Bicentenary of the porcelain works at
Sèvres (in 1956).

Gaston Planté
and Storage
Battery — A291

Designs: 12fr, Antoine Béclère and X-ray
apparatus. 18fr, Octave Terrillon, autoclave,
microscope and surgical instruments. 30fr, Etienne Oemichen and early helicopter.

1957, Apr. 13
821 A291 8fr gray blk & dp cl　　.30　.25
822 A291 12fr dk bl, blk & emer　.35　.25
823 A291 18fr rose red & mag　1.00　.90
824 A291 30fr green & slate grn　2.10　1.60
　　　Nos. 821-824 (4)　　　3.75　3.00

Uzès
Chateau — A292

1957, Apr. 27
825 A292 12fr slate bl & bis brn　.40　.40

Jean Moulin — A293

Portraits: 10fr, Honoré d'Estienne d'Orves.
12fr, Robert Keller. 18fr, Pierre Brossolette.
20fr, Jean-Baptiste Lebas.

1957, May 18
826 A293 8fr violet brown　　.90　.30
827 A293 10fr black & vio bl　.90　.30
828 A293 12fr brown & sl grn　1.00　.35
829 A293 18fr purple & blk　1.40　1.10
830 A293 20fr Prus bl & dk bl　1.40　.90
　　　Nos. 826-830 (5)　　　5.60　2.95
Issued in honor of the heroes of the French
Underground of World War II.
See Nos. 879-882, 915-919, 959-963, 990-
993.

Le Quesnoy — A294

1957, June 1
831 A294 8fr dk slate green　　.25　.25
See No. 837.

Symbols of
Justice — A295

1957, June 1
832 A295 12fr sepia & ultra　　.25　.25
French Cour des Comptes, 150th anniv.

Farm Woman Type of 1954
1957-59　　　　Perf. 14x13½
833　A236　6fr orange　　　.25　.25
833A A236 10fr brt green ('59)　.40　.25
834　A236 12fr red lilac　　　.25　.25
　　　Nos. 833-834 (3)　　　.90　.75
Nos. 833-834 issued without precancellation.

Symbols of Public
Works — A296

1957, June 20　Engr.　Perf. 13
835 A296 30fr sl grn, brn & ocher 1.50　1.00

Brest — A297

1957, July 6
836 A297 12fr gray grn & brn ol　.90　.75

Scenic Types of 1955, 1957
Designs: 15fr, Le Quesnoy. 35fr, Bordeaux.
70fr, Valentre bridge, Cahors.

1957, July 19　　　Unwmk.
837 A294 15fr dk bl grn & sep　.25　.25
838 A265 35fr dk bl grn & sl grn　2.90　.90
839 A265 70fr black & dull grn　16.00　1.60
　　　Nos. 837-839 (3)　　　19.15　2.75
For surcharge see Reunion No. 322.

Gallic Cock Type of 1954
1957　　Typo.　Perf. 14x13½
840 A237 5fr olive bister　　.25　.25
841 A237 10fr bright blue　　1.50　.25
842 A237 15fr plum　　　　1.25　.50
843 A237 30fr bright red　　9.00　2.10
844 A237 45fr green　　　　19.00　9.00
　　　Nos. 840-844 (5)　　　31.00　12.10
Nos. 840-844 are known only precanceled.
See second note after No. 132.

Leo Lagrange
and
Stadium — A298

1957, Aug. 31　Engr.　Perf. 13
845 A298 18fr lilac gray & blk　.40　.40
Intl. University Games, Paris, 8/31-9/8.

"United Europe" — A299

1957, Sept. 16
846 A299 20fr red brown & green　.40　.30
847 A299 35fr dk brown & blue　.90　.75
A united Europe for peace and prosperity.

Auguste Comte — A300

1957, Sept. 14
848 A300 35fr brown red & sepia　.40　.25
Centenary of the death of Auguste Comte,
mathematician and philosopher.

Roman
Amphitheater,
Lyon — A301

1957, Oct. 5　　Perf. 13
849 A301 20fr brn org & brn vio　.40　.25
2,000th anniv. of the founding of Lyon.

Sens River,
Guadeloupe
A302

Beynac-
Cazenac,
Dordogne
A303

Designs: 10fr, Elysee Palace. 25fr, Chateau de Valencay, Indre. 35fr, Rouen Cathedral. 50fr, Roman Ruins, Saint-Remy. 65fr, Evian-les-Bains.

1957, Oct. 19
850	A302	8fr green & lt brn	.25	.25
851	A302	10fr dk ol bis & vio brn	.25	.25
852	A302	18fr indigo & dk brn	.25	.25
853	A302	25fr bl gray & vio brn	.55	.25
854	A303	35fr car rose & lake	.25	.25
855	A302	50fr ol grn & ol bister	.35	.25
856	A302	65fr dk blue & indigo	.60	.30
		Nos. 850-856 (7)	2.50	1.80

See Nos. 907-909. See footnote after No. 4642. For overprint and surcharges see No. 1O1, Reunion Nos. 325, 328-329, 332-334.

Nicolaus Copernicus — A304

Portraits: 10fr, Michelangelo. 12fr, Miguel de Cervantes. 15fr, Rembrandt. 18fr, Isaac Newton. 25fr, Mozart. 35fr, Johann Wolfgang von Goethe.

1957, Nov. 9   Engr.   Perf. 13
857	A304	8fr dark brown	.65	.30
858	A304	10fr dark green	.65	.45
859	A304	12fr dark purple	.65	.45
860	A304	15fr brown or gry brn	.80	.60
861	A304	18fr deep blue	1.10	.80
862	A304	25fr lilac & claret	1.25	.90
863	A304	35fr blue	1.50	1.00
		Nos. 857-863 (7)	6.60	4.50

Louis Jacques Thénard — A305

1957, Nov. 30   Unwmk.
864	A305	15fr ol bis & grnsh blk	.40	.30

Centenary of the death of L. J. Thenard, chemist, and the founding of the Charitable Society of the Friends of Science.

Dr. Philippe Pinel — A306

French Physicians: 12fr, Fernand Widal. 15fr, Charles Nicolle. 35fr, René Leriche.

1958, Jan. 25
865	A306	8fr brown olive	.65	.45
866	A306	12fr brt vio blue	.65	.45
867	A306	15fr deep blue	1.00	.50
868	A306	35fr black	1.40	.80
		Nos. 865-868 (4)	3.70	2.20

Joseph Louis Lagrange — A307

French Scientists: 12fr, Urbain Jean Joseph Leverrier. 15fr, Jean Bernard Leon Foucault. 35fr, Claude Louis Berthollet.

1958, Feb. 15   Perf. 13
869	A307	8fr grnsh bl & vio bl	.65	.35
870	A307	12fr sepia & gray	.75	.35
871	A307	15fr slate grn & grn	1.40	.60
872	A307	35fr maroon & cop red	1.75	.90
		Nos. 869-872 (4)	4.55	2.20

Lourdes Type of 1954

1958
873	A241	20fr grnsh bl & ol	.30	.25

Le Havre
A308

Maubeuge
A309

Designs: 18fr, Saint-Die. 25fr, Sete.

1958, Mar. 29   Engr.   Perf. 13
874	A308	12fr ol grn & car rose	.55	.35
875	A309	15fr brt purple & brn	.60	.35
876	A309	18fr ultra & indigo	.90	.65
877	A308	25fr dk bl, bl grn & brn	1.25	.65
		Nos. 874-877 (4)	3.30	2.00

Reconstruction of war-damaged cities.

French Pavilion, Brussels — A310

1958, Apr. 12
878	A310	35fr brn, dk grn & bl	.30	.25

Issued for the Universal and International Exposition at Brussels.

Heroes Type of 1957

8fr, Jean Cavaillès. 12fr, Fred Scamaroni. 15fr, Simone Michel-Levy. 20fr, Jacques Bingen.

1958, Apr. 19
879	A293	8fr violet & black	.60	.45
880	A293	12fr ultra & green	.60	.45
881	A293	15fr brown & gray	1.50	.85
882	A293	20fr olive & ultra	1.25	.85
		Nos. 879-882 (4)	3.95	2.60

Issued in honor of the heroes of the French Underground in World War II.

Bowling — A311

Sports: 15fr, Naval joust. 18fr, Archery, vert. 25fr, Breton wrestling, vert.

1958, Apr. 26
883	A311	12fr rose & brown	.75	.75
884	A311	15fr bl, ol gray & grn	1.00	.75
885	A311	18fr green & brown	1.75	1.00
886	A311	25fr brown & indigo	2.50	1.75
		Nos. 883-886 (4)	6.00	4.25

Senlis Cathedral — A312

1958, May 17
887	A312	15fr ultra & indigo	.40	.25

Bayeux Tapestry Horsemen A313

1958, June 21
888	A313	15fr blue & carmine	.35	.25

Common Design Types pictured following the introduction.

Europa Issue, 1958
Common Design Type

1958, Sept. 13   Engr.   Perf. 13
Size: 22x36mm
889	CD1	20fr rose red	.40	.25
890	CD1	35fr ultra	1.25	.30

Foix Chateau — A314

1958, Oct. 11
891	A314	15fr ultra, grn & ol brn	.40	.25

City Halls, Paris and Rome — A315

1958, Oct. 11
892	A315	35fr gray, grnsh bl & rose red	.40	.25

Issued to publicize the cultural ties between Rome and Paris and the need for European unity.

UNESCO Building, Paris — A316

Design: 35fr, Different view of building.

1958, Nov. 1   Perf. 13
893	A316	20fr grnsh blue & ol bis	.25	.25
894	A316	35fr dk sl grn & red org	.25	.25

UNESCO Headquarters in Paris opening, Nov. 3.

Soldier's Grave in Wheat Field — A317

1958, Nov. 11
895	A317	15fr dp green & ultra	.30	.25

40th anniv. of the World War I armistice.

Arms of Marseille — A318

Cities: 70c, Lyon. 80c, Toulouse. 1fr, Bordeaux. 2fr, Nice. 3fr, Nantes. 5fr, Lille. 15fr, Algiers.

1958-59   Typo.   Perf. 14x13½
896	A318	50c dk blue & ultra	.25	.25
897	A318	70c multicolored	.25	.25
898	A318	80c red, blue & yel	.25	.25
899	A318	1fr dk bl, yel & red	.25	.25
900	A318	2fr dk bl, red & grn	.25	.25
901	A318	3fr multicolored	.25	.25
902	A318	5fr dk brown & red	.25	.25
903	A318	15fr multi ('59)	.25	.25
		Nos. 896-903 (8)	2.00	2.00

See Nos. 938, 940, 973, 1040-1042, 1091-1095, 1142-1144. For surcharges see Reunion Nos. 336, 345-346, 350-351, 353.

Arc de Triomphe and Flowers — A319

1959, Jan. 17   Engr.   Perf. 13
904	A319	15fr brn, bl, grn, cl & red	.40	.30

Paris Flower Festival.

Symbols of Learning and Medal — A320

1959, Jan. 24   Perf. 13
905	A320	20fr lake, blk & vio	.25	.25

Sesquicentennial of the Palm Leaf Medal of the French Academy.

Charles de Foucauld — A321

1959, Jan. 31
906	A321	50fr dp brn, bl & mar	.40	.30

Issued to honor Father Charles de Foucauld, explorer and missionary of the Sahara.

Type of 1957

Designs: 30fr, Elysee Palace. 85fr, Evian-les Bains. 100fr, Sens River, Guadeloupe.

1959, Feb. 10
907	A302	30fr dk slate green	2.00	.25
908	A302	85fr deep claret	3.00	.30
909	A302	100fr deep violet	25.00	.30
		Nos. 907-909 (3)	30.00	.85

Gallic Cock Type of 1954
1959		**Typo.**	**Perf. 14x13½**	
910	A237	8fr violet	.40	.25
911	A237	20fr yellow grn	1.50	.50
912	A237	40fr henna brn	3.25	1.60
913	A237	55fr emerald	15.00	6.00
		Nos. 910-913 (4)	20.15	8.35

Nos. 910-913 were issued with precancellation. See second note after No. 132. See Nos. 952-955.

Miners' Tools and School — A322

1959, Apr. 11   Engr.   Perf. 13
914	A322	20fr red, blk & blue	.25	.25

175th anniv. of the National Mining School.

Heroes Type of 1957

Portraits: No. 915, The five martyrs of the Buffon school. No. 916, Yvonne Le Roux. No. 917, Médéric-Védy. No. 918, Louis Martin-Bret. 30fr, Gaston Moutardier.

1959, Apr. 25   Engr.   Perf. 13
915	A293	15fr black & vio	.30	.25
916	A293	15fr mag & rose vio	.30	.25
917	A293	20fr green & grnsh bl	.30	.25
918	A293	20fr org brn & brn	.45	.30
919	A293	30fr magenta & vio	.50	.40
		Nos. 915-919 (5)	1.85	1.50

Dam at Foum el Gherza
A323

Marcoule Atomic Center
A324

Designs: 30fr, Oil field at Hassi Messaoud, Sahara. 50fr, C. N. I. T. Building (Centre National des Industries et des Techniques).

1959, May 23
920	A323	15fr olive & grnsh bl	.30	.25
921	A324	20fr brt car & red brn	.40	.40
922	A324	30fr dk blue, brn & grn	.40	.40
923	A323	50fr ol grn & sl blue	.65	.45
		Nos. 920-923 (4)	1.75	1.50

French technical achievements.

Marceline Desbordes-Valmore — A325

1959, June 20
924 A325 30fr blue, brn & grn   .25 .25
    Centenary of the death of Marceline Desbordes-Valmore, poet.

Pilots Goujon and Rozanoff — A326

1959, June 13
925 A326 20fr lt blue & lake brn   .40 .40
    Issued in honor of Charles Goujon and Col. Constantin Rozanoff, test pilots.

Tancarville Bridge — A327

1959, Aug. 1   Engr.   Perf. 13
926 A327 30fr dk blue, brn & ol   .40 .25

Marianne and Ship of State — A328

1959, July   Typo.   Perf. 14x13½
927 A328 25fr black & red   .30 .25
    See Nos. 942, 3521, 4410a, 4513. For surcharge see No. B336.

Jean Jaures — A329

1959, Sept. 12   Engr.   Perf. 13
928 A329 50fr chocolate   .40 .25
    Jean Jaures, socialist leader, birth cent.

Europa Issue, 1959
Common Design Type
1959, Sept. 19
Size: 22x36mm
929 CD2 25fr bright green   .30 .25
930 CD2 50fr bright violet   1.10 .55

Blood Donors — A330

1959, Oct. 17   Engr.
931 A330 20fr magenta & gray   .25 .25

French-Spanish Handshake A331

1959, Oct. 24   Perf. 13
932 A331 50fr blue, rose car & org   .45 .30
    300th anniv. of the signing of the Treaty of the Pyrenees.

Polio Victim Holding Crutches — A332

1959, Oct. 31
933 A332 20fr dark blue   .25 .25
    Vaccination against poliomyelitis.

Henri Bergson — A333

1959, Nov. 7
934 A333 50fr lt red brown   .35 .25
    Henri Bergson, philosopher, birth cent.

Avesnes-sur-Helpe — A334

Design: 30fr, Perpignan.

1959, Nov. 14
935 A334 20fr sepia & blue   .40 .25
936 A334 30fr brn, dp claret & bl   .40 .25

New NATO Headquarters, Paris — A335

1959, Dec. 12
937 A335 50fr green, brn & ultra   .45 .30
    10th anniv. of the NATO.

Types of 1958-59 and

Farm Woman A336   Sower A337

Designs: 5c, Arms of Lille. 15c, Arms of Algiers. 25c, Marianne and Ship of State.

Perf. 14x13½

1960-61	**Unwmk.**	**Typo.**	
938	A318 5c dk brown & red	2.60	.25
939	A336 10c brt green	.25	.25
940	A318 15c red, ultra, yel & grn	.50	.25
941	A337 20c grnsh bl & car rose	.25	.25
942	A328 25c ver & ultra	1.60	.25
b.	Booklet pane of 8	27.50	
c.	Booklet pane of 10	32.50	
942A	A337 30c gray & ultra ('61)	1.10	.30
	Nos. 938-942A (6)	6.30	1.55

    See Nos. 707-708, 833-834 for the Farm Woman type (A336), but with no decimals in denominations.
    For surcharges see Reunion Nos. 337-338, 341. For overprint see Algeria No. 286.

Laon Cathedral A338   Kerrata Gorge A339

Designs: 30c, Fougères Chateau. 50c, Mosque, Tlemcen. 65c, Sioule Valley. 85c, Chaumont Viaduct. 1fr, Cilaos Church, Reunion.

1960, Jan. 16   Engr.   Perf. 13
943 A338 15c blue & indigo   .25 .25
944 A338 30c blue, sepia & grn   1.75 .25
945 A339 45c brt vio & ol gray   .60 .25
946 A339 50c sl grn & lt cl   1.20 .25
947 A338 65c sl grn, bl & blk brn   1.10 .25
948 A338 85c blue, sep & grn   1.75 .25
949 A338 1fr vio bl, bl & grn   2.50 .25
    Nos. 943-949 (7)   9.15 1.75
    For surcharges see Reunion Nos. 335, 340, 342. For overprint see Algeria Nos. 288-289.

Pierre de Nolhac — A340

1960, Feb. 13
950 A340 20c black & gray   .45 .30
    Centenary of the birth of Pierre de Nolhac, curator of Versailles and historian.

Museum of Art and Industry, Saint-Etienne A341

1960, Feb. 20
951 A341 30c brn, car & slate   .45 .30

Gallic Cock Type of 1954

1960	**Typo.**	**Perf. 14x13½**	
952	A237 8c violet	.40	.25
953	A237 20c yellow grn	1.90	.30
954	A237 40c henna brn	7.50	1.75
955	A237 55c emerald	24.00	11.00
	Nos. 952-955 (4)	33.80	13.30

    Nos. 952-955 were issued only precanceled. See second note after No. 132. See Nos. 910-913.

View of Cannes — A342

1960, Mar. 5   Engr.   Perf. 13
956 A342 50c red brn & lt grn   .45 .40
    Meeting of European municipal administrators, Cannes, Mar., 1960.

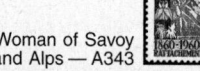

Woman of Savoy and Alps — A343

Woman of Nice and Shore — A344

1960   Unwmk.   Perf. 13
957 A343 30c slate green   .50 .40
958 A344 50c brn, yel & rose   .50 .30
    Cent. of the annexation of Nice and Savoy.

Heroes Type of 1957

Portraits: No. 959, Edmund Debeaumarché. No. 960, Pierre Massé. No. 961, Maurice Ripoche. No. 962, Leonce Vieljeux. 50c, Abbé René Bonpain.

1960, Mar. 26
959 A293 20c bister & blk   1.10 .90
960 A293 20c pink & rose cl   1.10 .90
961 A293 30c vio & brt vio   1.50 .90
962 A293 30c sl bl & brt bl   2.10 1.75
963 A293 50c sl grn & red brn   2.40 2.10
    Nos. 959-963 (5)   8.20 6.55
    Issued in honor of the heroes of the French Underground of World War II.

"Education" and Children — A345

1960, May 21   Engr.   Perf. 13
964 A345 20c rose lilac, pur & blk   .25 .25
    1st secondary school in Strasbourg, 150th anniv.

Blois Chateau — A346

View of La Bourboule A347

1960, May
965 A346 30c dk bl, sep & grn   .60 .45
966 A347 50c ol brown, car & grn   .60 .35

Lorraine Cross — A348

1960, June 18
967 A348 20c red brn, dk brn & yel grn   .45 .25
    20th anniv. of the French Resistance Movement in World War II.

Marianne — A349

1960, June 18   Typo.   Perf. 14x13½
968 A349 25c lake & gray   .25 .25
  a.   Booklet pane of 8   4.50
  b.   Booklet pane of 10   3.50
    See Nos. 3522, 4410b, 4514. For surcharge see Reunion No. 339. For overprint see Algeria No. 287.

Jean Bouin and Stadium — A350

1960, July 9   Engr.   Perf. 13
969 A350 20c blue, mag & ol gray   .35 .25
    17th Olympic Games, Rome, 8/25-9/11.

Europa Issue, 1960
Common Design Type
1960, Sept. 17   Perf. 13
Size: 36x22mm
970 CD3 25c green & bluish grn   .25 .25
971 CD3 50c maroon & red lilac   .25 .25

Lisieux Basilica — A351

1960, Sept. 24   Perf. 13
972 A351 15c blue, gray & blk   .25 .25

Arms Type of 1958-59

Design: Arms of Oran.

1960, Oct. 15   Typo.   Perf. 14x13½
973 A318 5c red, bl, yel & emer   .25 .25

Madame de Stael by François Gerard — A352

1960, Oct. 22   Engr.   Perf. 13
974 A352 30c dull claret & brn   .35 .25
Madame de Stael (1766-1817), writer.

Gen. J. B. E. Estienne — A353

1960, Nov. 5
975 A353 15c lt lilac & black   .35 .25
Centenary of the birth of Gen. Jean Baptiste Eugene Estienne.

Marc Sangnier and Youth Hostel at Bierville — A354

1960, Nov. 5
976 A354 20c blue, blk & lilac   .25 .25
Issued to honor Marc Sangnier, founder of the French League for Youth Hostels.

Badge of Order of Liberation — A355

1960, Nov. 14   Engr.   Perf. 13
977 A355 20c black & brt green   .40 .25
Order of Liberation, 20th anniversary.

Lapwings — A356

Birds: 30c, Puffin. 45c, European teal. 50c, European bee-eaters.

1960, Nov. 12
978 A356 20c multicolored   .25 .25
979 A356 30c multicolored   .25 .25
980 A356 45c multicolored   .60 .45
981 A356 50c multicolored   .55 .40
    Nos. 978-981 (4)   1.65 1.35
Issued to publicize wildlife protection.

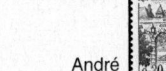

André Honnorat — A357

1960, Nov. 19
982 A357 30c blue, blk & green   .30 .25
Honnorat, statesman, fighter against tuberculosis and founder of the University City of Paris, an intl. students' community.

St. Barbara and Medieval View of School — A358

1960, Dec. 3   Engr.
983 A358 30c red, bl & ol brn   .30 .25
St. Barbara School, Paris, 500th anniv.

"Mediterranean" by Aristide Maillol — A359

1961, Feb. 18   Unwmk.   Perf. 13
984 A359 20c carmine & indigo   .25 .25
Aristide Maillol, sculptor, birth cent.

Marianne by Cocteau — A360

1961, Feb. 23
985 A360 20c blue & carmine   .25 .25
A second type has an extra inverted V-shaped mark (a blue flag top) at right of hair tip. Value unused $2.25, used 35 cents.
See Nos. 3523, 4410c, 4515.
For surcharge see Reunion No. 357.

Paris Airport, Orly — A361

1961, Feb. 25
986 A361 50c blk, dk bl, & bluish grn   .45 .25
Inauguration of new facilities at Orly airport.

George Méliès and Motion Picture Screen — A362

1961, Mar. 11
987 A362 50c pur, indigo & ol bis   .50 .35
Cent. of the birth of George Méliès, motion picture pioneer.

Jean Baptiste Henri Lacordaire — A363

1961, Mar. 25   Perf. 13
988 A363 30c lt brown & black   .30 .25
Cent. of the death of the Dominican monk Lacordaire, orator and liberal Catholic leader.

A364

1961, Mar. 25
989 A364 30c grn, red brn & red   .25 .25
Introduction of tobacco use into France, fourth centenary. By error stamp portrays Jan Nicquet instead of Jean Nicot.

Heroes Type of 1957

Portraits: No. 990, Jacques Renouvin. No. 991, Lionel Dubray. No. 992, Paul Gateaud. No. 993, Mère Elisabeth.

1961, Apr. 22
990 A293 20c blue & lilac   .75 .35
991 A293 20c gray grn & blue   .75 .35
992 A293 30c brown org & blk   1.40 .65
993 A293 30c violet & blk   .90 .80
    Nos. 990-993 (4)   3.80 2.15

Bagnoles-de-l'Orne — A365

1961, May 6
994 A365 20c olive, ocher, bl & grn   .25 .25

Dove, Olive Branch and Federation Emblem — A366

1961, May 6
995 A366 50c brt bl, grn & mar   .30 .25
World Federation of Ex-Service Men.

Deauville in 19th Century — A367

1961, May 13   Engr.
996 A367 50c rose claret   1.25 .90
Centenary of Deauville.

La Champmeslé — A368

French actors: No. 998, Talma. No. 999, Rachel. No. 1000, Gérard Philipe. No. 1001, Raimu.

1961, June 10   Unwmk.   Perf. 13
Dark Carmine Frame
997 A368 20c choc & yel grn   .60 .25
998 A368 30c brown & crimson   .60 .35
999 A368 30c yel grn & sl grn   .65 .35
1000 A368 50c olive & choc   1.10 .45
1001 A368 50c bl grn & red brn   1.10 .45
    Nos. 997-1001 (5)   4.05 1.85
Issued to honor great French actors and in connection with the Fifth World Congress of the International Federation of Actors.

Mont-Dore, Snowflake and Cable Car — A369

1961, July 1
1002 A369 20c orange & rose lilac   .25 .25

Pierre Fauchard — A370

1961, July 1
1003 A370 50c dk green & blk   .40 .30
Bicentenary of the death of Pierre Fauchard, 1st surgeon dentist.

St. Theobald's Church, Thann — A371

1961, July 1
1004 A371 20c dk grn, pur & red brn   .45 .25
800th anniversary of Thann.

Europa Issue, 1961
Common Design Type
1961, Sept. 16   Perf. 13
Size: 35x22mm
1005 CD4 25c vermilion   .25 .25
1006 CD4 50c ultramarine   .25 .25

Beach and Sailboats, Arcachon — A372

Designs: 15c, Saint-Paul, Maritime Alps. 45c, Sully-sur-Loire Chateau. 50c, View of Cognac. 65c, Rance Valley and Dinan. 85c, City hall and Rodin's Burghers, Calais. 1fr, Roman gates of Lodi, Medea, Algeria.

1961, Oct. 9   Engr.   Perf. 13
1007 A372 15c blue & purple   .25 .25
1008 A372 30c ultra, sl grn & lt brn   .25 .25
1009 A372 45c vio bl, red brn & grn   .25 .25
1010 A372 50c grn, Prus bl & sl   .75 .25
1011 A372 65c red brn, sl grn & bl   .25 .25
1012 A372 85c sl grn, sl & red brn   .35 .25
1013 A372 1fr dk bl, sl & bis   3.50 .25
    Nos. 1007-1013 (7)   5.60 1.75
For surcharges see Reunion Nos. 347-348.
For overprint see Algeria No. 290.

Blue Nudes, by Matisse A373

Paintings: 50c, "The Messenger," by Braque. 85c, "The Cardplayers," by Cézanne. 1fr, "The 14th July," by Roger de La Fresnaye.

1961, Nov. 10   Perf. 13x12
1014 A373 50c dk brn, bl, blk & gray   2.25 1.20
1015 A373 65c grn, vio, & ultra   3.75 1.90
1016 A373 85c blk, brn, red & ol   1.50 1.10
1017 A373 1fr multicolored   3.00 1.90
    Nos. 1014-1017 (4)   10.50 6.10

Liner France — A374

1962, Jan. 11   Engr.   Perf. 13
1018 A374 30c dk blue, blk & car   .60 .35
New French liner France.

Skier Going Downhill — A375

1962, Jan. 27   Perf. 13
1019 A375 30c shown   .25 .25
1020 A375 50c Slalom   .35 .25
Issued to publicize the World Ski Championships, Chamonix, Feb. 1962.

Maurice Bourdet — A376

1962, Feb. 17
1021 A376 30c slate   .30 .25
60th anniv. of the birth of Maurice Bourdet, radio commentator and resistance hero.

Pierre-Fidele Bretonneau
A377

1962, Feb. 17
1022　A377　50c brt lilac & blue　.35　.25
Centenary of the death of Pierre-Fidele Bretonneau, physician.

Chateau and Bridge, Laval, Mayenne — A378

1962, Feb. 24
1023　A378　20c bis brn & slate grn　.25　.25

Gallic Cock — A379

1962-65　　　　　　　　**Perf. 13**
1024　A379　25c ultra, car & brn　.25　.25
　　a.　Bklt. pane of 4 (horiz. strip)　2.50
1024B　A379　30c gray grn, red & brn ('65)　.85　.25
　　c.　Booklet pane of 5　5.00
　　d.　Booklet pane of 10　10.00

No. 1024 was also issued on experimental luminescent paper in 1963. Value $750. See Nos. 3524, 4410d, 4516.

Ramparts of Vannes
A380

Dunkirk
A381

Paris Beach, Le Touquet — A381a

1962　　　**Engr.**　　　**Perf. 13**
1025　A380　30c dark blue　.60　.50
1026　A381　95c grn, bis & red lil　.75　.40
1027　A381a　1fr grn, red brn & bl　.40　.25
　　Nos. 1025-1027 (3)　1.75　1.15

No. 1026 for the 300th anniv. of Dunkirk.

Stage Setting and Globe — A382

1962, Mar. 24　　　　**Unwmk.**
1028　A382　50c sl grn, ocher & mag　.40　.25
International Day of the Theater, Mar. 27.

Memorial to Fighting France, Mont Valerien
A383

Resistance Heroes' Monument, Vercors
A384

Design: 50c, Ile de Sein monument.

1962, Apr. 7
1029　A383　20c olive & slate grn　.50　.40
1030　A384　30c bluish black　.60　.45
1031　A384　50c blue & indigo　.75　.60
　　Nos. 1029-1031 (3)　1.85　1.45

Issued to publicize memorials for the French Underground in World War II.

Malaria Eradication Emblem and Swamp — A385

1962, Apr. 14　　　　**Engr.**
1032　A385　50c dk blue & dk red　.35　.25
WHO drive to eradicate malaria.

Nurses with Child and Hospital — A386

1962, May 5　　**Unwmk.**　　**Perf. 13**
1033　A386　30c bl grn, gray & red brn　.25　.25
National Hospital Week, May 5-12.

Glider — A387

20c, Planes showing development of aviation.

1962, May 12
1034　A387　15c orange red & brn　.30　.25
1035　A387　20c lil rose & rose cl　.35　.25
Issued to publicize sports aviation.

School Emblem — A388

1962, May 19　　　　**Engr.**
1036　A388　50c mar, ocher & dk vio　.40　.25
Watchmaker's School at Besançon, cent.

Louis XIV and Workers Showing Modern Gobelin — A389

1962, May 26　　**Unwmk.**　　**Perf. 13**
1037　A389　50c ol, sl grn & car　.40　.25
Gobelin tapestry works, Paris, 300th anniv.

Blaise Pascal — A390

1962, May 26
1038　A390　50c slate grn & dp org　.40　.25
Blaise Pascal (1623-1662), mathematician, scientist and philosopher.

Palace of Justice, Rennes — A391

1962, June 12
1039　A391　30c blk, grysh bl & grn　1.00　.75

Arms Type of 1958-59
5c, Amiens. 10c, Troyes. 15c, Nevers.

1962-63　　**Typo.**　　**Perf. 14x13½**
1040　A318　5c ver, ultra & yel　.25　.25
1041　A318　10c red, ultra & yel ('63)　.25　.25
1042　A318　15c ver, ultra & yel　.25　.25
　　Nos. 1040-1042 (3)　.75　.75

Phosphor Tagging
In 1970 France began to experiment with luminescence. Phosphor bands have been added to Nos. 1041, 1143, 1231, 1231C, 1292A-1294B, 1494-1498, 1560-1579B, etc.

Rose — A392

Design: 30c, Old-fashioned rose.

1962, Sept. 8　　**Engr.**　　**Perf. 13**
1043　A392　20c ol, grn & brt car　.45　.30
1044　A392　30c dk sl grn, ol & car　.55　.40

Europa Issue, 1962
Common Design Type
1962, Sept. 15
Size: 36x22mm
1045　CD5　25c violet　.25　.25
1046　CD5　50c henna brown　.35　.25

Space Communications Center, Pleumeur-Bodou, France — A394

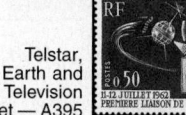

Telstar, Earth and Television Set — A395

1962, Sept. 29　　**Engr.**　　**Perf. 13**
1047　A394　25c gray, yel & grn　.25　.25
1048　A395　50c dk bl, grn & ultra　.40　.30

1st television connection of the US and Europe through Telstar satellite, July 11-12. For surcharges see Reunion Nos. 343-344.

"Bonjour Monsieur Courbet" by Gustave Courbet
A396

Paintings: 65c, "Madame Manet on Blue Sofa," by Edouard Manet. 1fr, "Guards officer on horseback," by Theodore Géricault, vert.

1962, Nov. 9　　**Perf. 13x12, 12x13**
1049　A396　50c multicolored　2.25　1.50
1050　A396　65c multicolored　2.25　1.40
1051　A396　1fr multicolored　4.50　2.00
　　Nos. 1049-1051 (3)　9.00　4.90

Bathyscaph "Archimede"
A397

1963, Jan. 26　**Unwmk.**　**Perf. 13**
1052　A397　30c dk blue & blk　.25　.25
French deep-sea explorations.

Flowers and Nantes Chateau — A398

1963, Feb. 11
1053　A398　30c vio bl, car & sl grn　.25　.25
Nantes flower festival.

St. Peter, Window at St. Foy de Conches — A399

50c, Jacob Wrestling with the Angel, by Delacroix.

1963, Mar. 2　　　　**Perf. 12x13**
1054　A399　50c multicolored　2.40　1.50
1055　A399　1fr multicolored　3.25　2.25
　　See Nos. 1076-1077.

Hungry Woman and Wheat Emblem — A400

1963, Mar. 21　　**Engr.**　　**Perf. 13**
1056　A400　50c slate grn & brn　.40　.25
FAO "Freedom from Hunger" campaign.

Cemetery and Memorial, Glières — A401

Design: 50c, Memorial, Ile de la Cité, Paris.

1963, Mar. 23　　**Unwmk.**　　**Perf. 13**
1057　A401　30c dk brown & olive　.40　.30
1058　A401　50c indigo　.40　.30

Heroes of the resistance against the Nazis.

Beethoven, Birthplace at Bonn and Rhine — A402

No. 1060, Emile Verhaeren, memorial at Roisin & residence. No. 1061, Giuseppe Mazzini, Marcus Aurelius statue & Via Appia, Rome. No. 1062, Emile Mayrisch, Colpach Chateau & blast furnace, Esch. No. 1063, Hugo de Groot, Palace of Peace, The Hague & St. Agatha Church, Delft.

1963, Apr. 27　　**Unwmk.**　　**Perf. 13**
1059　A402　20c ocher, sl & brt grn　.30　.25
1060　A402　20c purple, blk & mar　.30　.25
1061　A402　20c maroon, sl & ol　.30　.25
1062　A402　20c mar, dk brn & ocher　.30　.25
1063　A402　30c dk brn, vio & ocher　.30　.25
　　Nos. 1059-1063 (5)　1.50　1.25

Issued to honor famous men of the European Common Market countries.

Hotel des Postes and Stagecoach, 1863 — A403

1963, May 4
1064 A403 50c grayish black .35 .25
1st Intl. Postal Conference, Paris, 1863.

Lycée Louis-le-Grand, Belvédère, Panthéon and St. Etienne du Mont Church — A404

1963, May 18
1065 A404 30c slate green .30 .25
400th anniversary of the Jesuit Clermont secondary school, named after Louis XIV.

St. Peter's Church and Ramparts, Caen — A405

1963, June 1 **Unwmk.** **Perf. 13**
1066 A405 30c gray blue & brn .25 .25

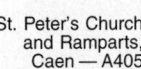

Radio Telescope, Nançay A406

1963, June 8 **Engr.**
1067 A406 50c dk bl & dk brn .45 .35

Amboise Chateau A407   Saint-Flour A408

Designs: 50c, Côte d'Azur Varoise. 85c, Vittel. 95c, Moissac.

1963, June 15
1068 A407 30c slate, grn & bis .25 .25
1069 A407 50c dk grn, dk bl & hn brn .30 .25
1070 A408 60c ultra, dk grn & hn brn .40 .25
1071 A407 85c dk grn, yel grn & brn 1.00 .25
1072 A408 95c brnsh black .60 .25
Nos. 1068-1072 (5) 2.55 1.25

For surcharge see Reunion No. 355.

Water Skiing Slalom — A409

1963, Aug. 31 **Unwmk.** **Perf. 13**
1073 A409 30c sl grn, blk & car .30 .25
World Water Skiing Championships, Vichy.

Europa Issue, 1963
Common Design Type
1963, Sept. 14
Size: 36x22mm

1074 CD6 25c red brown .25 .25
1075 CD6 50c green .35 .25

Art Type of 1963
Designs: 85c, "The Married Couple of the Eiffel Tower," by Marc Chagall. 95c, "The Fur Merchants," window, Chartres Cathedral.

1963, Nov. 9 **Engr.** **Perf. 12x13**
1076 A399 85c multicolored 1.10 .90
1077 A399 95c multicolored .50 .40

Philatec Issue
Common Design Type
1963, Dec. 14 **Unwmk.** **Perf. 13**
1078 CD118 25c dk gray, sl grn & dk car .25 .25

For surcharge see Reunion No. 349.

Radio and Television Center, Paris — A411

1963, Dec. 15 **Engr.**
1079 A411 20c org brn, slate & ol .25 .25

A412

Design: Fire Brigade Insignia, Symbols of Fire, Water and Civilian Defense.

1964, Feb. 8 **Engr.** **Perf. 13**
1082 A412 30c blue, org & red .40 .25
Issued to honor the fire brigades and civilian defense corps.

Handicapped Laboratory Technician — A413

1964, Feb. 22 **Unwmk.** **Perf. 13**
1083 A413 30c blue grn, org brn & brn .25 .25
Rehabilitation of the handicapped.

John II the Good (1319-64) by Girard d'Orleans A414

1964, Apr. 25 **Perf. 12x13**
1084 A414 1fr multicolored 1.10 .75

Stamp of 1900 A415   Mechanized Mail Handling A416

Designs: No. 1086, Stamp of 1900, Type A17. No. 1088, Telecommunications.

1964, May 9 **Perf. 13**
1085 A415 25c bister & dk car .25 .25
1086 A415 25c bister & blue .25 .25
1087 A416 30c blk, bl & org brn .25 .25
1088 A416 30c blk, car rose & bluish grn .25 .25
a. Strip of 4, #1085-1088 + label 1.10 1.00

Printed in sheets of 20 stamps, containing five No. 1088a. The label shows the Philatec emblem in green.

Type of Semi-Postal Issue
with "25e ANNIVERSAIRE" added
1964, May 9
1089 SP208 25c multicolored .25 .25
25th anniversary, night airmail service.

Madonna and Child from Rose Window of Notre Dame — A417

1964, May 23 **Perf. 12x13**
1090 A417 60c multicolored .50 .40
Notre Dame Cathedral, Paris, 800th anniv. See No. 5933c.

Arms Type of 1958-59
Arms: 1c, Niort. 2c, Guéret. 12c, Agen. 18c, Saint-Denis, Réunion. 30c, Paris.

1964-65 **Typo.** **Perf. 14x13½**
1091 A318 1c vio blue & yel .25 .25
1092 A318 2c emer, vio bl & yel .25 .25
1093 A318 12c black, red & yel .25 .25
1094 A318 18c multicolored .25 .25
1095 A318 30c vio bl & red ('65) .30 .25
a. Booklet pane of 10 15.00
Nos. 1091-1095 (5) 1.30 1.25

Gallic Coin — A418

Perf. 13½x14
1964-66 **Typo.** **Unwmk.**
1096 A418 10c emer & bister .75 .25
1097 A418 15c org & bister ('66) .30 .25
1098 A418 25c lilac & brn .45 .25
1099 A418 50c brt blue & brn .85 .75
Nos. 1096-1099 (4) 2.35 1.50

Nos. 1096-1099 are known only precanceled. See second note after No. 132. See Nos. 1240-1242, 1315-1318, 1421-1424.

Postrider, Rocket and Radar Equipment A419

1964, June 5 **Engr.** **Perf. 13**
1100 A419 1fr brn, dk red & dk bl 17.50 13.50

Sold for 4fr, including 3fr admission to PHILATEC. Issued in sheets of 8 stamps and 8 labels (2x8 subjects with labels in horizontal rows 1, 4, 5, 8; stamps in rows 2, 3, 6, 7). Commemorative inscriptions on side margins. Value $150.

Caesar's Tower, Provins A420   Chapel of Notre Dame du Haut, Ronchamp A421

1964-65
1101 A421 40c sl grn, dk brn & brn ('65) .25 .25
1102 A420 70c slate, grn & car .30 .25
1103 A421 1.25fr brt bl, sl grn & ol .70 .25
Nos. 1101-1103 (3) 1.25 .75

The 40c was issued in vertical coils in 1971. Every 10th coil stamp has a red control number printed twice on the back.
For surcharges see Reunion Nos. 352, 361.

Mandel — A422

1964, July 4 **Unwmk.** **Perf. 13**
1104 A422 30c violet brown .25 .25
Georges Mandel (1885-1944), Cabinet minister, executed by the Nazis.

Judo — A423

1964, July 4
1105 A423 50c dk blue & vio brn .25 .25
18th Olympic Games, Tokyo, 10/10-25/64.

Champlevé Enamel from Limoges, 12th Century — A424

Design: No. 1107, The Lady (Claude Le Viste?) with the Unicorn, 15th cent. tapestry.

1964 **Perf. 12x13**
1106 A424 1fr multicolored .75 .50
1107 A424 1fr multicolored .40 .30

No. 1106 shows part of an enamel sepulchral plate portraying Geoffrey IV, Count of Anjou and Le Maine (1113-1151), who was called Geoffrey Plantagenet.
Issue dates: No. 1106, July 4. No. 1107, Oct. 31.

Paris Taxis Carrying Soldiers to Front, 1914 — A425

1964, Sept. 5 **Unwmk.** **Perf. 13**
1108 A425 30c black, blue & red .25 .25
50th anniversary of Battle of the Marne.

Europa Issue, 1964
Common Design Type
1964, Sept. 12 **Engr.**
Size: 22x36mm

1109 CD7 25c dk car, dp ocher & grn .25 .25
1110 CD7 50c vio, yel grn & dk car .25 .25

Cooperation Issue
Common Design Type
1964, Nov. 6 **Unwmk.** **Perf. 13**
1111 CD119 25c red brn, dk brn & dk bl .25 .25

Joux Chateau — A427

1965, Feb. 6 **Engr.**
1112 A427 1.30fr redsh brn, brn red & dk brn .90 .25

"The English Girl from the Star" by Toulouse-Lautrec A428

St. Paul on the Damascus Road, Window, Cathedral of Sens A429

Leaving for the Hunt A430

Apocalypse Tapestry, 14th Century — A431

"The Red Violin" by Raoul Dufy — A432

Designs: No. 1115, "August" miniature of Book of Hours of Jean de France, Duc de Berry ("Les Très Riches Heures du Duc de Berry"), painted by Flemish brothers, Pol, Hermant and Jannequin Limbourg, 1411-16. No. 1116, Scene from oldest existing set of French tapestries, showing the Winepress of the Wrath of God (Revelations 14: 19-20).

1965   *Perf. 12x13, 13x12*
1113	A428	1fr multicolored	.40	.30
1114	A429	1fr multicolored	.40	.30
1115	A430	1fr multicolored	.30	.30
1116	A431	1fr multicolored	.30	.30
1117	A432	1fr blk, pink & car	.30	.30
		Nos. 1113-1117 (5)	1.70	1.50

No. 1114 issued to commemorate the 800th anniversary of the Cathedral of Sens.

Issued: No. 1113, 3/12; No. 1114, 6/5; No. 1115, 9/25; No. 1116, 10/30; No. 1117, 11/6.

Returning Deportees, 1945 — A433

1965, Apr. 1   Unwmk.   *Perf. 13*
1118   A433   40c Prussian green   .45   .25

20th anniv. of the return of people deported during World War II.

House of Youth and Culture, Troyes — A434

1965, Apr. 10   *Engr.*
1119   A434   25c ind, brn & dk grn   .25   .25

20th anniv. of the establishment of recreational cultural centers for young people.

Woman Carrying Flowers — A435

1965, Apr. 24   Unwmk.   *Perf. 13*
1120   A435   60c dk grn & ver   .30   .25

Tourist Campaign of Welcome & Amiability.

Flags of France, US, USSR and Great Britain Crushing Swastika — A436

1965, May 8
1121   A436   40c black, car & blue   .30   .25

20th anniv. of victory in World War II.

Telegraph Key, Syncom Satellite and Pleumeur-Bodou Station — A437

1965, May 17
1122   A437   60c dk blue, brn & blk   .30   .25

Centenary of the ITU.

Croix de Guerre — A438

1965, May 22   *Engr.*
1123   A438   40c red, brn & brt grn   .35   .25

50th anniv. of the Croix de Guerre medal.

Cathedral of Bourges A439

Moustiers-Sainte-Marie A440

Views: 30c, Road and tunnel, Mont Blanc. 60c, Aix-les-Bains, sailboat. 75c, Tarn Gorge. Lozère mountains. 95c, Vendée River, man poling boat, and windmill. 1fr, Prehistoric stone monuments, Carnac.

1965
1124	A439	30c bl, vio bl & brn vio	.25	.25
1125	A439	40c gray bl & redsh brn	.25	.25
1126	A440	50c grn, bl gray & bis	.25	.25
1127	A439	60c blue & red brn	.45	.25
1128	A439	75c brown, bl & grn	.75	.60
1129	A440	95c brown, grn & bl	4.50	.75
1130	A440	1fr gray, grn & brn	.75	.25
		Nos. 1124-1130 (7)	7.20	2.60

No. 1124 for the opening of the Mont Blanc Tunnel. No. 1125 (Bourges Cathedral) was issued in connection with the French Philatelic Societies Federation Congress, held at Bourges.

Issued: 40c, June 5; 50c, June 19; 30c, 60c, July 17; others, July 10.

For surcharges see Reunion Nos. 354, 362, 365.

Europa Issue, 1965
Common Design Type

1965, Sept. 25   *Perf. 13*
Size: 36x22mm
1131   CD8   30c red   .25   .30
1132   CD8   60c gray   .45   .25

Planting Seedling — A441

1965, Oct. 2
1133   A441   25c slate grn, yel grn & red brn   .25   .25

National reforestation campaign.

Etienne Régnault, "Le Taureau" and Coast of Reunion — A442

1965, Oct. 2
1134   A442   30c indigo & dk car   .25   .25

Tercentenary of settlement of Reunion.

Atomic Reactor and Diagram, Symbols of Industry, Agriculture and Medicine — A443

1965, Oct. 9
1135   A443   60c brt blue & blk   .50   .30

Atomic Energy Commission, 20th anniv.

Air Academy and Emblem — A444

1965, Nov. 6   *Perf. 13*
1136   A444   25c dk blue & green   .35   .30

Air Academy, Salon-de-Provence, 50th anniv.

French Satellite A-1 Issue
Common Design Type

Design: 60c, A-1 satellite.

1965, Nov. 30   *Engr.*   *Perf. 13*
1137	CD121	30c Prus bl, brt bl & blk	.25	.25
1138	CD121	60c blk, Prus bl & brt bl	.40	.25
a.		Strip of 2, #1137-1138 + label	.65	.65

Launching of France's 1st satellite, 11/26/65.
For surcharges see Reunion Nos. 358-359.

Arms of Auch — A446

Cities: 20c, Saint-Lô. 25c, Mont-de-Marsan.

Typographed, Photogravure (20c)
1966   *Perf. 14x13; 14 (20c)*
1142	A446	5c blue & red	.25	.25
1143	A446	20c vio bl, sil, gold & red	.25	.25
1144	A446	25c red brown & ultra	.30	.25
		Nos. 1142-1144 (3)	.80	.75

The 5c and 20c were issued in sheets and in vertical coils. In the coils, every 10th stamp has a red control number on the back.

For surcharges see Reunion Nos. 360-360A.

French Satellite D-1 Issue
Common Design Type

1966, Feb. 18   *Engr.*   *Perf. 13*
1148   CD122   60c blue blk, grn & cl   .25   .25

Horses from Bronze Vessel of Vix — A448

"The Newborn" by Georges de La Tour — A449

The Baptism of Judas (4th Century Bishop of Jerusalem) A450

"The Moon and the Bull" Tapestry by Jean Lurçat — A451

"Crispin and Scapin" by Honoré Daumier A452

1966   *Perf. 13x12, 12x13*
1149	A448	1fr multicolored	.40	.35
1150	A449	1fr multicolored	.40	.35
1151	A450	1fr multicolored	.40	.35
1152	A451	1fr multicolored	.40	.30
1153	A452	1fr multicolored	.40	.30
		Nos. 1149-1153 (5)	2.00	1.65

The design of No. 1149 is a detail from a 6th century B.C. vessel, found in 1953 in a grave near Vix, Cote d'Or.

The design of No. 1151 is from a stained glass window in the 13th century Sainte-Chapelle, Paris.

No. 1150 exists in an imperf, ungummed souv. sheet with 2 progressive die proofs, issued for benefit of the Postal Museum, and not postally valid. Value $2.

Issued: No. 1149, 3/26; No. 1150, 6/25; No. 1151, 10/22; No. 1152, 11/19; No. 1153, 12/10.

Chessboard, Knight, Emblems for King and Queen — A453

1966, Apr. 2   *Engr.*   *Perf. 13*
1154   A453   60c sepia, gray & dk vio bl   .45   .30

Issued to publicize the Chess Festival.

Rhone Bridge, Pont-Saint-Esprit — A454

1966, Apr. 23   Unwmk.   *Perf. 13*
1155   A454   25c black & dull blue   .25   .25

St. Michael Slaying the Dragon — A455

1966, Apr. 30   Litho. & Engr.
1156 A455 25c multicolored   .25   .25

Millenium of Mont-Saint-Michel.

Stanislas Leszczynski, Lunéville Chateau — A456

1966, May 6   Engr.
1157 A456 25c slate, grn & brn   .25   .25

200th anniv. of the reunion of Lorraine and Bar (Barrois) with France.

St. Andrew's and Sèvre River, Niort — A457

1966, May 28   Engr.   Perf. 13
1158 A457 40c brt bl, indigo & grn   .30   .25

Bernard Le Bovier de Fontenelle and 1666 Meeting Room — A458

1966, June 4
1159 A458 60c dk car rose & brn   .30   .25

300th anniversary, Académie des Sciences.

William the Conqueror, Castle and Norman Ships A459

1966, June 4
1160 A459 60c brown red & dp bl   .40   .30

900th anniversary of Battle of Hastings.

Tracks, Globe and Eiffel Tower — A460

1966, June 11
1161 A460 60c dk brn, car & dull bl   .50   .25

19th International Railroad Congress.

Oléron Bridge — A461

1966, June 20
1162 A461 25c Prus bl, brn & bl   .25   .25

Issued to commemorate the opening of Oléron Bridge, connecting Oléron Island in the Bay of Biscay with the French mainland.

Europa Issue, 1966
Common Design Type

1966, Sept. 24   Engr.   Perf. 13
Size: 22x36mm
1163 CD9 30c Prussian blue   .25   .25
1164 CD9 60c red   .30   .25

Vercingetorix at Gergovie, 52 B.C. — A462

Bishop Remi Baptizing King Clovis, 496 A.D. — A463

Design: 60c, Charlemagne attending school (page holding book for crowned king).

1966, Nov. 5   Perf. 13
1165 A462 40c choc, grn & gray bl   .30   .25
1166 A463 40c dk red brn & blk   .30   .25
1167 A463 60c pur, rose car & brn   .30   .25
     Nos. 1165-1167 (3)   .90   .75

Map of Pneumatic Post and Tube — A464

1966, Nov. 11
1168 A464 1.60fr mar & indigo   .60   .30

Centenary of Paris pneumatic post system.

Val Chateau — A465

1966, Nov. 19   Engr.   Perf. 13
1169 A465 2.30fr dk bl, sl grn & brn   1.50   .25

Rance Power Station — A466

1966, Dec. 3
1170 A466 60c dk bl, sl grn & brn   .45   .25

Tidal power station in the estuary of the Rance River on the English Channel.

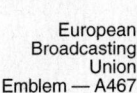

European Broadcasting Union Emblem — A467

1967, Mar. 4   Engr.   Perf. 13
1171 A467 40c dk blue & rose brn   .25   .25

3rd Intl. Congress of the European Broadcasting Union, Paris, Mar. 8-22.

Father Juniet's Gig by Henri Rousseau A468

Francois I by Jean Clouet — A469

The Bather by Jean-Dominique Ingres — A470

St. Eloi, the Goldsmith, at Work A471

1967   Engr.   Perf. 13x12, 12x13
1172 A468 1fr multicolored   .30   .25
1173 A469 1fr multicolored   .30   .25
1174 A470 1fr multicolored   .30   .25
1175 A471 1fr multicolored   .30   .25
    Nos. 1172-1175 (4)   1.20   1.00

The design of No. 1175 is from a 16th century stained glass window in the Church of Sainte Madeleine, Troyes.

Issued: No. 1172, 4/15; No. 1173, 7/1; No. 1174, 9/9; No. 1175, 10/7.

Snow Crystal and Olympic Rings — A472

1967, Apr. 22   Photo.   Perf. 13
1176 A472 60c brt & lt blue & red   .35   .25

Issued to publicize the 10th Winter Olympic Games, Grenoble, Feb. 6-18, 1968.

French Pavilion, EXPO '67 — A473

1967, Apr. 22   Engr.
1177 A473 60c dull bl & bl grn   .35   .30

Intl. Exhibition EXPO '67, Montreal, Apr. 28-Oct. 27, 1967.
For surcharge see Reunion No. 363.

Europa Issue, 1967
Common Design Type

1967, Apr. 29   Size: 22x36mm
1178 CD10 30c blue & gray   .25   .25
1179 CD10 60c brown & lt blue   .30   .25

Great Bridge, Bordeaux — A474

1967, May 8
1180 A474 25c olive, blk & brn   .25   .25

Nungesser, Coli and "L'Oiseau Blanc" — A475

1967, May 8
1181 A475 40c slate, dk & lt brn   .30   .25

40th anniv. of the attempted transatlantic flight of Charles Nungesser and François Coil, French aviators.

Gouin House, Tours — A476

1967, May 13   Engr.   Perf. 13
1182 A476 40c vio bl, red brn & red   .30   .25

Congress of the Federation of French Philatelic Societies in Tours.

Ramon and Alfort Veterinary School — A477

1967, May 27
1183 A477 25c brn, dp bl & yel grn   .25   .25

200th anniv. of the Alfort Veterinary School and to honor Professor Gaston Ramon (1886-1963).

Robert Esnault-Pelterie, Diamant Rocket and A-1 Satellite — A478

1967, May 27
1184 A478 60c slate & vio blue   .30   .25

Issued to honor Robert Esnault-Pelterie (1881-1957), aviation and space expert.

City Hall, Saint-Quentin A479   Saint-Germain-en-Laye A480

Views: 60c, Clock Tower, Vire. 75c, Beach, La Baule, Brittany. 95c, Harbor, Boulogne-sur-Mer. 1fr, Rodez Cathedral. 1.50fr, Morlaix; old houses, grotesque carving, viaduct.

1967
1185 A479 50c bl, sl bl & brn   .25   .25
1186 A479 60c dp bl, sl bl & dk red brn   .30   .25
1187 A480 70c rose car, red brn & bl   .30   .25
1188 A480 75c multicolored   1.10   .60
1189 A480 95c sky bl, lil & sl grn   1.10   .60
1190 A479 1fr indigo & bl gray   .45   .25
1191 A479 1.50fr brt bl, brt grn & red brn   .90   .35
    Nos. 1185-1191 (7)   4.40   2.55

Issued: 1fr, 1.50fr, June 10; 70c, June 17; 50c, 60c, 95c, July 8; 75c, July 24.

Orchids — A481

1967, July 29   Engr.   Perf. 13
1192 A481 40c dp car, brt pink &
pur   .50   .40
Orleans flower festival.

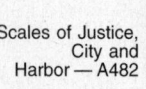
Scales of Justice,
City and
Harbor — A482

1967, Sept. 4
1193 A482 60c dk plum, dl bl &
ocher   .50   .30
9th Intl. Accountancy Cong., Paris, 9/6-12.

Cross of Lorraine,
Soldiers and
Sailors — A483

1967, Oct. 7   Engr.   Perf. 13
1194 A483 25c brn, dp ultra & bl   .25   .25
25th anniv. of the Battle of Bir Hacheim.

Marie Curie, Bowl
Glowing with
Radium — A484

1967, Oct. 23   Engr.   Perf. 13
1195 A484 60c dk blue & ultra   .30   .25
Marie Curie (1867-1934), scientist who discovered radium and polonium, Nobel prize winner for physics and chemistry.

Lions
Emblem — A485

1967, Oct. 28
1196 A485 40c dk car & vio bl   .70   .40
50th anniversary of Lions International.
For surcharge see Reunion No. 364.

Marianne (by
Cheffer) — A486

1967, Nov. 4   Engr.
1197 A486 25c dark blue   .25   .25
1198 A486 30c bright lilac   .25   .25
  a. Booklet pane of 5   6.00
  b. Booklet pane of 10   12.00

Coils (vertical) of Nos. 1197 and 1231 show a red number on the back of every 10th stamp.
See Nos. 1230-1231C, 3525, 4410e, 4517.
For surcharges see Reunion Nos. 367-368, 389.
Stamps of various colors and printing methods with denomination of €1 were limited printings sold in 2010. See footnote after No.3478.
A €1.16 stamp of type A486 with an attached label was included in a limited-edition booklet issued Nov. 4, 2020.

King Philip II (Philip
Augustus) at Battle of
Bouvines — A487

Designs: No. 1200, Election of Hugh Capet as King, horiz. 60c, King Louis IX (St. Louis) holding audience for the poor.

1967, Nov. 13   Engr.   Perf. 13
1199 A487 40c bl gray, blk & dk
blue   .30   .25
1200 A487 40c dp bluish grn &
blue   .30   .25
1201 A487 60c dp grn & dk red
brn   .40   .25
  Nos. 1199-1201 (3)   1.00   .75

Commemorative
Medal — A488

1968, Jan. 6   Engr.   Perf. 13
1202 A488 40c dk slate grn & bis   .25   .25
50th anniversary of postal checking service.

Various Road
Signs — A489

1968, Feb. 24
1203 A489 25c lil, red & dk bl grn   .25   .25
Issued to publicize road safety.

Prehistoric
Paintings,
Lascaux
Cave
A490

Arearea
(Merriment)
by Paul
Gauguin
A491

The Dance by
Emile Antoine
Bourdelle — A492

Portrait of the
Model by Auguste
Renoir — A493

1968   Engr.   Perf. 13x12, 12x13
1204 A490 1fr multicolored   .50   .30
1205 A491 1fr multicolored   .50   .30
1206 A492 1fr car & gray olive   .50   .30
1207 A493 1fr multicolored   .50   .30
  Nos. 1204-1207 (4)   2.00   1.20
Issued: No. 1204, 4/13; No. 1205, 9/21; No. 1206, 10/26; No. 1207, 11/9.

Audio-visual
Institute,
Royan — A494

1968, Apr. 13   Perf. 13
1208 A494 40c slate grn, brn &
Prus bl   .25   .25
5th Conference for World Cooperation with the theme of teaching living languages by audio-visual means.

Europa Issue, 1968
Common Design Type

1968, Apr. 27   Size: 36x22mm
1209 CD11 30c brt red lil & ocher   .25   .25
1210 CD11 60c brown & lake   .60   .30

Alain René Le
Sage — A495

1968, May 4
1211 A495 40c blue & rose vio   .25   .25
Alain René Le Sage (1668-1747), novelist and playwright.

Chateau de
Langeais — A496

1968, May 4
1212 A496 60c slate bl, grn & red
brn   .65   .30

Pierre
Larousse — A497

1968, May 11   Engr.   Perf. 13
1213 A497 40c rose vio & brown   .25   .25
Pierre Larousse (1817-75), grammarian, lexicographer and encyclopedist.

Gnarled Trunk and Fir
Tree — A498

1968, May 18   Engr.   Perf. 13
1214 A498 25c grnsh bl, brn & grn   .25   .25
Twinning of Rambouillet Forest in France and the Black Forest in Germany.

Map of Papal
Enclave, Valréas,
and John XXII
Receiving
Homage — A499

1968, May 25
1215 A499 60c brn, bis brn & pur   .40   .25
Papal enclave at Valréas, 650th anniv.

Louis XIV, Arms
of France and
Flanders — A500

1968, June 29
1216 A500 40c rose car, gray &
lemon   .25   .25
300th anniv. of the Treaty of Aachen which reunited Flanders with France.

Martrou Bridge,
Rochefort — A501

1968, July 20
1217 A501 25c sky bl, blk & dk
red brn   .25   .25

Letord Lorraine
Bimotor Plane
over Map of
France — A502

1968, Aug. 17   Engr.   Perf. 13
1218 A502 25c brt blue, indigo &
red   .40   .25
1st regularly scheduled air mail route in France from Paris to St. Nazaire, 50th anniv.

Tower de Constance,
Aigues-Mortes — A503

1968, Aug. 31
1219 A503 25c red brn, sky bl &
olive bister   .25   .25
Bicentenary of the release of Huguenot prisoners from the Tower de Constance, Aigues-Mortes.

Cathedral and
Pont Vieux,
Beziers — A504

1968, Sept. 7   Engr.   Perf. 13
1220 A504 40c ind, bis & grn   .95   .30

"Victory" over White
Tower of
Salonika — A505

1968, Sept. 28
1221 A505 40c red lilac & plum   .25   .25
50th anniv. of the armistice on the eastern front in World War I, Sept. 29, 1918.

Louis XV, Arms
of France and
Corsica — A506

1968, Oct. 5   Perf. 13
1222 A506 25c ultra, grn & blk   .25   .25
Return of Corsica to France, 200th anniv.

Relay
Race — A507

1968, Oct. 12
1223 A507 40c ultra, brt grn & ol
brn .40 .25
19th Olympic Games, Mexico City, 10/12-27.

A508

Design: Polar camp with helicopter, plane and Snocat tractor.

1968, Oct. 19
1224 A508 40c Prus bl, lt grnsh bl
& brn red .30 .25
20 years of French Polar expeditions.
For surcharge see Reunion No. 366.

Leon Bailby, Paris Opera Staircase and Hospital Beds — A509

1968, Oct. 26
1225 A509 40c ocher & maroon .25 .25
50th anniv. of the "Little White Beds" children's hospital fund.

"Victory" over Arc de Triomphe and Eternal Flame — A510

1968, Nov. 9 **Engr.** *Perf. 13*
1226 A510 25c dk car rose & dp
blue .25 .25
50th anniv. of the armistice which ended World War I.

Death of Bertrand Du Guesclin at Chateauneuf-de-Randon, 1380 — A511

No. 1228, King Philip IV (the Fair) and first States-General assembly, 1302, horiz. 60c, Joan of Arc leaving Vaucouleurs, 1429.

1968, Nov. 16
1227 A511 40c green, ultra & brn .30 .25
1228 A511 40c cop red, grn &
gray .30 .25
1229 A511 60c vio bl, sl bl & bis .40 .30
Nos. 1227-1229 (3) 1.00 .80
See No. 1260.

Marianne Type of 1967
1969-70 **Engr.** *Perf. 13*
1230 A486 30c green .35 .25
a. Booklet pane of 10 8.50
1231 A486 40c deep carmine .45 .25
a. Booklet pane of 5 (horiz. strip) 7.50
b. Booklet pane of 10 8.50
d. With label ('70) .50 .25

Typo. *Perf. 14x13*
1231C A486 30c blue green .25 .25
Nos. 1230-1231C (3) 1.05 .75

No. 1231d was issued in sheets of 50 with alternating labels showing coat of arms of Perigueux, arranged checkerwise, to commemorate the inauguration of the Perigueux stamp printing plant.
The 40c coil is noted after No. 1198.

Church of Brou, Bourg-en-Bresse A512

Views: 80c, Vouglans Dam, Jura. 85c, Chateau de Chantilly. 1.15fr, Sailboats in La Trinité-sur-Mer harbor.

1969 **Engr.** *Perf. 13*
1232 A512 45c olive, bl & red
brn .25 .25
1233 A512 80c ol bis, brn red
& dk brn .40 .25
1234 A512 85c sl grn, dl bl &
gray .75 .50
1235 A512 1.15fr brt bl, gray grn
& brn .75 .50
Nos. 1232-1235 (4) 2.15 1.50

"February" Bas-relief from Amiens Cathedral A513

Philip the Good, by Roger van der Weyden — A514

Sts. Savin and Cyprian before Ladicius, Mural, St. Savin, Vienne A515

The Circus, by Georges Seurat — A515a

1969 *Perf. 12x13*
1236 A513 1fr dk green & brn .40 .25
1237 A514 1fr multicolored .40 .25
1238 A515 1fr multicolored .40 .25
1239 A515a 1fr multicolored .40 .25
Nos. 1236-1239 (4) 1.60 1.00
Issue dates: No. 1236, Feb. 22; No. 1237, May 3; No. 1238, June 28; No. 1239, Nov. 8.

Gallic Coin Type of 1964-66
1969 **Typo.** *Perf. 13½x14*
1240 A418 22c brt green & vio .30 .25
1241 A418 35c red & ultra .85 .40
1242 A418 70c ultra & red brn 3.75 1.75
Nos. 1240-1242 (3) 4.90 2.40
Nos. 1240-1242 are known only precanceled. See note after No. 132.

Hautefort Chateau — A516

1969, Apr. 5 **Engr.** *Perf. 13*
1243 A516 70c blue, slate & bister .40 .25

Irises — A517

1969, Apr. 12 **Photo.**
1244 A517 45c multicolored .35 .25
3rd Intl. Flower Show, Paris, 4/23-10/5.

Europa Issue, 1969
Common Design Type
1969, Apr. 26 **Engr.** *Perf. 13*
Size: 36x22mm
1245 CD12 40c carmine rose .25 .25
1246 CD12 70c Prussian blue .30 .25

Albert Thomas and Thomas Memorial, Geneva — A518

1969, May 10 **Engr.** *Perf. 13*
1247 A518 70c mar, lt brn & ind .40 .25
ILO, 50th anniv., and honoring Thomas (1878-1932), director of the ILO (1920-32).

Garigliano Battle Scene, 1944 A519

1969, May 10
1248 A519 45c black & violet .40 .30
25th anniv. of the Battle of the Garigliano against the Germans.

Chateau du Marché, Chalons-sur-Marne A520

1969, May 24
1249 A520 45c bis, dull bl & grn .40 .30
Federation of French Philatelic Societies, 42nd congress.

Parachutists over Normandy Beach — A521

1969, May 31
1250 A521 45c inidgo & dk ultra .85 .40
Landing of Special Air Service and Free French commandos in Normandy, June 6, 1944, 25th anniv.

Monument of the French Resistance, Mt. Mouchet — A522

1969, June 7
1251 A522 45c dk grn, slate & ind .60 .45
25th anniv. of the battle of Mt. Mouchet between French resistance fighters and the Germans, June 2 and 10, 1944.

French Troops Landing in Provence A523

1969, Aug. 23 **Engr.** *Perf. 13*
1252 A523 45c slate & blk brn .75 .45
25th anniv. of the landing of French and American forces in Provence, Aug. 15, 1944.

Russian and French Aviators A524

1969, Oct. 18 **Engr.** *Perf. 13*
1253 A524 45c slate, dp bl & car .75 .45
Issued to honor the French aviators of the Normandy-Neman Squadron who fought on the Russian Front, 1942-45.

Kayak on Isère River — A525

1969, Aug. 2 **Engr.** *Perf. 13*
1254 A525 70c org brn, ol & dk bl .40 .25
Intl. Canoe and Kayak Championships, Bourg-Saint-Maurice, Savoy, July 31-Aug. 6.

A526

Design: Napoleon as young officer and his birthplace, Ajaccio.

1969, Aug. 16
1255 A526 70c brt grnsh bl, ol &
rose vio .40 .25
Napoleon Bonaparte (1769-1821).
For surcharge see Reunion No. 370.

Drops of Water and Diamond — A527

1969, Sept. 27
1256 A527 70c blk, dp bl & brt grn .40 .25
European Water Charter.

Mediterranean Mouflon — A528

1969, Oct. 11
1257 A528 45c ol, blk & org brn .60 .50
Issued to publicize wildlife protection.

Central School of Arts and Crafts — A529

1969, Oct. 18
1258 A529 70c dk grn, yel grn &
org .40 .25
Inauguration of the Central School of Arts and Crafts at Chatenay-Malabry.

Nuclear Submarine "Le Redoutable" A530

1969, Oct. 25
1259 A530 70c dp bl, grn & sl grn .40 .25

Type of 1968 and

Henri IV and Edict of Nantes A531

Designs: No. 1260, Pierre Terrail de Bayard wounded at Battle of Brescia (after a painting in Versailles). No. 1262, Louis XI, Charles the Bold and map of France.

1969, Nov. 8   Engr.   Perf. 13
1260 A511 80c brn, bister & blk   .45 .25
1261 A531 80c blk & vio bl   .45 .25
1262 A531 80c ol, dp grn & dk
              red brn   .45 .25
     Nos. 1260-1262 (3)   1.35 .75

"Firecrest" and Alain Gerbault — A532

1970, Jan. 10   Engr.   Perf. 13
1263 A532 70c ind, brt bl & gray .45 .30

Completion of Alain Gerbault's trip around the world aboard the "Firecrest," 1923-29, 40th anniv.

— A533

Design: Gendarmery emblem, mountain climber, helicopter, motorcyclists and motorboat.

1970, Jan. 31
1264 A533 45c sl grn, dk bl & brn .80 .40

National Gendarmery, founded 1791.

Field Ball Player — A534

1970, Feb. 21   Engr.   Perf. 13
1265 A534 80c slate green   .45 .40

7th Intl. Field Ball Games, Feb. 26-Mar. 8.

Alphonse Juin and Church of the Invalides A535

1970, Feb. 28
1266 A535 45c gray bl & dk brn   .35 .25

Issued to honor Marshal Alphonse Pierre Juin (1888-1967), military leader.

Aerotrain — A536

1970, Mar. 7
1267 A536 80c purple & gray   .45 .40

Introduction of the aerotrain, which reaches a speed of 320 miles per hour.

— A537

Design: Pierre Joseph Pelletier, Joseph Bienaimé Caventou, Quinine formula and cell.

1970, Mar. 21   Engr.   Perf. 13
1268 A537 50c slate grn, sky bl &
              dp car   .35 .25

Discovery of quinine, 150th anniversary.

Pink Flamingos — A538

1970, Mar. 21
1269 A538 45c olive, gray & pink .35 .25

European Nature Conservation Year, 1970.

Diamant B Rocket and Radar — A539

1970, Mar. 28
1270 A539 45c bright green   .50 .25

Space center in Guyana and the launching of the Diamant B rocket, Mar. 10, 1970.

Europa Issue, 1970
Common Design Type

1970, May 2   Engr.   Perf. 13
Size: 36x22mm

1271 CD13 40c deep carmine   .25 .25
1272 CD13 80c sky blue   .40 .25

Annunication, by Primitive Painter of Savoy, 1480 — A540

The Triumph of Flora, by Jean Baptiste Carpeaux A541

Diana Returning from the Hunt, by François Boucher A542

Dancer with Bouquet, by Edgar Degas — A543

1970   Perf. 12x13, 13x12
1273 A540 1fr multicolored   .50 .35
1274 A541 1fr red brown   .50 .35
1275 A542 1fr multicolored   .50 .35
1276 A543 1fr multicolored   .50 .35
     Nos. 1273-1276 (4)   2.00 1.40

Issued: No. 1273, 5/9; No. 1274, 7/4; No. 1275, 10/10; No. 1276, 11/14.

Arms of Lens, Miner's Lamp and Pit Head — A544

1970, May 16   Engr.   Perf. 13
1277 A544 40c scarlet   .25 .25

43rd Natl. Congress of the Federation of French Philatelic Societies, Lens, May 14-21.

Diamond Rock, Martinique A545

Haute Provence Observatory and Spiral Nebula A546

Designs: 95c, Chancelade Abbey, Dordogne. 1fr, Gosier Islet, Guadeloupe.

1970, June 20   Engr.   Perf. 13
1278 A545 50c sl grn, brt bl &
              plum   .30 .25
1279 A545 95c lt ol, car & brn   .80 .80
1280 A545 1fr sl grn, brt bl &
              dk car rose   .90 .25
1281 A546 1.30fr dk bl, vio bl &
              dk grn   1.10 .90
     Nos. 1278-1281 (4)   3.10 2.20

Hand Reaching for Freedom — A547

1970, June 27
1282 A547 45c vio bl, bl & bister .40 .25

Liberation of concentration camps, 25th anniv.

Handicapped Javelin Thrower — A548

1970, June 27
1283 A548 45c rose car, ultra &
              emer   .40 .25

Issued to publicize the International Games of the Handicapped, St. Etienne, June 1970.

Pole Vault — A549

1970, Sept. 11   Engr.   Perf. 13
1284 A549 45c car, bl & indigo   .45 .25

First European Junior Athletic Championships, Colombes, Sept. 11-13.

Royal Salt Works, Arc-et-Senans A550

1970, Sept. 26
1285 A550 80c bl, brn & dk grn   .70 .65

Restoration of the 18th cent. Royal Salt Works buildings, by Claude Nicolas Ledoux (1736-1806) at Arc-et-Senans, for use as a center for studies of all aspects of future human life.

Armand Jean du Plessis, Duc de Richelieu A551

Designs: No. 1287, Battle of Fontenoy, 1745. No. 1288, Louis XIV and Versailles.

1970, Oct. 17   Engr.   Perf. 13
1286 A551 45c blk, sl & car rose .50 .30
1287 A551 45c org, brn & indigo   .50 .30
1288 A551 45c sl grn, lem & org
              brn   .50 .30
     Nos. 1286-1288 (3)   1.50 .90

UN Headquarters in New York and Geneva — A552

1970, Oct. 24   Engr.   Perf. 13
1289 A552 80c ol, dp ultra & dk pur .40 .25

25th anniversary of the United Nations.

View of Bordeaux and France No. 43 — A553

1970, Nov. 7
1290 A553 80c vio bl & gray bl   .40 .25

Centenary of the Bordeaux issue.

Col. Denfert-Rochereau and Lion of Belfort, by Frederic A. Bartholdi — A554

1970, Nov. 14
1291 A554 45c dk bl, ol & red brn .40 .25

Centenary of the siege of Belfort during Franco-Prussian War.

Marianne (by Bequet) — A555

1971-74   Typo.   Perf. 14x13
1292 A555 45c sky blue   .30 .25
1292A A555 60c green ('74)   .50 .25

For surcharges see Reunion Nos. 371, 397-398.

Engr.   Perf. 13
1293 A555 50c rose carmine   .30 .25
 a. Bklt. pane of 5 (horiz. strip) 5.00
 b. Booklet pane of 10   10.00
1294 A555 60c green ('74)   4.00 .50
 a. Booklet pane of 10   65.00
1294B A555 80c car rose ('74)   .50 .25
 c. Booklet pane of 5   9.00
 d. Booklet pane of 10   12.00
  Nos. 1293-1294B (3)   4.80 .75

Nos. 1294 and 1294B issued also in vertical coils with control number on back of every 10th stamp.

No. 1293 issued only in booklets and in vertical coils with red control number on back of every 10th stamp.

See Nos. 1494-1498, 3526, 4410f, 4518, 6130-6133.

St. Matthew, Sculpture from Strasbourg Cathedral — A556

Winnower, by François Millet — A557

The Dreamer, by Georges Rouault — A558

1971   Engr.   Perf. 12x13
1295 A556 1fr dark red brown   .50 .40
1296 A557 1fr multicolored   .50 .40
1297 A558 1fr multicolored   .50 .40
  Nos. 1295-1297 (3)   1.50 1.20

Issued: No. 1295, 1/23; No. 1296, 4/3; No. 1297, 6/5.

Figure Skating Pair — A560

1971, Feb. 20   Engr.   Perf. 13
1299 A560 80c vio bl, sl & aqua   .50 .30

World Figure Skating Championships, Lyons, Feb. 23-28.

Underwater Exploration — A561

1971, Mar. 6
1300 A561 80c blue blk & bl grn   .45 .25

International Exhibition of Ocean Exploration, Bordeaux, Mar. 9-14.

Cape Horn Clipper "Antoinette" and Solidor Castle, Saint-Malo A562

1971, Apr. 10   Engr.   Perf. 13
1301 A562 80c blue, pur & slate   .80 .45

For surcharge see Reunion No. 372.

Pyrenean Chamois — A563

1971, Apr. 24   Engr.   Perf. 13
1302 A563 65c bl, dk brn & brn ol .50 .30

National Park of Western Pyrenees.

Europa Issue, 1971
Common Design Type and

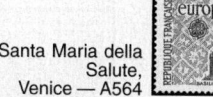

Santa Maria della Salute, Venice — A564

1971, May 8   Engr.   Perf. 13
1303 A564 50c blue gray & ol bis .30 .25

Size: 36x22mm
1304 CD14 80c rose lilac   .45 .40

Cardinal, Nobleman and Lawyer A565

Storming of the Bastille A566

Design: No. 1306, Battle of Valmy.

1971
1305 A565 45c bl, rose red & pur .45 .30
1306 A565 45c bl, ol bis & brn
        red   .50 .30
1307 A566 65c dk brn, gray bl &
        mag   .65 .45
  Nos. 1305-1307 (3)   1.60 1.05

No. 1305 commemorates the opening of the Estates General, May 5, 1789; No. 1306, Battle of Valmy (Sept. 20, 1792) between French and Prussian armies; 65c, Storming of the Bastille, Paris, July 14, 1789.

Issued: No. 1305, 5/8; No. 1306, 9/18; 65c, 7/10.

Grenoble — A568

1971, May 29   Engr.   Perf. 13
1308 A568 50c ocher, lil & rose red .35 .25

44th Natl. Cong. of the Federation of French Philatelic Societies, Grenoble, May 30-31.

"Rural Family Aid" Shedding Light on Village — A569

1971, June 5
1309 A569 40c vio, bl & grn   .25 .25

Aid for rural families.

For surcharge see Reunion No. 373.

Chateau and Fort de Sedan A570 | Pont d'Arc, Ardèche Gorge A571

Views: 60c, Sainte Chapelle, Riom. 65c, Fountain and tower, Dole. 90c, Tower and street, Riquewihr.

1971   Engr.   Perf. 13
1310 A571 60c black, grn & bl   .30 .25
1311 A571 65c lil, ocher & blk   .55 .25
1312 A571 90c grn, vio brn &
        red brn   .55 .25
1313 A570 1.10fr sl grn, Prus bl
        & brn   .65 .45
1314 A571 1.40fr sl grn, bl & dk
        brn   .75 .25
  Nos. 1310-1314 (5)   2.80 1.45

Issued: 60c, 6/19; 65c, 90c, 7/3; 1.10fr, 1.40fr, 6/12.
For surcharges see Reunion Nos. 374, 381.

Gallic Coin Type of 1964-66
1971, July 1   Typo.   Perf. 13½x14
1315 A418 26c lilac & brn   .30 .25
1316 A418 30c lt brown & brn   .35 .25
1317 A418 45c dull green & brn 1.20 .40
1318 A418 90c red & brown   1.50 .75
  Nos. 1315-1318 (4)   3.35 1.65

Nos. 1315-1318 are known only precanceled. See second paragraph after No. 132.

Bourbon Palace — A572

1971, Aug. 28   Engr.   Perf. 13
1319 A572 90c violet blue   .50 .35

59th Conf. of the Interparliamentary Union.

Embroidery and Tool Making — A573

1971, Oct. 16
1320 A573 90c brn red, brt lil & cl .50 .30

40th anniv. of the first assembly of presidents of artisans' guilds.
For surcharge see Reunion No. 375.

Reunion Chameleon A574

1971, Nov. 6   Photo.   Perf. 13
1321 A574 60c brn, yel, grn & blk .65 .45

Nature protection.

De Gaulle Issue
Common Design Type and

De Gaulle in Brazzaville, 1944 — A576

Designs: No. 1324, De Gaulle entering Paris, 1944. No. 1325, Pres. de Gaulle, 1970.

1971, Nov. 9   Engr.
1322 CD134 50c black   .65 .45
1323 A576 50c ultra   .65 .45
1324 A576 50c rose red   .65 .45

1325 CD134 50c black   .65 .45
 a. Strip of 4, #1322-1325 + label 3.00 2.50
  Nos. 1325a (1)   3.00 2.50

1st anniv. of the death of Charles de Gaulle. See Nos. 5947Bd, 5947Bf, Reunion Nos. 377, 380.

Antoine Portal and first Session of Academy A577

1971, Nov. 13
1326 A577 45c dk purple & mag   .40 .25

Sesquicentennial of the founding of the National Academy of Medicine; Baron Antoine Portal was first president.

L'Etude, by Jean Honoré Fragonard A578

Women in Garden, by Claude Monet — A579

St. Peter Presenting Pierre de Bourbon, by Maitre de Moulins — A580

Boats, by André Derain A581

1972   Engr.   Perf. 12x13, 13x12
1327 A578 1fr black & multi   .50 .40
1328 A579 1fr slate grn & multi 1.00 1.00
1329 A580 2fr dk brown & multi 1.25 1.00
1330 A581 2fr yellow & multi   1.25 1.00
  Nos. 1327-1330 (4)   4.00 2.90

Issued: No. 1327, 1/22; No. 1328, 6/17; No. 1329, 10/14; No. 1330, 12/16.

Map of South Indian Ocean, Penguin and Ships — A582

1972, Jan. 29   Perf. 13
1331 A582 90c black, bl & ocher   .50 .30

Bicentenary of discovery of the Crozet and Kerguelen Islands.

Slalom and Olympic Emblems — A583

1972, Feb. 7
1332 A583 90c dk olive & dp car　.50　.30
　11th Winter Olympic Games, Sapporo, Japan, Feb. 3-13.

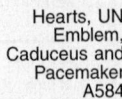

Hearts, UN Emblem, Caduceus and Pacemaker A584

1972, Apr. 8　Engr.　Perf. 13
1333 A584 45c dk car, org & gray　.35　.25
　"Your heart is your health," world health month.

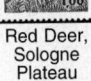

Red Deer, Sologne Plateau A585

Charlieu Abbey A585a

Bazoches-du-Morvand Chateau — A586

Saint-Just Cathedral, Narbonne A587

1972　　　　　　　　Perf. 13
1334 A585　1fr ocher & red brn　.50　.25
1335 A585a 1.20fr sl & dull brn　.65　.25
1336 A586　2fr sl grn, blk & red brn　1.00　.30
1337 A587 3.50fr bl, gray ol & car rose　1.50　.45
　Nos. 1334-1337 (4)　3.65　1.20
　Issued: 1fr, 9/10; 1.20fr, 4/29; 2fr, 9/9; 3.50fr, 4/8.
　For surcharge see Reunion No. 388.

Eagle Owl — A588

　Nature protection: 60c, Salmon, horiz.

1972
1338 A588 60c grn, ind & brt bl　1.50　.60
1339 A588 65c sl, ol brn & sep　.80　.50
　Issue dates: 60c, May 27; 65c, Apr. 15.

Europa Issue
Common Design Type and

Aix-la-Chapelle Cathedral — A589

1972, Apr. 22　Engr.　Perf. 13
1340 A589 50c yel, vio brn & dk ol　.25　.25

Photo.
Size: 22x36mm
1341 CD15 90c red org & multi　.50　.35
　Nos. 1341 (1)　.50　.35

Bouquet Made of Hearts and Blood Donors' Emblem — A590

1972, May 5　　　　Engr.
1342 A590 40c red　　　.30　.25
　20th anniv. of the Blood Donors Association of Post and Telecommunications Employees. For surcharge see Reunion No. 383.

Newfoundlander "Côte d'Emeraude" — A591

1972, May 6
1343 A591 90c org, vio bl & sl grn　.75　.55

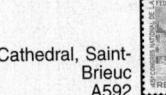

Cathedral, Saint-Brieuc A592

1972, May 20
1344 A592 50c lilac rose　　　.35　.25
　45th Congress of the Federation of French Philatelic Societies, Saint-Brieuc, May 21-22.

Hand Holding Symbol of Postal Code — A593

1972, June 3　Typo.　Perf. 14x13
1345 A593 30c green, blk & car　.25　.25
1346 A593 50c car, blk & yel　.30　.25
　Introduction of postal code system. For surcharges see Reunion Nos. 384-385.

Old and New Communications — A594

1972, July 1　Engr.　Perf. 13
1347 A594 45c slate & vio blue　.40　.25
　21st Intl. Congress of P.T.T. (Post, Telegraph & Telephone) Employees, Paris, 7/1-7.

Hurdler and Olympic Rings — A595

1972, July 8
1348 A595 1fr deep olive　　　.50　.25
　20th Olympic Games, Munich, 8/26-9/11.

Hikers and Mt. Aigoual — A596

1972, July 15　Photo.　Perf. 13
1349 A596 40c brt rose & multi　.75　.30
　Intl. Year of Tourism and 25th anniv. of the Natl. Hikers Association.

Bicyclist — A597

1972, July 22　　　　Engr.
1350 A597 1fr gray, brn & lil　1.20　.60
　World Bicycling Championships, Marseille, July 29-Aug. 2.

"Incroyables and Merveilleuses," 1794 — A598

　French History: 60c, Bonaparte at the Arcole Bridge. 65c, Egyptian expedition (soldiers and scientists finding antiquities; pyramids in background).

1972　　　Engr.　Perf. 13
1351 A598 45c ol, dk grn & car rose　.40　.30
1352 A598 60c red, blk & ind　.65　.35
1353 A598 65c ocher, ultra & choc　.65　.35
　Nos. 1351-1353 (3)　1.70　1.00
　. Issued: 45c, Oct. 7; 60c, 65c, Nov. 11.

Champollion, Rosetta Stone with Key Inscription — A599

1972, Oct. 14
1354 A599 90c vio bl, brn red & blk　.50　.30
　Sesquicentennial of the deciphering of hieroglyphs by Jean-François Champollion.

St. Teresa, Portal of Notre Dame of Alençon — A600

1973, Jan. 6　Engr.　Perf. 13
1355 A600 1fr Prus blue & indigo　.50　.30
　Centenary of the birth of St. Teresa of Lisieux, the Little Flower (Thérèse Martin, 1873-1897), Carmelite nun.

Anthurium (Martinique) — A601

1973, Jan. 20　　　　Photo.
1356 A601 50c gray & multi　　　.35　.25

Colors of France and Germany Interlaced A602

1973, Jan. 22
1357 A602 50c multicolored　　　.40　.25
　10th anniv. of the Franco-German Cooperation Treaty. See Germany No. 1101.

Polish Immigrants A603

1973, Feb. 3　Engr.　Perf. 13
1358 A603 40c slate grn, dp car & brn　.40　.25
　50th anniversary of Polish immigration into France, 1921-1923.

Last Supper, St. Austremoine Church, Issoire — A604

Kneeling Woman, by Charles Le Brun — A605

Angel, Wood, Moutier-D'Ahun A606

Lady Playing Archlute, by Antoine Watteau — A607

1973　　Engr.　Perf. 12x13
1359 A604 2fr brown & multi　1.25　.75
1360 A605 2fr dk red & yel　1.25　.75
1361 A606 2fr ol brn & vio brn　1.25　.75
1362 A607 2fr black & multi　1.25　.75
　Nos. 1359-1362 (4)　5.00　3.00
　Issued: No. 1359, 2/10; No. 1360, 4/28; No. 1361, 5/26; No. 1362, 9/22.

Tuileries Palace, Telephone Relays — A608

Oil Tanker, Francis I Lock — A609

Airbus A300-B — A610

1973
1363 A608 45c ultra, sl grn & bis   .30 .25
1364 A609 90c plum, blk & bl   .55 .25
1365 A610 3fr dk brn, bl & blk   1.25 .65
    Nos. 1363-1365 (3)   2.10 1.15
    French technical achievements.
    Issued: 45c, 5/15; 90c, 10/27; 3fr, 4/7.

Europa Issue 1973
Common Design Type and

City Hall, Brussels,
CEPT Emblem — A611

1973, Apr. 14   Engr.   Perf. 13
1366 A611 50c brt pink & choc   .40 .25
    Photo.
    Size: 36x22mm
1367 CD16 90c slate grn & multi 1.25 .75

Masonic Lodge
Emblem — A612

1973, May 12   Engr.   Perf. 13
1368 A612 90c magenta & vio bl   .50 .30
Bicentenary of the Free Masons of France.

Guadeloupe
Raccoon — A613

White
Storks — A614

1973
1369 A613 40c lilac, sepia & olive .35 .25
1370 A614 60c blk, aqua & org red   .50 .25
    Nature protection.
    Issue dates: 40c, June 23; 60c, May 12.

Tourist Issue

Doubs   Clos-Lucé,
Waterfall   Amboise
A615   A617

Palace of Dukes
of Burgundy,
Dijon — A616

Design: 90c, Gien Chateau.

1973   Engr.   Perf. 13
1371 A615 60c multicolored   .30 .25
1372 A616 65c red & purple   .30 .25
1373 A616 90c Prus bl, ind & brn .40 .25
1374 A617 1fr ocher, bl & sl grn .45 .25
    Nos. 1371-1374 (4)   1.45 1.00
    Issued: 60c, 9/8; 65c, 5/19; 90c, 8/18; 1fr,
6/23.
    For surcharge see Reunion No. 387.

Academy
Emblem — A618

1973, May 26
1375 A618 1fr lil, slate grn & red   .50 .30
Academy of Overseas Sciences, 50th anniv.

Racing Car and
Clocks — A619

1973, June 2
1376 A619 60c dk brown & blue   .50 .30
    24-hour automobile race at Le Mans, 50th
anniv.

Five-master
France
II — A620

1973, June 9
1377 A620 90c ultra, Prus bl &
    ind   .90 .45
For surcharge see Reunion No. 386.

Tower and Square,
Toulouse — A621

1973, June 9
1378 A621 50c purple & red brn   .30 .25
    46th Congress of the Federation of French
Philatelic Societies, Toulouse, June 9-12.

Dr. Armauer G.
Hansen — A622

1973, Sept. 29   Engr.   Perf. 13
1379 A622 45c grn, dk ol & ocher .30 .25
    Centenary of the discovery of the Hansen
bacillus, the cause of leprosy.

Ducretet and his
Transmission
Diagram — A623

1973, Oct. 6
1380 A623 1fr yel grn & magenta   .40 .30
    75th anniversary of the first transmission of
radio signals from the Eiffel Tower to the Pantheon by Eugene Ducretet (1844-1915).

Molière as
Sganarelle — A624

1973, Oct. 20
1381 A624 1fr dk red & olive brn   .45 .30
    Moliere (Jean-Baptiste Poquelin; 1622-
1673), playwright and actor.

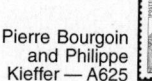

Pierre Bourgoin
and Philippe
Kieffer — A625

1973, Oct. 27
1382 A625 1fr red, rose cl & vio bl .45 .30
    Pierre Bourgoin (1907-70), and Philippe
Kieffer (1899-1963), heroes of the Free French
forces in World War II.

Napoleon, Jean Portalis and Palace of
Justice, Paris
A626

Exhibition
Halls
A627

The Coronation of
Napoleon, by Jean
Louis David — A628

1973   Engr.   Perf. 13
1383 A626 45c blue, choc & gray   .40 .30
1384 A627 60c ol, sl grn & brn   .40 .40
1385 A628 1fr sl grn, ol & claret .55 .40
    Nos. 1383-1385 (3)   1.35 1.10
    History of France. 45c, for the preparation of
the Code Napoleon; 60c, Napoleon's encouragement of industry; 1fr, his coronation.
    Issued: 45c, 11/3; 60c, 11/24; 1fr, 11/12.

Eternal Flame, Arc de
Triomphe — A629

1973, Nov. 10
1386 A629 40c pur, vio bl & red   .40 .30
    50th anniv. of the Eternal Flame at the Arc
de Triomphe, Paris.

Weather Vane — A630

1973, Dec. 1
1387 A630 65c ultra, blk & grn   .40 .30
    50th anniv. of the Dept. of Agriculture.

Human Rights Flame
and Man — A631

1973, Dec. 8   Engr.   Perf. 13
1388 A631 45c car, org & blk   .30 .25
    25th anniversary of the Universal Declara-
tion of Human Rights.

Postal Museum — A632

1973, Dec. 19
1389 A632 50c maroon & bister   .30 .25
    Opening of new post and philately museum,
Paris.

ARPHILA 75
Emblem — A633

1974, Jan. 19   Engr.   Perf. 13
1390 A633 50c brn, bl & brt lil   .30 .25
    ARPHILA 75 Philatelic Exhibition, Paris,
June 1975.
    For surcharge see Reunion No. 390.

Concorde over
Charles de Gaulle
Airport — A634

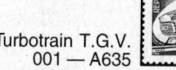

Turbotrain T.G.V.
001 — A635

Phenix Nuclear
Power
Station — A636

1974   Engr.   Perf. 13
1391 A634 60c pur & ol gray   .40 .30
1392 A635 60c multicolored   .85 .40
1393 A636 65c multicolored   .40 .30
    Nos. 1391-1393 (3)   1.65 1.00
    French technical achievements.
    Issued: No. 1391, 3/18; No. 1392, 8/31; 65c,
9/21.

Cardinal
Richelieu, by
Philippe de
Champaigne
A637

Painting by Joan
Miró — A638

Canal du Loing, by Alfred Sisley A639

"In Honor of Nicolas Fouquet," Tapestry by Georges Mathieu — A640

Engr., Photo. (#1395, 1397)
1974   **Perf. 12x13, 13x12**

1394	A637	2fr multicolored	1.25 1.00
1395	A638	2fr multicolored	1.25 1.00
1396	A639	2fr multicolored	1.25 1.00
1397	A640	2fr multicolored	1.25 1.00
		Nos. 1394-1397 (4)	5.00 4.00

Nos. 1394-1397 are printed in sheets of 25 with alternating labels publicizing "ARPHILA 75," Paris, June 6-16, 1975.
Issued: No. 1394, 3/23; No. 1395, 9/14; No. 1396, 11/9; No. 1397, 11/16.
For surcharges see Reunion Nos. 391-394.

French Alps and Gentian — A641

1974, Mar. 30   **Engr.**   **Perf. 13**
1398 A641 65c vio blue & gray   .40 .25
Centenary of the French Alpine Club.

Europa Issue 1974

"Age of Bronze," by Auguste Rodin A642

"Air," by Aristide Maillol A643

1974, Apr. 20   **Perf. 13**
1399 A642 50c brt rose lil & blk   .30 .25
1400 A643 90c olive & brown   .55 .40

Sea Rescue A644

1974, Apr. 27
1401 A644 90c multicolored   .50 .30
Reorganized sea rescue organization.
For surcharge see Reunion No. 395.

Council Building, View of Strasbourg and Emblem A645

1974, May 4   **Engr.**   **Perf. 13**
1402 A645 45c indigo, bister & bl   .30 .25
25th anniversary of the Council of Europe.

Tourist Issue

View of Salers A646

Basilica of St. Nicolas de Porte A647

Seashell over Corsica — A648

Design: 1.10fr, View of Lot Valley.

1974   **Engr.**   **Perf. 13**
1403 A646 65c yel grn & choc   .25 .25
1404 A646 1.10fr choc & sl grn   .45 .30
1405 A647 2fr gray & lilac   .80 .30
1406 A648 3fr multicolored   1.00 .40
    Nos. 1403-1406 (4)   2.50 1.25

Issued: 65c, 6/22; 1.10fr, 9/7; 2fr, 10/12; 3fr, 5/11.

Bison — A649

Giant Armadillo of Guyana — A650

1974
1407 A649 40c bis, choc & bl   .35 .25
1408 A650 65c slate, olive & grn   .35 .25
Nature protection.
Issued: No. 1407, 5/25; No. 1408, 10/19.

Americans Landing in Normandy and Arms of Normandy A651

General Marie-Pierre Koenig — A652

Order of the French Resistance A653

1974
1409 A651 45c grn, rose & ind   .80 .50
1410 A652 1fr multicolored   .50 .35
1411 A653 1fr multicolored   .65 .50
    Nos. 1409-1411 (3)   1.95 1.35

30th anniversary of the liberation of France from the Nazis. Design of No. 1410 includes diagram of battle of Bir-Hakeim and Free French and Bir-Hakeim memorials.
Issued: 45c, 6/8; No. 1410, 5/25; No. 1411, 11/23.
See No. B478.

Pfister House, 16th Century, Colmar — A654

1974, June 1
1412 A654 50c multicolored   .25 .25
47th Congress of the Federation of French Philatelic Societies, Colmar, May 30-June 4.

Chess — A655

1974, June 8
1413 A655 1fr dk brown & multi   .50 .30
21st Chess Olympiad, Nice, June 6-30.

Facade with Statue of Louis XIV, and 1675 Medal — A656

1974, June 15
1414 A656 40c indigo, bl & brn   .30 .25
300th anniversary of the founding of the Hotel des Invalides (Home for poor and sick officers and soldiers).

Peacocks Holding Letter, and Globe A657

1974, Oct. 5   **Engr.**   **Perf. 13**
1415 A657 1.20fr ultra, dp grn & dk car   .50 .30
Centenary of Universal Postal Union.
For surcharge see Reunion No. 396.

Copernicus and Heliocentric System A658

1974, Oct. 12
1416 A658 1.20fr multicolored   .50 .25
500th anniversary of the birth of Nicolaus Copernicus (1473-1543), Polish astronomer.

Tourist Issue

Palace of Justice, Rouen A659

Saint-Pol-de-Leon A660

Chateau de Rochechouart A661

1975   **Engr.**   **Perf. 13**
1417 A659 85c multicolored   .50 .30
1418 A660 1.20fr bl, bis & choc   .50 .30
1419 A661 1.40fr brn, ind & grn   .60 .30
    Nos. 1417-1419 (3)   1.60 .90

Issued: 85c, 1/25; 1.20fr, 1/18; 1.40fr, 1/11.

Snowy Egret — A662

1975, Feb. 15   **Engr.**   **Perf. 13**
1420 A662 70c brt blue & bister   .40 .30
Nature protection.

Gallic Coin — A663

1975, Feb. 16   **Typo.**   **Perf. 13½x14**
1421 A663 42c orange & mag   .90 .45
1422 A663 48c lt bl & red brn   1.00 .70
1423 A663 70c brt pink & red   1.75 1.00
1424 A663 1.35fr lt green & brn   2.40 1.25
    Nos. 1421-1424 (4)   6.05 3.40

Nos. 1421-1424 are known only precanceled. See second note after No. 132. See Nos. 1460-1463, 1487-1490.

The Eye — A664

Ionic Capital — A665

Graphic Art — A666

Ceres — A667

1975   **Engr.**   **Perf. 13**
1425 A664 1fr red, pur & org   .45 .30
1426 A665 2fr grn, sl grn & mag   .80 .55
1427 A666 3fr dk car & ol grn   1.25 .90
1428 A667 4fr red, sl grn & bis   1.60 1.25
    Nos. 1425-1428 (4)   4.10 3.00

Souvenir Sheet

1429   Sheet of 4   7.50 7.50
   a. A664 2fr dp car & slate blue   1.00 1.00
   b. A665 3fr brt bl, sl bl & dp car   1.40 1.40
   c. A666 4fr slate blue, brt bl & plum   2.00 2.00
   d. A667 6fr brt bl, sl bl & plum   2.50 2.50

ARPHILA 75, Intl. Philatelic Exhibition, Paris, 6/6-16. Issued: 1fr, 3/1; 2fr, 3/22; 3fr, 4/19; 4fr, 5/17; No. 1429, 4/2.

Pres. Georges
Pompidou — A668

1975, Apr. 3   Engr.   Perf. 13
1430 A668 80c black & gray   .40   .25
Georges Pompidou (1911-74), President of
France, 1969-74.

Paul as Harlequin, by
Picasso — A669

Europa; 1.20fr, Woman on Balcony, by Kees
van Dongen

1975, Apr. 26   Photo.   Perf. 13
1431 A669 80c multi   .45   .35
1432 A669 1.20fr multi, horiz.   .80   .70

Machines, Globe,
Emblem — A670

1975, May 3   Engr.
1433 A670 1.20fr blue, blk & red   .50   .30
World Machine Tool Exhib., Paris, 6/7-26.

Senate Assembly
Hall — A671

1975, May 24   Engr.   Perf. 13
1434 A671 1.20fr olive & dk car   .50   .30
Centenary of the Senate of the Republic.

Meter Convention Document, Atom
Diagram and Waves
A672

1975, May 31
1435 A672 1fr multicolored   .50   .30
Cent. of Intl. Meter Convention, Paris, 1875.

Metro Regional
Train — A673

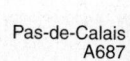

"Gazelle"
Helicopter — A674

1975
1436 A673 1fr blue & brt bl   .55   .30
1437 A674 1.30fr vio bl & grn   .60   .40
French technical achievements.
Issue dates: 1fr, June 21; 1.30fr, May 31.

Youth and Flasks,
Symbols of Study and
Growth — A675

1975, June 21
1438 A675 70c red pur & blk   .30   .25
Student Health Foundation.

People's Theater,
Bussang, and
Maurice
Pottecher — A676

1975, Aug. 9   Engr.   Perf. 13
1439 A676 85c multicolored   .35   .25
80th anniversary of the People's Theater at
Bussang, founded by Maurice Pottecher.

Regions of France

Central
France — A677

Limousin
A679

Aquitaine
A678

Picardy
A680

Burgundy
A681

Loire
A682

Guyana
A683

Auvergne
A684

Poitou-
Charentes
A685

Southern
Pyrenees — A686

Pas-de-Calais
A687

1975-76   Engr.   Perf. 13
1440 A677 25c blue & yel grn   .25   .25
1441 A678 60c multicolored   .25   .25
1442 A679 70c multicolored   .50   .35
1443 A680 85c bl, grn & org   .70   .35
1444 A681 1fr red, yel & mar   .70   .35

1445 A682 1.15fr bl, bis & grn   .70   .35
1446 A683 1.25fr multicolored   .65   .50
1447 A684 1.30fr dk bl & red   .85   .50
1448 A685 1.90fr sl, ol & Prus
             bl   1.00   .50
1449 A686 2.20fr multicolored   1.10 1.00
1450 A687 2.80fr car, bl & blk   1.40 1.00
       Nos. 1440-1450 (11)   8.10 5.40

Issued: 85c, 11/15; 1fr, 10/25; 1.15fr, 9/6;
1.30fr, 10/4/75; 1.90fr, 12/6; 2.80fr, 12/13;
25c, 1/31/76; 2.20fr, 1/10/76; 60c, 5/22/76;
70c, 5/29/76; 1.25fr, 10/16/76.

A690

French Flag, F.-H. Manhes, Jean Verneau,
Pierre Kaan

1975, Sept. 27
1453 A690 1fr multicolored   .60   .30
Liberation of concentration camps, 30th
anniversary. F.-H. Manhes (1889-1959), Jean
Verneau (1890-1944) and Pierre Kaan (1903-
1945) were French resistance leaders, imprisoned in concentration camps.

A691

Monument, by Joseph Riviere.

1975, Oct. 11
1454 A691 70c multicolored   .45   .30
Land Mine Demolition Service, 30th anniversary. Monument was erected in Alsace to
honor land mine victims.

Symbols of
Suburban
Living — A692

1975, Oct. 18
1455 A692 1.70fr brown, bl & grn   .75   .50
Creation of new towns.

Women and
Rainbow — A693

1975, Nov. 8   Photo.
1456 A693 1.20fr silver & multi   .50   .40
International Women's Year 1975.

Saint-Nazaire
Bridge — A694

1975, Nov. 8   Engr.
1457 A694 1.40fr bl, ind & grn   .60   .30

French and Russian
Flags — A695

1975, Nov. 22
1458 A695 1.20fr bl, red & ocher   .50   .30
Franco-Soviet diplomatic relations, 50th
anniv.

Frigate
Melpomene — A696

1975, Dec. 6
1459 A696 90c multicolored   1.00   .50

Gallic Coin Type of 1975

1976, Jan. 1   Typo.   Perf. 13½x14
1460 A663 50c lt green & brn   1.00   .65
1461 A663 60c lilac & brn   1.60   .95
1462 A663 90c orange & brn   2.00 1.25
1463 A663 1.60fr violet & brn   3.75 1.90
       Nos. 1460-1463 (4)   8.35 4.75

Nos. 1460-1463 are known only precanceled. See second note after No. 132.

Lintel, St. Genis
des Fontaines
Church — A697

Venus of
Brassempouy
(Paleolithic)
A698

"The Joy of Life,"
by Robert
Delaunay — A699

Ramses II,
from Abu
Simbel
Temple,
Egypt
A700

Still Life, by
Maurice de
Vlaminck
A701

1976 **Engr.** *Perf. 13*
1464 A697 2fr blue & slate bl 1.10 .60
1465 A698 2fr dk brn & yel 1.10 .60

Photo. *Perf. 12½x13*
1466 A699 2fr multicolored 1.10 .60

Engr. *Perf. 13x12½*
1467 A700 2fr multicolored .80 .50

Perf. 13
1468 A701 2fr multicolored .80 .50
Nos. 1464-1468 (5) 4.90 2.80
Issued: No. 1464, 1/24; No. 1465, 3/6; No. 1466, 7/24; No. 1467, 9/4; No. 1468, 12/18.

Tourist Issue

Chateau Fort de Bonaguil A702

Lodève Cathedral A703

Biarritz A704

Thiers A705

Ussel A706

Chateau de Malmaison A707

1976 **Engr.** *Perf. 13*
1469 A702 1fr multicolored .35 .25
1470 A703 1.10fr violet blue .40 .25
1471 A704 1.40fr multicolored .60 .25
1472 A705 1.70fr multicolored .60 .25
1473 A706 2fr multicolored .90 .25
1474 A707 3fr multicolored 1.10 .25
Nos. 1469-1474 (6) 3.95 1.50
Issued: 1fr, 2fr, 7/10; 1.10fr, 11/13; 1.40fr, 9/25; 1.70fr, 10/9; 3fr, 4/10.

Destroyers, Association Emblem — A708

1976, Apr. 24
1475 A708 1fr vio bl, mag & lem .50 .30
Naval Reserve Officers Assoc., 50th anniv.

Gate, Rouen — A709

1976, Apr. 24
1476 A709 80c olive gray & sal .35 .25
49th Congress of the Federation of French Philatelic Societies, Rouen, Apr. 23-May 2.

Young Person — A710

1976, Apr. 27
1477 A710 60c bl grn, ind & car .35 .25
JUVAROUEN 76, International Youth Philatelic Exhibition, Rouen, Apr. 25-May 2.

Europa Issue

Ceramic Pitcher, Strasbourg, 18th Century — A711

1.20fr, Sevres porcelain plate & CEPT emblem.

1976, May 8 **Photo.** *Perf. 13*
1478 A711 80c multicolored .30 .30
1479 A711 1.20fr multicolored .65 .55

Count de Vergennes and Benjamin Franklin A712

1976, May 15 **Engr.** *Perf. 13*
1480 A712 1.20fr multicolored .50 .30
American Bicentennial.

Battle of Verdun Memorial — A713

1976, June 12 **Engr.**
1481 A713 1fr multicolored .45 .25
Battle of Verdun, 60th anniversary.

Communication — A714

1976, June 12 **Photo.**
1482 A714 1.20fr multicolored .50 .40

Troncais Forest — A715

1976, June 19 **Engr.**
1483 A715 70c green & multi .35 .25
Protection of the environment.

Cross of Lorraine — A716

1976, June 19
1484 A716 1fr multicolored .50 .25
Association of Free French, 30th anniv.

Symphonie Communications Satellite — A717

1976, June 26 **Photo.**
1485 A717 1.40fr multicolored .65 .50
French technical achievements.

Gallic Coin Type of 1975
1976, July 1 **Typo.** *Perf. 13½x14*
1487 A663 52c ver & dk brn .40 .30
1488 A663 62c vio & dk brn 1.00 .70
1489 A663 95c tan & dk brn 1.00 .90
1490 A663 1.70fr dk bl & dk brn 2.75 1.40
Nos. 1487-1490 (4) 5.15 3.30
Nos. 1487-1490 are known only precanceled. See second note after No. 132.

Paris Summer Festival — A719

1976, July 10 **Engr.**
1491 A719 1fr multicolored .50 .30
Summer festival in Tuileries Gardens, Paris.

Emblem and Soldiers — A720

1976, July 8
1492 A720 1fr blk, dp bl & mag .50 .25
Officers Reserve Corps, centenary.

Sailing — A721

1976, July 17
1493 A721 1.20fr blue, blk & vio .50 .25
21st Olympic Games, Montreal, Canada, July 17-Aug. 1.

Marianne Type of 1971-74
1976 **Typo.** *Perf. 14x13*
1494 A555 80c green .40 .25

Engr. *Perf. 13*
1495 A555 80c green 1.25 .50
a. Booklet pane of 10 15.00
1496 A555 1fr carmine rose .50 .25
a. Booklet pane of 5 4.00
b. Booklet pane of 10 8.00
Nos. 1495-1496 (2) 1.75 .75
No. 1495 issued in booklets only. "POSTES" 6mm long on Nos. 1292A and 1494; 4mm on others.
Nos. 1494, 1496 were issued untagged in 1977.

Coil Stamps
1976, Aug. 1 **Engr.** *Perf. 13 Horiz.*
1497 A555 80c green .80 .55
1498 A555 1fr carmine rose .80 .55
Red control number on back of every 10th stamp.

Woman's Head, by Jean Carzou A722

1976, Sept. 18 **Engr.** *Perf. 13x12½*
1499 A722 2fr multicolored .90 .65

Old and New Telephones A723

1976, Sept. 25 **Engr.** *Perf. 13*
1500 A723 1fr multicolored .50 .25
Centenary of first telephone call by Alexander Graham Bell, Mar. 10, 1876.

Festival Emblem and Trophy, Pyrenees, Hercules and Pyrène — A724

1976, Oct. 2
1501 A724 1.40fr multicolored .65 .40
10th Intl. Tourist Film Festival, Tarbes, 10/4-10.

Police Emblem — A725

1976, Oct. 9 **Engr.** *Perf. 13*
1502 A725 1.10fr ultra, red & ol .50 .30
National Police, help and protection.

Atomic Particle Accelerator, Diagram — A726

1976, Oct. 22 **Photo.**
1503 A726 1.40fr multicolored .75 .45
European Center for Nuclear Research (CERN).

"Exhibitions" — A727

1976, Nov. 20 **Engr.** *Perf. 13*
1504 A727 1.50fr multicolored .75 .50
Trade Fairs and Exhibitions.

Abstract Design — A728

1976, Nov. 27 **Photo.**
1505 A728 1.10fr multicolored .50 .40
Customs Service.

Atlantic Museum, Port Louis A729

1976, Dec. 4 Engr.
1506 A729 1.45fr grnsh bl & olive .60 .50

Regions of France

Réunion A730

Martinique A731

Franche-Comté A732

Brittany A733

Languedoc-Roussillon A734

Rhône-Alps A735

Champagne-Ardennes A736

Alsace A737

Photo. (1.45fr, 1.50fr, 2.50fr); Engr.
1977 Perf. 13
1507 A730 1.45fr grn & lil rose .65 .40
1508 A731 1.50fr multicolored .65 .60
1509 A732 2.10fr multicolored .90 .65
1510 A733 2.40fr multicolored 1.10 .35
1511 A734 2.50fr multicolored 1.10 .85
1512 A735 2.75fr Prus blue 1.40 .80
1513 A736 3.20fr multicolored 1.40 .80
1514 A737 3.90fr multicolored 2.50 1.50
　Nos. 1507-1514 (8) 9.70 5.95
Issued: 1.45fr, 2/5; 1.50fr, 1/29; 2.10fr, 1/8; 2.40fr, 2/19; 2.50fr, 1/15; 2.75fr, 1/22; 3.20fr, 4/16; 3.90fr, 2/26.

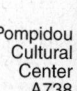

Pompidou Cultural Center A738

1977, Feb. 5 Engr. Perf. 13
1515 A738 1fr multicolored .35 .25
Inauguration of the Georges Pompidou National Center for Art and Culture, Paris.

Dunkirk Harbor — A739

1977, Feb. 12
1516 A739 50c multicolored .25 .25
Expansion of Dunkirk harbor facilities.

Bridge at Mantes, by Corot A740

Virgin and Child, by Rubens — A741

Tridimensional Design, by Victor Vasarely — A742

Head and Eagle, by Pierre-Yves Tremois — A743

1977 Engr. Perf. 13x12½
1517 A740 2fr multicolored .95 .75
　　 Perf. 12x13
1518 A741 2fr multicolored 1.10 .75
　　 Perf. 12½x13
1519 A742 3fr sl grn & pale lil 1.25 .75
　　 Photo.
1520 A743 3fr dark red & blk 1.40 1.25
　Nos. 1517-1520 (4) 4.70 3.50
Issue dates: No. 1517, Feb. 12; No. 1518, Nov. 5; No. 1519, Apr. 7; No. 1520, Sept. 17.

Hand Holding Torch and Sword — A744

1977, Mar. 5 Engr. Perf. 13
1521 A744 80c ultra & multi .45 .30
"France remembers its dead."

Pisces — A745

Zodiac Signs: 58c, Cancer. 61c, Sagittarius. 68c, Taurus. 73c, Aries. 78c, Libra. 1.05fr, Scorpio. 1.15fr, Capricorn. 1.25fr, Leo. 1.85fr, Aquarius. 2fr, Virgo. 2.10fr, Gemini.

1977-78 Engr. Perf. 13
1522 A745 54c violet blue .65 .30
1523 A745 58c emerald 1.00 .40
1524 A745 61c brt blue .55 .30
1525 A745 68c deep brown .85 .35
1526 A745 73c rose carmine 1.50 .80
1527 A745 78c vermilion .65 .35
1528 A745 1.05fr brt lilac 1.50 .75
1529 A745 1.15fr orange 2.25 1.40
1530 A745 1.25fr lt olive grn 1.25 .60
1531 A745 1.85fr slate grn 2.75 1.25
1532 A745 2fr blue green 3.00 1.75
1533 A745 2.10fr lilac rose 1.65 1.00
　Nos. 1522-1533 (12) 17.60 9.25
Issued: 54c, 68c, 1.05fr, 1.85fr, 4/1/77; others, 1978.

Nos. 1522-1533 are known only precanceled. See second note after No. 132.

Village in Provence — A746

Europa: 1.40fr, Brittany port.

1977, Apr. 23
1534 A746 1fr multicolored .45 .25
1535 A746 1.40fr multicolored 1.00 .35

Flowers and Gardening A747

1977, Apr. 23 Engr. Perf. 13
1536 A747 1.70fr multicolored .80 .50
National Horticulture Society, centenary.

Symbolic Flower — A748

1977, May 7
1537 A748 1.40fr multicolored .65 .40
Intl. Flower Show, Nantes, May 12-23.

Battle of Cambray — A749

1977, May 14
1538 A749 80c multicolored .40 .30
Capture of Cambray and the incorporation of Cambresis District into France, 300th anniv.

Carmes Church, School, Map of France — A750

1977, May 14
1539 A750 1.10fr multicolored .50 .30
Catholic Institutes in France.

Modern Constructions — A751

1977, May 21
1540 A751 1.10fr multicolored .50 .30
European Federation of the Construction Industry.

Annecy Castle — A752

1977, May 28
1541 A752 1fr multicolored .50 .30
Congress of the Federation of French Philatelic Societies, Annecy, May 28-30.

Tourist Issue

Abbey, Pont-à-Mousson A753

Abbey Tower, Saint-Amand-les-Eaux A754

Collegiate Church of Dorat A755

Fontenay Abbey A756

Bayeux Cathedral A757

Chateau de Vitré A758

1977 Engr. Perf. 13
1542 A753 1.25fr multicolored .50 .30
1543 A754 1.40fr multicolored .50 .30
1544 A755 1.45fr multicolored .55 .35
1545 A756 1.50fr multicolored .55 .25
1546 A757 1.90fr black & yel .75 .30
1547 A758 2.40fr black & yel .80 .30
　Nos. 1542-1547 (6) 3.65 1.80
　Issued: 1.25fr, 10/1; 1.40fr, 9/17; 1.45fr, 7/16; 1.50fr, 6/4; 1.90fr, 7/9; 2.40fr, 9/24.

Polytechnic School and "X" — A759

1977, June 4 Engr. Perf. 13
1548 A759 1.70fr multicolored .70 .30
Relocation at Palaiseau of Polytechnic School, founded 1794.

Soccer and Cup A760

1977, June 11
1549 A760 80c multicolored .60 .40
Soccer Cup of France, 60th anniversary.

De Gaulle Memorial — A761

Photo. & Embossed
1977, June 18
1550 A761 1fr gold & multi 1.00 .40
5th anniversary of dedication of De Gaulle memorial at Colombey-les-Deux-Eglises.
A €1.16 stamp of type A761 was included in a limited-edition booklet issued Nov. 4, 2020.

Stylized Map of France — A762

1977, June 18   Engr.   Perf. 13
1551 A762 1.10fr ultra & red   .50 .30
French Junior Chamber of Commerce.

Battle of Nancy — A763

1977, June 25
1552 A763 1.10fr blue & slate   .60 .40
Battle of Nancy between the Dukes of Burgundy and Lorraine, 500th anniversary.

Arms of Burgundy — A764

1977, July 2
1553 A764 1.25fr ol brn & slate
grn   .55 .25
Annexation of Burgundy by the French Crown, 500th anniversary.

Association Emblem — A765

1977, July 8
1554 A765 1.40fr ultra, olive & red .65 .25
French-speaking Parliamentary Association.

Red Cicada — A766

1977, Sept. 10   Photo.   Perf. 13
1555 A766 80c multicolored   .40 .30
Nature protection.

French Handicrafts A767

1977, Oct. 1   Engr.   Perf. 13
1556 A767 1.40fr multicolored   .40 .45
French craftsmen.

Industry and Agriculture — A768

1977, Oct. 22
1557 A768 80c brown & olive   .30 .25
Economic & Social Council, 30th anniv.

Table Tennis — A769

1977, Dec. 17   Engr.   Perf. 13
1558 A769 1.10fr multicolored   1.25 .75
French Table Tennis Federation, 50th anniv., and French team, gold medal winner, Birmingham.

Abstract, by Roger Excoffon A770

1977, Dec. 17   Perf. 13x12½
1559 A770 3fr multicolored   1.40 1.00

Sabine, after David — A771

1977-78   Engr.   Perf. 13
1560 A771   1c slate   .25 .25
1561 A771   2c brt violet   .25 .25
1562 A771   5c slate green   .25 .25
1563 A771   10c red brown   .25 .25
1564 A771   15c Prus blue   .25 .25
1565 A771   20c brt green   .25 .25
1566 A771   30c orange   .25 .25
1567 A771   50c red lilac   .25 .25
1568 A771   80c green   .50 .25
  a.   Booklet pane of 10   10.00
1569 A771   80c olive   .50 .25
1570 A771   1fr red   .60 .25
  a.   Booklet pane of 5   7.00
  b.   Booklet pane of 10   10.00
1571 A771   1fr green   .50 .25
  a.   Booklet pane of 10   7.00
1572 A771   1.20fr red   .55 .25
  a.   Booklet pane of 5   5.00
  b.   Booklet pane of 10   8.50
1573 A771   1.40fr brt blue   1.00 .25
1574 A771   1.70fr grnsh blue   .75 .25
1575 A771   2fr emerald   .90 .25
1576 A771   2.10fr lilac rose   1.00 .25
1577 A771   3fr dark brown   1.25 .25
  Nos. 1560-1577 (18)   9.55 4.50

Issued: Nos. 1560-1567, 1573, 1575, 1577, 4/3/78; Nos. 1568, 1570, 12/19/77; Nos. 1569, 1571, 1572, 1574, 1576, 6/5/78.

Coil Stamps

1978   Perf. 13 Horiz.
1578   A771   80c bright green   1.10 .90
1579   A771   1fr bright green   1.50 .90
1579A   A771   1fr bright red   1.10 .90
1579B   A771   1.20fr bright red   1.10 .90
  Nos. 1578-1579B (4)   4.80 3.60

See Nos. 1658-1677, 3527, 4410g, 4520, 5336-5343.
For similar design inscribed "REPUBLIQUE FRANCAISE" see type A900.

Percheron, by Jacques Birr A772

Osprey A773

1978   Photo.   Perf. 13
1580 A772 1.70fr multicolored   1.00 .80
Engr.
1581 A773 1.80fr multicolored   .90 .50
Nature protection.
Issue dates: 1.70fr, Jan. 7; 1.80fr, Oct. 14.

Tournament, 1662, Etching — A774

Institut de France and Pont des Arts, Paris, by Bernard Buffet A776

Horses, by Yves Brayer A777

1978   Engr.   Perf. 12x13
1582 A774 2fr black   1.00 .80
Perf. 13x12
1584 A776 3fr multicolored   1.40 1.25
1585 A777 3fr multicolored   1.40 1.25
  Nos. 1582-1585 (3)   3.80 3.30

Issued: 2fr, 1/14; No. 1584, 2/4; No. 1585, 12/9.

Communications School and Tower — A778

1978, Jan. 19   Engr.   Perf. 13
1586 A778 80c Prussian blue   .40 .25
Natl. Telecommunications School, cent.

Swedish and French Flags, Map of Saint Barthelemy A779

1978, Jan. 19
1587 A779 1.10fr multicolored   .55 .25
Centenary of the reunion with France of Saint Barthelemy Island, West Indies.

Regions of France

Ile de France A780

Tanker, Refinery, Flower, Upper Normandy A781

Lower Normandy A782

1978   Photo.   Perf. 13
1588 A780   1fr red, blue & blk   .45 .25
Engr.
1589 A781 1.40fr multicolored   .60 .30
Photo.
1590 A782 1.70fr multicolored   .80 .30
  Nos. 1588-1590 (3)   1.85 .85
Issued: 1fr, 3/4; 1.40fr, 1/21; 1.70fr, 3/31.

Stylized Map of France — A788

1978, Feb. 11   Engr.   Perf. 13
1596 A788 1.10fr dp ultra & green   .45 .25
Program of administrative changes, 15th anniv.

Young Stamp Collector — A789

1978, Feb. 25
1597 A789 80c multicolored   .35 .25
JUVEXNIORT, Youth Philatelic Exhibition, Niort, Feb. 25-March 5.

Tourist Issue

Verdon Gorge A790

Saint-Saturnin Church A792

Pont Neuf, Paris — A791

Our Lady of Bec-Hellouin Abbey — A793

Chateau D'Esquelbecq A794

Aubazine Abbey — A795

Fontevraud Abbey — A796

1978   Engr.   Perf. 13
1598 A790   50c multicolored   .25 .25
1599 A791   80c multicolored   .35 .25
1600 A792   1fr black   .45 .25
1601 A793   1.10fr multicolored   .50 .25
1602 A794   1.10fr multicolored   .50 .25
1603 A795   1.25fr carmine & brn   .60 .30
1604 A796   1.70fr multicolored   .80 .30
  Nos. 1598-1604 (7)   3.45 1.85

Issued: 1.25fr, 2/18; 50c, 3/6; No. 1601, 3/26; 80c, 5/27; 1fr, 6/10; 1.70fr, 6/3; No. 1602, 6/17.

See No. 5035b.

Fish and Corals — A797

1978, Apr. 15 Photo. Perf. 13
1605 A797 1.25fr multicolored .80 .70
Port Cros National Park, 15th anniversary.

Flowers, Butterflies and Houses — A798

1978, Apr. 22 Engr. Perf. 13
1606 A798 1.70fr multicolored 1.25 .50
Beautification of France campaign, 50th anniv.

Hands Shielding Source of Heat and Light — A799

1978, Apr. 22
1607 A799 1fr multicolored .50 .25
Energy conservation.

World War I Memorial near Lens — A800

1978, May 6
1608 A800 2fr lemon & magenta .50 .30
Colline Notre Dame de Lorette memorial of World War I.

Fountain of the Innocents, Paris — A801

Europa: 1.40fr, Flower Park Fountain, Paris.

1978, May 6
1609 A801 1fr multicolored .40 .25
1610 A801 1.40fr multicolored .75 .30

Maurois Palace, Troyes — A802

1978, May 13
1611 A802 1fr multicolored .45 .25
51st Congress of the Federation of French Philatelic Societies, Troyes, May 13-15.

Roland Garros Tennis Court and Player A803

1978, May 27
1612 A803 1fr multicolored 1.00 .40
Roland Garros Tennis Court, 50th anniv.

Hand and Plant — A804

1978, Sept. 9 Engr. Perf. 13
1613 A804 1.30fr brown, red & grn .50 .25
Encouragement of handicrafts.

Printing Office Emblem — A805

1978, Sept. 23
1614 A805 1fr multicolored .50 .25
National Printing Office, established 1538.

Fortress, Besançon, and Collegiate Church, Dole A806

Valenciennes and Maubeuge A807

1978
1615 A806 1.20fr multicolored .55 .25
1616 A807 1.20fr multicolored .55 .25
Reunion of Franche-Comté and Valenciennes and Maubeuge with France, 300th anniversary.
Issued: No. 1615, 9/23; No. 1616, 9/30.

Sower Type of 1906-1937 and Academy Emblem — A808

1978, Oct. 7
1617 A808 1fr multicolored .45 .30
Academy of Philately, 50th anniversary.

Gymnasts, Strasbourg Cathedral, Storks — A809

1978, Oct. 21
1618 A809 1fr multicolored .50 .30
19th World Gymnastics Championships, Strasbourg, Oct. 23-26.

Various Sports — A810

1978, Oct. 21
1619 A810 1fr multicolored .50 .30
Sports for all.

Polish Veterans' Monument — A811

1978, Nov. 11
1620 A811 1.70fr multicolored .75 .45
Polish veterans of World War II.

Railroad Car and Monument, Compiègne Forest, Rethondes A812

1978, Nov. 11 Engr. Perf. 13
1621 A812 1.20fr indigo .60 .30
60th anniversary of World War I armistice.

Handicapped People — A813

1978, Nov. 18
1622 A813 1fr multicolored .45 .25
Rehabilitation of the handicapped.

Human Rights Emblem — A814

1978, Dec. 9 Engr. Perf. 13
1623 A814 1.70fr dk brown & blue .80 .40
30th anniversary of Universal Declaration of Human Rights.

Child and IYC Emblem — A815

1979, Jan. 6 Engr. Perf. 13
1624 A815 1.70fr multicolored 1.25 .80
International Year of the Child.

"Music," 15th Century Miniature A816

1979, Jan. 13 Perf. 13x12½
1625 A816 2fr multicolored 1.00 .80

Diana Taking a Bath, d'Ecouen Castle — A817

Church at Auvers-on-Oise, by Vincent Van Gogh — A818

Head of Marianne, by Salvador Dali — A819

Fire Dancer from The Magic Flute, by Chaplain Midy — A820

1979 Photo. Perf. 12½x13
1626 A817 2fr multicolored 1.00 .80
1627 A818 2fr multicolored 1.50 .80
1628 A819 3fr multicolored 1.50 1.00
1629 A820 3fr multicolored 1.50 1.00
Nos. 1626-1629 (4) 5.50 3.60
Issued: No. 1626, 9/22; No. 1627, 10/27; No. 1628, 11/19; No. 1629, 11/26.

Orange Agaric — A821

Mushrooms: 83c, Death trumpet. 1.30fr, Olive wood pleurotus. 2.25fr, Cauliflower claveria.

1979, Jan. 15 Engr. Perf. 13
1630 A821 64c orange .40 .25
1631 A821 83c brown .40 .25
1632 A821 1.30fr yellow bister .85 .40
1633 A821 2.25fr brown purple 1.25 .85
Nos. 1630-1633 (4) 2.90 1.75
Nos. 1630-1633 are known only precanceled. See second note after No. 132.

Victor Segalen — A822

1979, Jan. 20
1634 A822 1.50fr multicolored .60 .30
Physician, explorer and writer (1878-1919).

Hibiscus and Palms — A823

1979, Feb. 3
1635 A823 35c multicolored .25 .25
International Flower Festival, Martinique.

Buddha, Stupas, Temple of Borobudur A824

1979, Feb. 24
1636 A824 1.80fr ol & slate grn .85 .40
Save the Temple of Borobudur, Java, campaign.

Boy, by Francisque Poulbot (1879-1946) — A825

1979, Mar. 24 Photo.
1637 A825 1.30fr multicolored .60 .25

Tourist Issue

Chateau de Maisons, Laffitte A826

Bernay and St. Pierre sur Dives Abbeys A827

View of Auray A827a

Steenvorde Windmill A828

Wall Painting, Niaux Cave — A829

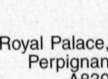

Royal Palace, Perpignan A830

1979		Engr.	Perf. 13	
1638	A826	45c multicolored	.45	.25
1639	A827	1fr multicolored	.45	.25
1640	A827a	1fr multicolored	.55	.25
1641	A828	1.20fr multicolored	.65	.25
1642	A829	1.50fr multicolored	.70	.40
1643	A830	1.70fr multicolored	.75	.60
	Nos. 1638-1643 (6)		3.55	2.00

Issued: 45c, 10/6; No. 1639, 6/16; No. 1640, 6/30; 1.20fr, 6/12; 1.50fr, 7/9; 1.70fr, 4/21.

Honey Bee — A831

1979, Mar. 31 Engr. Perf. 13
1644 A831 1fr multicolored .50 .30
Nature protection.

St. Germain des Prés Abbey — A832

1979, Apr. 21
1645 A832 1.40fr multicolored .60 .30

Simoun Mail Monoplanes, 1935, and Map of Mail Routes — A833

Europa: 1.70fr, Floating spheres used on Seine during siege of Paris, 1870.

1979, Apr. 28
1646 A833 1.20fr multicolored .75 .35
1647 A833 1.70fr multicolored 1.00 .50

Ship and View of Nantes — A834

1979, May 5 Engr. Perf. 13
1648 A834 1.20fr multicolored .55 .30
52nd National Congress of French Philatelic Societies, Nantes, May 5-7.

Royal Palace, 1789 — A835

1979, May 19
1649 A835 1fr car rose & pur .45 .25

European Elections — A836

1979, May 19 Photo. Perf. 13
1650 A836 1.20fr multicolored .55 .25
European Parliament, 1st direct elections, June 10.

Joan of Arc Monument A837

1979, May 24 Engr.
1651 A837 1.70fr brt lilac rose .70 .40
Joan of Arc, the Maid of Orleans (1412-1431).

Felix Guyon and Catheters — A840

1979, June 23
1652 A840 1.80fr sepia & blue .80 .35
Felix Guyon (1831-1920), urologist.

Lantern Tower, La Rochelle — A841

Towers: 88c, Chartres Cathedral. 1.40fr, Bourges Cathedral. 2.35fr, Amiens Cathedral.

1979, Aug. 13 Engr. Perf. 13
1653 A841 68c vio brn & blk .35 .25
1654 A841 88c ultra & blk .40 .25
1655 A841 1.40fr gray grn & blk .65 .50
1656 A841 2.35fr dull brn & blk 1.10 .60
Nos. 1653-1656 (4) 2.50 1.60

Nos. 1653-1656 are known only precanceled. See second note after No. 132. See Nos. 1684-1687, 1719-1722, 1814-1817.

Telecom '79 — A842

1979, Sept. 22
1657 A842 1.10fr multicolored .45 .25
3rd World Telecommunications Exhibition.

Sabine Type of 1977-78

1979-81		Engr.	Perf. 13	
1658	A771	40c brown ('81)	.25	.25
1659	A771	60c red brn ('81)	.25	.25
1660	A771	70c violet blue	.35	.25
1661	A771	90c brt lilac ('81)	.45	.30
1662	A771	1fr gray olive	.45	.25
1663	A771	1.10fr green	.50	.25
1664	A771	1.20fr green ('80)	.40	.25
1665	A771	1.30fr rose red	.55	.25
1666	A771	1.40fr rose red ('80)	.60	.25
1667	A771	1.60fr purple	.75	.30
1668	A771	1.80fr ocher	.80	.50
1669	A771	3.50fr lt ol grn ('81)	1.40	.60
1670	A771	4fr brt car ('81)	1.60	.40
1671	A771	5fr brt grnsh bl ('81)	2.00	.30
	Nos. 1658-1671 (14)		10.35	4.40

Coil Stamps

1979-80			Perf. 13 Horiz.	
1674	A771	1.10fr green	1.25	.60
1675	A771	1.20fr green ('80)	.70	.50
1676	A771	1.30fr rose red	1.25	.60
1677	A771	1.40fr rose red ('80)	.45	.40
	Nos. 1674-1677 (4)		3.65	2.10

Lorraine Region — A845

1979, Nov. 10
1678 A845 2.30fr multicolored 1.00 .30

Gears — A847

1979, Nov. 17 Perf. 13
1680 A847 1.80fr multicolored .80 .30
Central Technical School of Paris, 150th anniv.

Judo Throw — A848

1979, Nov. 24 Engr.
1681 A848 1.60fr multicolored .75 .40
World Judo Championships, Paris, Dec.

Violins — A849

1979, Dec. 10
1682 A849 1.30fr multicolored .60 .35

Eurovision A850

1980, Jan. 12 Engr. Perf. 13x13½
1683 A850 1.80fr multicolored .90 .70

Tower Type of 1979

Designs: 76c, Chateau d'Angers. 99c, Chateau de Kerjean. 1.60fr, Chateau de Pierrefonds. 2.65fr, Chateau de Tarascon.

1980, Jan. 21			Engr.	
1684	A841	76c grnsh bl & blk	.35	.30
1685	A841	99c slate grn & blk	.45	.30
1686	A841	1.60fr red & blk	.75	.55
1687	A841	2.65fr brn org & blk	1.25	.65
	Nos. 1684-1687 (4)		2.80	1.80

Nos. 1684-1687 are known only precanceled. See second note after No. 132.

Self-portrait, by Albrecht Dürer, Philexfrance '82 Emblem — A851

Woman Holding Fan, by Ossip Zadkine — A852

Abstract, by Raoul Ubak — A853

Hommage to J.S. Bach, by Jean Picart Le Doux — A854

Peasant, by Louis Le Nain — A855

Woman with Blue Eyes, by Modigliani A856

Abstract, by Hans Hartung — A857

Engraved, Photogravure (#1691, 1694)

1980		Perf. 12½x13, 13x12½		
1688	A851	2fr multicolored	1.00	.80
1689	A852	3fr multicolored	1.40	1.00
1690	A853	3fr multicolored	1.40	1.00
1691	A854	3fr multicolored	1.40	1.00
1692	A855	3fr multicolored	1.40	1.00
1693	A856	4fr multicolored	1.75	1.25
1694	A857	4fr ultra & black	1.75	1.25
		Nos. 1688-1694 (7)	10.10	7.30

Issued: No. 1688, 6/7; No. 1689, 1/19; No. 1690, 2/2; No. 1691, 9/20; No. 1693, 10/26; No. 1692, 11/10; No. 1694, 12/20.

Giants of the North Festival — A858

1980, Feb. 16			Perf. 13	
1695	A858	1.60fr multicolored	.75	.30

French Cuisine — A859

1980, Feb. 23				
1696	A859	90c red & lt brown	.60	.40

Woman Embroidering — A860

Photogravure and Engraved

1980, Mar. 29			Perf. 13	
1697	A860	1.10fr multicolored	.50	.30

Fight Against Cigarette Smoking — A861

1980, Apr. 5			Photo.	Perf. 13
1698	A861	1.30fr multicolored	.50	.25

Aristide Briand — A862

Europa: 1.80fr, St. Benedict.

1980, Apr. 26			Engr.	Perf. 13
1699	A862	1.30fr multicolored	.60	.30
1700	A862	1.80fr red & red brown	.85	.50

Aristide Briand (1862-1932), prime minister, 1909-1911, 1921-1922; St. Benedict, patron saint of Europe.

Liancourt, College, Map of Northwestern France — A863

1980, May 19			Engr.	Perf. 13
1701	A863	2fr dk green & pur	.80	.30

National College of Arts and Handicrafts (founded by Larochefoucauld Liancourt) bicentenary.

Cranes, Town Hall Tower, Dunkirk — A864

1980, May 24				
1702	A864	1.30fr multicolored	.60	.25

53rd Natl. Congress of French Federation of Philatelic Societies, Dunkirk, May 24-26.

Tourist Issue

Chateau de Maintenon A866

Cordes A865

Montauban A867

St. Peter's Abbey, Solesmes A868

Puy Cathedral — A869

1980			Engr.	Perf. 13
1703	A865	1.50fr multicolored	.55	.30
1704	A866	2fr multicolored	.80	.30
1705	A867	2.30fr multicolored	1.00	.30
1706	A868	2.30fr multicolored	1.25	.30
1707	A869	3.20fr multicolored	1.40	.50
		Nos. 1703-1707 (5)	5.00	1.70

Issued: No. 1703, 4/5; No. 1704, 6/7; No. 1705, 5/7; No. 1706, 9/20; No. 1707, 5/12.

Graellsia Isabellae — A870

1980, May 31			Photo.	
1708	A870	1.10fr multicolored	.70	.30

Association Emblem — A871

1980, June 10			Photo.	
1709	A871	1.30fr red & blue	.55	.25

Intl. Public Relations Assoc., 25th anniv.

Marianne, French Architecture A872

1980, June 21			Engr.	
1710	A872	1.50fr bluish & gray blk	.70	.30

Heritage Year.

Earth Sciences — A873

1980, July 5				
1711	A873	1.60fr dk brown & red	.70	.50

International Geological Congress.

Rochambeau's Landing — A874

1980, July 15				
1712	A874	2.50fr multicolored	1.10	.50

Rochambeau's landing at Newport, R.I. (American Revolution), bicentenary.

Message of Peace, by Yaacov Agam — A875

1980, Oct. 4		Photo.	Perf. 11½x13	
1713	A875	4fr multicolored	1.75	1.00

French Golf Federation A876

1980, Oct. 18			Engr.	
1714	A876	1.40fr multicolored	.60	.30

Comedie Francaise, 300th Anniversary A877

1980, Oct. 18				
1715	A877	2fr multicolored	.75	.40

Charles de Gaulle A878

1980, Nov. 10			Photo.	Perf. 13
1716	A878	1.40fr multicolored	.90	.50

40th anniversary of De Gaulle's appeal of June 18, and 10th anniversary of his death.

Guardsman — A879

1980, Nov. 24			Engr.	Perf. 13
1717	A879	1.70fr multicolored	.80	.45

Rambouillet Chateau — A880

1980, Dec. 6			Engr.	Perf. 13
1718	A880	2.20fr multicolored	1.00	.35

Tower Type of 1979

Designs: 88c, Imperial Chapel, Ajaccio. 1.14fr, Astronomical Clock, Besancon. 1.84fr, Coucy Castle ruins. 3.05fr, Font-de-Gaume cave drawing, Les Eyzies de Tayac.

1981, Jan. 11			Engr.	Perf. 13
1719	A841	88c dp mag & blk	.40	.25
1720	A841	1.14fr ultra & blk	.55	.30
1721	A841	1.84fr dk green & blk	.85	.50
1722	A841	3.05fr brn red & blk	1.40	.80
		Nos. 1719-1722 (4)	3.20	1.85

Nos. 1719-1722 are known only precanceled. See second note after No. 132.

Microelectronics A881

1981			Photo.	
1723	A881	1.20fr shown	.55	.30
1724	A881	1.20fr Biology	.55	.30
1725	A881	1.40fr Energy	.65	.30
1726	A881	1.80fr Marine exploration	.85	.50
1727	A881	2fr Telemetry	.90	.65
		Nos. 1723-1727 (5)	3.50	2.05

Issue dates: No. 1723, 2/5; others, 3/28.

Abstract, by Albert Gleizes — A882

1981, Feb. 28			Perf. 12½x13	
1728	A882	4fr multicolored	1.75	.90

The Footpath by Camille Pissaro
A883

1981, Apr. 18   Engr.   Perf. 13x12½
1729 A883 2fr multicolored   1.00 .80

Child Watering Smiling Map of France — A884

1981, Mar. 14   Engr.   Perf. 13
1730 A884 1.40fr multicolored   .65 .25

Sully Chateau, Rosny-sur-Seine
A885

1981, Mar. 21
1731 A885 2.50fr multicolored   1.10 .40

Tourist Issue

Roman Temple, Nimes — A886

1981, Apr. 11   Engr.   Perf. 13
1732 A886 1.70fr multicolored   .85 .30

Church of St. Jean, Lyon
A887

St. Anne d'Auray Basilica
A888

1981
1733 A887 1.40fr dk red & dk brn   .65 .30
1734 A888 2.20fr blue & black   1.00 .40
Issue dates: 1.40fr, May 30; 2.20fr, July 4.

Vaucelles Abbey — A889

Notre Dame of Louviers — A890

1981
1735 A889   2fr red & black   .90 .40
1736 A890 2.20fr red brn & dk brn   1.00 .50
Nos. 1732-1736 (5)   4.40 1.90
Issue dates: 2fr, Sept. 19; 2.20fr, Sept. 26.

Europa Issue

Folkdances
A891

1981, May 4   Perf. 13
1737 A891 1.40fr Bouree   .65 .25
1738 A891 2fr Sardane   1.00 .40

Bookbinding — A892

1981, Apr. 4   Perf. 13
1739 A892 1.50fr olive & car rose   .70 .40

Cadets — A893

1981, May 16
1740 A893 2.50fr multicolored   1.00 .30
Military College at St. Maixent centenary.

Man Drawing Geometric Diagram
A894

1981, May 23   Photo.
1741 A894 2fr shown   1.00 .75
1742 A894 2fr Faces   1.00 .75
a.   Pair, #1741-1742 + label   2.50 2.00
PHILEXFRANCE '82 Stamp Exhibition, Paris, June 11-21, 1982.

Theophraste Renaudot and Emile de Girardin — A895

1981, May 30   Engr.
1743 A895 2.20fr black & red   1.00 .30
350th anniversary of La Gazette (founded by Renaudot), and death centenary of founder of Le Journal (de Girardin).

Public Gardens, Vichy — A896

1981, June 6
1744 A896 1.40fr multicolored   .65 .30
54th National Congress of French Federation of Philatelic Societies, Vichy.

Higher National College for Commercial Studies Centenary
A897

1981, June 20   Perf. 13
1745 A897 1.40fr multicolored   .65 .30

Sea Shore Conservation
A898

1981, June 20
1746 A898 1.60fr multicolored   .75 .55

World Fencing Championship, Clermont-Ferrand, July 2-13 — A899

1981, June 27
1747 A899 1.80fr multicolored   .85 .45

Sabine, after David — A900

1981, Sept. 1   Engr.
1755 A900 1.40fr green   .70 .25
1756 A900 1.60fr red   .80 .25
1757 A900 2.30fr blue   1.40 .85
Nos. 1755-1757 (3)   2.90 1.35

Coil Stamps

1981   Engr.   Perf. 13 Horiz.
1758 A900 1.40fr green   .75 .50
1759 A900 1.60fr red   .75 .50

Highway Safety ("Drink or Drive") — A901

1981, Sept. 5   Perf. 13
1768 A901 1.60fr multicolored   .75 .30

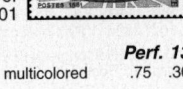

45th Intl. PEN Club Congress — A902

1981, Sept. 19   Perf. 13
1769 A902 2fr multicolored   1.00 .35

Jules Ferry, Statesman — A903

1981, Sept. 26   Perf. 12½x13
1770 A903 1.60fr multicolored   .75 .35
Free compulsory public school centenary.

Natl. Savings Bank Centenary
A904

1981, Sept. 21   Photo.   Perf. 13
1771 A904 1.40fr multicolored   .65 .25
1772 A904 1.60fr multicolored   .75 .25

The Divers, by Edouard Pignon
A905

1981, Oct. 3   Perf. 13x12½
1773 A905 4fr multicolored   1.75 .90

Alleluia, by Alfred Manessier
A906

1981, Dec. 19   Photo.   Perf. 12x13
1774 A906 4fr multicolored   1.75 .90

Tourist Issue

Saint-Emilion
A907

Crest
A908

1981   Engr.   Perf. 13x12½
1775 A907 2.60fr dk red & lt ol grn   1.10 .25
Perf. 13
1776 A908 2.90fr dk green   1.20 .25
Issued: No. 1775, 10/10; No. 1776, 11/28.

150th Anniv. of Naval Academy — A909

1981, Oct. 17   Perf. 13
1777 A909 1.40fr multicolored   .65 .30

A910

St. Hubert Kneeling before the Stag, 15th cent. sculpture.

1981, Oct. 24
1778 A910 1.60fr multicolored   .75 .30
Museum of hunting and nature.

A911

V. Schoelcher, J. Jaures, J. Moulin, the Pantheon.

1981, Nov. 2
1779 A911 1.60fr blue & dull pur   .75 .30

Intl. Year of the Disabled — A912

1981, Nov. 7
1780 A912 1.60fr multicolored   .75 .25

Men Leading Cattle, 2nd Cent. Roman Mosaic A913

1981, Nov. 14   Perf. 13x12
1781 A913 2fr multicolored   1.00 .75
Virgil's birth bimillennium.

Martyrs of Chateaubriant — A914

1981, Dec. 12   Engr.   Perf. 13
1782 A914 1.40fr multicolored   .70 .25

Liberty, after Delacroix — A915

1982   Engr.   Perf. 13
1783 A915 5c dk green   .25 .25
1784 A915 10c dull red   .25 .25
1785 A915 15c brt rose lilac   .35 .35
1786 A915 20c brt green   .25 .25
1787 A915 30c orange   .25 .25
1788 A915 40c brown   .25 .25
  a.   Bklt. pane of 5, 4 No.
     1784, No. 1788 ('87)   1.00
1789 A915 50c lilac   .25 .25
1790 A915 60c lt red brn   .30 .25
1791 A915 70c ultra   .35 .25
1792 A915 80c lt olive grn   .35 .25
1793 A915 90c brt lilac   .40 .25
1794 A915 1fr olive green   .30 .25
1795 A915 1.40fr green   .65 .25
1796 A915 1.60fr green   .75 .25
1797 A915 1.60fr red   .75 .25
1798 A915 1.80fr red   .85 .25
1799 A915 2fr brt yel grn   .85 .25
1800 A915 2.30fr blue   1.50 1.25
1801 A915 2.60fr blue   1.25 1.00
1802 A915 3fr chocolate   1.40 .30
1803 A915 4fr brt carmine   1.75 .30
1804 A915 5fr gray blue   2.25 .25
  Nos. 1783-1804 (22)   15.55 7.45

Coil Stamps
Perf. 13 Horiz.
1805 A915 1.40fr green   1.25 .90
1806 A915 1.60fr red   1.25 .90
1807 A915 1.60fr green   .85 .50
1807A A915 1.80fr red   .90 .50
  Nos. 1805-1807A (4)   4.25 2.80

  Issued: 5c-50c, 1fr-1.40fr, 2fr, 2.30fr, 5fr, No. 1797, 1/2; 1.80fr, 2.60fr, No. 1796, 6/1; 60c-90c, 3fr, 4fr, 11/3.
  See Nos. 1878-1897A, 2077-2080, 3528, 4410h, 4521. For surcharge see No. 2115.

Tourist Issue

St. Pierre and Miquelon A916   Corsica A917

Renaissance Fountain, Aix-en Provence — A918

Collonges-la-Rouge — A919

Castle of Henry IV, Pau — A920   Lille — A921

Chateau Ripaille, Haute-Savoie A921a

1982   Engr.   Perf. 12½
1808 A916 1.60fr dk blue & blk   1.25 .30
1809 A917 1.90fr blue & red   .90 .25
     Perf. 13
1810 A918 2fr multicolored   .90 .40
1811 A919 3fr multicolored   1.25 .40
1812 A920 3fr ultra & dk bl   1.25 .40
  Issued: 1.60fr, 1.90fr, Jan. 9; 2fr, June 21, No. 1811, July 5, No. 1812, May 15.
     Perf. 13x12½
1813 A921 1.80fr dull red & ol   .85 .25
1813A A921a 2.90fr multicolored   1.40 .80
  Nos. 1808-1813A (7)   7.80 2.80
  Issue dates: 1.80fr, Oct. 16; 2.90fr, Sept. 4.

Tower Type of 1979

97c, Tanlay Castle, Yonne. 1.25fr, Salses Fort, Pyrenees-Orientales. 2.03fr, Montlhery Tower, Essonne. 3.36fr, Chateau d'If Bouches-du-Rhone.

1982, Jan. 11   Engr.   Perf. 13
1814 A841 97c olive grn & blk   .45 .25
1815 A841 1.25fr red & blk   .55 .25
1816 A841 2.03fr sepia & blk   .95 .50
1817 A841 3.36fr ultra & blk   1.50 .80
  Nos. 1814-1817 (4)   3.45 1.80

  Nos. 1814-1817 are known only precanceled. See second note after No. 132.

800th Birth Anniv. of St. Francis of Assisi — A922

1982, Feb. 6   Photo. & Engr.
1818 A922 2fr black & blue   .90 .40

Posts and Mankind A923

Posts and Technology A924

1982, Feb. 13   Photo.
1819 A923 2fr multicolored   1.50 1.25
1820 A924 2fr multicolored   1.50 1.25
  a.   Pair, #1819-1820 + label   3.50 3.00
  PHILEXFRANCE '82 Stamp Exhibition, Paris, June 11-21.

Souvenir Sheet

Marianne, by Jean Cocteau — A925

1982, June 11
1821 A925 Sheet of 2   10.00 9.00
  a.   4fr red & blue   4.00 3.50
  b.   6fr blue & red   5.00 4.50
  Sold only with 20fr show admission ticket.

Scouting Year — A926

1982, Feb. 20   Engr.
1822 A926 2.30fr yel grn & blk   1.00 .30

31st Natl. Census — A927

1982, Feb. 27   Photo.
1823 A927 1.60fr multicolored   .75 .25

Bale-Mulhouse Airport Opening — A928

1982, Mar. 15   Engr.   Perf. 13
1824 A928 1.90fr multicolored   .90 .50

Fight Against Racism — A929

1982, Mar. 20
1825 A929 2.30fr brn & red org   1.00 .50

Blacksmith — A930

1982, Apr. 17
1826 A930 1.40fr multicolored   .65 .40

Europa 1982 — A931

1982, Apr. 24
1827 A931 1.60fr Treaty of Rome, 1957   .90 .30
1828 A931 2.30fr Treaty of Verdun, 843   1.20 .40

1982 World Cup — A932

1982, Apr. 28
1829 A932 1.80fr multicolored   .90 .30

Young Greek Soldier, Hellenic Sculpture, Agde — A933

1982, May 15   Perf. 12½x13
1830 A933 4fr multicolored   1.90 1.00

Embarkation for Ostia, by Claude Gellee A934

The Lacemaker, by Vermeer — A935

Turkish Chamber, by Balthus A936

1982   Photo.   Perf. 13x12½, 12½x13
1831 A934 4fr multicolored   1.90 1.00
1832 A935 4fr multicolored   1.90 1.00
1833 A936 4fr multicolored   1.90 1.00
  Nos. 1831-1833 (3)   5.70 3.00
  Issued: No. 1831, 6/19; No. 1832, 9/4; No. 1833, 11/6.

35th Intl. Film Festival, Cannes — A937

1982, May 15   Photo.   Perf. 13
1834 A937 2.30fr multicolored   1.00 .75

Natl. Space Studies Center, 20th Anniv. — A938

1982, May 15   Engr.
1835 A938 2.60fr multicolored   1.20 .50

A939

1982, June 4   Photo.
1836 A939 2.60fr multicolored   1.20 .50
  Industrialized Countries' Summit Meeting, Versailles, June 4-6.

A940

1982, June 4   Engr.   Perf. 13
1837 A940 1.60fr ol grn & dk grn   .75 .25
  Jules Valles (1832-1885), writer.

Frederic and Irene Curie, Radiation Diagrams — A941

1982, June 26
1838 A941 1.80fr multicolored   .85 .30

Electric Street Lighting Centenary A942

1982, July 10
1839 A942 1.80fr dk blue & vio   .90 .30

The Family, by Marc Boyan — A943

Photogravure and Engraved
1982, Sept. 18   Perf. 12½x13
1840 A943 4fr multicolored   1.75 1.00

Natl. Fed. of Firemen, Cent. — A944

1982, Sept. 18   Engr.   Perf. 13
1841 A944 3.30fr red & sepia   1.60 .40

Marionettes — A945

1982, Sept. 25
1842 A945 1.80fr multicolored   .90 .30

Rugby — A946

1982, Oct. 9
1843 A946 1.60fr multicolored   1.50 .30

Higher Education A947

1982, Oct. 16
1844 A947 1.80fr red & black   .90 .30

TB Bacillus Centenary A948

1982, Nov. 13
1845 A948 2.60fr red & black   1.10 .40

St. Teresa of Avila (1515-82) — A949

1982, Nov. 20
1846 A949 2.10fr multicolored   1.00 .45

Leon Blum (1872-1950), Politician — A950

1982, Dec. 18   Engr.   Perf. 13
1847 A950 1.80fr dk brn & brn   .85 .25

Cavelier de la Salle (1643-1687), Explorer — A951

1982, Dec. 18   Perf. 13x12½
1848 A951 3.25fr multicolored   1.25 .50

Spring — A952

1983, Jan. 17   Engr.   Perf. 13
1849 A952 1.05fr shown   .45 .25
1850 A952 1.35fr Summer   .50 .30
1851 A952 2.19fr Autumn   1.00 .75
1852 A952 3.63fr Winter   1.40 1.10
    Nos. 1849-1852 (4)   3.35 2.40

Nos. 1849-1852 known only precanceled. See second note after No. 132.

Provence-Alpes-Cote d'Azur — A953

Brantome (Perigord) A954

Concarneau A955

Noirlac Abbey — A956

1983   Photo.   Perf. 13
1853 A953 1fr multicolored   .45 .25
         Engr.
         Perf. 13x12½
1854 A954 1.80fr multicolored   .85 .25
         Perf. 13
1855 A955 3fr multicolored   1.25 .60
         Perf. 13x12½
1856 A956 3.60fr multicolored   1.60 .30
Issued: 1fr, 1/8; 1.80fr, 2/5; 3fr, 6/11; 3.60fr, 7/2.

Jarnac — A957

Charleville-Mezieres — A958

1983   Perf. 13x12½
1857 A957 2fr multicolored   .90 .35
1858 A958 3.10fr multicolored   1.40 .85
    Nos. 1853-1858 (6)   6.45 2.60
Issued: 2fr, Oct. 8; 3.10fr, Sept. 17.

Martin Luther (1483-1546) — A959

1983, Feb. 12   Engr.   Perf. 13
1859 A959 3.30fr dk brn & tan   1.40 .55

Alliance Francaise Centenary A960

1983, Feb. 19
1860 A960 1.80fr multicolored   .85 .30

Danielle Casanova (d. 1942), Resistance Leader — A961

1983, Mar. 8
1861 A961 3fr blk & red brn   1.25 .30

World Communications Year — A962

1983, Mar. 12   Photo.
1862 A962 2.60fr multicolored   1.10 .65

Manned Flight Bicentenary A963

1983, Mar. 19   Photo.   Perf. 13
1863   2fr Hot air balloon   .80 .55
1864   3fr Hydrogen balloon   1.25 .70
a.   A963 Pair, #1863-1864 + label   2.25 2.25

Female Nude, by Raphael — A964

Aurora-Set, by Dewasne A965

1983   Engr.   Perf. 13
1865 A964 4fr multicolored   1.75 1.00
         Photo.
1866 A965 4fr multicolored   1.75 1.00
Issued: No. 1866, 3/19; No. 1865, 4/9.

Illustration from Perrault's Folk Tales, by Gustave Dore — A966

1983, June 18   Engr.   Perf. 13
1867 A966 4fr red & black   1.75 1.00

Homage to Jean Effel — A967

1983, Oct. 15
1868 A967 4fr multicolored   1.75 1.00

Le Lapin Agile, by Utrillo A968

1983, Dec. 3   Perf. 13x12½
1869 A968 4fr multicolored   1.75 1.00

Thistle — A969

1983, Apr. 23   Engr.   Perf. 12½x12
1870 A969 1fr shown   .35 .30
1871 A969 2fr Martagon lily   .80 .30
1872 A969 3fr Aster   1.25 .60
1873 A969 4fr Aconite   1.75 .60
    Nos. 1870-1873 (4)   4.15 1.80

Europa 1983 — A970

1.80fr, Symbolic shutter. 2.60fr, Lens-to-screen diagram.

1983, Apr. 29   Perf. 13
1874 A970 1.80fr multi   1.00 .40
1875 A970 2.60fr multi   1.25 .75

Centenary of Paris Convention for the Protection of Industrial Property — A971

1983, May 14   Photo.   Perf. 13
1876 A971 2fr multicolored   .85 .30

French Philatelic Societies Congress, Marseille — A972

1983, May 21   Engr.   Perf. 13
1877 A972 1.80fr multicolored   .85 .35

Liberty Type of 1982

1983-87		**Engr.**	**Perf. 13**	
1878	A915	1.70fr green	.75	.25
1879	A915	1.80fr green	.80	.25
1880	A915	1.90fr green	1.25	.25
1881	A915	2fr red	.90	.25
1882	A915	2fr red	.90	.25
1883	A915	2.10fr red	.95	.25
1884	A915	2.20fr red	2.00	.25
a.	Booklet pane of 10		20.00	
b.	Bklt. pane, #1788, 4 #1884		8.50	
c.	With label ('87)		1.00	.25
1885	A915	2.80fr blue	1.25	.90
1886	A915	3fr blue	1.25	.50
1887	A915	3.20fr blue	1.50	.90
1888	A915	3.40fr blue	1.60	.75
1889	A915	3.60fr blue	1.60	.65
1890	A915	10fr purple	4.50	.25
1891	A915	(1.90fr) green	.90	.25
1892	A915	(2fr) green	.90	.25
	Nos. 1878-1892 (15)		21.05	6.20

Coil Stamps

		Engr.	**Perf. 13 Horiz.**	
1893	A915	1.70fr green	.90	.80
1894	A915	1.80fr green	1.00	.50
1895	A915	1.90fr green	1.25	.30
1896	A915	2fr red	1.00	.30
1897	A915	2.10fr red	1.10	.60
1897A	A915	2.20fr red	1.00	.50
	Nos. 1893-1897A (6)		6.25	3.00

No. 1891 is inscribed "A," No. 1892 "B."

No. 1884c was issued in sheets of 50 plus 50 alternating labels picturing the PHILEX-FRANCE '89 emblem to publicize the international philatelic exhibition.

Issued: 2.80fr, 10fr, No. 1881, 6/1; 1.70fr, 2.10fr, 3fr, 7/1/84; 1.80fr, 2.20fr, 3.20fr, 8/1/85; 3.40fr, No. 1891, 8/1/86; 1.90fr, 9/13/86; No. 1882, 10/15/87; 3.60fr, No. 1892, 8/1/87.

For surcharge see No. 2115.

50th Anniv. of Air France — A973

1983, June 18
1898 A973 3.45fr multicolored 1.50 .85

Treaties of Versailles and Paris Bicentenary A974

1983, Sept. 2 **Perf. 13x12½**
1899 A974 2.80fr multicolored 1.40 .60

Jewelry Making — A975

1983, Sept. 10 **Photo.** **Perf. 13**
1900 A975 2.20fr multicolored .90 .35

30th Anniv. of Customs Cooperation Council — A976

1983, Sept. 22 **Engr.** **Perf. 13x12½**
1901 A976 2.30fr multicolored 1.00 .40

Michaux's Bicycle — A977

1983, Oct. 1 **Engr.** **Perf. 13**
1902 A977 1.60fr multicolored 1.10 .30

Natl. Weather Forecasting — A978

1983, Oct. 22 **Engr.** **Perf. 12½x13**
1903 A978 1.50fr multicolored .70 .25

Berthie Albrecht (1893-1943) A979

1983, Nov. 5
1904 A979 1.60fr dk brown & olive .75 .30
1905 A979 1.60fr Rene Levy (1906-1943) .75 .30

Resistance heroines.

A980

1983, Dec. 16
1906 A980 2fr dk gray & red .80 .25

Pierre Mendes France (1907-1982), Premier.

Union Leader Waldeck-Rousseau A981

1984, Mar. 22 **Perf. 13**
1907 A981 3.60fr multi 1.60 .30

Trade Union centenary.

Homage to the Cinema, by Cesar — A982

1984, Feb. 4 **Engr.** **Perf. 12½x13**
1908 A982 4fr multicolored 1.75 1.00

Four Corners of the Sky, by Jean Messagier A983

1984, Mar. 31 **Photo.** **Perf. 13x12½**
1909 A983 4fr multicolored 1.75 1.00

Dining Room Corner, at Cannet, by Pierre Bonnard A984

Photogravure and Engraved
1984, Apr. 14 **Perf. 12½x12**
1910 A984 4fr multicolored 1.75 1.00

Pythia, by Andre Masson — A985

Painter at the Feet of His Model, by Helion — A986

1984 **Photo.** **Perf. 12x13**
1911 A985 5fr multicolored 2.25 1.00
1912 A986 5fr multicolored 2.25 1.00

Issue dates: No. 1911, 10/13; No. 1912, 12/1.

Guadeloupe A987

Design: Map, West Indian dancers.

1984, Feb. 25 **Perf. 13**
1913 A987 2.30fr multicolored 1.00 .30

Vauban Citadel, Belle Ile-en-Mer A988

Cordouan Lighthouse A989

1984 **Engr.** **Perf. 13**
1914 A988 2.50fr multicolored 1.10 .35
1915 A989 3.50fr multicolored 1.60 .40

Issued: No. 1914, 5/26; No. 1915, 6/23.

La Grande Chartreuse Monastery, 900th Anniv. — A990

Palais Ideal, Hauterives-Drome A991

Montsegur Chateau — A992

1984
1916 A990 1.70fr multicolored .80 .40
1917 A991 2.10fr multicolored .95 .30
1917A A992 3.70fr multicolored 1.60 .40
Nos. 1914-1917A (5) 6.05 1.85

Issued: 1.70fr, 7/7; 2.10fr, 6/30; 3.70fr, 9/15.

Flora Tristan (1803-44), Feminist — A992a

1984, Mar. 8
1918 A992a 2.80fr multicolored 1.25 .50

Playing Card Suits — A993

1984, Apr. 11 **Engr.**
1919 A993 1.14fr Hearts .50 .45
1920 A993 1.47fr Spades .65 .55
1921 A993 2.38fr Diamonds 1.00 .75
1922 A993 3.95fr Clubs 1.60 1.25
Nos. 1919-1922 (4) 3.75 3.00

Nos. 1919-1922 known only precanceled. See second note after No. 132.

450th Anniv. of Cartier's Landing in Quebec — A994

1984, Apr. 20 **Photo. & Engr.**
1923 A994 2fr multicolored .90 .25

See Canada No. 1011.

Philex '84, Dunkirk — A995

1984, Apr. 21 **Perf. 13x12½**
1924 A995 1.60fr multicolored .75 .35

Europa (1959-84) — A996

1984, Apr. 28 **Engr.** **Perf. 13**
1925 A996 2fr red brown .80 .30
1926 A996 2.80fr blue 1.25 .50

2nd European Parliament Election — A997

1984, Mar. 24 **Photo.** **Perf. 13**
1927 A997 2fr multicolored .90 .25

Foreign Legion — A998

1984, Apr. 30 **Engr.** **Perf. 13x12½**
1928 A998 3.10fr multicolored 1.40 .50

40th Anniv. of Liberation — A999

Photogravure and Engraved
1984, May 8 **Perf. 12½x13**
1929 A999 2fr Resistance .85 .50
1930 A999 3fr Landing 1.25 .60
a. Pair, #1929-1930 + label 2.50 2.00

Olympic Events A1000

1984, June 1 **Perf. 13**
1931 A1000 4fr multicolored 1.75 1.00

Intl. Olympic Committee, 90th anniv. and 1984 Summer Olympics.

Engraving — A1001

1984, June 8   **Engr.**
1932 A1001 2fr multicolored   .90 .25
        See No. 5864.

Bordeaux
A1002

1984, June 9   **Perf. 13x12½**
1933 A1002 2fr red   .85 .25

French Philatelic Societies Congress, Bordeaux.

Natl. Telecommunications College, 40th Anniv. — A1003

Design: Satellite, phone, keyboard.

1984, June 16   **Photo.**   **Perf. 13**
1934 A1003 3fr multicolored   1.25 .30

25th Intl. Geography Congress, Paris — A1004

1984, Aug. 25 **Engr.** **Perf. 13x12½**
1935 A1004 3fr Alps   1.25 .45

Telecom I Satellite — A1005

1984, Sept. 1   **Photo.**   **Perf. 13**
1936 A1005 3.20fr multicolored   1.50 .50

High-speed Train Mail Transport A1006

Design: Electric train, Paris-Lyon.

1984, Sept. 8
1937 A1006 2.10fr multicolroed   1.00 .25

Local Birds — A1007

Design: 1fr, Gypaetus barbatus. 2fr, Circaetus gallicus. 3fr, Accipiter nisus. 5fr, Peregrine falcon.

Photogravure and Engraved
1984, Sept. 22   **Perf. 12½x12**
1938 A1007 1fr multi   .45 .25
1939 A1007 2fr multi   .90 .25
1940 A1007 3fr multi   1.40 .75
1941 A1007 5fr multi   2.25 .55
        Nos. 1938-1941 (4)   5.00 1.80

Marx Dormoy (1888-1941) — A1008

1984, Sept. 22 **Engr.** **Perf. 13**
1942 A1008 2.40fr multicolored   1.00 .30

A1009

1984, Oct. 6 **Engr.** **Perf. 12½x13**
1943 A1009 3fr Automobile plans 1.40 .30

100th anniv. of the automobile.

A1010

1984, Nov. 3
1944 A1010 2.10fr multicolored   .95 .30

Pres. Vincent Auriol (1884-1966).

9th 5-Year Plan — A1011

1984, Dec. 8   **Photo.**   **Perf. 13**
1945 A1011 2.10fr dk blue & scar .95 .25

French Language Promotion — A1012

1985, Jan. 15 **Engr.** **Perf. 12½x13**
1946 A1012 3fr multicolored   1.25 .30

Tourism Issue

View of Vienne — A1013

Cathedral at Montpelier A1014

St. Michel de Cuxa (Codalet) Abbey A1015

Talmont Church, Saintonge Romane — A1016

Solutre — A1017

1985   **Perf. 13x12½**
1947 A1013 1.70fr ol blk & dk
                grn   .75 .25
1948 A1014 2.10fr sepia & org   .90 .25
1949 A1015 2.20fr multicolored   .90 .35
1950 A1016 3fr multicolored   1.25 .55
1951 A1017 3.90fr multicolored 1.50 .40
        Nos. 1947-1951 (5)   5.30 1.80

Issue dates: 1.70fr, Jan. 19; 2.10fr, Mar. 30; 2.20fr, July 6; 3fr, June 15; 3.90fr, Sept. 28.

French TV, 50th Anniv. — A1018

1985, Jan. 26   **Photo.**   **Perf. 13**
1952 A1018 2.50fr multicolored 1.10 .50

Months of the Year — A1019

1985, Feb. 11   **Engr.**
1953 A1019 1.22fr January   .60 .35
1954 A1019 1.57fr February   .70 .40
1955 A1019 2.55fr March   1.25 .90
1956 A1019 4.23fr April   2.00 1.25

1986, Feb. 10   **Engr.**   **Perf. 13**
1957 A1019 1.28fr May   .65 .35
1958 A1019 1.65fr June   .75 .40
1959 A1019 2.67fr July   1.25 1.00
1960 A1019 4.44fr August   2.25 1.60

1987, Feb. 16   **Engr.**
1961 A1019 1.31fr September   .70 .35
1962 A1019 1.69fr October   .75 .40
1963 A1019 2.74fr November   1.25 1.00
1964 A1019 4.56fr December   2.25 1.75
        Nos. 1953-1964 (12)   14.40 9.75

Nos. 1953-1964 are known only precanceled. See second note after No. 132.

St. Valentine, by Raymond Peynet — A1020

1985, Feb. 14 **Photo.** **Perf. 13x12½**
1965 A1020 2.10fr multicolored   .95 .25

Pauline Kergomard (1838-1925) A1021

1985, Mar. 8 **Engr.** **Perf. 13x12½**
1966 A1021 1.70fr int bl & cop red .75 .25

Stained Glass Window, Strasbourg Cathedral A1022

Still-life with Candle, Nicolas de Stael A1023

1985   **Engraved**   **Perf. 12x13**
1967 A1022 5fr multicolored   2.25 1.25

Photo.
Perf. 13x12
1968 A1023 5fr multicolored   2.25 1.00

Issue dates: No. 1967, 4/13; No. 1968, 6/1.

Untitled Abstract by Jean Dubuffet A1024

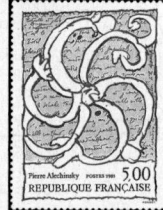

Octopus Overlaid on Manuscript, by Pierre Alechinsky A1025

Photogravure; Engraved (#1970)
1985   **Perf. 13x12½**
1969 A1024 5fr multicolored   2.25 1.00
1970 A1025 5fr multicolored   2.25 1.00

Issued: No. 1969, 10/14; No. 1970, 10/12.

The Dog, Abstract by Alberto Giacometti (1901-1966) A1026

1985, Dec. 7 **Engr.** **Perf. 13x12½**
1971 A1026 5fr grnsh blk & lt lem 2.25 1.00

Housing in Givors — A1027

Contemporary architecture by Jean Renaude.

1985, Apr. 20 **Engr.** **Perf. 13**
1972 A1027 2.40fr blk, yel org & ol
                grn   1.00 .50

Landevennec Abbey, 1500th Anniv. — A1028

1985, Apr. 20   **Perf. 13x12½**
1973 A1028 1.70fr green & brn
                vio   .75 .25

A1029

Europa: 2.10fr, Adam de la Halle (1240-1285), composer. 3fr, Darius Milhaud (1892-1974), composer.

1985, Apr. 27   **Perf. 12½x13**
1974 A1029 2.10fr dr bl, blk, &
                brt bl   .95 .30
1975 A1029 3fr dk bl, brt bl &
                blk   1.40 .50

A1030

1985, May 8   **Perf. 13x12½**
1976 A1030 2fr Return of peace .75 .50
1977 A1030 3fr Return of liberty 1.25 .50
  a. Pair, #1976-1977 + label 2.25 2.00
Liberation of France from German occupation forces, 40th anniv.

Natl. Philatelic Congress, Tours — A1031

Design: Tours Cathedral.

1985, May 25   **Perf. 12½x13**
1978 A1031 2.10fr multicolored .95 .30

Rabies Vaccine Cent. — A1032

Design: Pasteur inoculating patient.

1985, June 1   **Perf. 13x12½**
1979 A1032 1.50fr multicolored .70 .30

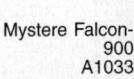
Mystere Falcon-900 A1033

1985, June 1   **Perf. 13**
1980 A1033 10fr blue 4.50 2.00

Lake Geneva Life-Saving Society Cent. — A1034

1985, June 15
1981 A1034 2.50fr blk, red & brt ultra 1.00 .40

UN, 40th Anniv. — A1035

1985, June 26   **Perf. 13x12½**
1982 A1035 3fr multicolored 1.10 .30

Huguenot Cross — A1036

1985, Aug. 31 **Engr.** **Perf. 12½x13**
1983 A1036 2.50fr dp vio, dk red brn & dk red 1.00 .30

King Louis XIV revoked the Edict of Nantes on Oct. 18, 1685, dispossessing French Protestants of religious and civil liberty.

A1037

Trees, leaves and fruit of the beech, elm, oak and spruce varieties: 2fr, Ulmus montana. 3fr, Quercus pedunculata. 5fr, Picea abies.

1985, Sept. 21 **Engr.** **Perf. 12½**
1984 A1037 1fr shown .45 .25
1985 A1037 2fr multicolored .90 .25
1986 A1037 3fr multicolored 1.25 .60
1987 A1037 5fr multicolored 2.25 .30
  Nos. 1984-1987 (4) 4.85 1.40

A1038

La France Mourning the Dead, Eternal Flame.

1985, Nov. 2 **Engr.** **Perf. 12½x13**
1988 A1038 1.80fr brn blk, org & lake .85 .25
Memorial Day.

A1039

1985, Nov. 9   **Engr.**
1989 A1039 3.20fr black & blue 1.25 .40
Charles Dullin, 1885-1949, impresario, theater.

A1040

1985, Nov. 16 **Engr.** **Perf. 13x12½**
1990 A1040 2.20fr red & black .90 .25
National information system.

Thai Ambassadors at the Court of King Louis XIV, Painting — A1041

1986, Jan. 25 **Engr.** **Perf. 13**
1991 A1041 3.20fr rose lake & blk 1.25 .65
Normalization of diplomatic relations with Thailand, 300th anniv.

Leisure, by Fernand Leger — A1042

1986, Feb. 1 **Photo.** **Perf. 13**
1992 A1042 2.20fr multicolored .90 .25
1936 Popular Front, 50th anniv.

Venice Carnival, Paris — A1043

1986, Feb. 12   **Perf. 12½x13**
1993 A1043 2.20fr multicolored .90 .25

La Marianne, Typograph by Raymond Gid — A1044

Photogravure & Engraved
1986, Mar. 3 **Perf. 12½x13½**
1994 A1044 5fr black & dk red 2.25 1.00

Tourism Issue

Filitosa, South Corsica — A1045

Loches Chateau — A1046

Norman Manor, St. Germain de Livet — A1047

Notre-Dame-en-Vaux Monastery, Marne — A1048

Market Square, Bastide de Monpazier, Dordogne — A1049

1986 **Engr.** **Perf. 13**
1995 A1045 1.80fr multicolored .85 .25
1996 A1046 2fr int blue & blk .90 .50
1997 A1047 2.20fr grnsh bl, brn & grn 1.00 .35
1998 A1048 2.50fr henna brn & sepia 1.10 .40
  Perf. 13x12½
1999 A1049 3.90fr blk & yel org 1.75 .90
  Nos. 1995-1999 (5) 5.60 2.40
Issued: 2.20fr, 3/3; 2fr, 6/14; 2.50fr, 6/9; 1.80fr, 3.90fr, 7/5.

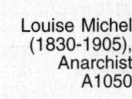
Louise Michel (1830-1905), Anarchist A1050

1986, Mar. 10   **Engr.**
2000 A1050 1.80fr dk red & gray blk .80 .25

City of Science and Industry, La Villette A1051

1986, Mar. 17
2001 A1051 3.90fr multicolored 1.60 .50

Center for Modern Asia-Africa Studies — A1052

1986, Apr. 12 **Photo.** **Perf. 13**
2002 A1052 3.20fr Map 1.25 .25

Skibet, Abstract by Maurice Esteve A1053

Virginia, Abstract by Alberto Magnelli A1054

Abstract, by Pierre Soulages A1055

The Dancer, by Jean Arp — A1056

Isabelle d'Este, by Leonardo da Vinci — A1057

Perf. 12½x13, 13x12½ (#2005, 2006)
1986 **Photo., Engr. (#2005, 2007)**
2003 A1053 5fr multicolored 2.25 1.00
2004 A1054 5fr multicolored 2.25 1.00
2005 A1055 5fr brt vio, blk & brn gray 2.25 1.00
2006 A1056 5fr multicolored 2.25 1.00
2007 A1057 5fr blk, red brn & grnsh yel 2.25 1.00
  Nos. 2003-2007 (5) 11.25 5.00
Issued: No. 2003, 4/14; No. 2004, 6/25; No. 2005, 6/22; Nos. 2006, 2007, 11/10.

Victor Basch (1863-1944), IPY Emblem — A1058

1986, Apr. 28 **Engr.** **Perf. 13**
2008 A1058 2.50fr black & yel grn 1.10 .25
International Peace Year.

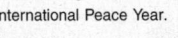
Europa 1986 — A1059

1986, Apr. 28   **Perf. 13x12½**
2009 A1059 2.20fr Civet cat 1.00 .30
2010 A1059 3.20fr Bat 1.40 .60

St. Jean-Marie Vianney, Curé of Ars — A1060

1986, May 3   **Engr.**   **Perf. 13x12½**
2011 A1060 1.80fr sepia, brn org & brn   .80   .25

Philatelic Societies Federation Congress, Nancy — A1061

1986, May 17   **Perf. 13**
2012 A1061 2.20fr Exposition Center   .90   .25

Mens World Volleyball Championship — A1062

1986, May 24   **Engr.**   **Perf. 13**
2013 A1062 2.20fr dk vio, brn vio & scar   .90   .30

Statue of Liberty, Cent. — A1063

1986, July 4   **Perf. 13**
2014 A1063 2.20fr scar & dk blue 1.00   .30
See US No. 2224.

1st Ascent of Mt. Blanc, 1786 — A1064

1986, Aug. 8   **Engr.**   **Perf. 13x12½**
2015 A1064 2fr J. Balmat, M.G. Paccard   .90   .50

Pierre-Louis Moreau de Maupertuis (1698-1759), La Condamine and Sextant — A1065

1986, Sept. 5
2016 A1065 3fr multicolored   1.25   .55

Lapland Expedition, 250th anniv., proved Earth's poles are flattened.
See Finland No. 741.

Marcassite — A1066

1986, Sept. 13   **Perf. 12½**
2017 A1066 2fr shown   .90   .25
2018 A1066 3fr Quartz   1.40   .25
2019 A1066 4fr Calcite   1.75   .70
2020 A1066 5fr Fluorite   2.25   .70
     Nos. 2017-2020 (4)   6.30 1.90

Souvenir Sheet

Natl. Film Industry, 50th Anniv. — A1067

Personalities and film scenes: a, Louis Feuillade, The Vampires. b, Max Linder. c, Sacha Guitry, Romance of the Trickster. d, Jean Renoir, The Grand Illusion. e, Marcel Pagnol, The Baker's Woman. f, Jean Epstein, The Three-Sided Mirror. g, Rene Clair, Women of the Night. h, Jean Gremillon, Talk of Love. i, Jacques Becker, Helmet of Gold. j, Francois Truffaut, The Young Savage.

1986, Sept. 20   **Photo.**   **Perf. 13x12½**
2021 A1067   Sheet of 10   10.00 10.00
   a.-j.   2.20fr any single   1.00   1.00

Scene from Le Grand Meaulnes, by Henry Alain-Fournier (b. 1886), Novelist — A1068

1986, Oct. 4   **Engr.**   **Perf. 12½x13**
2022 A1068 2.20fr black & dk red   .90   .25

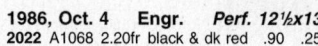

Professional Education, Cent. — A1069

1986, Oct. 4
2023 A1069 1.90fr brt vio & dp lil rose   .85   .25

World Energy Conf., Cannes — A1070

1986, Oct. 5   **Photo.**   **Perf. 13**
2024 A1070 3.40fr multicolored   1.50   .50

Mulhouse Technical Museum — A1071

1986, Dec. 1   **Engr.**
2025 A1071 2.20fr int blue, dk red & blk   1.00   .50

Museum at Orsay, Opening A1072

1986, Dec. 10   **Photo.**
2026 A1072 3.70fr bluish blk & pck bl   1.60   .60

Fulgence Bienvenue (1852-1934), and the Metro — A1073

1987, Jan. 17   **Engr.**   **Perf. 13**
2027 A1073 2.50fr vio brn, brn & dk grn   1.10   .30

A1074

1987, Jan. 24
2028 A1074 1.90fr grn & grnsh blk   .85   .25
Raoul Follereau (1903-1977), care for lepers.

A1075

1987, Mar. 7   **Engr.**   **Perf. 12½x13**
2029 A1075 1.90fr black & red   .85   .25
Cutlery industry, Thiers.

Tourist Issue

Redon, Ille et Vilaine — A1076

Azay-le-Rideau Chateau — A1077

Meuse District A1078

Etretat — A1079

Les Baux-de-Provence — A1080

1987   **Engr.**   **Perf. 13**
2030 A1076 2.20fr dp rose lil, blk & brn ol   1.00   .25
2031 A1077 2.50fr Prus blue & olive grn   1.25   .55

     Perf. 12½
2032 A1078 3.70fr multicolored   1.75 1.40

     Photo.   **Perf. 13**
2033 A1079 2.20fr multicolored   1.00   .25

     Engr.
2034 A1080   3fr dk ol bis & dp vio   1.25   .40
     Nos. 2030-2034 (5)   6.25 2.85

Issued: No. 2030, 3/7; No. 2033, 6/12; 2.50fr, 5/9; 3fr, 6/27; 3.70fr, 5/30.

Charles Edouard Jenneret (Le Corbusier) (1887-1965), Architect A1081

1987, Apr. 11   **Photo.**   **Perf. 13x12½**
2035 A1081 3.70fr Abstract   1.60   .50

Europa 1987 — A1082

Modern architecture: 2.20fr, Metal factory at Boulogne-Billancourt, by architect Claude Vasconi. 3.40fr, Rue Mallet-Stevens housing, by Robert Mallet-Stevens.

1987, Apr. 25   **Engr.**   **Perf. 13x12½**
2036 A1082 2.20fr dk blue & grn   1.00   .50
2037 A1082 3.40fr brn & dk grn   1.50   .65

Abstract Painting, by Bram van Velde A1083

Woman under Parasol, by Eugene Boudin (1824-1898) A1084

Precambrien, by Camille Bryen — A1085

World, Bronze Sculpture by Antoine Pevsner A1086

Perf. 12½x13, 13x12½ (Nos. 2039, 2041)
Photo., Engr. (Nos. 2039, 2041)
1987
2038 A1083 5fr multicolored   2.25 1.00
2039 A1084 5fr multicolored   2.25 1.00
2040 A1085 5fr multicolored   2.25 1.00
2041 A1086 5fr bister & blk   2.25 1.00
     Nos. 2038-2041 (4)   9.00 4.00

Issue dates: No. 2038, 4/25; No. 2039, 5/23; No. 2040, 9/12; No. 2041, 11/14.

Gaspard de Montagnes, from a Manuscript Illustration — A1087

1987, May 9   **Engr.**   **Perf. 13**
2042 A1087 1.90fr dp grn & sepia   .85   .25

Henri Pourrat (1887-1959), novelist.

Natl. Philatelic Societies Congress, Lens — A1088

1987, June 6   *Perf. 13x13½*
2043 A1088 2.20fr choc & red   .90 .30

Involvement of U.S. Forces in WW I, 70th Anniv. — A1089

Design: Stars and Stripes, troops, Gen. John J. Pershing (1860-1948), American army commander.

1987, June 13   *Perf. 13*
2044 A1089 3.40fr olive grn, saph & ver   1.50 .70

A1090

1987, June 17   *Photo.*
2045 A1090 2fr multicolored   .90 .50

6th Intl. Cable Car Transport Congress, Grenoble.

A1091

1987, June 20   *Litho.*
2046 A1091 1.90fr pale chalky blue & blk   .90 .50

Accession of Hugh Capet (c.938-996), 1st king of France, millenary.

A1092

1987, June 20   *Engr.*   *Perf. 12½x13*
2047 A1092 2.20fr multicolored   .90 .30

La Fleche Natl. Military School.

A1093

1987, June 27   *Photo.*   *Perf. 13*
2048 A1093 1.90fr multicolored   .90 .55

World Assembly of Expatriate Algerians, Nice. A 97c stamp of type A1091 was included in a limited-edition booklet issued Nov. 4, 2020.

World Wrestling Championships A1094

1987, Aug. 21   *Engr.*
2049 A1094 3fr brt pur, vio gray & brt olive grn   1.25 .60

Mushrooms — A1095

2fr, Gyroporus cyanescens. 3fr, Gomphus clavatus. 4fr, Morchella conica. 5fr, Russula virescens.

1987, Sept. 5   *Perf. 12½*
2050 A1095 2fr multicolored   .90 .25
2051 A1095 3fr multicolored   1.25 .30
2052 A1095 4fr multicolored   1.75 .60
2053 A1095 5fr multicolored   2.25 .60
   Nos. 2050-2053 (4)   6.15 1.75

William the Conqueror (c. 1027-1087) — A1096

1987, Sept. 5   *Perf. 13*
2054 A1096 2fr Bayeux Tapestry detail   .90 .30

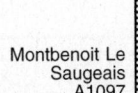

Montbenoit Le Saugeais A1097

Design: Abbey of Medieval Knights, cloisters, winter scene.

1987, Sept. 19
2055 A1097 2.50fr saph, blk & scar   1.10 .55

Pasteur Institute, Cent. — A1098

1987, Oct. 3
2056 A1098 2.20fr dp blue & dk red   .85 .25

Blaise Cendrars (1887-1961), Poet and Novelist — A1099

Pen and ink portrait by Modigliani.

1987, Nov. 6   *Perf. 12½*
2057 A1099 2fr brt grn, buff & blk   .90 .35

Treaty of Andelot, 1400th Anniv. — A1100

1987, Nov. 28   *Perf. 12½x13*
2058 A1100 3.70fr multicolored   1.60 .55

Gen. Leclerc (1902-1947), Marshal of France — A1101

1987, Nov. 28   *Perf. 13x12½*
2059 A1101 2.20fr multicolored   .90 .25

Liberty Type of 1982

1987-90   *Perf. 13*
2077 A915 3.70fr brt lilac rose   1.75 .30
2078 A915 (2.10fr) green ('90)   .95 .25
2079 A915 (2.30fr) red ('90)   1.00 .25
   Nos. 2077-2079 (3)   3.70 .80

Coil Stamp
Engr.
Perf. 13 Horiz.
2080 A915 2fr emerald green   .90 .30

Issued: 2fr, 8/1; 3.70fr, 11/16; Nos. 2078-2079, 1/2.
Nos. 2078-2079 are inscribed "C."

Franco-German Cooperation Treaty, 25th Anniv. — A1102

1988, Jan. 15   *Perf. 13*
2086 A1102 2.20fr Adenauer, De Gaulle   1.00 .30

See Fed. Rep. of Germany No. 1546.

Marcel Dassault (1892-1986), Aircraft Designer A1103

1988, Jan. 23   *Photo.*
2087 A1103 3.60fr brt ultra, gray blk & dk red   1.60 .70

Communications A1104

Angouleme Festival prize-winning cartoons.

1988, Jan. 29   *Photo.*   *Perf. 13½x13*
Booklet Stamps
2088 A1104 2.20fr Pellos   1.00 .40
2089 A1104 2.20fr Reiser   1.00 .40
2090 A1104 2.20fr Marijac   1.00 .40
2091 A1104 2.20fr Fred   1.00 .40
2092 A1104 2.20fr Moebius   1.00 .40
2093 A1104 2.20fr Gillon   1.00 .40
2094 A1104 2.20fr Bretecher   1.00 .40
2095 A1104 2.20fr Forest   1.00 .40
2096 A1104 2.20fr Mezieres   1.00 .40
2097 A1104 2.20fr Tardi   1.00 .40
2098 A1104 2.20fr Lob   1.00 .40
2099 A1104 2.20fr Bilal   1.00 .40
   a.   Bklt. pane of 12, #2088-2099   12.00 8.50

Great Synagogue, Rue Victoire, Paris — A1105

1988, Feb. 7   *Litho.*   *Perf. 13*
2100 A1105 2fr black & gold   .90 .25

The Four Elements — A1106

1988, Feb. 1   *Engr.*   *Perf. 13*
2101 A1106 1.36fr Air   .65 .40
2102 A1106 1.75fr Water   .80 .40
2103 A1106 2.83fr Fire   1.25 1.00
2104 A1106 4.75fr Earth   2.25 1.75
   Nos. 2101-2104 (4)   4.95 3.55

Nos. 2101-2104 known only precanceled. See second note after No. 132.

PHILEXFRANCE '89 — A1107

1988, Mar. 4
2105 A1107 2.20fr #1885, emblem   1.00 .25

Postal Training College, Cent. — A1108

1988, Mar. 29
2106 A1108 3.60fr multicolored   1.60 .40

Philex-Jeunes '88, Youth Stamp Show — A1109

1988, Apr. 8   *Perf. 13x12½*
2107 A1109 2fr multicolored   .90 .25

Blood Donation — A1110

1988, Apr. 9   *Photo.*   *Perf. 13½x13*
2108 A1110 2.50fr multicolored   1.10 .40

Europa 1988 — A1111

Communication and transportation.

1988, Apr. 30   *Engr.*   *Perf. 13*
2109 A1111 2.20fr Cables, satellites   1.00 .30
2110 A1111 3.60fr Rail cars   1.75 .40

Jean Monnet (1888-1979), Economist — A1112

1988, May 10   *Perf. 12½x13*
2111 A1112 2.20fr black & brn ol   1.00 .25

Philatelic Congress, Valence — A1113

1988, May 21   *Perf. 13x12½*
2112 A1113 2.20fr multicolored   1.00 .35

Intl. Medical Assistance A1114

1988, May 28   *Photo.*   *Perf. 13*
2113 A1114 3.60fr multicolored   1.60 .50

Aid to the Handicapped A1115

1988, May 28
2114 A1115 3.70fr multicolored   1.60 .50

No. 1884 Surcharged in European Currency Units

1988, Apr. 16   **Engr.**
2115 A915 2.20fr red   1.00 .25

Tourist Issue

Hermes Dicephalus (Roman Empire), Frejus — A1116

1988, June 12   **Engr.**   **Perf. 13x12½**
2116 A1116 3.70fr multicolored   1.75 .80

Ship Museum, Douarnenez A1117

Chateau Sedieres, Correze A1118

Cirque de Gavarnie A1119

1988   **Perf. 13, 12½x13 (#2118)**
2117 A1117 2fr multicolored   .90 .25
2118 A1118 2.20fr multicolored   1.00 .35
2119 A1119 3fr multicolored   1.25 .40

Issued: 2.20fr, 7/2; 2fr, 7/4; 3fr, 7/23.

View of Perouges, Ain — A1120

1988, Sept. 10   **Perf. 13x12½**
2120 A1120 2.20fr multicolored   1.00 .25
   Nos. 2116-2120 (5)   5.90 2.05

French Revolution, Bicent. A1121

Designs: 3fr, Assembly of the Three Estates, Vizille. 4fr, Day of the Tiles (Barricades), Grenoble.

1988, June 18   **Engr.**
2121 A1121 3fr multicolored   1.25 1.00
2122 A1121 4fr multicolored   1.75 1.00
   a.   Pair, #2121-2122 + label   3.50 3.00

PHILEXFRANCE '89.

Buffon's Natural History — A1122

1988, June 18   **Perf. 12½**
2123 A1122 2fr Otters   .90 .25
2124 A1122 3fr Stag   1.25 .30
2125 A1122 4fr Fox   1.75 .70
2126 A1122 5fr Badger   2.25 .60
   Nos. 2123-2126 (4)   6.15 1.85

Alpine Troops, Cent. — A1123

1988, June 25   **Perf. 13**
2127 A1123 2.50fr multicolored   1.10 .60

Roland Garros (1888-1918), 1st Pilot to Fly Across the Mediterranean, Sept. 23, 1913 — A1124

1988, July 2   **Engr.**   **Perf. 13x12½**
2128 A1124 2fr brt grn bl & olive   .90 .25

A1125

1988, Sept. 10   **Engr.**   **Perf. 13**
2129 A1125 2.20fr brt blue, gray & blk   1.00 .25

Nov. 11, 1918 Armistice Ending World War I, 70th anniv.

Homage to Leon Degand, Sculpture by Robert Jacobsen A1126

1988, Sept. 22   **Perf. 12½x13**
2130 A1126 5fr blk & dp claret   2.25 1.00

French-Danish cultural exchange program, 10th anniv. See Denmark No. 860.

Strasbourg, 2000th Anniv. — A1127

1988, Sept. 24   **Perf. 13**
2131 A1127 2.20fr Municipal arms 1.00 .25

St. Mihiel Sepulcher, by Ligier Richier (c. 1500-1567), Sculptor A1128

Composition, 1954, by Serge Poliakoff (1906-1969) — A1129

La Pieta de Villeneuve-les-Avignon, by Enguerrand Quarton (1444-1466) — A1130

Anthropometry of the Blue Period, by Yves Klein — A1131

1988-89   **Engr.**   **Perf. 13x12½**
2132 A1128 5fr black brown   2.25 1.00
     Photo.
2133 A1129 5fr multicolored   2.25 1.00
2134 A1130 5fr multicolored   2.25 1.00
2135 A1131 5fr multi ('89)   2.25 1.00
   Nos. 2132-2135 (4)   9.00 4.00

Issue dates: No. 2132, 10/15; No. 2133, 10/22; No. 2134, 12/10; No. 2135, 1/21.

Thermal Springs — A1132

1988, Nov. 21   **Engr.**   **Perf. 13x12½**
2136 A1132 2.20fr multicolored   1.00 .25

Metamecanique, by Jean Tinguely — A1133

1988, Nov. 25   **Photo.**
2137 A1133 5fr multicolored   2.25 1.00

See Switzerland No. 828.

UN Declaration of Human Rights, 40th Anniv. — A1134

1988, Dec. 12   **Litho.**   **Perf. 13**
2138 A1134 2.20fr dk bl & grnsh bl 1.00 .25

French Revolution, Bicent. A1135

1989, Jan. 1   **Photo.**   **Perf. 13x12½**
2139 A1135 2.20fr red & vio blue 1.00 .25

A1136

Design: Valentin Hauy (1745-1822), founder of the school for the blind, Paris, 1791.

Photo. & Embossed

1989, Jan. 28
2140 A1136 2.20fr multicolored   1.00 .40

A 97c stamp of type A1136 was included in a limited-edition booklet issued Nov. 4, 2020.

Estienne School, Cent. — A1137

1989, Feb. 4   **Engr.**   **Perf. 12½**
2141 A1137 2.20fr gray, black & red   1.00 .25

European Parliament Elections A1138

1989, Mar. 4   **Litho.**   **Perf. 13**
2142 A1138 2.20fr multicolored   1.00 .25

A1139

1989   **Engr.**   **Perf. 12½x13**
2143 A1139 2.20fr Liberty   1.00 .25
2144 A1139 2.20fr Equality   1.00 .25
2145 A1139 2.20fr Fraternity   1.00 .25
   a.   Strip of 3, #2143-2145 + label   3.00 2.50

Bicent. of the French revolution and the Declaration of Rights of Man and the Citizen. No. 2145a contains inscribed label picturing PHILEXFRANCE '89 emblem.
Issue dates: No. 2143, 3/18; No. 2144, 4/22; No. 2145, 5/27; No. 2145a, 7/14.

French-Soviet Joint Space Flight — A1140

1989, Mar. 4   **Litho.**   **Perf. 13**
2146 A1140 3.60fr multicolored   1.60 .50

Historic Sights, Paris — A1141

Designs: No. 2147, Arche de la Defense. No. 2148, Eiffel Tower. No. 2149, Grand Louvre. No. 2150, Notre Dame Cathedral. No. 2151, Bastille Monument and Opera de la Bastille. No. 2151a has a continuous design.

1989, Apr. 21   **Engr.**   **Perf. 13x12½**
2147 A1141 2.20fr multicolored   1.00 .75
2148 A1141 2.20fr multicolored   1.00 .75
2149 A1141 2.20fr multicolored   1.00 .75
2150 A1141 2.20fr multicolored   1.00 .75
2151 A1141 2.20fr multicolored   1.00 .75
   a.   Strip of 5, #2147-2151   5.00 5.00

Europa 1989 — A1142

Children's games.

1989, Apr. 29   **Perf. 13**
2152 A1142 2.20fr Hopscotch   1.00 .30
2153 A1142 3.60fr Catch (ball)   1.60 .60

ITU Plenipotentiaries Conference, Nice — A1143

1989, May 23 Litho.
2154 A1143 3.70fr dk bl, dl org & red 1.60 .40

Tourist Issue

Fontainebleau Forest — A1144

Vaux le Vicomte A1145

La Brenne A1146

1989, May 20 Engr. *Perf. 13*
2155 A1144 2.20fr multicolored .90 .30
Perf. 13x12½
2156 A1145 3.70fr ol bis & blk 1.60 .75
2157 A1146 4fr violet blue 1.60 .75
Nos. 2155-2157 (3) 4.10 1.80

Issued: 2.20fr, 5/20; 3.70fr, 7/14; 4fr, 8/25.

World Cycling Championships, Chambery A1147

1989, June 3 Litho. *Perf. 13*
2158 A1147 2.20fr multi 1.00 .25

Jehan de Malestroit, Dept. of Morbihan — A1148

1989, June 10 Engr. *Perf. 12½x13*
2159 A1148 3.70fr multicolored 1.60 .55

Preliminary Sketch (Detail) for *Oath of the Tennis Court*, by David A1149

Regatta with Wind Astern, by Charles Lapicque A1150

1989, June 19 Photo. *Perf. 13x12½*
2160 A1149 5fr multicolored 2.25 1.00
Perf. 12½
2161 A1150 5fr multicolored 2.25 1.00

No. 2160 for French revolution bicent.
Issued: No. 2160, 6/19; No. 2161, 9/23.

Souvenir Sheet

Revolution Bicentennial — A1151

Revolutionaries: a, Madame Roland (1754-1793). b, Camille Desmoulins (1760-1794). c, Condorcet (1743-1794). d, Kellermann (1735-1820).

1989, June 26 Engr. *Perf. 13*
2162 A1151 Sheet of 4 4.00 3.50
a.-d. 2.20fr any single 1.00 .60

A1152

2.20fr, 15th Summit of the Arch Meeting of Leaders from Industrial Nations, July 14-16.

1989, July 14 Photo.
2163 A1152 2.20fr multicolored 1.00 .35

Declaration of the Rights of Man and the Citizen, Versailles, Aug. 26, 1789 — A1153

Details of an anonymous 18th-19th cent. painting in Carnavalet Museum: No. 2168a, Preamble, Article I. No. 2168b, Articles VII-XI. No. 2168c, Articles II-VI. No. 2168d, Articles XII-XVII.

Litho. & Engr.

1989, Aug. 26 *Perf. 13x11½*
2164 A1153 2.50fr Preamble, Article I 1.00 .80
2165 A1153 2.50fr Art. II-VI 1.00 .80
2166 A1153 2.50fr Art. VII-XI 1.00 .80
2167 A1153 2.50fr Art. XII-XVII 1.00 .80
a. Strip, #2164-2167 + label 4.50 3.25

Souvenir Sheet
Perf. 13x12½
2168 A1153 Sheet of 4 10.00 10.00
a.-d. 5fr any single 2.25 2.00

No. 2168 contains 4 52x41mm stamps. Sold for 50fr, including admission fee to PHILEX-FRANCE '89.
Value of No. 2168 is for examples on plain paper. Examples on fluorescent paper seem to have been distributed in North America, and may not have been distributed widely or made available in Europe. Value $400.

Musical Instruments — A1154

1989 Litho. *Perf. 12x12½*
2169 A1154 1.39fr Harp .65 .50
2170 A1154 1.79fr Piano .80 .50
2171 A1154 2.90fr Trumpet 1.25 1.00
2172 A1154 4.84fr Violin 2.25 1.75
Nos. 2169-2172 (4) 4.95 3.75

Nos. 2169-2172 are known only precanceled. See second note after No. 132.

See Nos. 2233-2239, 2273-2283, 2303-2306, 2368-2371.

TGV Atlantic — A1155

1989, Sept. 23 Photo. *Perf. 13*
2173 A1155 2.50fr dk bl, sil & red 1.10 .50

Clermont-Ferrand Tramway, Cent. — A1156

1989, Oct. 28 Engr.
2174 A1156 3.70fr blk & dk ol bis 1.75 .40

Villers-Cotterets Ordinance, 450th Anniv. — A1157

1989, Oct. 28 Engr.
2175 A1157 2.20fr blk, dp cl & red 1.00 .25

Baron Augustin-Louis Cauchy (1789-1857), Mathematician A1158

1989, Nov. 10 *Perf. 13x12½*
2176 A1158 3.60fr red, blk & bl grn 1.60 .50

Marshal Jean de Lattre de Tassigny (1889-1952) A1159

1989, Nov. 18 *Perf. 13*
2177 A1159 2.20fr bl, blk & red 1.00 .25

Harki Soldiers of France — A1160

1989, Dec. 9 Photo.
2178 A1160 2.20fr multicolored 1.00 .30

Marianne — A1161

1990-92 Engr. *Perf. 13*
2179 A1161 10c brn blk .25 .25
a. Bklt. pane, #2180, 4 #2179 1.00
2180 A1161 20c lt green .25 .25
2181 A1161 50c brt violet .25 .25
2182 A1161 1fr orange .45 .25
2183 A1161 2fr apple grn .90 .25
2184 A1161 2.10fr dark grn .95 .25
2185 A1161 2.20fr dark grn 1.00 .25
2186 A1161 2.20fr emerald 1.00 .25
2187 A1161 2.30fr red 1.00 .25
a. Bklt. pane, #2180, 4 #2187 5.00
2188 A1161 2.50fr red 1.10 .25
2189 A1161 3.20fr blue 1.50 .75
2190 A1161 3.40fr blue 1.60 .40
2191 A1161 3.80fr lilac rose 1.75 .30
2192 A1161 4fr lilac rose 1.90 .25
2193 A1161 4.20fr lilac rose 1.90 .25
2194 A1161 5fr greenish blue 2.25 .25
2195 A1161 10fr violet 4.50 .25
2196 A1161 (2.20fr) dk grn 1.00 .25
2197 A1161 (2.50fr) red 1.10 .25
Nos. 2179-2197 (19) 24.65 5.45

Coil Stamps
Perf. 13 Horiz.
2198 A1161 2.10fr dk grn 1.00 .25
2199 A1161 2.20fr dk grn 1.00 .60
2200 A1161 2.30fr red 1.00 .25
2201 A1161 2.50fr red 1.10 .25
Nos. 2198-2201 (4) 4.10 1.35
Die Cut
Self-Adhesive
2202 A1161 2.30fr red 1.00 .25
a. Booklet pane of 10 10.00
2203 A1161 2.50fr red 1.10 .25
a. Booklet pane of 10 11.00
b. Booklet pane of 5 5.50
2204 A1161 (2.50fr) red 1.10 .25
a. Booklet pane of 10 11.00
Nos. 2202-2204 (3) 3.20 .75

Issued: No. 2187, 1/2; No. 2198, 1/1; 10c, 20c, 50c, 3.20fr, 3.80fr, 3/26; No. 2202, 1/29; Nos. 2182-2183, 2194-2195, 5/21; Nos. 2196-2197, 8/19/91; 2.20fr, 2.50fr, 3.40fr, 4fr, 9/30/91; Nos. 2179a, 2187a, 2199, 2201, 1991; 4.20fr, 9/24/92; Nos. 2203-2204, 1992; 2.10fr, 1993.
Peelable paper backing serves as booklet cover for Nos. 2202, 2203. No. 2203b has separate backing with no printing.
A €1.16 stamp of type A11161 was included in a limited-edition booklet issued Nov. 4, 2020.
Nos. 2196-2197, 2204 inscribed "D."
See Nos. 2333-2348, 3529, 4410i, 4522.

Lace Work — A1162

1990, Feb. 3 Engr. *Perf. 13x12½*
2205 A1162 2.50fr red 1.00 .40

1992 Winter Olympics, Albertville — A1163

1990, Feb. 9 Photo. *Perf. 13*
2206 A1163 2.50fr multicolored 1.00 .25

Charles de Gaulle (1890-1970) — A1164

1990, Feb. 24 Engr. *Perf. 12½x13*
2207 A1164 2.30fr brt vio, vio bl & blk 1.00 .25

See No. 5947Be.

Max Hymans (1900-1961), Planes and ACC Emblem — A1165

1990, Mar. 3 *Perf. 13*
2208 A1165 2.30fr brt vio, brt bl & dk ol grn 1.00 .25

Profile of a Woman, by Odilon Redon — A1166

Head of Christ,
Wissembourg
A1167

Cambodian
Dancer by
Auguste
Rodin — A1168

Jaune et Gris by
Roger
Bissiere — A1169

1990   Litho.   Perf. 13½x14
2209 A1166 5fr multicolored   2.25 1.00
            Perf. 12½x13
            Engr.
2210 A1167 5fr multicolored   2.25 1.00
2211 A1168 5fr multicolored   2.25 1.00
            Photo.
2212 A1169 5fr multicolored   2.25 1.00
      Nos. 2209-2212 (4)   9.00 4.00

Issue dates: No. 2209, Mar. 3; No. 2210,
June 16; No. 2211, June 9; No. 2212, Dec. 8.

Jean Guehenno (1890-
1978) — A1170

Litho. & Engr.
1990, Mar. 24   Perf. 13
2213 A1170 3.20fr buff & red brn 1.50 .40

Tourism Series

Flaran Abbey,
Gers — A1171

1990, Apr. 21   Engr.   Perf. 13
2214 A1171 3.80fr sepia & blk   1.75 .50

Cluny — A1172

Pont Canal de
Briare — A1173

Cap Canaille,
Cassis — A1174

1990
2215 A1172 2.30fr multicolored   1.00 .25
2216 A1173 2.30fr multicolored   1.00 .25
2217 A1174 3.80fr multicolored   1.75 1.00
      Nos. 2215-2217 (3)   3.75 1.50

Issued: No. 2215, 6/23; No. 2216, 7/7;
3.80fr, 7/14.

Europa
1990 — A1175

Post offices.

1990, Apr. 28   Engr.   Perf. 13
2218 A1175 2.30fr Macon   1.00 .30
2219 A1175 3.20fr Cerizay   1.50 .60

Arab World
Institute — A1176

1990, May 5   Perf. 12½x13
2220 A1176 3.80fr brt bl, dk red
            & dp bl   1.75 .40

Labor Day,
Cent. — A1177

1990, May 1   Photo.   Perf. 13
2221 A1177 2.30fr multicolored   1.00 .25

Villefranche-sur-Saone — A1178

1990, June 2   Engr.   Perf. 13x12½
2222 A1178 2.30fr multicolored   1.00 .25
National philatelic congress.

A1179

1990, June 6   Perf. 13x12½
2223 A1179 2.30fr La Poste   1.00 .25
Whitbread trans-global yacht race.

A1181

1990, June 17   Perf. 12½x13
2225 A1181 2.30fr multicolored   1.00 .25
De Gaulle's Call for French Resistance, 50th
anniv.

Franco-Brazilian
House, Rio de
Janeiro — A1182

1990, July 14   Perf. 13
2226 A1182 3.20fr multicolored   1.50 .70
      See Brazil No. 2255.

A1183

1990, Oct. 6   Engr.   Perf. 12½
2227 A1183 2fr Rutilus rutilus   .90 .25
2228 A1183 3fr Perca fluviatilis 1.25 .25
2229 A1183 4fr Salmo salar   1.75 .40
2230 A1183 5fr Esox lucius   2.25 .40
      Nos. 2227-2230 (4)   6.15 1.30

A1184

1990, Sept. 29   Photo.   Perf. 12½x13
2231 A1184 2.30fr multicolored   1.00 .30
Natl. Institute of Geography, 50th anniv.

Souvenir Sheet

French Revolution,
Bicentennial — A1185

Designs: a, Gaspard Monge. b, Abbe Gre-
goire. c, Creation of the Tricolor. d, Creation of
the French departments.

1990, Oct. 15   Engr.   Perf. 13
2232 A1185 Sheet of 4   4.50 4.00
  a.-d.   2.50fr any single   1.10 .90

Musical Instrument Type of 1989

Designs: 1.46fr, Accordion. 1.89fr, Breton
bagpipe. 3.06fr, Tambourin. 5.10fr, Hurdy-
gurdy.

1990, Sept. 1   Litho.   Perf. 13
2233 A1154 1.46fr multi   .65 .40
2234 A1154 1.89fr multi   .75 .60
2235 A1154 3.06fr multi   1.50 1.50
2236 A1154 5.10fr multi   2.50 2.40
      Nos. 2233-2236 (4)   5.40 4.90

1990, Nov.   Litho.   Perf. 13
2237 A1154 1.93fr like #2169   1.00 .60
2238 A1154 2.39fr like #2170   1.10 .80
2239 A1154 2.74fr like #2172   1.25 1.25
      Nos. 2237-2239 (3)   3.35 2.65

Nos. 2233-2239 are known only precanceled. See second note after No. 132.

Maurice Genevoix (1890-
1980), Novelist — A1186

1990, Nov. 12   Engr.   Perf. 13
2240 A1186 2.30fr lt green & blk 1.00 .25

A1187

1990, Dec. 15   Litho.
2241 A1187 3.20fr dk & lt blue 1.50 .70
Organization for Economic Cooperation and
Development, 30th Anniv.

"The Swing" by
Auguste Renoir
(1841-1919)
A1188

1991, Feb. 23   Engr.   Perf. 12½x13
2242 A1188 5fr multicolored   2.25 1.00

Youth Philatelic
Exhibition,
Cholet — A1189

1991, Mar. 30   Litho.   Perf. 13
2243 A1189 2.50fr multicolored 1.10 .40

Art Series

Le Noeud Noir by
Georges Seurat
(1859-1891)
A1190

Apres Nous La
Maternite, by Max
Ernst (1891-1976)
A1191

Volte Faccia by
Francois
Rouan — A1192

O Tableau
Noir by
Roberto
Matta (b.
1911)
A1193

1991   Engr.   Perf. 12½x13
2244 A1190 5fr pale yellow & blk 2.25 1.00

        Photo.   Perf. 13
2245 A1191 2.50fr multicolored   1.00 .70

        Engr.   Perf. 12½x13
2246 A1192 5fr black   2.25 1.00

        Photo.   Perf. 13x12½
2247 A1193 5fr multicolored   2.25 1.00
      Nos. 2244-2247 (4)   7.75 3.70

Issued: No. 2244, 4/13: No. 2245, 10/10;
No. 2246, 11/9; No. 2247, 11/30.

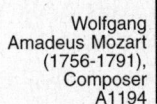

Wolfgang Amadeus Mozart (1756-1791), Composer A1194

1991, Apr. 9   **Photo.**   **Perf. 13**
2248   A1194   2.50fr bl, blk & red   1.10   .60

National Printing Office, 350th Anniv. — A1195

1991, Apr. 13
2249   A1195   4fr multicolored   1.75   .75

Tourism Series

Chevire Bridge, Nantes A1196

Carennac Castle A1197

Pipe Organ, Wasquehal A1198

Valley of Munster — A1199

1991   **Engr.**   **Perf. 13**
2250   A1196   2.50fr multicolored   1.10   .25
     Perf. 12x13
2251   A1197   2.50fr multicolored   1.10   .30
     Perf. 12
2252   A1198   4fr black & buff   1.75   .55
     Perf. 13x12½
2253   A1199   4fr violet   1.75   .55
     Nos. 2250-2253 (4)   5.70   1.65
   Issue dates: No. 2250, Apr. 27; Nos. 2251, 2253, July 6; No. 2252, June 22.

Europa — A1200

   2.50fr, Ariane launch site, French Guiana. 3.50fr, Television satellite.

1991, Apr. 27   **Perf. 12½x13**
2254   A1200   2.50fr multi   1.10   .40
2255   A1200   3.50fr multi   1.60   .55
   Compare with No. 2483.

Concours Lepine, 90th Anniv. — A1201

1991, Apr. 27   **Perf. 13**
2256   A1201   4fr multicolored   1.75   .75
   French Assoc. of Small Manufacturers and Inventors.

Philatelic Society Congress, Perpignan A1202

1991, May 18
2257   A1202   2.50fr multicolored   1.10   .25

French Open Tennis Championships, Cent. — A1203

1991, May 24   **Engr.**   **Perf. 13**
2258   A1203   3.50fr multicolored   1.60   .50

Souvenir Sheet

French Revolution, Bicent. — A1204

   Designs: a, Theophile Malo Corret, La Tour d'Auvergne (1743-1800). b, Liberty Tree. c, National police, bicent. d, Louis Antoine-Leon de St. Just (1767-1794).

1991, June 1   **Engr.**   **Perf. 13**
2259   A1204   Sheet of 4   4.50   3.50
  a.-d.   2.50fr any single   1.10   .80

A1205

1991, June 13   **Photo.**   **Perf. 13**
2260   A1205   2.50fr multicolored   1.10   .40
   Gaston III de Foix (Febus) (1331-1391), general.

Wildlife — A1206

   Designs: 2fr, Ursus arctos. 3fr, Testudo hermanni. 4fr, Castor fiber. 5fr, Alcedo atthis.

1991, Sept. 14   **Engr.**   **Perf. 12½**
2261   A1206   2fr multi   .90   .30
2262   A1206   3fr multi   1.25   .30
2263   A1206   4fr multi   1.75   .70
2264   A1206   5fr multi   2.25   .70
     Nos. 2261-2264 (4)   6.15   2.00

10th World Forestry Congress A1207

1991, Sept. 22   **Engr.**   **Perf. 13x12½**
2265   A1207   2.50fr multicolored   1.10   .25

School of Public Works, Cent. — A1208

1991, Oct. 5   **Litho. & Engr.**   **Perf. 13**
2266   A1208   2.50fr multicolored   1.10   .30
   A €1.16 stamp of type A1208 was included in a limited-edition booklet issued Nov. 4, 2020.

Marcel Cerdan (1916-1949), Middleweight Boxing Champion A1209

1991, Oct. 19   **Photo.**   **Perf. 13**
2267   A1209   2.50fr black & red   1.00   .30

Amnesty International, 30th Anniv. — A1210

1991, Oct. 19
2268   A1210   3.40fr multicolored   1.50   .60

1992 Winter Olympics, Albertville — A1211

1991, Nov. 14   **Engr.**   **Perf. 13**
2269   A1211   2.50fr Olympic flame   1.10   .25

Fifth Handicapped Olympics — A1212

1991, Dec. 7   **Perf. 13**
2270   A1212   2.50fr dk & lt blue   1.10   .25

Voluntary Attachment of Mayotte to France, Sesquicentennial A1213

1991, Dec. 21   **Engr.**
2271   A1213   2.50fr multicolored   1.10   .25

French Pavilion, Expo '92, Seville — A1214

Litho. & Engr.
1992, Jan. 18   **Perf. 13**
2272   A1214   2.50fr multicolored   1.10   .25

Musical Instruments Type of 1989
1992, Jan. 31   **Litho.**   **Perf. 13**
2273   A1154   1.60fr Guitar   60.00   25.00
2274   A1154   1.98fr like
         #2233   3.00   2.25
2275   A1154   2.08fr Saxo-
         phone   1.25   1.00

2276   A1154   2.46fr like
         #2234   1.25   1.00
2277   A1154   2.98fr Banjo   1.50   1.50
2278   A1154   3.08fr like
         #2235   6.00   4.00
2279   A1154   3.14fr like
         #2236   2.00   1.50
2280   A1154   3.19fr like
         #2169   7.00   4.00
2281   A1154   5.28fr Xylo-
         phone   3.00   1.50
2282   A1154   5.30fr like
         #2170   3.00   1.50
2283   A1154   5.32fr like
         #2172   3.00   1.50
     Nos. 2273-2283 (11)   91.00   44.75
     Perf. 12
2273a   A1154   1.60fr Guitar   7.50   4.50
2274a   A1154   1.98fr like #2233   150.00   140.00
2275a   A1154   2.08fr Saxophone   40.00   30.00
2276a   A1154   2.46fr like #2234   12.00   7.50
2278a   A1154   3.08fr like #2235   12.00   7.50
2279a   A1154   3.14fr like #2236   60.00   50.00
2280a   A1154   3.19fr like #2169   8.00   5.00
2281a   A1154   5.28fr Xylophone   30.00   20.00
2282a   A1154   5.30fr like #2170   75.00   60.00
2283a   A1154   5.32fr like #2172   25.00   20.00
     Nos. 2273a-2283a (10)   419.50   344.50
   Nos. 2273-2283 are known only precanceled. See 2nd note after No. 132. See Nos. 2303-2306.

1992 Summer Olympics, Barcelona A1215

1992, Apr. 3   **Photo.**   **Perf. 13**
2284   A1215   2.50fr multicolored   1.10   .25
   See Greece No. 1730.

Marguerite d'Angouleme (1492-1549) — A1216

1992, Apr. 11   **Litho.**   **Perf. 13**
2285   A1216   3.40fr multicolored   1.60   .75

Founding of Ajaccio, 500th Anniv. — A1217

   Virgin and Child Beneath a Garland by Botticelli.

1992, Apr. 30   **Photo.**   **Perf. 13**
2286   A1217   4fr multicolored   1.75   .60

Europa — A1218

   Discovery of America, 500th Anniv.: 2.50fr, Map, navigation instruments. 3.40fr, Sailing ship, map.

1992, May 9   **Engr.**   **Perf. 13x12½**
2287   A1218   2.50fr multicolored   1.25   .30
2288   A1218   3.40fr multicolored   1.75   .60

Intl. Bread and Cereal Congress — A1219

1992, May 30   **Litho.**   **Perf. 13**
2289   A1219   3.40fr multicolored   1.60   .70

Tourism Series

Ourcq Canal — A1220

1992, May 30　Engr.　Perf. 13
2290　A1220　4fr black, blue & grn　1.75　.40

Mt. Aiguille — A1221

1992, June 27　Engr.　Perf. 13
2291　A1221　3.40fr multicolored　1.60　.70
First ascension of Mt. Aiguille, 500th anniv.

Lorient — A1222

1992, July 4　Engr.　Perf. 13
2292　A1222　4fr multicolored　1.25　.25

Biron Castle — A1223

1992, July 4　Perf. 12½x13
2293　A1223　2.50fr multicolored　1.75　.40

Natl. Philatelic Societies Congress, Niort — A1224

1992, June 6　Photo.　Perf. 13
2294　A1224　2.50fr multicolored　1.10　.25
Natl. Art Festival.

1992 Olympic Games, Albertville and Barcelona A1225

1992, June 19　Perf. 12½x13½
2295　A1225　2.50fr multicolored　1.10　.30

Tautavel Man — A1226

1992, June 20　Photo.　Perf. 13
2296　A1226　3.40fr multicolored　1.60　.60

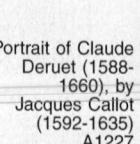

Portrait of Claude Deruet (1588-1660), by Jacques Callot (1592-1635) A1227

1992, June 27　Engr.　Perf. 12x13
2297　A1227　5fr buff & brown　2.25　1.00

Flowers — A1228

2fr, Pancratium maritimum. 3fr, Drosera rotundifolia. 4fr, Orchis palustris. 5fr, Nuphar luteum.

1992, Sept. 12　Engr.　Perf. 12½
2298　A1228　2fr multicolored　.90　.30
2299　A1228　3fr multicolored　1.25　.30
2300　A1228　4fr multicolored　1.75　.60
2301　A1228　5fr multicolored　2.25　.60
　　　Nos. 2298-2301 (4)　6.15　1.80

First French Republic, Bicent. — A1229

1992, Sept. 26　Perf. 13
2302　A1229　2.50fr multicolored　1.10　.25

Musical Instruments Type of 1989

1992, Oct.　Litho.　Perf. 13
2303　A1154　1.73fr like #2273　.80　.25
2304　A1154　2.25fr like #2275　1.00　.50
2305　A1154　3.51fr like #2277　2.00　1.00
2306　A1154　5.40fr like #2281　2.75　1.75
　　　Nos. 2303-2306 (4)　6.55　3.50

Nos. 2303-2306 are known only precancelled. See second note after No. 132.

Proclamation of First French Republic, Bicent. — A1230

Paintings or drawings by contemporary artists: No. 2307, Tree of Freedom, by Pierre Alechinsky. No. 2308, Portrait of a Young Man, by Martial Raysse. No. 2309, Marianne with Body and Head of Rooster, by Gerard Garouste. No. 2310, "Republique Francaise," by Jean-Charles Blais.

1992, Sept. 26　Engr.　Perf. 13
2307　A1230　2.50fr red　1.10　.25
2308　A1230　2.50fr red　1.10　.25
2309　A1230　2.50fr red　1.10　.25
2310　A1230　2.50fr red　1.10　.25
　　　Nos. 2307-2310 (4)　4.40　1.00

Single European Market — A1231

1992, Nov. 6　Photo.　Perf. 12½x13½
2311　A1231　2.50fr multicolored　1.10　.30

First Mail Flight from Nancy to Luneville, 80th Anniv. — A1232

1992, Nov. 12　Perf. 13
2312　A1232　2.50fr multicolored　1.10　.40

Marcel Paul (1900-1982), Minister of Industrial Production — A1233

1992, Nov. 13　Engr.
2313　A1233　4.20fr claret & blue　1.90　.50

Contemporary Art — A1234

No. 2314, Le Rendezvous d'Ephese, by Paul Delvaux, Belgium. No. 2315, Abstract painting, by Alberto Burri, Italy. No. 2316, Abstract painting, by Antoni Tapies, Spain. No. 2317, Portrait of John Edwards, by Francis Bacon, Great Britain.

1992　Photo.　Perf. 13x12½
2314　A1234　5fr multicolored　2.25　1.00
2315　A1234　5fr multicolored　2.25　1.00
2316　A1234　5fr multicolored　2.25　1.00
2317　A1234　5fr multicolored　2.25　1.00
　　　Nos. 2314-2317 (4)　9.00　4.00

Issued: No. 2314, 11/20; Nos. 2315-2317, 11/21.
See Nos. 2379-2390.

Gypsy Culture — A1235

1992, Dec. 5　Photo.　Perf. 13
2318　A1235　2.50fr multicolored　1.10　.25

Yacht "La Poste," Entrant in Whitbread Trans-Global Race — A1236

1993, Feb. 6　Engr.　Perf. 12
2319　A1236　2.50fr multicolored　1.10　.30
See No. 2375.

Water Birds — A1237

1993, Feb. 6　Perf. 12½x12
2320　A1237　2fr Harle piette　.90　.30
2321　A1237　3fr Fuligule nyroca　1.25　.30
2322　A1237　4fr Tadorne de belon　1.75　.60
2323　A1237　5fr Harle huppe　2.25　.70
　　　Nos. 2320-2323 (4)　6.15　1.90

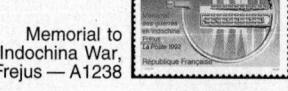

Memorial to Indochina War, Frejus — A1238

Litho. & Engr.
1993, Feb. 16　Perf. 13x13½
2324　A1238　4fr multicolored　1.75　.60

Stamp Day — A1239

1993, Mar. 6　Photo.　Perf. 13
2325　A1239　2.50fr red & multi　1.50　.80
2326　A1239　2.50fr +60c red & multi　1.25　1.00
　a.　Bklt. pane of 4 #2325, 3 #2326 + label　10.00

Mediterranean Youth Games, Agde — A1240

1993, Mar. 13　Photo.　Perf. 13
2327　A1240　2.50fr multicolored　1.10　.25

Human Rights, Intl. Mixed Masonic Order, Cent. — A1241

1993, Apr. 3　Engr.　Perf. 13
2328　A1241　3.40fr blue & black　1.60　.50

Contemporary Art — A1242

Europa: 2.50fr, Painting, Rouge Rythme Bleu, by Olivier Debre. 3.40fr, Sculpture, Le Griffu, by Germaine Richier, vert.

Perf. 13x12½, 12½x13
1993, Apr. 17　Litho.
2329　A1242　2.50fr multicolored　1.10　.30
2330　A1242　3.40fr multicolored　1.60　.80

Marianne Type of 1990

1993-96　Engr.　Perf. 13
2333　A1161　2fr blue　1.00　.25
2334　A1161　2.40fr emerald　1.25　.25
2335　A1161　2.70fr emerald　1.40　.25
2336　A1161　3.50fr apple green　1.60　.30
2337　A1161　3.80fr blue　1.75　.50
2338　A1161　4.40fr blue　2.00　.40
2339　A1161　4.50fr mag　2.00　.40
2340　A1161　(2.50fr) red　1.75　.25
　　　Complete booklet, 10 #2340　17.50
　　　Nos. 2333-2340 (8)　12.75　2.60

Perf. 13 Horiz.
Coil Stamps
2341　A1161　2.40fr emerald　1.10　.60
2342　A1161　2.70fr emerald　1.60　.25
2343　A1161　(2.80fr) red　1.75　.25

Self-Adhesive
Die Cut
2344　A1161　70c brown　13.00　9.00

Serpentine Die Cut Vert.
2345　A1161　70c brown　13.00　9.00
2346　A1161　1fr orange　4.25　2.50
　a.　Booklet pane, 3 #2348, 1 #2346　9.00
　　　Complete bklt., 2 #2346a　20.00

Die Cut
2347　A1161　(2.50fr) red　1.75　.25
　a.　Booklet pane of 10 (see footnote)　17.50
　b.　Bklt. pane of 4 + label　7.00
　c.　Booklet pane, #2344, 3 #2347 + label　30.00
　d.　Booklet pane of 10 (see footnote)　15.00

Serpentine Die Cut 6¾ Vert.
2348　A1161　(2.80fr) red　1.75　.25
　a.　Bklt. pane of 4 + label　7.00
　b.　Booklet pane of 10 (see footnote)　17.50
　c.　Booklet pane, #2345, 3 #2348 + label　19.00
　d.　Booklet pane of 10 (see footnote)　17.50
　e.　Booklet pane of 10 (see footnote)　17.50
　f.　Booklet pane of 10 (see footnote)

Nos. 2340, 2347 pay postage for the first class letter rate and sold for 2.50fr when first released. They have no denomination or letter inscription. Nos. 2343 and 2348 had a face value of 2.80fr when released.

No. 2347a has all stamps adjoining and has selvage covering backing paper (booklet cover), No. 2347d is comprised of two strips of 5 stamps each with yellow backing paper showing.

No. 2348b has the same format as No. 2347a. No. 2348d has a format similar to No. 2347d except there is a narrow selvage strip between the left six stamps and the right four stamps. No. 2348e is like No. 2348f but lacks the selvage strip. No. 2348f has a format similar to No. 2347a except it has a wide selvage strip between the left four stamps and the right six stamps.

Backing paper of Nos. 2347b and 2347c may have cuts along fold and were sold in a booklet for 20fr.

Issued: #2340, 2347, 4/19/93; 70c, July; 2fr, 7/31/94; Nos. 2341-2343, 4/1/94; Nos. 2345, 2348, 2/14/94; 1fr, 2.70fr, 3.80fr, 4.50fr, 3/18/96.

Tourism Series

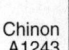

Chinon
A1243

1993, Apr. 24   Engr.   Perf. 13x12½
2355 A1243 4.20fr dk grn, ol grn & brn   2.00 .80

Village of
Minerve — A1244

1993, July 17   Perf. 13
2356 A1244 4.20fr red brown & yel grn   2.00 .50

Chaise-Dieu
Abbey — A1245

Montbeliard
A1246

1993
2357 A1245 2.80fr multicolored   1.25 .30
2358 A1246 4.40fr multicolored   2.00 .60
   Nos. 2355-2358 (4)   7.25 2.20
Issued: No. 2357, 9/4; No. 2358, 9/11.

Ninth European
Conference on
Protection of
Human
Rights — A1247

1993, May 8   Engr.   Perf. 12½x13
2359 A1247 2.50fr multicolored   1.10 .30

Django Reinhardt
(1910-1953),
Musician
A1248

1993, May 14   Litho.   Perf. 13
2360 A1248 4.20fr multicolored   1.90 .50

Louise Weiss (1893-
1983),
Suffragist — A1249

1993, May 15   Engr.   Perf. 13x12½
2361 A1249 2.50fr blk, buff & red   1.10 .30

Philatelic Society
Congress,
Lille — A1250

1993, May 29   Engr.   Perf. 13x12½
2362 A1250 2.50fr bl, dk bl & lil   1.10 .40

Natural History
Museum,
Bicent. — A1251

Litho. & Engr.
1993, June 5   Perf. 13
2363 A1251 2.50fr multicolored   1.10 .30

Martyrs and
Heroes of
the
Resistance
A1252

1993, June 18   Photo.   Perf. 13
2364 2.50fr red, black & gray   1.10 .60
2365 4.20fr red, black & gray   1.90 1.00
a. A1252 Pair, #2364-2365   3.00 1.50

A1254

1993, July 10   Engr.   Perf. 13x12½
2366 A1254 2.50fr multicolored   1.10 .30
Claude Chappe's Semaphore Telegraph, bicent.

A1255

1993, July 10   Engr.   Perf. 12½x13
2367 A1255 3.40fr bl, grn & red   1.50 .70
Train to Lake Artouste, Laruns, highest train ride in Europe.

Musical Instruments Type of 1989
1993, July 1   Litho.   Perf. 13
2368 A1154 1.82fr like #2171   .80 .25
2369 A1154 2.34fr like #2235   1.10 .60
2370 A1154 3.86fr like #2236   1.75 .90
2371 A1154 5.93fr like #2281   2.75 1.75
   Nos. 2368-2371 (4)   6.40 3.50
Nos. 2368-2371 are known only precanceled. See note after No. 132.

Liberation of Corsica,
50th Anniv. — A1256

1993, Sept. 9   Engr.   Perf. 13
2372 A1256 2.80fr lake, bl & blk   1.25 .30

Saint Thomas, by
Georges de la
Tour (1593-1652)
A1257

1993, Sept. 9   Photo.   Perf. 12½x13
2373 A1257 5fr multicolored   2.25 1.00

Service as Military
Hospital of Val de Grace
Monastery,
Bicent. — A1258

1993, Sept. 25   Engr.   Perf. 13
2374 A1258 3.70fr multicolored   1.60 .30

Whitbread Trans-Global Race Type
1993, Sept. 27   Engr.   Perf. 12
2375 A1236 2.80fr multicolored   1.25 .40

The Muses, by
Maurice Denis
(1870-1943)
A1259

1993, Oct. 2   Photo.   Perf. 12½x13
2376 A1259 5fr multicolored   2.25 1.00

The Clowns, by Albert
Gleizes (1881-
1953) — A1260

1993, Oct. 2   Photo.   Perf. 13½x12½
2377 A1260 2.80fr multicolored   1.25 .30
Natl. Circus Center, Chalons-sur-Marne.

Clock Tower Bellringer
Statues of
Lambesc — A1261

1993, Oct. 9   Engr.   Perf. 13x12½
2378 A1261 4.40fr multicolored   2.00 .60

European Contemporary Art Type
Designs: No. 2379, Abstract, by Takis. No. 2380, Abstract, by Maria Helena Vieira da Silva. No. 2381, Abstract Squares, by Sean Scully. No. 2382, Abstract, by Georg Baselitz, Germany.

1993-94   Photo.   Perf. 13x12½
2379 A1234 5fr blk & ver   2.25 1.00
2380 A1234 5fr multicolored   2.25 1.00
2381 A1234 6.70fr multicolored   3.00 1.00
   Perf. 13
2382 A1234 6.70fr multicolored   3.00 1.00
   Nos. 2379-2382 (4)   10.50 4.00
Issued: No. 2379, 10/9/93; No. 2380, 12/11/93; No. 2381, 1/29/94; No. 2382, 11/19/94.

Greetings — A1266

Greeting, artist: No. 2383, Happy Birthday, Claire Wendling. No. 2384, Happy Birthday, Bernard Olivie. No. 2385, Happy Anniversary, Stephane Colman. No. 2386, Happy Anniversary, Guillaune Sorel. No. 2387, With Love, Jean-Michel Thiriet. No. 2388, Please Write, Etienne Davodeau. No. 2389, Congratulations, Johan de Moor. No. 2390, Good luck, "Mezzo." No. 2391, Best Wishes, Nicolas de Crecy. No. 2392, Best Wishes, Florence Magnin. No. 2393, Merry Christmas, Thierry Robin. No. 2394, Merry Christmas, Patrick Prugne.

1993, Oct. 21   Photo.   Perf. 13½x13
Booklet Stamps
2383 A1266 2.80fr multicolored   1.25 .30
2384 A1266 2.80fr multicolored   1.25 .30
2385 A1266 2.80fr multicolored   1.25 .30
2386 A1266 2.80fr multicolored   1.25 .30
2387 A1266 2.80fr multicolored   1.25 .30
2388 A1266 2.80fr multicolored   1.25 .30
2389 A1266 2.80fr multicolored   1.25 .30
2390 A1266 2.80fr multicolored   1.25 .30
2391 A1266 2.80fr multicolored   1.25 .30
2392 A1266 2.80fr multicolored   1.25 .30
2393 A1266 2.80fr multicolored   1.25 .30
2394 A1266 2.80fr multicolored   1.25 .30
a. Bklt. pane, #2383-2394   15.00

   Perf. 12½
2383a A1266 2.80fr   1.25 .30
2384a A1266 2.80fr   1.25 .30
2385a A1266 2.80fr   1.25 .30
2386a A1266 2.80fr   1.25 .30
2387a A1266 2.80fr   1.25 .30
2388a A1266 2.80fr   1.25 .30
2389a A1266 2.80fr   1.25 .30
2390a A1266 2.80fr   1.25 .30
2391a A1266 2.80fr   1.25 .30
2392a A1266 2.80fr   1.25 .30
2393a A1266 2.80fr   1.25 .30
2394b A1266 2.80fr   1.25 .30
c. Booklet pane of 12, #2383a-2393a, 2394b   16.50

Souvenir Sheet

European Stamp Exhibition, Salon du Timbre — A1267

a, Rhododendrons. b, Flowers in park, Paris.

1993, Nov. 10   Perf. 13
2395 A1267 2.40fr #a.-b.+ 2 labels   12.00 10.00
Sold for 15fr.

Louvre Museum,
Bicent. — A1268

1993, Nov. 20
2396 A1268 2.80fr Louvre, 1793   1.25 1.00
2397 A1268 4.40fr Louvre, 1993   2.00 1.25
a. Pair, #2396-2397   3.50 2.50

Glassware,
1901
A1269

Cast Iron,
c. 1900
A1270

Furniture,
c. 1902
A1271

Stoneware,
c. 1898
A1272

Decorative arts by: No. 2398, Emile Galle (1846-1904). No. 2399, Hector Guimard (1867-1942). No. 2400, Louis Majorelle (1859-1926). No. 2401, Pierre-Adrien Dalpayrat (1844-1910).

   Perf. 13½x12½
1994. Jan. 22   Photo.
2398 A1269 2.80fr multicolored   1.25 .35
2399 A1270 2.80fr multicolored   1.25 .35
2400 A1271 4.40fr multicolored   2.00 .65
2401 A1272 4.40fr multicolored   2.00 .65
   Nos. 2398-2401 (4)   6.50 2.00

Stained Glass Window, St. Julian's Cathedral, Le Mans — A1273

1994, Feb. 12   Engr.   Perf. 12½x13
2402 A1273 6.70fr multicolored   3.00 1.00

City of Bastia — A1274

1994, Feb. 19   Perf. 13x12½
2403 A1274 4.40fr blue & brown   2.00 .60

Tourism Series

Argentat A1275

1994, June 18   Engr.   Perf. 12x12½
2404 A1275 4.40fr red brn & rose car   2.00 .60

European Parliamentary Elections A1276

1994, Feb. 26   Litho.   Perf. 13
2405 A1276 2.80fr multicolored   1.25 .25

Laurent Mourguet (1769-1844), Creator of Puppet, Guignol — A1277

1994, Mar. 4   Photo.   Perf. 13
2406 A1277 2.80fr multicolored   1.25 .30

French Polytechnic Institute, Bicent. — A1277a

1994, Mar. 11
2407 A1277a 2.80fr multicolored 1.25 .30

Stamp Day — A1278

1994, Mar. 12   Engr.   Perf. 13
2408 A1278 2.80fr blue & red   2.00 1.60
2409 A1278 2.80fr +60c blue & red   1.40 1.25
a.   Booklet pane of 4 #2408, 3 #2409 + 1 label   25.00

No. 2408 issued only in booklets.

Swedish Ballet Costume — A1279

Banquet for Gustavus III at the Trianon, 1784, by Lafrensen A1280

French-Swedish cultural relations: No. 2411, Tuxedo costume for Swedish ballet. No. 2412, Viking ships. No. 2413, Viking ship. No. 2415, Swedish, French flags.

1994, Mar. 18   Engr.   Perf. 13
2410 A1279 2.80fr multicolored   1.25 1.00
2411 A1279 2.80fr multicolored   1.25 1.00
2412 A1279 2.80fr multicolored   1.25 1.00
2413 A1279 2.80fr multicolored   1.25 1.00
2414 A1280 3.70fr multicolored   3.00 2.00
2415 A1280 3.70fr multicolored   3.00 2.00
a.   Booklet pane of #2410-2415   16.00

See Sweden Nos. 2065-2070.

Pres. Georges Pompidou (1911-1974) — A1281

1994, Apr. 9   Engr.   Perf. 13
2416 A1281 2.80fr olive brown   1.25 .30

Resistance of the Maquis, 50th Anniv. — A1282

1994, Apr. 9
2417 A1282 2.80fr multicolored   1.25 .30

Philexjeunes '94, Grenoble A1283

1994, Apr. 22   Photo.
2418 A1283 2.80fr multicolored   1.25 .30

Europa — A1284

Discoveries: 2.80fr, AIDS virus, by scientists of Pasteur Institute. 3.70fr, Formula for wave properties of matter, developed by Louis de Brogile.

1994, Apr. 30   Photo. & Engr.
2419 A1284 2.80fr multicolored   1.25 .30
a.   With label   1.25 .75
2420 A1284 3.70fr multicolored   1.75 .85

No. 2419a issued Dec. 1, 1994.

Opening of Channel Tunnel A1285

Designs: Nos. 2421, 2423, British lion, French rooster, meeting over Channel. Nos. 2422, 2424, Joined hands above speeding train.

1994, May 3   Photo.   Perf. 13
2421 A1285 2.80fr dk blue & multi   1.25 .30
2422 A1285 2.80fr dk blue & multi   1.25 .30
a.   Pair, #2421-2422   2.75 1.50
2423 A1285 4.30fr lt blue & multi   2.00 .90
2424 A1285 4.30fr multicolored   2.00 .90
a.   Pair, #2423-2424   4.50 2.25
Nos. 2421-2424 (4)   6.50 2.40

See Great Britain Nos. 1558-1561.

Asian Development Bank, Board of Governors Meeting, Nice — A1286

1994, May 3   Photo.   Perf. 13
2425 A1286 2.80fr multicolored   1.25 .30

Federation of French Philatelic Societies, 67th Congress, Martigues A1287

1994, May 20   Engr.   Perf. 12x12½
2426 A1287 2.80fr multicolored   1.25 .30

Court of Cassation A1288

Litho. & Engr.
1994, June 3   Perf. 13
2427 A1288 2.80fr multicolored   1.25 .30

D-Day, 50th Anniv. — A1289

No. 2429, Tank, crowd waving Allied flags.

1994, June 4   Engr.
2428 A1289 4.30fr multicolored   2.00 .50
2429 A1289 4.30fr multicolored   2.00 .50

Liberation of Paris, 50th anniv. (No. 2429).

Mount St. Victoire, by Paul Cezanne (1839-1906) A1290

1994, June 18   Photo.   Perf. 13
2430 A1290 2.80fr multicolored   1.25 .30

Intl. Olympic Committee, Cent. — A1291

1994, June 23   Litho.   Perf. 13
2431 A1291 2.80fr multicolored   1.25 .25

Saulx River Bridge, Rupt aux Nonains — A1292

1994, July 2   Engr.
2432 A1292 2.80fr blackish blue 1.25 .25

Organ, Poitiers Cathedral — A1293

1994, July 2   Perf. 13x12½
2433 A1293 4.40fr multicolored   2.00 .55

Allied Landings in Provence, 50th Anniv. — A1294

1994, Aug. 13   Engr.   Perf. 13
2434 A1294 2.80fr multicolored   1.25 .30

Moses and the Daughters of Jethro, by Nicolas Poussin (1594-1665) — A1295

1994, Sept. 10
2435 A1295 4.40fr yel brn & blk   1.90 .90

Natl. Conservatory of Arts and Crafts, Bicent. — A1296

1994, Sept. 24   Perf. 13x12½
2436 A1296 2.80fr Foucault's pendulum   1.25 .25

The Great Cascade, St. Cloud Park — A1297

1994, Sept. 24   Perf. 12½x13
2437 A1297 3.70fr multicolored   1.75 .60

Leaves — A1298

1994   Litho.   Perf. 13
2438 A1298 1.91fr Oak   .85 .40
2439 A1298 2.46fr Sycamore   1.10 .70
2440 A1298 4.24fr Chestnut   2.00 1.00
2441 A1298 6.51fr Holly   3.00 1.75
Nos. 2438-2441 (4)   6.95 3.85

Nos. 2438-2441 are known only precanceled. See second note after No. 132. See Nos. 2517-2520.

Ecole Normale Superieure (Teachers' School), Bicent. — A1299

1994, Oct. 8   Engr.   Perf. 13
2442 A1299 2.80fr red & dk bl   1.25 .25

Georges Simenon (1903-89), Writer — A1300

Litho. & Engr.
1994, Oct. 15   Perf. 13
2443 A1300 2.80fr multicolored   1.25 .25

See Belgium No. 1567, Switzerland No. 948.

Souvenir Sheet

European Stamp Exhibition — A1301

a, Flowers in park, Paris. b, Dalhias, vert.

1994, Oct. 15   Photo.   Perf. 13
2444 A1301 2.80fr Sheet of 2,
#a.-b.   10.00 9.00
No. 2444 sold for 16fr.

Natl. Drug Addiction
Prevention Day — A1302

1994, Oct. 15
2445 A1302 2.80fr multicolored 1.25 .25

Grand Lodge of
France,
Cent. — A1303

1994, Nov. 5   Engr.
2446 A1303 2.80fr multicolored 1.25 .25

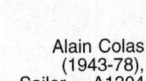

Alain Colas
(1943-78),
Sailor — A1304

1994, Nov. 19
2447 A1304 3.70fr green & black 1.60 .60

French Natl.
Press Federation,
50th
Anniv. — A1305

1994, Dec. 9   Photo.   Perf. 13
2448 A1305 2.80fr multicolored 1.25 .30

Champs
Elysees
A1306

1994, Dec. 31
2449 A1306 4.40fr multi + label 2.00 .75
See No. 5762d

Souvenir Sheet

Motion
Pictures,
Cent.
A1307

Faces on screen and: a, Projector at right. b, Projector facing away from screen. c, Projector facing screen. d, Reels of film.

1995, Jan. 14   Photo.   Perf. 13
2450 A1307 Sheet of 4   5.00 5.00
a.-d.   2.80fr any single   1.00 1.00

Normandy Bridge — A1308

1995, Jan. 20   Engr.   Perf. 13
2451 A1308 4.40fr multicolored 2.00 .75

European Notaries
Public — A1309

1995, Jan. 21   Perf. 13x12
2452 A1309 2.80fr multicolored 1.25 .30

Louis Pasteur (1822-
95) — A1310

1995, Feb. 18   Photo.   Perf. 13
2453 A1310 3.70fr multicolored 1.60 1.00

Art Series

St. Taurin's
Reliquary,
Evreaux
A1311

Study for
the Dream
of
Happiness,
by Pierre
Prud'hon
(1758-1823)
A1312

Abstract, by
Zao Wou-ki
A1313

Abstract, by
Per Kirkeby,
Denmark
A1314

1995   Photo. & Engr.   Perf. 12x13
2454 A1311 6.70fr multicolored 3.00 1.10
Engr.
Perf. 13x12
2455 A1312 6.70fr slate & blue 3.00 1.10
Litho.
Perf. 14
2456 A1313 6.70fr multicolored 3.00 1.10
Photo.
Perf. 13
2457 A1314 6.70fr multicolored 3.00 1.10
Nos. 2454-2457 (4)   12.00 4.40
Issued: No. 2454, 2/25; No. 2455, 5/12; No. 2456, 6/10; No. 2457, 9/23.

Tourism Series

Stenay Malt
Works — A1315

Remiremont,
Vosges — A1316

Nyons Bridge,
Drome — A1317

Barbizon, Home
of Landscape
Artists — A1318

1995   Engr.   Perf. 13x12½
2458 A1315 2.80fr ol & dk grn 1.25 .30
2459 A1316 2.80fr brn, grn & bl 1.25 .30
Perf. 12½x13
2460 A1317 4.40fr multicolored 2.00 .75
Photo.
Perf. 13½
2461 A1318 4.40fr multicolored 2.00 .75
Nos. 2458-2461 (4)   6.50 2.10
Issued: No. 2458, 2/25; No. 2459, 5/13; No. 2460, 5/20; No. 2461, 9/30.

A1319

John J. Audubon
(1785-1851) — A1320

Designs: No. 2462, Snowy egret. No. 2463, Band-tailed pigeon. 4.30fr, Common tern. 4.40fr, Brown-colored rough-legged buzzard.

1995, Feb. 25 Photo. Perf. 12½x12
2462 A1319 2.80fr multicolored 1.25 .40
2463 A1320 2.80fr multicolored 1.25 .40
2464 A1319 4.30fr multicolored 2.00 .75
2465 A1320 4.40fr multicolored 2.00 .75
a.   Souvenir sheet of 4, #2462-
       2465, perf. 13   7.00 7.00
Nos. 2462-2465 (4)   6.50 2.30

Stamp
Day — A1321

1995, Mar. 4   Engr.   Perf. 13
2466 A1321 2.80fr multicolored 2.00 1.00
2467 A1321 2.80fr +60c multi 1.50 1.25
a.   Booklet pane, 4 #2466, 3
       #2467+label   15.00
       Complete booklet, #2467   16.00
No. 2466 issued only in booklets.

Work Councils, 50th
Anniv. — A1322

1995, Mar. 7   Engr.   Perf. 13
2468 A1322 2.80fr dk bl, brn &
       sky bl   1.25 .30

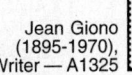

Advanced
Institute of
Electricity,
Cent. — A1323

1995, Mar. 11   Photo.
2469 A1323 3.70fr multicolored 1.75 .60

Institute of
Oriental
Languages,
Bicent. — A1324

1995, Mar. 25   Photo.   Perf. 13
2470 A1324 2.80fr multicolored 1.25 .30

Jean Giono
(1895-1970),
Writer — A1325

1995, Mar. 25   Engr.
2471 A1325 3.70fr multicolored 1.75 .60

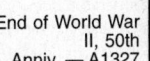

Iron and Steel Industry
in Lorraine — A1326

1995, Apr. 1   Perf. 13x12
2472 A1326 2.80fr multicolored 1.25 .30

End of World War
II, 50th
Anniv. — A1327

Europa: 2.80fr, Barbed wire, laurel wreath. 3.70fr, Broken sword, emblem of European Union.

1995, Apr. 29   Photo.   Perf. 13
2473 A1327 2.80fr multicolored 1.25 .40
2474 A1327 3.70fr multicolored 1.75 1.00

Forestry Profession,
Ardennes — A1328

1995, May 2   Engr.   Perf. 12½x13
2475 A1328 4.40fr multicolored 2.00 .60

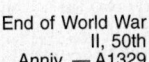

End of World War
II, 50th
Anniv. — A1329

1995, May 8   Photo.   Perf. 13
2476 A1329 2.80fr multicolored 1.25 .30

Natl.
Assembly
A1330

1995, May 13 Photo. Perf. 13x12½
2477 A1330 2.80fr multicolored 1.25 .60

French's People's Relief Assoc., 50th Anniv. — A1331

1995, May 20   Engr.   Perf. 12½x13
2478 A1331 2.80fr multicolored   1.25   .30

Scenes of France — A1332

No. 2479, Forest, Vosges. No. 2480, Massif, Brittany. No. 2481, Wetlands, cattle, Camargue. No. 2482, Volcanoes, Auvergne.

1995, May 27   Perf. 13
2479 A1332 2.40fr green   1.10   .25
2480 A1332 2.40fr green   1.10   .25
2481 A1332 2.80fr red   1.25   .30
2482 A1332 2.80fr red   1.25   .30
　　　　 Nos. 2479-2482 (4)   4.70 1.10

Ariane Rocket on Launch Pad, French Guiana — A1333

1995, March 28 Engr. Perf. 12½x13
2483 A1333 2.80fr bl, grn & red   1.25   .30
　　　　 Compare with No. 2254.

A1334

1995, June 2   Engr.   Perf. 13
2484 A1334 2.80fr multicolored   1.25   .30
　 68th Congress of French Federation of Philatelic Organizations, Orleans.

Town of Correze — A1335

1995, June 3
2485 A1335 4.40fr multi   2.00   .60

A1336

Fables of Jean de la Fontaine (1621-95): No. 2486, The Grasshopper and The Ant. No. 2487, The Frog Who Could Make Himself Larger than an Ox. No. 2488, The Wolf and the Lamb. No. 2489, The Crow and the Fox. No. 2490, The Cat, the Weasel, and the Small Rabbit. No. 2491, The Tortoise and the Hare.

1995, June 24   Photo.   Perf. 13
2486 A1336 2.80fr multicolored   1.40   .50
2487 A1336 2.80fr multicolored   1.40   .50
2488 A1336 2.80fr multicolored   1.40   .50
2489 A1336 2.80fr multicolored   1.40   .50
2490 A1336 2.80fr multicolored   1.40   .50
2491 A1336 2.80fr multicolored   1.40   .50
　a.　　 Strip, #2486-2491 + 2 labels   9.00 8.00

Velodrome d'Hiver Raid — A1337

1995, July 9   Photo.   Perf. 13
2492 A1337 2.80fr multicolored   1.25   .30

André Maginot (1877-1932), Creator of Maginot Line — A1338

1995, Sept. 9   Engr.   Perf. 13
2493 A1338 2.80fr multicolored   1.25   .30

Women's Grand Masonic Lodge of France, 50th Anniv. — A1339

1995, Sept. 16   Perf. 13x12½
2494 A1339 2.80fr multicolored   1.25   .30

Hospital Pharmacies, 500th Anniv. — A1340

1995, Sept. 23   Perf. 12½x13
2495 A1340 2.80fr multicolored   1.25   .30

Natl. School of Administration, 50th Anniv. — A1341

1995, Oct. 5   Photo.   Perf. 13
2496 A1341 2.80fr multicolored   1.25   .30

The Cradle, by Berthe Morisot (1841-95) A1342

1995, Oct. 7   Litho.   Perf. 13½x14
2497 A1342 6.70fr multicolored   3.00 1.00

The French Institute, Bicent. — A1343

1995, Oct. 14   Engr.   Perf. 12½x13
2498 A1343 2.80fr blk, grn & red   1.25   .30

Automobile Club of France, Cent. — A1344

1995, Nov. 4   Engr.   Perf. 13x12½
2499 A1344 4.40fr blk, bl & red   2.00   .60

UN, 50th Anniv. — A1345

1995, Nov. 16   Photo.   Perf. 13
2500 A1345 4.30fr multicolored   2.00   .60

Francis Jammes (1868-1938), Poet — A1346

1995, Dec. 2   Engr.   Perf. 13
2501 A1346 3.70fr black & blue   1.60   .60

A1347

1995, Dec. 9   Litho. & Engr.
2502 A1347 2.80fr Evry Cathedral 1.25 .30

A1348

1995, Dec. 12   Photo.   Perf. 13
2503 A1348 2.80fr multicolored   1.25   .30
　 1998 World Cup Soccer Championships, France.

Art Series

Abstract, by Lucien Wercollier A1349

Design: No. 2505, The Netherlands (Horizon), abstract photograph, by Jan Dibbets.

1996   Perf. 13x12½
2504 A1349 6.70fr multicolored   3.00 1.00
2505 A1349 6.70fr multicolored   3.00 1.00
　 Issued: No. 2504, 1/20; No. 2505, 2/10.

Arawak Civilization, Saint Martin — A1350

Design: 2.80fr, Dog figurine, 550 B.C.

1996, Feb. 10   Engr.   Perf. 13
2506 A1350 2.80fr multicolored   1.25   .30

The Augustus Bridge over the Nera River, by Camille Corot (1796-1875) A1351

1996, Mar. 2   Litho.   Perf. 13
2507 A1351 6.70fr multicolored   3.00 1.00

St. Patrick — A1352

1996, Mar. 16   Photo.   Perf. 13
2508 A1352 2.80fr multicolored   1.25   .30

The Sower, 1903 — A1353

1996, Mar. 16   Litho. & Engr.
2509 A1353 2.80fr multicolored   2.00 1.50
2510 A1353 2.80fr +60c multi   1.50 1.25
　a.　 Booklet pane, 4 #2509, 3
　　　 #2510 + label   13.00
　　　 Complete booklet, #2510a   15.00
　　　 Stamp Day.

Jacques Rueff (1896-1978), Economist A1354

1996, Mar. 23   Engr.   Perf. 13x12½
2511 A1354 2.80fr multicolored   1.25   .30

René Descartes (1596-1650) — A1355

1996, Mar. 30   Engr.   Perf. 12½x13
2512 A1355 4.40fr red   2.00   .75

Gas & Electric Industries, 50th Anniv. — A1356

1996, Apr. 6   Photo.   Perf. 13
2513 A1356 3fr multicolored   1.25   .30

Natl. Parks — A1357

1996, Apr. 20
2514 A1357   3fr Cévennes   1.25   .40
2515 A1357 4.40fr Vanoise   2.00   .75
2516 A1357 4.40fr Mercantour   2.00   .75
　　　 Nos. 2514-2516 (3)   5.25 1.90

See Nos. 2569-2572.

Leaf Type of 1994
1996, Mar.   Litho.   Perf. 13
2517 A1298 1.87fr Ash   .85   .25
2518 A1298 2.18fr Beech   1.00   .50
2519 A1298 4.66fr Walnut   2.10 1.00
2520 A1298 7.11fr Elm   3.00 1.75
　　　 Nos. 2517-2520 (4)   6.95 3.50

　 Nos. 2517-2520 are known only precanceled. Values for precanceled stamps in first column are for those which have not been through the post and have original gum. Values in second column are for postally used, gumless stamps.

Madame Marie de Sévigné (1626-96), Writer — A1358

1996, Apr. 27   **Photo.**   *Perf. 13*
2521 A1358 3fr multicolored   1.25   .40

Europa.

Natl. Institute of Agronomy Research, 50th Anniv. — A1359

1996, May 4   **Photo.**   *Perf. 13*
2522 A1359 3.80fr multicolored   1.75   .60

Joan of Arc's House, Domremy-La-Pucelle — A1360

1996, May 11
2523 A1360 4.50fr multicolored   2.10   .75

RAMOGE Agreement Between France, Italy, Monaco, 20th Anniv. — A1361

1996, May 14   **Photo. & Engr.**
2524 A1361 3fr multicolored   1.25   .30

See Monaco No. 1998, Italy No. 2077.

69th Congress of Federation of Philatelic Assoc., Clermont-Ferrand A1362

1996, May 24   **Engr.**   *Perf. 13*
2525 A1362 3fr brn, red & grn   1.25   .30

Tourism Series

Bitche, Moselle — A1363

Iles Sanguinaires, Ajaccio, Southern Corsica — A1364

Thoronet Abbey, Var — A1365

Chambéry Cathedral, Savoie — A1366

1996   **Engr.**   *Perf. 12½x13*
2526 A1363 3fr multicolored   1.25   .30
2527 A1364 3fr multicolored   1.25   .30
    Perf. 13x12½
2528 A1365 3.80fr brn & claret   1.75   .60
    Photo.
    Perf. 13
2529 A1366 4.50fr multicolored   2.00   .75
   Nos. 2526-2529 (4)   6.25 1.95

Issued: No. 2526, 5/25; No. 2527, 6/1; 3.80fr, 7/6; 4.50fr, 6/8.

1998 World Cup Soccer Championships, France — A1367

Various stylized soccer plays, name of host city in France.

1996, June 1   **Photo.**   *Perf. 13*
2530 A1367 3fr Lens   1.25   .30
2531 A1367 3fr Toulouse   1.25   .30
2532 A1367 3fr Saint-Etienne   1.25   .30
2533 A1367 3fr Montpellier   1.25   .30
   Nos. 2530-2533 (4)   5.00 1.20

See Nos. 2584-2587, 2623-2624, sheet of 10, No. 2624a.

Art Series

Gallo-Roman Bronze Statue of Horse, Neuvy-en-Sullias, Loiret — A1368

Imprints of Cello Fragments, by Arman A1369

1996   **Engr.**   *Perf. 13*
2534 A1368 6.70fr multicolored   3.00 1.00
    Photo.
2535 A1369 6.70fr multicolored   3.00 1.00

Issued: No. 2534, 6/8; No. 2535, 9/21.

Modern Olympic Games, Cent. — A1371

1996, June 15   **Photo.**   *Perf. 13*
2537 A1371 3fr multicolored   1.25   .30

A1372

1996, June 15   **Engr.**   *Perf. 12½x13*
2538 A1372 4.40fr deep purple   2.00   .70

Jacques Marette (1922-84), Member of Parliament.

A1373

1996, June 29   **Photo.**   *Perf. 13*
2539 A1373 3fr multicolored   1.25   .30

Train between Ajaccio and Vizzavona, cent.

A1374

1996, Sept. 6   **Engr.**   *Perf. 13x12½*
2540 A1374 3fr dark blue & yel   1.25   .30

Notre Dame de Fourvière Basilica, Lyon, cent.

Baptism of Clovis, 1500th Anniv. — A1375

1996, Sept. 14   *Perf. 13*
2541 A1375 3fr multicolored   1.25   .30

Henri IV High School, Bicent. — A1376

1996, Oct. 12   **Engr.**   *Perf. 12½x13*
2542 A1376 4.50fr brown & blue   2.00   .80

UNICEF, 50th Anniv. — A1377

1996, Oct. 19   **Photo.**   *Perf. 13*
2543 A1377 4.50fr multicolored   2.00   .80

Economic and Social Council, 50th Anniv. — A1378

1996, Oct. 26   **Engr.**   *Perf. 13*
2544 A1378 3fr red, black & blue   1.25   .30

UNESCO, 50th Anniv. — A1379

1996, Nov. 2   **Litho.**   *Perf. 13*
2545 A1379 3.80fr multicolored   1.75   .60

Autumn Stamp Show, 50th Anniv. — A1380

1996, Nov. 7   **Photo.**   *Perf. 13*
2546 A1380 3fr multicolored   1.25   .30

A1381

1996, Nov. 16
2547 A1381 3fr multicolored   1.25   .30

Creation of French Overseas Departments, 50th anniv.

André Malraux (1901-76), Writer — A1382

1996, Nov. 23   **Engr.**   *Perf. 13*
2548 A1382 3fr deep green black   1.25   .30

French School in Athens, 150th Anniv. — A1383

1996, Nov. 23   **Photo.**
2549 A1383 3fr multicolored   1.25   .30

Cannes Film Festival, 50th Anniv. — A1384

1996, Nov. 30
2550 A1384 3fr multicolored   1.25   .30

New National Library of France — A1385

1996, Dec. 14
2551 A1385 3fr multicolored   1.25   .30

Francois Mitterrand (1916-96) — A1386

1997, Jan. 4
2552 A1386 3fr multicolored   1.25   .30

Participatory Innovation — A1387

1997, Jan. 24   **Photo.**   *Perf. 13*
2553 A1387 3fr multicolored   1.25   .30

A1388

1997, Jan. 31   **Engr.**   *Perf. 12½x13*
2554 A1388 3fr multicolored   1.25   .30

Georges Pompidou Natl. Center of Art and Culture, 20th Anniv.

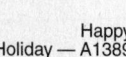

Happy Holiday — A1389

1997, Feb. 8   Photo.   Perf. 13
2555 A1389 3fr shown   1.25   .30
2556 A1389 3fr Happy birthday 1.25   .30

A1390

Photo. & Engr.   Perf. 12½x13
2557 A1390 3fr multicolored   1.25   .30
Natl. School of Bridges and Highways, 250th Anniv.

Saint-Laurent-du-Maroni, French Guiana — A1391

Photo. & Engr.   Perf. 12½x13
2558 A1391 3fr multicolored   1.25   .30

Art Series

Church Fresco, Tavant — A1392

Painting by Bernard Moninot A1393

The Thumb, Polished Bronze, by César — A1394

Grapes and Pomegranates, by Jean Baptiste Chardin — A1395

1997   Engr.   Perf. 13
2559 A1392 6.70fr multicolored 3.00 1.00
Photo.
2560 A1393 6.70fr multicolored 3.00 1.00
2561 A1394 6.70fr multicolored 3.00 1.00
2562 A1395 6.70fr multicolored 3.00 1.00
   Nos. 2559-2562 (4)   12.00 4.00

Issued: No. 2559, 3/1; No. 2560, 3/29; No. 2561, 9/13; No. 2562, 9/27.

Tourism Series

Millau A1396

Guimiliau Church Close A1398

Fresco, Saint Eutrope des Salles-Lavauguyon — A1397

Sablé-Sur-Sarthe A1399

1997   Engr.   Perf. 12½x13
2563 A1396 3fr grn & dk bl
             grn   1.25 .30
Perf. 13
2564 A1397 4.50fr multicolored   2.10 .75
2565 A1398 3fr multicolored   1.25 .30
Perf. 12½x13
2566 A1399 3fr multicolored   1.25 .30
   Nos. 2563-2566 (4)   5.85 1.65

Issued: No. 2563, 3/15; No. 2564, 6/14; No. 2565, 7/12; No. 2566, 9/20.

Vignette of Type A17 — A1400

Litho. & Engr.   Perf. 13½x13
2567 A1400 3fr multicolored   2.50 1.50
2568 A1400 3fr +60c multi   1.50 1.25
   a.   Booklet pane, 4 #2567, 3
         #2568 + label   15.00
        Complete booklet, #2568a 16.00

Stamp Day.
No. 2567 issued only in booklets.

National Parks Type of 1996

No. 2569, Parc des Ecrins. No. 2570, Guadeloupe Park. No. 2571, Parc des Pyrénées. No. 2572, Port-Cros Park.

1997, Apr. 12   Photo.   Perf. 13
2569 A1357 3fr multi   1.25 .40
2570 A1357 3fr multi   1.25 .40
2571 A1357 4.50fr multi   2.00 .70
2572 A1357 4.50fr multi   2.00 .70
   Nos. 2569-2572 (4)   6.50 2.20

Puss-in-Boots — A1401

1997, Apr. 26   Engr.   Perf. 13
2573 A1401 3fr blue   1.25 .30
Europa.

Philexjeunes '97, Nantes — A1402

1997, May 2   Litho.   Perf. 13
2574 A1402 3fr multicolored   1.25 .30

Cartoon Journey of a Letter — A1403

"Envelope": No. 2575, Writing letter. No. 2576, Climbing ladder to go into letter box. No. 2577, On wheels. No. 2578, Following postman carrying another "Envelope." No. 2579, Held by girl. No. 2580, At feet of girl reading long letter.

1997, May 8   Photo.   Perf. 13
2575 A1403 3fr multicolored   1.25 1.00
2576 A1403 3fr multicolored   1.25 1.00
2577 A1403 3fr multicolored   1.25 1.00
2578 A1403 3fr multicolored   1.25 1.00
2579 A1403 3fr multicolored   1.25 1.00
2580 A1403 3fr multicolored   1.25 1.00
   a.   Strip of 6, #2575-2580
         + label   8.00 8.00
Self-Adhesive
Serpentine Die Cut 11
2580B A1403 3fr like #2575   1.25 1.00
2580C A1403 3fr like #2576   1.25 1.00
2580D A1403 3fr like #2577   1.25 1.00
2580E A1403 3fr like #2578   1.25 1.00
2580F A1403 3fr like #2579   1.25 1.00
2580G A1403 3fr like #2580   1.25 1.00
   h.   Booklet pane, 2 each
         #2580B-2580G   15.00 15.00

By its nature No. 2580h is a complete booklet. The peelable paper backing serves as a booklet cover.
See Nos. 2648-2659.

Honoring French Soldiers in North Africa (1952-62) A1404

1997, May 10   Litho.   Perf. 13
2581 A1404 3fr multicolored   1.25 .30

French Federation of Philatelic Associations, 70th Congress, Versailles — A1405

1997, May 17   Photo.   Perf. 13
2582 A1405 3fr multicolored   1.25 .40
Printed with se-tenant label.

Château de Plessis-Bourré, Maine and Loire Rivers — A1406

1997, May 24   Litho. & Engr.
2583 A1406 4.40fr multicolored   2.00 1.25

1998 World Cup Soccer Championships Type

Stylized action scenes, name of host city in France.

1997, May 31   Photo.   Perf. 13½
2584 A1367 3fr Lyon   1.25 .30
2585 A1367 3fr Marseilles   1.25 .30
2586 A1367 3fr Nantes   1.25 .30
2587 A1367 3fr Paris   1.25 .30
   Nos. 2584-2587 (4)   5.00 1.20

Saint Martin of Tours (316-97) Apostle of the Gauls — A1408

1997, July 5   Engr.   Perf. 13
2588 A1408 4.50fr multicolored   2.00 .75

Marianne — A1409

1997, July 14   Engr.   Perf. 13
2589 A1409 10c brown   .25   .25
2590 A1409 20c brt blue
             grn   .25   .25
2591 A1409 50c purple   .25   .25
2592 A1409 1fr bright org   .45   .25
2593 A1409 2fr bright blue   1.00 .30
2594 A1409 2.70fr bright grn   1.25 .25
2595 A1409 (3fr) red   1.90 .25
2596 A1409 3.50fr apple grn   1.60 .25
2597 A1409 3.80fr blue   1.75 .25
2598 A1409 4.20fr dark org   1.90 .30
2599 A1409 4.40fr blue   2.00 .25
2600 A1409 4.50fr bright pink   2.10 .30
2601 A1409 5fr brt grn
             blue   5.25 .30
2602 A1409 6.70fr dark grn   3.00 .30
   a.   Souvenir sheet, #2594-
         2600, 2602   14.00 14.00
2603 A1409 10fr violet   4.50 .35
   a.   Souvenir sheet, #2589-
         2593, 2601, 2603   12.00 12.00
   Nos. 2589-2603 (15)   27.45 4.15

Self-Adhesive
Booklet Stamps
Die Cut x Serpentine Die Cut 7
2603B A1409 1fr brt org   2.25 .50
   c.   Booklet pane, #2603B, 3
         #2604   7.75
        Booklet, 2 #2603Bc   16.00
2604 A1409 (3fr) red   1.40 .25
   a.   Booklet pane of 10   14.00

Coil Stamps
Perf. 13 Horiz.
2604B A1409 2.70fr bright grn   1.25 .50
2605 A1409 (3fr) red   1.75 .25

Nos. 2595, 2604-2605 were valued at 3fr on day of issue.
Issued: Nos. 2602a, 2603a, 11/12/01. No. 2603B, 9/1/97.
See Nos. 2835-2835C, 2921-2922, 3530, 4410j, 4523.

1997 World Rowing Championships, Savoie — A1410

1997, Aug. 30   Engr.   Perf. 13x12½
2606 A1410 3fr blue & magenta   1.25 .30

Basque Corsairs A1411

1997, Sept. 13   Perf. 13
2607 A1411 3fr multicolored   1.25 .30

Saint-Maurice Basilica, Epinal — A1412

1997, Sept. 20   Perf. 13x12½
2608 A1412 3fr multicolored   1.25 .30

Fresh Fish Merchants, Port of Boulogne A1413

1997, Sept. 26   Perf. 13
2609 A1413 3fr multicolored   1.25 .30

Japan Year — A1414

1997, Oct. 4   Engr.   Perf. 13
2610 A1414 4.90fr multicolored   1.00 1.25

1997 World Judo Championships A1415

1997, Oct. 9 **Photo.** *Perf. 13*
2611 A1415 3fr multicolored 1.25 .30

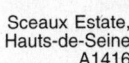

Sceaux Estate, Hauts-de-Seine A1416

1997, Oct. 11
2612 A1416 3fr multicolored 1.25 .30

Saar-Lorraine-Luxembourg Summit — A1417

1997, Oct. 16 **Photo.** *Perf. 13*
2613 A1417 3fr multicolored 1.25 .30
See Germany No. 1982, Luxembourg No. 972.

College of France — A1418

1997, Oct. 18 **Engr.**
2614 A1418 4.40fr multicolored 2.00 .70

Quality — A1419

1997, Oct. 18 **Photo.**
2615 A1419 4.50fr multicolored 2.00 .80

A1420

Season's Greetings — A1421

1997 **Photo.** *Perf. 13*
2616 A1420 3fr Cat & mouse 1.50 .30
Photo. & Embossed
2617 A1421 3fr Mailman 1.25 .30
Issued: No. 2616, 11/8; No. 2617, 11/22.

Protection of Abused Children — A1422

1997, Nov. 20 **Photo.**
2618 A1422 3fr multicolored 1.25 .30

A1423

Design: Marshal Jacques Leclerc (Philippe de Haute Cloque) (1902-47).

1997, Nov. 28 **Photo.** *Perf. 13*
2619 A1423 3fr multicolored 1.25 .30

Philexfrance '99, World Stamp Exposition A1424

1997, Dec. 6 **Engr.**
2620 A1424 3fr red & blue 1.25 .30

Abbey of Moutier D'Ahun, Creuse — A1425

1997, Dec. 13
2621 A1425 4.40fr multicolored 2.00 .70

Michel Debré (1912-96), Politician A1426

1998, Jan. 15 **Photo.**
2622 A1426 3fr multicolored 1.25 .30

1998 World Cup Soccer Championships Type

Stylized action scenes, name of host city in France.

1998, Jan. 24 *Perf. 13½*
2623 A1367 3fr Saint-Denis 1.25 .30
2624 A1367 3fr Bordeaux 1.25 .30
a. Sheet of 10, #2530-2533, #2584-2587, #2623-2624 + label 14.00 14.00

National Assembly, Bicent. — A1427

1998, Jan. 24 *Perf. 13*
2625 A1427 3fr multicolored 1.25 .30

Valentine's Day — A1428

1998, Jan. 31
2626 A1428 3fr multicolored 1.25 .30

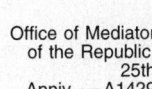

Office of Mediator of the Republic, 25th Anniv. — A1429

1998, Feb. 5
2627 A1429 3fr multicolored 1.25 .30

A1430

1998, Feb. 28 **Photo.** *Perf. 12½*
2628 A1430 3fr multicolored 1.25 .30
Self-Adhesive
Serpentine Die Cut
2629 A1430 3fr like #2628 1.25 .30
a. Booklet pane of 10 14.00 14.00
b. Sheet of 1 + 7 labels 17.00 16.00
1998 World Cup Soccer Championships, France.
The peelable paper backing of No. 2629a serves as a booklet cover.

A €1.16 stamp of type A1430 was included in a limited-edition booklet issued Nov. 4, 2020.
See No. 2665.

A1431

1998, Feb. 21 **Engr.** *Perf. 13½x13*
2630 A1431 3fr Detail of design A16 3.00 1.60
2631 A1431 3fr +60c like #2630 1.50 1.40
a. Booklet pane, 4 #2630, 3 #2631 + label 14.00
Complete booklet, #2631a 15.00
Stamp Day. No. 2630 issued only in booklets.

A1432

1998, Feb. 28 **Engr.** *Perf. 13*
2632 A1432 4.50fr blue 2.00 .75
Father Franz Stock (1904-48), prison chaplain.

Happy Birthday — A1433

1998, Mar. 13 **Photo.** *Perf. 13x13½*
2633 A1433 3fr multicolored 1.25 .30

Union of Mulhouse with France, Bicent. — A1434

1998, Mar. 14
2634 A1434 3fr multicolored 1.25 .30

Citeaux Abbey, 900th Anniv. — A1435

1998, Mar. 14 **Engr.** *Perf. 13*
2635 A1435 3fr multicolored 1.25 .30

Sous-Préfecture Hotel, Saint-Pierre, Réunion — A1436

1998, Apr. 4 **Engr.** *Perf. 13*
2636 A1436 3fr multicolored 1.25 .30
Réunion's architectural heritage.

"The Return," by René Magritte A1437

1998, Apr. 18 **Photo.**
2637 A1437 3fr multicolored 1.40 .50
See Belgium No. 1691.

Edict of Nantes, 400th Anniv. — A1438

1998, Apr. 18 **Litho.**
2638 A1438 4.50fr Henry IV 2.00 .75

Art Series

Detail from "Entry of the Crusaders into Constantinople," by Delacroix (1798-1863) A1439

Le Printemps, by Pablo Picasso (1881-1973) A1440

Neuf Moules Malic, by Marcel Duchamp (1887-1968) A1441

Vision After the Sermon, by Paul Gauguin (1848-1903) A1442

1998 **Engr.** *Perf. 12x13*
2639 A1439 6.70fr multicolored 3.00 1.00
Litho. *Perf. 13*
2640 A1440 6.70fr multicolored 3.00 1.00
Photo.
2641 A1441 6.70fr multicolored 3.00 1.00
2642 A1442 6.70fr multicolored 3.00 1.00
Issued: No. 2639, 4/25; No. 2640, 5/15; No. 2641, 10/17; No. 2642, 12/5.

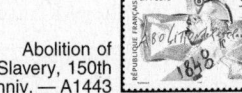

Abolition of Slavery, 150th Anniv. — A1443

1998, Apr. 25 **Litho.** *Perf. 13*
2643 A1443 3fr multicolored 1.25 .30

Tourism Series

Le Gois Causeway, Island of Noirmoutier, Vendée A1444

Bay of Somme, Picardy A1445

Château de Crussol, Ardèche A1446

Collegiate Church of Mantes A1447

1998, May 2   **Photo.**
2644	A1444	3fr multicolored	1.25	.30
2645	A1445	3fr multicolored	1.25	.30

Engr.
2646	A1446	3fr multicolored	1.25	.30
2647	A1447	4.40fr multicolored	2.00	.70
		Nos. 2644-2647 (4)	5.75	1.60

Issued: No. 2644, 5/2; No. 2645, 6/27; No. 2646, 7/4; No. 2647, 9/19.

Journey of a Letter Type

Historic "letters:" No. 2648, Dove carrying letter, Noah's Ark. No. 2649, Egyptian writing letter on papyrus. No. 2650, Soldier running to Athens with letter to victory at Marathon. No. 2651, Knight carrying letter on horseback. No. 2652, Writing letters with quill and ink. No. 2653, Astronaut carrrying letter in space from earth to the moon.

1998, May 9   **Photo.**   *Perf. 13x13½*
2648	A1403	3fr multicolored	1.25	1.00
2649	A1403	3fr multicolored	1.25	1.00
2650	A1403	3fr multicolored	1.25	1.00
2651	A1403	3fr multicolored	1.25	1.00
2652	A1403	3fr multicolored	1.25	1.00
2653	A1403	3fr multicolored	1.25	1.00
a.		Strip, #2648-2653 + label	8.00	6.50

Booklet Stamps
Self-Adhesive
Serpentine Die Cut 11
2654	A1403	3fr like #2648	1.25	1.00
2655	A1403	3fr like #2649	1.25	1.00
2656	A1403	3fr like #2650	1.25	1.00
2657	A1403	3fr like #2651	1.25	1.00
2658	A1403	3fr like #2652	1.25	1.00
2659	A1403	3fr like #2653	1.25	1.00
a.		Bklt. pane, 2 ea #2654-2659	16.00	14.00

By its nature No. 2659a is a complete booklet. The peelable paper backing serves as a booklet cover.

League of Human Rights, Cent. — A1448

1998, May 9   *Perf. 13*
2660	A1448	4.40fr multicolored	2.00	.70

Henri Collet (1885-1951), Composer A1449

1998, May 15   **Engr.**   *Perf. 12x13*
2661	A1449	4.50fr black, gray & buff	2.00	.80

French Federation of Philatelic Assoc., 71st Congress, Dunkirk — A1450

Photo. & Engr.
1998, May 29   *Perf. 13*
2662	A1450	3fr multicolored	1.25	.30

Mont-Saint-Michel A1451

1998, June 6   **Photo.**   *Perf. 13*
2663	A1451	3fr multicolored	1.40	.30

Natl. Music Festival — A1452

1998, June 13
2664	A1452	3fr multicolored	1.25	.50

Europa.

1998 World Cup Soccer Championships Type with Added
Inscription, "Champion du Monde"

1998, July 12   **Photo.**   *Perf. 12½*
2665	A1430	3fr multicolored	1.25	.30

Stéphane Mallarmé (1842-98), Poet — A1453

Photo. & Engr.
1998, Sept. 5   *Perf. 13*
2666	A1453	4.40fr multicolored	2.00	.70

Flowers — A1453a

1.87fr, Liseron. 2.18fr, Coquelicot. 4.66fr, Violette. 7.11fr, Bouton d'or.

1998, Sept. 9   **Litho.**   *Perf. 13*
2666A	A1453a	1.87fr multi	.85	.25
2666B	A1453a	2.18fr multi	1.00	.50
2666C	A1453a	4.66fr multi	2.10	1.00
2666D	A1453a	7.11fr multi	3.00	1.75
		Nos. 2666A-2666D (4)	6.95	3.50

Nos. 2666A-2666D are known only precanceled. See second note after No. 132.

Aéro Club of France, Cent. — A1454

1998, Sept. 12   **Photo.**
2667	A1454	3fr multicolored	1.25	.30

A1455

"The Little Prince," by Antoine de Saint-Exupéry (1900-44): a, Standing in uniform with sword, horiz. b, Seated on wall. c, "The Little Prince on Asteroid B-612." d, Pouring water from sprinkling can. e, Walking along cliff, fox, horiz.

1998, Oct. 23   **Photo.**   *Perf. 13*
2668		Strip of 5 + 2 labels	6.50	4.00
a.-e.		A1455 3fr any single	1.25	.70
f.		Souv. sheet, #2668a-2668e	8.00	8.00

Philexfrance '99. No. 2668f was released 9/12 and sold for 25fr.

Hall of Heavenly Peace, Imperial Palace, Beijing, China — A1456

1998, Sept. 12   **Photo.**   *Perf. 13x13½*
2669	A1456	3fr shown	1.25	.40
2670	A1456	4.90fr The Louvre, France	2.40	1.25

See People's Republic of China Nos. 2895-2896.

Garnier Palace, Home of the Paris Opera — A1457

1998, Sept. 19   **Photo.**   *Perf. 13*
2671	A1457	4.50fr multicolored	2.00	.70

Horses — A1458

1998, Sept. 27
2672	A1458	2.70fr Camargue	1.10	.30
2673	A1458	3fr Pottok	1.25	.40
2674	A1458	3fr French trotter	1.25	.40
2675	A1458	4.50fr Ardennais	2.10	.80
		Nos. 2672-2675 (4)	5.70	1.90

Paris Auto Show, Cent. — A1459

1998, Oct. 1   *Perf. 12*
2676	A1459	3fr multicolored	1.25	.30

5th Republic, 40th Anniv. — A1460

1998, Oct. 3   **Photo.**   *Perf. 13*
2677	A1460	3fr blue, gray & red	1.25	.30

Saint-Dié, Capital of Vosges Mountain Region — A1461

1998, Oct. 3   **Engr.**   *Perf. 13*
2678	A1461	3fr Tower of Liberty	1.25	.30

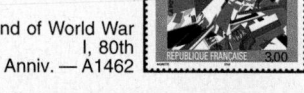

End of World War I, 80th Anniv. — A1462

1998, Oct. 17   **Photo.**   *Perf. 13x13½*
2679	A1462	3fr multicolored	1.25	.30

Intl. Union for the Conservation of Nature and Natural Resources, 50th Anniv. — A1463

1998, Nov. 3   **Litho.**
2680	A1463	3fr multicolored	1.25	.40

New Year A1464

Christmas A1465

1998, Nov. 7   **Photo.**   *Perf. 13*
Background Colors
2681	A1464	3fr deep blue	1.60	.70
2682	A1465	3fr green	1.60	.70
2683	A1464	3fr yellow	1.60	.70
2684	A1465	3fr red	1.60	.70
2685	A1465	3fr green	1.60	.70
a.		Strip of 5, #2681-2685	8.00	3.50

Issued in sheets of 10 stamps. Location of "Bonne Annee" and "Meilleurs Voeux" varies.

Doctors Without Borders — A1466

1998, Nov. 21   *Perf. 13x13½*
2686	A1466	3fr multicolored	1.25	.30

European Parliament, Strasbourg A1467

1998, Dec. 5   **Photo.**   *Perf. 13*
2687	A1467	3fr multicolored	1.25	.30

Universal Declaration of Human Rights, 50th Anniv. — A1468

No. 2688, Faces of people of various races, globe. No. 2689, René Cassin (1887-1976), principal author of Declaration, Eleanor Roosevelt (1884-1962), Chaillot Palace, Paris.

1998, Dec. 10   **Litho.**   *Perf. 13*
2688	A1468	3fr multicolored	1.25	.40
2689	A1468	3fr multicolored	1.25	.40

Discovery of Radium, Cent., ZOE Reactor, 50th Anniv. — A1469

1998, Dec. 15   **Photo.**   *Perf. 13*
2690	A1469	3fr multicolored	1.25	.30

Introduction of the Euro — A1470

1999   **Engr.**   *Perf. 13*
2691	A1470	3fr red & blue	1.25	.25

Booklet Stamps
Self-Adhesive
Die Cut x Serpentine Die Cut 7
2691A	A1470	3fr red & blue	1.25	.25
b.		Booklet pane of 10	12.50	

Issued: No. 2691, 1/1/99. No. 2691A, 2/15/99. Values are shown in both Francs and Euros on Nos. 2691-2691A. No. 2691Ab is a complete booklet.
Euro currency did not circulate until 2002.

French Postage Stamps, 150th Anniv. — A1471

1999, Jan. 1   Photo.   Perf. 13
Booklet Stamps

2692	A1471	3fr black & red	7.00 6.00
2693	A1471	3fr red & black	1.25 1.00
a.		Booklet pane, #2692, 4 #2693 + label	13.00
		Complete booklet, #2693a	14.00

No. 2692 has black denomination; No. 2693 has red denomination. Stamp Day.

Public Assistance Hospital, Paris, 150th Anniv. — A1472

1999, Jan. 9
2694	A1472	3fr multicolored	1.25 .30

Diplomatic Relations with Israël, 50th Anniv. — A1473

1999, Jan. 24
2695	A1473	4.40fr multicolored	2.00 .75

Festival Stamps — A1474

1999, Feb. 6   Photo.   Perf. 13
2696	A1474	3fr Stars, "Je t'aime"	1.25 .30
2697	A1474	3fr Rose	1.25 .30

Booklet Stamps
Self-Adhesive
Die Cut Perf. 10

2698	A1474	3fr like #2696	1.25 .30
2699	A1474	3fr like #2697	1.25 .30
a.		Bklt. pane, 5 ea #2698-2699	14.00

No. 2699a is a complete booklet.
A €1.16 stamp of type A1474 was included in a limited-edition booklet issued Nov. 4, 2020.

Art Series

St. Luke the Evangelist, Sculpture by Jean Goujon (1510-66) A1475

Painting, "Waterlillies in Moonlight," by Claude Monet (1840-1926) A1476

Stained Glass, Cathedral of Auch, by Arnauld de Moles, 16th Cent. — A1477

Charles I, King of England, by Sir Anthony Van Dyck — A1478

1999   Engr.   Perf. 13
2700	A1475	6.70fr multicolored	3.00 1.00

Litho.
2701	A1476	6.70fr multicolored	3.00 1.00

Engr.
2702	A1477	6.70fr multicolored	3.00 1.00

Photo.
Perf. 13¼x13
2703	A1478	6.70fr multicolored	3.00 1.00
		Nos. 2700-2703 (4)	12.00 4.00

Issued: No. 2700, 2/13; No. 2701, 5/29; No. 2702, 6/19; No. 2703, 11/11.

National Census — A1479

1999, Feb. 20   Photo.   Perf. 13½
2704	A1479	3fr multicolored	1.25 .30

Cultural Heritage of Lebanon A1480

Mosaic illustrating transformation of Zeus into bull, Natl. Museum of Beirut.

1999, Feb. 27   Perf. 12½
2705	A1480	4.40fr multicolored	2.00 .70

Asterix, by Albert Uderzo and Rene Goscinny — A1481

1999, Mar. 6   Photo.   Perf. 13¼
2706	A1481	3fr multicolored	1.25 .30
a.		Perf. 13¼x12¾	1.40 1.20

Booklet Stamp
Perf. 13¼x12¾
2707	A1481	3fr +60c like #2706	3.00 1.50
b.		Booklet pane, 4 #2706a, 3 #2707 + label	14.00
		Complete booklet, #2707b	15.00

Souvenir Sheet
2707A	A1481	3fr +60c like #2706	2.50 2.00

Stamp Day. Stamp design in No. 2707A continues into the margins.

Council of Europe, 50th Anniv. — A1482

1999, Mar. 19
2708	A1482	3fr multicolored	1.25 .30

Announcements A1483a

No. 2709, Marriage (Oui). No. 2710, It's a boy (C'est un garcon). No. 2711, It's a girl (C'est une fille). No. 2712, Thank you.

1999, Mar. 20   Perf. 13
2709	A1483	3fr multi	1.25 .30
2710	A1483	3fr multi	1.25 .30
2711	A1483	3fr multi	1.25 .30
2712	A1483a	3fr multi	1.25 .30
		Nos. 2709-2712 (4)	5.00 1.20

See Nos. 2721-2722.

Souvenir Sheet

PhilexFrance '99 — A1484

Works of art: a, Venus de Milo. b, Mona Lisa, by Da Vinci. c, Liberty Guiding the People, by Delacroix.

Litho. & Engr.
1999, Mar. 26   Perf. 13¼
2713	A1484	Sheet of 3	80.00 60.00
a.-b.		5fr each	17.50 12.50
c.		10fr multicolored	37.50 30.00

No. 2713 sold for 50fr, with 30fr serving as a donation to the Assoc. for the Development of Philately.

Elections to the European Parliament A1485

1999, Mar. 27   Photo.   Perf. 13
2714	A1485	3fr multicolored	1.25 .30

Richard I, the Lion-Hearted (1157-1199), King of England — A1486

1999, Apr. 10   Engr.   Perf. 13x12½
2715	A1486	3fr multicolored	1.25 .35

Tourism Series

Dieppe — A1487

Haut-Koenigsbourg Castle, Bas-Rhin — A1488

Birthpalce of Champollion, Figeac A1489

Chateau, Arnac-Pompadour A1490

1999   Engr.   Perf. 13½
2716	A1487	3fr multicolored	1.25 .30

Litho. & Engr.
Perf. 13
2717	A1488	3fr multicolored	1.40 .50
2718	A1489	3fr multicolored	1.25 .30

Engr.
2719	A1490	3fr multicolored	1.25 .30
		Nos. 2716-2719 (4)	5.15 1.40

Issued: No. 2716, 4/17; No. 2717, 5/15; No. 2718, 6/26; No. 2719, 7/10.

The Camargue Nature Preserve A1491

1999, Apr. 24   Photo.   Perf. 13x13½
2720	A1491	3fr multicolored	1.25 .30

Europa.

Announcements Type of 1999 and

A1492

No. 2721, Nice Holiday (bonnes vacances). No. 2722, Happy Birthday (joyeux anniversaire). No. 2723, Long Live Vacations (Vive les vacances).

1999, May 13   Photo.   Perf. 13
2721	A1483	3fr multi	1.25 .30
2722	A1483	3fr multi	1.25 .30
2723	A1492	3fr multi	1.25 .30
		Nos. 2721-2723 (3)	3.75 .90

Saint Pierre, Martinique A1493

1999, May 15
2724	A1493	3fr multicolored	1.25 .30

Detail of "Noctuelles" Dish, by Émile Gallé, School of Nancy Museum A1494

1999, May 22
2725	A1494	3fr multicolored	1.25 .30

Souvenir Sheet

World Old Roses Competition, Lyon — A1495

a, 4.50fr, Mme. Caroline Testout. b, 3fr, Mme. Alfred Carrière. c, 4.50fr, La France.

1999, May 28   Perf. 13½x13
2726	A1495	Sheet of 3, #a.-c.	5.50 4.50

Court of Saint-Emilion, 800th Anniv. — A1496

1999, May 29 Engr. Perf. 13¼x13
2727 A1496 3.80fr multicolored 1.75 .60

Hotel de la Monnaie, French Mint Headquarters A1497

1999, June 5 Engr. Perf. 13
2728 A1497 4.50fr brn org & bl 2.00 .75

A1498

1999, June 12 Photo. Perf. 13¼
2729 A1498 3fr multicolored 1.25 .30
Countess of Segur (1799-1874), children's storyteller.

Loving Welcome — A1499

1999, June 19 Perf. 13
2730 A1499 3fr multicolored 1.25 .30

René Caillié (1799-1838), Explorer of Africa — A1500

1999, June 26 Engr. Perf. 13¼
2731 A1500 4.50fr multicolored 2.00 .75

1st French Postage Stamps, 150th Anniv. — A1501

1999, July 2 Photo. Perf. 11¾x13
2732 A1501 6.70fr multicolored 3.00 1.00
PhilexFrance '99, World Philatelic Exhibition. No. 2732 was printed with a se-tenant label and contains a holographic image. Soaking in water may affect the hologram.

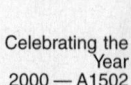

Celebrating the Year 2000 — A1502

1999, July 5 Photo. Perf. 13
2733 A1502 3fr multicolored 1.25 .30

Year 2000 Stamp Design Contest Winner A1503

1999, July 6
2734 A1503 3fr multicolored 1.25 .30

Total Solar Eclipse, Aug. 11, 1999 — A1504

1999, July 8 Perf. 12x12¼
2735 A1504 3fr multicolored 1.25 .30

Gathering of Tall Ships, Rouen, July 9-18 — A1505

Sailing ships: a, Simón Bolivar. b, Iskra. c, Statsraad Lehmkuhl. d, Asgard II. e, Belle Poule. f, Belem. g, Amerigo Vespucci. h, Sagres. i, Europa. j, Cuauhtemoc.

1999, July 10 Photo. Perf. 13
2736 1fr Sheet of 10 6.50 6.50
a.-j. A1505 any single .60 .50

1999 Rugby World Cup, Cardiff, Wales — A1506

1999, Sept. 11 Photo. Perf. 13¼
2737 A1506 3fr multicolored 1.25 .40
a. Miniature sheet of 10 12.50
Value is for stamp with surrounding selvage. One stamp in No. 2737a has a missing "F" in the printer's mark.

Frédéric Ozanam (1813-53), Historian — A1507

1999, Sept. 11 Engr. Perf. 13
2738 A1507 4.50fr multicolored 2.00 .75

Emmaus Movement, 50th Anniv. — A1508

1999, Sept. 26 Photo. Perf. 13
2739 A1508 3fr multicolored 1.25 .30

Cats and Dogs — A1509

Designs: No. 2740, Chartreux cat. No. 2741, European cat. No. 2742, Pyrenean Mountain dog. No. 2743, Brittany spaniel.

1999, Oct. 2 Photo. Perf. 13¼
2740 A1509 2.70fr multi 1.25 .30
2741 A1509 3fr multi 1.25 .30
2742 A1509 3fr multi 1.25 .30
2743 A1509 4.50fr multi 2.00 .75
Nos. 2740-2743 (4) 5.75 1.65

Frédéric Chopin (1810-49), Composer A1510

1999, Oct. 17 Engr. Perf. 13¼
2744 A1510 3.80fr multicolored 1.75 .75
See Poland No. 3484.

A1511

Best Wishes for Year 2000 — A1512

1999, Nov. 20 Photo. Perf. 13x13¼
2745 A1511 3fr multi 1.25 .30
2746 A1512 3fr multi 1.25 .30
No. 2746 was printed with se-tenant label.

Paris Metro, Cent. — A1513

1999, Dec. 4 Photo. Perf. 13
2747 A1513 3fr multi 1.25 .30

Council of State, Bicent. — A1514

1999, Dec. 11
2748 A1514 3fr multi 1.25 .30

Reconstruction of Lighthouses — A1515

2000, Jan. 1 Photo. Perf. 13x12¾
2749 A1515 3fr multi 1.25 .30
Reconstruction of San Juan de Salvamento Lighthouse, Argentina and replication of its design at La Rochelle, France.

Hearts — A1516

2000, Jan. 8 Photo. Perf. 13
2750 A1516 3fr Snakes 1.25 .30
2751 A1516 3fr Face 1.25 .30
a. Souvenir sheet, 3 #2750, 2 #2751 8.00 6.50

Self-Adhesive Booklet Stamps
Serpentine Die-Cut
2752 A1516 3fr Like #2750 1.25 .30
2753 A1516 3fr Like #2751 1.25 .30
a. Bklt. pane, 5 ea #2752-2753 12.50
Values for Nos. 2750-2751 are for stamps with surrounding selvage. No. 2753a is a complete booklet.

Bank of France, Bicent. — A1517

2000, Jan. 15 Litho. Perf. 13
2754 A1517 3fr multi 1.25 .30

Prefectorial Corps, Bicent. — A1518

2000, Feb. 17 Photo. Perf. 13x12¼
2755 A1518 3fr multi 1.25 .30

Art Series

Venus and the Graces Offering Gifts to a Young Girl, by Sandro Botticelli (1445-1510) A1519

The Waltz, by Camille Claudel — A1520

Visage Rouge, by Gaston Chaissac A1521

Carolingian Mosaic, Germigny-des-Prés — A1522

2000 Photo. Perf. 13¼x13
2756 A1519 6.70fr multi 3.00 1.00
2757 A1520 6.70fr multi 3.00 1.00
2758 A1521 6.70fr multi 3.00 1.00
2759 A1522 6.70fr multi 3.00 1.00
Issued: No. 2756, 2/25; No. 2757, 4/8; No. 2758, 9/23; 10/21.

Tourism Series

Carcassonne — A1523

Saint-Guilhem-Le-Désert — A1524

Gérardmer A1525

Abbey Church of
Ottmarsheim
A1526

2000 **Photo.** **Perf. 13**
2760 A1523 3fr multi 1.25 .30

Engr.
Perf. 13¼
2761 A1524 3fr multi 1.25 .30
2762 A1525 3fr multi 1.25 .30

Perf. 12¼x13
2763 A1526 3fr multi 1.25 .30
Nos. 2760-2763 (4) 5.00 1.20

Issued: No. 2760, 3/3; No. 2761, 4/8; No. 2762, 4/17; No. 2763, 6/17.

Tintin — A1527

2000, Mar. 11 **Photo.** **Perf. 13¼**
2764 A1527 3fr multi 1.25 .30
a. Perf. 13½x13 1.40 1.20

Perf. 13½x13
2765 A1527 3fr + 60c multi 2.50 2.00
a. Booklet pane, 4 #2764a, 3 #2765 + label 14.00
Complete booklet, #2765a 15.00
b. Souvenir sheet of 1 2.50 2.00

Stamp Day.

Bretagne
Parliament
Building
Restoration
A1528

2000, Mar. 25 **Photo.** **Perf. 13¼**
2766 A1528 3fr multi 1.25 .30

Madagascar
Periwinkles
A1529

2000, Mar. 25 **Litho.** **Perf. 13x13¼**
2767 A1529 4.50fr multi 2.00 .80

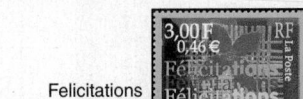

Felicitations
A1530

2000, Apr. 7 **Photo.** **Perf. 13x13¼**
2768 A1530 3fr multi 1.25 .30

The 20th
Century
A1531

No. 2769: a, France as World Cup soccer champions, 1998, vert. b, Marcel Cerdan wins middleweight boxing title, 1948. c, Charles Lindbergh flies solo across Atlantic, 1927. d, Jean-Claude Killy wins three Winter Olympics gold medals, 1968, vert. e, Carl Lewis wins four Olympic gold medals, 1984, vert.

Perf. 13¼x13 (vert. stamps), 13x13¼
2000, Apr. 15
2769 A1531 Sheet, 2 ea #a-e 14.00 14.00
a.-e. 3fr any single 1.40 .75

Top part of No. 2769 contains Nos. 2769a-2769e and is separated from bottom part of sheet by a row of rouletting.
See No. 2787, 2804, 2837, 2881, 2915.

Automobiles — A1532

No. 2770: a, Bugatti 35. b, Citroen Traction. c, Renault 4CV. d, Simca Chambord. e, Hispano-Suiza K6. f, Volkswagen Beetle. g, 1962 Cadillac. h, Peugeot 203. i, Citroen DS19. j, Ferrari 250 GTO.

2000, May 5 **Perf. 13¼x13**
2770 A1532 Sheet of 10, #a.-j. 7.50 7.50
a.-e. 1fr any single .45 .35
f.-j. 2fr any single .90 .60

Europa, 2000
Common Design Type

2000, May 9 **Photo.** **Perf. 13¼**
2771 CD17 3fr multi 1.25 .40

Henry-Louis
Duhamel du
Monceau (1700-
82), Agronomist
A1533

2000, May 13 **Engr.** **Perf. 13**
2772 A1533 4.50fr multi 2.00 .80

French Federation of
Philatelic Associations,
73rd Congress,
Nevers — A1534

2000, May 19 **Engr.** **Perf. 13¼**
2773 A1534 3fr multi 1.25 .30

Happy
Vacation — A1535

2000, June 1 **Photo.** **Perf. 13¼x13**
2774 A1535 3fr multi 1.25 .30

A1536

2000, June 3 **Engr.** **Perf. 13x12¼**
2775 A1536 3fr multi 1.25 .30
First Ascent of Annapurna, 50th anniv.

Nature — A1537

2.70fr, Agrias sardanapalus butterfly. No. 2777, Giraffe. No. 2778, Allosaurus. 4.50fr, Tulipa lutea.

2000, June 17 **Photo.** **Perf. 13¼**
2776 A1537 2.70fr multi 1.25 .30
2777 A1537 3fr multi, vert. 1.25 .30
2778 A1537 3fr multi, vert 1.25 .30
2779 A1537 4.50fr multi, vert 2.00 .75
a. Souvenir sheet, #2776-2779 6.00 6.00
Nos. 2776-2779 (4) 5.75 1.65

Antoine de Saint-
Exupéry (1900-44),
Aviator, Writer — A1538

2000, June 24 **Photo.** **Perf. 13¼x13**
2780 A1538 3fr multi 1.25 .30

Yellow Train of
Cerdagne,
Cent. — A1539

2000, July 14 **Perf. 13x13¼**
2781 A1539 3fr multi 1.25 .30

Folklore — A1540

2000, Aug. 12 **Photo.** **Perf. 13**
2782 A1540 4.50fr multi 2.00 .80

2000 Summer
Olympics,
Sydney — A1541

Designs: No. 2783, Cycling, fencing, relay racer. No. 2784, Relay racer, judo, diving.

2000, Sept. 9
2783 A1541 3fr multi 1.40 .30
2784 A1541 3fr multi 1.40 .30
a. Pair, #2783-2784 3.00 2.00
b. Sheet, 5 #2784a + label 15.00 15.00

Olymphilex 2000, Sydney (No. 2784b).

Brother Alfred
Stanke (1904-75)
A1542

2000, Sept. 23 **Engr.**
2785 A1542 4.40fr multi 2.00 .70

S.O.S. Amitié,
40th
Anniv. — A1543

2000, Sept. 30 **Litho.** **Perf. 13**
2786 A1543 3fr multi 1.40 .30

20th Century Type

No. 2787: a, Man on the Moon, 1969, vert. b, Paid vacations, 1936. c, Invention of washing machine, 1901, vert. d, Woman suffrage, 1944, vert. e, Universal Declaration of Human Rights, 1948.

Perf. 13¼x13 (vert. stamps), 13x13¼
2000, Sept. 30 **Photo.**
2787 A1531 Sheet, 2 each #a-e 14.00 14.00
a.-e. 3fr Any single 1.40 .50

The top and bottom parts of No. 2787 contains Nos. 2787a-2787e and are separated by a row of rouletting.

2001, Start of
New Millennium
A1544

2000, Oct. 14 **Litho.** **Perf. 13**
2788 A1544 3fr multi 1.40 .30

The Lovers'
Kiosk, by
Peynet — A1545

2000, Nov. 4 **Engr.** **Perf. 13¼x13**
2789 A1545 3fr multi 1.40 .50

Endangered
Birds — A1546

2000, Nov. 4 **Photo.** **Perf. 13¼**
2790 A1546 3fr Kiwi 1.40 .40
2791 A1546 5.20fr Falcon 2.50 1.50

See New Zealand Nos. 1688, 1694.

Start of the 3rd Millennium — A1547

2000, Nov. 9 **Photo.** **Perf. 13x13¼**
2792 A1547 3fr multi + label 1.40 .30

Issued in sheets of 10 stamps + 10 labels, which could be personalized for an extra fee.

Holiday Greetings
A1548

2000, Nov. 11 **Perf. 12¼x13**
2793 A1548 3fr Meilleurs voeux 1.40 .30

Perf. 13¼
2794 A1548 3fr Bonne année 1.40 .30

Union of Metallurgical &
Mining Industries,
Cent. — A1549

Engr. with Foil Application
2000, Dec. 9 **Perf. 13x13¼**
2795 A1549 4.50fr multi 2.10 .90

World Handball Championships A1550

2001, Jan. 20 **Photo.** *Perf. 13¼*
2796 A1550 3fr multi 1.40 .30

Heart — A1551

2001, Jan. 27
2797 A1551 3fr multi 1.40 .30
  a.   Souvenir sheet of 5 10.00 10.00

Value of No. 2797 is for stamp with surrounding selvage.

Art Series

The Peasant Dance, by Pieter Breughel, the Elder A1552

Hotel des Chevaliers de Saint-Jean-de-Jérusalem — A1553

Yvette Guilbert Singing "Linger, Longer, Loo," by Henri de Toulouse-Lautrec (1864-1901) A1554

Honfleur at Low Tide, by Johan Barthold Jongkind A1555

Engr., Photo (#2800), Litho (#2801)
2001 *Perf. 13x13¼, 13¼x13 (#2800)*
2798 A1552 6.70fr multi 3.00 1.00
2799 A1553 6.70fr multi 3.00 1.00
2800 A1554 6.70fr multi 3.00 1.00
2801 A1555 6.70fr multi 3.00 1.00
  Nos. 2798-2801 (4) 12.00 4.00

Issued: No. 2798, 2/3; No. 2799, 4/21; No. 2800, 9/8; No. 2801, 10/27.

Gaston Lagaffe, by André Franquin — A1556

2001, Feb. 24 **Photo.** *Perf. 13¼*
2802 A1556 3fr multi 1.40 .30
  a.   Perf. 13¼x13 1.40 1.20
       Perf. 13¼x13
2803 A1556 3fr +60c multi 3.00 1.50
  a.   Souvenir sheet of 1 6.00 3.50
  b.   Booklet pane, 5 #2802a, 3 #2803 18.00
    Booklet, #2803b 19.00

Stamp Day.

20th Century Type of 2000

No. 2804 — Communications: a, Television. b, Compact disc. c, Advertisements, vert. d, Radio, vert. e, Portable telephone, vert.

Perf. 13¼x13 (vert. stamps), 13x13¼
2001, Mar. 17 **Photo.**
2804 A1531 Sheet, 2 each #a-e 14.00 14.00
  a.-e.   3fr Any single 1.40 .75

Top part of No. 2804 contains Nos. 2804a-2804e and is separated from bottom part by a row of roulleting.

Announcements A1557

Designs: No. 2805, It's a girl. No. 2806, It's a boy. No. 2807, Thank you. 4.50fr, Yes (marriage).

2001 **Frame Color** *Perf. 13*
2805 A1557 3fr brt pink 1.40 .30
  a.   Litho., stamp + label 6.50 6.50
2806 A1557 3fr brt blue 1.40 .30
  a.   Litho., stamp + label 6.50 6.50
2807 A1557 3fr brt yel grn 1.40 .30
  a.   Litho., stamp + label 6.50 6.50
2808 A1557 4.50fr orange 2.10 .75
  Nos. 2805-2808 (4) 6.30 1.65

Issued: Nos. 2805-2808, 3/23; Nos. 2805a-2807a, 11/8.

Nos. 2805a-2807a were issued in sheets of 10 stamps and 10 labels that sold for 60fr on day of issue. The labels could be personalized. Frames on Nos. 2805 and 2806 look splotchy, while those on Nos. 2805a and 2806a have a distinct dot structure. The frame on No. 2807 has tightly spaced small dots, while on No. 2807a, the dots are more widely spaced.

Wildlife — A1558

2001, Apr. 21 **Photo.** *Perf. 13¼*
2809 A1558 2.70fr Squirrel 1.25 .40
2810 A1558 3fr Roe deer 1.40 .40
2811 A1558 3fr Hedgehog, horiz. 1.40 .40
2812 A1558 4.50fr Ermine 2.10 .75
  a.   Souvenir sheet, #2809-2812 7.00 6.50
  Nos. 2809-2812 (4) 6.15 1.95

Tourism Issue

Nogent-le-Rotrou A1559

Besançon A1560

Calais — A1561

Château de Grignan A1562

Engr., Litho & Engr. (#2813)
2001 *Perf. 13¼x13 (#2813), 13*
2813 A1559 3fr multi 1.40 .40
2814 A1560 3fr multi 1.40 .30
2815 A1561 3fr multi 1.40 .30
2816 A1562 3fr multi 1.40 .30
  Nos. 2813-2816 (4) 5.60 1.30

Issued: No. 2813, 4/28; No. 2814, 5/5; No. 2815, 6/16; No. 2816, 7/7.

Europa — A1563

2001, May 8 **Photo.** *Perf. 13*
2817 A1563 3fr multi 1.40 .35

Gardens of Versailles — A1564

2001, May 12
2818 A1564 4.40fr multi 2.00 .80

Singers — A1565

Designs: No. 2819, Claude François (1939-78). No. 2820, Léo Ferré (1916-93). No. 2821, Serge Gainsbourg (1928-91). No. 2822, Dalida (1933-87). No. 2823, Michel Berger (1947-92). No. 2824, Barbara (1930-97).

2001, May 19 **Photo.** *Perf. 13*
2819 A1565 3fr multi 1.40 .75
2820 A1565 3fr multi 1.40 .75
2821 A1565 3fr multi 1.40 .75
2822 A1565 3fr multi 1.40 .75
2823 A1565 3fr multi 1.40 .75
2824 A1565 3fr multi 1.40 .75
  a.   Souvenir sheet, #2819-2824 12.00 12.00
  Nos. 2819-2824 (6) 8.40 4.50

No. 2824a sold for 28fr with the Red Cross receiving 10fr of that.

Old Lyon — A1566

2001, May 19 **Engr.** *Perf. 13¼*
2825 A1566 3fr multi 1.40 .30

French Federation of Philatelic Associations 74th Congress, Tours — A1567

2001, June 1
2826 A1567 3fr multi 1.40 .30

Jean Vilar (1912-71), Actor — A1568

Litho. & Engr.
2001, June 7 *Perf. 13*
2827 A1568 3fr multi 1.40 .40

Vacation A1569

2001, June 10 **Litho.** *Perf. 13*
2828 A1569 3fr multi 1.40 .30
Booklet Stamp
Self-Adhesive
2829 A1569 3fr multi 1.40 .30
  a.   Booklet of 10 14.00

1 Euro Coin — A1570

2001, June 23 **Photo.** *Perf. 12½*
2830 A1570 3fr multi 1.40 .30

Value is for copy with surrounding selvage.

Albert Caquot (1881-1976), Engineer A1571

2001, June 30 **Engr.** *Perf. 13¼*
2831 A1571 4.50fr multi 2.00 .75

Law Guaranteeing Freedom of Association, Cent. — A1572

2001, July 1 **Photo.** *Perf. 13*
2832 A1572 3fr multi 1.40 .30

Trains A1573

No. 2833: a, Eurostar. b, American 220. c, Crocodile. d, Crampton. e, Garratt 59. f, Pacific Chapelon. g, Mallard. h, Capitole. i, Autorail Panoramique. j, 230 Class P8.

2001, July 6 **Photo.** *Perf. 13¼*
2833 A1573 Sheet of 10 10.00 8.00
  a.-j.   1.50fr Any single .90 .65

Geneva Convention on Refugees, UN High Commisioner for Refugees, 50th Anniv. — A1574

2001, July 28 *Perf. 13*
2834 A1574 4.50fr multi 2.00 .75

Marianne Type of 1997 Inscribed "RF" at Lower Left Instead of "La Poste"

2001 **Engr.** *Perf. 13*
2835 A1409 (3fr) red 1.40 .25
  d.   Sheet of 15 + 15 labels 60.00

Serpentine Die Cut 6¾ Vert.
Self-Adhesive

2835A	A1409 (3fr) red	1.40	.25
b.	Booklet of 10	15.00	
e.	No. 2835 with attached label	6.00	

No. 2835Ae is from a sheet having either small or large-sized labels that could be personalized.

2001, Aug. 1 Engr. *Perf. 13 Horiz.*
Coil Stamp
Water-Activated Gum

2835C	A1409 (3fr) red	1.40	.25

Issued: Nos. 2835, 2835C, 8/1; No. 2835A, 9/24. No. 2835Ae, 2004.
No. 2835d sold for €10.03. Labels could be personalized for an additional price.

Pierre de Fermat (1601-65), Mathematician A1575

2001, Aug. 19 Engr. *Perf. 13¼x13*

2836	A1575 4.50fr multi	2.00	.75

20th Century Type of 2000

No. 2837 — Science: a, First man in space. b, DNA. c, Chip cards. d, Laser. e, Penicillin.

Perf. 13¼x13 (vert. stamps), 13
2001, Sept. 22 Photo.

2837	A1531 Sheet, 2 each	14.00	14.00
	#a-e		
a.-e.	3fr Any single	1.40	.70

Top part of No. 2837 contains Nos. 2837a-2837e and is separated from bottom part of sheet by a row of rouletting.

Astrolabe Sculpture, Val-de-Reuil A1576

2001, Sept. 29 *Perf. 13*

2838	A1576 3fr multi	1.40	.30

Halloween A1577

2001, Oct. 20

2839	A1577 3fr multi	1.40	.30
a.	Souvenir sheet of 5 + 4 labels	8.00	8.00

Jean Pierre-Bloch (1905-99), Human Rights Advocate — A1578

2001, Nov. 8 Engr. *Perf. 13*

2840	A1578 4.50fr multi	2.00	.75

Albert Decaris (1901-88), Artist — A1579

2001, Nov. 9 Engr. *Perf. 13¼x13*

2841	A1579 3fr multi	1.40	.40

Jacques Chaban-Delmas (1915-2000), Politician — A1580

2001, Nov. 10 Engr. *Perf. 13x13¼*

2842	A1580 3fr multi	1.40	.40

Holiday Greetings A1581

Designs: Nos. 2843, 2845 Bonne Année (Happy New Year). Nos. 2844, 2846 Meilleurs Voeux (Best wishes).

2001, Nov. 9 Litho. *Perf. 13*

2843	A1581 3fr multi	1.40	.30
2844	A1581 3fr multi	1.40	.30

Serpentine Die Cut 11
Self-Adhesive
Booklet Stamps

2845	A1581 3fr multi	1.40	.30
2846	A1581 3fr multi	1.40	.30
a.	Booklet, 5 each # 2845-2846	14.00	

Fountains — A1582

Designs: 3fr, Nejjarine Fountain, Fez, Morocco. 3.80fr, Wallace Fountain, Paris.

2001, Dec. 14 Photo. *Perf. 13¼*

2847	A1582 3fr multi	1.40	.40
2848	A1582 3.80fr multi	1.75	1.00

See Morocco Nos. 914-915.

100 Cents = 1 Euro (€)

Marianne (With Euro Denominations) — A1583

2002, Jan. 1 Engr. *Perf. 13*

2849	A1583 1c yellow	.25	.25
2850	A1583 2c brown	.25	.25
2851	A1583 5c brt bl grn	.25	.25
2852	A1583 10c purple	.25	.25
2853	A1583 20c brt org	.60	.30
2854	A1583 41c brt green	1.20	.25
2855	A1583 50c dk blue	1.50	.25
2856	A1583 53c apple grn	1.60	.40
2857	A1583 58c blue	1.75	.50
2858	A1583 64c dark org	1.90	.50
2859	A1583 67c brt blue	2.00	.50
a.	67c deep blue	2.00	.50
2860	A1583 69c brt pink	2.10	.60
2861	A1583 €1 Prus blue	3.00	.80
2862	A1583 €1.02 dk green	3.00	.90
a.	Souvenir sheet, #2835, 2854, 2856-2858, 2859a, 2860, 2862	15.00	15.00
2863	A1583 €2 violet	6.00	1.50
a.	Souvenir sheet, #2849-2853, 2855, 2861, 2863	12.00	12.00
	Nos. 2849-2863 (15)	25.65	7.50

Coil Stamp
Perf. 13 Horiz.

2864	A1583 41c brt green	1.50	.30

See Nos. 2952-2957, 3043, 3043P-3043Q.

Orchids — A1584

Designs: 29c, Orchis insularis. 33c, Ophrys fuciflora.

2002, Jan. 2 Litho. *Perf. 13*

2865	A1584 29c multi	1.00	.30
2866	A1584 33c multi	1.50	.40

Nos. 2865-2866 are known only precanceled. See second note after No. 132.
See Nos. 2958-2959, 3046, 3168.

Heart of Voh, Photograph by Yann Arthurs-Bertrand A1585

2002, Jan. 18 Photo. *Perf. 13¼*

2867	A1585 46c multi	1.40	.40
a.	Souvenir sheet of 5	7.00	7.00

Value of No. 2867 is for stamp with surrounding selvage.

2002 Winter Olympics, Salt Lake City — A1586

2002, Jan. 26 *Perf. 13*

2868	A1586 46c multi	1.40	.30

Art Series

Sphere Concorde, by Jesús Rafael Soto — A1587

The Kiss, by Gustav Klimt — A1588

The Dancers, by Fernando Botero — A1589

Self-Portrait, by Elisabeth Vigée-Lebrun A1590

2002 Photo. *Perf. 13¼x13*

2869	A1587 75c multi	2.25	1.00
2870	A1588 €1.02 multi	3.00	1.00
2871	A1589 €1.02 multi	3.00	1.00

Engr.

2872	A1590 €1.02 multi	3.00	1.00
	Nos. 2869-2872 (4)	11.25	4.00

Issued: No. 2869, 11/11. No. 2870, 2/8; No. 2871, 4/27. No. 2872, 10/12.

Alain Bosquet (1919-98), Poet — A1591

2002, Feb. 16 Engr. *Perf. 13*

2873	A1591 58c multi	1.75	.80

It's A Girl — A1592

It's A Boy — A1593

Yes — A1594

2002, Feb. 23 Photo.

2874	A1592 46c multi	1.40	.30
2875	A1593 46c multi	1.40	.30
2876	A1594 69c multi	2.00	.80
	Nos. 2874-2876 (3)	4.80	1.40

Europa — A1595

2002, Mar. 2 *Perf. 13¼*

2877	A1595 46c multi	1.40	.30

Boule and Bill, by Jean Roba — A1596

Designs: 46c, Boule, Bill, bird. 46c+9c, Boule, Bill, ball.

2002, Mar. 16 *Perf. 13¼*

2878	A1596 46c multi	1.40	.50
a.	Perf. 13¼x13	1.40	1.20

Perf. 13¼x13

2879	A1596 46c +9c multi	3.00	1.50
a.	Souvenir sheet of 1	3.00	2.50
b.	Booklet pane, 5 #2878a, 3 #2879	18.00	—
	Booklet, #2879b	19.00	

Stamp Day. No. 2879 surtax for Red Cross. Stamp on No. 2879a has continuous design.

Nimes Amphitheater — A1597

Litho. & Engr.
2002, Mar. 22 *Perf. 13*

2880	A1597 46c multi	1.40	.30

20th Century Type of 2000

No. 2881 — Transportation: a, Concorde supersonic airplane. b, TGV train. c, Ocean liner France, vert. d, Mobylette motor scooter, vert. e, Citroen 2 CV automobile, vert.

Perf. 13, 13¼x13 (vert. stamps)
2002, Mar. 23 Photo.

2881	A1531 Sheet, 2 each	14.00	14.00
	#a-e		
a.-e.	46c Any single	1.40	.75

Top part of No. 2881 contains Nos. 2881a-2881e and is separated from bottom part of sheet by a row of rouletting.

Encounter of Matthew Flinders and Nicolas Boudin, Bicent. — A1598

Map of Australia, portrait and ship of: 46c, Flinders. 79c, Boudin.

2002, Apr. 4   **Perf. 13¼**
2882 A1598 46c multi   1.40   .40
2883 A1598 79c multi   2.25   1.50
   See Australia Nos. 2053-2054.

Tourism Series

La Charité-sur-
Loire
A1599

Collioure
A1600

Locronan
A1601

Neufchateau
A1602

Engraved (#2884, 2886), Photo.
(#2885)

2002   **Perf. 13¼**
2884 A1599 46c multi   1.40   .30
2885 A1600 46c multi   1.40   .30
2886 A1601 46c multi   1.40   .30
2887 A1602 46c multi   1.40   .30
   Nos. 2884-2887 (4)   5.60   1.20

   Issue dates: No. 2884, 4/6; No. 2885, 6/22; No. 2886, 7/13; No. 2887, 10/12/02.
   Numbers have been reserved for additional stamps in this set.

Birthday Greetings
A1603

Invitation — A1604

2002, Apr. 6   **Photo.**   **Perf. 13**
2888 A1603 46c multi   1.40   .30
   a.   Litho., stamp + label   6.00   6.00
2889 A1604 46c multi   1.40   .30
   a.   Litho., stamp + label   6.00   6.00

   Issued: Nos. 2888a, 2889a, 11/7. Nos. 2888a and 2889a were issued in sheets of 10 stamps and 10 labels that sold for €6.19 on day of issue. The labels could be personalized.
   No. 2888a has a duller blue in "Anniversaire" than No. 2888, but is otherwise quite similar in appearance. The gold ink on No. 2889a has a more coppery look than that on No. 2889.

100th Paris-Roubaix
Bicycle Race — A1605

2002, Mar. 13
2890 A1605 46c multi   1.40   .30

2002 World Cup Soccer
Championships, Japan and
Korea — A1606

   No. 2891: a, Flags, soccer ball and field (32mm diameter). b, Soccer player, year of French championship.

2002, Apr. 27   **Perf. 12¾**
2891 A1606   Horiz. pair   2.75   2.50
   a.-b.   46c Any single   1.40   .90
   c.   Sheet, 5 #2891   15.00   15.00
   Issued: No. 2891c, 5/18.
   See Argentina No. 2184, Brazil No. 2840, Germany No. 2163, Italy No. 2526 and Uruguay No. 1946.

Marine
Life — A1607

   Designs: 41c, Sea turtle (tortue luth), vert. No. 2893, Killer whale (orque). No. 2894, Dolphin (grand dauphin). 69c, Seal (phoque veau marin).

2002, May 4   **Perf. 13¼**
2892 A1607 41c multi   1.25   .30
2893 A1607 46c multi   1.25   .30
2894 A1607 46c multi   1.25   .30
2895 A1607 69c multi   2.00   .75
   a.   Souvenir sheet, #2892-2895   6.50   6.50
   Nos. 2892-2895 (4)   5.75   1.65

   Worldwide Fund for Nature (No. 2895a).

French Federation of Philatelic
Associations 75th Congress,
Marseilles — A1608

2002, May 17   **Engr.**   **Perf. 13**
2896 A1608 46c multi   1.40   .40

Legion of Honor,
Bicent. — A1609

2002, May 18   **Photo.**
2897 A1609 46c multi   1.40   .30

Rocamadour — A1610

2002, May 25   **Perf. 13¼**
2898 A1610 46c multi   1.40   .30

Louis Delgrés
(1766-1802),
Soldier — A1611

2002, May 25
2899 A1611 46c multi   1.40   .30

Vacation — A1612

2002, June 8   **Litho.**   **Perf. 13**
2900 A1612 46c multi   1.40   .30

Self-Adhesive
Serpentine Die Cut 11

2901 A1612 46c multi   1.40   .30
   a.   Booklet pane of 10   14.00

World Disabled
Athletics
Championships
A1613

2002, June 15   **Photo.**   **Perf. 13¼**
2902 A1613 46c multi   1.40   .30

Saint-Ser
Chapel — A1614

2002, June 22   **Engr.**   **Perf. 13x13¼**
2903 A1614 46c multi   1.40   .30

Metz Cathedral
Stained
Glass — A1615

2002, July 6   **Engr.**   **Perf. 13¼x13**
2904 A1615 46c multi   1.40   .40

Jazz Musicians — A1616

   Designs: No. 2905, Louis Armstrong (1901-71). No. 2906, Ella Fitzgerald (1918-96). No. 2907, Duke Ellington (1899-1974). No. 2908, Stéphane Grappelli (1908-97). No. 2909, Michel Petrucciani (1962-99), horiz. No. 2910, Sidney Bechet (1897-1959), horiz.

2002, July 13   **Photo.**   **Perf. 13**
2905 A1616 46c multi   1.40   .75
2906 A1616 46c multi   1.40   .75
2907 A1616 46c multi   1.40   .75
2908 A1616 46c multi   1.40   .75
2909 A1616 46c multi   1.40   .75
2910 A1616 46c multi   1.40   .75
   a.   Souvenir sheet, #2905-2910   12.00   12.00
   Nos. 2905-2910 (6)   8.40   4.50

   No. 2910a sold for €4.36, with the Red Cross receiving €1.60 of that.

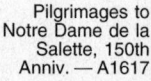

Pilgrimages to
Notre Dame de la
Salette, 150th
Anniv. — A1617

2002, Aug. 15   **Engr.**   **Perf. 13¼x13**
2911 A1617 46c multi   1.40   .30

Choreography — A1618

2002, Sept. 13   **Photo.**   **Perf. 13x13¼**
2912 A1618 53c multi   1.60   .70

Motorcycles — A1619

   No. 2913: a, Honda 750 four. b, Terrot 500 RGST. c, Majestic. d, Norton Commando 750. e, Voxan 1000 Café Racer. f, BMW R90S. g, Harley Davidson Hydra Glide. h, Triumph Bonneville 650. i, Ducati 916. j, Yamaha 500 XT.

2002, Sept. 14   **Perf. 13¼x13**
2913 A1619   Sheet of 10   12.00   12.00
   a.-e.   16c any single   .75   .60
   f.-j.   30c any single   .90   .90

Georges Perec (1936-
82), Writer — A1620

2002, Sept. 21   **Engr.**   **Perf. 13¼**
2914 A1620 46c multi   1.40   .30

20th Century Type of 2000

   No. 2915 — Photographs of everyday life: a, Family on motor scooter, 1955, vert. b, Man, horse and wagon, 1947. c, Woman ironing, 1950. d, Boy at fountain, 1950, vert. e, Girl in classroom, 1965, vert.

Perf. 13¼x13 (vert. stamps), 13

2002, Sept. 28   **Photo.**
2915 A1531   Sheet, 2 each
      #a-e   14.00   14.00
   a.-e.   46c Any single   1.40   .75

   Top part of No. 2915 contains Nos. 2915a-2915e and is separated from bottom part of sheet by a row of rouletting.

Emile Zola (1840-1902),
Novelist — A1621

2002, Oct. 5   **Perf. 13**
2916 A1621 46c multi   1.40   .30

Souvenir Sheet

European Capitals — A1622

   Attractions in Rome: a, Trevi Fountain. b, Coliseum, horiz. c, Trinità de Monti Church and Spanish Steps. d, St. Peter's Basilica, horiz.

2002, Nov. 7   **Perf. 13¼x13, 13x13¼**
2917 A1622   Sheet of 4   6.00   6.00
   a.-d.   46c Any single   1.40   .90

   See Nos. 2985, 3052, 3138, 3223, 3340, 3535, 3728, 3908, 3986, 4183, 4365.

Globe and
Microcircuits
A1623

2002, Nov. 8   **Photo.**   *Perf. 13*
2918 A1623 46c multi   1.40   .30
   a.   Litho., stamp + label   6.00   6.00

Issued: No. 2918a, 11/7. No. 2918a was issued in sheets of 10 stamps and 10 labels that sold for €6.19 on day of issue. The labels could be personalized.
No. 2918a has a hairline at top, above "RF" that No. 2918 does not have, but is otherwise quite similar in appearance.

Holiday Greetings
A1624

2002, Nov. 8   **Photo.**   *Perf. 13*
2919 A1624 46c multi   1.40   .30
   a.   Litho., stamp + label   6.00   6.00

Booklet Stamp
Self-Adhesive
Serpentine Die Cut 11
2920 A1624 46c multi   1.40   .30
   a.   Booklet pane of 10   14.00

Issued: No. 2919a, 11/7. No. 2919a was issued in sheets of 10 stamps and 10 labels that sold for €6.19 on day of issue. The labels could be personalized.
No. 2919a has a finer dot structure, which is most noticeable in the chimney smoke, than No. 2919.

Marianne Type of 1997 Inscribed "RF" at Lower Left
2002, Nov. 9   **Engr.**   *Perf. 13*
2921 A1409 (41c) bright green   1.20   .25
Coil Stamp
Perf. 13 Horiz.
2922 A1409 (41c) bright green   1.20   .25

Alexandre Dumas
(Father) (1802-70),
Writer — A1625

2002, Nov. 30   **Photo.**   *Perf. 13*
2924 A1625 46c multi   1.40   .30

Léopold Sédar
Senghor (1906-
2001), President
of Senegal,
Poet — A1626

2002, Dec. 20
2925 A1626 46c multi   1.40   .30

Hearts — A1627

2003, Jan. 11   *Perf. 13¼*
2926 A1627 46c Four hearts   1.40   .30
   a.   Souvenir sheet of 5   7.00   7.00
2927 A1627 69c Roses   2.00   .75

Values for Nos. 2926-2927 are for examples with surrounding selvage.

Thank
You — A1628

Birth — A1629

2003, Jan. 11   *Perf. 13*
2928 A1628 46c multi   1.40   .30
2929 A1629 46c brt org & brt bl   1.40   .30

Franco-German
Cooperation Treaty,
40th
Anniv. — A1630

2003, Jan. 16   *Perf. 13¼*
2930 A1630 46c multi   1.40   .40

A1631

2003, Feb. 8   **Photo.**   *Perf. 13*
2931 A1631 46c multi   1.40   .30

Delegation for Land-use Planning and Regional Action, 40th Anniv.

Geneviève de Gaulle
Anthonioz (1920-2002),
World War II Resistance
Fighter — A1632

2003, Feb. 11
2932 A1632 46c blk & ol brn   1.40   .30

Paris Chamber of
Commerce and
Industry,
Bicent. — A1633

2003, Feb. 22   *Perf. 13¼*
2933 A1633 46c multi   1.40   .30

Lucky Luke, by Morris
(Maurice De
Bevere) — A1634

Lucky Luke and Jolly Jumper: 46c, Skipping rope on ball on high wire. 46c+9c, Following dog, Rantanplan.

2003, Mar. 15   **Photo.**   *Perf. 13¼*
2934 A1634 46c multi   1.40   .65
   a.   Perf. 13¼x13   1.40   .65
Perf. 13¼x13
2935 A1634 46c +9c multi   3.50   2.00
   a.   Souvenir sheet of 1   3.00   2.50
   b.   Booklet pane, 5 #2934a, 3 #2935   17.50
     Complete booklet, #2935b   18.00

Stamp Day.

Birds — A1635

Designs: 41c, Colibri à tete bleue (Cyanophaia bicolor). No. 2937, Toucan ariel (Ramphastos vitellinus). No. 2938, Colibri grenat (Eulampis jugularis), vert. 69c, Terpsiphone de Bourbon (Terpsiphone bourbonnensis).

2003, Mar. 22   **Photo.**   *Perf. 13¼*
2936 A1635 41c multi   1.20   .30
2937 A1635 46c multi   1.40   .30
2938 A1635 46c multi   1.40   .30
2939 A1635 69c multi   2.00   .75
   a.   Souvenir sheet, #2936-2939   7.00   7.00
     Nos. 2936-2939 (4)   6.00   1.65

Nantes — A1636

2003, Apr. 4   **Engr.**
2940 A1636 46c multi   1.40   .30

Pierre Bérégovoy (1925-
93), Prime
Minister — A1637

2003, Apr. 30   **Engr.**   *Perf. 13x13¼*
2941 A1637 46c multi   1.40   .30

Milan Stefanik
(1880-1919),
Czechoslovakian
General — A1638

2003, May 3   *Perf. 13¼*
2942 A1638 50c multi   1.50   .40
   See Slovakia No. 428.

Europa — A1639

2003, May 8   **Photo.**
2943 A1639 50c multi   1.50   .40

Charter of
Fundamental Rights of
the European
Union — A1640

2003, May 8
2944 A1640 50c multi   1.50   .30

Aircraft Carrier
"Charles de
Gaulle" — A1641

2003, May 8   **Engr.**
2945 A1641 50c multi   1.50   .30

Aspects of Life in
the French
Regions — A1642

No. 2946: a, Beach cabins. b, Fishing net. c, Vineyards of Champagne. d, Camembert cheese, vert. e, Foie gras, vert. f, Petanque. g, Puppet show (Guignol), vert. h, Crepe, vert. i, Cassoulet. j, Limoges porcelain.

2003, May 24   **Photo.**   *Perf. 13*
2946   Sheet of 10   16.00   16.00
   a.-j.   A1642 50c Any single   1.50   1.30

No. 2946 has three vertical rows of rouletting, separating sheet into quarters.
Nos. 2946a-2946j were also issued in large booklets containing panes of 1 of each stamp. The booklet sold for €19.
See Nos. 2978, 3007, 3047, 3106, 3139, 3192, 3234, 3299, 3300-3301, 3357, 3427, 3505.

Art Series

"The Dying Slave"
and "The Rebel
Slave," by
Michelangelo
A1643

The Red Buoy, by
Paul
Signac — A1644

Untitled Abstract
by Vassily
Kandinsky
A1645

Marilyn, by Andy
Warhol — A1646

2003   **Engr.**   *Perf. 13¼x13*
2947 A1643 75c multi   2.50   1.25
   Photo.
2948 A1644 75c multi   2.50   1.25
   Litho.
2949 A1645 €1.11 multi   3.50   1.25
2950 A1646 €1.11 multi   3.50   1.40
     Nos. 2947-2950 (4)   12.00   5.15

Issued: No. 2947, 5/24. Nos. 2948, 2949, 7/5. No. 2950, 11/8.
A sheet containing 3 No. 2949 and 12 imperforate color progressive proofs was bound in a book that sold for €60.

Happy
Birthday — A1647

2003, May 31   **Photo.**   *Perf. 13¼*
2951 A1647 50c multi   1.50   .35
   a.   Souvenir sheet of 5   7.50   7.50
   b.   Litho., stamp + label   1.75   1.75

Issued: No. 2951b, 2004. No. 2951b was issued in sheets of 10 stamps + 10 labels that sold for €6.67 on day of issue. The labels could be personalized. The background on No. 2951 looks splotchy while that of No. 2951b has a dot structure.

Marianne With Euro Denominations Type of 2002
2003, June 1   **Engr.**   *Perf. 13*
2952 A1583 58c apple grn   1.75   .40
2953 A1583 70c yellow grn   2.00   .50
2954 A1583 75c bright blue   2.25   .25
2955 A1583 90c dark blue   2.60   1.00
2956 A1583 €1.11 red lilac   3.25   .25
2957 A1583 €1.90 vio brn   5.75   .40
   a.   Souvenir sheet, #2835, 2921, 2952-2957   22.00   22.00
     Nos. 2952-2957 (6)   17.60   2.80

No. 2957a issued 2/28/04.

Orchids Type of 2002
Designs: 30c, Platanthera chlorantha. 35c, Dactylorhiza savogiensis.

2003, June 1   Litho.   Perf. 13
2958 A1584 30c multi   1.00
2959 A1584 35c multi   1.50   .40

Nos. 2958-2959 are known only precanceled. See second note after No. 132.

French Federation of
Philatelic Associations
76th Congress,
Mulhouse — A1648

2003, June 6   Engr.   Perf. 13¼
2960 A1648 50c multi   1.50   .30

Vacation — A1649

Perf. 12¾x13¼
2003, June 14   Litho.
2961 A1649 50c multi   1.50   .30

Self-Adhesive
Booklet Stamp
Serpentine Die Cut 11
2962 A1649 50c multi   1.50   .30
a.   Booklet pane of 10   15.00

Tourism Issue

Notre Dame
de l'Epine
Basilica
A1650

Tulle
A1651

Arras
A1652

Pontarlier — A1653

Perf. 13x13¼, 13 (#2965)
2003, June 21   Engr.
2963 A1650 50c multi   1.50   .30
2964 A1651 50c multi   1.50   .30
2965 A1652 50c multi   1.50   .30
2966 A1653 50c multi   1.50   .30
    Nos. 2963-2966 (4)   6.00 1.20

Issued: Nos. 2963, 2964, 6/21. No. 2965, 9/20. No. 2966, 10/11.

French
Freemasonry,
275th
Anniv. — A1654

2003, June 28   Engr.   Perf. 13¼x13
2967 A1654 50c multi   1.50   .30

Tour de France
Bicycle Race,
Cent. — A1655

No. 2968: a, Maurice Garin, winner of 1903 race. b, Cyclist with arms raised.

2003, June 28   Photo.   Perf. 13
2968 A1655   Vert. pair   3.00 2.00
a.-b.   50c Either single   1.50   .30

Values are for stamps with surrounding selvage.

Saint-Père Church,
Yonne — A1656

2003, July 12   Engr.   Perf. 13¼
2969 A1656 50c multi   1.50   .30

World Track and Field Championships,
Paris — A1657

2003, July 19   Photo.   Perf. 13
2970 A1657 50c multi   1.50   .30

Characters From French
Literature — A1658

Designs: No. 2971, Eugène-François Vidocq (1775-1857), convict and police official. No. 2972, Esmerelda, from *Notre-Dame de Paris*, by Victor Hugo. No. 2973, Claudine, from *Claudine* novels, by Colette. No. 2974, Nana, from *Rougon-Macquart*, by Emile Zola. No. 2975, La Comte de Monte-Cristo, from *La Comte de Monte-Cristo*, by Alexandre Dumas (pere). No. 2976, Gavroche, from *Les Miserables*, by Hugo.

2003, Aug. 30   Photo.   Perf. 13
2971 A1658 50c multi   1.50   .75
2972 A1658 50c multi   1.50   .75
2973 A1658 50c multi   1.50   .75
2974 A1658 50c multi   1.50   .75
2975 A1658 50c multi   1.50   .75
2976 A1658 50c multi   1.50   .75
a.   Souvenir sheet, #2971-
     2976   14.00 14.00
    Nos. 2971-2976 (6)   9.00 4.50

No. 2976a sold for €4.60, with the Red Cross receiving €1.60 of that.

Ahmad Shah Massoud
(1953-2001), Afghan
Northern Alliance
Leader — A1659

2003, Sept. 9
2977 A1659 50c multi   1.50   .30

Aspects of Life in French Regions
Type of 2003

No. 2978: a, Chateau de Chenonceau. b, House, Alsace. c, Roof, Bourgogne. d, Genoese Tower, Corsica, vert. e, Arc de Triomphe,

vert. f, Farm house, Provence. g, Pointe du Raz, vert. h, Mont Blanc, vert. i, Basque house. j, Pont du Gard.

2003, Sept. 20   Photo.   Perf. 13
2978   Sheet of 10   15.00 15.00
a.-j.   A1642 50c Any single   1.50 1.25

No. 2978 has three vertical rows of rouletting, separating sheet into quarters.
Nos. 2978a-2978j were also issued in large booklets containing panes of 1 of each stamp. The booklet sold for €19.

Gardens and
Parks — A1660

No. 2979: a, Buttes-Chaumont Park. b, Jardin du Luxembourg.

2003, Sept. 27   Perf. 13¼x13
2979   Sheet of 2   12.00 12.00
a.-b.   A1660 €1.90 Either single 6.00 6.00

Salon du Timbre 2004. No. 2979 has four vertical rows of rouletting, separating sheet into fifths, with the two stamps in the central fifth.
See Nos. 3029, 3118, 3201, 3316, 3429.

Motor
Vehicles
A1661

No. 2980: a, 1954 Isobloc 648 DP 102 bus (Autocar). b, 1950 SFV 302 Tractor. c, 1938 Delahaye fire truck with mechanical aerial ladder. d, Renault Kangaroo Express postal van. e, 1932 Renault TN6 Paris city bus. f, 1910 Berliet 22hp Type M delivery truck. g, 1957 Berliet T100 heavy-duty truck. h, Citroen police van. i, Citroen DS ambulance. j, 1964 Hotchkiss fire truck.

2003, Oct. 24   Photo.   Perf. 13¼
2980   Sheet of 10   9.00 9.00
a.-e.   20c Any single   .55   .45
f.-j.   30c Any single   1.00   .75

Philexjeunes 2003 Philatelic Exhibition, Dunkerque.

A1662

Holiday Greetings
A1663

2003, Nov. 6   Photo.   Perf. 13
2981 A1662 50c multi   1.50   .35
a.   Litho., stamp + label   6.00 6.00

Litho.
2982 A1663 50c multi   1.50   .35
a.   Sheet of 10 + 10 labels   60.00 60.00

Booklet Stamp
Self-Adhesive
Serpentine Die Cut 11¼
2983 A1663 50c multi   1.50   .35
a.   Booklet pane of 10   16.00

Nos. 2981a, 2982a, 2004. Nos. 2981a and 2982 were issued in sheets of 10 stamps + 10 labels that sold for €6.67 each on day of

issue. The labels could be personalized. The background on No. 2981 looks splotchy while that of No. 2981a has a dot structure.
A souvenir sheet containing No. 2982 was sold for €6 by mail order only. It was not available through standing order subscriptions and was not offered in the philatelic bureau's sales catalog. 50,000 copies of this sheet were printed. Value $100.

Sower Type of 1903,
Cent. — A1664

Serpentine Die Cut 6¾ Vert.
2003, Nov. 6   Engr.
Booklet Stamp
2984 A1664 50c red   3.50 2.00
a.   Booklet pane, 5 each #
     2984, 2835A   25.00

See Nos. 4727b, 6147.

European Capitals Type of 2002

No. 2985 — Attractions in Luxembourg: a, Citadelle Saint-Esprit. b, Notre Dame Cathedral, horiz. c, Adolphe Bridge, horiz. d, Grand Duke's Palace.

Perf. 13¼x13, 13x13¼
2003, Nov. 7   Photo.
2985 A1622   Sheet of 4   7.50 7.50
a.-d.   50c Any single   1.50 1.00

Indian and
French Artisan's
Work — A1665

Designs: 50c, Illumination depicting rooster, France, 15th cent. 90c, Jewelry design, India, 19th cent.

2003, Nov. 29   Engr.   Perf. 13¼x13
2986 A1665 50c multi   1.50   .45
2987 A1665 90c multi   2.60 1.50

See India No. 2040.

Launch of the Queen
Mary 2 — A1666

2003, Dec. 12   Photo.   Perf. 13¼
2988 A1666 50c multi   1.50   .30

Greetings
A1667

Holes punched through dots in "i's."
2004, Jan. 9   Photo.   Perf. 13
2989 A1667 50c shown   1.50   .30
2990 A1667 50c Un grand merci   1.50   .30

No Holes Punched Through Dots of "i's"
Stamp + Label
2991 A1667 50c Like No. 2989   6.00 6.00
2992 A1667 50c Like No. 2990   6.00 6.00

Nos. 2991-2992 were issued in sheets of 10 stamps + 10 labels that sold for €6.67 on day of issue. The labels could be personalized. Compare with Types A2203 and SP411. See Nos. 3096-3097D, 3569A-3569B.

It's a
Boy — A1668

It's a Girl — A1669

2004   Litho.   Perf. 13
Stamp + Label
2993 A1668 50c multi   6.00 6.00
2994 A1669 50c multi   6.00 6.00

Booklet Stamps
Self-Adhesive
Serpentine Die Cut 11
2995 A1668 50c multi   1.50 .35
  a. Booklet pane of 10   15.00
2996 A1669 50c multi   1.50 .35
  a. Booklet pane of 10   15.00

Nos. 2993-2994 were issued in sheets of 10 stamps + 10 labels that sold for €6.67 on day of issue. The labels could be personalized. Nos. 2995-2996 issued 1/9/04.

Hearts — A1670

Designs: 50c, Chanel No. 5 perfume bottle. 75c, Woman, Eiffel Tower.

2004, Jan. 9   Photo.   Perf. 13
2997 A1670 50c multi   1.50 .35
  a. Souvenir sheet of 5   7.50 7.50
  b. Litho., stamp + label, perf. 13¼   6.00 6.00
2998 A1670 75c multi   2.25 .75
  a. Litho., stamp + label, perf. 13¼   6.00 6.00

Nos. 2997b and 2998a were each printed in sheets of 10 stamps + 10 labels that could be personalized and sold for €6.69 and €10 respectively. On No. 2997b, there are large brown dots arranged in circles in the shading on the green rectangles, while on No. 2997 the brown dots are small and arranged in rows. On No. 2998a, the dots in the sky are larger and father apart than the tiny dots found on No. 2998.
Values are for stamps with surrounding selvage.
See Nos. 3133, 3135.

Tourism Issue

Lille, 2004 European Cultural Capital — A1671

2004, Jan. 10   Photo.   Perf. 13
2999 A1671 50c multi   1.50 .35

Art Series

Statue of Liberty, Sculpted by Frederic Auguste Bartholdi (1834-1904) A1672

2004, Feb. 21   Engr.   Perf. 13¼x13
3000 A1672 90c multi   2.60 1.50

Queen Eleanor of Aquitaine (c. 1122-1204) — A1673

2004, Feb. 28   Perf. 13x13¼
3001 A1673 50c multi   1.50 .35

Stamp Day — A1674

Characters of Walt Disney: 45c, Donald Duck. 50c, Mickey Mouse. 75c, Minnie Mouse.

2004, Mar. 6   Photo.   Perf. 13¼
3002 A1674 50c multi   1.50 .35
  a. Perf. 13¼x13 (from booklet pane)   1.50 .35

Booklet Stamps
Perf. 13¼x13
3003 A1674 45c multi   2.25 1.00
3004 A1674 75c multi   2.25 .75
  a. Booklet pane, 2 #3003, 4 each #3002a, 3004   23.00 —
     Complete booklet, #3004a   24.00

Civil Code, Bicent. — A1675

2004, Mar. 12   Engr.   Perf. 13¼x13
3005 A1675 50c multi   1.50 .35

George Sand (1804-76), Writer — A1676

2004, Mar. 20   Engr.   Perf. 13¼x13
3006 A1676 50c multi   1.50 .35

Aspects of Life in French Regions Type of 2003

No. 3007: a, Cutlery. b, Produce of Provence, vert. c, Beaujolais grapes, vert. d, Bread. e, Woman wearing coif, vert. f, Oysters, vert. g, Quiche Lorraine. h, Bullfighting. i, Clafoutis. j, Bagpipers.

2004, Mar. 26   Photo.   Perf. 13
3007 Sheet of 10   15.00 15.00
  a.-j. A1642 50c Any single   1.50 1.25

No. 3007 has three vertical rows of rouletting, separating sheet into quarters.

Clermont-Ferrand A1677

2004, Mar. 26   Engr.   Perf. 13¼
3008 A1677 50c multi   1.50 .30

Entente Cordiale, Cent. — A1678

Designs: 50c, Coccinelle, by Sonia Delaunay. 75c, Lace 1 (trial proof) 1968, by Sir Terry Frost.

2004, Apr. 6   Photo.   Perf. 13¼
3009 A1678 50c multi   1.50 .35
3010 A1678 75c multi   2.25 .85

See Great Britain Nos. 2200-2201.

Road Safety — A1679

2004, Apr. 7
3011 A1679 50c multi   1.50 .30

See United Nations Offices in Geneva No. 424.

Art Series

La Méridienne d'Après Millet, by Vincent van Gogh A1680

2004, July 2   Photo.   Perf. 13x13¼
3012 A1680 75c multi   2.50 .95

Art Series

Un Combat de Coqs, by Jean-Léon Gérôme A1681

Galatée aux Sphères, by Salvador Dali — A1682

2004   Photo.   Perf. 13x13¼
3013 A1681 €1.11 multi   3.50 1.25
3014 A1682 €1.11 multi   3.50 1.25

Issued: No. 3013, 4/17; No. 3014, 6/19.

Tourism Issue

Bordeaux — A1683

Vaux-sur-Mer A1684   Notre Dame de l'Assomption Cathedral, Luçon A1685

2004   Litho. & Engr.   Perf. 13
3015 A1683 50c multi   1.50 .30

Engr.
Perf. 13¼
3016 A1684 50c multi   1.50 .30
3017 A1685 50c multi   1.50 .30

Issued: No. 3015, 4/26; No. 3016, 7/17; No. 3017, 10/2.

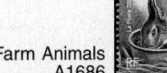

Farm Animals A1686

2004, Apr. 26   Photo.   Perf. 13¼
3018 A1686 45c Rabbit   1.25 .30
3019 A1686 50c Cow, vert.   1.50 .30
3020 A1686 50c Chicken   1.50 .30
3021 A1686 75c Burro, vert.   2.25 .90
  a. Souvenir sheet, #3018-3021   7.00 7.00

Expansion of the European Union — A1687

2004, May 1   Photo.   Perf. 13¼
3022 A1687 50c multi   1.50 .30

Battle of Dien Bien Phu, 50th Anniv. — A1688

2004, May 7   Perf. 13¼x13
3023 A1688 50c multi   1.50 .30

Europa — A1689

2004   Photo.   Perf. 13x13¼
3024 A1689 50c multi   1.50 .30

Litho.
Booklet Stamp
Self-Adhesive
Serpentine Die Cut 11
3025 A1689 50c multi   1.50 .30
  a. Booklet pane of 10   15.00

Issued: No. 3024, 5/9; No. 3025, 6/4.

Blake and Mortimer, Comic Book Characters by Edgar P. Jacobs — A1690

Blake and Mortimer and: 50c, Brick wall, vert. €1, Blue background.

2004, May 15   Photo.   Perf. 13¼
3026 A1690 50c multi   1.50 .30
3027 A1690 €1 multi   3.00 1.25

See Belgium No. 2020.

FIFA (Fédération Internationale de Football Association), Cent. — A1691

2004, May 20   Perf. 13¼x13
3028 A1691 50c multi   1.50 .30

Gardens and Parks Type of 2003

No. 3029: a, Jardin des Tuileries. b, Parc Floral de Paris.

2004, June 4   Perf. 13¼x13
3029 Sheet of 2   12.00 12.00
  a.-b. A1660 €1.90 Either single   5.75 5.00
  c. Souvenir sheet, #2979a-2979b, 3029a-3029b   35.00 35.00

Salon du Timbre 2004. No. 3029 has four vertical rows of rouletting, separating sheet into fifths, with the two stamps in the central fifth.

D-Day Invasion of France, 60th Anniv. — A1692

2004, June 5   **Perf. 13**
3030 A1692 50c multi   1.50   .30

Organ Donation — A1693

2004, June 22   **Perf. 13¼**
3031 A1693 50c multi   1.50   .30

Pierre Dugua de Mons, Leader of First French Settlement in Acadia, and Ship — A1694

Litho. & Engr.
2004, June 26   **Perf. 13**
3032 A1694 90c multi   2.75 1.00

See Canada No. 2044.

Napoleon I and the Imperial Guard — A1695

Designs: No. 3033, Light cavalry (Chasseur à cheval). No. 3034, Artilleryman and cannon (Artilleur à pied), horiz. No. 3035, Dragoon. No. 3036, Mameluke. No. 3037, Napoleon I. No. 3038, Grenadier (Grenadier à pied).

2004, June 26   **Photo.**
3033 A1695 50c multi   1.50   .75
3034 A1695 50c multi   1.50   .75
3035 A1695 50c multi   1.50   .75
3036 A1695 50c multi   1.50   .75
3037 A1695 50c multi   1.50   .75
3038 A1695 50c multi   1.50   .75
   a.   Souvenir sheet, #3033-3038   12.50 12.50
   Nos. 3033-3038 (6)   9.00 4.50

No. 3038a sold for €4.60, with the Red Cross receiving €1.60 of that.

French Federation of Philatelic Associations 77th Congress, Paris — A1696

Litho. & Engr.
2004, June 27   **Perf. 13¼x13**
3039 A1696 50c multi   1.50   .30

2004 Summer Olympics, Athens A1697

2004, June 28   **Photo.**   **Perf. 13¼**
3040   50c Modern athletes   1.50   .75
3041   50c Ancient athletes   1.50   .75
   a.   A1697 Pair, #3040-3041   3.25 2.25

Printed in sheets containing five of each stamp.
A souvenir sheet containing No. 3041 was issued Aug. 2 and sold for €2.51. Value $20.

Happy Birthday — A1698

2004, June 30   **Photo.**   **Perf. 13¼**
3042 A1698 50c multi   1.50   .30
   a.   Souvenir sheet of 5   7.50 7.50
   b.   Litho. stamp + label   6.00 6.00

No. 3042b printed in sheets of 10 stamps + 10 labels that could be personalized that sold for €8. No. 3042b has a dark green inscription at left with a distinct dot pattern. No. 3042 has a lighter green inscription.

Marianne Type of 1997 Inscribed "RF" at Lower Left and Type of 2002 With Euro Denominations

2004   **Litho.**   **Perf. 13**
3043   Sheet of 15 + 15 labels   60.00 60.00
   a.   A1583 1c orange yellow   .25 .25
   b.   A1583 2c brown   .25 .25
   c.   A1583 5c brt bl green   .25 .25
   d.   A1583 10c purple   .30 .30
   e.   A1583 20c orange   .60 .60
   f.   A1583 58c apple green   1.75 1.75
   g.   A1583 70c olive   2.10 2.10
   h.   A1583 75c sky blue   2.25 2.25
   i.   A1583 90c dark blue   2.75 2.75
   j.   A1583 €1 Prussian blue   3.00 3.00
   k.   A1583 €1.11 red lilac   3.25 3.25
   l.   A1583 €1.90 violet brown   5.75 5.75
   m.   A1583 €2 violet   6.00 6.00
   n.   A1409 (45c) green   1.40 1.40
   o.   A1409 (50c) red   1.50 1.50

Engr.
Serpentine Die Cut 6¾ Vert
Self-Adhesive
3043P A1583   75c brt blue + label   8.75 8.75
3043Q A1583   €1.11 purple + label   10.50 10.50
3043R A1583   €1.11 chocolate + label   — —

No. 3043 sold for €10.03. Stamps have a glossy varnish.
Labels on Nos. 3043P-3043R could be personalized.

Marianne and Emblem of World Fund to Combat AIDS, Tuberculosis and Smoking A1699

2004, July 1   **Engr.**   **Perf. 13**
3044 A1699 (50c) red   1.50   .35

Extreme Sports A1700

No. 3045: a, Skateboarding. b, Parachuting. c, Sailboarding. d, Surfing. e, Luge. f, BMX bicycling. g, Paragliding. h, Jetskiing. i, Snowboarding. j, Rollerblading.

2004, July 3   **Photo.**   **Perf. 13¼x13**
3045 A1700   Sheet of 10   7.50 7.50
   a.-e.   20c Any single   .60 .50
   f.-j.   30c Any single   .90 .75

Orchid Type of 2002

Design: 39c, Orchis insularis.

2004, Sept. 1   **Litho.**   **Perf. 13**
3046 A1584 39c multi   1.50   .75

No. 3046 known only precanceled. See second note after No. 132.

Aspects of Life in the French Regions Type of 2003

No. 3047: a, House, Normandy. b, Chambord Chateau. c, Gorges, Tarn, vert. d, Notre Dame Cathedral, Paris, vert. e, Windmill, vert. f, Cave dwellings. g, Creek, Cassis, vert. h, Cap-Ferret Lighthouse, vert. i, Castle ruins. j, Alpine chalet.

2004, Sept. 18   **Photo.**   **Perf. 13**
3047   Sheet of 10   15.00 15.00
   a.-j.   A1642 50c Any single   1.50 1.25

No. 3047 has three vertical rows of rouletting separating sheet into quarters.
Each stamp exists in booklet pane of 1 from booklet that sold for €19.

Halloween A1701

2004, Oct. 9   **Litho.**   **Perf. 13**
3048 A1701 50c multi   1.50   .30

Félix Eboué (1884-1944), Colonial Governor — A1702

2004, Oct. 16   **Photo.**
3049 A1702 50c multi   1.50   .30

Ouistreham Lighthouse — A1703

2004, Oct. 30   **Perf. 13¼**
3050 A1703 50c multi   1.50   .30

Marianne — A1704

Serpentine Die Cut 6¾ Vert.
2004, Nov. 10   **Engr.**
Booklet Stamp
Self-Adhesive
3051 A1704 50c multi   3.00 2.00
   a.   Booklet pane, 5 each #2835A, 3051   22.50

European Capitals Type of 2002

No. 3052 — Attractions in Athens: a, Greek Academy. b, Parthenon. c, Odeon of Herodes Atticus. d, Church of the Holy Apostles, vert.

Perf. 13x13¼, 13¼x13
2004, Nov. 11   **Photo.**
3052 A1622   Sheet of 4   7.50 7.50
   a.-d.   50c Any single   1.50   .90

A1705

A1706

A1707

A1708

A1709

Holiday Greetings A1710

2004, Nov. 12   **Photo.**   **Perf. 13**
3053 A1705 50c multi   1.50   .30

Litho.
3054 A1706 50c multi + label   6.00 6.00
3055 A1707 50c multi + label   6.00 6.00
3056 A1708 50c multi + label   6.00 6.00
3057 A1709 50c multi + label   6.00 6.00
3058 A1710 50c multi + label   6.00 6.00
   a.   Vert. strip of 5, #3054-3059 + 5 labels   30.00 30.00
     Miniature sheet, 2 #3058a + 10 labels   70.00 70.00

Booklet Stamps
Self-Adhesive
Serpentine Die Cut 11¼x11
3059 A1706 50c multi   1.50   .30
3060 A1707 50c multi   1.50   .30
3061 A1708 50c multi   1.50   .30
3062 A1709 50c multi   1.50   .30
3063 A1710 50c multi   1.50   .30
   a.   Booklet pane, 2 each #3059-3063   15.00
   Nos. 3053-3063 (11)   39.00 31.80

Miniature sheet containing Nos. 3054-3058 sold for €6.69. Labels could be personalized. No. 3055 exists in a souvenir sheet of 1 stamp without label that sold for €3. Value $35.

Henri Wallon (1812-1904), Historian and Politician — A1711

2004, Nov. 13   **Photo.**   **Perf. 13**
3064 A1711 50c multi   1.50   .30

Opening of Millau Viaduct A1712

2004, Dec. 14   **Photo.**   **Perf. 13**
3065 A1712 50c multi   2.50 1.00

Marianne — A1713

Inscribed "ITVF" at Bottom

2005-07   **Engr.**   **Perf. 13**
3066 A1713   1c yellow   .25 .25
   a.   Inscribed "Phil@poste" at bottom   .25 .25
3067 A1713   5c brn blk   .25 .25
   a.   Inscribed "Phil@poste" at bottom   .25 .25
3068 A1713   10c violet   .25 .25
3069 A1713   (45c) green   1.60 .25
   a.   Inscribed "Phil@poste" at bottom   1.60 .25

3070	A1713	(50c) red	3.00 .25

a. Sheet of 15 + 15 labels 70.00 70.00
b. Inscribed "Phil@poste" at bottom 2.00 .25
3071 A1713 55c dark blue 1.60 .50
3072 A1713 58c olive green 1.75 .40
3073 A1713 64c dark green 1.90 .40
3074 A1713 70c dark green 2.10 .50
3075 A1713 75c light blue 2.25 .25
3076 A1713 82c fawn 4.00 .50
3077 A1713 90c dark blue 2.75 .80
3078 A1713 €1 orange 3.00 .25
a. Inscribed "Phil@poste" at bottom 3.25 .75
3079 A1713 €1.11 red violet 3.25 .25
3080 A1713 €1.22 red violet 3.00 .30
3081 A1713 €1.90 chocolate 5.75 .50
3082 A1713 €1.98 chocolate 6.00 1.25
Nos. 3066-3082 (17) 42.70 6.95

Self-Adhesive (#3083-3085)
Serpentine Die Cut 6¾ Vert.
3083 A1713 (50c) red 1.50 .25
a. Booklet pane of 10 (see footnote) 15.00
b. Booklet pane of 10 (see footnote) 15.00
c. Booklet pane of 20 30.00
d. As #3083, with "Phil@poste" inscription 1.50 .25
e. Booklet pane, 10 #3083d 15.00
f. Booklet pane of 12 #3083d 15.00
g. No. 3083 with attached label 7.50
3084 A1713 82c fawn + label 12.00 12.00
3085 A1713 €1.22 red violet 15.00 15.00

Coil Stamps
Perf. 13 Horiz.
3086 A1713 (45c) green 2.00 .30
a. Inscribed "Phil@poste" at bottom 1.40 .25
3087 A1713 (50c) red 2.00 .25
c. Inscribed "Phil@poste" at bottom
3087A A1713 55c dark blue 2.50 1.25
b. Inscribed "Phil@poste" at bottom 1.60 .25
Nos. 3083-3087A (6) 35.00 29.05

Issued: Nos. 1c, 10c, (45c), (50c), 58c, 70c, 75c, 90c, €1, €1.11, €1.90, 1/8. 5c, 3071, 64c, 82c, €1.22, €1.98, 3/1. No. 3087A, 7/15. Nos. 3083d, 3083e, 10/1/06. Nos. 3066a, 3067a, 3069a, 3070b, 2006. No. 3083f, Jan. 2007. Nos. 3083g, 3084-3085, Apr. 2007. No. 3086a was issued in 2008 and sold for 50c. No. 3087b was issued in 2008 and sold for 55c.

Face values shown for Nos. 3069, 3070, 3083, 3086 and 3087 are those the stamps sold for on the day of issue. On day of issue, No. 3069a sold for 49c; No. 3070b for 54c.

No. 3070a sold for €10.03 and the labels could be personalized for an additional fee.

No. 3083a has a narrow strip of selvage separating the four stamps at left, from the six stamps, at right, and is on a white backing paper. No. 3083b is comprised of two horizontal strips of five stamps on a yellow backing paper. No. 3083d sold for 54c on day of issue.

No. 3083g was printed in sheets containing 15 stamps + 15 small or large-sized labels that could be personalized. Nos. 3084 and 3085 were each printed in sheets of 30 stamps + 30 large-sized labels that could be personalized.

A sheet of 10 litho. stamps similar to No. 3068 + 10 labels exists, but was not sold.

See Nos. 3211, 3211N, 3212, 3247-3255E, 3302, 3302N, 3383-3388A, 3389, 3531, 4410k, 4524.

Rabbi Shlomo Yitshaqi (Rashi) (1040-1105) A1714

2005, Jan. 16 Engr. Perf. 13¼
3088 A1714 50c multi 1.75 .30

Hearts — A1715

Designs: 53c, Polka dots. 82c, Bird and flowers.

2005, Jan. 29 Photo. Perf. 13¼
3089 A1715 53c multi 1.50 .30
a. Souvenir sheet of 5 7.50 7.50
b. Litho, stamp + label 6.00 6.00
3090 A1715 82c multi 2.50 1.00
a. Litho, stamp + label 6.00 6.00
Values are for stamps with surrounding selvage.
Sheets of 10 of No. 3089b sold for €6.86, and sheets of 10 of No. 3090a sold for €8.78.

Labels could be personalized for an additional fee.
See Nos. 3134, 3136.

New Year 2005 (Year of the Rooster) — A1716

Photo. & Embossed
2005, Jan. 29 Perf. 13½x13
3091 A1716 (50c) multi 1.75 .30
See No. 4969a.

Rotary International, Cent. — A1717

2005, Feb. 19 Photo. Perf. 13¼
3092 A1717 53c multi 1.50 .30
See No. 3227A.

 Titeuf A1718
 Nadia A1719
 Manu — A1720

2005, Feb. 28 Photo. Perf. 13¼
3093 A1718 (50c) red & multi 1.50 .30
a. Perf. 13¼x13 (booklet stamp) 1.50 .30

Booklet Stamps
3094 A1719 (45c) green & multi 3.00 .60
3095 A1720 (90c) blue & multi 2.50 1.00
a. Booklet pane, 2 #3094, 4 each #3093a, 3095 22.00
Complete booklet, #3095a 23.00
Characters from Titeuf, comic strip by Zep. Stamp Day.

Greetings Type of 2004 Inscribed "Lettre 20g"
Designs: Nos. 3096, 3097A, "Ceci est une invitation." Nos. 3097, 3097B, "Un grand merci."
No. 3097C, "Ceci est une invitation." No. 3097D, "Un grand merci."

2005-06 Photo. Perf. 13
Holes Punched Through Dots of "i's"
3096 A1667 (53c) brt lil rose & yel 2.00 .30
3097 A1667 (53c) brt yel grn & red lil 2.00 .30

Litho.
No Holes Punched Through Dots of "i's"
Stamp + Label
3097A A1667 (53c) brt lil rose & yel 5.00
3097B A1667 (53c) brt yel grn & red lil 5.00

Self-Adhesive
No Holes Punched Through Dots of "i's"
Serpentine Die Cut 11¼x11
Stamp + Label
3097C A1667 (53c) brt lil rose & yel 5.00 5.00
3097D A1667 (53c) brt yel grn & rrd lil 5.00 5.00

Nos. 3097A-3097B were issued in sheets of 10 stamps + 10 labels that sold for €8 on day of issue. The labels could be personalized.
Nos. 3097C-3097D were each issued in sheets of 10 stamps + 10 labels that sold for €8.61. Labels could be personalized.
Issued: Nos. 2096-3097B, 3/1/05. Nos. 3097C-3097D, 2006.

Art Series

The Guitarist, by Jean-Baptiste Greuze (1725-1805) A1721

White Bear, Sculpture by François Pompon A1722

Sicile, by Nicolas de Stael A1723

2005 Photo. Perf. 13x13¼
3098 A1721 82c multi 2.50 .50
3099 A1722 90c multi 3.00 1.25
3100 A1723 €1.22 multi 3.75 1.25
Issued: €1.22, 3/5. 90c, 7/2. 82c, 9/24.

Orchids — A1725

Designs: No. 3102, Cypripedium calceolus. No. 3103, Paphiopedilum Mabel Sanders. 55c, Oncidium papilio. 82c, Paphinia cristata, horiz.

2005, Mar. 11 Photo. Perf. 13¼
3102 A1725 53c multi 1.60 .30
3103 A1725 53c multi 1.60 .30
3104 A1725 55c multi 1.60 .30
3105 A1725 82c multi 2.50 .60
a. Souvenir sheet, #3102-3105 7.50 7.50
Nos. 3102-3105 (4) 7.30 1.50

Aspects of Life in French Regions Type of 2003
No. 3106: a, Nautical jousting. b, Clocks of Franche-Comte, vert. c, Cantal cheese and bread, vert. d, Dancers and accordion player. e, Bouillabaisse. f, P'tit Quinquin statue, vert. g, Rillettes (chopped pork). h, Sauerkraut and sausage, beer stein. i, Pelota, vert. j, Sugar cane, vert.

2005, Mar. 19 Photo. Perf. 13
3106 Sheet of 10 16.00 16.00
a.-j. A1642 53c Any single 1.50 1.25
No. 3106 has three vertical rows of rouletting, separating sheet into quarters.
Each stamp exists in a booklet pane of 1 from a booklet that sold for €19. Value $50.

Tourism Issue

Aix-en-Provence A1726

Gulf of Morbihan A1727

Villefranche-sur-Mer — A1728

La Roque-Gageac A1729

2005 Engr. Perf. 13¼, 13 (#3108)
3107 A1726 53c multi 1.60 .30
Photo.
3108 A1727 53c multi 1.60 .30
3109 A1728 53c multi 1.60 .30
Engr.
3110 A1729 53c multi 1.60 .30
Issued: No. 3107, 4/1; No. 3108, 5/5; No. 3109, 6/4; No. 3110, 7/23.

Happy Birthday — A1730

2005, Apr. 2 Photo. Perf. 13
3111 A1730 (53c) multi 2.00 .30
a. Souvenir sheet of 5 10.00 9.00
b. Litho, stamp + label 8.00 8.00

Litho.
Serpentine Die Cut 11
Self-Adhesive
3111C A1730 (53c) multi + label — —
Sheets of 10 and 10 labels of No. 3111b and 3111C each sold for €6.86. Labels could be personalized for an additional fee.

Albert Einstein (1879-1955), Physicist A1731

2005, Apr. 16 Perf. 13¼
3112 A1731 53c multi 1.60 .30

Alexis de Tocqueville (1805-59), Writer — A1732

2005, Apr. 23 Engr. Perf. 13x13¼
3113 A1732 90c multi 2.75 1.00

Liberation of Concentration Camp Internees, 60th Anniv. — A1733

2005, Apr. 24 Photo. Perf. 13¼
3114 A1733 53c multi 1.60 .30

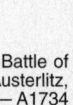

Battle of Austerlitz, Bicent. — A1734

Litho. & Engr.
2005, May 4   Perf. 13¼
3115 A1734 55c multi   1.60 .45

See Czech Republic No. 3273.

French Federation of Philatelic Associations, 78th Congress, Nancy — A1735

2005, May 5   Engr.   Perf. 13
3116 A1735 53c multi + label   1.60 .30

A souvenir sheet of one stamp without label exists. Value $12.

Europa — A1736

2005, May 8   Photo.   Perf. 13¼
3117 A1736 53c multi   1.60 .30

Gardens and Parks Type of 2003
Souvenir Sheet

No. 3118 — Sculptures in Jardin de la Fontaine, Nimes: a, Denomination in green. b, Denomination in white.

2005, May 15   Perf. 13¼x13
3118   Sheet of 2   12.00 12.00
a.-b.   A1660 €1.98 Either single   6.00 6.00

Salon du Timbre 2005. No. 3118 has four vertical rows of rouletting, separating sheet into fifths, with the two stamps in the central fifth.

Vacation — A1737

Serpentine Die Cut 11
2005, May 23   Litho.
Booklet Stamp
Self-Adhesive
3119 A1737 (53c) multi   2.00 .25
a.   Booklet pane of 10   20.00

Stories by Jules Verne (1828-1905) — A1738

Designs: No. 3120, Five Weeks in a Balloon (Cinq Semaines en Ballon). No. 3121, From the Earth to the Moon (De la Terre a la Lune). No. 3122, Journey to the Center of the Earth (Voyage au Centre de la Terre), horiz. No. 3123, Michael Strogoff, horiz. No. 3124, Around the World in Eighty Days (Le Tour du Monde en Quatre-vingts Jours). No. 3125, 20,000 Leagues Under the Sea (Vingt Mille Lieues Sous les Mers).

2005, May 28   Photo.   Perf. 13
3120 A1738 53c multi   1.60 .75
3121 A1738 53c multi   1.60 .75
3122 A1738 53c multi   1.60 .75
3123 A1738 53c multi   1.60 .75
3124 A1738 53c multi   1.60 .75
3125 A1738 53c multi   1.60 .75
a.   Souvenir sheet, #3120-3125   12.00 12.00
   Nos. 3120-3125 (6)   9.60 4.50

No. 3125a sold for €4.80 with the Red Cross receiving €1.62 of that.

Miniature Sheet

Gordon Bennett Cup, Cent. A1739

No. 3126 — Inscriptions: a, La Coupe Gordon Bennett (Car No. 1 facing right). b, La Coupe Gordon Bennett (Car No. 1 facing left). c, La Formule 1, vert. d, Le Rallye-Raid, vert. e, Les Rallyes. f, La Course d'endurance.

2005, June 2   Photo.   Perf.
3126 A1739   Sheet of 10, #a-b, 2 each #c-f   19.00 19.00
a.-f.   53c Any single   1.75 .85

A souvenir sheet containing No. 3126a sold for €3. Value $100.

Environmental Charter — A1740

2005, June 5   Litho.   Perf. 13
3127 A1740 53c multi, lt green   1.60 .30

Enactment of Handicapped Persons Rights Law — A1741

2005, June 18   Photo.   Perf. 13¼
3128 A1741 53c multi   1.60 .30

It's a Boy — A1742

It's a Girl — A1743

2005   Litho.   Perf. 13x13¼
3129 A1742 (53c) multi + label   5.00 5.00
3130 A1743 (53c) multi + label   5.00 5.00

Booklet Stamps
Self-Adhesive
Serpentine Die Cut 11¼x11
3131 A1742 (53c) multi   2.00 .30
a.   Booklet pane of 10   20.00
b.   Sheet of 10 + 10 labels   50.00
3132 A1743 (53c) multi   2.00 .30
a.   Booklet pane of 10   20.00
b.   Sheet of 10 + 10 labels   50.00

Sheets of 10 stamps and 10 labels of Nos. 3129 and 3130 each sold for €6.86. Nos. 3131b and 3132b each sold for €8.61. Labels could be personalized for an additional fee.

Hearts Types of 2004-05
Serpentine Die Cut
2005, July 15   Photo.
Self-Adhesive
3133 A1670 50c Like #2997   4.00 2.50
3134 A1715 53c Like #3089   4.00 3.00
3135 A1670 75c Like #2998   6.00 3.50
3136 A1715 82c Like #3090   6.00 4.00
   Nos. 3133-3136 (4)   20.00 13.00

Haras du Pin Natl. Stud Farm — A1744

2005, July 16   Perf. 13
3137 A1744 53c multi   1.60 .30

European Capitals Type of 2002

No. 3138 — Attractions in Berlin: a, Brandenburg Gate. b, Kaiser Wilhelm Memorial Church, vert. c, Philharmonic Hall. d, Reichstag.

Perf. 13x13¼, 13¼x13
2005, Aug. 27   Photo.
3138 A1622   Sheet of 4   7.00 7.00
a.-d.   53c Any single   1.75 1.00

Aspects of Life in the French Regions Type of 2003

No. 3139: a, Lake Annecy. b, Etretat Cliffs, vert. c, Pigeon house, vert. d, Wash house (lavoir). e, Banks of the Seine. f, Carnac megaliths. g, House, Sologne. h, Pilat Sand Dune. i, Stiff Lighthouse, vert. j, Stone hut (borie), vert.

2005, Sept. 17   Perf. 13
3139   Sheet of 10   17.00 17.00
a.-j.   A1642 53c Any single   1.60 1.25

No. 3139 has three vertical rows of rouletting, separating sheet into quarters. Nos. 3139a-3139j were also issued in large booklets containing panes of 1 of each stamp. The booklet sold for €19. Value $60.

Art Series

Les Halles Centrales, Designed by Victor Baltard (1805-74) A1745

2005, Sept. 17   Engr.   Perf. 13x13¼
3140 A1745 €1.22 multi   3.75 1.10

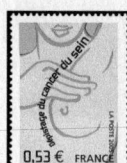

Breast Cancer Awareness — A1746

2005, Oct. 1   Photo.   Perf. 13¼
3141 A1746 53c multi   1.60 .30

A1747

A1748

A1749

A1750

A1751

A1752

A1753

A1754

A1755

Cat, Comics by Philippe Geluck — A1756

Serpentine Die Cut 11¼x11
2005, Oct. 1   Litho.
Booklet Stamps
Self-Adhesive
3142 A1747 (53c) multi   2.00 .30
3143 A1748 (53c) multi   2.00 .30
3144 A1749 (53c) multi   2.00 .30
3145 A1750 (53c) multi   2.00 .30
3146 A1751 (53c) multi   2.00 .30
3147 A1752 (53c) multi   2.00 .30
3148 A1753 (53c) multi   2.00 .30
3149 A1754 (53c) multi   2.00 .30
3150 A1755 (53c) multi   2.00 .30
3151 A1756 (53c) multi   2.00 .30
a.   Booklet pane of 10, #3142-3151   20.00

Raymond Aron (1905-83), Philosopher — A1757

2005, Oct. 7   Engr.   Perf. 13¼x13
3152 A1757 53c multi   1.60 .30

Souvenir Sheet

The Annunciation, by Raphael — A1758

No. 3153: a, Drawing of Angel, painting of Virgin Mary. b, Painting of Angel, drawing of Virgin Mary.

Litho. & Engr.
2005, Nov. 10   Perf. 13x13¼
3153 A1758   Sheet of 2   4.00 4.00
a.   53c multi   1.60 1.60
b.   55c multi   1.75 1.75

See Vatican City Nos. 1312-1314.

Marianne — A1759

Serpentine Die Cut 6¾ Vert.
2005, Nov. 11   Engr.
Booklet Stamp
Self-Adhesive
3154 A1759 53c red   3.50 3.00
a.   Booklet pane, 5 each #3083, 3154   25.00

See No. 4911.

Video Game Characters — A1760

No. 3155: a, Link. b, Pac-Man. c, Prince of Persia. d, Spyro. e, Donkey Kong. f, Mario. g, Adibou. h, Rayman. i, Lara Croft. j, The Sims.

2005, Nov. 11   Photo.   Perf. 13¼x13
3155	A1760	Sheet of 10	9.00	9.00
a.-e.		20c Any single	.60	.50
f.-j.		33c Any single	1.00	.75

Avicenna (980-1037), Scientist — A1761

2005, Nov. 12   Engr.   Perf. 13x13¼
3156	A1761	53c multi	1.60	.30

Holiday Greetings A1762

Designs: Nos. 3157, 3162, Bear, three penguins and sled. Nos. 3158, 3163, Two penguins, reindeer and sled. Nos. 3159, 3164, Two penguins, bear and sled. Nos. 3160, 3165, Three penguins. Nos. 3161, 3166, Two penguins, reindeer and snowman.

2005, Nov. 12   Litho.   Perf. 13
3157	A1762	(53c) multi + label	6.00	4.00
3158	A1762	(53c) multi + label	6.00	4.00
3159	A1762	(53c) multi + label	6.00	4.00
3160	A1762	(53c) multi + label	6.00	4.00
3161	A1762	(53c) multi + label	6.00	4.00
a.		Vert. strip of 5, #3157-3161, + 5 labels	30.00	30.00
		Miniature sheet, 2 #3161a	60.00	60.00

Booklet Stamps
Self-Adhesive
Serpentine Die Cut 11¼x11
3162	A1762	(53c) multi	2.00	.30
3163	A1762	(53c) multi	2.00	.30
3164	A1762	(53c) multi	2.00	.30
3165	A1762	(53c) multi	2.00	.30
3166	A1762	(53c) multi	2.00	.30
a.		Booklet pane, 2 each #3162-3166	16.00	
		Nos. 3157-3166 (10)	40.00	21.50

Miniature sheet containing Nos. 3157-3161 sold for €6.86. Labels could be personalized. No. 3161 exists in a souvenir sheet of one stamp without label, that sold for €3. Value $30.

Jacob Kaplan (1895-1994), Grand Rabbi of France — A1763

2005, Nov. 14   Engr.   Perf. 13
3167	A1763	53c multi	1.60	.30

Orchid Type of 2002

Design: Orchis insularis.

2005   Litho.   Perf. 13
3168	A1584	42c multi	2.50	.75

No. 3168 is known only precanceled. See second note after No. 132.

Law Separating Church and State, Cent. — A1764

2005, Dec. 3   Photo.   Perf. 13¼x13
3169	A1764	53c multi	1.60	.30

Hearts — A1765

Designs: (53c), Hearts, octagons and diamonds. (82c), Heart and stripes.

2006, Jan. 7   Photo.   Perf. 13¼
3170	A1765	(53c) multi	1.60	.30
a.		Souvenir sheet of 5	10.00	8.00
b.		Litho., stamp + label	5.00	5.00
3171	A1765	(82c) multi	3.00	1.00
a.		Litho., stamp + label	12.00	12.00

Self-Adhesive
Serpentine Die Cut
3172	A1765	(53c) Like #3170	4.00	3.00
a.		Sheet of 10 + 10 labels	40.00	
3173	A1765	(82c) Like #3171	6.00	4.50
a.		Sheet of 10 + 10 labels	60.00	

Values are for stamps with surrounding selvage. Sheets of 10 of No. 3170b sold for €6.86, and sheets of No. 3172a. No. 3172a sold for €8.61; No. 3173a for €11.54. Labels could be personalized for an additional fee.

New Year 2006 (Year of the Dog) — A1766

2006, Jan. 21   Photo.   Perf. 13¼x13
3174	A1766	(53c) multi	1.60	.30

A souvenir sheet containing No. 3174 sold for €3. Value $8.
See No. 4969b.

Impressionist Paintings — A1767

Designs: Nos. 3175a, 3176, Portraits from the Country, by Gustave Caillebotte. Nos. 3175b, 3183, Dancers, by Edgar Degas. Nos. 3175c, 3181, Marguerite Gachet in the Garden, by Vincent van Gogh. Nos. 3175d, 3179, Two Young Girls at the Piano, by Auguste Renoir. Nos. 3175e, 3177, The Butterfly Hunt, by Berthe Morisot. Nos. 3175f, 3184, Luncheon on the Grass, by Edouard Manet. Nos. 3175g, 3182, Evening Air, by Henri-Edmond Cross. Nos. 3175h, 3180, The Shepherdess (Young Peasant Girl with a Stick), by Camille Pissarro. Nos. 3175i, 3178, Mother and Child, by Mary Cassatt. Nos. 3175j, 3185, Women of Tahiti on the Beach, by Paul Gauguin.

2006   Litho.   Perf. 13¼
3175		Sheet of 10 +10 labels	60.00	60.00
a.-j.	A1767	(53c) Any single + label	5.00	5.00

Booklet Stamps
Self-Adhesive
Serpentine Die Cut 11¼x11
3176	A1767	(53c) multi	2.00	.30
3177	A1767	(53c) multi	2.00	.30
3178	A1767	(53c) multi	2.00	.30
3179	A1767	(53c) multi	2.00	.30
3180	A1767	(53c) multi	2.00	.30
3181	A1767	(53c) multi	2.00	.30
3182	A1767	(53c) multi	2.00	.30
3183	A1767	(53c) multi	2.00	.30
3184	A1767	(53c) multi	2.00	.30
3185	A1767	(53c) multi	2.00	.30
a.		Booklet pane of 10, #3176-3185	20.00	
b.		Sheet of 10, #3176-3185, + 10 labels	110.00	

Issued: No. 3175, 6/1; Nos. 3176-3185, 1/21. No. 3175 sold for €6.86. No. 3185b sold for €8.61. Labels could be personalized.

2006 Winter Olympics, Turin — A1768

2006, Feb. 4   Photo.   Perf. 13
3186	A1768	53c multi	1.60	.30

Spirou A1769

Fantasio, Spip and Spirou A1770

Fantasio — A1771

2006, Feb. 25   Perf. 13¼
3187	A1769	(53c) multi	2.00	.30
a.		Perf. 13¼x13 (booklet stamp)	1.25	.30

Booklet Stamps
Perf. 13¼x13
3188	A1770	(48c) multi	2.50	1.00
3189	A1771	(90c) multi	3.00	.75
a.		Booklet pane, 4 each #3187a, 3188, 2 #3189	23.00	—
		Complete booklet, #3189a	24.00	

Characters from Spirou, by Robert Velter. Stamp Day.

Courrières Coal Mine Disaster, Cent. — A1772

2006, Feb. 25   Perf. 13¼
3190	A1772	53c multi	1.60	.30

Douaumont Ossuary A1773

2006, Mar. 4   Engr.
3191	A1773	53c multi	1.60	.30

Aspects of Life in the French Regions Type of 2003

No. 3192: a, Yellow plums (mirabelle). b, Salt marsh (marais salants). c, Butter (beurre). d, Roquefort cheese, vert. e, Olive oil, vert. f, Carnival, vert. g, Grape harvests (vendanges), vert. h, Waiter at café, vert. i, Transhumance of livestock. j, Marshland gardens (hortillonages).

2006, Mar. 25   Photo.
3192		Sheet of 10	16.00	16.00
a.-j.	A1642	53c Any single	1.60	1.25

No. 3192 has three vertical rows of rouletting, separating sheet into quarters.

Nos. 3192a-3192j were also issued in large booklets containing panes of 1 of each stamp. The booklet sold for €19. Value $35.

Tourism Issue

Yvoire — A1774

Dijon — A1775

Antibes Juan-les-Pins A1776

Thionville A1777

2006   Photo.   Perf. 13
3193	A1774	53c multi	1.60	.30

Engr.
Perf. 13¼
3194	A1775	53c multi	1.60	.30

Litho. & Engr.
Perf. 13x13¼
3195	A1776	53c multi	1.60	.30

Engraved
3196	A1777	54c multi	1.60	.40
		Nos. 3193-3196 (4)	6.40	1.30

Issued: No. 3193, 3/25; No. 3194, 4/7. No. 3195, 7/15. No. 3196, 9/16.

Art Series

Prehistoric Drawings in Rouffignac Cave A1778

Bathers, by Paul Cézanne A1779

Untitled Painting by Claude Viallat — A1780

Beggars Receiving Alms at the Door of a House, by Rembrandt A1781

Engr., Photo. (#3198, 3199)
2006   Perf. 13x13¼
3197	A1778	55c multi	2.25	.75
3198	A1779	82c multi	2.50	1.00

Perf. 13¼x13

3199	A1780	€1.22 brt pink & bl grn	3.75 1.25
3200	A1781	€1.30 multi	4.75 1.25
	Nos. 3197-3200 (4)		13.25 4.25

Issued: 82c, 4/8; 55c, 5/27; No. 3199, 6/3. No. 3200, 11/10.

Gardens and Parks Type of 2003
Souvenir Sheet

No. 3201: a, Vallée-aux-Loups Park. b, Albert Kahn Gardens.

2006, Apr. 22   Photo.   Perf. 13¼x13

3201		Sheet of 2	13.00 13.00
a.-b.		A1660 €1.98 Either single	6.00 5.00
c.		Souvenir sheet, #3118a, 3118b, 3201a, 3201b	50.00 50.00

Salon du Timbre 2006. No. 3201 has four vertical rows of rouletting, separating sheet into fifths, with the two stamps in the central fifth.

No. 3201c issued 6/16.

Young Animals — A1782

Designs: No. 3202, Puppy. No. 3203, Kitten. 55c, Foal, horiz. 82c, Lamb, horiz..

2006, Apr. 22   Perf. 13¼

3202	A1782	53c multi	1.60 .30
3203	A1782	53c multi	1.60 .30
3204	A1782	55c multi	1.60 .30
3205	A1782	82c multi	2.40 1.75
a.		Souvenir sheet, #3202-3205	7.50 7.50
	Nos. 3202-3205 (4)		7.20 1.65

Europa — A1783

2006, Apr. 30

3206	A1783	53c multi	1.60 .30

Pierre Bayle (1647-1706), Philiosopher — A1784

2006, May 2   Engr.   Perf. 13x13¼

3207	A1784	53c blk & brn	1.60 .30

Remembrance of Slavery Day, 5th Anniv. — A1785

2006, May 10   Photo.   Perf. 13¼

3208	A1785	53c multi	1.60 .30

Vacation — A1786

Serpentine Die Cut 11¼x11
2006, May 27   Litho.
Booklet Stamp
Self-Adhesive

3209	A1786	(53c) multi	2.00 .25
a.		Booklet pane of 10	20.00

Miniature Sheet

2006 World Cup Soccer Championships, Germany — A1787

No. 3210: a, Replacement players (39x25mm). b, Fans (39x25mm). c, Player with ball near chest (32mm diameter). d, Player kicking ball (32mm diameter). e, Goalie throwing ball (32mm diameter). f, Player making scissor kick (32mm diameter). g, Two players (32mm diameter). h, Referee (25x39mm). i, Coach (39x25mm). j, Cameramen (39x25mm).

2006, May 27   Photo.   Perf. 12¾

3210	A1787	Sheet of 10	16.00 16.00
a.-j.		53c Any single	1.60 1.25

Marianne Type of 2005

2006   Litho.   Perf. 13

3211		Sheet of 15, #a-k, 2 each #l-m, + 15 labels	70.00 70.00
a.	A1713	1c yellow orange	.35 .35
b.	A1713	5c dark brown	.35 .35
c.	A1713	10c violet	.55 .55
d.	A1713	55c blue	2.75 2.75
e.	A1713	64c olive green	3.25 3.25
f.	A1713	75c light blue	3.50 3.50
g.	A1713	82c fawn	4.25 4.25
h.	A1713	90c dark blue	4.50 4.50
i.	A1713	€1 dull orange	5.00 5.00
j.	A1713	€1.22 red violet	6.00 6.00
k.	A1713	€1.98 brown	9.50 9.50
l.	A1713	(48c) green	2.50 2.50
m.	A1713	(53c) red	2.60 2.60

Serpentine Die Cut 11¼
Self-Adhesive

3211N		Sheet of 15, #3211No-3211Ny, 2 each #3211Nz, 3211Naa, + 15 labels	250.00
o.	A1713	1c yellow orange	.75 .75
p.	A1713	5c dark brown	.75 .75
q.	A1713	10c violet	1.25 1.25
r.	A1713	55c blue	6.75 6.75
s.	A1713	64c olive green	7.50 7.50
t.	A1713	75c light blue	8.75 8.75
u.	A1713	82c fawn	9.50 9.50
v.	A1713	90c dark blue	11.00 11.00
w.	A1713	€1 dull orange	12.00 12.00
x.	A1713	€1.22 red violet	15.00 15.00
y.	A1713	€1.98 brown	20.00 20.00
z.	A1713	(48c) green	5.50 5.50
aa.	A1713	(53c) red	6.25 6.25

Etched on Foil
Die Cut Perf. 13

3212	A1713	€5 silver	17.50 12.50

Nos. 3211a-3211m, 3211No-3211Naa and 3212 have "Phil@poste" inscription at bottom. Nos. 3211 and 3211N have stamps with a glossy varnish. No. 3211 sold for €12.04 and labels could be personalized. No. 3211N sold for €15.05 and labels could be personalized. No. 3212 was sold in a protective package.

Costumes From Operas by Wolfgang Amadeus Mozart — A1788

Designs: No. 3213, The Magic Flute. No. 3214, Don Giovanni. No. 3215, The Marriage of Figaro. No. 3216, The Clemency of Titus. No. 3217, The Abduction from the Seraglio (L'enlèvement au Sérail). No. 3218, Cosi Fan Tutte.

2006, June 17   Photo.   Perf. 13

3213	A1788	53c multi	1.60 .75
3214	A1788	53c multi	1.60 .75
3215	A1788	53c multi	1.60 .75
3216	A1788	53c multi	1.60 .75
3217	A1788	53c multi	1.60 .75
3218	A1788	53c multi	1.60 .75
a.		Souvenir sheet, #3213-3218	12.00 12.00
	Nos. 3213-3218 (6)		9.60 4.50

Nos. 3213-3218 were each printed in souvenir sheets containing one stamp that sold as a set for €15, and in booklet panes containing one stamp in a large book that sold for €19. Value: set of 6 sheets $40; set of 6 panes in book $50. No. 3218a sold for €4.80, with the Red Cross receiving €1.62 of that.

UNESCO World Heritage Sites — A1789

Designs: 53c, Provins. 90c, Mont Saint-Michel.

2006, June 17   Photo.   Perf. 13¼

3219	A1789	53c multi	1.60 .30
3220	A1789	90c multi	2.75 1.20

See United Nations Offices in Geneva Nos. 459-461.

Garnier Opera House, Paris A1790

2006, June 18   Engr.   Perf. 13x13¼

3221	A1790	53c multi + label	1.60 .40

French Federation of Philatelic Associations 79th Congress, Paris. No. 3221 exists in a souvenir sheet of 1 (without label), issued in 2007 that sold for €3. Value, $12. See No. 5762b.

Happy Birthday — A1791

2006, June 19   Photo.   Perf. 13

3222	A1791	(53c) multi	2.00 .30
a.		Souvenir sheet of 5	10.00 10.00
b.		Litho. stamp + label	6.00 6.00

Serpentine Die Cut 11
Self-Adhesive

3222C	A1791	(53c) multi + label	15.00 15.00

Sheets of 10 on No. 3222b sold for €6.86. No. 3222C was printed in sheets of 10 stamps + 10 labels that sold for €8.61. Labels could be personalized for an additional fee.

European Capitals Type of 2002
Souvenir Sheet

No. 3223 — Attractions in Nicosia, Cyprus: a, Chrysaliniotissa Church. b, Archaeological Museum. c, Famagusta Gate. d, Archbishop's residence (Archeveché).

2006, June 20   Photo.   Perf. 13x13¼

3223	A1622	Sheet of 4	7.00 7.00
a.-d.		53c Any single	1.60 1.00

Tango Dancing — A1792

2006, June 21   Photo.   Perf. 12¼

3224	A1792	53c Dancers	1.60 .30
3225	A1792	90c Musician	2.75 1.20

See Argentina Nos. 2395-2396.

La Poste's Business Foundation, 10th Anniv. — A1793

2006, June 22   Litho.   Perf. 13

3226	A1793	(53c) multi, tan	2.00 .30

French Open Golf Championship, Cent. — A1794

Photo. & Embossed

2006, June 24   Perf. 13

3227	A1794	53c multi	1.60 .30

A souvenir sheet containing No. 3227 sold for €3. Value $8.

Rotary International Type of 2005
Serpentine Die Cut 11

2006, July 1   Photo.
Self-Adhesive

3227A	A1717	53c multi	5.00 4.00

French Soccer Team's Second-Place Showing in 2006 World Cup — A1795

2006, July 5   Photo.   Perf. 13¼
Size: 35x26mm

3228	A1795	53c multi	1.60 .40

Litho.
Size: 35x22mm
Perf. 13

3229	A1795	53c multi + label	5.00 4.00

Serpentine Die Cut 11¼x11
Self-Adhesive

3229A	A1795	53c multi + label	13.00 13.00

No. 3229 was printed in sheets of 10 stamps and 10 labels that sold for €6.94. Value $55. No. 3229A was printed in sheets of 10 stamps + 10 labels that sold for €8.61. Value $150. Labels could be personalized.

Quai Branly Museum A1796

2006, July 8   Photo.   Perf. 13x13¼

3230	A1796	53c multi	1.60 .40

Reinstatement of Capt. Alfred Dreyfus, Cent. — A1797

2006, July 12   Engr.

3231	A1797	53c multi	1.60 .30

Claude-Joseph Rouget de Lisle (1760-1836), Composer of "La Marseillaise" A1798

2006, July 13   Photo.   Perf. 13¼

3232	A1798	53c multi	1.60 .30

Pablo Casals (1876-1973), Cellist — A1799

2006, July 29

3233	A1799	53c multi	1.60 .30

Aspects of Life in French Regions Type of 2003

No. 3234: a, Catalan Towers. b, La Croisette, Cannes. c, Brocéliande Forest. d, Volcanic craters, Auvergne, vert. e, Les Invalides, Paris, vert. f, Chateau de

Chaumont, Chaumont-sur-Loire. g, Ardèche Gorges, vert. h, Flour mill, Valmy, vert. i, Grotto of Messabielle, Lourdes. j, Calanches de Piana, Corsica.

2006, Sept. 2   Photo.   *Perf. 13*
3234   Sheet of 10   16.00 16.00
a.-j.   A1642 54c Any single   1.60   1.25

No. 3234 has three vertical rows of rouletting, separating sheet into quarters.

Nos. 3234a-3234j were also issued in large booklets containing panes of 1 of each stamp. The booklet sold for €19. Value $35.

A1800

A1801

A1802

A1803

A1804

A1805

A1806

A1807

A1808

Cubitus, Comics by Michel Rodrigue and Pierre Aucaigne — A1809

Serpentine Die Cut 11¼x11
2006, Sept. 20   Litho.
Self-Adhesive
Booklet Stamps
3235 A1800 (54c) multi   2.00   .30
3236 A1801 (54c) multi   2.00   .30
3237 A1802 (54c) multi   2.00   .30
3238 A1803 (54c) multi   2.00   .30
3239 A1804 (54c) multi   2.00   .30
3240 A1805 (54c) multi   2.00   .30
3241 A1806 (54c) multi   2.00   .30
3242 A1807 (54c) multi   2.00   .30
3243 A1808 (54c) multi   2.00   .30
3244 A1809 (54c) multi   2.00   .30
a.   Booklet pane of 10, #3235-
        3244   20.00

Sculptures by Constantin Brancusi (1876-1957) A1810

Designs: 54c, Sleeping Muse. 85c, Sleep.

2006, Sept. 25   Photo.   *Perf. 13¼*
3245 A1810 54c multi   1.60   .30
3246 A1810 85c multi   2.75   .90

See Romania Nos. 4878-4879.

Marianne Type of 2005
2006   Engr.   *Perf. 13*
Inscribed "Phil@poste" at Bottom
3247 A1713 10c gray   .30   .25
3248 A1713 60c dark blue 1.75   .40
3249 A1713 70c yel green 2.10   .40
3250 A1713 85c purple   2.75   .50
3251 A1713 86c fawn   2.75   .50
3252 A1713 €1.15 blue   3.50   .75
3253 A1713 €1.30 red violet 4.00 1.00
3254 A1713 €2.11 chocolate 6.25   .50
      Nos. 3247-3254 (8)   23.40 4.30

Coil Stamp
Perf. 13 Horiz.
3255 A1713 60c dark blue 2.00   .75

Serpentine Die Cut 11¼
Self-Adhesive
3255A A1713 (54c) red + label 12.00 12.00
f.   Inscribed "ITVF" at bot-
        tom + label   —   —

Inscribed "Phila@poste" at Bottom
3255B A1713 55c dk blue +
                label   —   —
3255C A1713 60c dark blue +
                label   13.00 13.00
3255D A1713 82c fawn + label 15.00 15.00
3255E A1713 86c fawn + label 13.00 13.00
      Nos. 3255A-3255E (4)   53.00 53.00

Issued: Nos. 3247-3255, 10/1, others, 2006. Nos. 3255A, 3255Af, 3255C and 3255E were printed in sheets of 15 stamps + 15 labels that could be personalized. Nos. 3255B and 3255D were printed in sheets containing 10 stamps + 10 large labels or 15 stamps and 15 small labels. Labels could be personalized. Sheets of Nos. 3255A and 3255Af each sold for €13.29; No. 3255C, €14.04; No. 3255E, €17.31. For Nos. 3255A, 3255C, 3255D and 3255E, adjacent labels came in large and small sizes.

Aviation Without Borders — A1811

2006, Oct. 7   Photo.   *Perf. 13*
3256 A1811 54c multi   1.60   .30

Henri Moissan (1852-1907), 1906 Nobel Chemistry Laureate A1812

2006, Oct. 14   Engr.   *Perf. 13¼x13*
3257 A1812 54c multi   1.60   .30

"Shared Memories," Intl. Conference on Veterans, Paris — A1813

2006, Oct. 26   Photo.   *Perf. 13¼*
3258 A1813 54c multi   1.60   .30

Marianne — A1814

Serpentine Die Cut 6¾ Vert.
2006, Nov. 8   Engr.
Self-Adhesive
Booklet Stamp
3259 A1814 54c red   4.00 3.00
a.   Booklet pane, 5 each
        #3083d, 3259   30.00

Compare with types A147 and A3213. See No. 4910.

Miniature Sheet

Flying Machines — A1815

No. 3260: a, Gustave Ponton d'Amécourt's helicopter. b, Alberto Santos-Dumont's monoplane, "Demoiselle," horiz. c, Jean Marie Le Bris's bird-shaped glider, horiz. d, Clément Ader's "Avion III," horiz. e, Henri Fabré's seaplane, horiz. f, Jean-Pierre Blanchard's balloon.

Litho. & Engr.
2006, Nov. 9   *Perf. 13*
3260 A1815 Sheet of 6   10.00 10.00
a.-f.   54c Any single   1.60   1.40

Inauguration of Aulnay-sous-Bois to Bondy Tram-Train Line — A1816

2006, Nov. 18   Photo.   *Perf. 13x13¼*
3261 A1816 54c multi   1.60   .30

Holiday Greetings A1817

Designs: No. 3262, Reindeer, sleigh, four penguins. No. 3263, Reindeer with fishing pole, three penguins. No. 3264, Reindeer, Christmas tree, two penguins. No. 3265, Reindeer skating, three penguins. No. 3266, Reindeer with gift boxes, three penguins.

2006, Nov. 25   Litho.   *Perf. 13¼*
3261A A1817 (54c) multi + la-
                 bel   2.00   .30
3261B A1817 (54c) multi + la-
                 bel   2.00   .30
3261C A1817 (54c) multi + la-
                 bel   2.00   .30
3261D A1817 (54c) multi + la-
                 bel   2.00   .30
3261E A1817 (54c) multi + la-
                 bel   2.00   .30
f.   Vert. strip of 5, #3261A-
        3261E, + 5 labels   12.00 12.00
      Miniature sheet, 2
        #3261Ef   30.00 30.00

Self-Adhesive
Booklet Stamps
Serpentine Die Cut 11¼x11
3262 A1817 (54c) multi   2.00   .30
3263 A1817 (54c) multi   2.00   .30
3264 A1817 (54c) multi   2.00   .30
3265 A1817 (54c) multi   2.00   .30
3266 A1817 (54c) multi   2.00   .30
a.   Booklet pane, 2 each
        #3262-3266   20.00
      Nos. 3262-3266 (5)   10.00 1.50

Miniature sheet containing Nos. 3261A-3261E sold for €6.94. Value $60. Labels could be personalized. Value $60.

A souvenir sheet containing a perf. 13 example of No. 3266 sold for €3. Value $17.50. A sheet containing 5 No. 3261A + 5 labels exists, but was not sold.

Grand Masonic Lodge of France — A1818

2006, Dec. 1   Photo.   *Perf. 13x13¼*
3267 A1818 54c multi   1.60   .30

Alain Poher (1909-96), Politician, and Senate Building A1819

2006, Dec. 2   Engr.   *Perf. 13¼*
3268 A1819 54c multi   1.60   .30

Opening of New Paris Tramway A1820

2006, Dec. 16   Photo.   *Perf. 13¼*
3269 A1820 54c multi   1.75   .30

Orchids Type of 2002
Designs: 31c, Platanthera chlorantha. 36c, Dactylorhiza savogiensis. 43c, Orchis insularis.

2007, Jan. 2   Litho.   *Perf. 13*
3270 A1584 31c multi   1.50   .50
3271 A1584 36c multi   1.50   .60
3272 A1584 43c multi   2.50   .75
      Nos. 3270-3272 (3)   5.50 1.85

Nos. 3270-3272 are known only precanceled. See second note after No. 132.

Hearts — A1821

"Givenchy" in: (54c), Black and white. (86c), Red.

2007, Jan. 6   Photo.   *Perf. 13¼*
Inscribed "Lettre 20 g"
3273 A1821 (54c) red & black 2.00   .30
a.   Souvenir sheet of 5   10.00 10.00
Inscribed "Lettre 50 g"
3274 A1821 (86c) black & red 3.00 1.00

Values are for stamps with surrounding selvage.

Serpentine Die Cut
Self-Adhesive
3275 A1821 (54c) Like #3273 16.00 13.00
Inscribed "Lettre 50 g"
3276 A1821 (86c) Like #3274 16.00 13.00

New Year 2007 (Year of the Pig) — A1822

2007, Jan. 27   Photo.   *Perf. 13¼x13*
3277 A1822 (54c) multi   2.00   .30
a.   Litho., stamp + label 8.00 8.00

Serpentine Die Cut 11
Self-Adhesive
3277B A1822 (54c) multi + la-
                 bel   15.00 15.00

No. 3277 has a somewhat blurrier image than No. 3277a. Sheets of 5 #3277a + 5 labels sold for €3.51. Value $15. Labels could be personalized. No. 3277 exists in a souvenir sheet of 1 that sold for €3. Value $12.

No. 3277B was printed in sheets of 10 + 10 labels that sold for €8.86. Value $150. Labels could be personalized.

See No. 4969c.

Egyptian Hippopotamus Figurine — A1823

Head of Aphrodite A1824

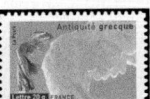
Winged Victory of Samothrace A1825

Fresco, Pompeii — A1826

King Amenemhet III of Egypt — A1827

Statue of Juno — A1828

Egyptian Harpist — A1829

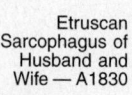

Etruscan Sarcophagus of Husband and Wife — A1830

Egyptian Statue of Seated Scribe — A1831

Head of Pericles — A1832

Serpentine Die Cut 11¼x11

2007, Jan. 27   Litho.
Booklet Stamps
Self-Adhesive

3279	A1823	(54c) multi	2.00	.30
3280	A1824	(54c) multi	2.00	.30
3281	A1825	(54c) multi	2.00	.30
3282	A1826	(54c) multi	2.00	.30
3283	A1827	(54c) multi	2.00	.30
3284	A1828	(54c) multi	2.00	.30
3285	A1829	(54c) multi	2.00	.30
3286	A1830	(54c) multi	2.00	.30
3287	A1831	(54c) multi	2.00	.30
3288	A1832	(54c) multi	2.00	.30
a.		Booklet pane of 10, #3279-3288	20.00	

Tourism Issue

Valenciennes A1833

2007   Engr.   *Perf. 13¼*
3289   A1833   54c red & blue   1.50   .30
    Issued: No. 3289, 2/3.

Tourism Issue

Limoges A1834

2007   Engr.   *Perf. 13¼*
3290   A1834   54c multi   2.25   .30
    Issued: No. 3290, 3/23.

Tourism Issue

Arcachon A1835

2007, May 19   Photo.   *Perf. 13¼*
3291   A1835   54c multi   2.25   .30

Tourism Issue

Castres — A1836

2007, July 20   Engr.   *Perf. 13¼*
3292   A1836   54c multi   1.60   .30

Tourism Issue

Firminy — A1837

2007, Sept. 15   Engr.   *Perf. 13¼*
3293   A1837   54c multi   1.75   .30

Rights of France — A1838

2007, Feb. 5   Photo.   *Perf. 13¼*
3294   A1838   54c multi   2.00   .30

Art Issue

Book Illumination from Sélestat Library — A1839

Galerie des Glaces, Versailles Palace A1840

La Barrière Fleurie, by Paul Sérusier A1841

Gallic Boar Ensign A1842

Perf. 12¼x13, 13¼x13 (#3297), 13x13¼ (#3296, 3298)
Engraved, Photo. (#3296, 3297, 3298A)

2007-08

3295	A1839	60c multi	1.75	.60
3296	A1840	85c multi	3.50	1.00
3297	A1841	86c multi	3.00	1.00
3298	A1842	€1.30 multi	4.50	1.25
		Nos. 3295-3298 (4)	12.75	3.85

Self-Adhesive
Serpentine Die Cut 11

3298A	A1840	85c multi	20.00	12.00

   Issued: No. 3295, 2/10. No. 3297, 10/13. No. 3298, 6/2. No. 3296, 11/10. No. 3298A, 2008.

Aspects of Life in the French Regions Type of 2003

   No. 3299: a, Baux-de-Provence. b, Banks of the Loire. c, Grande-Chartreuse Massif. d, Saint-Tropez. e, Doubs Waterfall, vert. f, Fontainebleau Forest, vert. g, Chantilly Castle. h, Saint-Malo. i, Ballon d'Alsace, vert. j, Midi Canal, vert.

2007, Feb. 24   Photo.   *Perf. 13*
3299   Sheet of 10   16.00   16.00
  a.-j.   A1642 54c Any single   1.50   1.25

   No. 3299 has three vertical rows of rouletting, separating sheet into quarters.
   Nos. 3299a-3299j were also issued in large booklets containing panes of 1 of each stamp. The booklet sold for €19.

Aspects of Life in French Regions Type of 2003 Inscribed "Lettre Prioritaire 20g"

   Designs: Nos. 3300-3301, Arc de Triomphe, vert.

2007, Feb.   Photo.   *Perf. 13*
3300   A1642 (54c) multi + label   8.00   8.00
Serpentine Die Cut 11x11¼
3301   A1642 (54c) multi + label   45.00   45.00

   Nos. 3300-3301 each were printed in sheets of 10 stamps + 10 different labels that sold for €6.85. Value of sheets: No. 3300, $80; No. 3301, $450.

Marianne Type of 2005
2007   Litho.   *Perf. 13*
Stamps Inscribed "Phil@poste"
Without Varnish

3302		Sheet of 15, #a-k, 2 each #l-m, + 15 labels	250.00	250.00
a.	A1713	1c yellow orange	1.25	1.25
b.	A1713	5c brown	1.65	1.65
c.	A1713	10c gray	3.00	3.00
d.	A1713	60c blue	11.50	11.50
e.	A1713	70c lt yellow green	13.50	13.50
f.	A1713	85c purple	16.00	16.00
g.	A1713	86c pink	17.00	17.00
h.	A1713	€1 orange	21.00	21.00
i.	A1713	€1.15 light blue	23.00	23.00
j.	A1713	€1.30 red violet	25.00	25.00
k.	A1713	€2.11 maroon	37.50	37.50
l.	A1713	(49c) blue green	10.00	10.00
m.	A1713	(54c) red	11.50	11.50

Litho.
Serpentine Die Cut 11¼
Self-Adhesive
Stamps Inscribed "Phil@poste"
Without Varnish

3302N		Sheet of 15, #3302No-3302Ny, 2 each #3302Nz, 3302Naa, + 15 labels	—	
o.	A1713	1c yellow orange	—	—
p.	A1713	5c brown	—	—
q.	A1713	10c gray	—	—
r.	A1713	60c blue	—	—
s.	A1713	70c lt yellow green	—	—
t.	A1713	85c purple	—	—
u.	A1713	86c pink	—	—
v.	A1713	€1 orange	—	—
w.	A1713	€1.15 light blue	—	—
x.	A1713	€1.30 red violet	—	—
y.	A1713	€2.11 maroon	—	—
z.	A1713	(49c) blue green	—	—
aa.	A1713	(54c) red	—	—

   Nos. 3302 and 3302N each sold for €14.40 and have personalizable labels.

Harry Potter — A1843

   Designs: (49c), Ron Weasley. (85c), Hermione Granger.

2007, Mar. 12   Photo.   *Perf. 13¼*
3303   A1843   (54c) red & multi   2.00   .30
  a.   Souvenir sheet of 1   2.50   2.00
  b.   Perf. 13¼x13 (booklet stamp)   2.00   .30

Booklet Stamps
Perf. 13¼x13

3304   A1843   (49c) grn & multi   2.50   1.00
3305   A1843   (85c) blue & multi   3.00   .60
  a.   Booklet pane of 10, 4 #3303b, 3 each #3304-3305   22.50   —
     Complete booklet, #3305a   22.50

   Stamp Day. Sheets of five serpentine die cut 11 self-adhesive stamps of each denomination and five labels that could not be personalized exist. Each sheet sold for €6.50. Value, set, $150.

Albert Londres (1884-1932), Journalist A1844

2007, Mar. 16   Engr.   *Perf. 13x13¼*
3306   A1844   54c multi   1.60   .30

   Six different souvenir sheets containing one No. 3306 exist. The set sold for €15. Value, set $45.

Audit Office, Bicent. — A1845

2007   *Perf. 13¼x13*
3307   A1845   54c multi   2.00   .30
Serpentine Die Cut 11
Self-Adhesive
3307A   A1845   54c multi   5.00   4.00
   Issued: No. 3307, 3/17; No. 3307A, 7/20.

Treaty of Rome, 50th Anniv. — A1846

2007, Mar. 23   Photo.   *Perf. 13¼*
3308   A1846   54c multi   1.50   .30

Sébastaen Le Prestre de Vauban (1633-1707), Military Engineer A1847

2007, Mar. 30   Engr.
3309   A1847   54c multi   1.50   .30

2007 Rugby World Cup — A1848

2007, Apr. 14   Photo.   *Perf. 13¼*
3310   A1848   54c multi   1.50   .30
  a.   Perf. 13x13¼ + label   5.00   5.00

Serpentine Die Cut 11¼
Self-Adhesive

3311 A1848 54c multi + label 12.50 12.50

No. 3310a was printed in sheets of 5 stamps and 5 labels that could be personalized that sold for €4.20. Value $60.
No. 3311 was printed in sheets of 10 + 10 labels that could be personalized. Sheets sold for €10.60. Value, sheet $125.

Endangered Animals in Overseas Departments — A1849

Designs: No. 3312, Antillean iguana. No. 3313, Raccoon, horiz. 60c, Jaguar, horiz. 86c, Barau's petrel, horiz..

2007, Apr. 28   Photo.   Perf. 13¼

3312 A1849 54c multi 1.50 .30
3313 A1849 54c multi 1.50 .30
3314 A1849 60c multi 1.75 .60
3315 A1849 86c multi 2.40 .60
a. Souvenir sheet, #3312-3315 7.25 7.25
Nos. 3312-3315 (4) 7.15 1.80

Gardens and Parks Type of 2003
Souvenir Sheet

No. 3316 — Parc de la Tete d'Or, Lyon: a, Red flowers. b, White flowers.

2007, Apr. 28   Perf. 13¼x13

3316 Sheet of 2 12.00 12.00
a.-b. A1660 €2.11 Either single 6.00 5.00

Salon du Timbre. No. 3316 has four vertical rows of rouletting, separating sheet into fifths, with the two stamps in the central fifth.

Vacations A1850

Designs: No. 3317, Wooden fence and red hollyhocks. No. 3318, Angelfish. No. 3319, Blue flowers. No. 3320, Blueberries. No. 3321, Canoes. No. 3322, Dyed wool hanging on rods. No. 3323, Glacier. No. 3324, Palm tree. No. 3325, Beach umbrellas and woman. No. 3326, Boxes of color pigments.

Serpentine Die Cut 11¼x11
2007, Apr. 28   Litho.
Booklet Stamps
Self-Adhesive

3317 A1850 (54c) multi 1.75 .30
3318 A1850 (54c) multi 1.75 .30
3319 A1850 (54c) multi 1.75 .30
3320 A1850 (54c) multi 1.75 .30
3321 A1850 (54c) multi 1.75 .30
3322 A1850 (54c) multi 1.75 .30
3323 A1850 (54c) multi 1.75 .30
3324 A1850 (54c) multi 1.75 .30
3325 A1850 (54c) multi 1.75 .30
3326 A1850 (54c) multi 1.75 .30
a. Booklet pane of 10, #3317-3326 17.50

Europa — A1851

2007, May 1   Photo.   Perf. 13¼

3327 A1851 60c multi 1.50 .40

Scouting, cent.

Intl. Sailing Federation, Cent. — A1852

2007, May 4   Perf. 13

3328 A1852 85c multi 2.25 .80

A souvenir sheet containing No. 3328 sold for €3. Value, $12.

Tintin and Snowy — A1853

Characters from Tintin comic strips and books, by Hergé: No. 3330, Professor Calculus (Tournesol). No. 3331, Captain Haddock. No. 3332, Thomson and Thompson (Dupondt). No. 3333, Bianca Castafiore. No. 3334, Chang (Tchang).

2007, May 12

3329 A1853 54c multi 1.50 .50
3330 A1853 54c multi 1.50 .50
3331 A1853 54c multi 1.50 .50
3332 A1853 54c multi 1.50 .50
3333 A1853 54c multi 1.50 .50
3334 A1853 54c multi 1.50 .50
a. Souvenir sheet, #3329-3334 13.50 13.50

No. 3334a sold for €5, with the Red Cross receiving €1.76 of that.

Religious Art — A1854

Designs: 54c, Nativity, 15th cent. miniature, from Armenia. 85c, The Smile of Reims.

2007, May 22   Perf. 13¼

3335 A1854 54c multi 1.60 .30
3336 A1854 85c multi 2.50 1.00

See Armenia Nos. 749-750.

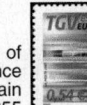

Inauguration of Eastern France TGV Train Service — A1855

2007, June 9

3337 A1855 54c multi 1.50 .30

French Federation of Philatelic Associations 80th Congress, Poitiers — A1856

2007, June 15   Engr.   Perf. 13¼x13¼

3338 A1856 54c multi + label 1.75 .30

Miniature Sheet

2007 Rugby World Cup, France A1857

No. 3339 — Inscriptions: a, Touche (Throw-in, 30x39mm elliptical). b, Melée (scrum). c, Attaque (player running with ball). d, Essai (try). e, Transformation (kick, 30x39mm elliptical). f, Passe (pass). g, Raffut (stiff-arm). h, Haka (dance). i, Plaquage (tackle). j, Supporteurs (fans).

2007, June 23   Perf. 13x13¼

3339 A1857 Sheet of 10 17.00 17.00
a.-j. 54c Any single 1.50 1.25

European Capitals Type of 2002
Souvenir Sheet

No. 3340 — Attractions in Brussels: a, Maison du Roi (Royal Palace). b, Hotel du Ville (City Hall), vert. c, Mannekin Pis, vert. d, Atomium.

Perf. 13x13¼, 13¼x13 (vert. stamps)
2007, June 30

3340 A1622 Sheet of 4 7.50 7.50
a.-d. 54c Any single 1.60 .90

Association of French Mayors, Cent. — A1858

2007, July 5   Photo.   Perf. 13¼

3341 A1858 54c multi 1.50 .30

Pierre Pfimlin (1907-2000), Mayor of Strasbourg — A1859

2007, July 7   Photo.   Perf. 13¼

3342 A1859 60c multi 1.75 .60

2007 Rugby World Cup, France — A1860

Litho. With Three-Dimensional Plastic Affixed
2007, Sept. 5   Serpentine Die Cut 11
Self-Adhesive

3343 A1860 €3 multi 10.00 6.00

Happy Birthday — A1861

2007, Sept. 8   Photo.   Perf. 13x13¼

3344 A1861 (54c) multi 5.00 .30
a. Litho., with attached label 2.40 2.40

No. 3344 was printed in a sheet of 5; No. 3344a was printed in a sheet of 5 + 5 labels that sold for €4.20.

Gift Boxes — A1862

Boxes and: Nos. 3345a, 3346, Butterflies. Nos. 3345b, 3348, Flowers. Nos. 3345c, 3347, Hearts. Nos. 3345d, 3350, Musical notes. Nos. 3345e, 3349, Bubbles.

2007, Sept. 8   Litho.   Perf. 13¼

3345 Sheet of 5 + 5 labels 12.00 12.00
a.-e. A1862 (54c) Any single + label 2.40 2.40

Self-Adhesive
Booklet Stamps
Serpentine Die Cut 11

3346 A1862 (54c) multi 1.60 .55
3347 A1862 (54c) multi 1.60 .55
3348 A1862 (54c) multi 1.60 .55
3349 A1862 (54c) multi 1.60 .55
3350 A1862 (54c) multi 1.60 .55
a. Booklet pane of 5 #3346-3350 8.00

No. 3345 sold for €4.20.

Sully Prudhomme (1839-1907), Poet — A1863

2007, Sept. 15   Engr.   Perf. 13¼

3351 A1863 €1.30 multi 3.75 1.25

A1864

A1865

A1866

A1867

Cows — A1868

Serpentine Die Cut 11
2007, Sept. 20   Litho.
Self-Adhesive
Booklet Stamps

3352 A1864 (54c) multi 1.60 .55
3353 A1865 (54c) multi 1.60 .55
3354 A1866 (54c) multi 1.60 .55
3355 A1867 (54c) multi 1.60 .55
3356 A1868 (54c) multi 1.60 .55
a. Booklet pane, 2 each #3352-3356 16.00
Nos. 3352-3356 (5) 8.00 2.75

Aspects of Life in French Regions Type of 2003

No. 3357: a, Sèvres porcelain. b, Grasse perfume. c, Christmas market. d, Marseille soap. e, Giants, vert. f, Basque beret, vert. g, Aubusson tapestries. h, Lyonnaise tavern. i, Slipper, vert. j, Canteloupe, vert.

2007, Sept. 29   Photo.   Perf. 13

3357 Sheet of 10 16.00 16.00
a.-j. A1642 54c Any single 1.60 .55

No. 3357 has three vertical rows of rouletting separating sheet into quarters.
Nos. 3357a-3357j were also issued in large booklets containing panes of 1 of each stamp. The booklet sold for €19. Value $55.

Space Age, 50th Anniv. A1869

2007, Oct. 4   Perf. 13x12½

3358 A1869 85c multi 2.40 1.00

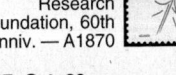

Medical Research Foundation, 60th Anniv. — A1870

2007, Oct. 20   Perf. 13¼

3359 A1870 54c multi 1.60 .30

Guy Moquet (1924-41), World War II Resistance Fighter — A1871

2007, Oct. 22   **Engr.**
3360   A1871   54c multi   1.60   .30

Dole — A1872

2007, Nov. 2
3361   A1872   54c multi   1.60   .30

Personalized Stamp With Country Name on Short Side — A1873

Personalized Stamp With Country Name on Long Side — A1874

Serpentine Die Cut 11¼ Syncopated
2007, Nov.   **Litho.**
Self-Adhesive
Inscribed: "Lettre Prioritaire 20 g"
3362   A1873   (54c) multi   6.00   6.00
3363   A1874   (54c) multi   6.00   6.00
Inscribed: "Monde 20 g"
3364   A1873   (85c) multi   6.00   6.00
3365   A1874   (85c) multi   6.00   6.00
Inscribed: "Lettre Prioritaire 50 g"
3366   A1873   (86c) multi   6.00   6.00
3367   A1874   (86c) multi   6.00   6.00
    Nos. 3362-3367 (6)   36.00 36.00

Nos. 3362-3367 were each printed in sheets of ten, having vignettes that could be personalized or chosen from a library of stock designs, two of which are shown on the illustrated stamps. Sheets of Nos. 3362 and 3363 each sold for €10.03, and sheets of Nos. 3364-3367 each sold for €13.38. Sheets were made available with different frame colors. Starting in 2008, numerous sheets containing a varying number of stamps with these frames and having various pre-selected vignettes were produced and sold by La Poste for various prices per sheet, each well above the franking value of the stamps at the time of issue. Any stamp with a vignette and/or frame color differing from the items shown is an equivalent item to those shown. Also starting in 2008, stamps were created bearing dozens of different rate inscriptions other than "Lettre Prioritaire 20g," "Monde 20g," and "Lettre Prioritaire 50g" inscriptions listed here. In 2019, a round stamp with similar features was produced in a souvenir sheet of 1.

Jean-Baptiste Charcot (1867-1936), Polar Explorer — A1875

Ship Pourquoi-Pas? — A1876

2007, Nov. 8   **Engr.**   ***Perf. 13x12¾***
3368   A1875   54c multi   1.60   .55
3369   A1876   60c multi   1.75   .60
   a.   Horiz. pair, #3368-3369   3.50 1.25

See Greenland No. 505. A sheet containing Nos. 3368-3369 sold for €4 in 2008.

Marianne — A1877

Serpentine Die Cut 6¾ Vert.
2007, Nov. 8   **Engr.**
Self-Adhesive
Booklet Stamp
3370   A1877   54c red   3.00 2.00
   a.   Booklet pane, 6 each
      #3083d, 3370   27.50

Miniature Sheet

Lighthouses — A1878

No. 3371: a, Cap Fréhel Lighthouse. b, Espiguette Lighthouse. c, D'ar-Men Lighthouse. d, Grand-Léjon Lighthouse. e, Porquerolles Lighthouse, horiz. f, Chassiron Lighthouse, horiz.

Litho. & Engr.
2007, Nov. 9   ***Perf. 13***
3371   A1878   Sheet of 6   9.75 9.75
   a.-f.   54c Any single   1.60   .55

2007 Women's World Handball Championships, France — A1879

2007, Nov. 10   **Photo.**   ***Perf. 13¼***
3372   A1879   54c multi   1.60   .30

Holiday Greetings A1880

No. 3377: a, Squirrel with stocking cap. b, Bird with party hat. c, Hedgehog with party cap. d, Dog with stocking cap. e, Deer with stocking cap.
No. 3378, Squirrel with stocking cap. No. 3379, Bird with party hat. No. 3380, Deer with stocking cap. No. 3381, Hedgehog with party hat. No. 3382, Dog with stocking cap.

2007, Nov. 24   **Litho.**   ***Perf. 13¼***
3377   Sheet of 5 + 5 labels   20.00 20.00
   a.-e.   A1880 (54c) Any single + label   2.50   2.50

Booklet Stamps
Self-Adhesive
Serpentine Die Cut 11
3378   A1880   (54c) multi   2.00   .30
3379   A1880   (54c) multi   2.00   .30
3380   A1880   (54c) multi   2.00   .30
3381   A1880   (54c) multi   2.00   .30
3382   A1880   (54c) multi   2.00   .30
   a.   Booklet pane, 2 each #3378-3382   20.00

No. 3377 sold for €4.20 and had labels that could not be personalized.
A souvenir sheet of 1 of No. 3381 sold for €3. Value, $12.

Marianne Type of 2005
2008   **Engr.**   ***Perf. 13***
3383   A1713   (65c) dk blue   2.50   .40
3384   A1713   72c yel green   2.25   .40
3385   A1713   88c fawn   2.75   .50
3386   A1713   €1.25 blue   4.00   .80
3387   A1713   €1.33 red vio   4.25   .85
3388   A1713   €2.18 choc   6.50 1.40
    Nos. 3383-3388 (6)   22.25 4.35

Coil Stamp
Perf. 13 Horiz.
3388A   A1713   (65c) dk blue   3.00   .40
   Issued: Nos. 3383-3388A, 3/1.

Marianne Type of 2005
Serpentine Die Cut 6¾ Vert.
2008   **Self-Adhesive**   **Engr.**
Booklet Stamp
3389   A1713   (60c) blue   2.50   .50
   a.   Booklet pane of 12   30.00
   Issued: No. 3389, 1/2.

Hearts — A1881

Designs: (54c), Face. (86c), (88c), Plant with heart-shaped leaves.

2008, Jan. 5   **Photo.**   ***Perf. 13¼***
3390   A1881   (54c) multi   1.60   .30
   a.   Souvenir sheet of 5   8.00 8.00
   b.   Sheet of 10 + 10 labels   20.00 —
3391   A1881   (86c) multi   2.60 1.00
Self-Adhesive
Serpentine Die Cut
3392   A1881   (54c) multi   16.00 12.00
3392A   A1881   (88c) multi   16.00 12.00
Values are for stamps with surrounding selvage.
Nos. 3390, 3390a, 3390b, 3391-3392 issued 1/5/08. No. 3390b was sold for €6.86. Labels could not be personalized.

New Year 2008 (Year of the Rat) — A1882

2008, Jan. 26   **Photo.**   ***Perf. 13¼x13***
3393   A1882   (54c) multi   1.60   .30
Printed in sheets of 5. A souvenir sheet of one No. 3393 sold for €3.
See No. 4969d.

Paintings — A1883

Designs: No. 3394, Legend of St. Francis: Sermon to the Birds, by Giotto di Bondone. No. 3395, Seaport at Sunset, by Claude Lorrain. No. 3396, The Birth of Venus, by Sandro Botticelli. No. 3397, Napoleon Bonaparte Crossing the Alps, by Jacques-Louis David. No. 3398, La Belle Jardinière (Madonna and Child with St. John the Baptist), by Raphael, vert. No. 3399, Head of a Girl in a Turban, by Jan Vermeer, vert. No. 3400, Summer, by Giuseppe Arcimboldo, vert. No. 3401, Mona Lisa, by Leonardo da Vinci, vert. No. 3402, Infant Maria Marguerita, by Diego Velásquez, vert. No. 3403, Money Changer with Wife, by Quentin Massys (Metsys), vert.

Serpentine Die Cut 11
2008, Jan. 26   **Litho.**
Booklet Stamps
Self-Adhesive
3394   A1883   (54c) multi   1.60   .55
3395   A1883   (54c) multi   1.60   .55
3396   A1883   (54c) multi   1.60   .55
3397   A1883   (54c) multi   1.60   .55
3398   A1883   (54c) multi   1.60   .55
3399   A1883   (54c) multi   1.60   .55
3400   A1883   (54c) multi   1.60   .55
3401   A1883   (54c) multi   1.60   .55
3402   A1883   (54c) multi   1.60   .55
3403   A1883   (54c) multi   1.60   .55
   a.   Booklet pane of 10, #3394-3403   16.00

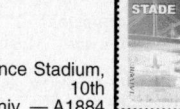

France Stadium, 10th Anniv. — A1884

2008, Jan. 28   **Photo.**   ***Perf. 13¼***
3404   A1884   54c multi   1.60   .30

Tourism Issue

Vendôme A1885

La Rochelle A1886

Toulon — A1887

Richelieu A1888   Le Havre A1889

2008   **Engr.**   ***Perf. 13¼***
3405   A1885   54c multi   1.60   .30
               Perf. 13
3406   A1886   55c multi   1.50   .30
3407   A1887   55c multi   1.50   .30
3408   A1888   55c multi   1.50   .30
3409   A1889   55c multi   1.50   .30
    Nos. 3405-3409 (5)   7.60 1.50

Issued: No. 3405, 2/2; No. 3406, 4/5; Nos. 3407-3408, 7/5; No. 3409, 9/13. A souvenir sheet of one of No. 3406 sold for €3.

Art Issue

Globes of Vincenzo Coronelli A1890

Young Girl Warming Her Hands at a Large Stove, by Jean-Jacues Henner — A1891

Untitled Work by Gérard Garouste A1892

A Theater Box Office, by Honoré Daumier A1893

Litho. & Engr., Photo (A1891-A1892), Engr. (A1893)

2008			**Perf. 13¼x13**	
3410	A1890	85c multi	3.00	1.25
3411	A1891	88c multi	3.00	.60
3412	A1892	€1.33 multi	4.00	1.25
3413	A1893	€1.33 choc & bl gray	4.50	1.00
	Nos. 3410-3413 (4)		14.50	4.10

Self-Adhesive
Serpentine Die Cut 11

3413A	A1891	88c multi	6.00	4.00
3413B	A1892	€1.33 multi	120.00	50.00
3413C	A1893	€1.33 choc & bl gray	200.00	75.00
	Nos. 3413A-3413C (3)		326.00	129.00

Issued: No. 3410, 2/11; No. 3412, 6/19; No. 3411, 10/18; No. 3413, 11/7.
A souvenir sheet containing No. 3410 sold for €3.

Emir Abdelkader (1808-83), Algerian Leader — A1894

2008, Feb. 20		**Engr.**	**Perf. 13¼**	
3414	A1894	54c multi	1.75	.30

Droopy Dog — A1895

Red-haired Woman — A1896

The Wolf — A1897

Design: €2.18, Droopy Dog, diff.

2008, Mar. 1		**Photo.**	**Perf. 13¼**	
3415	A1895	(55c) multi	1.75	.30
3416	A1896	(55c) multi	1.75	.30
3417	A1897	(55c) multi	1.75	.30
a.	Strip of 3, #3415-3417		5.25	1.90

Souvenir Sheet
Perf. 13x13¼

3418	A1895	€2.18 multi	6.75	6.75

Booklet Stamps
Self-Adhesive
Serpentine Die Cut 11

3419	A1895	(55c) multi	1.75	.30
3420	A1896	(55c) multi	1.75	.30
3421	A1897	(55c) multi	1.75	.30
a.	Booklet pane of 10, 4 #3419, 3 each #3420-3421		17.50	

Cartoon characters created by Tex Avery; Stamp Day. No. 3418 contains one 35x27mm stamp that has thermographic ink (on cartoon balloon) that when warmed, changes color allowing a message beneath the ink to appear.
Nos. 3419-3421 exist in three sheets, each containing 5 of each stamp + 5 non-personalizable labels. Each sheet sold for €6.50. Value, each $40.

Sound Recording Libraries A1898

2008, Mar. 15		**Photo.**	**Perf. 13¼**	
3422	A1898	55c multi	1.75	.30

Flowers — A1899

Designs: 37c, Aquilegia. 38c, Tulipa sp. 44c, Bellis perennis. 45c, Primula veris.

2008, Mar. 1		**Litho.**	**Perf. 13**	
3423	A1899	37c multi	1.25	.60
3424	A1899	38c multi	1.25	.60
3425	A1899	44c multi	1.75	.70
3426	A1899	45c multi	1.75	.70
	Nos. 3423-3426 (4)		6.00	2.60

Nos. 3423-3426 are known only precanceled. See second note after No. 132. Compare with types A2174-A2177.

Aspects of Life in French Regions Type of 2003

No. 3427: a, Chateau d'Ussé, Rigny-Ussé. b, Vézelay. c, Place des Vosges, Le Marais district, Paris. d, Le Marais Poitevin (Poitevin Marsh). e, Cugarel Windmill, Castelnaudary, vert. f, Red granite coastal rocks, vert. g, Honfleur. h, La Petite France district, Strasbourg. i, La Boétie House, Sarlat-la-Canéda, vert. j, Marfate Cirque, Reunion, vert.

2008, Mar. 29		**Photo.**	**Perf. 13**	
3427		Sheet of 10	17.50	17.50
a.-j.	A1642 55c Any single		1.75	1.25

No. 3427 has three vertical rows of rouletting, separating sheet into quarters. Nos. 3427a-3427j were also issued in a large booklet containing panes of 1 of each stamp. The booklet sold for €19.

Lyon A1900

Litho. & Engr.

2008, Apr. 4			**Perf. 13**	
3428	A1900	55c multi	1.75	.30

Gardens and Parks Type of 2003

No. 3429: a, Parc Longchamp, Marseille. b, Parc Borely, Marseille.

2008		**Photo.**	**Perf. 13¼x13**	
3429		Sheet of 2	13.50	13.50
a.-b.	A1660 €2.18 Either single		6.75	3.50
c.	Miniature sheet of 4, #3316a, 3316b, 3429a, 3429b		50.00	50.00

Salon du Timbre. No. 3429 has four vertical rows of rouletting, separating sheet into fifths, with the two stamps in the central fifth.
Issued: No. 3429, 4/12; No. 3429c, 6/14.

Prehistoric Animals — A1901

Designs: No. 3430, Phorusrhacos. No. 3431, Smilodon. 65c, Megaloceros, horiz. 88c, Mammoth, horiz.

2008, Apr. 19			**Perf. 13¼**	
3430	A1901	55c multi	1.75	.30
3431	A1901	55c multi	1.75	.30
3432	A1901	65c multi	2.00	.50
3433	A1901	88c multi	2.75	1.00
a.	Miniature sheet, #3430-3433		8.25	8.25
	Nos. 3430-3433 (4)		8.25	2.10

First Heart Transplant in Europe, 40th Anniv. — A1902

2008, Apr. 24			**Perf. 13¼x13**	
3434	A1902	55c red & black	1.60	.30

Valentré Bridge, Cahors — A1903

2008, Apr. 26		**Engr.**	**Perf. 13x13¼**	
3435	A1903	55c multi	1.60	.30

Europa — A1904

2008, May 4		**Photo.**	**Perf. 13x13¼**	
3436	A1904	55c multi	1.75	.30

Self-Adhesive
Serpentine Die Cut 11

3436A	A1904	55c multi	3.00	3.00

Quebec City, Canada, 400th Anniv. — A1905

2008, May 16		**Engr.**	**Perf. 13**	
3437	A1905	85c multi	2.75	1.00

See Canada No. 2269.
A souvenir sheet containing No. 3437 and Canada No. 2269 sold for $4.99 in Canada and was sold in France for €15 as part of a set additionally containing six different souvenir sheets containing only No. 3437.

Happy Birthday — A1906

2008, May 28			**Photo.**	
3438	A1906	(55c) multi	1.75	.30

Printed in sheets of 5.

It's a Boy — A1907

It's a Girl — A1908

2008, May 28		**Serpentine Die Cut 11**		

Booklet Stamps
Self-Adhesive

3439	A1907	(55c) multi, un-scratched panel	2.00	2.00
a.	Scratched panel			.60
b.	Booklet pane of 10 #3439		20.00	

3440	A1908	(55c) multi, un-scratched panel	2.00	2.00
a.	Scratched panel			.60
b.	Booklet pane of 10 #3440		20.00	

Scratch-off panels on Nos. 3439-3440 cover pictures and text for baby boy and girl, respectively.

Vacations A1909

Designs: No. 3441, Ferns. No. 3442, Butterfly on leaf. No. 3443, Hands holding plant's leaves. No. 3444, Coconut palm tree. No. 3445, Path beside forest lake. No. 3446, Golf ball, putter and hole. No. 3447, Water lily and lily pads. No. 3448, Watering cans and foliage. No. 3449, Sliced kiwi fruit. No. 3450, Shelled and unshelled peas.

Serpentine Die Cut 11
2008, May 28			**Litho.**	

Booklet Stamps
Self-Adhesive

3441	A1909	(55c) multi	1.75	.60
3442	A1909	(55c) multi	1.75	.60
3443	A1909	(55c) multi	1.75	.60
3444	A1909	(55c) multi	1.75	.60
3445	A1909	(55c) multi	1.75	.60
3446	A1909	(55c) multi	1.75	.60
3447	A1909	(55c) multi	1.75	.60
3448	A1909	(55c) multi	1.75	.60
3449	A1909	(55c) multi	1.75	.60
3450	A1909	(55c) multi	1.75	.60
a.	Booklet pane of 10, #3441-3450		17.50	

Evreux Belfry — A1910

2008, May 31		**Engr.**	**Perf. 13**	
3451	A1910	55c multi	1.60	.60

Grand Palais, Paris A1911

2008, June 14			**Perf. 13x13¼**	
3452	A1911	55c multi + label	1.60	.60

French Federation of Philatelic Associations 81st Congress, Paris. See No. 5762a.

Marianne and Stars A1912

Hand Depositing Ballot A1913

Tree in Hand A1914

Dove A1915

2008		**Engr.**	**Perf. 13**	
3453	A1912	1c yellow	.25	.25
3454	A1912	5c gray brown	.25	.25
3455	A1912	10c gray	.30	.25
3456	A1912	(50c) green	1.60	.40
3457	A1912	(55c) red	1.75	.40
3458	A1912	(65c) dark blue	2.10	.50
3459	A1912	72c olive green	2.25	.60
3460	A1912	85c purple	2.75	.70
3461	A1912	88c fawn	2.75	.70
3462	A1912	€1 orange	3.25	.80
3463	A1912	€1.25 blue	4.00	1.00
3464	A1912	€1.33 red violet	4.25	1.10
3465	A1912	€2.18 chocolate	7.00	2.40

Self-Adhesive (#3466)
Etched on Foil
Die Cut Perf. 13

3466	A1912	€5 silver	16.00	16.00
	Nos. 3453-3466 (14)		48.50	25.20

Litho.
Perf. 13

3467		Sheet of 15, #3467a-3467k, 2 each #3467l-3467m, + 15 labels	40.00	40.00
a.	A1912	1c yellow	.25	.25
b.	A1912	5c brown	.25	.25
c.	A1912	10c gray	.35	.35
d.	A1912	(65c) dark blue	2.40	2.40
e.	A1912	72c olive green	2.60	2.60
f.	A1912	85c purple	3.00	3.00
g.	A1912	88c fawn	3.25	3.25
h.	A1912	€1 orange	3.50	3.50
i.	A1912	€1.25 blue	4.50	4.50
j.	A1912	€1.33 red violet	4.75	4.75
k.	A1912	€2.18 brn violet	7.75	7.75
l.	A1912	(50c) green	1.75	1.75
m.	A1912	(55c) red	2.00	2.00

Coil Stamps
Perf. 13 Horiz.
Engr.

3468	A1912	(50c) green	3.50	2.00
3469	A1912	(55c) red	4.00	2.00
3470	A1912	(65c) dark blue	4.50	2.00

Booklet Stamps (Types A1913-A1915)
Self-Adhesive
Serpentine Die Cut 6¾ Vert.

3471	A1912	(55c) red	2.50	1.00
a.		Booklet pane of 20	50.00	
b.		Booklet pane of 10	25.00	
c.		Booklet pane of 12	30.00	
3472	A1913	55c red	2.50	1.00
3473	A1914	55c red	2.50	1.00
3474	A1915	55c red	2.50	1.00
a.		Booklet pane of 12, 6 #3471, 2 each #3472-3474	30.00	
3475	A1912	(65c) dark blue	2.50	1.00
a.		Booklet pane of 12	30.00	
3476	A1913	65c dark blue	2.50	1.00
3477	A1914	65c dark blue	2.50	1.00
3478	A1915	65c dark blue	2.50	1.00
a.		Booklet pane of 12, 6 #3475, 2 each #3476-3478	30.00	
	Nos. 3471-3478 (8)		20.00	8.00

Issued: No. 3457, 6/17; No. 3741c, 9/8; No. 3466, 7/1; No. 3475a, 2009; others, 6/14. On day of issue, No. 3467 sold for €12.54. Labels on No. 3467 could not be personalized.

No. 3471b is comprised of two horizontal strips of five stamps on a yellow backing paper. Nos. 3471 and 3475 were also printed in sheets of 100 later in 2008.

See Nos. 3532, 3551-3566, 3612-3616E, 3730, 3871-3882, 4410l, 4525.

Typographed, engraved and silk-screened perf. 13 stamps of types A486 and A1912 with denomination of €1 in red were produced in pairs with 2 labels and photogravure perf. 13 stamps of these types with denominations of €1 in blue, green and multicolored were printed in blocks of 8 + 8 labels. These items were created in very limited quantities in 2010.

Ecology — A1916

Designs: No. 3479, Tree. No. 3480, Bicycle. No. 3481, World map. No. 3482, Computer. No. 3483, Water droplets. No. 3484, Sun. No. 3485, Two plastic bottles. No. 3486, Three plastic bottles. No. 3487, Apple core. No. 3488, Strawberry.

Serpentine Die Cut 11
2008, June 14   **Photo.**
Booklet Stamps
Self-Adhesive

3479	A1916	(55c) multi	1.75	.50
3480	A1916	(55c) multi	1.75	.50
3481	A1916	(55c) multi	1.75	.50
3482	A1916	(55c) multi	1.75	.50
3483	A1916	(55c) multi	1.75	.50
3484	A1916	(55c) multi	1.75	.50
3485	A1916	(55c) multi	1.75	.50
3486	A1916	(55c) multi	1.75	.50
3487	A1916	(55c) multi	1.75	.50
3488	A1916	(55c) multi	1.75	.50
a.		Booklet pane of 10, #3479-3488	17.50	

Trapeze Artist
A1917

Bareback Rider
A1918

Clown
A1919

Lion Tamer
A1920

Clown
A1921

Juggler
A1922

2008, June 15   **Photo.**   *Perf. 13*

3489	A1917	55c multi	1.75	.60
3490	A1918	55c multi	1.75	.60
3491	A1919	55c multi	1.75	.60
3492	A1920	55c multi	1.75	.60
3493	A1921	55c multi	1.75	.60
3494	A1922	55c multi	1.75	.60
a.		Souvenir sheet, #3489-3494	16.50	16.50
	Nos. 3489-3494 (6)		10.50	3.60

No. 3494a sold for €5.10, with the Red Cross receiving €1.80 of that.

2008 Summer Olympics, Beijing — A1923

Designs: No. 3495, Equestrian, cycling. No. 3496, Swimming, rowing, horiz. No. 3497, Judo, fencing, horiz. No. 3498, Tennis, running.

Perf. 13¼x13, 13x13¼
2008, June 16

3495	A1923	55c multi	1.75	.60
3496	A1923	55c multi	1.75	.60
3497	A1923	55c multi	1.75	.60
a.		Pair, #3496-3497	3.50	1.75
3498	A1923	55c multi	1.75	.60
a.		Vert. pair, #3495, 3498	3.50	1.75
	Nos. 3495-3498 (4)		7.00	2.40

Nos. 3495-3498 were printed in a sheet of 10 containing 2 each #3495 and #3498 and 3 each #3496-3497.

Charles de Gaulle Memorial, Paris — A1924

2008, June 18   **Engr.**   *Perf. 13¼*

3499	A1924	55c multi	1.75	.60

Miniature Sheet

European Projects — A1925

No. 3500: a, Map of Europe, 1-euro coin. b, Flags of France and European Union, horiz (French Presidency of European Union). c, Earth and Galileo satellite, horiz. d, Students and flags (Erasmus higher education program).

2008, June 19   **Photo.**   *Perf. 13*

3500	A1925	Sheet of 4	7.00	7.00
a.-d.		55c Any single	1.75	.60

Miniature Sheet

Famous Ships A1926

No. 3501: a, Confiance. b, Grande Hermine, horiz. c, Boudeuse, horiz. d, Astrolabe, horiz. e, Hermione, horiz. f, Boussole.

2008, June 20

3501	A1926	Sheet of 6	10.50	10.50
a.-f.		55c Any single	1.75	.60

French and Brazilian Landscapes — A1927

Designs: 55c, Amazonian forest, Brazil. 85c, Glacier, France.

2008, July 13

3502	A1927	55c multi	1.75	.60
3503	A1927	85c multi	2.75	.90
a.		Horiz. pair, #3502-3503	4.50	2.25

See Brazil No. 3052.

Mediterranean Summit, Paris — A1928

2008, July 13   *Perf. 13¼*

3504	A1928	55c multi	1.75	.60

Aspects of Life in French Regions Type of 2003

No. 3505: a, Espadrilles. b, Stew (pot au feu). c, Chestnuts (chataigne). d, Fireworks (feu d'artifice). e, Epinal prints (l'image d'Epinal), vert. f, Lentils (lentille), vert. g, Reblochon cheese. h, Calissons (candy). i, Stilt walker (les échasses), vert. j, Mustard (moutarde), vert.

2008, Sept. 6   **Photo.**   *Perf. 13*

3505		Sheet of 10	15.00	15.00
a.-j.	A1642	55c Any single	1.50	.50

No. 3505 has three vertical rows of rouletting, separating sheet into quarters.
Nos. 3505a-3505j also were issued in large booklets containing panes of 1 of each stamp. The booklet sold for €19.

Josselin — A1929

2008, Sept. 20   **Engr.**   *Perf. 13¼*

3506	A1929	55c multi	1.75	.50

A1930

A1931

A1932

A1933

A1934

A1935

A1936

A1937

A1938

Garfield, Comic Strip by Jim Davis — A1939

Serpentine Die Cut 11¼x11
2008, Sept. 18   **Photo.**
Booklet Stamps
Self-Adhesive

3507	A1930	(55c) multi	1.75	.50
3508	A1931	(55c) multi	1.75	.50
3509	A1932	(55c) multi	1.75	.50
3510	A1933	(55c) multi	1.75	.50
3511	A1934	(55c) multi	1.75	.50
3512	A1935	(55c) multi	1.75	.50
3513	A1936	(55c) multi	1.75	.50
3514	A1937	(55c) multi	1.75	.50
3515	A1938	(55c) multi	1.75	.50
3516	A1939	(55c) multi	1.75	.50
a.		Booklet pane of 10, #3507-3516	17.50	
	Nos. 3507-3516 (10)		17.50	5.00

"I Am Sport" — A1940

2008, Oct. 2   **Photo.**   *Perf. 12½*

3517	A1940	55c multi	1.50	.50

Values are for stamps with surrounding selvage.

Fifth Republic, 50th Anniv. — A1941

2008, Oct. 4   *Perf. 13¼*

3518	A1941	55c multi	1.50	.50

Seascapes of Viet Nam and
France — A1942

Designs: 55c, Along Bay, Viet Nam. 85,
Strait of Bonifacio, France.

2008, Oct. 15   Photo.   Perf. 13x12¾
3519	A1942	55c multi	1.40	.45
3520	A1942	85c multi	2.25	.75

See Viet Nam Nos. 3340-3341.

Types of 1959-2008
Serpentine Die Cut 6¾ Vert.

2008, Nov. 6   Photo.
Booklet Stamps
Self-Adhesive
3521	A328	55c multi	1.40	.45
3522	A349	55c multi	1.40	.45
3523	A360	55c multi	1.40	.45
3524	A379	55c multi	1.40	.45
3525	A486	55c dark red	1.40	.45
3526	A555	55c rose carmine	1.40	.45
3527	A771	55c bright red	1.40	.45
3528	A915	55c red	1.40	.45
3529	A1161	55c red	1.40	.45
3530	A1409	55c red	1.40	.45
3531	A1713	55c red	1.40	.45
3532	A1912	55c red	1.40	.45
a.	Booklet pane of 12, #3521-3532		17.00	
	Nos. 3521-3532 (12)		16.80	5.40

Landmarks
of France
and Israel
A1943

Airplane, stamped first flight cover and: 55c,
Haifa waterfront, Israel. 85c, Eiffel Tower,
Paris.

2008, Nov. 6   Photo.   Perf. 13
3533	A1943	55c multi	1.40	.45
3534	A1943	85c multi	2.25	.75

First flight between France and Israel, 60th
anniv. See Israel Nos. 1750-1751.

European Capitals Type of 2002

No. 3535 — Attractions in Prague: a, Tour
du Petit Coté (Charles Bridge and Tower), vert.
b, Hotel de ville horloge astronomique et
calandrier (City Hall astronomical clock), vert.
c, Eglise Notre-Dame-de-Tyn (Tyn Cathedral),
vert. d, Le Chateau (Hradcany Castle).

Perf. 13¼x13, 13x13¼ (#3535d)
2008, Nov. 7   Photo.
3535	A1622	Sheet of 4	5.75	5.75
a.-d.		55c Any single	1.40	.45

A1944   A1945

A1946   A1947

A1948   A1949

A1950

A1951

A1952

A1953

A1954

A1955

A1956

Happy
Holidays — A1957

Serpentine Die Cut 11¼x11
2008, Nov. 8   Photo.
Booklet Stamps
Self-Adhesive
3536	A1944	(55c) multi	1.40	.45
3537	A1945	(55c) multi	1.40	.45
3538	A1946	(55c) multi	1.40	.45
3539	A1947	(55c) multi	1.40	.45
3540	A1948	(55c) multi	1.40	.45
3541	A1949	(55c) multi	1.40	.45

Serpentine Die Cut 11x11¼
3542	A1950	(55c) multi	1.40	.45
3543	A1951	(55c) multi	1.40	.45
3544	A1952	(55c) multi	1.40	.45
3545	A1953	(55c) multi	1.40	.45
3546	A1954	(55c) multi	1.40	.45
3547	A1955	(55c) multi	1.40	.45
3548	A1956	(55c) multi	1.40	.45
3549	A1957	(55c) multi	1.40	.45
a.	Booklet pane of 14, #3536-3549		20.00	
	Nos. 3536-3549 (14)		19.60	6.30

A souvenir sheet containing one perf.
13x13¼ stamp like No. 3543 with water-activated gum sold for €3.

End of World
War I, 90th
Anniv. — A1958

2008, Nov. 11   Engr.   Perf. 13¼
3550	A1958	55c multi	1.40	.45

Marianne and Stars Type of 2008
Serpentine Die Cut 6¾ Vert.

2008   Engr.   Self-Adhesive
3551	A1912	1c yellow	.25	.25
3552	A1912	5c gray brown	.25	.25
3553	A1912	10c gray	.30	.30
3554	A1912	(50c) green	1.40	1.40
3555	A1912	72c olive green	2.00	2.00
3556	A1912	85c purple	2.40	2.40
3557	A1912	88c fawn	2.50	2.50
3558	A1912	€1 orange	2.75	2.75
3559	A1912	€1.25 blue	3.50	3.50
3560	A1912	€1.33 red violet	3.75	3.75
3561	A1912	€2.18 chocolate	6.00	6.00
	Nos. 3551-3561 (11)		25.10	25.10

Serpentine Die Cut 6¾ Horiz.
Coil Stamps
3564	A1912	(50c) green	1.40	1.40
3565	A1912	(55c) red	1.50	1.50
3566	A1912	(65c) dark blue	1.90	1.90
	Nos. 3564-3566 (3)		4.80	4.80

Nos. 3551-3561 each were printed in sheets
of 100.

Flowers — A1959

Designs: 31c, Helianthus annuus. 33c,
Magnolia.

2008, Nov. 12   Litho.   Perf. 13
3567	A1959	31c multi	.80	.25
3568	A1959	33c multi	.85	.25

Nos. 3567-3568 are known only precanceled. See note under No. 132.

Trees and Map of Mediterranean
Area — A1960

2008, Nov. 20   Photo.   Perf. 13x12¾
3569	A1960	85c multi	2.50	.75

See Lebanon No. 645.

Greetings Type of 2004 Inscribed
"Lettre Prioritaire 20g"
Designs: No. 3569A, "Ceci est une invitation." No. 3569B, "Un grand merci."

2008   Photo.   Serpentine Die Cut 11
Self-Adhesive
3569A	A1667	(55c) brt lil rose & yel	1.60	1.60
3569B	A1667	(55c) brt yel grn & red lil	1.60	1.60

Louis Braille (1809-52), Educator of
the Blind — A1961

Engr. & Embossed
2009, Jan. 4   Perf. 13x12¾
3570	A1961	55c blk & violet	1.50	.50

New Year 2009 (Year
of the Ox) — A1962

2009, Jan. 10   Photo.   Perf. 13¼x13
3571	A1962	(55c) multi	1.50	.50

No. 3571 was printed in sheets of 5. A souvenir sheet of 1 sold for €3. Value, $8.
See No. 4970a.

Decorated   Decorated Clock,
Glasses, Nancy   Louvre
Museum — A1963   Museum — A1964

Marquetry,   Quimper Faience,
Valençay   Sèvres
Chateau — A1965   Museum — A1966

Enamelwork, Apt   Tapestry,
Cathedral   Malmaison
A1967   Chateau
                      A1968

Stained Glass, St.   Cabinetwork,
Joan of Arc   Louvre
Church,   Museum — A1970
Rouen — A1969

Wrought Iron,   Mosaic, Palace of
Army Museum,   Versailles
Paris   A1972
A1971

Jewelry,   Crystal, Clichy
Malmaison   Glassworks
Chateau   A1974
A1973

Booklet Stamps
Serpentine Die Cut 11
2009, Jan. 10   Self-Adhesive
3572	A1963	(55c) multi	1.50	.50
3573	A1964	(55c) multi	1.50	.50
3574	A1965	(55c) multi	1.50	.50
3575	A1966	(55c) multi	1.50	.50
3576	A1967	(55c) multi	1.50	.50
3577	A1968	(55c) multi	1.50	.50
3578	A1969	(55c) multi	1.50	.50
3579	A1970	(55c) multi	1.50	.50
3580	A1971	(55c) multi	1.50	.50
3581	A1972	(55c) multi	1.50	.50
3582	A1973	(55c) multi	1.50	.50
3583	A1974	(55c) multi	1.50	.50
a.	Booklet pane of 12, #3572-3583		18.00	
	Nos. 3572-3583 (12)		18.00	6.00

René I, Duke of
Anjou (1409-80)
A1975

2009, Jan. 16   Engr.   Perf. 13¼
3584	A1975	55c multi	1.50	.50

Hearts — A1976

Flowers and: (55c), One parrot. (88c), Two
parrots.

2009, Jan. 17   Photo.   Perf. 13¼
3585	A1976	(55c) multi	1.50	.50
a.	Souvenir sheet of 5		7.50	7.50
3586	A1976	(88c) multi	2.40	1.25

Self-Adhesive
Serpentine Die Cut
3587	A1976	(55c) multi	1.50	.50
3588	A1976	(88c) multi	2.40	1.25
a.	Booklet pane of 12		29.00	
	Nos. 3585-3588 (4)		7.80	3.50

Tourism Issue

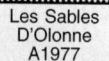

Les Sables D'Olonne — A1977

Menton — A1978

Chaumont — A1979

Château de la Bâtie d'Urfé — A1980

Bordeaux — A1981

Abbey of Royaumont — A1982

Photo., Engr. (#3590, 3592-3594)

2009   **Perf. 13¼, 13 (#3593)**

3589	A1977	55c multi	1.40	.45
3590	A1978	56c multi	1.40	.45
3591	A1979	56c multi	1.60	.55
3592	A1980	56c multi	1.60	.55

Perf. 13

3593	A1981	56c multi	1.60	.55
3594	A1982	56c multi	1.75	.60
		Nos. 3589-3594 (6)	9.35	3.15

Self-Adhesive
Serpentine Die Cut 11

3594A	A1981	56c multi	1.60	1.60

Issued: No. 3589, 1/31; No. 3590, 2/21; No. 3591, 5/16. No. 3592, 6/6; Nos. 3593, 3594A, 6/20. No. 3594, 9/26.

Miniature Sheet

World Alpine Skiing Championships, Val d'Isère — A1983

No. 3595: a, Super combined skier. b, Slalom skier. c, Downhill (Descente) skier. d, Giant slalom skier. e, Skiers at Val d'Isère.

2009, Jan. 31   **Photo.**   **Perf. 13x13¼**

3595	A1983	Sheet of 5	7.00	7.00
a.-e.		55c Any single	1.40	.45

France Foundation, 40th Anniv. — A1984

2009, Feb. 5   **Photo.**   **Perf. 13¼**

3596	A1984	55c multi	1.40	.45

Art Series

Angel, St. Cecilia Cathedral, Albi — A1985

La Promenade, by Hansi (Jean-Jacques Waltz) — A1986

Wrapping of Pont-Neuf, by Christo and Jeanne-Claude — A1987

Paintings by Pierre-Auguste Renoir — A1988

No. 3600: a, Monsieur et Madame Bernheim de Villers. b, Gabrielle à la Rose.

Perf. 13, 13x13¼ (#3598), 13¼x13 (#3599)

2009   **Litho. (#3597), Photo.**

3597	A1985	85c multi	2.25	1.10
3598	A1986	90c multi	2.75	1.40
3599	A1987	€1.35 multi	3.75	1.90
		Nos. 3597-3599 (3)	8.75	4.40

Souvenir Sheet
Perf. 13¼

3600	A1988	Sheet of 2	6.50	6.50
a.		85c multi	2.50	1.25
b.		€1.35 multi	4.00	2.00

Self-Adhesive
Serpentine Die Cut 11

3601	A1985	85c multi	2.50	2.50
3602	A1986	90c multi	2.75	2.75
3603	A1987	€1.35 multi	3.75	3.75

Issued: No. 3597, 2/7; No. 3598, 10/24; Nos. 3599, 3603, 6/13 No. 3600, 11/5. A souvenir sheet of 1 of No. 3597 sold for €3.

Road Runner and Wile E. Coyote — A1989

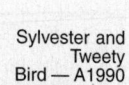

Sylvester and Tweety Bird — A1990

Daffy Duck and Bugs Bunny — A1991

Design: €1, Yosemite Sam, Wile E. Coyote, Sylvester, Tasmanian Devil, Bugs Bunny, Daffy Duck, Road Runner, Marvin the Martian and Tweety Bird.

2009, Feb. 28   **Photo.**   **Perf. 13x13¼**

3605	A1989	56c multi	1.40	.45
3606	A1990	56c multi	1.40	.45
3607	A1991	56c multi	1.40	.45
a.		Strip of 3, #3605-3607	4.25	1.40
		Nos. 3605-3607 (3)	4.20	1.35

Souvenir Sheet

3608	A1989	€1 multi	2.60	1.25

Booklet Stamps
Self-Adhesive
Litho.
Serpentine Die Cut 11

3609	A1989	(56c) multi	1.40	.45
3610	A1991	(56c) multi	1.40	.45
3611	A1990	(56c) multi	1.40	.45
a.		Booklet pane of 12, 4 each #3609-3611	17.00	
		Nos. 3609-3611 (3)	4.20	1.35

Stamp Day. No. 3608 contains one 80x26mm stamp. Sheets of five serpentine die cut 11 self-adhesive stamps like Nos. 3605-3607 and 5 labels each sold for €6.50.

Marianne and Stars Type of 2008

2009, Feb. 28   **Engr.**   **Perf. 13**

3612	A1912	73c ol grn	1.90	.50
3613	A1912	90c fawn	2.25	.55
3614	A1912	€1.30 blue	3.25	.85
3615	A1912	€1.35 red vio	3.50	.90
3616	A1912	€2.22 choc	5.75	1.40
		Nos. 3612-3616 (5)	16.65	4.20

Serpentine Die Cut 6¾ Vert.
Self-Adhesive

3616A	A1912	73c ol grn	1.90	1.90
3616B	A1912	90c fawn	2.25	2.25
3616C	A1912	€1.30 blue	3.25	3.25
3616D	A1912	€1.35 red vio	3.50	3.50
3616E	A1912	€2.22 choc	5.75	5.75
		Nos. 3616A-3616E (5)	16.65	16.65

Constitutional Council — A1992

2009, Mar. 5   **Photo.**   **Perf. 13¼**

3617	A1992	56c multi	1.40	.45

Self-Adhesive
Serpentine Die Cut 11

3617A	A1992	56c multi	1.60	1.60

Papal Palace, Avignon — A1993

2009, Mar. 7   **Engr.**   **Perf. 13x12¾**

3618	A1993	70c multi	1.90	.65

Portraits of Women by Titouan Lamazou — A1994

Designs: No. 3619, Helena, United States. No. 3620, Dayu, Indonesia. No. 3621, Deborah, France. No. 3622, Kabari, Bangladesh. No. 3623, Mei Mei, China. No. 3624, Malika, Morocco. No. 3625, Dayan, Colombia. No. 3626, Francine, Rwanda. No. 3627, Blessing, Nigeria. No. 3628, Nandita, India. No. 3629, Elmas, Turkey. No. 3630, Nadia, Brazil.

Serpentine Die Cut 11
2009, Mar. 9   **Litho.**
Booklet Stamps
Self-Adhesive

3619	A1994	(56c) multi	1.50	.50
3620	A1994	(56c) multi	1.50	.50
3621	A1994	(56c) multi	1.50	.50
3622	A1994	(56c) multi	1.50	.50
3623	A1994	(56c) multi	1.50	.50
3624	A1994	(56c) multi	1.50	.50
3625	A1994	(56c) multi	1.50	.50
3626	A1994	(56c) multi	1.50	.50
3627	A1994	(56c) multi	1.50	.50
3628	A1994	(56c) multi	1.50	.50
3629	A1994	(56c) multi	1.50	.50
3630	A1994	(56c) multi	1.50	.50
a.		Booklet pane of 12, #3619-3630	18.00	
		Nos. 3619-3630 (12)	18.00	6.00

Mâcon — A1995

2009, Mar. 27   **Engr.**   **Perf. 13x12¾**

3631	A1995	56c multi	1.50	.50

Souvenir Sheet

Protection of Polar Regions — A1996

No. 3632: a, Iceberg and bird. b, Emperor penguins, vert.

Perf. 13x13¼, 13¼x13 (85c)

2009, Mar. 28   **Litho. & Engr.**

3632	A1996	Sheet of 2	4.00	4.00
a.		56c multi	1.50	.50
b.		85c multi	2.50	.85

Aimé Césaire (1913-2008), Martinique Politician — A1997

2009, Apr. 17   **Photo.**   **Perf. 13¼x13**

3633	A1997	56c multi	1.50	.50

Flora of the French Regions — A1998

Designs: No. 3634, Plum (quetsche), Alsace. No. 3635, Plum (mirabelle), Lorraine. No. 3636, Birch tree, Centre. No. 3637, Bee orchid, Champagne-Ardenne. No. 3638, Lily, Paris. No. 3639, Bluebells, Ile de France. No. 3640, Gorse, Bretagne. No. 3641, Lily-of-the-valley, Pays de la Loire. No. 3642, Apples, Basse-Normandie. No. 3643, Beech leaves, Haute-Normandie. No. 3644, Rose, Picardie. No. 3645, Potatoes, Nord-Pas de Calais. No. 3646, Olives, Provence-Alpes-Côte d'Azur. No. 3647, Chestnut, Corse. No. 3648, Wild thyme, Languedoc-Roussillon. No. 3649, Yellow gentian, Auvergne. No. 3650, Boletus mushroom, Limousin. No. 3651, Saltwort, Poitou-Charentes. No. 3652, Maritime pine, Aquitaine. No. 3653, Norway spruce, Franche-Comté. No. 3654, Awara palm, French Guiana. No. 3655, Toulouse violet, Midi-Pyrénées. No. 3656, Blueberries, Rhône-Alpes. No. 3657, Black currants, Bourgogne.

Serpentine Die Cut 11
2009, Apr. 25   **Photo.**
Booklet Stamps
Self-Adhesive

3634	A1998	(56c) multi	1.50	.50
3635	A1998	(56c) multi	1.50	.50
a.		Booklet pane of 2, #3634-3635	3.00	
3636	A1998	(56c) multi	1.50	.50
3637	A1998	(56c) multi	1.50	.50
a.		Booklet pane of 2, #3636-3637	3.00	
3638	A1998	(56c) multi	1.50	.50
3639	A1998	(56c) multi	1.50	.50
a.		Booklet pane of 2, #3638-3639	3.00	
3640	A1998	(56c) multi	1.50	.50
3641	A1998	(56c) multi	1.50	.50
a.		Booklet pane of 2, #3640-3641	3.00	
3642	A1998	(56c) multi	1.50	.50
3643	A1998	(56c) multi	1.50	.50
a.		Booklet pane of 2, #3642-3643	3.00	
3644	A1998	(56c) multi	1.50	.50
3645	A1998	(56c) multi	1.50	.50
a.		Booklet pane of 2, #3644-3645	3.00	
		Complete booklet, #3635a, 3637a, 3639a, 3641a, 3643a, 3645a	18.00	
3646	A1998	(56c) multi	1.50	.50
3647	A1998	(56c) multi	1.50	.50
a.		Booklet pane of 2, #3646-3647	3.00	

3648	A1998 (56c) multi	1.50	.50
3649	A1998 (56c) multi	1.50	.50
a.	Booklet pane of 2, #3648-3649	3.00	
3650	A1998 (56c) multi	1.50	.50
3651	A1998 (56c) multi	1.50	.50
a.	Booklet pane of 2, #3650-3651	3.00	
3652	A1998 (56c) multi	1.50	.50
3653	A1998 (56c) multi	1.50	.50
a.	Booklet pane of 2, #3652-3653	3.00	
3654	A1998 (56c) multi	1.50	.50
3655	A1998 (56c) multi	1.50	.50
a.	Booklet pane of 2, #3654-3655	3.00	
3656	A1998 (56c) multi	1.50	.50
3657	A1998 (56c) multi	1.50	.50
a.	Booklet pane of 2, #3656-3657	3.00	
	Complete booklet, #3647a, 3649a, 3651a, 3653a, 3655a, 3657a	18.00	
	Nos. 3634-3657 (24)	36.00	12.00

Souvenir Sheet

Europa
A1999

No. 3658: a, Saturn. b, Exoplanet.

2009, May 3 Litho. Perf. 13¼x13

3658	A1999 Sheet of 2	4.00	4.00
a.-b.	70c Either single	2.00	.65

Intl. Year of Astronomy.

A2000   Vacations — A2001

Designs: No. 3659, Tennis ball on red clay court. No. 3660, Red-striped director's chair. No. 3661, Red turban. No. 3662, Ladybug. No. 3663, Red air mattress. No. 3664, Cherry tomatoes. No. 3665, Rooster. No. 3666, Poppy. No. 3667, License plate of Bonaire, Netherlands Antilles. No. 3668, Monarch butterfly. No. 3669, Raspberries. No. 3670, Doorknocker on red door. No. 3671, Flowers near house number. No. 3672, Red boat, rope and cleat.

Serpentine Die Cut 11
2009, May 13 Litho.
Booklet Stamps
Self-Adhesive

3659	A2000 (56c) multi	1.60	.55
3660	A2000 (56c) multi	1.60	.55
3661	A2000 (56c) multi	1.60	.55
3662	A2000 (56c) multi	1.60	.55
3663	A2000 (56c) multi	1.60	.55
3664	A2000 (56c) multi	1.60	.55
3665	A2001 (56c) multi	1.60	.55
3666	A2001 (56c) multi	1.60	.55
3667	A2001 (56c) multi	1.60	.55
3668	A2001 (56c) multi	1.60	.55
3669	A2001 (56c) multi	1.60	.55
3670	A2001 (56c) multi	1.60	.55
3671	A2001 (56c) multi	1.60	.55
3672	A2001 (56c) multi	1.60	.55
a.	Booklet pane of 14, #3659-3672	22.50	
	Nos. 3659-3672 (14)	22.40	7.70

Timber-frame Houses, Alsace — A2002

Azay-le-Rideau Chateau — A2003

Notre Dame Cathedral, Paris — A2004

Vineyards, Bordeaux A2005

Nice — A2006

Mont-Saint-Michel A2007

Eiffel Tower — A2008

Provence A2009

Serpentine Die Cut 11
2009, May 13 Litho.
Booklet Stamps
Self-Adhesive

3673	A2002 (85c) multi	2.40	.80
3674	A2003 (85c) multi	2.40	.80
3675	A2004 (85c) multi	2.40	.80
3676	A2005 (85c) multi	2.40	.80
3677	A2006 (85c) multi	2.40	.80
3678	A2007 (85c) multi	2.40	.80
3679	A2008 (85c) multi	2.40	.80
3680	A2009 (85c) multi	2.40	.80
a.	Booklet pane of 8, #3673-3680	19.50	
	Nos. 3673-3680 (8)	19.20	6.40

Nos. 3678 and 3679 each were printed in sheets of 50 in 2010.

John Calvin (1509-64), Theologian and Religious Reformer A2010

2009, May 22 Engr. Perf. 13¼

3681	A2010 56c multi	1.60	.55

Miniature Sheet

Chocolate — A2011

No. 3682: a, Cacao leaves, pods and beans. b, Aztec Indian. c, Spanish soldier. d, Castle. e, Map of French Atlantic coast. f, European man and woman of 16th cent. g, Production of chocolate. h, Chocolate bar. i, Cocoa service. j, Person eating chocolate bar.

2009, May 23 Photo. Perf. 13

3682	A2011 Sheet of 10	16.00	16.00
a.-j.	56c Any single	1.60	.55

No. 3682 is impregnated with a chocolate scent. €1.16 stamps having the designs Nos. 3682a-3682d, 3682f-3682k was included in a limited-edition booklet issued Nov. 4, 2020.

French Federation Of Philatelic Associations 82nd Congress, Tarbes — A2012

2009, June 12 Engr. Perf. 13x13¼

3683	A2012 56c multi + label	1.60	.55

Jean Moulin Memorial, Rhône — A2013

2009, June 20 Engr. Perf. 13¼
Serpentine Die Cut 11
Self-Adhesive

3684	A2013 56c multi	1.60	.55
3685	A2013 56c multi	1.60	1.60

Endangered Animals — A2014

Designs: No. 3686, Giant panda. No. 3687, Rhinoceros. 70c, Aurochs, horiz. 90c, California condor, horiz.

2009, June 20 Photo. Perf. 13¼

3686	A2014 56c multi	1.60	.55
3687	A2014 56c multi	1.60	.55
3688	A2014 70c multi	2.00	.65
3689	A2014 90c multi	2.50	.85
a.	Souvenir sheet of 4, #3686-3689	7.75	7.75
	Nos. 3686-3689 (4)	7.70	2.60

Gordon Bennett Aviation Cup, Cent. — A2015

2009, June 27 Engr. Perf. 13¼

3690	A2015 56c blk & brn	1.60	.55

Etienne Dolet (1509-46), Printer and Translator — A2016

2009, July 4 Engr. Perf. 13x13¼

3691	A2016 56c multi	1.60	.55

Miniature Sheet

Fair Attractions — A2017

Designs: a, Parachute jump. b, Ferris wheel. c, Roller coaster. d, Carousel. e, Candy apple. f, Fishing arcade game.

2009, Sept. 5 Photo. Perf. 13

3692	A2017 Sheet of 6	10.50	10.50
a.-f.	56c Any single	1.75	.60

A2018

Invitation — A2019

Designs: No. 3693, Yellow background, man with red violet pants and shoes. No. 3694, Red background, woman wearing dress. No.

3695, Red violet background, woman scattering papers. No. 3696, Light blue background, cow with flowers. No. 3697, Blue background, man with red violet pants and blue shoes. No. 3698, Brown black background, birthday cake with slice on cake server. No. 3699, Yellow green background, woman with brown pants and green shoes. No. 3700, Green background, man with blue pants and shoes. No. 3701, Brown background, cut birthday cake. No. 3702, Red violet background, woman with red violet pants and shoes. No. 3703, Pink background, woman with balloons. No. 3704, Red background, bird. No. 3705, Yellow green background, woman with green skirt and shoes. No. 3706, Orange background, woman scattering papers.

Serpentine Die Cut 11
2009, Sept. 5 Litho.
Booklet Stamps
Self-Adhesive

3693	A2018 (56c) multi	1.75	.60
3694	A2018 (56c) multi	1.75	.60
3695	A2018 (56c) multi	1.75	.60
3696	A2018 (56c) multi	1.75	.60
3697	A2018 (56c) multi	1.75	.60
3698	A2018 (56c) multi	1.75	.60
3699	A2018 (56c) multi	1.75	.60
3700	A2018 (56c) multi	1.75	.60
3701	A2019 (56c) multi	1.75	.60
3702	A2019 (56c) multi	1.75	.60
3703	A2019 (56c) multi	1.75	.60
3704	A2019 (56c) multi	1.75	.60
3705	A2019 (56c) multi	1.75	.60
3706	A2019 (56c) multi	1.75	.60
a.	Booklet pane of 14, #3693-3706	24.50	
	Nos. 3693-3706 (14)	24.50	8.40

Eugène Vaillé (1875-1959), First Conservator of the Postal Museum A2020

2009, Sept. 19 Engr. Perf. 13¼

3707	A2020 56c multi	1.75	.60

Self-Adhesive
Serpentine Die Cut 11

3708	A2020 56c multi	1.75	1.75

Souvenir Sheet

Jardin des Plantes, Paris A2021

No. 3709: a, Gazebo. b, Mexican Hothouse.

2009, Sept. 19 Photo. Perf. 13¼x13

3709	A2021 Sheet of 2	13.00	13.00
a.-b.	€2.22 Either single	6.50	3.25

Salon du Timbre.

A2022   Le Petit Nicolas, by René Goscinny — A2023

Designs: No. 3710, Nicolas, wearing striped shirt, holding envelope and book bag. No. 3711, Geoffroy. No. 3712, Eudes. No. 3713, Nicolas, wearing scarf, holding envelope and book bag. No. 3714, Nicolas writing. No. 3715, Joachim. No. 3716, "Chouette, des nouvelles!" No. 3717, Character at typewriter. No. 3718, "Vous me ferez cent lignes!" No. 3719, "Chère Maman. . ." No. 3720, "C'est toi la plus jolie!", vert. No. 3721, "J'ai fait le bonheur de tout le monde.", vert. No. 3722, "Moi, je veux pas grand chose réellement. . .", vert. No. 3723, "C'est pout toi, Maman!", vert.

Serpentine Die Cut 11
2009, Sept. 19 Litho.
Booklet Stamps
Self-Adhesive

3710	A2022	(56c) multi	1.75	.60
3711	A2022	(56c) multi	1.75	.60
3712	A2022	(56c) multi	1.75	.60
3713	A2022	(56c) multi	1.75	.60
3714	A2022	(56c) multi	1.75	.60
3715	A2022	(56c) multi	1.75	.60
3716	A2023	(56c) multi	1.75	.60
3717	A2023	(56c) multi	1.75	.60
3718	A2023	(56c) multi	1.75	.60
3719	A2023	(56c) multi	1.75	.60
3720	A2023	(56c) multi	1.75	.60
3721	A2023	(56c) multi	1.75	.60
3722	A2023	(56c) multi	1.75	.60
3723	A2023	(56c) multi	1.75	.60
a.	Booklet pane of 14, #3710-3723		24.50	

Nos. 3710-3723 (14) 24.50 8.40

René de Saint-Marceaux (1845-1915), Sculptor of UPU Monument A2024

Litho. & Engr.
2009, Oct. 9 Perf. 13x13¼
3724 A2024 70c multi 2.10 .70

See Switzerland No. 9O22.

Miniature Sheet

Dolls A2025

No. 3725: a, Porcelain doll. b, GéGé doll, horiz. c, Rag doll, horiz. d, Bella doll, horiz. e, Baigneur Petitcollin, horiz. f, Unglazed porcelain doll (poupée en biscuit).

2009, Oct. 17 Perf. 13
3725 A2025 Sheet of 6 10.50 10.50
a.-f. 56c Any single 1.75 .60

Juliette Dodu (1848-1909), Spy — A2026

2009, Oct. 28 Engr. Perf. 13¼
3726 A2026 56c multi 1.75 .60
Self-Adhesive
Serpentine Die Cut 11
3727 A2026 56c multi 1.75 1.75

European Capitals Type of 2002
Miniature Sheet

No. 3728 — Attractions in Lisbon: a, Hieronymites Monastery. b, Bairro Alto Quarter, vert. c, Belém Tower. d, Monument to the Discoveries.

Perf. 13x13¼, 13¼x13 (#3728b)
2009, Nov. 5 Photo.
3728 A1622 Sheet of 4 7.00 7.00
a.-d. 56c Any single 1.75 .60

Francisco de Miranda (1750-1816), Revolutionist in France and Venezuela A2027

2009, Nov. 6 Photo. Perf. 13¼
3729 A2027 85c multi 2.60 .90

See Venezuela No. 1693.

Marianne and Stars Type of 2008
Miniature Sheet
Photo., Engr. (#3456-3458)
2009, Nov. 6 Perf. 13
3730 Sheet of 13, #3456-3458, 3730a-3730j + label 31.00 31.00

a.	A1912	1c yellow	.25	.25
b.	A1912	5c gray brown	.25	.25
c.	A1912	10c gray	.30	.30
d.	A1912	73c olive green	2.25	2.25
e	A1912	85c purple	2.60	2.60
f.	A1912	90c fawn	2.75	2.75
g.	A1912	€1 orange	3.00	3.00
h.	A1912	€1.30 blue	4.00	4.00
i.	A1912	€1.35 red violet	4.00	4.00
j.	A1912	€2.22 chocolate	6.50	6.50

Euromed Postal Conference A2028

2009, Nov. 7 Engr. Perf. 13¼
3731 A2028 56c multi 1.75 .60

A2029   A2030

A2031   A2032

A2033   A2034

A2035   A2036

A2037   A2038

A2039   A2040

A2041   A2042

Serpentine Die Cut 11
2009, Nov. 7 Photo.
Booklet Stamps
Self-Adhesive

3732	A2029	(56c) multi	1.75	.60
3733	A2030	(56c) multi	1.75	.60
3734	A2031	(56c) multi	1.75	.60
3735	A2032	(56c) multi	1.75	.60
3736	A2033	(56c) multi	1.75	.60
3737	A2034	(56c) multi	1.75	.60
3738	A2035	(56c) multi	1.75	.60
3739	A2036	(56c) multi	1.75	.60
3740	A2037	(56c) multi	1.75	.60
3741	A2038	(56c) multi	1.75	.60
3742	A2039	(56c) multi	1.75	.60
3743	A2040	(56c) multi	1.75	.60
3744	A2041	(56c) multi	1.75	.60
3745	A2042	(56c) multi	1.75	.60
a.	Booklet pane of 14, #3732-3745		24.50	

Nos. 3732-3745 (14) 24.50 8.40

A souvenir sheet containing one No. 3743 sold for €3.

Helicopter Carrier Jeanne d'Arc — A2043

Sailors of the Jeanne d'Arc — A2044

2009, Nov. 21 Engr. Perf. 13x12¾
3746 A2043 56c multi 1.75 .60
3747 A2044 56c multi 1.75 .60
a. Horiz. pair, #3746-3747 3.50 1.20

A souvenir sheet containing Nos. 3746-3747 sold for €3.

Asterix, Comic Strip by René Goscinny and Albert Uderzo — A2045

No. 3749: a, Assurancetorix on rope (40x30mm). b, Eight characters, horiz. (80x26mm). c, Falbala with basket (30x40mm). d, Idefix and bone, horiz. (22x19mm). e, Obelix carrying rock (50x100mm).

2009, Dec. 2 Photo. Perf. 13
3748 A2045 56c multi 1.75 .60
3749 Sheet of 6, #3748, 3749a-3749e 15.50 15.50

a.	A2045 56c multi, perf. 13x13¼		2.50	2.50
b.	A2045 56c multi, perf. 13		2.50	2.50
c.	A2045 56c multi, perf. 13¼x13		2.50	2.50
d.	A2045 56c multi, perf. 13¼x12½		2.50	2.50
e.	A2045 56c multi, perf. 13x12¼		2.50	2.50

No. 3749 sold for €5.20, with the Red Cross receiving €1.84 of that. No. 3749e has a gritty substance affixed to the rock.

A2046   Hearts — A2047

Type I — Bow ties extend to perforations.
Type II — Bow ties do not touch perforations (red frame all around).

2010, Jan. 8 Photo. Perf. 13¼
3750 A2046 56c multi, type I 1.60 .55
Perf.
3751 A2046 56c multi, type II 1.60 .55
Perf. 13¼
3752 A2047 90c multi 2.50 1.25
Nos. 3750-3752 (3) 5.70 2.35
Self-Adhesive
Serpentine Die Cut
3753 A2046 56c multi, type I 1.60 1.60
3754 A2047 90c multi 2.50 2.50

Values for Nos. 3750, 3752 are for stamps with surrounding selvage. No. 3751 was printed in sheets of 5.

New Year 2010 (Year of the Tiger) — A2048

2010, Jan. 15 Photo. Perf. 13¼x13
3755 A2048 56c multi 1.60 .55

No. 3755 was printed in sheets of 5. A souvenir sheet of 1 sold for €3.
See No. 4970b.

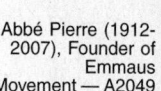

Abbé Pierre (1912-2007), Founder of Emmaus Movement — A2049

2010, Jan. 22 Engr. Perf. 13¼
3756 A2049 56c multi 1.60 .55
Self-Adhesive
Serpentine Die Cut 11
3757 A2049 56c multi 1.60 1.60

A souvenir sheet containing No. 3756 was printed in 2011 and sold for €3.

Musical Instruments in Art — A2050

Designs: No. 3758, Lyre, by Gustave Moreau. No. 3759, Harp (Harpe), by François André Vincent. No. 3760, Violincello (Violoncelle), by Karl Gustav Klingstedt. No. 3761, Guitar (Guitare), by Camille Roqueplan. No. 3762, Horn (Cor), by Daniel Rabel. No. 3763, Saxophone, by Marthe and Juliette Vesque. No. 3764, Organ (Orgue), by François Garas. No. 3765, Bugle (Clairon), by Auguste Mayer. No. 3766, Clavecin, by Louis Carrogis Carmontelle. No. 3767, Piano, by Pierre-Désiré Lamy. No. 3768, Tambourine (Tambourin), by Théodore Chassériau. No. 3769, Drums (Tambour), by Jacques-Antoine Delaistre.

Serpentine Die Cut 11
2010, Jan. 30 Photo.
Booklet Stamps
Self-Adhesive

3758	A2050	(56c) multi	1.60	.55
3759	A2050	(56c) multi	1.60	.55
3760	A2050	(56c) multi	1.60	.55
3761	A2050	(56c) multi	1.60	.55
3762	A2050	(56c) multi	1.60	.55
3763	A2050	(56c) multi	1.60	.55
3764	A2050	(56c) multi	1.60	.55
3765	A2050	(56c) multi	1.60	.55
3766	A2050	(56c) multi	1.60	.55
3767	A2050	(56c) multi	1.60	.55
3768	A2050	(56c) multi	1.60	.55
3769	A2050	(56c) multi	1.60	.55
a.	Booklet pane of 12, #3758-3769		19.50	

Nos. 3758-3769 (12) 19.20 6.60

See Nos. 3882A-3882B.

2010 Winter Olympics, Vancouver A2051

2010, Feb. 6 Perf. 13x13¼
3770 A2051 85c Figure skaters 2.40 1.25
3771 A2051 85c Skier 2.40 1.25
a. Horiz. pair, #3770-3771 4.80 2.50
b. Tete-beche block of 4, 2 #3771a 9.60 5.00

Art Issue

Museum of Art and Industry (La Piscine), Roubaix A2052

The Beach at Calais at Ebb Tide, by Joseph Mallord William Turner A2053

Maman, by Louise Bourgeois A2054

Allegory of Spring, by Sandro Botticelli A2055

No. 3775: a, Flora, Zephyrus and Chloris. b, The Three Graces.

2010		**Photo.**		*Perf. 13x13¼*	
3772	A2052	85c multi		2.10	1.10
3773	A2053	€1.35 multi		3.75	1.90
3774	A2054	€1.35 multi		3.50	1.75
	Nos. 3772-3774 (3)			9.35	4.75

		Perf. 13¼x13			
3775	A2055	Sheet of 2		6.25	6.25
a.		87c multi		2.40	1.25
b.		€1.40 multi		3.75	1.90

Self-Adhesive
Serpentine Die Cut 11
Photo.

3776	A2052	85c multi		2.10	2.10
3776A	A2055	87c Like		2.40	2.40
		#3775b			
3777	A2053	€1.35 multi		3.75	3.75
3778	A2054	€1.35 multi		3.50	3.50
3779	A2055	€1.40 Like		3.75	3.75
		#3775a			
	Nos. 3776-3779 (5)			15.50	15.50

Issued: Nos. 3772, 3776, 5/15; Nos. 3773, 3777, 2/19; Nos. 3774, 3778, 6/17; No. 3775, 11/8/10; Nos. 3776A, 3779, 11/18/10.

A2056

Stamp Day A2057

2010, Feb. 27	**Engr.**	*Perf. 13*	
3780 A2056	56c blue & red	1.60	.55

Souvenir Sheet
Litho. & Embossed
Perf. 13¼x13

3781 A2057	€2 multi	5.50	2.75

Protection of Water — A2058

Inscriptions: No. 3782, Grands mammifères marins (large marine mammals). No. 3783,

Marée noire (black tide). No. 3784, Irrigation. No. 3785, Plaisir de l'eau (pleasure of water). No. 3786, Inondation (flood). No. 3787, Source. No. 3788, Aigues vertes (green water). No. 3789, Secheresse (drought). No. 3790, Hydro-électricité (hydroelectricity). No. 3791, Géothermie (geothermal energy). No. 3792, Pluies acides (acid rain). No. 3793, Fonte des glaciers (melting of glaciers).

Serpentine Die Cut 11

2010, Feb. 27		**Photo.**	

Booklet Stamps
Self-Adhesive

3782	A2058	(56c) multi	1.60	.55
3783	A2058	(56c) multi	1.60	.55
3784	A2058	(56c) multi	1.60	.55
3785	A2058	(56c) multi	1.60	.55
3786	A2058	(56c) multi	1.60	.55
3787	A2058	(56c) multi	1.60	.55
3788	A2058	(56c) multi	1.60	.55
3789	A2058	(56c) multi	1.60	.55
3790	A2058	(56c) multi	1.60	.55
3791	A2058	(56c) multi	1.60	.55
3792	A2058	(56c) multi	1.60	.55
3793	A2058	(56c) multi	1.60	.55
a.		Booklet pane of 12, #3782-3793	19.50	
	Nos. 3782-3793 (12)		19.20	6.60

Savoy as Part of France, 150th Anniv. — A2059

2010, Mar. 27	**Engr.**	*Perf. 13¼x13*	
3794 A2059	56c multi	1.60	.55

Self-Adhesive
Serpentine Die Cut 11

3795 A2059	56c multi	1.60	1.60

Tourism Issue

Villeneuve lez Avignon A2060   Orcival Basilica A2061

Pornic A2062

Arcueil-Cachan Aqueduct Bridge — A2063

2010	**Engr.**	*Perf. 13¼*	
3796 A2060	56c multi	1.50	.50
3797 A2061	56c multi	1.40	.45

	Perf. 13		
3798 A2062	56c multi	1.40	.45

	Perf. 13¼		
3799 A2063	58c multi	1.60	.55
	Nos. 3796-3799 (4)	5.90	1.95

Self-Adhesive
Engr.
Serpentine Die Cut 11

3800 A2060	56c multi	1.50	1.50

Issued: Nos. 3796, 3800, 4/17; No. 3797, 5/13; No. 3798, 5/25; No. 3799, 9/24.

A2064

A2065

A2066

A2067   A2068

A2069   A2070

A2071   A2072

A2073   A2074

Campaign Against Violence Toward Women — A2075

Serpentine Die Cut 11

2010, Apr. 20		**Litho.**	

Booklet Stamps
Self-Adhesive

3801	A2064	(56c) multi	1.50	.50
3802	A2065	(56c) multi	1.50	.50
3803	A2066	(56c) multi	1.50	.50
3804	A2067	(56c) multi	1.50	.50
3805	A2068	(56c) multi	1.50	.50
3806	A2069	(56c) multi	1.50	.50
3807	A2070	(56c) multi	1.50	.50
3808	A2071	(56c) multi	1.50	.50
3809	A2072	(56c) multi	1.50	.50
3810	A2073	(56c) multi	1.50	.50
3811	A2074	(56c) multi	1.50	.50
3812	A2075	(56c) multi	1.50	.50
a.		Booklet pane of 12, #3801-3812	18.00	
	Nos. 3801-3812 (12)		18.00	6.00

Colmar — A2076

2010, Apr. 23	**Engr.**	*Perf. 13¼*	
3813 A2076	56c multi	1.50	.50

Self-Adhesive
Serpentine Die Cut 11

3814 A2076	56c multi	1.50	1.50

National Sheepcote, Rambouillet A2077

2010, May 1		*Perf. 13¼*	
3815 A2077	90c multi	2.40	1.25

Europa — A2078

2010, May 9		**Photo.**	
3816 A2078	70c multi	1.75	.60

Miniature Sheet

Stamp Bourse in Paris, 150th Anniv. A2079

No. 3817 — Famous philatelists: a, Pres. Franklin Delano Roosevelt (1882-1945). b, Lucien Berthelot (1903-85), President of International Philatelic Federation. c, Louis Yvert (1866-1950), stamp catalogue publisher, horiz. d, Arthur Maury (1844-1907), stamp catalogue publisher, horiz. e, Alberto Bolaffi (1874-1944), stamp catalogue publisher.

2010, May 13	**Engr.**	*Perf. 13*	
3817 A2079	Sheet of 5	7.00	7.00
a.-e.	56c Any single	1.40	.45

Deauville, 150th Anniv. — A2080

2010, May 14	**Photo.**	*Perf. 13¼*	
3818 A2080	85c multi	2.10	1.10

Mother Teresa (1910-97), Humanitarian A2081

2010, May 27	**Engr.**	*Perf. 13¼x13*	
3819 A2081	85c multi	2.10	1.10

Self-Adhesive
Serpentine Die Cut 11

3820 A2081	85c multi	2.10	2.10

Institute of Human Paleontology, Paris, Cent. — A2082

2010, June 1		*Perf. 13x12¾*	
3821 A2082	56c multi	1.40	.45

See Monaco No. 2597.

Nice as Part of France, 150th Anniv. — A2083

2010, June 11	**Photo.**	*Perf. 13¼*	
3822 A2083	56c multi	1.40	.45

Self-Adhesive
Serpentine Die Cut 11

3823 A2083	56c multi	1.40	1.40

Front Side of No. 3824

Rear Side of No. 3824
A2084

A2085

2010 World Cup Soccer Championships, South Africa — A2086

No. 3825: a, Soccer player and ball. b, Soccer players, vert. c, South African building, vert. d, Aerial view of Cape Town.

2010   **Photo.**   **Perf. 13x12¾**
3824   A2084   56c multi   2.75   .50
     Perf. 13x13¼, 13¼x13
3825   A2085   Sheet of 4   8.50   8.50
  a.-d.   85c Any single   2.10   1.10

Embossed and Etched on Silver
Die Cut Perf. 12¾
Self-Adhesive
3826   A2086   €5 silver   12.50   12.50

Issued: Nos. 3824, 3825, 6/13; No. 3826, 6/11. No. 3824 is gummed on both sides and sold for €1.12. Both sides of the stamp could be used. Values for used examples of No. 3824 are for stamps canceled on either or both sides.

Launch of Soyuz Space Flights From French Guiana — A2087

2010, June 12   **Photo.**   **Perf. 13¼**
3827   A2087   85c multi   2.25   1.10
    Self-Adhesive
    Serpentine Die Cut 11
3828   A2087   85c multi   2.25   2.25

Souvenir Sheet

Jardins de Giverny, by Claude Monet A2088

No. 3829: a, Bridge. b, Pond.

2010, June 12   **Perf. 13¼x13**
3829   A2088   Sheet of 2   11.50   11.50
  a.-b.   €2.22 Either single   5.75   3.00
  c.   Souvenir sheet, #3709a, 3709b, 3829a, 3829b   22.50   22.50

2010 Salon du Timbre (No. 3829c).

Regional Cuisine — A2089

Designs: No. 3830, Eclade (grilled mussels), Poitou-Charentes. No. 3831, Baeckaoffe (stew), Alsace. No. 3832, Tomme des Pyrénées cheese, Midi-Pyrénées. No. 3833, Tarte aux mirabelles (plum tart), Lorraine. No. 3834,

Potage aux cresson (watercress soup), Ile-de-France. No. 3835, Flamiche (leek pie), Picardy. No. 3836, Pont l'Evêque cheese, Basse-Normandie. No. 3837, Blanc-manger (blanc-mange), Antilles. No. 3838, Caviar, Aquitaine. No. 3839, Chapon (capon), Franche-Comté. No. 3840, Fourme d'Ambert cheese, Auvergne. No. 3841, Tarte tatin (upside-down apple tart), Centre.

No. 3842, Quenelles (dumplings), Rhône-Alpes. No. 3843, Escalope normande (veal cutlet), Haute-Normandie. No. 3844, Maroilles cheese, Nord-Pas-de-Calais. No. 3845, Clafoutis (baked fruit and batter), Limousin. No. 3846, Gougères (cheese pastry), Bourgogne. No. 3847, Tian (baked vegetables), Provence-Alpes-Côte d'Azur. No. 3848, Brocciu cheese, Corsica. No. 3849, Abricots rouges au miel (apricots in honey), Languedoc-Roussillon. No. 3850, Homard breton (lobster), Bretagne. No. 3851, Brochet au beurre blanc (pike with white butter), Pays de la Loire. No. 3852, Chaource cheese, Champagne-Ardennes. No. 3853, Paris-Brest (butter cream-filled pastry), Paris.

Serpentine Die Cut 11
2010, June 12   **Photo.**
    Booklet Stamps
    Self-Adhesive
3830   A2089   (56c) multi   1.40   .45
3831   A2089   (56c) multi   1.40   .45
3832   A2089   (56c) multi   1.40   .45
3833   A2089   (56c) multi   1.40   .45
  a.   Booklet pane of 4, #3830-3833   5.60
3834   A2089   (56c) multi   1.40   .45
3835   A2089   (56c) multi   1.40   .45
3836   A2089   (56c) multi   1.40   .45
3837   A2089   (56c) multi   1.40   .45
  a.   Booklet pane of 4, #3834-3837   5.60
3838   A2089   (56c) multi   1.40   .45
3839   A2089   (56c) multi   1.40   .45
3840   A2089   (56c) multi   1.40   .45
3841   A2089   (56c) multi   1.40   .45
  a.   Booklet pane of 4, #3838-3841   5.60
     Complete booklet, #3833a, 3837a, 3841a   17.00
3842   A2089   (56c) multi   1.40   .45
3843   A2089   (56c) multi   1.40   .45
3844   A2089   (56c) multi   1.40   .45
3845   A2089   (56c) multi   1.40   .45
  a.   Booklet pane of 4, #3842-3845   5.60
3846   A2089   (56c) multi   1.40   .45
3847   A2089   (56c) multi   1.40   .45
3848   A2089   (56c) multi   1.40   .45
3849   A2089   (56c) multi   1.40   .45
  a.   Booklet pane of 4, #3846-3849   5.60
3850   A2089   (56c) multi   1.40   .45
3851   A2089   (56c) multi   1.40   .45
3852   A2089   (56c) multi   1.40   .45
3853   A2089   (56c) multi   1.40   .45
  a.   Booklet pane of 4, #3850-3853   5.60
     Complete booklet, #3845a, 3849a, 3853a   17.00
    Nos. 3830-3853 (24)   33.60   10.80

Romanesque Art — A2090

Designs: No. 3854, Bas-relief, Tournus. No. 3855, Interior of Cistercian Abbey, Léoncel. No. 3856, Painting, St. Sever. No. 3857, Serrabone Priory, Boule d'Amont. No. 3858, Sculpture, L'Ile-Bouchard. No. 3859, Painting, Citeaux Abbey. No. 3860, Fresco from St. Martin's Church, Nohant-Vic. No. 3861, Bas-relief, Clermont-Ferrand. No. 3862, Fresco, St. Jacques-des-Guérets. No. 3863, Bas-relief, Angouleme. No. 3864, Painting of the Consecration of the third Abbey Church, Cluny. No. 3865, Bas-reliefs, tympanum of Saint-Foy Abbey Church, Conques.

Serpentine Die Cut 11
2010, June 14   **Photo.**
    Booklet Stamps
    Self-Adhesive
3854   A2090   (56c) multi   1.40   .45
3855   A2090   (56c) multi   1.40   .45
3856   A2090   (56c) multi   1.40   .45
3857   A2090   (56c) multi   1.40   .45
3858   A2090   (56c) multi   1.40   .45
3859   A2090   (56c) multi   1.40   .45
3860   A2090   (56c) multi   1.40   .45
3861   A2090   (56c) multi   1.40   .45
3862   A2090   (56c) multi   1.40   .45
3863   A2090   (56c) multi   1.40   .45
3864   A2090   (56c) multi   1.40   .45
3865   A2090   (56c) multi   1.40   .45
  a.   Booklet pane of 12, #3854-3865   17.00
    Nos. 3854-3865 (12)   16.80   5.40

See Nos. 3870A-3870B.

Miniature Sheet

Mills A2091

No. 3866: a, Windmill, Montbrun-Lauragais. b, Windmill, Cassel. c, Aigremonts Windmill, Bléré, horiz. d, Daudet Windmill, Fontvieille, horiz. e, Flour mill, Villeneuve-d'Ascq. f, Birlot Watermill, Ile-de-Bréhat, horiz.

    Litho. & Engr.
2010, June 15   **Perf. 13**
3866   A2091   Sheet of 6   8.50   8.50
  a.-f.   56c Any single   1.40   .45

2010 Youth Olympics, Singapore — A2092

2010, June 16   **Photo.**   **Perf. 13¼**
3867   A2092   85c multi   2.25   1.10

Souvenir Sheet

Charles de Gaulle's Appeal of June 18 Speech, 70th Anniv. A2093

2010, June 18   **Engr.**   **Perf. 13x13¼**
3868   A2093   56c multi   1.40   .45

See No. 5947Bc.

Conciergerie, Paris — A2094

2010, June 19
3869   A2094   56c multi + label   1.40   .45
French Federation of Philatelic Associations, 83rd Congress, Paris.

French Pavilion, Expo 2010, Shanghai A2095

2010, June 20   **Photo.**   **Perf. 13¼**
3870   A2095   85c multi   2.25   1.10

Romanesque Art Type of 2010
Designs: No. 3870A, Like #3855. No. 3870B, Like #3858.

Serpentine Die Cut 11
2010, June 21   **Litho.**
    Self-Adhesive
3870A   A2090   (56c) multi   1.40   1.40
3870B   A2090   (56c) multi   1.40   1.40

Nos. 3870A-3870B each were printed in sheets of 50. The red panels of Nos. 3855 and 3858 are splotchy, typical of photogravure printings. Under magnification black dots can be seen in the red panels on Nos. 3870A-3870B.

Marianne and Stars Type of 2008
2010, July 1   **Engr.**   **Perf. 13**
3871   A1912   75c olive green   1.90   .50
3872   A1912   87c purple   2.25   .55
3873   A1912   95c fawn   2.40   .60
3874   A1912   €1.35 blue   3.50   .90
3875   A1912   €1.40 red violet   3.50   .90
3876   A1912   €2.30 chocolate   5.75   1.50
    Nos. 3871-3876 (6)   19.30   4.95
    Self-Adhesive
Serpentine Die Cut 6¾ Vert.
3877   A1912   75c olive green   1.90   1.90
3878   A1912   87c purple   2.25   2.25
3879   A1912   95c fawn   2.40   2.40
3880   A1912   €1.35 blue   3.50   3.50
3881   A1912   €1.40 red violet   3.50   3.50
3882   A1912   €2.30 chocolate   5.75   5.75
    Nos. 3877-3882 (6)   19.30   19.30

Musical Instruments Type of 2010
Designs: No. 3882A, Like #3761. No. 3882B, Like #3767.

Serpentine Die Cut 11
2010, July 1   **Litho.**
    Self-Adhesive
3882A   A2050   (58c) multi   1.50   1.50
3882B   A2050   (58c) multi   1.50   1.50

Nos. 3882A-3882B were each printed in sheets of 50. The gray blue portions of Nos. 3761 and 3767 are splotchy, typical of photogravure printings, and not splotchy on Nos. 3882A and 3882B.

Independence of French Colonies in Africa, 50th Anniv. — A2096

2010, July 15   **Photo.**   **Perf. 13¼**
3883   A2096   87c multi   2.25   1.10
    Self-Adhesive
Serpentine Die Cut 11
3884   A2096   87c multi   2.25   2.25

Butterflies A2097

Designs: Nos. 3885, 3886b, Morpho menelaus. No. 3886a, Cerura vinula caterpillar. 75c, Thersamolycaena dispar, vert. 95c, Callophrys rubi.

   Litho. (#3885, 3886a), Litho. & Embossed
2010, Sept. 3   **Perf. 13¼**
3885   A2097   58c multi   1.50   .50
3886   Sheet of 4   7.50   7.50
  a.   A2097   58c multi   1.50   .50
  b.   A2097   58c multi   1.50   .50
  c.   A2097   75c multi   2.00   .65
  d.   A2097   95c multi   2.50   .85

Universal Israelite Alliance, 150th Anniv. — A2098

    Litho. & Engr.
2010, Sept. 7   **Perf. 13¼**
3887   A2098   58c multi   1.50   .50

A2099

A2100

A2101

A2102

A2103

A2104

A2105

A2106

A2107

A2108

A2109

Cartoons With
Letters — A2110

Serpentine Die Cut 11
2010, Oct. 11   Photo.
Booklet Stamps
Self-Adhesive

3888	A2099	(58c) multi	1.75	.60
3889	A2100	(58c) multi	1.75	.60
3890	A2101	(58c) multi	1.75	.60
3891	A2102	(58c) multi	1.75	.60
3892	A2103	(58c) multi	1.75	.60
3893	A2104	(58c) multi	1.75	.60
3894	A2105	(58c) multi	1.75	.60
3895	A2106	(58c) multi	1.75	.60
3896	A2107	(58c) multi	1.75	.60
3897	A2108	(58c) multi	1.75	.60
3898	A2109	(58c) multi	1.75	.60
3899	A2110	(58c) multi	1.75	.60
a.	Booklet pane of 12, #3888-3899		21.00

Nos. 3888-3899 (12)   21.00   7.20

Aviation
Pioneers — A2111

Designs: Nos. 3900, 3902, Elise Deroche (1882-1919).
No. 3901: a, Hubert Latham (1883-1912). b, Orville (1871-1948) and Wilbur Wright (1867-1912). c, Henry Farman (1874-1958). d, Jules Védrines (1881-1919). e, Léon Delagrange (1872-1910).

2010, Oct. 15   Photo.   Perf. 13
3900 A2111 58c multi   1.75 .60
3901   Sheet of 6, #3900,
                3901a-3901e   15.00 15.00
  a.-e. A2111 58c Any single   2.50 2.50

Self-Adhesive
Serpentine Die Cut 11
3902 A2111 58c multi   1.75 1.75

No. 3901 sold for € 5.40, with the Red Cross receiving €1.92 of that.

World Fencing
Championships,
Paris — A2112

Designs: 58c, Wheelchair fencing. 87c, Fencing.

2010, Oct. 22   Engr.   Perf. 13x13¼
3903 A2112 58c multi   1.75 .60
3904 A2112 87c multi   2.50 .85
  a. Horiz. pair, #3903-3904 + central label   4.25 1.50

Paris Bar
Association,
Bicent. — A2113

2010, Oct. 28   Photo.   Perf. 13¼
3905 A2113 58c black & lt blue   1.75 .60

Self-Adhesive
Serpentine Die Cut 11
3906 A2113 58c black & lt blue   1.75 1.75

Villeneuve-sur-Lot — A2114

2010, Oct. 30   Engr.   Perf. 13¼
3907 A2114 58c multi   1.75 .60

European Capitals Type of 2002
Miniature Sheet

No. 3908 — Attractions in Paris: a, Arc de Triomphe de l'Etoile. b, Notre Dame Cathedral. c, Garnier Opera House. d, Eiffel Tower, vert.

Perf. 13x13¼, 13¼x13 (#3908d)
2010, Nov. 4   Photo.
3908 A1622   Sheet of 4   7.00 7.00
  a.-d.   58c Any single   1.75 .60

A2115

A2116

A2117

A2118

A2119

A2120

A2121

A2122

A2123

A2124

A2125

A2126

A2127

"Best Wishes" — A2128

Serpentine Die Cut 11
2010, Nov. 5   Photo.
Booklet Stamps
Self-Adhesive

3909	A2115	(58c) multi	1.75	.60
3910	A2116	(58c) multi	1.75	.60
3911	A2117	(58c) multi	1.75	.60
3912	A2118	(58c) multi	1.75	.60
3913	A2119	(58c) multi	1.75	.60
3914	A2120	(58c) multi	1.75	.60
3915	A2121	(58c) multi	1.75	.60
3916	A2122	(58c) multi	1.75	.60
3917	A2123	(58c) multi	1.75	.60
3918	A2124	(58c) multi	1.75	.60
3919	A2125	(58c) multi	1.75	.60
3920	A2126	(58c) multi	1.75	.60
3921	A2127	(58c) multi	1.75	.60
3922	A2128	(58c) multi	1.75	.60
a.	Booklet pane of 14, #3909-3922, + 14 stickers		24.50

Nos. 3909-3922 (14)   24.50 8.40

A souvenir sheet containing one perf. 13x13¼ example of No. 3915 with water-activated gum sold for €3.

First French Revenue
Stamp, 150th
Anniv. — A2129

Serpentine Die Cut 6¾ Vert.
2010, Nov. 6   Engr.
Booklet Stamp
Self-Adhesive
3923 A2129 (58c) brown   1.60 .40
  a. Booklet pane of 12, 6 each #3471, 3923   19.50

Souvenir Sheet

Primitive
Flemish
Paintings
A2130

No. 3924: a, Madonna and Child, by Roger de la Pasture. b, Portrait of Laurent Froimont, by Rogier van der Weyden.

2010, Nov. 6   Photo.   Perf. 13
3924 A2130   Sheet of 2   10.00 10.00
  a.-b.   €1.80 Either single   5.00 2.50

See Belgium No. 2478.

Independence
Movements of Latin
America and the
Caribbean,
Bicent. — A2131

2010, Nov. 27   Perf. 13¼
3925 A2131 87c multi   2.40 .80

Hearts — A2132

Designs: 58c, Multicolored outlines of hearts. 95c, Red heart.

Photo., Photo. With Foil Application (95c)
2011, Jan. 7   Perf. 13
3926 A2132 58c multi   1.60 .55
  a.   Sheet of 5   8.00 8.00
3927 A2132 95c black & red   2.60 .85

Self-Adhesive
Serpentine Die Cut
3928 A2132 58c multi   1.60 1.60
3929 A2132 95c black & red   2.60 2.60

New Year 2011 (Year
of the
Rabbit) — A2133

2011, Jan. 14   Photo.   Perf. 13¼x13
3930 A2133 58c multi   1.60 .55

No. 3930 was printed in sheets of 5. A souvenir sheet of 1 sold for €3.
See No. 4970c.

Mulhouse Tram-
Train
A2134

2011, Jan. 14   Engr.   Perf. 13¼
3931 A2134 58c multi   1.60 .55

Fabric
Designs — A2135

Fabric designs from: Nos. 3932, 3936, French Polynesia. Nos. 3933, 3942, Japan. No. 3934, France, from 1780. No. 3935, Ivory Coast. No. 3937, Italy. No. 3938, Iran. No. 3939, Egypt. No. 3940, India. No. 3941, China. No. 3943, Peru. No. 3944, Morocco. No. 3945, France, from First Empire period.

Serpentine Die Cut 11
2011, Jan. 21   Photo.
Self-Adhesive
With Faint Blue Dots Behind Type
in Area Below Vignette
3932 A2135 (58c) multi   1.60 1.60
3933 A2135 (58c) multi   1.60 1.60

Booklet Stamps
Without Dots Behind Type In Area
Below Vignette

3934	A2135	(58c) multi	1.60	.55
3935	A2135	(58c) multi	1.60	.55
3936	A2135	(58c) multi	1.60	.55
3937	A2135	(58c) multi	1.60	.55
3938	A2135	(58c) multi	1.60	.55
3939	A2135	(58c) multi	1.60	.55
3940	A2135	(58c) multi	1.60	.55
3941	A2135	(58c) multi	1.60	.55
3942	A2135	(58c) multi	1.60	.55
3943	A2135	(58c) multi	1.60	.55
3944	A2135	(58c) multi	1.60	.55
3945	A2135	(58c) multi	1.60	.55
a.	Booklet pane of 12, #3934-3945		19.50

Nos. 3934-3945 (12)   19.20 6.60

Marie Curie (1867-
1934),
Chemist — A2136

2011, Jan. 27   **Engr.**   **Perf. 13¼**
3946 A2136 87c red & dk blue   2.40   .80

Self-Adhesive

Serpentine Die Cut 11
3947 A2136 87c red & dk blue   2.40   2.40

Intl. Year of Chemistry.

Art Issue

Plongée, by Jean Bazaine A2137

Le Kiosque des Noctambules, Sculpture by Jean-Michel Othoniel A2138

Buddha, by Odilon Redon — A2139

Dying Centaur, Sculpture, by Antoine Bourdelle (1861-1929) A2140

The Three Nymphs, Sculpture by Aristide Maillol (1861-1944) — A2140a

2011   **Photo.**   **Perf. 13x13¼**
3948 A2137 87c multi   2.50   1.25

Perf. 13¼x13
3949 A2138 €1.40 multi   3.75   1.90
3950 A2139 €1.40 multi   3.75   1.90
   Nos. 3948-3950 (3)   10.00   5.05

Souvenir Sheet

Engr.
3951   Sheet of 2   6.50   6.50
  a.   A2140 89c multi   2.50   1.25
  b.   A2140a €1.45 multi   4.00   2.00

Self-Adhesive

Serpentine Die Cut 11
3952 A2137   87c multi   2.50   2.50
3953 A2138   €1.40 multi   3.75   3.75
3954 A2139   €1.40 multi   3.75   3.75
3955 A2140   89c multi   2.50   2.50
3955A A2140a €1.45 multi   4.00   4.00
   Nos. 3952-3955A (5)   16.50   16.50

Issued: Nos. 3948, 3952, 3/18; Nos. 3949, 3953, 2/11; Nos. 3950, 3954, 4/1; Nos. 3951, 3955, 3955A, 11/4.

Marianne and Hand Planting Seedling A2141

Strawberry and Strawberry Plant — A2142

2011, Feb. 26   **Engr.**   **Perf. 13**
3956 A2141 58c multi   1.75   .60

Souvenir Sheet

Photo. & Engr.

Perf. 13¼x13
3957 A2142 €2 multi   5.75   3.00

Stamp Day. No. 3957 has printing and a strawberry-scented scratch-and-sniff panel on the reverse.

Hand Planting Seedling A2143

Leaf on Edge of Cliff — A2144

Flora and Earth — A2145

Hedgehog and Plants — A2146

Field — A2147

Tree With Various Fruits — A2148

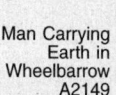

Man Carrying Earth in Wheelbarrow A2149

Heart-shaped Plants in Flower Pots — A2150

Hands Holding Potatoes A2151

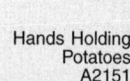

Man Watering Tree on Earth — A2152

Earth on Plant — A2153

Farmer's Field and House — A2154

Serpentine Die Cut 11

2011, Feb. 26   **Photo.**

Self-Adhesive

Smooth, Glossy Paper
3958 A2143 (58c) multi   1.75   1.75
3959 A2144 (58c) multi   1.75   1.75
3960 A2145 (58c) multi   1.75   1.75
   Nos. 3958-3960 (3)   5.25   5.25

Booklet Stamps

Rough, Textured Paper
3961 A2143 (58c) multi   1.75   .60
3962 A2144 (58c) multi   1.75   .60
3963 A2146 (58c) multi   1.75   .60
3964 A2147 (58c) multi   1.75   .60
3965 A2148 (58c) multi   1.75   .60
3966 A2149 (58c) multi   1.75   .60
3967 A2150 (58c) multi   1.75   .60
3968 A2151 (58c) multi   1.75   .60
3969 A2152 (58c) multi   1.75   .60
3970 A2153 (58c) multi   1.75   .60
3971 A2154 (58c) multi   1.75   .60
3972 A2145 (58c) multi   1.75   .60
  a.   Booklet pane of 12, #3961-3972   21.00
   Nos. 3961-3972 (12)   21.00   7.20

Stamp Day.

Tristan Corbière (1845-75), Poet — A2155

2011, Mar. 4   **Engr.**   **Perf. 13**
3973 A2155 75c multi   2.10   .70

Art of Miss.Tic (Radhia de Ruiter) — A2156

Woman and text: No. 3974, Femme de lêtre. No. 3975, Je suis la votelle du mot voyou. No. 3976, Femme de tête mais l'esprit de corps. No. 3977, Tout achever sauf le désir. No. 3978, Soyons heureuses en attendant le bonneur. No. 3979, Je crois en l'éternel féminin. No. 3980, L'homme est le passé de la femme. No. 3981, Le masculin l'emporte mais où? No. 3982, Je ne me suis pas laissé défaire. No. 3983, Mieux que rien c'est pas assez. No. 3984, Il fait un temps de chienne. No. 3985, Cueillir l'éros de la vie.

Serpentine Die Cut 11

2011, Mar. 8   **Photo.**

Booklet Stamps

Self-Adhesive
3974 A2156 (58c) black & red   1.75   .60
3975 A2156 (58c) black & red   1.75   .60
3976 A2156 (58c) black & red   1.75   .60
3977 A2156 (58c) black & red   1.75   .60
3978 A2156 (58c) black & red   1.75   .60
3979 A2156 (58c) black & red   1.75   .60
3980 A2156 (58c) black & red   1.75   .60
3981 A2156 (58c) black & red   1.75   .60
3982 A2156 (58c) black & red   1.75   .60
3983 A2156 (58c) black & red   1.75   .60
3984 A2156 (58c) black & red   1.75   .60
3985 A2156 (58c) black & red   1.75   .60
  a.   Booklet pane of 12, #3974-3985   21.00
   Nos. 3974-3985 (12)   21.00   7.20

Intl. Women's Day.

European Capitals Type of 2002

Miniature Sheet

No. 3986 — Attractions in Budapest: a, Parliament. b, Pont des Chaînes (Chain Bridge). c, Royal Palace. d, Bains Széchenyi (Széchenyi Baths), vert.

Perf. 13x13¼, 13¼x13 (#3986d)

2011, Mar. 25   **Photo.**
3986 A1622   Sheet of 4   7.00   7.00
  a.-d.   (58c) Any single   1.75   .60

Tourism Issue

Angers — A2157

Wooden Bridge, Crest — A2158

Autun A2159

Varengeville-sur-Mer A2160

Notre Dame Church, Royan A2161

2011   **Engr.**   **Perf. 13¼**
3987 A2157 58c multi   1.75   .60
3988 A2158 58c multi   1.75   .60

Perf. 13
3989 A2159 58c multi   1.75   .60

Perf. 13¼
3990 A2160 58c multi   1.75   .60
3991 A2161 60c multi   1.75   .60
   Nos. 3987-3991 (5)   8.75   3.00

Issued: No. 3990, 6/24. No. 3991, 10/23.

Gothic Houses of Worship — A2162

Designs: Nos. 3992, 4001, Notre Dame Cathedral, Strasbourg. Nos. 3993, 4002, Notre Dame Cathedral, Amiens. Nos. 3994, 4005, Sainte-Chapelle, Paris. No. 3995, St. Etienne Cathedral, Sens. No. 3996, Notre Dame Cathedral, Chartres. No. 3997, Notre Dame Cathedral, Laon. No. 3998, St. Etienne Cathedral, Metz. No. 3999, St. Pierre Cathedral, Beauvais. No. 4000, St. Etienne Cathedral, Bourges. No. 4003, Notre Dame Cathedral, Bayeux. No. 4004, Notre Dame Cathedral, Rouen. No. 4006, St. Denis Basilica, Saint-Denis.

Serpentine Die Cut 11

2011, Apr. 15   **Litho.**
3992 A2162 (58c) multi   1.75   1.75
3993 A2162 (58c) multi   1.75   1.75
3994 A2162 (58c) multi   1.75   1.75
   Nos. 3992-3994 (3)   5.25   5.25

Photo.

Booklet Stamps
3995 A2162 (58c) multi   1.75   .60
3996 A2162 (58c) multi   1.75   .60
3997 A2162 (58c) multi   1.75   .60
3998 A2162 (58c) multi   1.75   .60
3999 A2162 (58c) multi   1.75   .60
4000 A2162 (58c) multi   1.75   .60
4001 A2162 (58c) multi   1.75   .60
4002 A2162 (58c) multi   1.75   .60
4003 A2162 (58c) multi   1.75   .60
4004 A2162 (58c) multi   1.75   .60
4005 A2162 (58c) multi   1.75   .60
4006 A2162 (58c) multi   1.75   .60
  a.   Booklet pane of 12, #3995-4006   21.00
   Nos. 3995-4006 (12)   21.00   7.20

On lithographed stamps, "Phil@poste" is sharp and crisp, while on photogravure stamps it is muddy and unclear.

Dogs — A2163

Designs: No. 4007, Labrador retriever. No. 4008a, Berger allemand (German shepherd), vert. 75c, Caniche (poodle). 95c, Yorkshire terrier, vert.

Perf. 13¼, 13¼x13¼x12¾x13¼ (#4008b)

			Photo.
2011, Apr. 28			
4007	A2163 58c multi	1.75	.60
4008	Sheet of 4, #4008a-4008c, 4007	8.50	8.50
a.	A2163 58c multi	1.75	.60
b.	A2163 75c multi	2.25	.75
c.	A2163 95c multi	2.75	.90

Souvenir Sheet

Reims Cathedral, 800th Anniv. — A2164

No. 4009 — Stained-glass window depicting: a, King. b, Saint and man.

2011, May 6	**Engr.**		**Perf.**
4009	A2164 Sheet of 2	4.25	4.25
a.	58c multi	1.75	.60
b.	87c multi	2.50	.85

A souvenir sheet containing Nos. 4009a-4009b with a different sheet margin sold for €3.

Europa — A2165

2011, May 8	**Photo.**		**Perf. 13¼**
4010	A2165 75c multi	2.10	.70

Self-Adhesive
Serpentine Die Cut 11

4011	A2165 75c multi	2.10	2.10

Intl. Year of Forests.

Claude Bourgelat (1712-79), Founder of World's First Veterinary School — A2166

2011, May 14	**Engr.**		**Perf. 13¼**
4012	A2166 58c dark blue	1.75	.60

Self-Adhesive
Serpentine Die Cut 11

4013	A2166 58c dark blue	1.75	1.75

Regional Festivals and Traditions A2167

Inscriptions and location: Nos. 4014, 4018, La Braderie, Lille. Nos. 4015, 4033, La Saint-Vincent Tournante, Bourgogne. No. 4016, Le Théâtre des Cabotans, Amiens. No. 4017, Le Feu d'Artifices du 14 Juillet, Paris. No. 4019, Les Médiévales, Provins. No. 4020, La Bénédiction de la Mer, Port-en-Bessin-Huppain. No. 4021, La Fête du Hareng, Haute-Normandie. No. 4022, La Fête des Brodeuses, Pont-l'Abbé. No. 4023, La Fête des Chalands Fleuris, Saint-André-des-Eaux. No. 4024, La Force Basque, Biarritz, Hendaye and Esplette. No. 4025, Les Nuits Romanes, Poitou-Charentes. No. 4026, La Sardane, Céret. No. 4027, La Fête de la Transhumance, Midi-Pyrénées. No. 4028, La Saint Nicolas, Lorraine. No. 4029, Le Mariage de l'Ami Fritz, Marlenheim. No. 4030, Les Fêtes Johanniques, Reims. No. 4031, Les Soufflaculs, Saint-Claude. No. 4032, La Fête de l'Estive, allanche. No. 4034, La Foire aux Potirons, Tranzault. No. 4035, La Frairie des Petits Ventres, Limoges. No. 4036, La Fête du Citron, Menton. No. 4037, La Fête des Lumières, Lyon. No. 4038, L'Abolition de l'Esclavage, Réunion. No. 4039, Les Chants Corses, Corsica.

2011	**Litho.**	**Serpentine Die Cut 11**	
		Self-Adhesive	
4014	A2167 (58c) multi	1.75	1.75
4015	A2167 (58c) multi	1.75	1.75

Photo.
Booklet Stamps

4016	A2167 (58c) multi	1.75	.60
4017	A2167 (58c) multi	1.75	.60
4018	A2167 (58c) multi	1.75	.60
4019	A2167 (58c) multi	1.75	.60
a.	Booklet pane of 4, #4016-4019	7.00	
4020	A2167 (58c) multi	1.75	.60
4021	A2167 (58c) multi	1.75	.60
4022	A2167 (58c) multi	1.75	.60
4023	A2167 (58c) multi	1.75	.60
a.	Booklet pane of 4, #4020-4023	7.00	
4024	A2167 (58c) multi	1.75	.60
4025	A2167 (58c) multi	1.75	.60
4026	A2167 (58c) multi	1.75	.60
4027	A2167 (58c) multi	1.75	.60
a.	Booklet pane of 4, #4024-4027	7.00	
	Complete booklet, #4019a, 4023a, 4027a	21.00	
4028	A2167 (58c) multi	1.75	.60
4029	A2167 (58c) multi	1.75	.60
4030	A2167 (58c) multi	1.75	.60
4031	A2167 (58c) multi	1.75	.60
a.	Booklet pane of 4, #4028-4031	7.00	
4032	A2167 (58c) multi	1.75	.60
4033	A2167 (58c) multi	1.75	.60
4034	A2167 (58c) multi	1.75	.60
4035	A2167 (58c) multi	1.75	.60
a.	Booklet pane of 4, #4032-4035	7.00	
4036	A2167 (58c) multi	1.75	.60
4037	A2167 (58c) multi	1.75	.60
4038	A2167 (58c) multi	1.75	.60
4039	A2167 (58c) multi	1.75	.60
a.	Booklet pane of 4, #4036-4039	7.00	
	Complete booklet, #4031a, 4035a, 4039a	21.00	
	Nos. 4016-4039 (24)	42.00	14.40

The black text on No. 4014 is sharper than that on No. 4018. The black text on No. 4015 is sharper than that on No. 4033.

Issued: No. 4014, 6/30, Nos. 4016-4039, 5/28.

French Federation of Philatelic Associations 84th Congress, Metz — A2168

2011, June 10	**Engr.**		**Perf. 13x13¼**
4040	A2168 58c multi + label	1.75	.60

A souvenir sheet containing No. 4040 was issued in 2012 and sold fro €3.

Miniature Sheet

Bicycles A2169

No. 4041 — Inscriptions: a, Bicyclette à Pneumatiques. b, Draisienne, horiz. c, Vélocipède à Pédales, horiz. d, Vélo de Ville, horiz. e, Bicyclette à Chaine, horiz. f, Grand Bi.

Litho. & Engr.

2011, June 17			**Perf. 13**
4041	A2169 Sheet of 6	10.50	10.50
a.-f.	58c Any single	1.75	.60

Pres. Georges Pompidou (1911-74), and Pompidou Center, Paris — A2170

2011, June 22	**Engr.**		**Perf. 13¼**
4042	A2170 58c gray grn & brt bl	1.75	.60

Train des Pignes, Provence, Cent. — A2171

2011, June 24			
4043	A2171 58c multi	1.75	.60

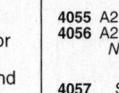

Organization for Economic Cooperation and Development, 50th Anniv. — A2172

2011, June 24	**Photo.**		
4044	A2172 87c multi	2.50	.85

World Judo Championships, Paris — A2173

2011, July 1			**Perf. 13x12¾**
4045	A2173 89c multi	2.50	.85

Aquilegia A2174

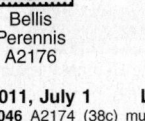

Tulipa Sp. A2175

Bellis Perennis A2176

Primula Veris A2177

2011, July 1	**Litho.**		**Perf. 13**
4046	A2174 (38c) multi	1.10	.25
4047	A2175 (39c) multi	1.10	.25
4048	A2176 (46c) multi	1.40	.30
4049	A2177 (47c) multi	1.40	.30
	Nos. 4046-4049 (4)	5.00	1.10

Nos. 4046-4049 are known only precanceled. See note after No. 132. Compare with Nos. 3423-3426.

"Ecopli 20g" A2178

"Lettre Prioritaire 20g" A2179

"Europe 20g" A2180

"Monde 20g" A2181

"Lettre Prioritaire 50g" A2182

"Lettre Prioritaire 100g" A2183

"Lettre Prioritaire 250g" — A2184

Engr., Litho. (#4057a-4057d)

2011			**Perf. 13**
4050	A2178 (55c) gray	1.60	.25
4051	A2179 (60c) red	1.75	.40
4052	A2180 (77c) dark blue	2.25	.60
4053	A2181 (89c) purple	2.50	.65
4054	A2182 (€1) fawn	3.00	.75
4055	A2183 (€1.45) red violet	4.25	1.10
4056	A2184 (€2.40) chocolate	6.75	2.40
	Nos. 4050-4056 (7)	22.10	6.15

Souvenir Sheet

4057	Sheet of 7, #4050-4052, 4057a-4057d, + label	21.50	21.50
a.	A2181 (89c) purple, litho.	2.50	2.50
b.	A2182 (€1) fawn, litho.	2.75	2.75
c.	A2183 (€1.45) red violet, litho.	4.00	4.00
d.	A2184 (€2.40) chocolate, litho.	6.75	6.75

Coil Stamps
Perf. 13 Horiz.

4058	A2179 (60c) red	1.75	.40
4059	A2180 (77c) blue	2.25	.60

Self-Adhesive
Serpentine Die Cut 6¾ Vert.

4060	A2178 (55c) gray	1.60	1.60
4061	A2179 (60c) red	1.75	1.75
a.	Booklet pane of 12	21.00	
b.	Booklet pane of 20	35.00	
c.	Booklet pane of 10	17.50	
4062	A2180 (77c) blue	2.25	2.25
a.	Booklet pane of 12	27.00	
4063	A2181 (89c) purple	2.50	2.50
4064	A2182 (€1) fawn	3.00	3.00
4065	A2183 (€1.45) red violet	4.25	4.25
4066	A2184 (€2.40) chocolate	6.75	6.75
	Nos. 4060-4066 (7)	22.10	22.10

Issued: Nos. 4050-4056, Nos. 4060-4066, 7/1; No. 4057, 11/3; Nos. 4058-4059, 7/6; No. 4061a, 7/1; Nos. 4061b-4061c, 4/16/12; No. 4062a, 8/16. See Nos. 4089-4090.

G20 and G8 Summits, Cannes and Deauville A2185

2011, July 8	**Photo.**		**Perf. 12¼**
4067	A2185 89c multi	2.50	.85

Self-Adhesive
Serpentine Die Cut 11

4068	A2185 89c multi	2.50	2.50

A2186

2011 Rugby World Cup, New Zealand — A2187

No. 4069: a, Player with ball behind scrum. b, Player carrying ball, vert. c, Auckland skyline, vert. d, Lake and mountains, New Zealand.
€5, Two players.

Perf. 13¼x13, 13x13¼

2011, July 8			**Photo.**
4069	A2186 Sheet of 4	10.00	10.00
a.-d.	89c Any single	2.50	.85

Embossed and Etched on Silver
Self-Adhesive
Die Cut Perf. 12¾

4070	A2187 €5 silver	14.00	14.00

Protection of Water Type of 2010
Serpentine Die Cut 11

2011, Sept. 9			**Litho.**
		Self-Adhesive	
4071	A2058 (60c) Like #3782	1.75	1.75
4072	A2058 (60c) Like #3787	1.75	1.75

Nos. 4071-4072 have a dot structure not found on Nos. 3782 and 3787, which are printed by photogravure.

Souvenir Sheet

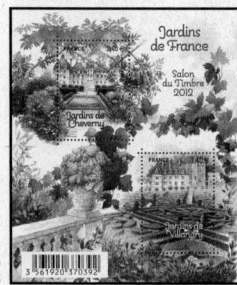

Gardens
A2188

No. 4073: a, Cheverny Gardens. b, Villandry Gardens.

2011, Sept. 16 Photo. Perf. 13¼x13
| 4073 | A2188 | Sheet of 2 | 13.00 | 13.00 |
| a.-b. | | €2.40 Either single | 6.50 | 3.25 |

Salon du Timbre 2012.

Firefighters of Paris, Bicent. — A2189

No. 4074: a, Horse-drawn fire wagon (38x38mm). b, Fireman holding hose (26x40mm). c, Firemen attending to victim on gurney, ambulance (26x40mm). d, Fireman with rescue dog (30x40mm). e, Firefighter's badge (26x40mm). f, Firemen in truck holding flag, Arc de Triomphe (26x40mm). g, Fireman wearing helmet without visor (30x40mm). h, Fireman in antique fire truck (40x26mm). i, Fireman and modern ladder truck (40x26mm). j, j, Fireman wearing helmet with visor (30x40mm).

Perf. 13, 13¼ (#4074a), 13¼x13 (#4074d, 4074g, 4074j)
2011, Sept. 16
| 4074 | A2189 | Sheet of 10 | 17.50 | 17.50 |
| a.-j. | | 60c Any single | 1.75 | .60 |

Self-Adhesive
Serpentine Die Cut 11
| 4075 | A2189 | 60c Like #4074b | 1.75 | 1.75 |
| 4076 | A2189 | 60c Like #4074i | 1.75 | 1.75 |

A set of six souvenir sheets, each containing one example of Nos. 4074a, 4074b, 4074f, 4074h, 4074i, and 4074j, sold for €15.

TGV Train Service, 30th Anniv. — A2190

2011, Sept. 27 Perf. 13¼
| 4077 | A2190 | 60c multi | 1.75 | .60 |

Self-Adhesive
Serpentine Die Cut 11
| 4078 | A2190 | 60c multi | 1.75 | 1.75 |

A2191   A2192

A2193   A2194

Marianne, Stars and Leaf
A2193   A2194

2011, Sept. 30 Engr. Perf. 13
4079	A2191	(57c) green	1.60	.25
4080	A2192	(95c) yellow		
		green	2.60	.55
4081	A2193	(€1.40) blue		
		green	4.00	.80

4082	A2194	(€2.30) dk bl		
		green	6.25	1.25
Nos. 4079-4082 (4)			14.45	2.85

Coil Stamp
Perf. 13 Horiz.
| 4083 | A2191 | (57c) green | 1.60 | .25 |

Self-Adhesive
Serpentine Die Cut 6¾ Vert.
4084	A2191	(57c) green	1.60	1.60
a.		Booklet pane of 10	16.00	
b.		Booklet pane of 12	19.50	
c.		Booklet pane of 20	32.00	
4085	A2192	(95c) yellow		
		green	2.60	2.60
4086	A2193	(€1.40) blue		
		green	4.00	4.00
4087	A2194	(€2.30) dk bl		
		green	6.25	6.25

Serpentine Die Cut 6¾ Horiz.
| 4088 | A2191 | (57c) green | 1.60 | .40 |
| *Nos. 4084-4088 (5)* | | | 16.05 | 14.85 |

Marianne and Stars Types of 2011
Serpentine Die Cut 6¾ Horiz.
2011, Oct. 1 Engr.
Coil Stamps
Self-Adhesive
| 4089 | A2179 | (60c) red | 1.75 | .40 |
| 4090 | A2180 | (77c) dark blue | 2.10 | .60 |

Souvenir Sheet

World Weight Lifting Championships, Paris — A2195

No. 4091: a, Male weight lifter (43mm diameter). b, Female weight lifter (49mm diameter).

2011, Oct. 7 Photo. Perf.
4091	A2195	Sheet of 2	4.25	4.25
a.		60c multi	1.75	.60
b.		89c multi	2.50	.85

Souvenir Sheets

Chantilly Lace
A2196

Lace of Puy-en-Velay Region — A2197

Alençon Lace
A2198

Calais Lace
A2199

Litho. with Lace Affixed
2011, Oct. 8
4092	A2196	€2.50 multi	7.00	7.00
4093	A2197	€2.50 multi	7.00	7.00
4094	A2198	€2.50 multi	7.00	7.00
4095	A2199	€2.50 multi	7.00	7.00
Nos. 4092-4095 (4)			28.00	28.00

National Center for Space Studies, 50th Anniv. — A2200

2011, Oct. 12 Engr. Perf. 13¼
| 4096 | A2200 | 60c multi | 1.75 | .60 |

Discovery of Clipperton Island, 200th Anniv. — A2201

2011, Oct. 21
| 4097 | A2201 | €1 multi | 2.75 | .90 |

Second-Place Finish of French Team in 2011 Rugby World Cup Championships A2202

2011, Oct. 23 Photo.
| 4098 | A2202 | 60c multi | 1.75 | .60 |

Values are for stamp with surrounding selvage.

Words of Ben — A2203

"Ben" (artist Benjamin Vautier) and inscription: No. 4099, Je suis timbré. No. 4100, J'aime écrire. No. 4101, Les mots c'est la vie. No. 4102, Entre nous. . . No. 4103, Cette idée. . . voyage. No. 4104, Pour l'instant tout va bien. No. 4105, Enfin de l'art. No. 4106, J'ai quelque chose à dire. No. 4107, Mots d'amour. No. 4108, Ceci est un lettre. No. 4109, Garderem lo moral. No. 4110, Vous êtes formidables!

Serpentine Die Cut 11
2011, Oct. 24 Photo.
Booklet Stamps
Self-Adhesive
4099	A2203	(60c) multi	1.75	.60
4100	A2203	(60c) multi	1.75	.60
4101	A2203	(60c) multi	1.75	.60
4102	A2203	(60c) multi	1.75	.60
4103	A2203	(60c) multi	1.75	.60
4104	A2203	(60c) multi	1.75	.60
4105	A2203	(60c) multi	1.75	.60
4106	A2203	(60c) multi	1.75	.60
4107	A2203	(60c) multi	1.75	.60
4108	A2203	(60c) multi	1.75	.60
4109	A2203	(60c) multi	1.75	.60
4110	A2203	(60c) multi	1.75	.60
a.		Booklet pane of 12, #4099-4110	21.00	
Nos. 4099-4110 (12)			21.00	7.20

Compare with types A1667 and SP411.

Gaston Monnerville (1897-1991), Senate President — A2204

2011, Nov. 7 Engr. Perf. 13¼
| 4111 | A2204 | 60c multi | 1.75 | .60 |

Henri Mouhot (1826-61), Explorer of Southeast Asia — A2205

2011, Nov. 7
| 4112 | A2205 | 89c multi | 2.50 | .85 |

Christmas — A2206

Paintings: No. 4113, Adoration of the Shepherds, by Robert Campin, Master of Flémalle. No. 4114, Adoration of the Shepherds, by Mathias Stormer. No. 4115, The Newborn, by Georges de La Tour. No. 4116, Adoration of the Magi, by Italian School artist. No. 4117, Adoration of the Magi, by Francisco de Zurbaran. No. 4118, Nativity, by Jean Fouquet. No. 4119, Nativity, by the Master of the Nativity in the Louvre. No. 4120, Triptych of the Adoration of the Magi, by the Master of 1518. No. 4121, Adoration of the Magi, by Peter Paul Rubens. No. 4122, Adoration of the Infant Jesus, by the Master of Moulins. No. 4123, Adoration of the Child, by the Master of the St. Bartholomew Altarpiece. No. 4124, Scenes from the Life of Christ — Nativity, by Mariotto di Nardo.

Serpentine Die Cut 11
2011, Nov. 7 Photo.
Booklet Stamps
Self-Adhesive
4113	A2206	(60c) multi	1.75	.60
4114	A2206	(60c) multi	1.75	.60
4115	A2206	(60c) multi	1.75	.60
4116	A2206	(60c) multi	1.75	.60
4117	A2206	(60c) multi	1.75	.60
4118	A2206	(60c) multi	1.75	.60
4119	A2206	(60c) multi	1.75	.60
4120	A2206	(60c) multi	1.75	.60
4121	A2206	(60c) multi	1.75	.60
4122	A2206	(60c) multi	1.75	.60
4123	A2206	(60c) multi	1.75	.60
4124	A2206	(60c) multi	1.75	.60
a.		Booklet pane of 12, #4113-4124	21.00	
Nos. 4113-4124 (12)			21.00	7.20

A souvenir sheet containing one perf. 13x13¼ example of No. 4115 with water-activated gum sold for €3.

Discovery of Insulin, 90th Anniv. — A2207

2011, Nov. 17 Photo. Perf. 13¼
| 4125 | A2207 | 60c multi | 1.75 | .60 |

Serpentine Die Cut 11
Self-Adhesive
| 4126 | A2207 | 60c multi | 1.75 | .60 |

Year of Overseas Territories
A2208

Drawings of: No. 4127, Carved rocks, Guadeloupe. No. 4128, Harbor, Cayenne, French Guiana. No. 4129, Beach scence, New Caledonia. No. 4130, Tattoo designs of tiki and compass rose, French Polynesia. No. 4131, Tree blossoms, St. Martin. No. 4132, Buildings, St. Pierre and Miquelon. No. 4133, House, Martinique. No. 4134, Man on path near Morne Langevin, Reunion. No. 4135, Pirogue, near Mt. Choungi, Mayotte. No. 4136, Building, Saint-Barthélemy. No. 4137, Kava bowl and building, Wallis and Futuna Islands. No. 4138, Penguins, French Southern and Antarctic Territories (T.A.A.F.).

Serpentine Die Cut 11
2011, Nov. 25 Photo.
Booklet Stamps
Self-Adhesive
4127	A2208	(60c) multi	1.75	.60
4128	A2208	(60c) multi	1.75	.60
4129	A2208	(60c) multi	1.75	.60
4130	A2208	(60c) multi	1.75	.60
4131	A2208	(60c) multi	1.75	.60
4132	A2208	(60c) multi	1.75	.60
4133	A2208	(60c) multi	1.75	.60
4134	A2208	(60c) multi	1.75	.60
4135	A2208	(60c) multi	1.75	.60
4136	A2208	(60c) multi	1.75	.60
4137	A2208	(60c) multi	1.75	.60
4138	A2208	(60c) multi	1.75	.60
a.		Booklet pane of 12, #4127-4138	21.00	
Nos. 4127-4138 (12)			21.00	7.20

New Year 2012 (Year of the Dragon) — A2209

2012, Jan. 6   Perf. 13¼x13
4139 A2209 60c multi   1.60 .55

No. 4139 was printed in sheets of 5. A souvenir sheet of one sold for €3. See No. 4970d.

A2210

Hearts — A2211

2012, Jan. 13   Photo.   Perf. 13
4140 A2210 €1 red & black   2.75 .95

Self-Adhesive
Serpentine Die Cut
4141 A2210 €1 red & black   2.75 2.75

On Plastic
4142 A2211 60c red & black   1.60 1.60
a.   Souvenir sheet of 5   8.00

Brass Relief, France, 18th Cent. — A2212

Bronze Relief, China, 2nd Cent. — A2213

Copper and Silver Relief, Egypt, 14th Cent. — A2214

Marble Relief, Andalusia, 11th Cent. — A2215

Sardonyx Relief, Italy, 13th Cent. — A2216

Stone Relief, Egypt, 1440 B.C. — A2217

Litho., Engr. (olive gray stamps)
Serpentine Die Cut 11
2012, Jan. 20   Self-Adhesive
Booklet Stamps
4143 A2211 (60c) multi   1.60 .55
4144 A2212 (60c) olive gray   1.60 .55
4145 A2213 (60c) multi   1.60 .55
4146 A2214 (60c) olive gray   1.60 .55
4147 A2214 (60c) multi   1.60 .55
4148 A2215 (60c) olive gray   1.60 .55
4149 A2215 (60c) multi   1.60 .55
4150 A2215 (60c) multi   1.60 .55
4151 A2216 (60c) multi   1.60 .55
4152 A2216 (60c) olive gray   1.60 .55
4153 A2217 (60c) multi   1.60 .55

4154 A2217 (60c) olive gray   1.60 .55
a.   Booklet pane of 12, #4143-4154   19.50
   Nos. 4143-4154 (12)   19.20 6.60

Art Issue

Morning Sun, by Edward Hopper A2218

2012, Feb. 3   Photo.   Perf. 13x13¼
4155 A2218 €1.45 multi   4.00 2.00

Self-Adhesive
Serpentine Die Cut 11
4156 A2218 €1.45 multi   4.00 4.00

Flowers — A2219

Designs: No. 4157, Arums. No. 4158, Tulips. No. 4159, Roses. No. 4160, Violets. No. 4161, Pansies (Pensée). No. 4162, Lily of the valley (Muguet). No. 4163, Irises. No. 4164, Dahlias. No. 4165, Poppies (Coquelicot). No. 4166, Peonies (Pivoine). No. 4167, Daisies (Marguerite). No. 4168, Pinks (Oeillet).

Serpentine Die Cut 11
2012, Feb. 10   Self-Adhesive
Booklet Stamps
4157 A2219 (60c) multi   1.60 .55
4158 A2219 (60c) multi   1.60 .55
4159 A2219 (60c) multi   1.60 .55
4160 A2219 (60c) multi   1.60 .55
4161 A2219 (60c) multi   1.60 .55
4162 A2219 (60c) multi   1.60 .55
4163 A2219 (60c) multi   1.60 .55
4164 A2219 (60c) multi   1.60 .55
4165 A2219 (60c) multi   1.60 .55
4166 A2219 (60c) multi   1.60 .55
4167 A2219 (60c) multi   1.60 .55
4168 A2219 (60c) multi   1.60 .55
a.   Booklet pane of 12, #4157-4168   19.50
   Nos. 4157-4168 (12)   19.20 6.60

Grand Mosque of Paris, 90th Anniv. — A2220

2012, Feb. 11   Engr.   Perf. 13¼
4169 A2220 60c multi   1.60 .55

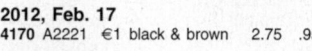

Henri Queuille (1884-1970), Prime Minister — A2221

2012, Feb. 17
4170 A2221 €1 black & brown   2.75 .95

Portraits of Women — A2222

Details of paintings: No. 4171, Young Woman in a Ball Gown, by Berthe Morisot. No. 4172, Portrait of Lydia Cassat, by Mary Cassatt. No. 4173, Biskra Woman, by Marie Caire. No. 4174, Woman with Turban, by Marie Laurencin. No. 4175, Madame Molé-Raymond, by Elisabeth Vigée-Lebrun. No. 4176, Portrait of

a Young Woman, by Edgar Degas. No. 4177, Mandy, by Edouard Barnard Lintott. No. 4178, Orphan Girl at the Cemetery, by Eugène Delacroix. No. 4179, Woman with a Mirror, by Titian. No. 4180, Madeleine Bernard, by Paul Gauguin. No. 4181, Young Woman, by Hippolyte Flandrin. No. 4182, Portrait of Berthe Morisot with a Bouquet of Violets, by Edouard Manet.

Serpentine Die Cut 11
2012, Mar. 8   Photo.
Booklet Stamps
Self-Adhesive
4171 A2222 (60c) multi   1.60 .55
4172 A2222 (60c) multi   1.60 .55
4173 A2222 (60c) multi   1.60 .55
4174 A2222 (60c) multi   1.60 .55
4175 A2222 (60c) multi   1.60 .55
4176 A2222 (60c) multi   1.60 .55
4177 A2222 (60c) multi   1.60 .55
4178 A2222 (60c) multi   1.60 .55
4179 A2222 (60c) multi   1.60 .55
4180 A2222 (60c) multi   1.60 .55
4181 A2222 (60c) multi   1.60 .55
4182 A2222 (60c) multi   1.60 .55
a.   Booklet pane of 12, #4171-4182   19.50
   Nos. 4171-4182 (12)   19.20 6.60

European Capitals Type of 2002
Miniature Sheet

No. 4183 — Attractions in Copenhagen, Denmark: a, The Little Mermaid statue. b, Amalienborg Palace, horiz. c, Rosenborg Castle. d, Nyhavn, horiz.

Perf. 13¼x13, 13x13¼ (horiz. stamps)
2012, Mar. 23   Photo.
4183 A1622   Sheet of 4   6.50 6.50
a.-d.   60c Any single   1.60 .55

Tourism Issue

Moulins A2223

2012, Mar. 23   Engr.   Perf. 13x12¾
4184 A2223 60c multi   1.60 .55

Miniature Sheet

Way of St. James A2224

No. 4185: a, Via Turonensis in Paris. b, Via Lemovicensis in Vézelay, horiz. c, Via Podiensis in Puy-en Velay, horiz. d, Via Tolosana in Arles.

Litho. & Engr.
2012, Mar. 30   Perf. 13
4185 A2224   Sheet of 4   8.50 8.50
a.-d.   77c Any single   2.10 .70

Fruits — A2225

Designs: No. 4186, Pineapple (Ananas). No. 4187, Melon. No. 4188, White grapes (Raisins blancs). No. 4189, Hazel nuts (Noisettes). No. 4190, Kiwis. No. 4191, Gooseberries (Groseilles à maquereaux). No. 4192, Green papayas (Papayes vertes). No. 4193, Dates (Dattes). No. 4194, Bananas (Bananes vertes). No. 4195, Mangos (Mangues). No. 4196, Pippin apples (Pommes "Reinette grise"). No. 4197, Pear (Poire William).

Serpentine Die Cut 11
2012, Mar. 30   Photo.
Booklet Stamps
Self-Adhesive
4186 A2225 (57c) multi   1.50 .50
4187 A2225 (57c) multi   1.50 .50
4188 A2225 (57c) multi   1.50 .50
4189 A2225 (57c) multi   1.50 .50
4190 A2225 (57c) multi   1.50 .50
4191 A2225 (57c) multi   1.50 .50
4192 A2225 (57c) multi   1.50 .50
4193 A2225 (57c) multi   1.50 .50
4194 A2225 (57c) multi   1.50 .50

4195 A2225 (57c) multi   1.50 .50
4196 A2225 (57c) multi   1.50 .50
4197 A2225 (57c) multi   1.50 .50
a.   Booklet pane of 12, #4186-4197   18.00
   Nos. 4186-4197 (12)   18.00 6.00

Tourism Issue

Epernay A2226

2012, Apr. 13   Engr.   Perf. 13¼
4198 A2226 60c multi   1.60 .55

Tropical Fish — A2227

Designs: No. 4199, Amphiprion ocellaris. No. 4200a, Phycodurus eques, horiz. No. 4200b, Heniochus acuminatus, horiz. No. 4200c, Pomacanthus imperator.

2012, Apr. 20   Photo.   Perf. 13¼
4199 A2227 60c multi   1.60 .55
4200   Sheet of 4, #4199, 4200a-4200c   8.00 8.00
a.   A2227 60c multi   1.60 .55
b.   A2227 77c multi   2.10 .70
c.   A2227 €1 multi   2.60 .90

Art — A2228

Designs: No. 4201, Douglas Castle, painting by unknown Chinese artist. No. 4202, Crab, sculpture by Cheung Yee. Nos. 4203, 4205, The Racecourse — Amateur Jockeys Close to a Carriage, painting by Edgar Degas. No. 4204, The Horse, sculpture by Raymnond Duchamp-Villon.

2012, May 3   Photo.   Perf. 13¼
4201 A2228 60c multi   1.60 .55
4202 A2228 60c multi   1.60 .55
4203 A2228 89c multi   2.40 .80
4204 A2228 89c multi   2.40 .80
   Nos. 4201-4204 (4)   8.00 2.70

Self-Adhesive
Serpentine Die Cut 11
4205 A2228 89c multi   2.40 2.40

See Hong Kong Nos. 1490-1493.

Cubist Art — A2229

Designs: No. 4206, La Table Louis-Philippe, by Roger de La Fresnaye. No. 4207, Three Figures Under a Tree, by Pablo Picasso. No. 4208, The Three Poets, by Louis Marcoussis, vert. No. 4209, Still Life with a Red Ball, by Auguste Herbin, vert. No. 4210, The Blue Bird, by Jean Metzinger, vert. No. 4211, The 14th of July, by Fernand Léger, vert. No. 4212, Music, by Frantisek Kupka. No. 4213, Rugby, by André Lhote. No. 4214, The War Song, Portrait of Florent Schmitt, by Albert Gleizes, vert. No. 4215, The Book, by Juan Gris, vert. No. 4216, Compotier et Cartes, by Georges Braque, vert. No. 4217, Marine, by Lyonel Feininger, vert.

2012, May 10   Serpentine Die Cut 11
Booklet Stamps
Self-Adhesive
4206 A2229 (60c) multi   1.50 .50
4207 A2229 (60c) multi   1.50 .50
4208 A2229 (60c) multi   1.50 .50
4209 A2229 (60c) multi   1.50 .50
4210 A2229 (60c) multi   1.50 .50
4211 A2229 (60c) multi   1.50 .50
4212 A2229 (60c) multi   1.50 .50
4213 A2229 (60c) multi   1.50 .50
4214 A2229 (60c) multi   1.50 .50

4215	A2229	(60c) multi	1.50	.50
4216	A2229	(60c) multi	1.50	.50
4217	A2229	(60c) multi	1.50	.50
a.		Booklet pane of 12, #4206-4217	18.00	
		Nos. 4206-4217 (12)	18.00	6.00

Pacific 231 K8 Locomotive, Cent. — A2230

2012, May 11   Engr.   Perf. 13¼
4218	A2230	60c multi	1.50	.50

Self-Adhesive
Serpentine Die Cut 11
4219	A2230	60c multi	1.50	1.50

A souvenir sheet of one of No. 4218 sold for €3.

St. Joan of Arc (c. 1412-31) — A2231

Photo. & Engr.
2012, May 11   Perf. 13
4220	A2231	77c multi	2.00	.65

See Vatican City No. 1499.

Souvenir Sheet

Battle of Denain, 300th Anniv. A2232

2012, May 12   Photo.   Perf. 13¼
4221	A2232	77c multi	2.00	.65

Birds — A2233

Designs: No. 4222a, Little bustard (Outarde canepetière). No. 4222b, Bluethroat (Gorgebleue à miroir), horiz. No. 4222c, Osprey (Balbuzard pêcheur). No. 4222d, 4223, Atlantic puffin (Macareux moine).

Perf. 13¼x13, 13x13¼ (#4222b)
2012, May 12
4222		Sheet of 4	6.00	6.00
a.-d.	A2233	57c Any single	1.50	.50

Self-Adhesive
Serpentine Die Cut 11
4223	A2233	57c multi	1.50	1.50

Bird Protection League, cent.

Europa A2234

2012, May 20   Engr.   Perf. 13
4224	A2234	77c multi	2.00	.65

Self-Adhesive
Serpentine Die Cut 11
4225	A2234	77c multi	2.00	2.00

Tourism Issue

Chateau de Suscinio A2235

2012, May 26   Perf. 13¼
4226	A2235	60c multi	1.50	.50

Souvenir Sheet

Saint-Cloud Park, Paris — A2236

No. 4227: a, Cascade. b, Reflecting ponds,

2012, June 9   Photo.   Perf. 13x13¼
4227	A2236	Sheet of 2	12.00	12.00
a.-b.		€2.40 Either single	6.00	3.00
c.		Souvenir sheet of 4, #4073a, 4073b, 4227a, 4227b	24.00	24.00

2012 Salon du Timbre, Paris.

Historic Residences A2237

Designs: Nos. 4228, 4245, Palais du Luxembourg, Paris. No. 4229, Château Guillaume-le-Conquérant, Falaise. No. 4230, Château des Comtes de Foix. No. 4231, Château de Boulogne sur Mer. No. 4232, Château de Saumur. No. 4233, Château d' Anjony, Tournemire. No. 4234, Château de Pompadour. No. 4235, Citadelle de Corte. No. 4236, Forteresse de Salses. No. 4237, Château d'If. No. 4238, Hôtel de Mauroy, Troyes. No. 4239, Maison Pfister, Colmar. No. 4240, Château du Taureau, Baie de Morlaix. No. 4241, Palais Ducal de Nevers. No. 4242, Château d'Azay-le-Rideau. No. 4243, Château de Puyguilhem. No. 4244, Château de Crazannes. No. 4246, Château de Vaux-le-Vicomte. No. 4247, Château de Brémontier-Merval. No. 4248, Château de Lesdiguières, Vixille. No. 4249, Château de Pierrefonds. No. 4250, Villa Palladienne de Syam. No. 4251, Maison Souques-Pagès, Pointe-à-Pitre. No. 4252, Villa Majorelle, Nancy.

Serpentine Die Cut 11
2012, June 9   Litho.
Self-Adhesive
4228	A2237	(60c) multi	1.50	1.50

Photo.
Booklet Stamps
4229	A2237	(60c) multi	1.50	.50
4230	A2237	(60c) multi	1.50	.50
4231	A2237	(60c) multi	1.50	.50
4232	A2237	(60c) multi	1.50	.50
a.		Booklet pane of 4, #4229-4232	6.00	
4233	A2237	(60c) multi	1.50	.50
4234	A2237	(60c) multi	1.50	.50
4235	A2237	(60c) multi	1.50	.50
4236	A2237	(60c) multi	1.50	.50
a.		Booklet pane of 4, #4233-4236	6.00	
4237	A2237	(60c) multi	1.50	.50
4238	A2237	(60c) multi	1.50	.50
4239	A2237	(60c) multi	1.50	.50
4240	A2237	(60c) multi	1.50	.50
a.		Booklet pane of 4, #4237-4240	6.00	
		Complete booklet, #4232a, 4236a, 4240a	18.00	
4241	A2237	(60c) multi	1.50	.50
4242	A2237	(60c) multi	1.50	.50
4243	A2237	(60c) multi	1.50	.50
4244	A2237	(60c) multi	1.50	.50
a.		Booklet pane of 4, #4241-4244	6.00	
4245	A2237	(60c) multi	1.50	.50
4246	A2237	(60c) multi	1.50	.50
4247	A2237	(60c) multi	1.50	.50
4248	A2237	(60c) multi	1.50	.50
a.		Booklet pane of 4, #4245-4248	6.00	
4249	A2237	(60c) multi	1.50	.50
4250	A2237	(60c) multi	1.50	.50
4251	A2237	(60c) multi	1.50	.50
4252	A2237	(60c) multi	1.50	.50
a.		Booklet pane of 4, #4249-4252	6.00	
		Complete booklet, #4244a, 4248a, 4252a	18.00	
		Nos. 4229-4252 (24)	36.00	12.00

Lettering, most evident in the "Phil@poste" inscription at bottom, is sharp on No. 4228 and fuzzy on No. 4245.

Miniature Sheet

Soldiers A2238

No. 4253: a, Croisé (crusader), 12th cent. b, Vercingetorix (c. 82-46 B.C.), Gallic chieftain, horiz. c, Fantassin (foot soldier), 16th cent. d, Tambour (drummer), 18th cent. e, Grognard (member of Napoleon's Old Guard). f, Fantassin (foot soldier), 1914.

Litho. & Engr.
2012, June 10   Perf. 13
4253	A2238	Sheet of 6	9.00	9.00
a.-f.		60c Any single	1.50	.50

A set of six souvenir sheets, each containing one example of Nos. 4253a-4253f, sold for €15.

Handball — A2239

Embossed and Etched on Silver
2012, June 11   Die Cut Perf. 12¾
Self-Adhesive
4254	A2239	€5 silver	12.50	12.50

2012 Summer Olympics, London — A2240

2012, June 12   Photo.   Perf. 13
4255	A2240	89c multi	2.25	.75

Miles Davis (1926-91), Jazz Trumpet Player A2241

Edith Piaf (1915-63), Singer A2242

2012, June 12   Perf. 13
4256	A2241	60c multi	1.50	.50
4257	A2242	89c multi	2.25	.75
a.		Horiz. pair, #4256-4257	3.75	1.25

See United States Nos. 4692-4693.

Vegetables A2243

Designs: No. 4258, Peas (petits pois). No. 4259, Salad greens (salades). Nos. 4260, Pimentos (piments). No. 4261, Green beans (haricots vers). No. 4262, Broccoli (chou brocoli). No. 4263, Zucchini (courgettes). No. 4264, Snap beans (haricots mange-tout). No. 4265, Leeks (poireaux). No. 4266, Green peppers (poivron "Lamuyo"). No. 4267, Artichoke (artichaut "Gros Camus"). No. 4268, Squashes (potirons vers). No. 4269, Cabbage (chou cabus).

Serpentine Die Cut 11
2012, June 13   Self-Adhesive
Booklet Stamps
4258	A2243	(57c) multi	1.40	.45
4259	A2243	(57c) multi	1.40	.45
4260	A2243	(57c) multi	1.40	.45
4261	A2243	(57c) multi	1.40	.45
4262	A2243	(57c) multi	1.40	.45
4263	A2243	(57c) multi	1.40	.45
4264	A2243	(57c) multi	1.40	.45
4265	A2243	(57c) multi	1.40	.45
4266	A2243	(57c) multi	1.40	.45
4267	A2243	(57c) multi	1.40	.45
4268	A2243	(57c) multi	1.40	.45
4269	A2243	(57c) multi	1.40	.45
a.		Booklet pane of 12, #4258-4269	17.00	
		Nos. 4258-4269 (12)	16.80	5.40

First Heart-Lung Transplant in Europe, 30th Anniv. — A2244

2012, June 14   Perf. 13¼
4270	A2244	60c multi	1.50	.50

Issenheim Altarpiece, 500th Anniv. — A2245

Sheet with Altarpiece Doors Closed (Covering Stamps)

No. 4271: a, St. Augustine, "Le Retable d'Issenheim" at right (19x56mm). b, St. Hieronymus, "Le Retable d'Issenheim" at left (19x56mm). c, St. Anthony (34x65mm).

Perf. 13¼x13, 13 (#4271c)
2012, June 15   Litho.
4271	A2245	Sheet of 3	12.50	12.50
a.-b.		€1.50 Either single	3.75	1.25
c.		€2 multi	5.00	1.75

Card stock doors printed on both sides that depict artwork on the two alterpiece doors, are pasted on top of each other at the left and right of the stamps. Values for the sheet are for examples with all four doors affixed.

Musée d'Orsay, Paris — A2246

2012, June 16   Engr.   Perf. 13x13¼
4272	A2246	60c multi + label	1.50	.50

French Federation of Philatelic Associations, 85th Congress, Paris.

Tourism Issue

Pointe Saint-
Mathieu
A2247

2012, June 22   **Perf. 13¼**
4273   A2247   57c multi   1.40   .45

Souvenir Sheet

2012 World Karate Championships,
Paris — A2248

No. 4274: a, Karateka kicking. b, Eiffel
Tower. c, Karateka kicking, horiz.

Perf. 13¼x13, 13x13¼ (#4274c)
2012, Sept. 7   **Photo.**
4274   A2248   Sheet of 3   7.25   7.25
a.-c.   89c Any single   2.40   .80

2012 World Pétanque Championships,
Marseille — A2249

Photo. & Embossed
2012, Sept. 14   **Perf. 13x13¼**
4275   A2249   89c multi   2.40   .80

Art Issue

Figures Representing Seven
Continents, by Jaume Plensa, Place
Masséna, Nice — A2250

2012, Sept. 14   **Photo.**
4276   A2250   €1.45 multi   3.75   1.90

Camp des Milles, World War II
Internment Camp — A2251

2012, Sept. 21   **Engr.**
4277   A2251   60c multi   1.60   .55

Tourism Issue

Verneuil-sur-Avre
A2252

2012, Sept. 21   **Perf. 13¼**
4278   A2252   60c multi   1.60   .55

Marianne and
Stars — A2253

2012, Oct. 1   **Perf. 13**
4279   Souvenir sheet of 3,
     #4051, 4079, 4279a   5.00   5.00
a.   A2253 60c orange   1.60   .55

Torch, Marianne
and
Stars — A2254

The Temptation of St. Anthony, by
Hieronymus Bosch — A2255

Items on
Fire — A2256

Designs: No. 4282, Lava (La lave). No.
4283, Welder (la soudure). No. 4284, Glass-
blowing (Le travail du verre). No. 4285, Flame
of the Unknown Soldier, Paris (La flamme du
soldat inconnu). No. 4286, Halloween jack
o'lantern. No. 4287, People around Midsummer's Eve bonfire (Feu de la Saint-Jean). No.
4288, Fire fighters and fire (Les pompiers).
No. 4289, Charcoal fire (Les braises). No.
4290, Candles (bougies). No. 4291, Light
show (Spectacle). No. 4292, Sunset (Coucher
de soleil). No. 4293, Birthday candles on cake
(Bougies d'anniversaire).

2012, Oct. 13   **Engr.**   **Perf. 13**
4280   A2254   60c orange & red   1.60   .55

Souvenir Sheet
Litho. & Engr.
Perf. 13x13¼
4281   A2255   €2 multi   5.25   2.60

Photo.
Booklet Stamps
Self-Adhesive
4282   A2256   (60c) multi   1.60   .55
4283   A2256   (60c) multi   1.60   .55
4284   A2256   (60c) multi   1.60   .55
4285   A2256   (60c) multi   1.60   .55
4286   A2256   (60c) multi   1.60   .55
4287   A2256   (60c) multi   1.60   .55
4288   A2256   (60c) multi   1.60   .55
4289   A2256   (60c) multi   1.60   .55
4290   A2256   (60c) multi   1.60   .55
4291   A2256   (60c) multi   1.60   .55
4292   A2256   (60c) multi   1.60   .55
4293   A2256   (60c) multi   1.60   .55
a.   Booklet pane of 12, #4282-
     4293   19.50
Nos. 4282-4293 (12)   19.20   6.60

Stamp Day. An illustration and a bar code is
found on the reverse of the sheet margin of
No. 4281.

Historic Residences Type of 2012
Design: (60c), Chaâteau d'If.

Serpentine Die Cut 11
2012, Oct. 29   **Litho.**
Self-Adhesive
4294   A2237   (60c) multi   1.60   1.60

Lettering, most evident in the "Phil@poste"
inscription at bottom, is sharp on No. 4294 and
fuzzy on No. 4237.

Court
House,
Lyon
A2257

2012, Oct. 26   **Engr.**   **Perf. 13**
4295   A2257   60c multi   1.60   .55

Lion of Belfort Statue, by Frédéric
Auguste Bartholdi
A2258

2012, Nov. 2   **Perf. 13x13¼**
4296   A2258   60c multi + label   1.60   .55

Timbres Passion 2012 Stamp Exhibition,
Belfort. A souvenir sheet containing No. 4296
was issued in 2013 and sold for €3.

King Henri IV of France (1553-1610),
Co-Prince of Andorra — A2259

2012, Nov. 8
4297   A2259   60c multi   1.60   .55
a.   Sheet of 10, 5 each #4297,
     French Andorra #710   16.00   16.00

See French Andorra No. 710.

Souvenir Sheet

The
Masked
Ball,
Opera by
Daniel
Auber
A2260

No. 4298: a, Auber (1782-1871). b, King
Gustav III of Sweden (1746-92), main character in opera.

Litho. & Engr.
2012, Nov. 9   **Perf. 13¼**
4298   A2260   Sheet of 2   3.75   3.75
a.   60c multi   1.60   .55
b.   77c multi   2.00   .65

See Sweden No. 2697.

Souvenir Sheet

Organ
from
Church
of St.
Jacques,
Lunéville
A2261

No. 4299 — Various details of organ's ornamentation: a, 89c. b, €1.45, vert.

Perf. 13x13¼, 13¼x13
2012, Nov. 10   **Engr.**
4299   A2261   Sheet of 2   6.25   6.25
a.   89c multi   2.40   .80
b.   €1.45 multi   3.75   1.25

Laurent
Bonnevay (1870-
1957), Politician,
and Apartment
Building
A2262

2012, Nov. 12   **Engr.**   **Perf. 13¼**
4300   A2262   57c multi   1.50   .50

Bonnevay Law on rent-controlled housing,
cent.

Souvenir Sheet

French
History
A2263

No. 4301: a, Intercession by St. Geneviève
on behalf of Paris, c. 480. b, Clovis at Battle of
Vouillé, 507, horiz.

Perf. 13¼x13, 13x13¼
2012, Nov. 12
4301   A2263   Sheet of 2   7.00   7.00
a.-b.   €1.35 Either single   3.50   1.10

A2264   A2265

A2266   A2267

A2268   A2269

A2270   A2271

A2272   A2273

A2274   Greetings
     Stamps — A2275

Booklet Stamps
Serpentine Die Cut 11
2012, Nov. 12   **Photo.**
Self-Adhesive
4302   A2264   (57c) multi   1.50   .50
4303   A2265   (57c) multi   1.50   .50
4304   A2266   (57c) multi   1.50   .50
4305   A2267   (57c) multi   1.50   .50
4306   A2268   (57c) multi   1.50   .50
4307   A2269   (57c) multi   1.50   .50
4308   A2270   (57c) multi   1.50   .50
4309   A2271   (57c) multi   1.50   .50
4310   A2272   (57c) multi   1.50   .50
4311   A2273   (57c) multi   1.50   .50
4312   A2274   (57c) multi   1.50   .50
4313   A2275   (57c) multi   1.50   .50
a.   Booklet pane of 12, #4302-
     4313   18.00
Nos. 4302-4313 (12)   18.00   6.00

A souvenir sheet containing one perf.
13x13¼ example of No. 4309 with water-activated gum sold for €3.
See No. 4329.

Elysée Treaty,
50th
Anniv. — A2276

2013, Jan. 2   **Litho.**   **Perf. 13**
4314   A2276   80c multi   2.25   .75

See Germany No. 2703.

New Year 2013 (Year of the Snake) — A2277

2013, Jan. 4   Photo.   *Perf. 13¼x13*
4315 A2277 63c multi   1.75   .60

No. 4315 was printed in sheets of 5. A souvenir sheet of one sold for €3.
See No. 4971a.

Bronze Sculpture of Goat — A2278

Terra Cotta Figurine of Rabbit, From Studio of Bernard Palissy — A2279

Bronze Sculpture of Buffalo — A2280

Brass Sculpture of Rooster — A2281

Bronze Sculpture of Tiger, by Antoine Louis Barye — A2282

Porcelain Figurine of Rats and Egg — A2283

Glazed Clay Figurine of Pig — A2284

Bronze Sculpture of Monkey, by Jacques Lehmann A2285

Enameled Stone Sculpture of Dog — A2286

Earthenware Figurine of Dragon — A2287

Gold Sculpture of Snake — A2288

Bronze Sculpture of Horse, by Edgar Degas — A2289

2013, Jan. 4   *Serpentine Die Cut 11*
Booklet Stamps
Self-Adhesive
4316 A2278 (58c) multi   1.60   .55
4317 A2279 (58c) multi   1.60   .55
4318 A2280 (58c) multi   1.60   .55
4319 A2281 (58c) multi   1.60   .55
4320 A2282 (58c) multi   1.60   .55
4321 A2283 (58c) multi   1.60   .55
4322 A2284 (58c) multi   1.60   .55
4323 A2285 (58c) multi   1.60   .55
4324 A2286 (58c) multi   1.60   .55
4325 A2287 (58c) multi   1.60   .55
4326 A2288 (58c) multi   1.60   .55
4327 A2289 (58c) multi   1.60   .55
  a.   Booklet pane of 12, #4316-
          4327   19.50
    Nos. 4316-4327 (12)   19.20 6.60

Marseille, 2013 European Capital of Culture — A2290

2013, Jan. 12   Photo.   *Perf. 13¼*
4328 A2290 80c multi   2.25   .75

Greetings Type of 2012
Serpentine Die Cut 11
2013, Jan. 14   Litho.
Self-Adhesive
4329 A2265 (58c) multi   1.60 1.60

Lettering, most evident in the "Phil@poste" inscription at bottom, is sharp on No. 4329 and fuzzy on No. 4303.

Souvenir Sheet

Notre Dame Cathedral, Paris, 850th Anniv. — A2291

No. 4330 — Stained-glass window depicting: a, Peasant with scythe (44x44mm). b, Madonna and Child (42mm diameter).

Litho., Sheet Margin Litho. & Engr.
2013, Jan. 19   *Perf.*
4330 A2291   Sheet of 2   7.25 7.25
  a.   €1.05 multi   3.00 1.00
  b.   €1.55 multi   4.25 1.40
  c.   Sheet of 2, #4330a, 4330b,
          lithographed sheet mar-
          gin   13.50 13.50
No. 4330c has a different margin design and sold for €5.
A €1.16 stamp having the design of No. 4330a was included in a limited-edition booklet issued Nov. 4, 2020.

Art Issue

Landscape, by Chaim Soutine (1893-1943) A2292

2013, Jan. 25   Photo.   *Perf. 13¼x13*
4331 A2292 €1.55 multi   4.25 2.10

A2293

A2294

Hearts A2295

No. 4334: a, Two white hearts embellished with flowers. b, Bird with long tail. c, Swan facing left. d, Swan facing right.

2013, Jan. 25   *Perf. 13¼*
4332 A2293 58c multi   1.60   .55
4333 A2294 97c multi   2.75   .90

Souvenir Sheet
Perf.
4334 A2295   Sheet of 5,
               #4332, 4334a-
               4334d   8.00 8.00
  a.-d. 58c Any single   1.60   .55
Self-Adhesive
Serpentine Die Cut
4335 A2293 58c multi   1.60 1.60
4336 A2294 97c multi   2.75 2.75
Values for Nos. 4332-4333 are for stamps with surrounding selvage.

Art Issue

85.8 Degree Arc x 16, Sculpture, by Bernar Venet A2296

2013, Feb. 1   *Perf. 13x13¼*
4337 A2296 €1.55 multi   4.25 2.10

Animal Proverbs and Idioms — A2297

Designs: No. 4338, Qui vole un oeuf vole un boeuf ("Who steals an egg steals an ox"). No. 4339, Etre serrés come des sardines ("Be packed like sardines"). No. 4340, Etre heureux comme un poisson dans l'eau ("Be happy as a fish in water"). No. 4341, Pleurer des larmes de crocodile ("Cry crocodile tears"). No. 4342, Quand les poules auront des dents ("When chickens have teeth" or "When pigs fly"). No. 4343, Avaler des couleuvres ("To swallow snakes" or "To endure affronts"). No. 4344, Le chat parti, les souris dansent ("The cat's away, the mice will play"). No. 4345, Sauter du coq à l'âne ("Jump from the rooster to the donkey" or "Jump from one thing to another"). No. 4346, Se regarder en chiens de faience ("To stare like clay dogs" or "To stare menacingly at each other"). No. 4347, Ménager la chèvre et le chou ("To take care of the goat and the cabbage" or "To run with the hares and hunt with the hounds"). No. 4348, Cela ne se trouve pas sous les sabots d'un cheval ("That is not under the hooves of a horse"). No. 4349, Pratique la politique de l'autruche ("Practice the policy of an ostrich" or "Bury one's head in the sand like an ostrich").

2013, Feb. 4   *Serpentine Die Cut 11*
Booklet Stamps
Self-Adhesive
4338 A2297 (58c) multi   1.60   .55
4339 A2297 (58c) multi   1.60   .55
4340 A2297 (58c) multi   1.60   .55
4341 A2297 (58c) multi   1.60   .55
4342 A2297 (58c) multi   1.60   .55
4343 A2297 (58c) multi   1.60   .55
4344 A2297 (58c) multi   1.60   .55
4345 A2297 (58c) multi   1.60   .55
4346 A2297 (58c) multi   1.60   .55
4347 A2297 (58c) multi   1.60   .55
4348 A2297 (58c) multi   1.60   .55
4349 A2297 (58c) multi   1.60   .55
  a.   Booklet pane of 12, #4338-
          4349   19.50
    Nos. 4338-4349 (12)   19.20 6.60
Compare types A2297 and A2498.

Raphael Elizé (1891-1945), First Black Mayor in France — A2298

2013, Feb. 15   Engr.   *Perf. 13¼*
4350 A2298 63c multi   1.75   .60

Miniature Sheet

Way of St. James A2299

No. 4351: a, Via Lemovicensis in Neuvy-Saint-Sépulchre. b, Via Turonensis in Aulnay. c, Via Tolosana in Saint-Gilles, horiz. d, Via Podiensis in Conques, horiz.

Litho. & Engr.
2013, Feb. 22   *Perf. 13*
4351 A2299   Sheet of 4   8.50 8.50
  a.-d. 80c Any single   2.10   .70

50th International Agricultural Show, Paris — A2300

2013, Feb. 25   Photo.   *Perf. 13¼*
4352 A2300 95c multi   2.50   .85

Intl. Women's Day — A2301

Qualities of women in Aicha des Gazelles Rally, Morocco: No. 4353, Courage. No. 4354, Partage (sharing). No. 4355, Dépassement de soi (surpassing oneself). No. 4356, Entraide (mutual aid). No. 4357, Enthousiasme (enthusiasm). No. 4358, Solidarité (solidarity). No. 4359, Esprit d'équipe (team spirit). No. 4360, Engagement. No. 4361, Emotion. No. 4362, Performance. No. 4363, Confiance (confidence). No. 4364, Respect.

2013, Mar. 8   *Serpentine Die Cut 11*
Booklet Stamps
Self-Adhesive
4353 A2301 (58c) multi   1.50   .50
4354 A2301 (58c) multi   1.50   .50
4355 A2301 (58c) multi   1.50   .50
4356 A2301 (58c) multi   1.50   .50
4357 A2301 (58c) multi   1.50   .50
4358 A2301 (58c) multi   1.50   .50
4359 A2301 (58c) multi   1.50   .50
4360 A2301 (58c) multi   1.50   .50
4361 A2301 (58c) multi   1.50   .50
4362 A2301 (58c) multi   1.50   .50
4363 A2301 (58c) multi   1.50   .50
4364 A2301 (58c) multi   1.50   .50
  a.   Booklet pane of 12, #4353-
          4364   18.00
    Nos. 4353-4364 (12)   18.00 6.00
See No. 4406.

European Capitals Type of 2002
Miniature Sheet

No. 4365 — Attractions in Madrid, Spain: a, Plaza Mayor. b, Almudena Cathedral, horiz. c, Palace of Communication (Cibeles Palace), horiz. d, Royal Palace, horiz.

Perf. 13¼x13 (#4365a), 13x13¼
2013, Mar. 15
4365 A1622   Sheet of 4   6.50 6.50
  a.-d. 63c Any single   1.60   .55

Opening of Jacques Chaban-Delmas Vertical Lift Bridge, Bordeaux A2302

2013, Mar. 16   *Perf. 13¼*
4366 A2302 58c multi   1.50   .50

Water Towers, Designed by Philolaos Tloupas, Valence — A2303

2013, Mar. 22   Engr.
4367 A2303 58c multi   1.50   .50

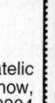

Spring Philatelic Show, Mâcon — A2304

2013, Apr. 5   *Perf. 13¼*
4368 A2304 63c multi   1.75   .60

Horses — A2305

Horse breeds and horses at work: No. 4369, Breton horse. No. 4370, Norman Cob horse. No. 4371, Boulonnais horse. No. 4372, Trait du Nord horse. No. 4373, Ardennais horse. No. 4374, Comtois horse. No. 4375, Poitevin Mulsassier horse. No. 4376, Horse pulling wagon (Attelage en roulotte). No. 4377, Percheron horse. No. 4378, Horse working in vineyard (Travail de la vigne). No. 4379, Auxois horse. No. 4380, Horse pulling logs in forest (Débardage en forêt).

Serpentine Die Cut 11
2013, Apr. 5   *Photo.*
Booklet Stamps
Self-Adhesive
4369	A2305	(58c)	multi	1.50	.50
4370	A2305	(58c)	multi	1.50	.50
4371	A2305	(58c)	multi	1.50	.50
4372	A2305	(58c)	multi	1.50	.50
4373	A2305	(58c)	multi	1.50	.50
4374	A2305	(58c)	multi	1.50	.50
4375	A2305	(58c)	multi	1.50	.50
4376	A2305	(58c)	multi	1.50	.50
4377	A2305	(58c)	multi	1.50	.50
4378	A2305	(58c)	multi	1.50	.50
4379	A2305	(58c)	multi	1.50	.50
4380	A2305	(58c)	multi	1.50	.50
a.	Booklet pane of 12, #4369-4380			18.00	
	Nos. 4369-4380 (12)			18.00	6.00

Champs-Elysées Theater, Paris, Cent. — A2306

2013, Apr. 8   Engr.   *Perf. 13¼*
4381 A2306 €1.05 multi   2.75   .90

Chateau des Vaux, Home of Apprentices of Auteuil — A2307

2013, Apr. 12
4382 A2307 58c multi   1.50   .50

Bats — A2308

Designs: No. 4383, Rhinolophus ferrumequinum.
No. 4384: a, Pteropus seychellensis comorensis, vert. b, Plecotus macrobullaris, vert. c, Myotis nattereri.

2013, Apr. 19   *Photo.*
4383 A2308 58c multi   1.50   .50
Miniature Sheet
4384	Sheet of 4, #4383, 4384a-4384c		8.00	8.00
a.	A2308 58c multi		1.50	.50
b.	A2308 80c multi		2.10	.70
c.	A2308 €1.05 multi		2.75	.90

Notre Dame de Melun Collegiate Church, 1000th Anniv. — A2309

2013, Apr. 20   Engr.
4385 A2309 63c multi   1.75   .60

Impressionist Paintings Depicting Water — A2310

Designs: No. 4386, L'Ile de la Grande Jatte, Neuilly-sur-Seine, by Alfred Sisley. No. 4387, L'Estaque - Vue du Golfe de Marseille (Gulf of Marseille as Seen from L'Estaque), by Paul Cézanne. No. 4388, Sur la Plage (On the Beach), by Edouard Manet. No. 4389, L'Anse des Pilotes au Havre, Haute Mer Après Midi, Soleil, by Camille Pissarro. No. 4390, Régates à Argenteuil (Regatta at Argenteuil), by Claude Monet. No. 4391, Alphonsine Fournaise, by Pierre-Auguste Renoir. No. 4392, La Rivière Blanche (Breton Boy by the Aven River), by Paul Gauguin. No. 4393, L'Homme à la Barre (Man at the Helm), by Théo van Rysselberghe. No. 4394, Les Pecheurs à la Ligne, Étude pour la Grande Jatte (Fishermen), by Georges Seurat. No. 4395, Dans le Port de Rouen (In the Port of Rouen), by Albert Lebourg. No. 4396, La Nuit Etoilée, Arles (Starry Night Over the Rhone), by Vincent van Gogh. No. 4397, La Jetée de Deauville (The Jetty at Deauville), by Louis-Eugène Boudin.

Serpentine Die Cut 11
2013, Apr. 29   *Photo.*
Booklet Stamps
Self-Adhesive
4386	A2310	(58c)	multi	1.50	.50
4387	A2310	(58c)	multi	1.50	.50
4388	A2310	(58c)	multi	1.50	.50
4389	A2310	(58c)	multi	1.50	.50
4390	A2310	(58c)	multi	1.50	.50
4391	A2310	(58c)	multi	1.50	.50
4392	A2310	(58c)	multi	1.50	.50
4393	A2310	(58c)	multi	1.50	.50
4394	A2310	(58c)	multi	1.50	.50
4395	A2310	(58c)	multi	1.50	.50
4396	A2310	(58c)	multi	1.50	.50
4397	A2310	(58c)	multi	1.50	.50
a.	Booklet pane of 12, #4386-4397			18.00	
	Nos. 4386-4397 (12)			18.00	6.00

See Nos. 4449-4452.

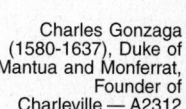

Rixheim A2311

2013, May 3   Litho. & Engr.   *Perf. 13*
4398 A2311 63c multi   1.75   .60

A souvenir sheet of one No. 4398 sold for €3.

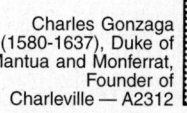

Charles Gonzaga (1580-1637), Duke of Mantua and Monferrat, Founder of Charleville — A2312

2013, May 6   Engr.   *Perf. 13¼*
4399 A2312 80c red & black   2.25   .75

World Table Tennis Championships, Paris — A2313

Designs: 63c, Female player (blue shirt). 95c, Male player (red shirt).

2013, May 13   *Perf. 13x13¼*
4400 A2313 63c multi   1.75   .60
4401 A2313 95c multi   2.50   .80
| a. | Horiz. pair, #4400-4401, + central label | | 4.25 | 1.40 |

Cathedral and Jules Verne Circus, Amiens — A2314

2013, May 17
4402 A2314 63c multi + label   1.75   .60

French Federation of Philatelic Associations, 86th Congress, Amiens. A souvenir sheet containing No. 4402 was issued in 2014 and sold for €3.20.

Europa A2315

Designs: No. 4403, Mail coach, 1840. No. 4404, Renault Kangoo ZE mail van.

2013, May 19   *Photo.*
4403		80c multi	2.25	.75
4404		80c multi	2.25	.75
a.	A2315	Horiz. pair, #4403-4404	4.50	1.50

Souvenir Sheet

Works of André Le Nôtre (1613-1700), Landscape Architect for King Louis XVI — A2316

No. 4405 — Fountains and gardens at: a, Versailles. b, Chantilly.

2013, May 31   *Perf. 13x13¼*
4405	A2316	Sheet of 2	14.00	14.00
a.-b.		€2.55 Either single	7.00	2.50
c.		Sheet of 2, #4405a-4405b, different sheet margin	24.00	24.00

No. 4405c sold for €9.

Intl. Women's Day Type of 2013
Serpentine Die Cut 11
2013, June 1   Litho.
Self-Adhesive
4406 A2301 (58c) Like #4359   1.60   1.60

No. 4406 has a dot structure not found on No. 4359, which is printed by photogravure.

Abbaye-aux-Dames, Saintes — A2317

2013, June 14   Engr.   *Perf. 13¼*
4407 A2317 63c multi   1.75   .60

Jacques Baumel (1918-2006), Politician A2318

2013, June 15
4408 A2318 €1.05 multi   3.00   1.00

Miniature Sheet

100th Tour de France Bicycle Race A2319

No. 4409: a, Rider wearing yellow jersey, Annecy in background (40x30mm). b, Rider wearing polka-dot jersey near Bagnères-de-Bigorre (26x40mm). c, Rider wearing light blue and dark blue jersey near Mont Ventoux (26x40mm). d, Peloton going along Alpe d'Huez mountain road (40x40mm). e, Rider wearing green jersey in foreground, Calvi in background (40x26mm). f, Rider wearing white jersey, Versailles Palace in background (40x30mm). g, Rider wearing yellow jersey winning race, Arc de Triomphe, Paris (30x40mm). h, Rider in red and black jersey, Mont-Saint-Michel (40x26mm).

Perf. 13x13¼ (#4409a, 4409f), 13¼x13 (#4409g), 13
2013, June 29   *Photo.*
4409	A2319	Sheet of 8	15.50	15.50
a.-d.		58c Any single	1.50	.50
e.-f.		80c Either single	2.10	.70
g.-h.		95c Either single	2.50	.85

A souvenir sheet containing Nos. 4409e and 4409g sold for €4.

Types of 1959-2008
Miniature Sheet
2013			Engr.	*Perf. 13*
4410		Sheet of 12	21.00	21.00
a.	A328	63c black	1.75	.60
b.	A349	63c black	1.75	.60
c.	A360	63c black	1.75	.60
d.	A379	63c black	1.75	.60
e.	A486	63c black	1.75	.60
f.	A555	63c black	1.75	.60
g.	A771	63c black	1.75	.60
h.	A915	63c black	1.75	.60
i.	A1161	63c black	1.75	.60
j.	A1409	63c black	1.75	.60
k.	A1713	63c black	1.75	.60
l.	A1912	63c black	1.75	.60
m.	Booklet pane of 12, #4410a-4410l		21.00	

No. 4410 was only sold together with No. 4437a.
Issued: No. 4410, 7/15; No. 4410m, 11/6.

Marianne and Children A2320

Marianne and Children "Ecopli" A2321

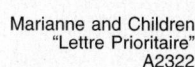

Marianne and Children "Lettre Prioritaire" A2322

Marianne and Children "Europe" A2323

Marianne and Children "Monde" — A2324

Type A2322 gram limits (at LL): Nos. 4415, 4422, 4428, 4435, 20g. Nos. 4419, 4432, 50g. Nos. 4420, 4433, 100g. Nos. 4421, 4434, 250g.

2013, July 15   Engr.   *Perf. 13*
4411	A2320	1c yellow	.25	.25
4412	A2320	5c dk brown	.25	.25
4413	A2320	10c brown	.25	.25
4414	A2321	(56c) dk gray	1.50	.30
4415	A2322	(63c) red	1.75	.35
a.	As No. 4415, engraved, glossy paper (#4437g)		1.75	1.75

b.	As No. 4415, photogravure, glossy paper (#4437g)		1.75	1.75
c.	As No. 4415, litho., glossy paper (#4437g)		1.75	1.75
d.	As No. 4415, typo., glossy paper (#4437g)		1.75	1.75
e.	As No. 4415, silk-screened, glossy paper (#4437g)		1.75	1.75
f.	No. 4415a with overprint "Marianne 1944-2014" (#4437o)		1.75	1.75
g.	No. 4415b with overprint "Marianne 1944-2014" (#4437o)		1.75	1.75
h.	No. 4415c with overprint "Marianne 1944-2014" (#4437o)		1.75	1.75
i.	No. 4415d with overprint "Marianne 1944-2014" (#4437o)		1.75	1.75
j.	No. 4415e with overprint "Marianne 1944-2014" (#4437o)		1.75	1.75
4416	A2323	(80c) blue	2.10	.45
4417	A2324	(95c) purple	2.50	.65
4418	A2320	€1 orange	2.60	.65
4419	A2322	(€1.05) fawn	2.75	.70
4420	A2322	(€1.55) red violet	4.00	1.00
4421	A2322	(€2.55) chocolate	6.75	2.40
	Nos. 4411-4421 (11)		24.70	7.25

Coil Stamps
Perf. 13 Horiz.

4422	A2322	(63c) red	1.75	.35
4423	A2323	(80c) blue	2.10	.45

Self-Adhesive
Serpentine Die Cut 6¾ Vert.

4424	A2320	1c yellow	.25	.25
4425	A2320	5c dk brown	.25	.25
4426	A2320	10c brown	.25	.25
4427	A2321	(56c) dk gray	1.50	1.50
4428	A2322	(63c) red	1.75	.35
a.	Booklet pane of 10		17.50	
b.	Booklet pane of 12		21.00	
c.	Booklet pane of 20		35.00	
4429	A2323	(80c) blue	2.10	.45
a.	Booklet pane of 12		25.50	
4430	A2324	(95c) purple	2.50	2.50
4431	A2320	€1 orange	2.60	2.60
4432	A2322	(€1.05) fawn	2.75	2.75
4433	A2322	(€1.55) red violet	4.00	4.00
4434	A2322	(€2.55) chocolate	6.75	6.75
	Nos. 4424-4434 (11)		24.70	21.65

Coil Stamps
Serpentine Die Cut 6¾ Horiz.

4435	A2322	(63c) red	1.75	.35
4436	A2323	(80c) blue	2.10	.45

Issued: Nos. 4415a-4415e, 11/6; Nos. 4415f-4415j, 11/6/14. No. 4415e uses an ink that is shinier than that used on No. 4415a that causes the small lettering at the base of the stamp to be indistinct. Nos. 4415f-4415j had a franking value of 66c on day of issue. Compare with types A2534, A2536. See No. 4519. For overprint, see No. 5447.

Marianne and Tree "Lettre Verte" — A2325

Type A2325 gram limits (at LL): Nos. 4437, 4441, 4442, 4446, 20g. Nos. 4438, 4443, 50g. Nos. 4439, 4444, 100g. Nos. 4440, 4445, 250g.

2013, July 15   Engr.   Perf. 13

4437	A2325	(58c) green	1.50	.25
a.	Souvenir sheet of 2, #4415, 4437		3.25	3.25
b.	As No. 4437, engraved, glossy paper (#4437g)		1.60	1.60
c.	As No. 4437, photogravure, glossy paper (#4437g)		1.60	1.60
d.	As No. 4437, litho., glossy paper (#4437g)		1.60	1.60
e.	As No. 4437, typo., glossy paper (#4437g)		1.60	1.60
f.	As No. 4437, silk-screened, glossy paper (#4437g)		1.60	1.60
g.	Sheet of 40, 8 each #4415a, 4437b, 4 each #4415b, 4415e, 4437d, 4437e, 2 each #4415c, 4415d, 4437c, 4437f, + label		67.00	67.00
h.	Booklet pane of 2, #4415, 4437		3.50	—
	Complete booklet, #4410m, 4437h		24.50	
i.	Booklet pane of 2, #4079, 4437		3.00	—
j.	No. 4437b with overprint "Marianne 1944-2014" (#4437o)		1.60	1.60
k.	No. 4437c with overprint "Marianne 1944-2014" (#4437o)		1.60	1.60
l.	No. 4437d with overprint "Marianne 1944-2014" (#4437o)		1.60	1.60
m.	No. 4437e with overprint "Marianne 1944-2014" (#4437o)		1.60	1.60
n.	No. 4437f with overprint "Marianne 1944-2014" (#4437o)		1.60	1.60
o.	Sheet of 40, 8 each #4415f, 4437j, 4 each #4415g, 4415j, 4437l, 4437m, 2 each #4415h, 4415i, 4437k, 4437n, + label		67.00	67.00
4438	A2325	(97c) yel grn	2.60	.55
4439	A2325	(€1.45) dk bl grn	3.75	.80
4440	A2325	(€2.35) dk bl grn	6.25	1.25
	Nos. 4437-4440 (4)		14.10	2.85

Coil Stamp
Perf. 13 Horiz.

4441	A2325	(58c) green	1.50	.25

Self-Adhesive
Serpentine Die Cut 6¾ Vert.

4442	A2325	(58c) green	1.50	.25
a.	Booklet pane of 10		15.00	
b.	Booklet pane of 12		18.00	
4443	A2325	(97c) yel grn	2.60	2.60
4444	A2325	(€1.45) dk bl grn	3.75	3.75
4445	A2325	(€2.35) dk bl grn	6.25	6.25
	Nos. 4442-4445 (4)		14.10	12.85

Coil Stamp
Serpentine Die Cut 6¾ Horiz.

4446	A2325	(58c) green	1.50	.25

Issued: Nos. 4437b-4437h, 11/6, No. 4437i-4437o, 11/6/14. No. 4437a was only sold together with No. 4410. No. 4437a is 144x106mm. A 209x103mm sheet similar to No. 4437a was sold with a folder for €4.
No. 4437f uses an ink that is shinier than that used on No. 4437b that causes the small lettering at the base of the stamp to be indistinct. Nos. 4437j-4437n each had a franking value of 61c on day of issue.
The 80x52mm label on No. 4437g depicting an enlarged example of Type A2325 is not valid for postage. The 80x52mm label on No. 4437o was also overprinted "Marianne 1944-2014" but is not valid for postage.
Compare with type A2535.
See No. 4512. For overprint, see No. 5448.

Gaston Doumergue (1863-1937), Politician — A2326

2013, Aug. 1   Engr.   Perf. 13¼

4447	A2326	58c dark blue	1.60	.55

Pierre-Georges Latécoère (1883-1943), Aircraft Manufacturer A2327

2013, Aug. 15   Photo.

4448	A2327	€1.05 multi	3.00	1.00

Impressionist Paintings Type of 2013

Designs: No. 4449, Like #4387. No. 4450, Like #4389. No. 4451, Like #4390. No. 4452, Like #4396.

Serpentine Die Cut 11
2013, Aug. 26   Litho.
Self-Adhesive

4449	A2310	(58c) multi	1.60	1.60
4450	A2310	(58c) multi	1.60	1.60
4451	A2310	(58c) multi	1.60	1.60
4452	A2310	(58c) multi	1.60	1.60
	Nos. 4449-4452 (4)		6.40	6.40

Nos. 4449-4452 each have a dot structure in the colored panels at right that is not found on the photogravure stamps. The appearance of "France" on Nos. 4449-4452 appears lighter and grayer than that found on the photogravure stamps.

Patronage Law, 10th Anniv. — A2328

2013, Sept. 5   Photo.   Perf. 13¼

4453	A2328	63c multi	1.75	.60

Sculpture of Virgin Mary and Infant Jesus A2329

Keystone, Sainte-Chapelle de Vincennes A2330

Mirror With Ivory Carving of Chess Players A2331

Annunciation of the Virgin, Reims Cathedral A2332

Carving of Rooster, St. Pierre's Cathedral, Poitiers — A2333

Decorated Mirror of Louis d'Anjou — A2334

Marriage of the Virgin, Notre Dame Cathedral, Paris — A2335

Angel From Canopy of King Charles VII — A2336

Illumination From Les Très Riches Heures du Duc de Berry A2337

Reliquary Medallion A2338

Illumination from Heures de François de Guise — A2339

Bas-relief of Man Presenting Flower to Woman — A2340

Serpentine Die Cut 11
2013, Sept. 6   Photo.
Booklet Stamps
Self-Adhesive

4454	A2329	(63c) multi	1.75	.60
4455	A2330	(63c) multi	1.75	.60
4456	A2331	(63c) multi	1.75	.60
4457	A2332	(63c) multi	1.75	.60
4458	A2333	(63c) multi	1.75	.60
4459	A2334	(63c) multi	1.75	.60
4460	A2335	(63c) multi	1.75	.60
4461	A2336	(63c) multi	1.75	.60
4462	A2337	(63c) multi	1.75	.60
4463	A2338	(63c) multi	1.75	.60
4464	A2339	(63c) multi	1.75	.60
4465	A2340	(63c) multi	1.75	.60
a.	Booklet pane of 12, #4454-4465		21.00	
	Nos. 4454-4465 (12)		21.00	7.20

Gothic art.

French Heritage — A2341

Designs: No. 4466, House of the Lumière Brothers, Lyon. No. 4467, Buffon Museum, Montbard. No. 4468, House of George Sand, Nohant. No. 4469, House of Georges Clemenceau, Saint-Vincent-sur-Jard. No. 4470, Château de La Motte-Tilly, La Motte-Tilly. No. 4471, Castle and ramparts, Carcassonne. No. 4472, Château de Carrouges, Carrouges. No. 4473, Château de Champs-sur-Marne, Champs-sur-Marne. No. 4474, Aligned stones of Carnac. No. 4475, Roman structures (Mausoleum of the Julii, Triumphal arch of Glanum), Saint-Rémy-de-Provence. No. 4476, Mosaics at Montcaret archaeological site. No. 4477, Gallo-Roman Villa, Montmaurin.

Serpentine Die Cut 11
2013, Sept. 6   Photo.
Booklet Stamps
Self-Adhesive

4466	A2341	(58c) multi	1.60	.55
4467	A2341	(58c) multi	1.60	.55
4468	A2341	(58c) multi	1.60	.55
4469	A2341	(58c) multi	1.60	.55
a.	Booklet pane of 4, #4466-4469		6.50	
4470	A2341	(58c) multi	1.60	.55
4471	A2341	(58c) multi	1.60	.55
4472	A2341	(58c) multi	1.60	.55
4473	A2341	(58c) multi	1.60	.55
a.	Booklet pane of 4, #4470-4473		6.50	
4474	A2341	(58c) multi	1.60	.55
4475	A2341	(58c) multi	1.60	.55
4476	A2341	(58c) multi	1.60	.55
4477	A2341	(58c) multi	1.60	.55
a.	Booklet pane of 4, #4474-4477		6.50	
	Complete booklet, #4469a, 4473a, 4477a		19.50	
	Nos. 4466-4477 (12)		19.20	6.60

Judicial Police of Paris, Cent. — A2342

2013, Sept. 13   Photo.   Perf. 13¼

4478	A2342	63c multi	1.75	.60

Art Issue

Faience Vase, by Théodore Deck (1823-91) A2343

2013, Sept. 20   Photo.   Perf. 13¼x13

4479	A2343	€1.55 multi	4.25	2.10

Alexandre Yersin (1863-1943), Bacteriologist A2344

Yersin as: 63c, Older man. 95c, Young man.

2013, Sept. 20   Engr.   Perf. 13x13¼

4480	A2344	63c multi	1.75	.60
4481	A2344	95c multi	2.60	.85

See Viet Nam Nos. 3488-3489.

Art Issue
Souvenir Sheet

Paintings by Georges Braque (1882-1963) — A2345

No. 4482: a, Le Guéridon. b, Le Salon.

2013, Sept. 27   Photo.   Perf. 13x13¼

4482	A2345	Sheet of 2	8.50	8.50
a.-b.	€1.55 Either single		4.25	2.10

St. Bernard of Clairvaux (1090-1153), Abbot, and His Birthplace, Fontaine-lès-Dijon — A2346

2013, Oct. 4 Engr. Perf. 13¼
4483 A2346 58c multi 1.60 .55

Miniature Sheet

Theatrical Masks — A2347

No. 4484: a, Balinese Topeng. b, Greek theater mask, horiz. c, Korean Sandae mask. d, Japanese Noh theater mask. e, Italian Commedia dell'arte mask, horiz. f, Javanese shadow theater mask.

2013, Oct. 4 Litho. & Engr. Perf. 13
4484 A2347 Sheet of 6 9.75 9.75
  a.-f. 58c Any single 1.60 .55
A set of six souvenir sheets, each containing one each of Nos. 4484a-4484f, sold for €15.

Marianne and Balloon — A2348

Balloons and Paraglider — A2349

Man Blowing on Fire — A2350 Bottle of Air in Water — A2351

Man Pumping Air Into Tire — A2352 Paramedics Tending to Man Wearing Oxygen Mask — A2353

Hang Glider — A2354 Sailboat — A2355

Birds — A2356 Hummingbird and Flowers — A2357

Horn Player — A2358 Runner — A2359

Polynesian Canoe — A2360 Wind Turbine — A2361

2013, Oct. 12 Engr. Perf. 13
4485 A2348 58c multi 1.60 .55

Photo. & Embossed
Souvenir Sheet
Perf. 13¼x13
4486 A2349 €2.35 multi 6.50 3.25

Photo.
Booklet Stamps
Self-Adhesive
Serpentine Die Cut 11
4487 A2350 (63c) multi 1.75 .60
4488 A2351 (63c) multi 1.75 .60
4489 A2352 (63c) multi 1.75 .60
4490 A2353 (63c) multi 1.75 .60
4491 A2354 (63c) multi 1.75 .60
4492 A2356 (63c) multi 1.75 .60
4493 A2356 (63c) multi 1.75 .60
4494 A2357 (63c) multi 1.75 .60
4495 A2358 (63c) multi 1.75 .60
4496 A2359 (63c) multi 1.75 .60
4497 A2360 (63c) multi 1.75 .60
4498 A2361 (63c) multi 1.75 .60
  a. Booklet pane of 12, #4487-4498 21.00
  Nos. 4487-4498 (12) 21.00 7.20
Stamp Day. See Nos. 4535-4536.

Miniature Sheet

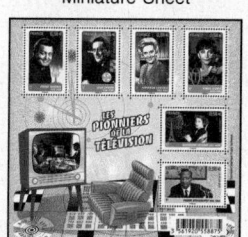

Television Personalities — A2362

No. 4499: a, Pierre Sabbagh (1918-94), news reporter and producer. b, Léon Zitrone (1914-95), news and sports reporter. c, Catherine Langeais (1923-98), show host. d, Denise Glaser (1920-83), show host and producer. e, Jacqueline Joubert (1921-2005), show host and producer, horiz. f, Pierre Desgraupes (1918-93), news reporter, horiz.

2013, Oct. 18 Photo. Perf. 13
4499 A2362 Sheet of 6 9.75 9.75
  a.-f. 58c Any single 1.60 .55

Little Pleasures — A2363

Designs: No. 4500, People and tea set (Thé partagé). No. 4501, Tree of life (Arbre de vie). No. 4502, Peacock holding letter (Paon messager). No. 4503, Carousel (Carrousel). No. 4504, Tree and falling coins (Pluie d'écus). No. 4505, Robin (Le rouge-gorge). No. 4506, Child and dove (Enfant de paix). No. 4507, Flying horse and rider (Cheval porte-bonheur). No. 4508, Cookies, pastries and snacks (Gourmandises). No. 4509, Citrus fruit and blossoms (Magie d'agrumes). No. 4510, Mother, child and flowers (Bienveillance). No. 4511, Shoe filled with gifts (L'escarpin).

Serpentine Die Cut 11
2013, Oct. 25 Photo.
Booklet Stamps
Self-Adhesive
4500 A2363 (58c) multi 1.60 .55
4501 A2363 (58c) multi 1.60 .55
4502 A2363 (58c) multi 1.60 .55
4503 A2363 (58c) multi 1.60 .55
4504 A2363 (58c) multi 1.60 .55

4505 A2363 (58c) multi 1.60 .55
4506 A2363 (58c) multi 1.60 .55
4507 A2363 (58c) multi 1.60 .55
4508 A2363 (58c) multi 1.60 .55
4509 A2363 (58c) multi 1.60 .55
4510 A2363 (58c) multi 1.60 .55
4511 A2363 (58c) multi 1.60 .55
  a. Booklet pane of 12, #4500-4511 19.50
  Nos. 4500-4511 (12) 19.20 6.60
A souvenir sheet containing a perf. 12¾ example of No. 4510 with water-activated gum sold for €3.

Types of 1959-2013
Serpentine Die Cut 11
2013, Nov. 6 Engr.
Booklet Stamps
Self-Adhesive
4512 A2325 (58c) green 1.60 .35
4513 A328 63c black 1.75 .60
4514 A349 63c black 1.75 .60
4515 A360 63c black 1.75 .60
4516 A379 63c black 1.75 .60
4517 A486 63c black 1.75 .60
4518 A555 63c black 1.75 .60
4519 A2322 (63c) red 1.75 .60
4520 A771 63c black 1.75 .60
4521 A915 63c black 1.75 .60
4522 A1161 63c black 1.75 .60
4523 A1409 63c black 1.75 .60
4524 A1713 63c black 1.75 .60
4525 A1912 63c black 1.75 .60
  a. Booklet pane of 14, #4512-4525 24.50
  Nos. 4512-4525 (14) 24.35 8.15

Trade Treaty Between France and Denmark, 350th Anniv. — A2364

Map and compass rose with ship at: 63c, Right. 80c, Left.

2013, Nov. 7 Engr. Perf. 13
4526 A2364 63c multi 1.75 .60
4527 A2364 80c multi 2.25 .75
See Denmark Nos. 1663-1664.

Fashion — A2365

Designs: No. 4528, Finished dresses on three dress forms. No. 4529, Flower, three women wearing white dresses. No. 4530, Three dress forms. No. 4531, Three women wearing white dresses.

2013, Nov. 8 Photo. Perf. 13¼
4528 A2365 63c multi 1.75 .60
4529 A2365 63c multi 1.75 .60
4530 A2365 95c multi 2.60 .85
4531 A2365 95c multi 2.60 .85
  Nos. 4528-4531 (4) 8.70 2.90
See Singapore Nos. 1640-1643.

Souvenir Sheet

French History A2366

No. 4532: a, Battle of Muret, 1213. b, Capture of Tournoel, 1212.

2013, Nov. 8 Engr. Perf. 13x13¼
4532 A2366 Sheet of 2 8.00 8.00
  a.-b. €1.45 Either single 4.00 1.40

National Order of Merit, 50th Anniv. — A2367

2013, Nov. 9 Engr. Perf. 13¼
4533 A2367 63c blue 1.75 .60

2013 French Kickboxing World Championships, Clermont-Ferrand — A2368

2013, Nov. 16 Photo. Perf. 13
4534 A2368 95c multi 2.60 .85

Sailboat and Horn Player Types of 2013
Serpentine Die Cut 11
2013, Nov. 18 Litho.
Self-Adhesive
4535 A2355 (63c) multi 1.75 1.75
4536 A2358 (63c) multi 1.75 1.75
"Phil@poste" is sharper on Nos. 4535-4536 than on Nos. 4492 and 4495.

Items with Spirals — A2369

Spirals in: No. 4537, Solarium shell (Coquillage solarium). No. 4538, Pottery design from Iznik, Turkey (Céramique Iznik). No. 4539, Spirograph. No. 4540, Red rose (Rose rouge). No. 4541, Ammonite fossil (Fossile d'ammonite). No. 4542, Chinese highway interchange (Echangeur Shanghai Nanpu). No. 4543, Kite (Cerf-volant). No. 4544, Cyclone Ingrid. No. 4545, Tree rings (Sapin-coupe transversale). No. 4546, Basket (Vannerie). No. 4547, Lighthouse staircase (Phare de la Coubre). No. 4548, School of barracudas (Banc des barracudas).

Serpentine Die Cut 11
2014, Jan. 4 Photo.
Booklet Stamps
Self-Adhesive
4537 A2369 (66c) multi 1.75 .60
4538 A2369 (66c) multi 1.75 .60
4539 A2369 (66c) multi 1.75 .60
4540 A2369 (66c) multi 1.75 .60
4541 A2369 (66c) multi 1.75 .60
4542 A2369 (66c) multi 1.75 .60
4543 A2369 (66c) multi 1.75 .60
4544 A2369 (66c) multi 1.75 .60
4545 A2369 (66c) multi 1.75 .60
4546 A2369 (66c) multi 1.75 .60
4547 A2369 (66c) multi 1.75 .60
4548 A2369 (66c) multi 1.75 .60
  a. Booklet pane of 12, #4537-4548 21.00
  Nos. 4537-4548 (12) 21.00 7.20
See Nos. 4566-4567, 4698.

Hearts — A2370

"Baccarat" and: 61c, Chandelier. €1.02, Goblet.

Silk-Screened, Engraved & Embossed
2014, Jan. 7 Perf. 13
4549 A2370 61c multi 1.75 .60
  a. Souvenir sheet of 5 8.75 8.75
4550 A2370 €1.02 multi 2.75 .90
Silk-Screened & Engraved
Serpentine Die Cut
Self-Adhesive
4551 A2370 61c multi 1.75 1.75
4552 A2370 €1.02 multi 2.75 2.75
See No. 4651.

Anne, Duchess of Brittany (1477-1514) A2371

Litho. & Engr.

2014, Jan. 11   *Perf. 13*
4553 A2371 66c multi   1.75 .60

A souvenir sheet of one sold for €3.20.

Signs of the Zodiac — A2372

Designs: No. 4554, Aries (Bélier). No. 4555, Taurus (Taureau). No. 4556, Gemini (Gémeaux). No. 4557, Cancer. No. 4558, Leo (Lion). No. 4559, Virgo (Vierge). No. 4560, Libra (Balance). No. 4561, Scorpio (Scorpion). No. 4562, Sagittarius (Sagittaire). No. 4563, Capricorn (Capricorne). No. 4564, Aquarius (Verseau). No. 4565, Pisces (Poissons).

Serpentine Die Cut 11

2014, Jan. 20   **Photo.**

Booklet Stamps
Self-Adhesive
4554	A2372	(61c) multi	1.75	.60
4555	A2372	(61c) multi	1.75	.60
4556	A2372	(61c) multi	1.75	.60
4557	A2372	(61c) multi	1.75	.60
4558	A2372	(61c) multi	1.75	.60
4559	A2372	(61c) multi	1.75	.60
4560	A2372	(61c) multi	1.75	.60
4561	A2372	(61c) multi	1.75	.60
4562	A2372	(61c) multi	1.75	.60
4563	A2372	(61c) multi	1.75	.60
4564	A2372	(61c) multi	1.75	.60
4565	A2372	(61c) multi	1.75	.60
a.		Booklet pane of 12, #4554-4565	21.00	
		Nos. 4554-4565 (12)	21.00	7.20

Items With Spirals Type of 2014

Designs: No. 4566, Like #4542. No. 4567, Like #4543.

Serpentine Die Cut 11

2014, Jan. 27   **Litho.**

Self-Adhesive
4566	A2369	(66c) multi	1.75	1.75
4567	A2369	(66c) multi	1.75	1.75

"Phil@poste" is sharper on Nos. 4566-4567 than on Nos. 4542-4543.

New Year 2014 (Year of the Horse) — A2373

2014, Jan. 31   **Photo.**   *Perf. 13¼x13*
4568 A2373 66c multi   1.75 .60

No. 4568 was printed in sheets of 5. A souvenir sheet of one sold for €3.20.
See No. 4971b.

Art Issue

Bust of Julius Caesar — A2374

2014, Feb. 14   **Engr.**   *Perf. 13¼x13*
4569 A2374 €1.65 multi   4.50 2.25

Cattle Breeds — A2375

Inscriptions: No. 4570, La Bretonne Pie Noir. No. 4571, L'Armoricaine. No. 4572, La Béarnaise. No. 4573, La Maraîchine. No. 4574, La Mirandaise. No. 4575, La Villard de Lans. No. 4576, La Saosnoise. No. 4577, La Nantaise. No. 4578, La Bordelaise. No. 4579, La Lourdaise. No. 4580, La Casta. No. 4581, La Ferrandaise.

Serpentine Die Cut 11

2014, Feb. 22   **Photo.**

Booklet Stamps
Self-Adhesive
4570	A2375	(61c) multi	1.75	.60
4571	A2375	(61c) multi	1.75	.60
4572	A2375	(61c) multi	1.75	.60
4573	A2375	(61c) multi	1.75	.60
4574	A2375	(61c) multi	1.75	.60
4575	A2375	(61c) multi	1.75	.60
4576	A2375	(61c) multi	1.75	.60
4577	A2375	(61c) multi	1.75	.60
4578	A2375	(61c) multi	1.75	.60
4579	A2375	(61c) multi	1.75	.60
4580	A2375	(61c) multi	1.75	.60
4581	A2375	(61c) multi	1.75	.60
a.		Booklet pane of 12, #4570-4581	21.00	
		Nos. 4570-4581 (12)	21.00	7.20

Art Issue

Tokyo 04, Photograph by Maxime Bruno A2376

2014, Feb. 28   **Litho.**   *Perf. 13x13¼*
4582 A2376 €1.65 multi   4.50 2.25

Miniature Sheet

Way of St. James A2377

No. 4583: a, Via Lemovicensis in Bazas. b, Via Podiensis in Moissac. c, Via Tolosana in Auch. d, Via Turonensis in Pons.

Litho. & Engr.

2014, Mar. 14   *Perf. 13*
4583 A2377   Sheet of 4   9.00 9.00
  a.-d.   83c Any single   2.25 .75

Alexandre Glais-Bizoin (1800-77), Politician A2378

2014, Mar. 15   **Engr.**   *Perf. 13x13¼*
4584 A2378 66c multi   1.90 .65

Bears — A2379

Designs: No. 4585, Giant panda (Panda géant).
No. 4586: a, Spectacled bear (Ours andin). b, Kermode bear (Ours Kermode). c, Polar bear (Ours polaire).

2014, Mar. 21   **Photo.**   *Perf. 13¼*
4585 A2379 61c multi   1.75 .60

Miniature Sheet
4586   Sheet of 4, #4585, 4586a-4586c   7.00 7.00
  a.-c.   A2379 61c Any single   1.75 .60

Diplomatic Relations Between France and People's Republic of China, 50th Anniv. A2380

Designs: 66c, Qinhuai River, Nanjing. 98c, Seine River, Paris.

2014, Mar. 27   **Engr.**   *Perf. 13x13¼*
4587 A2380 66c multi   1.90 .65
4588 A2380 98c multi   2.75 .90

See No. 5933b and People's Republic of China Nos. 4172-4173.

Art Issue

Painting by Joan Mitchell (1925-92) A2381

2014, Mar. 28   **Litho.**   *Perf. 13¼x13*
4589 A2381 €1.65 multi   4.50 2.25

Sell and Buy Used Items A2382

Turn Off Appliances A2383

Fruits and Vegetables A2384

Fix Leaks Quickly A2385

Sort and Recycle Paper A2386

Control Indoor Temperatures A2387

Conserve Water — A2388

People in Carpool — A2389

Use Public Transportation A2390

Save Energy A2391

Drive Ecologically Friendly Automobiles A2392

Recycle Waste Products A2393

Serpentine Die Cut 11

2014, Apr. 3   **Photo.**

Booklet Stamps
Self-Adhesive
4590	A2382	(61c) multi	1.75	.60
4591	A2383	(61c) multi	1.75	.60
4592	A2384	(61c) multi	1.75	.60
4593	A2385	(61c) multi	1.75	.60
4594	A2386	(61c) multi	1.75	.60
4595	A2387	(61c) multi	1.75	.60
4596	A2388	(61c) multi	1.75	.60
4597	A2389	(61c) multi	1.75	.60
4598	A2390	(61c) multi	1.75	.60
4599	A2391	(61c) multi	1.75	.60
4600	A2392	(61c) multi	1.75	.60
4601	A2393	(61c) multi	1.75	.60
a.		Booklet pane of 12, #4590-4601	21.00	
		Nos. 4590-4601 (12)	21.00	7.20

Opera Theater, Clermont-Ferrand A2394

2014, Apr. 4   **Engr.**   *Perf. 13¼*
4602 A2394 61c multi   1.75 .60

Spring Philatelic Show, Clermont-Ferrand.

Marguerite Duras (1914-96), Writer and Film Director — A2395

2014, Apr. 4   **Engr.**   *Perf. 13¼*
4603 A2395 €1.10 multi   3.00 1.00

Arrest and Deportation of Jews at Izieu Orphanage, 70th Anniv. — A2396

Litho. & Engr.

2014, Apr. 6   *Perf. 13x13¼*
4604 A2396 61c multi   1.75 .60

Miniature Sheet

European Capitals — A2397

No. 4605 — Attractions in Vienna: a, Secession Building. b, Belvedere Palace, horiz. c, Karlskirche (St. Charles' Church). d, Hofburg Palace, horiz.

Perf. 13¼x13, 13x13¼

2014, Apr. 18   **Photo.**
4605 A2397   Sheet of 4 + 3 labels   7.75 7.75
  a.-d.   66c Any single   1.90 .65

Souvenir Sheet

French History A2398

No. 4606: a, St. Louis (1214-70) (35x66mm). b, Battle of Bouvines, 1214 (52x41mm).

2014, Apr. 25 Engr. Perf. 13x13¼

4606	A2398	Sheet of 2	9.50	9.50
a.-b.		€1.65 Either single	4.75	2.25
c.		Souvenir sheet of 4, #4532a, 4532b, 4606a, 4606b	17.00	17.00

Salon du Timbre 2014 (No. 4606c). Issued: No. 4606c, 6/23/14.

Palace of Poitiers
A2399

2014, May 1 Engr. Perf. 13x13¼

4607	A2399	61c multi + label	1.75	.60

Vacation — A2400

Designs: No. 4608, Dog with sunglasses eating ice cream bar. No. 4609, Snail with trailer for shell. No. 4610, Crab building sand castle. No. 4611, Cats dancing. No. 4612, Turtle playing lute, turtle dancing. No. 4613, Lobster holding beach gear. No. 4614, Chicken and egg wearing headphones. No. 4615, Fish surfing. No. 4616, Ram with backpack and mountain climbing gear. No. 4617, Rabbits on tandem bicycle. No. 4618, Frogs with umbrellas in swan boat. No. 4619, Geese, tent, snails on picnic plate.

Serpentine Die Cut 11
2014, May 3 Photo.
Booklet Stamps
Self-Adhesive

4608	A2400	(61c) multi	1.75	.60
4609	A2400	(61c) multi	1.75	.60
4610	A2400	(61c) multi	1.75	.60
4611	A2400	(61c) multi	1.75	.60
4612	A2400	(61c) multi	1.75	.60
4613	A2400	(61c) multi	1.75	.60
4614	A2400	(61c) multi	1.75	.60
4615	A2400	(61c) multi	1.75	.60
4616	A2400	(61c) multi	1.75	.60
4617	A2400	(61c) multi	1.75	.60
4618	A2400	(61c) multi	1.75	.60
4619	A2400	(61c) multi	1.75	.60
a.		Booklet pane of 12, #4608-4619	21.00	
		Nos. 4608-4619 (12)	21.00	7.20

Harp Created by Jean Henri Naderman, 1787 — A2401

2014, May 4 Photo. Perf. 13¼x13

4620	A2401	83c multi	2.25	.75

Europa.

Opening of English Channel Tunnel, 20th Anniv. — A2402

2014, May 6 Engr. Perf. 13¼

4621	A2402	66c multi	1.90	.65

Tourism Series

Boulogne-sur-Mer — A2403

2014, May 9 Engr. Perf. 13x12¾

4622	A2403	61c multi	1.75	.60

D-Day, 70th Anniv. A2404

2014, June 5 Photo. Perf. 13x12¾

4623	A2404	66c multi	1.90	.65

Two souvenir sheets of one, issued in 2014 and in 2015, each sold for €3.20.

Tourism Issue

Pontigny Abbey, Yonne — A2405

2014, June 7 Engr. Perf. 13¼

4624	A2405	61c multi	1.75	.60

Massacre of Tulle, 70th Anniv. — A2406

2014, June 9 Photo. Perf. 13¼

4625	A2406	66c multi	1.90	.65

Souvenir Sheet

Benjamin Rabier (1864-1939), Comic Book Illustrator — A2407

No. 4626: a, Duckling hatching, ring with rabbits, chick and chicken (41x41mm). b, Rabier, chicken, rabbit and duck (30x41mm).

2014, June 14 Engr. Perf. 13¼

4626	A2407	Sheet of 2	5.00	5.00
a.		66c multi	1.90	.65
b.		€1.10 multi	3.00	1.00

A 200x95mm sheet containing Nos. 4626a and 4626b, but having a different margin design sold for €6.

See Nos. 4676, 4680.

Trains — A2408

Designs: No. 4627, Buddicom No. 33, Haute-Normandie. No. 4628, Z 209, Vallée de Chamonix. No. 4629, Pacific Chapelon Nord 3.1192, Paris, Gare du Nord. No. 4630, Micheline XM 5005, Haute-Marne. No. 4631, Mikado 141 R 1187, Côte Vermeille. No. 4632, BB 12125, Moselle. No. 4633, Z 6181, Ile-de-France. No. 4634, BB 66001, Les Cévennes. No. 4635, BB 9004, Les Landes. No. 4636, RTG T 2057, Gare de Boulogne-Aroglisseurs. No. 4637, CC 6572, Limoges, Gare des Bénédictins. No. 4638, TGV Duplex, Gare de Belfort-Montbéliard TGV.

Serpentine Die Cut 11
2014, June 14 Photo.
Booklet Stamps
Self-Adhesive

4627	A2408	(66c) multi	1.90	.65
4628	A2408	(66c) multi	1.90	.65
4629	A2408	(66c) multi	1.90	.65
4630	A2408	(66c) multi	1.90	.65
a.		Booklet pane of 4, #4627-4630	7.60	
4631	A2408	(66c) multi	1.90	.65
4632	A2408	(66c) multi	1.90	.65
4633	A2408	(66c) multi	1.90	.65
4634	A2408	(66c) multi	1.90	.65
a.		Booklet pane of 4, #4631-4634	7.60	
4635	A2408	(66c) multi	1.90	.65
4636	A2408	(66c) multi	1.90	.65
4637	A2408	(66c) multi	1.90	.65

4638	A2408	(66c) multi	1.90	.65
a.		Booklet pane of 4, #4635-4638	7.60	
		Complete booklet, #4630a, 4634a, 4638a	23.00	
		Nos. 4627-4638 (12)	22.80	7.80

Paris Zoo, 80th Anniv. A2409

2014, June 15 Photo. Perf. 13

4639	A2409	98c multi	2.75	.95

A souvenir sheet containing No. 4639 sold for €3.20.

Jean Jaurès (1859-1914), Assassinated Socialist Party Leader — A2410

Jaurès: 61c, Without hat. €1.02, With hat.

2014, June 17 Engr. Perf. 13¼

4640	A2410	61c blue	1.75	.60
4641	A2410	€1.02 red	2.75	.95
a.		Horiz. pair, #4640-4641	4.50	2.25

See Nos. 4675, 4679.

Miniature Sheet

The 1950s A2411

No. 4642: a, Automobile. b, Electricity advertisement, vert. c, People packing for vacation, vert. d, Vendor in movie theater. e, Musicians. f, Two women modeling fashions, veret.

2014, June 18 Photo. Perf. 13

4642	A2411	Sheet of 6	11.50	11.50
a.-f.		66c Any single	1.90	.65

See Nos. 4677, 4678.

A set of 10 miniature sheets containing reproductions of old French stamps (Nos. 641, 722, 764, 850, B34, B92, B97, B172, B248 and C22) with denominations was produced in limited quantities and offered only as a complete set. Each sheet contained five reproductions of one of the ten stamps in different colors, one with a €2.20 denomination and four with €2.45 denominations. **Similar sets were produced in limited quantities in subsequent years with reproductions of different stamps having different new denomninations of more than €1.40.**

Ceres — A2412

2014, June 18 Engr. Imperf.
With Printer's Inscription at Base of Stamp

4643	A2412	€1 rose carmine	2.75	1.40
4644	A2412	€1 red	2.75	1.40

Typo.

4645	A2412	€1 vermilion	2.75	1.40
a.		With printer information at top of stamp	2.75	1.40
4646	A2412	€1 rose	2.75	1.40
a.		With printer information at top of stamp	2.75	1.40
		Nos. 4643-4646 (4)	11.00	5.60

Printed in sheets of 20 containing Nos. 4645a, 4646a, 5 each Nos. 4643-4644, 4 each Nos. 4645-4646. See No. 4727a.

Tourism Issue

Coareze — A2413

Locmariaquer A2414

2014 Engr. Perf. 13¼

4647	A2413	61c multi	1.75	.60
4648	A2414	61c multi	1.75	.60

Issued: No. 4647, 6/19; No. 4648, 6/20. See Nos. 4673, 4674.

French Institute, Paris A2415

2014, June 21 Engr. Perf. 13x13¼

4649	A2415	61c multi + label	1.75	.60

French Federation of Philatelic Associations, 87th Congress, Paris. See Nos. 4672, 5762c.

Art Issue

The Seine at Pont du Carrousel, by Jean Dufy (1888-1964) A2416

2014, June 22 Litho. Perf. 13x13¼

4650	A2416	€1.65 multi	4.50	2.25

See No. 4681.

Baccarat Hearts Type of 2014
Silk-Screened & Engraved
2014, June 23 Perf.

4651	A2370	€3 multi	8.25	4.25

No. 4651 was printed in sheets of 5.

National Institute of Health and Medical Research, 50th Anniv. — A2417

2014, July 3 Photo. Perf. 13¼

4652	A2417	66c multi	1.75	.60

Jeanne Antoine Poisson, Marquise de Pompadour (1721-64), Patron of the Arts — A2418

2014, July 4 Engr. Perf. 13¼

4653	A2418	66c multi	1.75	.60

Art Issue

Les Boîtes de Conserve, by Jean Fautrier (1898-1964) — A2419

2014, July 11 Engr. Perf. 13x13¼
4654 A2419 €1.65 multi 4.50 2.25

General Mobilization of World War I Troops, Cent. — A2420

2014, Aug. 2 Engr. Perf. 13x13¼
4655 A2420 66c blue & red 1.75 .60

Miniature Sheet

2014 World Equestrian Games, Normandy — A2421

No. 4656: a, Dressage (40x30mm). b, Endurance (40x30mm). c, Concours complet d'équitation (40x40mm). d, Para-dressage (30x40mm). e, Voltige (30x40mm). f, Attelage (40x40mm). g, Saut d'obstacles (40x30mm). h, Reining (40x30mm).

2014, Aug. 23 Photo. Perf. 13x13¼
4656 A2421 Sheet of 8 17.50 8.75
a.-d. 61c Any single 1.60 .55
e.-h. €1.02 Any single 2.75 .90

A souvenir sheet containing examples of Nos. 4656e and 4656f with different perforations, sold for €6.

Charles Péguy (1873-1914), Writer — A2422

2014, Sept. 5 Engr. Perf. 13¼
4657 A2422 €1.55 multi 4.00 1.40

Renaissance Objets d'Art — A2423

Designs: No. 4658, Gardens of Château de Villandry. No. 4659, Clock, Rouen. No. 4660, Stairway sculpture, by Jean Goujon. No. 4661, Sculpture of salamander, Château de Fontainbleau. No. 4662, Buckle of King Charles IX. No. 4663, Detail of tapestry depicting Jupiter and Latona. No. 4664, Portrait of King Francis I, by Jean Clouet. No. 4665, Stainedd-glass window depicting angel playing flute, Sainte-Etienne Cathedral, Sens. No. 4666, Enamel painting of Ulysses, by Léonard Limousin. No. 4667, Book cover by Etienne Roffet. No. 4668, Armor of King Henri II. No. 4669, Stained-glass emblem of Queen Anne of Brittany depicting ermine and crown.

Serpentine Die Cut 11
2014, Sept. 6 Photo.
Booklet Stamps
Self-Adhesive
4658 A2423 (61c) multi 1.60 .55
4659 A2423 (61c) multi 1.60 .55
4660 A2423 (61c) multi 1.60 .55
4661 A2423 (61c) multi 1.60 .55
4662 A2423 (61c) multi 1.60 .55
4663 A2423 (61c) multi 1.60 .55
4664 A2423 (61c) multi 1.60 .55
4665 A2423 (61c) multi 1.60 .55
4666 A2423 (61c) multi 1.60 .55
4667 A2423 (61c) multi 1.60 .55
4668 A2423 (61c) multi 1.60 .55
4669 A2423 (61c) multi 1.60 .55
a. Booklet pane of 12, #4658-4669 19.50
Nos. 4658-4669 (12) 19.20 6.60

Souvenir Sheet

First Battle of the Marne, Cent. — A2424

No. 4670: a, Troops and automobile. b, Troops on horseback.

Photo. & Litho.
2014, Sept. 12 Perf. 13¼
4670 A2424 Sheet of 2 4.25 2.10
a. 66c multi 1.75 .60
b. 98c multi 2.50 .85

A souvenir sheet containing Nos. 4670a and 4670b but with as different margin sold for €5.

Art Issue

Mural on Necker Hospital Staircase, by Keith Haring (1958-90) A2425

2014, Sept. 19 Photo. Perf. 12¼x13
4671 A2425 €2.65 multi 6.75 3.50

Types of 2014
Serpentine Die Cut 11
2014, Sept. 25 Photo.
Booklet Stamps
Self-Adhesive
4672 A2415 61c Like #4649 + label (22x16mm) 1.60 .55
4673 A2413 61c Like #4647 (22x16mm) 1.60 .55
4674 A2414 61c Like #4648 (21x16mm) 1.60 .55
4675 A2410 61c Like #4640 (15x22mm) 1.60 .55
4676 A2407 66c Like #4626a (21x22mm) 1.75 .60
4677 A2411 66c Like #4642e (30x22mm) 1.75 .60
4678 A2411 66c Like #4642a (30x22mm) 1.75 .60
4679 A2410 €1.02 Like #4641 (15x22mm) 2.60 .85
4680 A2407 €1.10 Like #4626b (15x22mm) 2.75 .90
4681 A2416 €1.65 Like #4650 (46x38mm) 4.25 1.40
a. Booklet pane of 10, #4672-4681 + label 21.50
Nos. 4672-4681 (10) 21.25 7.15

Sense of Smell — A2426

Designs: No. 4682, Man and woman in love. No. 4683, Dog with magnifying glass. No. 4684, Coffee pot and cup. No. 4685, Skunks. No. 4686, Perfume atomizer. No. 4687, Athletic shoe and flowers. No. 4688, Fish with clothespin on nose. No. 4689, Cheese and foxes. No. 4690, Roast chicken. No. 4691, Woman smelling rose. No. 4692, Mother and baby. No. 4693, Face, herbs and spices.

Serpentine Die Cut 11
2014, Oct. 1 Photo.
Booklet Stamps
Self-Adhesive
4682 A2426 (61c) multi 1.60 .55
4683 A2426 (61c) multi 1.60 .55
4684 A2426 (61c) multi 1.60 .55
4685 A2426 (61c) multi 1.60 .55
4686 A2426 (61c) multi 1.60 .55
4687 A2426 (61c) multi 1.60 .55
4688 A2426 (61c) multi 1.60 .55
4689 A2426 (61c) multi 1.60 .55
4690 A2426 (61c) multi 1.60 .55
4691 A2426 (61c) multi 1.60 .55
4692 A2426 (61c) multi 1.60 .55
4693 A2426 (61c) multi 1.60 .55
a. Booklet pane of 12, #4682-4693 19.50
Nos. 4682-4693 (12) 19.20 6.60

Douai Court House 300th Anniv. — A2427

2014, Oct. 3 Engr. Perf. 13¼
4694 A2427 83c multi 2.10 .70

Green Turtle — A2428

2014, Oct. 9 Litho. Perf. 13x13¼
4695 A2428 98c multi 2.50 .85

See Comoro Islands No. , French Southern & Antarctic Territories No. 511, Malagasy Republic No. 1637, Mauritius No. 1144, Seychelles No. 904.

Salsa Dancers — A2429

Break Dancers A2430

2014, Oct. 11 Engr. Perf. 13¼
4696 A2429 61c multi 1.50 .50

Souvenir Sheet
Litho.
Perf. 13¼x13
4697 A2430 €2.45 multi 6.25 2.10
Stamp Day.

Items With Spirals Type of 2014
Serpentine Die Cut 11
2014, Oct. 15 Litho.
Self-Adhesive
4698 A2369 (66c) Like #4540 1.75 1.75
"Phil@poste" is sharper on No. 4698 than on No. 4540.

Maximilien Vox (1894-1974), Creator of Typographical Classification System — A2431

2014, Oct. 17 Engr. Perf. 13¼
4699 A2431 €1.10 multi 2.75 .90

Miniature Sheet

Cameras — A2432

No. 4700: a, 1865 Derogy four-lens camera. b, 1902 Girard Le Reve folding camera. c, 1930 Kodak Beau Brownie camera. d, 1898 Bazin & Leroy Stereocycle camera. e, 1910 folding camera, horiz. f, 1935 Gaumont Spido Reportage camera.

Litho. & Engr.
2014, Oct. 24 Perf. 13
4700 A2432 Sheet of 6 10.50 5.25
a.-f. 66c Any single 1.75 .60

A set of six souvenir sheets containing one example of Nos. 4700a-4700f sold as a set for €16.

A2433

A2434

A2435
A2436

A2437

A2438

A2439

A2440
A2441
A2442

A2443

A2444

Serpentine Die Cut 11
2014, Oct. 24 Photo.
Booklet Stamps
Self-Adhesive
4701 A2433 (61c) multi 1.50 .50
4702 A2434 (61c) multi 1.50 .50
4703 A2435 (61c) multi 1.50 .50
4704 A2436 (61c) multi 1.50 .50
4705 A2437 (61c) multi 1.50 .50
4706 A2438 (61c) multi 1.50 .50
4707 A2439 (61c) multi 1.50 .50
4708 A2440 (61c) multi 1.50 .50
4709 A2441 (61c) multi 1.50 .50
4710 A2442 (61c) multi 1.50 .50
4711 A2443 (61c) multi 1.50 .50
4712 A2444 (61c) multi 1.50 .50
a. Booklet pane of 12, #4701-4712 18.00
Nos. 4701-4712 (12) 18.00 6.00

A souvenir sheet containing one perf. 13¼ example of a stamp like No. 4706 sold for €3.20.

New French Industries A2445

Serpentine Die Cut 11
2014, Oct. 27   **Photo.**
Self-Adhesive
4713 A2445 (98c) multi   —   —

New French Industries A2446

Inscriptions: No. 4714, Usine du futur. No. 4715, Transition numérique. No. 4716, Développement durable. No. 4717, Patrimoine. No. 4718, Gastronomie. No. 4719, Transition énergétique. No. 4720, Elégance. No. 4721, Economi sociale et solidaire. No. 4722, Electromobilité. No. 4723, Exportations. No. 4724, Métiers d'art. No. 4725, Innovation 2030.

Serpentine Die Cut 11
2014, Oct. 27   **Photo.**
Booklet Stamps
Self-Adhesive
4714	A2446	(61c) multi	1.50	.50
4715	A2446	(61c) multi	1.50	.50
4716	A2446	(61c) multi	1.50	.50
4717	A2446	(61c) multi	1.50	.50
4718	A2446	(61c) multi	1.50	.50
4719	A2446	(61c) multi	1.50	.50
4720	A2446	(61c) multi	1.50	.50
4721	A2446	(61c) multi	1.50	.50
4722	A2446	(61c) multi	1.50	.50
4723	A2446	(61c) multi	1.50	.50
4724	A2446	(61c) multi	1.50	.50
4725	A2446	(61c) multi	1.50	.50
a.		Booklet pane of 12, #4714-4725	18.00	
		Nos. 4714-4725 (12)	18.00	6.00

Public Sale of Blue Cornflowers Made by World War I Veterans, 80th Anniv. — A2447

2014, Nov. 6 **Photo.**   **Perf. 13¼**
4726 A2447 €1.10 multi   2.75 .90

Types of 2003-14
2014, Nov. 6   **Engr.**   **Perf. 13**
4727		Sheet of 4, #4079, 4437, 4727a, 4727b	6.00	3.00
a.		A2412 61c green (20x26mm)	1.50	.50
b.		A1664 61c green	1.50	.50
c.		Booklet pane of 12, 6 each #4727a-4727b	18.00	
		Complete booklet, #4437b, 4727c	21.00	

Evariste de Parny (1753-1814), Poet — A2448

2014, Nov. 7 **Engr.**   **Perf. 13¼**
4728 A2448 83c multi   2.10 .70

Republican Security Companies (Riot Control Forces), 70th Anniv. — A2449

2014, Dec. 8 **Photo.**   **Perf. 13x12¾**
4729 A2449 €1.10 multi   2.75 .90

Handicrafts A2450

Inscriptions: Nos. 4730, 4742, Pierres précieuses (jewelery making). No. 4731, Bois (sanding wood). No. 4732, Verre (glass making). No. 4733, Métal (blacksmithing). No. 4734, Tissu (embroidery). No. 4735, Terre (pottery making). No. 4736, Papier (paper making). No. 4737, Tissu (weaving). No. 4738, Cuir (leather work). No. 4739, Bois (barrel making). No. 4740, Pierre (sculpting). No. 4741, Végétal (flower arranging).

2015 Litho. *Serpentine Die Cut 11*
Self-Adhesive
4730 A2450 (76c) multi   1.75 1.75
Photo.
Booklet Stamps
4731	A2450	(76c) multi	1.75	.60
4732	A2450	(76c) multi	1.75	.60
4733	A2450	(76c) multi	1.75	.60
4734	A2450	(76c) multi	1.75	.60
4735	A2450	(76c) multi	1.75	.60
4736	A2450	(76c) multi	1.75	.60
4737	A2450	(76c) multi	1.75	.60
4738	A2450	(76c) multi	1.75	.60
4739	A2450	(76c) multi	1.75	.60
4740	A2450	(76c) multi	1.75	.60
4741	A2450	(76c) multi	1.75	.60
4742	A2450	(76c) multi	1.75	.60
a.		Booklet pane of 12, #4731-4742	21.00	
		Nos. 4731-4742 (12)	21.00	7.20

No. 4730 has a visible dot pattern in the upper right part of the vignette and a sharper "Phil@poste" than No. 4742. Issued: Nos. 4730, 1/5; others 1/3.

Marianne and Children "Lettre Suivie" — A2450a

2015-16 Litho. *Die Cut*
Self-Adhesive
4742B A2450a (€1.08) red lilac   —   —
                    + label, background dots close together
c.		red lilac, background dots farther apart	—	—
d.		€1.10 As "c," magenta	—	—
e.		lt magenta, finer background dots	—	—
f.		As "e," dots and circles in background, coarse portrait with jagged curved lines	—	—

Issued: No. 4742B, 1/1. No. 4742Bd, 1/1/16. Sheet margins differ. No. 4742B has a green panel at left and destination and date lines over green background. No. 4742Bc is like No. 4742B, but with destination and date lines over a white background. No. 4742Bd has a magenta panel at left with "Indemnisation**" and "€" at lower left. Nos. 4742Be and 4742Bf are like No. 4742Bd, but with "Epaisseur 3cm max" at lower left.

Art Issue

The Great Wave, by Katsushika Hokusai (1760-1849) A2451

2015, Jan. 16 **Photo.**   **Perf. 13x13¼**
4743 A2451 €1.90 multi   4.50 2.25

Hearts — A2452

"JC de Castelbajac," people kissing and: 68c, Hearts. €1.15, Flowers.

2015, Jan. 23   **Photo.**   **Perf.**
With White Frame Around Stamp
4744 A2452 68c multi   1.60 .55

Without White Frame Around Stamp
Perf. 13
4745	A2452	68c multi	1.60	.55
4746	A2452	€1.15 multi	2.60	.85

Self-Adhesive
Serpentine Die Cut
4747	A2452	68c multi	1.60	1.60
4748	A2452	€1.15 multi	2.60	2.60

No. 4744 was printed in sheets of 5. Values for Nos. 4745-4748 are for examples with surrounding selvage. Designs on Nos. 4745-4748 continue onto the surrounding selvage.

New Year 2015 (Year of the Goat) — A2453

2015, Jan. 30 Photo. Perf. 13¼x13
4749 A2453 76c multi   1.75 .60

No. 4749 was printed in sheets of 5. A souvenir sheet of one sold for €3.20. See No. 4971c.

Drawings of Hands — A2454

Drawing by: No. 4750, Alphonse Legros. No. 4751, Unknown 18th century Italian School artist. No. 4752, Paul Delaroche. No. 4753, Gustave Moreau. No. 4754, Eugène Carrière. No. 4755, Pablo Picasso. No. 4756, Annibale Carrache. No. 4757, Unknown 17th century Italian School artist (four hands holding handles). No. 4758, Louis Tocque (one hand). No. 4759, Pierre Mignard. No. 4760, Tocque (two hands holding hoop with flowers). No. 4761, Unknown 17th Italian School artist (hand, water drop and goblet).

Serpentine Die Cut 11
2015, Jan. 30   **Litho.**
Booklet Stamps
Self-Adhesive
4750	A2454	(68c) multi	1.60	.55
4751	A2454	(68c) multi	1.60	.55
4752	A2454	(68c) multi	1.60	.55
4753	A2454	(68c) multi	1.60	.55
4754	A2454	(68c) multi	1.60	.55
4755	A2454	(68c) multi	1.60	.55
4756	A2454	(68c) multi	1.60	.55
4757	A2454	(68c) multi	1.60	.55
4758	A2454	(68c) multi	1.60	.55
4759	A2454	(68c) multi	1.60	.55
4760	A2454	(68c) multi	1.60	.55
4761	A2454	(68c) multi	1.60	.55
a.		Booklet pane of 12, #4750-4761	19.50	
		Nos. 4750-4761 (12)	19.20	6.60

Landmine Removal Service, 70th Anniv. — A2455

2015, Feb. 20 **Photo.**   **Perf. 13¼**
4762 A2455 €1.20 multi   2.75 .90

Goat Breeds — A2456

Inscriptions: No. 4763, La Créole. No. 4764, La Poitevine. No. 4765, L'Alpine. No. 4766, La Chèvre du Massif Central. No. 4767, La Lorraine. No. 4768, La Rove. No. 4769, La Chèvre des Fossés. No. 4770, La Saanen. No. 4771, La Pyrénéenne. No. 4772, L'Angora. No. 4773, La Provençale. No. 4774, La Corse.

Serpentine Die Cut 11
2015, Feb. 21   **Photo.**
Booklet Stamps
Self-Adhesive
4763	A2456	(68c) multi	1.50	.50
4764	A2456	(68c) multi	1.50	.50
4765	A2456	(68c) multi	1.50	.50
4766	A2456	(68c) multi	1.50	.50
4767	A2456	(68c) multi	1.50	.50
4768	A2456	(68c) multi	1.50	.50
4769	A2456	(68c) multi	1.50	.50
4770	A2456	(68c) multi	1.50	.50
4771	A2456	(68c) multi	1.50	.50
4772	A2456	(68c) multi	1.50	.50
4773	A2456	(68c) multi	1.50	.50
4774	A2456	(68c) multi	1.50	.50
a.		Booklet pane of 12, #4763-4774	18.00	
		Nos. 4763-4774 (12)	18.00	6.00

Souvenir Sheet

Enamel Art of Léonard Limosin (c. 1505-77) A2457

No. 4775: a, The Judgment of Paris. b, Eritrean Sibyl (Sybila Richea), vert.

Perf. 13x13¼, 13¼x13
2015, Feb. 27   **Photo.**
4775	A2457	Sheet of 2	8.50	8.50
a.-b.		€1.90 Either single	4.25	1.40
c.		Souvenir sheet of 2, #4775a-4775b, #4775a at right	14.00	14.00

No. 4775c sold for €6.20.

Souvenir Sheet

Basilica of Saint-Denis — A2458

No. 4776: a, Tombs (41x30mm). b, Stained-glass window (41x41mm).

2015, Mar. 14 **Engr.**   **Perf. 13¼**
4776	A2458	Sheet of 2	4.50	4.50
a.		76c multi	1.75	.60
b.		€1.25 multi	2.75	.90

A souvenir sheet of 2, containing Nos. 4776a-4776b, with No. 4776a at left sold for €6.20.

Spring Philatelic Show, Paris A2459

2015, Mar. 19 **Engr.**   **Perf. 13x12¾**
4777 A2459 68c multi   1.50 .50

Belgian Government in Exile in Sainte-Adresse, Cent. — A2460

Mailboxes, Belgian government officials in exile and: 76c, French and Belgian flags, building. 95c, Ministerial residence.

2015, Mar. 19 **Photo.**   **Perf. 13¼**
4778	A2460	76c multi	1.75	.60
4779	A2460	95c multi	2.10	.70
a.		Souvenir sheet of 2, #4778-4779	7.00	7.00

No. 4779a sold for €3.20. See Belgium No. 2748.

Art Issue

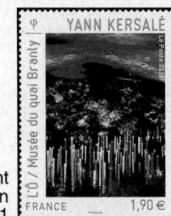

L'O, Light Sculpture by Yann Kersalé — A2461

2015, Mar. 20	Photo.		Perf. 13¼
4780 A2461 €1.90 multi		4.25	2.10

Nicole Mangin (1878-1919), World War I Physician A2462

2015, Mar. 21	Engr.		Perf. 13x13¼
4781 A2462 68c multi		1.50	.50

Renaissance Architecture A2463

Designs: No. 4782, Château d'Amboise. No. 4783, Château de Valençay. No. 4784, Palais Ducal de Nevers. No. 4785, Château de Villandry. No. 4786, Château d'Ancy-le-Franc. No. 4787, Palais du Louvre. No. 4788, Château de Chambord. No. 4789, Château d'Ecouen. No. 4790, Château d'Azay-le-Rideau. No. 4791, Château de Chenonceau. No. 4792, Château d'Anet. No. 4793, Château de Blois.

Serpentine Die Cut 11

2015, Mar. 27		Litho.
Booklet Stamps		
Self-Adhesive		
4782 A2463 (68c) multi	1.50	.50
4783 A2463 (68c) multi	1.50	.50
4784 A2463 (68c) multi	1.50	.50
4785 A2463 (68c) multi	1.50	.50
4786 A2463 (68c) multi	1.50	.50
4787 A2463 (68c) multi	1.50	.50
4788 A2463 (68c) multi	1.50	.50
4789 A2463 (68c) multi	1.50	.50
4790 A2463 (68c) multi	1.50	.50
4791 A2463 (68c) multi	1.50	.50
4792 A2463 (68c) multi	1.50	.50
4793 A2463 (68c) multi	1.50	.50
a. Booklet pane of 12, #4782-4793	18.00	
Nos. 4782-4793 (12)	18.00	6.00

Saintes-Maries-de-la-Mer Religious Procession, 700th Anniv. — A2464

2015, Mar. 29	Engr.		Perf. 13¼
4794 A2464 68c multi		1.50	.50

Miniature Sheet

European Capitals — A2465

No. 4795 — Attractions in Riga, Latvia: a, Nativity Cathedral. b, St. Peter's Church, horiz. c, House of the Blackheads, horiz. d, National Opera.

Perf. 13¼x13, 13x13¼

2015, Apr. 3		Photo.
4795 A2465 Sheet of 4	7.00	7.00
a.-d. 76c Any single	1.75	.60

Croix de Guerre, Cent. — A2466

2015, Apr. 8	Engr.		Perf. 13¼
4796 A2466 76c multi		1.75	.60

Souvenir Sheet

French History A2467

No. 4797: a, Coronation of Charlemagne, 768. b, Educational reforms of Charlemagne, 789, horiz.

Perf. 13¼x13, 13x13¼

2015, Apr. 10		Engr.
4797 A2467 Sheet of 2	8.50	8.50
a.-b. €1.90 Either single	4.25	1.40

French and Indian Cooperation in Space, 50th Anniv. — A2468

Designs: 76c, Saral satellite. €1.20, Megha-Tropiques satellite.

2014, Apr. 10	Photo.		Perf. 13¼
4798 A2468 76c multi		1.75	.60
4799 A2468 €1.20 multi		2.75	.90

See India Nos. 2725-2726.

Chalon-sur-Saône A2469

2015, Apr. 17	Engr.		Perf. 13¼
4800 A2469 68c multi		1.60	.55

Liberation of Concentration Camps, 70th Anniv. — A2470

2015, Apr. 24	Photo.		Perf. 13¼
4801 A2470 76c multi		1.75	.60

Miniature Sheet

Way of St. James A2471

No. 4802 — Sites in: a, Oloron-Sainte-Marie. b, Aire-sur l'Adour, vert. c, Saint-Jean-Pied-de Port. d, Blaye.

Litho. & Engr.

2015, Apr. 24		Perf. 13
4802 A2471 Sheet of 4	9.00	9.00
a.-d. 95c Any single	2.25	.75

Europa — A2472

2015, May 2	Photo.		Perf. 13¼
4803 A2472 95c multi		2.25	.75

Paintings of Flowers — A2473

Designs: No. 4804, Irises and Red Geraniums, by Paul Cézanne. No. 4805, Peonies, by Paul Gauguin. No. 4806, Carnations, by Jeanne Magnin. No. 4807, Wisteria, by Pierre Bracquemond. No. 4808, Daisies and Hydrangea, by Emile Boutin. No. 4809, Roses and Anémones, by Vincent van Gogh. No. 4810, Gladioluses, by Auguste Renoir. No. 4811, Wildflowers by Odilon Redon. No. 4812, Peonies, by Edouard Manet. No. 4813, Roses, by Gustave Caillebotte. No. 4814, Queens Daisies, by Marie Duhem. No. 4815, Roses, by Henri Fantin-Latour.

Serpentine Die Cut 11

2015, May 2		Litho.
Booklet Stamps		
Self-Adhesive		
4804 A2473 (68c) multi	1.60	.55
4805 A2473 (68c) multi	1.60	.55
4806 A2473 (68c) multi	1.60	.55
4807 A2473 (68c) multi	1.60	.55
4808 A2473 (68c) multi	1.60	.55
4809 A2473 (68c) multi	1.60	.55
4810 A2473 (68c) multi	1.60	.55
4811 A2473 (68c) multi	1.60	.55
4812 A2473 (68c) multi	1.60	.55
4813 A2473 (68c) multi	1.60	.55
4814 A2473 (68c) multi	1.60	.55
4815 A2473 (68c) multi	1.60	.55
a. Booklet pane of 12, #4804-4815	19.50	
Nos. 4804-4815 (12)	19.20	6.60

Victory in World War II, 70th Anniv. — A2474

2015, May 7	Photo.		Perf. 13¼
4816 A2474 68c multi		1.50	.50

Marshal Jacques II de Chabannes, Lord of La Palice (1470-1525) A2475

2015, May 15	Engr.		Perf. 13¼
4817 A2475 76c multi		1.75	.60

Mâcon A2476

2015, May 22	Engr.		Perf. 13x13¼
4818 A2476 68c multi + label		1.50	.50

French Federation of Philatelic Associations, 88th Congress, Mâcon.

17th World Convention of Rose Societies, Lyon — A2477

Designs: 76c, Red and pink roses. €1.20, Pink and yellow roses.

2015, May 29	Photo.		Perf. 13¼
4819 A2477 76c multi		1.75	.60
4820 A2477 €1.20 multi		2.75	.90
a. Horiz. pair, #4819-4820		4.50	2.25

A souvenir sheet containing Nos. 4819-4820 sold for €6.20.

Service Central d'Etat Civil, 50th Anniv. — A2478

2015, June 6	Engr.		Perf. 13¼
4821 A2478 €1.25 multi		2.75	.90

The 1960's A2479

No. 4822: a, Radio France Headquarters. b, Men and women dancing, vert. c, Movie poster for Les Demoiselles de Rochefort, vert. d, 1961 Peugeot 404 convertible. e, Ocean liner SS France. f, Women wearing short dresses, vert.

2015, June 12	Photo.		Perf. 13
4822 A2479 Sheet of 6		10.50	10.50
a.-f. 76c Any single		1.75	.60

Hartmannswillerkopf National Monument — A2480

2015, June 19	Engr.		Perf. 13¼
4823 A2480 95c multi		2.10	.70

Saint-Martial Church, Lestards A2481

2015, June 24	Engr.		Perf. 13¼
4824 A2481 68c multi		1.50	.50

A2482

A2483

A2484

A2485

A2486

A2487

A2488

A2489

A2490

A2491

A2492

Vacations
A2493

Serpentine Die Cut 11
2015, June 29   **Photo.**
Booklet Stamps
Self-Adhesive

4825	A2482	(68c) multi	1.50	.50
4826	A2483	(68c) multi	1.50	.50
4827	A2484	(68c) multi	1.50	.50
4828	A2485	(68c) multi	1.50	.50
4829	A2486	(68c) multi	1.50	.50
4830	A2487	(68c) multi	1.50	.50
4831	A2488	(68c) multi	1.50	.50
4832	A2489	(68c) multi	1.50	.50
4833	A2490	(68c) multi	1.50	.50
4834	A2491	(68c) multi	1.50	.50
4835	A2492	(68c) multi	1.50	.50
4836	A2493	(68c) multi	1.50	.50
a.		Booklet pane of 12, #4825-4836	18.00	
		Nos. 4825-4836 (12)	18.00	6.00

Haguenau, 900th
Anniv. — A2494

2015, July 3   **Engr.**   **Perf. 13¼**
4837 A2494 68c multi   1.50   .50

Martin Nadaud
(1815-98),
Mason and
Politician
A2495

2015, July 3   **Engr.**   **Perf. 13¼**
4838 A2495 68c multi   1.50   .50

Gilberto Bosques
(1892-1995),
Mexican Diplomat
Who Saved Jews
In World War
II — A2496

Bosques and: 76c, Notre Dame de la Garde Basilica, Marseilles, and signed travel visa. €1.20, Embassy, Mexican consular handstamp.

2015, July 16   **Litho.**   **Perf. 13**
4839 A2496 76c multi   1.75   .60
4840 A2496 €1.20 multi   2.75   .90
  a.   Horiz. pair, #4839-4840 4.50 2.25

See Mexico Nos. 2940-2941.

Animal
Eyes — A2497

Eye of: No. 4841, Requin à aileron blanc du lagon (whitetip reef shark). No. 4842, Petit-duc du Grant (southern white-faced owl). No. 4843, Rainette à yeux rouges (red-eyed tree frog). No. 4844, Toucan. No. 4845, Coq de race Brahma (Brahma chicken). No. 4846, Agame (agama lizard). No. 4847, Ara hyacinthe (hyacinth macaw). No. 4848, Iguane des Fidji (Fiji banded iguana). No. 4849, Tarente géante (giant wall gecko). No. 4850, Serpentaire (serpent eagle). No. 4851, Poisson-lime gribouillé (scrawled filefish). No. 4852, Gypaète barbu (bearded vulture).

Serpentine Die Cut 11
2015, July 31   **Photo.**
Booklet Stamps
Self-Adhesive

4841	A2497	(76c) multi	1.75	.60
4842	A2497	(76c) multi	1.75	.60
4843	A2497	(76c) multi	1.75	.60
4844	A2497	(76c) multi	1.75	.60
4845	A2497	(76c) multi	1.75	.60
4846	A2497	(76c) multi	1.75	.60
4847	A2497	(76c) multi	1.75	.60
4848	A2497	(76c) multi	1.75	.60
4849	A2497	(76c) multi	1.75	.60
4850	A2497	(76c) multi	1.75	.60
4851	A2497	(76c) multi	1.75	.60
4852	A2497	(76c) multi	1.75	.60
a.		Booklet pane of 12, #4841-4852	21.00	
		Nos. 4841-4852 (12)	21.00	7.20

Animal Proverbs
and
Idioms — A2498

Designs: No. 4853, Un froid de canard ("Freezing cold"). No. 4854, Rire comme une baleine ("Laughing like a whale"). No. 4855, Comme un chien dans un jeu de quilles ("Like a bull in a China shop"). No. 4856, Prendre le taureau par les cornes ("Take the bull by the horns"). No. 4857, Fier comme un paon ("Proud as a peacock"). No. 4858, Donner de la confiture aux cochons ("Cast pearls before swine"). No. 4859, Avoir un appétit d'oiseau ("Have the appetite of a bird"). No. 4860, Donner sa langue au chat ("Cat got your tongue?"). No. 4861, Etre le bouc émissaire ("Be the scapegoat"). No. 4862, Faire le pied de grue ("To cool one's heels"). No. 4863, Araignée du soir espoir ("A spider in the evening, hope"). No. 4864, Poser un lapin ("To stand someone up").

Serpentine Die Cut 11
2015, Aug. 28   **Photo.**
Booklet Stamps
Self-Adhesive

4853	A2498	(68c) multi	1.60	.55
4854	A2498	(68c) multi	1.60	.55
4855	A2498	(68c) multi	1.60	.55
4856	A2498	(68c) multi	1.60	.55
4857	A2498	(68c) multi	1.60	.55
4858	A2498	(68c) multi	1.60	.55
4859	A2498	(68c) multi	1.60	.55
4860	A2498	(68c) multi	1.60	.55
4861	A2498	(68c) multi	1.60	.55
4862	A2498	(68c) multi	1.60	.55
4863	A2498	(68c) multi	1.60	.55
4864	A2498	(68c) multi	1.60	.55
a.		Booklet pane of 12, #4853-4864	19.50	
		Nos. 4853-4864 (12)	19.20	6.60

Compare types A2498 and A2297.

Souvenir Sheet

Battle of Huningue, 200th
Anniv. — A2499

2015, Aug. 29   **Photo.**   **Perf. 13¼**
4865 A2499 €1.25 multi   3.00 1.00

2015 World Rowing
Championships,
Aiguebelette — A2500

Boat with: 76c, Two female rowers. €1.20, Male rowers (35x26mm).

2015, Aug. 30   **Photo.**   **Perf. 13x13¼**
4866 A2500 76c multi   1.75   .60
4867 A2500 €1.20 multi   2.75   .90
  a.   Horiz. pair, #4866-4867 4.50 2.25

Marianne and
Children "Europe"
With Data Matrix
Code — A2501

Marianne and
Children "Monde"
With Data Matrix
Code — A2502

2015, Sept. 4   **Engr.**   **Perf. 13**
4868 A2501 (95c) blue   2.25   .75
4869 A2502 (€1.20) purple   2.75   .90

Self-Adhesive
Serpentine Die Cut 6¾ Vert.
4870 A2501 (95c) blue   2.25   .75
  a.   Booklet pane of 6   13.50
4871 A2502 (€1.20) purple   2.75   .90

The Data Matrix codes on types A2501 and A2502 differ, but all examples of stamps of either type have identical codes. Compare with Types A2538-A2539.

Art Issue

Woman with
White Stockings,
by Suzanne
Valadon (1865-
1938)
A2503

2015, Sept. 18   **Photo.**   **Perf. 13¼x13**
4872 A2503 €1.90 multi   4.25 2.10

*Freedom, Equality,
Fraternity,* Painting by
Jonone in National
Assembly — A2504

2015, Sept. 19   **Photo.**   **Perf. 13¼**
4873 A2504 76c multi   1.75   .60

Landing of French on
Mauritius, 300th
Anniv. — A2505

2015, Sept. 25   **Photo.**   **Perf. 13¼**
4874 A2505 76c multi   1.75   .60

See Mauritius No. 1147.

Sense of
Sight — A2506

Designs: No. 4875, Room with a window (Chambre avec vue). No. 4876, Eye chart (A ma vue). No. 4877, Land in sight (Terre en vue). No. 4878, Eye (A vue d'oeil). No. 4879, Sun on horizon (Déjà vue). No. 4880, Women viewed through binoculars (Jumelles en vue). No. 4881, Planets (Vue imprenable). No. 4882, Nose and butterfly (A vue de nez). No. 4883, Diver and pool (Vue plongeante). No. 4884, Clouds (A perte de vue). No. 4885, Woman wearing mask (Ni vue, ni connue). No. 4886, Ghost and pink flying elephant (Vue de l'esprit).

Serpentine Die Cut 11
2015, Sept. 25   **Photo.**
Booklet Stamps
Self-Adhesive

4875	A2506	(68c) multi	1.60	.55
4876	A2506	(68c) multi	1.60	.55
4877	A2506	(68c) multi	1.60	.55
4878	A2506	(68c) multi	1.60	.55
4879	A2506	(68c) multi	1.60	.55
4880	A2506	(68c) multi	1.60	.55
4881	A2506	(68c) multi	1.60	.55
4882	A2506	(68c) multi	1.60	.55
4883	A2506	(68c) multi	1.60	.55
4884	A2506	(68c) multi	1.60	.55
4885	A2506	(68c) multi	1.60	.55
4886	A2506	(68c) multi	1.60	.55
a.		Booklet pane of 12, #4875-4886	19.50	
		Nos. 4875-4886 (12)	19.20	6.60

Jean-Henri Fabre (1823-1915),
Entomologist — A2507

2015, Oct. 2   **Litho.**   **Perf. 13¼**
4887 A2507 €2.60 multi   6.00 2.00

A souvenir sheet of one of No. 4887 sold for €6.20.

A2508

Design: Pierre Laroque (1907-97), Director of Social Security, and Ambroise Croizat (1901-51), Politician.

2015, Oct. 6   **Photo.**   **Perf. 13x13¼**
4888 A2508 68c multi   1.50   .50

French Social Security System, 70th anniv.

Tango
Dancers — A2509

Ballet
Preljocaj
A2510

Litho. & Engr.

2015, Oct. 10   **Perf. 13¼**
4889 A2509   68c multi   1.50   .50

Photo.
Souvenir Sheet
4890 A2510 €1.15 multi   2.60   .85

Stamp Day. A souvenir sheet of one No. 4889 was produced in 2016 and sold for €3.20.

Saint-Gobain
Corporation,
350th
Anniv. — A2511

Litho. & Engr.

2015, Oct. 14   **Perf. 13¼**
4891 A2511 68c multi   1.50   .50

Laure Diebold-
Mutschler
(1915-65),
Resistance Leader in
World War II — A2512

2015, Oct. 16   **Engr.**   **Perf. 13¼**
4892 A2512 68c multi   1.50   .50

 A2513   A2514

A2515   A2516

A2517   A2518

 A2519   A2520

 A2521   A2522

 A2523   Happy New Year — A2524

Serpentine Die Cut 11
2015, Oct. 30   **Photo.**
Booklet Stamps
Self-Adhesive
4893 A2513 (68c) multi   1.50   .50
4894 A2514 (68c) multi   1.50   .50
4895 A2515 (68c) multi   1.50   .50
4896 A2516 (68c) multi   1.50   .50
4897 A2517 (68c) multi   1.50   .50
4898 A2518 (68c) multi   1.50   .50
4899 A2519 (68c) multi   1.50   .50
4900 A2520 (68c) multi   1.50   .50
4901 A2521 (68c) multi   1.50   .50
4902 A2522 (68c) multi   1.50   .50
4903 A2523 (68c) multi   1.50   .50
4904 A2524 (68c) multi   1.50   .50
  a. Booklet pane of 12, #4893-4904   18.00
  Nos. 4893-4904 (12)   18.00   6.00

A souvenir sheet containing one perf. 12¾ example of a stamp like No. 4902 sold for €3.20.

Types of 1944-45 with Denominations in Euro Currency and Types of 2005-06
2015, Nov. 5   **Engr.**   **Perf. 13x12¾**
4905 A144 €1 dark blue   2.10   .70
     Perf. 12¾x13
4906 A147 €1 dark blue   2.10   .70
     Perf. 13
4907 A151 €4 dark blue   8.50   2.60
  Nos. 4905-4907 (3)   12.70   4.00
Booklet Stamps
4908 A147 76c red, 15x19mm design   1.60   .55
4909 A144 76c red, 15x19mm design   1.60   .55
  a. Booklet pane of 2, #4908-4909   3.25   —
4910 A1814 76c red   1.60   .55
4911 A1759 76c red   1.60   .55
  a. Booklet pane of 12, 6 each #4910-4911   19.50   —
  Complete booklet, #4909a, 4911a   23.00
  Nos. 4908-4911 (4)   6.40   2.20

Nos. 4905-4907 were printed in sheets of 14 containing 6 each Nos. 4905-4906 and 2 No. 4907.

Tapestry
Depicting
the Sacrifice
of Abraham
A2525

Unicorn
Hide,
Tapetry by
Nicolas
Buffe
A2526

2015, Nov. 6   **Litho.**   **Perf. 13**
Flocked Paper
4912 A2525 76c multi   1.60   .55
4913 A2526 €1.20 multi   2.60   .85
  a. Horiz. pair, #4912-4913, + central label   4.25   1.40

Aubusson, International City of Tapestries.

Miniature Sheet

Music
Boxes
A2527

No. 4914 — Inscriptions: a, La pendule à orgues. b, La leçon de chant. c, L'automate magicien. d, Boîte à musique danseuse. e, L'oiseau chanteur, horiz. f, La joueuse de typanon.

Litho. & Engr.
2015, Nov. 6   **Perf. 13**
4914 A2527 Sheet of 6   9.00   9.00
  a.-f. 68c Any single   1.50   .50

Nos. 4914a-4914f were each printed in souvenir sheets containing one stamp that sold as a set for €16.

Souvenir Sheet

Roland Barthes (1915-80),
Semiotician — A2528

2015, Nov. 12   **Engr.**   **Perf. 13¼**
4915 A2528 €1.15 multi   2.50   .85

Roosters — A2529

Designs: No. 4916, Coq gaulois.
No. 4917: a, Coq de Houdan. b, Coq meusien. c, Coq de Marans.

2015, Nov. 13   **Photo.**   **Perf. 13¼**
4916 A2529 68c multi   1.50   .50
4917   Sheet of 4, #4916, 4917a-4917c   6.00   6.00
  a.-c. A2529 68c Any single   1.50   .50

Two souvenir sheets, one containing Nos. 4916 and 4917b, and the other containing Nos. 4917a and 4917c, sold as a set for €6.20.

National Forestry
Office, 50th
Anniv. — A2530

2015, Nov. 20   **Photo.**   **Perf. 13¼**
4918 A2530 68c multi   1.50   .50

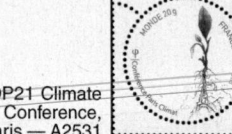

COP21 Climate
Conference,
Paris — A2531

2015, Nov. 24   **Photo.**   **Perf. 13¼**
4919 A2531 (€1.20) multi   2.60   .85

Values are for stamps with surrounding selvage.

Launch of
Astérix
Satellite,
50th
Anniv.
A2532

2015, Nov. 26   **Photo.**   **Perf. 13¼**
4920 A2532 68c multi   1.50   .50
  a. Tete-beche pair   3.00   1.00

A €1.16 stamp of type A2532 was included in a limited-edition booklet issued Nov. 4, 2020.

City
Halls — A2533

City Hall in: No. 4921, La Pernelle. No. 4922, Brunstatt. No. 4923, Chambourcy. No. 4924, Châteaugiron. No. 4925, Sennecey-le-Grand. No. 4926, Saint-Nicolas-de-la-Grave. No. 4927, Caudebec-en-Caux. No. 4928, Cercy-la-Tour. No. 4929, Clamart. No. 4930, Créteil. No. 4931, Toul. No. 4932, Le Pêchereau.

Serpentine Die Cut 11
2015, Dec. 10   **Photo.**
Booklet Stamps
Self-Adhesive
4921 A2533 (70c) multi   1.60   .55
4922 A2533 (70c) multi   1.60   .55
4923 A2533 (70c) multi   1.60   .55
4924 A2533 (70c) multi   1.60   .55
4925 A2533 (70c) multi   1.60   .55
4926 A2533 (70c) multi   1.60   .55
4927 A2533 (70c) multi   1.60   .55
4928 A2533 (70c) multi   1.60   .55
4929 A2533 (70c) multi   1.60   .55
4930 A2533 (70c) multi   1.60   .55
4931 A2533 (70c) multi   1.60   .55
4932 A2533 (70c) multi   1.60   .55
  a. Booklet pane of 12, #4921-4932   19.50
  Nos. 4921-4932 (12)   19.20   6.60

Marianne and Children,
"Ecopli" Without Gram Limit
Inscription
A2534

Marianne and Tree, "Lettre
Verte" Without Gram Limit
Inscription
A2535

Marianne and Children,
"Lettre Prioritaire" Without
Gram Limit
Inscription — A2536

2016, Jan. 1   **Engr.**   **Perf. 13**
4933 A2534 (68c) gray black   1.50   .30
4934 A2535 (70c) emerald   1.60   .35
4935 A2536 (80c) red   1.75   .45
  Nos. 4933-4935 (3)   4.85   1.10
Coil Stamps
Perf. 13 Horiz.
4936 A2535 (70c) green   1.60   .35
4937 A2536 (80c) red   1.75   .45
Self-Adhesive
Serpentine Die Cut 6¾ Vert.
4938 A2534 (68c) gray black   1.50   .30
4939 A2535 (70c) emerald   1.60   .35
  a. Booklet pane of 10   16.00
  b. Booklet pane of 12   19.50
4940 A2536 (80c) scarlet   1.75   .45
  a. Booklet pane of 10   17.50
  b. Booklet pane of 12   21.00
  c. Booklet pane of 20   35.00
  Nos. 4938-4940 (3)   4.85   1.10

Compare with types A2321, A2322 and A2325. See No. B775.

Marianne and Children "Europe" With
Data Matrix Code Without Gram Limit
Inscription
A2538

Marianne and Children "Monde" With Data Matrix Code Without Gram Limit Inscription
A2539

2016, Jan. 1   Engr.   Perf. 13

4942	A2538	(€1) blue	2.25	.75
4943	A2539	(€1.25) purple	2.75	.90

Self-Adhesive
Serpentine Die Cut 6¾ Vert.

4944	A2538	(€1) blue	2.25	.75
a.		Booklet pane of 6	—	
4945	A2539	(€1.25) dp reddish vio	2.75	.90

Compare with types A2501-A2502. Data Matrix codes differ on types A2501 and A2538, and on types A2502 and A2539.

Minerals — A2540

Designs: No. 4946, Gold (or), No. 4947, Labradorite. No. 4948, Topaz (topaze). No. 4949, Amethyst (amethyste). No. 4950, Olivine. No. 4951, Quartz. No. 4952, Turquoise. No. 4953, Fluorite. No. 4954, Sulfur (soufre). No. 4955, Ruby (rubis). No. 4956, Silver (argent). No. 4957, Copper (cuivre).

Serpentine Die Cut 11

2016, Jan. 7   Photo.
Booklet Stamps
Self-Adhesive

4946	A2540	(80c) multi	1.75	.60
4947	A2540	(80c) multi	1.75	.60
4948	A2540	(80c) multi	1.75	.60
4949	A2540	(80c) multi	1.75	.60
4950	A2540	(80c) multi	1.75	.60
4951	A2540	(80c) multi	1.75	.60
4952	A2540	(80c) multi	1.75	.60
4953	A2540	(80c) multi	1.75	.60
4954	A2540	(80c) multi	1.75	.60
4955	A2540	(80c) multi	1.75	.60
4956	A2540	(80c) multi	1.75	.60
4957	A2540	(80c) multi	1.75	.60
a.		Booklet pane of 12, #4946-4957	21.00	
		Nos. 4946-4957 (12)	21.00	7.20

A2541   A2542

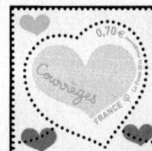

Winning Designs in Children's Stamp Design Contest — A2543

2016, Jan. 11   Photo.   Perf. 13¼

4958	A2541	70c multi	1.60	.55
4959	A2542	70c multi	1.60	.55
4960	A2543	70c multi	1.60	.55
a.		Horiz. strip of 3, #4958-4960	5.00	1.75
		Nos. 4958-4960 (3)	4.80	1.65

Hearts — A2544

"Courrèges" and: Nos. 4961, 4965, Light blue heart, bright pink denomination. No. 4962, No. 4966, White heart, slate denomination.

No. 4963 — "Courrèges," light blue heart and denomination in: a, Pale yellow. b, Light blue. c, Dark blue. d, Bright orange.
No. 4964 — "Courrèges," and heart in: a, Bright pink. b, Bright green. c, Bright yellow. d, Dark blue. e, Bright orange.

Photo., Litho. (#4964)

2016   Perf. 13

4961	A2544	70c multi	1.60	.55
4962	A2544	€1.40 multi	3.25	1.10

Perf.

4963		Sheet of 5, #4961, 4963a-4963d	8.00	8.00
a.-d.		A2544 70c Any single	1.60	.55
4964		Sheet of 5	34.00	34.00
a.-e.		A2544 €3 Any single	6.75	3.50

Self-Adhesive
Serpentine Die Cut

4965	A2544	70c multi	1.60	.55
4966	A2544	€1.40 multi	3.25	1.10

Issued: No. 4964, 5/19; others, 1/15. Values for Nos. 4961-4962 are for stamps with surrounding selvage.

Art Issue

Black, Red Over Black on Red, by Mark Rothko (1903-70) A2545

2016, Jan. 22   Photo.   Perf. 13¼x13

4967	A2545	€1.60 multi	3.50	1.75

New Year Types of 2005-15 and

New Year 2016 (Year of the Monkey) — A2546

2016, Jan. 29   Photo.   Perf. 13¼x13

4968	A2546	80c multi	1.75	.90
4969		Sheet of 4	8.75	8.75
a.	A1716	80c multi	2.10	2.10
b.	A1766	80c multi	2.10	2.10
c.	A1822	80c multi	2.10	2.10
d.	A1882	80c multi	2.10	2.10
4970		Sheet of 4	8.75	8.75
a.	A1962	80c multi	2.10	2.10
b.	A2048	80c multi	2.10	2.10
c.	A2133	80c multi	2.10	2.10
d.	A2209	80c multi	2.10	2.10
4971		Sheet of 4, #4968, 4971a-4971c	8.75	8.75
a.	A2277	80c multi	2.10	2.10
b.	A2373	80c multi	2.10	2.10
c.	A2453	80c multi	2.10	2.10
		Nos. 4969-4971 (3)	26.25	26.25

No. 4968 was printed in sheets of 5. A souvenir sheet of 1 #4968 sold for €3.20. Nos. 4969-4971 sold as a set for €12.

Sense of Hearing — A2549

Ear, playback buttons and: No. 4972, Cricket. No. 4973, Various insects. No. 4974, Man's head and singing angels. No. 4975, Marbles rolling down stairs. No. 4976, Pinball game. No. 4977, Water drip. No. 4978, Bird. No. 4979, Lion. No. 4980, Musicians. No. 4981, Sea shell. No. 4982, Harp, lyre, hands, butterflies and flowers. No. 4983, Children.

Serpentine Die Cut 11

2016, Jan. 30   Litho.
Booklet Stamps
Self-Adhesive

4972	A2549	(70c) multi	1.60	.55
4973	A2549	(70c) multi	1.60	.55
4974	A2549	(70c) multi	1.60	.55
4975	A2549	(70c) multi	1.60	.55
4976	A2549	(70c) multi	1.60	.55
4977	A2549	(70c) multi	1.60	.55
4978	A2549	(70c) multi	1.60	.55
4979	A2549	(70c) multi	1.60	.55
4980	A2549	(70c) multi	1.60	.55
4981	A2549	(70c) multi	1.60	.55
4982	A2549	(70c) multi	1.60	.55

4983	A2549	(70c) multi	1.60	.55
a.		Booklet pane of 12, #4972-4983	19.50	
		Nos. 4972-4983 (12)	19.20	6.60

Marguerite Long (1874-1966), Pianist — A2550

2016, Feb. 12   Engr.   Perf. 13¼

4984	A2550	70c multi	1.50	.50

Art Issue

Annie Hall, by Jan Toorop (1858-1928) A2551

2016, Feb. 19   Litho.   Perf. 13

4985	A2551	€2.80 multi	6.25	3.25

Georges Charpak (1924-2010), 1992 Nobel Laureate in Physics — A2552

2016, Feb. 26   Engr.   Perf. 13¼

4986	A2552	70c gold & multi	1.50	.50

Roosters — A2557

Inscriptions: No. 4987, Coq Barbezieux. No. 4988, Coq Bourbonnais. No. 4989, Coq Gaulois. No. 4990, Coq Gournay. No. 4991, Coc Coucou de Rennes. No. 4992, Coq Faverolles. No. 4993, Coq d'Alsace. No. 4994, Coq Bresse. No. 4995, Coq Meusien. No. 4996, Coq Marans. No. 4997, Coq Gâtinais. No. 4998, Coq La Flèche.

Serpentine Die Cut 11

2016, Feb. 27   Photo.
Booklet Stamps
Self-Adhesive

4987	A2557	(70c) multi	1.50	.50
4988	A2557	(70c) multi	1.50	.50
4989	A2557	(70c) multi	1.50	.50
4990	A2557	(70c) multi	1.50	.50
4991	A2557	(70c) multi	1.50	.50
4992	A2557	(70c) multi	1.50	.50
4993	A2557	(70c) multi	1.50	.50
4994	A2557	(70c) multi	1.50	.50
4995	A2557	(70c) multi	1.50	.50
4996	A2557	(70c) multi	1.50	.50
4997	A2557	(70c) multi	1.50	.50
4998	A2557	(70c) multi	1.50	.50
a.		Booklet pane of 12, #4987-4998	18.00	
		Nos. 4987-4998 (12)	18.00	6.00

Pierre Messmer (1916-2007), Prime Minister — A2558

2016, Mar. 11   Engr.   Perf. 13¼

4999	A2558	80c multi	1.90	.65

Sophie Germain (1776-1831), Mathematician A2559

2016, Mar. 18   Engr.   Perf. 13¼

5000	A2559	70c multi	1.60	.55

Notre-Dame-des-Missions Church, Epinay-sur-Seine — A2560

2016, Mar. 18   Engr.   Perf. 13¼

5001	A2560	70c multi	1.60	.55

Auteuil Apprentices, 150th Anniv. — A2561

2016, Mar. 18   Photo.   Perf. 13¼

5002	A2561	70c multi	1.60	.55

2016 European Soccer Championships, France — A2562

2016   Photo.   Perf. 13

5003	A2562	€1 multi	2.25	.75
a.		Souvenir sheet of 5	11.50	11.50
5004	A2562	€2 multi	4.50	2.25

Issued: No. 5003, 3/26; No. 5004, 5/19. Values are for stamps with surrounding selvage. No. 5004 was printed in sheets of 5 and has varnish covering the trophy in the design.

Sculptor A2563

2016, Mar. 31   Engr.   Perf. 12¼

5005	A2563	70c multi	1.60	.55

Spring Philatelic Show, Belfort A2564

2016, Apr. 1   Engr.   Perf. 13x12¾

5006	A2564	70c multi	1.60	.55

Portraits — A2565

Designs: No. 5007, Portrait of a Young Boy, by Paul Gauguin. No. 5008, Portrait of the Artist's Son, by Paul Cézanne. No. 5009, Young Woman Wearing a Black Hat, by Pierre-Auguste Renoir. No. 5010, Young Woman with a Low-cut Dress and Flower in Hair, by Berthe Morisot. No. 5011, Margot Lux with a Wide Hat, by Mary Cassatt. No. 5012, Portrait of Irma Brunner, La Viennoise, by Edouard Manet. No. 5013, Portrait of Léon Bonnat, by Edgar Degas. No. 5014, Self-portrait, by Gustave Caillebotte. No. 5015, Portrait of a Young Girl, by Armand Guillaumin. No. 5016, Self-portrait, by Vincent van Gogh. No. 5017, Portrait of Blanche Hoschedé, by Claude Monet. No. 5018, Woman with a Green Scarf, by Camille Pissarro.

Serpentine Die Cut 11

2016, Apr. 2			Litho.

Booklet Stamps
Self-Adhesive

5007	A2565	(70c) multi	1.60	.55
5008	A2565	(70c) multi	1.60	.55
5009	A2565	(70c) multi	1.60	.55
5010	A2565	(70c) multi	1.60	.55
5011	A2565	(70c) multi	1.60	.55
5012	A2565	(70c) multi	1.60	.55
5013	A2565	(70c) multi	1.60	.55
5014	A2565	(70c) multi	1.60	.55
5015	A2565	(70c) multi	1.60	.55
5016	A2565	(70c) multi	1.60	.55
5017	A2565	(70c) multi	1.60	.55
5018	A2565	(70c) multi	1.60	.55
a.		Booklet pane of 12, #5007-5018	19.50	
		Nos. 5007-5018 (12)	19.20	6.60

National Center of Costume and Scenography, Moulins — A2566

Litho. & Engr.

2016, Apr. 8			Perf. 13x13¼
5019	A2566	80c multi	1.90	.65

A souvenir sheet containing No. 5019 sold for €3.20.

Edmond Locard (1877-1966), Forensic Scientist — A2567

2016, Apr. 15		Engr.	Perf. 13¼
5020	A2567	70c multi	1.60	.55

Marquis de Jouffroy d'Abbans (1751-1832) and Steamboat A2568

2016, Apr. 22		Engr.	Perf. 13¼
5021	A2568	€1.25 red & blue	3.00	1.00

Steamboat navigation on the Seine, 200th anniv.

Deposits and Consignments Fund, 200th Anniv. — A2569

Engr. & Embossed

2016, Apr. 28			Perf. 13¼
5022	A2569	80c black & red	1.90	.60

A self-adhesive version of this stamp on a cream-colored paper was printed in sheets of 4 that were produced in limited quantities.

Europa — A2570

2016, May 8		Photo.	Perf. 13¼
5023	A2570	€1 multi	2.25	.75

Think Green Issue.

Saint-Brevin-les-Pins — A2571

2016, May 13		Photo.	Perf. 13¼
5024	A2571	70c multi	1.60	.55

Soccer Plays — A2572

Inscriptions: No. 5025, Frappe (kick). No. 5026, Coup du sombrero (heading ball). No. 5027, Amorti poitrine (chest stop). No. 5028, Coup franc laucarne (corner kick). No. 5029, Reprise de volée (volley). No. 5030, Aile de pigeon (pigeon wing). No. 5031, Arrêt gardien (goalie's save). No. 5032, Coup du foulard (behind-the-planted-leg kick). No. 5033, Coup de pied retourné (bicycle kick). No. 5034, Joueuse qui gagne (winning player).

Serpentine Die Cut 11

2016, May 19			Litho.

Booklet Stamps
Self-Adhesive

5025	A2572	(70c) multi	1.60	.55
5026	A2572	(70c) multi	1.60	.55
5027	A2572	(70c) multi	1.60	.55
5028	A2572	(70c) multi	1.60	.55
5029	A2572	(70c) multi	1.60	.55
5030	A2572	(70c) multi	1.60	.55
5031	A2572	(70c) multi	1.60	.55
5032	A2572	(70c) multi	1.60	.55
5033	A2572	(70c) multi	1.60	.55
5034	A2572	(70c) multi	1.60	.55
a.		Booklet pane of 10, #5025-5034	16.00	
		Nos. 5025-5034 (10)	16.00	5.50

Types of 1947-78
Souvenir Sheet

Engr., Sheet Margin Photo. & Embossed With Foil Application

2016, May 19			Perf. 13
5035		Sheet of 3	13.50	13.50
a.	A169	€2 blue	4.50	2.25
b.	A791	€2 gray & dull brown	4.50	2.25
c.	SP171	€2 gray black	4.50	2.25

2016 Paris-Philex Stamp Show.

Bees — A2573

Inscriptions: No. 5036, Collète.
No. 5037: a, Osmie, vert. b, Anthophore. c, Mégachile, vert.

2016, May 20		Photo.	Perf. 13¼
5036	A2573	70c multi	1.60	.55
5037		Sheet of 4, #5036, 5037a-5073c	6.50	6.50
a.-c.	A2573	70c Any single	1.60	.55

Two souvenir sheets, one containing Nos. 5036 and 5037a, and the other containing Nos. 5037b and 5037c, sold as a set for €6.20.

Place des Vosges, Paris A2574

2016, May 21		Engr.	Perf. 13x13¼
5038	A2574	70c multi + label	1.60	.55

French Federation of Philatelic Associations, 89th Congress, Paris.

Miniature Sheet

The 1970's A2575

No. 5039: a, Renault 5 automobile. b, Women's fashions, vert. c, Skiers, chair lift and resort, vert. d, L'île aux Enfants children's televison show. e, Parc des Princes Stadium, Paris. f, People dancing at discotheque, vert.

2016, May 21		Photo.	Perf. 13
5039	A2575	Sheet of 6	11.50	11.50
a.-f.		80c Any single	1.90	.60

Louise Labé (c. 1524-1566), Poet — A2576

2016, May 22		Engr.	Perf. 13x13¼
5040	A2576	€1.40 multi	3.25	1.10

Battle of Verdun, Cent. A2577

Litho. & Engr.

2016, May 29			Perf. 13x12¾
5041	A2577	70c multi	1.60	.55

A souvenir sheet containing No. 5041 sold for €3.20. A souvenir sheet issued in 2017 containing No. 5041, a denominated proof of No. 5041 with black, brown and yellow inks, and a non-denominated proof of No. 5041 with red, yellow and blue inks sold for €6.20.

Saint-Etienne School of Mines, 200th Anniv. — A2578

2016, June 3			Perf. 13¼
5042	A2578	70c multi	1.60	.55

Diplomatic Relations Between France and South Korea, 130th Anniv. — A2579

Designs: 80c, Korean Celadon incense burner, 12th. cent. €1.25, French reliquary.

2016, June 3		Photo.	Perf. 13¼
5043	A2579	80c multi	1.90	.60
5044	A2579	€1.25 multi	2.75	.90

See South Korea No. 2469.

French History A2580

No. 5045: a, Catherine de Medici (1519-89), Queen of France. b, 1520 meeting of King Henry VIII of England and King François I of France at Field of the Cloth of Gold, horiz.

Perf. 13¼x13, 13x13¼

2016, June 3			Engr.
5045	A2580	Sheet of 2	6.50	6.50
a.-b.		€1.40 Either single	3.25	1.60

A 200x95mm sheet containing Nos. 5045a and 5045b, but with a different margin design sold for €6.20.

First Women in French Government, 80th Anniv. — A2581

2016, June 4		Photo.	Perf. 13
5046	A2581	70c red & black	1.60	.55

Cécile Brunschvicg (1877-1946), Undersecretary of State for National Education; Irène Joliot-Curie (1897-1956), Undersecretary of State for Scientific Research; Suzanne Lacore (1875-1975), Undersecretary of State for Public Health.

Art Issue

Lost Illusions, by Charles Gleyre (1806-74) A2582

2016, June 5		Engr.	Perf. 13x13¼
5047	A2582	€1.60 multi	3.75	1.90

Holy Cross Abbey, Quimperlé A2583

2016, June 17		Engr.	Perf. 13¼
5048	A2583	70c multi	1.60	.55

League of Education, 150th Anniv. — A2584

2016, June 23		Photo.	Perf. 13¼
5049	A2584	€1 multi	2.25	.75

Pierre Mauroy (1928-2013), Prime Minister — A2585

2016, June 24		Engr.	Perf. 13¼
5050	A2585	80c multi	1.90	.60

Academy of Sciences, 350th Anniv. — A2586

2016, June 28		Photo.	Perf. 13¼
5051	A2586	€2.50 multi	5.75	1.90

Souvenir Sheet

Battle of the Somme, Cent. A2587

No. 5052: a, Soldiers shaking hands, castle and British tank. b, Damaged Albert Cathedral, Theipval Memorial, Visitor's Center.

2016, July 1 **Photo.** **Perf. 13¼**
5052 A2587 Sheet of 2 4.25 4.25
a. 80c multi 1.90 .60
b. €1 multi 2.25 .75

A 200x95mm sheet containing Nos. 5052a and 5052b, but with a different margin design sold for €6.20.

A2588

A2589 A2590

A2591

A2592 A2593

A2594 A2595

A2596

A2597

A2598

Summer Vacation — A2599

Serpentine Die Cut 11
2016, July 2 **Photo.**
Booklet Stamps
Self-Adhesive
5053 A2588 (70c) multi 1.60 .55
5054 A2589 (70c) multi 1.60 .55
5055 A2590 (70c) multi 1.60 .55
5056 A2591 (70c) multi 1.60 .55
5057 A2592 (70c) multi 1.60 .55
5058 A2593 (70c) multi 1.60 .55
5059 A2594 (70c) multi 1.60 .55
5060 A2595 (70c) multi 1.60 .55
5061 A2596 (70c) multi 1.60 .55
5062 A2597 (70c) multi 1.60 .55
5063 A2598 (70c) multi 1.60 .55
5064 A2599 (70c) multi 1.60 .55
a. Booklet pane of 12, #5053-5064 19.50
Nos. 5053-5064 (12) 19.20 6.60

Mediterranean Sea Fish — A2600

2016, July 9 **Photo.** **Perf. 13x12½**
5065 A2600 €1 multi 2.25 .75

Flowers — A2601

Inscriptions: No. 5066, Oiseau de paradis (bird-of-paradise flower). No. 5067, Coquelicot (poppy). No. 5068, Muguet (lily-of-the-valley). No. 5069, Balisier (heliconia). No. 5070, Lys rouge (red lily). No. 5071, Iris. No. 5072, Rose. No. 5073, Tournesol (sunflower). No. 5074, Jonquille (jonquil). No. 5075, Marguerite (daisy). No. 5076, Belle-de-nuit (four o'clock flower). No. 5077, Passiflore (passionflower).

Serpentine Die Cut 11
2016, July 30 **Photo.**
Booklet Stamp
Self-Adhesive
5066 A2601 (80c) multi 1.75 .60
5067 A2601 (80c) multi 1.75 .60
5068 A2601 (80c) multi 1.75 .60
5069 A2601 (80c) multi 1.75 .60
5070 A2601 (80c) multi 1.75 .60
5071 A2601 (80c) multi 1.75 .60
5072 A2601 (80c) multi 1.75 .60
5073 A2601 (80c) multi 1.75 .60
5074 A2601 (80c) multi 1.75 .60
5075 A2601 (80c) multi 1.75 .60
5076 A2601 (80c) multi 1.75 .60
5077 A2601 (80c) multi 1.75 .60
a. Booklet pane of 12, #5066-5077 21.00
Nos. 5066-5077 (12) 21.00 7.20

Eagle Dam, Soursac, and World War II Resistance Fighters — A2602

2016, Sept. 2 **Engr.** **Perf. 13x12¾**
5078 A2602 €3.20 multi 7.25 2.40

Animal Proverbs and Idioms — A2603

Designs: No. 5079, Courir plusieurs lièvres à la fois ("to try to do more than one thing at once"). No. 5080, Quand on parle du loup on en voit la queue ("speak of the devil and he appears"). No. 5081, Avoir des oursins dans le porte-monnaie ("to be stingy"). No. 5082, Avoir une mémoire d'éléphant ("have the memory of an elephant"). No. 5083, Muet comme une carpe ("silent like a carp"). No. 5084, La part du lion ("the lion's share"). No. 5085, Dormir comme un loir ("to sleep like a log"). No. 5086, Etre le dindon de la farce ("being the butt of the joke"). No. 5087, Peigner la girafe ("to do nothing effective"). No. 5088, C'est le serpent qui se mord la queue ("to be in a vicious cycle"). No. 5089, Monter sur ses grands chevaux ("to get carried away"). No. 5090, Bayer aux corneilles ("to stand and gape").

Serpentine Die Cut 11
2016, Sept. 3 **Photo.**
Booklet Stamps
Self-Adhesive
5079 A2603 (70c) multi 1.60 .55
5080 A2603 (70c) multi 1.60 .55
5081 A2603 (70c) multi 1.60 .55
5082 A2603 (70c) multi 1.60 .55
5083 A2603 (70c) multi 1.60 .55
5084 A2603 (70c) multi 1.60 .55
5085 A2603 (70c) multi 1.60 .55
5086 A2603 (70c) multi 1.60 .55
5087 A2603 (70c) multi 1.60 .55
5088 A2603 (70c) multi 1.60 .55
5089 A2603 (70c) multi 1.60 .55
5090 A2603 (70c) multi 1.60 .55
a. Booklet pane of 12, #5079-5090 19.50
Nos. 5079-5090 (12) 19.20 6.60

Léo Ferré (1916-93), Musician A2604

2016, Sept. 8 **Photo.** **Perf. 12¼**
5091 A2604 €1.40 multi 3.25 1.10

Françoise Giroud (1916-2003), Minister of Culture — A2605

2016, Sept. 9 **Engr.** **Perf. 13x13¼**
5092 A2605 80c lt blue & maroon 1.75 .60

Characters From *Les Legendaires*, Cartoons by Patrick Sobral — A2606

Designs: No. 5093, Danael. No. 5094, Jadina and Shimy.

2016, Sept. 16 **Photo.** **Perf. 13¼**
5093 A2606 70c multi 1.60 .55
5094 A2606 70c multi 1.60 .55
a. Horiz. pair, #5093-5094, + 2 alternating labels 3.20 1.10

A2607 A2608

A2609 A2610

A2611 A2612

A2613 A2614

A2615 A2616

A2617

Stars and Heavenly Bodies — A2618

Serpentine Die Cut 11
2016, Oct. 1 **Photo.**
Booklet Stamps
Self-Adhesive
5095 A2607 (70c) multi 1.60 .55
5096 A2608 (70c) multi 1.60 .55
5097 A2609 (70c) multi 1.60 .55
5098 A2610 (70c) multi 1.60 .55
5099 A2611 (70c) multi 1.60 .55
5100 A2612 (70c) multi 1.60 .55
5101 A2613 (70c) multi 1.60 .55
5102 A2614 (70c) multi 1.60 .55
5103 A2615 (70c) multi 1.60 .55
5104 A2616 (70c) multi 1.60 .55
5105 A2617 (70c) multi 1.60 .55
5106 A2618 (70c) multi 1.60 .55
a. Booklet pane of 12, #5095-5106 19.50
Nos. 5095-5106 (12) 19.20 6.60

Charleston Dancers — A2619

Ballet Dancer in *Swan Lake* A2620

2016, Oct. 8 **Engr.** **Perf. 13¼**
5107 A2619 70c multi 1.60 .55
Souvenir Sheet
Photo. & Embossed
Perf. 13¼x13
5108 A2620 €1.40 multi 3.25 1.10
Stamp Day.

Eclair Airplane Propellers, Cent. — A2621

2016, Oct. 13 **Photo.** **Perf. 13¼**
5109 A2621 70c multi 1.60 .55

St. Étienne Cathedral, Toul — A2622

2016, Oct. 21 **Engr.** **Perf. 13x13¼**
5110 A2622 70c multi + label 1.60 .55

Architecture of Paris and Lisbon A2623

Designs: 80c, Rua Augusta Arch, Lisbon. €1, Buildings along Rue Royale, Paris.

2016, Oct. 21 **Engr.** **Perf. 13x12½**
5111 A2623 80c multi 1.75 .60
5112 A2623 €1 multi 2.25 .75
See Portugal Nos. 3847-3848.

Pres. François Mitterrand (1916-96) — A2624

2016, Oct. 26　Engr.　Perf. 13¼
5113　A2624　80c multi　　1.75　.60

Miniature Sheet

European Capitals — A2625

No. 5114 — Attractions in Amsterdam, Netherlands: a, Begijnhof (Le Béguinage). b, Rijksmuseum. c, Westerkerk, vert. d, Canals and buildings.

Perf. 13¼x13½, 13½x13¼
2016, Nov. 3　　　　Photo.
5114　A2625　Sheet of 4　　7.00　7.00
　a.-d.　　80c Any single　　1.75　.60

A2626　　　　　　A2626a

Peace and Commerce ("Type Sage") With Denominations in Euro Currency).
Type I: The "N" of "INV" is under the "B" of "REPUBLIQUE."
Type II: The "N" of "INV" is under the "U" of "REPUBLIQUE."

2016, Nov. 3　Engr.　Perf. 12¾x13¼
Type I
5115　A2626　€1 dark green　　2.25　.75
Type II
5116　A2626　€1 dark green　　2.25　.75
　a.　Pair, #5115-5116　　　4.50　1.50

Booklet Stamps
Type I
Design Size: 15x19mm
Perf. 12¾x13
5117　A2626　80c red　　　1.75　.45
5118　A2626a　80c black　　1.75　.45
　a.　Booklet pane of 2, #5117-5118　　　　　3.50　—
　b.　Booklet pane of 12, 6 each #5117-5118　　21.00　—
　　　Complete booklet, #5118a, 5118b　　　　24.50

Nos. 5115-5116 were printed in sheets containing 10 of each stamp.

Brive-la-Gaillarde — A2627

2016, Nov. 4　Engr.　Perf. 13x12¾
5119　A2627　70c multi　　1.50　.50

Miniature Sheet

Pens
A2628

No. 5120: a, Person dipping Sergent-Major pen into ink, 19th cent. b, Calames (ancient reed pen). c, Monk with quill pen, 12th cent. d, Metallic pen nibs, 19th cent. e, Cat, writer with fountain pen, horiz. f, Voltaire writing with quill pen, 1775.

Litho. & Engr.
2016, Nov. 4　　　　Perf. 13
5120　A2628　Sheet of 6　　9.00　9.00
　a.-f.　　70c Any single
　g.　Souvenir sheet of 3, #5120a, 5120d, 5120e　　6.75　6.75
　h.　Souvenir sheet of 3, #5120b, 5120c, 5120f　　6.75　6.75

Nos. 5120g and 5120h were sold as a set for €6.20.

Restoration and Reopening of Bièvre River — A2629

2016, Nov. 5　Photo.　Perf. 13¼
5121　A2629　70c multi　　1.50　.50

Art Issue
Souvenir Sheet

Paintings by Marie Laurencin (1883-1956) — A2630

No. 5122: a, Portrait of Baroness Gourgaud in Black Mantilla, 1923. b, Young Girl with Guitar, 1940.

2016, Nov. 6　Photo.　Perf. 13¼x13
5122　A2630　Sheet of 2　　7.00　7.00
　a.-b.　　€1.60 Either single　　3.50　1.75

National Office of Veterans and War Victims, Cent. — A2631

2016, Nov. 9　Photo.　Perf. 13¼
5123　A2631　70c multi　　1.50　.50

Jewelery Making — A2632

2016, Nov. 10　Engr.　Perf. 12¼
5124　A2632　€1 multi　　2.25　.75

A2633　　　　　A2634

A2635　　　　　A2636

A2637　　　　　A2638

A2639　　　　　A2640

A2641　　　　　A2642

A2643

Contest Stamps With Scratch-off Panel — A2644

Serpentine Die Cut 11
2016, Nov. 14　　　　Photo.
Booklet Stamps
Self-Adhesive
Unscrached Panels
5125　A2633　(70c) multi　　1.50　.50
　a.　Scratched panel　　　　　.35
5126　A2634　(70c) multi　　1.50　.50
　a.　Scratched panel　　　　　.35
5127　A2635　(70c) multi　　1.50　.50
　a.　Scratched panel　　　　　.35
5128　A2636　(70c) multi　　1.50　.50
　a.　Scratched panel　　　　　.35
5129　A2637　(70c) multi　　1.50　.50
　a.　Scratched panel　　　　　.35
5130　A2638　(70c) multi　　1.50　.50
　a.　Scratched panel　　　　　.35
5131　A2639　(70c) multi　　1.50　.50
　a.　Scratched panel　　　　　.35
5132　A2640　(70c) multi　　1.50　.50
　a.　Scratched panel　　　　　.35
5133　A2641　(70c) multi　　1.50　.50
　a.　Scratched panel　　　　　.35
5134　A2642　(70c) multi　　1.50　.50
　a.　Scratched panel　　　　　.35
5135　A2643　(70c) multi　　1.50　.50
　a.　Scratched panel　　　　　.35

5136　A2644　(70c) multi　　1.50　.50
　a.　Scratched panel　　　　　.35
　b.　Booklet pane of 12, #5125-5136　　　　18.00
　　　Nos. 5125-5136 (12)　18.00　6.00

Gold scratch-off panels on Nos. 5125-5136 hide codes that could be entered at the contest website for a chance to win various prizes.

Stained-Glass Windows — A2645

Window from: No. 5137, Notre Dame Cathedral, Coutances. No. 5138, Saint-Denis Chapel, Paris. No. 5139, Notre Dame Cathedral, Chartres. No. 5140, Saint-Nazaire Basilica, Carcassonne. No. 5141, Notre Dame Cathedral, Strasbourg. No. 5142, Saint-Savin-de-Gartempe Abbey, Saint-Savin. No. 5143, Saint-Etienne Cathedral, Bourges. No. 5144, Saint-Julien Cathedral, Le Mans. No. 5145, Saint-Denis Basilica, Saint-Denis. No. 5146, Notre Dame Cathedral, Bayeux. No. 5147, Saint-Pierre Cathedral, Beauvais. No. 5148, Notre Dame Cathedral, Paris.

Serpentine Die Cut 11
2016, Nov. 26　　　　Photo.
Booklet Stamps
Self-Adhesive
5137　A2645　(70c) multi　　1.50　.50
5138　A2645　(70c) multi　　1.50　.50
5139　A2645　(70c) multi　　1.50　.50
5140　A2645　(70c) multi　　1.50　.50
5141　A2645　(70c) multi　　1.50　.50
5142　A2645　(70c) multi　　1.50　.50
5143　A2645　(70c) multi　　1.50　.50
5144　A2645　(70c) multi　　1.50　.50
5145　A2645　(70c) multi　　1.50　.50
5146　A2645　(70c) multi　　1.50　.50
5147　A2645　(70c) multi　　1.50　.50
5148　A2645　(70c) multi　　1.50　.50
　a.　Booklet pane of 12, #5137-5148　　　　18.00
　　　Nos. 5137-5148 (12)　18.00　6.00

French Academy in Rome, 350th Anniv. — A2646

2016, Nov. 30　Photo.　Perf. 13¼
5149　A2646　€1 chestnut & red　　2.25　.75

A souvenir sheet of one sold for €3.50. See Italy No. 3433

Landscape Reflections A2647

Designs: No. 5150, Nusa Dua, Bali, Indonesia. No. 5151, Siwa Oasis, Egypt. No. 5152, Mont Blanc, France. No. 5153, Laguna Colorada, Bolivia. No. 5154, Mount Shompole, Tanzania. No. 5155, Moremi Game Reserve, Botswana. No. 5156, Mount Fuji, Japan. No. 5157, Dolomites, Italy. No. 5158, Avenue of Baobabs, Madagascar. No. 5159, Mountains, Sermersooq Municipality, Greenland. No. 5160, Everglades, United States. No. 5161, Mountains, Ultima Esperanza Province, Chile.

Serpentine Die Cut 11
2017, Jan. 7　　　　Photo.
Booklet Stamps
Self-Adhesive
5150　A2647　(85c) multi　　1.90　.65
5151　A2647　(85c) multi　　1.90　.65
5152　A2647　(85c) multi　　1.90　.65
5153　A2647　(85c) multi　　1.90　.65
5154　A2647　(85c) multi　　1.90　.65
5155　A2647　(85c) multi　　1.90　.65
5156　A2647　(85c) multi　　1.90　.65
5157　A2647　(85c) multi　　1.90　.65
5158　A2647　(85c) multi　　1.90　.65
5159　A2647　(85c) multi　　1.90　.65
5160　A2647　(85c) multi　　1.90　.65
5161　A2647　(85c) multi　　1.90　.65
　a.　Booklet pane of 12, #5150-5161　　　　23.00
　　　Nos. 5150-5161 (12)　22.80　7.80

Art Issue
Souvenir Sheet

Art by Marc Chagall (1887-1985) — A2648

No. 5162: a, Peace (stained-glass window), 1976. b, Paradise (painting), 1961.

2017, Jan. 13   Photo.   Perf. 13¼
5162 A2648 Sheet of 2   7.50 4.00
a.-b.   €1.70 Either single   3.75 1.90

A2649   Hearts — A2650

2017, Jan. 20   Photo.   Perf. 13¼
5163 A2649 73c multi   1.60   .55
a.   Souvenir sheet of 5   8.00 8.00
5164 A2650 €1.46 multi   3.25 1.10

Self-Adhesive
Serpentine Die Cut
5165 A2649 73c multi   1.60   .55
5166 A2650 €1.46 multi   3.25 1.10

Values for Nos. 5163-5164 are for stamps with surrounding selvage.

Tourism Issue

Chateau de Pailly — A2651

2017, Jan. 28   Engr.   Perf. 13¼
5167 A2651 73c multi   1.60   .55

Rat — A2652   Ox — A2653

Tiger — A2654   Rabbit — A2655

Dragon   Snake
A2656   A2657

Horse — A2658   Goat — A2659

Monkey   Rooster
A2660   A2661

Dog — A2662   Pig — A2663

Serpentine Die Cut 11
2017, Jan. 28   Photo.
Booklet Stamps
Self-Adhesive
5168 A2652 (73c) multi   1.60   .55
5169 A2653 (73c) multi   1.60   .55
5170 A2654 (73c) multi   1.60   .55
5171 A2655 (73c) multi   1.60   .55
5172 A2656 (73c) multi   1.60   .55
5173 A2657 (73c) multi   1.60   .55
5174 A2658 (73c) multi   1.60   .55
5175 A2659 (73c) multi   1.60   .55
5176 A2660 (73c) multi   1.60   .55
5177 A2661 (73c) multi   1.60   .55
5178 A2662 (73c) multi   1.60   .55
5179 A2663 (73c) multi   1.60   .55
a.   Booklet pane of 12, #5168-5179   19.50
      Nos. 5168-5179 (12)   19.20 6.60

New Year 2017 (Year of the Rooster).

Women and Lucien Neuwirth (1924-2013), Politician A2664

2017, Feb. 9   Photo.   Perf. 13¼
5180 A2664 85c multi   1.90   .65

Passage of Neuwirth Law legalizing birth control, 50th anniv.

Art Issue

La Vue de Village, by Frédéric Bazille (1841-70) A2665

2017, Feb. 17   Photo.   Perf. 13¼x13
5181 A2665 €1.70 multi   3.75 1.90

Farm Animals — A2666

Designs: No. 5182, Bélier (ram). No. 5183, Laperau (rabbit). No. 5184, Anesse (female donkey). No. 5185, Dindon (turkey). No. 5186, Oie (goose). No. 5187, Veau (calf). No. 5188, Porcelet (piglet). No. 5189, Anon (male donkey). No. 5190, Canard (duck). No. 5191, Brebis (ewe). No. 5192, Vache (cow). No. 5193, Poule (hen).

Serpentine Die Cut 11
2017, Feb. 24   Photo.
Booklet Stamps
Self-Adhesive
5182 A2666 (73c) multi   1.60   .55
5183 A2666 (73c) multi   1.60   .55
5184 A2666 (73c) multi   1.60   .55

5185 A2666 (73c) multi   1.60   .55
5186 A2666 (73c) multi   1.60   .55
5187 A2666 (73c) multi   1.60   .55
5188 A2666 (73c) multi   1.60   .55
5189 A2666 (73c) multi   1.60   .55
5190 A2666 (73c) multi   1.60   .55
5191 A2666 (73c) multi   1.60   .55
5192 A2666 (73c) multi   1.60   .55
5193 A2666 (73c) multi   1.60   .55
a.   Booklet pane of 12, #5182-5193   19.50
      Nos. 5182-5193 (12)   19.20 6.60

Anne Morgan (1873-1952), Philanthropist and Provider of War Relief — A2667

2017, Feb. 24   Engr.   Perf. 13¼
5194 A2667 85c multi   1.90   .65

Montmartre — A2668

2017, Mar. 9   Engr.   Perf. 13x12¾
5195 A2668 73c multi   1.60   .55

Spring Philatelic Show, Paris.

Miniature Sheet

European Capitals — A2669

No. 5196 — Attractions in Valletta, Malta: a, Palais des Grand Maîtres (Grandmaster's Palace). b, Gallarija (building balconies). c, St. John's Co-cathedral, vert. d, Fort Saint Elmo (canals and buildings).

Perf. 13x13¼, 13¼x13
2017, Mar. 10   Photo.
5196 A2669 Sheet of 4   7.75 7.75
a.-d.   85c Any single   1.90   .65

Germaine Ribière (1917-99), Resistance Fighter Who Saved Jews in World War II — A2670

2017, Mar. 10   Engr.   Perf. 13¼
5197 A2670 €1.10 multi   2.40   .80

Waltzers — A2671

2017, Mar. 11   Engr.   Perf. 13¼
5198 A2671 73c multi   1.60   .55

The Star, by Edgar Degas (1834-1917) — A2672

Souvenir Sheet
Photo.
Perf. 13¼x13
5199 A2672 €1.46 multi   3.25 1.10

Stamp Day. A souvenir sheet containing No. 5198 was issued in 2018 and sold for €4.

Law on Commercial And Industrial Credit, Cent. — A2673

2017, Mar. 13   Photo.   Perf. 13¼
5200 A2673 85c multi   1.90   .65

French-Algerian War Ceasefire, 55th Anniv. — A2674

2017, Mar. 15   Photo.   Perf. 13¼
5201 A2674 €1.30 multi   2.75   .90

Maurice Faure (1922-2014), Politician — A2675

2017, Mar. 25   Engr.   Perf. 13¼
5202 A2675 85c multi   1.90   .65

Photographs of Items Looking Like Masks, by Michelangelo Durazzo — A2676

Mask number: No. 5203, 7. No. 5204, 13. No. 5205, 12. No. 5206, 9. No. 5207, 32. No. 5208, 29. No. 5209, 26. No. 5210, 35. No. 5211, 3. No. 5212, 17. No. 5213, 21. No. 5214, 44.

Serpentine Die Cut 11
2017, Mar. 31   Photo.
Booklet Stamps
Self-Adhesive
5203 A2676 (73c) multi   1.60   .55
5204 A2676 (73c) multi   1.60   .55
5205 A2676 (73c) multi   1.60   .55
5206 A2676 (73c) multi   1.60   .55
5207 A2676 (73c) multi   1.60   .55
5208 A2676 (73c) multi   1.60   .55
5209 A2676 (73c) multi   1.60   .55
5210 A2676 (73c) multi   1.60   .55
5211 A2676 (73c) multi   1.60   .55
5212 A2676 (73c) multi   1.60   .55
5213 A2676 (73c) multi   1.60   .55
5214 A2676 (73c) multi   1.60   .55
a.   Booklet pane of 12, #5203-5214   19.50
      Nos. 5203-5214 (12)   19.20 6.60

Ironwork A2677

2017, Mar. 31   Engr.   Perf. 12¼
5215 A2677 73c multi   1.60   .55

Souvenir Sheet

Battle of Vimy Ridge, Cent. A2678

No. 5216: a, Pillars and statue. b, Statue of weeping woman.

2017, Apr. 7	**Engr.**		**Perf. 13¼**	
5216	A2678	Sheet of 2	5.00	5.00
a.		85c multi	1.90	.65
b.		€1.30 multi	3.00	1.00

See Canada Nos. 2981-2982.

Souvenir Sheet

Second Battle of Chemin des Dames, Cent. A2679

No. 5217: a, Seven Senegalese soldiers. b, Eight soldiers in Dragon Cavern.

2017, Apr. 14	**Photo.**		**Perf. 13¼**	
5217	A2679	Sheet of 2	5.00	5.00
a.-b.		€1.10 Either single	2.40	.80

A 200x95mm sheet containing Nos. 5217a and 5217b, but with a different margin design sold for €6.20.

Jean-Baptiste Charcot (1867-1936), Polar Explorer, and Ship Pourquoi-Pas? — A2680

2017, Apr. 22	**Engr.**		**Perf. 13x12¾**	
5218	A2680	€1.30 multi	3.00	1.00

A souvenir sheet containing No. 5218 sold for €3.20.

Concours Lépine Inventor's Show — A2681

2017, Apr. 27	**Photo.**		**Perf. 13¼**	
5219	A2681	€1.30 multi	3.00	1.00

Flowers in Objets d' Art — A2682

Inscription: No. 5220, Cristal pierres & or (crystal stones and gold). No. 5221, Bois peint & doré (painted and gilded wood). No. 5222, Argent travaillé (worked silver). No. 5223, Faïence & glaçure, peinte (glazed and painted faience). No. 5224, Bronze doré (gilded bronze). No. 5225, Mosaïque, pierres dures (stone mosaic). No. 5226, Porcelaine tendre (soft porcelain). No. 5227, Bois sculpté (sculpted wood). No. 5228, Laine & soie (wool and silk). No. 5229, Bois gravé (engraved wood). No. 5230, Perles, diamants, or & argent (pearls, diamonds, gold and silver). No. 5231, Coton & fil de soie, broderie (cotton and silk thread embroidery).

Serpentine Die Cut 11

2017, Apr. 28   **Photo.**

Booklet Stamps
Self-Adhesive

5220	A2682	(73c) multi	1.60	.55
5221	A2682	(73c) multi	1.60	.55
5222	A2682	(73c) multi	1.60	.55
5223	A2682	(73c) multi	1.60	.55
5224	A2682	(73c) multi	1.60	.55
5225	A2682	(73c) multi	1.60	.55
5226	A2682	(73c) multi	1.60	.55
5227	A2682	(73c) multi	1.60	.55
5228	A2682	(73c) multi	1.60	.55
5229	A2682	(73c) multi	1.60	.55
5230	A2682	(73c) multi	1.60	.55
5231	A2682	(73c) multi	1.60	.55
a.		Booklet pane of 12, #5220-5231	19.50	
		Nos. 5220-5231 (12)	19.20	6.60

Cholet A2683

2017, Apr. 28	**Engr.**		**Perf. 13x13¼**	
5232	A2683	73c multi + label	1.60	.55

French Federation of Philatelic Associations, 90th Congress, Cholet.

Bid of Paris to Host 2024 Summer Olympics and Paralympics — A2684

2017, May 13	**Photo.**		**Perf. 13x13¼**	
5233	A2684	73c multi + label	1.75	.60

For overprint, see No. 5303.

Chambord, Azay-le-Rideau and Chenonceau Chateaus — A2685

2017, May 14	**Photo.**		**Perf. 13x12¾**	
5234	A2685	€1.10 multi	2.50	.85

Europa.

Coupe de France Soccer Tournament, Cent. — A2686

2017, May 19	**Photo.**		**Perf. 13¼**	
5235	A2686	73c multi	1.75	.60

Saint-Benoît-sur-Loire Abbey — A2687

2017, May 19	**Engr.**		**Perf. 13¼**	
5236	A2687	73c multi	1.75	.60

Insects — A2688

Designs: No. 5237, Coccinelle (ladybug). No. 5238: a, Demoiselle (banded damselfly). b, Hanneton (cockchafer), vert. c, Carabe (beetle), vert.

2017, May 19	**Photo.**		**Perf. 13¼**	
5237	A2688	73c multi	1.75	.60
5238		Sheet of 4, #5237, 5238a-5238c	7.00	7.00
a.-c.		A2688 73c Any single	1.75	.60

Two souvenir sheets, one containing Nos. 5237 and 5238c, and the other containing Nos. 5238a and 5238b, sold as a set for €6.20.

National Sea Rescue Society, 50th Anniv. — A2689

2017, May 23	**Photo.**		**Perf. 13¼**	
5239	A2689	85c multi	1.90	.65

Lions Clubs International, Cent. — A2690

2017, May 27	**Photo.**		**Perf. 13¼**	
5240	A2690	85c multi	1.90	.65

Haunted House Ride — A2691   Bumper Cars — A2692

Cotton Candy — A2693   Carousel — A2694

Candy Apples — A2695   Duck Hooking Game — A2696

Stuffed Animal Prizes — A2697   Ferris Wheel — A2698

Roller Coaster — A2699   Bowling — A2700

Swing Ride — A2701   Slide — A2702

Serpentine Die Cut 11

2017, June 2   **Photo.**

Booklet Stamps
Self-Adhesive

5241	A2691	(73c) multi	1.75	.60
5242	A2692	(73c) multi	1.75	.60
5243	A2693	(73c) multi	1.75	.60
5244	A2694	(73c) multi	1.75	.60
5245	A2695	(73c) multi	1.75	.60
5246	A2696	(73c) multi	1.75	.60
5247	A2697	(73c) multi	1.75	.60
5248	A2698	(73c) multi	1.75	.60
5249	A2699	(73c) multi	1.75	.60
5250	A2700	(73c) multi	1.75	.60
5251	A2701	(73c) multi	1.75	.60
5252	A2702	(73c) multi	1.75	.60
a.		Booklet pane of 12, #5241-5252	21.00	
		Nos. 5241-5252 (12)	21.00	7.20

Louis Vicat (1786-1861), Buildings and Bridge — A2703

2017, June 2	**Photo.**		**Perf. 13¼**	
5253	A2703	€1.30 multi	3.00	1.00

Invention of artificial cement by Vicat, 200th anniv.

Art Issue

Woman, Sculpture by Jeanne Bardey (1872-1954) A2704

2017, June 2	**Engr.**		**Perf. 13¼x13**	
5254	A2704	€1.70 multi	4.00	2.00

Rochefort-en-Terre — A2705

2017, June 14	**Engr.**		**Perf. 13¼**	
5255	A2705	73c multi	1.75	.60

Arrival of American Troops in World War I, Cent. — A2706

2017, June 23	**Engr.**		**Perf. 13¼**	
5256	A2706	€1.30 multi	3.00	1.00

Joachim Murat (1767-1815), French Marshal and Admiral and King of Naples — A2707

2017, June 23	**Engr.**		**Perf. 13¼**	
5257	A2707	85c multi	2.00	.70

Harness Race at Rambouillet Hippodrome A2708

2017, June 24	**Photo.**		**Perf. 13¼**	
5258	A2708	73c multi	1.75	.60

Diplomatic Relations Between France and the Philippines, 70th Anniv. — A2709

Unnamed painting by: 85c, Philippine painter Macario Vitalis (1898-1989). €1.30, French painter Jacques Villon (1875-1963).

2017, June 26	**Photo.**		**Perf. 13¼**	
5259	A2709	85c multi	2.00	.70
5260	A2709	€1.30 multi	3.00	1.00
a.		Souvenir sheet of 2, #5259-5260	7.50	7.50

No. 5260a sold for €3.20. See Philippines No. 3732.

Souvenir Sheet

French History A2710

No. 5261: a, Anne of France (1461-1522), Duchess of Beaujeu (41x53mm oval stamp). b, Treaty of Picquigny, 1475 (53x42mm).

Perf., Perf. 13x13¼ (#5261b)

2017, June 30   **Engr.**

5261	A2710	Sheet of 2	7.00	7.00
a.-b.		€1.46 Either single	3.50	1.25

A 200x95mm sheet containing Nos. 5261a and 5261b, but with a different margin design sold for €6.50.

Grains — A2711

Designs: No. 5262, Avoine (oats). No. 5263, Blé dur (durum wheat). No. 5264, Mais (corn). No. 5265, Millet. No. 5266, Riz (rice). No. 5267, Seigle (rye). No. 5268, Blé tendre (soft wheat). No. 5269, Epeautre (spelt). No. 5270, Orge (barley). No. 5271, Petit épautre (einkorn wheat). No. 5272, Sorgho (sorghum). No. 5273, Triticale.

Serpentine Die Cut 11

2017, June 30   **Photo.**

Booklet Stamps
Self-Adhesive

5262	A2711	(85c) multi	2.00	.70
5263	A2711	(85c) multi	2.00	.70
5264	A2711	(85c) multi	2.00	.70
5265	A2711	(85c) multi	2.00	.70
5266	A2711	(85c) multi	2.00	.70
5267	A2711	(85c) multi	2.00	.70
5268	A2711	(85c) multi	2.00	.70
5269	A2711	(85c) multi	2.00	.70
5270	A2711	(85c) multi	2.00	.70
5271	A2711	(85c) multi	2.00	.70
5272	A2711	(85c) multi	2.00	.70
5273	A2711	(85c) multi	2.00	.70
a.		Booklet pane of 12, #5262-5273	24.00	
		Nos. 5262-5273 (12)	24.00	8.40

Cherbourg-en-Cotentin — A2712

2017, July 7   **Engr.**   **Perf. 13¼**

5274	A2712	73c multi	1.75	.60

Trees of the Mediterranean Area — A2713

2017, July 10   **Photo.**   **Perf. 13¼**

5275	A2713	€1.10 multi	2.60	.90

2017 World Wrestling Championships, Paris — A2714

2017, July 22   **Photo.**   **Perf. 13x12¾**

5276	A2714	€1.30 multi	3.25	1.10

Espelette Pepper A2715   Woman Holding Strawberry A2716

Loaf of Bread, Croissant and Roll — A2717   Chocolate Bar Elephant — A2718

Beans — A2719   Lobster — A2720

Woman Drinking Citrus Juice — A2721   Cows and Cheese — A2722

Tomato and Olive Salad — A2723   Toucan With Cup of Coffee — A2724

Toast With Flavored Honey — A2725   People Drinking Mint Tea — A2726

Serpentine Die Cut 11

2017, Aug. 5   **Photo.**

Booklet Stamps
Self-Adhesive

5277	A2715	(73c) multi	1.75	.60
5278	A2716	(73c) multi	1.75	.60
5279	A2717	(73c) multi	1.75	.60
5280	A2718	(73c) multi	1.75	.60
5281	A2719	(73c) multi	1.75	.60
5282	A2720	(73c) multi	1.75	.60
5283	A2721	(73c) multi	1.75	.60
5284	A2722	(73c) multi	1.75	.60
5285	A2723	(73c) multi	1.75	.60
5286	A2724	(73c) multi	1.75	.60
5287	A2725	(73c) multi	1.75	.60
5288	A2726	(73c) multi	1.75	.60
a.		Booklet pane of 12, #5277-5288	21.00	
		Nos. 5277-5288 (12)	21.00	7.20

Sense of taste.

Le Havre, 500th Anniv. — A2727

2017, Aug. 31   **Engr.**   **Perf. 13¼**

5289	A2727	85c multi	2.10	.70

Bridges — A2728

Designs: No. 5290, Pont du Gard, Vers-Pont-du-Gard, France. No. 5291, Pont du Diable, Saint-Jean-de-Fos, France. No. 5292, Morlaix Viaduct, Morlaix, France. No. 5293, Digoin Canal Bridge, Digoin, France. No. 5294, Garabit Viaduct, Ruynes-en-Margeride, France. No. 5295, Tower Bridge, London. No. 5296, Pont Valentré, Cahors, France. No. 5297, Ponte Vecchio, Florence. No. 5298, U Bein Bridge, Amarapura, Myanmar. No. 5299, Manhattan and Brooklyn Bridges, New York City. No. 5300, Pont Alexandre III and Pont de la Concorde, Paris. No. 5301, Rochefort-Martrou Transporter Bridge, Rochefort, France.

Serpentine Die Cut 11

2017, Sept. 1   **Photo.**

Booklet Stamps
Self-Adhesive

5290	A2728	(73c) multi	1.75	.60
5291	A2728	(73c) multi	1.75	.60
5292	A2728	(73c) multi	1.75	.60
5293	A2728	(73c) multi	1.75	.60
5294	A2728	(73c) multi	1.75	.60
5295	A2728	(73c) multi	1.75	.60
5296	A2728	(73c) multi	1.75	.60
5297	A2728	(73c) multi	1.75	.60
5298	A2728	(73c) multi	1.75	.60
5299	A2728	(73c) multi	1.75	.60
5300	A2728	(73c) multi	1.75	.60
5301	A2728	(73c) multi	1.75	.60
a.		Booklet pane of 12, #5290-5301	21.00	
		Nos. 5290-5301 (12)	21.00	7.20

Normandie-Niemen Air Regiment, 75th Anniv. — A2729

2017, Sept. 1   **Engr.**   **Perf. 13x12¾**

5302	A2729	€1.30 multi	3.25	1.10

A souvenir sheet containing No. 5302, a denominated example of No. 5302 with black and red inks only, and a non-denominated example of No. 5302 without the black and red inks sold for €6.20. See Russia No. 7843.

No. 5233 Overprinted in Dark Blue

Method and Perf. As Before
2017, Sept. 13

5303	A2684	73c multi + label	1.75	.60

Selection of Paris as host city of 2024 Summer Olympics.

Art Issue

The Kiss, Sculpture by Auguste Rodin (1840-1917) A2730

2017, Sept. 15   **Engr.**   **Perf. 13¼x13**

5304	A2730	€1.30 multi	3.25	1.60

A souvenir sheet containing No. 5304 sold for €3.20.

Nadia Boulanger (1887-1979), Conductor and Teacher — A2731

2017, Sept. 16   **Engr.**   **Perf. 13¼x13**

5305	A2731	85c multi	2.00	.70

Jeanne Lanvin (1867-1946), Fashion Designer A2732

2017, Sept. 23   **Photo.**   **Perf. 13¼x13**

5306	A2732	€1.46 multi	3.50	1.25

A souvenir sheet containing No. 5306 sold for €3.20.

Characters Maestro, Nabot and Globus From *Hello Maestro!* Animated Television Series — A2733

2017, Sept. 23   **Photo.**   **Perf. 13¼**

5307	A2733	73c multi	1.75	.60
a.		Miniature sheet of 10		

Woman in Hoop A2734   Elephant Act A2735

Rabbit in Magician's Hat A2736   Mime A2737

Lion Tamer A2738   Acrobat A2739

Human Tower A2740   Clown Playing Guitar A2741

Ringmaster A2742   Unicyclist A2743

Trick Rider on Horse A2744   Aerial Contortionist A2745

Serpentine Die Cut 11

2017, Sept. 29   **Photo.**

Booklet Stamps
Self-Adhesive

5308	A2734	(73c) multi	1.75	.60
5309	A2735	(73c) multi	1.75	.60
5310	A2736	(73c) multi	1.75	.60
5311	A2737	(73c) multi	1.75	.60
5312	A2738	(73c) multi	1.75	.60
5313	A2739	(73c) multi	1.75	.60
5314	A2740	(73c) multi	1.75	.60
5315	A2741	(73c) multi	1.75	.60
5316	A2742	(73c) multi	1.75	.60
5317	A2743	(73c) multi	1.75	.60
5318	A2744	(73c) multi	1.75	.60
5319	A2745	(73c) multi	1.75	.60
a.		Booklet pane of 12, #5308-5319	21.00	
		Nos. 5308-5319 (12)	21.00	7.20

Circus acts.

Electronic Military
Transmissions,
150th
Anniv. — A2746

2017, Sept. 29   **Photo.**   *Perf. 13¼*
5320   A2746   €1.46 multi   3.50   1.25

Father Victor Dillard (1897-1945),
Minister to Deported French Slaves of
Germany in World War II — A2747

2017, Oct. 6   **Engr.**   *Perf. 13¼*
5321   A2747   73c multi   1.75   .60

Miniature Sheet

Actors and Actresses — A2748

No. 5322: a, Magali Noel (1931-2015). b,
Bruno Crémer (1929-2010). c, Odile Versois
(1930-80). d, Jean-Claude Brialy (1933-2007).

2017, Oct. 13   **Photo.**   *Perf. 13¼*
5322   A2748   Sheet of 4   8.00   8.00
a.-d.   85c Any single   2.00   .70

Joseph Peyré
(1892-1968),
Writer — A2749

2017, Oct. 20   **Engr.**   *Perf. 13¼*
5323   A2749   €1.10 multi   2.60   .90

A2750

A2751

A2752

A2753

A2754

A2755

A2756

A2757

A2758

A2759

A2760

Contest Stamps
With Scratch-off
Panel — A2761

Serpentine Die Cut 11
2017, Nov. 6   **Photo.**
     Booklet Stamps
     Self-Adhesive
5324   A2750   (73c) gold & multi   1.75   .60
  a.   Scratched panel   .40
5325   A2751   (73c) gold & multi   1.75   .60
  a.   Scratched panel   .40
5326   A2752   (73c) gold & multi   1.75   .60
  a.   Scratched panel   .40
5327   A2753   (73c) gold & multi   1.75   .60
  a.   Scratched panel   .40
5328   A2754   (73c) gold & multi   1.75   .60
  a.   Scratched panel   .40
5329   A2755   (73c) gold & multi   1.75   .60
  a.   Scratched panel   .40
5330   A2756   (73c) gold & multi   1.75   .60
  a.   Scratched panel   .40
5331   A2757   (73c) gold & multi   1.75   .60
  a.   Scratched panel   .40
5332   A2758   (73c) gold & multi   1.75   .60
  a.   Scratched panel   .40
5333   A2759   (73c) gold & multi   1.75   .60
  a.   Scratched panel   .40
5334   A2760   (73c) gold & multi   1.75   .60
  a.   Scratched panel   .40
5335   A2761   (73c) gold & multi   1.75   .60
  a.   Scratched panel   .40
  b.   Booklet pane of 12, #5324-
       5335   21.00
     Nos. 5324-5335 (12)   21.00   7.20

**Sabine Type of 1977-78 With
Denominations in Euros**
2017, Nov. 9   **Engr.**   *Perf. 13*
5336   A771   €1 red   2.40   .80
5337   A771   €1 green   2.40   .80
  a.   Pair, #5336-5337   4.80   1.60
      Size: 30x47mm
5338   A771   €5 red   12.00   4.00
5339   A771   €5 green   12.00   4.00
  a.   Horiz. pair, #5338-5339   24.00   8.00
     Nos. 5336-5339 (4)   28.80   9.60
     Booklet Stamps
5340   A771   73c green   1.75   .60
5341   A771   85c red   2.00   .65
  a.   Booklet pane of 12, 6 each
       #5340-5341   22.50
      Size: 30x47mm
5342   A771   €1.46 green   3.50   1.25
5343   A771   €1.70 red   4.00   1.40
  a.   Booklet pane of 2, #5342-
       5343   7.50

Complete booklet, #5341a,
   5343a   30.00
   Nos. 5340-5343 (4)   11.25   3.90
Nos. 5336-5339 were printed in sheets of 12
containing 5 each Nos. 5336-5337 and 1 each
Nos. 5338-5339.

Souvenir Sheet

Tulle
Lace
A2762

No. 5344: a, Butterfly. b, Rose.

     Photo. & Engr.
2017, Nov. 9   *Perf. 13¼*
5344   A2762   Sheet of 2   4.00   4.00
a.-b.   85c Either single   2.00   .65

Augustin-Alphonse Marty (1862-1940),
Reformer of Military Postal
System — A2763

2017, Nov. 10   **Engr.**   *Perf. 13¼x13*
5345   A2763   73c multi   1.75   .60

Art Issue

Spaces and
Lights, by
Geneviève
Asse — A2764

2017, Nov. 10   **Photo.**   *Perf. 13¼x13*
5346   A2764   €1.70 multi   4.00   2.00

Miniature Sheet

Postal
Balances
and
Scales
A2765

No. 5347 — Inscription: a, Balance
Romaine. b, Pèse-lettres Type "Roberval,"
horiz. c, Balance de Guichet. d, Balance à
Fléau. e, Balance à Trébuchet, horiz. f, Pèse-
lettres de Poche.

     Litho. & Engr.
2017, Nov. 11   *Perf. 13*
5347   A2765   Sheet of 6   10.50   10.50
a.-f.   73c Any single   1.75   .60
  g.   Souvenir sheet of 3,
       #5347a, 5347c, 5347e   7.50   7.50
  h.   Souvenir sheet of 3,
       #5347b, 5347d, 5347f   7.50   7.50
Nos. 5347g and 5347h were sold together
for €6.20.

Cabinetmaking
A2766

2017, Nov. 12   **Engr.**   *Perf. 12¼*
5348   A2766   €1.10 multi   2.60   .85

Photographs of
Natural
Phenomena
A2767

Inscriptions: No. 5357, Détail de marbre
(detail of marble, buff panel). No. 5358, Détail
de marbre (detail of marble, red panel). No.
5359, Tronc d'arbre (tree trunk). No. 5360,
Eau gelée (ice crystals). No. 5361, Sable-
traces de crabes (sand balls made by crabs).
No. 5362, Bulles d'air dans la glace (air bubbles in ice). No. 5363, Lichen crustacé sur un
rocher (lichen covering rock). No. 5364, Roche
chargeé de fer (iron in rock). No. 5365,
Flyschs à helminthoides (worm trails). No.
5366, Concrétions (rock concretions). No.
5367, Début de rouille (beginnings of rust).
No. 5368, Minerai de fer sur la roche (iron ore
in rock).

Serpentine Die Cut 11
2018, Jan. 5   **Photo.**
     Booklet Stamps
     Self-Adhesive
5357   A2767   (95c) multi   2.40   .80
5358   A2767   (95c) multi   2.40   .80
5359   A2767   (95c) multi   2.40   .80
5360   A2767   (95c) multi   2.40   .80
5361   A2767   (95c) multi   2.40   .80
5362   A2767   (95c) multi   2.40   .80
5363   A2767   (95c) multi   2.40   .80
5364   A2767   (95c) multi   2.40   .80
5365   A2767   (95c) multi   2.40   .80
5366   A2767   (95c) multi   2.40   .80
5367   A2767   (95c) multi   2.40   .80
5368   A2767   (95c) multi   2.40   .80
  a.   Booklet pane of 12, #5357-
       5368   29.00
     Nos. 5357-5368 (12)   28.80   9.60

Heart and   Heart and
Faces — A2768   Lips — A2769

2018, Jan. 12   **Photo.**   *Perf. 13¼*
5369   A2768   80c blk & red   2.00   .65
  a.   Souvenir sheet of 5   10.00   10.00
5370   A2769   €1.60 blk & red   4.00   1.40
     Self-Adhesive
    Serpentine Die Cut
5371   A2768   80c blk & red   2.00   .65
5372   A2769   €1.60 blk & red   4.00   1.40
Values for Nos. 5369-5370 are for stamps
with surrounding selvage.

Art Issue

Le Quai aux Fleurs, Notre-Dame, by
Léonard Foujita (1886-1968) — A2770

2018, Jan. 26   **Photo.**   *Perf. 13x13¼*
5373   A2770   €1.90 multi   4.75   2.40

Clermont-Ferrand Short Film Festival, 40th Anniv. — A2771

2018, Feb. 2 Photo. Perf. 13¼
5374 A2771 €1.30 multi 3.25 1.10

Sculptures of Dogs — A2772

Designs: No. 5375, African wooden sculpture of dog. No. 5376, Sculpture of spaniel by Antoine-Louis Barye (1795-1875). No. 5377, Sculpture of Boston terrier by François Pompon (1855-1933). No. 5378, Japanese sculpture of dog on table. No. 5379, Oriental sculptures of two dogs facing left. No. 5380, Egyptian sculpture of dog. No. 5381, Oriental sculpture of dog and bowl. No. 5382, Sculpture of basset hound by Barye. No. 5383, Chinese sculpture of dog. No. 5384, Two European sculptures of spaniels. No. 5385, Sculpture of dog by Louis de Monard (1873-1939). No. 5386, Asian sculpture of dog with ball.

Serpentine Die Cut 11
2018, Feb. 2 Photo.
Booklet Stamp
Self-Adhesive
5375 A2772 (80c) multi 2.00 .65
5376 A2772 (80c) multi 2.00 .65
5377 A2772 (80c) multi 2.00 .65
5378 A2772 (80c) multi 2.00 .65
5379 A2772 (80c) multi 2.00 .65
5380 A2772 (80c) multi 2.00 .65
5381 A2772 (80c) multi 2.00 .65
5382 A2772 (80c) multi 2.00 .65
5383 A2772 (80c) multi 2.00 .65
5384 A2772 (80c) multi 2.00 .65
5385 A2772 (80c) multi 2.00 .65
5386 A2772 (80c) multi 2.00 .65
a. Booklet pane of 12, #5375-5386 24.00
Nos. 5375-5386 (12) 24.00 7.80

Art Issue

Desir, Sculpture by Annette Messager A2773

2018, Feb. 16 Photo. Perf. 13x13¼
5387 A2773 €1.90 multi 4.75 2.40

Suzanne Noel (1878-1954), Plastic Surgeon — A2774

2018, Mar. 2 Photo. Perf. 13¼
5388 A2774 95c multi 2.40 .80

17th Century Tableware A2775

Designs: No. 5389, Cup made in Nevers. No. 5390, Plate made in Lille. No. 5391, Terrine made in Vincennes. No. 5392, Plate made in Moustiers-Sainte-Marie. No. 5393, Decorative cruet made in Strasbourg. No. 5394, Plate made in Limoges. No. 5395, Plate made in Moulins. No. 5396, Dessert service made in Gien. No. 5397, Tureen made in Sceaux. No. 5398, Plates made in Lyon. No. 5399, Plate and ewer made in Sèvres. No. 5400, Pot with lid made in Chantilly.

Serpentine Die Cut 11
2018, Mar. 2 Photo.
Booklet Stamp
Self-Adhesive
5389 A2775 (80c) multi 2.00 .65
5390 A2775 (80c) multi 2.00 .65
5391 A2775 (80c) multi 2.00 .65
5392 A2775 (80c) multi 2.00 .65
5393 A2775 (80c) multi 2.00 .65
5394 A2775 (80c) multi 2.00 .65
5395 A2775 (80c) multi 2.00 .65
5396 A2775 (80c) multi 2.00 .65
5397 A2775 (80c) multi 2.00 .65
5398 A2775 (80c) multi 2.00 .65
5399 A2775 (80c) multi 2.00 .65
5400 A2775 (80c) multi 2.00 .65
a. Booklet pane of 12, #5389-5400 24.00
Nos. 5389-5400 (12) 24.00 7.80

Stamp Day — A2776

Automobiles: 80c, Alpine Renault A110. €1.60, Renault Maxi 5 Turbo.

2018, Mar. 10 Engr. Perf. 13¼
5401 A2776 80c multi 2.00 .65
Souvenir Sheet
Photo.
Perf. 13
5402 A2776 €1.60 multi 4.00 1.40
No. 5402 contains one 52x41mm stamp.

Art Issue

Plans Par Couleurs, by Frantisek Kupka (1871-1957) A2777

2018, Mar. 18 Photo. Perf. 12¼x13
5403 A2777 €1.90 multi 4.75 2.40
A souvenir sheet containing a perf. 13¼ example of No. 5403 and three labels sold for €4.

Savings Banks, 200th Anniv. — A2778

2018, Mar. 22 Photo. Perf. 13¼
5404 A2778 95c multi 2.40 .80

Tourist Attractions A2779

Designs: No. 5405, Umbrellas on beach, Deauville. No. 5406, Chaîne des Puys. No. 5407, Dune of Pilat. No. 5408, Eiffel Tower and Tour Montparnasse, Paris. No. 5409, Vineyard, Bourgogne. No. 5410, Mont Blanc massif. No. 5411, Field, Alpes-de-Haute-Provence. No. 5412, Rocks on beach, Belle-Ile-en-Mer.

Serpentine Die Cut 11
2018, Mar. 23 Photo.
Booklet Stamps
Self-Adhesive
5405 A2779 (€1.30) multi 3.25 1.10
5406 A2779 (€1.30) multi 3.25 1.10
5407 A2779 (€1.30) multi 3.25 1.10
5408 A2779 (€1.30) multi 3.25 1.10
5409 A2779 (€1.30) multi 3.25 1.10
5410 A2779 (€1.30) multi 3.25 1.10
5411 A2779 (€1.30) multi 3.25 1.10
5412 A2779 (€1.30) multi 3.25 1.10
a. Booklet pane of 8, #5405-5412 26.00
Nos. 5405-5412 (8) 26.00 8.80

A2780

2018, Mar. 24 Photo. Perf. 13x13¼
5413 A2780 80c multi + label 2.00 .65
Posts, Telegraphs and Telecommunications Sporting Association, 120th Anniv.

Leatherwork A2781

2018, Mar. 30 Engr. Perf. 12¼
5414 A2781 €1.30 multi 3.25 1.10

Sorgues A2782

2018, Apr. 6 Engr. Perf. 13
5415 A2782 95c multi 2.25 .75
Spring Philatelic Show, Sorgues.

Sosthène Mortenol (1859-1930), Naval Hero — A2783

Litho. & Engr.
2018, Apr. 13 Perf. 13x13¼
5416 A2783 €1.20 multi 3.00 1.00

Miniature Sheet

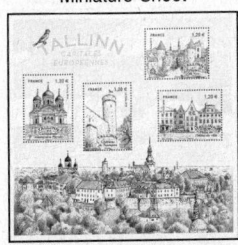

European Capitals — A2784

No. 5417 — Attractions in Tallinn, Estonia: a, Viru Gate. b, Alexander Nexsky Cathedral, vert. c, Toompea Castle, vert. d, Town Hall Square.

Perf. 13x13¼, 13¼x13
2018, Apr. 20 Photo.
5417 A2784 Sheet of 4 12.00 12.00
a.-d. €1.20 Any single 3.00 1.00

Souvenir Sheet

Vrai Guignolet Puppet Theater, Paris, 200th Anniv. — A2785

No. 5418: a, Two puppets with red and green headdresses. b, Two puppets, hot air balloon in background.

2018, May 10 Engr. Perf. 13
5418 A2785 Sheet of 2 12.00 12.00
a.-b. €2.60 Either single 6.00 2.00

Deux Rives Pedestrian Bridge, Strasbourg A2786

2018, May 18 Photo. Perf. 13¼
5419 A2786 €1.20 multi 3.00 1.00
Europa.

A2787 A2788

A2789 A2790

A2791 A2792

A2793 A2794

A2795 A2796

A2797 Emojis — A2798

Serpentine Die Cut 11
2018, May 18 Photo.
Booklet Stamps
Self-Adhesive
5420 A2787 (80c) multi 1.90 .65
5421 A2788 (80c) multi 1.90 .65
5422 A2789 (80c) multi 1.90 .65
5423 A2790 (80c) multi 1.90 .65
5424 A2791 (80c) multi 1.90 .65
5425 A2792 (80c) multi 1.90 .65
5426 A2793 (80c) multi 1.90 .65
5427 A2794 (80c) multi 1.90 .65
5428 A2795 (80c) multi 1.90 .65
5429 A2796 (80c) multi 1.90 .65
5430 A2797 (80c) multi 1.90 .65
5431 A2798 (80c) multi 1.90 .65
a. Booklet pane of 12, #5420-5431 23.00
Nos. 5420-5431 (12) 22.80 7.80

Lucie (1912-2007) and Raymond Aubrac (1914-2012), World War II Resistance Leaders — A2799

2018, May 26 Engr. Perf. 13x13¼
5432 A2799 €1.30 multi 3.00 1.00

United Nations Peacekeepers, 70th Anniv. — A2800

2018, May 29 Photo. Perf. 13
5433 A2800 €1.30 multi 3.00 1.00

A2801

Photographs of Earth Features Taken By Thomas Pesquet on the International Space Station: No. 5434, Snow and three lines of trees, Russia, taken Feb. 16, 2017. No. 5435, Paris, France, taken Apr. 14, 2017. No. 5436, Betsiboka River, Madagascar, taken May 6, 2017. No. 5437, Bijagos Archipelago, Guinea-Bissau, taken Feb. 4, 2017. No. 5438, Green River, Utah, taken Apr. 14, 2017. No. 5439, Persian Gulf islands, taken Dec. 31, 2016. No. 5440, Irrigated fields in desert, Saudi Arabia, taken Jan. 1, 2017. No. 5441, Fields, Spain, taken Apr. 12, 2017. No. 5442, Road in wilderness, Canada, taken Dec. 26, 2016. No. 5443, Melting ice in Himalayas, People's Republic of China, taken Apr. 27, 2017. No. 5444, Ile de Noirmoutier, France, taken Feb. 16, 2017. No. 5445, Coral reef and volcanic islands, French Polynesia, taken Mar. 16, 2017.

Serpentine Die Cut 11

2018, June 2			Photo.
Self-Adhesive			
Booklet Stamps			
5434	A2801	(80c) multi	1.90 .65
5435	A2801	(80c) multi	1.90 .65
5436	A2801	(80c) multi	1.90 .65
5437	A2801	(80c) multi	1.90 .65
5438	A2801	(80c) multi	1.90 .65
5439	A2801	(80c) multi	1.90 .65
5440	A2801	(80c) multi	1.90 .65
5441	A2801	(80c) multi	1.90 .65
5442	A2801	(80c) multi	1.90 .65
5443	A2801	(80c) multi	1.90 .65
5444	A2801	(80c) multi	1.90 .65
5445	A2801	(80c) multi	1.90 .65
a.		Booklet pane of 12, #5434-5445	23.00
		Nos. 5434-5445 (12)	22.80 7.80

Elysée Palace, Paris
A2802

2018, June 7		Engr.	Perf. 13
5446	A2802	95c multi + label	2.25 .75

French Federation of Philatelic Associations, 91st Congress, Paris.

Nos. 4413 and 4437 Overprinted in Blue or Red

2018, June 8		Engr.	Perf. 13
5447	A2320	10c brown (Bl)	— —
5448	A2325	(80c) green (R)	— —

Nos. 5447-5448 were sold only at the Paris Philex show on the day of issue. The entire 250,000-stamp print run of No. 5448 sold out on the day of issue.

Miniature Sheets

A2803

Paris Philex 2018 Stamp Show
A2804

No. 5449 — French stamps depicting Paris landmarks of 1939-56 redrawn: a, Grand Trianon, Versailles (like #794). b, Church of the Invalides, vert. (like #B203). c, Eiffel Tower, vert. (like #B85). d, Alexander III Bridge, Petit Palais (like #C24).

No. 5450 — French Orphan Relief stamps of 1917-19 redrawn: a, Widow at gate, vert. (like #B3). b, War orphans, vert. (like #B4). c, Woman plowing (like #B5). d, Woman plowing (like #B6). e, "Trench of Bayonets" (like #B7). f, Lion of Belfort (like #B8). g, "La Marseillaise" (like #B9). h, "La Marseiillaise" (like #B10).

Engr., Sheet Margin Litho. With Foil Application

2018, June 7			Perf. 13
5449	A2803	Sheet of 4	23.50 23.50
a.		€2 brown lake	4.75 4.75
b.		€2 brown lake	4.75 4.75
c.		€2 brown lake	4.75 4.75
d.		€4 brown lake	9.25 9.25

Typo.

5450	A2804	Sheet of 8	71.00 71.00
a.		€1 violet brown	2.40 2.40
b.		€1 sage green	2.40 2.40
c.		€2 sage green	4.75 4.75
d.		€2 light blue	4.75 4.75
e.		€3 gray grn & lilac	7.00 7.00
f.		€3 brn pur & lt brn	7.00 7.00
g.		€3 brn rose & maroon	7.00 7.00
h.		€15 lt blue & gray grn	35.00 35.00

Art Issue

Self-portrait, by Edouard Vuillard (1868-1940)
A2805

2018, June 8		Photo.	Perf. 13x12¾
5451	A2805	€1.30 multi	3.00 1.50

No. 5451 was printed in sheets of 9 + 8 triangular labels.

Souvenir Sheet

French History
A2806

No. 5452: a, Treaty of the Pyrenees, 1659. b, Queen Maria Theresa (1638-83).

2018, June 9		Engr.	Perf. 13
5452	A2806	Sheet of 2	12.00 12.00
a.-b.		€2.60 Either single	6.00 6.00
c.		Souvenir sheet of 2, #5452a-5452b, with different sheet margin	18.50 18.50

No. 5452c sold for €8.

Birds — A2807

Designs: No. 5453, Mésange bleue (European blue tit).
No. 5454: a, Rouge-gorge (European robin). b, Moineau (sparrow). c, Pie (magpie).

2018, June 10		Photo.	Perf. 13¼
5453	A2807	80c multi	1.90 .65

Souvenir Sheet

5454		Sheet of 4, #5453, 5454a-5454c	7.75 7.75
a.-c.		A2807 80c Any single	1.90 .95
d.		Souvenir sheet of 2, #5454a-5454b	7.00 7.00
e.		Souvenir sheet of 2, #5453, 5454c	7.00 7.00

Nos. 5454d-5454e sold together as a set for €6.

Trois-Fontaines Abbey, 900th Anniv. — A2808

2018, June 15		Photo.	Perf. 13¼x13
5455	A2808	95c multi	2.25 .75

Tourism Issue

Kayserberg — A2809

2018, June 20		Photo.	Perf. 13x12¾
5456	A2809	80c multi	1.90 .65

Ploumanc'h Lighthouse, Perros-Guirec
A2810

2018, June 22		Photo.	Perf. 13¼
5457	A2810	80c multi	1.90 .65

Mickey Mouse and Eiffel Tower — A2811

Mickey Mouse and Mont-Saint-Michel Abbey — A2812

Mickey Mouse and Azay-le-Rideau Chateau — A2813

Mickey Mouse and Pont Saint-Bénézet, Avignon — A2814

Mickey Mouse and Bonifacio, Corsica — A2815

Mickey Mouse and Beach — A2816

Mickey Mouse and Etretat Cliffs — A2817

Mickey Mouse and Auvergne Region Volcano — A2818

Mickey Mouse and Cable Car — A2819

Mickey Mouse and Lumière Monument, Lyon — A2820

Mickey Mouse and Saint-Tropez A2821

Mickey Mouse and Strasbourg Cathedral
A2822

Serpentine Die Cut 11

2018, June 29			Photo.
Booklet Stamps			
Self-Adhesive			
5458	A2811	(80c) multi	1.90 .65
5459	A2812	(80c) multi	1.90 .65
5460	A2813	(80c) multi	1.90 .65
5461	A2814	(80c) multi	1.90 .65
5462	A2815	(80c) multi	1.90 .65
5463	A2816	(80c) multi	1.90 .65
5464	A2817	(80c) multi	1.90 .65
5465	A2818	(80c) multi	1.90 .65
5466	A2819	(80c) multi	1.90 .65
5467	A2820	(80c) multi	1.90 .65
5468	A2821	(80c) multi	1.90 .65
5469	A2822	(80c) multi	1.90 .65
a.		Booklet pane of 12, #5458-5869	23.00
		Nos. 5458-5469 (12)	22.80 7.80

Ryder Cup, Flags of United States and European Union — A2823

2018		Photo.	Perf. 13x13¼
5470	A2823	€1.30 multi + label	3.00 1.00
a.		Sheet of 4 + 4 labels, sheet margin with white background	12.00 12.00
5470B	A2823	€2.60 multi + label	6.00 2.00

42nd Ryder Cup Matches, Guyancourt. Issued: No. 5470, 6/30; No. 5470B, 9/15. No. 5470B was printed in sheets of 4.

Camargue Region House — A2824

2018, July 6		Photo.	Perf. 13¼
5471	A2824	€1.30 multi	3.00 1.00

Viaur Viaduct A2825

2018, July 6		Photo.	Perf. 13x12¾
5472	A2825	95c multi	2.25 .75

Marianne and Denomination A2826

Marianne "Ecopli" A2827

Marianne "Lettre Verte" A2828

Marianne "Lettre Prioritaire" A2829

Marianne "Europe" With Data Matrix Code — A2830

Marianne "Monde" With Data Matrix Code — A2831

2018, July 20 — Engr. — Perf. 13

5473	A2826	1c yellow	.25	.25
5474	A2826	5c dk brown	.25	.25
5475	A2826	10c brown	.25	.25
a.		Souvenir sheet of 3, #5473-5475	.60	.60
5476	A2826	(78c) dk gray	1.90	.50
5477	A2828	(80c) emerald	1.90	.50
5478	A2829	(95c) red	2.25	.55
a.		Souvenir sheet of 2, #5477-5478	6.75	6.75
b.		Booklet pane of 12, 6 each #5477-5478	25.00	—
c.		Tete-beche pair (6034a)	4.50	4.50
5479	A2826	€1 orange	2.40	.60
a.		Souvenir sheet of 2, #5476, 5479	6.75	6.75
5480	A2830	(€1.20) dull blue	2.75	.70
5481	A2831	(€1.30) purple	3.00	.75
a.		Souvenir sheet of 5, #5476-5478, 5480-5481	12.00	12.00
b.		Souvenir sheet of 2, #5480-5481	9.50	9.50
		Nos. 5473-5481 (9)	14.95	4.35

Coil Stamps
Perf. 13 Horiz.

5482	A2828	(80c) emerald	1.90	.50
5483	A2829	(95c) red	2.25	.55

Self-Adhesive
Serpentine Die Cut 6¾ Vert.

5484	A2826	1c yellow	.25	.25
5485	A2826	5c dk brown	.25	.25
5486	A2826	10c brown	.25	.25
5487	A2827	(78c) dk gray	1.90	.50
5488	A2828	(80c) emerald	1.90	.50
a.		Booklet pane of 12	23.00	
5489	A2829	(95c) red	2.25	.55
a.		Booklet pane of 10	22.50	
b.		Booklet pane of 12	27.00	
c.		Booklet pane of 20	45.00	
5490	A2826	€1 orange	2.40	.60
5491	A2830	(€1.20) dull blue	2.75	.70
5492	A2831	(€1.30) purple	3.00	.75
		Nos. 5484-5492 (9)	14.95	4.35

Coil Stamps
Serpentine Die Cut 6¾ Horiz.

5493	A2828	(80c) emerald	1.90	.50
5494	A2829	(95c) red	2.25	.55

Issued: No. 5478b, 11/12/18; No. 5478c, 6/17/21. Nos. 5475a, 5478a, 5479a and 5481b sold as a set for €10.
Compare types A2831 and A2888.
See Nos. 5558-5561, 5756, 6036, 6129. For overprints, see Nos. 5539-5540, 5932.

Trees — A2832

Designs: No. 5495, Betula papyrifera. No. 5496, Adansonia digitata. No. 5497, Cedrus libani. No. 5498, Carpinus betulus. No. 5499, Quercus robur. No. 5500, Fraxinus excelsior. No. 5501, Acer saccharum. No. 5502, Pinus sylvestris. No. 5503, Sequoiadendron giganteum. No. 5504, Ginkgo biloba. No. 5505, Olea europaea. No. 5506, Fagus sylvatica.

Serpentine Die Cut 11
2018, Aug. 3 — Photo.
Booklet Stamps
Self-Adhesive

5495	A2832	(95c) multi	2.25	.75
5496	A2832	(95c) multi	2.25	.75
5497	A2832	(95c) multi	2.25	.75
5498	A2832	(95c) multi	2.25	.75
5499	A2832	(95c) multi	2.25	.75
5500	A2832	(95c) multi	2.25	.75
5501	A2832	(95c) multi	2.25	.75
5502	A2832	(95c) multi	2.25	.75
5503	A2832	(95c) multi	2.25	.75
5504	A2832	(95c) multi	2.25	.75
5505	A2832	(95c) multi	2.25	.75
5506	A2832	(95c) multi	2.25	.75
a.		Booklet pane of 12, #5495-5506	27.00	
		Nos. 5495-5506 (12)	27.00	9.00

Teapot From Jiangsu, China — A2833

Teapot From China — A2834

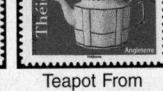

Teapot From England — A2835

Teapot From Sèvres, France A2836

Teapot From Delft, Netherlands A2837

Teapot From Jingdezhen, China — A2838

Teapot From Sèvres, France — A2839

Teapot From Kyoto, Japan — A2840

Teapot From Paris, France — A2841

Teapot From Moscow, Russia — A2842

Teapot From Venice, Italy — A2843

Teapot From Lille, France — A2844

Serpentine Die Cut 11
2018, Aug. 31 — Photo.
Booklet Stamps
Self-Adhesive

5507	A2833	(80c) multi	1.90	.65
5508	A2834	(80c) multi	1.90	.65
5509	A2835	(80c) multi	1.90	.65
5510	A2836	(80c) multi	1.90	.65
5511	A2837	(80c) multi	1.90	.65
5512	A2838	(80c) multi	1.90	.65
5513	A2839	(80c) multi	1.90	.65
5514	A2840	(80c) multi	1.90	.65
5515	A2841	(80c) multi	1.90	.65
5516	A2842	(80c) multi	1.90	.65
5517	A2843	(80c) multi	1.90	.65
5518	A2844	(80c) multi	1.90	.65
a.		Booklet pane of 12, #5507-5518	23.00	
		Nos. 5507-5518 (12)	22.80	7.80

Mickey Mouse, 90th Anniv. — A2845

2018, Sept. 5 — Photo. — Perf. 13¼x13

5519	A2845	€1.30 multi	3.00	1.00

Miniature Sheet

Stage Actors and Actresses — A2846

No. 5520: a, François-Joseph Talma (1763-1826). b, Rachel Félix (1821-58). c, Sarah Bernhardt (1844-1923). d, Benoît-Constant Coquelin (Coquelin Aîné) (1841-1909).

2018, Sept. 7 — Photo. — Perf. 13¼

5520	A2846	Sheet of 4 + 5 labels	11.00	11.00
a.-d.		€1.20 Any single	2.75	.90

Ceramics A2847

2018, Sept. 15 — Engr. — Perf. 13

5521	A2847	€1.30 multi	3.00	1.00

A souvenir sheet of 1 sold for €4.

Pierre Schoendoerffer (1928-2012), Film Director and War Reporter A2848

2018, Sept. 21 — Engr. — Perf. 13¼

5522	A2848	€1.30 multi	3.00	1.00

Louise de Bettignies (1880-1918), World War I Secret Agent — A2849

2018, Sept. 28 — Photo. — Perf. 13¼

5523	A2849	80c multi	1.90	.65

Rose Valland (1898-1980), Art Historian and World War II Resistance Leader — A2850

2018, Sept. 28 — Photo. — Perf. 13¼

5524	A2850	€1.20 multi	2.75	.90

Françoise Dolto (1908-88), Pediatrician and Psychoanalyst A2851

2018, Oct. 5 — Photo. — Perf. 13¼

5525	A2851	95c multi	2.25	.75

A2852

A2853

A2854

A2855

A2856

A2857

A2858

A2859

A2860

A2861

A2862

A2863

Photographs of Snowflakes

Serpentine Die Cut 11
2018, Oct. 5 — Photo.
Booklet Stamps
Self-Adhesive

5526	A2852	(80c) multi	1.90	.65
5527	A2853	(80c) multi	1.90	.65
5528	A2854	(80c) multi	1.90	.65
5529	A2855	(80c) multi	1.90	.65
5530	A2856	(80c) multi	1.90	.65
5531	A2857	(80c) multi	1.90	.65
5532	A2858	(80c) multi	1.90	.65
5533	A2859	(80c) multi	1.90	.65
5534	A2860	(80c) multi	1.90	.65
5535	A2861	(80c) multi	1.90	.65
5536	A2862	(80c) multi	1.90	.65
5537	A2863	(80c) multi	1.90	.65
a.		Booklet pane of 12, #5526-5537	23.00	
		Nos. 5526-5537 (12)	22.80	7.80

Elise (1898-1983) and Célestin (1896-1966) Freinet, Educational Reformers A2864

2018, Oct. 12 — Photo. — Perf. 13¼

5538	A2864	95c multi	2.25	.75

Nos. 5480-5481 Overprinted in Red or Blue

Methods and Perfs. As Before
2018, Oct. 15

5539	A2830	(€1.20) dull blue (R)	2.75	1.40
5540	A28310	(€1.30) purple (Bl)	3.00	1.50

Art Issue

Photograph of Woman Reading Letter by Sophie Calle A2865

2018, Oct. 19 — Photo. — Perf. 13x13¼

5541	A2865	€1.90 multi	4.50	2.25

Périgueux — A2866

2018, Oct. 26 — Engr. — Perf. 13x13¼

5542	A2866	80c multi + label	1.90	.65

Postal Checks,
Cent. — A2867

2018, Oct. 31   **Photo.**   *Perf. 12¼*
5543   A2867   80c multi   1.90   .65

Vases — A2868

Vase by: 95c, Emile Gallé (1846-1904),
France. €1.20, Antonija Krasnik (1874-1956),
Croatia.

2018, Nov. 8   **Photo.**   *Perf. 12¼*
5544   A2868   95c multi   2.25   .75
5545   A2868   €1.20 multi   2.75   .90

See Croatia Nos. 1092-1093.

"Bonne Année"
A2869

House and
Trees
A2870

Heart and
Flowers
A2871

Reindeer and
Flowers
A2872

"Bonne Année"
A2873

Candle,
Flowers and
Hearts
A2874

Christmas
Ornament
A2875

Reindeer
A2876

Gift
A2877

"Joyeuses
Fêtes"
A2878

"Joie"
A2879

Head of
Reindeer
A2880

Serpentine Die Cut 11
2018, Nov. 8   **Photo.**
Booklet Stamps
Self-Adhesive

5546	A2869	(80c) gold & multi	1.90	.65
		Scratched panel		.40
5547	A2870	(80c) gold & multi	1.90	.65
		Scratched panel		.40
5548	A2871	(80c) gold & multi	1.90	.65
		Scratched panel		.40
5549	A2872	(80c) gold & multi	1.90	.65
		Scratched panel		.40
5550	A2873	(80c) gold & multi	1.90	.65
		Scratched panel		.40
5551	A2874	(80c) gold & multi	1.90	.65
		Scratched panel		.40
5552	A2875	(80c) gold & multi	1.90	.65
		Scratched panel		.40
5553	A2876	(80c) gold & multi	1.90	.65
		Scratched panel		.40
5554	A2877	(80c) gold & multi	1.90	.65
		Scratched panel		.40
5555	A2878	(80c) gold & multi	1.90	.65
		Scratched panel		.40
5556	A2879	(80c) gold & multi	1.90	.65
		Scratched panel		.40
5557	A2880	(80c) gold & multi	1.90	.65
		Scratched panel		.40
a.		Booklet pane of 12, #5546-5557	23.00	
		Nos. 5546-5557 (12)	22.80	7.80

Christmas and New Year's greetings.

Marianne Types of 2018 and

Marianne
A2881

2018, Nov. 12   **Engr.**   *Perf. 13*
Booklet Stamps
Size: 30x46mm

5558	A2826	€1.60 green	3.75	1.25
5559	A2826	€1.90 red	4.50	1.50
a.		Booklet pane of 2, #5558-5559	8.25	—
		Complete booklet, #5478b, 5559a	33.50	

Self-Adhesive
Design Size: 15x23mm (Nos. 5560-5561)
Photo.
Serpentine Die Cut 11

5560	A2828	(80c) green	1.90	.50
5561	A2829	(95c) red	2.25	.60
5562	A2881	(€3.20) black & gray	7.25	2.40
a.		Bkt. pane of 13, #5562, 6 each #5560-5561	32.50	
		Nos. 5560-5562 (3)	11.40	3.50

Marianne "Lettre Suivie" — A2881a

2018 ?   **Litho.**   *Die Cut*
Self-Adhesive
5563   A2881a   (€1.28) cerise + label   —   —

Ivan Turgenev
(1818-83),
Writer — A2882

2018, Nov. 9   **Photo.**   *Perf. 13¼*
5565   A2882   €1.30 multi   3.00   1.00

Miniature Sheet

Hats
A2883

No. 5566: a, Capeline. b, Haut de forme (top
hat). c, Cloche. d, Mambo (pork pie hat), horiz.
e, Toque. f, Chapeau melon (bowler hat),
horiz.

Litho. & Engr.
2018, Nov. 9   *Perf. 13*

5566	A2883	Sheet of 6	13.50	13.50
a.-f.		95c Any single	2.25	.75
g.		Souvenir sheet of 3, #5566a, 5566d, 5566f	9.25	9.25
h.		Souvenir sheet of 3, #5566b, 5566c, 5566e	9.25	9.25

Nos. 5566g and 5566h were sold together
for €8.

Souvenir Sheet

World War I Armistice, Cent. — A2884

No. 5567: a, Soldiers celebrating. b, Civilians celebrating.

2018, Nov. 11   **Photo.**   *Perf. 13¼*

5567	A2884	Sheet of 2	12.00	12.00
a.-b.		€2.60 Either stamp	6.00	2.00
c.		Souvenir sheet of 2, #5567a-5567b, different sheet margin	18.50	18.50

No. 5567c sold for €8.

A2885

General Henri M.
Berthelot (1861-
1931)
A2886

2018, Nov. 27   **Photo.**   *Perf. 13¼*

5568	A2885	€1.30 multi	3.00	1.00
5569	A2886	€1.30 multi	3.00	1.00
a.		Souvenir sheet of 2, #5568-5569	9.25	9.25

No. 5569a sold for €4. See Romania Nos.
6201-6202.

Universal Declaration
of Human Rights, 70th
Anniv. — A2887

2018, Dec. 10   **Photo.**   *Perf. 13¼*
5570   A2887   88c multi   2.00   .65

Marianne
"International" and
Data Matrix
Code — A2888

2019, Jan. 1   **Engr.**   *Perf. 13*
5571   A2888   (€1.30) purple   3.00   .75
Booklet Stamp
Self-Adhesive
Serpentine Die Cut 6¾ Vert.
5572   A2888   (€1.30) purple   3.00   .75
   a.   Booklet pane of 6   18.00

Compare types A2831 and A2888.

A2889

A2890

A2891

A2892

A2893

A2894   A2895

A2896

A2897

A2898

A2899

African Fabric
Patterns — A2900

Serpentine Die Cut 11
2019, Jan. 4   **Photo.**
Booklet Stamps
Self-Adhesive

5573	A2889	(88c) multi	2.10	.70
5574	A2890	(88c) multi	2.10	.70
5575	A2891	(88c) multi	2.10	.70
5576	A2892	(88c) multi	2.10	.70
a.		Larger dots in flowers and background	2.10	.70
5577	A2893	(88c) multi	2.10	.70
5578	A2894	(88c) multi	2.10	.70
5579	A2895	(88c) multi	2.10	.70
5580	A2896	(88c) multi	2.10	.70
5581	A2897	(88c) multi	2.10	.70
5582	A2898	(88c) multi	2.10	.70
5583	A2899	(88c) multi	2.10	.70
5584	A2900	(88c) multi	2.10	.70
a.		Booklet pane of 12, #5573-5584	25.50	
		Nos. 5573-5584 (12)	25.20	8.40

No. 5576a was printed only in sheets of 50.

Emilie du Châtelet
(1706-49),
Philosopher,
Mathematician and
Physicist — A2901

2019, Jan. 18   **Photo.**   *Perf. 13¼*
5585   A2901   88c multi   2.10   .70

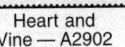

Heart and Vine — A2902

Heart and Vendôme Column, Paris — A2903

2019, Jan. 18   Photo.   Perf. 13¼
5586	A2902	88c multi	2.10	.70
a.		Souvenir sheet of 5	10.50	10.50
5587	A2903	€1.76 multi	4.00	1.40

Self-Adhesive
Serpentine Die Cut
5588	A2902	88c multi	2.10	.70
5589	A2903	€1.76 multi	4.00	1.40

Values for Nos. 5586-5589 are for stamps with surrounding selvage.

New Year 2019 (Year of the Pig) — A2904

Designs: 88c, Pig holding Chinese lantern. €1.30, Three pigs on Chinese lantern.

2019, Jan. 25   Photo.   Perf. 13
5590		Sheet of 5, #5590a, 4 #5590b	10.50	10.50
a.	A2904	88c 33x40mm stamp	2.10	.70
b.	A2904	88c 29x35mm stamp	2.10	.70
5591		Sheet of 5, #5591a, 4 #5591b	15.00	15.00
a.	A2904	€1.30 33x40mm stamp	3.00	1.00
b.	A2904	€1.30 29x35mm stamp	3.00	1.00

Architectural Details of French Buildings — A2905

Designs: No. 5592, Chapelle Sainte-Marie, Nevers. No. 5593, Château de Vitré. No. 5594, Grand Palais, Paris. No. 5595, Château de Chambord. No. 5596, Notre Dame Cathedral, Strasbourg. No. 5597, Pavilion de l'Horloge, Louvre Museum, Paris. No. 5598, Saline Royale (Royal Saltworks), Arc-et-Senans. No. 5599, Museum of Grenoble. No. 5600, Church, Saint-Nectaire. No. 5601, Notre-Dame-des-Champs Church, Avranches. No. 5602, Maison Carrée, Nîmes. No. 5603, Saint-Front Cathedral, Périgueux.

Serpentine Die Cut 11
2019, Feb. 1   Photo.
Booklet Stamps
Self-Adhesive
5592	A2905	(€1.05) multi	2.40	.80
5593	A2905	(€1.05) multi	2.40	.80
5594	A2905	(€1.05) multi	2.40	.80
5595	A2905	(€1.05) multi	2.40	.80
a.		Larger and coarser dot structure	2.40	.80
5596	A2905	(€1.05) multi	2.40	.80
a.		Larger and coarser dot structure	2.40	.80
5597	A2905	(€1.05) multi	2.40	.80
5598	A2905	(€1.05) multi	2.40	.80
5599	A2905	(€1.05) multi	2.40	.80
5600	A2905	(€1.05) multi	2.40	.80
5601	A2905	(€1.05) multi	2.40	.80
5602	A2905	(€1.05) multi	2.40	.80
5603	A2905	(€1.05) multi	2.40	.80
a.		Booklet pane of 12, #5592-5603	29.00	
		Nos. 5592-5603 (12)	28.80	9.60

Nos. 5595a and 5596a were both printed in sheets of 50. The larger and coarser dot structure can best be seen in the upper left triangle.

Louise de Vilmorin (1902-69), Writer — A2906

2019, Feb. 8   Photo.   Perf. 13¼
5604	A2906	€1.05 multi	2.40	.80

Sister Cities of Dinan, France and Dinant, Belgium A2907

2019, Feb. 15   Photo.   Perf. 13x12¾
5605	A2907	€1.30 multi	3.00	1.00

Saltwater Fish — A2908

Designs: No. 5606, Thunnus thynnus. No. 5607, Scorpaena scrofa. No. 5608, Dicentrarchus labrax. No. 5609, Zeus faber. No. 5610, Sparus aurata. No. 5611, Scophthalmus maximus. No. 5612, Solea solea. No. 5613, Scomber scombrus. No. 5614, Epinephelus marginatus. No. 5615, Ssrdina pilchardus. No. 5616, Raja clavata. No. 5617, Gadus morhua.

Serpentine Die Cut 11
2019, Feb. 22   Photo.
Booklet Stamps
Self-Adhesive
5606	A2908	(88c) multi	2.00	.65
5607	A2908	(88c) multi	2.00	.65
5608	A2908	(88c) multi	2.00	.65
5609	A2908	(88c) multi	2.00	.65
5610	A2908	(88c) multi	2.00	.65
5611	A2908	(88c) multi	2.00	.65
5612	A2908	(88c) multi	2.00	.65
5613	A2908	(88c) multi	2.00	.65
5614	A2908	(88c) multi	2.00	.65
5615	A2908	(88c) multi	2.00	.65
5616	A2908	(88c) multi	2.00	.65
5617	A2908	(88c) multi	2.00	.65
a.		Booklet pane of 12, #5606-5617	24.00	
		Nos. 5606-5617 (12)	24.00	7.80

Art Series

Calendula (Marigold), Photograph by Valérie Belin — A2909

2019, Feb. 22   Litho.   Perf. 13
5618	A2909	€2.10 multi	4.75	2.40

Citroen Automobiles A2910

Designs: 88c, Citroen Type A 10 HP. €1.76, Citroen Traction.

2019, Mar. 9   Photo.   Perf. 13¼
5619	A2910	88c multi	2.00	.65

Souvenir Sheet
Perf. 13x13¼
5620	A2910	€1.76 sil & multi	4.00	1.40

Stamp Day. No. 5620 contains one 52x41mm stamp.

Fontaine Saint-Michel, Paris — A2911

2019, Mar. 14   Engr.   Perf. 13
5621	A2911	88c multi	2.00	.65

Spring Philatelic Show, Paris.

Ceres — A2912

Photo. & Typo.
2019, Mar. 14   Imperf.
5622	A2912	20c black	.85	.85
a.		Tête bêche pair	2.00	
5623	A2912	88c black	2.00	.65
a.		As #5623, with inverted vignette	—	—
b.		Pair, #5623-5623a	—	—

No. 5622 was printed in sheets of 150 (with one stamp inverted) that sold for €55. No. 5623 was printed in sheets of 20 (with one stamp with inverted vignette). See Nos. 5754-5755.

Crystal Production A2913

2019, Mar. 15   Engr.   Perf. 13¼
5624	A2913	€1.30 indigo & slate vio	3.00	1.00

A souvenir sheet containing No. 5624 sold for €4.

Miniature Sheet

European Capitals — A2914

No. 5625 — Attractions in Helsinki, Finland: a, Lutheran Cathedral. b, Kruununhaka. c, Suomenlinna. d, Sibelius Monument.

2019, Mar. 16   Photo.   Perf. 13x13¼
5625	A2914	Sheet of 4	12.00	12.00
a.-d.		€1.30 Any single	3.00	1.00

Sculptures of Nude Women — A2915

Designs: No. 5626, Sculpture by Charles Despiau. No. 5627, Sculpture by Antoine Bourdelle. No. 5628, Ancient Egyptian sculpture. No. 5629, Ancient Greek sculpture (Venus de Milo). No. 5630, Sculpture by Edgar Degas. No. 5631, Ancient Oriental sculpture. No. 5632, Sculpture by Jacquio Ponce. No. 5633, Sculpture by Aristide Maillol. No. 5634, Nepalese sculpture. No. 5635, Statue by unknown artist in style of Etienne Maurice Falconet. No. 5636, Statue from Upper Paleolithic era. No. 5637, Sculpture from Ivory Coast (Côte d'Ivoire).

Serpentine Die Cut 11
2019, Mar. 29   Photo.
Booklet Stamps
Self-Adhesive
5626	A2915	(88c) multi	2.00	.65
5627	A2915	(88c) multi	2.00	.65
5628	A2915	(88c) multi	2.00	.65
5629	A2915	(88c) multi	2.00	.65
5630	A2915	(88c) multi	2.00	.65
5631	A2915	(88c) multi	2.00	.65
5632	A2915	(88c) multi	2.00	.65
5633	A2915	(88c) multi	2.00	.65
5634	A2915	(88c) multi	2.00	.65
5635	A2915	(88c) multi	2.00	.65
5636	A2915	(88c) multi	2.00	.65
5637	A2915	(88c) multi	2.00	.65
a.		Booklet pane of 12, #5626-5637	24.00	
		Nos. 5626-5637 (12)	24.00	7.80

Souvenir Sheet

Diplomatic Relations Between France and Poland, Cent. — A2916

No. 5638: a, Charles de Gaulle (1890-1970), as army captain (later president of France). b, Józef Haller (1873-1960), Polish lieutenant general.

2019, Apr. 2   Photo.   Perf. 13¼
5638	A2916	Sheet of 2	5.00	5.00
a.		88c multi	2.00	.65
b.		€1.30 multi	3.00	1.00

A souvenir sheet containing Nos. 5638a-5638b with a different sheet margin sold for €6. See Poland No. 4409.

Souvenir Sheet

Mogador Theater, Paris, Cent. A2917

No. 5639: a, Seats in theater. b, Architectural detail depicting ram's head.

2019, Apr. 2   Photo.   Perf. 13¼
5639	A2917	Sheet of 2	6.00	6.00
a.-b.		€1.30 Either single	3.00	1.00

A souvenir sheet containing Nos. 5639a-5639b with a different sheet margin sold for €6.

Woman Suffrage in France, 75th Anniv. — A2918

2019, Apr. 19   Photo.   Perf. 13¼
5640	A2918	88c multi	2.00	.65

Souvenir Sheet

Paintings A2919

No. 5641: a, The Gulf of Marseille Seen From L'Estaque, by Paul Cézanne (1839-1906). b, Mohammed V Square, Casablanca, by Jacques Majorelle (1886-1962).

2019, Apr. 26   Photo.   Perf. 13¼
5641	A2919	Sheet of 2	5.00	5.00
a.		88c multi	2.00	.65
b.		€1.30 multi	3.00	1.00

See Morocco No. 1269.

Art Issue

Lascaux
Cave
Drawings
A2920

2019, Apr. 26   Engr.   *Perf. 13x12*
5642 A2920 88c multi   2.00 1.00

A souvenir sheet containing a perf. 13x13¼ example of No. 5642 sold for €4.

A2921
                 A2922

A2923
                 A2924

A2925
                 A2926

A2927
                 A2928

A2929
                 A2930

A2931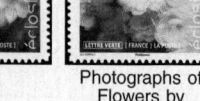

Photographs of
Flowers by
Jacques du
Sordet — A2932

Serpentine Die Cut 11
2019, May 3   Photo.
Booklet Stamps
Self-Adhesive
5643 A2921 (88c) multi   2.00 .65
5644 A2922 (88c) multi   2.00 .65
5645 A2923 (88c) multi   2.00 .65
5646 A2924 (88c) multi   2.00 .65
5647 A2925 (88c) multi   2.00 .65
5648 A2926 (88c) multi   2.00 .65
5649 A2927 (88c) multi   2.00 .65
5650 A2928 (88c) multi   2.00 .65
5651 A2929 (88c) multi   2.00 .65
5652 A2930 (88c) multi   2.00 .65
5653 A2931 (88c) multi   2.00 .65
5654 A2932 (88c) multi   2.00 .65
  a.   Booklet pane of 12, #5643-
       5654   24.00
     Nos. 5643-5654 (12)   24.00 7.80

Lighthouse,
Fresnel Lens and
Augustin Fresnel
(1788-1827),
Physicist
A2933

2019, May 3   Engr.   *Perf. 13¼*
5655 A2933 €1.05 multi   2.40 .80

Stylized
Birds
A2934

2019, May 10   Photo.   *Perf. 13*
5656 A2934 €1.30 multi   3.00 1.00

Europa.

Endangered
Flora — A2935

Designs: No. 5657, Violette de Rouen.
No. 5658: a, Saxifrage oeil-de-bouc. b,
Faujasie écailleuse. c, Dracocépahale
d'Autriche.

2019, May 17   Photo.   *Perf. 13¼*
5657 A2935 88c multi   2.00 .65

Miniature Sheet
5658   Sheet of 4, #5657,
             5658a-5658c   8.00 8.00
  a.-c. A2935 88c Any single   2.00 .65
  d.   Souvenir sheet of 2, #5657,
        5658b   6.75 6.75
  e.   Souvenir sheet of 2, #5658a,
        5658c   6.75 6.75

Nos. 5658d and 5658e were sold together
for €6.

Miniature Sheet

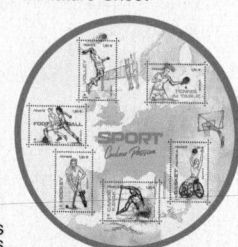

Sports
A2936

No. 5659: a, Volleyball. b, Table tennis,
horiz. c, Soccer, horiz. d, Field hockey. e,
Kayaking, horiz. f, Wheelchair basketball.

2019, May 18   Litho.   *Perf. 13*
5659 A2936   Sheet of 6 18.00 18.00
  a.-f.   €1.30 Any single   3.00 1.00

Château de Chambord, 500th
Anniv. — A2937

2019, May 31   Engr.   *Perf. 13x12¾*
5660 A2937 88c multi   2.00 .65

A souvenir sheet containing No. 5660 sold
for €4.

Characters from Astérix
Comic Strips — A2938

Designs: No. 5661, Falbala. No. 5662, Obé-
lix. No. 5663, Panoramix. No. 5664,
Ordralfabétix. No. 5665, Abraracourcix. No.
5666, Bonemine. No. 5667, Cétautomatix. No.
5668, Assurancetourix. No. 5669, Agece-
nonix. No. 5670, Mrs. Agecanonix. No. 5671,
Idéfix. No. 5672, Astérix.

Serpentine Die Cut 11
2019, June 6   Photo.
Booklet Stamps
Self-Adhesive
5661 A2938 (88c) multi   2.00 .65
5662 A2938 (88c) multi   2.00 .65
5663 A2938 (88c) multi   2.00 .65
5664 A2938 (88c) multi   2.00 .65
5665 A2938 (88c) multi   2.00 .65

5666 A2938 (88c) multi   2.00 .65
5667 A2938 (88c) multi   2.00 .65
5668 A2938 (88c) multi   2.00 .65
5669 A2938 (88c) multi   2.00 .65
5670 A2938 (88c) multi   2.00 .65
5671 A2938 (88c) multi   2.00 .65
5672 A2938 (88c) multi   2.00 .65
  a.   Booklet pane of 12, #5661-
       5672   24.00
     Nos. 5661-5672 (12)   24.00 7.80

Art Issue

Self-Portrait
with a Black
Dog, by
Gustave
Courbet
(1819-77)
A2939

2019, June 7   Photo.   *Perf. 13x13¼*
5673 A2939 €2.10 multi   4.75 2.40

Opéra Comédie, Montpellier — A2940

2019, June 7   Engr.   *Perf. 13x13¼*
5674 A2940 €1.05 multi + label 2.40 .80

French Federation of Philatelic Associations, 92nd Congress, Montpellier.

Saint-Philbert-de-Grand-Lieu
Abbey — A2941

2019, June 14   Photo.   *Perf. 13¼*
5675 A2941 88c multi   2.00 .65

Fountain of the
Quatre-Vallées,
Tarbes — A2942

2019, June 21   Photo.   *Perf. 13¼*
5676 A2942 88c multi   2.00 .65

Reuze-Papa and Reuze-Maman
Statues, Cassel — A2943

2019, June 27 Photo.   *Perf. 13x12¾*
5677 A2943 88c multi   2.00 .65

A2944
                 A2945

A2946
                 A2947

A2948
                 A2949

A2950   A2951

A2952   A2953

A2954

Vacation — A2955

Serpentine Die Cut 11
2019, June 28   Photo.
Booklet Stamps
Self-Adhesive
5678 A2944 (88c) multi   2.00 .65
5679 A2945 (88c) multi   2.00 .65
5680 A2946 (88c) multi   2.00 .65
5681 A2947 (88c) multi   2.00 .65
5682 A2948 (88c) multi   2.00 .65
5683 A2949 (88c) multi   2.00 .65
5684 A2950 (88c) multi   2.00 .65
5685 A2951 (88c) multi   2.00 .65
5686 A2952 (88c) multi   2.00 .65
5687 A2953 (88c) multi   2.00 .65
5688 A2954 (88c) multi   2.00 .65
5689 A2955 (88c) multi   2.00 .65
  a.   Booklet pane of 12, #5678-
       5689   24.00
     Nos. 5678-5689 (12)   24.00 7.80

Françoise
d'Aubigne,
Marquise de
Maintenon (1635-
1719), Second
Wife of King
Louis
XIV — A2956

2019, June 28   Photo.   *Perf. 13*
5690 A2956 €1.05 multi   2.40 .80

Values are for stamps with surrounding
selvage.

A2957

2019, July 5   Engr.   *Perf. 13*
5691 A2957 €1.05 multi   2.40 .80

Awarding of Legion of Honor and Croix de
Guerre to city of Reims, cent.

Mediterranean Women's Costumes and Euromed Postal Emblem — A2958

2019, July 5 **Photo.** *Perf. 13¼*
5692 A2958 €1.30 multi 3.00 1.00

First Man on the Moon, 50th Anniv. — A2959

2019, July 19 **Photo.** *Perf. 13x13¼*
5693 A2959 €1.30 multi 3.00 1.00

Lighthouses — A2960

Designs: No. 5694, Dunkerque Lighthouse. No. 5695, Goury Lighthouse. No. 5696, Ile Vierge Lighthouse. No. 5697, Kéréon Lighthouse. No. 5698, Ar-Men Lighthouse. No. 5699, Pilier Lighthouse. No. 5700, Chassiron Lighthouse. No. 5701, Cordouan Lighthouse. No. 5702, Biarritz Lighthouse. No. 5703, Cap Béar Lighthouse. No. 5704, Cap Camarat Lighthouse. No. 5705, Lavezzi Lighthouse.

Serpentine Die Cut 11
2019, Aug. 2 **Photo.**
Booklet Stamps
Self-Adhesive
5694 A2960 (€1.05) multi 2.40 .80
5695 A2960 (€1.05) multi 2.40 .80
5696 A2960 (€1.05) multi 2.40 .80
5697 A2960 (€1.05) multi 2.40 .80
5698 A2960 (€1.05) multi 2.40 .80
5699 A2960 (€1.05) multi 2.40 .80
5700 A2960 (€1.05) multi 2.40 .80
5701 A2960 (€1.05) multi 2.40 .80
5702 A2960 (€1.05) multi 2.40 .80
5703 A2960 (€1.05) multi 2.40 .80
5704 A2960 (€1.05) multi 2.40 .80
5705 A2960 (€1.05) multi 2.40 .80
a. Booklet pane of 12, #5694-5705 29.00
Nos. 5694-5705 (12) 28.80 9.60

Liberation of Paris, 75th Anniv. — A2961

2019, Aug. 25 **Photo.** *Perf. 13x12¾*
5706 A2961 €1.30 multi 3.00 1.00
A souvenir sheet containing No. 5706 sold for €4.

Monte Cinto, Corsica — A2962

2019, Sept. 6 **Photo.** *Perf. 13¼*
5707 A2962 88c multi 1.90 .65

Astérix Comic Strips, 60th Anniv. — A2963

2019, Sept. 6 **Photo.** *Perf. 13x13¼*
5708 A2963 88c multi 1.90 .65
No. 5708 was printed in sheets of 5.

Protection of Architectural Treasures A2964

Designs: No. 5709, Notre Dame Church, Rigny. No. 5710, Longuay Abbey, Aubepierre-sur-Aube. No. 5711, Château de Bon Repos, Jarrie. No. 5712, Château de Carneville. No. 5713, Canal du Midi. No. 5714, Grande Forge de Buffon. No. 5715, Fort Cicogne, Glénan Archipelago. No. 5716, Pont du Moulin, Thorame-Haute. No. 5717, Saint-François Convent, Pino. No. 5718, Saint-Léger Church, Barly. No. 5719, Château de Bouteville. No. 5720, Château de Lassay.

Serpentine Die Cut 11
2019, Sept. 12 **Photo.**
Booklet Stamps
Self-Adhesive
5709 A2964 (88c) multi 1.90 .65
5710 A2964 (88c) multi 1.90 .65
5711 A2964 (88c) multi 1.90 .65
5712 A2964 (88c) multi 1.90 .65
5713 A2964 (88c) multi 1.90 .65
5714 A2964 (88c) multi 1.90 .65
5715 A2964 (88c) multi 1.90 .65
5716 A2964 (88c) multi 1.90 .65
5717 A2964 (88c) multi 1.90 .65
5718 A2964 (88c) multi 1.90 .65
5719 A2964 (88c) multi 1.90 .65
5720 A2964 (88c) multi 1.90 .65
a. Booklet pane of 12, #5709-5720 23.00
Nos. 5709-5720 (12) 22.80 7.80

Le Creusot Buildings and Steam Hammer A2965

2019, Sept. 20 **Photo.** *Perf. 13¼*
5721 A2965 88c multi 1.90 .65

Bookbinding A2966

2019, Sept. 20 **Engr.** *Perf. 13x13¼*
5722 A2966 €1.05 multi 2.40 .80

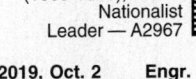

Mohandas K. Gandhi (1869-1948), Indian Nationalist Leader — A2967

2019, Oct. 2 **Engr.** *Perf. 13¼*
5723 A2967 €1.30 multi 3.00 1.00

Suez Canal, 150th Anniv. A2968

2019, Oct. 3 **Photo.** *Perf. 13x13¼*
5724 A2968 €1.30 multi 3.00 1.00
A souvenir sheet containing No. 5724 sold for €4.

Alexandre Varenne (1870-1947), Founder of *La Montagne* Newspaper A2969

2019, Oct. 4 **Engr.** *Perf. 13*
5725 A2969 88c multi 2.00 .70

Sèvres Plate A2970

Sèvres Plate A2972

Casteldurante Plate A2974

Sienne Plate A2976

Plate by Unknown Manufacturer A2978

Sèvres Plate A2980

Sèvres Plate A2971

Creil & Montereau Plate A2973

Sèvres Plate A2975

Creil & Montereau Plate A2977

Limoges Plate A2979

Sèvres Plate A2981

Serpentine Die Cut 11
2019, Oct. 4 **Photo.**
Booklet Stamps
Self-Adhesive
5726 A2970 (88c) multi 2.00 .70
5727 A2971 (88c) multi 2.00 .70
5728 A2972 (88c) multi 2.00 .70
5729 A2973 (88c) multi 2.00 .70
5730 A2974 (88c) multi 2.00 .70
5731 A2975 (88c) multi 2.00 .70
5732 A2976 (88c) multi 2.00 .70
5733 A2977 (88c) multi 2.00 .70
5734 A2978 (88c) multi 2.00 .70
5735 A2979 (88c) multi 2.00 .70
5736 A2980 (88c) multi 2.00 .70
5737 A2981 (88c) multi 2.00 .70
a. Booklet pane of 12, #5726-5737 24.00
Nos. 5726-5737 (12) 24.00 8.40

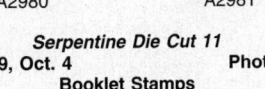

ESCP Europe Business School, Paris, 200th Anniv. — A2982

2019, Oct. 11 **Photo.** *Perf. 13¼*
5738 A2982 €1.30 multi 3.00 1.00

Souvenir Sheet

National Opera of Paris, 350th Anniv. A2983

No. 5739: a, Dancer's feet. b, Performer's head.

2019, Oct. 18 **Engr.** *Perf. 13¼*
5739 A2983 Sheet of 2 6.00 6.00
a.-b. €1.30 Either single 3.00 1.00
A souvenir sheet containing Nos. 5739a-5739b with a different sheet margin sold for €6.

Art Issue

St. Anne, the Virgin Mary and Jesus Playing With a Lamb, by Leonardo da Vinci (1452-1519) A2984

2019, Oct. 25 **Photo.** *Perf. 13*
5740 A2984 €2.10 multi 4.75 2.40
a. Souvenir sheet of 1 9.00 9.00
No. 5740a sold for €4.

Polar Bear A2985

Owl A2986

Fox's Body — A2987

Fox's Tails — A2988

Reindeer's Antlers — A2989

Polar Bear's Head A2990

Reindeer A2991

Owl's Head and Chest A2992

Fox's Head A2993

Fox's Head and Tail — A2994

Reindeer's Head — A2995

Polar Bear's Body — A2996

Serpentine Die Cut 11

2019, Nov. 2 — Photo.

Booklet Stamps
Self-Adhesive

5741	A2985	(88c) multi	2.00	.70
5742	A2986	(88c) multi	2.00	.70
5743	A2987	(88c) multi	2.00	.70
5744	A2988	(88c) multi	2.00	.70
5745	A2989	(88c) multi	2.00	.70
5746	A2990	(88c) multi	2.00	.70
5747	A2991	(88c) multi	2.00	.70
5748	A2992	(88c) multi	2.00	.70
5749	A2993	(88c) multi	2.00	.70
5750	A2994	(88c) multi	2.00	.70
5751	A2995	(88c) multi	2.00	.70
5752	A2996	(88c) multi	2.00	.70
a.		Booklet pane of 12, #5741-5752	24.00	
		Nos. 5741-5752 (12)	24.00	8.40

Paper art by Lila Poppins.

Ceres — A2997

2019, Nov. 7 — Engr. — Imperf.

5753	A2997	€5 black	11.00	11.00

No. 5753 was printed in sheets of 4.

Ceres and Marianne Types of 2018-19

2019, Nov. 7 — Engr. — Imperf.

Booklet Stamps
Size: 15x19mm

5754	A2912	€1.05 black	2.40	.80
a.		Booklet pane of 12, 6 each #5478, 5754	28.00	—

Size: 40x53mm
Perf. 13

5755	A2912	€2.10 black	4.75	1.60
5756	A2829	€2.10 red	4.75	1.60
a.		Booklet pane of 2, #5755-5756	9.50	—
		Complete booklet, #5754a, 5756a	37.50	

Renovation of Postal Museum, Paris — A2998

2019, Nov. 7 — Engr. — Perf. 13

5757	A2998	88c mag & dp ultra	2.00	.70

Souvenir Sheet

French History A2999

No. 5758 — Negotiators of the 1529 Treaty of Cambrai (Ladies' Peace): a, Archduchess Margaret of Austria (1480-1530). b, Louise of Savoy (1476-1531).

2019, Nov. 7 — Engr. — Perf. 13

5758	A2999	Sheet of 2	11.50	11.50
a.-b.		€2.60 Either single	5.75	1.90
c.		Souvenir sheet of 2, #5758a-5758b, different sheet margin	18.00	18.00

No. 5758c sold for €8.

Miniature Sheet

Husband and Wife Actors and Actresses — A3000

No. 5759: a, Jean Desailly (1920-2008). b, Simone Valère (1921-2010). c, Jean-Louis Barrault (1910-94). d, Madeleine Renaud (1900-94).

2019, Nov. 8 — Photo. — Perf. 13¼

5759	A3000	Sheet of 4	9.75	9.75
a.-d.		€1.05 Any single	2.40	.80

Tromelin Island, French Southern and Antarctic Territories A3001

2019, Nov. 9 — Engr. — Perf. 13x13¼

5760	A3001	€1.30 multi	3.00	1.00

Art Issue

Unnamed Painting by Fabienne Verdier A3002

2019, Nov. 15 — Photo. — Perf. 13

5761	A3002	€2.10 multi	4.75	2.40

Types of 1995-2014
Miniature Sheet

No. 5762 — Sites in Paris: a, Grand Palais. b, Opéra Garnier. c, French Institute. d, Champs Elysées.

Engr., Sheet Margin Litho. & Embossed With Foil Application
Perf. 13x13¼, 13 (#5762d)

2019, Dec. 3

5762		Sheet of 4	22.50	22.50
a.	A1911	€2 sepia	4.50	1.50
b.	A1790	€2 sepia	4.50	1.50
c.	A2415	€2 sepia	4.50	1.50
d.	A1306	€4 sepia	9.00	3.00

Le Carré d'Encre Stamp Shop, Paris, 10th anniv.

Lille, 2020 World Capital of Design — A3003

2020, Jan. 3 — Photo. — Perf. 13¼

5763	A3003	97c multi	2.25	.75

Butterfly Wing Details — A3004

Designs: No. 5764, Ornithoptera goliath. No. 5765, Zerynthia rumina. No. 5766, Melitaea phoebe. No. 5767, Agrias claudina. No. 5768, Morpho hecuba. No. 5769, Papilio demoleus. No. 5770, Agatasa calydonia (white area near center). No. 5771, Parnassius nomion. No. 5772, Agatasa calydonia ("L" in "Lettre" over black area). No. 5773, Papilio

machaon. No. 5774, Graellsia isabellae. No. 5775, Morpho peleides.

Serpentine Die Cut 11

2020, Jan. 3 — Photo.

Booklet Stamps
Self-Adhesive

5764	A3004	(€1.16) multi	2.60	.90
5765	A3004	(€1.16) multi	2.60	.90
5766	A3004	(€1.16) multi	2.60	.90
5767	A3004	(€1.16) multi	2.60	.90
5768	A3004	(€1.16) multi	2.60	.90
5769	A3004	(€1.16) multi	2.60	.90
5770	A3004	(€1.16) multi	2.60	.90
5771	A3004	(€1.16) multi	2.60	.90
5772	A3004	(€1.16) multi	2.60	.90
5773	A3004	(€1.16) multi	2.60	.90
5774	A3004	(€1.16) multi	2.60	.90
5775	A3004	(€1.16) multi	2.60	.90
a.		Booklet pane of 12, #5764-5775	31.50	
		Nos. 5764-5775 (12)	31.20	10.80

A3005   Hearts — A3006

2020, Jan. 10 — Photo. — Perf. 13½

5776	A3005	97c red, blk & dk blue	2.25	.75
a.		Souvenir sheet of 5	11.50	11.50
5777	A3006	€1.94 blk, red & dk blue	4.25	1.40

Self-Adhesive
Serpentine Die Cut

5778	A3005	97c red, blk & dk blue	2.25	.75
5779	A3006	€1.94 blk, red & dk blue	4.25	1.40

Values for Nos. 5776-5777 are for stamps with surrounding selvage.

New Year 2020 (Year of the Rat) — A3007

Designs: 97c, Rat and flower. €1.40, Rat in robe.

2020, Jan. 17 — Photo. — Perf. 13

5780		Sheet of 5, #5780a, 4 #5780b	11.50	11.50
a.	A3007	97c 33x40mm stamp	2.25	.75
b.	A3007	97c 29x35mm stamp	2.25	.75
5781		Sheet of 5, #5781a, 4 #5781b	16.50	16.50
a.	A3007	€1.40 33x40mm stamp	3.25	1.10
b.	A3007	€1.40 29x35mm stamp	3.25	1.10

Art Issue

Portrait Presumed to be Madeleine, by Marie-Guillemine Benoist (1768-1826) A3008

2020, Feb. 4 — Photo. — Perf. 13¼x13

5782	A3008	€2.32 multi	5.25	2.60

Animals and Their Reflections in Water — A3009

Inscriptions: No. 5783, Zèbres des plaines (Plains zebras). No. 5784, Tigre de Sibérie (Siberian tiger). No. 5785, Couple de lions (Lions) No. 5786, Phoque gris (Gray seal). No. 5787, Ours polaire (Polar bear). No. 5788, Manchots royaux (King penguins). No. 5789, Flamants roses (Greater flamingos). No. 5790, Lama (Llama). No. 5791, Grenouilles vertes (Green frogs). No. 5792, Héron crabier (Squacco heron). No. 5793, Goéland argenté (European herring gull). No. 5794, Rorqual à bosse (Humpback whale).

Serpentine Die Cut 11

2020, Feb. 7 — Photo.

Booklet Stamps
Self-Adhesive

5783	A3009	(97c) multi	2.25	.75
5784	A3009	(97c) multi	2.25	.75
5785	A3009	(97c) multi	2.25	.75
5786	A3009	(97c) multi	2.25	.75
5787	A3009	(97c) multi	2.25	.75
5788	A3009	(97c) multi	2.25	.75
5789	A3009	(97c) multi	2.25	.75
5790	A3009	(97c) multi	2.25	.75
5791	A3009	(97c) multi	2.25	.75
5792	A3009	(97c) multi	2.25	.75
5793	A3009	(97c) multi	2.25	.75
5794	A3009	(97c) multi	2.25	.75
a.		Booklet pane of 12, #5783-5794	27.00	
		Nos. 5783-5794 (12)	27.00	9.00

Jacqueline de Romilly (1913-2010), Writer — A3010

2020, Feb. 7 — Engr. — Perf. 13¼

5795	A3010	€1.16 multi	2.60	.90

René Guy Cadou (1920-51), Poet — A3011

2020, Feb. 14 — Engr. — Perf. 13¼

5796	A3011	97c black & lt blue	2.25	.75

Organ Building A3012

2020, Feb. 21 — Engr. — Perf. 13x13¼

5797	A3012	€1.40 multi	3.25	1.10

A souvenir sheet containing No. 5797 sold for €4.50.

Boris Vian (1920-59), Writer and Musician A3013

2020, Mar. 6 — Photo. — Perf. 13¼x12¼

5798	A3013	97c multi	2.10	.70

A souvenir sheet containing No. 5798 sold for €4.50. See No. 5845.

Drawing of Tulips A3014   Sundial A3015

Nautilus Shell Mounted on Decorative Base
A3016

Indian Painting of Butterfly
A3017

Owl
A3018

Herring Fishing, by Adriaen Van der Kabel (1631-1705)
A3019

Woman in Blue, by Jean-Baptiste-Camille Corot (1796-1875)
A3020

Seashell
A3021

Ewer
A3022

Rhinoceros, by Albrecht Dürer (1471-1528)
A3023

Drawings of Armadillos
A3024

Armillary Sphere
A3025

Serpentine Die Cut 11

2020, Mar. 6 **Photo.**

Booklet Stamps
Self-Adhesive

5799	A3014	(97c)	multi	2.10	.70
5800	A3015	(97c)	multi	2.10	.70
5801	A3016	(97c)	multi	2.10	.70
5802	A3017	(97c)	multi	2.10	.70
5803	A3018	(97c)	multi	2.10	.70
5804	A3019	(97c)	multi	2.10	.70
5805	A3020	(97c)	multi	2.10	.70
5806	A3021	(97c)	multi	2.10	.70
5807	A3022	(97c)	multi	2.10	.70
5808	A3023	(97c)	multi	2.10	.70
5809	A3024	(97c)	multi	2.10	.70
5810	A3025	(97c)	multi	2.10	.70
a.	Booklet pane of 12, #5799-5810			25.50	

Nos. 5799-5810 (12) 25.20 8.40

Miniature Sheet

European Capitals — A3026

No. 5811 — Attractions in Dublin, Ireland: a, Trinity College. b, Ha'penny Bridge. c, St. Patrick's Cathedral. d, Dublin Castle.

2020, Mar. 13 **Photo.** *Perf. 13*

5811	A3026	Sheet of 4		12.00	12.00
a.-d.	€1.40 Any single			3.00	1.00

Andrèe Chedid (1920-2011), Writer — A3027

2020, Mar. 20 **Photo.** *Perf. 13¼*

5812	A3027	€1.40 multi		3.00	1.00

Dole
A3028

2020, Mar. 27 **Engr.** *Perf. 13x12¾*

5813	A3028	97c multi		2.10	.70

Spring Philatelic Show, Dole.

A3029

A3029a

A3030

Félix Nadar (1820-1910), Photographer — A3031

2020, Apr. 3 **Photo.** *Perf. 13¼x13*

5814	Sheet of 4 + 8 labels			12.00	12.00
a.	A3029 €1.40 multi			3.00	1.00
b.	A3029a €1.40 multi			3.00	1.00
c.	A3030 €1.40 multi			3.00	1.00
d.	A3031 €1.40 multi			3.00	1.00

Bird Eggs — A3032

Inscriptions: No. 5817, Faucon crécerelle (common kestrel). No. 5818, Corneille noire (carrion crow). No. 5819, Gobemouche gris (spotted flycatcher). No. 5820, Autriche d'Afrique (common ostrich). No. 5821, Hirondelle rustique (barn swallow). No. 5822, Bruant fou (rock bunting). No. 5823, Moineau domestique (house sparrow). No. 5824, Grive musicienne (song thrush). No. 5825, Poule pondeuse rouse (chicken). No. 5826, Dinde (turkey). No. 5827, Vanneau huppé (northern lapwing). No. 5828, Emeu d'Australie (emu).

Serpentine Die Cut 11

2020, Apr. 3 **Photo.**

Booklet Stamps
Self-Adhesive

5817	A3032	(97c)	multi	2.10	.70
5818	A3032	(97c)	multi	2.10	.70
5819	A3032	(97c)	multi	2.10	.70
5820	A3032	(97c)	multi	2.10	.70
5821	A3032	(97c)	multi	2.10	.70
5822	A3032	(97c)	multi	2.10	.70
5823	A3032	(97c)	multi	2.10	.70
5824	A3032	(97c)	multi	2.10	.70
5825	A3032	(97c)	multi	2.10	.70
5826	A3032	(97c)	multi	2.10	.70
5827	A3032	(97c)	multi	2.10	.70
5828	A3032	(97c)	multi	2.10	.70
a.	Booklet pane of 12, #5817-5828			25.50	

Nos. 5817-5828 (12) 25.20 8.40

Art Issue

The Virgin of Loretto, by Raphael (1483-1520)
A3033

2020, Apr. 17 **Engr.** *Perf. 13*

5829	A3033	€2.32 multi		5.25	2.60

A souvenir sheet containing No. 5829 sold for €6.50.

A3034

A3035

A3036

A3037

A3038

A3039

A3040

A3041

A3042

A3043

Cosmos Flowers
A3044 A3045

Serpentine Die Cut 11

2020, Apr. 30 **Photo.**

Booklet Stamps
Self-Adhesive

5830	A3034	(97c)	multi	2.10	.70
5831	A3035	(97c)	multi	2.10	.70
5832	A3036	(97c)	multi	2.10	.70
5833	A3037	(97c)	multi	2.10	.70
5834	A3038	(97c)	multi	2.10	.70
5835	A3039	(97c)	multi	2.10	.70
5836	A3040	(97c)	multi	2.10	.70
5837	A3041	(97c)	multi	2.10	.70
5838	A3042	(97c)	multi	2.10	.70
5839	A3043	(97c)	multi	2.10	.70
5840	A3044	(97c)	multi	2.10	.70
5841	A3045	(97c)	multi	2.10	.70
a.	Booklet pane of 12, #5830-5841			25.50	

Nos. 5830-5841 (12) 25.20 8.40

Horse-drawn Carriage and Maps of Postal Routes — A3046

2020, May 7 **Engr.** *Perf. 13¼x13*

5842	A3046	€1.40 multi		3.25	1.10

Europa.

Souvenir Sheet

French Hydrographic Service, 300th Anniv. — A3047

No. 5843: a, Hydrographer on ship with flag taking sounding. b, Ship, compass wheel and star.

2020, May 22 **Photo.** *Perf. 13¼*

5843	A3047	Sheet of 2		6.50	6.50
a.-b.	€1.40 Either single			3.25	1.10

A souvenir sheet containing Nos. 5843a-5843b having a different sheet margin sold for €6.50.

Frédéric Dard (1921-2000), Writer of Crime Novels — A3048

2020, June 12 **Litho.** *Perf. 13¼*

5844	A3048	97c multi		2.25	.75

Boris Vian Type of 2020

2020, June 12 **Photo.** *Perf. 13¼*

5845	A3013	€1.16 multi		2.60	.85
a.	Tete-beche pair			5.25	1.75

No. 5845 was printed in sheets of 6 + 6 labels.

Flowers Used for Perfumes
A3049

No. 5846, Rose de Mai.
No. 5847: a, Tubéreuse (tuberose), vert. b, Violette (violet). c, Fleur d'oranger (orange blossoms), vert.

2020, June 12 **Photo.** *Perf. 13¼*

5846	A3049	97c multi		2.25	.75

Miniature Sheet

5847	Sheet of 4, #5846, 5847a-5847c			9.00	9.00
a.-c.	A3049 97c Any single			2.25	.75
d.	Souvenir sheet of 2, #5846, 5847c			7.25	7.25
e.	Souvenir sheet of 2, #5847a, 5847b			7.25	7.25

Nos. 5847d and 5847e sold as a set for €6.50. Nos. 5847 and 5847d are impregnated with an orange blossom scent.

University of Montpellier Buildings, François de la Peyronie (1678-1747), Surgeon, and Paul Joseph Barthez (1734-1806), Physician — A3050

2020, June 13   Photo.   Perf. 13x12¾
5848 A3050 €1.16 multi   2.60   .85
University of Montpellier Faculty of Medicine, 800th anniv.

Snacks With Faces A3051

Woman in Hammock A3052

Book Reader, Cloud and Birds — A3053

Woman Pulling Suitcase — A3054

Woman's Feet in Sandals — A3055

Surfer — A3056

Children in Inflatable Pool Toys — A3057

Woman With Shells in Hair — A3058

Flowers and Butterflies A3059

Fisherman in Boat A3060

Vacationers Carrying Gear — A3061

Tandem Bicycle — A3062

Serpentine Die Cut 11
2020, June 19   Photo.
Booklet Stamps
Self-Adhesive
5849 A3051 (97c) multi   2.25   .75
5850 A3052 (97c) multi   2.25   .75
5851 A3053 (97c) multi   2.25   .75
5852 A3054 (97c) multi   2.25   .75
5853 A3055 (97c) multi   2.25   .75
5854 A3056 (97c) multi   2.25   .75
5855 A3057 (97c) multi   2.25   .75
5856 A3058 (97c) multi   2.25   .75
5857 A3059 (97c) multi   2.25   .75
5858 A3060 (97c) multi   2.25   .75
5859 A3061 (97c) multi   2.25   .75
5860 A3062 (97c) multi   2.25   .75
  a.   Booklet pane of 12, #5849-
          5860   27.00
       Nos. 5849-5860 (12)   27.00 9.00

Tourism Issue

Rodemack — A3063

2020, June 26   Engr.   Perf. 13¼
5861 A3063 97c multi   2.25   .75

Olympe de Gouges (1748-93), Playwright A3064

2020, June 26   Photo.   Perf. 13¼x13
5862 A3064 €2.32 multi   5.25 1.75

Souvenir Sheet

Map of Corsica and GR 20 Hiking Trail A3065

2020, June 26   Photo.   Perf. 13¼
5863 A3065 €1.16 multi   2.60   .85
GR 20 Hiking Trail, 50th anniv.

Engraving Type of 1984
2020, June 26   Engr.   Perf. 13
5864 A1001 €4 multi   9.00 3.00
No. 5864 was printed in sheets of 6.

Saint-Vaast-la-Hougue — A3066

2020, July 2   Photo.   Perf. 13x12¾
5865 A3066 97c multi   2.25   .75

St. Odile of Alsace (c. 662-720) A3067

2020, July 3   Photo.   Perf. 13¼
5866 A3067 97c multi   2.25   .75

Bouillabaise Ingredients — A3068

2020, July 10   Litho.   Perf. 13¼
5867 A3068 €1.40 multi   3.25 1.10

Luis Mariano (1914-70), Opera Singer — A3069

2020, July 10   Photo.   Perf. 13
5868 A3069 €1.16 multi   2.75   .95

Bès-Bédène — A3070

2020, July 17   Engr.   Perf. 13x12¾
5869 A3070 97c multi   2.25   .75

Souvenir Sheet

Exterior Decorations of Notre Dame Cathedral, Paris — A3071

2020, July 17   Engr.   Perf. 13
5870 A3071 €1.40 multi   3.25 1.10

Amiens Cathedral, 800th Anniv. — A3072

2020, July 27   Engr.   Perf. 13¼
5871 A3072 €1.16 black & gold 2.75 .95

Raving Rabbid Behind Stamp A3073

Raving Rabbid With Tape Dispenser A3074

Raving Rabbid on Upside-Down Picture A3075

Raving Rabbid Drawing Stamp A3076

Raving Rabbid in Hole A3077

Raving Rabbid Licking Stamp A3078

Raving Rabbid Painting — A3079

Raving Rabbid Writing — A3080

Stamps Stuck on Raving Rabbid A3081

Raving Rabbids Holding Envelope Upside Down A3082

Raving Rabbid With Magnifying Glass — A3083

Group of Raving Rabbids — A3084

Serpentine Die Cut 11
2020, July 24   Photo.
Booklet Stamps
Self-Adhesive
5872 A3073 (97c) multi   2.25   .75
5873 A3074 (97c) multi   2.25   .75
5874 A3075 (97c) multi   2.25   .75
5875 A3076 (97c) multi   2.25   .75
5876 A3077 (97c) multi   2.25   .75
5877 A3078 (97c) multi   2.25   .75
5878 A3079 (97c) multi   2.25   .75
5879 A3080 (97c) multi   2.25   .75
5880 A3081 (97c) multi   2.25   .75
5881 A3082 (97c) multi   2.25   .75
5882 A3083 (97c) multi   2.25   .75
5883 A3084 (97c) multi   2.25   .75
  a.   Booklet pane of 12, #5872-
          5883   27.00
       Nos. 5872-5883 (12)   27.00 9.00

Raving Rabbids video game characters.

Lighthouses — A3085

Designs: No. 5884, Cayeux Lighthouse. No. 5885, Grand Léjon Lighthouse. No. 5886, Créac'h Lighthouse. No. 5887, Saint Mathieu Lighthouse. No. 5888, La Vieille Lighthouse. No. 5889, Eckmühl Lighthouse. No. 5890, Four du Croisic Lighthouse. No. 5891, Cap Ferret Lighthouse. No. 5892, Espiguette Lighthouse. No. 5893, Sanguinaires Lighthouse. No. 5894, Bel Air Lighthouse. No. 5895, Caravelle Lighthouse.

Serpentine Die Cut 11
2020, Aug. 28   Photo.
Booklet Stamps
Self-Adhesive
5884 A3085 (€1.16) multi   2.75   .95
5885 A3085 (€1.16) multi   2.75   .95
5886 A3085 (€1.16) multi   2.75   .95
5887 A3085 (€1.16) multi   2.75   .95
5888 A3085 (€1.16) multi   2.75   .95
5889 A3085 (€1.16) multi   2.75   .95
5890 A3085 (€1.16) multi   2.75   .95
5891 A3085 (€1.16) multi   2.75   .95
5892 A3085 (€1.16) multi   2.75   .95
5893 A3085 (€1.16) multi   2.75   .95
5894 A3085 (€1.16) multi   2.75   .95
5895 A3085 (€1.16) multi   2.75   .95
  a.   Booklet pane of 12, #5884-
          5895   33.00
       Nos. 5884-5895 (12)   33.00 11.40

Raving Rabbids Video Game Characters — A3086

2020, Sept. 4   Photo.   Perf. 13x12¾
5896 A3086 97c multi   2.25   .75

Tourism Issue

La Roche-sur-Yon
A3087

2020, Sept. 7   Photo.   Perf. 13¼
5897 A3087 97c red & black   2.25   .75

Health Care Workers — A3088   Helicopter Pilot and Ambulance Crew — A3089

Postal Worker Delivering Mail — A3090   Post Office Clerk — A3091

Store Cashier — A3092   Bus Driver — A3093

Health Care Workers Cleaning A3094   Health Care Worker and Woman in Wheelchair A3095

Police Officers — A3096   Sanitation Workers — A3097

Truck Driver — A3098   Farm Workers — A3099

Serpentine Die Cut 11
2020, Sept. 11   Photo.
Booklet Stamps
Self-Adhesive

5898 A3088	(97c) multi	2.25	.75
5899 A3089	(97c) multi	2.25	.75
5900 A3090	(97c) multi	2.25	.75
5901 A3091	(97c) multi	2.25	.75
5902 A3092	(97c) multi	2.25	.75
5903 A3093	(97c) multi	2.25	.75
5904 A3094	(97c) multi	2.25	.75
5905 A3095	(97c) multi	2.25	.75
5906 A3096	(97c) multi	2.25	.75
5907 A3097	(97c) multi	2.25	.75
5908 A3098	(97c) multi	2.25	.75
5909 A3099	(97c) multi	2.25	.75
a.	Booklet pane of 12, #5898-5909	27.00	
	Nos. 5898-5909 (12)	27.00	9.00

Salute to French workers during COVID-19 pandemic.

Château of the Dukes of Bourbon, Montluçon — A3100

2020, Sept. 18   Engr.   Perf. 13¼
5910 A3100 €1.16 multi   2.75   .95

Miniature Sheet

Sports A3101

No. 5911: a, Gymnastics. b, Badminton, vert. c, Taekwondo. d, Sailboarding, vert. e, Rowing. f, Pole vault.

Perf. 13x13¼, 13¼x13
2020, Sept. 18   Photo.
5911 A3101 Sheet of 6   19.50 19.50
a.-f. €1.40 Any single   3.25   1.10

Miniature Sheet

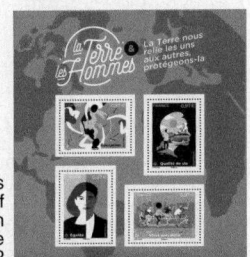

Aspects of French Life A3102

No. 5912: a, Education. b, Quality of life, vert. c, Equality, vert. d, Living together.

2020, Sept. 18   Photo.   Perf. 13¼
5912 A3102 Sheet of 4   9.00   9.00
a.-d. 97c Any single   2.25   .75

Pres. Jacques Chirac (1932-2019) — A3103

2020, Sept. 26   Engr.   Perf. 13¼
5913 A3103 97c multi   2.25   .75

Peugeot 204 Cabriolet A3104

Peugeot 404 Berline A3105

2020, Sept. 26   Engr.   Perf. 13x13¼
5914 A3104 97c multi   2.25   .75
5915 A3104 €1.16 multi   2.75   .95

Souvenir Sheet
Litho.
5916 A3105 €1.94 multi   4.50   1.50

Stamp Day. No. 5915 was printed in sheets of 6. Nos. 5914 and 5916 were intended to have been issued on Mar. 28, 2020, but were delayed because of the COVID-19 pandemic.

Art Issue

Zamer, Artwork by Mohamed Bourouissa A3106

2020, Oct. 9   Photo.   Perf. 13¼x13
5917 A3106 €2.32 multi   5.50   2.75

Annexation of Béarn as French Province by King Louis XIII, 400th Anniv. — A3107

2020, Oct. 16   Photo.   Perf. 13¼
5918 A3107 €1.16 multi   2.75   .95

Steam-Powered Vehicle Invented by Nicolas-Joseph Cugnot (1725-1804), 250th Anniv. — A3108

2020, Oct. 16   Engr.   Perf. 13x12¾
5919 A3108 €1.16 ochre & black   2.75   .95

A3109   A3110

A3111   A3112

A3113   A3114

A3115   A3116

Owl, Courrier Suivi Emblem, Tracking Number and Encryption — A3117

Serpentine Die Cut 11
2020, Oct. 16   Photo.
Booklet Stamps
Self-Adhesive

5920 A3109	(€1.42)	multi	3.50	1.75
5921 A3110	(€1.42)	multi	3.50	1.75
5922 A3111	(€1.42)	multi	3.50	1.75
5923 A3112	(€1.42)	multi	3.50	1.75
5924 A3113	(€1.42)	multi	3.50	1.75
5925 A3114	(€1.42)	multi	3.50	1.75
5926 A3115	(€1.42)	multi	3.50	1.75
5927 A3116	(€1.42)	multi	3.50	1.75
5928 A3117	(€1.42)	multi	3.50	1.75
a.	Booklet pane of 9, #5920-5928		31.50	
	Nos. 5920-5928 (9)		31.50	15.75

On the day of issue, Nos. 5920-5928 paid the 97c lettre verte rate plus the 45c letter tracking fee. Tracking numbers on each stamp are repeated in booklet selvage below that stamp. Letters bearing these stamps could be tracked by entering the tracking number on the La Poste website. The tracking numbers and encryption on each stamp differ.
Compare with types A3391-A3399.

Ludwig van Beethoven (1770-1827), Composer — A3118

2020, Oct. 23   Photo.   Perf. 13¼
5929 A3118 €1.40 multi   3.25   1.10

Hôtel de Mora, Moulins A3119

2020, Oct. 30   Engr.   Perf. 13x13¼
5930 A3119 97c multi + label   2.25   .75

2020 Stamp Passion Youth Philatelic Exhibition. Moulins.

Emblem of French Tennis Federation, Tennis Ball, and Suzannne Lenglen (1899-1938), Tennis Player — A3120

2020, Oct. 30   Photo.   Perf. 13
5931 A3120 €1.16 reddish org   2.75   .95

French Tennis Federation, cent., naming of new tennis court at Roland Garros Stadium after Lenglen, 25th anniv.

No. 5477 Overprinted

Method and Perf. As Before
2020, Nov. 4
5932 A2828 (97c) emerald   2.40   .80

A booklet printed in limited quantities was issued on Nov. 4, 2020, containing 97c stamps of types A1091 and A1136, €1.16 stamps of type A486 + label, A761, A1161, A1208, A1430, A1474, and A2532, and €1.16 stamps having the designs of Nos. 3682a-3682d, 3682f-3682k, and 4330a.

Types of 1947-2014 Redrawn With Denominations in Euros
Engr., Sheet Margin Litho. with Foil Application
2020, Nov. 4   Perf. 13¼x13

5933	Sheet of 4		29.00	29.00
a.	SP171 €2 dark green, like #B217		4.75	4.75
b.	A2380 €2 dark green, like #4588		4.75	4.75

c.   A417 €4 dark green, like #1090   9.75   9.75
d.   AP11 €4 dark green, like #C22   9.75   9.75

Notre Dame Cathedral, Paris.

 A3121

 A3122

A3123   A3124

A3125   A3126

A3127   A3128

A3129   A3130

 A3131

Christmas
A3132

Serpentine Die Cut 11

2020, Nov. 4   **Photo.**
Booklet Stamps
Self-Adhesive

5934	A3121	(97c)	multi	2.40	.80
5935	A3122	(97c)	multi	2.40	.80
5936	A3123	(97c)	multi	2.40	.80
5937	A3124	(97c)	multi	2.40	.80
5938	A3125	(97c)	multi	2.40	.80
5939	A3126	(97c)	multi	2.40	.80
5940	A3127	(97c)	multi	2.40	.80
5941	A3128	(97c)	multi	2.40	.80
5942	A3129	(97c)	multi	2.40	.80
5943	A3130	(97c)	multi	2.40	.80
5944	A3131	(97c)	multi	2.40	.80
5945	A3132	(97c)	multi	2.40	.80

a.   Booklet pane of 12, #5934-5945   29.00
Nos. 5934-5945 (12)   28.80   9.60

On back of No. 5945a there is a scratch inscribed "Grattez ici" off for a 100% winning game.

Charles de Gaulle (1890-1970), Wearing General's Uniform A3133

De Gaulle (1890-1970), As President of France A3134

2020, Nov. 5   **Engr.**   **Perf. 13¼**

5946	A3133	€1.16 multi	2.75	.90
5947	A3134	€1.16 multi	2.75	.90
a.		Horiz. pair, #5946-5947	5.50	1.90

Charles de Gaulle Types of 1971-2010 Redrawn
Miniature Sheet
Perf. 13x13¼, 13¼x13

2020, Nov. 5   **Engr.**

5947B		Sheet of 4	48.00	48.00
a.	A2093	€5 blue	12.00	12.00
b.	A576	€5 black (like #1324)	12.00	12.00
c.	A1164	€5 multi	12.00	12.00
d.	CD134	€5 red violet (like #1325)	12.00	12.00

Ceres — A3135

2020, Nov. 6   **Litho.**   **Imperf.**
Booklet Stamps

5948	A3135	10c green	.25	.25
5949	A3135	€1.40 red	3.50	1.25
a.		Booklet pane of 12, 6 each #5948-5949	22.50	

Size: 36x45mm

5950	A3135	€3.50 green	8.40	3.00
5951	A3135	€3.50 red	8.40	3.00
a.		Booklet pane of 2, #5950-5951	17.00	
		Complete booklet, #5949a, 5951a	39.50	

Metal Engraving A3136

2020, Nov. 6   **Engr.**   **Perf. 13**
5952   A3136   €1.40 multi   3.50   1.25

A souvenir sheet containing No. 5952 sold for €4.50.

Palais Galliera, Paris A3137

2020, Nov. 7   **Engr.**   **Perf. 13x13¼**
5953   A3137   €1.16 multi + label   2.75   .90

French Federation of Philatelic Associations, 93rd Congress, Paris.

Souvenir Sheet

French History A3138

No. 5954: a, Matilda of Flanders (c. 1031-83), Queen of England, Duchess of Normandy and wife of William the Conqueror. b, William the Conqueror (c. 1028-87), King of England and Duke of Normandy.

2020, Nov. 7   **Engr.**   **Perf. 13**

5954	A3138	Sheet of 2	13.50	13.50
a.-b.		€2.80 Either single	6.75	6.75
c.		Souvenir sheet of 2, #5954a-5954b, with different sheet margin	20.50	20.50

No. 5954c sold for €8.50.

Order of Liberation, 80th Anniv. — A3139

2020, Nov. 16   **Engr.**   **Perf. 13**
5955   A3139   €1.40 multi   3.50   1.25

For overprint, see No. 6150.

Aerial View of Vineyard, Bas-Rhin Department A3140   Aerial View of Orchard, Loiret Department A3141

Aerial View of Salt Marsh, Bouches-du-Rhône Department A3142   Aerial View of Beach, Corse-du-Sud Department A3143

Aerial View of Pasture, Lozère Department A3144   Aerial View of Basalt Columns, Lozère Department A3145

Aerial View of Coast, Morbihan Department A3146   Aerial View of Oyster Farm, Charente-Maritime Department A3147

Aerial View of Salt Marshes, Vendée Department A3148   Aerial View of Vegetable Fields, Seine-Maritime Department A3149

Aerial View of Salt Meadows, Somme Department A3150   Aerial View of Wheat and Rapeseed Fields, Côte d'Or Department A3151

Serpentine Die Cut 11
2021, Jan. 2   **Photo.**
Booklet Stamps
Self-Adhesive

5956	A3140	(€1.28) multi	3.25	1.10
5957	A3141	(€1.28) multi	3.25	1.10
5958	A3142	(€1.28) multi	3.25	1.10
5959	A3143	(€1.28) multi	3.25	1.10
5960	A3144	(€1.28) multi	3.25	1.10
5961	A3145	(€1.28) multi	3.25	1.10
5962	A3146	(€1.28) multi	3.25	1.10
5963	A3147	(€1.28) multi	3.25	1.10
5964	A3148	(€1.28) multi	3.25	1.10
5965	A3149	(€1.28) multi	3.25	1.10
5966	A3150	(€1.28) multi	3.25	1.10
5967	A3151	(€1.28) multi	3.25	1.10
a.		Booklet pane of 12, #5956-5967	39.00	
		Nos. 5956-5967 (12)	39.00	13.20

Birds — A3152

Designs: No. 5968, Pinguouin torda (razor-billed auk).
No. 5969: a, Tuit tuit (Reunion cuck-ooshrike), horiz. b, Oriole de Martinque (Martinique oriole). c, Grive à pattes jaunes (forest thrush).

2021, Jan. 8   **Photo.**   **Perf. 13¼**

5968	A3152	€1.08 multi	2.60	.85
		Souvenir Sheet		
5969		Sheet of 4, #5968, 5969a-5969c	10.50	10.50
a.-c.	A3152	€1.08 Any single	2.60	.85
d.		Souvenir sheet of 2, #5968, 5969b	8.00	8.00
e.		Souvenir sheet of 2, #5969a, 5969c	8.00	8.00

Nos. 5969d and 5969e were sold as a set for €6.50.

Madeleine Brès (1842-1921), First French Woman to Obtain Medical Degree — A3153

2021, Jan. 15   **Photo.**   **Perf. 13¼**
5970   A3153   €1.08 multi   2.60   .85

Heart and Bottle of Chanel No. 5 Perfume — A3154

2021, Jan. 22   **Photo.**   **Perf. 13¼**

5971	A3154	€1.08 red & black	2.60	.85
a.		Souvenir sheet of 5	13.00	13.00
5972	A3154	€2.16 pink & black	5.25	1.75

Self-Adhesive
Serpentine Die Cut

5973	A3154	€1.08 red & black	2.60	.85
5974	A3154	€2.16 pink & black	5.25	1.75

Values for Nos. 5971-5972 are for stamps with surrounding selvage.

New Year 2021 (Year of the Ox) — A3155

Designs: €1.08, Man on ox. €1.50, Ox.

2021, Feb. 5   **Photo.**   **Perf. 13¼x13**

5975		Sheet of 5, #5975a, 4 #5975b	13.00	13.00
a.	A3155	€1.08 multi, 33x40mm stamp	2.60	.85
b.	A3155	€1.08 multi, 29x35mm stamp	2.60	.85
5976		Sheet of 5, #5976a, 4 #5976b	19.00	19.00
a.	A3155	€1.50 multi, 33x40mm stamp	3.75	1.25
b.	A3155	€1.50 multi, 29x35mm stamp	3.75	1.25

Art Issue

Untitled (Skull), by Jean-Michel Basquiat (1960-88) A3156

2021, Feb. 5   *Photo.*   *Perf. 13*
5977 A3156 €2.56 multi   6.25 3.25

Stained-Glass Window Craftsmanship A3157

Engr. & Embossed
2021, Feb. 12   *Perf. 13*
5978 A3157 €1.50 multi   3.75 1.25

A souvenir sheet containing No. 5978 sold for €4.50.

Camel Tracks — A3158

African Lion Tracks — A3159

Chacma Baboon Tracks — A3160

Mallard Duck Tracks — A3161

Jaguar Tracks — A3162

Grizzly Bear Tracks — A3163

Gentoo Penguin Tracks — A3164

Hedgehog Tracks — A3165

African Elephant Tracks — A3166

Gray Heron Tracks — A3167

Roe Deer Tracks — A3168

Alpine Chamois Tracks — A3169

Serpentine Die Cut 11
2021, Feb. 12   *Photo.*
Booklet Stamps
Self-Adhesive

5979	A3158	(€1.08) multi	2.60	.85
5980	A3159	(€1.08) multi	2.60	.85
5981	A3160	(€1.08) multi	2.60	.85
5982	A3161	(€1.08) multi	2.60	.85
5983	A3162	(€1.08) multi	2.60	.85
5984	A3163	(€1.08) multi	2.60	.85
5985	A3164	(€1.08) multi	2.60	.85
5986	A3165	(€1.08) multi	2.60	.85
5987	A3166	(€1.08) multi	2.60	.85
5988	A3167	(€1.08) multi	2.60	.85
5989	A3168	(€1.08) multi	2.60	.85

5990	A3169	(€1.08) multi	2.60	.85
a.		Booklet pane of 12, #5979-5990	31.50	
		Nos. 5979-5990 (12)	31.20	10.20

National School of Charters, Paris, 200th Anniv. A3170

2021, Feb. 22   *Engr.*   *Perf. 13*
5991 A3170 €2.56 multi   6.25 2.10

The Kid, Motion Picture with Charlie Chaplin and Jackie Coogan, Cent. — A3171

2021, Feb. 26   *Engr.*   *Perf. 12¾x13*
5992 A3171 €1.50 blk & gray   3.75 1.25

A souvenir sheet issued in 2022 containing No. 5992 sold for €4.50.

Simone de Beauvoir (1908-86), Feminist Writer — A3172

2021, Mar. 5   *Engr.*   *Perf. 13¼*
5993 A3172 €1.28 dp vio & lil   3.00 1.00

Agricultural Order of Merit — A3173

2021, Mar. 12   *Photo.*   *Perf. 13x12¾*
5994 A3173 €1.08 multi   2.60 .85

Camille Saint-Saens (1835-1921), Composer — A3174

2021, Mar. 19   *Engr.*   *Perf. 13¼*
5995 A3174 €1.28 org brn & grnsh blue   3.00 1.00

Dans le Circle (Entire Painting), by Vassily Kandinsky (1866-1944) — A3175

A3176

A3177

A3178

A3179

A3180

A3182

A3181

A3183

A3184

Dans le Circle (Details) — A3185

Serpentine Die Cut 11
2021, Mar. 26   *Photo.*
Booklet Stamps
Self-Adhesive

5996	A3175	(€1.08) multi	2.60	.85
5997	A3176	(€1.08) org & multi	2.60	.85
5998	A3177	(€1.08) dk grn & multi	2.60	.85
5999	A3178	(€1.08) dk red brn & multi	2.60	.85
6000	A3179	(€1.08) purple & multi	2.60	.85
6001	A3180	(€1.08) org brn & multi	2.60	.85
6002	A3181	(€1.08) yel brown & multi	2.60	.85
6003	A3182	(€1.08) dark blue & multi	2.60	.85
6004	A3183	(€1.08) choc & multi	2.60	.85
6005	A3184	(€1.08) black & multi	2.60	.85
6006	A3185	(€1.08) Prus. blue & multi	2.60	.85
a.		Booklet pane of 12, #5997-6006, 2 #5996	31.50	
		Nos. 5996-6006 (11)	28.60	9.35

Miniature Sheet

European Capitals — A3186

No. 6007 — Attractions in Stockholm, Sweden: a, Royal Opera House. b, City Hall, vert. c, Royal Palace. d, Buildings in Gamla Stan District.

2021, Mar. 26   *Photo.*   *Perf. 13¼*
6007	A3186	Sheet of 4	14.00	14.00
a.-d.		€1.50 Any single	3.50	1.25

Tourism Issue

Pont-en-Royans — A3187

2021, Apr. 2   *Photo.*   *Perf. 13x12¾*
6008 A3187 €1.28 multi   3.25 1.10

Publication of *The Little Prince*, Children's Book by Antoine de Saint-Exupéry (1900-44), 75th Anniv. — A3188

2021, Apr. 9   *Photo.*   *Perf. 13¼*
6009 A3188 €1.08 multi   2.60 .85

Charles Baudelaire (1821-67), Poet — A3189

2021, Apr. 9   *Engr.*   *Perf. 13¼*
6010 A3189 €1.28 multi   3.25 1.10

Bel Group, Cheese Manufacturers, 156th Anniv. — A3190

2021, Apr. 16   *Photo.*   *Perf. 13*
6011 A3190 €1.08 multi   2.60 .85

No. 6011 was printed in sheets of 8.

Souvenir Sheet

Napoleon Bonaparte (1769-1821), Emperor — A3191

No. 6012: a, Napoleon and laurels. b, Napoleon on St. Helena looking at ocean, horiz.

Litho., Engr. & Embossed With Foil Application
2021, Apr. 17   *Perf. 13*
6012	A3191	Sheet of 2	7.50	7.50
a.-b.		€1.50 Either single	3.75	1.25

A souvenir sheet containing Nos. 6012a-6012b with a different sheet margin sold for €6.50.

Souvenir Sheet

Stained-Glass Window Depicting Adam and Eve, Notre Dame Cathedral, Paris — A3192

2021, Apr. 23   *Engr.*   *Perf.*
6013 A3192 €1.50 multi   3.75 1.25

Tourism Issue

Bibracte Archaelogical Site, Mont Beuvray — A3193

2021, May 6 **Photo.** **Perf. 13x12¾**
6014 A3193 €1.28 multi 3.25 1.10

Gladiolus Fabric Pattern — A3194

Rose and Lily of the Valley Fabric Pattern — A3195

Rose Fabric Pattern — A3196

Hydrangea and Peony Fabric Pattern — A3197

Rose Fabric Pattern — A3198

Iris and Tulip Fabric Pattern — A3199

Lilac Fabric Pattern — A3200

Sunflower and Anemone Fabric Pattern — A3201

Rose and Lilac Fabric Pattern — A3202

Tulip Fabric Pattern — A3203

Hyacinth and Crocus Fabric Pattern — A3204

Poppy Fabric Pattern — A3205

Serpentine Die Cut 11
2021, May 7 **Photo.**
Booklet Stamps
Self-Adhesive
6015 A3194 (€1.08) multi 2.75 .90
6016 A3195 (€1.08) multi 2.75 .90
6017 A3196 (€1.08) multi 2.75 .90
6018 A3197 (€1.08) multi 2.75 .90
6019 A3198 (€1.08) multi 2.75 .90
6020 A3199 (€1.08) multi 2.75 .90
6021 A3200 (€1.08) multi 2.75 .90
6022 A3201 (€1.08) multi 2.75 .90
6023 A3202 (€1.08) multi 2.75 .90
6024 A3203 (€1.08) multi 2.75 .90
6025 A3204 (€1.08) multi 2.75 .90
6026 A3205 (€1.08) multi 2.75 .90
  a. Booklet pane of 12, #6015-6026 33.00
  Nos. 6015-6026 (12) 33.00 10.80

Endangered Animals — A3206

2021, May 21 **Photo.** **Perf. 13¼**
6027 A3206 €1.50 blk & grn 3.75 1.25
  Europa.

Chamonix Guides Company, 200th Anniv. — A3207

2021, May 21 **Photo.** **Perf. 13¼**
6028 A3207 €1.08 multi 2.75 .90

Art Issue

Untitled (Seated Model in Profile in Evening Dress and Jacket), Photograph by Dora Maar (1907-97) A3208

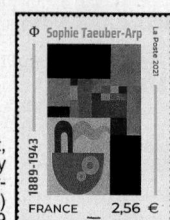

The Boat, Painting by Sophie Taeuber-Arp (1889-1943) A3209

2021, May 28 **Photo.** **Perf. 13¼**
6029 A3208 €2.56 multi 6.25 3.25
6030 A3209 €2.56 multi 6.25 3.25

Traffic Laws, Cent. A3210

2021, June 11 **Photo.** **Perf. 13x12¾**
6031 A3210 €1.08 multi 2.60 .85

Elsa Triolet (1896-1970), Writer — A3211

2021, June 12 **Photo.** **Perf. 13¼**
6032 A3211 €1.28 multi 3.00 1.00

French Pavilion at Expo 2020, Dubai A3212

2021, June 17 **Photo.** **Perf. 13**
6033 A3212 €1.50 multi 3.50 1.25

Marianne Type of 2018 and

Marianne — A3213

2021, June 17 **Engr.** **Perf. 13**
Booklet Stamps
6034 A3213 €1.08 emerald 2.60 .85
  a. Tete-beche pair 5.25 5.25
  b. Booklet pane of 12, 6 each #5478, 6034 29.50 —
Size: 30x46mm
6035 A3213 €2.16 emerald 5.25 1.75
6036 A2826 €2.56 red 6.25 2.10
  a. Booklet pane of 2, #6035-6036 11.50 —
  Complete booklet, #6034b, 6036a 41.00
Compare type A3213 with types A147 and A1814.

A3214 A3215

A3216 A3217

A3218 A3219

A3220 A3221

A3222 A3223

Publication of *The Little Prince,* by Antoine de Saint-Exupery (1900-44), 75th Anniv.
A3224 A3225

Serpentine Die Cut 11
2021, June 17 **Photo.**
Booklet Stamps
Self-Adhesive
6037 A3214 (€1.08) multi 2.60 .85
6038 A3215 (€1.08) multi 2.60 .85
6039 A3216 (€1.08) multi 2.60 .85
6040 A3217 (€1.08) multi 2.60 .85
6041 A3218 (€1.08) multi 2.60 .85
6042 A3219 (€1.08) multi 2.60 .85
6043 A3220 (€1.08) multi 2.60 .85
6044 A3221 (€1.08) multi 2.60 .85
6045 A3222 (€1.08) multi 2.60 .85
6046 A3223 (€1.08) multi 2.60 .85
6047 A3224 (€1.08) multi 2.60 .85
6048 A3225 (€1.08) multi 2.60 .85
  a. Booklet pane of 12, #6037-6048 31.50
  Nos. 6037-6048 (12) 31.20 10.20

20th Century Chess Set — A3226

Four 19th Century Chess Pieces — A3227

19th Century Chess Set — A3228

The Chess Game, Painting by Maria Helena Vieira da Silva (1908-92) A3229

Illustration From Treatise on Chess A3230

The Chess Board, Painting by Victor Vasarely (1906-97) A3231

Cavalier, Photomontage by Dora Maar (1907-97) A3232

19th Century Silver and Copper Chess Set A3233

Decorative Mirror Case Depicting Chess Players, c. 1300 — A3234

Chess Set Designed by Jean Puiforcat (1897-1945) A3235

Three 19th Century Chess Pieces — A3236

Porcelain Chess Set Designed by Jean-Jacques Prolongeau (1917-94) A3237

Serpentine Die Cut 11
2021, June 17 **Photo.**
Booklet Stamps
Self-Adhesive
6049 A3226 (€1.08) multi 2.60 .85
6050 A3227 (€1.08) multi 2.60 .85
6051 A3228 (€1.08) multi 2.60 .85
6052 A3229 (€1.08) multi 2.60 .85
6053 A3230 (€1.08) multi 2.60 .85
6054 A3231 (€1.08) multi 2.60 .85
6055 A3232 (€1.08) multi 2.60 .85
6056 A3233 (€1.08) multi 2.60 .85
6057 A3234 (€1.08) multi 2.60 .85
6058 A3235 (€1.08) multi 2.60 .85
6059 A3236 (€1.08) multi 2.60 .85
6060 A3237 (€1.08) multi 2.60 .85
  a. Booklet pane of 12, #6049-6060 31.50
  Nos. 6049-6060 (12) 31.20 10.20

Miniature Sheet

Sports
A3238

No. 6061: a, Breakdancing. b, Wheelchair fencing, horiz. c, Skateboarding. d, Rock climbing. e, Judo, horiz. f, Rugby sevens.

2021, June 18 Photo. Perf. 13
6061 A3238 Sheet of 6 21.00 21.00
a.-f. €1.50 Any single 3.50 1.25

Solar Impulse Experimental Solar-Powered Aircraft — A3239

2021, June 19 Photo. Perf. 13x12¾
6062 A3239 €1.08 multi 2.60 .85

Tourism Issue

Hunspach, 2020 Favorite Village in France
A3240

2021, July 1 Photo. Perf. 13
6063 A3240 €1.08 multi 2.60 .85

Saint-Louis Royal Chapel, Dreux — A3241

Engr. With Foil Application
2021, July 2 Perf. 13
6064 A3241 €1.28 gold & dk blue 3.00 1.00

A souvenir sheet containing No. 6064 sold for €4.50.

Gien Faience Factory, 200th Anniv. — A3242

2021, July 2 Engr. Perf. 13
6065 A3242 €2.56 blue & dk blue 6.25 2.10

A souvenir sheet containing No. 6065 sold for €6.50.

Souvenir Sheet

Jean de La Fontaine (1621-95), Fabulist — A3243

No. 6066: a, Characters from fable "The Frog and the Ox" (53x41mm). b, House of Jean de La Fontaine, Château-Thierry (30x41mm).

Perf. 13x13¼ (#6066a), 13¼ (#6066b)
2021, July 8 Engr.
6066 A3243 Sheet of 2 10.50 10.50
a.-b. €2.16 Either single 5.25 1.75

Coral Ear Pendant, Maltese Cross, and Coulas Bracelet — A3244

2021, July 9 Photo. Perf. 13¼x13
6067 A3244 €1.50 multi 3.75 1.25

Traditional Mediterranean jewelry.

Tourist Attractions A3245

Designs: No. 6068, Puy de Sancy Volcano. No. 6069, Rochers des Deux Jumeaux (Twin Rocks). No. 6070, Forêt de Fontainebleau (Fontainebleau Forest). No. 6071, Grand Ballon Mountain. No. 6072, Cascade des Tufs waterfall. No. 6073, Désert de Platé limestone outcropping. No. 6074, Dune du Pilat et Banc d'Arguin sand dune. No. 6075, Pointe du Raz promontory. No. 6076, Terril No. 74A slag heap. No. 6077, Colorado Provençal ocher quarry. No. 6078, Paysage de l'Aubrac plateau grassland. No. 6079, Loire River.

Serpentine Die Cut 11
2021, July 9 Photo.
Booklet Stamps
Self-Adhesive
6068 A3245 (€1.08) multi 2.60 .85
6069 A3245 (€1.08) multi 2.60 .85
6070 A3245 (€1.08) multi 2.60 .85
6071 A3245 (€1.08) multi 2.60 .85
6072 A3245 (€1.08) multi 2.60 .85
6073 A3245 (€1.08) multi 2.60 .85
6074 A3245 (€1.08) multi 2.60 .85
6075 A3245 (€1.08) multi 2.60 .85
6076 A3245 (€1.08) multi 2.60 .85
6077 A3245 (€1.08) multi 2.60 .85
6078 A3245 (€1.08) multi 2.60 .85
6079 A3245 (€1.08) multi 2.60 .85
a. Booklet pane of 12, #6068-6079 31.50
Nos. 6068-6079 (12) 31.20 10.20

Speleologists in Cave — A3246

2021, July 23 Photo. Perf. 13
6080 A3246 €1.50 multi 3.75 1.25

Children's Stories — A3247

Designs: No. 6081, Le Petit Chaperon Rouge (Little Red Riding Hood). No. 6082, Le Chat Botté (Puss in Boots). No. 6083, Le Petit Poucer (Tom Thumb). No. 6084, Les Musiciens de Brème (The Musicians of Bremen). No. 6085, La Petite Poucette (Thumbelina). No. 6086, Le Vilain Petit Canard (The Ugly Duckling). No. 6087, Aladin (Aladdin). No. 6088, Peau d'Ane (Donkeyskin). No. 6089, La Barbe Bleue (Bluebeard). No. 6090, La Belle au Bois Dormant (Sleeping Beauty). No. 6091, La Princesse au Petit Pois (The Princess and the Pea). No. 6092, Cendrillon (Cinderella).

Serpentine Die Cut 11
2021, Sept. 3 Photo.
Booklet Stamps
Self-Adhesive
6081 A3247 (€1.08) multi 2.50 .85
6082 A3247 (€1.08) multi 2.50 .85
6083 A3247 (€1.08) multi 2.50 .85
6084 A3247 (€1.08) multi 2.50 .85
6085 A3247 (€1.08) multi 2.50 .85
6086 A3247 (€1.08) multi 2.50 .85

6087 A3247 (€1.08) multi 2.50 .85
6088 A3247 (€1.08) multi 2.50 .85
6089 A3247 (€1.08) multi 2.50 .85
6090 A3247 (€1.08) multi 2.50 .85
6091 A3247 (€1.08) multi 2.50 .85
6092 A3247 (€1.08) multi 2.50 .85
a. Booklet pane of 12, #6081-6092 30.00
Nos. 6081-6092 (12) 30.00 10.20

Art Issue

In My Humble Opinion, Drawing by Camille Henrot A3248

2021, Sept. 10 Photo. Perf. 13x13¼
6093 A3248 €2.56 multi 6.00 3.00

Miniature Sheet

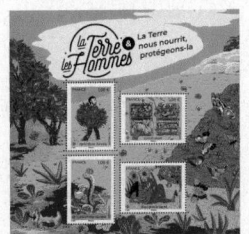

Environmental Protection — A3249

No. 6094: a, Agriculture durable (sustainable agriculture). b, Circuit court (locally produced produce), horiz. c, Consommer durable (sustainable consuming). d, Bien-être et santé (well-being and health), horiz.

2021, Sept. 17 Photo. Perf. 13¼
6094 A3249 Sheet of 4 10.00 10.00
a.-d. €1.08 Any single 2.50 .85

Featherwork A3250

Litho. & Engr.
2021, Sept. 24 Perf. 13
6095 A3250 €1.50 multi 3.50 1.25

Citroen Méhari — A3251

2021, Sept. 25 Engr. Perf. 13
6096 A3251 €1.08 multi 2.50 .85

Citroen 2CV A3252

Souvenir Sheet
Photo.
Perf. 13x13¼
6097 A3252 €2.16 multi 5.00 5.00
Stamp Day.

Gustave Roussy (1874-1948), Neurologist A3253

2021, Oct. 1 Engr. Perf. 13¼
6098 A3253 €1.28 multi 3.00 1.00

Valenciennes City Hall — A3254

2021, Oct. 8 Engr. Perf. 13x13¼
6099 A3254 €1.28 multi + label 3.00 1.00

French Federation of Philatelic Associations 94th Congress, Valenciennes.

National Center for Space Studies (CNES), 60th Anniv. — A3255

2021, Oct. 8 Photo. Perf. 13¼
6100 A3255 €1.50 multi 3.50 1.25

Mailbox of Japan A3256

Mailbox of France A3257

2021, Oct. 8 Litho. Perf. 13
6101 A3256 €1.28 red & blue 3.00 1.00
6102 A3257 €1.50 yellow & blue 3.50 1.25
a. Pair, #6101-6102 6.50 2.25

Joint issue between France and Japan. See Japan Nos. 4549-4550.
A souvenir sheet containing Nos. 6101-6102 sold for €6.50.

Souvenir Sheet

Goldorak (Grandizer) — A3258

No. 6103 — Scenes from Goldorak (Grandizer) animated television series: a, Goldorak, Koji Kabuto, Blaki. b, Goldorak, Gandal, Duke Fleed, Emperor of Darkness.

2021, Oct. 8 Photo. Perf. 13¼x13
6103 A3258 Sheet of 2 7.00 2.50
a.-b. €1.50 Either single 3.50 1.25

Paintings of Stars and Celestial Objects — A3259

Various paintings with inscriptions of: No. 6104, Tutoyer les étoiles. No. 6105, Naine blanche, Géant rouge ou bleue. No. 6106, Mesurer la distance qui nous sépare. No. 6107, A la lumière de l'infiniti lointain. No. 6108, Interroger le coeur des nébuleuses. No. 6109, Où brillent les jeunes étoiles turbulentes. No. 6110, Nova, Supernova, Pulsar. No. 6111, Chaque étoile porte un nom. No. 6112, Des millions d'étoiles en mouvement. No. 6113, Au fond des galaxies en fuite. No. 6114, Nous sommes poussière d'étoiles. No. 6115, Dans l'univers en expansion infinie.

Serpentine Die Cut 11
2021, Oct. 8   Photo.
Booklet Stamps
Self-Adhesive

6104	A3259	(€1.08) multi	2.50	.85
6105	A3259	(€1.08) multi	2.50	.85
6106	A3259	(€1.08) multi	2.50	.85
6107	A3259	(€1.08) multi	2.50	.85
6108	A3259	(€1.08) multi	2.50	.85
6109	A3259	(€1.08) multi	2.50	.85
6110	A3259	(€1.08) multi	2.50	.85
6111	A3259	(€1.08) multi	2.50	.85
6112	A3259	(€1.08) multi	2.50	.85
6113	A3259	(€1.08) multi	2.50	.85
6114	A3259	(€1.08) multi	2.50	.85
6115	A3259	(€1.08) multi	2.50	.85

   a.   Booklet pane of 12, #6104-6115   30.00

   Nos. 6104-6115 (12)   30.00   10.20

Georges Brassens (1921-81), Singer — A3260

2021, Oct. 22   Photo.   *Perf. 13¼*

6116	A3260	€1.08 multi	2.50	.85

Deer, Owl and Gift
A3261

Fox
A3262

Penguins
A3263

Fawn
A3264

Trees, Star, and Seeds
A3265

Snowflakes and Ornaments
A3266

Flowers and Stars — A3267

Fawns, Foxes and Trees — A3268

Squirrels, Acorns and Snowflake
A3269

Fox and Gifts
A3270

Bear Wearing Scarf
A3271

Deer and Penguins
A3272

Serpentine Die Cut 11
2021, Oct. 29   Photo.
Booklet Stamps
Self-Adhesive

6117	A3261	(€1.08) multi	2.50	.85
6118	A3262	(€1.08) multi	2.50	.85
6119	A3263	(€1.08) multi	2.50	.85
6120	A3264	(€1.08) multi	2.50	.85
6121	A3265	(€1.08) multi	2.50	.85
6122	A3266	(€1.08) multi	2.50	.85
6123	A3267	(€1.08) multi	2.50	.85
6124	A3268	(€1.08) multi	2.50	.85

6125	A3269	(€1.08) multi	2.50	.85
6126	A3270	(€1.08) multi	2.50	.85
6127	A3271	(€1.08) multi	2.50	.85
6128	A3272	(€1.08) multi	2.50	.85

   a.   Booklet pane of 12, #6117-6128   30.00

   Nos. 6117-6128 (12)   30.00   10.20

Christmas.

Marianne and Denomination Type of 2018

2021, Nov. 4   Engr.   *Perf. 12¾*
Size: 25x32mm

6129	A2826	€7 gold	16.00	8.00

   No. 6129 was printed in sheets of 4.

Marianne Type of 1971-74 With Euro Denominations

2021, Nov. 4   Engr.   *Perf. 13*
Booklet Stamps

6130	A555	€1.08 grnsh blue	2.50	.65
6131	A555	€1.08 red	3.00	.75

   a.   Booklet pane of 12, 6 each #6130-6131   33.00   —

Size: 40x52mm

6132	A555	€1.50 grnsh blue	3.50	.90
6133	A555	€1.50 red	3.50	.90

   a.   Booklet pane of 2, #6132-6133   7.00   —

   Complete booklet, #6131a, 6133a   40.00

A3273

A3274

A3275

A3276

A3277

A3278

A3279

A3280

A3281

A3282

A3283

Stamp Boxes — A3284

Serpentine Die Cut
2021, Nov. 4   Photo.
Booklet Stamps
Self-Adhesive

6134	A3273	(€1.08) multi	2.50	.85

Serpentine Die Cut 11

6135	A3274	(€1.08) multi	2.50	.85
6136	A3275	(€1.08) multi	2.50	.85
6137	A3276	(€1.08) multi	2.50	.85
6138	A3277	(€1.08) multi	2.50	.85
6139	A3278	(€1.08) multi	2.50	.85
6140	A3279	(€1.08) multi	2.50	.85
6141	A3280	(€1.08) multi	2.50	.85
6142	A3281	(€1.08) multi	2.50	.85
6143	A3282	(€1.08) multi	2.50	.85
6144	A3283	(€1.08) multi	2.50	.85
6145	A3284	(€1.08) multi	2.50	.85

   a.   Booklet pane of 12, #6134-6145   30.00

   Nos. 6134-6145 (12)   30.00   10.20

Souvenir Sheet

Roger North and Jean Farcigny, Founders of Autumn Philatelic Show
A3285

2021, Nov. 4   Engr.   *Perf. 13x13¼*

6146	A3285	€1.28 multi	3.00	1.00

   Autumn Philatelic Show, 75th anniv.

Sower Type of 2003

2021, Nov. 4   Engr.   *Perf. 13¼x13*

6147		Sheet of 6, 4 #6147a, 2 #6147b	55.00	55.00

   a.   A1664 €3 dull purple   6.75   3.00

   b.   A1664 €6 grnsh blue   14.00   7.00

Souvenir Sheet

French History
A3286

   No. 6148: a, Jeanne Hachette, heroine of the 1472 Siege of Beauvais. b, King Louis XI (1423-83).

2021, Nov. 5   Engr.   *Perf. 13*

6148	A3286	Sheet of 2	13.50	13.50

   a.-b.   €3 Either single   6.75   6.75

   c.   Souvenir sheet of 2, #6148a-6148b, with different sheet margin   19.50   19.50

   No. 6148c sold for €8.50.

Gustave Flaubert (1821-80), Writer — A3287

2021, Nov. 6   Photo.   *Perf. 13¼*

6149	A3287	€1.28 multi	3.00	1.00

   A souvenir sheet containing No. 6149 sold for €4.50.

No. 5955 Overprinted in Red

Method and Perf. As Before
2021, Nov. 15

6150	A3139	€1.40 multi	3.25	1.10

   The overprint marks the last issue to be printed in sheets of 30 stamps.

Valéry Giscard d'Estaing (1926-2020), President of France — A3288

2021, Nov. 19   Engr.   *Perf. 13¼*

6151	A3288	€1.28 multi	3.00	1.00

First Written Mention of a Christmas Tree in Municipal Archives of Sélestat, 500th Anniv. — A3289

Photo. With Foil Application
2021, Nov. 20   *Perf. 13¼*

6152	A3289	€1.50 gold & multi	3.50	1.25

   A souvenir sheet containing No. 6152 sold for €4.50.

Great Barrier Reef, Australia — A3290

Strokkur Geyser, Iceland — A3291

Iceberg in Lake Sassolo, Switzerland
A3292

Ice Cliff, Norway
A3293

Okavango Delta, Botswana
A3294

Iguazú Falls, Brazil and Argentina
A3295

Stream and Waterfall, New Zealand — A3296

Atlantic Ocean Waves, France — A3297

Gorges du Chéran, France — A3298

Trappstegsforsen Rapids, Sweden — A3299

Ahé Atoll, French Polynesia
A3300

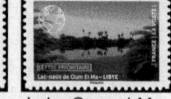

Lake Oum el Ma, Libya
A3301

Serpentine Die Cut 11
2022, Jan. 7   Photo.
Booklet Stamps
Self-Adhesive

6153	A3290	(€1.43) multi	3.25	1.10
6154	A3291	(€1.43) multi	3.25	1.10
6155	A3292	(€1.43) multi	3.25	1.10
6156	A3293	(€1.43) multi	3.25	1.10
6157	A3294	(€1.43) multi	3.25	1.10
6158	A3295	(€1.43) multi	3.25	1.10
6159	A3296	(€1.43) multi	3.25	1.10
6160	A3297	(€1.43) multi	3.25	1.10
6161	A3298	(€1.43) multi	3.25	1.10

6162	A3299	(€1.43) multi	3.25	1.10
6163	A3300	(€1.43) multi	3.25	1.10
6164	A3301	(€1.43) multi	3.25	1.10
a.		Booklet pane of 12, #6153-6164	39.00	
		Nos. 6153-6164 (12)	39.00	13.20

French Presidency of the Council of the European Union — A3302

Litho. & Engr.

2022, Jan. 10			**Perf. 13¼**	
6165	A3302	€1.65 multi	3.75	1.25

Molière (1622-73), Playwright and Actor A3303

2022, Jan. 14   Engr.   Perf. 13x13¼

6166	A3303	€1.43 black & gold	3.25	1.10

A souvenir sheet containing No. 6166 sold for €4.50.

Daniel Boulanger (1922-2014), Writer and Actor — A3304

2022, Jan. 21   Photo.   Perf. 13¼

6167	A3304	€1.43 multi	3.25	1.10

A3305

New Year 2022 (Year of the Tiger) — A3306

2022, Jan. 22   Photo.   Perf. 13¼x13

6168		Sheet of 5, #6168a, 4 #6168b	13.00	13.00
a.		A3305 €1.16 multi, 33x40mm stamp	2.60	.85
b.		A3305 €1.16 multi, 29x35mm stamp	2.60	.85
6169		Sheet of 5, #6169a, 4 #6169b	19.00	19.00
a.		A3306 €1.65 multi, 33x40mm stamp	3.75	1.25
b.		A3306 €1.65 multi, 29x35mm stamp	3.75	1.25

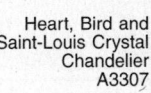

Heart, Bird and Saint-Louis Crystal Chandelier A3307

2022, Jan. 28   Litho.   Perf. 13¼

6170	A3307	€1.16 sil & multi	2.60	.85
a.		Souvenir sheet of 5	13.00	13.00
6171	A3307	€2.32 multi	5.25	1.75

Self-Adhesive
Serpentine Die Cut

6172	A3307	€1.16 multi	2.60	.85
6173	A3307	€2.32 multi	5.25	1.75

Values for Nos. 6170-6171 are for stamps with surrounding selvage.

Louis Pasteur (1822-95), Microbiologist, and His Birthplace, Dole — A3308

2022, Feb. 4   Engr.   Perf. 13¼

6174	A3308	€1.16 multi	2.60	.85

A souvenir sheet containing No. 6174 sold for €4.50.

Violin Making — A3309

2022, Feb. 11   Engr.   Perf. 13¼

6175	A3309	€1.65 multi	3.75	1.25

A souvenir sheet containing No. 6175 sold for €4.50.

Silhouettes of Animals — A3310

Silhouette of: No. 6176, African elephant. No. 6177, Giant kangaroo. No. 6178, Yellow-crested cockatoo. No. 6179, King penguins. No. 6180, European fallow deer. No. 6181, Baboons. No. 6182, Bottlenose dolphins. No. 6183, Guanacos. No. 6184, Lion. No. 6185, White stork and nest. No. 6186, Leopard. No. 6187, Great egrets and black-headed gull.

Serpentine Die Cut 11
2022, Feb. 11   Photo.
Booklet Stamps
Self-Adhesive

6176	A3310	(€1.16) multi	2.60	.85
6177	A3310	(€1.16) multi	2.60	.85
6178	A3310	(€1.16) multi	2.60	.85
6179	A3310	(€1.16) multi	2.60	.85
6180	A3310	(€1.16) multi	2.60	.85
6181	A3310	(€1.16) multi	2.60	.85
6182	A3310	(€1.16) multi	2.60	.85
6183	A3310	(€1.16) multi	2.60	.85
6184	A3310	(€1.16) multi	2.60	.85
6185	A3310	(€1.16) multi	2.60	.85
6186	A3310	(€1.16) multi	2.60	.85
6187	A3310	(€1.16) multi	2.60	.85
a.		Booklet pane of 12, #6176-6187	31.50	
		Nos. 6176-6187 (12)	31.20	10.20

Shells and Crustaceans A3311

Designs: No. 6188, Crevette bouquet (common prawn).
No. 6189: a, Tourteau (brown crab). b, Coquille Saint-Jacques (great scallop). c, Lambi (queen conch).

2022, Feb. 18   Photo.   Perf. 13¼

6188	A3311	€1.16 multi	2.60	.85

Souvenir Sheet

6189		Sheet of 4, #6188, 6189a-6189c	10.50	10.50
a.-c.		A3311 €1.16 Any single	2.60	.85
d.		Souvenir sheet of 2, #6188, 6189a	7.25	7.25
e.		Souvenir sheet of 2, #6189b, 6189c	7.25	7.25

Nos. 6189d and 6189e were sold as a set for €6.50.

Art Issue

The Tree of Paradise, Painting by Séraphine Louis (1864-1942) A3312

Portrait of a Lion, Painting by Rosa Bonheur (1822-99) A3313

2022   Photo.   Perf. 13¼x13

6190	A3312	€2.86 multi	6.50	3.25

Litho.

6191	A3313	€2.86 multi	6.50	3.25

Issued: No. 6190, 2/25; No. 6191, 3/4. A souvenir sheet containing No. 6191 sold for €6.50.

Lion of Belfort Statue and Territoire de Belfort City Hall — A3314

2022, Mar. 11   Photo.   Perf. 13¼

6192	A3314	€1.16 multi	2.60	.85

Departmental status of Terretoire de Belfort, cent.

Famous Explorers and Travelers — A3315

Designs: No. 6193, Marco Polo (1254-1324). No. 6194, Ferdinand Magellan (1480-1521). No. 6195, James Cook (1728-79). No. 6196, Jeanne Barret (1740-1807). No. 6197, Gertrude Bell (1868-1926). No. 6198, Isabelle Eberhardt (1877-1904). No. 6199, Christopher Columbus (1451-1506). No. 6200, Jacques Cartier (1491-1557). No. 6201, Roald Amundsen (1872-1928). No. 6202, Nellie Bly (1864-1922). No. 6203, Alexandra David-Néel (1868-1969). No. 6204, Amelia Earhart (1897-1937).

Serpentine Die Cut 11
2022, Mar. 11   Photo.
Booklet Stamps
Self-Adhesive

6193	A3315	(€1.16) multi	2.60	.85
6194	A3315	(€1.16) multi	2.60	.85
6195	A3315	(€1.16) multi	2.60	.85
6196	A3315	(€1.16) multi	2.60	.85
6197	A3315	(€1.16) multi	2.60	.85
6198	A3315	(€1.16) multi	2.60	.85
6199	A3315	(€1.16) multi	2.60	.85
6200	A3315	(€1.16) multi	2.60	.85
6201	A3315	(€1.16) multi	2.60	.85
6202	A3315	(€1.16) multi	2.60	.85
6203	A3315	(€1.16) multi	2.60	.85
6204	A3315	(€1.16) multi	2.60	.85
a.		Booklet pane of 12, #6193-6204	31.50	
		Nos. 6193-6204 (12)	31.20	10.20

TER Train — A3316

Hikers A3317

2022, Mar. 12   Engr.   Perf. 13¼

6205	A3316	€1.16 multi	2.50	.85

Souvenir Sheet
Photo.
Perf. 13x13¼

6206	A3317	€2.32 multi	5.25	5.25

Stamp Day.

Château de Villers-Cotterêts A3318

2022, Mar. 19   Engr.   Perf. 13¼

6207	A3318	€1.65 multi	3.75	1.25

Opening of Villers-Cotterêts International City of the French Language Project.

Odeillo Solar Furnace — A3319

2022, Mar. 25   Photo.   Perf. 13¼

6208	A3319	€1.16 multi	2.60	.85

Portrait of Henri Rouart (1833-1912), Painter and Engineer, by Edgar Degas (1834-1917) — A3320

2022, Apr. 8   Photo.   Perf. 13¼

6209	A3320	€1.43 multi	3.00	1.00

Souvenir Sheet

Pipe Organ of Notre Dame Cathedral, Paris — A3321

2022, Apr. 15   Engr.   Perf. 13

6210	A3321	€1.65 multi	3.50	3.50

Miniature Sheet

European Capitals — A3322

No. 6211 — Attractions in Ljubljana, Slovenia: a, Dragon Bridge. b, St. Nicholas's Cathedral, vert. c, Ljubljana Castle. d, Tivoli Park.

Litho. & Engr.

2022, Apr. 22			**Perf. 13¼**	
6211	A3322	Sheet of 4	14.00	14.00
a.-d.		€1.65 Any single	3.50	1.25

Legend of the
Mélusine
A3323

2022, May 6 Engr. Perf. 13¼x13
6212 A3323 €1.65 gold & black 3.50 1.25
Europa.

Poppy and
Candy
Lozenge
A3324

Chestnut
Catkins and
Candied
Chestnut
A3325

Acacia
Flowers and
Gum
A3326

Marshmallow
Flowers and
Marshmallow
Candy
A3327

Mint and
Bêtise de
Cambrai
Candy
A3328

Anise and
Anis de
Flavigny
Candy
A3329

Cacao
Flowers and
Chocolate
Candy
A3330

Violets and
Violet
Candy
A3331

Bergamot
Flower and
Bergamote
de Nancy
Candy
A3332

Coconut
Flowers and
Coconut
Ball Candy
A3333

Licorice
Flower and
Candy
A3334

Almond
Blossoms
and
Dragées
A3335

Serpentine Die Cut 11
2022, May 6 Photo.
Booklet Stamps
Self-Adhesive
6213 A3324 (€1.16) multi 2.50 .85
6214 A3325 (€1.16) multi 2.50 .85
6215 A3326 (€1.16) multi 2.50 .85
6216 A3327 (€1.16) multi 2.50 .85
6217 A3328 (€1.16) multi 2.50 .85
6218 A3329 (€1.16) multi 2.50 .85
6219 A3330 (€1.16) multi 2.50 .85
6220 A3331 (€1.16) multi 2.50 .85
6221 A3332 (€1.16) multi 2.50 .85
6222 A3333 (€1.16) multi 2.50 .85
6223 A3334 (€1.16) multi 2.50 .85
6224 A3335 (€1.16) multi 2.50 .85
 a. Booklet pane of 12, #6213-6224 30.00
 Nos. 6213-6224 (12) 30.00 10.20

Solitude (c. 1772-1802), Guadeloupian Slave Executed by French Colonial Forces — A3336

2022, May 13 Litho. Perf. 13¼
6225 A3336 €1.16 multi 2.50 .85

Tourism Issue

Church and Priory Gardens, Souvigny, and Anne of France (1461-1522), Regent for King Charles VIII — A3337

2022, May 13 Engr. Perf. 13¼x13
6226 A3337 €1.43 multi 3.00 1.00

Jeanne Moreau (1928-2017), Actress — A3338

2022, May 20 Photo. Perf. 13¼
6227 A3338 €1.43 multi 3.00 1.00

Emile Erckmann (1822-99), and Alexandre Chatrian (1826-90), Writers — A3339

2022, May 20 Engr. Perf. 13x13¼
6228 A3339 €2.86 multi 6.25 2.10

Balata Garden, Fort-de-France, Martinique — A3340

2022, May 27 Photo. Perf. 13¼
6229 A3340 €1.65 multi 3.50 1.25
 A souvenir sheet containing No. 6229 sold for €4.50.

Art Issue

Swallow Stories, Photograph by Sarah Moon A3341

2022, May 27 Photo. Perf. 13x13¼
6230 A3341 €2.86 multi 6.25 3.25

Alain Resnais (1922-2014), Movie Director — A3342

2022, June 3 Photo. Perf. 13¼
6231 A3342 €1.16 multi 2.40 .80

Sympathy
A3343

Excitement
A3344

Triumph
A3345

Romance
A3346

Desire
A3347

Admiration
A3348

Satisfaction
A3349

Joy
A3350

Adoration
A3351

Bliss
A3352

Calm
A3353

Amusement
A3354

Serpentine Die Cut 11
2022, June 3 Photo.
Booklet Stamps
Self-Adhesive
6232 A3343 (€1.16) multi 2.40 .80
6233 A3344 (€1.16) multi 2.40 .80
6234 A3345 (€1.16) multi 2.40 .80
6235 A3346 (€1.16) multi 2.40 .80
6236 A3347 (€1.16) multi 2.40 .80
6237 A3348 (€1.16) multi 2.40 .80
6238 A3349 (€1.16) multi 2.40 .80
6239 A3350 (€1.16) multi 2.40 .80
6240 A3351 (€1.16) multi 2.40 .80
6241 A3352 (€1.16) multi 2.40 .80
6242 A3353 (€1.16) multi 2.40 .80
6243 A3354 (€1.16) multi 2.40 .80
 a. Booklet pane of 12, #6232-6243 29.00
 Nos. 6232-6243 (12) 28.80 9.60

Pasteur Type of Semi-Postals of 1936 With Euro Denominations
Miniature Sheet
Engr., Sheet Margin Engr. & Embossed With Foil Application
2022, June 23 Perf. 13
6244 Sheet of 4, 2 each #6244a-6244b 25.50 25.50
 a. SP22 €2 dark blue 4.25 2.10
 b. SP22 €4 dp gray blue 8.50 4.25

Types of 1946-2008
Miniature Sheet
No. 6245 — Palaces in Paris: a, Chaillot Palace. b, Luxembourg Palace. c, Elysée Palace. d, Grand Palace.

Engr., Sheet Margin Litho. With Foil Application
2022, June 23 Perf. 13
6245 Sheet of 4 25.00 25.00
 a. A178 €3 blue 6.25 3.25
 b. A160 €3 blue 6.25 3.25
 c. A302 €3 blue 6.25 3.25
 d. A1961 €3 blue 6.25 3.25
 2022 Paris Philex.

Cité Internationale Universitaire de Paris — A3355

2022, June 23 Engr. Perf. 13x13¼
6246 A3355 €1.43 multi + label 3.00 1.00
 French Federation of Philatelic Associations 95th Congress, Paris.

Funerary Mask of King Tutankhamun A3356

Photo. With Foil Application
2022, June 23 Perf. 13¼x13
6247 A3356 €1.65 gold & multi 3.50 1.25
 A souvenir sheet containing No. 6247 sold for €4.50.

Sower With Euro Denominations — A3357

2022, June 23   Typo.   *Perf. 13*
Booklet Stamps

6248	A3357	€1.16 green	2.40	.60
6249	A3357	€1.43 red	3.00	.75
a.	Booklet pane of 12, 6 each #6248-6249		32.50	—

Size: 40x52mm

6250	A3357	€2.32 green	5.00	2.50
6251	A3357	€2.86 red	6.00	3.00
a.	Booklet pane of 2, #6250-6251		11.00	—
	Complete booklet, #6249a, 6251a		43.50	

A3358

A3359

A3360

A3361

A3362

A3363

A3364

A3365

A3366

A3367

A3368

Illustrations From Old Post Cards — A3369

Serpentine Die Cut 11
2022, June 23   Photo.
Booklet Stamps
Self-Adhesive

6252	A3358	(€1.16) multi	2.40	.80
6253	A3359	(€1.16) multi	2.40	.80
6254	A3360	(€1.16) multi	2.40	.80
6255	A3361	(€1.16) multi	2.40	.80
6256	A3362	(€1.16) multi	2.40	.80
6257	A3363	(€1.16) multi	2.40	.80
6258	A3364	(€1.16) multi	2.40	.80
6259	A3365	(€1.16) multi	2.40	.80
6260	A3366	(€1.16) multi	2.40	.80
6261	A3367	(€1.16) multi	2.40	.80
6262	A3368	(€1.16) multi	2.40	.80
6263	A3369	(€1.16) multi	2.40	.80
a.	Booklet pane of 12, #6252-6263		29.00	
	Nos. 6252-6263 (12)		28.80	9.60

French post cards, 150th anniv.

Miniature Sheet

Fire Fighters A3370

No. 6264 — Inscription: a, Soldat du feu (fire soldier). b, Soldat de la vie (soldier of life). c, Sauveteur de demain (lifeguard of tomorrow). d, Soldat du climat (climate soldier).

2022, June 23   Photo.   *Perf. 13¼*

6264	A3370	Sheet of 4	9.75	9.75
a.-d.	€1.16 Any single		2.40	.80

National Federation of Fire Fighters, 140th anniv.

Miniature Sheet

Sports A3371

No. 6265: a, Boxing. b, Handball. c, Wheelchair tennis. d, Equestrian jumping. e, Diving. f, Archery.

2022, June 23   Photo.   *Perf. 13*

6265	A3371	Sheet of 6	21.00	21.00
a.-f.	€1.65 Any single		3.50	1.25

Souvenir Sheet

Ceres A3373

Photo., Sheet Margin Typo.
2022, June 23   *Perf. 13x13¼*

6267	A3373	€3.30 pink & brown	7.00	7.00

French postal cards, 150th anniv.

Tourism Issue

Sancerre, 2021 Favorite Village in France A3374

2022, June 30   Photo.   *Perf. 13*

6268	A3374	€1.16 multi	2.40	.80

Col du Tourmalet Mountain Pass — A3387

2022, July 8   Photo.   *Perf. 13¼*

6281	A3387	€1.16 multi	2.40	.80

Underwater Archaeology — A3388

2022, July 8   Photo.   *Perf. 13¼*

6282	A3388	€1.65 multi	3.50	1.25

Château de Commequiers A3389

2022, July 15   Photo.   *Perf. 13¼*

6283	A3389	€1.43 multi	3.00	1.00

Marcel Proust (1871-1922), Writer — A3390

2022, July 22   Engr.   *Perf. 13¼x13*

6284	A3390	€1.65 multi	3.50	1.25

A souvenir sheet containing No. 6284 sold for €4.50.

A3391

A3392

A3393

A3394

A3395

A3396

A3397

A3398

Owl, Courrier Suivi Emblem, Tracking Number and Encryption — A3399

Serpentine Die Cut 11
2022, Aug. 19   Photo.
Booklet Stamps
Self-Adhesive

6285	A3391	(€1.66) multi	3.50	1.75
6286	A3392	(€1.66) multi	3.50	1.75
6287	A3393	(€1.66) multi	3.50	1.75
6288	A3394	(€1.66) multi	3.50	1.75
6289	A3395	(€1.66) multi	3.50	1.75
6290	A3396	(€1.66) multi	3.50	1.75
6291	A3397	(€1.66) multi	3.50	1.75
6292	A3398	(€1.66) multi	3.50	1.75
6293	A3399	(€1.66) multi	3.50	1.75
a.	Booklet pane of 9, #6285-6293		31.50	
	Nos. 6285-6293 (9)		31.50	15.75

On the day of issue, Nos. 6285-6293 paid the €1.16 lettre verte rate plus the 50c letter tracking fee. Tracking numbers on each stamp are repeated in booklet selvage below that stamp. Letters bearing these stamps could be tracked by entering the tracking number on the La Poste website. The tracking numbers and encryption on each stamp differ.

Compare with types A3109-A3117.

Details From Famous Paintings — A3400

Detail from: No. 6294, Liberty Leading the People, by Eugène Delacroix (1798-1863). No. 6295, Mona Lisa, by Leonardo da Vinci (1452-1519). No. 6296, The Card Players, by Paul Cézanne (1839-1906). No. 6297, La Grande Odalisque, by Jean-Auguste-Dominique Ingres (1780-1867). No. 6298, 1889 Self-portrait, by Vincent van Gogh (1853-90). No. 6299, The Intervention of the Sabine Women, by Jacques-Louis David (1748-1825). No. 6300, Pierrot, by Jean-Antoine Watteau (1684-1721). No. 6301, François I of France, by Jean Clouet (1480-1541). No. 6302, Helena Fourment with Children, by Peter Paul Rubens (1577-1640). No. 6303, Spring, by Giuseppe Arcimboldo (c. 1526-93). No. 6304, Two Young Girls at the Piano, by Pierre-Auguste Renoir (1841-1919). No. 6305, Marquise de Pompadour, by Maurice Quentin de La Tour (1704-88).

Serpentine Die Cut 11
2022, Sept. 2   Photo.
Booklet Stamps
Self-Adhesive

6294	A3400	(€1.16) multi	2.25	.75
6295	A3400	(€1.16) multi	2.25	.75
6296	A3400	(€1.16) multi	2.25	.75
6297	A3400	(€1.16) multi	2.25	.75
6298	A3400	(€1.16) multi	2.25	.75
6299	A3400	(€1.16) multi	2.25	.75
6300	A3400	(€1.16) multi	2.25	.75
6301	A3400	(€1.16) multi	2.25	.75
6302	A3400	(€1.16) multi	2.25	.75
6303	A3400	(€1.16) multi	2.25	.75
6304	A3400	(€1.16) multi	2.25	.75
6305	A3400	(€1.16) multi	2.25	.75
a.	Booklet pane of 12, #6294-6305		27.00	
	Nos. 6294-6305 (12)		27.00	9.00

Art Issue

Painting by Françoise Pétrovitch
A3401

2022, Sept. 9 **Litho.** **Perf. 13¼**
6306 A3401 €2.32 multi 4.50 2.25

Petit Louvre, La Pacaudière
A3402

2022, Sept. 9 **Photo.** **Perf. 13¼**
6307 A3402 €1.16 multi 2.25 .75

Tourism Issue

Familistère de Guise Housing Complex — A3403

2022, Sept. 16 **Engr.** **Perf. 13¼**
6308 A3403 €1.65 multi 3.25 1.10

Miniature Sheet

Renewable Energy Sources — A3404

No. 6309: a, Underwater generator. b, Wind generators, girl with pinwheel, horiz. c, People on sand dune with solar panels, horiz. d, Woman holding fruits, leaves and branches.

2022, Sept. 16 **Photo.** **Perf. 13¼**
6309 A3404 Sheet of 4 9.00 9.00
a.-d. €1.16 Any single 2.25 .75

Blind Man and Guide Dog — A3405

Photo. & Embossed
2022, Sept. 23 **Perf. 13¼**
6310 A3405 €1.16 black & red 2.25 .75

Coppersmithing
A3406

Engr. & Embossed
2022, Sept. 30 **Perf. 13**
6311 A3406 €1.65 multi 3.25 1.10

Frédéric Passy (1822-1912), 1901 Nobel Peace Laureate — A3408

2022, Oct. 7 **Engr.** **Perf. 13¼**
6313 A3408 €1.65 multi 3.25 1.10

Ada Lovelace (1815-52), Mathematician
A3409

2022, Oct. 11 **Photo.** **Perf. 13¼**
6314 A3409 €1.65 multi 3.25 1.10

A souvenir sheet containing No. 6314 sold for €4.50.

Lakes of the Orient Forest Regional Natural Park — A3410

2022, Oct. 14 **Photo.** **Perf. 13¼**
6315 A3410 €1.16 multi 2.40 .80

Tourism Issue

Notre Dame Bridge, Notre-Dame-et-Saint-Privat Cathedral, and Gévaudan Museum, Mende — A3411

2022, Oct. 21 **Engr.** **Perf. 13x12¾**
6316 A3411 €1.65 multi 3.25 1.10

A3412

A3413

A3414

A3414

A3415

A3416

A3417

A3418

A3419

A3420

A3421

A3422

Christmas
A3423

Serpentine Die Cut 11
2022, Nov. 2 **Photo.**
Booklet Stamps
Self-Adhesive
6318 A3412 (€1.16) multi 2.40 .80
6319 A3413 (€1.16) multi 2.40 .80
6320 A3414 (€1.16) multi 2.40 .80
6321 A3415 (€1.16) multi 2.40 .80
6322 A3416 (€1.16) multi 2.40 .80
6323 A3417 (€1.16) multi 2.40 .80
6324 A3418 (€1.16) multi 2.40 .80
6325 A3419 (€1.16) multi 2.40 .80
6326 A3420 (€1.16) multi 2.40 .80
6327 A3421 (€1.16) multi 2.40 .80
6328 A3422 (€1.16) multi 2.40 .80
6329 A3423 (€1.16) multi 2.40 .80
a. Booklet pane of 12, #6318-6329 29.00
Nos. 6318-6329 (12) 28.80 9.60

Raymond Devos (1922-2006), Comedian and Actor — A3424

2022, Nov. 3 **Photo.** **Perf. 13¼**
6330 A3424 €1.16 multi 2.40 .80

Souvenir Sheet

French History
A3425

No. 6331: a, Marie Leszczynska (1703-68), Queen Consort of King Louis XV. b, King Louis XV (1710-74).

2022, Nov. 3 **Engr.** **Perf.**
6331 A3425 Sheet of 2 14.00 14.00
a.-b. €3.30 Either single 7.00 7.00
c. Souvenir sheet of 2, #6631a-6631b, with different sheet margin 17.50 17.50

No. 6331c sold for €8.50.

1902 Grimaud Playing Cards — A3426

Designs: No. 6332, Queen of Spades. No. 6333, Queen of Hearts. No. 6334, Queen of Diamonds. No. 6335, Queen of Clubs. No. 6336, Ace of Spades. No. 6337, Ace of Hearts. No. 6338, Ace of Diamonds. No. 6339, Ace of Clubs. No. 6340, King of Spades. No. 6341, King of Hearts. No. 6342, King of Diamonds. No. 6343, King of Clubs.

Serpentine Die Cut 11
2022, Nov. 3 **Photo.**
Booklet Stamps
Self-Adhesive
6332 A3426 (€1.16) multi 2.40 .80
6333 A3426 (€1.16) multi 2.40 .80
6334 A3426 (€1.16) multi 2.40 .80
6335 A3426 (€1.16) multi 2.40 .80
6336 A3426 (€1.16) multi 2.40 .80
6337 A3426 (€1.16) multi 2.40 .80
6338 A3426 (€1.16) multi 2.40 .80
6339 A3426 (€1.16) multi 2.40 .80
6340 A3426 (€1.16) multi 2.40 .80
6341 A3426 (€1.16) multi 2.40 .80
6342 A3426 (€1.16) multi 2.40 .80
6343 A3426 (€1.16) multi 2.40 .80
a. Booklet pane of 12, #6332-6343 29.00
Nos. 6332-6343 (12) 28.80 9.60

Subject index of French commemorative Issues

FRANCE

SEMI-POSTAL STAMPS

No. 162 Surcharged in Red

and

SP2

1914 Unwmk. Typo. Perf. 14x13½

B1	A22	10c + 5c red	5.00	4.25
	Never hinged		7.00	
B2	SP2	10c + 5c red	32.50	3.25
	Never hinged		90.00	
a.	Booklet pane of 10		600.00	
	Never hinged		800.00	

Issue dates: No. B1, Aug. 11; No. B2, Sept. 10.
See Nos. B746a, B746b.
For overprint see Offices in Morocco No. B8.

Widow at Grave SP3

War Orphans SP4

Woman Plowing SP5

"Trench of Bayonets" SP6

Lion of Belfort — SP7

"La Marseillaise" SP8

1917-19

B3	SP3	2c + 3c vio brn	4.50	5.00
	Never hinged		10.00	
B4	SP4	5c + 5c grn ('19)	21.00	9.50
	Never hinged		60.00	
B5	SP5	15c + 10c gray green	30.00	27.50
	Never hinged		85.00	
B6	SP5	25c + 15c dp bl	80.00	57.50
	Never hinged		175.00	
B7	SP6	35c + 25c slate & vio	135.00	125.00
	Never hinged		350.00	
B8	SP7	50c + 50c pale brn & dk brn	225.00	180.00
	Never hinged		650.00	
B9	SP8	1fr + 1fr cl & mar	425.00	400.00
	Never hinged		1,100.	
B10	SP8	5fr + 5fr dp bl & blk	1,600.	1,550.
	Never hinged		4,000.	
	Nos. B3-B10 (8)		2,521.	2,355.

See No. B20-B23. For surcharges see No. B12-B19. For similar stamps with euro denominations, see No. 5450.

Hospital Ship and Field Hospital — SP9

1918, Aug.

B11	SP9	15c + 5c sl & red	125.00	60.00
	Never hinged		250.00	

See No. B746d.

Semi-Postal Stamps of 1917-19 Surcharged

1922, Sept. 1

B12	SP3	2c + 1c violet brn	.50	.80
	Never hinged		1.00	
B13	SP4	5c + 2½c green	.80	1.25
	Never hinged		1.50	
B14	SP5	15c + 5c gray grn	1.25	1.60
	Never hinged		2.60	
B15	SP5	25c + 5c deep bl	2.30	2.50
	Never hinged		4.75	
B16	SP6	35c + 5c slate & vio	13.00	15.00
	Never hinged		30.00	
B17	SP7	50c + 10c pale brn & dk brn	19.00	24.00
	Never hinged		39.00	
a.	Pair, one without surcharge			
B18	SP8	1fr + 25c cl & mar	32.50	37.50
	Never hinged		60.00	
B19	SP8	5fr + 1fr bl & blk	150.00	155.00
	Never hinged		275.00	
	Nos. B12-B19 (8)		219.35	237.65
	Set, never hinged		415.00	

Style and arrangement of surcharge differs for each denomination.

Types of 1917-19

1926-27

B20	SP3	2c + 1c violet brn	1.50	1.40
	Never hinged		4.00	
B21	SP7	50c + 10c ol brn & dk brn	20.00	12.50
	Never hinged		72.50	
B22	SP8	1fr + 25c dp rose & red brn	55.00	42.50
	Never hinged		150.00	
B23	SP8	5fr + 1fr sl bl & blk	105.00	100.00
	Never hinged		240.00	
	Nos. B20-B23 (4)		181.50	156.40

Sinking Fund Issues

Types of Regular Issues of 1903-07 Surcharged in Red or Blue

1927, Sept. 26

B24	A22	40c + 10c lt blue (R)	5.75	5.75
	Never hinged		10.50	
B25	A20	50c + 25c green (Bl)	8.25	9.00
	Never hinged		14.00	

Surcharge on No. B25 differs from illustration.

Type of Regular Issue of 1923 Surcharged in Black

B26	A23	1.50fr + 50c orange	14.50	14.00
	Never hinged		37.50	
a.	Pair, one without surcharge		2,000.	
	Nos. B24-B26 (3)		28.50	28.75

See Nos. B28-B33, B35-B37, B39-B41.

Industry and Agriculture SP10

1928, May Engr. Perf. 13½

B27	SP10	1.50fr + 8.50fr dull blue	140.00	150.00
	Never hinged		225.00	
a.	Blue green		500.00	550.00
	Never hinged		725.00	

Types of 1903-23 Issues Surcharged like Nos. B24-B26

1928, Oct. 1 Perf. 14x13½

B28	A22	40c + 10c gray lil (R)	13.00	14.00
	Never hinged		32.50	
B29	A20	50c + 25c org brn (Bl)	32.50	29.00
	Never hinged		60.00	
B30	A23	1.50fr + 50c rose lilac (Bk)	52.50	42.50
	Never hinged		100.00	
	Nos. B28-B30 (3)		98.00	85.50

Types of 1903-23 Issues Surcharged like Nos. B24-B26

1929, Oct. 1

B31	A22	40c + 10c green	18.00	19.00
	Never hinged		37.50	

B32	A20	50c + 25c lilac rose	30.00	30.00
	Never hinged		60.00	
B33	A23	1.50fr + 50c chestnut	60.00	65.00
	Never hinged		130.00	
	Nos. B31-B33 (3)		108.00	114.00

"The Smile of Reims" — SP11

1930, Mar. 15 Engr. Perf. 13

B34	SP11	1.50fr + 3.50fr red vio	80.00	82.50
	Never hinged		130.00	
a.	Booklet pane of 4		300.00	
	Never hinged		525.00	
b.	Booklet pane of 8		600.00	
	Never hinged		1,050.	
	Complete booklet, #B34b		1,100.	

Booklets containing No. B34 have two panes of 4 (No. B34a) connected by a gutter, the complete piece constituting #B34b, which is stapled into the booklet through the gutter. See footnote after No. 4642.

Types of 1903-07 Issues Surcharged like Nos. B24-B25

1930, Oct. 1 Perf. 14x13½

B35	A22	40c + 10c cerise	20.00	21.00
	Never hinged		70.00	
B36	A20	50c + 25c gray brown	37.50	42.50
	Never hinged		120.00	
B37	A22	1.50fr + 50c violet	65.00	70.00
	Never hinged		190.00	
	Nos. B35-B37 (3)		122.50	133.50

Allegory, French Provinces — SP12

1931, Mar. 1 Perf. 13

B38	SP12	1.50fr + 3.50fr green	125.00	140.00
	Never hinged		300.00	

Types of 1903-07 Issues Surcharged like Nos. B24-B25

1931, Oct. 1 Perf. 14x13½

B39	A22	40c + 10c ol grn	40.00	45.00
	Never hinged		100.00	
B40	A20	50c + 25c gray vio	100.00	110.00
	Never hinged		235.00	
B41	A22	1.50fr + 50c deep red	100.00	110.00
	Never hinged		200.00	
	Nos. B39-B41 (3)		240.00	265.00

> **Catalogue values for unused stamps in this section, from this point to the end of the section, are for Never Hinged items.**

"France" Giving Aid to an Intellectual SP13

Symbolic of Music — SP14

1935, Dec. 9 Engr. Perf. 13

B42	SP13	50c + 10c ultra	4.00	2.50
			2.50	
B43	SP14	50c + 2fr dull red	125.00	45.00
	Hinged		55.00	

The surtax was for the aid of distressed and exiled intellectuals.
For surcharge see No. B47.

Statue of Liberty — SP15

1936-37

B44	SP15	50c + 25c dk blue ('37)	7.50	5.00
			4.00	
B45	SP15	75c + 50c violet	20.00	10.00
	Hinged		9.50	

Surtax for the aid of political refugees. For surcharge see No. B47.

Children of the Unemployed — SP16

1936, May

B46	SP16	50c + 10c copper red	7.50	5.00
	Hinged		4.50	

The surtax was for the aid of children of the unemployed.

No. B43 Surcharged in Black

1936, Nov.

B47	SP14	20c on 50c + 2fr dull red	4.75	3.50
	Hinged		3.25	

Jacques Callot SP17

Anatole France (Jacques Anatole Thibault) SP18

Hector Berlioz — SP19

Victor Hugo — SP20

Auguste Rodin — SP21

Louis Pasteur — SP22

1936-37 Engr.

B48	SP17	20c + 10c brn car	4.50	2.50
	Hinged		2.25	
B49	SP18	30c + 10c emer ('37)	5.00	2.75
	Hinged		2.25	
B50	SP19	40c + 10c emer	4.50	2.75
	Hinged		2.25	
B51	SP20	50c + 10c copper red	8.75	3.75
	Hinged		3.75	
B52	SP21	90c + 10c rose red ('37)	13.00	6.50
	Hinged		6.00	
B53	SP22	1.50fr + 10c deep ultra	40.00	20.00
	Hinged		20.00	
	Nos. B48-B53 (6)		75.75	38.25

The surtax was used for relief of unemployed intellectuals. See No. 6244.

1938

B54	SP18	30c + 10c brn car	3.00	1.75
	Hinged		1.75	

B55 SP17	35c + 10c dull green	3.50	2.40
Hinged		2.40	
B56 SP19	55c + 10c dull vio	10.00	4.00
Hinged		6.00	
B57 SP20	65c + 10c ultra	11.50	4.00
Hinged		6.00	
B58 SP21	1fr + 10c car lake	8.50	4.50
Hinged		4.75	
B59 SP22	1.75fr + 25c dp blue	35.00	17.00
Hinged		17.00	
Nos. B54-B59 (6)		71.50	33.65

Tug of War — SP23

Foot Race SP24

Hiking SP25

1937, June 16

B60 SP23	20c + 10c brown	3.00	2.25
Hinged		1.60	
B61 SP24	40c + 10c red brn	3.00	2.25
Hinged		1.60	
B62 SP25	50c + 10c black brn	3.00	2.25
Hinged		1.60	
Nos. B60-B62 (3)		9.00	6.75

The surtax was for the Recreation Fund of the employees of the Post, Telephone and Telegraph.

Pierre Loti (Louis Marie Julien Viaud) — SP26

1937, Aug.

B63 SP26	50c + 20c rose car	7.50	5.00
Hinged		3.75	

The surtax was for the Pierre Loti Monument Fund.

"France" and Infant — SP27

1937-39

B64 SP27	65c + 25c brown vio	5.25	2.75
Hinged		3.25	
B65 SP27	90c + 30c pck bl ('39)	3.50	2.75
Hinged		2.10	

The surtax was used for public health work.

Winged Victory of Samothrace — SP28

1937, Aug.

B66 SP28	30c blue green	175.00	40.00
Hinged		65.00	
B67 SP28	55c red	175.00	40.00
Hinged		65.00	

On sale at the Louvre for 2.50fr. The surtax of 1.65fr was for the benefit of the Louvre Museum.

Jean Baptiste Charcot — SP29

1938-39

B68 SP29	65c + 35c dk bl grn	3.00	3.00
Hinged		1.60	

B69 SP29	90c + 35c brt red vio ('39)	30.00	13.50
Hinged		11.00	

Surtax for the benefit of French seamen.

Palace of Versailles — SP30

1938, May 9

B70 SP30	1.75fr + 75c dp bl	37.50	19.00
Hinged		19.00	

Natl. Exposition of Painting and Sculpture at Versailles.

The surtax was for the benefit of the Versailles Concert Society.

French Soldier — SP31

1938, May 16

B71 SP31	55c + 70c brown vio	8.50	5.25
Hinged		4.75	
B72 SP31	65c + 1.10fr pck bl	8.50	5.25
Hinged		4.75	

The surtax was for a fund to erect a monument to the glory of the French Infantrymen.

Monument — SP32

1938, May 25

B73 SP32	55c + 45c vermilion	22.50	12.50
Hinged		10.00	

The surtax was for a fund to erect a monument in honor of the Army Medical Corps.

Reims Cathedral — SP33

1938, July 10

B74 SP33	65c + 35c ultra	17.50	10.50
Hinged		8.50	

Completion of the reconstruction of Reims Cathedral, July 10, 1938.

"France" Welcoming Her Sons — SP34

1938, Aug. 8

B75 SP34	65c + 60c rose car	8.50	5.75
Hinged		4.00	

The surtax was for the benefit of French volunteers repatriated from Spain.

Curie Issue
Common Design Type

1938, Sept. 1

B76 CD80	1.75fr + 50c dp ultra	21.00	12.50
Hinged		8.75	

Victory Parade Passing Arc de Triomphe — SP36

1938, Oct. 8

B77 SP36	65c + 35c brown car	5.75	4.50
Hinged		3.25	

20th anniversary of the Armistice.

Student and Nurse — SP37

1938, Dec. 1

B78 SP37	65c + 60c pck blue	15.00	8.25
Hinged		8.00	

The surtax was for Student Relief.

Blind Man and Radio — SP38

1938, Dec.

B79 SP38	90c + 25c brown vio	15.00	9.00
Hinged		8.00	

The surtax was used to help provide radios for the blind.

Civilian Facing Firing Squad — SP39

1939, Feb. 1

B80 SP39	90c + 35c black brn	17.00	10.50
Hinged		8.75	

The surtax was used to erect a monument to civilian victims of World War I.

Red Cross Nurse — SP40

1939, Mar. 24

B81 SP40	90c + 35c dk sl grn, turq bl & red	13.00	8.25
Hinged		6.75	

75th anniv. of the Intl. Red Cross Society. See No. B746c.

Army Engineer — SP41

1939, Apr. 3

B82 SP41	70c + 50c vermilion	12.50	8.25
Hinged		6.00	

Army Engineering Corps. The surtax was used to erect a monument to those members who died in World War I.

Ministry of Post, Telegraph and Telephone SP42

1939, Apr. 8

B83 SP42	90c + 35c turq blue	37.50	20.00
Hinged		19.00	

The surtax was used to aid orphans of employees of the postal system. Opening of the new building for the Ministry of Post, Telegraph and Telephones.

Mother and Child — SP43

1939, Apr. 24

B84 SP43	90c + 35c red	3.75	2.50
Hinged		2.40	

The surtax was used to aid children of the unemployed.

50th Anniv. of the Eiffel Tower — SP44

1939, May 5

B85 SP44	90c + 50c red violet	15.00	9.00
Hinged		8.75	

The surtax was used for celebration festivities. For stamp with euro denominations see No. 5449c.

Puvis de Chavannes SP45

Claude Debussy SP46

Honoré de Balzac — SP47

Claude Bernard — SP48

1939-40

B86	SP45 40c + 10c ver	1.75	1.00
		.80	
B87	SP46 70c + 10c brn vio	8.25	2.50
Hinged		3.50	
B87A	SP46 80c + 10c brn vio ('40)	9.00	7.50
Hinged		4.25	
B88	SP47 90c + 10c brt red vio	7.25	2.50
Hinged		3.25	
B88A	SP47 1fr + 10c brt red vio ('40)	9.00	7.50
Hinged		4.25	
B89	SP48 2.25fr + 25c brt ultra	28.00	11.50
Hinged		14.50	
B89A	SP48 2.50fr + 25c brt ultra ('40)	9.00	7.50
Hinged		4.25	
Nos. B86-B89A (7)		72.25	40.00

The surtax was used to aid unemployed intellectuals.

Mothers and Children SP49 SP50

1939, June 15

B90 SP49	70c + 80c bl, grn & vio	5.25	4.50
Hinged		3.25	

B91 SP50 90c + 60c dk brn, dl 8.50 5.25
vio & brn
Hinged 4.75

The surtax was used to aid France's repopulation campaign.

"The Letter" by Jean Honoré Fragonard — SP51

1939, July 6
B92 SP51 40c + 60c multi 4.25 2.75
Hinged 2.40

The surtax was used for the Postal Museum. See footnote after No. 4642.

Statue of Widow and Children — SP52

1939, July 20
B93 SP52 70c + 30c brown vio 25.00 12.00
Hinged 12.00

Surtax for the benefit of French seamen.

French Soldier — SP53

Colonial Trooper — SP54

1940, Feb. 15
B94 SP53 40c + 60c sepia 3.25 2.75
Hinged 1.50
B95 SP54 1fr + 50c turq blue 3.25 2.75
Hinged 1.50

The surtax was used to assist the families of mobilized men.

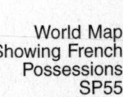

World Map Showing French Possessions SP55

1940, Apr. 15
B96 SP55 1fr + 25c scarlet 2.50 1.50
Hinged 1.50

Marshal Joseph J. C. Joffre SP56

Marshal Ferdinand Foch SP57

Gen. Joseph S. Gallieni — SP58

Woman Plowing — SP59

1940, May 1
B97 SP56 80c + 45c choc 6.00 3.75
Hinged 3.00

B98 SP57 1fr + 50c dk vio 4.50 3.00
2.50
B99 SP58 1.50fr + 50c brown 4.50 3.00
red
Hinged 2.50
B100 SP59 2.50fr + 50c indigo 12.00 7.50
& dl bl
Hinged 6.00
Nos. B97-B100 (4) 27.00 17.25

The surtax was used for war charities. See footnote after No. 4642.

Doctor, Nurse, Soldier and Family — SP60

Nurse and Wounded Soldier — SP61

1940, May 12
B101 SP60 80c + 1fr dk grn & 7.25 3.50
red
3.50
B102 SP61 1fr + 2fr sep & 9.00 3.50
red
Hinged 3.50

The surtax was used for the Red Cross. See Nos. B747a, B747e.

Nurse with Injured Children — SP62

1940, Nov. 12
B103 SP62 1fr + 2fr sepia 1.25 .80
Hinged .80

The surtax was used for victims of the war.

Wheat Harvest — SP63

Sowing — SP64

Picking Grapes — SP65

Grazing Cattle — SP66

1940, Dec. 2
B104 SP63 80c + 2fr brn blk 3.00 1.50
Hinged 1.40
B105 SP64 1fr + 2fr chest- 3.00 1.50
nut
Hinged 1.40
B106 SP65 1.50fr + 2fr brt vio 3.00 1.50
Hinged 1.40
B107 SP66 2.50fr + 2fr dp grn 3.25 1.75
Hinged 1.75
Nos. B104-B107 (4) 12.25 6.25

The surtax was for national relief.

Prisoners of War
SP67   SP68

1941, Jan. 1
B108 SP67 80c + 5fr dark grn 1.50 1.50
B109 SP68 1fr + 5fr rose brn 1.50 1.50

The surtax was for prisoners of war.

Science Fighting Cancer — SP69

1941, Feb. 20
B110 SP69 2.50fr + 50c slate blk 1.50 1.25
& brn

Surtax used for the control of cancer.

No. 417 Surcharged in Blue

+10c

1941, Mar. 4
B111 A109 1fr + 10c crimson .25 .25

Men Hauling Coal — SP70

"France" Aiding Needy Man — SP71

1941
B112 SP70 1fr + 2fr sepia 2.25 1.00
B113 SP71 2.50fr + 7.50fr dk bl 7.50 2.00

The surtax was for Marshal Pétain's National Relief Fund.

Liner Pasteur — SP72

1941, July 17   Red Surcharge
B114 SP72 1fr + 1fr on 70c dk bl .30 .30
grn

World Map, Mercator Projection SP73

1941
B115 SP73 1fr + 1fr multi .65 .45

Fisherman — SP74

1941, Oct. 23
B116 SP74 1fr + 9fr dk blue grn .80 .70

Surtax for benefit of French seamen.

Arms of Various Cities

Nancy SP75

Lille SP76

Rouen SP77

Bordeaux SP78

Toulouse SP79

Clermont-Ferrand SP80

Marseille SP81

Lyon SP82

Rennes SP83

Reims SP84

Montpellier SP85

Paris SP86

1941   *Perf. 14x13*
B117 SP75 20c + 30c brn 2.75 2.00
blk
B118 SP76 40c + 60c org 2.75 2.00
brn
B119 SP77 50c + 70c grnsh 2.75 2.00
blue
B120 SP78 70c + 80c rose 2.75 2.00
vio
B121 SP79 80c + 1fr dp 2.75 2.00
rose
B122 SP80 1fr + 1fr black 2.75 2.00
B123 SP81 1.50fr + 2fr dk bl 2.75 2.00
B124 SP82 2fr + 2fr dk vio 2.75 2.00
B125 SP83 2.50fr + 3fr brt grn 2.75 2.00
B126 SP84 3fr + 5fr org brn 2.75 2.00
B127 SP85 5fr + 6fr brt ul- 2.75 2.00
tra
B128 SP86 10fr + 10fr dk 2.75 2.00
red
Nos. B117-B128 (12) 33.00 24.00

Count de La Pérouse — SP87

1942, Mar. 23   *Perf. 13*
B129 SP87 2.50fr + 7.50fr ultra 1.25 1.40

Jean Francois de Galaup de La Pérouse, (1741-88), French navigator and explorer. The surtax was for National Relief.

Planes over Fields — SP88

1942, Apr. 4
B130 SP88 1.50fr + 3.50fr lt vio 2.40 2.40

The surtax was for the benefit of French airmen and their familes.

Alexis
Chabrier — SP89

1942, May 18
B131 SP89 2fr + 3fr sepia   1.25 1.25
Emmanuel Chabrier (1841-1894), composer, birth centenary. The surtax was for works of charity among musicians.

Symbolical of
French Colonial
Empire — SP90

1942, May 18
B132 SP90 1.50fr + 8.50fr black   1.10 1.10
The surtax was for National Relief.

Jean de
Vienne — SP91

1942, June 16
B133 SP91 1.50fr + 8.50fr sepia   1.10 1.10
600th anniv. of the birth of Jean de Vienne, 1st admiral of France. The surtax was for the benefit of French seamen.

Type of Regular Issue,
1941 Surcharged in
Carmine

1942, Sept. 10   *Perf. 14x13½*
B134 A116 1.50fr + 50c brt ultra   .25 .25
The surtax was for national relief ("Secours National").

Arms of Various Cities

Chambéry
SP92

La
Rochelle
SP93

Poitiers
SP94

Orléans
SP95

Grenoble
SP96

Angers
SP97

Dijon
SP98

Limoges
SP99

Le Havre
SP100

Nantes
SP101

Nice
SP102

St.
Etienne
SP103

    Perf. 14x13

		Unwmk.	Engr.
1942, Oct.			
B135	SP92	50c + 60c blk	3.50 3.25
B136	SP93	60c + 70c grnsh blue	3.50 3.25
B137	SP94	80c + 1fr rose	3.50 3.25
B138	SP95	1fr + 1.30fr dk green	3.50 3.25
B139	SP96	1.20fr + 1.50fr rose vio	3.50 3.25
B140	SP97	1.50fr + 1.80fr slate bl	3.50 3.25
B141	SP98	2fr + 2.30fr deep rose	3.50 3.25
B142	SP99	2.40fr + 2.80fr slate grn	3.50 3.25
B143	SP100	3fr + 3.50fr dp violet	3.50 3.25
B144	SP101	4fr + 5fr lt ultra	3.50 3.25
B145	SP102	4.50fr + 6fr red	3.50 3.25
B146	SP103	5fr + 7fr brt red vio	3.50 3.25
Nos. B135-B146 (12)			42.00 39.00

The surtax was for national relief.

Tricolor
Legion — SP104

1942, Oct. 12   *Perf. 13*
B147 SP104 1.20 + 8.80fr dk blue   10.00 10.00
   a.   Vert. pair, #B147, B148 + albino impression   22.50 25.00
B148 SP104 1.20 + 8.80fr crim   10.00 10.00
These stamps were printed in sheets of 20 stamps and 5 albino impressions arranged: 2 horizontal rows of 5 dark blue stamps, 1 row of 5 albino impressions, and 2 rows of 5 crimson stamps.

Marshal Henri Philippe
Pétain

SP105   SP106

1943, Feb. 8
B149 SP105 1fr + 10fr rose red   2.75 2.75
B150 SP105 1fr + 10fr blue   2.75 2.75
B151 SP106 2fr + 12fr rose red   2.75 2.75
B152 SP106 2fr + 12fr blue   2.75 2.75
   a.   Strip, #B149-B152 + label   12.50 12.50
The surtax was for national relief. Printed in sheets of 20, the 10 blue stamps at left, the 10 rose red at right, separated by a vert. row of 5 white labels bearing a tri-colored battle-ax.

Marshal
Pétain
SP107

"Work"
SP108

"Family"
SP109

"State"
SP110

Marshal Pétain — SP111

1943, June 7
B153 SP107 1.20fr + 1.40fr dull vio   12.00 11.00
B154 SP108 1.50fr + 2.50fr red   12.00 11.00
B155 SP109 2.40fr + 7fr brn   12.00 11.00
B156 SP110 4fr + 10fr dk violet   12.00 11.00
B157 SP111 5fr + 15fr red brn   12.00 11.00
   a.   Strip of 5, #B153-B157   100.00 100.00
Pétain's 87th birthday.
The surtax was for national relief.

Civilians Under Air
Attack — SP112

1943, Aug. 23
B158 SP112 1.50fr + 3.50fr black   .40 .40
Surtax was for bomb victims at Billancourt, Dunkirk, Lorient, Saint-Nazaire.

Civilians
Doing Farm
Work
SP113

Prisoner's Family
Doing Farm Work
SP114

1943, Sept. 27
B159 SP113 1.50fr + 8.50fr sepia   .75 .75
B160 SP114 2.40fr + 7.60fr dk grn   .80 .80
The surtax was for families of war prisoners.

Michel de
Montaigne — SP115

1.20fr+1.50fr, Francois Clouet. 1.50fr+3fr, Ambrose Paré. 2.40fr+4fr, Chevalier Pierre de Bayard. 4fr+6fr, Duke of Sully. 5fr+10fr, Henri IV.

1943, Oct. 2
B161 SP115 60c + 80c Prus green   1.75 1.75
B162 SP115 1.20fr + 1.50fr black   1.50 1.50
B163 SP115 1.50fr + 3fr deep ultra   1.50 1.50
B164 SP115 2.40fr + 4fr red   1.50 1.50
B165 SP115 4fr + 6fr dull brn red   1.75 1.75
B166 SP115 5fr + 10fr dull green   1.75 1.75
Nos. B161-B166 (6)   9.75 9.75
The surtax was for national relief. Issued to honor famous 16th century Frenchmen.

Picardy
Costume — SP121

Designs: 18th Century Costumes: 1.20fr+2fr, Brittany. 1.50fr+4fr, Ile de France.

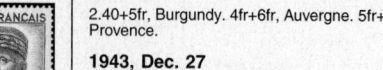

2.40+5fr, Burgundy. 4fr+6fr, Auvergne. 5fr+7fr, Provence.

1943, Dec. 27
B167 SP121 60c + 1.30fr sepia   1.60 1.60
B168 SP121 1.20fr + 2fr lt vio   1.60 1.60
B169 SP121 1.50fr + 4fr turq blue   1.60 1.60
B170 SP121 2.40fr + 5fr rose car   1.60 1.60
B171 SP121 4fr + 6fr chlky blue   2.50 2.50
B172 SP121 5fr + 7fr red   2.50 2.50
Nos. B167-B172 (6)   11.40 11.40
The surtax was for national relief. See footnote after No. 4642.

Admiral
Tourville — SP127

1944, Feb. 21
B173 SP127 4fr + 6fr dull red brn   .60 .60
300th anniv. of the birth of Admiral Anne-Hilarion de Cotentin Tourville (1642-1701).

Charles Gounod — SP128

1944, Mar. 27   *Perf. 14x13*
B174 SP128 1.50fr + 3.50fr sepia   .75 .60
50th anniv. of the death of Charles Gounod, composer (1818-1893).

Marshal
Pétain — SP129

Farming — SP130

Industry — SP131

1944, Apr. 24   *Perf. 13*
B175 SP129 1.50fr + 3.50fr sepia   3.00 3.00
B176 SP130 2fr + 3fr dp ultra   .50 .45
B177 SP131 4fr + 6fr rose red   .50 .45
Nos. B175-B177 (3)   4.00 3.90
Marshal Henri Pétain's 88th birthday.

Modern Streamliner,
19th Cent.
Train — SP132

1944, Aug. 14
B178 SP132 4fr + 6fr black   1.50 1.50
Centenary of the Paris-Rouen, Paris-Orléans railroad.

Molière (Jean-Baptiste Poquelin) — SP133

Designs: 80c+2.20fr, Jules Hardouin Mansart. 1.20fr+2.80fr, Blaise Pascal. 1.50fr+3.50fr, Louis II de Bourbon. 2fr+4fr, Jean-Baptiste Colbert. 4fr+6fr, Louis XIV.

1944, July 31
B179	SP133	50c + 1.50fr rose car	1.50	1.00
B180	SP133	80c + 2.20fr dk green	1.50	1.00
B181	SP133	1.20fr + 2.80fr black	1.50	1.00
B182	SP133	1.50fr + 3.50fr brt ultra	1.50	1.00
B183	SP133	2fr + 4fr dull brn red	1.50	1.00
B184	SP133	4fr + 6fr red	1.50	1.00
		Nos. B179-B184 (6)	9.00	6.00

Noted 17th century Frenchmen.

Angoulême SP139

Chartres SP140

Amiens SP141

Beauvais SP142

Albi — SP143

1944, Nov. 20
B185	SP139	50c + 1.50fr black	.60	.40
B186	SP140	80c + 2.20fr rose vio	.60	.40
B187	SP141	1.20fr + 2.80fr brn car	.60	.40
B188	SP142	1.50fr + 3.50fr dp blue	.60	.40
B189	SP143	4fr + 6fr orange red	.60	.40
		Nos. B185-B189 (5)	3.00	2.00

French Cathedrals.

Coat of Arms of Renouard de Villayer — SP144

1944, Dec. 9   Engr.
B190	SP144	1.50fr + 3.50fr dp brn	.25	.25

Stamp Day.

Sarah Bernhardt — SP145

1945, May 16   Unwmk.   Perf. 13
B191	SP145	4fr + 1fr dk violet brn	.30	.25

100th anniv. of the birth of Sarah Bernhardt, actress.

War Victims — SP146

1945, May 16
B192	SP146	4fr + 6fr dk violet brn	.25	.25

The surtax was for war victims of the P.T.T.

Tuberculosis Patient — SP147

1945, May 16   Typo.   Perf. 14x13½
B193	SP147	2fr + 1fr red orange	.25	.25

Surtax for the aid of tuberculosis victims. For surcharge see No. 561.

Boy and Girl — SP148

1945, July 9   Engr.   Perf. 13
B194	SP148	4fr + 2fr Prus green	.25	.25

The surtax was used for child welfare.

Burning of Oradour Church — SP149

1945, Oct. 13
B195	SP149	4fr + 2fr sepia	.25	.25

Destruction of Oradour, June, 1944.

Louis XI and Post Rider — SP150

1945, Oct. 13
B196	SP150	2fr + 3fr deep ultra	.35	.25

Stamp Day.
For overprint see French West Africa No. B2.

Ruins of Dunkirk — SP151

Ruins of Rouen — SP152

Ruins of Caen — SP153

Ruins of Saint-Malo SP154

1945, Nov. 5
B197	SP151	1.50fr + 1.50fr red brown	.40	.30
B198	SP152	2fr + 2fr violet	.40	.30
B199	SP153	2.40fr + 2.60fr blue	.40	.30
B200	SP154	4fr + 4fr black	.40	.30
		Nos. B197-B200 (4)	1.60	1.20

The surtax was to aid the suffering residents of Dunkirk, Rouen, Caen and Saint Malo.

Alfred Fournier SP155

Henri Becquerel SP156

1946, Feb. 4   Engr.   Perf. 13
B201	SP155	2fr + 3fr red brown	.30	.25
B202	SP156	2fr + 3fr violet	.30	.25

Issued to raise funds for the fight against venereal disease (No. B201) and for the struggle against cancer (No. B202).
No. B202 for the 50th anniv. of the discovery of radioactivity by Henri Becquerel.
See No. B221.

Church of the Invalides, Paris — SP157

1946, Mar. 11
B203	SP157	4fr + 6fr red brown	.30	.25

The surtax was to aid disabled war veterans. For stamp with euro denominations, see No. 5449b.

French Warships SP158

1946, Apr. 8
B204	SP158	2fr + 3fr gray black	.75	.40

The surtax was for naval charities.

"The Letter" by Jean Siméon Chardin — SP159

1946, May 25
B205	SP159	2fr + 3fr brown red	.40	.30

The surtax was used for the Postal Museum.

Fouquet de la Varane — SP160

1946, June 29
B206	SP160	3fr + 2fr sepia	.50	.25

Stamp Day.

François Villon — SP161

Designs: 3fr+1fr, Jean Fouquet. 4fr+3fr, Philippe de Commynes. 5fr+4fr, Joan of Arc. 6fr+5fr, Jean de Gerson. 10fr+6fr, Charles VII.

1946, Oct. 28
B207	SP161	2fr + 1fr dk Prus grn	1.25	.90
B208	SP161	3fr + 1fr dk blue vio	1.25	.90
B209	SP161	4fr + 3fr henna brn	1.25	.90
B210	SP161	5fr + 4fr ultra	1.25	.90
B211	SP161	6fr + 5fr sepia	1.25	.90
B212	SP161	10fr + 6fr red	1.25	.90
		Nos. B207-B212 (6)	7.50	5.40

Church of St. Sernin, Toulouse SP167

Notre Dame du Port, Clermont-Ferrand SP168

Cathedral of St. Front, Perigueux SP169

Cathedral of St. Julien, Le Mans SP170

Cathedral of Notre Dame, Paris SP171

1947   Engr.
B213	SP167	1fr + 1fr car rose	.85	.60
B214	SP168	3fr + 2fr dk bl vio	2.25	1.40
B215	SP169	4fr + 3fr henna brn	1.10	.90
B216	SP170	6fr + 4fr dp bl	1.10	.90
B217	SP171	10fr + 6fr dk gray grn	2.25	1.60
		Nos. B213-B217 (5)	7.55	5.40

See Nos. 5035c, 5933a.

François Michel le Tellier de Louvois — SP172

1947, Mar. 15
B218	SP172	4.50fr + 5.50fr car rose	1.10	.55

Stamp Day, Mar. 15, 1947.

Submarine Pens, Shipyard and Monument SP173

1947, Aug. 2
B219 SP173 6fr + 4fr bluish black .50 .30

British commando raid on the Nazi U-boat base at St. Nazaire, 1942.

Liberty Highway Marker — SP174

1947, Sept. 5
B220 SP174 6fr + 4fr dk green .75 .55

The surtax was to help defray maintenance costs of the Liberty Highway.

Fournier Type of 1946

1947, Oct. 20
B221 SP155 2fr + 3fr indigo .30 .25

Louis Braille — SP175

1948, Jan. 19
B222 SP175 6fr + 4fr purple .30 .25

Etienne Arago — SP176

1948, Mar. 6
B223 SP176 6fr + 4fr black brn .45 .25
Stamp Day, March 6-7, 1948.

Alphonse de Lamartine — SP177

Designs: 3fr+2fr, Alexandre A. Ledru-Rollin. 4fr+3fr, Louis Blanc. 5fr+4fr, Albert (Alexandre Martin). 6fr+5fr, Pierre J. Proudhon. 10fr+6fr, Louis Auguste Blanqui. 15fr+7fr, Armand Barbés. 20fr+8fr, Dennis A. Affre.

1948, Apr. 5 Engr. Perf. 13
B224 SP177 1fr + 1fr dk grn 1.10 .75
B225 SP177 3fr + 2fr henna brn 1.10 .75
B226 SP177 4fr + 3fr vio brn 1.10 .75
B227 SP177 5fr + 4fr lt bl grn 2.50 1.50
B228 SP177 6fr + 5fr indigo 2.25 1.10
B229 SP177 10fr + 6fr car rose 2.25 1.10
B230 SP177 15fr + 7fr sl blk 2.50 1.50
B231 SP177 20fr + 8fr purple 2.50 1.50
Nos. B224-B231 (8) 15.30 8.95

Centenary of the Revolution of 1848.

Dr. Léon Charles Albert Calmette SP178

1948, June 18
B232 SP178 6fr + 4fr dk grnsh bl .75 .35

1st Intl. Congress on the Calmette-Guerin bacillus vaccine.

Farmer — SP179

Designs: 5fr+3fr, Fisherman. 8fr+4fr, Miner. 10fr+6fr, Metal worker.

1949, Feb. 14
B233 SP179 3fr + 1fr claret .65 .45
B234 SP179 5fr + 3fr dk blue .75 .45
B235 SP179 8fr + 4fr indigo .75 .45
B236 SP179 10fr + 6fr dk red .80 .45
Nos. B233-B236 (4) 2.95 1.80

Étienne François de Choiseul and Post Cart — SP180

1949, Mar. 26
B237 SP180 15fr + 5fr dk green .80 .45
Stamp Day, Mar. 26-27, 1949.

Baron de la Brède et de Montesquieu — SP181

Designs: 8fr+2fr, Voltaire. 10fr+3fr, Antoine Watteau. 12fr+4fr, Georges de Buffon. 15fr+5fr, Joseph F. Dupleix. 25fr+10fr, A. R. J. Turgot.

1949, Nov. 14
B238 SP181 5fr + 1fr dk grn 2.50 1.50
B239 SP181 8fr + 2fr indigo 2.50 1.50
B240 SP181 10fr + 3fr brn red 3.00 1.90
B241 SP181 12fr + 4fr purple 3.50 1.90
B242 SP181 15fr + 5fr rose car 3.75 2.25
B243 SP181 25fr + 10fr ultra 4.50 3.00
Nos. B238-B243 (6) 19.75 12.05

"Spring" — SP182

Designs: 8fr+2fr, Summer. 12fr+3fr, Autumn. 15fr+4fr, Winter.

1949, Dec. 19
B244 SP182 5fr + 1fr green 1.50 .90
B245 SP182 8fr + 2fr yel org 1.90 1.10
B246 SP182 12fr + 3fr purple 1.90 1.50
B247 SP182 15fr + 4fr dp blue 3.50 1.75
Nos. B244-B247 (4) 8.80 5.25

Postman — SP183

1950, Mar. 11
B248 SP183 12fr + 3fr dp bl 3.00 1.75

Stamp Day, Mar. 11-12, 1950. See footnote after No. 4642.

André de Chénier — SP184

8fr+3fr, J. L. David. 10fr+4fr, Lazare Carnot. 12fr+5fr, G. J. Danton. 15fr+6fr, Maximilian Robespierre. 20fr+10fr, Louis Hoche.

1950, July 10 Engr. Perf. 13
Frames in Indigo
B249 SP184 5fr + 2fr brn vio 10.00 5.25
B250 SP184 8fr + 3fr blk brn 10.00 5.50
B251 SP184 10fr + 4fr lake 11.00 6.00
B252 SP184 12fr + 5fr red brn 13.00 6.00
B253 SP184 15fr + 6fr dk grn 14.00 6.00
B254 SP184 20fr + 10fr dk vio bl 14.00 6.00
Nos. B249-B254 (6) 72.00 34.50

Alexandre Brongniart, Bust by Houdon — SP185

15fr+3fr, "L'Amour" by Etienne M. Falconet.

1950, Dec. 22
B255 SP185 8fr + 2fr ind & car 2.00 1.25
B256 SP185 15fr + 3fr red brn & car 2.25 1.25

The surtax was for the Red Cross.

Mail Car Interior — SP186

1951, Mar. 10 Unwmk. Perf. 13
B257 SP186 12fr + 3fr lilac gray 3.00 2.25
Stamp Day, Mar. 10-11, 1951.

Alfred de Musset — SP187

8fr+2fr, Eugène Delacroix. 10fr+3fr, J.-L. Gay-Lussac. 12fr+4fr, Robert Surcouf. 15fr+5fr, C. M. Talleyrand. 30fr+10fr, Napoleon I.

Frames in Dark Brown

1951, June 2
B258 SP187 5fr + 1fr dk grn 5.25 3.00
B259 SP187 8fr + 2fr vio brn 7.50 3.00
B260 SP187 10fr + 3fr grnsh black 6.75 3.00
B261 SP187 12fr + 4fr dk vio brn 6.75 3.75
B262 SP187 15fr + 5fr brn car 6.75 3.75
B263 SP187 30fr + 10fr indigo 12.00 6.00
Nos. B258-B263 (6) 45.00 22.50

Child at Prayer by Le Maître de Moulins SP188

18th Century Child by Quentin de la Tour SP189

1951, Dec. 15 Cross in Red
B264 SP188 12fr + 3fr dk brown 3.00 1.75
B265 SP189 15fr + 5fr dp ultra 3.50 2.00
The surtax was for the Red Cross.

Stagecoach of 1844 — SP190

1952, Mar. 8 Perf. 13
B266 SP190 12fr + 3fr dp green 3.50 2.25
Stamp Day, Mar. 8, 1952.

Gustave Flaubert — SP191

Portraits: 12fr+3fr, Edouard Manet. 15fr+4fr, Camille Saint-Saens. 18fr+5fr, Henri Poincaré. 20fr+6fr, Georges-Eugene Haussmann. 30fr+7fr, Adolphe Thiers.

1952, Oct. 18
Frames in Dark Brown
B267 SP191 8fr + 2fr dk blue 6.75 3.00
B268 SP191 12fr + 3fr vio blue 6.75 3.00
B269 SP191 15fr + 4fr dk grn 6.75 3.00
B270 SP191 18fr + 5fr dk brn 7.50 3.75
B271 SP191 20fr + 6fr car 8.25 4.50
B272 SP191 30fr + 7fr purple 9.00 4.50
Nos. B267-B272 (6) 45.00 21.75

Cupid from Diana Fountain Versailles SP192

15fr+5fr, Similar detail, cupid facing left.

1952, Dec. 13 Cross in Red
B273 SP192 12fr + 3fr dk grn 4.25 2.50
B274 SP192 15fr + 5fr indigo 4.25 2.50
a. Booklet pane of 10 225.00
Complete booklet 375.00

The surtax was for the Red Cross.

Count d'Argenson — SP193

1953, Mar. 14
B275 SP193 12fr + 3fr dp blue 2.50 1.50
Day of the Stamp. Surtax for the Red Cross.

St. Bernard — SP194

12fr+3fr, Olivier de Serres. 15fr+4fr, Jean Philippe Rameau. 18fr+5fr, Gaspard Monge. 20fr+6fr, Jules Michelet. 30fr+7fr, Marshal Hubert Lyautey.

1953, July 9
B276 SP194 8fr + 2fr ultra 6.00 3.00
B277 SP194 12fr + 3fr dk grn 6.00 3.00
B278 SP194 15fr + 4fr brn car 9.00 4.50
B279 SP194 18fr + 5fr dk blue 10.00 5.25
B280 SP194 20fr + 6fr dk pur 10.00 5.25
B281 SP194 30fr + 7fr brown 10.00 5.25
Nos. B276-B281 (6) 51.00 26.25

The surtax was for the Red Cross.

Madame Vigée-Lebrun and her Daughter — SP195

Design: 15fr+5fr, "The Return from Baptism," by Louis Le Nain.

1953, Dec. 12   **Cross in Red**
B282 SP195 12fr + 3fr red brn   7.50 3.75
   a.   Bkt. pane, 4 each, gutter
     btwn.   85.00
B283 SP195 15fr + 5fr indigo   10.00 5.25

The surtax was for the Red Cross.

Count Antoine de La Vallette — SP196

1954, Mar. 20   Engr.   *Perf. 13*
B284 SP196 12fr + 3fr dp grn &
     choc   3.75 2.25

Stamp Day, Mar. 20, 1954.

Louis IX — SP197

Portraits: 15fr+5fr, Jacques Benigne Bossuet. 18fr+6fr, Sadi Carnot. 20fr+7fr, Antoine Bourdelle. 25fr+8fr, Dr. Emile Roux. 30fr+10fr, Paul Valéry.

1954, July 10
B285 SP197 12fr + 4fr dp bl   17.50 10.00
B286 SP197 15fr + 5fr pur   21.00 10.00
B287 SP197 18fr + 6fr dk
     brn   21.00 10.00
B288 SP197 20fr + 7fr crim   26.00 13.00
B289 SP197 25fr + 8fr ind   26.00 13.00
B290 SP197 30fr + 10fr dp
     claret   26.00 13.00
    Nos. B285-B290 (6)   137.50 69.00

See Nos. B303-B308, B312-B317.

"The Sick Child," by Eugene Carrière — SP198

Design: 15fr+5fr, "Young Girl with Doves," by Jean Baptiste Greuze.

1954, Dec. 18   **Cross in Red**
B291 SP198 12fr + 3fr vio
     gray & in-
     digo   10.00 4.50
   a.   Bkt. pane, 4 each, gutter
     btwn.   110.00
B292 SP198 15fr + 5fr dk brn
     & org brn   10.50 6.00

No. B291a for 90th anniv. of the Red Cross. The surtax was for the Red Cross.

Balloon Post, 1870 — SP199

1955, Mar. 19   Unwmk.   *Perf. 13*
B293 SP199 12fr + 3fr multi   3.75 2.25

Stamp Day, Mar. 19-20, 1955.

King Philip II — SP200

Portraits: 15fr+6fr, Francois de Malherbé. 18fr+7fr, Sebastien de Vauban. 25fr+8fr, Charles G. de Vergennes. 30fr+9fr, Pierre S. de Laplace. 50fr+15fr, Pierre Auguste Renoir.

1955, June 11
B294 SP200 12fr + 5fr brt
     pur   13.50 7.50
B295 SP200 15fr + 6fr dp bl   13.50 7.50
B296 SP200 18fr + 7fr dp
     green   13.50 7.50
B297 SP200 25fr + 8fr gray   19.00 9.00
B298 SP200 30fr + 9fr rose
     brn   26.00 10.00
B299 SP200 50fr + 15fr blue
     grn   26.00 11.00
    Nos. B294-B299 (6)   111.50 52.50

See Nos. B321-B326.

Child with Cage by Pigalle — SP201

Design: 15fr+5fr, Child with Goose, by Boethus of Chalcedon.

1955, Dec. 17   **Cross in Red**
B300 SP201 12fr + 3fr claret   6.50 3.75
B301 SP201 15fr + 5fr dk bl   5.25 3.00
   a.   Booklet pane of 10   150.00
     Complete booklet   300.00

The surtax was for the Red Cross.

Francois of Taxis — SP202

1956, Mar. 17   Engr.   *Perf. 13*
B302 SP202 12fr + 3fr ultra, grn
     & dk brn   2.25 1.10

Stamp Day, Mar. 17-18, 1956.

Portrait Type of 1954

Portraits: No. 303, Guillaume Budé. No. B304, Jean Goujon. No. B305, Samuel de Champlain. No. B306, Jean Simeon Chardin. No. B307, Maurice Barrès. No. B308, Maurice Ravel.

1956, June 9   *Perf. 13*
B303 SP197 12fr + 3fr saph   4.00 3.00
B304 SP197 12fr + 3fr lil gray   4.00 3.00
B305 SP197 12fr + 3fr brt red   5.25 3.00
B306 SP197 15fr + 5fr green   6.75 4.50
B307 SP197 15fr + 5fr vio brn   6.75 4.50
B308 SP197 15fr + 5fr dp vio   9.00 4.50
    Nos. B303-B308 (6)   35.75 22.50

Peasant Boy by Le Nain — SP203

Design: 15fr+5fr, Gilles by Watteau.

1956, Dec. 8   Unwmk.
       Cross in Red
B309 SP203 12fr + 3fr ol gray   2.25 1.10
   a.   Bkt. pane, 4 ea, gutter
     btwn.   40.00
B310 SP203 15fr + 5fr rose lake   2.50 1.25

The surtax was for the Red Cross.

Genoese Felucca, 1750 — SP204

1957, Mar. 16   *Perf. 13*
B311 SP204 12fr + 3fr bluish gray
     & brn blk   1.60 1.00

Day of the Stamp, Mar. 16, 1957, and honoring the Maritime Postal Service.

Portrait Type of 1954
1957, June 15

Portraits: No. B312, Jean de Joinville. No. B313, Bernard Palissy. No. B314, Quentin de la Tour. No. B315, Hugues Félicité Robert de

---

Lamennais. No. B316, George Sand. No. B317, Jules Guesde.

B312 SP197 12fr + 3fr ol gray
     & ol grn   1.90 1.10
B313 SP197 12fr + 3fr grnsh
     blk & grnsh
     bl   1.90 1.10
B314 SP197 15fr + 5fr cl & brt
     red   3.00 1.40
B315 SP197 15fr + 5fr ultra &
     ind   2.75 1.40
B316 SP197 18fr + 7fr grnsh
     blk & dk grn   3.25 1.60
B317 SP197 18fr + 7fr dk vio
     brn & red
     brn   3.25 1.60
    Nos. B312-B317 (6)   16.05 8.20

Blind Man and Beggar, Engraving by Jacques Callot — SP205

Design: 20fr+8fr, Women beggars.

1957, Dec. 7   Engr.   *Perf. 13*
B318 SP205 15fr + 7fr ultra &
     red   3.50 1.75
   a.   Bkt. pane, 4 ea, gutter
     btwn.   45.00 45.00
B319 SP205 20fr + 8fr dk vio
     brn & red   4.50 2.40

The surtax was for the Red Cross.

Motorized Mail Distribution SP206

1958, Mar. 15
B320 SP206 15fr + 5fr multi   1.20 .75

Stamp Day, Mar. 15.

Portrait Type of 1955

Portraits: No. B321, Joachim du Bellay. No. B322, Jean Bart. No. B323, Denis Diderot. No. B324, Gustave Courbet. 20fr+8fr, J. B. Carpeaux. 35fr+15fr, Toulouse-Lautrec.

1958, June 7   Engr.   *Perf. 13*
B321 SP200 12fr + 4fr yel grn   1.40 .90
B322 SP200 12fr + 4fr dk blue   1.40 .90
B323 SP200 15fr + 5fr dull cl   1.50 1.00
B324 SP200 15fr + 5fr ultra   1.60 1.10
B325 SP200 20fr + 8fr brt red   1.60 1.00
B326 SP200 35fr + 15fr green   2.10 1.10
    Nos. B321-B326 (6)   9.60 6.00

St. Vincent de Paul — SP207

Portrait: 20fr+8fr, J. H. Dunant.

1958, Dec. 6   Unwmk.
      Cross in Carmine
B327 SP207 15fr + 7fr grayish
     grn   1.00 .45
   a.   Bkt. pane, 4 each, gutter
     btwn.   20.00
B328 SP207 20fr + 8fr violet   1.00 .45

The surtax was for the Red Cross. See No. B747d.

Plane Landing at Night — SP208

1959, Mar. 21
B329 SP208 20fr + 5fr sl grn, blk
     & rose   .45 .30

Issued for Stamp Day, Mar. 21, and to publicize night air mail service.
The surtax was for the Red Cross.
See No. 1089.

Geoffroi de Villehardouin and Ships — SP209

Designs: No. B331, André Le Nôtre and formal garden. No. B332, Jean Le Rond d'Alembert, books and wheel. No. B333, David d'Angers, statue and building. No. B334, M. F. X. Bichat and torch. No. B335, Frédéric Auguste Bartholdi, Statue of Liberty and Lion of Belfort.

1959, June 13   Engr.   *Perf. 13*
B330 SP209 15fr + 5fr vio blue   1.00 .60
B331 SP209 15fr + 5fr dk sl grn   1.00 .60
B332 SP209 20fr + 10fr olive bis   .90 .60
B333 SP209 20fr + 10fr dk gray   1.10 .65
B334 SP209 30fr + 10fr dk car
     rose   1.00 .65
B335 SP209 30fr + 10fr org brn   1.20 .65
    Nos. B330-B335 (6)   6.20 3.75

The surtax was for the Red Cross.

No. 927 Surcharged

1959, Dec.   Typo.   *Perf. 14x13½*
B336 A328 25fr + 5fr black & red   .25 .25

Surtax for the flood victims at Frejus.

Charles Michel de l'Épée — SP210

Design: 25fr+10fr, Valentin Hauy.

1959, Dec. 5   Engr.   *Perf. 13*
      Cross in Carmine
B337 SP210 20fr + 10fr blk & cl   1.60 1.00
   a.   Bkt. pane, 4 each, gutter
     btwn.   30.00
B338 SP210 25fr + 10fr dk blue
     & blk   2.00 1.10

The surtax was for the Red Cross.

Ship Laying Underwater Cable — SP211

1960, Mar. 12
B339 SP211 20c + 5c grnsh bl
     & dk bl   1.10 .90

Issued for the Day of the Stamp. The surtax went to the Red Cross.

Refugee Girl Amid Ruins — SP212

1960, Apr. 7
B340 SP212 25c + 10c grn, brn &
     ind   .30 .25

World Refugee Year, July 1, 1959-June 30, 1960. The surtax was for aid to refugees.

Michel de L'Hospital SP213

No. B342, Henri de la Tour D'Auvergne, Viscount of Turenne. No. B343, Nicolas Boileau (Despreaux). No. B344, Jean-Martin Charcot, M.D. No. B345, Georges Bizet. 50c+15c, Edgar Degás.

1960, June 11   **Engr.**   **Perf. 13**

B341	SP213 10c + 5c pur & rose car	1.10	.90
B342	SP213 20c + 10c ol & vio brn	1.90	1.60
B343	SP213 20c + 10c Prus grn & dp yel grn	1.50	1.25
B344	SP213 30c + 10c rose car & rose red	2.60	2.25
B345	SP213 30c + 10c dk bl & vio bl	3.00	2.50
B346	SP213 50c + 15c sl bl & gray	3.50	2.75
	Nos. B341-B346 (6)	13.60	11.25

The surtax was for the Red Cross.
See Nos. B350-B355.

Staff of the Brotherhood of St. Martin — SP214

25c+10c, St. Martin, 16th cent. wood sculpture.

1960, Dec. 3   **Unwmk.**   **Perf. 13**

B347	SP214 20c + 10c rose cl & red	2.60	2.25
a.	Bkt. pane, 4 each, gutter btwn.	32.50	
B348	SP214 25c + 10c lt ultra & red	2.60	2.25

The surtax was for the Red Cross.

Letter Carrier, Paris 1760 — SP215

1961, Mar. 18   **Perf. 13**

B349	SP215 20c + 5c sl grn, brn & red	.60	.45

Stamp Day. Surtax for Red Cross.

Famous Men Type of 1960

Designs: 15c+5c, Bertrand Du Guesclin. No. B351, Pierre Puget. No. B352, Charles Coulomb. 30c+10c, Antoine Drouot. 45c+10c, Honoré Daumier. 50c+15c, Guillaume Apollinaire.

1961, May 20   **Engr.**

B350	SP213 15c + 5c red brn & blk	1.60	1.50
B351	SP213 20c + 10c dk grn & lt bl	1.50	1.50
B352	SP213 20c + 10c ver & rose car	1.75	1.50
B353	SP213 30c + 10c blk & brn org	1.75	1.50
B354	SP213 45c + 10c choc & dk grn	2.60	2.25
B355	SP213 50c + 15c dk car rose & vio	2.60	2.25
	Nos. B350-B355 (6)	11.80	10.50

"Love" by Rouault — SP216

Designs from "Miserere" by Georges Rouault: 25c+10c, "The Blind Consoles the Seeing."

1961, Dec. 2   **Perf. 13**

B356	SP216 20c + 10c brn, blk & red	1.90	1.50
a.	Bkt. pane, 4 each, gutter btwn.	30.00	
B357	SP216 25c + 10c brn, blk & red	2.25	1.90

The surtax was for the Red Cross.

Medieval Royal Messenger — SP217

1962, Mar. 17

B358	SP217 20c + 5c rose red, bl & sepia	.60	.55

Stamp Day. Surtax for Red Cross.

Denis Papin, Scientist — SP218

Portraits: No. B360, Edme Bouchardon, sculptor. No. B361, Joseph Lakanal, educator. 30c+10c, Gustave Charpentier, composer. 45c+15c, Edouard Estauniè, writer. 50c+20c, Hyacinthe Vincent, physician and bacteriologist.

1962, June 2   **Engr.**

B359	SP218 15c + 5c bluish grn & dk gray	1.50	1.25
B360	SP218 20c + 10c cl brn	1.50	1.25
B361	SP218 20c + 10c gray & sl	1.50	1.25
B362	SP218 30c + 10c brt bl & ind	1.90	1.60
B363	SP218 45c + 15c org brn & choc	2.10	1.75
B364	SP218 50c + 20c grnsh bl & blk	2.00	1.75
	Nos. B359-B364 (6)	10.50	8.85

The surtax was for the Red Cross.

Rosalie Fragonard by Fragonard — SP219

Design: 25c+10c, Child dressed as Pierrot.

1962, Dec. 8   **Cross in Red**

B365	SP219 20c + 10c redsh brown	.90	.75
a.	Bkt. pane, 4 ea, gutter btwn.	32.00	
B366	SP219 25c + 10c dull grn	1.50	1.40

The surtax was for the Red Cross.
For surcharges see Reunion Nos. B16-B17.

Jacques Amyot, Classical Scholar — SP220

30c+10c, Pierre de Marivaux, playwright. 50c+20c, Jacques Daviel, surgeon.

1963, Feb. 23   **Unwmk.**   **Perf. 13**

B367	SP220 20c + 10c mar, gray & pur	.75	.65
B368	SP220 30c + 10c Prus grn & mar	.75	.65
B369	SP220 50c + 20c ultra, ocher & ol	.90	.75
	Nos. B367-B369 (3)	2.40	2.05

The surtax was for the Red Cross.

Roman Chariot — SP221

1963, Mar. 16   **Engr.**

B370	SP221 20c + 5c brn org & vio brn	.25	.25

Stamp Day. Surtax for Red Cross.

Étienne Méhul, Composer SP222

Designs: 30c+10c, Nicolas-Louis Vauquelin, chemist. 50c+20c, Alfred de Vigny, poet.

1963, May 25   **Unwmk.**   **Perf. 13**

B371	SP222 20c + 10c dp bl, dk brn & dp org	.90	.75
B372	SP222 30c + 10c mag, gray & blk	.75	.65
B373	SP222 50c + 20c sl, blk & brn	1.20	1.00
	Nos. B371-B373 (3)	2.85	2.40

The surtax was for the Red Cross.

"Child with Grapes" by David d'Angers and Centenary Emblem — SP223

25c+10c, "The Fifer," by Edouard Manet.

1963, Dec. 9   **Unwmk.**   **Perf. 13**

B374	SP223 20c + 10c black & red	.65	.55
a.	Bkt. pane, 4 each, gutter btwn.	9.00	9.00
B375	SP223 25c + 10c sl grn & red	.65	.55

Cent. of the Intl. and French Red Cross. Surtax for the Red Cross.
For surcharges see Reunion Nos. B18-B19.

Post Rider, 18th Century — SP224

1964, Mar. 14   **Engr.**

B376	SP224 20c + 5c Prus green	.25	.25

Issued for Stamp Day.

Resistance Memorial by Watkin, Luxembourg Gardens SP225

De Gaulle's 1940 Poster "A Tous les Francais" SP226

Street Fighting in Paris and Strasbourg. SP227

Designs: 20c+5c, "Deportation," concentration camp with watchtower and barbed wire. No. B379, Allied troops landing in Normandy and Provence.

1964   **Engr.**   **Perf. 13**

B377	SP225 20c + 5c slate blk	.45	.40

Perf. 12x13

B378	SP226 25c + 5c dk red, bl, red & blk	.75	.60

Perf. 13

B379	SP227 30c + 5c blk, bl & org brn	.60	.55
B380	SP227 30c + 5c org brn, cl & blk	.60	.55
B381	SP225 50c + 5c dk grn	.60	.55
	Nos. B377-B381 (5)	3.00	2.65

20th anniv. of liberation from the Nazis. Issue dates: Nos. B377, B381, 3/21; No. B378, 6/18; No. B379, 6/6; No. B380, 8/22.

President René Coty — SP229

Portraits: No. B383, John Calvin. No. B384, Pope Sylvester II (Gerbert).

1964   **Unwmk.**   **Perf. 13**

B382	SP229 30c + 10c dp cl & blk	.30	.25
B383	SP229 30c + 10c dk grn, blk & brn	.30	.25
B384	SP229 30c + 10c slate & cl	.30	.25
	Nos. B382-B384 (3)	.90	.75

The surtax was for the Red Cross.
Issued: No. B382, 4/25; No. B383, 5/25; No. B384, 6/1.

Jean Nicolas Corvisart — SP230

Portrait: 25c+10c, Dominique Larrey.

Cross in Carmine

1964, Dec. 12   **Engr.**

B385	SP230 20c + 10c black	.30	.25
a.	Bkt. pane, 4 ea, gutter btwn.	3.50	
B386	SP230 25c + 10c black	.30	.25

Jean Nicolas Corvisart (1755-1821), physician of Napoleon I, and Dominique Larrey (1766-1842), Chief Surgeon of the Imperial Armies. The surtax was for the Red Cross.
For surcharges see Reunion Nos. B20-B21.

Paul Dukas, Composer — SP231

No. B387, Duke François de La Rochefoucauld, writer. No. B388, Nicolas Poussin, painter. No. B389, Duke Charles of Orléans, poet.

1965, Feb.   **Engr.**   **Perf. 13**

B387	SP231 30c + 10c org brn & dk bl	.30	.25
B388	SP231 30c + 10c car & dk red brn	.30	.25
B389	SP231 40c + 10c dk red brn, dk red & Prus bl	.45	.40
B390	SP231 40c + 10c dk brn & sl bl	.45	.40
	Nos. B387-B390 (4)	1.50	1.30

The surtax was for the Red Cross.
Issued: Nos. B387, B390 2/13; Nos. B388-B389 2/20.

Packet "La Guienne" — SP232

1965, Mar. 29   **Unwmk.**   **Perf. 13**

B391	SP232 25c + 10c multi	.40	.40

Issued for Stamp Day, 1965. "La Guienne" was used for transatlantic mail service. Surtax was for the Red Cross.

Infant with Spoon by Auguste Renoir — SP233

Design: 30c+10c, Coco Writing (Renoir's son Claude).

1965, Dec. 11   **Engr.**   *Perf. 13*
Cross in Carmine

B392	SP233 25c + 10c slate	.25	.25
a.	Bklt. pane, 4 ea, gutter btwn.	2.75	
B393	SP233 30c + 10c dull red brn	.25	.25

The surtax was for the Red Cross.
For surcharges see Reunion Nos. B22-B23.

Francois Mansart and Carnavalet Palace, Paris — SP234

No. B395, St. Pierre Fourier and Basilica of St. Pierre Fourier, Mirecourt. No. B396, Marcel Proust and St. Hilaire Bridge, Illiers. No. B397, Gabriel Fauré, monument and score of "Penelope." No. B398, Elie Metchnikoff, microscope and Pasteur Institute. No. B399, Hippolyte Taine and birthplace.

1966   **Engr.**   *Perf. 13*

B394	SP234 30c + 10c dk red brn & grn	.25	.25
B395	SP234 30c + 10c blk & gray grn	.25	.25
B396	SP234 30c + 10c ind, sep & grn	.25	.25
B397	SP234 30c + 10c bis brn & ind	.25	.25
B398	SP234 30c + 10c blk & dl brn	.25	.25
B399	SP234 30c + 10c grn & ol brn	.25	.25
	Nos. B394-B399 (6)	1.50	1.50

The surtax was for the Red Cross.
Issued: Nos. B394-B396, 2/12; others, 6/25.

Engraver Cutting Die and Tools — SP235

1966, Mar. 19   **Engr.**   *Perf. 13*

B400	SP235 25c + 10c slate, brn pur & dp org	.25	.25

Stamp Day. Surtax for Red Cross.

Angel of Victory, Verdun Fortress, Marching Troops — SP236

1966, May 28   *Perf. 13*

B401	SP236 30c + 5c Prus bl, ultra & dk grn	.25	.25

Victory of Verdun, 50th anniversary.

First Aid on Battlefield, 1859 — SP237

No. B403, Nurse giving first aid to child, 1966.

Cross in Carmine

1966, Dec. 10   **Engr.**   *Perf. 13*

B402	SP237 25c + 10c green	.25	.25
a.	Bklt. pane, 4 ea, gutter btwn.	3.50	
B403	SP237 30c + 10c slate	.30	.25

The surtax was for the Red Cross.
See No. B746e. For surcharges see Reunion Nos. B24-B25.

Emile Zola — SP238

No. B405, Beaumarchais (pen name of Pierre Augustin Caron). No. B406, St. Francois de Sales (1567-1622). No. B407, Albert Camus (1913-1960).

1967   **Engr.**   *Perf. 13*

B404	SP238 30c + 10c sl bl & bl	.30	.25
B405	SP238 30c + 10c rose brn & lil	.30	.25
B406	SP238 30c + 10c dl vio & pur	.30	.25
B407	SP238 30c + 10c brn & dl cl	.30	.25
	Nos. B404-B407 (4)	1.20	1.00

The surtax was for the Red Cross.
Issued: Nos. B404-B405, 2/4; others, 6/24.

Letter Carrier, 1865 — SP239

1967, Apr. 8

B408	SP239 25c + 10c indigo, grn & red	.30	.25

Issued for Stamp Day.

Ivory Flute Player — SP240

30c+10c, Violin player, ivory carving.

Cross in Carmine

1967, Dec. 16   **Engr.**   *Perf. 13*

B409	SP240 25c + 10c dl vio & lt brn	.30	.25
a.	Bklt. pane, 4 ea, gutter btwn.	3.50	
B410	SP240 30c + 10c grn & lt brn	.35	.25

The surtax was for the Red Cross.
For surcharges see Reunion Nos. B26-B27.

Ski Jump and Long Distance Skiing — SP241

Designs: 40c+10c, Ice hockey. 60c+20c, Olympic flame and snowflakes. 75c+25c, Woman figure skater. 95c+35c, Slalom.

1968, Jan. 27

B411	SP241 30c + 10c ver, gray & brn	.30	.30
B412	SP241 40c + 10c lil, lem & brt mag	.30	.30
B413	SP241 60c + 20c dk grn, org & brt vio	.40	.40
B414	SP241 75c + 25c brt pink, yel grn & blk	.50	.50
B415	SP241 95c + 35c bl, brt pink & red brn	.60	.50
	Nos. B411-B415 (5)	2.10	2.00

Issued for the 10th Winter Olympic Games, Grenoble, Feb. 6-18.

Rural Mailman, 1830 — SP242

1968, Mar. 16   **Engr.**   *Perf. 13*

B416	SP242 25c + 10c multi	.25	.25

Issued for Stamp Day.

François Couperin, Composer, and Instruments SP243

Portraits: No. B418, Gen. Louis Desaix de Veygoux (1768-1800) and scene showing his death at the Battle of Marengo, Italy. No. B419, Saint-Pol-Roux (pen name of Paul-Pierre Roux, 1861-1940), Christ on the Cross and ruins of Camaret-sur-Mer. No. B420, Paul Claudel (poet and diplomat, 1868-1955) and Joan of Arc at the stake.

1968   **Engr.**   *Perf. 13*

B417	SP243 30c + 10c pur & rose lil	.25	.25
B418	SP243 30c + 10c dk grn & brn	.25	.25
B419	SP243 30c + 10c cop red & ol bis	.25	.25
B420	SP243 30c + 10c dk brn & lil	.25	.25
	Nos. B417-B420 (4)	1.00	1.00

Issue dates: Nos. B417-B418, Mar. 23; Nos. B419-B420, July 6.

Spring, by Nicolas Mignard — SP244

Paintings by Nicolas Mignard; 30c+10c, Fall. No. B423, Summer. No. B424, Winter.

1968-69   *Perf. 13*
Cross in Carmine

B421	SP244 25c + 10c pur & dk bl	.30	.25
a.	Bklt. pane, 4 ea #B421-B422 with gutter btwn.)	3.00	
B422	SP244 30c + 10c org brn & car red	.30	.30
B423	SP244 40c + 15c dk brn & brn ('69)	.45	.30
a.	Bklt. pane, 4 ea #B423, B424 with gutter btwn.)	3.50	
B424	SP244 40c + 15c pur & Prus bl ('69)	.45	.30
	Nos. B421-B424 (4)	1.50	1.15

The surtax was for the Red Cross.
For surcharges see Reunion Nos. B28-B31.

Mailmen's Omnibus, 1881 — SP245

1969, Mar. 15   **Engr.**   *Perf. 13*

B425	SP245 30c + 10c brn, grn & blk	.25	.25

Issued for Stamp Day.
For surcharge see Reunion No. B32.

Gen. Francois Marceau — SP246

Portraits: No. B427, Charles Augustin Sainte-Beuve (1804-1869), writer. No. B428, Albert Roussel (1869-1937), musician. No. B429, Marshal Jean Lannes (1769-1809). No. B430, Georges Cuvier (1769-1832), naturalist. No. B431, André Gide, (1869-1951), writer.

1969

B426	SP246 50c + 10c brn red	.40	.35
B427	SP246 50c + 10c slate bl	.40	.35
B428	SP246 50c + 10c dp vio bl	.40	.35
B429	SP246 50c + 10c choc	.40	.35
B430	SP246 50c + 10c dp plum	.40	.35
B431	SP246 50c + 10c blue grn	.40	.35
	Nos. B426-B431 (6)	2.40	2.10

The surtax was for the Red Cross.
Issued: Nos. B426-B428, Mar. 24; No. B429, May 10; Nos. B430-B431, May 17.

Gen. Jacques Leclerc, La Madeleine and Battle SP247

1969, Aug. 23   **Engr.**   *Perf. 13*

B432	SP247 45c + 10c slate & brn	.75	.60

Liberation of Paris, 8/25/44, 25th anniv.

Inscribed Liberation de Strasbourg
1969, Nov. 22   *Perf. 13*

B433	SP247 70c + 10c brn, choc & olive	2.75	2.00

25th anniv. of the liberation of Strasbourg.

Philibert Delorme, Architect, and Chateau d'Anet — SP248

Designs: No. B435, Louis Le Vau (1612-1670), architect, and Vaux-le-Vicomte Chateau, Paris. No. B436, Prosper Merimée (1803-1870), writer, and Carmen. No. B437, Alexandre Dumas (1802-1870), writer, and Three Musketeers. No. B438, Edouard Branly (1844-1940), physicist, electric circuit and convent of the Carmes, Paris. No. B439, Maurice de Broglie (1875-1960), physicist, and X-ray spectrograph.

1970   **Engr.**   *Perf. 13*

B434	SP248 40c + 10c slate grn	.40	.35
B435	SP248 40c + 10c dk car	.40	.35
B436	SP248 40c + 10c Prus blue	.40	.35
B437	SP248 40c + 10c violet bl	.40	.35
B438	SP248 40c + 10c dp brown	.40	.35
B439	SP248 40c + 10c dk gray	.40	.35
	Nos. B434-B439 (6)	2.40	2.10

The surtax was for the Red Cross.
Issued: No. B434-B436, 2/14; others, 4/11.

City Mailman, 1830 — SP249

1970, Mar. 14

B440	SP249 40c + 10c blk, ultra & dk car rose	.30	.25

Issued for Stamp Day.
For surcharge see Reunion No. B33.

"Life and Death" — SP250

1970, Apr. 4

B441	SP250 40c + 10c brt bl, ol & car rose	.25	.25

Issued to publicize the fight against cancer in connection with Health Day, Apr. 7.

Marshal de Lattre de Tassigny SP251

1970, May 8   **Engr.**   *Perf. 13*

B442	SP251 40c + 10c slate & vio bl	.50	.30

25th anniv. of the entry into Berlin of French troops under Marshal Jean de Lattre de Tassigny, May 8, 1945.

Lord and Lady, Dissay Chapel Fresco — SP252

No. B444, Angel holding whips, from fresco in Dissay Castle Chapel, Vienne, c. 1500.

1970, Dec. 12   Engr.   Perf. 13
Cross in Carmine
B443 SP252 40c + 15c green .30 .25
  a.   Bklt. pane, 4 ea, gutter btwn. 12.50
B444 SP252 40c + 15c cop red .30 .25

The surtax was for the Red Cross.
For surcharges see Reunion Nos. B34-B35.

Daniel-Francois Auber and "Fra Diavolo" Music — SP253

No. B446, Gen. Charles Diego Brosset (1898-1944), Basilica of Fourvière. No. B447, Victor Grignard (1871-1935), chemist, Nobel Prize medal. No. B448, Henri Farman (1874-1958), plane. No. B449, Gen. Charles Georges Delestraint (1879-1945), scroll. No. B450, Jean Eugène Robert-Houdin (1805-71), magician's act.

1971   Engr.   Perf. 13
B445 SP253 50c + 10c brn vio
    & brn .50 .30
B446 SP253 50c + 10c dk sl
    grn & ol gray .50 .30
B447 SP253 50c + 10c brn red
    & olive .50 .30
B448 SP253 50c + 10c vio bl &
    vio .50 .30
B449 SP253 50c + 10c pur & cl .60 .45
B450 SP253 50c + 10c sl grn &
    bl grn .60 .45
    Nos. B445-B450 (6) 3.20 2.10

The surtax was for the Red Cross.
Issued: Nos. B445-B446, 3/6; No. B447, 5/8; No. B448, 5/29; Nos. B449-B450, 10/16.

Army Post Office, 1914-1918 SP254

1971, Mar. 27   Engr.   Perf. 13
B451 SP254 50c + 10c ol, brn &
    bl .40 .30

Stamp Day, 1971.
For surcharge see Reunion No. B36.

Girl with Dog, by Greuze — SP255

Design: 50c+10c, "The Dead Bird," by Jean-Baptiste Greuze (1725-1805).

1971, Dec. 11   Cross in Carmine
B452 SP255 30c + 10c violet bl .55 .45
  a.   Bklt. pane, 4 each, gutter btwn. 6.00
B453 SP255 50c + 10c dp car .55 .45

The surtax was for the Red Cross.
For surcharges see Reunion Nos. B37-B38.

Aristide Bergès (1833-1904) — SP256

No. B455, Paul de Chomedey (1612-76), founder of Montreal, and arms of Neuville-sur-Vanne. No. B456, Edouard Belin (1876-1963), inventor. No. B457, Louis Blériot (1872-1936), aviation pioneer. No. B458, Adm. François Joseph, Count de Grasse (1722-88), hero of

the American Revolution. No. B459, Théophile Gautier (1811-72), writer.

1972   Engr.   Perf. 13
B454 SP256 50c + 10c blk & grn .50 .40
B455 SP256 50c + 10c blk & bl .50 .40
B456 SP256 50c + 10c blk & lil
    rose .50 .40
B457 SP256 50c + 10c red & blk .50 .40
B458 SP256 50c + 10c org & blk .50 .40
B459 SP256 50c + 10c blk & brn .50 .40
    Nos. B454-B459 (6) 3.00 2.40

The surtax was for the Red Cross.
Issued: Nos. B454-B455, 2/19; No. B456, 6/24; No. B457, 7/1; Nos. B458-B459, 9/9.

Rural Mailman, 1894 — SP257

1972, Mar. 18   Engr.   Perf. 13
B460 SP257 50c + 10c bl, yel &
    ol gray .50 .40

Stamp Day 1972.
For surcharge see Reunion No. B39.

Nicolas Desgenettes — SP258

Designs: 30c+10c, René Nicolas Dufriche, Baron Desgenettes, M.D. (1762-1837). 50c+10c, François Joseph Broussais, M.D. (1772-1838).

1972, Dec. 16   Engr.   Perf. 13
B461 SP258 30c + 10c sl grn &
    red .40 .30
  a.   Bklt. pane, 4 ea, gutter btwn. 7.00
B462 SP258 50c + 10c red .45 .40

The surtax was for the Red Cross.
See No. B747b. For surcharges see Reunion Nos. B40-B41.

Mail Coach, 1835 — SP260

1973, Mar. 24   Engr.   Perf. 13
B470 SP260 50c + 10c grnsh blue .40 .25

Stamp Day, 1973.
For surcharge see Reunion No. B42.

Mary Magdalene — SP261

50c+10c, Mourning woman. Designs are from 15th cent. Tomb of Tonnerre.

1973, Dec. 1
B471 SP261 30c + 10c sl grn &
    red .40 .30
  a.   Bklt. pane, 4 each, gutter
    btwn. 6.00
B472 SP261 50c + 10c dk gray &
    red .45 .40

Surtax was for the Red Cross.
For surcharges see Reunion Nos. B43-B44.

St. Louis-Marie de Montfort — SP262

Portraits: No. B474, Francis Poulenc (1899-1963), composer. No. B475, Jules Barbey d'Aurevilly (1808-1889), writer. No. B476, Jean Giraudoux (1882-1944), writer.

1974, Feb. 23   Engr.   Perf. 13
B473 SP262 50c + 10c multi .50 .40
B474 SP262 50c + 10c multi .50 .40
B475 SP262 50c + 15c multi .60 .50
B476 SP262 80c + 15c multi .60 .50
    Nos. B473-B476 (4) 2.20 1.80

Issue dates: No. B473, Mar. 9; No. B474, July 20; Nos. B475-B476, Nov. 16.

Automatically Sorted Letters — SP263

1974, Mar. 9   Engr.   Perf. 13
B477 SP263 50c + 10c multi .30 .25

Stamp Day 1974. Automatic letter sorting center, Orleans-la-Source, opened 1/30/73.
For surcharge see Reunion No. B45.

Order of Liberation and 5 Honored Cities SP264

1974, June 15   Engr.   Perf. 13
B478 SP264 1fr + 10c multi .55 .30

30th anniv. of liberation from the Nazis.

"Summer" — SP265

Designs: B481, "Spring" (girl on swing). B482, "Fall" (umbrella and rabbits).

1974, Nov. 30   Engr.   Perf. 13
B479 SP265 60c + 15c multi .45 .40
  a.   Bklt. pane, 4 ea, gutter
    btwn. 6.00
B480 SP266 80c + 15c multi .45 .40

For surcharges see Reunion Nos. B46-B47.

"Winter" — SP266

1975, Nov. 29
B481 SP265 60c + 15c multi .40 .30
  a.   Bklt. pane, 4 ea, gutter btwn. 4.75
B482 SP266 80c + 20c multi .50 .40

Surtax was for the Red Cross.

Dr. Albert Schweitzer SP267

Edmond Michelet SP268

André Siegfried and Map — SP269

No. B483, Albert Schweitzer (1875-1965), medical missionary. No. B484, Edmond Michelet (1899-1970), Resistance hero, statesman. No. B485, Robert Schuman (1886-1963), promoter of United Europe. No. B486, Eugene Thomas (1903-69), minister of PTT. No. B487, André Siegfried (1875-1959), political science professor, writer.

1975   Engr.   Perf. 13
B483 SP267 80c + 20c multi .50 .40
B484 SP268 80c + 20c bl & ind .50 .40
B485 SP268 80c + 20c blk & ind .50 .40
B486 SP268 80c + 20c blk & sl .50 .40
B487 SP269 80c + 20c blk & bl .50 .40
    Nos. B483-B487 (5) 2.50 2.00

Issued: No. B483, 1/11; No. B484, 2/22; No. B485, 5/10; No. B486, 6/28; No. B487, 11/15.

Second Republic Mailman's Badge — SP270

1975, Mar. 8   Photo.
B488 SP270 80c + 20c multi .45 .35

Stamp Day.

"Sage" Type of 1876 — SP271

1976, Mar. 13   Engr.   Perf. 13
B489 SP271 80c + 20c blk & lil .40 .35

Stamp Day 1976.

Marshal A. J. de Moncey — SP272

No. B491, Max Jacob (1876-1944), Dadaist writer, by Picasso. No. B492, Jean Mounet-Sully (1841-1916), actor. No. B493, Gen. Pierre Daumesnil (1776-1832). No. B494, Eugène Fromentin (1820-1876), painter.

1976 Engr. Perf. 13

B490	SP272 80c + 20c multi	.40	.30
B491	SP272 80c + 20c red brn & ol	.40	.30
B492	SP272 80c + 20c multi	.40	.30
B493	SP272 1fr + 20c multi	.50	.30
B494	SP272 1fr + 20c multi	.50	.30
	Nos. B490-B494 (5)	2.20	1.50

Issued: No. B490, 5/22; No. B491, 7/22; No. B492, 8/28; No. B493, 9/4; No. B494, 9/25.

Anna de Noailles — SP273

1976, Nov. 6 Engr. Perf. 13

B495	SP273 1fr + 20c multi	.50	.30

Anna de Noailles (1876-1933), writer & poet.

St. Barbara — SP274

Design: 1fr+25c, Cimmerian Sibyl. Sculptures from Brou Cathedral.

1976, Nov. 20 Cross in Carmine

B496	SP274 80c + 20c violet	.45	.40
a.	Bklt. pane, 4 ea, gutter btwn.	6.00	
B497	SP274 1fr + 25c dk brown	.65	.45

Surtax was for the Red Cross.

Marckolsheim Relay Station Sign — SP275

1977, Mar. 26 Engr. Perf. 13

B498	SP275 1fr + 20c multi	.40	.25

Stamp Day.

Edouard Herriot, Statesman and Writer — SP276

Designs: No. B500, Abbé Breuil (1877-1961), archaeologist. No. B501, Guillaume de Machault (1305-1377), poet and composer. No. B502, Charles Cross (1842-1888).

1977 Engr. Perf. 13

B499	SP276 1fr + 20c blk	.40	.30
B500	SP276 1fr + 20c multi	.40	.30
B501	SP276 1fr + 20c multi	.40	.30
B502	SP276 1fr + 20c multi	.40	.30
	Nos. B499-B502 (4)	1.60	1.20

Issued: No. B499, 10/8; No. B500, 10/15; No. B501, 11/12; No. B502, 12/3.

Christmas Figurine, Provence — SP277

1fr+25c, Christmas figurine (woman), Provence.

1977, Nov. 26

B503	SP277 80c + 20c red & ind	.40	.30
a.	Bklt. pane, 4 ea, gutter btwn.	4.50	
B504	SP277 1fr + 25c red & sl grn	.45	.30

Surtax was for the Red Cross.

Marie Noel, Writer — SP278

No. B506, Georges Bernanos (1888-1948), writer. No. B507, Leon Tolstoy (1828-1910), Russian writer. No. B508, Charles Marie Leconte de Lisle (1818-1894), poet. No. B509, Voltaire (1694-1778) and Jean Jacques Rousseau (1712-1778). No. B510, Claude Bernard (1813-1878), physiologist.

1978 Engr. Perf. 13

B505	SP278 1fr + 20c multi	.40	.30
B506	SP278 1fr + 20c multi	.40	.30
B507	SP278 1fr + 20c multi	.40	.30
B508	SP278 1fr + 20c multi	.40	.30
B509	SP278 1fr + 20c multi	.40	.30
B510	SP278 1fr + 20c multi	.40	.30
	Nos. B505-B510 (6)	2.40	1.80

Issued: No. B505, 2/11; No. B506, 2/18; No. B507, 4/15; No. B508, 3/26; No. B509, 7/1; No. B510, 9/16.

Mail Collection, 1900 — SP279

1978, Apr. 8 Engr. Perf. 13

B511	SP279 1fr + 20c multi	.40	.30

Stamp Day 1978.

SP280

1fr+25c, The Hare & the Tortoise. 1.20fr+30c, The City Mouse & the Country Mouse.

1978, Dec. 2 Engr. Perf. 13

B512	SP280 1fr + 25c multi	.60	.50
a.	Bklt. pane, 4 ea, gutter btwn.	6.00	
B513	SP280 1.20fr + 30c multi	.65	.55

Surtax was for the Red Cross.

SP281

No. B514, Ladislas Marshal de Berchény (1689-1778). No. B515, Leon Jouhaux (1879-1954), labor leader. No. B516, Peter Abelard (1079-1142), theologian and writer. No. B517, Georges Courteline (1860-1929), humorist. No. B518, Simone Weil (1909-1943), social philosopher. No. B519, André Malraux (1901-1976), novelist.

1979 Engr. Perf. 13

B514	SP281 1.20fr + 30c multi	.50	.40
B515	SP281 1.20fr + 30c multi	.50	.40
B516	SP281 1.20fr + 30c multi	.50	.40
B517	SP281 1.20fr + 30c multi	.50	.40
B518	SP281 1.30fr + 30c multi	.60	.40
B519	SP281 1.30fr + 30c multi	.60	.40
	Nos. B514-B519 (6)	3.20	2.40

Issued: No. B514, 1/13; No. B515, 5/12; No. B516, 6/9; No. B517, 6/25; No. B518, 11/12; No. B519, 11/26.

General Post Office, from 1908 Post Card — SP282

1979, Mar. 10 Engr. Perf. 13

B520	SP282 1.20fr + 30c multi	.50	.30

Stamp Day 1979.

Woman, Stained-Glass Window — SP283

Stained-glass windows, Church of St. Joan of Arc, Rouen: 1.30fr+30c, Simon the Magician.

1979, Dec. 1 Perf. 13

B521	SP283 1.10fr + 30c multi	.50	.40
B522	SP283 1.30fr + 30c multi	.60	.45
a.	Bklt. pane, 4 each #521-522, with gutter btwn., perf. 12½x13	6.00	

Surtax was for the Red Cross.

Eugene Viollet le Duc (1814-1879), Architect SP284

Jean-Marie de Le Mennais (1780-1860), Priest and Educator SP285

No. B524, Jean Monnet (1888-1979), economist and diplomat. No. B525, Viollet le Duc (1814-1879), architect and writer. No. B526, Frederic Mistral (1830-1914), poet. No. B527, Saint-John Perse (Alexis Leger, 1887-1975), poet and diplomat. No. B528, Pierre Paul de Riquet (1604-1680), canal builder.

1980 Engr. Perf. 13

B523	SP284 1.30fr + 30c multi	.60	.55
B524	SP285 1.30fr + 30c multi	.60	.55
B525	SP285 1.40fr + 30c blue	.60	.55
B526	SP285 1.40fr + 30c black	.60	.55
B527	SP285 1.40fr + 30c multi	.60	.55
B528	SP284 1.40fr + 30c multi	.60	.55
	Nos. B523-B528 (6)	3.60	3.30

Issued: No. B523, Feb. 16; Nos. B524-B526, Sept. 6; Nos. B527-B528, Oct. 11.

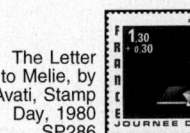

The Letter to Melie, by Avati, Stamp Day, 1980 SP286

1980, Mar. 8 Photo.

B529	SP286 1.30fr + 30c multi	.50	.40

Filling the Granaries, Choir Stall Detail, Amiens Cathedral — SP287

No. B531, Grapes from the Promised Land.

1980, Dec. 6 Engr. Perf. 13

B530	SP287 1.20fr + 30c red & dk red brn	.50	.40
B531	SP287 1.40fr + 30c red & dk red brn	.60	.40
a.	Bklt. pane, 4 #B530-B531, with gutter btwn., perf. 12½x13	6.50	

Sister Anne-Marie Javouhey (1779-1851), Founded Congregation of St. Joseph of Cluny — SP288

No. B532, Louis Armand (1905-71), railway engineer. No. B533, Louis Jouvet (1887-1951), theater director. No. B534, Marc Boegner (1881-1970), peace worker. No. B536, Jacques Offenbach (1819-80), composer. No. B537, Pierre Teilhard de Chardin (1881-1955), philosopher.

1981 Engr. Perf. 13

B532	SP288 1.20 + 30c multi	.55	.45
B533	SP288 1.20 + 30c multi	.55	.45
B534	SP288 1.40 + 30c multi	.55	.45
B535	SP288 1.40 + 30c multi	.55	.45
B536	SP288 1.40 + 30c multi	.55	.45
B537	SP288 1.40 + 30c multi	.55	.45
	Nos. B532-B537 (6)	3.30	2.70

Issued: No. B532, 5/23; No. B533, 6/13; No. B534, 11/14; No. B535, 2/7; No. B536, 2/14; No. B537, 5/23.

The Love Letter, by Goya SP289

1981, Mar. 7 Perf. 13x12½

B538	SP289 1.40 + 30c multi	.65	.60

Stamp Day 1981.

Scourges of the Passion — SP290

Stained-glass Windows, Church of the Sacred Heart, Audincourt: 1.60fr+30c, "Peace."

1981, Dec. 5 Photo. Perf. 13

B539	SP290 1.40 + 30c multi	.60	.55
B540	SP290 1.60 + 30c multi	.75	.65
a.	Bklt. pane, 4 ea, gutter btwn.	6.00	

Guillaume Postel (1510-1581), Theologian SP291

No. B542, Henri Mondor (1885-1962), physician. No. B543, Andre Chantemesse (1851-1919), Scientist. No. B544, Louis Pergaud (1882-1915), writer. No. B545, Robert Debre (1882-1978), writer. No. B546, Gustave Eiffel (1832-1923), engineer.

1982 Engr. Perf. 13

B541	SP291 1.40 + 30c multi	.60	.50
B542	SP291 1.40 + 30c dk brn & dk bl	.60	.50
B543	SP291 1.60 + 30c multi	.60	.50
B544	SP291 1.60 + 40c multi	.60	.50
B545	SP291 1.60 + 40c dk blue	.65	.60
B546	SP291 1.80 + 40c sepia	.65	.60
	Nos. B541-B546 (6)	3.70	3.20

Woman Reading, by Picasso SP292

1982, Mar. 27 Perf. 13x12½

B547	SP292 1.60 + 40c multi	.75	.60

Stamp Day.

SP293

Jules Verne books: 1.60fr+30c, Five Weeks in a Balloon. 1.80fr+40c, 20,000 Leagues under the Sea.

1982, Nov. 20   Perf. 13
B548 SP293 1.60 + 30c multi   .65   .50
B549 SP293 1.80 + 40c multi   .75   .60
  a.   Bklt. pane, 4 each #B548-
      B549, with gutter btwn.,
      perf. 12½x13   8.00

Surtax was for Red Cross.

SP294

No. B550, Andre Messager (1853-1929). No. B551, J.A. Gabriel (1698-1782), architect. No. B552, Hector Berlioz (1803-69), composer. No. B553, Max Fouchet (1913-80). No. B554, Rene Cassin (1887-1976). No. B555, Stendhal (Marie Henri Beyle, 1783-1842).

1983   Engr.   Perf. 12½x13
B550 SP294 1.60 + 30c multi   .65   .60
B551 SP294 1.60 + 30c multi   .65   .60
B552 SP294 1.80 + 40c dp lil &
      blk   .65   .60
B553 SP294 1.80 + 40c multi   .75   .60
B554 SP294 2fr + 40c multi   .80   .65
B555 SP294 2fr + 40c multi   .80   .65
   Nos. B550-B555 (6)   4.30 3.70

Issued: No. B550, 1/15; No. B551, 4/16; No. B552, 1/22; No. B553, 4/30; No. B554, 6/25; No. B555, 11/12.

Man Dictating a Letter, by Rembrandt SP295

Photo. & Engr.
1983, Feb. 26   Perf. 13X12½
B556 SP295 1.80 + 40c multi   .90   .60

Stamp Day.

Virgin with Child, Baillon, 14th Cent. — SP296

Design: No. B558, Virgin with Child, Genainville, 16th Cent.

1983, Nov. 26   Engr.   Perf. 13
B557 SP296 1.60 + 40c shown   .65   .45
B558 SP296 2fr + 40c multi   .75   .45
  a.   Bklt. pane, 4 #B557-B558,
      with gutter btwn., perf.
      12½x13   6.50

Emile Littre (1801-1881), Physician SP297

No. B560, Jean Zay (1904-44). No. B561, Pierre Corneille (1606-1684. No. B562, Gaston Bachelard (1884-1962). No. B563, Jean Paulhan (1884-1968). No. B564, Evariste Galois (1811-1832).

1984   Engr.   Perf. 13
B559 SP297 1.60fr + 40c plum &
      blk   .65   .60
B560 SP297 1.60fr + 40c dk grn
      & blk   .65   .60
B561 SP297 1.70fr + 40c dp vio
      & blk   .75   .60

B562 SP297 2fr + 40c gray &
      blk   .75   .60
B563 SP297 2.10fr + 40c dk brn
      & blk   .90   .65
B564 SP297 2.10fr + 40c ultra &
      blk   .90   .65
   Nos. B559-B564 (6)   4.60 3.70

SP298

Diderot Holding a Letter, by L.M. Van Loo.

1984, Mar. 17   Engr.   Perf. 12½x13
B565 SP298 2fr + 40c multi   .90   .60

SP299

The Rose Basket, by Caly.

1984, Nov. 24   Photo.   Perf. 12½x13
B566 SP299 2.10fr + 50c pnksh
      (basket) &
      multi   .80   .60
  a.   Salmon (basket) & multi,
      perf. 13½x13   .90   .60
  b.   As "a," bklt. pane of 10 + 2
      labels   9.00

Surtax was for the Red Cross.

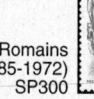

Jules Romains (1885-1972) SP300

Authors: No. B568, Jean-Paul Sartre (1905-1980). No. B569, Romain Rolland (1866-1944). No. B570, Roland Dorgeles (1885-1973). No. B571, Victor Hugo (1802-1885). No. B572, Francois Mauriac (1885-1970).

1985, Feb. 23   Engr.   Perf. 13
B567 SP300 1.70fr + 40c   1.10   .90
B568 SP300 1.70fr + 40c   1.10   .90
B569 SP300 1.70fr + 40c   1.10   .90
B570 SP300 2.10fr + 50c   1.25 1.00
B571 SP300 2.10fr + 50c   1.25 1.00
B572 SP300 2.10fr + 50c   1.25 1.00
  a.   Bklt. pane, 1 each + 2 la-
      bels, perf. 15x14½   15.00
   Nos. B567-B572 (6)   7.05 5.70

SP301

Stamp Day: Canceling apparatus invented by Eugene Daguin (1849-1888).

1985, Mar. 16   Engr.   Perf. 12½x13
B573 SP301 2.10fr + 50c brn blk
      & bluish gray   .90   .60

SP302

Issenheim Altarpiece retable.

1985, Nov. 23   Photo.
B574 SP302 2.20fr + 50c multi   .80   .60
  a.   As "b," bklt. pane of 10   8.00
  b.   Perf. 13½x13   .90   .60

Surtax for the Red Cross.

SP303

Famous men: No. B575, Francois Arago (1786-1853), physician, politician. No. B576, Henri Moissan (1852-1907), chemist. No. B577, Henri Fabre (1882-1984), engineer. No. B578, Marc Seguin (1786-1875), engineer. No. B579, Paul Heroult (1863-1914), chemist.

1986, Feb. 22   Engr.   Perf. 13
B575 SP303 1.80fr + 40c multi   .75   .65
B576 SP303 1.80fr + 40c multi   .75   .65
B577 SP303 1.80fr + 40c multi   .75   .65
B578 SP303 2.20fr + 50c multi   .80   .65
B579 SP303 2.20fr + 50c multi   .80   .65
  a.   Bklt. pane of 5, #B575-B579,
      + 3 labels   6.00
   Nos. B575-B579 (5)   3.85 3.25

SP304

1986, Mar. 1   Engr.   Perf. 13x12½
B580 SP304 2.20fr + 50c brn blk   4.50 4.50

Pierre Cot (1895-1977).

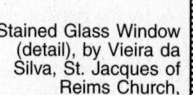

Mail Britzska — SP305

1986, Apr. 5   Perf. 13
B581 SP305 2.20fr + 60c pale
      tan & dk vio
      brn   .85   .60

Booklet Stamp
B582 SP305 2.20fr + 60c buff &
      blk   .85   .60
  a.   Bklt. pane of 6 + 2 labels   6.00

Stamp Day. See Nos. B590-B591, B599-B600, B608-B609.

Stained Glass Window (detail), by Vieira da Silva, St. Jacques of Reims Church, Marne — SP306

1986, Nov. 24   Photo.   Perf. 12½x13
B583 SP306 2.20fr + 60c multi   .85   .60
  a.   As "b," bklt. pane of 10   9.00
  b.   Perf. 13½x13   .90   .60

Surtaxed to benefit the natl. Red Cross.

Physicians and Biologists SP307

No. B584, Charles Richet (1850-1935). No. B585, Eugene Jamot (1879-1937). No. B586, Bernard Halpern (1904-1978). No. B587, Alexandre Yersin (1863-1943). No. B588, Jean Rostand (1894-1977). No. B589, Jacques Monod (1910-1976).

1987, Feb. 21   Engr.   Perf. 13
B584 SP307 1.90fr + 50c deep
      ultra   .75   .60
B585 SP307 1.90fr + 50c dull lil   .75   .60
B586 SP307 1.90fr + 50c grnsh
      gray   .75   .60
B587 SP307 2.20fr + 50c grnsh
      gray   .85   .65
B588 SP307 2.20fr + 50c deep
      ultra   .85   .65
B589 SP307 2.20fr + 50c dull lil   .85   .65
  a.   Bklt. pane of 6, #B584-B589   5.00
   Nos. B584-B589 (6)   4.80 3.75

Stamp Day Type of 1986

Stamp Day 1987: Berline carriage.

1987, Mar. 14   Engr.
B590 SP305 2.20fr + 60c buff &
      sepia   .85   .60

Booklet Stamp
B591 SP305 2.20fr + 60c pale &
      dk bl   .85   .60
  a.   Bklt. pane of 6 + 2 labels   6.00

Flight Into Egypt, Retable by Melchior Broederlam — SP308

1987, Nov. 21 Photo. Perf. 12½x13
B592 SP308 2.20fr +60c multi   .85   .60
  a.   As "b," bklt. pane of 10 + 2
      labels   8.00
  b.   Perf. 13½x13   .90   .60

Surtaxed to benefit the Red Cross.

Explorers SP309

Profiles & maps: No. B593, Marquis Abraham Duquesne (1610-1688), naval commander. No. B594, Pierre Andre de Suffren (1729-1788). No. B595, Jean-Francois de La Perouse (1741-1788). No. B596, Mahe de La Bourdonnais (1699-1753). No. B597, Louis-Antoine de Bougainville (1729-1811). No. B598, Jules Dumont d'Urville (1790-1842).

1988, Feb. 20   Engr.   Perf. 13
B593 SP309 2fr + 50c multi   .75   .50
B594 SP309 2fr + 50c multi   .75   .50
B595 SP309 2fr + 50c multi   .75   .50
B596 SP309 2.20fr + 50c multi   .85   .60
B597 SP309 2.20fr + 50c multi   .85   .60
B598 SP309 2.20fr + 50c multi   .85   .60
  a.   Bklt. pane of 6, #B593-B598   4.50

Stamp Day Type of 1986

Stamp Day 1988: Postal coach.

1988, Mar. 29   Engr.
B599 SP305 2.20fr +60c dk lilac   .85   .60

Booklet Stamp
B600 SP305 2.20fr +60c sepia   .85   .60
  a.   Bklt. pane of 6 + 2 labels   5.00

Intl. Red Cross, 125th Anniv. — SP310

1988, Nov. 19   Engr.   Perf. 12½x13
B601 SP310 2.20fr +60c multi   .85   .60
  a.   As "b," bklt. pane of 10+2
      labels   8.00
  b.   Perf. 13½x13   .85   .75

See No. B747c.

Revolution Leaders and Heroes — SP311

No. B602, Emmanuel Joseph Sieyes (1748-1836). No. B603, Honore Gabriel Riqueti, Comte de Mirabeau (1749-91). No. B604, Louis Marie de Noailles (1756-1804). No. B605, Lafayette. No. B606, Antoine Pierre Joseph Marie Barnave (1761-93). No. B607, Jean Baptiste Drouet (1763-1824).

1989, Feb. 25   Engr.   Perf. 13
B602 SP311 2.20fr +50c multi   .85   .60
B603 SP311 2.20fr +50c multi   .85   .60
B604 SP311 2.20fr +50c multi   .85   .60
B605 SP311 2.20fr +50c multi   .85   .60
B606 SP311 2.20fr +50c multi   .85   .60
B607 SP311 2.20fr +50c multi   .85   .60
  a.   Bklt. pane, 1 each + 2 labels   5.00

French Revolution, bicent.

Stamp Day Type of 1986

Design: Paris-Lyon stagecoach.

1989, Apr. 15 — Engr. — Perf. 13

B608	SP305	2.20fr +60c pale bl & dk bl	.85	.60

Booklet Stamp

B609	SP305	2.20fr +60c pale lil & pur	.85	.60
a.		Bkkt. pane of 6 + 2 labels	6.00	

Stamp Day 1989.

Bird From a Silk Tapestry, Lyon, 18th Cent. — SP312

1989, Nov. 18 — Photo. — Perf. 12½x13

B610	SP305	2.30fr +60c multi	.85	.60
a.		As "b," bklt. pane of 10	9.00	
b.		Perf. 13½x13	.90	.60

Surtax for the natl. Red Cross.

1992 Winter Olympics, Albertville SP313

1990, Feb. 9 — Engr. — Perf. 13

B611	SP313	2.30fr +20c red, bl & blk	.90	.70

See Nos. B621-B627, B636-B637, B639.

Stamp Day — SP314

1990, Mar. 17 — Photo.

B612	SP314	2.30fr +60c ultra, bl & brt yel	.90	.70

Booklet Stamp

B613	SP314	2.30fr +60c ultra, grn, yel & brt grn	.90	.70
a.		Bklt. pane of 6 + 2 labels	6.00	

SP315

Quimper or Brittany Ware Faience plate.

1990, May 5 — Photo. — Perf. 12½x13

B614	SP315	2.30fr +60c multi	.90	.70
a.		As "b," bklt. pane of 10+2 labels	9.00	
b.		Perf. 13½x13	.95	.70

Surcharge benefited the Red Cross.

SP316

No. B615, Aristide Bruant. No. B616, Maurice Chevalier. No. B617, Tino Rossi. No. B618, Edith Piaf. No. B619, Jacques Brel. No. B620, Georges Brassens.

1990, June 16 — Photo. — Perf. 13

B615	SP316	2.30fr +50c multi	.90	.70
B616	SP316	2.30fr +50c multi	.90	.70
B617	SP316	2.30fr +50c multi	.90	.70
B618	SP316	2.30fr +50c multi	.90	.70
B619	SP316	2.30fr +50c multi	.90	.70
B620	SP316	2.30fr +50c multi	.90	.70
a.		Bklt. pane, 1 each +2 labels	5.00	

Albertville Olympic Type

Designs: No. B621, Ski jumping. No. B622, Speed skiing. No. B623, Slalom skiing. No. B624, Cross-country skiing. No. B625, Ice hockey. No. B626, Luge. No. B627, Curling.

1990-91 — Engr. — Perf. 13

B621	SP313	2.30fr +20c multi	.90	.70
B622	SP313	2.30fr +20c multi	.90	.70
B623	SP313	2.30fr +20c multi	.90	.70
B624	SP313	2.30fr +20c multi	.90	.70
B625	SP313	2.30fr +20c multi	.90	.70
B626	SP313	2.30fr +20c multi	.90	.70
B627	SP313	2.50fr +20c multi	.90	.70
		Nos. B621-B627 (7)	6.30	4.90

Issued: No. B621, 12/22/90; No. B622, 12/29/90; No. B623, 1/19/91; No. B624, 2/2/91; No. B625, 2/9/91; No. B626, 3/2/91; No. B627, 4/20/91.

No. B624 inscribed "La Poste 1992."

Paul Eluard (1895-1952) SP317

Poets: No. B629, Andre Breton (1896-1966). No. B630, Louis Aragon (1897-1982). No. B631, Francis Ponge (1899-1988). No. B632, Jacques Prevert (1900-1977). No. B633, Rene Char (1907-1988).

1991, Feb. 23 — Engr. — Perf. 12½x13

B628	SP317	2.50fr +50c multi	1.00	.75
B629	SP317	2.50fr +50c multi	1.00	.75
B630	SP317	2.50fr +50c multi	1.00	.75
B631	SP317	2.50fr +50c multi	1.00	.75
B632	SP317	2.50fr +50c multi	1.00	.75
B633	SP317	2.50fr +50c multi	1.00	.75
a.		Bklt. pane, 1 each +2 labels, perf. 13	6.00	

Stamp Day — SP318

Designs: No. B634, Postal sorting with blue machine. No. B635, Postal sorting with purple machine.

1991, Mar. 16 — Photo. — Perf. 13

B634	SP318	2.50fr +60c multi	1.00	.75
B635	SP318	2.50fr +60c multi	1.00	.75
a.		Bklt. pane of 6 + 2 labels	6.00	

Winter Olympics Type of 1990

No. B636, Acrobatic skiing. No. B637, Alpine skiing.

1991 — Engr. — Perf. 13

B636	SP313	2.50fr +20c multi	1.00	.75
B637	SP313	2.50fr +20c multi	1.00	.75

Issued: No. B636, Aug. 3; No. B637, Aug. 17.

Nos. B636-B637 inscribed "La Poste 1992."

The Harbor of Toulon by Francois Nardi — SP319

1991, Dec. 2 — Photo. — Perf. 13x12½

B638	SP319	2.50fr +60c multi	1.00	.75
a.		Perf. 13x13½	1.10	.75
b.		As "a," bklt. pane of 10 + 2 labels	9.00	

Surtax for the Red Cross.

Winter Olympics Type of 1990
Miniature Sheet

No. B639: a, like #B611. b, like #B621. c, like #B622. d, like #B623. e, like #B624. f, like #B625.

1992, Feb. 8 — Engr. — Perf. 13

B639		Sheet of 10 + label	15.00	15.00
a.-f.	SP313	2.50fr +20c multi	1.00	.75

No. B639 contains one each B626-B627, B636-B637, B639a-B639f. Central label is litho.

Stamp Day — SP320

Designs: Careers in Post, Welcome — No. B640, gray people. No. B641, red people.

1992, Mar. 7 — Litho. — Perf. 13

B640	SP320	2.50fr +60c gray people	1.00	.75

Booklet Stamp
Photo.

B641	SP320	2.50fr +60c red people	1.00	.75
a.		Bklt. pane of 6 + 2 labels	6.00	

SP321

Composers: No. B642, Cesar Franck (1822-1890). No. B643, Erik Satie (1866-1925). No. B644, Florent Schmitt (1870-1958). No. B645, Arthur Honegger (1892-1955). No. B646, Georges Auric (1899-1983). No. B647, Germaine Tailleferre (1892-1983).

1992, Apr. 11 — Photo. — Perf. 13

B642	SP321	2.50fr +50c multi	1.00	.75
B643	SP321	2.50fr +50c multi	1.00	.75
B644	SP321	2.50fr +50c multi	1.00	.75
B645	SP321	2.50fr +50c multi	1.00	.75
B646	SP321	2.50fr +50c multi	1.00	.75
B647	SP321	2.50fr +50c multi	1.00	.75
a.		Bklt. pane of 6, #B642-B647	6.00	

SP322

1992, Nov. 28 — Photo. — Perf. 13½x13

B648	SP322	2.50fr +60c multi	1.00	.70
a.		Bklt. pane of 10 + 2 labels	9.00	

Mutual Aid, Strasbourg. Surtax for the Red Cross.

Writers — SP323

No. B649, Guy de Maupassant (1850-93). No. B650, Alain (Emile Chartier) (1868-1951). No. B651, Jean Cocteau (1889-1963). No. B652, Marcel Pagnol (1895-1974). No. B653, Andre Chamson (1900-83). No. B654, Marguerite Yourcenar (1903-87).

1993, Apr. 24 — Engr. — Perf. 13

B649	SP323	2.50fr +50c multi	1.00	.75
B650	SP323	2.50fr +50c multi	1.00	.75
B651	SP323	2.50fr +50c multi	1.00	.75
B652	SP323	2.50fr +50c multi	1.00	.75
B653	SP323	2.50fr +50c multi	1.00	.75
B654	SP323	2.50fr +50c multi	1.00	.75
a.		Bklt. pane of 6, #B649-B654 + 2 labels	6.00	

When Nos. B650-B654 are normally centered, inscriptions at base of the lower panel are not parallel to the perforations at bottom. On all six stamps the lower panel is not centered between the side perforations.

SP324

St. Nicolas, Image of Metz.

1993, Nov. 27 — Engr. — Perf. 12½x13

B655	SP324	2.80fr +60c multi	1.10	.75
a.		Perf. 13½x13	1.20	.75
b.		As "a," Bklt. pane of 10 +2 labels	12.00	

Surtax for Red Cross.

SP325

Stage and Screen Personalities: No. B656, Yvonne Printemps (1894-1977). No. B657, Fernandel (1903-71). No. B658, Josephine Baker (1906-75). No. B659, Bourvil (1917-70). No. B660, Yves Montand (1921-91). No. B661, Coluche (1944-86).

1994, Sept. 17 — Photo. — Perf. 13

B656	SP325	2.80fr +60c multi	1.10	.75
B657	SP325	2.80fr +60c multi	1.10	.75
B658	SP325	2.80fr +60c multi	1.10	.75
B659	SP325	2.80fr +60c multi	1.10	.75
B660	SP325	2.80fr +60c multi	1.10	.75
B661	SP325	2.80fr +60c multi	1.10	.75
a.		Bklt. pane, #B656-B661 + 2 labels	6.00	

SP326

Designs: No. B662, St. Vaast, Arras Tapestry. No. B663, Brussels tapestry from Reydams workshop, Horse Museum, Saumur.

1994-95 — Photo. — Perf. 12½x13

B662	SP326	2.80fr +60c multi	1.10	.75
a.		Perf. 13½x13	1.20	.75
b.		Bklt. pane, 10 #B662a + 2 labels	12.00	
		Complete booklet, #B662b	13.00	
B663	SP326	2.80fr +60c multi	1.10	.75
a.		Perf. 13½x13	1.20	.75
b.		Bklt. pane, 10 #B663a + 2 labels	12.00	
		Complete booklet, #B663b	13.00	

Surtax for Red Cross.

Issued: No. B662, 11/26/94; No. B663, 5/13/95.

SP327

Provencal Nativity Figures: No. B664, The Shepherd. No. B665, The Miller. No. B666, The Simpleton and the Tambour Player. No. B667, The Fishmonger. No. B668, The Scissor Grinder. No. B669, The Elders.

1995, Nov. 25 — Engr. — Perf. 13

B664	SP327	2.80fr +60c multi	1.10	.85
B665	SP327	2.80fr +60c multi	1.10	.85
B666	SP327	2.80fr +60c multi	1.10	.85
B667	SP327	2.80fr +60c multi	1.10	.85
B668	SP327	2.80fr +60c multi	1.10	.85
B669	SP327	2.80fr +60c multi	1.10	.85
a.		Booklet pane, Nos. B664-B669 + 2 labels	7.50	
		Complete booklet, No. B669a	11.00	

SP328

Famous Fictional Detectives and Criminals: No. B670, Rocambole. No. B671, Arsène Lupin. No. B672, Joseph Rouletabille. No. B673, Fantômas. No. B674, Commissioner Maigret. No. B675, Nestor Burma.

1996, Oct. 5 — Photo. — Perf. 13

B670	SP328	3fr +60c multi	1.10	.85
B671	SP328	3fr +60c multi	1.10	.85
B672	SP328	3fr +60c multi	1.10	.85
B673	SP328	3fr +60c multi	1.10	.85
B674	SP328	3fr +60c multi	1.10	.85
B675	SP328	3fr +60c multi	1.10	.85
a.		Booklet pane, #B670-B675 + 2 labels	7.50	
		Complete booklet, #B675a	11.00	

Christmas — SP329

1996, Nov. 16   Photo.   Perf. 12¾x13

B676	SP329	3fr +60c multi	1.10	.85
		Perf. 13¼x13	1.20	.85
b.		Booklet pane, 10 #B676a + 2 labels	12.00	—
		Complete booklet, #B676b	13.00	

Surtax for Red Cross.

Adventure Heroes — SP330

No. B677, Sir Lancelot. No. B678, Pardaillan. No. B679, D'Artagnan. No. B680, Cyrano de Bergerac. No. B681, Captain Fracasse. No. B682, Le Bossu.

1997, Oct. 25   Photo.   Perf. 13

B677	SP330	3fr +60c multi	1.10	.85
B678	SP330	3fr +60c multi	1.10	.85
B679	SP330	3fr +60c multi	1.10	.85
B680	SP330	3fr +60c multi	1.10	.85
B681	SP330	3fr +60c multi	1.10	.85
B682	SP330	3fr +60c multi	1.10	.85
a.		Booklet pane, #B677-B682 + 2 labels	7.50	
		Complete booklet, #B682a	7.50	

Christmas, New Year — SP331

1997, Nov. 6   Photo.   Perf. 12¾x13

B683	SP331	3fr +60c multi	1.10	.90
a.		Perf. 13¼x13	1.20	.95
b.		Booklet pane, 10 #B683a + 2 labels	12.00	
		Complete booklet, #B683b	13.00	

Surtax for the Red Cross.

SP332

Actors of the French Cinema: No. B684, Romy Schneider (1938-82). No. B685, Simone Signoret (1921-85). No. B686, Jean Gabin (1904-76). No. B687, Louis de Funés (1914-83). No. B688, Bernard Blier (1916-89). No. B689, Lino Ventura (1919-87).

1998, Oct. 3   Photo.   Perf. 13

B684	SP332	3fr +60c multi	1.10	.85
B685	SP332	3fr +60c multi	1.10	.85
B686	SP332	3fr +60c multi	1.10	.85
B687	SP332	3fr +60c multi	1.10	.85
B688	SP332	3fr +60c multi	1.10	.85
B689	SP332	3fr +60c multi	1.10	.85
a.		Booklet pane, #B684-B689 + label	7.50	
		Complete booklet, #B689a	8.00	

Christmas — SP333

1998, Nov. 5   Photo.   Perf. 12½x13

B690	SP333	3fr +60c multi	1.10	.85
a.		Perf. 13½x13	1.20	.85
b.		Booklet pane, 10 #B690a + 2 labels	12.00	
		Complete booklet, #B690b	13.00	

Surtax for Red Cross.

Famous Photographers SP334

Photographs by: No. B691, Robert Doisneau (1912-94). No. B692, Brassaï (Gyula Halasz) (1899-1984). No. B693, Jacques Lartigue (1894-1986). No. B694, Henri Cartier-Bresson (1908-2004). No. B695, Eugene Atget (1857-1927). No. B696, Felix Nadar (1820-1910).

1999, July 10   Photo.   Perf. 13

B691	SP334	3fr +60c multi	1.10	.85
B692	SP334	3fr +60c multi	1.10	.85
B693	SP334	3fr +60c multi	1.10	.85
B694	SP334	3fr +60c multi	1.10	.85
B695	SP334	3fr +60c multi	1.10	.85
B696	SP334	3fr +60c multi	1.10	.85
a.		Booklet pane, #B691-B696	7.50	
		Complete booklet, #B696a	8.00	

New Year 2000 — SP335

1999, Nov. 10   Photo.   Perf. 12¾x13

B697	SP335	3fr +60c multi	1.20	.85
a.		Perf. 13½x13	1.25	.85
b.		Booklet pane, 10 #B697a + 2 labels	9.00	
		Complete booklet, #B697b	10.00	

Surtax for Red Cross.

Adventurers — SP336

No. B698, Eric Tabarly (1931-98), sailor. No. B699, Alexandra David-Néel (1868-1969), opera singer, Asian traveler. No. B700, Haroun Tazieff (1914-98), vulcanologist. No. B701, Paul-Emile Victor (1907-55), ethnologist, polar explorer. No. B702, Jacques-Yves Cousteau (1910-97), oceanographer. No. B703, Norbert Casteret (1897-1987), speleologist.

2000, Sept. 16   Photo.   Perf. 13¼x13

B698	SP336	3fr +60c multi	1.20	.85
B699	SP336	3fr +60c multi	1.20	.85
B700	SP336	3fr +60c multi	1.20	.85
B701	SP336	3fr +60c multi	1.20	.85
B702	SP336	3fr +60c multi	1.20	.85
B703	SP336	3fr +60c multi	1.20	.85
a.		Booklet pane, #B698-B703	7.00	
		Booklet, #B703a	7.50	

Toy Airplane — SP337

2000, Nov. 9   Photo.   Perf. 13¼x13

B704	SP337	3fr +60c multi	1.10	.85
a.		Booklet pane of 10 + 2 labels	12.00	
		Booklet, #B704a	13.00	

Surtax for Red Cross.

Santa Claus and Tree Ornaments — SP338

2001, Nov. 8   Photo.   Perf. 12¾x13

B705	SP338	3fr +60c multi	1.10	.85
a.		Perf 13½x13	1.20	.85
b.		Booklet pane of 10	11.00	
		Booklet, #B705a	11.00	

Surtax for Red Cross.

Infant Jesus Asleep, by Giovanni Battista Salvi — SP339

2002, Nov. 7   Photo.   Perf. 12¾x13

B706	SP339	46c +9c multi	1.10	.85
a.		Perf. 13½x13	1.20	.85
b.		As "a," booklet pane of 10	11.00	
		Booklet, #B706b	11.00	

Surtax for Red Cross.

Virgin with Grapes, by Pierre Mignard — SP340

2003, Nov. 6   Photo.   Perf. 13¼x13
Booklet Stamp

B707	SP340	50c +(16c) multi	1.50	1.00
a.		Booklet pane of 10	15.00	
		Complete booklet, #B707a	15.00	

Surtax for Red Cross.

Virgin With Child, Attributed to Cretan School — SP341

2004, Nov. 10   Photo.   Perf. 13¼x13
Booklet Stamp

B708	SP341	50c +(16c) multi	1.50	1.00
a.		Booklet pane of 10 + 2 labels	15.00	
		Complete booklet, #B708a	15.00	

Surtax for Red Cross.

Dec. 26, 2004 Tsunami Victim Relief — SP342

2005, Jan. 13   Engr.   Perf. 13

B709	SP342	(50c) +20c red	1.75	.50

Virgin and Child, by Hans Memling — SP343

2005, Nov. 10   Photo.   Perf. 13½x13
Booklet Stamp

B710	SP343	53c +(17c) multi	1.50	1.00
a.		Booklet pane of 10 + 2 labels	15.00	
		Complete booklet, #B710a	15.00	

Surtax for Red Cross.

SP344   Children's Art — SP345

2006, Nov. 25   Photo.   Perf. 13½x13
Booklet Stamps

B711	SP344	(54c) +(17c) multi	1.90	.85
B712	SP345	(54c) +(17c) multi	1.90	.85
a.		Booklet pane, 5 each #B711-B712, + 2 labels	19.00	
		Complete booklet, #B712a	19.00	

Surtax for Red Cross.

Red Cross
SP346   SP347

Serpentine Die Cut 11

2007, Nov. 24   Photo.
Self-Adhesive
Booklet Stamps

B713	SP346	(54c) +(17c) multi	1.90	.85
B714	SP347	(54c) +(17c) multi	1.90	.85
a.		Booklet pane, 5 each #B713-B714	19.00	

Surtax for Red Cross.

Red Cross
SP348   SP349

Serpentine Die Cut 11x11¼

2008, Nov. 8   Photo.
Booklet Stamps
Self-Adhesive

B715	SP348	(55c) +(18c) multi	1.90	.85
B716	SP349	(55c) +(18c) multi	1.90	.85
a.		Booklet pane of 10, 2 each #B715-B716	19.00	

Surtax for Red Cross.

Miniature Sheet

Red Cross SP350

No. B717: a, Henri Dunant. b, Battle of Solferino. c, Pélias et Nélée, by Georges Braque, horiz. d, Geneva Conventions. e, Globe and symbols of the International Red Cross and Red Crescent Societies.

2009, Sept. 19   Photo.   Perf. 13

B717	SP350	Sheet of 5	12.00	12.00
a.-e.		56c +(40c) Any single	2.50	2.50

Surtax for Red Cross.

Haiti Earthquake Relief — SP351

2010, Jan. 19   Engr.   Perf. 13

B718	SP351	(56c) +44c red	2.25	1.50

Self-Adhesive
Serpentine Die Cut 11

B719	SP351	(56c) +44c red	4.50	4.00

Surtax was for French Red Cross relief efforts in Haiti.

Miniature Sheet

Red Cross SP352

No. B720: a, Woman on telephone. b, Man assisting unconscious woman. c, Red Cross emblem, horiz. d, Woman performing Heimlich maneuver on choking man. e, Cardio-pulmonary resuscitation.

Photo., Photo. & Embossed
(#B720c)

2010, Nov. 5   *Perf. 13*
B720	SP352	Sheet of 5	12.00 8.00
a.-e.	58c +(40c) Any single		2.00 1.25

Surtax for Red Cross.

Miniature Sheet

Singers SP353

No. B721: a, Colette Renard (1924-2010). b, Henri Salvador (1917-2008). c, Serge Reggiani (1922-2004). d, Claude Nougaro (1929-2004). e, Daniel Balavoine (1952-86). f, Gilbert Bécaud (1927-2001).

2011, Oct. 14   **Photo.**   *Perf. 13*
B721	SP353	Sheet of 6	12.00 9.00
a.-f.	60c + (33⅓c) Any single		2.00 1.50

Surtax for Red Cross.

Miniature Sheet

Red Cross SP354

No. B722: a, People carrying person on litter. b, Three hands. c, Red Cross, horiz. d, Red Cross volunteer teaching illiterates. e, Red Cross volunteer giving bottle to infant.

2011, Nov. 4
B722	SP354	Sheet of 5	10.00 7.50
a.-e.	60c + (40c) Any single		2.00 1.50

Surtax for Red Cross.

Miniature Sheet

Movie Stars SP355

No. B723: a, Françoise Dorléac (1942-67). b, Jean Marais (1913-98). c, Jacqueline Maillan (1923-92). d, Michel Serrault (1928-2007). e, Philippe Noiret (1930-2006). f, Annie Girardot (1931-2011).

2012, Oct. 19
B723	SP355	Sheet of 6	12.00 9.00
a.-f.	60c + (33⅓c) Any single		2.00 1.50

Surtax for Red Cross.

Miniature Sheet

Red Cross SP356

No. B724: a, Heart and hands. b, Man carrying man with injured foot. c, Red Cross, horiz. d, Three parachutists. e, People and dog hugging heart.

2012, Nov. 8
B724	SP356	Sheet of 5	12.50 12.50
a.-e.	57c + (40c) Any single		2.50 2.50

Surtax for Red Cross.

Loire River — SP357

The Loire River at: No. B725, Mont Gerbier de Jonc. No. B726, Lac de Grangent. No. B727, Bec d'Allier. No. B728, Gien. No. B729, Pointe de Coupain. No. B730, Blois. No. B731, Candes-Saint-Martin. No. B732, Ingrandes-sur-Loire. No. B733, Champtoceaux. No. B734, Marais de Brière.

2013, June 1   *Serpentine Die Cut 11*
Booklet Stamps
Self-Adhesive
B725	SP357	(58c+20c) multi	1.60 .50
B726	SP357	(58c+20c) multi	1.60 .50
B727	SP357	(58c+20c) multi	1.60 .50
B728	SP357	(58c+20c) multi	1.60 .50
B729	SP357	(58c+20c) multi	1.60 .50
B730	SP357	(58c+20c) multi	1.60 .50
B731	SP357	(58c+20c) multi	1.60 .50
B732	SP357	(58c+20c) multi	1.60 .50
B733	SP357	(58c+20c) multi	1.60 .50
B734	SP357	(58c+20c) multi	1.60 .50
a.	Booklet pane of 10, #B725-B734		18.00
	Nos. B725-B734 (10)		16.00 5.00

Surtax for the Red Cross.

Red Cross SP358

No. B735: a, One stylized person. b, Two stylized people. c, Red Cross, horiz. d, Three stylized people. e, Four stylized people.

2013, Nov. 7   **Photo.**   *Perf. 13*
B735	SP358	Sheet of 5	10.00 7.50
a.-e.	58c + (40c) Any single		1.75 1.25

Surtax for Red Cross.

Flowers — SP359

Designs: No. B736, Roses. No. B737, Daisies (Marguerite). No. B738, Tulips (Tulipe). No. B739, Sunflowers (Tournesol). No. B740, Irises. No. B741, Orchids (Orchidée). No. B742, Jonquils (Jonquille). No. B743, Lilies (Lys). No. B744, Carnations (Oeillet). No. B745, Gardenias (Gardénia).

Serpentine Die Cut 11
2014, May 24   **Photo.**
Booklet Stamps
Self-Adhesive
B736	SP359	(61c) + (20c) multi	1.75 1.00
B737	SP359	(61c) + (20c) multi	1.75 1.00
B738	SP359	(61c) + (20c) multi	1.75 1.00
B739	SP359	(61c) + (20c) multi	1.75 1.00
B740	SP359	(61c) + (20c) multi	1.75 1.00
B741	SP359	(61c) + (20c) multi	1.75 1.00
B742	SP359	(61c) + (20c) multi	1.75 1.00
B743	SP359	(61c) + (20c) multi	1.75 1.00
B744	SP359	(61c) + (20c) multi	1.75 1.00
B745	SP359	(61c) + (20c) multi	1.75 1.00
a.	Booklet pane of 10, #B736-B745		20.00
	Nos. B736-B745 (10)		17.50 10.00

Red Cross, 150th anniv. Surtax for Red Cross.

Semi-Postal Stamps of 1914-88
Redrawn

2014, June 14   **Litho.**
B746		Sheet of 5	14.00 14.00
a.	SP2 61c +30c like #B2, perf. 13¼		2.50 2.50
b.	A22 61c +30c like #B1, perf. 13¼		2.50 2.50
c.	SP40 61c +30c like #B81, perf. 13		2.50 2.50
d.	SP9 61c +30c like #B11, perf. 13x13¼		2.50 2.50

---

e.	SP237 61c +30c like #B403, perf. 13		2.50 2.50
B747		Sheet of 5	14.00 14.00
a.	SP60 61c +30c like #B101, perf. 13¼		2.50 2.50
b.	SP258 61c +30c like #B462, perf. 13		2.50 2.50
c.	SP310 61c +30c like #B601, perf. 13		2.50 2.50
d.	SP207 61c +30c like #B328, perf. 13		2.50 2.50
e.	SP61 61c +30c like #B102, perf. 13x13¼		2.50 2.50

Nos. B746-B747 sold together as a set for €12.

Miniature Sheet

French Red Cross, 150th Anniv. SP360

No. B748: a, Jean-Henri Dunant, 1864. b, White angel with Red Cross arm band treating soldier, 1914. c, Red cross and 150th anniv. emblem, horiz. d, Red Cross worker giving aid to refugee, 1945. e, Red Cross workers in Haiti, 2010.

2014, Nov. 7   **Photo.**   *Perf. 13*
B748	SP360	Sheet of 5	10.00 8.00
a.-e.	61c+(30c) Any single		2.00 1.25

Surtax for the Red Cross.

SP361

SP362

SP363

SP364

SP365

SP366

SP367

Red Cross Workers in Action — SP368

Serpentine Die Cut 11
2015, May 16   **Litho.**
Booklet Stamps
Self-Adhesive
B749	SP361	(68c+25c) multi	2.10 2.10
B750	SP362	(68c+25c) multi	2.10 2.10
B751	SP363	(68c+25c) multi	2.10 2.10
B752	SP364	(68c+25c) multi	2.10 2.10
B753	SP365	(68c+25c) multi	2.10 2.10
B754	SP366	(68c+25c) multi	2.10 2.10
B755	SP367	(68c+25c) multi	2.10 2.10

B756	SP368	(68c+25c) multi	2.10 2.10
a.	Booklet pane of 8, #B749-B756		17.00
	Nos. B749-B756 (8)		16.80 16.80

Surtax for the Red Cross.

Miniature Sheet

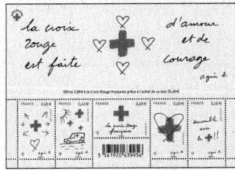

Red Cross SP369

No. B757: a, Red cross, heart and arrows. b, Sun, red crosses, ambulance. c, Red cross and text, horiz. d, Red cross and heart. e, Red Cross and text, diff.

2015, Nov. 7   **Photo.**   *Perf. 13*
B757	SP369	Sheet of 5	11.50 11.50
a.-e.	68c+(40c) Any single		2.25 2.25

Surtax for the Red Cross.

SP370

SP371

SP372

SP373

SP374

SP375

SP376

Red Cross Workers — SP377

Serpentine Die Cut 11
2016, Apr. 30   **Litho.**
Booklet Stamps
Self-Adhesive
B758	SP370	(70c+25c) multi	2.25 2.25
B759	SP371	(70c+25c) multi	2.25 2.25
B760	SP372	(70c+25c) multi	2.25 2.25
B761	SP373	(70c+25c) multi	2.25 2.25
B762	SP374	(70c+25c) multi	2.25 2.25
B763	SP375	(70c+25c) multi	2.25 2.25
B764	SP376	(70c+25c) multi	2.25 2.25
B765	SP377	(70c+25c) multi	2.25 2.25
a.	Booklet pane of 8, #B758-B765		18.00
	Nos. B758-B765 (8)		18.00 18.00

Surtax for the Red Cross.

Miniature Sheet

Red Cross SP378

No. B766: a, Head on top of cross. b, Heads and three crosses. c, Cross in winged and crowned heart, horiz. d, Flags with cross and heart. e, Stylized person with cross as torso and arms.

2016, Nov. 5   **Photo.**   *Perf. 13*
B766	SP378	Sheet of 5	12.00	12.00
a.-e.	70c+(40c) Any single		2.40	2.40

Surtax for the Red Cross.

SP379

SP380

SP381   SP382

SP383

SP384

SP385

Work of the Red Cross — SP386

Serpentine Die Cut 11
2017, May 5   **Photo.**
Booklet Stamps
Self-Adhesive
B767	SP379	(73c+25c) multi	2.25	2.25
B768	SP380	(73c+25c) multi	2.25	2.25
B769	SP381	(73c+25c) multi	2.25	2.25
B770	SP382	(73c+25c) multi	2.25	2.25
B771	SP383	(73c+25c) multi	2.25	2.25
B772	SP384	(73c+25c) multi	2.25	2.25
B773	SP385	(73c+25c) multi	2.25	2.25
B774	SP386	(73c+25c) multi	2.25	2.25
a.	Booklet pane of 8, #B767-B774		18.00	
	Nos. B767-B774 (8)		18.00	18.00

Surtax for Red Cross.

Marianne and Children "Lettre Prioritaire" Without Gram Limit Inscription Type of 2016
2017, Oct. 20   **Photo.**   *Perf. 13*
B775	A2536	(85c+66c) red	3.50	3.50

No. B775 was printed in sheets of 3 that sold for €4.55, €2 of which was for the Red Cross.

Flowers — SP387

Designs: No. B776, Anemones and shell. No. B777, Asters and daisies (asters et marguerites), keys. No. B778, Dahlias, eglantine roses and peaches. No. B779, Snapdragons and cornflowers (moufliers et bleuets), elephant figurine. No. B780, Peonies (pivoines), cat figurine. No. B781, Ranunculus (renoncules), letter and shell. No. B782, Roses, hourglass. No. B783, Calendulas (soucis) and oranges. No. B784, Sunflowers and blue thistles (tournesols et chardons bleus), teapot and owl figurine. No. B785, Zinnias, snail and butterflies.

Serpentine Die Cut 11
2018, May 4   **Photo.**
Booklet Stamps
Self-Adhesive
B776	SP387	(80c+20c) multi	2.40	2.40
B777	SP387	(80c+20c) multi	2.40	2.40
B778	SP387	(80c+20c) multi	2.40	2.40
B779	SP387	(80c+20c) multi	2.40	2.40
B780	SP387	(80c+20c) multi	2.40	2.40
B781	SP387	(80c+20c) multi	2.40	2.40
B782	SP387	(80c+20c) multi	2.40	2.40
B783	SP387	(80c+20c) multi	2.40	2.40
B784	SP387	(80c+20c) multi	2.40	2.40
B785	SP387	(80c+20c) multi	2.40	2.40
a.	Booklet pane of 10, #B776-B785		24.00	
	Nos. B776-B785 (10)		24.00	24.00

Surtax was for Red Cross.

Marianne and Red Cross — SP388

2018, Oct. 26   **Photo.**   *Perf. 13*
B786	SP388	(95c+66c) multi	3.75	3.75

No. B786 was printed in sheets of 3 that sold for €4.85, €2 of which was for the Red Cross.

SP389

SP391

SP393

SP395

SP397

SP390

SP392

SP394

SP396

Photographs of People by Christian Guémy — SP398

Serpentine Die Cut 11
2019, May 10   **Photo.**
Booklet Stamps
Self-Adhesive
B787	SP389	(88c+20c) multi	2.50	2.50
B788	SP390	(88c+20c) multi	2.50	2.50
B789	SP391	(88c+20c) multi	2.50	2.50
B790	SP392	(88c+20c) multi	2.50	2.50
B791	SP393	(88c+20c) multi	2.50	2.50
B792	SP394	(88c+20c) multi	2.50	2.50
B793	SP395	(88c+20c) multi	2.50	2.50
B794	SP396	(88c+20c) multi	2.50	2.50
B795	SP397	(88c+20c) multi	2.50	2.50
B796	SP398	(88c+20c) multi	2.50	2.50
a.	Booklet pane of 10, #B787-B796		25.00	
	Nos. B787-B796 (10)		25.00	25.00

Surtax for Red Cross.

Souvenir Sheet

Red Cross Workers SP399

No. B797: a, Red Cross worker in food storeroom. b, Nurse at dispensary. c, Red Cross worker at clothing warehouse.

2019, Oct. 18   **Photo.**   *Perf. 13*
B797	SP399	Sheet of 3	11.50	11.50
a.-c.	€1.05+(66c) Any single		3.75	3.75

No. B786 sold for €5.15, €2 of which was for the Red Cross.

SP400

SP401

SP402

SP403

SP404

SP405

SP406

SP407

SP408

Rhythm, Joy of Life, Painting by Robert Delaunay (1885-1941) SP409

Serpentine Die Cut 11
2020, May 15   **Photo.**
Booklet Stamps
Self-Adhesive
B798	SP400	(97c+20c) multi	2.60	2.60
B799	SP401	(97c+20c) multi	2.60	2.60
B800	SP402	(97c+20c) multi	2.60	2.60
B801	SP403	(97c+20c) multi	2.60	2.60
B802	SP404	(97c+20c) multi	2.60	2.60
B803	SP405	(97c+20c) multi	2.60	2.60
B804	SP406	(97c+20c) multi	2.60	2.60
B805	SP407	(97c+20c) multi	2.60	2.60
B806	SP408	(97c+20c) multi	2.60	2.60
B807	SP409	(97c+20c) multi	2.60	2.60
a.	Booklet pane of 10, #B798-B807 + sticker		26.00	
	Nos. B798-B807 (10)		26.00	26.00

Surtax was for Red Cross.

Souvenir Sheet

SP410

No. B808: a, Henry Dunant (1828-1910), co-founder of Red Cross. b, Gustave Moynier (1826-1910), co-founder of Red Cross. c, Volunteers collecting donations for Red Cross, horiz.

2020, Oct. 2   **Photo.**   *Perf. 13¼*
B808	SP410	Sheet of 3	13.00	13.00
a.-c.	€1.16 +(66c) Any single		4.25	4.25

No. B808 sold for €5.48, of which €2 was for the Red Cross.

Words of Ben — SP411

"Ben" (artist Benjamin Vautier), Red Cross, and inscription: No. B809, Important! No. B810, Chaque instant est unique. No. B811, Il va falloir s'adapter. No. B812, Un grand merci. No. B813, On peut le faire. No. B814, Vous êtes formidables! No. B815, Il faut oser. No. B816, J'aime la vie. No. B817, Nous finirons par vaincre. No. B818, Mots d'amour.

Serpentine Die Cut 11
2021, Apr. 23   **Photo.**
Booklet Stamps
Self-Adhesive
B809	SP411	(€1.08) +(20c) multi	3.25	3.25
B810	SP411	(€1.08) +(20c) multi	3.25	3.25
B811	SP411	(€1.08) +(20c) multi	3.25	3.25
B812	SP411	(€1.08) +(20c) multi	3.25	3.25
B813	SP411	(€1.08) +(20c) multi	3.25	3.25
B814	SP411	(€1.08) +(20c) multi	3.25	3.25
B815	SP411	(€1.08) +(20c) multi	3.25	3.25
B816	SP411	(€1.08) +(20c) multi	3.25	3.25
B817	SP411	(€1.08) +(20c) multi	3.25	3.25
B818	SP411	(€1.08) +(20c) multi	3.25	3.25
a.	Booklet pane of 10, #B809-B818		32.50	
	Nos. B809-B818 (10)		32.50	32.50

Surtax was for Red Cross. Compare with types A1667 and A2203.

Souvenir Sheet

SP412

No. B819: a, Food aid worker packing groceries. b, Red Cross workers wearing protective face masks. c, Red Cross worker administering vaccination.

2021, Oct. 22   Photo.   Perf. 13¼
B819 SP412 Sheet of 3   13.50 13.50
 a.-c.   €1.28 +(66c) Any single   4.50 4.50

No. B819 sold for €5.84, of which €2 was for the Red Cross.

SP413

SP414

SP415

SP416

SP417

SP418

SP419

SP420

SP421

Woolen Fabric Designs From the Mulhouse Museum of Printed Textiles — SP422

Serpentine Die Cut 11
2022, Apr. 22   Photo.
Booklet Stamps
Self-Adhesive

B820	SP413	(€1.16) + (20c) multi	3.00	3.00
B821	SP414	(€1.16) + (20c) multi	3.00	3.00
B822	SP415	(€1.16) + (20c) multi	3.00	3.00
B823	SP416	(€1.16) + (20c) multi	3.00	3.00
B824	SP417	(€1.16) + (20c) multi	3.00	3.00
B825	SP418	(€1.16) + (20c) multi	3.00	3.00
B826	SP419	(€1.16) + (20c) multi	3.00	3.00
B827	SP420	(€1.16) + (20c) multi	3.00	3.00
B828	SP421	(€1.16) + (20c) multi	3.00	3.00
B829	SP422	(€1.16) + (20c) multi	3.00	3.00

 a.   Booklet pane of 10, #B820-B829   30.00
      Nos. B820-B829 (10)   30.00 30.00

Surtax was for Red Cross.

Solidarity With Ukraine After Russian Invasion — SP423

2022, June 23   Photo.   Perf. 13
B830 SP423 (€1.16) +84c multi   4.25 4.25

Surtax was for Red Cross fund for Ukrainian relief efforts.

Souvenir Sheet

International Humanitarian Law — SP424

No. B831: a, Hands, people and globe stand. b, Refugees, stylized heads and balance scale. c, Face on flags, vert.

2022, Oct. 21   Photo.   Perf. 13¼
B831 SP424 Sheet of 3   11.00 11.00
 a.-c.   €1.16 +(66c) Any single   3.50 3.50

No. B831 sold for €5.48, of which €2 was for the Red Cross.

AIR POST STAMPS

Nos. 127, 130 Overprinted in Dark Blue or Black

Perf. 14x13½
1927, June 25   Unwmk.
C1 A18 2fr org & bl (DB)   200.00 225.00
    Never hinged   400.00
C2 A18 5fr dk bl & buff   200.00 225.00
    Never hinged   400.00

On sale only at the Intl. Aviation Exhib. at Marseilles, June, 1927. One set could be purchased by each holder of an admission ticket. Excellent counterfeits exist.

Nos. 242, 196 Surcharged

1928, Aug. 23
C3 A33 10fr on 90c   2,400. 1,800.
    Never hinged   3,500.
 a. Inverted surcharge 16,500. 16,500.
    Never hinged   25,000.
 b. Space between "10" and bars 6½mm   3,100. 3,100.
    Never hinged   5,100.
C4 A23 10fr on 1.50fr   10,000. 8,250.
    Never hinged   14,000.
 a. Space between "10" and bars 6½mm   13,000. 13,000.
    Never hinged   20,000.

Nos. C3-C4 received their surcharge in New York by order of the French consul general. They were for use in paying the 10fr fee for letters leaving the liner Ile de France on a catapulted hydroplane when the ship was one day off the coast of France on its eastward voyage.

The normal space between "10" and bars is 4½mm, but on 10 stamps in each pane of 50 the space is 6½mm. Counterfeits exist.

View of Marseille, Church of Notre Dame at Left — AP1

1930-31   Engr.   Perf. 13
C5 AP1 1.50fr dp car   21.00 4.00
    Never hinged   40.00
 a. With perf. initials "E.I.P.A.30"   2,750. 3,750.
    Never hinged   3,600.
C6 AP1 1.50fr dk bl ('31) 19.00 2.25
    Never hinged   35.00
 a. 1.50fr ultramarine   50.00 21.00
    Never hinged   90.00
 b. As "a," with perf. initials "E.I.P.A.30"   450.00 350.00
    Never hinged   700.00

Nos. C5a, C6a were sold at the Intl. Air Post Exhib., Paris, Nov. 6-20, 1930, at face value plus 5fr, the price of admission.
Forgeries abound of Nos. C5a and C6b. Certificates from recognized authorities are recommended.

Blériot's Monoplane AP2

1934, Sept. 1   Perf. 13
C7 AP2 2.25fr violet   24.00 6.00
    Never hinged   32.50

1st flight across the English Channel, by Louis Blériot.

Plane over Paris — AP3

1936
C8   AP3 85c deep green   2.25   2.25
     Never hinged   6.50
C9   AP3 1.50fr blue   10.50 5.50
     Never hinged   18.00
C10 AP3 2.25fr violet   18.00 7.00
     Never hinged   35.00
C11 AP3 2.50fr rose   32.50 8.25
     Never hinged   45.00
C12 AP3 3fr ultra   26.00 2.50
     Never hinged   37.50
C13 AP3 3.50fr orange brn 62.50 24.00
     Never hinged   105.00
C14 AP3 50fr emerald   825.00 325.00
     Never hinged   1,450.
 b. 50fr green   850.00 350.00
     Never hinged   1,500.
     Nos. C8-C14 (7)   976.75 374.50

Monoplane over Paris — AP4

Paper with Red Network Overprint
1936, July 10   Perf. 12½
C15 AP4 50fr ultra   625.00 310.00
     Never hinged   1,700.

Airplane and Galleon AP5

Airplane and Globe AP6

1936, Aug. 17   Perf. 13
C16 AP5 1.50fr dk ultra   17.50 5.25
     Never hinged   35.00
C17 AP6 10fr Prus green   290.00 130.00
     Never hinged   700.00

100th air mail flight across the South Atlantic.

> **Catalogue values for unused stamps in this section, from this point to the end of the section, are for Never Hinged items.**

Centaur and Plane AP7

Iris AP8

Zeus Carrying Hebe — AP9

Chariot of the Sun — AP10

1946-47   Engr.   Unwmk.
C18 AP7 40fr dk green   .55   .25
C19 AP8 50fr rose pink   .60   .25
C20 AP9 100fr dk blue ('47) 6.25 3.25
C21 AP10 200fr red   5.25 1.50
     Nos. C18-C21 (4)   12.65 5.25

Issued: 50fr, 200fr, 5/27; 40fr, 7/1; 100fr, Jan.
For surcharges see Reunion Nos. C35-C38.

Ile de la Cité, Paris, and Gull AP11

1947, May 7
C22 AP11 500fr dk Prus grn 45.00 27.50

UPU 12th Cong., Paris, May 7-July 7. See footnote after No. 4642. See No. 5933d.

View of Lille — AP12

Air View of Paris AP13

200fr, Bordeaux. 300fr, Lyon. 500fr, Marseille.

1949-50   Unwmk.   Perf. 13

C23	AP12	100fr sepia	1.20	.40
C24	AP12	200fr dk bl grn	11.50	.75
C25	AP12	300fr purple	15.00	9.00
C26	AP12	500fr brt red	55.00	4.75
C27	AP13	1000fr blk, dull gray vio ('50)	130.00	24.00
	Nos. C23-C27 (5)		212.70	38.90

For surcharges see Reunion Nos. C39-C41.

Alexander III Bridge and Petit Palais, Paris AP14

1949, June 13

C28	AP14	100fr brown car	5.25	5.25

International Telegraph and Telephone Conference, Paris, May-July 1949.

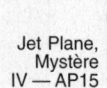

Jet Plane, Mystère IV — AP15

Planes: 200fr, Noratlas. 500fr, Miles Magister. 1000fr, Provence.

1954, Jan. 16

C29	AP15	100fr red brn & bl	2.25	.25
C30	AP15	200fr blk brn & vio bl	9.00	.25
C31	AP15	500fr car & org	175.00	10.50
C32	AP15	1000fr vio brn, bl grn & ind	95.00	14.00
	Nos. C29-C32 (4)		281.25	25.00

See No. C37. For surcharges see Reunion Nos. C42-C45, C48.

Maryse Bastié and Plane — AP16

1955, June 4   Unwmk.   Perf. 13

C33	AP16	50fr dp plum & rose pink	5.25	3.75

Issued to honor Maryse Bastié, 1898-1952.

Morane Saulnier 760 Paris — AP17

Designs: 500fr, Caravelle. 1000fr, Alouette helicopter.

1957-59   Engr.   Perf. 13

C34	AP17	300fr sl grn, grnsh bl & sep ('59)	5.00	2.25
C35	AP17	500fr dp ultra & blk	21.00	3.00
C36	AP17	1000fr lil, ol blk & blk ('58)	45.00	19.00
	Nos. C34-C36 (3)		71.00	24.25

See Nos. C38-C41. For surcharges see Reunion Nos. C46-C47, C49-C51.

Types of 1954-59

Planes: 2fr, Noratlas. 3fr, MS760, Paris. 5fr, Caravelle. 10fr, Alouette helicopter.

1960, Jan. 11

C37	AP15	2fr vio bl & ultra	1.10	.25
a.		2fr ultramarine	3.00	.75
C38	AP17	3fr sl grn, grnsh bl & sep	1.20	.25
C39	AP17	5fr dp ultra & blk	2.25	.65
C40	AP17	10fr lil, ol blk & blk	10.00	2.00
	Nos. C37-C40 (4)		14.55	3.15

Type of 1957-59

Design: 2fr, Jet plane, Mystère 20.

1965, June 12   Engr.   Perf. 13

C41	AP17	2fr slate bl & indigo	.75	.25

Concorde Issue
Common Design Type

1969, Mar. 2   Engr.   Perf. 13

C42	CD129	1fr indigo & brt bl	.75	.35

The 0.95fr stamp in this design was prepared but not issued. Value $30,000.

Jean Mermoz, Antoine de Saint-Exupéry and Concorde — AP19

1970, Sept. 19   Engr.   Perf. 13

C43	AP19	20fr blue & indigo	8.00	.55

Jean Mermoz (1901-36) and writer Antoine de Saint-Exupéry (1900-44), aviators and air mail pioneers.

Balloon, Gare d'Austerlitz, Paris — AP20

1971, Jan. 16   Engr.   Perf. 13

C44	AP20	95c bl, vio bl, org & sl grn	.75	.55

Centenary of the balloon post from besieged Paris, 1870-71.

Didier Daurat, Raymond Vanier and Plane Landing at Night AP21

1971, Apr. 17   Engr.   Perf. 13

C45	AP21	5fr Prus bl, blk & lt grn	1.75	.25

Didier Daurat (1891-1969) and Raymond Vanier (1895-1965), aviation pioneers. For surcharge see Reunion No. C52.

Hélène Boucher, Maryse Hilsz and Caudron-Renault and Moth-Morane Planes — AP22

Design: 15fr, Henri Guillaumet, Paul Codos, Latécoère 521, Guillaumet's crashed plane in Andes, skyscrapers.

1972-73   Engr.   Perf. 13

C46	AP22	10fr plum, red & sl	3.50	.40
C47	AP22	15fr dp car, gray & brn ('73)	5.25	.75

Hélène Boucher (1908-34), Maryse Hilsz (1901-46), Henri Guillaumet (1902-40) and Paul Codos (1896-1960), aviation pioneers. Issue dates: 10fr, June 10; 15fr, Feb. 24.

Concorde AP23

1976, Jan. 10   Engr.   Perf. 13

C48	AP23	1.70fr brt bl, red & blk	.75	.40

First flight of supersonic jet Concorde from Paris to Rio de Janeiro, Jan. 21.

Planes over the Atlantic, New York-Paris AP24

1977, June 4   Engr.   Perf. 13

C49	AP24	1.90fr multicolored	.75	.40

1st transatlantic flight by Lindbergh from NY to Paris, 50th anniv., and 1st attempted westbound flight by French aviators Charles Nungesser and Francois Coli.

Plane over Flight Route — AP25

1978, Oct. 14   Engr.   Perf. 13

C50	AP25	1.50fr multicolored	.60	.35

65th anniversary of first airmail route from Villacoublay to Pauillac, Gironde.

Rocket, Concorde, Exhibition Hall — AP26

1979, June 9   Engr.   Perf. 13

C51	AP26	1.70fr ultra, org & brn	.75	.60

33rd International Aerospace and Space Show, Le Bourget, June 11-15.

First Nonstop Transatlantic Flight, Paris-New York — AP27

1980, Aug. 30   Engr.   Perf. 13

C52	AP27	2.50fr vio brn & ultra	.90	.30

34th Intl. Space and Aeronautics Exhibition, June 5-14 — AP28

1981, June 6   Engr.   Perf. 13

C53	AP28	2fr multicolored	1.20	.40

Dieudonné Costes and Joseph Le Brix and their Breguet Bi-plane AP29

1981, Sept. 12   Engr.

C54	AP29	10fr dk brown & red	3.50	.40

1st So. Atlantic crossing, Oct. 14-15, 1927.

Seaplane Late-300 AP30

1982, Dec. 4   Engr.

C55	AP30	1.60fr multicolored	.75	.40

Farman F-60 Goliath AP31

Planes: 20fr, CAMS-53 seaplane. 30fr, Wibault 283 Monoplane. 50fr, Dewoitine 338.

1984-87   Engr.

C56	AP31	15fr dark blue	5.00	.75
C57	AP31	20fr dp org ('85)	6.50	.75
C58	AP31	30fr brt vio ('86)	10.00	1.50
C59	AP31	50fr green ('87)	15.00	4.50
	Nos. C55-C59 (5)		37.25	7.90

Issued: 15fr, 3/3; 20fr, 3/2; 30fr, 10/11; 50fr, 4/11.

Breguet XIV — AP32

1997, Nov. 15   Photo.   Perf. 13x13¼

C60	AP32	20fr shown	9.00	3.00
a.		Perf. 13x12½	6.00	1.50
C61	AP32	30fr Potez 25	12.50	3.50
a.		Perf. 13x12½	10.00	2.25

Issued: No. C60 11/15/97; No. C60a, 7/13/98; 30fr, 7/13/98.

Airbus A300-B4 AP33

1999, Apr. 10   Photo.   Perf. 13x13¼

C62	AP33	15fr multicolored	15.00	3.00
a.		Perf. 13x12½	5.25	1.25

Couzinet 70 — AP34

2000, Feb. 12   Perf. 13¼x13¼

C63	AP34	50fr multi	17.50	6.00
a.		Perf. 13x12½	22.50	7.50

First Flight of Airbus A300, 30th Anniv. AP35

2002, Oct. 26   Photo.   Perf. 13¼x13¼

C64	AP35	€3 multi	7.00	1.50

No. C64 was issued both in panes of 40 and 10, same perforation.

Jacqueline Auriol (1917-2000), Pilot, and Jet — AP36

Litho. & Engr.

2003, June 21   Perf. 13

C65	AP36	€4 multi	9.00	2.25
a.		Miniature sheet of 10	90.00	

Marie Marvingt (1875-1963), Pilot — AP37

Litho. & Engr.

2004, June 29   Perf. 13¼x13

C66	AP37	€5 multi	11.00	3.00
a.		Sheet of 10	110.00	

Adrienne Bolland (1895-1975),
Pilot — AP38

Litho. & Engr.

2005, Oct. 22			**Perf. 13**	
C67	AP38	€2 multi	4.50	1.50
a.	Miniature sheet of 10		45.00	—

Airbus A380
AP39

2006, June 23	Photo.		**Perf. 13x13¼**	
C68	AP39	€3 multi	6.50	1.50
a.	Miniature sheet of 10		65.00	—

Helicopters,
Cent.
AP40

2007, Feb. 19	Photo.		**Perf. 13x12½**	
C69	AP40	€3 multi	6.50	1.50
a.	Perf. 13x13¼		9.00	2.25

No. C69 was issued in panes of 40; No.
C69a in panes of 10.

French
Acrobatic
Patrol
AP41

Litho. & Engr.

2008, Sept. 13			**Perf. 13**	
C70	AP41	€3 multi	6.50	1.50

Louis
Blériot
(1872-1936)
and Blériot
XI Airplane
AP42

Litho. & Engr.

2009, July 25			**Perf. 13x12¾**	
C71	AP42	€2 multi	4.50	1.25

First flight across English Channel, cent.

Henri Fabre
(1882-1984)
and Le
Canard
Seaplane
AP43

Litho. & Engr.

2010, Mar. 27			**Perf. 13**	
C72	AP43	€3 multi	6.50	1.50

First seaplane flight, cent.

Henri Pequet (1888-1974), Pilot for
First Official Air Mail Flight in
India — AP44

2011, Feb. 18				
C73	AP44	€2 multi	4.50	1.25

First French Airmail Flight Between
Nancy and Luneville, Cent.
AP45

2012, July 30				
C74	AP45	€3 multi	6.50	1.50

First Parachute Jump by Adolphe
Pégoud (1889-1915), Cent. — AP46

2013, June 13				
C75	AP46	€2.55 multi	5.50	1.50
a.	Miniature sheet of 10		65.00	65.00

First Trans-Mediterranean Flight by
Roland Garros, Cent. — AP47

2013, Sept. 21	Photo.		**Perf. 13x12¾**	
C76	AP47	€3.40 multi	8.00	1.50

Caroline Aigle (1974-2007), First
Female Fighter Pilot in French Air
Force — AP48

Litho. & Engr.

2014, Apr. 5			**Perf. 13**	
C77	AP48	€3.55 multi	8.50	1.50

Gaston Caudron (1882-1915), Pilot
and Aircraft Manufacturer — AP49

Litho. & Engr.

2015, June 15			**Perf. 13**	
C78	AP49	€4.10 multi	9.00	2.00

Edouard Nieuport (1875-1911), Aviator
and Airplane Manufacturer, and
Nieuport 11 — AP50

Litho. & Engr.

2016, June 10			**Perf. 13**	
C79	AP50	€4.80 multi	11.00	5.50

Georges Guynemer (1894-1917), Ace
Fighter Pilot in World War I, and Spad
XIII — AP51

Litho. & Engr.

2017, Sept. 8			**Perf. 13**	
C80	AP51	€5.10 multi	12.00	6.00
a.	Miniature sheet of 10			

Michel Coiffard (1892-1918), and
Maurice Boyau (1888-1918), World
War I Flying Aces
AP52

Litho. & Engr.

2018, Nov. 10			**Perf. 13**	
C81	AP52	€3.80 multi	8.75	4.50

First Flight
of the
Concorde,
50th Anniv.
AP53

2019, Mar. 1	Photo.		**Perf. 13**	
C82	AP53	€4.20 multi	9.50	4.75

Ballons
Montés,
150th Anniv.
AP54

Litho. & Engr.

2020, Nov. 5			**Perf. 13**	
C83	AP54	€4.64 multi	11.50	5.75
a.	Miniature sheet of 10		115.00	

Pierre Clostermann (1921-2006), and
Claire Roman (1906-41), World War II
Pilots
AP55

Litho. & Engr.

2021, Apr. 4			**Perf. 13**	
C84	AP55	€4.71 multi	11.50	5.75
a.	Miniature sheet of 10		115.00	

**Antoine de Saint-Exupery Air Post
Semi-Postal Type of 1948 Redrawn**
Miniature Sheet
**Engr., Sheet Margin Engr. With Foil
Application**

2021, June 17			**Perf. 13**	
C85	Sheet of 6, 2 each		57.00	57.00
	#C85a-C85c			
a.	SPAP1 €4 violet		9.50	9.50
b.	SPAP1 €4 yellow green		9.50	9.50
c.	SPAP1 €4 dp bluish grn		9.50	9.50

A sheet containing five redrawn stamps of
type SPAP1 (two €1.50, two €7.50 stamps,
and a larger €12 stamp) was printed in limited
quantities.

Dewoitine
D1 and
Aircraft
Carrier
Béarn
AP56

Litho. & Engr.

2022, Nov. 3			**Perf. 13**	
C87	AP56	€5.26 multi	11.00	5.50

AIR POST SEMI-POSTAL STAMPS

**Catalogue values for unused
stamps in this section are for
Never Hinged items.**

Antoine de Saint-
Exupéry
SPAP1

Col. Jean
Dagnaux
SPAP2

1948   Unwmk.   Engr.   Perf. 13

CB1	SPAP1	50fr + 30fr vio brn	2.75	1.60
CB2	SPAP2	100fr + 70fr dk blue	3.75	2.75

See No. C85.

Modern Plane and
Ader's
"Eole" — SPAP3

1948, Feb.

CB3	SPAP3	40fr + 10fr dk blue	1.60	1.50

50th anniv. of the flight of Clément Ader's
plane, the Eole, in 1897.

POSTAGE DUE STAMPS

D1

1859-70   Unwmk.   Litho.   Imperf.

J1	D1	10c black	30,500.	240.00
J2	D1	15c black ('70)	140.00	250.00

In the lithographed stamps the central bar of
the "E" of "CENTIMES" is very short, and the
accent on "a" slants at an angle of 30 degree,
for the 10c and 17 degree for the 15c, while on
the typographed the central bar of the "E" is
almost as wide as the top and bottom bars and
the accent on the "a" slants at an angle of 47
degree.

No. J2 is known rouletted unofficially.

1859-78   Typo.

J3	D1	10c black	30.00	17.50
J4	D1	15c black ('63)	35.00	15.00
J5	D1	20c black ('77)	4,100.	
J6	D1	25c black ('71)	150.00	50.00
a.	Double impression		6,000.	
J7	D1	30c black ('78)	225.00	125.00
J8	D1	40c blue ('71)	325.00	425.00
a.	40c ultramarine		6,500.	5,700.
b.	40c Prussian blue		2,600.	
J9	D1	60c bister ('71)	475.00	1,050.
J10	D1	60c black ('78)	60.00	110.00
a.	60c dark blue		600.00	725.00
J10B	D1	60c black		2,700.

The 20c & 60c black were not put into use.
Nos. J3, J4, J6, J8 and J9 are known rouletted unofficially and Nos. J4, J6, J7 and J10
pin-perf. unofficially.

D2

1882-92   Perf. 14x13½

J11	D2	1c black	2.50	2.50
J12	D2	2c black	30.00	26.00
J13	D2	3c black	30.00	25.00
J14	D2	4c black	60.00	40.00
J15	D2	5c black	130.00	32.50
J16	D2	10c black	110.00	2.50
J17	D2	15c black	77.50	10.50
J18	D2	20c black	350.00	140.00
J19	D2	30c black	210.00	2.50
J20	D2	40c black	140.00	60.00
J21	D2	50c blk ('92)	600.00	175.00
J22	D2	60c blk ('84)	600.00	57.50
J23	D2	1fr black	750.00	350.00
J24	D2	2fr blk ('84)	1,400.	825.00
J25	D2	5fr blk ('84)	3,000.	1,600.

Excellent counterfeits exist of Nos. J23-J25.
See Nos. J26-J45A. For overprints and
surcharges see Offices in China Nos. J1-J6,
J33-J40, Offices in Egypt, Alexandria J1-J5,
Port Said J1-J8, Offices in Zanzibar 60-62, J1-
J5, Offices in Morocco 9-10, 24-25, J1-J5,
J10-J12, J17-J22, J35-J41.

1884
J26	D2	1fr brown	400.00	90.00
J27	D2	2fr brown	190.00	130.00
J28	D2	5fr brown	450.00	325.00

1893-1941
J29	D2	5c blue ('94)	.25	.30
a.		Grayish paper (GC) ('16)	3.50	2.50
J30	D2	10c brown	.25	.30
a.		Grayish paper (GC) ('16)	3.50	.75
J31	D2	15c lt grn ('94)	28.00	1.40
a.		Grayish paper (GC) ('16)	22.50	1.50
J32	D2	20c ol grn ('06)	6.50	.65
a.		Grayish paper (GC) ('16)	11.00	.75
J33	D2	25c rose ('23)	6.50	3.75
J34	D2	30c red ('94)	.25	.25
a.		Grayish paper (GC) ('16)	3.75	.75
J35	D2	30c org red ('94)	475.00	85.00
J36	D2	40c rose ('25)	11.50	4.50
J37	D2	45c grn ('24)	9.00	5.25
J38	D2	50c brn vio ('95)	.50	.30
a.		50c lilac	.50	.30
b.		Grayish paper (GC) ('16)	11.00	.75
J39	D2	60c lt grn ('25)	1.00	.55
J40	D2	1fr rose, *straw* ('96)	475.00	375.00
J41	D2	1fr red brn, *straw* ('20)	9.50	.30
J42	D2	1fr red brn ('35)	1.25	.40
J43	D2	2fr red org ('10)	225.00	65.00
J44	D2	2fr brt vio ('26)	.65	.75
J45	D2	3fr magenta ('26)	.65	.75
J45A	D2	5fr red org ('41)	1.40	2.25

 D3

1908-25
J46	D3	1c olive grn	1.00	1.25
J47	D3	10c violet	1.10	.30
a.		Imperf., pair	175.00	
J48	D3	20c bister ('19)	40.00	1.25
J49	D3	30c bister ('09)	14.00	.40
J50	D3	50c red ('09)	275.00	60.00
J51	D3	60c red ('25)	2.75	3.75
		Nos. J46-J51 (6)	333.85	66.95

"Recouvrements" stamps were used to recover charges due on undelivered or refused mail which was returned to the sender.

For surcharges see Offices in Morocco Nos. J6-J9, J13-J16, J23-J26, J42-J45.

Nos. J49-J50 Surcharged

1917
J52	D3	20c on 30c bister	20.00	4.00
J53	D3	40c on 50c red	10.50	4.00
a.		Double surcharge	475.00	

In Jan. 1917 several values of the current issue of postage stamps were handstamped "T" in a triangle and used as postage due stamps.

Recouvrements Stamps of 1908-25 Surcharged

1926
J54	D3	50c on 10c lilac	3.50	3.25
J55	D3	60c on 1c ol grn	7.00	5.00
J56	D3	1fr on 60c red	18.00	10.00
J57	D3	2fr on 60c red	18.00	10.50
		Nos. J54-J57 (4)	46.50	28.75

 D4

1927-31
J58	D4	1c olive grn ('28)	1.00	1.00
J59	D4	10c rose ('31)	1.90	1.40
J60	D4	30c bister	4.50	.50
J61	D4	60c red	4.50	.50
J62	D4	1fr violet	14.00	3.25
J63	D4	1fr Prus grn ('31)	17.00	.55
J64	D4	2fr blue	80.00	42.50
J65	D4	2fr olive brn ('31)	150.00	26.00
		Nos. J58-J65 (8)	272.90	75.70

Nos. J62 to J65 have the numerals of value double-lined.

Nos. J64, J62 Surcharged in Red or Black

1929
J66	D4	1.20fr on 2fr blue	42.50	11.00
J67	D4	5fr on 1fr vio (Bk)	65.00	15.00

No. J61 Surcharged

1931
J68	D4	1fr on 60c red	30.00	2.75

> Catalogue values for unused stamps in this section, from this point to the end of the section, are for Never Hinged items.

 Sheaves of Wheat — D5

Perf. 14x13½
1943-46		Unwmk.	Typo.	
J69	D5	10c sepia	.25	.25
J70	D5	30c brt red vio	.25	.25
J71	D5	50c blue grn	.25	.25
J72	D5	1fr brt ultra	.25	.25
J73	D5	1.50fr rose red	.25	.25
J74	D5	2fr turq blue	.25	.25
J75	D5	3fr brn org	.30	.25
J76	D5	4fr dp vio ('45)	4.50	2.25
J77	D5	5fr brt pink	.40	.25
J78	D5	10fr red org ('45)	2.50	.60
J79	D5	20fr ol bis ('46)	8.00	2.25
		Nos. J69-J79 (11)	17.20	7.10

Type of 1943 Inscribed "Timbre Taxe"
1946-53				
J80	D5	10c sepia ('47)	.75	.40
J81	D5	30c brt red vio ('47)	.75	.40
J82	D5	50c blue grn ('47)	19.00	6.50
J83	D5	1fr brt ultra ('47)	.25	.25
J85	D5	2fr turq blue	.25	.25
J86	D5	3fr brown org	.25	.25
J87	D5	4fr deep violet	.25	.25
J88	D5	5fr brt pink ('47)	.25	.25
J89	D5	10fr red org ('47)	.25	.25
J90	D5	20fr olive bis ('47)	1.25	.30
J91	D5	50fr dk green ('50)	19.00	.75
J92	D5	100fr dp green ('53)	65.00	6.00
		Nos. J80-J92 (12)	107.25	15.85

For surcharges see Reunion Nos. J36-J44.

 Sheaves of Wheat — D6

1960		Typo.	Perf. 14x13½	
J93	D6	5c bright pink	2.75	.40
J94	D6	10c red orange	3.75	.25
J95	D6	20c olive bister	3.50	.75
J96	D6	50c dark green	9.75	.75
J97	D6	1fr deep green	40.00	1.50
		Nos. J93-J97 (5)	59.75	3.65

For surcharges see Reunion Nos. J46-J48.
For overprints see Algeria Nos. J49-J53.

 D7

Flowers: 5c, Centaury. 10c, Gentian. 15c, Corn poppy. 20c, Violets. 30c, Forget-me-not. 40c, Columbine. 50c, Clover. 1fr, Soldanel.

1964-71		Typo.	Perf. 14x13½	
J98	D7	5c car rose, red & grn ('65)	.25	.25
J99	D7	10c car rose, brt bl & grn ('65)	.25	.25
J100	D7	15c brn, grn & red ('71)	.25	.25
J101	D7	20c dk grn, grn & vio ('71)	.25	.25
J102	D7	30c brn, ultra & grn	.25	.25
J103	D7	40c dk grn, scar & yel ('71)	.25	.25
J104	D7	50c vio bl, car & grn ('65)	.25	.25
J105	D7	1fr vio bl, lil & grn ('65)	.40	.25
		Nos. J98-J105 (8)	2.15	2.00

For surcharges see Reunion Nos. J49-J55.

D8

Designs: 10c, Ampedus Cinnabarinus. 20c, Dorcadion fuliginator. 30c, Leptura cordigera. 40c, Paederus littoralis. 50c, Pyrochroa coccinea. 1fr, Scarites laevigatus. 2fr, Trichius gallicus. 3fr, Adalia alpina. 4fr, Apoderus coryli. 5fr, Trichodes alvearius.

1982-83		Engr.	Perf. 13	
J106	D8	10c multicolored	.25	.25
J107	D8	20c multicolored	.25	.25
J108	D8	30c multicolored	.25	.25
J109	D8	40c multicolored	.25	.25
J110	D8	50c multicolored	.25	.25
J111	D8	1fr multicolored	.40	.25
J112	D8	2fr multicolored	.65	.25
J113	D8	3fr multicolored	1.00	.25
J114	D8	4fr multicolored	1.40	.25
J115	D8	5fr multicolored	1.75	.25
		Nos. J106-J115 (10)	6.45	2.50

Issued: 30c, 40c, 3fr, 5fr, 1/3/83; others, 1/4/82.

MILITARY STAMPS

Regular Issue Overprinted in Black or Red

1901-39		Unwmk.	Perf. 14x13½	
M1	A17	15c orange ('01)	65.00	6.00
a.		Inverted overprint	300.00	150.00
b.		Imperf., pair	425.00	
M2	A19	15c pale red ('03)	65.00	6.00
M3	A20	15c slate grn ('04)	52.50	6.00
a.		No period after "M"	110.00	57.50
b.		Imperf., pair	290.00	
M4	A20	10c rose ('06)	30.00	8.25
a.		No period after "M"	82.50	45.00
b.		Imperf., pair	350.00	
M5	A22	10c red ('07)	1.75	1.00
a.		Inverted overprint	105.00	65.00
b.		Imperf., pair	190.00	
M6	A20	50c vermilion ('29)	4.75	1.00
a.		No period after "M"	32.50	18.00
b.		Period in front of F	32.50	18.00
M7	A45	50c rose red ('34)	2.75	.55
a.		No period after "M"	29.00	16.00
M8	A45	65c brt ultra (R) ('38)	.30	.30
a.		No period after "M"	29.00	16.00
M9	A45	90c ultra (R) ('39)	.40	.35
		Nos. M1-M9 (9)	222.45	29.45

"F. M." are initials of Franchise Militaire (Military Frank). See No. S1.

> Catalogue values for unused stamps in this section, from this point to the end of the section, are for Never Hinged items.

 M1

1946-47			Typo.	
M10	M1	dark green	1.75	.65
M11	M1	rose red ('47)	.30	.25

Nos. M10-M11 were valid also in the French colonies.

Flag — M2

1964, July 20			Perf. 13x14	
M12	M2	multicolored	.30	.35

OFFICIAL STAMPS

FOR THE COUNCIL OF EUROPE
For use only on mail posted in the post office in the Council of Europe Building, Strasbourg.

> Catalogue values for unused stamps in this section are for Never Hinged items.

For French stamp inscribed "Conseil de l'Europe" see No. 679.

France No. 854 Overprinted: "CONSEIL DE L'EUROPE"
Unwmk.
1958, Jan. 14		Engr.	Perf. 13	
1O1	A303	35fr car rose & lake	.75	2.00

 Council of Europe Flag — O1

1958-59		Flag in Ultramarine		
1O2	O1	8fr red org & brn vio	.25	.25
1O3	O1	20fr yel & lt brn	.25	.25
1O4	O1	25fr lil rose & sl grn ('59)	.60	.30
1O5	O1	35fr red	.40	.25
1O6	O1	50fr lilac rose ('59)	.75	.75
		Nos. 1O2-1O6 (5)	2.25	1.80

1963, Jan. 3		Flag in Ultramarine		
1O7	O1	20c yel & lt brn	.90	.65
1O8	O1	25c lil rose & sl grn	1.40	1.10
1O9	O1	50c lilac rose	1.90	1.60
		Nos. 1O7-1O9 (3)	4.20	3.35

Centime value stamps shown the denomination as "0,20," etc.

1965-71
Flag in Ultramarine & Yellow
1O10	O1	25c ver, yel & sl grn	.75	.55
1O11	O1	30c ver & yel	.35	.35
1O12	O1	40c ver, yel & gray	.75	.55
1O13	O1	50c ver, yel & grn	1.50	1.10
1O14	O1	60c ver, yel & vio	1.10	1.00
1O15	O1	70c ver, yel & dk brn	2.25	2.10
		Nos. 1O10-1O15 (6)	6.70	5.65

Issue dates: 25c, 30c, 60c, 1/16/65; 50c, 2/20/71; others, 3/24/69.

Type of 1958 Inscribed "FRANCE"
Flag in Ultramarine & Yellow
1975-76		Engr.	Perf. 13	
1O16	O1	60c org, yel & emer	.60	.55
1O17	O1	80c yel & mag	.75	.60
1O18	O1	1fr car, yel & gray ol ('76)	1.50	1.25
1O19	O1	1.20fr org, yel & bl	4.00	2.25
		Nos. 1O16-1O19 (4)	6.85	4.65

Issue dates: 1fr, 10/16; others, 11/22.

 New Council Headquarters, Strasbourg — O2

1977, Jan. 22		Engr.	Perf. 13	
1O20	O2	80c car & multi	.80	.50
1O21	O2	1fr brown & multi	.75	.30
1O22	O2	1.40fr gray & multi	1.50	.75
		Nos. 1O20-1O22 (3)	3.05	1.55

 Human Rights Emblem in Upper Left Corner

1978, Oct. 14				
1O23	O2	1.20fr red lilac & multi	.45	.40
1O24	O2	1.70fr blue & multi	.60	.55

30th anniversary of the Universal Declaration of Human Rights.

Council Headquarters Type of 1977
1980, Nov. 24		Engr.	Perf. 13	
1O25	O2	1.40fr olive	.50	.50
1O26	O2	2fr blue gray	.75	.75

New Council Headquarters, Strasbourg — O3

1981-84   **Engr.**
1027	O3	1.40fr multicolored	.50 .50
1028	O3	1.60fr multicolored	.50 .40
1029	O3	1.70fr emerald	.60 .40
1030	O3	1.80fr multicolored	.70 .60
1031	O3	2fr multicolored	.75 .40
1032	O3	2.10fr red	.75 .60
1033	O3	2.30fr multicolored	.85 .60
1034	O3	2.60fr multicolored	.90 .75
1035	O3	2.80fr multicolored	1.00 .75
1036	O3	3fr brt blue	1.10 .90
		Nos. 1027-1036 (10)	7.65 5.90

Issued: 1.40, 1.60, 2.30fr, 11/21; 1.80, 2.60fr, 11/13/82; 2, 2.80fr, 11/21/83; 1.70, 2.10, 3fr, 11/5/84.

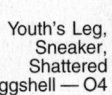

Youth's Leg, Sneaker, Shattered Eggshell — O4

1985, Aug. 31   **Engr.**   *Perf. 13*
1037	O4	1.80fr brt green	.70 .60
1038	O4	2.20fr vermilion	.75 .60
1039	O4	3.20fr brt blue	1.10 1.00
		Nos. 1037-1039 (3)	2.55 2.20

New Council Headquarters, Strasbourg — O5

1986-87   **Engr.**   *Perf. 13*
1040	O5	1.90fr green	.70 .60
1041	O5	2fr brt yel grn	.90 .60
1042	O5	2.20fr red	.75 .60
1043	O5	3.40fr blue	1.20 1.00
1044	O5	3.60fr brt blue	1.40 1.10
		Nos. 1040-1044 (5)	4.95 3.90

Issued: 1.90, 2.20, 3.40fr, 12/13; 2, 3.60fr, 10/10/87.

Council of Europe, 40th Anniv. — O6

1989, Feb. 4   **Litho. & Engr.**
1045	O6	2.20fr multicolored	.90 .70
1046	O6	3.60fr multicolored	1.40 1.10

Denominations also inscribed in European Currency Units (ECUs).

Map of Europe — O7

1990-91   **Litho.**   *Perf. 13*
1047	O7	2.30fr multicolored	.90 .75
1048	O7	2.50fr multicolored	.90 .75
1049	O7	3.20fr multicolored	1.10 1.00
1050	O7	3.40fr multicolored	1.10 1.00
		Nos. 1047-1050 (4)	4.00 3.50

Issued: 2.30fr, 3.20fr, 5/26/90; 2.50fr, 3.40fr, 11/23/91.

36 Heads, by Hundertwasser — O8

1994, Jan. 15   **Litho.**   *Perf. 13*
1051	O8	2.80fr multicolored	1.40 .75
1052	O8	3.70fr multicolored	2.25 1.00

Palace of Human Rights, Strasbourg — O9

1996, June 1   **Litho.**   *Perf. 13*
1053	O9	3fr multicolored	1.50 .75
1054	O9	3.80fr multicolored	1.75 1.00

Charioteer of Delphi — O10

1999, Sept. 18   **Photo.**   *Perf. 13*
1055	O10	3fr shown	1.40 .75
1056	O10	3.80fr Nike	1.75 1.00

Girl, Penguin and Boy — O11

2001, Dec. 1   **Litho.**   *Perf. 13*
1057	O11	3fr red & multi	2.00 .70
1058	O11	3.80fr grn & multi	2.40 1.00

Hiker on Stars — O12

2003, Oct. 18   **Litho.**   *Perf. 13*
1059	O12	50c Hiker facing left	2.00 .70
1060	O12	75c Hiker facing right	2.50 1.20

O13

O14

2005, Sept. 18   **Litho.**   *Perf. 13*
1061	O13	55c multi	2.00 .75
1062	O14	75c multi	2.50 1.20

Map of Europe — O15

Sculpture by Mariano González Beltrán — O16

2007, June 23   **Litho.**   *Perf. 13*
1063	O15	60c multi	2.00 .75
1064	O16	85c multi	2.50 1.25

Council of Europe, 60th Anniv. — O17

European Court of Human Rights, 50th Anniv. — O18

2009, May 16   **Litho.**   *Perf. 13*
1065	O17	56c multi	2.00 .75
1066	O18	70c multi	2.50 1.25

Tree — O19   Chain — O20

2010, Sept. 17   **Litho.**   *Perf. 13*
1067	O19	75c multi	2.10 .75
1068	O20	87c multi	2.40 1.25

European Human Rights Convention, 60th anniv. (No. 1068).

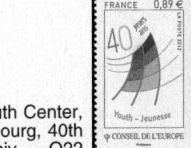

Map of Europe and Flags — O21

2011, Sept. 9   **Litho.**   *Perf. 13*
1069	O21	89c multi	2.50 1.25

European Social Charter, 50th anniv.

European Youth Center, Strasbourg, 40th Anniv. — O22

2012, Sept. 28
1070	O22	89c multi	2.40 1.25

Balance of Rights and Responsibilties of Citizens in a Democracy O23

2013, Sept. 27   **Litho.**   *Perf. 13*
1071	O23	95c multi	2.60 1.25

European Directorate for the Quality of Medicines and Health Care, 50th Anniv. O24

European Cultural Cooperation, 60th Anniv. O25

2014, Oct. 3   **Photo.**   *Perf. 13*
1072	O24	83c multi	2.10 1.00
1073	O25	98c multi	2.50 1.25

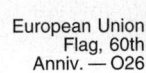

European Union Flag, 60th Anniv. — O26

2015, Oct. 2   **Litho.**   *Perf. 13*
1074	O26	95c multi	2.25 1.10

European Social Charter — O27

2016, Oct. 14   **Litho.**   *Perf. 13*
1075	O27	€1 multi	2.25 2.25

Council of Europe Cultural Routes 30th Anniv. — O28

2017, Oct. 13   **Litho.**   *Perf. 13*
1076	O28	€1.10 multi	2.60 2.60

Framework Convention for the Protection of National Minorities, 20th Anniv. — O29

2018, Oct. 12   **Litho.**   *Perf. 13*
1077	O29	€1.20 multi	2.75 2.75

Council of Europe, 70th Anniv. — O30

European Court of Human Rights, 60th Anniv. — O31

2019, May 5   **Litho.**   *Perf. 13¼*
1078	O30	€1.30 multi	3.00 3.00
1079	O31	€1.30 multi	3.00 3.00

European Convention on Human Rights, 70th Anniv. — O32

European Court of Human Rights Building, 25th Anniv. — O33

2020, Sept. 4   **Litho.**   *Perf. 13¼*
1080	O32	€1.40 mutli	3.25 3.25
1081	O33	€1.40 dk blue	3.25 3.25

Freedom of Expression — O34

Digital Printing
2021, Sept. 30   *Perf. 13¼*
1082	O34	€1.50 multi	3.50 3.50

Gender Equality — O35

Digital Printing

2022, Sept. 2			**Perf. 13¼**
1O83	O35	€1.65 multi	3.25 3.25

FOR THE UNITED NATIONS EDUCATIONAL, SCIENTIFIC AND CULTURAL ORGANIZATION

For use only on mail posted in the post office in the UNESCO Building, Paris.

> Catalogue values for unused stamps in this section are for Never Hinged items.

For French stamps inscribed "UNESCO" see Nos. 572, 893-894, 2545.

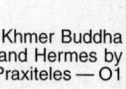

Khmer Buddha and Hermes by Praxiteles — O1

1961-65	Unwmk.	Engr.	**Perf. 13**
2O1	O1 20c dk gray, ol bis & bl	.25	.55
2O2	O1 25c blk, lake & grn	.40	.90
2O3	O1 30c choc & bis brn ('65)	.90	.60
2O4	O1 50c blk, red & vio bl	.90	1.75
2O5	O1 60c grnsh bl, red brn & rose lil ('65)	1.00	1.40
	Nos. 2O1-2O5 (5)	3.45	5.20

Book and Globe — O2

1966, Dec. 17

2O6	O2 25c gray	.30	.25
2O7	O2 30c dark red	.45	.35
2O8	O2 60c green	.75	.65
	Nos. 2O6-2O8 (3)	1.50	1.25

20th anniversary of UNESCO.

Human Rights Flame — O3

1969-71	Engr.		**Perf. 13**
2O9	O3 30c sl grn, red & dp brn	.30	.30
2O10	O3 40c dk car rose, red & dp brn	.45	.40
2O11	O3 50c ultra, car & brn ('71)	.75	.60
2O12	O3 70c pur, red & sl	1.50	1.40
	Nos. 2O9-2O12 (4)	3.00	2.70

Universal Declaration of Human Rights.

Type of 1969 Inscribed "FRANCE" — O3a

1975, Nov. 15	Engr.		**Perf. 13**
2O13	O3a 60c bl grn, red & choc	.60	.55
2O14	O3a 80c ocher, red & red brn	.90	.60
2O15	O3a 1.20fr ind, red & brn	3.00	2.25
	Nos. 2O13-2O15 (3)	4.50	3.40

O4

1976-78	Engr.		**Perf. 13**
2O16	O4 80c multi	.65	.55
2O17	O4 1fr multi	.35	.30
2O18	O4 1.20fr multi	.50	.40
2O19	O4 1.40fr multi	1.25	.90
2O20	O4 1.70fr multi	.75	.60
	Nos. 2O16-2O20 (5)	3.50	2.75

Issued: 1.20, 1.70fr, 10/14/78; others, 10/23/76.

Slave Quarters, Senegal — O5

Designs: 1.40fr, Mohenjo-Daro excavations, Pakistan. 2fr, Sans-Souci Palace, Haiti.

1980, Nov. 17	Engr.		**Perf. 13**
2O21	O5 1.20fr multi	.50	.50
2O22	O5 1.40fr multi	.55	.50
2O23	O5 2fr multi	.80	.65
	Nos. 2O21-2O23 (3)	1.85	1.65

Hue, Vietnam — O7

Designs: 1.40fr, Building, Fez, Morocco. 1.60fr, Seated deity, Sukhothai, Thailand. 2.30fr, Fort St. Elmo, Malta, horiz. 2.60fr, St. Michael Church ruins, Brazil.

1981-82

2O24	O7 1.40fr multi	.50	.35
2O25	O7 1.60fr multi	.50	.35
2O26	O7 1.80fr shown	.70	.55
2O27	O7 2.30fr multi	.60	.50
2O28	O7 2.60fr multi	.75	.55
	Nos. 2O24-2O28 (5)	3.05	2.30

Issued: 1.80fr, 2.60fr, 10/23/82; others, 12/12/81.

Mosque, Chinguetti, Mauritania — O8

Roman Theater and Female Standing Sculpture, Carthage, Tunisia — O8a

Architecture: 1.70fr, Church, Lalibela, Ethiopia. 2.10fr, San'a, Yemen. 2.20fr, Old Town Square and wrought iron latticework, Havana. 2.80fr, Enclosure wall interior, Istanbul. 3fr, Church, Kotor, Yugoslavia. 3.20fr, Temple of Anuradhapura and bas-relief of two women, Sri Lanka.

1983-85			Engr.
2O29	O8 1.70fr multi	.55	.35
2O30	O8a 1.80fr multi	.65	.55
2O31	O8 2fr multi	.75	.40
2O32	O8 2.10fr multi	.75	.60
2O33	O8a 2.20fr multi	.75	.60
2O34	O8 2.80fr multi	1.00	.60
2O35	O8 3fr multi	1.10	.90
2O36	O8 3.20fr multi	1.10	1.00
	Nos. 2O29-2O36 (8)	6.65	5.00

Issued: 2fr, 2.80fr, 10/10; 1.70fr, 2.10fr, 3fr, 10/22/84; 1.80fr, 2.20fr, 3.20fr, 10/26/85.

Tikal Temple, Guatemala — O9

3.40fr, Bagerhat Mosque, Bangladesh.

1986, Dec. 6	Engr.		**Perf. 13**
2O37	O9 1.90fr shown	.75	.65
2O38	O9 3.40fr multicolored	1.25	1.20

The Parthenon, Athens — O10

3.60fr, Temple of Philae, Egypt.

1987, Dec. 5	Engr.	**Perf. 13x12½**
2O39	O10 2fr shown	.90 .60
2O40	O10 3.60fr multicolored	1.40 1.20

Shibam, Yemen People's Democratic Republic — O11

2.30fr, San Francisco de Lima, Peru, vert.

Perf. 13x12½, 12½x13

1990, Apr. 7		Engr.
2O41	O11 2.30fr multicolored	.90 .75
2O42	O11 3.20fr shown	1.20 1.00

Bagdaon Temple, Nepal — O12

3.40fr, Citadel of Harat, Afghanistan, horiz.

1991, Nov. 23

2O43	O12 2.50fr choc & dk red	.90	.75
2O44	O12 3.40fr grn, brn & ol	1.20	1.00

Tassili N'Ajjer Natl. Park, Algeria — O13

Design: 2.80fr, Angkor Wat Archaeological Park, Cambodia, vert.

1993, Oct. 23	Litho.	**Perf. 13**
2O45	O13 2.80fr multicolored	1.25 .75
2O46	O13 3.70fr multicolored	1.50 1.00

UNESCO, 50th Anniv. — O14

Designs: 3fr, Uluru Natl. Park, Australia. 3.80fr, Los Glaciares Natl. Park, Argentina.

1996, June 1	Litho.	**Perf. 13**
2O47	O14 3fr multicolored	1.50 .75
2O48	O14 3.80fr multicolored	2.00 1.00

Detail of Dionysus Fresco, Pompeii O15

Moai Statues, Easter Island O16

1998, Oct. 24	Litho.	**Perf. 13**
2O49	O15 3fr multicolored	1.50 .75
2O50	O16 3.80fr multicolored	1.90 1.25

Sphinx and Pyramids, Egypt — O17

Komodo Dragon, Komodo Natl. Park, Indonesia — O18

2001, Dec. 1	Litho.	**Perf. 13**
2O51	O17 3fr multi	2.00 .75
2O52	O18 3.80fr multi	2.50 1.00

Reindeer, Lapland O19

Church of the Resurrection, St. Petersburg, Russia O20

2003, Dec. 6	Litho.	**Perf. 13**
2O53	O19 50c multi	2.00 .75
2O54	O20 75c multi	2.50 1.40

Bison in Bialowieza Forest, Poland O21

Petra, Jordan O22

2005, Nov. 26	Litho.	**Perf. 13**
2O55	O21 55c multi	2.00 .75
2O56	O22 90c multi	2.50 1.40

Siberian Tiger — O23

Luang Prabang, Laos — O24

2006, Dec. 7	Litho.	**Perf. 13**
2O57	O23 60c multi	2.00 .75
2O58	O24 85c multi	2.50 1.25

Ksar d'Ait-Ben-Haddou, Morocco — O25

Koala, Australia — O26

2007, Dec. 13	Litho.	**Perf. 13**
2O59	O25 60c multi	2.00 .75
2O60	O26 85c multi	2.50 1.40

Gorilla — O27

Machu Picchu, Peru — O28

2008, Dec. 3   Litho.   *Perf. 13*
2O61   O27 65c multi   2.00   1.00
2O62   O28 85c multi   2.50   1.25

Polar Bear — O29

Suzhou, China — O30

2009, Dec. 9   Litho.   *Perf. 13*
2O63   O29 70c multi   2.10   1.00
2O64   O30 85c multi   2.50   1.25

Alhambra, Spain — O31

Alpaca — O32

2010, Dec. 1   Litho.   *Perf. 13*
2O65   O31 75c multi   2.00   1.00
2O66   O32 87c multi   2.40   1.20

Bactrian Camel — O33

Milford Sound, New Zealand — O34

2011, Oct. 19
2O67   O33 77c multi   2.10   1.00
2O68   O34 89c multi   2.50   1.25

Stonehenge, Great Britain — O35

African Elephants — O36

2012, Nov. 22
2O69   O35 77c multi   2.00   1.00
2O70   O36 89c multi   2.40   1.20

Japanese Cranes O37

Sigiriya UNESCO World Heritage Site, Sri Lanka O38

2013, Nov. 7   Litho.   *Perf. 13*
2O71   O37 58c multi   1.60   .80
2O72   O38 95c multi   2.60   1.25

Trulli of Alberobello UNESCO World Heritage Site, Italy O39

Hyacinth Macaw O40

2014, Nov. 8   Litho.   *Perf. 13x13¼*
2O73   O39 83c multi   2.10   1.00

Perf. 13¼x13
2O74   O40 98c multi   2.50   1.25

African Gnu O41

Sagrada Familia Basilica, Barcelona O42

2015, Nov. 6   Litho.   *Perf. 13*
2O75   O41   95c multi   2.00   2.00
2O76   O42 1.20 multi   2.60   2.60

UNESCO, 70th anniv.

Florida Panther O43

Ruins, Ephesus, Turkey O44

2016, Sept. 9   Litho.   *Perf. 13*
2O77   O43   €1 multi   2.25   2.25
2O78   O44 €1.25 multi   2.75   2.75

Samarkand, Uzbekistan O45

Orangutan O46

2017, June 30   Litho.   *Perf. 13*
2O79   O45 €1.10 multi   2.50   2.50
2O80   O46 €1.30 multi   3.00   3.00

UNESCO Man and Biosphere Program — O47

2018, Sept. 7   Photo.   *Perf. 12¼*
2O81   O47 €1.30 multi   3.00   3.00

International Year of Indigenous Languages O48

2019, Sept. 13   Litho.   *Perf. 13¼*
2O82   O48 €1.30 multi   3.00   3.00

UNESCO, 75th Anniv. — O49

2020, Sept. 11   Litho.   *Perf. 13*
2O83   O49 €1.40 multi   3.25   3.25

"United Against Racism and Discrimination" O50

Digital Printing
2021, Sept. 17   *Perf. 13*
2O84   O50 €1.50 multi   3.50   3.50

Florence Cathedral — O51

Digital Printing
2022, Sept. 9   *Perf. 13¼*
2O85   O51 €1.65 multi   3.25   3.25

Convention Concerning the Protection of the World Cultural and Natural Heritage, 50th anniv.

NEWSPAPER STAMPS

Coat of Arms — N1

1868	Unwmk.	Typo.	*Imperf.*
P1	N1 2c lilac	300.00	65.00
P2	N1 2c (+ 2c) blue	600.00	275.00

Perf. 12½

P3	N1 2c lilac	52.50	25.00
P4	N1 2c (+ 4c) rose	250.00	100.00
P5	N1 2c (+ 2c) blue	75.00	35.00
P6	N1 5c lilac	1,250.	550.00

Nos. P2, P4, and P5 were sold for face plus an added fiscal charge indicated in parenthesis. Nos. P1, P3 and P6 were used simply as fiscals.

The 2c rose and 5c lilac imperforate and the 5c rose and 5c blue, both imperforate and perforated, were never put into use.

Nos. P1-P6 were reprinted for the 1913 Ghent Exhibition and the 1937 Paris Exhibition (PEXIP).

No. 109 Surcharged in Red

1919		*Perf. 14x13½*	
P7	A16 ½c on 1c gray	.30	.30
a.	Inverted surcharge	1,200.	1,150.
c.	Grayish paper (GC) ('16)	.30	.30

No. 156 Surcharged

1933			
P8	A22 ½c on 1c olive bister	.30	.30

PARCEL POST STAMPS

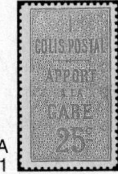

Inscribed "I APPORT A LA GARE" — PP1

Perfs As Noted

1892	Unwmk.		Typo.
Q1	PP1 25c brown, *yel*, perf 13½	825.00	290.00
	Never hinged	1,500.	
Q2	PP1 25c brown, *yel*, perf 11	30.00	24.00
	Never hinged	45.00	
a.	Printed on both sides	400.00	
	Never hinged	650.00	

Inscribed "II VALEUR DECLAREE" — PP2

Q3	PP2 10c red, perf 13½	1,000.	275.00
	Never hinged	1,750.	
Q4	PP2 10c red, perf 10x13½	875.00	325.00
	Never hinged	1,600.	
Q5	PP2 10c org red, perf 11	30.00	14.00
	Never hinged	42.50	
Q6	PP2 10c red, imperf	22.50	16.50
	Never hinged	32.50	

Inscribed "III LIVRAISON PAR EXPRESS" — PP3

Q7	PP3 25c green, perf 13½	57.50	32.50
	Never hinged	115.00	
Q8	PP3 25c green, perf 11	45.00	24.00
	Never hinged	70.00	

See Nos. Q22-Q26.

Locomotive — PP4

A set of six stamps, in the design above, was prepared in 1901 as postal tax stamps for expedited parcels but were not issued. All are perf 14x13½. Values: 5c gray, $3, never hinged $4; 10c yellow green, $3, never hinged $5; 20c rose, $20, never hinged $29; 50c blue, $7, never hinged $11.50; 1fr brown, $8, never hinged $12; 2fr brown red, $37.50, never hinged $57.50.

PP5

Large Trefoil

Type I: Large Trefoil Under "N" of "MAJORATION"

1918		*Perf. 11*	
Q9	PP5 5c black	1.25	.85
	Never hinged	2.00	

Q10	PP5	15c brn lilac	1.25	.85
		Never hinged	2.00	

Imperforate

Q11	PP5	5c black	3.25	2.50
		Never hinged	6.25	
Q12	PP5	15c brn lilac	9.00	4.25
		Never hinged	14.00	
		Nos. Q9-Q12 (4)	14.75	8.45

40c values, perforated 11 and imperf, in orange, were prepared but not issued. Value, perf or imperf, $375.

PP5a

Small Trefoil

Type II: Small Trefoil Under "O" of "MAJORATION"

Q13	PP5a	5c black	140.00	45.00
		Never hinged	275.00	
Q14	PP5a	35c red	3.75	2.50
		Never hinged	5.00	
Q15	PP5a	50c vio blue	4.50	1.60
		Never hinged	7.00	
Q16	PP5a	1fr yellow	4.25	1.60
		Never hinged	7.00	

Imperforate

Q17	PP5a	5c black	130.00	45.00
		Never hinged	260.00	
Q18	PP5a	15c brn lilac	30.00	16.50
		Never hinged	50.00	
Q19	PP5a	35c red	3.25	2.50
		Never hinged	6.75	
Q20	PP5a	50c vio blue	24.00	14.00
		Never hinged	40.00	
Q21	PP5a	1fr yellow	18.50	12.50
		Never hinged	30.00	
		Nos. Q13-Q21 (9)	358.25	141.20

See Nos. Q41-Q44, Q143-Q145.
For surcharges, see Nos. Q28-Q40.

Type of 1892

1918-23   **Perf. 10½x11**

Q22	PP1	30c brn, *yel*	37.50	16.50
		Never hinged	55.00	
a.		Imperf	200.00	
		Never hinged	290.00	
Q23	PP1	60c brn, *straw* ('23)	47.50	30.00
		Never hinged	70.00	
		Imperf	190.00	
		Never hinged	275.00	
Q24	PP2	15c vermilion ('22)	16.00	11.00
		Never hinged	23.00	
Q25	PP3	30c green	40.00	21.00
		Never hinged	57.50	
a.		Imperf	240.00	
		Never hinged	325.00	
Q26	PP3	60c green ('23)	75.00	50.00
		Never hinged	110.00	
		Nos. Q22-Q26 (5)	216.00	128.50

PP6

1924, Oct.   **Perf. 14**

Q27	PP6	15c rose & blue	4.00	3.75
		Never hinged	5.00	
a.		Imperf	550.00	
		Never hinged	750.00	

No. Q27 is a postal tax stamp, issued to show the collection of a new 15c excise fee on rail parcels. On July 3, 1925, its use was extended to all fiscal categories.

Surcharged in Black or Red (R) on Nos. Q9//Q16 and Types of 1918

1926   **Perf. 13**

Q28	PP5	20c on 2fr rose	1.90	1.10
		Never hinged	2.75	
Q29	PP5	30c on 2fr yellow	1.90	1.10
		Never hinged	2.75	
a.		"0f30" omitted	190.00	
		Never hinged	250.00	
Q30	PP5	40c on 3fr gray	1.90	1.40
		Never hinged	2.75	
Q31	PP5	45c on 3fr orange	1.90	1.40
		Never hinged	2.75	
a.		Period after "f" omitted	19.00	19.00
		Never hinged	30.00	

Q32	PP5	95c on 1fr yel	8.00	2.75
		Never hinged	12.50	
a.		Imperf	90.00	
		Never hinged	150.00	
Q33	PP5	1.35fr on 3fr vio	10.50	4.50
		Never hinged	14.00	
		On postal document		70.00
a.		Imperf	150.00	
		Never hinged	225.00	
Q34	PP5	1.45fr on 5fr blk (R)	1.90	1.00
		Never hinged	2.75	
Q35	PP5	1.75fr on 2fr blue	10.50	4.50
		Never hinged	14.00	
Q36	PP5	1.85fr on 10c org	1.90	1.20
		Never hinged	2.75	
Q37	PP5	1.95fr on 15c brn lilac	2.50	1.75
		Never hinged	3.50	
a.		Imperf	110.00	
		Never hinged	175.00	
Q38	PP5	2.35fr on 25c grn	1.90	1.00
		Never hinged	2.75	
a.		Imperf	110.00	
		Never hinged	175.00	
Q39	PP5	2.90fr on 35c red	2.50	1.00
		Never hinged	3.50	
a.		Dots before and after "f"	140.00	
		Never hinged	200.00	
b.		Imperf	125.00	
		Never hinged	190.00	
Q40	PP5	3.30fr on 50c blue violet (R)	2.50	1.25
		Never hinged	3.50	
a.		Double surcharge	250.00	
		Never hinged	375.00	
b.		Imperf	90.00	
		Never hinged	140.00	
		Nos. Q28-Q40 (13)	49.80	23.95

Type of 1918

1926   **Perf. 11**

Q41	PP5	10c orange	2.00	1.25
		Never hinged	3.75	
a.		Imperf	4.00	
		Never hinged	6.50	
Q42	PP5	25c pale green	2.00	1.25
		Never hinged	3.75	
a.		Imperf	4.00	
		Never hinged	6.50	
Q43	PP5	2fr pale blue	25.00	14.50
		Never hinged	42.50	
a.		Imperf	50.00	
		Never hinged	80.00	
Q44	PP5	3fr violet	110.00	67.50
		Never hinged	190.00	
a.		Imperf	225.00	
		Never hinged	360.00	
		Nos. Q41-Q44 (4)	139.00	84.50

Inscribed "APPORT A LA GARE" — PP7

No. 51

1926

Q45	PP7	1fr on 60c brn, *yel*	13.50	10.50
		Never hinged	24.00	
a.		Imperf	190.00	
		Never hinged	300.00	
Q46	PP7	1fr brn, *yel*	17.50	13.00
		Never hinged	30.00	
Q47	PP7	1.30fr on 1fr brn, *yel*	17.50	12.50
		Never hinged	30.00	
Q48	PP7	1.50fr brn, *yel*	20.00	11.50
		Never hinged	32.50	
Q49	PP7	1.65fr brn, *yel*	15.00	12.50
		Never hinged	24.00	
Q50	PP7	1.90fr on 1fr brn, *yel*	17.50	12.50
		Never hinged	30.00	
Q51	PP7	2.10fr on 1.65fr brn, *yel*	17.50	12.50
		Never hinged	30.00	
		Nos. Q45-Q51 (7)	118.50	85.00

See Nos. Q91-Q95, footnote following No. Q102, Q143-Q145.
For overprints and surcharges, see Nos. Q76-Q78, Q83-Q86, Q91-Q92, boxed note following Q95, Q96-Q99, Q107-QQ109, boxed note following Q159.

PP8

Type I   Type II

Type III

1926-38

Q52	PP8	15c brown, *yel*, type I	7.50	3.00
		Never hinged	11.00	
a.		Imperf	180.00	
		Never hinged	275.00	
Q53	PP8	15c brown, *yel*, type II ('32)	8.00	4.25
		Never hinged	11.50	
a.		Type III ('38)	210.00	
		Never hinged	275.00	
b.		As "a," imperf	240.00	
		Never hinged	300.00	

Nos. Q52-Q53a were issued for use in Paris only. No. Q53a was prepared but not issued.

Inscribed "VALEUR DECLAREE" — PP9

The additional numerals overprinted on Nos. Q56-Q63 and on Nos. Q72-Q75 indicate the weight category of the parcels being sent.

1926

Q54	PP9	50c on 15c red	3.00	1.60
		Never hinged	5.00	
a.		Imperf	180.00	
		Never hinged	275.00	
Q55	PP9	50c red	750.00	750.00
		Never hinged	1,200.	
a.		Imperf	1,200.	
		Never hinged	1,650.	
Q56	PP9	50c red, ovptd. "1"	4.50	2.00
		Never hinged	7.00	
a.		Imperf	200.00	
		Never hinged	300.00	
b.		Double overprint "1"	300.00	
		Never hinged	400.00	
Q57	PP9	55c on 15c red, ovptd. "1"	6.75	5.00
		Never hinged	11.50	
a.		Imperf	190.00	
		Never hinged		
Q58	PP9	55c on 50c red, ovptd. "1"	6.75	5.00
		Never hinged	11.50	
Q59	PP9	65c on 15c red	2.50	2.50
		Never hinged	4.25	
Q60	PP9	65c on 50c red, ovptd. "1"	15.00	8.25
		Never hinged	27.50	
Q61	PP9	1.50fr on 50c red, ovptd. "3"	7.00	5.00
		Never hinged	12.00	
a.		Imperf	275.00	
		Never hinged	375.00	
Q62	PP9	2.00fr on 50c red, ovptd. "4"	8.25	3.75
		Never hinged	14.00	
Q63	PP9	2.50fr on 50c red, ovptd. "5"	15.00	8.25
		Never hinged	26.50	
		Nos. Q54-Q63 (10)	818.75	791.35

See Nos. Q79, Q93, Q150-Q152.
For overprints and surcharges, see No. Q87, boxed note following No. Q95, Q100, Q110, Q123-Q124, Q138.

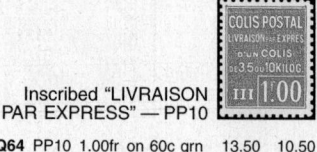

Inscribed "LIVRAISON PAR EXPRESS" — PP10

Q64	PP10	1.00fr on 60c grn	13.50	10.50
		Never hinged	24.00	
a.		Imperf	225.00	
		Never hinged	325.00	
Q65	PP10	1.00fr green	125.00	75.00
		Never hinged	250.00	
Q66	PP10	1.30fr on 1fr grn	16.50	12.50
		Never hinged	29.00	
Q67	PP10	1.50fr green	16.50	15.00
		Never hinged	32.50	
Q68	PP10	1.65fr green	16.50	15.00
		Never hinged	32.50	
Q69	PP10	1.90fr on 1.50fr grn	16.50	12.50
		Never hinged	30.00	

Q70	PP10	2.10fr on 1.65fr grn	30.00	14.00
		Never hinged	50.00	
		Nos. Q64-Q70 (7)	234.50	154.50

For overprints and surcharges, see Nos. Q80-Q82, Q88-Q90, Q94, boxed note following Q95, Q101-Q105, Q111-Q113, Q125-Q132, Q139-Q141, Q146-Q149.

Inscribed "INTERETS A LA LIVRAISON" — PP11

No. Q72

No. Q73

Q71	PP11	50c lilac	3.00	1.60
		Never hinged	5.00	
a.		Imperf	225.00	190.00
		Never hinged	325.00	
Q72	PP11	50c lil, ovptd. "1"	6.75	4.25
		Never hinged	10.00	
a.		Imperf	200.00	
		Never hinged	300.00	
Q73	PP11	1.50fr on 50c lil, ovptd. "3"	7.50	5.00
		Never hinged	11.50	
a.		Imperf	200.00	
		Never hinged	300.00	
Q74	PP11	2.00fr on 50c lil ovptd. "4"	10.00	7.00
		Never hinged	16.00	
Q75	PP11	2.50fr on 50c lil ovptd. "5"	10.00	7.00
		Never hinged	16.50	
a.		Imperf	210.00	
		Never hinged	310.00	
		Nos. Q71-Q75 (5)	37.25	24.85

1926 Issues Overprinted   A

1928

Inscribed "APPORT A LA GARE"

Q76	PP7	1.00fr brn, *yel*	16.50	14.00
		Never hinged	25.00	
a.		Imperf	190.00	190.00
		Never hinged	300.00	
Q77	PP7	1.50fr brn, *yel*	16.50	13.00
		Never hinged	25.00	
Q78	PP7	1.65fr brn, *yel*	16.50	13.00
		Never hinged	25.00	

Inscribed "VALEUR DECLAREE"

Q79	PP9	50c red	5.75	4.25
		Never hinged	8.25	
a.		Imperf	190.00	190.00
		Never hinged	300.00	
b.		Inverted overprint	210.00	
		Never hinged	310.00	

Inscribed "LIVRAISON PAR EXPRESS"

Q80	PP10	1.00fr green	17.00	13.50
		Never hinged	26.00	
Q81	PP10	1.50fr green	17.00	13.50
		Never hinged	26.00	
Q82	PP10	1.65fr green	17.00	13.50
		Never hinged	27.50	
		Nos. Q76-Q82 (7)	106.25	84.75

1926 Issues Surcharged   1ᶠ.45

1928

Inscribed "APPORT A LA GARE"

Q83	PP7	1.45fr on 60c brn, *yel*	7.00	6.75
		Never hinged	10.00	
Q84	PP7	1.45fr on 1fr brn, *yel*	40.00	32.50
		Never hinged	70.00	
Q85	PP7	2.15fr on 1.50fr brn, *yel*	62.50	42.50
		Never hinged	105.00	

Q86 PP7 2.35fr on 1.65fr
    brn, *yel* 62.50 42.50
    Never hinged 105.00

Inscribed "VALEUR DECLAREE"

Q87 PP9 75c on 50c red 2.10 1.60
    Never hinged 3.25
  a. Imperf 210.00
    Never hinged 400.00

Inscribed "LIVRAISON PAR EXPRESS"

Q88 PP10 1.45fr on 1fr
    green 62.50 42.50
    Never hinged 105.00
Q89 PP10 2.15fr on 1.50fr
    green 62.50 42.50
    Never hinged 105.00
Q90 PP10 2.35fr on 1.65fr
    green 62.50 42.50
    Never hinged 105.00
    Nos. Q83-Q90 (8) 361.60 253.35

Types of 1926

1933

Inscribed "APPORT A LA GARE"

Q91 PP7 1.45fr brn, *yel* 55.00 25.00
    Never hinged 82.50
Q92 PP7 2.35fr brn, *yel* 1,400.
    Never hinged 1,900.

A 2.15fr value, brown on yellow paper, was prepared but not issued without overprint or surcharge.

For overprints and surcharges, see Nos. Q96, Q98, Q99, Q107-Q109, Q115, Q116, Q118, Q120-Q122, Q135-Q137.

Inscribed "VALEUR DECLAREE"

Q93 PP9 75c red 18.00 3.25
    Never hinged 22.50
  a. Imperf 180.00

For overprints and surcharges on No. Q93, see Nos. Q110, Q123, Q124, Q138.

A 1.15fr black in this design, imperf, was prepared but not issued. Value, $400.

Inscribed "LIVRAISON PAR EXPRESS"

Q94 PP10 1.45fr yel grn 450.00 300.00
    Never hinged 675.00

Two other values, 2.15fr and 2.35fr were prepared but not issued without overprint or surcharge.

For overprints and surcharges, see Nos. Q101, Q103, Q105, Q111-Q113, Q125, Q126, Q128, Q130-Q132. Q139-Q141.

PP12

Inscribed "COLIS ENCOMBRANT"

1934

Q95 PP12 2fr blue 45.00 21.00
    Never hinged 70.00

For overprints and surcharges, see Nos. Q106, Q114, Q133, Q134, Q142.

B

Nos. Q46, Q48, Q49, Q55, Q65, Q67 and Q68 overprinted "B" were not issued. Values: 1fr (No. Q46), $95; never hinged $130; 1.50fr (No. Q48), $95, never hinged $130; 1.65fr (No. Q49), $95, never hinged $130; 50c (No. Q55), $95, never hinged $130; 1fr (No. Q65), $92.50, never hinged $140; 1.50fr (No. Q67), $92.50, never hinged $140; 1.65fr (No. Q68), $92.50, never hinged $140.

C

Stamps and Types of 1926-34 Overprinted

Q97 PP7 2.15fr on 1.50fr
    brn, *yel* 37.50 31.00
    Never hinged 57.50
Q98 PP7 2.15fr brn, *yel* 25.00 19.00
    Never hinged 37.50
Q99 PP7 2.35fr brn, *yel* 25.00 19.00
    Never hinged 37.50

Inscribed "VALEUR DECLAREE"

Q100 PP9 75c red 17.50 16.50
    Never hinged 25.00
  a. Imperf 225.00
    Never hinged 325.00

Inscribed "LIVRAISON PAR EXPRESS"

Q101 PP10 1.45fr green 17.50 16.50
    Never hinged 25.00
Q102 PP10 2.15fr on 1.50fr
    grn 17.50 16.50
    Never hinged 25.00
Q103 PP10 2.15fr green 42.50 30.00
    Never hinged 67.50
  a. Imperf 210.00
    Never hinged 315.00
Q104 PP10 2.35fr on 1.65fr
    grn 250.00 110.00
    Never hinged 350.00
Q105 PP10 2.35fr green 17.50 12.50
    Never hinged 26.00

Inscribed "COLIS ENCOMBRANT"

Q106 PP12 2fr blue 37.50 35.00
    Never hinged 57.50
    Nos. Q96-Q106 (11) 494.25 312.75

For overprints and surcharges, see Nos. Q146-Q149.

Types of 1933-34 Surcharged

1937

Inscribed "APPORT A LA GARE"

Q107 PP7 1.85fr on 1.45fr
    brn, *yel* 15.00 12.50
    Never hinged 26.00
Q108 PP7 2.75fr on 2.15fr
    brn, *yel* 26.00 17.50
    Never hinged 45.00
Q109 PP7 3.05fr on 2.55fr
    brn, *yel* 50.00 26.00
    Never hinged 90.00

Inscribed "VALEUR DECLAREE"

Q110 PP9 .95fr on 75c
    red 42.50 25.00
    Never hinged 67.50

Inscribed "LIVRAISON PAR EXPRESS"

Q111 PP10 1.85fr on 1.45fr
    grn 70.00 45.00
    Never hinged 120.00
Q112 PP10 2.75fr on 2.15fr
    grn 70.00 45.00
    Never hinged 120.00
Q113 PP10 3.05fr on 2.35fr
    grn 70.00 45.00
    Never hinged 120.00

Inscribed "COLIS ENCOMBRANT"

Q114 PP12 2.60fr on 2fr bl 17.50 17.50
    Never hinged 26.00
    Nos. Q107-Q114 (8) 361.00 233.50

Stamps and Types of 1926-34 Overprinted

D

1937

Inscribed "APPORT A LA GARE"

Q115 PP7 1.45fr brn, *yel* 3.00 2.50
    Never hinged 4.50
Q116 PP7 1.85fr on 1.45fr
    brn, *yel* 3.00 2.50
    Never hinged 4.50
Q117 PP7 2.15fr on 1.50fr
    brn, *yel* 2.50 2.50
    Never hinged 4.25
Q118 PP7 2.15fr brn, *yel* 42.50 35.00
    Never hinged 62.50
Q119 PP7 2.35fr on 1.65fr
    brn, *yel* 575.00 475.00
    Never hinged 800.00
Q120 PP7 2.35fr brn, *yel* 3.00 2.50
    Never hinged 4.50
Q121 PP7 2.75fr on 2.15fr
    brn, *yel* 3.25 2.50
    Never hinged 5.75
Q122 PP7 3.05fr on 2.35fr
    brn, *yel* 6.50 6.25
    Never hinged 10.00

Inscribed "VALEUR DECLAREE"

Q123 PP9 75c red 3.75 3.50
    Never hinged 5.50
  a. Pair, one without over-
    print 225.00
    Never hinged 350.00
Q124 PP9 95c on 75c red 3.00 3.00
    Never hinged 3.75

Inscribed "LIVRAISON PAR EXPRESS"

Q125 PP10 1.45fr green 4.25 3.25
    Never hinged 6.25
Q126 PP10 1.85fr on 1.45fr
    green 5.75 4.25
    Never hinged 8.25
Q127 PP10 2.15fr on 1.50fr
    grn 375.00 325.00
    Never hinged 500.00
Q128 PP10 2.15fr green 18.50 16.50
    Never hinged 27.50
Q129 PP10 2.35fr on 1.65fr
    grn 675.00 725.00
    Never hinged 775.00
Q130 PP10 2.35fr green 11.00 10.50
    Never hinged 15.00
Q131 PP10 2.75fr on 2.15fr
    grn 35.00 45.00
    Never hinged 55.00
Q132 PP10 3.05fr on 2.35fr
    grn 35.00 45.00
    Never hinged 55.00

Inscribed "COLIS ENCOMBRANT"

Q133 PP12 2fr blue 3.00 2.10
    Never hinged 4.50
  a. Pair, imperf between 130.00
    Never hinged 210.00
Q134 PP12 2.60fr on 2fr bl 3.25 2.50
    Never hinged 5.50
    Nos. Q115-Q134 (20) 1,811. 1,714.

For additional surcharges, see Nos. Q146-Q149.

Stamps and Types of 1933-34 Surcharged

1938

Inscribed "APPORT A LA GARE"

Q135 PP7 2.30fr on 1.45fr
    brn, *yel* 3.75 3.00
    Never hinged 5.50
Q136 PP7 3.45fr on 2.15fr
    brn, *yel* 3.75 3.00
    Never hinged 5.50
Q137 PP7 3.85fr on 2.35fr
    brn, *yel* 3.75 3.00
    Never hinged 5.50

Inscribed "VALEUR DECLAREE"

Q138 PP9 1.15fr on 75c
    red 1.60 1.60
    Never hinged 2.50

Inscribed "LIVRAISON PAR EXPRESS"

Q139 PP10 2.30fr on 1.45fr
    grn 3.75 3.00
    Never hinged 5.50
Q140 PP10 3.45fr on 2.15fr
    grn 3.75 3.00
    Never hinged 5.50
Q141 PP10 3.85fr on 2.35fr
    grn 3.75 3.00
    Never hinged 5.50

Inscribed "COLIS ENCOMBRANT"

Q142 PP12 3.25fr on 2fr bl 1.60 1.60
    Never hinged 2.50
    Nos. Q135-Q142 (8) 25.70 21.20

For Nos. Q135-Q138, Q140-Q142 overprinted "E," see editor's note following No. Q159.

Type of 1918

1938   11, Imperf (#Q161)

Q143 PP5 10c gray black 17.50 16.00
  a. Imperf 26.00
    Never hinged 42.50
Q144 PP5 20c brown lilac 17.50 16.00
  a. Imperf 26.00
    Never hinged 62.50
Q145 PP5 25c green, imperf 50.00 20.00
    Never hinged 80.00
    Nos. Q143-Q145 (3) 85.00 52.00

Two additional values, a 10c rose lilac and a 15c ultramarine, were prepared with this set but not issued. Values, each stamp: $90, never hinged $150. Both stamps also exist imperf. Values, each: $82.50; never hinged $150.

Nos. Q103, Q105, Q112, Q113 Overprinted

D

1938   Perf. 11

Q146 PP10 2.30fr on 2.15fr
    green 62.50 62.50
    Never hinged 80.00
Q147 PP10 2.30fr on 2.35fr
    green 62.50 62.50
    Never hinged 80.00
Q148 PP10 2.30fr on 2.75fr
    on 2.15fr
    green 125.00 100.00
    Never hinged 175.00
Q149 PP10 2.30fr on 3.05fr
    on 2.35fr
    green 125.00 100.00
    Never hinged 175.00
    Nos. Q146-Q149 (4) 375.00 325.00

Types of 1926 and

PP13   PP13a

PP14   PP15

PP16

1938-39

Q150 PP9 1fr red ('39) 2.50 2.50
    Never hinged 4.00
Q151 PP9 1.15fr red 1.25 1.25
    Imperf 2.10
    Never hinged 225.00
Q152 PP9 5fr red ('39) 2.50 2.75
    Never hinged 4.00
Q153 PP13 2.40fr brown,
    yel 2.50 2.75
    Never hinged 4.00
Q154 PP13a 3.50fr brown,
    yel 2.50 2.75
    Never hinged 4.00
Q155 PP13 3.80fr brown,
    yel 2.50 2.75
    Never hinged 4.00
    Imperf 125.00
    Never hinged 190.00
Q156 PP14 2.50fr grn yel
    ('39) 2.50 2.25
    Never hinged 4.00
Q157 PP14 7.50fr grn yel
    ('39) 2.75 2.50
    Never hinged 4.25
Q158 PP15 1fr lilac
    ('39) 9.50 6.75
    Never hinged 14.00
Q159 PP16 3.20fr blue 11.00 7.50
    Never hinged 16.00
    Nos. Q150-Q159 (10) 39.50 33.75

Two additional values, 3.45fr and 3.85fr, type PP7, brown on yellow paper, imperforate, were prepared but not issued. Values, each: $140; never hinged, $225.

E

Nos. Q135-Q138, Q140-Q142 were overprinted "E" in 1939, in anticipation of new rates to take effect April 1, but were not issued. Values: 2.30fr on 1.45fr, $675, never hinged $1,000; 3.45fr on 2.15fr, $875, never hinged $1,300; 3.85fr on 2.35fr, $875, never hinged $1,300; 1.15fr on 75c, $300, never hinged $450; 3.45fr on 2.15fr, $2,800, never hinged $4,000; 3.85fr on 2.35fr, $2,800, never hinged $4,000; 3.25fr on 2fr, $675, never hinged $1,000.

In 1941, two sets were prepared in anticipation of new rate increases on April 1. They were not issued.

Six stamps in a new design, consisting of a 10c greenish gray, 30c blue, 50c brown, 1fr blue violet, 2fr orange and 5fr red. Values: 10c $185, never hinged $275; 30c $240, never hinged $350; 50c $240, never hinged $350; 1fr $185, never hinged $275; 2fr $185, never hinged $275; 5fr $185, never hinged $275.

Nos. Q93, Q153-Q155 and Q159 overprinted "E." Values: 75c; other values $575, never hinged.

PP17

PP18

Without Denominations

1941			Perf. 12½	
Q160	PP17	(2.70fr) brown	5.00	4.00
	Never hinged		8.25	
Q161	PP17	(3.90fr) blue	5.00	4.00
	Never hinged		8.25	
Q162	PP17	(4.20fr) green	5.00	4.00
	Never hinged		8.25	
Q163	PP18	(3.50fr) blue	9.50	8.50
	Never hinged		12.50	
	Nos. Q160-Q163 (4)		24.50	20.50

Five stamps in the designs of PP20-PP22 below, but with blank value tablets, were prepared with Nos. Q160-Q163 but were not issued. Values: (1fr) brown, (5fr) red and (2.50fr) blue, each $60, never hinged $80; (7.50fr) green, $260, never hinged $360; (1fr) violet, $110, never hinged $160.
See Nos. Q178-Q181, Q200-Q206.

"Domicile"
PP19

"Valeur
Declaree"
PP20

"Remboursement"
PP21

"Interet A La
Livraison"
PP22

"Encombrant"
PP23

1941		Perf. 12½, 13 (#Q167-171)		
Q164	PP19	2.70fr brown	6.00	5.00
	Never hinged		10.00	
Q165	PP19	3.90fr blue	6.00	5.00
	Never hinged		10.00	
Q166	PP19	4.20fr green	6.00	5.00
	Never hinged		10.00	
Q167	PP20	1fr brown	2.40	1.10
	Never hinged		3.75	
Q168	PP20	5fr red	1.20	1.50
	Never hinged		1.90	
Q169	PP21	2.50fr blue	1.20	1.50
	Never hinged		1.90	
Q170	PP21	7.50fr green	3.50	3.00
	Never hinged		5.25	
Q171	PP22	1fr violet	.85	.75
Q172	PP23	3.50fr blue	32.50	16.00
	Never hinged		47.50	
	Nos. Q164-Q172 (9)		59.65	38.85

See Nos. Q173-Q177, Q186-Q194, Q200-Q206.
For surcharges, see footnote following No. Q177, Nos. Q182-Q185, Q207-Q210.

Types of 1941 with Bold Numerals

1942, Feb.			Perf. 13	
Q173	PP20	1fr brown	1.25	1.10
	Never hinged		1.90	
Q174	PP20	5fr red	4.00	5.00
	Never hinged		6.00	
Q175	PP21	2.50fr blue	1.25	1.10
	Never hinged		1.90	
Q176	PP21	7.50fr green	6.00	6.50
	Never hinged		9.75	
Q177	PP22	1fr violet	60.00	
	Never hinged		95.00	
	Nos. Q173-Q177 (5)		72.50	13.70

See Nos. Q173-Q177, Q186-Q194, Q200-Q206. See No. Q194.

Nine stamps from the 1941-42 issues were surcharged "+3F / C.N.S. / Cheminots" to raise funds for a philatelic exhibition organized by railroad employees, which took place in Paris on Dec. 26 and 27, 1942. They were not valid for postage. Value, set: $110; never hinged $150.

Type of 1941 Inscribed
in Value Tablets

1943			Perf. 12½	
Q178	PP17	(3fr) brown	2.60	2.60
	Never hinged		4.00	
Q179	PP17	(4.30fr) blue	2.60	2.60
	Never hinged		4.00	
Q180	PP17	(4.70fr) green	2.60	2.60
	Never hinged		4.00	
Q181	PP18	(3.50fr) blue	6.00	6.00
	Never hinged		12.00	
	Nos. Q178-Q181 (4)		13.80	13.80

Stamps of 1941 Surcharged in Deep Blue or Red

1943				
Q182	PP19	3fr on 2.70fr brn	12.50	12.50
	Never hinged		19.00	
Q183	PP19	4.3fr on 3.90fr blue (R)	2.25	2.60
	Never hinged		4.00	
Q184	PP19	4.7fr on 4.20fr green (R)	3.00	2.60
	Never hinged		4.50	
Q185	PP23	3.9fr on 3.50fr blue (R)	3.00	3.00
	Never hinged		4.50	
	Nos. Q182-Q185 (4)		20.75	20.70

Denominations in Black or Red

1943			Unwmk.	
Q186	PP19	3fr brn	3.50	3.75
	Never hinged		5.00	
Q187	PP19	4.3fr blue (R)	9.00	5.25
	Never hinged		11.50	
Q188	PP19	4.7fr green (R)	10.00	2.25
	Never hinged		13.50	
Q189	PP23	3.9fr blue (R)	65.00	52.50
	Never hinged		97.50	
	Nos. Q186-Q189 (4)		87.50	63.75

1943			Wmk. 407	
Q190	PP19	3fr brn	11.00	9.75
	Never hinged		19.00	
Q191	PP19	4.3fr blue	19.00	12.00
	Never hinged		30.00	
Q192	PP19	4.7fr green	19.00	12.00
	Never hinged		30.00	
Q193	PP23	3.9fr blue	12.00	12.00
	Never hinged		19.00	
	Nos. Q190-Q193 (4)		61.00	45.75

1944				
Q194	PP21	20fr orange	4.50	6.00
	Never hinged		6.00	

Hydroelectric
Dam — PP24

Electric
Train — PP25

Power Line — PP26

1944			Perf. 12½	
Q195	PP24	1fr dk mauve	6.00	6.00
	Never hinged		8.25	
Q196	PP24	5fr red brn	6.00	6.00
	Never hinged		8.25	
Q197	PP25	2.5fr blue	6.00	6.00
	Never hinged		8.25	
Q198	PP25	7.5fr green	6.00	6.00
	Never hinged		8.25	
Q199	PP26	1fr violet	6.00	6.00
	Never hinged		8.25	
	Nos. Q195-Q199 (5)		30.00	30.00

A 20fr orange, design PP25, was prepared but not issued. Values: $1,050; never hinged, $1,600.
Nos. Q195-Q199 exist unwatermarked, but were not issued in this form Values, each: $275; never hinged $375.

Types of 1941 Inscribed "G" in Value Tablets

1945			Unwmk.	
Q200	PP17	(5fr) brown	5.00	5.25
	Never hinged		6.50	
Q201	PP17	(7.20fr) blue	5.00	5.25
	Never hinged		6.50	
Q202	PP17	(7.60fr) green	5.00	5.25
	Never hinged		6.50	
	Nos. Q200-Q203 (4)		20.50	21.75

			Wmk. 407	
Q204	PP17	(5fr) brown	15.00	15.00
	Never hinged		21.00	
Q205	PP17	(7.20fr) blue	11.00	11.00
	Never hinged		16.50	
Q206	PP17	(7.60fr) green	11.00	11.00
	Never hinged		16.50	
	Nos. Q204-Q206 (3)		37.00	37.00

Nos. Q190-Q193
Surcharged

1945			Wmk. 407	
Q207	PP19	5fr on 3fr brown	5.50	5.50
	Never hinged		8.00	

Q208	PP19	7.2fr on 4.30fr blue	5.50	5.50
	Never hinged		8.00	
Q209	PP19	7.8fr on 4.70fr green	5.50	5.50
	Never hinged		8.00	
Q210	PP23	6.6fr on 3.90fr blue	6.75	6.75
	Never hinged			
	Nos. Q207-Q210 (4)		23.25	23.25

Nos. Q186-Q189 were also surcharged but were not issued. Values, each: $40; never hinged $67.50.

Electric Train
PP27

Transformer
PP28

1945		Denominations in Black		
Q211	PP27	5fr mauve	14.00	14.00
	Never hinged		20.00	
Q212	PP27	7.2fr blue	13.50	13.50
	Never hinged		20.00	
Q213	PP27	7.8fr green	13.50	13.50
	Never hinged		20.00	

		Denomination in Purple		
Q214	PP28	6.6fr blue	6.00	6.00
	Never hinged		8.25	
	Nos. Q211-Q214 (4)		47.00	47.00

Nos. Q211-Q213 without watermark were not issued. Value, set: $45; never hinged, $72.50.

A set of ten stamps in the design of the first three images were prepared in 1945 but were not issued. Value, each: $300; never hinged $475.

Four stamps of types PP27-PP28, inscribed "H" in the value tablet, were prepared but not issued. Value, set: $2,400; never hinged $4,000.

Locomotive — PP29

Nos. Q215-216, Q222-Q223:
16x22mm; Nos. Q217-Q221, Q224-Q228: 18.5x22mm

1944		Wmk. 407	Perf. 13	
Q215	PP29	1fr deep green	3.75	1.10
	Never hinged		7.50	
Q216	PP29	2fr violet	5.25	1.50
	Never hinged		11.00	
Q217	PP29	5fr ultramarine	24.00	1.50
	Never hinged		32.50	
Q218	PP29	10fr red	12.00	1.50
	Never hinged		20.00	
Q219	PP29	20fr olive green	10.00	1.50
	Never hinged		16.00	
Q220	PP29	50fr red orange	19.00	1.50
	Never hinged		26.00	
Q221	PP29	100fr gray black	35.00	1.50
	Never hinged		52.50	
	Nos. Q215-Q221 (7)		109.00	10.10

		Unwmk.		
Q222	PP29	1fr deep green	9.75	4.75
	Never hinged		15.00	
Q223	PP29	2fr violet	12.50	4.75
	Never hinged		19.00	

Q224	PP29	5fr ultramarine	40.00	4.75
		Never hinged	65.00	
Q225	PP29	10fr red	26.00	4.75
		Never hinged	37.50	
Q226	PP29	20fr olive green	19.00	4.75
		Never hinged	30.00	
Q227	PP29	50fr red orange	37.50	4.75
		Never hinged	55.00	
Q228	PP29	100fr gray black	67.50	5.25
		Never hinged	97.50	
		Nos. Q222-Q228 (7)	212.25	33.75

Nos. Q215-Q234 were issued for use on small packets. Effective January 1, 1946, the parcel and small packet services were unified, and all issued thereafter were valid for both services.
See Nos. Q229-Q254.

Nos. Q229-Q230: 16x22mm; Nos. Q231-Q254: 18.5x22mm

1944-45   Wmk. 407

Q229	PP29	3fr gray	6.00	1.50
		Never hinged	11.00	
Q230	PP29	4fr black	9.75	2.25
		Never hinged	15.00	
Q231	PP29	7fr violet	62.50	2.60
		Never hinged	100.00	
Q232	PP29	8fr yel grn	18.00	2.25
		Never hinged	30.00	
Q233	PP29	9fr dk blue	30.00	4.00
		Never hinged	50.00	
Q234	PP29	30fr red brn	82.50	1.50
		Never hinged	125.00	
		Nos. Q229-Q234 (6)	208.75	14.10

1946

Q235	PP29	6fr claret	16.00	1.50
		Never hinged	23.00	
Q236	PP29	40fr yel brn	24.00	1.50
		Never hinged	35.00	
Q237	PP29	60fr lake red	26.00	1.50
		Never hinged	37.50	
Q238	PP29	70fr violet	175.00	26.00
		Never hinged	260.00	
Q239	PP29	80fr yel grn	24.00	2.25
		Never hinged	35.00	
Q240	PP29	90fr dk blue	140.00	25.00
		Never hinged	225.00	
Q241	PP29	200fr emer grn	30.00	2.25
		Never hinged	47.50	
		Nos. Q235-Q241 (7)	435.00	60.00

1947

Q242	PP29	5fr pale blue	19.00	1.90
		Never hinged	30.00	
Q243	PP29	7fr pale vio	250.00	16.00
		Never hinged	400.00	
Q244	PP29	9fr pale bl	190.00	15.00
		Never hinged	290.00	
Q245	PP29	30fr pale gray brn	67.50	1.90
		Never hinged	100.00	
Q246	PP29	70fr pale viol	175.00	6.75
		Never hinged	260.00	
Q247	PP29	90fr pale ultra	130.00	2.25
		Never hinged	200.00	
Q248	PP29	100fr yellow	350.00	2.25
		Never hinged	490.00	
		Nos. Q242-Q248 (7)	1,182.00	46.05

1948

Q249	PP29	500fr yel org	80.00	2.25
		Never hinged	120.00	
Q250	PP29	1000fr yel	290.00	16.00
		Never hinged	425.00	

1951-52

Q251	PP29	10fr grn	52.50	7.50
		Never hinged	82.50	
Q252	PP29	20fr vio	52.50	13.50
		Never hinged	82.50	
Q253	PP29	50fr blue	65.00	9.00
		Never hinged	100.00	
Q254	PP29	100fr rose ver	19.00	1.50
		Never hinged	26.00	
		Nos. Q251-Q254 (4)	189.00	31.50

National Railway Company — PP30

1960

Q255	PP30	5c orange	11.50	2.10
		Never hinged	17.50	
Q256	PP30	10c red	10.50	8.25
		Never hinged	16.00	
Q257	PP30	20c dp red	8.75	3.75
		Never hinged	13.50	
Q258	PP30	30c dp red	8.75	3.75
		Never hinged	13.50	
Q259	PP30	40c dp red	8.75	7.50
		Never hinged	13.50	
Q260	PP30	50c dp red	8.75	4.25
		Never hinged	13.50	
Q261	PP30	60c dp red	7.50	4.25
		Never hinged	11.00	
Q262	PP30	70c dp red	7.50	4.25
		Never hinged	11.00	
Q263	PP30	80c dp red	11.50	4.25
		Never hinged	17.50	
Q264	PP30	90c dp red	11.50	4.25
		Never hinged	17.50	
Q265	PP30	1fr blue	13.00	2.25
		Never hinged	20.00	

Q266	PP30	2fr blue	13.00	2.25
		Never hinged	20.00	
Q267	PP30	3fr blue	13.00	2.25
		Never hinged	20.00	
Q268	PP30	4fr blue	13.00	2.25
		Never hinged	20.00	
Q269	PP30	5fr blue	13.00	2.25
		Never hinged	20.00	
Q270	PP30	10fr yellow	15.00	2.50
		Never hinged	22.50	
Q271	PP30	20fr dp grn	20.00	16.00
		Never hinged	30.00	
		Nos. Q255-Q271 (17)	195.00	76.35

1960   Unwmk.

Q272	PP30	5c orange	14.00	6.25
		Never hinged	32.50	
Q273	PP30	20c dp red	210.00	55.00
		Never hinged	325.00	
Q274	PP30	30c dp red	150.00	55.00
		Never hinged	325.00	
Q275	PP30	40c dp red	110.00	30.00
		Never hinged	160.00	
Q276	PP30	70c dp red	22.50	7.50
		Never hinged	32.50	
Q277	PP30	80c dp red	22.50	6.50
		Never hinged	32.50	
Q278	PP30	90c dp red	22.50	6.50
		Never hinged	32.50	
Q279	PP30	1fr blue	20.00	3.75
		Never hinged	30.00	
Q280	PP30	2fr blue	20.00	3.75
		Never hinged	30.00	
Q281	PP30	3fr blue	20.00	3.75
		Never hinged	30.00	
Q282	PP30	4fr blue	20.00	3.75
		Never hinged	30.00	
Q283	PP30	5fr blue	20.00	3.75
		Never hinged	30.00	
Q284	PP30	10fr yellow	25.00	6.25
		Never hinged	37.50	
Q285	PP30	20fr dp grn	30.00	21.00
		Never hinged	45.00	
		Nos. Q272-Q285 (14)	706.50	212.75

FRANCHISE STAMPS

No. 276 Overprinted

1939   Unwmk.   Perf. 14x13½

S1	A45	90c ultramarine	1.90	*2.50*
		Never hinged	2.75	
a.		Period following "F"	30.00	30.00
		Never hinged	50.00	

No. S1 was for the use of Spanish refugees in France. "F" stands for "Franchise."

OCCUPATION STAMPS

FRANCO-PRUSSIAN WAR
Issued under German Occupation
(Alsace and Lorraine)

OS1

Network Points Up

1870   Typo.   Unwmk.   Perf. 13½x14
Network with Points Up

N1	OS1	1c bronze green	75.00	100.00
a.		1c olive grn	75.00	100.00
N2	OS1	2c dark brown	125.00	175.00
a.		2c red brown	115.00	175.00
N3	OS1	4c gray	135.00	100.00
N4	OS1	5c yel grn	125.00	14.00
N5	OS1	10c bistre brn	110.00	5.75
a.		10c yellow brown	110.00	6.50
b.		Network lemon yellow	135.00	10.00
N6	OS1	20c ultra	115.00	16.50
N7	OS1	25c brown	150.00	100.00
a.		25c black brown	145.00	100.00

There are three varieties of the 4c and two of the 10c, differing in the position of the figures of value, and several other setting varieties.

Network Points Down

Network with Points Down

N8	OS1	1c olive grn	350.00	625.00
N9	OS1	2c red brn	150.00	550.00
N10	OS1	4c gray	150.00	200.00
N11	OS1	5c yel grn	6,500.	650.00
N12	OS1	10c bister	150.00	21.50
a.		Network lemon yellow	225.00	50.00
N13	OS1	20c ultra	225.00	90.00
N14	OS1	25c brown	450.00	300.00

Official imitations have the network with points downward. The "P" of "Postes" is 2½mm from the border in the imitations and 3mm in the originals.
The word "Postes" measures 12¾ to 13mm on the imitations, and from 11 to 12½mm on the originals.
The imitations are perf. 13½x14½; originals, perf. 13½x14¼.
The stamps for Alsace and Lorraine were replaced by stamps of the German Empire on Jan. 1, 1872.

WORLD WAR I
German Stamps of 1905-16 Surcharged

1916   Wmk. 125   Perf. 14, 14½

N15	A16	3c on 3pf brown	1.25	1.25
N16	A16	5c on 5pf green	1.25	1.25
N17	A22	8c on 7½pf org	2.00	2.00
N18	A16	10c on 10pf car	2.00	2.00
N19	A22	15c on 15pf yel brn	1.25	1.25
N20	A16	25c on 20pf blue	1.25	1.25
a.		25c on 20pf ultramarine	2.00	2.00
N21	A16	40c on 30pf org & blk, *buff*	2.90	2.75
N22	A16	50c on 40pf lake & blk	2.90	2.75
N23	A16	75c on 60pf mag	12.50	12.50
N24	A16	1fr on 80pf lake & blk, *rose*	12.50	12.50

N25	A17	1fr25c on 1m car	47.50	47.50
a.		Double surcharge		
N26	A21	2fr50c on 2m gray bl	47.50	47.50
a.		Double surcharge		
		Nos. N15-N26 (12)	134.80	134.50

These stamps were also used in parts of Belgium occupied by the German forces.

> **Catalogue values for unused stamps in this section, from this point to the end of the section, are for Never Hinged items.**

WORLD WAR II
Alsace
Issued under German Occupation

Stamps of Germany 1933-36 Overprinted in Black

Elfaß

1940   Wmk. 237   Perf. 14

N27	A64	3pf olive bister	.80	.55
N28	A64	4pf dull blue	.80	.55
N29	A64	5pf brt green	.80	.55
N30	A64	6pf dark green	.80	.55
a.		Inverted overprint	1,500.	
N31	A64	8pf vermilion	.80	.55
a.		Inverted overprint	4,000.	
N32	A64	10pf chocolate	.80	.55
N33	A64	12pf dp carmine	1.00	.55
N34	A64	15pf maroon	1.00	.55
N35	A64	20pf brt blue	1.65	.75
N36	A64	25pf ultra	1.65	.75
N37	A64	30pf olive grn	1.65	.75
N38	A64	40pf red violet	2.90	*1.00*
N39	A64	50pf dk grn & blk	7.00	3.25

N40	A64	60pf claret & blk	7.00	3.25
N41	A64	80pf dk blue & blk	17.50	7.00
N42	A64	100pf orange & blk	17.50	7.00
		Nos. N27-N42 (16)	63.65	28.15

Lorraine
Issued under German Occupation

Stamps of Germany 1933-36 Overprinted in Black

Lothringen

1940   Wmk. 237   Perf. 14

N43	A64	3pf olive bister	1.00	.75
N44	A64	4pf dull blue	1.00	.75
N45	A64	5pf brt green	1.00	*4.00*
N46	A64	6pf dark green	1.00	.75
N47	A64	8pf vermilion	1.00	.75
N48	A64	10pf chocolate	1.50	.85
N49	A64	12pf deep carmine	1.50	.85
N50	A64	15pf maroon	1.50	.75
a.		Inverted surcharge		
N51	A64	20pf brt blue	1.65	1.00
N52	A64	25pf ultra	1.40	1.00
N53	A64	30pf olive grn	2.10	1.00
N54	A64	40pf red violet	2.50	1.25
N55	A64	50pf dk grn & blk	6.00	3.00
N56	A64	60pf claret & blk	6.00	3.00
N57	A64	80pf dk blue & blk	18.00	7.50
N58	A64	100pf orange & blk	18.00	7.50
		Nos. N43-N58 (16)	65.15	34.70

Besetztes Gebiet Nordfrankreich
These three words, in a rectangular frame covering two stamps, were hand-stamped in black on Nos. 267, 367 and 369 and used in the Dunkerque region in July-August, 1940. The German political officer of Dunkerque authorized the overprint. The prevalence of forgeries and later favor overprints make expertization mandatory.

ALLIED MILITARY GOVERNMENT

> **Stamps formerly listed in this section as Nos. 2N1-2N20 are now listed with regular stamps of France as Nos. 475-476H and 523A-523J.**

FRANCE OFFICES ABROAD

OFFICES IN CHINA

Prior to 1923 several of the world powers maintained their own post offices in China for the purpose of sending and receiving overseas mail. French offices were maintained in Canton, Hoi Hao (Hoihow), Kwangchowan (Kouang-tchéou-wan), Mongtseu (Mong-tseu), Packhoi (Paknoi), Tong King (Tchongking), Yunnan Fou (Yunnanfu).

100 Centimes = 1 Franc
100 Cents = 1 Piaster
100 Cents = 1 Dollar

Peace and Commerce Stamps of France Ovptd. in Red, Carmine or Black

1894-1900		**Unwmk.**	**Perf. 14x13½**
1	A15	5c grn, grnsh (R)	3.25	3.00
2	A15	5c yel grn, I (R) ('00)	4.25	3.00
a.		Type II	47.50	32.50
3	A15	10c blk, lav, I (R)	9.25	3.00
a.		Type II	27.50	17.50
4	A15	15c bl (R), quadrille paper	12.50	4.25
5	A15	20c red, grn	7.50	5.00
6	A15	25c blk, rose (C)	9.25	2.50
a.		Double overprint	225.00	
b.		Pair, one without overprint	550.00	
d.		Imperf	120.00	45.00
7	A15	30c brn, bis	9.25	6.25
8	A15	40c red, straw	9.25	7.50
9	A15	50c car, rose, I	26.00	17.50
a.		Carmine overprint	62.50	
b.		Type II (Bk)	25.00	16.00
10	A15	75c dp vio, org (R)	80.00	60.00
11	A15	1fr brnz grn, straw	17.00	8.50
a.		Double overprint	425.00	450.00
12	A15	2fr brn, az ('00)	30.00	29.00
12A	A15	5fr red lil, lav	75.00	60.00
b.		Red overprint	525.00	
		Nos. 1-12A (13)	292.50	209.50

For surcharges and overprints see Nos. 13-17, J7-J10, J20-J23.

No. 11 Surcharged in Black

13	A15	25c on 1fr brnz grn, straw	125.00	75.00

No. 6 Surcharged in Red

1901			
14	A15	2c on 25c blk, rose	1,100.	340.00
15	A15	4c on 25c blk, rose	1,350.	450.00
16	A15	6c on 25c blk, rose	1,100.	375.00
17	A15	16c on 25c blk, rose	325.00	200.00
a.		Black surcharge		7,250.
		Nos. 14-17 (4)	3,875.	1,365.

Stamps of Indo-China Surcharged in Black

Two types of Nos. 18-33: type I, 13mmx3mm, "C" and "H" wide, "E" with fine serifs; type II, 12½mmx2¾mm, "C" and "H" narrower, "E" with heavy serifs.

1902-04			
18a	A3	1c blk, lil bl	2.50	2.50
19	A3	2c brn, buff	4.25	4.25
20a	A3	4c claret, lav	4.25	3.40
21a	A3	5c yellow grn	5.00	3.40
22	A3	10c red	6.75	6.00
23	A3	15c gray	7.50	6.75
24a	A3	20c red, grn	9.25	8.50
25a	A3	25c blk, rose	12.50	12.50
26	A3	25c blue	10.00	8.50

27a	A3	30c brn, bis	9.25	8.50
28a	A3	40c red, straw	25.00	21.00
29	A3	50c car, rose	67.50	67.50
30	A3	50c brn, azure	10.00	9.25
31a	A3	75c vio, org	40.00	37.50
32a	A3	1fr brnz grn, straw	45.00	42.50
33a	A3	5fr red lil, lav	97.50	90.00
		Nos. 18a-33a (16)	356.25	332.05

The Chinese characters surcharged on Nos. 18-33 are the Chinese equivalents of the French values and therefore differ on each denomination. Two printings exist, differing slightly in the size of "CHINE." Values above are for the less expensive variety. See the *Scott Classic Specialized Catalogue of Stamps and Covers* for detailed listings. Many varieties of surcharge exist.

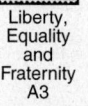

Liberty, Equality and Fraternity A3

"Rights of Man" A4

A5

1902-03			**Typo.**
34	A3	5c green	6.00	3.75
35	A4	10c rose red ('03)	3.00	2.10
36	A4	15c pale red	3.00	2.10
37	A4	20c brn vio ('03)	8.50	7.25
38	A4	25c blue ('03)	6.75	3.40
39	A4	30c lilac ('03)	9.25	7.50
40	A5	40c red & pale bl	19.00	16.00
41	A5	50c bis brn & lav	23.00	19.00
42	A5	1fr claret & ol grn	30.00	19.00
43	A5	2fr gray vio & yel	62.50	45.00
44	A5	5fr dk bl & buff	92.50	72.50
		Nos. 34-44 (11)	263.50	197.60

For surcharges and overprints see Nos. 45, 57-85, J14-J16, J27-J30.

Surcharged in Black

1903			
45	A4	5c on 15c pale red	17.50	12.00
a.		Inverted surcharge	135.00	75.00

Stamps of Indo-China, 1904-06, Surcharged as Nos. 18-33 in Black

1904-05			
46	A4	1c olive grn	2.10	2.10
47	A4	2c vio brn, buff	2.10	2.10
47A	A4	4c cl, bluish	975.00	800.00
48	A4	5c deep grn	2.10	2.10
49	A4	10c carmine	3.00	3.00
50	A4	15c org brn, bl (I)	3.00	3.00
51	A4	20c red, grn	11.50	11.00
52	A4	25c deep blue	10.00	6.00
53	A4	40c blk, bluish	8.50	6.00
54	A4	1fr pale grn	360.00	300.00
55	A4	2fr brn, org	42.50	37.50
56	A4	10fr org brn, grn	165.00	155.00
		Nos. 46-56 (12)	1,585.	1,328.

Many varieties of the surcharge exist.

Stamps of 1902-03 Surcharged in Black

1907			
57	A3	2c on 5c green	2.50	1.60
58	A4	4c on 10c rose red	2.50	1.75
a.		Pair, one without surcharge	—	
59	A4	6c on 15c pale red	3.40	2.50
60	A4	8c on 20c brn vio	6.00	6.00
a.		"8" inverted	75.00	75.00
61	A4	10c on 25c blue	2.10	1.25
62	A5	20c on 50c bis brn & lav	6.25	3.75
a.		Double surcharge		
b.		Triple surcharge	440.00	440.00
63	A5	40c on 1fr claret & ol grn	22.00	13.50

64	A5	2pi on 5fr dk bl & buff	23.00	13.50
a.		Double surcharge	2,300.	1,900.
		Nos. 57-64 (8)	67.75	43.85

Stamps of 1902-03 Surcharged in Black

1911-22			
65	A3	2c on 5c green	2.10	1.50
66	A4	4c on 10c rose red	2.50	1.75
67	A4	6c on 15c org	5.00	2.10
68	A4	8c on 20c brn vio	2.10	1.80
69	A4	10c on 25c bl ('21)	4.25	2.10
70	A4	20c on 50c bl ('22)	55.00	55.00
71	A5	40c on 1fr cl & ol grn	7.50	6.00

No. 44 Surcharged

73	A5	$2 on 5fr bl & buff ('22)	175.00	200.00
		Nos. 65-73 (8)	253.45	270.25

Types of 1902-03 Surcharged like Nos. 65-71

1922			
75	A3	1c on 5c org	6.00	6.75
76	A4	2c on 10c grn	6.75	7.50
77	A4	3c on 15c org	9.25	11.00
78	A4	4c on 20c red brn	11.00	13.50
79	A4	5c on 25c dk vio	6.00	6.00
80	A4	10c on 30c red	12.00	11.00
82	A4	10c on 50c blue	14.50	12.00
83	A5	20c on 1fr claret & ol grn	35.00	40.00
84	A5	40c on 2fr org & pale bl	45.00	55.00
85	A5	$1 on 5fr dk bl & buff	150.00	160.00
		Nos. 75-85 (10)	295.50	322.75

POSTAGE DUE STAMPS

Postage Due Stamps of France Handstamped in Red or Black

1901-07		**Unwmk.**	**Perf. 14x13½**
J1	D2	5c lt bl (R)	7.50	4.25
a.		Double overprint	160.00	
J2	D2	10c choc (R)	11.00	6.00
a.		Double overprint	160.00	
J3	D2	15c lt grn (R)	11.00	7.50
a.		Pair, one stamp without ovpt.	275.00	
b.		Imperf, single	160.00	
J4	D2	20c ol grn (R) ('07)	12.50	11.00
J5	D2	30c carmine	17.00	12.00
a.		Double overprint	160.00	
J6	D2	50c lilac	17.00	12.50
a.		Triple overprint	160.00	
b.		Pair, one stamp without overprint	275.00	
		Nos. J1-J6 (6)	76.00	53.25

Stamps of 1894-1900 Handstamped in Carmine

1903			
J7	A15	5c yel grn	—	2,250.
a.		Purple handstamp	—	
b.		5c green, greenish	—	
J8	A15	10c blk, lavender	—	
a.		Purple handstamp	—	
J9	A15	15c blue	2,750.	1,250.
a.		Purple handstamp	—	
J10	A15	30c brn, bister	1,500.	350.00

Same Handstamp on Stamps of 1902-03 in Carmine

1903			
J14	A3	5c green	—	2,000.
a.		Purple handstamp	—	
J15	A4	10c rose red	750.	425.00
a.		Purple handstamp	—	
J16	A4	15c pale red	750.	325.00
a.		Purple handstamp	—	

Stamps of 1894-1900 Handstamped in Carmine

1903			
J20	A1	5c yellow green	—	1,100.
a.		Purple handstamp	—	
b.		5c green, greenish	—	
J21	A1	10c blk, lavender	—	
a.		Purple handstamp	—	
J22	A1	15c blue	1,250.	350.
a.		Purple handstamp	—	
J23	A1	30c brn, bister	600.	325.
a.		Purple handstamp	—	

Same Handstamp on Stamps of 1902-03 in Carmine or Purple

1903			
J27	A3	5c green (C)	—	1,750.
a.		Purple handstamp	—	
J28	A4	10c rose red (C)	340.	225.
a.		Purple handstamp	—	
J29	A4	15c pale red (C)	675.	225.
a.		Purple handstamp	—	
J30	A4	30c lilac (P)	—	

The handstamps on Nos. J7-J30 are found inverted, double, etc.

The cancellations on these stamps should have dates between Sept. 1, and Nov. 30, 1903, to be genuine.

Postage Due Stamps of France, 1893-1910 Surcharged like Nos. 65-71

1911			
J33	D2	2c on 5c blue	3.00	2.50
a.		Double surcharge	140.00	—
J34	D2	4c on 10c choc	3.00	2.50
a.		Double surcharge	140.00	—
J35	D2	8c on 20c ol grn	3.40	3.00
a.		Double surcharge	140.00	—
J36	D2	20c on 50c lilac	3.40	3.00
		Nos. J33-J36 (4)	12.80	11.00

1922			
J37	D2	1c on 5c blue	82.50	95.00
J38	D2	2c on 10c brn	145.00	165.00
J39	D2	4c on 20c brn	145.00	165.00
J40	D2	10c on 50c brn vio	125.00	185.00
		Nos. J37-J40 (4)	497.50	610.00

CANTON

Stamps of Indo-China, 1892-1900, Overprinted in Red

1901		**Unwmk.**	**Perf. 14x13½**
1	A3	1c blk, lil bl	2.10	2.10
1A	A3	2c brn, buff	2.50	2.50
2	A3	4c claret, lav	4.25	4.25
2A	A3	5c grn, grnsh	600.00	600.00
3	A3	5c yel grn	3.40	3.40
4	A3	10c blk, lavender	7.25	7.25
5	A3	15c blue, quadrille paper	6.75	6.75
6	A3	15c gray	7.50	7.50
a.		Double overprint	19.00	
7	A3	20c red, grn	22.50	22.50
8	A3	25c blk, rose	13.50	13.50
9	A3	30c brn, bister	32.50	32.50
10	A3	40c red, straw	32.50	32.50
11	A3	50c car, rose	35.00	35.00
12	A3	75c dp vio, org	35.00	35.00
13	A3	1fr brnz grn, straw	45.00	45.00
14	A3	5fr red lil, lav	250.00	250.00
		Nos. 1-14 (16)	1,100.	1,100.

The Chinese characters in the overprint on Nos. 1-14 read "Canton." On Nos. 15-64, they restate the denomination of the basic stamp.

Surcharged in Black

(CANTON overprint)

1903-04			
15	A3	1c blk, lil bl	4.25	4.25
16	A3	2c brn, buff	4.50	4.25
17	A3	4c claret, lav	4.50	4.25
18	A3	5c yellow green	4.25	4.25
19	A3	10c rose red	4.50	4.25
20	A3	15c gray	4.50	4.25
21	A3	20c red, grn	21.00	17.50
22	A3	25c blue	7.50	7.50
23	A3	25c blk, rose ('04)	10.00	8.50
24	A3	30c brn, bister	27.50	21.00
25	A3	40c red, straw	67.50	55.00
26	A3	50c car, rose	340.00	310.00

27	A3	50c brn, *az* ('04)		85.00	72.50
28	A3	75c dp vio, *org*		67.50	67.50
a.		"INDO-CHINE" inverted		55,000.	
29	A3	1fr brnz grn,		67.50	67.50
		straw		67.50	67.50
30	A3	5fr red lil, *lav*		67.50	67.50
		Nos. 15-30 (16)		787.50	720.00

Many varieties of the surcharge exist on Nos. 15-30.

Stamps of Indo-China, 1892-1906, Surcharged in Red or Black

A second printing of the 1906 surcharges of Canton, Hoi Hao, Kwangchowan, Mongtseu, Packhoi, Tong King and Yunnan Fou was made in 1908. The inks are grayish instead of full black and vermilion instead of carmine. Values are for the cheaper variety which usually is the second printing.

The 4c and 50c of the 1892 issue of Indo-China are known with this surcharge and similarly surcharged for other cities in China. The surcharges on these two stamps are always inverted. It is stated that they were irregularly produced and never issued.

1906

31	A4	1c ol grn (R)		2.50	2.50
32	A4	2c vio brn, *buff*		2.50	2.50
33	A4	4c cl, *bluish* (R)		2.50	2.50
34	A4	5c dp grn (R)		2.10	2.10
35	A4	10c carmine		3.00	3.00
36	A4	15c org brn, *bl*		22.50	22.50
37	A4	20c red, *grn*		12.50	12.50
38	A4	25c deep blue		5.00	5.00
39	A4	30c pale brn		17.00	17.00
40	A4	35c blk, *yel* (R)		12.50	12.50
41	A4	40c blk, *bluish* (R)		21.00	21.00
42	A4	50c bister brn		14.50	14.50
43	A3	75c dp vio, *org* (R)		67.50	67.50
44	A4	1fr pale grn		30.00	30.00
45	A4	2fr brn, *org* (R)		42.50	42.50
46	A3	5fr red lil, *lav*		92.50	92.50
47	A4	10fr org brn, *grn*		85.00	85.00
		Nos. 31-47 (17)		435.10	435.10

Surcharge exists inverted on 1c, 25c & 1fr.

Stamps of Indo-China, 1907, Srchd. in Red or Blue

Chinese Characters

1908

48	A5	1c ol brn & blk		1.25	1.25
49	A5	2c brn & blk		1.25	1.25
50	A5	4c bl & blk		2.50	1.25
51	A5	5c grn & blk		2.50	2.10
52	A5	10c red & blk (Bl)		3.40	2.50
53	A5	15c vio & blk		4.25	3.40
54	A6	20c vio & blk		5.00	5.00
55	A6	25c bl & blk		5.00	4.25
56	A6	30c brn & blk		8.50	8.50
57	A6	35c ol grn & blk		8.50	8.50
58	A6	40c brn & blk		11.00	8.50
59	A6	50c car & blk (Bl)		11.00	8.50
60	A7	75c ver & blk (Bl)		11.00	10.00
61	A8	1fr car & blk (Bl)		18.00	15.00
62	A9	2fr grn & blk		45.00	37.50
63	A10	5fr bl & blk		62.50	55.00
64	A11	10fr pur & blk		92.50	92.50
		Nos. 48-64 (17)		293.15	265.00

Nos. 48-64 Surcharged with New Values in Cents or Piasters in Black, Red or Blue

1919

65	A5	⅖c on 1c		1.25	1.25
66	A5	⅘c on 2c		1.25	1.25
67	A5	1⅗c on 4c (R)		1.25	1.25
68	A5	2c on 5c		1.60	1.60
69	A5	4c on 10c (Bl)		2.10	1.60
a.		Chinese "2" instead of "4"		42.50	42.50
70	A5	6c on 15c		2.50	2.10
71	A5	8c on 20c		4.25	2.10
72	A6	10c on 25c		5.00	1.60
73	A6	12c on 30c		2.10	2.10
a.		Double surcharge		140.00	140.00
74	A6	14c on 35c		2.10	1.60
a.		Closed "4"		10.00	10.00
75	A6	16c on 40c		2.50	1.60
76	A6	20c on 50c (Bl)		2.50	2.10
77	A7	30c on 75c (Bl)		2.50	2.10
78	A8	40c on 1fr (Bl)		12.50	7.50
79	A9	80c on 2fr (R)		19.00	12.00
80	A10	2pi on 5fr (R)		32.50	32.50
81	A11	4pi on 10fr (R)		32.50	32.50
		Nos. 65-81 (17)		127.40	106.75

HOI HAO

Stamps of Indo-China Overprinted in Red

1901   **Unwmk.**   **Perf. 14x13½**

1	A3	1c blk, *lil bl*		3.40	3.40
2	A3	2c brn, *buff*		4.25	4.25
3	A3	4c claret, *lav*		4.25	4.25
4	A3	5c yel grn		5.00	5.00
5	A3	10c blk, *lavender*		13.50	12.00
6	A3	15c blue		1,850.	800.00
7	A3	15c gray		7.50	5.00
8	A3	20c red, *grn*		32.50	25.00
9	A3	25c blk, *rose*		17.00	12.50
10	A3	30c brn, *bister*		67.50	67.50
11	A3	40c red, *straw*		67.50	67.50
12	A3	50c car, *rose*		67.50	67.50
13	A3	75c dp vio, *org*		250.00	225.00
14	A3	1fr brnz grn,			
		straw		800.00	740.00
15	A3	5fr red lil, *lav*		800.00	675.00
		Nos. 1-15 (15)		3,990.	2,714.

The Chinese characters in the overprint on Nos. 1-15 read "Hoi Hao." On Nos. 16-66, they restate the denomination of the basic stamp.

Surcharged in Black

1903-04

16	A3	1c blk, *lil bl*		2.50	2.50
17	A3	2c brn, *buff*		2.50	2.50
18	A3	4c claret, *lav*		4.25	4.25
19	A3	5c yel grn		4.25	4.25
20	A3	10c red		4.25	4.25
21	A3	15c gray		5.00	5.00
22	A3	20c red, *grn*		7.50	7.50
23	A3	25c blue		5.00	5.00
24	A3	25c blk, *rose* ('04)		8.50	8.50
25	A3	30c brn, *bister*		6.75	6.75
26	A3	40c red, *straw*		32.50	32.50
27	A3	50c car, *rose*		30.00	30.00
28	A3	50c brn, *az* ('04)		170.00	170.00
29	A3	75c dp vio, *org*		50.00	50.00
a.		"INDO-CHINE" inverted		45,000.	
30	A3	1fr brnz grn,			
		straw		67.50	67.50
31	A3	5fr red lil, *lav*		225.00	225.00
		Nos. 16-31 (16)		625.50	625.50

Many varieties of the surcharge exist on Nos. 1-31.

Stamps of Indo-China, 1892-1906, Surcharged in Red or Black

1906

32	A4	1c ol grn (R)		8.50	8.50
33	A4	2c vio brn, *buff*		8.50	8.50
34	A4	4c cl, *bluish* (R)		8.50	8.50
35	A4	5c dp grn (R)		8.50	8.50
36	A4	10c carmine		8.50	8.50
37	A4	15c org brn, *bl*		32.50	32.50
38	A4	20c red, *grn*		13.50	13.50
39	A4	25c deep blue		11.00	11.00
40	A4	30c pale brn		13.50	13.50
41	A4	35c blk, *yel* (R)		21.00	21.00
42	A4	40c blk, *bluish* (R)		21.00	21.00
43	A4	50c gray brn		21.00	21.00
44	A3	75c dp vio, *org* (R)		62.50	62.50
45	A4	1fr pale grn		62.50	62.50
46	A4	2fr brn, *org* (R)		62.50	62.50
47	A3	5fr red lil, *lav*		135.00	135.00
48	A4	10fr org brn, *grn*		150.00	150.00
		Nos. 32-48 (17)		648.50	648.50

Stamps of Indo-China, 1907, Srchd. in Red or Blue

Chinese Characters

1908

49	A5	1c ol brn & blk		1.70	1.70
50	A5	2c brn & blk		1.70	1.70
51	A5	4c bl & blk		1.70	1.70
52	A5	5c grn & blk		3.00	3.00
53	A5	10c red & blk (Bl)		3.00	3.00
54	A5	15c vio & blk		6.75	6.75
55	A6	20c vio & blk		7.50	7.50
56	A6	25c bl & blk		7.50	7.50
57	A6	30c brn & blk		7.50	7.50
58	A6	35c ol grn & blk		7.50	7.50
59	A6	40c brn & blk		8.50	8.50
60	A6	50c car & blk (Bl)		10.00	10.00

62	A7	75c ver & blk (Bl)		10.00	10.00
63	A8	1fr car & blk (Bl)		29.00	29.00
64	A9	2fr grn & blk		42.50	42.50
65	A10	5fr bl & blk		75.00	75.00
66	A11	10fr pur & blk		110.00	110.00
		Nos. 49-66 (17)		332.85	332.85

Nos. 49-66 Surcharged with New Values in Cents or Piasters in Black, Red or Blue

1919

67	A5	⅖c on 1c		1.25	1.25
68	A5	⅘c on 2c		1.25	1.25
69	A5	1⅗c on 4c (R)		2.10	2.10
70	A5	2c on 5c		2.50	2.50
71	A5	4c on 10c (Bl)		3.00	3.00
a.		Chinese "2" instead of "4"		14.50	14.50
72	A5	6c on 15c		2.50	2.50
73	A6	8c on 20c		4.25	4.25
a.		"S" of "CENTS" omitted		170.00	170.00
74	A6	10c on 25c		6.75	6.75
75	A6	12c on 30c		4.25	4.25
76	A6	14c on 35c		3.40	3.40
a.		Closed "4"		42.50	42.50
77	A6	16c on 40c		4.25	4.25
79	A6	20c on 50c (Bl)		3.40	3.40
80	A7	30c on 75c (Bl)		11.00	11.00
81	A8	40c on 1fr (Bl)		22.00	22.00
82	A9	80c on 2fr (R)		62.50	62.50
83	A10	2pi on 5fr (R)		92.50	92.50
a.		Triple surch. of new value		750.00	750.00
84	A11	4pi on 10fr (R)		225.00	225.00
		Nos. 67-84 (17)		451.90	451.90

KWANGCHOWAN

A Chinese Territory leased to France, 1898 to 1945.

Stamps of Indo-China, 1892-1906, Surcharged in Red or Black

1906   **Unwmk.**   **Perf. 14x13½**

1	A4	1c ol grn (R)		8.50	8.50
2	A4	2c vio brn, *buff*		8.50	8.50
3	A4	4c cl, *bluish* (R)		8.50	8.50
4	A4	5c dp grn (R)		8.50	8.50
5	A4	10c carmine		8.50	8.50
6	A4	15c org brn, *bl*		32.50	32.50
7	A4	20c red, *grn*		13.50	13.50
8	A4	25c deep blue		11.00	11.00
9	A4	30c pale brn		13.50	13.50
10	A4	35c blk, *yel* (R)		21.00	21.00
11	A4	40c blk, *bluish* (R)		21.00	21.00
12	A4	50c bister brn		25.00	25.00
13	A3	75c dp vio, *org* (R)		67.50	67.50
14	A4	1fr pale grn		42.50	42.50
15	A4	2fr brn, *org* (R)		55.00	55.00
16	A3	5fr red lil, *lav*		225.00	225.00
17	A4	10fr org brn, *grn*		275.00	275.00
		Nos. 1-17 (17)		845.00	845.00

Various varieties of the surcharge exist on Nos. 2-10.

Stamps of Indo-China, 1907, Srchd. in Red or Blue

Value in Chinese

1908

18	A5	1c ol brn & blk		1.70	1.70
19	A5	2c brn & blk		1.70	1.70
20	A5	4c bl & blk		1.70	1.70
21	A5	5c grn & blk		1.70	1.70
22	A5	10c red & blk (Bl)		3.00	3.00
23	A5	15c vio & blk		4.25	4.25
24	A5	20c vio & blk		6.75	6.75
25	A6	25c bl & blk		6.75	6.75
26	A6	30c brn & blk		10.00	10.00
27	A6	35c ol grn & blk		14.50	14.50
28	A6	40c brn & blk		14.50	14.50
30	A6	50c car & blk (Bl)		17.00	17.00
31	A7	75c ver & blk (Bl)		17.00	17.00
32	A8	1fr car & blk (Bl)		24.00	24.00
33	A9	2fr grn & blk		32.50	32.50
34	A10	5fr bl & blk		75.00	75.00
35	A11	10fr pur & blk		105.00	105.00
a.		Double surcharge		1,050.	
b.		Triple surcharge		1,050.	
		Nos. 18-35 (17)		335.75	335.75

The Chinese characters overprinted on Nos. 1 to 35 repeat the denomination of the basic stamp.

Nos. 18-35 Srchd. in Cents or Piasters in Black, Red or Blue

1919

36	A5	⅖c on 1c		1.25	.85
37	A5	⅘c on 2c		1.25	.85
38	A5	1⅗c on 4c (R)		1.25	.85
39	A5	2c on 5c		2.10	1.25
a.		"2 CENTS" inverted		97.50	
40	A5	4c on 10c (Bl)		3.75	3.40
41	A5	6c on 15c		2.10	2.10
42	A6	8c on 20c		4.25	4.25
43	A6	10c on 25c		14.50	13.50
44	A6	12c on 30c		3.40	3.40
45	A6	14c on 35c		3.40	3.40
a.		Closed "4"		45.00	37.50
46	A6	16c on 40c		2.10	2.10
48	A6	20c on 50c (Bl)		2.10	2.10
49	A7	30c on 75c (Bl)		11.00	11.00
50	A8	40c on 1fr (Bl)		12.00	12.00
a.		"40 CENTS" inverted			
51	A9	80c on 2fr (R)		20.00	20.00
52	A10	2pi on 5fr (R)		175.00	175.00
53	A11	4pi on 10fr (R)		32.50	32.50
		Nos. 36-53 (17)		291.95	288.55

Stamps of Indo-China, 1922-23, Overprinted in Black, Red or Blue

1923

54	A12	⅒c blk & sal (Bl)		.35	.35
55	A12	⅕c dp bl & blk (R)		.35	.35
a.		Black overprint		135.00	
56	A12	⅖c ol brn & blk (R)		.40	.40
57	A12	⅘c brt rose & blk		.60	.60
58	A12	1c yel brn & blk			
		(Bl)		.60	.60
59	A12	2c gray grn & blk			
		(R)		.95	.95
60	A12	3c vio & blk (R)		1.00	1.00
61	A12	4c org & blk		1.25	1.25
62	A12	5c car & blk		1.25	1.25
63	A13	6c dl red & blk		1.25	1.25
64	A13	7c ol grn & blk		1.70	1.70
65	A13	8c black (R)		2.50	2.50
66	A13	9c yel & blk		2.50	2.50
67	A13	10c bl & blk		2.10	2.10
68	A13	11c vio & blk		2.10	2.10
69	A13	12c brn & blk		2.10	2.10
70	A13	15c org & blk		3.00	3.00
71	A13	20c bl & blk, *straw*			
		(R)		3.00	3.00
72	A13	40c ver & blk, *bluish*			
		(Bl)		3.40	3.40
73	A13	1pi bl grn & blk,			
		grnsh		7.50	7.50
74	A13	2pi vio brn & blk,			
		pnksh (Bl)		17.00	17.00
		Nos. 54-74 (21)		54.90	54.90

Accent omitted varieties exist for Nos. 54-74. For detailed listings, see "Scott Classic Specialized Catalogue of Stamps and Covers 1840-1940".

Indo-China Stamps of 1927 Overprinted in Black or Red

1927

75	A14	⅒c lt ol grn (R)		.35	.35
76	A14	⅕c yellow		.35	.35
77	A14	⅖c lt blue (R)		.50	.50
78	A14	⅘c dp brown		.50	.50
79	A14	1c orange		.85	.85
80	A14	2c blue grn (R)		1.25	1.25
81	A14	3c indigo		1.25	1.25
82	A14	4c lilac rose		1.25	1.25
83	A14	5c deep violet		1.25	1.25
84	A15	6c deep red		1.25	1.25
85	A15	7c lt brown		1.25	1.25
86	A15	8c gray grn (R)		1.25	1.25
87	A15	9c red violet		1.70	1.70
88	A15	10c lt bl (R)		1.70	1.70
89	A15	11c orange		1.70	1.70
90	A15	12c myr grn (R)		1.70	1.70
91	A16	15c dl rose & ol			
		brn		3.00	3.00
92	A16	20c vio & sl (R)		2.50	2.50
93	A17	25c org brn & lil			
		rose		2.50	2.50
94	A17	30c dp bl & ol gray			
		(R)		1.70	1.70
95	A18	40c ver & lt bl		1.70	1.70
96	A18	50c lt grn & sl (R)		2.50	2.50
97	A19	1pi dk bl, blk & yel			
				4.25	4.25
98	A19	2pi red, dp bl &			
		org (R)		6.00	6.00
a.		Double overprint		160.00	
		Nos. 75-98 (24)		42.25	42.25

Accent omitted varieties exist for Nos. 75-90. For detailed listings, see "Scott Classic Specialized Catalogue of Stamps and Covers 1840-1940".

Stamps of Indo-China, 1931-41, Overprinted in Black or Red

1937-41			Perf. 13, 13½	
99	A20	⅒c Prus blue	.25	.25
100	A20	⅕c lake	.25	.25
101	A20	⅖c orange red	.40	.40
102	A20	½c red brown	.35	.35
103	A20	⅘c dk violet	.35	.35
104	A20	1c black brown	.35	.35
105	A20	2c dk green	.35	.35
a.	Inverted overprint		140.00	
106	A21	3c dk green	.75	.75
107	A21	3c yel brn ('41)	.35	.35
108	A21	4c dk blue (R)	1.00	1.00
109	A21	4c dk green ('41)	.35	.35
110	A21	4c yel org ('41)	2.75	2.75
111	A21	5c dp violet	.95	.95
112	A21	5c dp green ('41)	.50	.50
113	A21	6c orange red	.65	.65
114	A21	7c black ('41)	.65	.65
115	A21	8c rose lake ('41)	.75	.75
116	A21	9c blk, yel ('41)	1.00	1.00
d.	Black overprint		9.25	9.25
117	A22	10c dk blue (R)	1.10	1.10
118	A22	10c ultra, pink (R) ('41)	.85	.85
119	A22	15c dk bl (R)	.75	.75
120	A22	18c bl (R) ('41)	.65	.65
121	A22	20c rose	.75	.75
122	A22	21c olive grn	.75	.75
123	A22	22c green ('41)	.60	.60
124	A22	25c dp violet	3.00	3.00
125	A22	25c dk bl (R) ('41)	.85	.85
126	A22	30c orange brn	.85	.85
127	A23	50c dk brown	1.10	1.10
128	A23	60c dl violet	1.10	1.10
129	A23	70c lt bl (R) ('41)	.85	.85
130	A23	1pi yel green	2.10	2.10
131	A23	2pi red	2.25	2.25
	Nos. 99-131 (33)		29.55	29.55

Accent omitted varieties exist for Nos. 99-124 and No. 126. For detailed listings, see "Scott Classic Specialized Catalogue of Stamps and Covers 1840-1940".

Common Design Types pictured following the introduction.

Colonial Arts Exhibition Issue
Common Design Type
Souvenir Sheet

1937		Engr.		Imperf.
132	CD79	30c grn & sepia	9.25	11.00

New York World's Fair Issue
Common Design Type

1939		Unwmk.	Perf. 12½x12	
133	CD82	13c car lake	1.25	1.25
134	CD82	23c ultra	1.25	1.25

Petain Issue
Indo-China Nos. 209-209A
Overprinted "KOUANG TCHEOU" in Blue or Red

1941		Engr.	Perf. 12½x12	
135	A27a	10c car lake (B)	.85	
136	A27a	25c blue (R)	.85	

Nos. 135-136 were issued by the Vichy government in France, but were not placed on sale in Kwangchowan.
For surcharges, see Nos. B9-B10.

Indo-China Types of 1937-41 without "RF" Overprinted "KOUANG TCHEOU" in Blue or Red

1942-44				
137	A20	⅖c orange red	.25	
138	A20	½c red brown	.25	
139	A20	1c black brown	.35	
140	A20	2c dark green	.65	
141	A21	3c yellow brown	.65	
142	A21	4c yellow orange	.35	
143	A21	5c deep green	.50	
144	A21	9c black, yellow	.35	
145	A22	10c ultra, pink (R)	.60	
146	A22	18c blue (R)	190.00	
147	A22	22c green	.60	
148	A22	30c orange brown	.65	
149	A23	50c dark brown	.60	
150	A23	60c dull violet	.65	
151	A23	70c light blue (R)	.85	
152	A23	1pi yellow green	1.30	
153	A23	2pi red	1.40	
	Nos. 137-153 (17)		200.00	

Nos. 137-153 were issued by the Vichy government in France, but were not placed on sale in Kwangchowan.

SEMI-POSTAL STAMPS

French Revolution Issue
Common Design Type

1939		Unwmk.	Photo.	Perf. 13	
Name and Value typo. in Black					
B1	CD83	6c + 2c green	9.25	9.25
B2	CD83	7c + 3c brown	9.25	9.25
B3	CD83	9c + 4c red org	9.25	9.25
B4	CD83	13c + 10c rose pink	9.25	9.25
B5	CD83	23c + 20c blue	9.25	9.25
	Nos. B1-B5 (5)		46.25	46.25

Indo-China Nos. B19A and B19C Overprinted "KOUANG-TCHEOU" in Blue or Red, and Common Design Type

1941		Photo.	Perf. 13½	
B6	SP1	10c + 10c red (B)	.85	
B7	CD86	15c + 30c mar & car	.85	
B8	SP2	25c + 10c blue (R)	.85	
	Nos. B6-B8 (3)		2.55	

Nos. B6-B8 were issued by the Vichy government in France, but were not placed on sale in Kwangchowan.

Indo-China Nos. B21A-B21B Overprinted in Blue or Red

1944		Engr.	Perf. 12½x12	
B9	A27a	5c + 15c on 25c deep blue (R)	1.00	
B10	A27a	+25c on 10c car lake	1.10	

Colonial Development Fund.
Nos. B9-B10 were issued by the Vichy government in France, but were not placed on sale in Kwangchowan.

AIR POST SEMI-POSTAL STAMPS

Indo-China Nos. CB2-CB4 Overprinted "KOUANG-TCHEOU" in Blue or Red

Methods and Perfs as Before

1942, June 22				
CB1	SPAP1	15c + 35c green (R)	.95	
CB2	SPAP2	20c + 60c brown	.95	
CB3	SPAP3	30c +90c car red	.95	
	Nos. CB1-CB3 (3)		2.85	

Native children's welfare fund.
Nos. CB1-CB3 were issued by the Vichy government in France, but were not placed on sale in Kwangchowan.

Colonial Education Fund
Indo-China No. CB5 Overprinted "KOUANG-TCHEOU" in Blue or Red

Perf. 12½x13½

1942, June 22			Engr.	
CB4	CD86a	12c + 18c blue & red	1.00	

No. CB4 was issued by the Vichy government in France, but was not placed on sale in Kwangchowan.

MONGTSEU (MENGTSZ)

Stamps of Indo-China Surcharged in Black

1903-04		Unwmk.	Perf. 14x13½	
1	A3	1c blk, lil bl	7.50	7.50
2	A3	2c brn, buff	6.75	6.75
3	A3	4c claret, lav	8.50	8.50
4	A3	5c yel grn	6.00	6.00
5	A3	10c red	9.25	9.25
6	A3	15c gray	10.00	10.00
7	A3	20c red, grn	12.50	12.50
7C	A3	25c blk, rose	725.00	725.00
8	A3	25c blue	12.50	12.50
9	A3	30c brn, bister	11.00	11.00
10	A3	40c red, straw	75.00	75.00
11	A3	50c car, rose	440.00	440.00
12	A3	50c brn, az ('04)	150.00	150.00
13	A3	75c dp vio, org	120.00	120.00
a.	"INDO-CHINE" inverted		67,500.	

14	A3	1fr brnz grn, straw	110.00	110.00
15	A3	5fr red lil, lav	110.00	110.00
	Nos. 1-15 (16)		1,814.	1,814.

Many surcharge varieties exist on Nos. 1-15.

Stamps of Indo-China, 1892-1906, Surcharged in Red or Black

1906				
16	A4	1c ol grn (R)	5.00	5.00
17	A4	2c vio brn, buff	5.00	5.00
18	A4	4c cl, bluish (R)	5.00	5.00
19	A4	5c dp grn (R)	6.00	6.00
20	A4	10c carmine	5.00	5.00
21	A4	15c org brn, bl	35.00	35.00
22	A4	20c red, grn	13.50	13.50
23	A4	25c deep blue	10.00	10.00
24	A4	30c pale brn	13.50	13.50
25	A4	35c blk, yel	12.50	12.50
26	A4	40c blk, bluish (R)	20.00	20.00
27	A4	50c bister brn	21.00	21.00
28	A3	75c dp vio, org	67.50	67.50
a.	"INDO-CHINE" inverted		67,500.	
29	A4	1fr pale grn	42.50	42.50
30	A4	2fr brn, org (R)	55.00	55.00
31	A3	5fr red lil, lav	140.00	140.00
32	A4	10fr org brn, grn	150.00	150.00
a.	Chinese characters inverted		1,750.	2,100.
	Nos. 16-32 (17)		606.50	606.50

Inverted varieties of the surcharge exist on Nos. 19, 22 and 32.

Stamps of Indo-China, 1907, Srchd. in Red or Blue

Value in Chinese

1908				
33	A5	1c ol brn & blk	1.25	1.25
34	A5	2c brn & blk	1.25	1.25
35	A5	4c bl & blk	1.25	1.25
36	A5	5c grn & blk	1.25	1.25
37	A5	10c red & blk (Bl)	3.00	3.00
38	A5	15c vio & blk	3.00	3.00
39	A6	20c vio & blk	6.00	6.00
40	A6	25c bl & blk	15.00	15.00
41	A6	30c brn & blk	6.75	6.75
42	A6	35c ol grn & blk	7.50	7.50
43	A6	40c brn & blk	5.00	5.00
44	A6	50c car & blk (Bl)	6.75	6.75
45	A7	75c ver & blk (Bl)	14.50	14.50
46	A7	1fr car & blk (Bl)	13.50	13.50
47	A8	2fr grn & blk	19.00	19.00
48	A9	5fr bl & blk	105.00	105.00
49	A10	10fr pur & blk	125.00	125.00
	Nos. 33-50 (17)		335.00	335.00

The Chinese characters overprinted on Nos. 1 to 50 repeat the denomination of the basic stamp.

Nos. 33-50 Srchd. in Cents or Piasters in Black, Red or Blue

1919				
51	A5	⅖c on 1c	1.70	1.70
52	A5	⅖c on 2c	1.70	1.70
53	A5	1⅗c on 4c	1.70	1.70
54	A5	2c on 5c	1.70	1.70
55	A5	4c on 10c (Bl)	3.00	3.00
56	A5	6c on 15c	3.00	3.00
57	A6	8c on 20c	6.75	6.75
58	A6	10c on 25c	5.00	5.00
59	A6	12c on 30c	5.00	5.00
60	A6	14c on 35c	3.40	3.40
a.	Closed "4"		21.00	21.00
61	A6	16c on 40c	4.25	4.25
63	A6	20c on 50c (Bl)	5.00	5.00
64	A7	30c on 75c (Bl)	9.25	9.25
65	A8	40c on 1fr (Bl)	10.00	10.00
66	A9	80c on 2fr (R)	10.00	10.00
a.	Triple surch., one inverted		550.00	550.00
67	A10	2pi on 5fr (R)	200.00	200.00
a.	Triple surch., one inverted		625.00	625.00
b.	Double surcharge		925.00	925.00
68	A11	4pi on 10fr (R)	30.00	30.00
	Nos. 51-68 (17)		301.45	301.45

PAKHOI

Stamps of Indo-China Surcharged in Black

1903-04		Unwmk.	Perf. 14x13½	
1	A3	1c blk, lil bl	6.75	6.75
2	A3	2c brn, buff	6.75	6.75
3	A3	4c claret, lav	6.75	6.75
4	A3	5c yel grn	5.00	5.00
5	A3	10c red	5.00	5.00
6	A3	15c gray	5.00	5.00
7	A3	20c red, grn	11.00	11.00
8	A3	25c blue	9.25	9.25
9	A3	25c blk, rose('04)	6.75	6.75
10	A3	30c brn, bister	8.50	8.50
11	A3	40c red, straw	57.50	57.50
12	A3	50c car, rose	340.00	340.00
13	A3	50c brn, az ('04)	47.50	47.50
14	A3	75c dp vio, org	67.50	67.50
a.	"INDO-CHINE" inverted		47,500.	
15	A3	1fr brnz grn, straw	67.50	67.50
16	A3	5fr red lil, lav	135.00	135.00
	Nos. 1-16 (16)		785.75	785.75

Many varieties of the surcharge exist.

Stamps of Indo-China 1892-1906, Surcharged in Red or Black

1906				
17	A4	1c ol grn (R)	8.50	8.50
18	A4	2c vio brn, buff	8.50	8.50
19	A4	4c cl, bluish (R)	8.50	8.50
20	A4	5c dp grn (R)	8.50	8.50
21	A4	10c carmine	8.50	8.50
22	A4	15c org brn,bl	32.50	32.50
23	A4	20c red, grn	13.50	13.50
24	A4	25c deep blue	11.00	11.00
25	A4	30c pale brn	13.50	13.50
26	A4	35c blk, yel (R)	21.00	21.00
27	A4	40c blk, bluish(R)	21.00	21.00
28	A4	50c bister brn	21.00	21.00
29	A3	75c dp vio, org (R)	67.50	67.50
30	A4	1fr pale grn	42.50	42.50
31	A4	2fr brn, org(R)	55.00	55.00
32	A3	5fr red lil, lav	140.00	140.00
33	A4	10fr org brn, grn	150.00	150.00
	Nos. 17-33 (17)		631.00	631.00

Various surcharge varieties exist on Nos. 17-24.

Stamps of Indo-China, 1907, Surcharged "PAKHOI" and Value in Chinese in Red or Blue

1908				
34	A5	1c ol brn & blk	1.25	1.25
35	A5	2c brn & blk	1.25	1.25
36	A5	4c bl & blk	1.25	1.25
37	A5	5c grn & blk	1.70	1.70
38	A5	10c red & blk (Bl)	1.70	1.70
39	A5	15c vio & blk	2.10	2.10
40	A6	20c vio & blk	2.50	2.50
41	A6	25c bl & blk	3.00	3.00
42	A6	30c brn & blk	3.40	3.40
43	A6	35c ol grn & blk	3.40	3.40
44	A6	40c brn & blk	3.40	3.40
46	A6	50c car & blk (Bl)	3.40	3.40
47	A7	75c ver & blk (Bl)	7.25	7.25
48	A7	1fr car & blk (Bl)	7.50	7.50
49	A9	2fr grn & blk	16.00	16.00
50	A10	5fr bl & blk	85.00	85.00
51	A11	10fr pur & blk	150.00	150.00
	Nos. 34-51 (17)		294.10	294.10

The Chinese characters overprinted on Nos. 1 to 51 repeat the denomination of the basic stamps.

Nos. 34-51 Surcharged with New Values in Cents or Piasters in Black, Red or Blue

1919				
52	A5	⅖c on 1c	1.25	1.25
a.	"PAK-HOI" and Chinese double		170.00	
53	A5	⅖c on 2c	1.25	1.25
54	A5	1⅗c on 4c (R)	1.25	1.25
55	A5	2c on 5c	2.50	2.50
56	A5	4c on 10c (Bl)	3.40	3.40
57	A5	6c on 15c	1.70	1.70
58	A6	8c on 20c	3.40	3.40
59	A6	10c on 25c	5.00	5.00
60	A6	12c on 30c	1.70	1.70
a.	"12 CENTS" double		675.00	
61	A6	14c on 35c	1.25	1.25
a.	Closed "4"		14.50	14.50
62	A6	16c on 40c	3.00	3.00
64	A6	20c on 50c (Bl)	2.10	2.10
65	A7	30c on 75c (Bl)	9.25	9.25
66	A8	40c on 1fr (Bl)	12.50	12.50
67	A9	80c on 2fr (R)	10.00	10.00

68	A10	2pi on 5fr (R)	16.00	16.00
69	A11	4pi on 10fr (R)	35.00	35.00
		Nos. 52-69 (17)	110.55	110.55

TCHONGKING (CHUNGKING)

Stamps of Indo-China
Surcharged in Black

1903-04   Unwmk.   Perf. 14x13½

1	A3	1c blk, *lil bl*	5.00	5.00
2	A3	2c brn, *buff*	5.00	5.00
3	A3	4c claret, *lav*	6.00	6.00
4	A3	5c yel grn	6.00	6.00
5	A3	10c red	6.00	6.00
6	A3	15c gray	6.00	6.00
7	A3	20c red, *grn*	8.50	8.50
8	A3	25c blue	55.00	55.00
9	A3	25c blk, *rose* ('04)	10.00	10.00
10	A3	30c brn, *bister*	15.00	15.00
11	A3	40c red, *straw*	62.50	62.50
12	A3	50c car, *rose*	225.00	225.00
13	A3	50c brn, *az* ('04)	140.00	140.00
14	A3	75c vio, *org*	45.00	45.00
15	A3	1fr brnz grn, *straw*	60.00	60.00
16	A3	5fr red lil, *lav*	105.00	105.00
		Nos. 1-16 (16)	760.00	760.00

Many surcharge varieties exist on Nos. 1-14.
Stamps of Indo-China and French China, issued in 1902 with similar overprint, but without Chinese characters, were not officially authorized.

Stamps of Indo-China,
1892-1906, Surcharged in
Red or Black

1906

17	A4	1c ol grn (R)	8.50	8.50
18	A4	2c vio brn, *buff*	8.50	8.50
19	A4	4c cl, *bluish* (R)	8.50	8.50
20	A4	5c dp grn (R)	8.50	8.50
21	A4	10c carmine	8.50	8.50
22	A4	15c org brn, *bl*	32.50	32.50
23	A4	20c red, *grn*	13.50	13.50
24	A4	25c deep blue	11.00	11.00
25	A4	30c pale brn	13.50	13.50
26	A4	35c blk, *yellow* (R)	21.00	21.00
27	A4	40c blk, *bluish* (R)	21.00	21.00
28	A4	50c bis brn	25.00	25.00
29	A3	75c dp vio, *org* (R)	67.50	67.50
30	A4	1fr pale grn	42.50	42.50
31	A4	2fr brn, *org* (R)	55.00	55.00
32	A3	5fr red lil, *lav*	140.00	140.00
33	A4	10fr org brn, *grn*	150.00	150.00
		Nos. 17-33 (17)	635.00	635.00

Variety "T" omitted in surcharge occurs once in each sheet of Nos. 17-33. For detailed listings, see "Scott Classic Specialized Catalogue of Stamps and Values". Other surcharge varieties exist. Inverted surcharge on 1c and 2c are of private origin.

Stamps of Indo-China, 1907, Surcharged "TCHONGKING" and Value in Chinese in Red or Blue

1908

34	A5	1c ol brn & blk	.85	.85
35	A5	2c brn & blk	.85	.85
36	A5	4c bl & blk	1.25	1.25
37	A5	5c grn & blk	2.10	2.10
38	A5	10c red & blk (Bl)	2.10	2.10
39	A5	15c vio & blk	3.00	3.00
40	A6	20c vio & blk	3.00	3.00
41	A6	25c bl & blk	5.50	5.50
42	A6	30c brn & blk	3.40	3.40
43	A6	35c ol grn & blk	7.50	7.50
44	A6	40c brn & blk	15.00	15.00
45	A6	50c car & blk (Bl)	12.00	12.00
46	A7	75c ver & blk (Bl)	10.00	10.00
47	A8	1fr car & blk (Bl)	13.50	13.50
48	A9	2fr grn & blk	85.00	85.00
49	A10	5fr bl & blk	37.50	37.50
50	A11	10fr pur & blk	225.00	225.00
		Nos. 34-50 (17)	427.55	427.55

The Chinese characters overprinted on Nos. 1 to 50 repeat the denomination of the basic stamp.

Nos. 34-50 Surcharged with New Values in Cents or Piasters in Black, Red or Blue

1919

51	A5	⅚c on 1c	1.25	1.25
52	A5	⅚c on 2c	1.25	1.25
53	A5	1⅚c on 4c (R)	1.25	1.25
54	A5	2c on 5c	1.70	1.70
55	A5	4c on 10c (Bl)	1.25	1.25
56	A5	6c on 15c	1.70	1.70
57	A6	8c on 20c	3.00	1.25
58	A6	10c on 25c	8.50	8.50
59	A6	12c on 30c	3.00	1.25
60	A6	14c on 35c	2.10	1.70
a.		Closed "4"	35.00	35.00
61	A6	16c on 40c	2.10	1.70
a.		"16 CENTS" double	125.00	125.00
62	A6	20c on 50c (Bl)	11.00	10.00
63	A7	30c on 75c (Bl)	9.25	6.75
64	A8	40c on 1fr (R)	9.25	6.75
65	A9	80c on 2fr (R)	9.25	6.75
66	A10	2pi on 5fr (R)	9.25	9.25
67	A11	4pi on 10fr (R)	17.50	17.50
		Nos. 51-67 (17)	92.60	79.80

YUNNAN FOU

(Formerly Yunnan Sen, later known as Kunming)

Stamps of Indo-China
Surcharged in Black

1903-04   Unwmk.   Perf. 14x13½

1	A3	1c blk, *lil bl*	6.75	6.75
2	A3	2c brn, *buff*	6.75	6.75
3	A3	4c claret, *lav*	7.50	7.50
4	A3	5c yel green	6.75	6.75
5	A3	10c red	7.50	7.50
6	A3	15c gray	7.50	7.50
7	A3	20c red, *grn*	12.50	12.50
8	A3	25c blue	7.50	7.50
9	A3	30c brn, *bister*	12.50	12.50
10	A3	40c red, *straw*	75.00	60.00
11	A3	50c car, *rose*	350.00	350.00
12	A3	50c brn, *az* ('04)	180.00	180.00
13	A3	75c dp vio, *org*	67.50	62.50
a.		"INDO-CHINE" inverted		47,500.
14	A3	1fr brnz grn, *straw*	67.50	62.50
15	A3	5fr red lil, *lav*	125.00	125.00
		Nos. 1-15 (15)	940.25	915.25

The Chinese characters overprinted on Nos. 1 to 15 repeat the denomination of the basic stamp.
Many varieties of the surcharge exist.

Stamps of Indo-China,
1892-1906, Surcharged in
Red or Black

1906   Unwmk.   Perf. 14x13½

17	A4	1c ol grn (R)	5.00	5.00
18	A4	2c vio brn, *buff*	5.00	5.00
19	A4	4c cl, *bluish* (R)	5.00	5.00
20	A4	5c dp grn (R)	5.00	5.00
21	A4	10c carmine	5.00	5.00
22	A4	15c org brn, *bl*	35.00	35.00
23	A4	20c red, *grn*	13.50	13.50
24	A4	25c deep blue	11.00	11.00
25	A4	30c pale brn	13.50	13.50
26	A4	35c blk, *yel* (R)	17.00	17.00
27	A4	40c blk, *bluish* (R)	17.00	17.00
28	A4	50c bister brn	21.00	21.00
29	A3	75c dp vio, *org* (R)	67.50	67.50
30	A4	1fr pale grn	42.50	42.50
31	A4	2fr brn, *org* (R)	55.00	55.00
32	A3	5fr red lil, *lav*	140.00	140.00
33	A4	10fr org brn, *grn*	150.00	150.00
		Nos. 17-33 (17)	608.00	608.00

Various varieties of the surcharge exist on Nos. 18, 20, 21 and 27.

Stamps of Indo-China, 1907, Surcharged "YUNNANFOU," and Value in Chinese in Red or Blue

1908

34	A5	1c ol brn & blk	1.25	1.25
35	A5	2c brn & blk	1.25	1.25
36	A5	4c bl & blk	2.10	2.10
37	A5	5c grn & blk	3.00	3.00
38	A5	10c red & blk (Bl)	3.00	3.00
39	A5	15c vio & blk	6.75	6.75
40	A6	20c vio & blk	6.25	6.25
41	A6	25c bl & blk	9.25	9.25
42	A6	30c brn & blk	7.50	7.50
43	A6	35c ol grn & blk	7.50	7.50
44	A6	40c brn & blk	8.50	8.50
45	A6	50c car & blk (Bl)	9.25	9.25
46	A7	75c ver & blk (Bl)	11.00	11.00
47	A8	1fr car & blk (Bl)	17.00	17.00
48	A9	2fr grn & blk	29.00	29.00
a.		"YUNANNFOU"	2,500.	2,500.
49	A10	5fr bl & blk	60.00	60.00
a.		"YUNANNFOU"	2,500.	2,500.
50	A11	10fr pur & blk	120.00	120.00
a.		"YUNANNFOU"	2,500.	2,500.
		Nos. 34-50 (17)	302.60	302.60

The Chinese characters overprinted on Nos. 17-50 repeat the denomination of the basic stamp.

Nos. 34-50 Surcharged with New Values in Cents or Piasters in Black, Red or Blue

1919

51	A5	⅚c on 1c	1.25	1.25
52	A5	⅚c on 2c	1.25	1.25
53	A5	1⅚c on 4c (R)	1.25	1.25
54	A5	2c on 5c	1.70	1.70
55	A5	4c on 10c (Bl)	1.25	1.25
56	A5	6c on 15c	1.70	1.70

Nos. 34-50 Surcharged with New Values in Cents or Piasters in Black, Red or Blue

1919

51	A5	⅚c on 1c	1.25	1.25
a.		New value double	140.00	
52	A5	⅚c on 2c	1.25	1.25
53	A5	1⅚c on 4c (R)	1.25	1.25
54	A5	2c on 5c	2.10	2.10
a.		Triple surcharge	210.00	
55	A5	4c on 10c (Bl)	1.70	1.70
56	A5	6c on 15c	3.00	3.00
57	A6	8c on 20c	2.10	2.10
58	A6	10c on 25c	3.75	3.75
59	A6	12c on 30c	9.25	9.25
60	A6	14c on 35c	14.50	14.50
a.		Closed "4"	140.00	140.00
61	A6	16c on 40c	9.25	9.25
62	A6	20c on 50c (Bl)	3.00	3.00
63	A7	30c on 75c (Bl)	9.25	9.25
64	A8	40c on 1fr (R)	35.00	35.00
65	A9	80c on 2fr (R)	14.50	14.50
a.		Triple surch., one inverted	250.00	
66	A10	2pi on 5fr (R)	67.50	67.50
67	A11	4pi on 10fr (R)	35.00	35.00
		Nos. 51-67 (17)	213.65	213.65

OFFICES IN CRETE

Austria, France, Italy and Great Britain maintained their own post offices in Crete during the period when that country was an autonomous state.

100 Centimes = 1 Franc

Liberty,
Equality
and
Fraternity
A1

"Rights
of Man"
A2

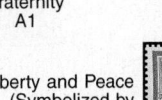

Liberty and Peace
(Symbolized by
Olive
Branch) — A3

Perf. 14x13½

		1902-03	**Unwmk.**	**Typo.**
1	A1	1c dark gray	2.35	2.75
a.	A1	1c light gray	2.35	2.75
2	A1	2c violet brown	2.35	2.75
3	A1	3c red orange	2.35	2.75
4	A1	4c yellow brown	2.35	2.75
5	A1	5c green	2.35	2.75
6	A2	10c rose red	2.75	2.75
7	A2	15c pale red ('03)	4.25	3.00
8	A2	20c brown vio ('03)	5.25	4.00
9	A2	25c blue ('03)	6.75	4.50
10	A2	30c lilac ('03)	6.75	4.50
11	A3	40c red & pale bl	13.00	13.00
12	A3	50c bis brn & lav	18.00	15.00
13	A3	1fr claret & ol grn	24.50	22.50
14	A3	2fr gray vio & yel	25.00	37.50
a.		Imperf., pair	675.00	
15	A3	5fr dk blue & buff	62.50	60.00
		Nos. 1-15 (15)	180.50	180.50
		Set, never hinged	375.00	

A4

A5

		1903	**Black Surcharge**	
16	A4	1pi on 25c blue	55.00	47.50
17	A5	2pi on 50c bis brn & lav	75.00	57.50
18	A5	4pi on 1fr claret & ol grn	110.00	100.00
19	A5	8pi on 2fr gray vio & yel	140.00	145.00
20	A5	20pi on 5fr dk bl & buff	235.00	225.00
		Nos. 16-20 (5)	615.00	575.00

OFFICES IN EGYPT

French post offices formerly maintained in Alexandria and Port Said.

100 Centimes = 1 Franc

ALEXANDRIA

Stamps of France Ovptd. in
Red, Blue or Black

1899-1900   Unwmk.   Perf. 14x13½

1	A15	1c blk, *lil bl* (R)	2.10	2.10
a.		Double overprint	150.00	
b.		Triple overprint	180.00	
2	A15	2c brn, *buff* (Bl)	3.25	2.50
3	A15	3c gray, *grysh* (Bl)	3.25	2.50
4	A15	4c cl, *lav* (R)	4.25	3.25
5	A15	5c yel grn, (I) (R)	6.00	3.25
		Type II (R)	160.00	97.50
6	A15	10c blk, *lav*, (I) (R)	9.25	7.50
		Type II (R)	62.50	37.50
7	A15	15c blue (R)	9.25	4.25
8	A15	20c red, *grn* (R)	14.50	7.50
9	A15	25c blk, *rose* (R)	7.50	4.25
a.		Inverted overprint	97.50	
b.		Double ovpt., one invtd.	160.00	
10	A15	30c brn, *bis*	15.00	12.00
11	A15	40c red, *straw*	13.50	13.50
12	A15	50c car, *rose* (II)	35.00	17.50
		Type I	150.00	27.50
13	A15	1fr brnz grn, *straw*	32.50	22.50
14	A15	2fr brn, *az* ('00)	82.50	80.00
15	A15	5fr red lil, *lav*	120.00	110.00
		Nos. 1-15 (15)	357.85	292.60

A2

A3

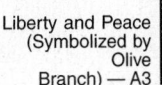

A4

1902-13

16	A2	1c pale gray	.80	.65
17	A2	2c violet brn	.75	.75
18	A2	3c red orange	.75	.75
19	A2	4c yellow brn	1.00	.85
20	A2	5c green	5.00	4.25
21	A3	10c rose red	1.50	.75
22	A3	15c orange ('13)	1.75	1.25
a.		15c pale red ('03)	4.75	1.60
23	A3	20c brn vio ('03)	3.00	1.50
24	A3	25c blue ('03)	1.75	.75
25	A3	30c violet ('03)	7.50	4.25
26	A4	40c red & pale bl	5.00	2.50
27	A4	50c bis brn & lav	11.00	3.00
28	A4	1fr cl & ol grn	10.00	4.25
29	A4	2fr gray vio & yel	24.00	12.00
30	A4	5fr dk bl & buff	29.00	17.00
		Nos. 16-30 (15)	102.80	54.50

The 2c, 5c, 10c, 20c and 25c exist imperf.
Value, each $55.
See #77-86. For surcharges see #31-73, B1-B4.

Stamps of 1902-03
Surcharged Locally in
Black

1921

31	A2	2m on 5c green	7.50	5.00
32	A2	3m on 3c red org	14.50	12.00
a.		Wider numeral	140.00	125.00
33	A3	4m on 10c rose	6.75	6.00
34	A3	5m on 1c gray	14.50	12.00
35	A2	5m on 4c yel brn	19.00	13.50
36	A3	6m on 15c orange	6.75	6.00
a.		Wider numeral	110.00	110.00
37	A3	8m on 20c brn vio	7.50	6.00
a.		Wider numeral	80.00	60.00
38	A3	10m on 25c blue	4.25	4.25
a.		Inverted surcharge	45.00	45.00
b.		Double surcharge	45.00	45.00
39	A3	12m on 30c vio	17.50	17.50
40	A2	15m on 2c vio brn	14.50	14.50

Nos. 26-30
Surcharged

41	A4	15m on 40c	25.00	19.00
42	A4	15m on 50c (#27a)	12.00	12.00
43	A4	30m on 1fr	175.00	175.00
44	A4	60m on 2fr	250.00	250.00
a.		Wider numerals	1,050.	1,050.
45	A4	150m on 5fr	350.00	350.00

Port Said Nos. 20 and 19 Surcharged like Nos. 32 and 40

45A	A2	3m on 3c red org	150.00	150.00
46	A2	15m on 2c vio brn	150.00	150.00
		Nos. 31-46 (17)	1,225.	1,203.

Alexandria No. 28 Srchd.

1921

46A	A4	30m on 15m on 1fr	1,200.	*1,350.*

The surcharge "15 Mill." was made in error and is canceled by a bar.

The surcharges were lithographed on Nos. 31, 33, 38, 39 and 42 and typographed on the other stamps of the 1921 issue. Nos. 34, 36 and 37 were surcharged by both methods.

Alexandria Stamps of 1902-03 Surcharged in Paris

1921-23

47	A2	1m on 1c slate	3.25	2.50
48	A2	2m on 5c green	2.25	1.90
49	A3	4m on 10c rose	2.75	2.50
50	A3	4m on 10c green ('23)	2.50	2.50
51	A3	5m on 3c red org ('23)	6.75	5.00
52	A3	6m on 15c orange	2.25	1.90
53	A3	8m on 20c brn vio	2.25	2.25
54	A3	10m on 25c blue	1.40	1.25
55	A3	10m on 30c vio	4.25	3.25
56	A3	15m on 50c bl ('23)	3.25	3.00

Nos. 27-30 and Type of 1902 Surcharged

57	A4	15m on 50c	5.00	3.25
58	A4	30m on 1fr	4.25	3.00
59	A4	60m on 2fr	2,250.	*2,400.*
60	A4	60m on 2fr org & pale bl ('23)	13.50	13.00
61	A4	150m on 5fr	13.50	8.50
		Nos. 47-58,60-61 (14)	67.15	52.80

Stamps and Types of 1902-03 Surcharged with New Values and Bars in Black

1925

62	A2	1m on 1c slate	1.25	1.25
63	A2	2m on 5c orange	1.25	1.25
64	A2	2m on 5c green	1.75	1.75
65	A3	4m on 10c green	1.10	.85
66	A2	5m on 3c red org	1.50	1.25
67	A3	6m on 15c orange	1.40	1.25
68	A3	8m on 20c brn vio	1.75	1.40
69	A3	10m on 25c blue	1.10	1.00
70	A3	15m on 50c blue	2.40	1.40
71	A4	30m on 1fr cl & ol grn	3.50	2.90
72	A4	60m on 2fr org & pale bl	4.25	3.50
73	A4	150m on 5fr dk bl & buff	6.00	5.00
		Nos. 62-73 (12)	27.25	22.80

Types of 1902-03 Issue

1927-28

77	A2	3m orange ('28)	2.50	2.10
81	A3	15m slate blue	2.50	2.10
82	A3	20m rose lil ('28)	6.75	5.00
84	A4	50m org & blue	11.00	9.35
85	A4	100m sl bl & buff	15.00	12.00
86	A4	250m gray grn & red	25.00	16.00
		Nos. 77-86 (6)	62.75	46.55

SEMI-POSTAL STAMPS

Regular Issue of 1902-03 Surcharged in Carmine

1915   Unwmk.   Perf. 14x13½

B1	A3	10c + 5c rose	1.25	1.25

Sinking Fund Issue

Type of 1902-03 Issue Surcharged in Blue or Black

1927-30

B2	A3	15m + 5m deep org	6.00	6.00
B3	A3	15m + 5m red vio ('28)	9.25	9.25
	a.	15m + 5m violet ('30)	15.00	15.00

Type of 1902-03 Issue Surcharged as in 1927-28

1929

B4	A3	15m + 5m fawn	12.00	12.00

POSTAGE DUE STAMPS

Postage Due Stamps of France, 1893-1920, Surcharged in Paris in Black

1922   Unwmk.   Perf. 14x13½

J1	D2	2m on 5c blue	2.50	2.50
J2	D2	4m on 10c brown	2.50	2.50
J3	D2	10m on 30c rose red	3.00	3.00
J4	D2	15m on 50c brn vio	3.25	3.25
J5	D2	30m on 1fr red brn, *straw*	4.50	4.50
		Nos. J1-J5 (5)	15.75	15.75

D3

1928   Typo.

J6	D3	1m slate	1.60	1.60
J7	D3	2m light blue	1.25	1.25
J8	D3	4m lilac rose	1.75	1.75
J9	D3	5m gray green	2.00	2.00
J10	D3	10m light red	2.50	2.50
J11	D3	20m violet brn	2.25	2.25
J12	D3	30m green	5.00	5.00
J13	D3	40m lt violet	6.25	6.25
		Nos. J6-J13 (8)	22.60	22.60

Nos. J6-J13 were also available for use in Port Said.

PORT SAID

Stamps of France Overprinted in Red, Blue or Black

1899-1900   Unwmk.   Perf. 14x13½

1	A15	1c blk, *lil bl* (R)	2.10	1.70
2	A15	2c brn, *buff* (bl)	2.10	1.70
3	A15	3c gray, *grysh* (Bl)	2.10	2.10
4	A15	4c claret, *lav* (Bl)	1.75	*2.10*
5	A15	5c yel grn (I) (R)	11.00	5.00
	a.	Type II (R)	55.00	25.00
6	A15	10c blk, *lav* (I) (R)	14.00	12.50
	a.	Type II (R)	72.50	55.00
7	A15	15c blue (R)	14.00	8.50
8	A15	20c red, *grn*	17.00	11.00
9	A15	25c blk, *rose* (R)	14.00	5.00
	a.	Double overprint	300.00	
	b.	Inverted overprint	300.00	
10	A15	30c brn, *bister*	17.00	14.00
	a.	Inverted overprint	325.00	
11	A15	40c red, *straw*	14.00	14.00
12	A15	50c car, *rose* (II)	20.00	14.00
	a.	Type I	300.00	100.00
	b.	Double overprint (II)	425.00	
13	A15	1fr brnz grn, *straw*	30.00	17.50
14	A15	2fr brn, *az* ('00)	75.00	65.00
15	A15	5fr red lil, *lav*	120.00	92.50
		Nos. 1-15 (15)	354.05	266.60

Regular Issue Surcharged in Red

1899

16	A15	25c on 10c blk, *lav*	130.00	35.00
	a.	Inverted surcharge	250.00	

With Additional Surcharge "25c" in Red

17	A15	25c on 10c blk, *lav*	475.00	160.00
	a.	"25" inverted	1,500.	1,400.
	b.	"25" in black		2,600.
	c.	As "b," "VINGT CINQ" inverted		3,400.
	d.	As "b," "25" vertical		3,400.
	e.	As "c" and "d"		3,400.

A2

A3

A4

1902-03   Typo.

18	A2	1c pale gray ('16)	.65	.65
19	A2	2c violet brn	.75	.75
20	A2	3c red orange	.85	.75
21	A2	4c yellow brown	1.10	.90
22	A2	5c blue green ('04)	1.20	.85
	a.	5c yellow green	5.00	3.00
23	A3	10c rose red	1.60	1.10
24	A3	15c pale red ('03)	3.25	2.25
	a.	15c orange	5.00	3.00
25	A3	20c brn vio ('03)	3.25	2.25
26	A3	25c blue ('03)	2.50	1.60
27	A3	30c gray violet ('03)	6.75	5.00
28	A4	40c red & pale bl	6.00	4.25
29	A4	50c bis brn & lav	9.25	6.75
30	A4	1fr claret & ol grn	12.00	9.25
31	A4	2fr gray vio & yel	15.00	15.00
32	A4	5fr dk bl & buff	35.00	32.50
		Nos. 18-32 (15)	99.15	83.85

See Nos. 83-92. For surcharges see Nos. 33-80, B1-B4.

Stamps of 1902-03 Surcharged Locally

1921

33	A2	2m on 5c green	10.00	10.00
	a.	Inverted surcharge	50.00	50.00
34	A3	4m on 10c rose	9.25	9.25
	a.	Inverted surcharge	50.00	50.00
35	A2	5m on 1c slate	14.00	14.00
	b.	5m on 1c light gray	26.00	26.00
	c.	Surcharged "2 Millièmes" on #35	67.50	67.50
36	A2	5m on 2c	24.00	24.00
	a.	Surcharged "2 Millièmes"	75.00	75.00
	b.	As "a," inverted	160.00	160.00
37	A2	5m on 3c	15.00	15.00
	a.	Inverted surcharge	62.50	62.50
	b.	On Alexandria #18	400.00	400.00
38	A2	5m on 4c	11.00	11.00
	a.	Inverted surcharge	80.00	80.00
39	A2	10m on 2c	25.00	25.00
40	A2	10m on 4c	35.00	35.00
	a.	Inverted surcharge	85.00	85.00
	b.	Double surcharge	100.00	105.00
41	A3	10m on 25c	9.25	9.25
	a.	Inverted surcharge	85.00	85.00
42	A3	12m on 30c	42.50	42.50
43	A2	15m on 4c	10.00	10.00
	a.	Inverted surcharge	85.00	85.00
	b.	Double surcharge	92.50	97.50
44	A3	15m on 15c pale red	67.50	67.50
	a.	Inverted surcharge	160.00	160.00
45	A3	15m on 20c	67.50	67.50
	a.	Inverted surcharge	160.00	160.00
46	A4	30m on 50c	300.00	300.00
47	A4	60m on 50c	350.00	350.00
48	A4	150m on 50c	400.00	400.00

Nos. 46, 47 and 48 have a bar between the numerals and "Millièmes," which is in capital letters.

Same Surcharge on Stamps of French Offices in Turkey, 1902-03

49	A2	2m on 2c vio brn	160.00	160.00
50	A2	5m on 1c gray	150.00	150.00
	a.	"5" inverted	7,250.	
		Nos. 33-50 (18)	1,700.	1,700.

Nos. 28-32 Surcharged

51	A4	15m on 40c	60.00	60.00
52	A4	15m on 50c	85.00	85.00
	b.	Bar below 15	50.00	50.00
53	A4	30m on 1fr	300.00	300.00
54	A4	60m on 2fr	85.00	92.50
55	A4	150m on 5fr	250.00	*275.00*
		Nos. 51-55 (5)	780.00	812.50

Overprinted "MILLtEMES"

51a	A4	15m on 40c	425.00	425.00
52a	A4	15m on 50c	500.00	500.00
53a	A4	30m on 1fr	1,400.	1,400.
54a	A4	60m on 2fr	400.00	400.00
55a	A4	150m on 5fr	1,050.	1,050.
		Nos. 51a-55a (5)	3,775.	3,775.

Stamps of 1902-03 Surcharged in Paris

1921-23

56	A2	1m on 1c slate	1.60	1.60
57	A2	2m on 5c green	1.60	1.60
58	A3	4m on 10c rose	2.50	2.50
59	A3	5m on 3c red org	9.25	9.25
60	A3	6m on 15c orange	3.25	3.25
	a.	6m on 15c pale red	14.00	14.00
61	A3	8m on 20c brn vio	5.00	5.00
62	A3	10m on 25c blue	2.50	2.50
63	A3	10m on 30c violet	7.50	7.50
64	A3	15m on 50c blue	6.75	6.75

Nos. 29-32 and Type of 1902 Surcharged

65	A4	15m on 50c	6.00	6.00
66	A4	30m on 1fr	9.25	9.25
67	A4	60m on 2fr	130.00	130.00
68	A4	60m on 2fr org & pale blue	12.50	12.50
69	A4	150m on 5fr	20.00	20.00
		Nos. 56-69 (14)	217.70	217.70

Stamps and Types of 1902-03 Surcharged

1925

70	A2	1m on 1c light gray	.75	.75
71	A2	2m on 5c green	1.10	1.10
72	A3	4m on 10c rose red	.90	.90
73	A2	5m on 3c red org	1.10	1.10
74	A3	6m on 15c orange	1.10	1.10
75	A3	8m on 20c brn vio	1.00	1.00
76	A3	10m on 25c blue	1.40	1.40
77	A3	15m on 50c blue	1.60	1.60
78	A4	30m on 1fr cl & ol grn	2.75	2.75
79	A4	60m on 2fr org & pale blue	2.50	2.50
80	A4	150m on 5fr dk bl & buff	2.50	2.50
		Nos. 70-80 (11)	18.45	18.45

Type of 1902-03 Issue and

A5

1927-28

83	A5	3m orange ('28)	2.10	2.10
87	A3	15m slate bl	2.50	2.50
88	A3	20m rose lil ('28)	2.50	2.50
90	A4	50m org & blue	4.50	4.50
91	A4	100m slate bl & buff	6.00	6.00
92	A4	250m gray grn & red	9.25	9.25
		Nos. 83-92 (6)	26.85	26.85

SEMI-POSTAL STAMPS

Regular Issue of 1902-03 Surcharged in Carmine

1915   Unwmk.   Perf. 14x13½

B1	A3	10c + 5c rose	1.60	1.60

Sinking Fund Issue
Type of 1902-03 Issue Surcharged like Alexandria Nos. B2-B3 in Blue or Black

1927-30

B2	A3	15m + 5m dp org (Bl)	5.00	5.00
B3	A3	15m + 5m red vio ('28)	8.50	8.50
b.		15m + 5m violet ('30)	14.00	14.00
B4	A3	15m + 5m fawn ('29)	10.00	10.00
		Nos. B2-B4 (3)	23.50	23.50

POSTAGE DUE STAMPS

Postage Due Stamps of France, 1893-1906, Srchd. Locally in Black

1921   Unwmk.   Perf. 14x13½

J1	D2	12m on 10c brown	62.50	67.50
J2	D2	15m on 5c blue	92.50	105.00
J3	D2	30m on 20c ol grn	92.50	105.00
a.		Inverted surcharge	1,100.	1,100.
J4	D2	30m on 50c red vio	3,000.	3,400.

Same Surcharged in Red or Blue

1921

J5	D2	2m on 5c bl (R)	55.00	60.00
a.		Blue surcharge	300.00	300.00
b.		Accent omitted from "è" of "Millièmes"	190.00	200.00
c.		Second "m" of "Millièmes" inverted	190.00	200.00
d.		"S" of "Millièmes" omitted	190.00	250.00
J6	D2	4m on 10c brn (Bl)	55.00	62.50
a.		Surcharged "15 Millièmes"	725.00	725.00
b.		Accent omitted from "è" of "MiLLièMES"	190.00	200.00
c.		Second "m" of "Millièmes" inverted	190.00	200.00
d.		"S" of "Millièmes" omitted	190.00	225.00
J7	D2	10m on 30c red (Bl)	55.00	60.00
a.		Inverted surcharge	160.00	160.00
b.		Accent omitted from "è" of "Millièmes"	190.00	190.00
c.		Second "M" of "Millièmes" inverted	190.00	190.00
d.		"S" of "Millièmes" omitted	190.00	225.00
e.		"Q" for "0" in surcharge (1Qm)	1,450.	1,500.
J8	D2	15m on 50c brn vio (Bl)	67.50	72.50
a.		Inverted surcharge	160.00	160.00
b.		Accent omitted from "è" of "Millièmes"	190.00	190.00
c.		Second "m" of "Millièmes" inverted	190.00	190.00
d.		"S" of "Millièmes" omitted	210.00	240.00
e.		As "a," accent omitted from è of "Millièmes"	425.00	
		Nos. J5-J8 (4)	232.50	255.00

Alexandria Nos. J6-J13 were also available for use in Port Said.

OFFICES IN TURKEY (LEVANT)

Various powers maintained post offices in the Turkish Empire before World War I by authority of treaties which ended with the signing of the Treaty of Lausanne in 1923. The foreign post offices were closed Oct. 27, 1923.

100 Centimes = 1 Franc
25 Centimes = 40 Paras = 1 Piaster

Stamps of France Surcharged in Black or Red

1885-1901   Unwmk.   Perf. 14x13½

1	A15	1pi on 25c yel, straw	550.00	16.00
a.		Inverted surcharge	2,500.	2,400.
2	A15	1pi on 25c blk, rose (R) ('86)	4.25	1.25
		Never hinged	8.00	
a.		Inverted surcharge	400.00	325.00

3	A15	2pi on 50c car, rose (II) ('90)	18.00	3.00
		Never hinged	35.00	
a.		Type I ('01)	375.00	50.00
		Never hinged	725.00	
4	A15	3pi on 75c car, rose	30.00	15.00
		Never hinged	60.00	
5	A15	4pi on 1fr brnz grn, straw	30.00	15.00
		Never hinged	60.00	
6	A15	8pi on 2fr brn, az ('00)	37.50	25.00
		Never hinged	67.50	
7	A15	20pi on 5fr red lil, lav ('90)	110.00	60.00
		Never hinged	225.00	
		Nos. 1-7 (7)	779.75	135.25

A2

A3

A4

Nos. 29, 32, 36 and Types of A4 Surcharged

No. 34

No. 35

1902-07   Typo.   Perf. 14x13½

21	A2	1c gray	.65	.65
		Never hinged	1.25	
22	A2	2c vio brn	.65	.65
23	A2	3c red org	.65	.65
24	A2	4c yel brn	3.00	1.10
a.		Imperf., pair	90.00	
25	A3	5c lt yel green ('03)	2.00	.80
26	A3	10c rose red	1.00	.65
27	A3	15c pale red ('03)	3.00	1.25
28	A3	20c brn vio ('03)	3.25	2.00
29	A3	25c blue ('07)	45.00	60.00
a.		Imperf., pair	425.00	
30	A3	30c lilac ('03)	6.00	3.00
31	A4	40c red & pale bl	6.00	3.25
32	A4	50c bis brn & lav ('07)	190.00	225.00
a.		Imperf., pair	925.00	
33	A4	1fr claret & ol grn ('07)	425.00	450.00
a.		Imperf., pair	1,100.	

Black Surcharge

34	A3	1pi on 25c bl ('03)	1.20	.65
a.		Second "I" omitted	32.50	25.00
b.		Double surcharge	72.50	60.00
35	A4	2pi on 50c bis brn & lavender	4.25	1.60
36	A4	4pi on 1fr cl & ol grn	5.00	2.10
a.		Imperf., pair	750.00	
37	A4	8pi on 2fr gray vio & yel	20.00	15.00
38	A4	20pi on 5fr dk bl & buff	10.00	6.00
		Nos. 21-38 (18)	726.65	774.35

Nos. 29, 32-33 were used during the early part of 1907 in the French Offices at Harar and Diredawa, Ethiopia. Djibouti and Port Said stamps were also used.

No. 27 Surcharged in Green

1905

39	A3	1pi on 15c pale red	2,100.	325.
a.		"Piastte"	7,000.	1,700.

Stamps of France 1900-21 Surcharged

On A22

On A20

On A18

1921-22

40	A22	30pa on 5c grn	1.00	1.00
41	A22	30pa on 5c org	1.00	.85
42	A22	1pi20pa on 10c red	1.10	1.10
43	A22	1pi20pa on 10c grn	1.10	.85
44	A22	3pi30pa on 25c bl	1.60	1.00
45	A22	4pi20pa on 30c org	1.60	1.10
a.		"4" omitted	1,050.	
46	A20	7pi20pa on 50c bl	1.60	1.25
47	A18	15pi on 1fr car & ol grn	3.00	2.10
48	A18	30pi on 2fr org & pale bl	12.50	10.00
49	A18	75pi on 5fr dk bl & buff	11.00	7.50
		Nos. 40-49 (10)	35.50	26.75

Stamps of France, 1903-07, Handstamped

1923

52	A22	1pi20pa on 10c red	62.50	60.00
54	A20	3pi30pa on 15c gray grn (GC)	25.00	25.00
55	A22	7pi20pa on 35c vio	30.00	30.00
b.		1pi20pa on 35c violet	1,400.	1,400.
		Nos. 52-55 (3)	117.50	115.00

CAVALLE (CAVALLA)

Stamps of France Ovptd. or Srchd. in Carmine, Red, Blue or Black

1893-1900   Unwmk.   Perf. 14x13½

1	A15	5c grn, grnsh (R)	25.00	21.00
a.		Type II (C)	25.00	21.00
2	A15	5c yel grn (I) ('00) (R)	21.00	21.00
3	A15	10c blk, lav (II)	26.00	26.00
a.		10c black, lavender (I)	180.00	150.00
4	A15	15c blue (R)	47.50	30.00
a.		15c blue (C)	47.50	30.00
5	A15	1pi on 25c blk, rose	28.00	20.00
6	A15	2pi on 50c car, rose	92.50	65.00
7	A15	4pi on 1fr brnz grn, straw (R)	97.50	87.50
b.		4pi on 1fr brnz grn, straw (C)	95.00	87.50
8	A15	8pi on 2fr brn, az ('00) (Bk)	120.00	120.00
		Nos. 1-8 (8)	457.50	390.50
		Set, never hinged	1,000.	

A3

A4

A5

A6

1902-03

9	A3	5c green	2.25	1.75
a.		5c yel grn	2.50	2.00
10	A4	10c rose red ('03)	2.25	1.75
11	A4	15c orange	2.25	1.75
a.		15c pale red ('03)	12.50	12.50

Surcharged in Black

12	A5	1pi on 25c bl	4.75	3.00
13	A6	2pi on 50c bis brn & lav	13.00	7.00
14	A6	4pi on 1fr cl & ol grn	16.00	13.00
15	A6	8pi on 2fr gray vio & yel	21.00	19.00
		Nos. 9-15 (7)	61.50	47.25

DEDEAGH (DEDEAGATCH)

Stamps of France Ovptd. or Srchd. in Carmine, Red, Blue or Black

1893-1900   Unwmk.   Perf. 14x13½

1	A15	5c grn, grnsh (II) (R)	18.00	15.00
a.		Type II (C)	18.00	15.00

2	A15	5c yel grn (I) ('00) (R)	14.50	14.00
3	A15	10c blk, lav (II)	27.50	20.00
b.		As"a," double overprint	300.00	
4	A15	15c blue (II) (R)	37.50	30.00
a.		Type II (C)	37.50	30.00
5	A15	1pi on 25c blk, rose	42.50	37.50
6	A15	2pi on 50c car, rose	70.00	50.00
7	A15	4pi on 1fr brnz grn, straw (R)	82.50	70.00
8	A15	8pi on 2fr brn, az ('00) (Bk)	120.00	95.00
		Nos. 1-8 (8)	412.50	331.50
		Set, never hinged	1,000.	

A3

A4

A5

A6

1902-03

9	A3	5c green ('03)	3.00	2.50
a.		5c yellow green	3.50	3.00
10	A4	10c rose red ('03)	3.50	2.75
11	A4	15c orange	5.00	3.75
a.		15c rose red ('03)	7.00	6.00
15	A5	1pi on 25c bl ('03)	3.50	2.75
16	A6	2pi on 50c bis brn & lav	11.50	10.00
a.		Double surcharge	300.00	
17	A6	4pi on 1fr cl & ol grn	22.50	18.50
18	A6	8pi on 2fr gray vio & yel	32.50	27.50
		Nos. 9-18 (7)	81.50	67.75
		Set, never hinged	175.00	

PORT LAGOS

Stamps of France Ovptd. or Srchd. in Carmine, Red or Blue

1893   Unwmk.   Perf. 14x13½

1	A15	5c grn, grnsh (R)	30.00	32.50
a.		5c grn, grnsh (C)	30.00	32.50
2	A15	10c blk, lav	62.50	47.50
3	A15	15c blue (R)	92.50	72.50
a.		15c blue (C)	97.50	77.50
4	A15	1pi on 25c blk, rose	77.50	62.50
5	A15	2pi on 50c car, rose	185.00	97.50
6	A15	4pi on 1fr brnz grn, straw (R)	112.50	97.50
		Nos. 1-6 (6)	560.00	410.00
		Set, never hinged	1,300.	

VATHY (SAMOS)

Stamps of France Ovptd. or Srchd. in Carmine, Red, Blue or Black

1894-1900   Unwmk.   Perf. 14x13½

1	A15	5c grn, grnsh (R)	8.75	8.00
a.		5c grn, grnsh (II) (C)	10.00	8.75
2	A15	5c yel grn (I) ('00) (R)	8.75	7.50
a.		Type II	87.50	87.50
3	A15	10c blk, lav (I)	17.50	15.00
a.		Type II	50.00	47.50
4	A15	15c blue (R)	17.50	15.00
5	A15	1pi on 25c blk, rose	17.50	11.50
6	A15	2pi on 50c car, rose	30.00	27.50
7	A15	4pi on 1fr brnz grn, straw (R)	42.50	35.00
8	A15	8pi on 2fr brn, az ('00) (Bk)	75.00	75.00
9	A15	20pi on 5fr lil, lav ('00) (Bk)	110.00	110.00
		Nos. 1-9 (9)	327.50	304.50
		Set, never hinged	600.00	

OFFICES IN ZANZIBAR

Until 1906 France maintained post offices in the Sultanate of Zanzibar, but in that year Great Britain assumed direct control over this protectorate and the French withdrew their postal system.

16 Annas = 1 Rupee

Stamps of France Surcharged in Red, Carmine, Blue or Black

1894-96		Unwmk.	Perf. 14x13½	
1	A15	½a on 5c grn, grnsh	10.00	7.50
2	A15	1a on 10c blk, lav (Bl)	15.00	12.50
3	A15	1½a on 15c bl ('96)	22.50	21.00
a.		"ANNAS"	100.00	92.50
4	A15	2a on 20c red, grn ('96) (Bk)	19.00	15.00
a.		"ANNA"	2,300.	2,300.
5	A15	2½a on 25c blk, rose (Bl)	12.50	9.25
a.		Double surcharge	250.00	250.00
6	A15	3a on 30c brn, bis ('96)	21.00	18.00
7	A15	4a on 40c red, straw ('96) (Bk)	29.00	25.00
8	A15	5a on 50c car, rose (Bl)	37.50	32.50
9	A15	7½a on 75c vio, org ('96)	500.00	400.00
10	A15	10a on 1fr brnz grn, straw	67.50	55.00
11	A15	50a on 5fr red lil, lav ('96) (Bk)	325.00	260.00
		Nos. 1-11 (11)	1,059.	855.75
1894				
12	A15	½a & 5c on 1c blk, lil bl (R)	200.00	220.00
13	A15	1a & 10c on 3c gray, grysh (R)	180.00	200.00
14	A15	2½a & 25c on 4c cl, lav (Bk)	230.00	275.00
15	A15	5a & 50c on 20c red, grn (Bk)	250.00	275.00
16	A15	10a & 1fr on 40c red, straw (Bk)	475.00	525.00
		Nos. 12-16 (5)	1,335.	1,495.

There are two distinct types of the figures 5c, four of the 25c and three of each of the others of this series.

Stamps of France Srchd. in Red, Carmine, Blue or Black

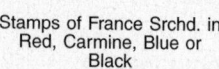

1896-1900				
17	A15	½a on 5c grn, grnsh (R)	11.00	8.50
18	A15	½a on 5c yel grn (I) (R)	7.50	6.75
a.		Type II	9.25	7.50
19	A15	1a on 10c blk, lav (II) (Bl)	9.25	7.50
a.		Type I	22.50	19.00
20	A15	1½a on 15c bl (R)	11.00	9.25
21	A15	2a on 20c red, grn	9.25	9.25
a.		"ZANZIBAR" double	210.00	210.00
b.		"ZANZIBAR" triple	210.00	210.00
22	A15	2½a on 25c blk, rose (Bl)	11.00	9.25
a.		Inverted surcharge	275.00	210.00
23	A15	3a on 30c brn, bis	11.00	9.25
24	A15	4a on 40c red, straw	13.50	10.00
25	A15	5a on 50c rose, rose (II) (Bl)	45.00	32.50
a.		Type I	125.00	100.00
26	A15	10a on 1fr brnz grn, straw (R)	29.00	25.00
27	A15	20a on 2fr brn, az	35.00	29.00
a.		"ZANZIBAS"	675.00	750.00
b.		"ZANZIBAR" triple		1,600.
28	A15	50a on 5fr lil, lav	67.50	62.50
a.		"ZANZIBAS"	9,250.	
		Nos. 17-28 (12)	260.00	218.75

For surcharges see Nos. 50-54.

A4

A5

1897				
29	A4	2½a & 25c on ½a on 5c grn, grnsh		
30	A4	2½a & 25c on 1a on 10c lav	1,300.	240.
31	A4	2½a & 25c on 1½a on 15c blue	4,500.	1,100.
32	A5	5a & 50c on 3a on 30c brn, bis	4,400.	950.
33	A5	5a & 50c on 4a on 40c red, straw	4,400.	950.
			4,500.	1,300.

Printed on the Margins of Sheets of French Stamps

A6

A7

Perf. 14x13½ on one or more sides

1897				
34	A6	2½a & 25c grn, grnsh		1,300.
35	A6	2½a & 25c blk, lav		4,000.
36	A6	2½a & 25c blue		3,000.
37	A7	5a & 50c brn, bis		2,900.
38	A7	5a & 50c red, straw		4,000.

There are 5 varieties of figures in the above surcharges.

Surcharged in Red or Black

A8

A9

A10

1902-03			Perf. 14x13½	
39	A8	½a on 5c grn (R)	6.75	6.00
40	A9	1a on 10c rose red ('03)	7.50	7.50
41	A9	1½a on 15c pale red ('03)	15.00	14.00
42	A9	2a on 20c brn vio ('03)	18.00	15.00
43	A9	2½a on 25c bl ('03)	18.00	15.00
44	A9	3a on 30c lil ('03)	13.00	13.00
a.		5a on 30c (error)	325.00	375.00
45	A10	4a on 40c red & pale bl	30.00	25.00
46	A10	5a on 50c bis brn & lav	25.00	21.00
47	A10	10a on 1fr cl & ol grn	32.50	29.00
48	A10	20a on 2fr gray vio & yel	85.00	75.00
49	A10	50a on 5fr dk bl & buff	100.00	92.50
		Nos. 39-49 (11)	350.75	313.00

For see Reunion Nos. 55-59.

Nos. 23-24 Surcharged in Black

a

b

c

1904				
50	A15 (a)	25c & 2½a on 4a on 40c		1,000.
51	A15 (b)	50c & 5a on 3a on 30c		1,200.
52	A15 (b)	50c & 5a on 4a on 40c	6,500.	1,200.
53	A15 (c)	1fr & 10a on 3a on 30c		2,000.
54	A15 (c)	1fr & 10a on 4a on 40c		2,000.

Nos. 39-40, 44 Surcharged in Red or Black

d

e

f

g

55	A8 (d)	25c & 2a on ½a on 5c (R)		
56	A9 (e)	25c & 2½a on 1a on 10c	3,100.	140.00
a.		Inverted surcharge		1,500.
57	A9 (e)	25c & 2½a on 3a on 30c	6,500.	150.00
a.		Inverted surcharge		2,400.
b.		Double surch., both invtd.		4,100.
58	A9 (f)	50c & 5a on 3a on 30c		2,600.
59	A9 (g)	1fr & 10a on 3a on 30c	1,250.	
				2,000.

No. J1-J3 With Various Surcharges Overprinted: "Timbre" in Red

60	D1	½a on 5c blue		450.00

Overprinted "Affrancht" in Black

61	D1	1a on 10c brn		450.00

With Red Bars Across "CHIFFRE" and "TAXE"

62	D1	1½a on 15c grn		1,000.

The illustrations are not exact reproductions of the new surcharges but are merely intended to show their relative positions and general styles.

POSTAGE DUE STAMPS

Postage Due Stamps of France Srchd. in Red, Blue or Black Like Nos. 17-28

1897		Unwmk.	Perf. 14x13½	
J1	D2	½a on 5c blue (R)	21.00	12.50
J2	D2	1a on 10c brn (Bl)	21.00	12.50
a.		Inverted surcharge	160.00	190.00
J3	D2	1½aon 15c grn (R)	32.50	12.50
J4	D2	3a on 30c car (Bk)	29.00	21.00
J5	D2	5a on 50c lil (Bl)	32.50	25.00
a.		2 ½a on 50c lilac (Bl)	1,400.	1,300.
		Nos. J1-J5 (5)	136.00	83.50

For overprints see Nos. 60-62.

REUNION

LOCATION — An island in the Indian Ocean about 400 miles east of Madagascar

GOVT. — Department of France

AREA — 970 sq. mi.

POP. — 490,000 (est. 1974)

CAPITAL — St. Denis

The colony of Réunion became an integral part of the Republic, acquiring the same status as the departments in metropolitan France, under a law effective Jan. 1, 1947.

On Jan. 1, 1975, stamps of France replaced those inscribed or overprinted "CFA."

100 Centimes = 1 Franc

Catalogue values for unused stamps in this country are for Never Hinged items, beginning with Scott 224 in the regular postage section, Scott B15 in the semi-postal section, Scott C18 in the airpost section, and Scott J26 in the postage due section.

For French stamps inscribed "Reunion" see Nos. 949, 1507.

A1

A2

1852		Unwmk.	Typo.	Imperf.
1	A1	15c black, blue	39,000.	25,000.
2	A2	30c black, blue	39,000.	25,000.

Four varieties of each value.

The reprints are printed on a more bluish paper than the originals. They have a frame of a thick and a thin line, instead of one thick and two thin lines. Value, $62.50 each.

Stamps of French Colonies Surcharged or Overprinted in Black

a

Overprint Type "a"

1885				
3	A1(a)	5c on 40c org, yelsh	450.00	375.00
a.		Inverted surcharge	2,250.	2,100.
b.		Double surcharge	2,250.	2,100.
4	A1(a)	25c on 40c org, yelsh	70.00	55.00
a.		Inverted surcharge	1,000.	900.00
b.		Double surcharge	1,000.	900.00
5	A5(a)	5c on 30c brn, yelsh	70.00	57.50
a.		"5" inverted	3,500.	3,000.
b.		Double surcharge	1,100.	900.00
c.		Inverted surcharge	1,000.	900.00
6	A4(a)	5c on 40c org, yelsh (I)	62.50	45.00
a.		5c on 40c org, yelsh (II)	2,500.	2,500.
b.		Inverted surcharge (I)	1,100.	900.00
c.		Double surcharge (I)	1,100.	900.00
7	A8(a)	5c on 30c brn, yelsh	22.50	18.00
8	A8(a)	5c on 40c ver, straw	135.00	115.00
a.		Inverted surcharge	950.00	850.00
b.		Double surcharge	925.00	850.00
9	A8(a)	10c on 40c ver, straw	27.50	22.50
a.		Inverted surcharge	950.00	850.00
b.		Double surcharge	950.00	850.00
10	A8(a)	20c on 30c brn, yelsh	90.00	75.00

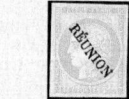
b

Overprint Type "b"
With or Without Accent on "E"

1891				
11	A4	40c org, yelsh (I)	575.00	550.00
a.		40c orange, yelsh (II)	6,750.	6,750.
b.		Double overprint	750.00	750.00
12	A7	80c car, pnksh	80.00	62.50
13	A8	30c brn, yelsh	52.50	52.50
14	A8	40c ver, straw	42.50	42.50
15	A8	75c car, rose	475.00	475.00
16	A8	1fr brnz grn, straw	62.50	52.50

Perf. 14x13½

17	A9	1c blk, lil bl	4.75	4.00
a.		Inverted overprint	60.00	60.00
b.		Double overprint	52.50	52.50
18	A9	2c brn, buff	6.50	5.00
a.		Inverted overprint	40.00	40.00
19	A9	4c claret, lav	10.00	8.00
a.		Inverted overprint	72.50	72.50
20	A9	5c grn, grnsh	11.50	9.00
a.		Inverted overprint	60.00	60.00
b.		Double overprint	60.00	57.50
21	A9	10c blk, lav	40.00	40.00
a.		Inverted overprint	90.00	80.00
b.		Double overprint	100.00	80.00

No.	Type	Description	Unused	Used
22	A9	15c blue	57.50	9.00
a.		Inverted overprint	120.00	110.00
23	A9	20c red, *grn*	45.00	30.00
a.		Inverted overprint	175.00	150.00
b.		Double overprint	175.00	150.00
24	A9	25c blk, *rose*	50.00	7.25
a.		Inverted overprint	125.00	120.00
25	A9	35c dp vio, *yel*	45.00	35.00
b.		Inverted overprint	180.00	175.00
26	A9	40c red, *straw*	72.50	62.50
a.		Inverted overprint	240.00	225.00
27	A9	75c car, *rose*	675.00	575.00
a.		Inverted overprint	1,600.	1,400.
28	A9	1fr brnz grn, *straw*	575.00	500.00
a.		Inverted overprint	1,600.	1,500.
b.		Double overprint	1,600.	1,400.

The varieties "RUNION," "RUENION," "REUNIONR," "REUINON," "EUNION," "REUNIN," "REUNIOU" and "REUNOIN" are found on most stamps of this group. See *Scott Classic Specialized Catalogue of Stamps and Covers* for detailed listings. There are also many broken letters.

For surcharges see Nos. 29-33, 53-55.

No. 23 with Additional Surcharge in Black

c

d

e

f

1891

No.	Type	Description	Unused	Used
29	A9(c)	02c on 20c red, *grn*	14.50	14.50
a.		Inverted surcharge	90.00	90.00
b.		No "c" after "02"	57.50	57.50
30	A9(c)	15c on 20c red, *grn*	18.00	18.00
a.		Inverted surcharge	70.00	70.00
31	A9(d)	2c on 20c red, *grn*	5.00	5.00
32	A9(e)	2c on 20c red, *grn*	6.00	5.75
33	A9(f)	2c on 20c red, *grn*	10.00	10.00
		Nos. 29-33 (5)	53.50	53.25

The varieties "RUNION" and "RUENION" appear on several stamps from this set. See *Scott Classic Specialized Catalogue of Stamps and Covers* for listings.

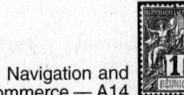

Navigation and
Commerce — A14

1892-1905 Typo. Perf. 14x13½
Name of Colony in Blue or Carmine

No.	Type	Description	Unused	Used
34	A14	1c blk, *lil bl*	2.00	1.25
35	A14	2c brn, *buff*	2.00	1.25
36	A14	4c claret, *lav*	3.25	2.25
37	A14	5c grn, *grnsh*	7.25	2.25
38	A14	5c yel grn ('00)	1.75	1.75
39	A14	10c blk, *lav*	9.50	3.50
40	A14	10c red ('00)	4.50	4.50
41	A14	15c bl, quadrille paper	30.00	3.50
42	A14	15c gray ('00)	10.00	3.50
43	A14	20c red, *grn*	20.00	9.00
44	A14	25c blk, *rose*	22.50	3.50
a.		"Reunion" double	425.00	450.00
45	A14	25c blue ('00)	29.00	27.50
46	A14	30c brn, *bis*	23.00	12.00
47	A14	40c red, *straw*	32.50	19.00
48	A14	50c car, *rose*	80.00	42.50
a.		"Reunion" in red and blue	500.00	500.00
49	A14	50c brn, *az* ("Reunion" in car) ('00)	57.50	50.00
50	A14	50c brn, *az* ("Reunion" in bl) ('05)	57.50	50.00
51	A14	75c dp vio, *org*	62.50	45.00
a.		"Reunion" double	375.00	375.00
52	A14	1fr brnz grn, *straw*	50.00	35.00
a.		"Reunion" double	360.00	375.00
		Nos. 34-52 (19)	504.75	317.25

Perf. 13½x14 stamps are counterfeits.
For surcharges and overprint see Nos. 56-59, 99-106, Q1.

French Colonies No. 52 Surcharged in Black

g

h

j

1893

No.	Type	Description	Unused	Used
53	A9(g)	2c on 20c red, *grn*	3.25	3.25
54	A9(h)	2c on 20c red, *grn*	6.00	6.00
55	A9(j)	2c on 20c red, *grn*	22.50	22.50
		Nos. 53-55 (3)	31.75	31.75

Reunion Nos. 47-48, 51-52 Surcharged in Black

1901

No.	Type	Description	Unused	Used
56	A14	5c on 40c red, *straw*	7.00	7.00
a.		Inverted surcharge	47.50	47.50
b.		No bar	240.00	240.00
c.		Thin "5"	1,400.	1,200.
d.		"5" inverted	1,400.	1,200.
57	A14	5c on 50c car, *rose*	7.75	7.25
a.		Inverted surcharge	47.50	47.50
b.		No bar	240.00	240.00
c.		Thin "5"		
58	A14	15c on 75c vio, *org*	22.50	22.50
a.		Inverted surcharge	57.50	57.50
b.		No bar	240.00	240.00
c.		Thin "5" and small "1"	47.50	47.50
d.		As "c," inverted	800.00	800.00
59	A14	15c on 1fr brnz grn, *straw*	19.00	19.00
a.		Inverted surcharge	57.50	57.50
b.		No bar	240.00	240.00
c.		Thin "5" and small "1"	47.50	47.50
d.		As "c," inverted		
		Nos. 56-59 (4)	56.25	55.75

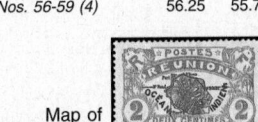

Map of
Réunion — A19

Coat of Arms and
View of St.
Denis — A20

View of St.
Pierre — A21

1907-30 Typo.

No.	Type	Description	Unused	Used
60	A19	1c vio & lt rose	.30	.30
61	A19	2c brn & ultra	.30	.30
62	A19	4c ol grn & red	.40	.40
a.		Center double	225.00	
63	A19	5c grn & red	1.35	.40
64	A19	5c org & vio ('22)	.30	.30
65	A19	10c car & grn	2.75	.30
66	A19	10c grn ('22)	.30	.30
67	A19	10c brn red & org red, *bluish* ('26)	.70	.70
68	A19	15c blk & ultra ('17)	.55	.40
a.		Center double	250.00	250.00
69	A19	15c gray grn & bl grn ('26)	.40	.40
70	A19	15c bl & lt red ('28)	.55	.45
71	A20	20c gray grn & bl grn	.45	.45
a.		Center omitted	1,100.	1,100.
72	A20	25c dp bl & vio brn	7.00	4.00
73	A20	25c lt brn & bl ('22)	.55	.55
74	A20	30c yel brn & grn	1.50	1.00

No.	Type	Description	Unused	Used
75	A20	30c rose & pale rose ('22)	1.50	1.50
76	A20	30c gray & car rose ('26)	.55	.55
77	A20	30c dp grn & yel grn ('28)	1.20	1.20
78	A20	35c ol grn & bl	1.75	1.10
79	A20	40c gray grn & brn ('25)	.70	.70
80	A20	45c vio & car rose	1.90	1.10
81	A20	45c red brn & ver ('25)	.90	.90
82	A20	45c vio & red org ('28)	3.00	2.75
83	A20	50c red brn & ultra	5.00	1.75
84	A20	50c bl & ultra ('22)	1.40	1.40
85	A20	50c yel & vio ('26)	1.10	1.10
86	A20	60c dk bl & yel brn ('25)	1.10	1.10
87	A20	65c vio & lt bl ('28)	1.60	1.40
88	A20	75c red & car rose	.80	.70
89	A20	75c ol brn & red vio ('28)	2.50	2.25
90	A20	90c brn red & brt red ('30)	9.00	8.25
91	A21	1fr ol grn & bl	1.50	1.40
92	A21	1fr blue ('25)	.95	.95
93	A21	1fr yel brn & lav ('28)	1.50	.70
94	A21	1.10fr org brn & rose lil ('28)	1.50	1.40
95	A21	1.50fr dk bl & ultra ('30)	16.00	16.00
96	A21	2fr red & grn	6.75	4.25
97	A21	3fr red vio ('30)	14.50	9.50
98	A21	5fr car & vio brn	11.50	6.75
		Nos. 60-98 (39)	105.60	79.05

For surcharges see Nos. 107-121, 178-180, B1-B3.

Stamps of 1892-1900 Surcharged in Black or Carmine

1912
Spacing between figures of surcharge 1.5mm (5c), 2mm (10c)

No.	Type	Description	Unused	Used
99	A14	5c on 2c brn, buff	1.60	1.60
100	A14	5c on 15c gray (C)	1.40	1.40
a.		Inverted surcharge	210.00	210.00
101	A14	5c on 20c red, grn	2.40	2.40
102	A14	5c on 25c blk, rose (C)	1.60	1.60
103	A14	5c on 30c brn, bis (C)	1.40	1.40
104	A14	10c on 40c red, straw	1.40	1.40
105	A14	10c on 50c brn, az (C)	5.75	5.75
106	A14	10c on 75c dp vio, org	9.50	9.50
		Nos. 99-106 (8)	25.05	25.05

Two spacings between the surcharged numerals are found on Nos. 99 to 106. For detailed listings, see the *Scott Classic Specialized Catalogue of Stamps and Covers.*

No. 62
Surcharged

1917

No.	Type	Description	Unused	Used
107	A19	1c on 4c ol grn & red	2.00	2.00
a.		Inverted surcharge	80.00	80.00
b.		Double surcharge	70.00	70.00
c.		In pair with unsurcharged #62	625.00	625.00

Stamps and
Types of 1907-30
Surcharged in
Black or Red

1922-33

No.	Type	Description	Unused	Used
108	A20	40c on 20c grn & yel	.80	.80
a.		Double surcharge, one inverted	175.00	175.00
b.		Center double	175.00	175.00
c.		Surcharge omitted	1,200.	1,200.
109	A20	50c on 45c red brn & ver ('33)	1.20	1.20
109A	A20	50c on 45c vio & red org ('33)	325.00	275.00
b.		Double surcharge	1,750.	
110	A20	50c on 65c vio & lt bl ('33)	1.20	1.20
111	A20	60c on 75c red & rose	.85	.85
a.		Double surcharge	225.00	225.00
112	A19	65c on 15c blk & ultra (R) ('25)	2.00	2.00
113	A19	85c on 15c blk & ultra (R) ('25)	2.00	2.00
114	A20	85c on 75c red & cer ('25)	2.25	2.25
115	A20	90c on 75c brn red & rose red ('25)	2.25	2.25
		Nos. 108-109,110-115 (8)	12.55	12.55

Stamps and Type
of 1907-30 Srchd.
in Black or Red

1924-27

No.	Type	Description	Unused	Used
116	A21	25c on 5fr car & brn	1.10	1.10
a.		Double surcharge	110.00	
117	A21	1.25fr on 1fr bl (R) ('26)	1.10	1.10
a.		Double surcharge	125.00	
118	A21	1.50fr on 1fr ind & ultra, *bluish* ('27)	1.50	1.50
a.		Double surcharge	140.00	
b.		Surcharge omitted	200.00	
119	A21	3fr on 5fr dl red & lt bl ('27)	4.25	3.00
120	A21	10fr on 5fr bl grn & brn red ('27)	19.50	17.00
121	A21	20fr on 5fr brn & mag ('27)	24.00	19.00
		Nos. 116-121 (6)	51.45	42.70

Common Design Types pictured following the introduction.

Colonial Exposition Issue
Common Design Types
1931 Engr. Perf. 12½
Name of Country Typo. in Black

No.	Type	Description	Unused	Used
122	CD70	40c dp green	5.50	5.50
123	CD71	50c violet	5.50	5.50
124	CD72	90c red orange	5.50	5.50
125	CD73	1.50fr dull blue	5.50	5.50
		Nos. 122-125 (4)	22.00	22.00

Cascade of
Salazie
A22

Waterfowl Lake
and Anchain Peak
A23

Léon Dierx
Museum, St.
Denis — A24

Perf. 12, 12½ and Compound
1933-40 Engr.

No.	Type	Description	Unused	Used
126	A22	1c violet	.25	.25
127	A22	2c dark brown	.25	.25
128	A22	3c rose vio ('40)	.25	.25
129	A22	4c olive green	.25	.25
130	A22	5c red orange	.25	.25
131	A22	10c ultramarine	.25	.25
132	A22	15c black	.25	.25
133	A22	20c indigo	.30	.25
134	A22	25c red brown	.40	.30
135	A22	30c dark green	.40	.40
136	A23	35c green ('38)	.55	.55
137	A23	40c ultramarine	.55	.55
138	A23	40c brn blk ('40)	.40	.40

139	A23	45c red violet	1.00	1.00
140	A23	45c green ('40)	.45	.45
141	A23	50c red	.30	.30
142	A23	55c brn org ('38)	1.50	1.00
143	A23	60c dull bl ('40)	.45	.45
144	A23	65c olive green	1.10	.80
145	A23	70c ol grn ('40)	.65	.65
146	A23	75c dark brown	5.00	4.25
147	A23	80c black ('38)	1.00	.80
148	A23	90c carmine	2.50	2.10
149	A23	90c dl rose vio ('39)	1.00	1.00
150	A23	1fr green	2.00	.70
151	A23	1fr dk car ('38)	2.50	.70
152	A23	1fr black ('40)	.70	.70
153	A24	1.25fr orange brown	.70	.55
154	A24	1.25fr brt car rose ('39)	1.00	1.00
155	A22	1.40fr pck bl ('40)	1.00	1.00
156	A24	1.50fr ultramarine	.40	.40
157	A24	1.60fr dk car rose ('40)	1.40	1.40
158	A24	1.75fr olive green	1.00	.65
159	A22	1.75fr dk bl ('38)	1.40	.70
160	A24	2fr vermilion	.55	.55
161	A22	2.25fr brt ultra ('39)	2.00	2.00
162	A24	2.50fr chnt ('40)	1.40	1.40
163	A24	3fr purple	.55	.55
164	A24	5fr magenta	.55	.55
165	A24	10fr dark blue	1.10	1.10
166	A24	20fr red brown	1.50	1.50
		Nos. 126-166 (41)	39.05	32.55

For overprints and surcharges see Nos. 177A, 181-220, 223, C1.
60c, 1fr without "RF," see Nos. 237A-238B.

Paris International Exposition Issue
Common Design Types

1937   **Perf. 13**

167	CD74	20c dp vio	2.25	2.25
168	CD75	30c dk grn	2.25	2.25
169	CD76	40c car rose	2.25	2.25
170	CD77	50c dk brn & blk	2.10	2.10
171	CD78	90c red	2.10	2.10
172	CD79	1.50fr ultra	2.25	2.25
		Nos. 167-172 (6)	13.20	13.20
		Set, never hinged	20.00	

Colonial Arts Exhibition Issue
Souvenir Sheet
Common Design Type

1937   **Imperf.**

173	CD74	3fr ultra	8.50	10.00
		Never hinged	16.00	

New York World's Fair Issue
Common Design Type

1939   **Engr.**   **Perf. 12½x12**

174	CD82	1.25fr car lake	1.40	1.40
175	CD82	2.25fr ultra	1.40	1.40
		Set, never hinged	4.50	

For overprints, see Nos. 221-222.

St. Denis Roadstead and Marshal Pétain — A25

1941   **Unwmk.**   **Perf. 11½x12**

176	A25	1fr brown		.80
177	A25	2.50fr blue		.80
		Set, never hinged	2.00	

Nos. 176-177 were issued by the Vichy government in France, but were not placed on sale in Réunion.
For surcharges, see Nos. B13-B14.

No. 144 Surcharged in Carmine

1943

177A		1fr on 65c olive grn	1.10	.65
		Never hinged	1.60	

De Pronis Landing on Reunion — A25a

1943   **Perf. 12½x12**

177B	A25a	60c blk brn & red	.55
177C	A25a	80c green & blue	.40
177D	A25a	1.50fr dk brn red	.35
177E	A25a	4fr ultra & red	.35
177F	A25a	5fr red brn & black	.55
177G	A25a	10fr violet & green	.65
		Nos. 177B-177G,C13A-C13F (12)	5.70
		Set, never hinged	8.00

300th Ann. of French settlement on Réunion. Nos. 177B-177G were issued by the Vichy government in France, but were not placed on sale in Réunion.

Stamps of 1907 Overprinted in Blue Violet

q

1943   **Unwmk.**   **Perf. 14x13½**

178	A19(q)	4c ol gray & pale red	6.00	6.00
179	A20(q)	75c red & lil rose	1.75	1.75
180	A21(q)	5fr car & vio brn	60.00	60.00

Stamps of 1933-40 Overprinted in Carmine, Black or Blue Violet

181	A22(r)	1c rose vio (C)	1.00	1.00
182	A22(r)	2c blk brn (C)	1.00	1.00
183	A22(r)	3c rose vio (C)	1.00	1.00
184	A22(r)	4c ol yel (C)	1.00	1.00
185	A22(r)	5c red org	1.00	1.00
186	A22(r)	10c ultra (C)	1.00	1.00
187	A22(r)	15c blk (C)	1.00	1.00
188	A22(r)	20c ind (C)	1.00	1.00
189	A22(r)	25c red brn (BIV)	1.25	1.25
190	A22(r)	30c dk grn (C)	1.40	1.40
191	A23(q)	35c green	1.00	1.00
192	A23(q)	40c dl ultra (C)	1.00	1.00
193	A23(q)	40c brn blk (C)	1.00	1.00
194	A23(q)	45c red vio (C)	1.00	1.00
195	A23(q)	45c green	1.00	1.00
196	A23(q)	50c org red	1.00	1.00
197	A23(q)	55c brn org	1.00	1.00
198	A23(q)	60c dl bl (C)	3.00	3.00
199	A23(q)	65c ol grn	1.00	1.00
200	A23(q)	70c ol grn (C)	2.25	2.25
201	A23(q)	75c dk brn (C)	5.25	5.25
202	A23(q)	80c blk (C)	1.00	1.00
203	A23(q)	90c dl rose vio	1.00	1.00
204	A23(q)	1fr green	1.00	1.00
205	A23(q)	1fr dk car	1.00	1.00
206	A23(q)	1fr blk (C)	3.00	3.00
207	A24(q)	1.25fr org brn (BIV)	1.00	1.00
208	A24(q)	1.25fr brt car rose	3.00	3.00
209	A22(r)	1.40fr pck bl (C)	2.00	2.00
210	A24(q)	1.50fr ultra (C)	1.00	1.00
211	A22(r)	1.60fr dk car rose	2.10	2.10
212	A24(q)	1.75fr ol grn (C)	2.75	2.75
213	A22(r)	1.75fr dk bl (C)	4.50	4.50
214	A24(q)	2fr vermilion	1.00	1.00
215	A22(r)	2.25fr brt ultra (C)	4.50	4.50
216	A22(r)	2.50fr chnt (BIV)	7.50	7.50
217	A24(q)	3fr pur (C)	1.00	1.00
218	A24(q)	5fr brn lake (BIV)	2.10	2.10
219	A24(q)	10fr dk bl (C)	8.50	8.50
220	A24(q)	20fr red brn (BIV)	13.00	13.00

New York World's Fair Issue Overprinted in Black or Carmine

221	CD82(q)	1.25fr car lake	4.00	4.00
222	CD82(q)	2.25fr ultra (C)	4.00	4.00
		Nos. 178-222 (45)	165.85	165.85
		Set, never hinged	235.00	

No. 177A Overprinted

1943   **Unwmk.**   **Perf. 12½**

223	A23	1fr on 65c ol grn	.85	.85

> **Catalogue values for unused stamps in this section, from this point to the end of the section, are for Never Hinged items.**

Produce of Réunion — A26

1943   **Photo.**   **Perf. 14½x14**

224	A26	5c dull brown	.25	.25
225	A26	10c blue & lt blue	.25	.25
226	A26	25c emerald	.25	.25
227	A26	30c dp orange	.25	.25
228	A26	40c dk slate grn	.25	.25
229	A26	80c rose violet	.65	.50
230	A26	1fr red brown	.25	.25
231	A26	1.50fr crimson	.65	.50
232	A26	2fr black	.65	.50
233	A26	2.50fr ultra	1.00	.70
234	A26	4fr dk violet	1.25	.90
235	A26	5fr bister	1.25	.90
236	A26	10fr dark brown	1.75	1.40
237	A26	20fr dark green	2.75	1.75
		Nos. 224-237 (14)	11.45	8.65

For surcharges see Nos. 240-247.

Type of 1933-40 without "RF"

1944   **Engr.**   **Perf. 12½**

237A	A23	60c dull blue	1.40	1.00
237B	A23	1fr black & blue	1.40	1.00

Nos. 237A-237B were issued by the Vichy government in France, but were not placed on sale in Réunion.

Eboue Issue
Common Design Type

1945   **Engr.**   **Perf. 13**

238	CD91	2fr black	1.00	1.00
239	CD91	25fr Prussian green	1.40	1.00

Nos. 224, 226 and 233 Surcharged in Carmine or Black

1945   **Perf. 14½x14**

240	A26	50c on 5c dl brn (C)	.30	.25
241	A26	60c on 5c dl brn (C)	.30	.25
242	A26	70c on 5c dl brn (C)	.30	.25
243	A26	1.20fr on 5c dl brn (C)	.70	.50
244	A26	2.40fr on 25c emer	.70	.50
245	A26	3fr on 25c emer	1.25	.90
246	A26	4.50fr on 25c emer	1.25	.90
247	A26	15fr on 2.50fr ultra (C)	1.75	1.10
		Nos. 240-247 (8)	6.55	4.65

Various double and inverted overprints exist for Nos. 240-247.

Cliff A27

Cutting Sugar Cane A28

Cascade A29

Banana Tree A30

Mountain Scene — A31

Ship Approaching Réunion — A32

1947   **Unwmk.**   **Photo.**   **Perf. 13½**

249	A27	10c org & grnsh blk	.25	.25
250	A27	30c org & brt bl	.25	.25
251	A27	40c org & brn	.25	.25
252	A28	50c bl grn & brn	.25	.25
253	A28	60c dk bl & brn	.25	.25
254	A28	80c brn & ol brn	.55	.45
255	A29	1fr dl bl & vio brn	.55	.45
256	A29	1.20fr bl grn & gray	.80	.65
257	A29	1.50fr org & brn vio	.80	.65
258	A30	2fr gray bl & bl grn	.80	.65
259	A30	3fr vio brn & bl grn	.80	.65
260	A30	3.60fr dl red & rose red	.90	.70
261	A30	4fr gray bl & buff	.80	.70
262	A31	5fr rose lil & brn	1.25	.70
263	A31	6fr bl & brn	1.50	.75
264	A31	10fr org & ultra	3.25	1.50
265	A32	15fr gray bl & vio brn	4.75	2.75
266	A32	20fr bl & org	6.50	4.00
267	A32	25fr rose lil & brn	8.00	4.25
		Nos. 249-267 (19)	32.50	20.10

Nos. 249-267 exist imperf. Value, set $100.

Stamps of France, 1945-49, Surcharged type "a" or "b" in Black or Carmine

On A147

Others

1949   **Unwmk.**   **Perf. 14x13½, 13**

268	A153	10c on 30c	.30	.25
269	A153	30c on 50c	.60	.25
270	A146	50c on 1fr	1.40	.90
271	A146	60c on 2fr	8.00	1.40
272	A147	1fr on 3fr	2.00	.70
273	A147	2fr on 4fr	8.00	1.40
274	A147	2.50fr on 5fr	20.00	11.00
275	A147	3fr on 6fr	2.25	1.40
276	A147	4fr on 10fr	2.00	1.60
277	A162	5fr on 20fr (C)	10.00	1.40
278	A147	6fr on 12fr	29.00	2.25
279	A160	7fr on 12fr	9.00	3.00
280	A165	8fr on 25fr (C)	37.50	3.25
281	A165	10fr on 25fr (C)	2.75	1.40
282	A174	11fr on 18fr (C)	16.00	2.25
		Nos. 268-282 (15)	148.80	32.65

The letters "C. F. A." are the initials of "Colonies Francaises d'Afrique," referring to the currency which is expressed in French Africa francs.
The surcharge on Nos. 277, 279, 282 includes two bars.

1950   **Perf. 14x13½**

283	A182	10c on 50c bl, red & yel	.55	.55
284	A182	1fr on 2fr grn, yel & red (#619)	10.00	3.50
285	A147	2fr on 5fr lt grn	18.00	4.25
		Nos. 283-285 (3)	28.55	8.30

France Nos. 630 & 623 Surcharged

1950-51   **Perf. 13**
286 A188 5fr on 20fr dk red   10.00 1.75
287 A185 8fr on 25fr dp ultra   10.00 1.75
         ('51)

Stamps of France, 1951-52, Surcharged in Black or Red

No. 288   No. 292

1951-52   **Perf. 14x13½, 13**
288 A182 50c on 1fr bl, red &   .70   .70
         yel
289 A182 1fr on 2fr vio bl, red   .70   .70
         & yel (#662)
290 A147 2fr on 5fr dl vio   4.25 2.00
291 A147 3fr on 6fr grn   8.00 1.60
292 A220 5fr on 20fr dk pur   3.00 1.75
         (R; '52)
293 A147 6fr on 12fr red org   9.00 2.00
         ('52)
294 A215 8fr on 40fr vio (R)   6.50   .70
         ('52)
295 A147 9fr on 18fr cerise   21.00 4.25
296 A208 15fr on 30fr ind (R)   11.00 2.25
         Nos. 288-296 (9)   64.15 15.95

The surcharge on Nos. 292, 294 and 296 include two bars.

France No. 697 Surcharged in Black

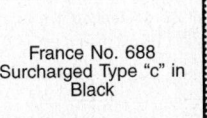

1953   **Perf. 14x13½**
297 A182 50c on 1fr blk, red &   .35   .25
         yel

France No. 688 Surcharged Type "c" in Black

Perf. 13
298 A230 3fr on 6fr dp plum &   1.20   .80
         car

France Nos. 703 and 705 Surcharged in Red or Blue

No. 299

No. 300

1954
299 A235 8fr on 40fr (R)   38.50 7.50
300 A235 20fr on 75fr   80.00 32.50

France Nos. 698, 721, 713, and 715 Surcharged in Black

No. 301   No. 304

301 A182 1fr on 2fr   4.75 2.10
302 A241 4fr on 10fr   4.50 1.25
303 A238 8fr on 40fr   11.00 1.60
304 A238 20fr on 75fr   14.50 1.60

The surcharge on Nos. 303 and 304 includes two bars.

France Nos. 737, 719 and 722-724 Surcharged in Black or Red

a

b

305 A182(b) 1fr on 2fr   .50   .50
306 A241(a) 2fr on 6fr (R)   .80   .50
307 A242(a) 6fr on 12fr   11.00 1.75
308 A241(b) 9fr on 18fr   12.00 5.00
309 A241(a) 10fr on 20fr   8.00 1.40
         Nos. 299-309 (11)   185.55 55.70

The surcharge on Nos. 306-308 includes two bars; on No. 309 three bars.

France No. 720 Surcharged in Red

1955   **Perf. 13**
310 A241 3fr on 8fr brt bl & dk   1.40 1.10
         grn

France Nos. 785, 774-779 Surcharged in Black or Red

No. 311   No. 317

1955-56   **Typo., Engr.**
Perf. 14x13½, 13
311 A182 50c on 1fr   .45   .30
312 A265 2fr on 6fr ('56)   1.20   .70
313 A265 3fr on 8fr   1.00   .50
314 A265 4fr on 10fr   1.25   .50
315 A265 5fr on 12fr (R)   1.30   .50
316 A265 6fr on 18fr (R)   1.00   .50
317 A265 10fr on 25fr   1.75   .50
         Nos. 311-317 (7)   7.95 3.50

The surcharge on Nos. 312-317 includes two bars.

France Nos. 801-804 Surcharged in Black or Red

No. 318   No. 319

No. 320   No. 321

1956   **Engr.**   **Perf. 13**
318 A280(a) 8fr on 30fr (R)   5.25 1.10
319 A280(b) 9fr on 40fr   7.75 3.00
320 A280(a) 15fr on 50fr   9.25 1.60
321 A280(a) 20fr on 75fr (R)   8.50 2.25
         Nos. 318-321 (4)   30.75 7.95

The surcharge on Nos. 318, 319 and 321 includes two bars.

France Nos. 837 and 839 Surcharged in Red

1957   **Perf. 13**
322 A294 7fr on 15fr   1.20   .55
323 A265 17fr on 70fr   6.75 2.10

The surcharge on Nos. 322-323 includes two bars.
No. 322 has three types of "7" in the sheet of 50. There are 34 of the "normal" 7; 10 of a slightly thinner 7, and 6 of a slightly thicker 7.

France Nos. 755-756, 833-834, 851-855, 908, 949 Surcharged in Black or Red Type "a", "b" or

d

Typographed, Engraved

1957-60   **Perf. 14x13½, 13**
324 A236(b) 2fr on 6fr   .30   .30
325 A302(b) 3fr on 10fr ('58)   .50   .50
326 A236(b) 4fr on 12fr   3.50   .75
327 A236(b) 5fr on 10fr   2.25 1.10
328 A303(b) 6fr on 18fr   1.25   .50
329 A302(a) 9fr on 25fr (R)
         ('58)   1.25   .65
330 A252(a) 10fr on 20fr (R)   1.75   .30
331 A252(a) 12fr on 25fr   6.75   .50
332 A303(a) 17fr on 35fr   3.75 1.75
333 A302(a) 20fr on 50fr   1.75   .80
334 A302(a) 25fr on 85fr   4.00 1.60
335 A339(d) 50fr on 1fr ('60)   3.00   .75
         Nos. 324-335 (12)   30.05 9.50

The surcharge includes two bars on Nos. 324, 326-327, 329-331, 333 and 335.

France Nos. 973, 939 and 968 Surcharged

e   f

1961-63   **Typo.**   **Perf. 14x13½**
336 A318(e) 2fr on 5c multi   .30   .25
  a. Double surcharge   300.00
  b. Inverted surcharge   1,000.   —
337 A336(e) 5fr on 10c brt
         grn   1.30   .50
338 A336(b) 5fr on 10c brt
         grn ('63)   1.60   .75
339 A349(f) 12fr on 25c lake
         & gray   .30   .30
         Nos. 336-339 (4)   3.50 1.80

The surcharge on No. 337 includes three bars. No. 338 has "b" surcharge and two bars.

France Nos. 943, 941 and 946 Surcharged in Black or Red

Engraved, Typographed

1961 **Unwmk.** **Perf. 13, 14x13½**
340 A338 7fr on 15c   1.00   .80
341 A337 10fr on 20c   .30   .30
342 A339 20fr on 50c (R)   17.00 4.50
         Nos. 340-342 (3)   18.30 5.60

Surcharge on No. 342 includes 3 bars.

France Nos. 1047-1048 Surcharged

No. 343

No. 344

1963, Jan. 2   **Engr.**   **Perf. 13**
343 A394 12fr on 25c   1.00   .95
344 A395 25fr on 50c   1.00   .95

1st television connection of the US and Europe through the Telstar satellite, July 11-12, 1962.

France Nos. 1040-1041, 1007 and 1009 Surcharged

No. 345   No. 346

No. 347

No. 348

Typographed, Engraved

1963   **Perf. 14x13½, 13**
345 A318 2fr on 5c   .30   .30
346 A318 5fr on 10c   .25   .25
347 A372 7fr on 15c   .60   .50
348 A372 20fr on 45c   1.25   .75
         Nos. 345-348 (4)   2.40 1.80

Two-line surcharge on No. 345; No. 347 has currency expressed in capital "F" and two heavy bars through old value; two thin bars on No. 348.

France No. 1078
Surcharged

1964, Feb. 8 **Engr.** *Perf. 13*
349 CD118 12fr on 25c 1.25 1.25
"PHILATEC," Intl. Philatelic and Postal Techniques Exhib., Paris, June 5-21, 1964.

France Nos. 1092, 1094
and 1102 Surcharged

Typographed, Engraved
1964 *Perf. 14x13½, 13*
350 A318 1fr on 2c .25 .25
351 A318 6fr on 18c .30 .30
352 A420 35fr on 70c 1.50 .95
  Nos. 350-352 (3) 2.05 1.50
Surcharge on No. 352 includes two bars.

France Nos. 1095, 1126, 1070
Surcharged

No. 353

No. 354

No. 355

1965
353 A318 15fr on 30c .50 .30
354 A440 25fr on 50c 1.00 .95
355 A408 30fr on 60c 1.50 1.00
  Nos. 353-355 (3) 3.00 2.25
Two bars obliterate old denomination on Nos. 354-355.

Etienne Regnault, "Le Taureau" and Coast of Reunion — A33

1965, Oct. 3 **Engr.** *Perf. 13*
356 A33 15fr bluish blk & dk car 1.00 .65
Tercentenary of settlement of Reunion.

France No. 985 Surcharged

1966, Feb. 13 **Engr.** *Perf. 13*
357 A360 10fr on 20c bl & car 1.60 .70

French Satellite A-1 Issue
France Nos. 1137-1138 Surcharged
in Red

1966, Mar. 27 **Engr.** *Perf. 13*
358 CD121 15fr on 30c 1.10 1.00
359 CD121 30fr on 60c 1.30 1.10
  a. Strip of 2 + label 3.50 3.00

France Nos. 1142, 1143, 1101 and
1127 Surcharged

No. 360

No. 361

1967-69 **Typo.** *Perf. 14x13*
360 A446 2fr on 5c bl & red .30 .30

Photo. *Perf. 13*
360A A446 10fr on 20c multi ('69) .30 .30

Engr.
361 A421 20fr on 40c multi 1.10 .95
362 A439 30fr on 60c bl & red brn 1.30 .75

EXPO '67 Issue
France No. 1177 Surcharged

1967, June 12 **Engr.** *Perf. 13*
363 A473 30fr on 60c dl bl & bl grn 2.40 1.75
EXPO '67, Montreal, Apr. 28-Oct. 27.

Lions Issue
France No. 1196 Surcharged in Blue

1967, Oct. 29 **Engr.** *Perf. 13*
364 A485 20fr on 40c 3.00 1.20
50th anniversary of Lions International.

France No. 1130 Surcharged in
Violet Blue

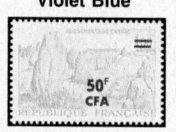

1968, Feb. 26 **Engr.** *Perf. 13*
365 A440 50fr on 1fr 2.75 1.60

France No. 1224 Surcharged

1968, Oct. 21 **Engr.** *Perf. 13*
366 A508 20fr on 40c multi 1.50 1.00
20 years of French Polar expeditions.

France Nos. 1230-1231
Surcharged

1969, Apr. 13 **Engr.** *Perf. 13*
367 A486 15fr on 30c green .65 .50
368 A486 20fr on 40c dp car .70 .30

France No. 1255 Surcharged

1969, Aug. 18 **Engr.** *Perf. 13*
370 A526 35fr on 70c multi 1.60 1.35
Napoleon Bonaparte (1769-1821).

France No. 1293
Surcharged

1971, Jan. 16 **Engr.** *Perf. 13*
371 A555 25fr on 50c rose car .90 .30

France No. 1301 Surcharged

1971, Apr. 13 **Engr.** *Perf. 13*
372 A562 40fr on 80c multi 2.00 1.40

France No. 1309
Surcharged

1971, June 5 **Engr.** *Perf. 13*
373 A569 15fr on 40c multi 1.00 .70
Aid for rural families.

France No. 1312
Surcharged

1971, Aug. 30 **Engr.** *Perf. 13*
374 A571 45fr on 90c multi 1.15 .95

France No. 1320 Surcharged

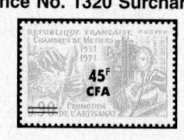

1971, Oct. 18 **Engr.** *Perf. 13*
375 A573 45fr on 90c multi 1.40 1.00
40th anniversary of the first assembly of presidents of artisans' guilds.

Réunion
Chameleon
A34

1971, Nov. 8 **Photo.** *Perf. 13*
376 A34 25fr multi 1.40 1.10
Nature protection.

Common Design Type and

De Gaulle in Brazzaville,
1944 — A35

Designs: No. 377, Gen. de Gaulle, 1940. No. 379, de Gaulle entering Paris, 1944. No. 380, Pres. de Gaulle, 1970.

1971, Nov. 9 **Engr.**
377 CD134 25fr black 1.60 1.60
378 A35 25fr ultra 1.60 1.60
379 A35 25fr rose red 1.60 1.60
380 CD134 25fr black 1.60 1.60
  a. Strip of 4 + label 9.25 8.00
Charles de Gaulle (1890-1970), president of France.
Nos. 377-380 printed se-tenant in sheets of 20 containing 5 strips of 4 plus labels with Cross of Lorraine and inscription. Exists imperf. Value, strip $200.

France No. 1313 Surcharged

1972, Jan. 17 **Engr.** *Perf. 13*
381 A570 50fr on 1.10fr multi 1.40 1.15

Map of South Indian Ocean, Penguin and Ships — A36

1972, Jan. 31 **Engr.** *Perf. 13*
382 A36 45fr blk, bl & ocher 2.25 2.25
Bicentenary of the discovery of the Crozet and Kerguelen Islands.

France No. 1342
Surcharged in Red

1972, May. 8 **Engr.** *Perf. 13*
383 A590 15fr on 40c red 1.00 .95
20th anniv. of Blood Donors' Assoc. of Post and Telecommunications Employees.

France Nos. 1345-1346 Surcharged

1972, June 5 **Typo.** *Perf. 14x13*
384 A593 15fr on 30c multi .45 .45
385 A593 25fr on 50c multi .75 .65
Introduction of postal code system.

France No. 1377 Surcharged in Ultramarine

1973, June 12   **Engr.**   *Perf. 13*
386 A620 45fr on 90c multi   2.00 1.35

France No.
1374
Surcharged
in
Ultramarine

France No. 1336
Srchd. in Red

1973   **Engr.**   *Perf. 13*
387 A617 50fr on 1fr multi (U)   1.15 .95
388 A586 100fr on 2fr multi (R)   2.00 1.10

On No. 388, two bars cover "2.00".
Issue dates: 50fr, June 24; 100fr, Oct. 13.

France No. 1231C
Surcharged in Black

1973, Nov.   **Typo.**   *Perf. 14x13*
389 A486 15fr on 30c bl grn   5.00 .80

France No. 1390 Surcharged in Red

1974, Jan. 20   **Engr.**   *Perf. 13*
390 A633 25fr on 50c multi   .70 .70

ARPHILA 75 Phil. Exhib., Paris, June 1975.

France Nos. 1394-1397 Surcharged in Black, Ultramarine or Brown

No. 391

No. 394

Engr. (#391, 393), Photo. (#392, 394)
1974   *Perf. 12x13, 13x12*
391 A637 100fr on 2fr (Blk)   2.50 2.40
392 A638 100fr on 2fr (U)   3.25 2.40
393 A639 100fr on 2fr (Br)   3.25 2.40
394 A640 100fr on 2fr (U)   3.25 2.40
       Nos. 391-394 (4)   12.25 9.60

Nos. 391-394 printed in sheets of 25 with
alternating labels publicizing "ARPHILA 75,"
Paris June 6-16, 1975.
Two bars obliterate original denomination on
Nos. 391-393.

France No. 1401 Surcharged in Red

1974, Apr. 29   **Engr.**   *Perf. 13*
395 A644 45fr on 90c multi   1.90 1.40

Reorganized sea rescue organization.

France No. 1415 Surcharged in Ultramarine

1974, Oct. 6   **Engr.**   *Perf. 13*
396 A657 60fr on 1.20fr multi   1.60 1.35

Centenary of Universal Postal Union.

France Nos. 1292A and 1294B Surcharged in Ultramarine

1974, Oct. 19   **Typo.**   *Perf. 14x13*
397 A555 30fr on 60c grn   1.75 1.60
       Engr.
       Perf. 13
398 A555 40fr on 80c car rose   2.10 1.75

SEMI-POSTAL STAMPS

   No. 65
Surcharged in
Black or Red

1915   **Unwmk.**   *Perf. 14x13½*
B1 A19 10c + 5c (Bk)   160.00 120.00
   a. Inverted surcharge   450.00 350.00
B2 A19 10c + 5c (R)   1.75 1.75
   a. Inverted surcharge   77.50 77.50
   b. Double surcharge, both in-
       verted   675.00 675.00

No. 65
Surcharged in
Red

1916
B3 A19 10c + 5c   1.90 1.90

Curie Issue
Common Design Type

1938   *Perf. 13*
B4 CD80 1.75fr + 50c brt ultra   14.00 14.00
      Never hinged   24.00

French Revolution Issue
Common Design Type

1939   **Photo.**   **Unwmk.**
Name and Value Typo. in Black
B5 CD83 45c + 25c grn   12.50 12.50
B6 CD83 70c + 30c brn   12.50 12.50
B7 CD83 90c + 35c red
       org   12.50 12.50
B8 CD83 1.25fr + 1fr rose
       pink   12.50 12.50
B9 CD83 2.25fr + 2fr blue   12.50 12.50
       Nos. B5-B9 (5)   62.50 62.50
      Set, never hinged   110.00

See CB1.

Common Design Type and

Artillery
Colonel
SP1

Colonial Infantry
SP2

1941   **Unwmk.**   *Perf. 13½*
B10 SP1 1fr + 1fr red   1.60
B11 CD86 1.50fr + 3fr claret   1.60
B12 SP2 2.50fr + 1fr blue   1.60
       Nos. B10-B12 (3)   4.80
      Set, never hinged   6.50

Nos. B10-B12 were issued by the Vichy
government in France, but were not placed on
sale in Reunion. Nos. B10-B12 exist imperf.
Value, set $200.

Nos. 176-177 Surcharged in Black or Red

1944   **Engr.**   *Perf. 12½x12*
B13 50c + 1.50fr on 2.50fr deep
     blue (R)   .80
B14 + 2.50fr on 1fr yel brn   .80
      Set, never hinged   2.00

Colonial Development Fund.
Nos. B13-B14 were issued by the Vichy
government in France, but were not placed on
sale in Réunion.

Catalogue values for unused
stamps in this section, from this
point to the end of the section, are
for Never Hinged items.

Red Cross Issue
Common Design Type

1944   *Perf. 14½x14*
B15 CD90 5fr + 20fr black   1.60 1.10

The surtax was for the French Red Cross
and national relief.

France Nos. B365-B366
Surcharged in Black

1962, Dec. 10   **Engr.**   *Perf. 13*
B16 SP219 10 + 5fr on 20 + 10c   2.50 2.50
B17 SP219 12 + 5fr on 25 + 10c   2.75 2.75

The surtax was for the Red Cross.

France Nos. B374-B375
Surcharged in Red

1963, Dec. 9
B18 SP223 10 + 5fr on 20 + 10c   3.00 3.00
B19 SP223 12 + 5fr on 25 + 10c   3.00 3.00

Centenary of the Intl. Red Cross. The surtax
was for the Red Cross.

France Nos. B385-B386
Surcharged in Dark Blue

1964, Dec. 13   **Unwmk.**   *Perf. 13*
B20 SP230 10 + 5fr on 20 + 10c   1.75 1.75
B21 SP230 12 + 5fr on 25 + 10c   1.90 1.90

Jean Nicolas Corvisart (1755-1821) and
Dominique Larrey (1766-1842), physicians.
The surtax was for the Red Cross.

France Nos. B392-B393
Surcharged in Black

1965, Dec. 12   **Engr.**   *Perf. 13*
B22 SP233 12 + 5fr on 25 + 10c   1.60 1.60
B23 SP233 15 + 5fr on 30 + 10c   1.60 1.60

The surtax was for the Red Cross.

France Nos. B402-B403
Surcharged in Black

1966, Dec. 11   **Engr.**   *Perf. 13*
B24 SP237 12 + 5fr on 25 + 10c   1.50 1.50
B25 SP237 15 + 5fr on 30 + 10c   1.50 1.50

The surtax was for the Red Cross.

France Nos. B409-B410
Surcharged in Black

1967, Dec. 17   **Engr.**   *Perf. 13*
B26 SP240 12 + 5fr on 25 + 10c   3.00 3.00
B27 SP240 15 + 5fr on 30 + 10c   3.75 3.75

Surtax for the Red Cross.

France Nos. B421-B424
Surcharged in Black

1968-69   **Engr.**   *Perf. 13*
B28 SP244 12 + 5fr on 25 + 10c   1.70 1.50
B29 SP244 15 + 5fr on 30 + 10c   1.90 1.50
B30 SP244 20 + 7fr on 40 + 15c
      ('69)   1.60 1.50
B31 SP244 20 + 7fr on 40 + 15c
      ('69)   1.60 1.50
      Nos. B28-B31 (4)   6.80 6.00

The surtax was for the Red Cross.

France No. B425 Surcharged in Black

1969, Mar. 17   **Engr.**   *Perf. 13*
B32 SP245 15fr + 5fr on 30c +
      10c   1.40 1.40
      Stamp Day.

France No. B440
Surcharged in Black

1970, Mar. 16   Engr.   *Perf. 13*
B33 SP249 20fr + 5fr on 40c + 10c   1.10   .95
Stamp day.

France Nos. B443-B444
Surcharged in Black

1970, Dec. 14   Engr.   *Perf. 13*
B34 SP252 20 + 7fr on 40 + 15c   2.40   2.00
B35 SP252 20 + 7fr on 40 + 15c   2.40   2.40
The surtax was for the Red Cross.

France No. B451 Surcharged in Black

1971, Mar. 29   Engr.   *Perf. 13*
B36 SP254 25fr + 5fr on 50c + 10c   1.10   .90
Stamp Day.

France Nos. B452-B453
Surcharged in Black

1971, Dec. 13
B37 SP255 15fr + 5fr on 30c + 10c   1.40   1.40
B38 SP255 25fr + 5fr on 50c + 10c   1.40   1.40
The surtax was for the Red Cross.

France No. B460
Surcharged in Black

1972, Mar. 20   Engr.   *Perf. 13*
B39 SP257 25fr + 5fr on 50c + 10c   1.20   1.20
Stamp Day.

France Nos. B461-B462
Surcharged in Red or Green

1972, Dec. 16   Engr.   *Perf. 13*
B40 SP258 15 + 5fr on 30 + 10c   1.20   1.20
B41 SP258 25 + 5fr on 50 + 10c (G)   1.40   1.40
Surtax was for the Red Cross.

France No. B470 Surcharged in Red

1973, Mar. 26   Engr.   *Perf. 13*
B42 SP260 25fr +5fr on 50c +10c   1.40   1.40
Stamp Day.

France Nos. B471-B472
Surcharged in Red

1973, Dec. 3   Engr.   *Perf. 13*
B43 SP261 15 +5fr on 30c +10c   1.40   1.40
B44 SP261 25 +5fr on 50c +10c   1.40   1.40
Surtax was for the Red Cross.

France No. B477
Surcharged

1974, Mar. 11   Engr.   *Perf. 13*
B45 SP263 25fr + 5fr on 50c + 10c   1.10   1.10
Stamp Day.

France Nos. B479-B480
Surcharged in Green or Red

1974, Nov. 30   Engr.   *Perf. 13*
B46 SP265 30 + 7fr on 60 + 15c (G)   1.40   1.40
B47 SP266 40 + 7fr on 80 + 15c (R)   1.40   1.40
Surtax was for the Red Cross.

AIR POST STAMPS

No. 141 Ovptd. in Blue

1937, Jan. 23   Unwmk.   *Perf. 12½*
C1 A23 50c red   290.00   250.00
   a.   Vert. pair, one without overprint   1,800.   1,800.
   b.   Inverted overprint   6,000.
   c.   As "b," in pair with unoverprinted stamp   26,000.
Flight of the "Roland Garros" from Reunion to France by aviators Laurent, Lenier and Touge in Jan.-Feb., 1937.

Airplane and Landscape — AP2

1938, Mar. 1   Engr.   *Perf. 12½*
C2 AP2 3.65fr slate blue & car   1.00   .90
C3 AP2 6.65fr brown & org red   1.00   .90
C4 AP2 9.65fr car & ultra   1.00   .90
C5 AP2 12.65fr brown & green   2.00   1.50
   Nos. C2-C5 (4)   5.00   4.20
   Set, never hinged   7.00
For overprints see Nos. C14-C17.

Plane and Bridge over East River AP3

Plane and Landscape AP4

1942, Oct. 19   *Perf. 12x12½*
C6 AP3 50c olive & pur   .35
C7 AP3 1fr dk bl & scar   .35
C8 AP3 2fr brn & blk   .60
C9 AP3 3fr rose lil & grn   1.10
C10 AP3 5fr red org & red brn   1.10
Frame Engr., Center Photo.
C11 AP4 10fr dk grn, red org & vio   1.10
C12 AP4 20fr dk bl, brn vio & red   1.10
C13 AP4 50fr brn car, Prus grn & bl   1.60
   Nos. C6-C13 (8)   7.30
   Set, never hinged   9.50
Nos. C6-C13 were issued by the Vichy government in France, but were not placed on sale in Réunion.

De Poivre AP4a

1943   *Perf. 12½x12*
C13A AP4a 1fr sepia & red   .25
C13B AP4a 2fr green & blue   .35
C13C AP4a 3fr dk brown red   .40
C13D AP4a 5fr ultra & red   .55
C13E AP4a 10fr red brn & blk   .55
C13F AP4a 20fr violet & green   .75
   Nos. C13A-C13F (6)   2.85
   Set, never hinged   4.00
300th Ann. of French settlement on Réunion. Nos. C13A-C13F were issued by the Vichy government in France, but were not placed on sale in Réunion.

Nos. C2-C5 Overprinted in Black or Carmine

1943   Unwmk.   *Perf. 12½*
C14 AP2 3.65fr sl bl & car   5.50   5.50
C15 AP2 6.65fr brn & org red   5.50   5.50
C16 AP2 9.65fr car & ultra (C)   5.50   5.50
C17 AP2 12.65fr brn & grn   5.50   5.50
   Nos. C14-C17 (4)   22.00   22.00
   Set, never hinged   32.50

> **Catalogue values for unused stamps in this section, from this point to the end of the section, are for Never Hinged items.**

Common Design Type
1944   Photo.   *Perf. 14½x14*
C18 CD87 1fr dk org   .50   .30
C19 CD87 1.50fr brt red   .50   .30
C20 CD87 5fr brn red   .70   .45
C21 CD87 10fr black   1.10   .80
C22 CD87 25fr ultra   1.25   .95
C23 CD87 50fr dk grn   1.25   .95
C24 CD87 100fr plum   1.75   1.25
   Nos. C18-C24 (7)   7.05   5.00

Victory Issue
Common Design Type
1946, May 8   Engr.   *Perf. 12½*
C25 CD92 8fr olive gray   1.10   .90
European victory of the Allied Nations in WWII.

Chad to Rhine Issue
Common Design Types
1946, June 6
C26 CD93 5fr orange   1.40   .85
C27 CD94 10fr sepia   1.40   .85
C28 CD95 15fr grnsh blk   1.40   .85
C29 CD96 20fr lilac rose   1.90   1.25

C30 CD97 25fr greenish blue   1.90   1.25
C31 CD98 50fr green   2.25   1.50
   Nos. C26-C31 (6)   10.25   6.55

Shadow of Plane AP5

Plane over Réunion — AP6

Air View of Réunion and Shadow of Plane AP7

Perf. 13x12½
1947, Mar. 24   Photo.   Unwmk.
C32 AP5 50fr ol grn & bl gray   11.00   8.00
C33 AP6 100fr dk brn & org   17.00   12.50
C34 AP7 200fr dk bl & org   21.00   14.00
   Nos. C32-C34 (3)   49.00   34.50

France, Nos. C18-C21
Surcharged in Carmine or Black

1949   Unwmk.   *Perf. 13*
C35 AP7 20fr on 40fr (C)   3.75   1.25
C36 AP8 25fr on 50fr   4.75   1.40
C37 AP9 50fr on 100fr (C)   11.00   4.25
C38 AP10 100fr on 200fr   55.00   21.00
   Nos. C35-C38 (4)   74.50   27.90

France Nos. C24, C26 and C27 Surcharged in Black

No. C39

No. C40

No. C41

1949-51
C39 AP12 100fr on 200fr ('51)   145.00   26.50
C40 AP12 200fr on 500fr   55.00   21.00
C41 AP13 500fr on 1000fr ('51)   325.00   210.00
   Nos. C39-C41 (3)   525.00   257.50

France Nos. C29-C32 Surcharged in Blue or Red

No. C42

No. C43

No. C44

No. C45

1954, Feb. 10
C42 AP15 50fr on 100fr 3.50 1.25
C43 AP15 100fr on 200fr (R) 5.50 1.40
C44 AP15 200fr on 500fr 45.00 12.50
C45 AP15 500fr on 1000fr 37.50 12.50
Nos. C42-C45 (4) 91.50 27.65

France Nos. C35-C36 Surcharged in Red or Black

No. C46

No. C47

1957-58   **Engr.**   *Perf. 13*
C46 AP17 200fr on 500fr (R) 25.00 6.75
C47 AP17 500fr on 1000fr
   ('58) 25.00 13.00

France Nos. C37, C39-C40 Surcharged in Red or Black

No. C48

No. C49

No. C50

1961-64
C48 AP15 100fr on 2fr 6.75 1.40
C49 AP17 200fr on 5fr 7.00 3.25
C50 AP17 500fr on 10fr (B;'64) 16.00 6.25
Nos. C48-C50 (3) 29.75 10.90

France No. C41 Surcharged in Red

1967, Jan. 27   **Engr.**   *Perf. 13*
C51 AP17 100fr on 2fr sl bl & ind 2.25 .80

France No. C45 Surcharged in Red

1972, May 14   **Engr.**   *Perf. 13*
C52 AP21 200fr on 5fr multi 5.00 1.75

AIR POST SEMI-POSTAL STAMP

French Revolution Issue
Common Design Type

1939   **Unwmk.**   *Perf. 13*
Name and Value Typo. in Orange
CB1 CD83 3.65fr + 4fr brn blk 25.00 25.00
   Never hinged 37.50

Felix Guyon Hospital, St. Denis SPAP1

Perf. 13½x12½

1942, June 22   **Engr.**
CB2 SPAP1 1.50fr + 3.50fr lt grn 1.00
CB3 SPAP1 2fr + 6fr yel brn 1.00
   Set, never hinged 2.50

   Native children's welfare fund.
   Nos. CB2-CB3 were issued by the Vichy government in France, but were not placed on sale in Réunion.

Colonial Education Fund
Common Design Type

1942, June 22
CB4 CD86a 1.20fr + 1.80fr blue
    & red .90
   Never hinged 1.25

   No. CB4 was issued by the Vichy government in France, but was not placed on sale in Réunion.

POSTAGE DUE STAMPS

D1

1889-92   **Unwmk. Type-set**   *Imperf.*
Without Gum
J1 D1 5c black 29.00 16.00
J2 D1 10c black 35.00 16.00
J3 D1 15c black ('92) 67.50 42.50
J4 D1 20c black 50.00 27.50
J5 D1 30c black 45.00 27.50
Nos. J1-J5 (5) 226.50 129.50

   Ten varieties of each value.
   Nos. J1-J2, J4-J5 issued on yellowish paper in 1889; Nos. J1-J3, J5 on bluish white paper in 1892.
   Nos. J1-J5 exist with double impression. Values, each $125-$190.

D2

1907   **Typo.**   *Perf. 14x13½*
J6 D2 5c carmine, *yel* .90 .90
J7 D2 10c blue, *bl* .90 .90
J8 D2 15c black, *bluish* 1.50 1.50
J9 D2 20c carmine 1.50 1.50
J10 D2 30c green, *grnsh* 2.25 2.25
J11 D2 50c red, *green* 2.60 2.60
J12 D2 60c carmine, *bl* 2.60 2.60
J13 D2 1fr violet 3.00 3.00
Nos. J6-J13 (8) 15.25 15.25
   Set, never hinged 27.50

Type of 1907 Issue Surcharged

1927
J14 D2 2fr on 1fr org red 12.50 12.50
J15 D2 3fr on 1fr org brn 12.50 12.50
   Set, never hinged 40.00

Arms of Réunion — D3

1933   **Engr.**   *Perf. 13x13½*
J16 D3 5c deep violet .25 .25
J17 D3 10c dark green .25 .25
J18 D3 15c orange brown .25 .25
J19 D3 20c light red .35 .35
J20 D3 30c olive green .35 .35
J21 D3 50c ultramarine .80 .80
J22 D3 60c black brown .80 .80
J23 D3 1fr light violet .80 .80
J24 D3 2fr deep blue .80 .80
J25 D3 3fr carmine 1.00 1.00
Nos. J16-J25 (10) 5.65 5.65
   Set, never hinged 8.75

> **Catalogue values for unused stamps in this section, from this point to the end of the section, are for Never Hinged items.**

Numeral — D4

1947   **Unwmk.**   **Photo.**   *Perf. 13*
J26 D4 10c dark violet .25 .25
J27 D4 30c brown .25 .25
J28 D4 50c blue green .25 .25
J29 D4 1fr orange .60 .45
J30 D4 2fr red violet .60 .45
J31 D4 3fr red brown .85 .65
J32 D4 4fr blue 1.50 1.10
J33 D4 5fr henna brown 2.00 1.40
J34 D4 10fr slate green 2.00 1.40
J35 D4 20fr violet blue 2.00 .90
Nos. J26-J35 (10) 10.30 7.10

France, Nos. J83-J92 Surcharged in Black

1949-53
J36 D5 10c on 1fr brt ultra .25 .25
J37 D5 50c on 2fr turq bl .45 .40
J38 D5 1fr on 3fr brn org .60 .40
J39 D5 2fr on 4fr dp vio .60 .40
J40 D5 3fr on 5fr brt pink 6.50 2.75
J41 D5 5fr on 10fr red org 1.10 .70
J42 D5 10fr on 20fr ol bis 2.00 2.00
J43 D5 20fr on 50fr dk grn
   ('50) 12.50 5.50
J44 D5 50fr on 100fr dp grn
   ('53) 30.00 13.00
Nos. J36-J44 (9) 54.00 25.40

France Nos. J93, J95-J96 Surcharged

1962-63   **Typo.**   *Perf. 14x13½*
J46 D6 1fr on 5c brt pink
   ('63) 3.00 1.10
J47 D6 10fr on 20c ol bis ('63) 5.50 2.75
J48 D6 20fr on 50c dk grn 22.00 12.50
Nos. J46-J48 (3) 30.50 16.35

France Nos. J98-J102, J104-J105 Surcharged

1964-71   **Unwmk.**   *Perf. 14x13½*
J49 D7 1fr on 5c .25 .25
J50 D7 5fr on 10c .30 .25
J51 D7 7fr on 15c .50 .45
J52 D7 10fr on 20c ('71) 1.40 .55
J53 D7 15fr on 30c .65 .45

J54 D7 20fr on 50c .80 .55
J55 D7 50fr on 1fr 1.40 1.25
Nos. J49-J55 (7) 5.30 3.75

PARCEL POST STAMPS

Frame Typographed; Center Handstamped PP1

1890-1903   **Unwmk.**   **Typo.**   *Imperf.*
Q1 PP1 10c black, *yellow*,
   black frame 400.00 200.00
Q2 PP1 10c black, *yellow*,
   ultra frame 110.00 100.00
Q3 PP1 10c black, *yellow*, bl
   grn frame 30.00 27.50

No. 40 Overprinted

1906   **Unwmk.**   *Perf. 14x13½*
Q4 A14 10c red 22.50 22.50

Fiscal Stamps Surcharged — PP2

1907-23   **Unwmk.**   **Typo.**   *Perf. 14*
Q5 PP2 10c blk on grayish
   brn ('07) 17.50 15.00
Q6 PP2 10c red on gray
   ('23) 17.50 15.00

FRENCH COLONIES

'french 'kä-lə-nēz

From 1859 to 1906 and from 1943 to 1945 special stamps were issued for use in all French Colonies which did not have stamps of their own.

100 Centimes = 1 Franc

Catalogue values for unused stamps in this country are for Never Hinged items, beginning with Scott B1 in the semi-postal section and Scott J23 in the postage due section.

Perforations: Nos. 1-45 are known variously perforated privately.
Gum: Many of Nos. 1-45 were issued without gum. Some were gummed locally.
Reprints: Nos. 1-7, 9-12, 24, 26-42, 44 and 45 were reprinted officially in 1887. These reprints are ungummed and the colors of both design and paper are deeper or brighter than the originals. Value for Nos. 1-6, $20 each.

Eagle and Crown — A1

1859-65		**Unwmk.**	**Typo.**	**Imperf.**
1	A1	1c ol grn, *pale bl* ('62)	24.00	27.50
2	A1	5c yel grn, *grnsh* ('62)	24.00	16.00
3	A1	10c bister, *yel*	32.50	8.00
a.		Pair, one sideways	1,000.	525.00
4	A1	20c bl, *bluish* ('65)	35.00	13.50
5	A1	40c org, *yelsh*	27.50	13.50
6	A1	80c car rose, *pnksh* ('65)	110.00	60.00
		Nos. 1-6 (6)	253.00	138.50

For surcharges, see Reunion Nos. 1-4.

Napoleon III
A2   A3

Ceres
A4

Napoleon III
A5

1871-72				**Imperf.**
7	A2	1c ol grn, *pale bl* ('72)	80.00	80.00
8	A3	5c yel grn, *grnsh* ('72)	1,000.	400.00
9	A4	10c bis, *yelsh*	375.00	130.00
a.		Tête bêche pair	55,000.	22,500.
10	A4	15c bis, *yelsh* ('72)	325.00	13.00
11	A4	20c blue, *bluish*	750.00	125.00
a.		Tête bêche pair	—	18,000.
12	A4	25c bl, *bluish* ('72)	175.00	13.00
13	A5	30c brn, *yelsh*	175.00	60.00
14	A4	40c org, *yelsh* (I)	250.00	13.00
a.		Type II	3,500.	650.00
b.		Pair, types I & II	7,250.	1,750.
15	A5	80c rose, *pnksh*	1,100.	115.00
		Nos. 7-15 (9)	4,230.	949.00

For 40c types I-II see illustrations over France #1.
For surcharges, see Reunion Nos. 5-6.
See note after France No. 9 for additional information on Nos. 8-9, 11-12, 14.

Ceres
A6   A7

1872-77				**Imperf.**
16	A6	1c ol grn, *pale bl* ('73)	13.00	14.50
17	A6	2c red brn, *yelsh* ('76)	475.00	750.00
18	A6	4c gray ('76)	11,000.	475.00
19	A6	5c grn, *pale bl* ('76)	17.50	9.50
20	A7	10c bis, *rose* ('76)	240.00	13.00
21	A7	15c bister ('77)	525.00	100.00
22	A7	30c brn, *yelsh*	130.00	21.00
23	A7	80c rose, *pnksh* ('73)	625.00	140.00

No. 17 was used only in Cochin China, 1876-77. Excellent forgeries of Nos. 17 and 18 exist.
With reference to the stamps of France and French Colonies in the same designs and colors see the note after France No. 9.

Peace and Commerce — A8

1877-78		**Type I**		**Imperf.**
24	A8	1c grn, *grnsh*	35.00	45.00
25	A8	4c grn, *grnsh*	24.00	14.50
26	A8	30c brn, *yelsh* ('78)	52.50	52.50
27	A8	40c ver, *straw*	35.00	21.00
28	A8	75c rose, *rose* ('78)	75.00	100.00
29	A8	1fr brnz grn, *straw*	60.00	67.50
		Nos. 24-29 (6)	281.50	300.50

		Type II		
30	A8	2c grn, *grnsh*	17.50	11.00
31	A8	5c grn, *grnsh*	24.00	5.50
32	A8	10c grn, *grnsh*	125.00	24.00
33	A8	15c gray, *grnsh*	250.00	72.50
34	A8	20c red brn, *straw*	52.50	9.50
35	A8	25c ultra *bluish*	52.50	8.75
a.		25c blue, *bluish* ('78)	4,250.	175.00
36	A8	35c vio blk, *org* ('78)	67.50	32.50
		Nos. 30-36 (7)	589.00	163.75
		Nos. 24-36 (13)	870.50	464.25

		Type II		
1878-80				
38	A8	1c blk, *lil bl*	21.00	21.00
39	A8	2c brn, *buff*	21.00	24.00
40	A8	4c claret, *lav*	32.50	45.00
41	A8	10c blk, *lav* ('79)	120.00	27.50
42	A8	15c blue ('79)	35.00	17.50
43	A8	20c red, *grn* ('79)	87.50	17.50
44	A8	25c blk, *red* ('79)	600.00	275.00
45	A8	40c yel, *straw* ('80)	725.00	32.50
		Nos. 38-45 (8)	1,642.	460.00

No. 44 was used only in Mayotte, Nossi-Be and New Caledonia. Forgeries exist.
The 3c yellow, 3c gray, 15c yellow, 20c blue, 25c rose and 5fr lilac were printed together with the reprints, and were never issued.
For stamps of type A8 surcharged and with "SPM" see St. Pierre & Miquelon Nos. 1-8.

Commerce — A9

1881-86				**Perf. 14x13½**
46	A9	1c blk, *lil bl*	5.50	4.75
47	A9	2c brn, *buff*	5.50	4.75
48	A9	4c claret, *lav*	5.50	5.50
49	A9	5c grn, *grnsh*	6.50	3.25
50	A9	10c blk, *lavender*	11.00	4.75
51	A9	15c blue	16.00	3.25
52	A9	20c red, *yel grn*	52.50	18.00
53	A9	25c yel, *straw*	17.50	5.50
54	A9	25c blk, *rose* ('86)	24.00	3.25
55	A9	30c brn, *bis*	45.00	21.00
56	A9	35c vio blk, *yel org*	40.00	30.00
a.		35c violet black, *yellow*	100.00	52.50
57	A9	40c ver, *straw*	45.00	27.50
58	A9	75c car, *rose*	120.00	60.00
59	A9	1fr brnz grn, *straw*	80.00	45.00
		Nos. 46-59 (14)	474.00	236.50

Nos. 46-59 exist imperforate. They are proofs and were not used for postage, except the 10c.
For stamps of type A9 surcharged with numerals see: Cochin China, Diego Suarez, Gabon, Malagasy (Madagascar), Nossi-Be, New Caledonia, Reunion, Senegal, Tahiti.
For stamps of type A9 surcharged and with "MQE" see Martinique Nos. 3-4. For stamps of

type A9 surcharged and with "SPM" see St. Pierre & Miquelon Nos. 9-11, 15-18.

SEMI-POSTAL STAMPS

Catalogue values for unused stamps in this section are for Never Hinged items.

Resistance Fighters — SP1

1943		**Unwmk.**	**Litho.**	**Rouletted**
B1	SP1	1.50fr + 98.50fr ind & gray	47.50	65.00
		Without label	21.00	35.00

The surtax was for the benefit of patriots and the French Committee of Liberation.
No. B1 was printed in sheets of 10 (5x2) with adjoining labels showing the Lorraine cross.

Colonies Offering Aid to France — SP2

1943				**Perf. 12**
B2	SP2	9fr + 41fr redsh pur	3.50	10.50

Surtax for the benefit of French patriots.

Patriots and Map of France — SP3

1943				
B3	SP3	50c + 4.50fr yel grn	1.25	10.50
B4	SP3	1.50fr + 8.50fr cerise	1.25	10.50
B5	SP3	3fr + 12fr grnsh bl	1.25	10.50
B6	SP3	5fr + 15fr olive gray	1.25	1.50
		Nos. B3-B6 (4)	5.00	33.00

Surtax for the aid of combatants and patriots.

Refugee Family — SP4

1943				
B7	SP4	10fr + 40fr dull blue	5.25	12.50

The surtax was for refugee relief work.

Woman and Child with Wing — SP5

1944				
B8	SP5	10fr + 40fr grnsh blk	6.75	21.00

Surtax for the benefit of aviation.
Nos. B1-B8 were prepared for use in the French Colonies, but after the landing of Free French troops in Corsica they were used there and later also in Southern France. They became valid throughout France in Nov. 1944.

POSTAGE DUE STAMPS

D1

1884-85		**Unwmk.**	**Typo.**	**Imperf.**
J1	D1	1c black	4.00	4.00
J2	D1	2c black	4.00	4.00
J3	D1	3c black	4.00	4.00
J4	D1	4c black	4.75	4.00
J5	D1	5c black	6.50	3.25
J6	D1	10c black	8.75	6.50
J7	D1	15c black	13.00	10.50
J8	D1	20c black	16.00	10.50
J9	D1	30c black	17.50	8.75
J10	D1	40c black	21.00	8.75
J11	D1	60c black	27.50	16.00
J12	D1	1fr brown	35.00	27.50
a.		1fr black	300.00	
J13	D1	2fr brown	35.00	27.50
a.		2fr black	300.00	325.00
J14	D1	5fr brown	110.00	67.50
a.		5fr black	425.00	450.00

Nos. J12a, J13a and J14a were not regularly issued.

1894-1906				
J15	D1	5c blue	1.60	1.60
J16	D1	10c brown	1.60	1.60
J17	D1	15c pale green	1.60	1.60
J18	D1	20c olive grn ('06)	1.60	1.60
J19	D1	30c carmine	2.75	1.60
J20	D1	50c lilac	2.75	1.60
J21	D1	60c brown, *buff*	4.50	2.75
a.		60c dark violet, *buff*	4.75	2.75
J22	D1	1fr red, *buff*	7.50	4.50
a.		1fr rose, *buff*	27.50	19.00
		Nos. J15-J22 (8)	23.90	16.85

For overprints see New Caledonia Nos. J1-J8.

Catalogue values for unused stamps in this section, from this point to the end of the section, are for Never Hinged items.

D2

1945		**Litho.**		**Perf. 12**
J23	D2	10c slate blue	.45	16.00
J24	D2	15c yel green	.45	16.00
J25	D2	25c deep orange	.45	16.00
J26	D2	50c greenish blk	1.00	16.00
J27	D2	60c copper brn	1.00	16.00
J28	D2	1fr deep red lil	1.00	16.00
J29	D2	2fr red	1.00	16.00
J30	D2	4fr slate gray	4.50	20.00
J31	D2	5fr brt ultra	4.50	20.00
J32	D2	10fr purple	22.50	52.50
J33	D2	20fr dull brown	4.00	20.00
J34	D2	50fr deep green	7.25	27.50
		Nos. J23-J34 (12)	48.10	252.00

FRENCH CONGO

'french 'käŋ˳gō

LOCATION — Central Africa
GOVT. — French possession

French Congo was originally a separate colony, but was joined in 1888 to Gabon and placed under one commissioner-general with a lieutenant-governor presiding in Gabon and another in French Congo. In 1894 the military holdings in Ubangi were attached to French Congo, and in 1900 the Chad military protectorate was added. Postal service was not established in Ubangi or Chad, however, at that time. In 1906 Gabon and Middle Congo were separated and French Congo ceased to exist as such. Chad and Ubangi remained attached to Middle Congo as the joint dependency of "Ubangi-Chari-Chad," and Middle Congo stamps were used there.

Issues of the Republic of the Congo are listed under Congo People's Republic (ex-French).

100 Centimes = 1 Franc

Watermarks

Wmk. 122 Thistle Branch

Wmk. 123 — Rose Branch

Wmk. 124 Olive Branch

Stamps of French Colonies Surcharged Horizontally in Red or Black

Congo français 5c.

1891   Unwmk.   Perf. 14x13½

1	A9	5c on 1c blk, *lil bl* (R)	6,500.	4,750.
a.		Double surcharge	20,000.	
2	A9	5c on 1c blk, *lil bl*	200.00	110.00
a.		Double surcharge	650.00	425.00
3	A9	5c on 15c blue	350.00	180.00
a.		Double surcharge	725.00	375.00
5	A9	5c on 25c blk, *rose*	130.00	52.50
a.		Inverted surcharge	275.00	115.00
b.		Surcharge vertical	600.00	600.00
c.		Double surcharge	600.00	600.00

First "O" of "Congo" is a Capital, "Francais" with Capital "F"

1891-92

6	A9	5c on 20c red, *grn*	1,300.	425.00
7	A9	5c on 25c blk, *rose*	200.00	100.00
a.		Surcharge vertical	250.00	110.00
8	A9	10c on 25c blk, *rose*	240.00	67.50
a.		Inverted surcharge	400.00	160.00
b.		Surcharge vertical	300.00	100.00
d.		Double surcharge	400.00	225.00
9	A9	10c on 40c red, *straw*	2,750.	400.00
10	A9	15c on 25c blk, *rose*	225.00	52.50
a.		Surcharge vertical	260.00	92.50
c.		Double surcharge	400.00	200.00

First "O" of Congo small Surcharge Vert., Down or Up No Period

11	A9	5c on 25c blk, *rose*	300.00	135.00
12	A9	10c on 25c blk, *rose*	300.00	
13	A9	15c on 25c blk, *rose*	425.00	190.00

The listings Nos. 5a and 12 are being re-evaluated. The Catalogue Editors would appreciate any information on these stamps.

Postage Due Stamps of French Colonies Surcharged in Red or Black Reading Down or Up

1892   Imperf.

14	D1	5c on 5c blk (R)	200.00	140.00
a.		Double surcharge	1,450.	
15	D1	5c on 20c blk (R)	200.00	140.00
16	D1	5c on 30c blk (R)	260.00	180.00
17	D1	10c on 1fr brown	200.00	140.00
a.		Double surcharge	4,100.	
b.		Surcharge horiz.		2,400.
c.		"Congo" omitted		475.00
		Nos. 14-17 (4)	860.00	600.00

Excellent counterfeits of Nos. 1-17 exist.

Navigation and Commerce — A3

1892-1900   Typo.   Perf. 14x13½
Colony Name in Blue or Carmine

18	A3	1c blk, *lil bl*	1.60	1.60
a.		Name double	225.00	175.00
19	A3	2c brn, *buff*	4.00	3.25
a.		Name double	225.00	175.00
20	A3	4c claret, *lav*	4.00	3.25
a.		Name in blk and in blue	225.00	175.00
21	A3	5c grn, *grnsh*	8.00	8.00
22	A3	10c blk, *lavender*	24.00	20.00
a.		Name double	850.00	600.00
23	A3	10c red ('00)	4.00	4.00
24	A3	15c blue, quadrille paper	55.00	20.00
25	A3	15c gray ('00)	12.00	8.00
26	A3	20c red, *grn*	24.00	20.00
27	A3	25c blk, *rose*	24.00	16.00
28	A3	25c blue ('00)	12.00	12.00
29	A3	30c brn, *bis*	40.00	24.00
30	A3	40c red, *straw*	55.00	32.50
31	A3	50c car, *rose*	55.00	40.00
32	A3	50c brn, *az* ('00)	16.00	16.00
a.		Name double	775.00	775.00
33	A3	75c dp vio, *org*	47.50	40.00
34	A3	1fr brnz grn, *straw*	55.00	40.00
		Nos. 18-34 (17)	441.10	308.60

Perf. 13½x14 stamps are counterfeits.
For surcharges see Nos. 50-51.
No. 21 exists in yellow green on pale green. The stamp was prepared but not issued. Value, $4,000.

Leopard — A4

Type I

Type II

Bakalois Woman A5

Coconut Grove A6

Design A4 exists in two types. Type 1: end of left tusk extends behind and above right tusk. Type 2: end of left tusk does not appear behind right tusk. Type 2 of design A4 appears in position 91 of each pane of 100. For detailed listings, see the *Scott Catalogue Classic Specialized of Stamps & Covers.*

1900-04   Wmk. 122   Perf. 11

35	A4	1c brn vio & gray lilac (1)	.80	.80
a.		Background inverted	75.00	75.00
36	A4	2c brn & yel (1)	.80	.80
a.		Imperf., pair	80.00	80.00
b.		Pair, imperf between	100.00	110.00
37	A4	4c scar & gray bl	1.60	1.20
a.		Background inverted	95.00	87.50
b.		Type 2	55.00	55.00
38	A4	5c grn & gray grn (1)	2.75	1.60
a.		Imperf., pair	140.00	140.00
39	A4	10c red & rose pink (1)	8.00	3.25
a.		Imperf., pair	140.00	140.00
40	A4	15c dl vio & ol grn (1)	2.40	1.20
a.		Imperf., pair	110.00	

Wmk. 123

41	A5	20c yel grn & org (1)	2.40	2.00
42	A5	25c bl & pale bl	3.50	2.40
43	A5	30c car rose & org	5.50	2.40
44	A5	40c org brn & brt grn	8.00	2.75
a.		Imperf., pair	110.00	110.00
b.		Center and value inverted	200.00	170.00
45	A5	50c gray vio & lil	8.00	6.50
46	A5	75c red vio & org	20.00	11.00
a.		Imperf., pair	110.00	110.00

Wmk. 124

47	A6	1fr gray lil & ol	24.00	20.00
a.		Center and value inverted	300.00	300.00
b.		Imperf., pair	140.00	140.00
48	A6	2fr car & brn	47.50	32.50
a.		Imperf., pair	300.00	300.00
49	A6	5fr brn org & gray	87.50	72.50
a.		5fr ocher & gray	750.00	950.00
b.		Center and value inverted	450.00	450.00
c.		Wmk. 123	500.00	500.00
d.		Imperf., pair	800.00	800.00
		Nos. 35-49 (15)	222.75	160.90

For surcharges see Nos. 52-53.

Nos. 26 and 29 Surcharged in Black

Valeur 5

1900   Unwmk.   Perf. 14x13½

50	A3	5c on 20c red, *grn*	26,000.	6,000.
a.		Double surcharge		18,000.
51	A3	15c on 30c brn, *bis*	20,000.	2,600.
a.		Double surcharge		6,000.

Nos. 43 and 48 Surcharged in Black

a

b

1903   Wmk. 123   Perf. 11

52	A5	5c on 30c	325.00	160.00
a.		Inverted surcharge	2,750.	

Wmk. 124

53	A6	10c on 2fr	375.00	160.00
a.		Inverted surcharge	2,750.	
b.		Double surcharge	3,250.	

Counterfeits of the preceding surcharges are known.

FRENCH EQUATORIAL AFRICA

'french ē-kwə-'tōr-ē-əl 'a-fri-kə

LOCATION — North of Belgian Congo and south of Libya
GOVT. — French Colony
AREA — 959,256 square miles
POP. — 4,491,785
CAPITAL — Brazzaville

In 1910 Gabon and Middle Congo, with its military dependencies, were politically united as French Equatorial Africa. The component colonies were granted administrative autonomy. In 1915 Ubangi-Chari-Chad was made an autonomous civilian colony and in 1920 Chad was made a civil colony. In 1934 the four colonies were administratively united as one colony, but this federation was not completed until 1936. Each colony had its own postal administration until 1936. The postal issues of the former colonial subdivisions are listed under the names of those colonies.

In 1958, French Equatorial Africa was divided into four republics: Chad, Congo, Gabon and Central African Republic (formerly Ubangi-Chari).

Stamps other than Nos. 189-192 are inscribed with "Afrique Equatoriale Francaise" or "AEF" and the name of one of the component colonies are listed under those colonies.

100 Centimes = 1 Franc

Catalogue values for unused stamps in this country are for Never Hinged items, beginning with Scott 142 in the regular postage section, Scott B8A in the semi-postal section, Scott C17 in the airpost section, and Scott J12 in the postage due section.

Stamps of Gabon, 1932, Overprinted "Afrique Equatoriale Francaise" and Bars Similar to "a" and "b" in Black
Perf. 13x13½, 13½x13

1936			Unwmk.	
1	A16	1c brown violet	.40	.80
2	A16	2c black, *rose*	.80	.80
3	A16	4c green	1.20	1.60
4	A16	5c grnsh blue	1.20	1.60
5	A16	10c red, *yel*	1.20	1.60
6	A17	40c brown violet	4.00	3.25
7	A17	50c red brown	3.25	2.40
8	A17	1fr grn, *bl*	32.50	16.00
9	A18	1.50fr dull blue	8.00	4.00
10	A18	2fr brown red	20.00	16.00
		Nos. 1-10 (10)	72.55	48.05

Stamps of Middle Congo, 1933 Overprinted in Black

a

b

c

1936				
11	A4 (b)	1c lt brown	.40	.50
12	A4 (b)	2c dull blue	.40	.50
13	A4 (b)	4c olive green	1.60	1.60
14	A4 (b)	5c red violet	.80	1.00
15	A4 (b)	10c slate	1.60	1.25
16	A4 (b)	15c dk violet	2.00	1.60
17	A4 (b)	20c red, *pink*	2.00	1.60
18	A4 (b)	25c orange	4.00	2.40
19	A5 (a)	40c orange brn	5.50	2.75
20	A5 (c)	50c black violet	5.50	2.40
21	A5 (c)	75c black, *pink*	5.50	4.75
22	A5 (a)	90c carmine	5.50	4.00
23	A5 (c)	1.50fr dark blue	4.75	2.00

24	A6 (a)	5fr slate blue	55.00	35.00
25	A6 (a)	10fr black	35.00	30.00
26	A6 (a)	20fr dark brown	35.00	32.50
		Nos. 11-26 (16)	164.55	123.85

Other overprints inscribed "Afrique Equitoriale Française" in a different type font on earlier Middle Congo stamps are listed under Middle Congo.

Common Design Types pictured following the introduction.

Paris International Exposition Issue
Common Design Types

1937, Apr. 15		Engr.	Perf. 13	
27	CD74	20c dark violet	2.40	2.40
28	CD75	30c dark green	2.40	2.40
29	CD76	40c carmine rose	2.40	2.40
30	CD77	50c dk brn & bl	2.40	2.40
31	CD78	90c red	3.25	3.25
32	CD79	1.50fr ultra	3.25	3.25
		Nos. 27-32 (6)	16.10	16.10

Logging on Loème River — A1

People of Chad — A2

Pierre Savorgnan de Brazza — A3

Emile Gentil — A4

Paul Crampel — A5

Governor Victor Liotard — A6

Two types of 25c:
Type I — Wide numerals (4mm).
Type II — Narrow numerals (3½mm).

1937-40		Photo.	Perf. 13½x13	
33	A1	1c brown & yel	.25	.25
34	A1	2c violet & grn	.25	.25
35	A1	3c blue & yel ('40)	.25	.30
36	A1	4c magenta & bl	.25	.30
37	A1	5c dk lt green	.25	.30
38	A2	10c magenta & blue	.25	.30
39	A2	15c blue & buff	.25	.30
40	A2	20c brown & yellow	.25	.30
41	A2	25c cop red & bl (I)	.80	.30
a.		Type II	2.75	2.00
42	A3	30c gray grn & grn	.80	.55
43	A3	30c chlky bl, ind & buff ('40)	.40	.50
44	A2	35c dp grn & yel ('38)	.80	.80
45	A3	40c cop red & bl	.40	.30
46	A3	45c dk bl & lt grn	4.75	3.50
47	A3	45c dp grn & lt grn ('40)	.40	.80
48	A3	50c brown & yellow	.50	.25
49	A3	55c pur & bl ('38)	.80	.80
50	A3	60c mar & gray bl ('40)	.80	.85
51	A4	65c dk bl & grn	.80	.40
52	A4	70c dp vio & buff ('40)	.80	.95
53	A4	75c ol blk & dl yel	5.50	4.50
54	A4	80c brn & yel ('38)	.40	.80
55	A4	90c copper red & buff	.55	.40
56	A4	1fr dk vio & lt grn	2.40	1.20
57	A4	1fr cer & dl org ('38)	4.00	1.60
58	A4	1fr bl grn & sl grn ('40)	.40	.55
59	A5	1.25fr cop red & buff	2.40	1.20
60	A5	1.40fr dk brn & pale grn ('40)	1.20	1.25
61	A5	1.50fr dk & lt blue	1.60	.80

62	A5	1.60fr dp vio & buff ('40)	1.60	1.25
63	A5	1.75fr brn & yel	2.00	1.20
64	A5	1.75fr bl & lt bl ('38)	.80	.80
65	A5	2fr dk & lt green	1.60	.80
66	A6	2.15fr brn, vio & yel ('38)	1.20	.80
67	A6	2.25fr bl & lt bl ('39)	1.60	1.60
68	A6	2.50fr rose lake & buff ('40)	2.00	1.40
69	A6	3fr dk blue & buff	.80	.50
70	A6	3fr dk & lt green	1.60	1.20
71	A6	10fr dk violet & bl	3.25	3.25
72	A6	20fr ol blk & dl yel	4.00	3.50
		Nos. 33-72 (40)	52.95	40.90

For overprints and surcharges see Nos. 80-127, 129-141, B2-B3, B10-B13, B22-B23.

Colonial Arts Exhibition Issue
Souvenir Sheet
Common Design Type

1937			Imperf.	
73	CD79	3fr red brown	12.00	16.00
		Never hinged	16.00	

Count Louis Edouard Bouet-Willaumez and His Ship "La Malouine" — A7

1938, Dec. 5			Perf. 13½	
74	A7	65c gray brown	1.25	1.25
75	A7	1fr deep rose	1.25	1.25
76	A7	1.75fr blue	1.60	1.60
77	A7	2fr dull violet	2.40	2.40
		Nos. 74-77 (4)	6.50	6.50
		Set, never hinged	8.85	

Centenary of Gabon.

New York World's Fair Issue
Common Design Type

1939, May 10		Engr.	Perf. 12½x12	
78	CD82	1.25fr car lake	.80	1.60
79	CD82	2.25fr ultra	.80	1.60
		Set, never hinged	2.40	

Libreville View and Marshal Petain — A7a

1941		Engr.	Perf. 12½x12	
79A	A7a	1fr bluish green	.40	
79B	A7a	2.50fr blue	.40	
		Set, never hinged	1.60	

Nos. 79A-79B were issued by the Vichy government in France, but were not placed on sale in French Equatorial Africa.
For surcharges, see Nos. B36-B37.

Stamps of 1936-40, Overprinted in Carmine or Black

Nos. 80-82, 84-88, 93

Nos. 83, 89-92, 94-125

1940-41			Perf. 13½x13	
80	A1	1c brn & yel (C)	4.00	4.00
81	A1	2c vio & grn (C)	4.00	4.00
82	A1	3c blue & yel (C)	4.00	4.00
83	A4	4c ol grn (No. 13)	24.00	16.00
b.		Inverted overprint	120.00	150.00
84	A1	5c dk grn & lt grn	4.00	4.00
85	A2	10c magenta & bl	4.00	4.00
86	A2	15c blue & buff (C)	4.00	4.00
87	A2	20c brn & yel (C)	4.00	4.00
88	A2	25c cop red & bl	4.00	4.00
89	A3	30c gray grn & grn	16.00	16.00
90	A3	30c gray grn & grn ('41)	16.00	16.00
91	A3	30c chlky bl, ind & buff (C) ('41)	16.00	16.00
92	A3	30c chlky bl, ind & buff ('41)	16.00	16.00
93	A2	35c dp grn & yel (C)	4.00	4.00
94	A3	40c cop red & bl	4.00	4.00
b.		Inverted overprint		100.00
95	A3	45c dp grn & yel grn (C)	4.00	4.00
96	A3	45c dp grn & yel grn ('41)	16.00	16.00

97	A3	50c brn & yel (C)	4.00	4.00
98	A3	50c brn & yel ('41)	8.00	8.00
99	A3	55c pur & bl (C)	4.00	4.00
100	A3	55c pur & bl ('41)	16.00	16.00
101	A3	60c mar & gray bl	4.00	4.00
102	A4	65c dk bl & grn	4.00	4.00
103	A4	70c dp vio & buff	4.00	4.00
104	A4	75c ol blk & dl yel	80.00	80.00
105	A4	80c brown & yellow	4.00	4.00
106	A4	90c cop red & buff	4.00	4.00
107	A4	1fr bl grn & sl grn	8.00	8.00
108	A4	1fr bl grn & sl grn (C) ('41)	20.00	20.00
109	A3	1fr cer & dl org	4.00	4.00
110	A5	1.40fr dk brn & pale grn	4.00	4.00
111	A5	1.50fr dk bl & lt bl	4.00	4.00
112	A5	1.60fr dp vio & buff	4.00	4.00
113	A5	1.75fr brown & yel	4.00	4.00
114	A6	2.15fr brn, vio & yel	4.00	4.00
115	A6	2.25fr bl & lt bl (C)	4.00	4.00
116	A6	2.25fr bl & lt bl ('41)	16.00	16.00
117	A6	2.50fr rose lake & buff (C)	4.00	4.00
118	A6	3fr dk bl & buff (C)	4.00	4.00
119	A6	3fr dk bl & buff ('41)	16.00	16.00
120	A6	5fr dk grn & lt grn (C)	4.00	4.00
121	A6	5fr dk grn & lt grn ('41)	140.00	140.00
122	A6	10fr dk vio & bl (C)	3.25	3.25
123	A6	10fr dk vio & bl ('41)	130.00	130.00
124	A6	20fr ol blk & dl yel (C)	4.00	4.00
125	A6	20fr ol blk & dl yel ('41)	16.00	16.00
		Nos. 80-125 (46)	673.25	665.25

For overprints and surcharges see Nos. 129-132, B12-B13, B22-B23.
For types of Nos. 38//61 without "RF," see Nos. 155A-155B.

Double Overprint

80a	A1	1c	325.00	225.00
81a	A1	2c	32.50	
82a	A1	3c	32.50	
83a	A4	4c	75.00	
84a	A1	5c	32.50	
85a	A2	10c	32.50	40.00
86a	A2	15c	32.50	
87a	A2	20c	32.50	
88a	A2	25c	55.00	
89a	A3	30c	110.00	120.00
90a	A3	30c	47.50	55.00
91a	A3	30c	47.50	47.50
93a	A3	35c	250.00	
94a	A3	40c	47.50	
96a	A3	45c	75.00	
98a	A3	50c	110.00	75.00
100a	A3	55c	75.00	
102a	A4	65c	45.00	
103a	A4	70c	47.50	
104a	A4	75c	175.00	
105a	A4	80c	45.00	
106a	A4	90c	45.00	
b.		one inverted	120.00	
109a	A4	1fr One inverted	120.00	
110a	A5	1.40fr	47.50	
111a	A5	1.50fr	47.50	
114a	A6	2.15fr	40.00	
115a	A6	2.25fr	60.00	
116a	A6	2.25fr	47.50	
117a	A6	2.50fr	60.00	
119a	A6	3fr	60.00	
123a	A6	10fr	60.00	67.50
124a	A6	20fr	60.00	
		Nos. 96a-124a (17)	1,035.	

Nos. 48, 51 Surcharged in Black or Carmine

1940				
126	A3	75c on 50c	.80	.80
a.		Double surcharge	40.00	
127	A4	1fr on 65c (C)	.80	.80
a.		Double surcharge	32.50	
		Set, never hinged	3.20	

Middle Congo No. 67 Overprinted in Carmine like No. 80
Perf. 13½

128	A4	4c olive green	65.00	65.00

Stamps of 1940 With Additional Overprint in Black

1940			Perf. 13½x13	
129	A4	80c brown & yel	24.00	16.00
a.		Overprint without "2"	150.00	
130	A4	1fr bl & sl grn	24.00	20.00
131	A3	1fr cer & dull org	24.00	16.00
132	A5	1.50fr dk bl & lt bl	24.00	16.00
		Nos. 129-132 (4)	96.00	68.00

Arrival of General de Gaulle in Brazzaville, capital of Free France, Oct. 24, 1940.
These stamps were sold affixed to post cards and at a slight increase over face value.

to cover the cost of the cards. Values for unused stamps are for examples without gum. For surcharges see Nos. B12-B13, B22-B23.

Stamps of 1937-40 Overprinted in Black

1 mm between lines

2 mm between lines

1941

133	A1	1c brown & yel	4.00	4.00
134	A1	2c violet & grn	4.00	4.00
135	A1	3c blue & red	4.00	4.00
136	A1	5c dk & lt green	4.00	4.00
137	A2	10c magenta & bl	4.00	4.00
138	A2	15c blue & buff	4.00	4.00
139	A2	20c brown & yel	4.00	4.00
140	A2	25c copper red & bl	4.00	4.00
141	A2	35c dp grn & yel	4.00	4.00
a.		Double overprint	120.00	
		Nos. 133-141 (9)	36.00	36.00
		Set, never hinged	55.00	

There are 2 settings of the overprint on Nos. 133-141 and C10. The 1st has 1mm between lines of the overprint (Nos. 133-141), the 2nd has 2mm. Value, set with 2mm spacing $95.

Catalogue values for unused stamps in this section, from this point to the end of the section, are for Never Hinged items.

Phoenix — A8

1941   Photo.   Perf. 14x14½

142	A8	5c brown	.30	.25
143	A8	10c dark blue	.30	.25
a.		Denomination doubled	125.00	
144	A8	25c emerald	.30	.25
145	A8	30c deep orange	.30	.25
146	A8	40c slate grn	.55	.30
147	A8	80c red brown	.55	.30
148	A8	1fr deep red lilac	.55	.30
149	A8	1.50fr brt red	.75	.40
150	A8	2fr gray	.75	.40
151	A8	2.50fr brt ultra	.95	.70
152	A8	4fr dull violet	.95	.70
153	A8	5fr yellow bister	.95	.70
154	A8	10fr deep brown	1.40	1.00
155	A8	20fr deep green	1.75	1.25
		Nos. 142-155 (14)	10.35	7.05

For surcharges see #158-165, B14-B21, B24-B35.

Types of 1937-40 without "RF"

1944   Perf. 13½

155A	A2	10c magenta & blue	1.20
155B	A2	15c blue & buff	1.60
155C	A3	60c mar & gray blue	1.60
155D	A5	1.50fr dk & lt blue	2.00
		Nos. 155A-155D (4)	6.40

Nos. 155A-155D were issued by the Vichy government in France, but were not sold in French Equatorial Africa.

Eboue Issue
Common Design Type

1945   Unwmk.   Engr.   Perf. 13

156	CD91	2fr black	.65	.50
157	CD91	25fr Prussian green	1.90	1.50

Nos. 156-157 exist imperforate. Value, set $65.

Nos. 142, 144 and 151 Surcharged with New Values and Bars in Red, Carmine or Black

1946   Perf. 14x14½

158	A8	50c on 5c (R)	.80	.65
159	A8	60c on 5c (R)	.80	.65
160	A8	70c on 5c (R)	.80	.65
161	A8	1.20fr on 5c (C)	.80	.65
162	A8	2.40fr on 25c	1.40	1.00
163	A8	4fr on 25c	1.40	1.00
164	A8	4.50fr on 25c	1.75	1.20
165	A8	15fr on 2.50fr (C)	1.90	1.40
		Nos. 158-165 (8)	9.65	7.20

Black Rhinoceros and Rock Python A9

Jungle Scene A10

Mountainous Shore Line — A11

Gabon Forest A12

Niger Boatman A13

Young Bacongo Woman — A14

1946   Unwmk.   Engr.   Perf. 12½

166	A9	10c deep blue	.40	.25
167	A9	30c violet blk	.40	.25
168	A9	40c dp orange	.40	.25
169	A10	50c violet bl	.80	.50
170	A10	60c dk carmine	.80	.50
171	A10	80c dk ol grn	.80	.50
172	A11	1fr dp orange	.80	.30
173	A11	1.20fr dp claret	.80	.65
174	A11	1.50fr dk green	1.20	.95
175	A12	2fr dk vio brn	.40	.25
176	A12	3fr rose carmine	.80	.25
177	A12	3.60fr red brown	3.25	2.50
178	A12	4fr deep blue	.80	.30
179	A13	5fr dk brown	.80	.25
180	A13	6fr deep blue	1.25	.30
181	A13	10fr black	2.40	.75
182	A14	15fr brown	2.40	.80
183	A14	20fr dp claret	2.40	.80
184	A14	25fr black	3.25	.80
		Nos. 166-184 (19)	24.15	11.40

Imperforates
Most French Equatorial Africa stamps from 1951 onward exist imperforate in issued and trial colors, and also in small presentation sheets in issued colors.

Pierre Savorgnan de Brazza — A15

1951, Nov. 5   Perf. 13

185	A15	10fr indigo & dk grn	1.60	.40

Cent. of the birth of Pierre Savorgnan de Brazza, explorer.

Military Medal Issue
Common Design Type
Engraved and Typographed

1952, Dec. 1   Perf. 13

186	CD101	15fr multicolored	8.00	5.50

Lt. Gov. Adolphe L. Cureau — A16

1954, Sept. 20   Engr.

187	A16	15fr ol grn & red brn	2.00	.80

Savannah Monitor — A17

1955, May 2   Unwmk.

188	A17	8fr dk grn & claret	2.40	1.25

International Exhibition for Wildlife Protection, Paris, May 1955.

FIDES Issue
Common Design Type

Designs: 5fr, Boali Waterfall and Power Plant, Ubangi-Chari. 10fr, Cotton, Chad. 15fr, Brazzaville Hospital, Middle Congo. 20fr, Libreville Harbor, Gabon.

1956, Apr. 25   Perf. 13x12½

189	CD103	5fr dk brn & claret	.65	.30
190	CD103	10fr blk & bluish grn	.65	.30
191	CD103	15fr ind & gray vio	.80	.40
192	CD103	20fr dk red & red org	1.10	.65
		Nos. 189-192 (4)	3.20	1.65

Coffee Issue

Coffee — A19

1956, Oct.   Engr.   Perf. 13

193	A19	10fr brn vio & vio bl	1.60	.40

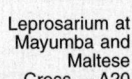

Leprosarium at Mayumba and Maltese Cross — A20

1957, Mar. 11

194	A20	15fr grn, bl grn & red	2.00	.80

Issued in honor of the Knights of Malta.

Giant Eland — A21

1957, Nov. 4

195	A21	1fr shown	.80	.40
196	A21	2fr Lions	.80	.40
197	A21	3fr Elephant, vert.	.80	.40
198	A21	4fr Greater kudu, vert.	.90	.40
		Nos. 195-198 (4)	3.30	1.60

WHO Building, Brazzaville — A22

1958, May 19   Engr.   Perf. 13

199	A22	20fr dk green & org brn	1.60	.80

10th anniv. of WHO.

Flower Issue
Common Design Type

1958, July 7   Photo.   Perf. 12x12½

200	CD104	10fr Euadania	1.60	.65
201	CD104	25fr Spathodea	2.00	.95

Human Rights Issue
Common Design Type

1958, Dec. 10   Engr.   Perf. 13

202	CD105	20fr Prus grn & dk bl	2.40	1.25

SEMI-POSTAL STAMPS

Common Design Type

1938, Oct. 24   Engr.

B1	CD80	1.75fr + 50c brt ultra	24.00	24.00
		Never hinged	32.50	

Nos. 51, 64 Surcharged in Black or Red

1938, Nov. 7   Perf. 13x13½

B2	A4	65c + 35c dk bl & lt grn (R)	2.40	2.40
B3	A4	1.75fr + 50c bl & lt bl	4.00	4.00
		Set, never hinged	12.00	

The surtax was for welfare.

French Revolution Issue
Common Design Type
Name and Value Typo. in Black

1939, July 5   Photo.

B4	CD83	45c + 25c green	16.00	16.00
B5	CD83	70c + 30c brown	16.00	16.00
B6	CD83	90c + 35c red org	16.00	16.00
B7	CD83	1.25fr + 1fr rose pink	16.00	16.00
B8	CD83	2.25fr + 2fr blue	16.00	16.00
		Nos. B4-B8 (5)	80.00	80.00
		Set, never hinged	120.00	

Surtax used for the defense of the colonies.

Catalogue values for unused stamps in this section, from this point to the end of the section, are for Never Hinged items.

Common Design Type and

Native Artilleryman SP1

Gabon Infantryman SP2

1941   Photo.   Perf. 13½

B8A	SP1	1fr + 1fr red	3.50
B8B	CD86	1.50fr + 3fr maroon	3.50
B8C	SP2	2.50fr + 1fr blue	3.50
		Nos. B8A-B8C (3)	10.50

Nos. B8A-B8C were issued by the Vichy government in France, but were not placed on sale in French Equatorial Africa.

Brazza and Stanley Pool — SP3

1941   Photo.   Perf. 14½x14

B9	SP3	1fr + 2fr dk brn & red	2.00	1.60

The surtax was for a monument to Pierre Savorgnan de Brazza.

Nos. 67, 71 Srchd. in Red

1943, June 28   Perf. 13½x13

B10	A6	2.25fr + 50fr	47.50	32.50
B11	A6	10fr + 100fr	120.00	80.00

Nos. 129 and 132
with Add'l. Srch.
in Carmine

1944

B12	A4	80c + 10fr	65.00 40.00
B13	A5	1.50fr + 15fr	65.00 40.00

Surcharged Vertically on
Nos. 142-146, 148, 150-
151

Perf. 14x14½

B14	A8	5c + 10fr brown	40.00 27.50
B15	A8	10c + 10fr dk bl	40.00 27.50
B16	A8	25c + 10fr emer	40.00 27.50
B17	A8	30c + 10fr dp org	40.00 27.50
B18	A8	40c + 10fr dk sl grn	40.00 27.50
B19	A8	1fr + 10fr dp red lil	40.00 27.50
B20	A8	2fr + 20fr gray	40.00 27.50
B21	A8	2.50fr + 25fr brt ultra	40.00 27.50
		Nos. B12-B21 (10)	450.00 300.00

Nos. 129 and 132
with Add'l. Srch.
in Carmine

1944   **Perf. 13½x13**

B22	A4	80c + 10fr	65.00 40.00
B23	A5	1.50fr + 15fr	65.00 40.00

Surcharged Vertically on
Nos. 142-146, 148, 150-
155

Perf. 14x14½

B24	A8	5c + 10fr brn	40.00 27.50
B25	A8	10c + 10fr dk bl	40.00 27.50
B26	A8	25c + 10fr emer	40.00 27.50
B27	A8	30c + 10fr dp org	40.00 27.50
B28	A8	40c + 10fr dk sl grn	40.00 27.50
B29	A8	1fr + 10fr dp red lil	40.00 27.50
B30	A8	2fr + 20fr gray	40.00 27.50
B31	A8	2.50fr + 25fr brt ultra	40.00 27.50
B32	A8	4fr + 40fr dl vio	40.00 27.50
B33	A8	5fr + 50fr yel bis	40.00 27.50
B34	A8	10fr + 100fr dp brn	40.00 27.50
B35	A8	20fr + 200fr dp grn	40.00 27.50
		Nos. B22-B35 (14)	610.00 410.00

Nos. B12 to B35 were issued to raise funds
for the Committee to Aid the Fighting Men and
Patriots of France.

Nos. 79A-79B
Srchd. in Black or
Red

1944   **Engr.**   **Perf. 12½x12**

B36	50c + 1.50fr on 2.50fr deep blue (R)	.80
B37	+ 2.50fr on 1fr green	.80

Colonial Development Fund.
Nos. B36-B37 were issued by the Vichy
government in France, but were not placed on
sale in French Equatorial Africa.

Red Cross Issue
Common Design Type

1944   **Photo.**   **Perf. 14½x14**

B38	CD90	5fr + 20fr royal blue	1.60 1.20

The surtax was for the French Red Cross
and national relief.

Tropical Medicine Issue
Common Design Type

1950, May 15   **Engr.**   **Perf. 13**

B39	CD100	10fr + 2fr dk bl grn & vio brn	7.25 5.50

The surtax was for charitable work.

AIR POST STAMPS

Hydroplane over
Pointe-Noire
AP1

Trimotor over
Stanley
Pool — AP2

1937   **Unwmk.**   **Photo.**   **Perf. 13½**

C1	AP1	1.50fr ol blk & yel	.40 .40
C2	AP1	2fr mag & blue	.55 .55
C3	AP1	2.50fr grn & buff	.55 .55
C4	AP1	3.75fr brn & lt grn	.80 .80
C5	AP2	4.50fr cop red & bl	.90 .90
C6	AP2	6.50fr bl & lt grn	1.60 1.60
C7	AP2	8.50fr red brn & yel	1.60 1.60
C8	AP2	10.75fr vio & lt grn	1.60 1.60
		Nos. C1-C8 (8)	8.00 8.00

For overprints and surcharges see Nos. C9-
C16, CB6.

**Nos. C1, C3-C7 Overprinted in Black
like Nos. 133-141**

No. C10

1940-41

C9	AP1	1.50fr ('41)	240.00 240.00
C10	AP1	2.50fr	4.00 4.00
a.		Double overprint	275.00 275.00
b.		Inverted overprint	275.00 275.00
C11	AP1	3.75fr ('41)	240.00 240.00
a.		Double overprint	275.00 275.00
C12	AP2	4.50fr	4.50 4.50
a.		Double overprint	275.00 275.00
C13	AP2	6.50fr	4.00 4.00
a.		Double overprint	130.00 130.00
C14	AP2	8.50fr	4.00 4.00

No. C8
Surcharged in
Carmine

C15	AP2	50fr on 10.75fr	12.00 12.00

No. C3
Surcharged in
Black

C16	AP1	10fr on 2.50fr ('41)	95.00 95.00
		Nos. C9-C16 (8)	603.50 603.50

Counterfeits of Nos. C9 and C11 exist.
See note following No. 141.

> **Catalogue values for unused
> stamps in this section, from this
> point to the end of the section, are
> for Never Hinged items.**

Common Design Type

1941   **Photo.**   **Perf. 14½x14**

C17	CD87	1fr dark orange	.65 .30
C18	CD87	1.50fr brt red	.95 .50
C19	CD87	5fr brown red	1.60 .90
C20	CD87	10fr black	1.75 1.00
C21	CD87	25fr ultra	1.60 1.20
C22	CD87	50fr dark green	1.60 1.20
C23	CD87	100fr plum	2.25 1.25
		Nos. C17-C23 (7)	10.40 6.35

Types of 1937 without "RF" and

Sikorsky 5.43
Seaplane and
Canoe — AP2a

Perf. 13½, 13 (#C23M)

1943, Oct. 18-1944   **Unwmk.**

C23A	AP1	1.50fr ol blk & yel	.40
C23B	AP1	2fr mag & blue	.40
C23C	AP1	2.50fr grn & buff	.40
C23D	AP1	3.75fr brn & lt grn	.80
C23E	AP2	4.50fr cop red & bl	.80
C23F	AP2	5fr green	1.20
C23G	AP2	6.50fr bl & lt grn	1.20
C23H	AP2	8.50fr red brn & yel	1.20
C23I	AP2	10fr gray & brn ('44)	1.20
C23J	AP2	10.75fr vio & lt grn	1.20
C23K	AP2	20fr yel & brn red ('44)	1.60
C23L	AP2	50fr gray grn & blk ('44)	2.40
C23M	AP2a	100fr red brn ('44)	1.60
		Nos. C23A-C23M (13)	14.40

Issue dates: Nos. C23I, C23K-L, 4/3/44;
C23M, 6/26/44.
Nos. C23A-C23M were issued by the Vichy
government in France, but were not sold in
French Equatorial Africa.

Victory Issue
Common Design Type

Perf. 12½

1946, May 8   **Unwmk.**   **Engr.**

C24	CD92	8fr lilac rose	1.60 1.25

Chad to Rhine Issue
Common Design Types

1946, June 6

C25	CD93	5fr dk violet	1.60 1.20
C26	CD94	10fr slate green	1.60 1.20
C27	CD95	15fr deep blue	2.75 2.00
C28	CD96	20fr red orange	2.75 2.00
C29	CD97	25fr sepia	2.75 2.00
C30	CD98	50fr brown carmine	3.25 2.40
		Nos. C25-C30 (6)	14.70 10.80

Palms and
Village
AP3

Village and
Waterfront
AP4

Bearers in
Jungle
AP5

1946   **Engr.**   **Perf. 13**

C31	AP3	50fr red brn	3.50 .80
C32	AP4	100fr grnsh blk	5.25 1.25
C33	AP5	200fr deep blue	12.00 2.00
		Nos. C31-C33 (3)	20.75 4.05

UPU Issue
Common Design Type

1949, July 4

C34	CD99	25fr green	16.00 12.00

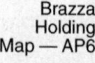

Brazza
Holding
Map — AP6

1951, Nov. 5

C35	AP6	15fr brn, indigo & red	2.40 1.60

Cent. of the birth of Pierre Savorgnan de
Brazza, explorer.

Archbishop
Augouard
and St. Anne
Cathedral,
Brazzaville
AP7

1952, Dec. 1

C36	AP7	15fr ol grn, dk brn & vio brn	6.50 2.40

Cent. of the birth of Archbishop Philippe-
Prosper Augouard.

Anhingas
AP8

1953, Feb. 16

C37	AP8	500fr grnsh blk, blk & slate	47.50 8.00

Liberation Issue
Common Design Type

1954, June 6

C38	CD102	15fr vio & vio brn	12.00 8.00

Log
Rafts — AP9

Designs: 100fr, Fishing boats and nets,
Lake Chad. 200fr, Age of mechanization.

1955, Jan. 24   **Engr.**

C39	AP9	50fr ind, brn & dk grn	2.40 .80
C40	AP9	100fr aqua, dk grn & blk brn	8.00 1.60
C41	AP9	200fr red & deep plum	12.00 2.40
		Nos. C39-C41 (3)	22.40 4.80

Gov. Gen.
Félix Eboué,
View of
Brazzaville
and the
Pantheon
AP10

1955, Apr. 30   **Unwmk.**   **Perf. 13**

C42	AP10	15fr sep, brn & slate bl	6.50 2.40

Gen. Louis Faidherbé
and African
Sharpshooter — AP11

1957, July 20

C43	AP11	15fr sepia & org ver	3.50 2.00

Centenary of French African Troops.

AIR POST SEMI-POSTAL STAMPS

French Revolution Issue
Common Design Type

1939   **Unwmk.**   **Photo.**   **Perf. 13**
Name and Value Typo. in Orange

CB1	CD83	4.50fr + 4fr brn blk	40.00 40.00

SPAP1

SPAP2

SPAP3

Unwmk.

1942, June 22   Engr.   Perf. 13

CB2	SPAP1 1.50fr + 3.50fr green		.80
CB3	SPAP2 2fr + 6fr brown		.80
CB4	SPAP3 3fr + 9fr carmine		.80
	Nos. CB2-CB4 (3)		2.40

Native children's welfare fund.

Nos. CB2-CB4 were issued by the Vichy government in France, but were not placed on sale in French Equatorial Africa.

Colonial Education Fund
Common Design Type

1942, June 22

CB5	CD86a 1.20fr + 1.80fr bl & red		.80

No. CB5 was issued by the Vichy government in France, but was not placed on sale in French Equatorial Africa.

No. C8 Surcharged in Red like Nos. B10-B11

1943, June 28   Perf. 13½

CB6	AP2 10.75fr + 200fr		400.00	240.00

Counterfeits exist.

POSTAGE DUE STAMPS

Numeral of Value on
Equatorial Butterfly — D1

1937   Unwmk.   Photo.   Perf. 13

J1	D1	5c redsh pur & lt bl	.25	.40
J2	D1	10c cop red & buff	.25	.40
J3	D1	20c dk grn & grn	.30	.50
J4	D1	25c red brn & buff	.30	.50
J5	D1	30c cop red & lt bl	.50	.55
J6	D1	45c mag & yel grn	.75	.80
J7	D1	50c dk ol grn & buff	.80	.95
J8	D1	60c redsh pur & yel	.95	1.10
J9	D1	1fr brown & yel	1.00	1.20
J10	D1	2fr dk bl & buff	1.40	1.50
J11	D1	3fr red brn & lt grn	1.50	1.75
	Nos. J1-J11 (11)		8.00	9.65
	Set, never hinged		12.00	

Catalogue values for unused stamps in this section, from this point to the end of the section, are for Never Hinged items.

D2

1947   Engr.

J12	D2	10c red	.40	.25
J13	D2	30c dp org	.40	.25
J14	D2	50c greenish bl	.50	.30
J15	D2	1fr carmine	.55	.40
J16	D2	2fr emerald	.65	.50
J17	D2	3fr dp red lil	.65	.50
J18	D2	4fr dp ultra	1.60	1.20
J19	D2	5fr red brown	1.60	1.20
J20	D2	10fr peacock blue	2.00	1.60
J21	D2	20fr sepia	2.10	1.90
	Nos. J12-J21 (10)		10.45	8.10

FRENCH GUIANA

'french gē-'a-nə

LOCATION — On the northeast coast of South America bordering on the Atlantic Ocean.
GOVT. — French colony
AREA — 34,740 sq. mi.
POP. — 28,537 (1946)
CAPITAL — Cayenne

French Guiana became an overseas department of France in 1946.

100 Centimes = 1 Franc

Catalogue values for unused stamps in this country are for Never Hinged items, beginning with Scott 171 in the regular postage section, Scott B12 in the semipostal section, Scott C9 in the airpost section, and Scott J22 in the postage due section.

See France No. 1446 for French stamp inscribed "Guyane."

Stamps of French Colonies
Surcharged in Black

1886, Dec.   Unwmk.   Imperf.

1	A8 5c on 2c grn, grnsh, srch 12mm high	750.00	675.00
a.	Double surcharge	1,900.	1,900.
b.	Surcharge 10½mm high	900.00	825.00
c.	No "f" after "O"	950.00	850.00

Perf. 14x13½

2	A9 5c on 2c brn, buff, srch 12mm high	650.00	600.00
a.	No "f" after "O"	525.00	450.00
b.	As "a," double surcharge	1,700.	1,700.

Nos. 1-2 unused are valued without gum.

Stamps of French Colonies
Overprinted in Black

"Av" of Date Line Inverted-Reversed

1887, Apr.   Imperf.

4	A8 20c on 35c blk, org	70.00	57.50
a.	Double surcharge	225.00	225.00
b.	No "f" after "O"	150.00	150.00

Date Line Reads "Avril 1887"

5	A8 5c on 2c grn, grnsh	175.00	125.00
a.	Double surcharge	900.00	900.00
b.	No "f" after "O"	375.00	375.00
c.	Pair, one stamp without surcharge	1,500.	
6	A8 20c on 35c blk, org	375.00	375.00
a.	Double surcharge	1,250.	1,250.
b.	No "f" after "O"	850.00	850.00
c.	Vertical pair, #6 + #4	2,200.	
7	A7 25c on 30c brn, yelsh	55.00	47.50
a.	Double surcharge	900.00	900.00
b.	No "f" after "O"	275.00	275.00

Nos. 4-7 unused are valued without gum.

French Colonies Nos. 22 and 26 Surcharged

8	A7 5c on 30c brn, yelsh	155.00	140.00
a.	Double surcharge	800.00	800.00
b.	Inverted surcharge	1,200.	1,200.
c.	Pair, one without surcharge	1,600.	
9	A8 5c on 30c brn, yelsh	1,500.	1,500.

Nos. 8-9 unused are valued without gum.

**French Colonies Nos. 22 and 28
Surcharged**

1888

10	A7 5c on 30c brn, yelsh	155.00	140.00
b.	Double surcharge	500.00	500.00
c.	Inverted surcharge	600.00	600.00
11	A8 10c on 75c car, rose	400.00	290.00
	No gum	290.00	
a.	Double surcharge	1,100.	1,100.
b.	Pair, one stamp without surcharge	2,500.	

No. 10 unused is valued without gum.

Stamps of French Colonies
Overprinted in Black

1892, Feb. 20   Imperf.

12	A8 2c grn, grnsh	850.00	975.00
a.	Inverted overprint	3,500.	
13	A7 30c brn, yelsh	155.00	155.00
a.	Inverted overprint	575.00	575.00
14	A8 35c blk, orange	2,850.	3,000.
15	A8 40c red, straw	175.00	140.00
16	A8 75c car, rose	180.00	140.00
	Inverted overprint	625.00	550.00
17	A8 1fr brnz grn, straw	210.00	160.00
a.	Inverted overprint	800.00	800.00
b.	Double overprint	800.00	800.00
c.	Triple overprint	1,800.	1,800.

Nos. 12-14 unused are valued without gum.

1892   Perf. 14x13½

18	A9 1c blk, lil bl	47.50	35.00
19	A9 2c brn, buff	45.00	37.50
20	A9 4c claret, lav	42.50	37.50
21	A9 5c grn, grnsh	47.50	35.00
a.	Inverted overprint	150.00	150.00
b.	Double overprint	150.00	150.00
22	A9 10c blk, lavender	67.50	40.00
a.	Inverted overprint	200.00	200.00
b.	Double overprint	275.00	275.00
23	A9 15c blue	67.50	45.00
a.	Double overprint	275.00	200.00
24	A9 20c red, grn	55.00	42.50
a.	Inverted overprint	225.00	225.00
25	A9 25c blk, rose	75.00	35.00
a.	Double overprint	275.00	275.00
b.	Triple overprint	300.00	300.00
26	A9 30c brn, bis	47.50	40.00
27	A9 35c blk, orange	225.00	225.00
a.	Inverted overprint	575.00	575.00
28	A9 40c red, straw	135.00	135.00
a.	Inverted overprint	300.00	300.00
29	A9 75c car, rose	145.00	125.00
30	A9 1fr brnz grn, straw	250.00	220.00
a.	Double overprint	375.00	
	Nos. 18-30 (13)	1,250.	1,053.

**French Colonies No. 51
Surcharged**

1892, Dec.

31	A9 5c on 15c blue	70.00	47.50
a.	Double surcharge	300.00	275.00
b.	No "f" after "O"	160.00	135.00
c.	Pair, one stamp without surcharge	1,700.	1,700.

Navigation and
Commerce — A12

**1892-1904   Typo.   Perf. 14x13½
Name of Colony in Blue or Carmine**

32	A12 1c blk, lil bl	2.00	1.75
33	A12 2c brn, buff	1.45	1.45
34	A12 4c claret, lav	2.00	1.90
a.	"GUYANE" double	275.00	
35	A12 5c grn, grnsh	12.50	11.00
36	A12 5c yel grn ('04)	2.40	1.60
37	A12 10c blk, lavender	13.50	8.25
38	A12 10c red ('00)	4.75	1.60
39	A12 15c blue, quadrille paper	42.50	4.00
40	A12 15c gray, lt gray ('00)	122.50	110.00
41	A12 20c red, grn	25.00	18.00
42	A12 25c blk, rose	20.00	5.50
43	A12 25c blue ('00)	22.50	22.50
44	A12 30c brn, bis	24.00	18.00
45	A12 40c red, straw	24.00	16.00
46	A12 50c car, rose	35.00	18.00

47	A12	50c brn, az ('00)	26.00	26.00
48	A12	75c dp vio ('00) org	37.50	27.50
49	A12	1fr brn grn, straw	18.00	14.00
50	A12	2fr vio, rose ('02)	180.00	16.00
	Nos. 32-50 (19)		615.60	323.05

Perf. 13½x14 stamps are counterfeits.
For surcharges see Nos. 87-93.

Great
Anteater
A13

Washing
Gold
A14

Palm Grove at
Cayenne — A15

1905-28

51	A13	1c black	.40	.40
52	A13	2c blue	.40	.40
a.	Imperf	57.50		
53	A13	4c red brn	.40	.40
54	A13	5c green	1.25	1.10
55	A13	5c org ('22)	.40	.45
56	A13	10c rose	1.50	1.10
57	A13	10c grn ('22)	.65	.40
58	A13	10c red, bluish ('25)	.45	.45
59	A13	15c violet	1.75	1.25
60	A14	20c red brn	.65	.65
61	A14	25c blue	3.00	1.60
62	A14	25c vio ('22)	.60	.50
63	A14	30c black	2.50	1.00
64	A14	30c rose ('22)	.50	.60
65	A14	30c red org ('25)	.45	.45
66	A14	30c dk grn, grnsh ('28)	1.35	1.35
67	A14	35c blk, yel ('06)	.65	.65
68	A14	40c rose	1.50	.85
69	A14	40c black ('22)	.40	.95
70	A14	45c olive ('07)	1.00	.95
71	A14	50c violet	4.25	3.50
72	A14	50c blue ('22)	.55	.65
73	A14	50c gray ('25)	.80	.80
74	A14	60c lil, rose ('25)	.65	.65
75	A14	65c myr grn ('26)	.85	.80
76	A14	75c green	1.60	1.40
77	A14	85c magenta ('26)	.85	.80
78	A15	1fr rose	.90	.85
a.	Imperf	82.50		
79	A15	1fr bl, bluish ('25)	.85	.80
80	A15	1fr bl, yel grn ('28)	2.75	2.75
81	A15	1.10fr lt red ('28)	1.50	1.50
82	A15	2fr blue	1.35	1.35
83	A15	2fr org red, yel ('26)	2.75	2.40
84	A15	5fr blue	8.50	6.50
a.	Imperf	82.50		
85	A15	10fr grn, yel ('24)	14.00	14.50
a.	Printed on both sides	140.00		
86	A15	20fr brn lake ('24)	17.50	17.50
	Nos. 51-86 (36)		79.45	71.75

For surcharges see Nos. 94-108, B1-B2.

**Issue of 1892 Surcharged in Black
or Carmine**

1912

**Spacing between figures of
surcharge 1.5mm (5c), 2mm (10c)**

87	A12	5c on 2c brn, buff (C)	1.60	2.00
88	A12	5c on 4c cl, lav (C)	1.20	1.60
89	A12	5c on 20c red, grn	1.75	1.90
90	A12	5c on 25c blk, rose (C)	4.00	4.75
91	A12	5c on 30c brn, bis (C)	1.75	1.90
92	A12	10c on 40c red, straw	1.40	1.90
a.	Pair, one stamp without surcharge	1,250.		
93	A12	10c on 50c car, rose	4.25	5.25
a.	Double surcharge	550.00		
	Nos. 87-93 (7)		15.95	19.30

Two spacings between the surcharged numerals are found on Nos. 87 to 93. For detailed listings, see the *Scott Classic Specialized Catalogue of Stamps and Covers.*

No. 59 Surcharged in Various Colors

1922

94	A13	1c on 15c vio (Bk)	.65	.75
a.		Double surcharge	90.00	
95	A13	2c on 15c vio (Bl)	.65	.75
a.		Inverted surcharge	97.50	
b.		In pair with unovptd. stamp	250.00	
c.		No. 95a, in pair with unovptd. stamp	850.00	
96	A13	4c on 15c vio (G)	.65	.75
a.		Double surcharge	90.00	
b.		In pair with unovptd. stamp	275.00	
97	A13	5c on 15c vio (R)	.65	.75
a.		In pair with unovptd. stamp	275.00	
		Nos. 94-97 (4)	2.60	3.00

Type of 1905-28 Srchd. in Blue

1923

98	A15	10fr on 1fr grn, *yel*	22.50	24.00
99	A15	20fr on 5fr lilac, *rose*	22.50	24.00

Stamps and Types of 1905-28 Srchd. in Black or Red

1924-27

100	A13	25c on 15c vio ('25)	.85	.85
a.		Triple surcharge	130.00	130.00
b.		In pair with unovptd. stamp	260.00	
101	A15	25c on 2fr bl ('24)	.90	.95
a.		Double surcharge	140.00	
b.		Triple surcharge	150.00	
102	A14	65c on 45c ol (R) ('25)	1.75	1.90
103	A14	85c on 45c ol (R) ('25)	1.75	1.90
104	A14	90c on 75c red ('27)	1.50	1.50
105	A15	1.05fr on 2fr lt yel brn ('27)	1.50	1.50
106	A15	1.25fr on 1fr ultra (R) ('26)	1.60	1.75
107	A15	1.50fr on 1fr lt bl ('27)	1.60	1.75
108	A15	3fr on 5fr vio ('27)	1.75	2.00
a.		No period after "F"	12.00	12.00
		Nos. 100-108 (9)	13.20	14.10

Carib Archer A16

Shooting Rapids, Maroni River A17

Government Building, Cayenne — A18

1929-40   **Perf. 13½x14**

109	A16	1c gray lil & grnsh bl	.25	.25
a.		Imperf	35.00	
110	A16	2c dk red & bl grn	.25	.25
a.		Imperf	35.00	
111	A16	3c gray lil & grnsh bl ('40)	.30	.30
112	A16	4c ol brn & red vio	.30	.30
113	A16	5c Prus bl & red org	.30	.30
114	A16	10c mag & brn	.30	.30
115	A16	15c yel brn & red org	.30	.30
a.		Imperf	35.00	
116	A16	20c dk bl & ol grn	.30	.30
117	A16	25c dk red & dk brn	.50	.50

Perf. 14x13½

118	A17	30c dl & lt grn	.70	.70
119	A17	30c grn & brn ('40)	.50	.50
120	A17	35c Prus grn & ol grn ('38)	1.10	1.10
121	A17	40c org brn & ol gray	.30	.30
122	A17	45c grn & dk brn	1.20	1.20
123	A17	45c ol grn & lt grn ('40)	.70	.70
124	A17	50c dk bl & ol gray	.40	.40
a.		Imperf	35.00	

125	A17	55c vio bl & car ('38)	1.50	1.50
126	A17	60c sal & grn ('40)	.75	.75
a.		Imperf	47.50	
127	A17	65c sal & grn	1.10	1.10
128	A17	70c ind & sl bl ('40)	1.30	1.30
129	A17	75c ind & sl bl	1.15	1.15
130	A17	80c blk & vio bl ('38)	.80	.80
131	A17	90c dk red & ver	1.10	1.10
132	A17	90c red vio & brn ('39)	1.30	1.30
133	A17	1fr lt vio & brn	.70	.70
134	A17	1fr car & lt red ('38)	2.10	2.10
135	A17	1fr blk & vio bl ('40)	.80	.80
136	A18	1.05fr ver & olive	6.25	6.25
137	A18	1.10fr ol brn & red vio	7.25	5.75
138	A18	1.25fr blk brn & bl grn ('33)	.80	.80
139	A18	1.25fr rose & lt red ('39)	1.10	1.10
140	A18	1.40fr ol brn & red vio ('40)	1.30	1.30
141	A18	1.50fr dk bl & lt bl	.40	.40
142	A18	1.60fr ol brn & bl grn ('40)	1.30	1.30
143	A18	1.75fr brn red & blk brn ('33)	2.25	2.25
144	A18	1.75fr vio bl ('38)	1.75	1.75
145	A18	2fr dk grn & rose red	.65	.65
146	A18	2.25fr vio bl ('39)	1.30	1.30
147	A18	2.50fr cop red & brn ('40)	1.30	1.30
148	A18	3fr brn red & red vio	.75	.75
149	A18	5fr dl vio & yel	1.25	1.25
150	A18	10fr ol gray & dp ultra	1.50	1.50
151	A18	20fr indigo & ver	2.50	2.50
		Nos. 109-151 (43)	51.95	50.45

For types A16-A18 without "RF," see Nos. 170C-170E.

Common Design Types
pictured following the introduction.

Colonial Exposition Issue
Common Design Types

1931   **Engr.**   **Perf. 12½**
Name of Country in Black

152	CD70	40c dp green	5.50	5.50
153	CD71	50c violet	5.50	5.50
154	CD72	90c red orange	5.50	5.50
155	CD73	1.50fr dull blue	5.50	5.50
		Nos. 152-155 (4)	22.00	22.00

Recapture of Cayenne by d'Estrées, 1676 — A19

Products of French Guiana — A20

1935, Oct. 21   **Perf. 13**

156	A19	40c gray brn	5.75	5.75
157	A19	50c dull red	10.00	8.00
158	A19	1.50fr ultra	5.75	5.75
159	A20	1.75fr lilac rose	12.50	11.50
160	A20	5fr brown	10.00	9.00
161	A20	10fr blue green	10.50	10.00
		Nos. 156-161 (6)	54.50	50.00

Tercentenary of the founding of French possessions in the West Indies.

Paris International Exposition Issue
Common Design Types

1937, Apr. 15

162	CD74	20c deep violet	1.75	1.75
163	CD75	30c dark green	1.75	1.75
164	CD76	40c car rose	1.75	1.75
165	CD77	50c dark brown	1.75	1.75
166	CD78	90c red	1.75	1.75
167	CD79	1.50fr ultra	2.25	2.25
		Nos. 162-167 (6)	11.00	11.00

Colonial Arts Exhibition Issue
Souvenir Sheet
Common Design Type

1937   **Imperf.**

168	CD75	3fr violet	11.50	13.50

New York World's Fair Issue
Common Design Type

1939, May 10   **Engr.**   **Perf. 12½x12**

169	CD82	1.25fr car lake	1.30	1.30
170	CD82	2.25fr ultra	1.30	1.30

View of Cayenne and Marshal Petain — A21a

1941   **Engr.**   **Perf. 12½x12**

170A	A21a	1fr deep lilac	.80	.80
170B	A21a	2.50fr blue	.80	.80

For surcharges, see Nos. B11A-B11B.

Types of 1929-40 without "RF"

1944   **Methods and Perfs as Before**

170C	A16	15c yel brn & red org		1.10
170D	A17	1fr black & vio blue		1.10
170E	A18	1.50fr dk blue & lt blue		1.40
		Nos. 170C-170E (3)		3.60

Nos. 170C-170E were issued by the Vichy government in France, but were not issued in French Guiana.

> **Catalogue values for unused stamps in this section, from this point to the end of the section, are for Never Hinged items.**

Eboue Issue
Common Design Type

1945   **Engr.**   **Perf. 13**

171	CD91	2fr black	.95	.80
172	CD91	25fr Prussian green	1.50	1.20

This issue exists imperforate.

Arms of Cayenne — A22

1945   **Litho.**   **Perf. 12**

173	A22	10c dp gray violet	.30	.25
174	A22	30c brown org	.35	.25
175	A22	40c lt blue	.35	.25
176	A22	50c violet brn	.75	.60
177	A22	60c orange yel	.75	.60
178	A22	70c pale brown	.75	.60
179	A22	80c lt green	.75	.60
180	A22	1fr blue	.35	.25
181	A22	1.20fr brt violet	.75	.60
182	A22	1.50fr dp orange	1.00	.75
183	A22	2fr black	1.10	.85
184	A22	2.40fr red	1.10	.85
185	A22	3fr pink	1.10	.85
186	A22	4fr dp ultra	1.30	1.00
187	A22	4.50fr dp yel grn	1.30	1.00
188	A22	5fr orange brn	1.30	1.00
189	A22	10fr dk violet	1.30	1.00
190	A22	15fr rose carmine	1.30	1.00
191	A22	20fr olive green	1.50	1.25
		Nos. 173-191 (19)	17.40	12.55

Hammock A23

Guiana Girl A26

Maroni River Bank — A24

Inini Scene — A25

Toucans — A27

Parrots — A28

Perf. 13.

1947, June 2   **Unwmk.**   **Engr.**

192	A23	10c dk blue grn	.30	.25
193	A23	30c brt red	.30	.25
194	A23	50c dk vio brn	.30	.25
195	A24	60c grnsh blk	.60	.45
196	A24	1fr red brn	.85	.60
197	A24	1.50fr black brn	.85	.60
198	A25	2fr dp yel grn	1.10	.75
199	A25	2.50fr dp ultra	1.10	.75
200	A25	3fr red brn	1.00	.70
201	A26	4fr black brn	2.50	1.25
202	A26	5fr deep blue	1.75	1.10
203	A26	6fr red brown	1.75	1.10
204	A27	10fr deep ultra	7.25	4.75
205	A27	15fr black brn	7.25	5.00
206	A27	20fr red brn	9.25	5.00
207	A28	25fr brt bl grn	13.00	8.50
208	A28	40fr black brn	11.00	8.00
		Nos. 192-208 (17)	60.15	39.30

SEMI-POSTAL STAMPS

Regular Issue of 1905-28 Surcharged in Red

1915   **Unwmk.**   **Perf. 13½x14**

B1	A13	10c + 5c rose	17.50	18.00
a.		Inverted surcharge	250.00	250.00
b.		Double surcharge	250.00	250.00

Regular Issue of 1905-28 Surcharged in Rose

B2	A13	10c + 5c rose	1.60	1.60

Curie Issue
Common Design Type

1938   **Perf. 13**

B3	CD80	1.75fr + 50c brt ultra	13.50	13.50

French Revolution Issue
Common Design Type

1939   **Photo.**
Name and Value in Black

B4	CD83	45c + 25c green	11.50	11.50
B5	CD83	70c + 30c brown	11.50	11.50
B6	CD83	90c + 35c red org	11.50	11.50
B7	CD83	1.25fr + 1fr rose pink	11.50	11.50
B8	CD83	2.25fr + 2fr blue	11.50	11.50
		Nos. B4-B8 (5)	57.50	57.50

Common Design Type and

Colonial Infantryman SP1

Colonial Policeman SP2

1941   **Photo.**   **Perf. 13½**

B9	SP1	1fr + 1fr red		1.30
B10	CD86	1.50fr + 3fr maroon		1.50
B11	SP2	2.50fr + 1fr blue		1.30
		Nos. B9-B11 (3)		4.10

Nos. B9-B11 were issued by the Vichy government in France, but were not placed on sale in French Guiana.

Nos. 170A-170B Srchd. in Black or Red

1944   **Engr.**   **Perf. 12½x12**

B11A		50c + 1.50fr on 2.50fr deep blue (R)		.80
B11B		+ 2.50fr on 1fr dp lilac		.80

Colonial Development Fund.

Nos. B11A-B11B were issued by the Vichy government in France, but were not placed on sale in French Guiana.

Catalogue values for unused stamps in this section, from this point to the end of the section, are for Never Hinged items.

Red Cross Issue
Common Design Type

1944			Perf.	14½x14
B12	CD90	5fr + 20fr dk copper brn	1.75	1.25

The surtax was for the French Red Cross and national relief.

AIR POST STAMPS

Cayenne — AP1

Perf. 13½

1933, Nov. 20		Unwmk.		Photo.
C1	AP1	50c orange brn	.30	.30
C2	AP1	1fr yellow grn	.50	.50
C3	AP1	1.50fr dk blue	.70	.70
C4	AP1	2fr orange	.70	.70
C5	AP1	3fr black	.85	.85
C6	AP1	5fr violet	.85	.85
C7	AP1	10fr olive grn	.85	.85
C8	AP1	20fr scarlet	1.25	1.25
		Nos. C1-C8 (8)	6.00	6.00

For No. C1 without "RF," see No. C8A.
A 20fr violet exists, but was not regularly issued. Value, $175.

Catalogue values for unused stamps in this section, from this point to the end of the section, are for Never Hinged items.

Type of 1933 without "RF" and

AP1a   AP1b

Perf. 13½, 13 (#C8C)

1941-44		Photo, Engr.	(#C8C)
C8A	AP1	50c orange brn	1.00
C8B	AP1a	50f bl grn & red brown ('42)	1.40
C8C	AP1b	100f dk blue ('44)	1.60
		Nos. C8A-C8C (3)	4.00

Nos. C8A-C8C were issued by the Vichy government in France, but were not placed on sale in French Guiana.

Common Design Type

1945		Photo.	Perf.	14½x14
C9	CD87	50fr dark green	1.30	1.10
C10	CD87	100fr plum	2.50	2.00

Victory Issue
Common Design Type

1946, May 8		Engr.	Perf.	12½
C11	CD92	8fr black	1.75	1.25

Chad to Rhine Issue
Common Design Types

1946, June 6				
C12	CD93	5fr dk slate bl	1.75	1.50
C13	CD94	10fr lilac rose	1.75	1.50
C14	CD95	15fr dk vio brn	1.75	1.50
C15	CD96	20fr dk slate grn	2.00	1.60
C16	CD97	25fr vio brown	2.40	2.00
C17	CD98	50fr bright lilac	3.00	2.25
		Nos. C12-C17 (6)	12.65	10.35

Eagles
AP2

Tapir — AP3

Toucans AP4

1947, June 2		Engr.	Perf.	13
C18	AP2	50fr deep green	22.50	17.50
C19	AP3	100fr red brown	15.00	13.00
C20	AP4	200fr dk gray bl	30.00	24.00
		Nos. C18-C20 (3)	67.50	54.50

AIR POST SEMI-POSTAL STAMP

French Revolution Issue
Common Design Type
Unwmk.

1939, July 5		Photo.	Perf.	13
Name & Value Typo. in Orange				
CB1	CD83	5fr + 4fr brn blk	22.00	22.00

Nurse with Mother & Child SPAP1

Unwmk.

1942, June 22		Engr.	Perf.	13
CB2	SPAP1	1.50fr + 50c green		1.00
CB3	SPAP1	2fr + 6fr brn & red		1.00

Native children's welfare fund.
Nos. CB2-CB3 were issued by the Vichy government in France, but were not placed on sale in French Guiana.

Colonial Education Fund
Common Design Type

1942, June 22			
CB4	CD86a	1.20fr + 1.80fr blue & red	1.10

No. CB4 was issued by the Vichy government in France, but was not placed on sale in French Guiana.

POSTAGE DUE STAMPS

Postage Due Stamps of France, 1893-1926, Overprinted

1925-27		Unwmk.	Perf.	14x13½
J1	D2	5c light blue	.70	.75
a.	In pair with unovptd. stamp		375.00	
J2	D2	10c brown	1.00	1.10
J3	D2	20c olive green	1.10	1.25
J4	D2	50c violet brown	1.50	1.60
J5	D2	3fr magenta ('27)	11.00	12.50

Surcharged in Black

J6	D2	15c on 20c ol grn	1.00	1.10
a.	Blue surcharge		67.50	
J7	D2	25c on 5c lt bl	1.30	1.40
a.	In pair with unovptd. stamp		375.00	

J8	D2	30c on 20c ol grn	1.50	1.60
J9	D2	45c on 10c brn	1.50	1.60
J10	D2	60c on 5c lt bl	1.50	1.60
J11	D2	1fr on 20c ol grn	2.25	2.40
J12	D2	2fr on 50c vio brn	2.25	2.40
		Nos. J1-J12 (12)	26.60	29.30

Royal Palms — D3   Guiana Girl — D4

1929, Oct. 14		Typo.	Perf.	13½x14
J13	D3	5c indigo & Prus bl	.45	.50
J14	D3	10c bis brn & Prus grn	.45	.50
J15	D3	20c grn & rose red	.45	.50
J16	D3	30c ol brn & rose red	.45	.50
J17	D3	50c vio & ol brn	.95	1.00
J18	D3	60c brn red & ol brn	1.30	1.40
J19	D4	1fr dp bl & org brn	1.75	1.90
J20	D4	2fr brn red & bluish grn	2.00	2.10
J21	D4	3fr violet & blk	4.25	4.50
		Nos. J13-J21 (9)	12.05	12.90

Catalogue values for unused stamps in this section, from this point to the end of the section, are for Never Hinged items.

D5

1947, June 2		Engr.	Perf.	14x13
J22	D5	10c dk car rose	.35	.35
J23	D5	30c dull green	.45	.45
J24	D5	50c black	.45	.45
J25	D5	1fr brt ultra	.55	.55
J26	D5	2fr dk brown red	.55	.55
J27	D5	3fr deep violet	1.00	.80
J28	D5	4fr red	1.30	1.10
J29	D5	5fr brown violet	1.50	1.25
J30	D5	10fr blue green	2.25	1.90
J31	D5	20fr lilac rose	3.00	2.25
		Nos. J22-J31 (10)	11.40	9.65

FRENCH GUINEA

ˈfrench ˈgi-nē

LOCATION — On the coast of West Africa, between Portuguese Guinea and Sierra Leone.
GOVT. — French colony
AREA — 89,436 sq. mi.
POP. — 2,058,442 (est. 1941)
CAPITAL — Conakry

French Guinea stamps were replaced by those of French West Africa around 1944-45. French Guinea became the Republic of Guinea Oct. 2, 1958. See "Guinea" for issues of the republic.

100 Centimes = 1 Franc

See French West Africa No. 66 for additional stamp inscribed "Guinee" and "Afrique Occidentale Francaise."

Navigation and Commerce — A1

Perf. 14x13½

1892-1900		Typo.		Unwmk.
Name of Colony in Blue or Carmine				
1	A1	1c black, lilac bl	2.40	1.60
2	A1	2c brown, buff	2.40	2.00
3	A1	4c claret, lav	3.25	2.00
4	A1	5c green, grnsh	8.00	8.00
5	A1	10c blk, lavender	8.00	4.75
6	A1	10c red ('00)	45.00	40.00

7	A1	15c blue, quadrille paper	16.00	8.00
8	A1	15c gray, lt gray ('00)	100.00	87.50
9	A1	20c red, grn	20.00	16.00
10	A1	25c black, rose	16.00	8.00
11	A1	25c blue ('00)	24.00	24.00
12	A1	30c brown, bis	40.00	32.50
13	A1	40c red, straw	40.00	32.50
a.	"GUINEE FRANCAISE" double		475.00	475.00
14	A1	50c car, rose	47.50	35.00
15	A1	50c brown, az ('00)	40.00	40.00
16	A1	75c dp vio, org	65.00	47.50
17	A1	1fr brnz grn, straw	50.00	40.00
		Nos. 1-17 (17)	527.55	429.35

Perf. 13½x14 stamps are counterfeits.
For surcharges see Nos. 48-54.

Fulah Shepherd — A2

1904				
18	A2	1c black, yel grn	1.20	1.20
19	A2	2c vio brn, buff	1.20	1.20
20	A2	4c carmine, bl	1.60	1.60
21	A2	5c green, grnsh	1.60	1.60
22	A2	10c carmine	4.00	2.40
23	A2	15c violet, rose	12.00	5.50
24	A2	20c carmine, grn	16.00	16.00
25	A2	25c blue	16.00	10.00
26	A2	30c brown	24.00	24.00
27	A2	40c red, straw	35.00	24.00
28	A2	50c brown, az	32.50	24.00
29	A2	75c green, org	32.50	32.50
30	A2	1fr brnz grn, straw	47.50	47.50
31	A2	2fr red, org	87.50	87.50
32	A2	5fr green, yel grn	120.00	120.00
		Nos. 18-32 (15)	432.60	399.00

For surcharges see Nos. 55-62.

Gen. Louis Faidherbé — A3   Oil Palm — A4

Dr. Noel Eugène Ballay — A5

1906-07				
Name of Colony in Red or Blue				
33	A3	1c gray	.80	.80
34	A3	2c brown	1.20	1.20
35	A3	4c brown, bl	1.60	1.60
36	A3	5c green	4.00	2.00
37	A3	10c carmine (B)	24.00	1.60
38	A4	20c black, blue	8.00	4.00
39	A4	25c blue, pnksh	8.00	6.50
40	A4	30c brown, pnksh	8.00	4.00
41	A4	35c black, yellow	6.50	2.40
42	A4	45c choc, grnsh gray	8.00	4.00
43	A4	50c dp violet	16.00	12.00
44	A4	75c blue, org	12.00	4.00
45	A5	1fr black, az	20.00	24.00
46	A5	2fr blue, pink	40.00	45.00
47	A5	5fr car, straw (B)	60.00	65.00
		Nos. 33-47 (15)	218.10	178.10

Regular Issues Surcharged in Black or Carmine

1912				
On Issue of 1892-1900				
48	A1	5c on 2c brown, buff	1.60	2.00
49	A1	5c on 4c cl, lav (C)	1.25	1.60
50	A1	5c on 15c blue (C)	1.25	1.60
51	A1	5c on 20c red, grn	4.00	5.25
52	A1	5c on 30c brn, bis (C)	5.50	6.50
53	A1	10c on 40c red, straw	2.40	3.25
54	A1	10c on 75c dp vio, org	9.50	9.00
a.	Double surcharge, inverted		325.00	

On Issue of 1904				
55	A2	5c on 2c vio brn, buff	1.20	1.20
a.	Pair, one without surcharge		650.00	
b.	Inverted surcharge		210.00	
56	A2	5c on 4c car, blue	1.20	1.20
57	A2	5c on 15c violet, rose	1.20	1.20
58	A2	5c on 20c car, grn	1.60	1.60

59	A2	5c on 25c blue (C)	1.60	2.00
60	A2	5c on 30c brown (C)	2.00	3.25
61	A2	10c on 40c red, straw	2.00	3.25
62	A2	10c on 50c brn, az (C)	5.50	6.50
		Nos. 48-62 (15)	40.30	49.90

Two spacings between the surcharged numerals are found on Nos. 48 to 62. For detailed listings, see the *Scott Classic Specialized Catalogue of Stamps and Covers.*

Ford at Kitim — A6

1913-33			Perf. 13½x14	
63	A6	1c violet & bl	.25	.25
a.		Imperf.	72.50	
64	A6	2c brn & vio brn	.25	.25
a.		Double impression of vio brn	160.00	
65	A6	4c gray & black	.25	.25
66	A6	5c yel grn & bl grn	1.20	.40
a.		Booklet pane of 4		
		Complete booklet, 10 #66a	275.00	
67	A6	5c brn vio & grn ('22)	.40	.25
68	A6	10c red org & rose	1.20	.40
a.		Booklet pane of 4		
		Complete booklet, 10 #68a	550.00	
69	A6	10c yel grn & bl grn ('22)	.55	.25
70	A6	10c vio & ver ('25)	.80	.40
a.		Imperf.	45.00	
71	A6	15c vio brn & rose, chalky paper ('16)	.80	.40
a.		Booklet pane of 4		
		Complete booklet, 10 #71a	1,200.	
72	A6	15c gray grn & yel grn ('25)	.40	.40
73	A6	15c red brn & rose lil ('27)	.40	.30
74	A6	20c brn & vio	.40	.40
75	A6	20c grn & bl grn ('26)	.80	.80
76	A6	20c brn red & brn ('27)	.80	.50
77	A6	25c ultra & blue	2.75	1.60
78	A6	25c black & vio ('22)	.80	.80
79	A6	30c vio brn & grn	1.60	1.20
80	A6	30c red org & rose ('22)	1.20	1.10
81	A6	30c rose red & grn ('25)	.30	.30
82	A6	30c dl grn & bl grn ('28)	1.60	1.60
83	A6	35c blue & rose	.55	.55
84	A6	40c green & gray	1.20	1.20
85	A6	45c brown & red	1.20	1.20
86	A6	50c ultra & black	6.50	4.75
87	A6	50c ultra & bl ('22)	1.60	.80
88	A6	50c yel brn & ol ('25)	.80	.80
89	A6	60c vio, pnksh ('25)	.80	.80
90	A6	65c yel brn & sl bl ('26)	2.00	1.20
91	A6	75c red & ultra	1.60	1.60
92	A6	75c indigo & dl bl ('25)	.80	1.20
93	A6	75c mag & yel grn ('27)	1.60	1.20
94	A6	85c ol grn & red brn ('26)	1.20	1.20
95	A6	90c brn red & rose ('30)	5.50	4.75
96	A6	1fr violet & black	1.60	2.40
97	A6	1.10fr vio & ol brn ('28)	8.00	8.00
98	A6	1.25fr vio & yel brn ('33)	2.40	1.60
99	A6	1.50fr dk bl & lt bl ('30)	6.50	2.40
100	A6	1.75fr ol brn & vio ('33)	1.75	1.60
101	A6	2fr org & vio brn	4.00	4.00
102	A6	3fr red vio ('30)	8.00	5.50
103	A6	5fr black & vio	16.00	16.00
104	A6	5fr dl bl & blk ('22)	4.00	2.40
		Nos. 63-104 (42)	94.35	77.00

For surcharges see Nos. 105-115, B1.

Nos. 66, 68 and 77 pasted on colored cardboard and overprinted "VALEUR D'ECHANGE" were used as emergency currency in 1920.

Type of 1913-33 Surcharged

1922
105 A6 60c on 75c violet, pnksh .40 .40

Stamps and Type of 1913-33 Surcharged

1924-27
106	A6	25c on 2fr org & brn (R)	.40	.40
107	A6	25c on 5fr dull bl & blk	.40	.40
108	A6	65c on 75c rose & ultra ('25)	1.60	1.60
109	A6	85c on 75c rose & ultra ('25)	2.40	2.00
110	A6	90c on 75c brn red & cer ('27)	3.25	3.25
111	A6	1.25fr on 1fr dk bl & ultra ('26)	1.20	1.60
112	A6	1.50fr on 1fr dp bl & lt bl ('27)	2.40	2.40
113	A6	3fr on 5fr mag & sl ('27)	4.00	4.00
114	A6	10fr on 5fr bl & bl grn, bluish ('27)	8.00	8.00
115	A6	20fr on 5fr rose lil & brn ol, pnksh ('27)	20.00	20.00
		Nos. 106-115 (10)	43.65	43.65

Common Design Types pictured following the introduction.

Colonial Exposition Issue
Common Design Types
1931 Engr. Perf. 12½
Name of Country in Black
116	CD70	40c deep green	4.75	4.75
a.		"GUINÉE FRANCAISE" omitted	55.00	67.50
117	CD71	50c violet	4.75	4.75
118	CD72	90c red orange	4.75	4.75
a.		"GUINÉE FRANCAISE" omitted	55.00	70.00
119	CD73	1.50fr dull blue	5.50	5.50
a.		"GUINÉE FRANCAISE" omitted	55.00	67.50
		Nos. 116-119 (4)	19.75	19.75
		Set, never hinged	32.00	

Paris International Exposition Issue
Common Design Types
1937 Perf. 13
120	CD74	20c deep violet	2.00	2.00
121	CD75	30c dark green	2.00	2.00
122	CD76	40c car rose	2.40	2.40
123	CD77	50c dark brown	1.60	1.60
124	CD78	90c red	1.60	1.60
125	CD79	1.50fr ultra	2.40	2.40
		Nos. 120-125 (6)	12.00	12.00
		Set, never hinged	20.25	

Colonial Arts Exhibition Issue
Souvenir Sheet
Common Design Type
1937 Imperf.
126 CD76 3fr Prussian green 12.00 16.00
Never hinged 16.00

Guinea Village — A7

Hausa Basket Workers — A8

Forest Waterfall A9 · Guinea Women A10

1938-40			Perf. 13	
128	A7	2c vermilion	.25	.25
129	A7	3c ultra	.25	.25
130	A7	4c green	.25	.25
131	A7	5c rose car	.25	.25
132	A7	10c peacock blue	.25	.25
133	A7	15c violet brown	.25	.25
134	A8	20c dk carmine	.30	.25
135	A8	25c pck blue	.40	.25
136	A8	30c ultra	.40	.25
137	A8	35c green	.55	.50
138	A8	40c blk brn ('40)	.40	.40
139	A8	45c dk green ('40)	.40	.40
140	A8	50c red brown	.55	.50
141	A8	55c dk ultra	1.20	.80
142	A9	60c dk ultra ('40)	1.20	1.20
143	A9	65c green	1.20	1.20
144	A9	70c green ('40)	1.20	1.20
145	A9	80c rose violet	.80	.55
146	A9	90c rose vio ('39)	1.25	1.25
147	A9	1fr orange red	2.40	2.00
148	A9	1fr brn blk ('40)	.40	.40
149	A9	1.25fr org red ('39)	1.40	1.40
150	A9	1.40fr brown ('40)	1.20	1.20
151	A9	1.50fr violet	2.40	2.00
152	A10	1.60fr org red ('40)	1.60	1.60
153	A10	1.75fr ultra	.80	.80
154	A10	2fr magenta	1.20	.80
155	A10	2.25fr brt ultra ('39)	1.75	1.75
156	A10	2.50fr brn blk ('40)	1.60	1.60
157	A10	3fr peacock blue	.95	.40
158	A10	5fr rose violet	.95	.80
159	A10	10fr slate green	1.60	1.60
160	A10	20fr chocolate	2.40	2.40
		Nos. 128-160 (33)	32.00	28.60
		Set, never hinged	45.00	

For surcharges see Nos. B8-B11.

Caillié Issue
Common Design Type
1939 Engr. Perf. 12½x12
161	CD81	90c org brn & org	.40	.80
162	CD81	2fr brt violet	.40	1.20
163	CD81	2.25fr ultra & dk bl	.40	1.20
		Nos. 161-163 (3)	1.20	3.20
		Set, never hinged	2.40	

René Caillié, French explorer, death cent.

New York World's Fair Issue
Common Design Type
1939
164	CD82	1.25fr carmine lake	.80	1.60
165	CD82	2.25fr ultra	.80	1.60
		Set, never hinged	2.40	

Ford at Kitim and Marshal Petain — A11

1941			Perf. 12x12½	
166	A11	1fr green	.40	—
167	A11	2.50fr deep blue	.40	—
		Set, never hinged	1.60	

For surcharges, see Nos. B15-B16.

Types of 1933-40 without "RF"
1943-44			Perf. 13	
168	A7	10c peacock blue	.40	
169	A8	20c dk carmine	.40	
170	A8	30c ultramarine	.40	
171	A8	40c black brown	1.20	
172	A9	60c dk ultramarine	1.20	
173	A9	1.50fr violet	1.20	
174	A10	2fr magenta	1.60	
		Nos. 168-174 (7)	6.40	
		Set, never hinged	9.50	

Nos. 168-174 were issued by the Vichy government in France, but were not placed on sale in French Guinea.

SEMI-POSTAL STAMPS

Regular Issue of 1913 Surcharged in Red

1915 Unwmk. Perf. 13½x14
B1 A6 10c + 5c org & rose 1.60 1.60

Curie Issue
Common Design Type
1938 Engr. Perf. 13
B2 CD80 1.75fr + 50c brt ultra 8.75 8.75
Never hinged 14.00

French Revolution Issue
Common Design Type
1939 Photo.
Name and Value Typo. in Black
B3	CD83	45c + 25c green	9.50	9.50
B4	CD83	70c + 30c brown	9.50	9.50
B5	CD83	90c + 35c red org	9.50	9.50
B6	CD83	1.25fr + 1fr rose	9.50	9.50
B7	CD83	2.25fr + 2fr blue	9.50	9.50
		pink		
		Nos. B3-B7 (5)	47.50	47.50
		Set, never hinged	80.00	

Stamps of 1938, Surcharged in Black

1941 Unwmk. Perf. 13
B8	A8	50c + 1fr red brn	4.00	4.00
B9	A9	80c + 2fr rose vio	8.00	8.00
B10	A9	1.50fr + 2fr brn	8.00	8.00
B11	A10	2fr + 3fr magenta	8.00	8.00
		Nos. B8-B11 (4)	28.00	28.00
		Set, never hinged	55.00	

Common Design Type and

Senegalese Soldier SP1 · Colonial Infantryman SP2

1941 Unwmk. Perf. 13
B12	SP1	1fr + 1fr red	1.25	
B13	CD86	1.50fr + 3fr maroon	1.40	
B14	SP2	2.50fr + 1fr blue	1.40	
		Nos. B12-B14 (3)	4.05	
		Set, never hinged	6.50	

Nos. B12-B14 were issued by the Vichy government in France, but were not placed on sale in the French Guinea.

Nos. 166-167 Surcharged in Black or Red

1944 Engr. Perf. 12½x12
B15		50c + 1.50fr on 2.50fr deep blue (R)	.40	
B16		+ 2.50fr on 1fr green	.40	
		Set, never hinged	1.60	

Colonial Development Fund.
Nos. B15-B16 were issued by the Vichy government in France, but were not placed on sale in French Guinea.

AIR POST STAMPS

Common Design Type

1940 Unwmk. Engr. Perf. 12½x12

C1	CD85	1.90fr ultra	.40	.40
C2	CD85	2.90fr dark red	.40	.40
C3	CD85	4.50fr dk gray grn	.80	.80
C4	CD85	4.90fr yellow bis	.80	.80
C5	CD85	6.90fr pte orange	1.60	1.60
	Nos. C1-C5 (5)		4.00	4.00
	Set, never hinged		6.00	

Common Design Types

1942   **Engr.**

C6	CD88	50c car & blue	.25
C7	CD88	1fr brown & blk	.30
C8	CD88	2fr dk grn & red brn	.30
C9	CD88	3fr dk bl & scar	.50
C10	CD88	5fr vio & brn red	.80

Frame Engraved, Center Typographed

C11	CD89	10fr multicolored	.80
C12	CD89	20fr multicolored	1.20
C13	CD89	50fr multicolored	1.60 —
	Nos. C6-C13 (8)		5.75
	Set, never hinged		12.00

There is doubt whether Nos. C6-C12 were officially placed in use.

AIR POST SEMI-POSTAL STAMPS

Dahomey types SPAP1-SPAP3 inscribed "Guinée Frcaise" or "Guinée"

Perf. 13½x12½, 13 (#CB3)
Photo, Engr. (#CB3)

1942, June 22

CB1	SPAP1	1.50fr + 3.50fr grn	.40	5.50
CB2	SPAP2	2fr + 6fr brown	.40	5.50
CB3	SPAP3	3fr + 9fr car red	.40	5.50
	Nos. CB1-CB3 (3)		1.20	16.50
	Set, never hinged		2.40	

Native children's welfare fund.

Colonial Education Fund
Common Design Type
Perf. 12½x13½

1942, June 22   **Engr.**

CB4	CD86a	1.20fr + 1.80fr blue & red	.40	5.50
	Never hinged		.80	

POSTAGE DUE STAMPS

Fulah Woman — D1

1905 Unwmk. Typo. Perf. 14x13½

J1	D1	5c blue	1.60	3.25
J2	D1	10c brown	2.40	3.25
J3	D1	15c green	8.00	6.50
J4	D1	30c rose	8.00	6.50
J5	D1	50c black	12.00	13.00
J6	D1	60c dull orange	12.00	16.00
J7	D1	1fr violet	40.00	47.50
	Nos. J1-J7 (7)		84.00	96.00

Heads and Coast — D2

1906-08

J8	D2	5c grn, *grnsh* ('08)	20.00	13.00
J9	D2	10c violet brn ('08)	8.00	5.50
J10	D2	15c dk blue ('08)	8.00	5.50
J11	D2	20c blk, *yellow*	8.00	5.50
J12	D2	30c red, *straw* ('08)	27.50	26.00
J13	D2	50c violet ('08)	24.00	26.00
J14	D2	60c blk, *buff* ('08)	24.00	21.00
J15	D2	1fr blk, *pnksh* ('08)	16.00	13.50
	Nos. J8-J15 (8)		135.50	116.00

D3

1914

J16	D3	5c green	.40	.55
J17	D3	10c rose	.40	.65
J18	D3	15c gray	.40	.80
J19	D3	20c brown	.80	.80
J20	D3	30c blue	.80	.80
J21	D3	50c black	1.00	1.25
J22	D3	60c orange	2.00	2.40
J23	D3	1fr violet	2.00	2.40
	Nos. J16-J23 (8)		7.80	9.65

Type of 1914 Issue Surcharged

1927

J24	D3	2fr on 1fr lil rose	8.00	8.00
a.		No period after "F"	27.50	32.50
J25	D3	3fr on 1fr org brn	8.00	8.00

D4

1938   **Engr.**

J26	D4	5c dk violet	.25	.30
J27	D4	10c carmine	.25	.30
J28	D4	15c green	.25	.30
J29	D4	20c red brown	.25	.40
J30	D4	30c rose violet	.25	.40
J31	D4	50c chocolate	.80	.70
J32	D4	60c peacock blue	.80	1.10
J33	D4	1fr vermilion	.80	1.10
J34	D4	2fr ultra	.80	1.10
J35	D4	3fr black	1.60	1.60
	Nos. J26-J35 (10)		6.05	7.30

For No. J27 without "RF," see No. J36.

Type of 1938 without "RF"

1944

J36	D4	10c carmine	.80
	Never hinged		1.20

No. J36 was issued by the Vichy government in France, but was not placed on sale in French Guinea.

FRENCH INDIA

ˈfrench ˈin-dē-ə

LOCATION — East coast of India bordering on Bay of Bengal.
GOVT. — French Territory
AREA — 196 sq. mi.
POP. — 323,295 (1941)
CAPITAL — Pondichéry

French India was an administrative unit comprising the five settlements of Chandernagor, Karikal, Mahé, Pondichéry and Yanaon. These united with India in 1949 and 1954.

100 Centimes = 1 Franc
24 Caches = 1 Fanon (1923)
8 Fanons = 1 Rupie

> **Catalogue values for unused stamps in this country are for Never Hinged items, beginning with Scott 210 in the regular postage section, Scott B14 in the semipostal section, and Scott C7 in the airpost section.**

Navigation and Commerce — A1

Perf. 14x13½

1892-1907 Typo. Unwmk.
Colony Name in Blue or Carmine

1	A1	1c blk, *lil bl*	1.40	1.00
2	A1	2c brn, *buff*	2.40	1.50
3	A1	4c claret, *lav*	3.00	2.50
4	A1	5c grn, *grnsh*	6.00	3.75
5	A1	10c blk, *lavender*	13.50	2.75
6	A1	10c red ('00)	5.00	2.40
7	A1	15c blue, quadrille paper	16.00	5.50

8	A1	15c gray, *lt gray* ('00)	30.00	30.00
9	A1	20c red, *grn*	8.00	5.50
10	A1	25c blk, *rose*	5.25	2.75
11	A1	25c blue ('00)	19.00	16.00
12	A1	30c brn, *bis*	57.50	50.00
13	A1	35c blk, *yel* ('06)	19.00	9.00
14	A1	40c red, *straw*	7.50	7.25
15	A1	45c blk, *gray grn* ('07)	5.25	6.00
16	A1	50c car, *rose*	7.25	7.25
17	A1	50c brn, *az* ('00)	16.00	17.50
18	A1	75c dp vio, *org*	9.75	9.50
19	A1	1fr brnz grn, *straw*	14.00	14.50
	Nos. 1-19 (19)		245.80	194.65

Perf. 13½x14 stamps are counterfeits.

Nos. 10 and 16 Surcharged in Carmine or Black

1903

20	A1	5c on 25c blk, *rose*	400.00	240.00
21	A1	10c on 25c blk, *rose*	375.00	225.00
22	A1	15c on 25c blk, *rose*	125.00	115.00
23	A1	40c on 50c car, *rose* (Bk)	525.00	425.00
	Nos. 20-23 (4)		1,425.	1,005.

Counterfeits of Nos. 20-23 abound.

A2

Revenue Stamp Surcharged in Black

1903

24	A2	5c gray blue	30.00	30.00

The bottom of the revenue stamps were cut off.

Brahma   Kali Temple near
A5   Pondichéry
             A6

1914-22 Perf. 13½x14, 14x13½

25	A5	1c gray & blk	.30	.30
a.		1c light gray & black	.55	.55
26	A5	2c brn vio & blk	.30	.30
27	A5	2c grn & brn vio ('22)	.45	.45
28	A5	3c brown & blk	.40	.40
29	A5	4c orange & blk	.40	.40
30	A5	5c bl grn & blk	.70	.70
31	A5	5c vio brn & blk ('22)	.60	.60
32	A5	10c dp rose & blk	1.25	1.25
33	A5	10c grn & blk ('22)	.90	.90
34	A5	15c vio & blk	1.10	1.10
35	A5	20c org red & blk	2.00	2.00
36	A5	25c blue & blk	2.00	2.00
37	A5	25c ultra & fawn ('22)	1.60	1.60
38	A5	30c ultra & blk	4.00	4.00
39	A5	30c rose & blk ('22)	1.75	1.75
40	A6	35c choc & blk	2.25	2.25
41	A6	40c org red & blk	2.25	2.25
42	A6	45c bl grn & blk	2.25	2.25
43	A6	50c dp rose & blk	2.25	2.25
44	A6	50c ultra & bl ('22)	3.00	3.00
45	A6	75c blue & blk	4.50	4.50
46	A6	1fr yellow & blk	4.50	4.50
47	A6	2fr violet & blk	6.75	6.75
48	A6	5fr ultra & blk	3.50	3.50
49	A6	5fr rose & blk ('22)	4.50	4.50
	Nos. 25-49 (25)		54.50	54.50

For surcharges see Nos. 50-79, 113-116, 156A, B1-B5.

No. 34 Surcharged in Various Colors

1922

50	A5	1c on 15c (Bk)	.80	.80
51	A5	2c on 15c (Bl)	.80	.80
53	A5	5c on 15c (R)	.80	.80
	Nos. 50-53 (3)		2.40	2.40

Stamps and Types of 1914-22 Surcharged with New Values in Caches, Fanons and Rupies in Black, Red or Blue

No. 55

No. 69

No. 78

1923-28

54	A5	1ca on 1c gray & blk (R)	.30	.30
a.		Imperf.	50.00	50.00
55	A5	2ca on 5c vio brn & blk	.50	.50
a.		Horizontal pair, imperf. between	—	
b.		Imperf.	45.00	45.00
56	A5	3ca on 3c brn & blk	.55	.55
57	A5	4ca on 4c org & blk	.80	.80
58	A5	6ca on 10c grn & blk	.95	.95
a.		Double surcharge	175.00	
59	A6	6ca on 45c bl grn & blk (R)	.95	.95
60	A5	10ca on 20c dp red & bl grn ('28)	2.50	2.50
61	A5	12ca on 15c vio & blk	.95	.95
62	A5	15ca on 20c org & blk	1.50	1.50
63	A6	16ca on 35c lt bl & yel brn ('28)	2.60	2.60
64	A5	18ca on 30c rose & blk	2.40	2.40
65	A6	20ca on 45c grn & dl red ('28)	2.00	1.50
66	A5	1fa on 25c dp grn & rose red ('28)	3.50	3.50
67	A6	1fa3ca on 35c choc & blk (Bl)	1.10	1.10
68	A6	1fa6ca on 40c org & blk (R)	1.50	1.25
69	A6	1fa12ca on 50c ultra & bl (Bl)	1.75	1.50
70	A6	1fa12ca on 75c bl & blk (Bl)	1.25	1.25
a.		Double surcharge	145.00	
71	A6	1fa16ca on 75c brn red & grn ('28)	3.50	3.00
72	A5	2fa9ca on 25c ultra & fawn (Bl)	1.50	1.20
73	A6	2fa12ca on 1fr vio & dk brn ('28)	3.00	3.00
74	A6	3fa3ca on 1fr yel & blk (R)	1.75	1.45
a.		Double surcharge	145.00	
75	A6	6fa6ca on 2fr vio & blk	5.25	4.50
76	A6	1r on 1fr grn & dp bl (R) ('26)	9.50	7.75
77	A6	2r on 5fr rose & blk (R)	7.50	7.00
a.		Double surcharge	145.00	
78	A6	3r on 2fr gray & bl vio (R) ('26)	21.00	19.00
79	A6	5r on 5fr rose & blk, *grnsh* ('26)	27.50	24.00
	Nos. 54-79 (26)		105.60	95.00

Nos. 60, 63, 66 and 73 have the original value obliterated by bars.

A7

A8

1929

80	A7	1ca dk gray & blk	.25	.25
81	A7	2ca vio brn & blk	.25	.25
82	A7	3ca grn & blk	.25	.25
83	A7	4ca org & blk	.30	.30
84	A7	6ca gray grn & grn	.30	.30
85	A7	10ca brn, red & grn	.30	.30
86	A8	12ca grn & lt grn	.75	.70
87	A7	16ca brt bl & blk	.95	.95

88	A7	18ca brn red & ver	.95	.95
89	A7	20ca dk bl & grn, *bluish*	.75	.75
90	A8	1fa gray grn & rose red	.75	.70
91	A8	1fa6ca red org & blk	.75	.70
92	A8	1fa12ca dp bl & ultra	.75	.70
93	A8	1fa16ca rose red & grn	.95	.95
94	A8	2fa12ca brt vio & brn	1.20	1.00
95	A8	6fa6ca dl vio & blk	1.20	1.00
a.		Imperf.	50.00	
96	A8	1r gray grn & dp bl	1.10	1.00
97	A8	2r rose & blk	1.60	1.20
a.		Imperf.	50.00	
98	A8	3r lt gray & gray lil	3.00	2.25
99	A8	5r rose & blk, *grnsh*	3.00	2.40
		Nos. 80-99 (20)	19.35	16.90

For overprints and surcharges see Nos. 117-134, 157-176, 184-209G.

Common Design Types pictured following the introduction.

Colonial Exposition Issue
Common Design Types

1931		**Engr.**	***Perf. 12½***	
100	CD70	10ca deep green	4.50	4.50
101	CD71	12ca violet	4.50	4.50
102	CD72	18ca red orange	4.50	4.50
103	CD73	1fa12ca dull blue	4.50	4.50
		Nos. 100-103 (4)	18.00	18.00

Paris International Exposition Issue
Common Design Types

1937			***Perf. 13***	
104	CD74	8ca dp violet	2.00	4.00
105	CD75	12ca dk green	2.25	4.00
106	CD76	16ca car rose	2.25	4.00
107	CD77	20ca dk brown	1.40	4.00
108	CD78	1fa12ca red	1.75	4.00
109	CD79	2fa12ca ultra	2.25	4.00
		Nos. 104-109 (6)	11.90	24.00

For overprints see Nos. 135-139, 177-181.

Colonial Arts Exhibition Issue
Souvenir Sheet
Common Design Type

1937			***Imperf.***	
110	CD79	5fa red violet	9.25	12.50

For overprint see No. 140.

New York World's Fair Issue
Common Design Type

1939		**Engr.**	***Perf. 12½x12***	
111	CD82	1fa12ca car lake	1.25	4.00
112	CD82	2fa12ca ultra	1.75	4.00

For overprints see Nos. 141-142, 182-183.

Temple near Pondichéry and Marshal Petain — A9

1941		**Engr.**	***Perf. 12½x12***	
112A	A9	1fa16ca car & red	.80	
c.		Denomination omitted	55.00	
112B	A9	4fa4ca blue	.80	
d.		Denomination omitted	200.00	

Nos. 112A-112B were issued by the Vichy government in France, but were not placed on sale in French India.

For surcharges, see Nos. B13B-B13C.

Nos. 62, 64, 67, 72 Overprinted in Carmine or Blue (#116)

a

b

1941		**Unwmk.**	***Perf. 13½x14***	
113	A5 (a)	15ca on 20c	85.00	85.00
114	A5 (a)	18ca on 30c	16.00	16.00
115	A6 (a)	1fa3ca on 35c	130.00	130.00
a.		Horiz. overprint	125.00	125.00
116	A5 (b)	2fa9ca on 25c	1,600.	1,150.
a.		Overprint "a" (Bl)	1,400.	1,150.
b.		Overprint "b" (C)	2,100.	2,100.

Nos. 81-99 Overprinted Type "a" in Carmine or Blue

1941				
117	A7	2ca (C)	12.50	12.50
118	A7	3ca (C)	4.75	4.75
119	A7	4ca (C)	13.50	13.50
120	A7	6ca (C)	4.75	4.75
121	A7	10ca (Bl)	6.50	6.50
122	A8	12ca (C)	4.75	4.75
123	A7	16ca (C)	4.75	4.75
123A	A7	18ca (Bl)	675.00	675.00
124	A7	20ca (C)	4.75	4.75
125	A8	1fa (Bl)	4.75	4.75
126	A8	1fa6ca (C)	4.75	4.75
127	A8	1fa12ca (C)	6.50	6.50
128	A8	1fa16ca (C)	4.75	4.75
129	A8	2fa12ca (C)	4.75	4.75
130	A8	6fa6ca (C)	4.75	4.75
131	A8	1r (C)	4.75	4.75
132	A8	2r (C)	4.75	4.75
133	A8	3r (C)	6.50	6.50
134	A8	5r (C)	10.50	10.50
		Nos. 117-123, 124-134 (18)	113.00	113.00

Same Overprints on Paris Exposition Issue of 1937

1941			***Perf. 13***	
135	CD74 (b)	8ca (C)	10.00	10.00
135A	CD74 (b)	8ca (Bl)	275.00	275.00
d.		Blk. overprint	1,000.	1,000.
135B	CD74 (a)	8ca (C)	180.00	180.00
135C	CD74 (a)	8ca (Bl)	250.00	250.00
136	CD75 (a)	12ca (C)	6.00	6.00
137	CD76 (a)	16ca (Bl)	6.00	6.00
a.		Blk. overprint	175.00	175.00
138	CD78 (a)	1fa12ca (Bl)	6.00	6.00
139	CD79 (a)	2fa12ca (C)	6.00	6.00
		Nos. 135-139 (8)	739.00	739.00

Inverted overprints exist.

Souvenir Sheet
No. 110 Overprinted "FRANCE LIBRE" Diagonally in Blue Violet

Two types of overprint:
I — Overprint 37mm. With serifs.
II — Overprint 24mm, as type "a" shown above No. 113. No serifs.

1941		**Unwmk.**	***Imperf.***	
140	CD79	5fa red vio (I)	800.00	725.00
a.		Type II	1,000.	1,000.
b.		As No. 140, inverted surcharge	5,000.	2,000.

Overprinted on New York World's Fair Issue, 1939

			Perf. 12½x12	
141	CD82 (a)	1fa12ca (Bl)	4.75	4.75
142	CD82 (a)	2fa12ca (C)	5.50	5.50

Lotus Flowers — A10

1942	**Unwmk.**	**Photo.**	***Perf. 14x14½***	
143	A10	2ca brown	.30	.30
144	A10	3ca dk blue	.30	.30
145	A10	4ca emerald	.30	.30
146	A10	6ca dk orange	.30	.30
147	A10	12ca grnsh blk	.30	.30
148	A10	16ca rose violet	.30	.30
149	A10	20ca dk red brn	.65	.65
150	A10	1fa brt red	.70	.65
151	A10	1fa18ca slate blk	.90	.80
152	A10	6fa6ca brt ultra	1.60	1.50
153	A10	1r dull violet	1.40	1.40
154	A10	2r bister	1.75	1.60
155	A10	3r chocolate	1.75	1.60
156	A10	5r dk green	2.25	2.00
		Nos. 143-156 (14)	12.80	12.00

Stamps of 1923-39 Overprinted in Blue or Carmine

c

d

1942-43		***Perf. 13½x14, 14x13½***		
Overprinted on No. 64				
156A	A5 (c)	18ca on 30c (B)	300.00	230.00

Overprinted on #81-82, 84, 86-99

157	A7 (c)	2ca (C)	3.75	3.75
a.		"FRANCE LIBRE" in black	250.00	175.00
b.		As No. 157, blk. overprint	375.00	375.00
c.		As No. 157, bl. overprint	500.00	500.00
158	A7 (c)	3ca (C)	2.40	2.40
159	A7 (c)	6ca (Bl)	3.25	3.25
a.		Car. overprint	325.00	
b.		Blk. overprint	725.00	
c.		Blk.-Blk. overprint	50.00	35.00
160	A8 (d)	12ca (Bl)	3.75	3.75
161	A7 (c)	16ca (C)	3.25	3.25
162	A7 (c)	18ca (Bl)	2.40	2.40
163	A7 (c)	20ca (Bl)		
			('43)	7.25	5.50
164	A7 (c)	20ca (C)	2.40	2.40
a.		Double overprint, one bl. one car.	1,350.	475.00
165	A8 (d)	1fa (Bl)	2.40	2.40
166	A8 (d)	1fa6ca (Bl)	3.25	3.25
a.		Bl. overprint	300.00	225.00
167	A8 (d)	1fa12ca (Bl)	3.25	3.25
168	A8 (d)	1fa16ca (Bl)	3.25	3.25
169	A8 (d)	2fa12ca (Bl)	100.00	80.00
170	A8 (d)	2fa12ca (C)	3.25	3.25
171	A8 (d)	6fa6ca (C)	4.00	4.00
172	A8 (d)	1r (C)	7.25	7.25
173	A8 (d)	2r (C)	7.25	7.25
174	A8 (d)	3r (C)	7.25	7.25
175	A8 (d)	3r (Bl)		
			('43)	200.00	175.00
176	A8 (d)	5r (C)	7.25	7.25
		Nos. 156A-176 (21)	676.85	560.10

Same Overprints on Paris International Exposition Issue of 1937

			Perf. 13	
177	CD74 (c)	8ca (Bl)	7.25	7.25
178	CD75 (d)	12ca (Bl)	7.25	7.25
179	CD76 (d)	16ca (Bl)	1,300.	1,300.
180	CD78 (d)	1fa12ca (Bl)	7.25	7.25
181	CD79 (d)	2fa12ca (C)	7.25	7.25

Same Overprint on New York World's Fair Issue, 1939

			Perf. 12½x12	
182	CD82 (d)	1fa12ca (Bl)	7.25	7.25
183	CD82 (d)	2fa12ca (C)	7.25	7.25

No. 87 Surcharged in Carmine

1942-43			***Perf. 13½x14***	
184	A7	1ca on 16ca	75.00	45.00
185	A7	4ca on 16ca ('43)	75.00	45.00
186	A7	10ca on 16ca	55.00	35.00
187	A7	15ca on 16ca	55.00	35.00
188	A7	1fa3ca on 16ca ('43)	72.50	45.00
189	A7	2fa9ca on 16ca ('43)	72.50	45.00
190	A7	3fa3ca on 16ca ('43)	55.00	35.00
		Nos. 184-190 (7)	460.00	285.00

Nos. 95-99 Srchd. in Carmine

1943			***Perf. 14x13½***	
191	A8	1ca on 6fa6ca	11.00	11.00
192	A8	4ca on 6fa6ca	12.50	12.50
193	A8	10ca on 6fa6ca	11.00	11.00
194	A8	15ca on 6fa6ca	11.00	11.00
195	A8	1fa3ca on 6fa6ca	11.00	11.00
196	A8	2fa9ca on 6fa6ca	12.50	12.50
197	A8	3fa3ca on 6fa6ca	12.50	12.50
198	A8	1ca on 1r	4.75	4.75
199	A8	2ca on 1r	1.60	1.60
200	A8	4ca on 1r	1.60	1.60
201	A8	6ca on 2r	1.60	1.60
202	A8	10ca on 2r	1.75	1.75
203	A8	12ca on 2r	1.60	1.60
204	A8	15ca on 3r	1.60	1.60
205	A8	16ca on 3r	1.60	1.60
206	A8	1fa3ca on 3r	1.60	1.60
207	A8	1fa6ca on 5r	2.00	2.00
208	A8	1fa12ca on 5r	2.40	2.40
209	A8	1fa16ca on 5r	2.40	2.40
		Nos. 191-209 (19)	106.00	106.00

In 1943, 200 each of 27 stamps were overprinted in red or dark blue, "FRANCE TOUJOURS" and a Lorraine Cross within a circle measuring 17½mm in diameter. Overprinted were Nos. 81-99, 104-109, 111-112. Values, set: $25,000 unused; $6,000 used.

No. 95 Surcharged in Carmine

1943		**Unwmk.**	***Perf. 14x13½***	
209A	A8	1ca on 6fa6ca	35.00	27.50
209B	A8	4ca on 6fa6ca	35.00	27.50
209C	A8	10ca on 6fa6ca	24.00	16.00
209D	A8	15ca on 6fa6ca	24.00	16.00
209E	A8	1fa3ca on 6fa6ca	32.50	27.50
209F	A8	2fa9ca on 6fa6ca	32.50	27.50
209G	A8	3fa3ca on 6fa6ca	27.50	27.50
		Nos. 209A-209G (7)	218.00	169.50

Catalogue values for unused stamps in this section, from this point to the end of the section, are for Never Hinged items.

Eboue Issue
Common Design Type

1945		**Engr.**	***Perf. 13***	
210	CD91	3fa8ca black	.80	.70
211	CD91	5r1fa16ca Prus grn	1.40	1.25

Nos. 210 and 211 exist imperforate.

Apsaras — A11

Designs: 6ca, 8ca, 10ca, Dvarabalagar. 12ca, 15ca, 1fa, Vishnu. 1fa6ca, 2fa, 2fa2ca, Dvarabalagar (foot raised). 2fa12ca, 3fa, 5fa, Temple Guardian. 7fa12ca, 1r2fa, 1r4fa12ca, Tigoupalagar.

1948		**Photo.**	***Perf. 13x13½***	
212	A11	1ca dk ol grn	.50	.25
213	A11	2ca orange brn	.50	.25
214	A11	4ca vio, *cr*	.55	.30
215	A11	6ca yellow org	1.50	.65
216	A11	8ca gray blk	1.50	1.10
217	A11	10ca dl yel grn, *pale grn*	1.50	1.10
218	A11	12ca violet brn	1.00	.65
219	A11	15ca Prus grn	1.00	.65
220	A11	1fa vio, *pale rose*	1.50	.80
221	A11	1fa6ca brown red	1.50	.85
222	A11	2fa dk green	1.50	.85
223	A11	2fa2ca blue, *cr*	1.50	1.15
224	A11	2fa12ca brown	1.90	1.15
225	A11	3fa dp orange	3.25	1.25
226	A11	5fa red vio, *rose*	3.00	1.25
227	A11	7fa12ca dk brown	3.25	1.25
228	A11	1r2fa blue blk	6.00	4.50
229	A11	1r4fa12ca olive grn	6.50	5.00
		Nos. 212-229 (18)	37.95	23.00

Brahman Ascetic — A12

1952				
230	A12	18ca rose red	2.75	2.00
231	A12	1fa15ca vio blue	3.75	2.50
232	A12	4fa olive grn	4.25	3.50
		Nos. 230-232 (3)	10.75	8.00

Military Medal Issue
Common Design Type

1952		**Engr. and Typo.**	***Perf. 13***	
233	CD101	1fa multi	5.50	7.00

SEMI-POSTAL STAMPS

Regular Issue of 1914 Surcharged in Red

Two printings: 1st, surcharge at bottom of stamp; 2nd, surcharge centered toward top.

1915   **Unwmk.**   *Perf. 14x13½*

B1	A5	10c + 5c rose & blk		
		(1st)	2.10	2.10
b.		Inverted surcharge	210.00	210.00

There were two printings of this surcharge. In the first, it was placed at the bottom of the stamp; in the second, it was centered toward the top.

Regular Issue of 1914
Surcharged in Red

1916

B2	A5	10c + 5c rose & blk	21.00	21.00
a.		Inverted surcharge	210.00	210.00
b.		Double surcharge	210.00	210.00

No. 32 Surcharged

B3   A5   10c + 5c rose & blk   3.50   3.50

No. 32 Surcharged

B4   A5   10c + 5c rose & blk   1.60   1.60

No. 32 Surcharged

B5   A5   10c + 5c rose & blk   2.25   2.25

Curie Issue
Common Design Type

1938   **Engr.**   *Perf. 13*

B6	CD80	2fa12ca + 20ca brt ultra	10.00	10.00

French Revolution Issue
Common Design Type

1939   **Photo.**
Name and Value Typo. in Black

B7	CD83	18ca + 10ca grn	5.75	6.50
B8	CD83	1fa6ca + 12ca brn	5.75	6.50
B9	CD83	1fa12ca + 16ca red org	5.75	6.50
B10	CD83	1fa16ca + 1fa16ca rose pink	5.75	6.50
B11	CD83	2fa12ca + 3fa blue	5.75	6.50
		Nos. B7-B11 (5)	28.75	32.50

Common Design Type and

Non-Commissioned
Officer, Native
Guard — SP1

Sepoy — SP2

1941   **Photo.**   *Perf. 13½*

B12	SP1	1fa16ca + 1fa16ca red	1.25
B13	CD86	2fa12ca + 5fa mar	1.25
B13A	SP2	4fa4ca + 1fa16ca bl	1.25
		Nos. B12-B13A (3)	3.75

Nos. B12-B13A were issued by the Vichy government in France, but were not placed on sale in French India.

Nos. 112A-112B
Srchd. in Black or
Red

1944   **Engr.**   *Perf. 12½x12*

B13B		20ca + 2fa12ca on 4fa4ca deep blue (R)	1.00
B13C		+ 4fa4ca on 1fa16ca car & red	1.00

Colonial Development Fund.
Nos. B13B-B13C were issued by the Vichy government in France, but were not placed on sale in French India.

> Catalogue values for unused stamps in this section, from this point to the end of the section, are for Never Hinged items.

Red Cross Issue
Common Design Type

1944   **Photo.**   *Perf. 14½x14*

B14   CD90   3fa + 1r4fa dk ol brn   1.50   1.25

The surtax was for the French Red Cross and national relief.

Tropical Medicine Issue
Common Design Type

1950   **Engr.**   *Perf. 13*

B15   CD100   1fa + 10ca ind & dp bl   6.00   4.00

The surtax was for charitable work.

AIR POST STAMPS

Common Design Type

1942   **Unwmk. Photo.**   *Perf. 14½x14*

C1	CD87	4fa dark orange	.90	2.00
C2	CD87	1r bright red	.90	2.00
C3	CD87	2r brown red	1.50	2.00
C4	CD87	5r black	1.50	3.00
C5	CD87	8r ultra	2.25	3.00
C6	CD87	10r dark green	2.25	3.00
		Nos. C1-C6 (6)	9.30	15.00

> Catalogue values for unused stamps in this section, from this point to the end of the section, are for Never Hinged items.

Victory Issue
Common Design Type

1946   **Engr.**   *Perf. 12½*

C7   CD92   4fa dk blue green   1.00   4.00

Chad to Rhine Issue
Common Design Types

1946, June 6

C8	CD93	2fa12ca olive bis	1.40	2.00
C9	CD94	5fa dark blue	1.40	2.00
C10	CD95	7fa12ca dk purple	2.25	2.00
C11	CD96	1r2fa green	2.25	3.00
C12	CD97	1r4fa12ca dk car	2.75	3.00
C13	CD98	3r1fa violet brn	2.75	3.00
		Nos. C8-C13 (6)	12.80	15.00

A 3r ultramarine and red, picturing the Temple of Chindambaram, was sold at Paris June 7 to July 8, 1948, but not placed on sale in the colony. Values: $10 never hinged, $7 hinged.

Bas-relief
Figure of
Goddess
AP1

Wing and   Bird over
Temple — AP2   Palms — AP3

Perf. 12x13, 13x12

1949   **Photo.**   **Unwmk.**

C14	AP1	1r yellow & plum	6.00	10.00
C15	AP2	2r green & dk grn	6.00	10.00
C16	AP3	5r lt bl & vio brn	27.50	30.00
		Nos. C14-C16 (3)	39.50	50.00

UPU Issue
Common Design Type

1949   **Engr.**   *Perf. 13*

C17   CD99   6fa lilac rose   11.50   8.75

Universal Postal Union, 75th anniv.

Liberation Issue
Common Design Type

1954, June 6

C18   CD102   1fa sepia & vio brn   11.00   8.00

AIR POST SEMI-POSTAL STAMPS

Girl's
School — SPAP1

Perf. 12½x13½

1942, June 22   **Unwmk.**   **Photo.**

CB1	SPAP1	2fa12ca + 5fa20ca green	.95
CB2	SPAP1	3fa8ca + 1r2fa yel brn	.95

Native children's welfare fund.
Nos. CB1-CB2 were issued by the Vichy government in France, but were not placed on sale in French India.

Colonial Education Fund
Common Design Type

1942, June 22

CB3   CD86a   2fa + 3fa blue & red   .90

No. CB3 was issued by the Vichy government in France, but was not placed on sale in French India.

POSTAGE DUE STAMPS

Postage Due Stamps of France Surcharged like Nos. 54-75 in Black, Blue or Red

1923   **Unwmk.**   *Perf. 14x13½*

J1	D2	6ca on 10c brn	1.25	1.25
J2	D2	12ca on 25c rose (Bk)	1.25	1.25
J3	D2	15ca on 20c ol grn (R)	1.60	1.60
J4	D2	1fa6ca on 30c red	1.60	1.60
J5	D2	1fa12a on 50c brn vio	2.75	2.75
J6	D2	1fa15ca on 5c bl (Bk)	3.00	3.00
J7	D2	3fa3ca on 1fr red brn, straw	3.25	3.25
		Nos. J1-J7 (7)	14.70	14.70

Types of Postage Due Stamps of French Colonies, 1884-85, Surcharged with New Values as in 1923 in Red or Black Bars over Original Values

1928

J8	D1	4ca on 20c gray lil	1.60	1.60
J9	D1	1fa on 30c orange	3.25	3.25
J10	D1	1fa16ca on 5c bl blk (R)	3.25	3.25
J11	D1	3fa on 1fr lt grn	3.75	3.75
		Nos. J8-J11 (4)	11.85	11.85

D3

1929   **Typo.**

J12	D3	4ca deep red	.50	.50
J13	D3	6ca blue	.65	.65
J14	D3	12ca green	.65	.65
J15	D3	1fa brown	1.25	1.25
J16	D3	1fa12ca lilac gray	1.25	1.25
J17	D3	1fa16ca buff	1.75	1.75
J18	D3	3fa lilac	2.10	2.10
		Nos. J12-J18 (7)	8.15	8.15

D4

1948   **Unwmk. Photo.**   *Perf. 13x13½*

J19	D4	1ca dk violet	.30	.30
J20	D4	2ca dk brown	.50	.50
J21	D4	6ca blue green	.50	.50
J22	D4	12ca dp orange	.70	.70
J23	D4	1fa dk car rose	.80	.80
J24	D4	1fa12ca brown	.80	.80
J25	D4	2fa dk slate bl	1.25	1.25
J26	D4	2fa12ca henna brn	1.60	1.60
J27	D4	5fa dk olive grn	2.25	2.25
J28	D4	1r dk blue vio	3.00	3.00
		Nos. J19-J28 (10)	11.70	11.70

FRENCH MOROCCO

'french mə-'rä-ˌkō

LOCATION — Northwest coast of Africa
GOVT. — French Protectorate
AREA — 153,870 sq. mi.
POP. — 8,340,000 (estimated 1954)
CAPITAL — Rabat

French Morocco was a French Protectorate from 1912 until 1956 when it, along with the Spanish and Tangier zones of Morocco, became the independent country, Morocco.

Stamps inscribed "Tanger" were for use in the international zone of Tangier in northern Morocco.

100 Centimos = 1 Peseta
100 Centimes = 1 franc (1917)

Catalogue values for unused stamps in this country are for Never Hinged items, beginning with Scott 177 in the regular postage section, Scott B26 in the semipostal section, Scott C27 in the airpost section, Scott CB23A in the airpost semi-postal section, and Scott J46 in the postage due section.

French Offices in Morocco

Stamps of France
Surcharged in Red or Black

Type I. The "N" of "INV" is under the "B" of "REPUBLIQUE."
Type II. The "N" of "INV" is under the "U" of "REPUBLIQUE."

1891-1900 Unwmk.		Perf. 14x13½	
1	A15 5c on 5c grn, grnsh (R)	16.00	4.00
a.	Imperf., pair	175.00	
2	A15 5c on 5c yel grn (II) (R) ('99)	32.50	27.50
a.	Type I	32.50	27.50
3	A15 10c on 10c blk, lav (II) (R)	32.50	4.00
a.	Type I	45.00	20.00
b.	10c on 25c black, rose	1,300.	1,400.
4	A15 20c on 20c red, grn	40.00	32.50
5	A15 25c on 25c blk, rose (R)	32.50	4.00
a.	Double surcharge	225.00	
b.	Imperf., pair	175.00	
6	A15 50c on 50c car, rose (II)	105.00	47.50
a.	Type I	375.00	260.00
7	A15 1p on 1fr brnz grn, straw	120.00	80.00
8	A15 2p on 2fr brn, az (Bk) ('00)	240.00	240.00
	Nos. 1-8 (8)	618.50	439.50

No. 3b was never sent to Morocco.

France Nos. J15-J16
Overprinted in Carmine

1893			
9	D2 5c black	3,250.	1,300.
10	D2 10c black	2,900.	900.

Counterfeits exist.

Surcharged in Red or Black

A3

A4

A5

1902-10			
11	A3 1c on 1c gray (R) ('08)	2.40	1.20
12	A3 2c on 2c vio brn ('08)	2.40	1.20
13	A3 3c on 3c red org ('08)	3.25	1.60
14	A3 4c on 4c yel brn ('08)	13.00	8.00
15	A3 5c on 5c grn (R)	12.00	4.00
a.	Double surcharge		340.00
b.	Triple surcharge	340.00	
16	A4 10c on 10c rose red ('03)	8.00	4.00
a.	Surcharge omitted	225.00	
17	A4 20c on 20c brn vio ('03)	40.00	24.00
18	A4 25c on 25c bl ('03)	40.00	24.00
19	A4 35c on 35c vio ('10)	40.00	24.00
20	A5 50c on 50c bis brn & lav ('03)	67.50	16.00
21	A5 1p on 1fr cl & ol grn ('03)	120.00	80.00
22	A5 2p on 2fr gray vio & yel ('03)	160.00	120.00
	Nos. 11-22 (12)	508.55	288.00

Nos. 11-14 exist spelled CFNTIMOS or GENTIMOS.
The 25c on 25c with surcharge omitted is listed as No. 81a.
For overprints and surcharges see Nos. 26-37, 72-79, B1, B3.

Postage Due Stamps Nos.
J1-J2 Handstamped

1903			
24	D2 5c on 5c light blue	1,500.	1,400.
25	D2 10c on 10c chocolate	2,800.	2,600.

Nos. 24 and 25 were used only on Oct. 10, 1903. Used stamps were not canceled, the overprint serving as a cancellation.
Numerous counterfeits exist.

Types of 1902-10 Issue
Surcharged in Red or Blue

1911-17			
26	A3 1c on 1c gray (R)	1.20	.90
27	A3 2c on 2c vio brn	1.20	1.20
28	A3 3c on 3c orange	1.20	1.20
29	A3 5c on 5c green (R)	1.20	.80
30	A4 10c on 10c rose	1.20	.80
a.	Imperf., pair	275.00	
31	A4 15c on 15c org ('17)	3.50	2.40
32	A4 20c on 20c brn vio	5.50	4.00
33	A4 25c on 25c blue (R)	2.40	1.60
34	A4 35c on 35c violet (R)	12.00	5.50
35	A5 40c on 40c red & pale bl ('17)	8.00	5.50
36	A5 50c on 50c bis brn & lav (R)	27.50	16.00
37	A5 1p on 1fr cl & ol grn	24.00	12.00
	Nos. 26-37 (12)	88.90	51.90

For surcharges see Nos. B1, B3.

Stamps of this design were issued by the Cherifien posts in 1912-13. The Administration Cherifinne des Postes, Telegraphes et Telephones was formed in 1911 under French guidance. See Morocco in *Scott Classic Specialized Catalogue of Stamps & Covers* for listings.

French Protectorate
Issue of 1911-17 Overprinted
"Protectorat Francais"

A6

A7

A8

1914-21			
38	A6 1c on 1c lt gray	.40	.50
a.	1c dk gray ('22)	.55	.80
39	A6 2c on 2c vio brn	.80	.50
40	A6 3c on 3c orange	1.20	.65
41	A6 5c on 5c green	1.20	.50
a.	New value omitted	275.00	275.00
42	A7 10c on 10c rose	.80	.30
a.	New value omitted	550.00	550.00
43	A7 15c on 15c org ('17)	.80	.80
a.	New value omitted	120.00	120.00
44	A7 20c on 20c brn vio	4.75	3.50
a.	"Protectorat Francais" double	300.00	300.00
45	A7 25c on 25c blue	3.25	.80
a.	New value omitted	350.00	350.00
46	A7 25c on 25c violet ('21)	1.25	.40
a.	"Protectorat Francais" omitted	80.00	80.00
b.	"Protectorat Francais" double	175.00	175.00
c.	"Protectorat Francais" dbl. (R + Bk)	175.00	175.00
47	A7 30c on 30c vio ('21)	20.00	9.00
48	A7 35c on 35c violet	4.75	1.60
49	A8 40c on 40c red & pale bl	20.00	8.75
a.	New value omitted	375.00	375.00
50	A8 45c on 45c grn & bl ('21)	55.00	40.00
51	A8 50c on 50c bis brn & lav	2.40	.80
a.	"Protectorat Francais" invtd.	200.00	200.00
b.	"Protectorat Francais" double	450.00	450.00
52	A8 1p on 1fr cl & ol grn	5.50	.80
a.	"Protectorat Francais" invtd.	350.00	350.00
b.	New value double	200.00	200.00
c.	New value dbl., one invtd.	210.00	210.00
53	A8 2p on 2fr gray vio & yel	8.00	4.00
a.	New value omitted	175.00	175.00
b.	"Protectorat Francais" omitted	110.00	110.00
c.	New value double		225.00
d.	New value dbl., one invtd.		
54	A8 5p on 5fr dk bl & buff	15.00	8.00
	Nos. 38-54 (17)	145.10	80.90

For surcharges see Nos. B2, B4-B5.

Tower of Hassan,
Rabat — A9

Mosque of the Andalusians,
Fez — A10

City Gate Chella
A11

Koutoubiah, Marrakesh
A12

Bab Mansour, Meknes — A13

Roman Ruins, Volubilis — A14

1917	Engr.	Perf. 13½x14, 14x13½	
55	A9 1c grnsh gray	.40	.40
56	A9 2c brown lilac	.40	.40
57	A9 3c orange brn	.40	.80
a.	Imperf., pair	87.50	
58	A10 5c yellow grn	.40	.40
59	A10 10c rose red	.80	.40
60	A10 15c dark gray	.80	.40
a.	Imperf., pair	65.00	
61	A11 20c red brown	4.00	2.40
62	A11 25c dull blue	4.00	1.25
63	A11 30c gray violet	4.75	3.25

64	A12 35c orange	4.75	4.00
65	A12 40c ultra	1.60	1.60
66	A12 45c gray green	32.50	16.00
67	A13 50c dk brown	5.50	4.00
a.	Imperf., pair	65.00	
68	A13 1fr slate	16.00	4.00
a.	Imperf., pair	65.00	
69	A14 2fr black brown	160.00	95.00
70	A14 5fr dk gray grn	47.50	40.00
71	A14 10fr black	47.50	40.00
	Nos. 55-71 (17)	331.30	214.30

See note following No. 115. See Nos. 93-105. For surcharges see Nos. 120-121.

Types of the 1902-10 Issue
Overprinted

1918-24		Perf. 14x13½	
72	A3 1c dk gray	.40	.80
73	A3 2c violet brn	.40	.80
74	A3 3c red orange	1.20	1.20
75	A3 5c green	1.20	1.20
76	A3 5c orange ('23)	2.40	2.00
77	A4 10c rose	2.40	1.60
78	A4 10c green ('24)	2.40	1.60
79	A4 15c orange	1.60	1.20
80	A4 20c violet brn	2.40	2.40
81	A4 25c blue	2.40	2.40
a.	"TANGER" omitted	550.00	550.00
82	A4 30c red org ('24)	4.00	2.75
83	A4 35c violet	4.00	2.40
84	A5 40c red & pale bl	4.00	2.40
85	A5 50c bis brn & lav	27.50	16.00
86	A5 50c blue ('24)	24.00	13.50
87	A5 1fr claret & ol grn	16.00	8.00
88	A5 2fr org & pale bl ('24)	80.00	72.50
89	A5 5fr dk bl & buff ('24)	67.50	65.00
	Nos. 72-89 (18)	243.80	197.75

Types of 1917 and

Tower of Hassan, Rabat
A15

Bab Mansour, Meknes
A16

Roman Ruins, Volubilis — A17

1923-27	Photo.	Perf. 13½	
90	A15 1c olive green	.25	.25
91	A15 2c brown vio	.25	.25
92	A15 3c yellow brn	.25	.25
93	A10 5c orange	.25	.25
94	A10 10c yellow grn	.25	.25
95	A10 15c dk gray	.25	.25
96	A11 20c red brown	.25	.25
97	A11 20c red vio ('27)	.40	.40
98	A11 25c ultra	.40	.40
99	A11 30c deep red	.40	.40
100	A11 30c turq bl ('27)	1.20	.80
101	A12 35c violet	1.20	.80
102	A12 40c orange red	.25	.25
103	A12 45c deep green	.40	.40
104	A12 50c dull turq	.40	.40
105	A12 50c ol grn ('27)	.80	.40
106	A16 60c lilac	1.20	.80
107	A16 75c red vio ('27)	.80	.40
108	A16 1fr deep brown	.80	.80
109	A16 1.05fr red brn ('27)	1.60	.80
110	A16 1.40fr dull rose ('27)	.80	.80
111	A16 1.50fr turq bl ('27)	1.20	.40
112	A17 2fr olive brn	1.60	1.20
113	A17 3fr dp red ('27)	1.60	1.20
114	A17 5fr dk gray grn	4.00	2.75
115	A17 10fr black	12.00	4.75
	Nos. 90-115 (26)	32.80	19.90

Nos. 90-110, 112-115 exist imperf. The stamps of 1917 were line engraved. Those of 1923-27 were printed by photogravure and have in the margin at lower right the imprint "Helio Vaugirard".
See No. B36. For surcharges see Nos. 122-123.

No. 102 Surcharged in Black

1930

120	A12	15c on 40c org red	1.60	1.60
a.		Surcharge bars omitted	72.50	72.50
b.		Pair, one with surcharge omitted		350.00

Nos. 100, 106 and 110 Surcharged in Blue Similarly to No. 176

1931

121	A11	25c on 30c turq blue	2.50	2.10
a.		Inverted surcharge	140.00	140.00
122	A16	50c on 60c lilac	1.20	.40
a.		Inverted surcharge	150.00	150.00
b.		Double surcharge	150.00	150.00
c.		Surcharge bars omitted	90.00	
123	A16	1fr on 1.40fr rose	3.25	1.60
a.		Inverted surcharge	150.00	150.00
b.		Surcharge bars omitted	90.00	
		Nos. 121-123 (3)	6.95	4.10

Old Treasure House and Tribunal, Tangier — A18

Roadstead at Agadir — A19

Post Office at Casablanca A20

Moulay Idriss of the Zehroun — A21

Kasbah of the Oudayas, Rabat — A22

Court of the Medersa el Attarine at Fez — A23

Kasbah of Si Madani el Glaoui at Ouarzazat A24

Saadiens' Tombs at Marrakesh A25

1933-34 Engr. Perf. 13

124	A18	1c olive blk	.25	.25
125	A18	2c red violet	.25	.25
126	A19	3c dark brown	.25	.25
127	A19	5c brown red	.25	.25
128	A20	10c blue green	.30	.30
129	A20	15c black	.40	.30
130	A20	20c red brown	.40	.30
131	A21	25c dark blue	.40	.30
132	A21	30c emerald	.40	.30
133	A21	40c black brn	.40	.30
134	A22	45c brown vio	.80	.65
135	A22	50c dk blue grn	.80	.30
a.		Booklet pane of 10	—	
b.		Booklet pane of 20	—	
		Complete booklet, #135b	2,000.	
136	A22	65c brown red	.40	.30
a.		Booklet pane of 10	—	
b.		Booklet pane of 20	—	
		Complete booklet, #136b	65.00	
137	A23	75c red violet	.80	.30
138	A23	90c orange red	.40	.30
139	A23	1fr deep brown	1.20	.50
140	A23	1.25fr black ('34)	1.60	1.50

141	A24	1.50fr ultra	.40	.30
142	A24	1.75fr myr grn ('34)	.80	.40
143	A24	2fr yellow brn	4.75	.80
144	A24	3fr car rose	55.00	6.50
145	A25	5fr red brown	12.00	2.50
146	A25	10fr black	10.00	6.50
147	A25	20fr bluish gray	9.50	7.25
		Nos. 124-147 (24)	101.75	30.90

Booklets containing Nos. 135 and 136 each have two panes of 10 (Nos. 135a, 136a) connected by a gutter, the complete piece constituting No. 135b or 136b, which is stapled into the booklet through the gutter.

For surcharges see Nos. 148, 176, B13-B20.

No. 135 Srchd. in Red

1939

148	A22	40c on 50c dk bl grn	.95	.50

Mosque of Salé A26

Sefrou A27

Cedars A28

Goatherd A29

Ramparts of Salé — A30

Scimitar-horned Oryxes — A31

Valley of Draa — A32

Fez — A33

1939-42

149	A26	1c rose violet	.25	.25
150	A27	2c emerald	.25	.25
151	A27	3c ultra	.25	.25
152	A26	5c dk bl grn	.25	.25
153	A27	10c brt red vio	.25	.25
154	A28	15c dk green	.25	.25
155	A28	20c black grn	.25	.25
156	A29	30c deep blue	.25	.25
157	A29	40c chocolate	.25	.25
158	A29	45c Prus green	.50	.50
159	A30	50c rose red	1.40	.90
159A	A30	50c Prus grn ('40)	.30	.25
160	A30	60c turq blue	1.25	.75
160A	A30	60c choc ('40)	.30	.25
161	A31	70c dk violet	.25	.25
162	A32	75c grnsh blk	.50	.50
163	A32	80c pck bl ('40)	.30	.25
163A	A32	80c dk grn ('42)	.40	.25
164	A30	90c ultra	.30	.25
165	A28	1fr chocolate	.30	.25
165A	A32	1.20fr rose vio ('42)	.80	.40
166	A32	1.25fr henna brn	1.10	.65
167	A32	1.40fr rose violet	.65	.30
168	A30	1.50fr cop red ('40)	.30	.25
168A	A30	1.50fr rose ('42)	.25	.25
169	A33	2fr Prus green	.25	.25
170	A33	2.25fr dark blue	.65	.50

170A	A26	2.40fr red ('42)	.30	.30
171	A26	2.50fr scarlet	.90	.70
171A	A26	2.50fr dp blue ('40)	1.10	.65
172	A33	3fr black brown	.50	.30
172A	A32	4fr dp ultra ('42)	.40	.40
172B	A32	4.50fr grnsh blk ('42)	.80	.80
173	A31	5fr dark blue	.65	.50
174	A31	10fr red	1.25	.90
174A	A31	15fr Prus grn ('42)	4.75	4.00
175	A31	20fr dk vio brn	2.00	1.75
		Nos. 149-175 (37)	24.70	19.55
		Set, never hinged	32.50	

See Nos. 197-219. For surcharges see Nos. 244, 261-262, B21-B24, B26, B28, B32.

No. 136 Srchd. in Black

1940

176	A22	35c on 65c brown red	1.75	.95
a.		Pair, one without surcharge	3.25	2.40

The surcharge was applied on alternate rows in the sheet, making No. 176a. This was done to make a pair equal 1fr, the new rate.

> **Catalogue values for unused stamps in this section, from this point to the end of the section, are for Never Hinged items.**

One Aim Alone-Victory — A34

1943 Litho. Perf. 12

177	A34	1.50fr deep blue	.40	.25

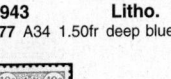

Tower of Hassan, Rabat — A35

1943

178	A35	10c rose lilac	.30	.25
179	A35	30c blue	.30	.25
180	A35	40c lake	.30	.25
181	A35	50c blue green	.30	.25
182	A35	60c dk vio brn	.30	.25
183	A35	70c rose violet	.30	.25
184	A35	80c gray green	.30	.30
185	A35	1fr car lake	.30	.25
186	A35	1.20fr violet	.30	.25
187	A35	1.50fr red	.30	.25
188	A35	2fr lt bl grn	.30	.25
189	A35	2.40fr car rose	.30	.35
190	A35	3fr olive brn	.30	.30
191	A35	4fr dk ultra	.30	.30
192	A35	4.50fr slate blk	.40	.25
193	A35	5fr dull blue	.55	.25
194	A35	10fr orange brn	.55	.40
195	A35	15fr slate grn	1.60	.55
196	A35	20fr deep plum	2.40	.80
		Nos. 178-196 (19)	9.70	6.00

Types of 1939-42
Perf. 13½x14, 14x13½

1945-47		Typo.	Unwmk.	
197	A27	10c red violet	.40	.25
199	A29	40c chocolate	.40	.25
200	A30	50c Prus grn	.40	.25
203	A28	1fr choc ('46)	.40	.35
204	A32	1.20fr vio brn ('46)	.40	.30
205	A27	1.30fr blue ('47)	.80	.40
206	A30	1.50fr deep red	.40	.25
207	A33	2fr Prus grn	.40	.25
209	A33	3fr black brn	.40	.25
210	A29	3.50fr dk red ('47)	1.20	.80
212	A31	4.50fr magenta ('47)	.80	.40
214	A31	5fr indigo	1.20	.55
215	A32	6fr chlky bl ('46)	.80	.35
216	A31	10fr red	2.00	.80
217	A31	15fr Prus grn	2.40	.80
218	A31	20fr dk vio brn	3.25	1.40
219	A31	25fr black brn	3.25	2.10
		Nos. 197-219 (17)	18.90	9.75

For surcharges see Nos. 261-263, B26, B28, B32.

The Terraces A37

Mountain District A39

Fortress — A38

Marrakesh — A40

Gardens of Fez A41

Ouarzazat District A42

1947		Engr. Unwmk.	Perf. 13	
221	A37	10c black brn	.40	.25
222	A37	30c brt red	.40	.25
223	A37	50c brt grnsh bl	.40	.25
224	A37	60c brt red vio	.40	.25
225	A38	1fr black	.40	.25
226	A38	1.50fr blue	.40	.25
227	A39	2fr brt green	.80	.40
228	A39	3fr brown red	.40	.25
229	A40	4fr dk bl vio	.40	.25
230	A41	5fr dk green	1.20	.55
231	A40	6fr crimson	.40	.25
232	A41	10fr dp blue	1.20	.40
233	A42	15fr dk grn	1.60	1.20
234	A42	20fr henna brn	1.60	.80
235	A42	25fr purple	2.40	1.20
		Nos. 221-235 (15)	12.40	6.80

1948-49

236	A37	30c purple	.40	.25
237	A38	2fr vio brn ('49)	.80	.40
238	A40	4fr green	.80	.35
239	A41	8fr org ('49)	1.60	.80
240	A41	10fr blue	1.20	.40
241	A42	10fr car rose	.80	.80
242	A38	12fr red	1.20	.80
243	A42	18fr deep blue	2.40	1.20
		Nos. 236-243 (8)	9.20	5.00

For surcharges see Nos. 263, 293-294.

No. 175 Surcharged with New Value and Wavy Lines in Carmine

1948

244	A31	8fr on 20fr dk vio brn	1.20	.80

Fortified Oasis — A43

Walled City — A44

1949

245	A43	5fr blue green	1.20	.40
246	A44	15fr red	1.60	.80
247	A44	25fr ultra	1.60	.80
		Nos. 245-247 (3)	4.40	2.00

See No. 300.

Detail,
Gate of
Oudayas,
Rabat
A45

Nejjarine
Fountain,
Fez
A46

Garden, Meknes — A47

1949   **Perf. 14x13**
248 A45 10c black   .40   .25
249 A45 50c rose brn   .40   .25
250 A45 1fr blue vio   .40   .25
251 A46 2fr dk car rose   .40   .25
252 A46 3fr dark blue   .80   .25
253 A46 5fr brt green   1.20   .25
254 A47 8fr dk bl grn   1.60   .80
255 A47 10fr brt red   1.60   .80
        Nos. 248-255 (8)   6.80 3.10

Postal
Administration
Building,
Meknes — A48

1949, Oct.   **Perf. 13**
256 A48 5fr dark green   2.40 2.00
257 A48 15fr deep carmine   2.40 2.00
258 A48 25fr deep blue   2.75 2.40
        Nos. 256-258 (3)   7.55 6.40
        75th anniv. of the UPU.

Todra
Valley — A49

1950
259 A49 35fr red brown   1.60   .40
260 A49 50fr indigo   1.60   .40
        See No. 270.

Nos. 204 and 205
Srchd. in Black or
Blue

1950   **Perf. 14x13½, 13½x14**
261 A32 1fr on 1.20fr vio brn (Bk)   .40   .35
262 A27 1fr on 1.30fr blue (Bl)   .40   .25
   The surcharge is transposed and spaced to
fit the design on No. 262.

**No. 231 Surcharged with New Value
and Wavy Lines in Black**
1951   **Perf. 13**
263 A40 5fr on 6fr crimson   .80   .25

Statue of Gen. Jacques
Leclerc — A50

1951, Apr. 28   **Engr.**
264 A50 10fr blue green   2.40 2.00
265 A50 15fr deep carmine   2.75 2.00
266 A50 25fr indigo   2.75 2.00
        Nos. 264-266 (3)   7.90 6.00
   Unveiling of a monument to Gen. Leclerc at
Casablanca, Apr. 28, 1951. See No. C39.

Loustau Hospital,
Oujda — A51

Designs: 15fr, New Hospital, Meknes. 25fr,
New Hospital, Rabat.

1951
267 A51 10fr indigo & pur   2.00 1.60
268 A51 15fr Prus grn & red brn   2.00 1.60
269 A51 25fr dk brn & ind   2.40 2.00
        Nos. 267-269 (3)   6.40 5.20
        See No. C41.

Todra Valley Type of 1950

1951
270 A49 30fr ultramarine   1.60   .40

Pigeons at
Fountain
A52

Karaouine
Mosque,
Fez
A53

Patio,
Oudayas
A54

Oudayas
Point,
Rabat
A55

Patio of Old
House — A56

Type I   Type II
(No.   (No.
275)   276)

                        Perf. 14x13, 13
1951-53   **Engr.   Unwmk.**
271 A52 5fr magenta ('52)   .40   .25
272 A53 6fr bl grn ('52)   .40   .40
273 A52 8fr brown ('52)   .40   .40
273A A53 10fr rose red ('53)   .40   .35
274 A53 12fr dp ultra ('52)   .80   .40
275 A54 15fr red brn (I)   2.75   .25
276 A54 15fr red brn (II)   1.20   .25
277 A55 15fr pur ('52)   1.20   .40
278 A55 18fr red ('52)   2.00 1.20
279 A56 20fr dp grnsh bl ('52)   2.40   .80
        Nos. 271-279 (10)   11.95 4.70
        See Nos. 297-299.

8th-10th Cent.
Capital — A57

   Capitals: 20fr, 12th Cent. 25fr, 13th-14th
Cent. 50fr, 17th Cent.

1952, Apr. 5   **Perf. 13**
280 A57 15fr deep blue   3.25 2.40
281 A57 20fr red   3.25 2.40
282 A57 25fr purple   3.25 2.40
283 A57 50fr deep green   3.25 2.40
        Nos. 280-283 (4)   13.00 9.60

Casablanca
Monument — A58

1952 Sept. 22   **Engr. & Typo.**
284 A58 15fr multicolored   3.50 2.40
   Creation of the French Military Medal, cent.

Daggers of South
Morocco — A59

   Designs: 20fr and 25fr, Antique brooches.

1953, Mar. 27   **Engr.**
285 A59 15fr dk car rose   4.00 3.25
286 A59 20fr violet brn   4.00 3.25
287 A59 25fr dark blue   4.00 3.25
        Nos. 285-287 (3)   12.00 9.75
        See No. C46.

Post Rider and Public
Letter-writer — A60

1953, May 16
288 A60 15fr violet brown   2.00 1.60
   Stamp Day, May 16, 1953.

Bine el Ouidane
Dam — A61

1953, Nov. 3   **Perf. 13**
290 A61 15fr indigo   2.00 1.60
        See No. 295.

Mogador Fortress — A62

   Design: 30fr, Moorish knights.

1953, Dec. 4
291 A62 15fr green   2.40 1.60
292 A62 30fr red brown   2.40 1.60
        Issued to aid Army Welfare Work.

**Nos. 226 and 243 Surcharged with
New Value and Wavy Lines in Black**
1954
293 A38 1fr on 1.50fr blue   .40   .25
294 A42 15fr on 18fr dp bl   1.20   .65

Dam Type of 1953
1954, Mar. 8
295 A61 15fr red brn & indigo   1.60 1.20

Station of Rural
Automobile
Post — A63

1954, Apr. 10
296 A63 15fr dk blue grn   1.40   .80
   Stamp Day, April 10, 1954.

Types of 1951-53
1954   **Engr.   Perf. 14x13**
297 A52 15fr dk blue green   1.20   .40
              Typo.
298 A52 5fr magenta   1.20   .40
299 A55 15fr rose violet   1.60   .40
        Nos. 297-299 (3)   4.00 1.20

Walled City Type of 1949
1954   **Engr.   Perf. 13**
300 A44 25fr purple   2.40   .80

Marshal Lyautey at
Rabat
A64

Lyautey,
Builder of
Cities
A65

   Designs: 15fr, Marshal Lyautey at Khenifra.
50fr, Hubert Lyautey, Marshal of France.

1954, Nov. 17
301 A64 5fr indigo   2.40 2.00
302 A64 15fr dark green   3.25 2.75
303 A65 30fr rose brown   4.00 3.25
304 A65 50fr dk red brn   4.00 3.25
        Nos. 301-304 (4)   13.65 11.25
        Marshal Hubert Lyautey, birth cent.

Franco-Moslem
Education
A66

Moslem
Student at
Blackboard
A67

   Designs: 30fr, Moslem school at Camp
Boulhaut. 50fr, Moulay Idriss College at Fez.

1955, Apr. 16   Unwmk.   Perf. 13
305 A66 5fr indigo   2.00 1.60
306 A67 15fr rose lake   2.40 2.00
307 A66 30fr chocolate   2.40 2.00
308 A67 50fr dk blue grn   2.75 2.40
        Nos. 305-308 (4)   9.55 8.00
        Franco-Moslem solidarity.

Map and Rotary
Emblem — A68

1955, June 11
309 A68 15fr bl & org brn   2.00 1.20
        Rotary Intl., 50th anniv.

Post Office,
Mazagan — A69

1955, May 24
310 A69 15fr red   1.20   .80
        Stamp Day.

Bab el
Chorfa,
Fez
A70

Mahakma
(Courthouse),
Casablanca
A71

Fortress,
Safi — A72

   Designs: 50c, 1fr, 2fr, 3fr, Mrissa Gate,
Salé. 10fr, 12fr, 15fr, Minaret at Rabat. 30fr,
Menara Garden Marrakesh. 40fr, Tafraout Vil-
lage. 50fr, Portuguese cistern, Mazagan. 75fr,
Garden of Oudaya, Rabat.

FRENCH MOROCCO

801

1955   Perf. 13½x13, 13x13½, 13

311	A70	50c brn vio	.40	.25
312	A70	1fr blue	.40	.25
313	A70	2fr red lilac	.40	.25
314	A70	3fr bluish blk	.40	.25
315	A70	5fr vermilion	1.60	.40
316	A70	6fr green	.75	.35
317	A70	8fr orange brn	1.20	.40
318	A70	10fr violet brn	1.60	.40
319	A70	12fr greenish bl	.80	.40
320	A70	15fr magenta	1.10	.25
321	A71	18fr dk green	2.00	.80
322	A71	20fr brown lake	1.20	.40
323	A72	25fr brt ultra	2.75	.40
324	A72	30fr green	2.40	.80
325	A72	40fr orange red	2.40	.40
326	A72	50fr black brn	8.00	.80
327	A71	75fr greenish bl	2.40	1.20
		Nos. 311-327 (17)	29.80	8.00

Succeeding issues, released under the Kingdom, are listed under Morocco in Vol. 4.

___

SEMI-POSTAL STAMPS

French Protectorate

No. 30 Surcharged in Red

1914   Unwmk.   Perf. 14x13½
B1 A4 10c + 5c on 10c   *24,000. 28,000.*

Known only with inverted red surcharge.

No. 42 Surcharged in Red

B2	A7	10c + 5c on 10c rose	6.50 6.50
a.		Double surcharge	175.00 175.00
b.		Inverted surcharge	225.00 225.00
c.		"c" omitted	110.00 110.00

On Nos. B1 and B2 the cross is set up from pieces of metal (quads), the horizontal bar being made from two long pieces, the vertical bar from two short pieces. Each cross in the setting of twenty-five differs from the others.

No. 30 Handstamp Surcharged in Red

B3	A4	10c + 5c on 10c rose	*1,650. 1,400.*

No. B3 was issued at Oujda. The surcharge ink is water-soluble.

No. 42 Surcharged in Vermilion or Carmine

B4	A7	10c + 5c on 10c (V)	25.00 25.00
a.		Double surcharge	240.00 240.00
b.		Inverted surcharge	240.00 240.00
c.		Double surch., one invtd.	200.00 200.00
B5	A7	10c +5c on 10c (C)	475.00 525.00
a.		Inverted surcharge	1,600. 1,600.

On Nos. B4-B5 the horizontal bar of the cross is single and not as thick as on Nos. B1-B2.

No. B5 was sold largely at Casablanca.

Carmine Surcharge SP1   Black Overprint SP2

1915
B6	SP1	5c + 5c green	3.25 2.40
a.		Inverted surcharge	300.00 300.00
B7	SP2	10c + 5c rose	4.75 4.75

No. B6 was not issued without the Red Cross surcharge. No. B7 was used in Tangier.

France No. B2 Overprinted in Black

B8	SP2	10c + 5c red	7.50 7.50

No. 30 Surcharged in Carmine — SP4

1917
B9	SP4	10c + 5c on 10c rose	3.25 3.25

On No. B9 the horizontal bar of the cross is made from a single, thick piece of metal.

Marshal Hubert Lyautey — SP5

1935, May 15   Photo.   Perf. 13x13½
B10	SP5	50c + 50c red	9.50 9.50
B11	SP5	1fr + 1fr dk grn	11.00 11.00
B12	SP5	5fr + 5fr blk brn	45.00 45.00
		Nos. B10-B12 (3)	65.50 65.50
		Set, never hinged	98.00

Stamps of 1933-34 Surcharged in Blue or Red

1938   Perf. 13
B13	A18	2c + 2c red vio	5.50 5.50
B14	A19	3c + 3c dk brn	5.50 5.50
B15	A20	20c + 20c red brn	5.50 5.50
B16	A21	40c + 40c blk brn (R)	5.50 5.50
B17	A22	65c + 65c brn red	5.50 5.50
B18	A23	1.25fr + 1.25fr blk (R)	5.50 5.50
B19	A24	2fr + 2fr yel brn	5.50 5.50
B20	A25	5fr + 5fr red brn	5.50 5.50
		Nos. B13-B20 (8)	44.00 44.00
		Set, never hinged	64.00

Stamps of 1939 Srchd. in Black

1942
B21	A29	45c + 2fr Prus grn	6.75 4.75
B22	A30	90c + 4fr ultra	6.75 4.75
B23	A32	1.25fr + 6fr henna brn	8.00 6.50
B24	A26	2.50fr + 8fr scarlet	8.00 6.50
		Nos. B21-B24 (4)	29.50 22.50
		Set, never hinged	40.00

The arrangement of the surcharge differs slightly on each denomination.

> Catalogue values for unused stamps in this section, from this point to the end of the section, are for Never Hinged items.

No. 207 Surcharged in Black

1945   Unwmk.   Perf. 13½x14
B26	A33	2fr + 1fr Prus green	.80 .50

For surcharge see No. B28.

Mausoleum of Marshal Lyautey — SP7

1945   Litho.   Perf. 11½
B27	SP7	2fr + 3fr dark blue	.80 .40

The surtax was for French works of solidarity.

No. B26 Surcharged in Red

1946   Perf. 13½x14
B28	A33	3fr (+ 1fr) on 2fr + 1fr	.40 .25

Statue of Marshal Lyautey — SP8

Perf. 13½x14, 13
1946, Dec. 16   Engr.
B29	SP8	2fr + 10fr black	2.40 1.60
B30	SP8	3fr + 15fr cop red	2.40 1.60
B31	SP8	10fr + 20fr brt bl	3.25 2.40
		Nos. B29-B31 (3)	8.05 5.60

The surtax was for works of solidarity.

No. 212 Surcharged in Rose Violet

1947, Mar. 15   Perf. 13½x14
B32	A31	4.50fr + 5.50fr magenta	2.00 1.60

Stamp Day, 1947.

Map and Symbols of Prosperity from Phosphates SP9

1947   Perf. 13
B33	SP9	4.50fr + 5.50fr green	1.60 1.20

25th anniv. of the exploitations of the Cherifien Office of Phosphates.

Power SP10   Health SP11

1948, Feb. 9
B34	SP10	6fr + 9fr red brn	3.25 2.40
B35	SP11	10fr + 20fr dp ultra	3.25 2.40

The surtax was for combined works of Franco-Moroccan solidarity.

Type of Regular Issue of 1923, Inscribed: "Journee du Timbre 1948"

1948, Mar. 6
B36	A16	6fr + 4fr red brown	1.20 .80

Stamp Day, Mar. 6, 1948.

Battleship off Moroccan Coast — SP12

1948, Aug.
B37	SP12	6fr + 9fr purple	2.00 1.60

The surtax was for naval charities.

Wheat Field near Meknes — SP13

Designs: 2fr+5fr, Olive grove, Taroudant. 3fr+7fr, Net and coastal view. 5fr+10fr, Aguedal Gardens, Marrakesh.

1949, Apr. 12   Engr.   Unwmk.
Inscribed: "SOLIDARITÉ 1948"
B38	SP13	1fr + 2fr orange	2.00 1.60
B39	SP13	2fr + 5fr car	2.00 1.60
B40	SP13	3fr + 7fr pck bl	2.00 1.60
B41	SP13	5fr + 10fr dk brn vio	2.00 1.60
a.		Sheet of 4, #B38-B41	27.50 24.00
		Nos. B38-B41,CB31-CB34 (8)	17.60 14.40

Gazelle Hunter, from 1899 Local Stamp — SP14

1949, May 1
B42	SP14	10fr + 5fr choc & car rose	2.00 1.60

Stamp Day and 50th anniversary of Mazagan-Marrakesh local postage stamp.

Moroccan Soldiers, Flag — SP15

1949
B43	SP15	10fr + 10fr bright red	1.60 1.40

The surtax was for Army Welfare Work.

Rug Weaving — SP16

Designs: 2fr+5fr, Pottery making, 3fr+7fr, Bookbinding. 5fr+10fr, Copper work.

Inscribed: "SOLIDARITE 1949"

1950, Apr. 11
B44	SP16	1fr + 2fr dp car	2.75 2.40
B45	SP16	2fr + 5fr dk brnsh bl	2.75 2.40
B46	SP16	3fr + 7fr dk pur	2.75 2.40
B47	SP16	5fr + 10fr red brn	2.75 2.40
a.		Sheet of 4, #B44-B47	32.50 24.00
		Nos. B44-B47,CB36-CB39 (8)	20.60 17.60

Ruins of Sala Colonia at Chella — SP17

1950, Sept. 25   Engr.   Perf. 13
B48	SP17	10fr + 10fr dp mag	2.00 *1.60*
B49	SP17	15fr + 15fr indigo	2.00 1.60

The surtax was for Army Welfare Work.

___

AIR POST STAMPS

French Protectorate

Biplane over
Casablanca
AP1

1922-27   Photo.   Unwmk.   Perf. 13½

C1	AP1	5c dp org ('27)	.50	.50
C2	AP1	25c dp ultra	1.20	.50
C3	AP1	50c grnsh blue	.40	.40
C4	AP1	75c dp blue	80.00	16.00
C5	AP1	75c dp green	.80	.40
C6	AP1	80c vio brn ('27)	2.40	.80
C7	AP1	1fr vermilion	1.20	.80
C8	AP1	1.40fr brn lake		
		('27)	2.40	1.25
C9	AP1	1.90fr dp blue ('27)	2.75	1.60
C10	AP1	2fr black vio	2.40	1.20
a.		2fr deep violet	2.25	1.40
C11	AP1	3fr gray blk	2.75	2.00
		Nos. C1-C11 (11)	96.80	26.15

The 25c, 50c, 75c deep green and 1fr each were printed in two of three types, differing in frameline thickness, or hyphen in "Helio-Vaugirard" imprint.Values are for the more common types.

Imperf., Pairs

C1a	AP1	5c	65.00	65.00
C2a	AP1	25c	72.50	72.50
C3a	AP1	50c	72.50	72.50
C4a	AP1	75c	550.00	550.00
C5a	AP1	75c	72.50	72.50
C6a	AP1	80c	72.50	72.50
C7a	AP1	1fr	90.00	90.00
C10b	AP1	2fr	225.00	225.00

Nos. C8-C9
Srchd. in Blue or
Black

1931, Apr. 10

C12	AP1	1fr on 1.40fr		
		(B)	2.40	2.40
a.		Inverted surcharge	310.00	310.00
C13	AP1	1.50fr on 1.90fr		
		(Bk)	2.40	2.40

Rabat and Tower
of Hassan — AP2

Casablanca
AP3

1933, Jan.   Engr.

C14	AP2	50c dark blue	.80	.80
C15	AP2	80c orange brn	.80	.65
C16	AP2	1.50fr brown red	.80	.80
C17	AP2	2.50fr carmine rose	6.50	1.20
C18	AP3	5fr violet	3.25	1.75
C19	AP3	10fr dp green	1.20	1.20
		Nos. C14-C19 (6)	13.35	6.40

For surcharges see Nos. CB22-CB23.

Storks and
Minaret,
Chella
AP4

Plane and Map of
Morocco
AP5

1939-40   Perf. 13

C20	AP4	80c Prus green	.25	.25
C21	AP4	1fr dk red	.25	.25
C22	AP5	1.90fr ultra	.40	.30
C23	AP5	2fr red vio ('40)	.40	.30
C24	AP5	3fr chocolate	.50	.25

C25	AP4	5fr violet	1.40	.80
C26	AP5	10fr turq blue	1.25	.55
		Nos. C20-C26 (7)	4.45	2.70

> **Catalogue values for unused stamps in this section, from this point to the end of the section, are for Never Hinged items.**

Plane over Oasis — AP6

1944   Litho.   Perf. 11½

C27	AP6	50c Prus grn	.50	.35
C28	AP6	2fr ultra	.50	.35
C29	AP6	5fr scarlet	.50	.35
C30	AP6	10fr violet	1.40	1.10
C31	AP6	50fr black	2.00	1.60
C32	AP6	100fr dp bl & red	4.00	3.25
		Nos. C27-C32 (6)	8.90	7.00

For surcharge see No. CB24.

Plane — AP7

1945   Engr.   Perf. 13

C33	AP7	50fr sepia	1.20	.95

Moulay
Idriss
AP8

La Medina
AP9

1947-48

C34	AP8	9fr dk rose car	.40	.30
C35	AP8	40fr dark blue	1.20	.80
C36	AP8	50fr dp claret ('47)	1.60	.40
C37	AP9	100fr dp grnsh bl	3.25	1.20
C38	AP9	200fr henna brn	8.00	1.60
		Nos. C34-C38 (5)	14.45	4.30

Leclerc Type of Regular Issue

1951, Apr. 28

C39	A50	50fr purple	3.25 2.75

Unveiling of a monument to Gen. Leclerc at Casablanca, Apr. 28, 1951.

Kasbah of the
Oudayas,
Rabat — AP11

1951, May 22

C40	AP11	300fr purple	24.00 12.00

Ben Smine
Sanatorium
AP12

1951, June 4

C41	AP12	50fr pur & Prus grn	3.50 2.75

Fortifications,
Chella — AP13

Plane Near
Marrakesh
AP14

Fort, Anti-
Atlas
Mountains
AP15

View of Fez — AP16

1952, Apr. 19   Unwmk.   Perf. 13

C42	AP13	10fr blue green	1.60	.80
C43	AP14	40fr red	2.40	.80
C44	AP15	100fr brown	5.50	1.60
C45	AP16	200fr purple	10.50	4.00
		Nos. C42-C45 (4)	20.00	7.20

Antique
Brooches — AP17

1953, Mar. 27

C46	AP17	50fr dark green	4.00 3.25

"City" of the
Agdal,
Meknes — AP18

20fr, Yakoub el Mansour, Rabat. 40fr, Ainchock, Casablanca. 50fr, El Aliya, Fedala.

1954, Mar. 8

C47	AP18	10fr olive brown	4.00	2.75
C48	AP18	20fr purple	4.00	2.75
C49	AP18	40fr red brown	4.00	2.75
C50	AP18	50fr deep green	4.00	2.75
		Nos. C47-C50 (4)	16.00	11.00

Franco-Moroccan solidarity.

Naval Vessel and
Sailboat — AP19

1954, Oct. 18

C51	AP19	15fr dk blue green	2.00	1.60
C52	AP19	30fr violet blue	2.40	2.00

Village in
the Anti-
Atlas
AP20

"Ksar es Souk,"
Rabat and Plane
AP21

200fr, Estuary of Bou Regreg, Rabat and Plane.

1955, July 25   Engr.   Perf. 13

C53	AP20	100fr brt violet	2.75	.80
C54	AP20	200fr brt carmine	6.50	1.20
C55	AP21	500fr grnsh blue	16.00	4.00
		Nos. C53-C55 (3)	25.25	6.00

AIR POST SEMI-POSTAL STAMPS

French Protectorate

Moorish
Tribesmen
SPAP1

Designs: 25c, Moor plowing with camel and burro. 50c, Caravan nearing Saffi. 75c, Walls, Marrakesh. 80c, Sheep grazing at Azrou. 1fr, Gate at Fez. 1.50fr, Aerial view of Tangier. 2fr, Aerial view of Casablanca. 3fr, Storks on old wall, Rabat. 5fr, Moorish fete.

Perf. 13½

1928, July 26   Photo.   Unwmk.

CB1	SPAP1	5c dp blue	5.25	5.25
CB2	SPAP1	25c brn org	5.25	5.25
CB3	SPAP1	50c red	5.25	5.25
CB4	SPAP1	75c org brn	5.25	5.25
CB5	SPAP1	80c olive grn	5.25	5.25
CB6	SPAP1	1fr orange	5.25	5.25
CB7	SPAP1	1.50fr Prus bl	5.25	5.25
CB8	SPAP1	2fr dp brown	5.25	5.25
CB9	SPAP1	3fr dp violet	5.25	5.25
CB10	SPAP1	5fr brown blk	5.25	5.25
		Nos. CB1-CB10 (10)	52.50	52.50

These stamps were sold in sets only and at double their face value. The money received for the surtax was divided among charitable and social organizations. The stamps were not sold at post offices but solely by subscription to the Moroccan Postal Administration.

Overprinted in
Red or Blue (25c,
50c, 75c, 1fr)

1929, Feb. 1

CB11	SPAP1	5c dp blue	5.25	5.25
CB12	SPAP1	25c brown org	5.25	5.25
CB13	SPAP1	50c red	5.25	5.25
CB14	SPAP1	75c org brn	5.25	5.25
CB15	SPAP1	80c olive grn	5.25	5.25
CB16	SPAP1	1fr orange	5.25	5.25
CB17	SPAP1	1.50fr Prus bl	5.25	5.25
CB18	SPAP1	2fr dp brown	5.25	5.25
CB19	SPAP1	3fr dp violet	5.25	5.25
CB20	SPAP1	5fr brown blk	5.25	5.25
		Nos. CB11-CB20 (10)	52.50	52.50

These stamps were sold at double their face values and only in Tangier. The surtax benefited various charities.

Marshal Hubert
Lyautey
SPAP10

1935, May 15   Perf. 13½

CB21	SPAP10	1.50fr + 1.50fr		
		blue	20.00	20.00

Nos. C14, C19
Surcharged in
Red

1938   Perf. 13

CB22	AP2	50c + 50c dk bl	8.00	8.00
CB23	AP3	10fr + 10fr bl grn	5.50	5.50

> **Catalogue values for unused stamps in this section, from this point to the end of the section, are for Never Hinged items.**

Plane over
Oasis — SPAP11

1944   Litho.   Perf. 11½

CB23A	SPAP11	1.50fr + 98.50fr	2.40 1.60

The surtax was for charity among the liberated French.

No. C29 Surcharged in Black

1946, June 18   *Perf. 11*
CB24 AP6 5fr + 5fr scarlet   1.60 1.20

6th anniv. of the appeal made by Gen. Charles de Gaulle, June 18, 1940. The surtax was for the Free French Association of Morocco.

Statue of Marshal Lyautey — SPAP12

1946, Dec.   Engr.   Perf. 13
CB25 SPAP12 10fr +30fr dk grn   6.50 2.75

The surtax was for works of solidarity.

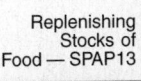

Replenishing Stocks of Food — SPAP13

Agriculture SPAP14

1948, Feb. 9   Unwmk.
CB26 SPAP13 9fr +26fr dp grn   2.00 1.60
CB27 SPAP14 20fr +35fr brown   2.00 1.60

The surtax was for combined works of Franco-Moroccan solidarity.

Tomb of Marshal Hubert Lyautey — SPAP15

1948, May 18   Perf. 13
CB28 SPAP15 10fr +25fr dk grn   1.60 1.25

Lyautey Exposition, Paris, June, 1948.

P.T.T. Clubhouse SPAP16

1948, June 7   Engr.
CB29 SPAP16 6fr + 34fr dk grn   2.40 2.00
CB30 SPAP16 9fr +51fr red brn   2.40 2.00

The surtax was used for the Moroccan P.T.T. employees vacation colony at Ifrane.

View of Agadir — SPAP17

Designs: 6fr+9fr, Fez. 9fr+16fr, Atlas Mountains. 15fr+25fr, Valley of Draa.

1949, Apr. 12   Perf. 13
Inscribed: "SOLIDARITÉ 1948"
CB31 SPAP17 5fr +5fr dk grn   2.40 2.00
CB32 SPAP17 6fr +9fr org
                      red   2.40 2.00
CB33 SPAP17 9fr +16fr blk
                      brn   2.40 2.00

CB34 SPAP17 15fr +25fr ind   2.40 2.00
  a.   Sheet of 4, #CB31-CB34   32.50 24.00
        Nos. CB31-CB34 (4)   9.60 8.00

Plane over Globe — SPAP18

1950, Mar. 11   Engr. & Typo.
CB35 SPAP18 15fr + 10fr bl grn
                      & car   1.60 1.25

Day of the Stamp, Mar. 11-12, 1950, and 25th anniv. of the 1st post link between Casablanca and Dakar.

Scenes and Map: Northwest Corner — SPAP19

Designs (quarters of map): 6fr+9fr, NE, 9fr+16fr, SW. 15fr+25fr, SE.

1950, Apr. 11   Engr.
Inscribed: "SOLIDARITE 1949"
CB36 SPAP19 5fr +5fr dp ul-
                      tra   2.40 2.00
CB37 SPAP19 6fr +9fr Prus
                      grn   2.40 2.00
CB38 SPAP19 9fr +16fr dk
                      brn   2.40 2.00
CB39 SPAP19 15fr +25fr brn
                      red   2.40 2.00
  a.   Sheet of 4, #CB36-CB39   32.50 24.00
        Nos. CB36-CB39 (4)   9.60 8.00

Arch of Triumph of Caracalla at Volubilis SPAP20

1950, Sept. 25   Unwmk.
CB40 SPAP20 10fr + 10fr sepia   2.00 1.60
CB41 SPAP20 15fr + 15fr bl grn   2.00 1.60

The surtax was for Army Welfare Work.

Casablanca Post Office and First Air Post Stamp — SPAP21

1952, Mar. 8   Perf. 13
CB42 SPAP21 15fr + 5fr red brn
                      & dp grn   4.75 4.00

Day of the Stamp, Mar. 8, 1952, and 30th anniv. of French Morocco's 1st air post stamp.

POSTAGE DUE STAMPS

French Offices in Morocco

France Postage Due Stamps and Types Surcharged in Red or Black

1896   Unwmk.   Perf. 14x13½
          On Stamps of 1891-93
J1 D2 5c on 5c lt bl (R)   12.00   5.50
J2 D2 10c on 10c choc (R)   16.00   6.50
J3 D2 30c on 30c car   32.50   24.00
  a.   Pair, one without surcharge
J4 D2 50c on 50c lilac   32.50   27.50
  a.   "S" of "CENTIMOS" omitted 340.00 250.00
J5 D2 1p on 1fr lil brn   350.00 325.00

1909-10   On Stamps of 1908-10
J6 D3 1c on 1c ol grn (R)   4.00   4.00
J7 D3 10c on 10c violet   40.00   32.50
J8 D3 30c on 30c bister   55.00   40.00
J9 D3 50c on 50c red   80.00   72.50
        Nos. J6-J9 (4)   179.00 149.00

Postage Due Stamps of France Surcharged in Red or Blue

1911   On Stamps of 1893-96
J10 D2 5c on 5c blue (R)   4.75   4.75
J11 D2 10c on 10c choc (R)   16.00   16.00
  a.   Double surcharge   225.00 260.00
J12 D2 50c on 50c lil (Bl)   20.00   20.00
          On Stamps of 1908-10
J13 D3 1c on 1c ol grn (R)   4.00   3.25
J14 D3 10c on 10c vio (R)   8.00   8.00
J15 D3 30c on 30c bis (R)   12.00   12.00
J16 D3 50c on 50c red (Bl)   16.00   16.00
        Nos. J10-J16 (7)   80.75   80.00

For surcharges see Nos. J23-J26.

French Protectorate

France Postage Due Stamps of 1911 Issue Overprinted

1915-17
J17 D4 1c on 1c black   .80   .80
  a.   New value double   175.00
J18 D4 5c on 5c blue   3.25   2.00
J19 D4 10c on 10c choc   4.00   2.00
J20 D4 20c on 20c ol grn   4.00   2.00
J21 D4 30c on 30c rose red,
                      grayish   8.00   5.50
J22 D4 50c on 50c vio brn   12.00   8.00
        Nos. J17-J22 (6)   32.05   20.30

Nos. J13 to J16 With Additional Overprint "Protectorat Francais"

1915
J23 D3 1c on 1c ol grn   1.60   1.60
J24 D3 10c on 10c violet   4.00   3.25
J25 D3 30c on 30c bister   4.00   4.00
J26 D3 50c on 50c red   4.00   4.00
        Nos. J23-J26 (4)   13.60   12.85

D5

1917-26   Typo.
J27 D5 1c black   .25   .25
J28 D5 5c deep blue   .40   .25
J29 D5 10c brown   .40   .40
J30 D5 20c olive green   2.50   1.60
J31 D5 30c rose   .40   .40
J32 D5 50c lilac brown   .80   .40
J33 D5 1fr red brn, *straw* ('26) .85 .80
J34 D5 2fr violet ('26)   2.40   1.60
        Nos. J27-J34 (8)   8.00   5.70

See #J49-J56, Morocco #J1-J4. For surcharges see #J46-J48.

Postage Due Stamps of France, 1882-1906 Overprinted

1918
J35 D2 1c black   1.20   1.20
J36 D2 5c blue   2.40   2.40
J37 D2 10c chocolate   2.00   2.00
J38 D2 15c green, *grayish*   4.75   4.75
J39 D2 20c olive green   6.50   6.50
J40 D2 30c rose red, *grayish* 16.00 16.00
J41 D2 50c violet brown   24.00 24.00
        Nos. J35-J41 (7)   56.85   56.85

Postage Due Stamps of France, 1908-19 Overprinted

1918
J42 D3 1c olive green   1.20   1.20
J43 D3 10c violet   2.75   2.75
J44 D3 20c bister, *grayish*   8.00   8.00
J45 D3 40c red   20.00   20.00
        Nos. J42-J45 (4)   31.95   31.95

> **Catalogue values for unused stamps in this section, from this point to the end of the section, are for Never Hinged items.**

Nos. J31 and J29 Surcharged

1944   Unwmk.   Perf. 14x13½
J46 D5 50c on 30c rose   3.25   2.40
J47 D5 1fr on 10c brown   5.50   4.00
J48 D5 3fr on 10c brown   13.00   9.50
        Nos. J46-J48 (3)   21.75   15.90

Type of 1917-1926

1945-52   Typo.
J49 D5 1fr brn lake ('47)   1.20   .80
J50 D5 2fr rose lake ('47)   1.60   .80
J51 D5 3fr ultra   .80   .35
J52 D5 4fr red orange   .80   .30
J53 D5 5fr green   1.60   .50
J54 D5 10fr yellow brn   2.00   .50
J55 D5 20fr carmine ('50)   2.00   .90
J56 D5 30fr dull brn ('52)   2.75   1.60
        Nos. J49-J56 (8)   12.75   5.75

PARCEL POST STAMPS

French Protectorate

PP1

1917   Unwmk.   Perf. 13½x14
Q1 PP1 5c green   1.20   .80
Q2 PP1 10c carmine   1.20   .80
Q3 PP1 20c lilac brown   1.20   1.00
Q4 PP1 25c blue   1.60   .80
Q5 PP1 40c dark brown   2.40   1.60
Q6 PP1 50c red orange   4.00   .80
Q7 PP1 75c pale slate   4.00   2.40
Q8 PP1 1fr ultra   5.50   .80
Q9 PP1 2fr gray   12.00   1.60
Q10 PP1 5fr violet   12.00   1.60
Q11 PP1 10fr black   20.00   1.60
        Nos. Q1-Q11 (11)   65.10   13.80

FRENCH POLYNESIA

'french ,pä-lə-'nē-zhə

(French Oceania)

LOCATION — South Pacific Ocean
GOVT. — French Overseas Territory
AREA — 1,522 sq. mi.
POP. — 242,073 (1999 est.)
CAPITAL — Papeete

In 1903 various French Establishments in the South Pacific were united to form a single colony. Most important of the island groups are the Society Islands, the Marquesas Islands, the Tuamotu group and the Gambier, Austral, and Rapa Islands. Tahiti, largest of the Society group, ranks first in importance.

100 Centimes = 1 Franc

> Catalogue values for unused stamps in this country are for Never Hinged items, beginning with Scott 136 in the regular postage section, Scott B11 in the semipostal section, Scott C2 in the airpost section, Scott J18 in the postage due section, and Scott O1 in the officials section.

Navigation and Commerce — A1

Perf. 14x13½

1892-1907   Typo.   Unwmk.
Name of Colony in Blue or Carmine

1	A1	1c black, *lil bl*	1.60	1.60
2	A1	2c brown, *buff*	2.75	2.75
3	A1	4c claret, *lav*	4.50	4.00
4	A1	5c green, *grnsh*	13.50	9.50
5	A1	5c yellow grn ('06)	5.00	2.40
6	A1	10c blk, *lavender*	30.00	12.50
7	A1	10c red ('00)	5.00	2.40
8	A1	15c blue, quadrille paper	35.00	12.00
9	A1	15c gray, *lt gray* ('00)	10.00	7.25
10	A1	20c red, *grn*	17.50	16.00
11	A1	25c black, *rose*	60.00	30.00
12	A1	25c blue ('00)	32.50	16.00
13	A1	30c brown, *bis*	16.00	14.50
14	A1	35c black, *yel* ('06)	11.00	9.50
15	A1	40c red, *straw*	132.50	80.00
16	A1	45c blk, *gray grn* ('07)	6.75	6.75
17	A1	50c car, *rose*	10.00	10.00
a.		50c rose, *pale rose*	10.00	9.00
18	A1	50c brown, *az* ('00)	275.00	250.00
19	A1	75c dp vio, *org*	12.00	12.00
20	A1	1fr brnz grn, *straw*	13.50	12.00
		Nos. 1-20 (20)	694.10	512.65

Perf. 13½x14 stamps are counterfeits.
For overprint and surcharge see Nos. 55, B1.

Tahitian Girl
A2

Kanakas
A3

Fautaua Valley — A4

1913-30

21	A2	1c violet & brn	.25	.25
22	A2	2c brown & blk	.25	.25
23	A2	4c orange & bl	.35	.35
24	A2	5c grn & yel grn	1.60	.90
a.		Double impression of yel grn	500.00	
25	A2	5c bl & blk ('22)	.50	.50
26	A2	10c rose & org	2.25	2.25
27	A2	10c bl grn & yel grn ('22)	1.25	1.25

28	A2	10c org red & brn red, *bluish* ('26)	1.40	1.40
29	A2	15c org & blk ('15)	.85	.65
a.		Imperf., pair	175.00	
30	A2	20c black & vio	1.10	1.00
a.		Imperf., pair	175.00	
31	A2	20c grn & bl grn ('26)	1.00	1.00
32	A2	20c brn red & dk brn ('27)	1.60	1.60
33	A3	25c ultra & blue	1.50	1.25
34	A3	25c vio & rose ('22)	.75	.75
35	A3	30c gray & brown	5.00	4.00
a.		Imperf., pair	325.00	
36	A3	30c rose & red org ('22)	3.25	3.25
37	A3	30c blk & red org ('26)	.75	.75
38	A3	30c slate bl & bl grn ('27)	1.75	1.75
39	A3	35c green & rose	1.25	1.25
40	A3	40c black & green	1.10	1.10
41	A3	45c orange & red	1.10	1.10
42	A3	50c dk brown & blk	17.50	13.50
43	A3	50c ultra & bl ('22)	1.25	1.25
44	A3	50c gray & bl vio ('26)	1.10	1.10
45	A3	60c green & blk ('25)	1.25	1.25
46	A3	65c ol brn & red vio ('27)	3.25	3.25
47	A3	75c vio brn & vio	2.50	2.50
48	A3	90c brn red & rose ('30)	16.50	16.50
a.		Imperf., pair	225.00	
49	A4	1fr rose & black	6.25	4.25
50	A4	1.10fr vio & dk brn ('28)	1.60	1.60
51	A4	1.40fr bis brn & vio ('27)	4.00	4.00
52	A4	1.50fr ind & bl ('30)	16.50	16.50
53	A4	2fr dk brown & grn	6.25	4.25
54	A4	5fr violet & bl	11.00	11.00
a.		Imperf., pair	500.00	
		Nos. 21-54 (34)	117.80	107.55

For surcharges see Nos. 56-71, B2-B4.

No. 7 Overprinted

1915

55	A1	10c red	6.75	6.75
a.		Inverted overprint	225.00	225.00

For surcharge see No. B1.

No. 29 Surcharged

1916

56	A2	10c on 15c org & blk	3.50	3.50

No. 22 Surcharged

No. 41 Surcharged

No. 29 Surcharged

1921

57	A2	5c on 2c brn & blk	36.00	36.00
58	A3	10c on 45c org & red	36.00	36.00
59	A2	25c on 15c org & blk	9.00	9.00
		Nos. 57-59 (3)	81.00	81.00

On No. 58 the new value and date are set wide apart and without bar.

Types of 1913-30 Issue Surcharged in Black or Red

1923-27

60	A3	60c on 75c bl & brn	.75	.75
61	A4	65c on 1fr dk bl & ol (R) ('25)	2.25	2.25
62	A4	85c on 1fr dk bl & ol (R) ('25)	2.25	2.25
63	A3	90c on 75c brn red & cer ('27)	3.00	3.00
		Nos. 60-63 (4)	8.25	8.25

No. 26 Surcharged

1924

64	A2	45c on 10c rose & org	3.00	3.00
a.		Inverted surcharge	2,400.	2,400.

Stamps and Type of 1913-30 Surcharged with New Value and Bars in Black or Red

1924-27

65	A4	25c on 2fr dk brn & grn	1.10	1.10
66	A4	25c on 5fr vio & bl	1.10	1.10
67	A4	1.25fr on 1fr dk bl & ultra (R) ('26)	1.20	1.20
68	A4	1.50fr on 1fr dk bl & lt bl ('27)	4.00	4.00
69	A4	20fr on 5fr org & brt vio ('27)	32.50	26.00
		Nos. 65-69 (5)	39.90	33.40

Surcharged in Black or Red

1926

70	A4	3fr on 5fr gray & blue	3.25	2.50
71	A4	10fr on 5fr grn & blk (R)	7.25	7.25

Papetoai Bay, Moorea — A5

1929, Mar. 25

72	A5	3fr green & dk brn	8.00	8.00
73	A5	5fr lt blue & dk brn	15.00	15.00
74	A5	10fr lt red & dk brn	45.00	45.00
75	A5	20fr lilac & dk brn	57.50	57.50
		Nos. 72-75 (4)	125.50	125.50

For overprints see Nos. 128, 130, 132, 134.

Common Design Types pictured following the introduction.

Colonial Exposition Issue
Common Design Types

1931, Apr. 13   Engr.   Perf. 12½
Name of Country Printed in Black

76	CD70	40c deep green	7.50	7.50
77	CD71	50c violet	7.50	7.50
78	CD72	90c red orange	7.50	7.50
79	CD73	1.50fr dull blue	7.50	7.50
		Nos. 76-79 (4)	30.00	30.00

Spear Fishing — A12

Tahitian Girl — A13

Idols — A14

1934-40   Photo.   Perf. 13½, 13½x13

80	A12	1c gray black	.25	.25
81	A12	2c claret	.35	.35
82	A12	3c lt blue ('40)	.35	.35
83	A12	4c orange	.60	.60
84	A12	5c violet	.90	.90
85	A12	10c dark brown	.40	.40
86	A12	15c green	.60	.60
87	A12	20c red	.60	.60
88	A13	25c gray blue	.90	.90
89	A13	30c yellow green	1.20	1.20
90	A13	30c org brn ('40)	.80	.80
91	A14	35c brt green ('38)	4.00	4.00
92	A13	40c red violet	.60	.60
93	A13	45c brown orange	9.00	9.00
94	A13	45c dk green ('39)	1.60	1.60
95	A13	50c violet	.60	.60
96	A13	55c blue ('38)	6.75	6.75
97	A13	60c black ('39)	.75	.75
98	A13	65c brown	3.25	3.25
99	A13	70c brt pink ('39)	1.40	1.40
100	A13	75c olive green	9.00	9.00
101	A13	80c violet brn ('38)	2.00	2.00
102	A13	90c rose red	.90	.90
103	A14	1fr red brown	.90	.90
104	A14	1.25fr brown violet	8.25	8.25
105	A14	1.25fr rose red ('39)	1.25	1.25
106	A14	1.40fr org yel ('39)	1.25	1.25
107	A14	1.50fr blue	.90	.90
108	A14	1.60fr dull vio ('39)	1.40	1.40
109	A14	1.75fr olive	6.75	6.75
110	A14	2fr red	1.10	1.10
111	A14	2.25fr dp blue ('39)	1.25	1.25
112	A14	2.50fr black ('39)	1.25	1.25
113	A14	3fr brn org ('39)	1.50	1.50
114	A14	5fr red violet ('39)	1.00	1.00
115	A14	10fr dk grn ('39)	3.00	3.00
116	A14	20fr dk brn ('39)	3.00	3.00
		Nos. 80-116 (37)	80.10	80.10

For overprints see Nos. 126-127, 129, 131, 133, 135.

Paris International Exposition Issue
Common Design Types

1937   Engr.   Perf. 13

117	CD74	20c deep violet	3.50	3.50
118	CD75	30c dark green	3.50	3.50
119	CD76	40c carmine rose	3.50	3.50
120	CD77	50c dk brn & blue	4.25	4.25
121	CD78	90c red	4.25	4.25
122	CD79	1.50fr ultra	5.00	5.00
		Nos. 117-122 (6)	24.00	24.00

Colonial Arts Exhibition Issue
Souvenir Sheet
Common Design Type

1937   Imperf.

123	CD78	3fr emerald	36.00	52.50
		Never hinged	55.00	

New York World's Fair Issue
Common Design Type

1939, May 10   Engr.   Perf. 12½x12

124	CD82	1.25fr carmine lake	2.40	2.40
125	CD82	2.25fr ultra	2.40	2.40
		Set, never hinged	8.00	

Fautaua Valley and Marshal Petain — A15

1941   Engr.   Perf. 12½x12

125A	A15	1fr bluish green	1.10	
c.		Denomination ("1F") omitted	80.00	
125B	A15	2.50fr deep blue	1.25	
		Set, never hinged	3.25	

Nos. 125A-125B were issued by the Vichy government in France, but were not placed on sale in the French Polynesia.

For surcharges, see Nos. B12B-B12C.

Stamps of 1929-39 Ovptd. in Black or Red

1941   Perf. 14x13½, 13½x13

126	A14	1fr red brn (BK)	7.00	9.50
a.		Inverted overprint	1,200.	
127	A14	2.50fr black	8.00	11.00
a.		Inverted overprint	1,200.	
128	A5	3fr grn & dk brn	9.00	9.00
129	A14	3fr brn org (Bk)	10.00	12.00
130	A5	5fr lt bl & dk brn	9.00	9.00
131	A14	5fr red vio (Bk)	10.00	10.00

132	A5	10fr lt red & dk brn	25.00 30.00
133	A14	10fr dark green	90.00 110.00
134	A5	20fr lil & dk brn	135.00 135.00
135	A14	20fr dark brown	75.00 95.00
		Nos. 126-135 (10)	378.00 430.50
		Set, never hinged	480.00

Types of 1934-39 without "RF"

1942-44 Photo. Perf. 13½

135A	A12	10c brown	.65
135B	A13	30c red orange	.85
135C	A14	1.50fr blue	1.00
135D	A14	10fr dark green	1.75
135E	A14	20fr dark brown	2.50
		Nos. 135A-135E (5)	6.75

Nos. 135A-135E were issued by the Vichy government in France, but were not placed on sale in French Polynesia.

> Catalogue values for unused stamps in this section, from this point to the end of the section, are for Never Hinged items.

Ancient Double Canoe — A16

1942 Photo. Perf. 14½x14

136	A16	5c dark brown	.40 .25
137	A16	10c dk gray bl	.40 .25
138	A16	25c emerald	.40 .25
139	A16	30c red orange	.40 .25
140	A16	40c dk slate grn	.40 .25
141	A16	80c red brown	.40 .25
142	A16	1fr rose violet	.50 .35
143	A16	1.50fr brt red	.65 .50
144	A16	2fr gray black	1.00 .75
145	A16	2.50fr brt ultra	2.50 1.75
146	A16	4fr dull violet	1.75 1.25
147	A16	5fr bister	1.75 1.25
148	A16	10fr deep brown	2.50 1.90
149	A16	20fr deep green	3.00 2.10
		Nos. 136-149 (14)	16.05 11.35

For surcharges see Nos. 152-159.

Eboue Issue
Common Design Type

1945 Engr. Perf. 13

150	CD91	2fr black	1.00 .75
151	CD91	25fr Prus green	2.60 2.10

Nos. 150 and 151 exist imperforate.

Nos. 136, 138 and 145 Surcharged with New Values and Bars in Carmine or Black

1946 Perf. 14½x14

152	A16	50c on 5c (C)	.65 .50
153	A16	60c on 5c (C)	.65 .50
154	A16	70c on 5c (C)	.65 .50
155	A16	1.20fr on 5c (C)	.80 .65
156	A16	2.40fr on 25c (Bk)	1.60 1.25
157	A16	3fr on 25c (Bk)	1.00 .75
158	A16	4.50fr on 25c (Bk)	2.00 1.50
159	A16	15fr on 2.50fr (C)	2.40 1.75
		Nos. 152-159 (8)	9.75 7.40

Coast of Moorea A17

Fisherman and Catch A18

Tahitian Girl — A20

House at Faa — A19

Island of Borabora — A21

Island Women — A22

1948 Unwmk. Engr. Perf. 13

160	A17	10c brown	.50 .35
161	A17	30c blue green	.50 .35
162	A17	40c deep blue	.50 .35
163	A18	50c red brown	.50 .35
164	A18	60c dk brown ol	.65 .50
165	A18	80c brt blue	.65 .50
166	A19	1fr red brown	.65 .35
167	A19	1.20fr slate	.65 .50
168	A19	1.50fr deep ultra	.65 .50
169	A20	2fr sepia	1.10 .75
170	A20	2.40fr red brown	1.25 1.00
171	A20	3fr purple	11.50 2.50
172	A20	4fr blue black	2.40 1.40
173	A21	5fr sepia	3.75 1.65
174	A21	6fr steel blue	3.75 2.10
175	A21	10fr dk brown ol	4.75 1.75
176	A22	15fr vermilion	7.25 2.75
177	A22	20fr slate	7.25 3.25
178	A22	25fr sepia	9.00 5.00
		Nos. 160-178 (19)	57.25 25.85

Imperforates
Most French Polynesia stamps from 1948 onward exist imperforate in issued and trial colors, and also in small presentation sheets in issued colors.

Military Medal Issue
Common Design Type

1952, Dec. 1 Engr. & Typo.

179	CD101	3fr multicolored	13.50 10.00

Girl of Bora Bora — A23

1955, Sept. 26 Engr.

180	A23	9fr dk brn, blk & red	11.00 7.25

FIDES Issue
Common Design Type
Design: 3fr, Dry dock at Papeete.

1956, Oct. 22 Engr. Perf. 13x12½

181	CD103	3fr grnsh blue	4.00 2.00

Girl Playing Guitar — A24

Designs: 4fr, 7fr, 9fr, Man with headdress. 10fr, 20fr, Girl with shells on beach.

1958, Nov. 3 Unwmk. Perf. 13

182	A24	10c grn & redsh brn	.65 .55
183	A24	25c slate grn, cl & car	.80 .60
184	A24	1fr brt bl, brn & red org	1.00 .65
185	A24	2fr brn, vio brn & vio	1.10 .65
186	A24	4fr sl grn & org yel	1.50 1.00
187	A24	7fr red brn, grn & org	3.00 1.60
188	A24	9fr vio brn, grn & org	5.50 2.25
189	A24	10fr dk bl, brn & car	5.00 2.25
190	A24	20fr pur, rose red & brn	9.00 5.00
		Nos. 182-190 (9)	27.55 14.55

See Nos. 304-306.

Human Rights Issue
Common Design Type

1958, Dec. 10

191	CD105	7fr dk gray & dk bl	13.00 8.75

Flower Issue
Common Design Type

1959, Jan. 3 Photo. Perf. 12½x12

192	CD104	4fr Breadfruit	6.50 4.00

Spear Fishing A25

Tahitian Dancers A26

1960, May 16 Engr. Perf. 13

193	A25	5fr green, brn & lil	1.25 1.00
194	A26	17fr ultra, brt grn & red brn	6.00 2.50

Post Office, Papeete — A27

1960, Nov. 19 Unwmk. Perf. 13

195	A27	16fr green, bl & claret	5.50 3.25

Saraca Indica — A28

1962, July 12 Photo. Perf. 13

196	A28	15fr shown	15.00 14.00
197	A28	25fr Hibiscus	24.00 16.00

Map of Australia and South Pacific A29

1962, July 18 Perf. 13x12

198	A29	20fr multicolored	17.50 7.75

5th South Pacific Conf., Pago Pago, July 1962.

Spined Squirrelfish A30

Fish: 10fr, One-spot butterflyfish. 30fr, Radiate lionfish. 40fr, Horned boxfish.

1962, Dec. 15 Engr. Perf. 13

199	A30	5fr black, mag & bis	4.25 1.90
200	A30	10fr multicolored	6.25 2.75
201	A30	30fr multicolored	12.50 7.75
202	A30	40fr multicolored	15.50 11.50
		Nos. 199-202 (4)	38.50 23.90

Soccer A30a

Design: 50fr, Throwing the javelin.

1963, Aug. 29 Photo. Perf. 12½

203	A30a	20fr brt ultra & brn	9.00 6.25
204	A30a	50fr brt car rose & ultra	16.00 9.25

South Pacific Games, Suva, 8/29-9/7.

Red Cross Centenary Issue
Common Design Type

1963, Sept. 2 Engr. Perf. 13

205	CD113	15fr vio brn, gray & car	15.00 12.00

Human Rights Issue
Common Design Type

1963, Dec. 10 Unwmk. Perf. 13

206	CD117	7fr green & vio bl	15.00 10.00

Philatec Issue
Common Design Type

1964, Apr. 9 Unwmk. Perf. 13

207	CD118	25fr grn, dk sl grn & red	18.00 12.50

Tahitian Dancer — A31

1964, May 14 Engr. Perf. 13

208	A31	1fr multicolored	.40 .40
209	A31	3fr dp claret, blk & org	.90 .90

Soldiers, Truck and Battle Flag — A32

1964, July 10 Photo. Perf. 12½

210	A32	5fr multicolored	11.00 4.25

Issued to honor the Tahitian Volunteers of the Pacific Battalion. See No. C31.

Tuamotu Scene — A33

Views: 4fr, Borabora. 7fr, Papeete Harbor. 8fr, Paul Gauguin's tomb, Marquesas. 20fr, Mangareva, Gambier Islands.

1964, Dec. 1 Litho. Perf. 12½x13

211	A33	2fr multicolored	.90 .50
212	A33	4fr multicolored	1.50 .50
213	A33	7fr multicolored	3.00 1.25
214	A33	8fr multicolored	4.00 1.75
215	A33	20fr multicolored	9.50 2.50
		Nos. 211-215, C32 (6)	28.40 10.50

Painting from a School Dining Room — A34

1965, Nov. 29 Engr. Perf. 13

216	A34	20fr dk brn, sl grn & dk car	20.00 12.00

Publicizing the School Canteen Program. See No. C38.

Outrigger Canoe on Lagoon — A35

Ships: 11fr, Large cruising yacht, vert. 12fr, Motorboat for sport fishing. 14fr, Outrigger canoes in lagoon. 19fr, Schooner, vert. 22fr, Modern coaster "Oiseau des Iles II."

1966, Aug. 30 Engr. Perf. 13

217	A35	10fr brt ultra, emer & mar	2.75 .90
218	A35	11fr mar, dk bl & sl grn	2.75 1.60
219	A35	12fr emer, dk bl & red lil	3.75 1.75
220	A35	14fr brn, bl & slate grn	5.50 2.00
221	A35	19fr scar, sl grn & dp bl	6.50 2.10
222	A35	22fr multicolored	9.50 4.00
		Nos. 217-222 (6)	30.75 12.35

High Jump — A36

Designs: 20fr, Pole vault, vert. 40fr, Women's basketball, vert. 60fr, Hurdling.

1966, Dec. 15   Engr.   Perf. 13
223 A36 10fr dk red, lem & blk   2.25   1.50
224 A36 20fr blue, emer & blk   5.25   2.00
225 A36 40fr emer, brt pink &
blk   10.00   5.00
226 A36 60fr dull yel, bl & blk   17.00   8.50
    Nos. 223-226 (4)   34.50   17.00
2nd South Pacific Games, Nouméa, New Caledonia, Dec. 8-18.

Poi Pounder — A37

1967, June 15   Engr.   Perf. 13
227 A37 50fr orange & blk   17.00   10.00
Society for Oceanic Studies, 50th anniv.

Javelin Throwing — A38

5fr, Spring dance. 15fr, Horse race. 16fr, Fruit carriers' race. 21fr, Canoe race.

1967, July 11
228 A38 5fr multi, horiz.   1.10   .90
229 A38 13fr multi   4.50   1.50
230 A38 15fr multi, horiz.   4.50   1.60
231 A38 16fr multi   4.50   2.75
232 A38 21fr multi, horiz.   9.50   5.00
    Nos. 228-232 (5)   24.10   11.75
Issued to publicize the July Festival.

Earring — A39

Art of the Marquesas Islands: 10fr, Carved mother-of-pearl. 15fr, Decorated canoe paddle. 23fr, Oil vessel. 25fr, Carved stilt stirrups. 30fr, Fan handles. 35fr, Tattooed man. 50fr, Tikis.

1967-68   Engr.   Perf. 13
233 A39 10fr dp cl, dl red & ultra   2.25   .65
234 A39 15fr black & emerald   3.00   1.25
235 A39 20fr ol gray, dk car &
lt bl   5.25   2.00
236 A39 23fr dk brn, ocher &
bl   6.50   4.00
237 A39 25fr dk brn, dk bl & lil   6.50   3.75
238 A39 30fr brown & red lilac   8.25   4.00
239 A39 35fr ultra & dk brn   14.00   6.25
240 A39 50fr brn, sl grn & lt bl   15.00   7.25
    Nos. 233-240 (8)   60.75   29.15
Issued: 20fr, 25fr, 30fr, 50fr, 12/19/67; others 2/28/68.

WHO Anniversary Issue
Common Design Type
1968, May 4   Engr.   Perf. 13
241 CD126 15fr bl grn, mar &
dp vio   11.00   4.75
242 CD126 16fr org, lil & bl grn   11.00   8.00

Human Rights Year Issue
Common Design Type
1968, Aug. 10   Engr.   Perf. 13
243 CD127 15fr blue, red & brn   12.00   6.00
244 CD127 16fr brn, brt pink &
ultra   12.00   8.00

Tiare Apetahi — A40

Flower: 17fr, Tiare Tahiti.

1969, Mar. 27   Photo.   Perf. 12½x13
245 A40 9fr multicolored   2.10   1.10
246 A40 17fr multicolored   4.25   2.10

3rd South Pacific Games, Port Moresby, Papua and New Guinea, Aug. 13-23 — A41

1969, Aug. 13   Engr.   Perf. 13
247 A41 9fr Boxer, horiz.   3.25   1.25
248 A41 17fr High jump   7.25   2.00
249 A41 18fr Runner   9.00   3.50
250 A41 22fr Long jump   12.00   7.25
    Nos. 247-250 (4)   31.50   14.00

ILO Issue
Common Design Type
1969, Nov. 24   Engr.   Perf. 13
251 CD131 17fr org, emer & ol   12.00   5.75
252 CD131 18fr org, dk brn &
vio bl   12.00   6.75

Territorial Assembly — A42

Buildings: 14fr, Governor's Residence. 17fr, House of Tourism. 18fr, Maeva Hotel. 24fr, Taharaa Hotel.

1969, Dec. 22   Photo.   Perf. 12½x12
253 A42 13fr black & multi   2.75   1.25
254 A42 14fr black & multi   4.25   1.50
255 A42 17fr black & multi   7.00   3.50
256 A42 18fr black & multi   7.75   4.00
257 A42 24fr black & multi   13.50   7.00
    Nos. 253-257 (5)   35.25   17.25

Stone Figure with Globe — A43

Designs: 40fr, Globe, plane, map of Polynesia and men holding "PATA" sign, horiz. 60fr, Polynesian carrying globe.

1970, Apr. 7   Engr.   Perf. 13
258 A43 20fr deep plum, gray
& bl   6.75   3.25
259 A43 40fr emer, rose lil &
ultra   11.00   5.25
260 A43 60fr red brn, bl & dk
brn   19.00   10.00
    Nos. 258-260 (3)   36.75   18.50
Issued to publicize the 1970 Pacific Area Travel Association Congress (PATA).

UPU Headquarters Issue
Common Design Type
1970, May 20   Engr.   Perf. 13
261 CD133 18fr mar, pur & brn   10.00   4.75
262 CD133 20fr lil rose, ol & ind   10.00   5.25

Night Fishing — A44

1971, May 11   Photo.   Perf. 13
263 A44 10fr multicolored   12.50   5.25
    Nos. 263,C71-C73 (4)   37.50   19.75

Flowers — A45

Designs: Various flowers. 12fr is horiz.

Perf. 12½x13, 13x12½
1971, Aug. 27
264 A45 8fr multicolored   2.25   1.00
265 A45 12fr multicolored   3.50   1.75
266 A45 22fr multicolored   5.75   3.00
    Nos. 264-266 (3)   11.50   5.75
Day of a Thousand Flowers.

Water-skiing Slalom A46

Designs: 20fr, Water-skiing, jump, vert. 40fr, Figure water-skiing.

1971, Oct. 11   Engr.   Perf. 13
267 A46 10fr grnsh bl, dk red
& brn   6.25   2.00
268 A46 20fr car, emer & brn   9.00   4.00
269 A46 40fr brn, grn & lil   20.00   12.00
    Nos. 267-269 (3)   35.25   18.00
World water-skiing championships, Oct. 1971.

De Gaulle Issue
Common Design Type
30fr, As general, 1940. 50fr, As president, 1970.

1971, Nov. 9   Engr.   Perf. 13
270 CD134 30fr red lilac & blk   22.50   11.00
271 CD134 50fr red lilac & blk   29.00   18.50

Map of Tahiti and Jerusalem Cross — A47

1971, Dec. 18   Photo.   Perf. 13x12½
272 A47 28fr lt blue & multi   14.00   8.50
2nd rally of French Boy Scouts and Guides, Taravao, French Polynesia.

"Alcoholism" — A48

1972, Mar. 24   Photo.   Perf. 13
273 A48 20fr brown & multi   11.50   5.75
Fight against alcoholism.

Mother and Child — A49

1973, Sept. 26   Photo.   Perf. 12½x13
274 A49 28fr pale yellow & multi   9.50   5.00
Day nursery.

A 50fr multicolored stamp for the Second Medical Conference was prepared for release in 1973, but not issued. Between 50 and 75 examples were sold.

Polynesian Golfer — A50

Design: 24fr, Atimaono Golf Course.

1974, Feb. 27   Photo.   Perf. 13
275 A50 16fr multicolored   8.50   3.25
276 A50 24fr multicolored   10.50   5.25
Atimaono Golf Course.

Hand Throwing Life Preserver to Puppy A51

1974, May 9   Photo.   Perf. 13
277 A51 21fr brt blue & multi   12.00   5.00
Society for the Protection of Animals.

Around a Fire, on the Beach — A52

Polynesian Views: 2fr, Lagoons and mountains. 6fr, Pebble divers. 10fr, Lonely Mountain and flowers, vert. 15fr, Sailing ship at sunset. 20fr, Lagoon and mountain.

1974, May 22
278 A52 2fr multicolored   .90   .60
279 A52 5fr multicolored   1.10   .90
280 A52 6fr multicolored   1.90   1.10
281 A52 10fr multicolored   2.10   1.25
282 A52 15fr multicolored   4.25   1.75
283 A52 20fr multicolored   7.00   2.10
    Nos. 278-283 (6)   17.25   7.70

Polynesian Woman and UPU Emblem — A53

1974, Oct. 9   Engr.   Perf. 13
284 A53 65fr multicolored   12.00   7.75
Centenary of Universal Postal Union.

Lion, Sun and Emblem — A54

1975, June 17   Photo.
285 A54 26fr multicolored   12.00   5.00
15th anniv. of Lions Intl. in Tahiti.

Fish and Leaf — A55

1975, July 9   Litho.   Perf. 12
286 A55 19fr dp ultra & green   10.00 4.25

Polynesian Association for the Protection of Nature.

Georges Pompidou, Pres. of France — A55a

1976, Feb. 16   Engr.   Perf. 13
287 A55a 49fr dk violet & black   11.00 7.00

See France No. 1430.

Alain Gerbault and Sailboat — A56

1976, May 25   Photo.   Perf. 13
288 A56 90fr multicolored   13.50 9.00

Alain Gerbault's arrival in Bora Bora, 50th anniv.

Turtle — A57

Design: 42fr, Hand protecting bird.

1976, June 24   Litho.   Perf. 12½
289 A57 18fr multicolored   14.00 4.25
290 A57 42fr multicolored   20.00 11.00

World Ecology Day.

A. G. Bell, Telephone, Radar and Satellite A58

1976, Sept. 15   Engr.   Perf. 13
291 A58 37fr multicolored   10.00 5.00

Centenary of first telephone call by Alexander Graham Bell, Mar. 10, 1876.

Dugout Canoes A59

1976, Dec. 16   Litho.   Perf. 13x12½
292 A59 25fr Marquesas   3.75 2.75
293 A59 30fr Raiatea   4.75 4.75
294 A59 75fr Tahiti   9.50 5.75
295 A59 100fr Tuamotu   12.00 7.00
     Nos. 292-295 (4)   30.00 20.25

Sailing Ship — A60

Designs: Various sailing vessels.

1977, Dec. 22   Litho.   Perf. 13
296 A60 20fr multicolored   6.25 2.00
297 A60 50fr multicolored   7.25 2.25
298 A60 85fr multicolored   9.00 3.75
299 A60 120fr multicolored   15.00 5.75
     Nos. 296-299 (4)   37.50 13.75

Hibiscus — A61

Designs: 10fr, Vanda orchids. 16fr, Pua (fagraea berteriana). 22fr, Gardenia.

1978-79   Photo.   Perf. 12½x13
300 A61 10fr multicolored   1.10 .50
301 A61 13fr multicolored   2.50 1.00
302 A61 16fr multicolored   2.75 1.75
303 A61 22fr multicolored   1.75 1.00
     Nos. 300-303 (4)   8.10 4.25

Issued: 13fr, 16fr, 8/23; 10fr, 22fr, 1/25/79.

Girl with Shells on Beach — A62

Design A24 with "1958 1978" added: 28fr, Man with headdress. 36fr, Girl playing guitar.

1978, Nov. 3   Engr.   Perf. 13
304 A62 20fr multicolored   3.00 .75
305 A62 28fr multicolored   3.75 1.50
306 A62 36fr multicolored   5.75 2.25
  a. Souvenir sheet of 3   27.50 27.50
     Nos. 304-306 (3)   12.50 4.50

20th anniv. of stamps inscribed: Polynesie Francaise. No. 306a contains Nos. 304-306 in changed colors.

Ships — A63

1978, Dec. 29   Litho.   Perf. 13x12½
307 A63 15fr Tahiti   1.50 .80
308 A63 30fr Monowai   2.75 1.25
309 A63 75fr Tahitien   4.50 3.25
310 A63 100fr Mariposa   8.50 3.25
     Nos. 307-310 (4)   17.25 8.55

Porites Coral — A64

Design: 37fr, Montipora coral.

1979, Feb. 15   Perf. 13x12½
311 A64 32fr multicolored   2.50 1.25
312 A64 37fr multicolored   3.75 2.00

Raiatea — A65

Landscapes: 1fr, Moon over Bora Bora. 2fr, Mountain peaks, Ua Pou. 3fr, Sunset over Motu Tapu. 5fr, Motu. 6fr, Palm and hut, Tuamotu.

1979, Mar. 8   Photo.   Perf. 13x13½
313 A65 1fr multicolored   .25 .25
314 A65 2fr multicolored   .25 .25
315 A65 3fr multicolored   .30 .25
316 A65 4fr multicolored   .45 .25
317 A65 5fr multicolored   .80 .35
318 A65 6fr multicolored   1.00 .60
     Nos. 313-318 (6)   3.05 1.95

See Nos. 438-443 for redrawn designs.

Dance Costumes — A66

1979, July 14   Litho.   Perf. 12½
319 A66 45fr Fetia   1.75 1.00
320 A66 51fr Teanuanua   2.75 1.25
321 A66 74fr Temaeva   3.75 2.25
     Nos. 319-321 (3)   8.25 4.50

Hill, Great Britain No. 53, Tahiti No. 28 — A67

1979, Aug. 1   Engr.   Perf. 13
322 A67 100fr multicolored   5.00 3.00

Sir Rowland Hill (1795-1879), originator of penny postage.

Hastula Strigilata — A68

Shells: 28fr, Scabricola variegata. 35fr, Fusinus undatus.

1979, Aug. 22   Litho.   Perf. 12½
323 A68 20fr multicolored   1.50 .50
324 A68 28fr multicolored   2.00 1.00
325 A68 35fr multicolored   2.75 2.00
     Nos. 323-325 (3)   6.25 3.50

Statue Holding Rotary Emblem — A69

1979, Nov. 30   Litho.   Perf. 13
326 A69 47fr multicolored   2.75 2.00

Rotary International, 75th anniversary; Papeete Rotary Club, 20th anniversary. For overprint see No. 330.

Myripristis Murdjan — A70

Fish: 8fr, Napoleon. 12fr, Emperor.

1980, Jan. 21   Litho.   Perf. 12½
327 A70 7fr multicolored   1.00 .50
328 A70 8fr multicolored   1.00 .65
329 A70 12fr multicolored   1.65 .95
     Nos. 327-329 (3)   3.65 2.10

No. 326 Overprinted and Surcharged in Gold

1980, Feb. 23   Litho.   Perf. 13
330 A69 77fr on 47fr multi   5.75 3.25

Rotary International, 75th anniversary.

CNEXO Fish Hatchery — A71

1980, Mar. 17   Photo.   Perf. 13x13½
331 A71 15fr shown   1.75 .90
332 A71 22fr Crayfish   1.75 .90

Papeete Post Office Building Opening — A72

1980, Apr. 30   Photo.   Perf. 13x12½
333 A72 50fr multicolored   2.50 1.50

Tiki and Festival Emblem — A73

1980, June 30   Photo.   Perf. 13½
334 A73 34fr shown   1.25 .90
335 A73 39fr Drum (pahu)   2.00 1.30
336 A73 49fr Ax (to'i)   2.75 1.75
  a. Souv. sheet of 3, #334-336   13.50 13.00
     Nos. 334-336 (3)   6.00 3.95

South Pacific Arts Festival, Port Moresby, Papua New Guinea.

Titmouse Henparrot — A74

25fr, White sea-swallow, horiz. 45fr, Minor frigate bird, horiz.

Perf. 13x12½, 12½x13
1980, Oct. 20   Photo.
337 A74 25fr multi   1.50 .70
338 A74 35fr shown   1.75 .90
339 A74 45fr multi   2.75 1.10
     Nos. 337-339 (3)   6.00 2.70

Charles de Gaulle — A75

1980, Nov. 9   Engr.   Perf. 12½x13
340 A75 100fr multicolored   5.00 3.25

Naso Vlamingi (Karaua) — A76

16fr, Lutjanus vaigensis (toau). 24fr, Plectropomus leopardus (tonu).

1981, Feb. 5   Litho.   Perf. 12½
341 A76 13fr shown   1.00 .50
342 A76 16fr multi   1.10 .60
343 A76 24fr multi   2.25 .75
    Nos. 341-343 (3)   4.35 1.85

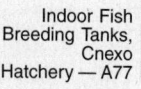

Indoor Fish Breeding Tanks, Cnexo Hatchery — A77

1981, May 14   Photo.   Perf. 13x13½
344 A77 23fr shown   1.10 .80
345 A77 41fr Mussels   2.00 1.10

Folk Dancers — A78

Perf. 13x13½, 13½x13
1981, July 10   Litho.
346 A78 26fr shown   1.25 .65
347 A78 28fr Dancer   1.25 1.10
348 A78 44fr Dancers, vert. 2.10 1.50
    Nos. 346-348 (3)   4.60 3.25

Sterna Bergii A79

53fr, Ptilinopus purpuratus, vert. 65fr, Estrilda astrild, vert.

1981, Sept. 24   Litho.   Perf. 13
349 A79 47fr shown   1.75 1.00
350 A79 53fr multi   1.75 1.20
351 A79 65fr multi   2.25 1.50
    Nos. 349-351 (3)   5.75 3.70
    See Nos. 370-372.

Huahine Island — A80

1981, Oct. 22   Litho.   Perf. 12½
352 A80 34fr shown   1.40 .75
353 A80 134fr Maupiti   3.25 2.00
354 A80 136fr Bora-Bora   3.25 2.00
    Nos. 352-354 (3)   7.90 4.75

A81

1982, Feb. 4   Photo.   Perf. 13x13½
355 A81 30fr Parrotfish   1.00 .75
356 A81 31fr Regal angel   1.40 .75
357 A81 45fr Spotted bass 1.50 1.25
    Nos. 355-357 (3)   3.90 2.75

Pearl Industry — A82

1982, Apr. 22   Photo.   Perf. 13x13½
358 A82 7fr Pearl beds   .85 .45
359 A82 8fr Extracting pearls .85 .45
360 A82 10fr Pearls   1.20 1.10
    Nos. 358-360 (3)   2.90 2.00

Tahiti "No. 1A," Emblem A83

1982, May 12   Engr.   Perf. 13
361 A83 150fr multicolored 4.75 3.50
  a.   Souvenir sheet   16.00 16.00

PHILEXFRANCE Stamp Exhibition, Paris, June 11-21. No. 361a contains No. 361 in changed colors.

King Holding Carved Scepter — A84

Designs: Coronation ceremony.

1982, July 12   Photo.   Perf. 13½x13
362 A84 12fr shown   .50 .25
363 A84 13fr King, priest   .50 .25
364 A84 17fr Procession   1.00 .50
    Nos. 362-364 (3)   2.00 1.00

Championship Emblem — A85

1982, Aug. 13   Perf. 13
365 A85 90fr multicolored   2.75 2.00

4th Hobie-Cat 16 World Catamaran Sailing Championship, Tahiti, Aug. 15-21.

First Colloquium on New Energy Sources — A86

1982, Sept. 29   Litho.
366 A86 46fr multicolored   1.75 1.00

Motu, Tuamotu Islet — A87

1982, Oct. 12   Litho.   Perf. 13
367 A87 20fr shown   .70 .35
368 A87 33fr Tupai Atoll   .90 .45
369 A87 35fr Gambier Islds. 1.25 .55
    Nos. 367-369 (3)   2.85 1.35

Bird Type of 1981

37fr, Sacred egret. 39fr, Pluvialis dominica, vert. 42fr, Lonchura castaneothorax.

1982, Nov. 17   Litho.   Perf. 13
370 A79 37fr multi   1.40 .55
371 A79 39fr multi   1.40 .65
372 A79 42fr multi   1.75 .90
    Nos. 370-372 (3)   4.55 2.10

Fish — A88

8fr, Acanthurus lineatus. 10fr, Caranx melampygus. 12fr, Carcharhinus melanopterus.

1983, Feb. 9   Litho.   Perf. 13x13½
373 A88 8fr multi   .70 .35
374 A88 10fr multi   .90 .35
375 A88 12fr multi   1.40 .50
    Nos. 373-375 (3)   3.00 1.20

The Way of the Cross, Sculpture by Damien Haturau — A89

1983, Mar. 9   Litho.   Perf. 13
376 A89 7fr shown   .25 .25
377 A89 21fr Virgin and Child .70 .60
378 A89 23fr Christ   .90 .60
    Nos. 376-378 (3)   1.85 1.45

Traditional Hats — A90

1983, May 24   Litho.   Perf. 13x12½
379 A90 11fr Acacia   .45 .30
380 A90 13fr Niau   .60 .30
381 A90 25fr Ofe   .80 .50
382 A90 35fr Ofe, diff.   1.10 .60
    Nos. 379-382 (4)   2.95 1.70
    See Nos. 393-396.

Chieftain in Traditional Costume, Sainte-Christine Isld. — A91

Traditional Costumes, Marquesas Islds.

1983, July 12   Photo.   Perf. 13
383 A91 15fr shown   .70 .30
384 A91 17fr Man   .90 .40
385 A91 28fr Woman   1.10 .50
    Nos. 383-385 (3)   2.70 1.20
    See Nos. 397-399, 419-421.

Polynesian Crowns A92

Various flower garlands.

1983, Oct. 19   Litho.   Perf. 13
386 A92 41fr multicolored 1.25 .90
387 A92 44fr multicolored 1.40 .95
388 A92 45fr multicolored 1.50 1.00
    Nos. 386-388 (3)   4.15 2.85
    See Nos. 400-402.

Martin Luther (1483-1546) — A93

1983, Nov. 10   Engr.   Perf. 13
389 A93 90fr black, brn & lil gray 2.25 1.10

Tiki Carvings — A94

Various carvings.

1984, Feb. 8   Litho.   Perf. 12½x13
390 A94 14fr multicolored   .50 .25
391 A94 16fr multicolored   .60 .45
392 A94 19fr multicolored   .75 .45
    Nos. 390-392 (3)   1.85 1.15

Hat Type of 1983

1984, June 20   Litho.   Perf. 13x12½
393 A90 20fr Aeho ope   .50 .35
394 A90 24fr Paeore   .60 .35
395 A90 26fr Ofe fei   .75 .50
396 A90 33fr Hua   .80 .50
    Nos. 393-396 (4)   2.65 1.70

Costume Type of 1983

34fr, Tahitian playing nose flute. 35fr, Priest, Oei-eitia. 39fr, Tahitian adult and child.

1984, July 11   Litho.   Perf. 13
397 A91 34fr multi   .75 .50
398 A91 35fr multi   .90 .50
399 A91 39fr multi   .90 .50
    Nos. 397-399 (3)   2.55 1.50

Garland Type of 1983

1984, Oct. 24   Litho.   Perf. 13x12½
400 A92 46fr Moto'i Lei   .90 .50
401 A92 47fr Pitate Lei   1.00 .60
402 A92 53fr Bougainvillea Lei 1.25 .80
    Nos. 400-402 (3)   3.15 1.90

4th Pacific Arts Festival, Noumea, New Caledonia, Dec. 8-22 — A95

1984, Nov. 20   Litho.   Perf. 13
403 A95 150fr Statue, head-dress 3.50 2.25
    See No. C213.

Paysage D'Anaa, by Jean Masson A96

Paintings: 50fr, Sortie Du Culte, by Jacques Boulaire. 75fr, La Fete, by Robert Tatin. 85fr, Tahitiennes Sur La Plage, by Pierre Heyman.

Perf. 12½x13, 13x12½
1984, Dec. 12   Litho.
404 A96 50fr multi, vert. 1.25 .70
405 A96 65fr multicolored 1.40 .90
406 A96 75fr multicolored 1.90 1.00
407 A96 85fr multicolored 2.25 1.75
    Nos. 404-407 (4)   6.80 4.35

Tiki Carvings — A97

1985, Jan. 23   Litho.   Perf. 13½
408 A97 30fr multicolored   .60 .35
409 A97 36fr multicolored   .80 .45
410 A97 40fr multicolored   .90 .75
    Nos. 408-410 (3)   2.30 1.55

Polynesian Faces — A98

1985, Feb. 20   Photo.   Perf. 12½x13
411 A98 22fr multicolored   .40   .30
412 A98 39fr multicolored   .75   .40
413 A98 44fr multicolored   .95   .70
        Nos. 411-413 (3)   2.10 1.40

Early Tahiti — A99

Designs: 42fr, Entrance to Papeete. 45fr, Girls, vert. 48fr, Papeete market.

Perf. 13x12½, 12½x13
1985, Apr. 24   Litho.
414 A99 42fr multicolored   .90   .55
415 A99 45fr multicolored   1.25   .75
416 A99 48fr multicolored   1.40   .85
        Nos. 414-416 (3)   3.55 2.15

5th Intl. Congress on Coral Reefs, Tahiti — A100

Design: Local reef formation.

1985, May 28   Litho.   Perf. 13½
417 A100 140fr multicolored   3.00 2.00

Printed se-tenant with label picturing congress emblem.

National Flag — A101

1985, June 28
418 A101 9fr Flag, natl. arms   .65   .30

Costume Type of 1983

18th-19th Cent. Prints, Beslu Collection: 38fr, Tahitian dancer. 55fr, Man and woman from Otahiti, 1806. 70fr, Traditional chief.

1985, July 17   Perf. 13
419 A91 38fr multicolored   .95   .65
420 A91 55fr multicolored   1.25   .90
421 A91 70fr multicolored   1.75 1.25
        Nos. 419-421 (3)   3.95 2.80

Local Foods A103

Designs: 25fr, Roasted pig. 35fr, Pit fire. 80fr, Fish in coconut milk. 110fr, Fafaru.

1985-86   Litho.   Perf. 13
422   A103 25fr multi   .85   .60
423   A103 35fr multi   1.10   .65
423A A103 80fr multi   1.90 1.50
423B A103 110fr multi   2.40 1.90
        Nos. 422-423B (4)   6.25 4.65

Issued: 25fr, 35fr, 11/14; 80fr, 110fr, 5/20/86.
See Nos. 458-459, 474-475.

Catholic Churches A104

90fr, St. Anne's, Otepipi. 100fr, St. Michael's Cathedral, Rikitea. 120fr, Cathedral, exterior.

1985, Dec. 11   Litho.   Perf. 13
424 A104 90fr multi   1.75 1.00
425 A104 100fr multi   1.90 1.00
426 A104 120fr multi   2.25 1.50
        Nos. 424-426 (3)   5.90 3.50

Nos. 424-426 printed se-tenant with labels picturing local religious art.

Crabs — A105

1986, Jan. 22   Perf. 13½
427 A105 18fr Fiddler   .90   .50
428 A105 29fr Hermit   1.40   .65
429 A105 31fr Coconut   2.40   .65
        Nos. 427-429 (3)   4.70 1.80

Faces of Polynesia — A106

1986, Feb. 19   Perf. 12½x13, 13½x12½
430 A106 43fr Boy, fish   1.00   .50
431 A106 49fr Boy, coral   1.25   .50
432 A106 51fr Boy, turtle, vert. 1.40 .60
        Nos. 430-432 (3)   3.65 1.60

Old Tahiti A107

Designs: 52fr, Papeete. 56fr, Harpoon fishing. 57fr, Royal Palace, Papeete.

1986, Mar. 18   Perf. 13x12½
433 A107 52fr multi   1.00   .55
434 A107 56fr multi   1.10   .55
435 A107 57fr multi   1.25   .70
        Nos. 433-435 (3)   3.35 1.80

Tiki Rock Carvings — A108

Designs: 58fr, Atuona, Hiva Oa. 59fr, Ua Huka Hill, Hane Valley.

1986, Apr. 16
436 A108 58fr multi   1.40   .70
437 A108 59fr multi   1.40   .70

Landscapes Type Redrawn

1986-88   Litho.   Perf. 13½
438 A65 1fr multi, type 2 ('88) 2.50   .35
    a.   Type 1 ('86)   4.50 1.25
    b.   Type 3 ('91)   18.50 4.50
439 A65 2fr multicolored   .40   .25
440 A65 3fr multicolored   .45   .25
441 A65 4fr multicolored ('87) 1.75   .40
442 A65 5fr multicolored   .75   .30
443 A65 6fr multicolored   .65   .30
        Nos. 438-443 (6)   6.50 1.85

Nos. 438-443 printed in sharper detail, and box containing island name is taller. Nos. 439-443 margin is inscribed "CARTOR" instead of "DELRIEU."

No. 438 has three types of inscription below design: type 1, photographer's name at left, no inscription at right; type 2, photographer's name at left 9.5mm long, printer's name (Cartor) at right; type 3, photographer's name at left 12.5mm long, Cartor at right.

Traditional Crafts — A109

Perf. 13x12½, 12½x13
1986, July 17
444 A109 8fr Quilting, vert.   .25   .25
445 A109 10fr Baskets, hats   .25   .25
446 A109 12fr Grass skirts   .80   .30
        Nos. 444-446 (3)   1.30   .80

Building a Pirogue (Canoe) — A110

1986, Oct. 21   Litho.   Perf. 13½
447 A110 46fr Boat-builders   1.00   .65
448 A110 50fr Close-up   1.10   .85

Medicinal Plants — A111

Designs: 40fr, Phymatosorus. 41fr, Barringtonia asiatica. 60fr, Ocimum bacilicum.

1986, Nov. 19   Perf. 13
449 A111 40fr multi   .90   .50
450 A111 41fr multi   1.00   .50
451 A111 60fr multi   1.60   .90
        Nos. 449-451 (3)   3.50 1.90

See Nos. 495-497.

Polynesians — A112

1987, Jan. 21   Litho.   Perf. 13½
452 A112 28fr Old man   .60   .35
453 A112 30fr Mother and child .75   .50
454 A112 37fr Old woman   1.00   .60
        Nos. 452-454 (3)   2.35 1.45

Crustaceans A113

34fr, Carpilius maculatus. 35fr, Parribacus antarticus. 39fr, Justitia longimana.

1987, Feb. 18   Perf. 12½x13
455 A113 34fr multicolored   2.00   .65
456 A113 35fr multicolored   2.00   .65
457 A113 39fr multicolored   2.50   .65
        Nos. 455-457 (3)   6.50 1.95

Local Foods Type of 1985

1987, Mar. 19   Litho.   Perf. 13
458 A103 33fr Papaya poe   1.10   .70
459 A103 65fr Chicken fafa   2.00 1.00

Polynesian Petroglyphs — A114

1987, May 13   Perf. 12½
460 A114 13fr Tipaerui, Tahiti .35   .25
461 A114 21fr Turtle, Raiatea Is. .60   .35

Calling Devices and Musical Instruments, Museum of Tahiti and the Isles — A115

1987, July 1   Perf. 13½
462 A115 20fr Wood horn   .65   .30
463 A115 26fr Triton's conch   .80   .65
464 A115 33fr Nose flutes   1.00   .70
        Nos. 462-464 (3)   2.45 1.65

Medicinal Plants — A116

46fr, Thespesia populnea. 53fr, Ophioglossum reticulatum. 54fr, Dicrocephala latifolia.

1987, Sept. 16   Perf. 12½x13
465 A116 46fr olive green   1.00   .55
466 A116 53fr reddish lilac   1.40   .55
467 A116 54fr dp bluish grn   1.50   .55
        Nos. 465-467 (3)   3.90 1.65

Ancient Weapons and Tools A117

Designs: 25fr, Adze, war club, chisel, flute. 27fr, War clubs, tatooing comb, mallet. 32fr, Headdress, necklaces, nose flute.

1987, Oct. 14   Engr.   Perf. 13
468 A117 25fr lt olive grn & blk   .60   .30
469 A117 27fr Prus grn & int blue .75   .45
470 A117 32fr brt olive bis & brn
                 blk   .80   .55
        Nos. 468-470 (3)   2.15 1.40

Catholic Missionaries A118

Monsignors: 95fr, Rene Ildefonse Dordillon (1808-1888), bishop of the Marquesas Isls. 105fr, Tepano Jaussen (1815-1891), first bishop of Polynesia. 115fr, Paul Laurent Maze (1885-1976), archbishop of Papeete.

1987, Dec. 9   Litho.
471 A118 95fr multicolored   1.90 1.40
472 A118 105fr multicolored   2.10 1.50
473 A118 115fr multicolored   2.40 1.60
        Nos. 471-473 (3)   6.40 4.50

Local Foods Type of 1985

Designs: 40fr, Crayfish (varo). 75fr, Bananas in coconut milk.

1988, Jan. 12   Litho.   Perf. 13
474 A103 40fr multi   1.90   .55
475 A103 75fr multi   2.75 1.10

Nos. 474-475 are vert.

Authors A119

62fr, James Norman Hall (1887-1951). 85fr, Charles Bernard Nordhoff (1887-1947).

1988, Feb. 10
476 A119 62fr multicolored   1.40   .75
477 A119 85fr multicolored   1.90   .85

Traditional Housing A120

11fr, Taranpoo Opoa Is., Raiatea. 15fr, Tahaa Village. 17fr, Community meeting house, Tahiti.

1988, Mar. 16   Litho.   *Perf. 13x12½*
478	A120	11fr multicolored	.50	.30
479	A120	15fr multicolored	.60	.30
480	A120	17fr multicolored	.60	.30
		Nos. 478-480 (3)	1.70	.90

Point Venus Lighthouse, 120th Anniv. — A121

1988, Apr. 21   Litho.   *Perf. 13*
| 481 | A121 | 400fr multicolored | 8.50 | 5.50 |

Tapa-cloth Paintings by Paul Engdahl — A122

1988, May 20
482	A122	52fr multicolored	1.25	.75
483	A122	54fr multicolored	1.40	.85
484	A122	64fr multicolored	1.50	1.10
		Nos. 482-484 (3)	4.15	2.70

POLYSAT (Domestic Communications Network) — A123

1988, June 15   Litho.   *Perf. 12½x12*
| 485 | A123 | 300fr multicolored | 6.00 | 4.75 |

Tahitian Dolls — A124

Designs: 42fr, Wearing grass skirt and headdress. 45fr, Wearing print dress and straw hat, holding guitar. 48fr, Wearing print dress and straw hat, holding straw bag.

1988, June 27   *Perf. 13x12½*
486	A124	42fr multicolored	1.00	.60
487	A124	45fr multicolored	1.25	.60
488	A124	48fr multicolored	1.50	.75
		Nos. 486-488 (3)	3.75	1.95

Visiting a Marae at Nuku Hiva, Engraving by J. & E. Verreaux — A125

1988, Aug. 1   Engr.   *Perf. 13*
| 489 | A125 | 68fr black brown | 2.00 | 1.25 |

Size: 143x101mm
| 490 | A125 | 145fr violet brn & grn | 5.25 | 4.00 |

SYDPEX '88, July 30-Aug. 7, Australia. No. 490 pictures a Russian navy officer (probably Krusenstern) visiting the Marquesas Islanders; denomination LR.

Map Linking South America and South Pacific Islands A126

1988, Aug. 30   Engr.
| 491 | A126 | 350fr multicolored | 7.50 | 4.50 |

Eric de Bisschop (1890-1958), explorer who tried to prove that there was an exchange of peoples between the South Pacific islands and So. America, rather than that the island populations originated from So. America.

Seashells — A127

1988, Sept. 21   Litho.   *Perf. 13½*
492	A127	24fr Kermia barnardi	.60	.35
493	A127	35fr Vexillum suavis	1.00	.50
494	A127	44fr Berthelinia	1.40	.75
		Nos. 492-494 (3)	3.00	1.60

Medicinal Plants Type of 1986

23fr, Davallia solida. 36fr, Rorippa sarmentosa. 49fr, Lindernia crustacea.

1988, Oct. 18   Engr.   *Perf. 13*
495	A111	23fr carmine lake	.75	.30
496	A111	36fr purple brown	1.10	.45
497	A111	49fr deep blue	1.25	.70
		Nos. 495-497 (3)	3.10	1.45

Protestant Missionaries A128

80fr, Henry Nott (1774-1844). 90fr, Papeiha (1800-40). 100fr, Samuel Raapoto (1921-76).

1988, Dec. 7   Litho.
498	A128	80fr multi	1.50	.90
499	A128	90fr multi	2.00	1.25
500	A128	100fr multi	2.25	1.40
		Nos. 498-500 (3)	5.75	3.55

Tahiti Post Office — A129

1989, Jan. 12   Engr.
| 501 | A129 | 30fr P.O., 1875 | .75 | .40 |
| 502 | A129 | 40fr P.O., 1915 | 1.00 | .55 |

Center for Arts and Crafts — A130

29fr, Marquesas Is. lidded bowl. 31fr, Mother-of-pearl pendant.

1989, Feb. 15   Litho.   *Perf. 12½*
| 503 | A130 | 29fr multi | .80 | .40 |
| 504 | A130 | 31fr multi | .90 | .45 |

Copra Industry

Extracting Coconut Meat From Shell — A131a

Drying Coconut Meat in Sun — A131

1989, Mar. 16   Litho.   *Perf. 13*
| 505 | A131a | 55fr multicolored | 55.00 | 40.00 |
| 506 | A131 | 70fr multicolored | 2.50 | 2.00 |

Tapa Art — A132

43fr, Wood statue (pole), Marquesas Islands, vert. 51fr, Hand-painted bark tapestry, Society Is. 56fr, Concentric circles, Tubuai, Austral Islands.

1989, Apr. 18   Litho.   *Perf. 13½*
507	A132	43fr multicolored	.90	.60
508	A132	51fr shown	1.25	.75
509	A132	56fr multicolored	1.50	.90
		Nos. 507-509 (3)	3.65	2.25

Polynesian Environment — A133

Design: 140fr, Diving for seashells.

1989, May 17   Litho.   *Perf. 13x12½*
| 510 | A133 | 120fr shown | 2.25 | 1.50 |
| 511 | A133 | 140fr multicolored | 2.75 | 1.75 |

Polynesian Folklore — A134

Designs: 47fr, Stone-lifting contest, vert. 61fr, Dancer, vert. 67fr, Folk singers.

Perf. 13x12½, 12½x13

1989, June 28   Litho.
512	A134	47fr multicolored	1.10	.55
513	A134	61fr multicolored	1.40	.70
514	A134	67fr multicolored	1.75	.75
		Nos. 512-514 (3)	4.25	2.00

Bounty Castaways, from an Etching by Robert Dodd A135

1989, July 7   Engr.   *Perf. 13*
| 515 | A135 | 100fr dp blue & bl grn | 2.40 | 1.50 |

Souvenir Sheet
Imperf
| 516 | A135 | 200fr dk ol grn & dk brn | 12.00 | 12.00 |

PHILEXFRANCE '89 and 200th annivs. of the mutiny on the *Bounty* and the French revolution.
No. 515 printed se-tenant with label picturing exhibition emblem.

1989, Aug. 7   Engr.   *Perf. 13x13½*
| 517 | A136 | 52fr yel brn & myrtle grn | 1.40 | .75 |

Miniature Sheet

Messages A137

a, Get well soon. b, Good luck. c, Happy birthday. d, Keep in touch. e, Congratulations.

1989, Sept. 27   Litho.   *Perf. 12½*
| 518 | A137 | 42fr Sheet of 5, #a.-e. | 12.00 | 12.00 |

Sea Shells — A138

1989, Oct. 12   Litho.   *Perf. 13½*
523	A138	60fr Triphoridae	1.60	.80
524	A138	69fr Muricidae favartia	1.75	.90
525	A138	73fr Muricidae morula	2.00	1.00
		Nos. 523-525 (3)	5.35	2.70

Te Faaturama, c. 1892, by Gauguin — A139

1989, Nov. 19   Litho.   *Perf. 12½x13*
| 526 | A139 | 1000fr multicolored | 22.00 | 12.50 |

Legends — A140

Designs: 66fr, Maui, birth of the islands, vert. 82fr, Mt. Rotui, the pierced mountain. 88fr, Princess Hina and the eel King of Lake Vaihiria.

1989, Dec. 6   Litho.   *Perf. 13*
527	A140	66fr olive brn & blk	1.40	.90
528	A140	82fr buff & blk	1.90	1.10
529	A140	88fr cream & blk	2.00	1.15
		Nos. 527-529 (3)	5.30	3.15

Vanilla Orchid — A141

1990, Jan. 11   Litho.
| 530 | A141 | 34fr Flower | 1.35 | .60 |
| 531 | A141 | 35fr Bean pods | 1.60 | .60 |

Reverend-Father Patrick O'Reilly (1900-1988) — A136

Marine Life — A142

1990, Feb. 9   Litho.   *Perf. 13½*
| 532 | A142 | 40fr Kuhlia marginata | 1.30 | .55 |
| 533 | A142 | 50fr Macrobrachium | 1.50 | .70 |

Tahiti, Center of Polynesian Triangle A143

Maohi settlers and maps of island settlements: 58fr, Hawaiian Islands. 59fr, Easter Island. 63fr, New Zealand.

1990, Mar. 14   Engr.   Perf. 13
534 A143 58fr black   1.75   .85
535 A143 59fr bluish gray   45.00 25.00
536 A143 63fr olive green   2.25   .95
537 A143 71fr Prussian blue   2.50 1.10
        Nos. 534-537 (4)   51.50 27.90
            See Nos. 544-545.

Papeete Village, Cent. A144

1990, May 16   Litho.
538 A144 150fr New City Hall   3.25 1.75
539 A144 250fr Old Town Hall   4.75 3.00

A145

Designs: Endangered birds.

1990, June 5   Perf. 13½
540 A145 13fr Porzana tabuensis   .75 .25
541 A145 20fr Vini ultramarina   1.75 .35

A146

1990, July 10   Perf. 13
542 A146 39fr multicolored   1.10 .65
    Lions Club in Papeete, 30th anniv.

Gen. Charles de Gaulle, Birth Cent. A147

1990, Sept. 2   Litho.
543 A147 200fr multi   4.50 3.25

No. 536 with Different Colors and Inscriptions
1990, Aug. 24   Engr.   Perf. 13
544 A143 125fr Man, map   3.00 2.00
        Souvenir Sheet
            Imperf
545 A143 230fr like No. 544   6.00 6.00
        New Zealand 1990.

Intl. Tourism Day — A148

1990, Sept. 27   Litho.   Perf. 12½
546 A148 8f red & yellow pareo   1.10 .35
547 A148 10fr yellow pareo   1.10 .35
548 A148 12fr blue pareo   1.10 .75
        Nos. 546-548 (3)   3.30 1.45

Polynesian Legends A149

170fr, Legend of the Uru. 290fr, Pipiri-ma, vert. 375fr, Hiro, God of Thieves, vert.

1990, Nov. 7   Litho.   Perf. 13
549 A149 170fr multicolored   4.00 2.50
550 A149 290fr multicolored   7.50 4.00
551 A149 375fr multicolored   11.00 5.00
        Nos. 549-551 (3)   22.50 11.50

Tiare Flower — A150

Designs: 28fr, Flower crown, lei. 30fr, Flowers in bloom. 37fr, Lei.

1990, Dec. 5   Perf. 12½
552 A150 28fr multicolored   .70 .45
553 A150 30fr multicolored   .95 .45
554 A150 37fr multicolored   1.20 .55
        Nos. 552-554 (3)   2.85 1.45

Pineapple — A151

Design: 44fr, Pineapple field.

1991, Jan. 9   Die Cut
        Self-adhesive
555 A151 42fr multicolored   1.25 .90
556 A151 44fr multicolored   1.75 1.10
    Nos. 555-556 are on paper backing perf. 12½.

Marine Life — A152

1991, Feb. 7   Perf. 12½
557 A152 7fr Nudibranch   .45 .25
558 A152 9fr Galaxaura tenera   .70 .25
559 A152 11fr Adusta cumingii   .70 .25
        Nos. 557-559 (3)   1.85 .75

Maohi Islands — A153

18th Century scenes of: 68fr, Woman of Easter Island, vert. 84fr, Twin-hulled canoe, Hawaii. 94fr, Maori village, New Zealand.

1991, Mar. 13   Engr.   Perf. 13
560 A153 68fr olive   47.50 32.50
561 A153 84fr black   2.50 1.75
562 A153 94fr brown   3.00 1.75
        Nos. 560-562 (3)   53.00 36.00

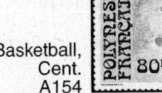

Basketball, Cent. A154

1991, May 15   Litho.   Perf. 13
563 A154 80fr multicolored   1.75 1.25

Birds — A155

1991, June 5   Perf. 13½
564 A155 17fr Halcyon gambieri   .60 .25
565 A155 21fr Vini kuhlii   .90 .35

Still Life with Oranges in Tahiti by Paul Gauguin A156

1991, June 9   Litho.   Perf. 13
566 A156 700fr multicolored   17.50 9.50

Sculptures of the Marquesas Islands A157

56fr, White Tiki with Club, vert. 102fr, Warriors Carrying Tired Man, vert. 110fr, Native Canoe.

1991, July 17   Litho.   Perf. 13
567 A157 56fr multicolored   1.25 .85
568 A157 102fr multicolored   2.25 1.50
569 A157 110fr multicolored   2.50 1.75
        Nos. 567-569 (3)   6.00 4.10

Wolfgang Amadeus Mozart, Death Bicent. A158

1991, Aug. 28   Engr.   Perf. 13x12½
570 A158 100fr multicolored   3.00 1.75

Stone Fishing A159

25fr, Fishing boats, vert. 57fr, Man hurling stone, vert. 62fr, Trapped fish.

1991, Oct. 9   Litho.   Perf. 13
571 A159 25fr multi   .60 .40
572 A159 57fr multi   1.25 .90
573 A159 62fr multi   1.50 1.25
        Nos. 571-573 (3)   3.35 2.55

Phila Nippon '91 — A160

Designs: 50fr, Drawings of marine life by Jules-Louis Lejeune, vert. 70fr, Sailing ship, La Coquille. 250fr, Contains designs from Nos. 574-575.

Perf. 12½x13, 13x12½
1991, Nov. 16   Engr.
574 A160 50fr multicolored   1.30 .55
575 A160 70fr multicolored   1.75 1.25
        Size: 100x75mm
            Imperf
576 A160 250fr multicolored   6.00 6.00
        Nos. 574-576 (3)   9.05 7.80

Central Bank for Economic Cooperation, 50th Anniv. — A161

1991, Dec. 2   Litho.   Perf. 13x12½
577 A161 307fr multicolored   7.00 4.50

Christmas A162

Perf. 12½x13, 13x12½
1991, Dec. 11   Litho.
578 A162 55fr Scuba divers   1.25 .75
579 A162 83fr Underwater scene   1.75 1.35
580 A162 86fr Nativity, vert.   1.75 1.35
        Nos. 578-580 (3)   4.75 3.45

Tourism A163

Designs: 2fr, Horses, beach. 3fr, Girl holding fish. 4fr, Waterfalls, vert. 5fr, Sailing. 6fr, Waterfalls, helicopter, vert.

1992, Feb. 12   Perf. 13
581 A163 1fr shown   .25 .25
582 A163 2fr multicolored   .35 .25
583 A163 3fr multicolored   .50 .30
584 A163 4fr multicolored   .60 .35
585 A163 5fr multicolored   .75 .40
586 A163 6fr multicolored 1.00 .45
        Nos. 581-586 (6)   3.45 2.00

Views from Space A164

Designs: 46fr, Tahiti. 72fr, Mataiva. 76fr, Bora Bora. 230fr, Satellite imaging system.

1992, Mar. 18   Litho.   Perf. 13x12½
587 A164 46fr multi   1.75 .90
588 A164 72fr multi   2.00 1.25
589 A164 76fr multi   2.25 1.40
        Size: 130x100mm
            Imperf
590 A164 230fr multi   6.00 5.75
        Nos. 587-590 (4)   12.00 9.30
        International Space Year.

World Health
Day — A165

1992, Apr. 7   *Perf. 13½*
591 A165 136fr multicolored   3.00 2.25

Discovery of
America,
500th Anniv.
A166

1992, May 22   *Perf. 13*
592 A166 130fr multicolored   3.00 2.25
Size: 140x100mm
Imperf
593 A166 250fr multicolored   6.00 6.00
World Columbian Stamp Expo '92, Chicago.

Traditional
Dances
A167

Dance from: 95fr, Tahiti. 105fr, Hawaii.
115fr, Tonga.

1992, June 17   Engr.   *Perf. 13*
594 A167 95fr brown black   1.90 1.60
595 A167 105fr olive brown   2.10 1.75
596 A167 115fr red brn & olive
      grn   2.50 1.75
   Nos. 594-596 (3)   6.50 5.10

Tattoos — A168

1992, July 8   Litho.   *Perf. 12½*
597 A168 61fr Hand   1.90 1.25
598 A168 64fr Man, vert.   2.00 1.25

Children's
Games — A169

Designs: 22fr, Outrigger canoe models.
31fr, String game. 45fr, Stilt game, vert.

1992, Aug. 5   *Perf. 13½*
599 A169 22fr multi   .50 .35
600 A169 31fr multi   .75 .45
601 A169 45fr multi   1.25 .70
   Nos. 599-601 (3)   2.50 1.50

Herman Melville, 150th
Anniv. of Arrival in
French
Polynesia — A170

1992, Sept. 16   *Perf. 12½*
602 A170 78fr multicolored   4.50 1.25

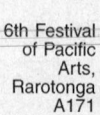

6th Festival
of Pacific
Arts,
Rarotonga
A171

40fr, Men on raft. 65fr, Pirogues, Tahiti.

1992, Oct. 16   Engr.   *Perf. 13*
603 A171 40fr lake   1.50 .60
604 A171 65fr blue   2.00 1.00

First French
Polynesian
Postage
Stamps,
Cent.
A172

1992, Nov. 18   Photo.   *Perf. 13*
605 A172 200fr multicolored   4.75 3.25

Paintings — A173

55fr, Two Women Talking, by Erhard Lux.
60fr, Bouquet of Flowers, by Uschi. 75fr,
Spearfisherman, by Pierre Kienlen. 85fr,
Mother Nursing Child, by Octave Morillot.

1992, Dec. 9   *Perf. 12½x13*
606 A173 55fr multicolored   1.50 .75
607 A173 60fr multicolored   1.75 1.40
608 A173 75fr multicolored   1.90 1.50
609 A173 85fr multicolored   2.50 1.60
   Nos. 606-609 (4)   7.65 5.25

Net Thrower — A174

1993, Feb. 10   Litho.   *Die Cut*
Self-Adhesive
Size: 26x36mm
610 A174 46fr blue & multi   1.50 1.00
Size: 17x23mm
611 A174 46fr green & multi   1.50 1.00
  a.   Booklet pane of 10   15.00

Bonito Fishing — A175

1993, Mar. 10   *Perf. 13½*
612 A175 68fr Line & hook   1.60 1.25
613 A175 84fr Boat, horiz.   1.90 1.50
614 A175 86fr Drying catch   2.10 1.50
   Nos. 612-614 (3)   5.60 4.25

Allied
Airfield on
Bora Bora,
50th Anniv.
A176

1993, Apr. 5   *Perf. 13*
615 A176 120fr multicolored   3.00 2.25

Jacques
Boullaire,
Artist, Birth
Cent.
A177

Various scenes depicting life on: 32fr,
Moorea. 36fr, Tuamotu. 39fr, Rurutu. 51fr,
Nuku Hiva.

1993, May 6   Engr.
616 A177 32fr brown black   .90 .50
617 A177 36fr brick red   .90 .65
618 A177 39fr violet   1.25 .90
619 A177 51fr light brown   1.50 1.00
   Nos. 616-619 (4)   4.55 3.05

Sports Festival — A178

1993, May 15   Litho.   *Perf. 12½*
620 A178 30fr multicolored   .85 .50

Australian
Mathematics
Competition, 15th
Anniv. — A179

1993, July 1   Litho.   *Perf. 13½*
621 A179 70fr multicolored   1.75 1.10

Intl. Symposium on
Inter-Plate Volcanism,
French University of
the Pacific,
Punaauia — A180

1993, Aug. 2   Litho.   *Perf. 13*
622 A180 140fr tan, blk & brn   3.50 2.50

Taipei '93 — A181

1993, Aug. 14   Litho.   *Perf. 13½*
623 A181 46fr multicolored   1.75 .85
Exists without the Cartor imprint. Value,
unused $17.50.

Tourism — A182

14fr, Boat tour. 20fr, Groom preparing for
traditional wedding. 29fr, Beachside brunch.

1993, Sept. 27
624 A182 14fr multi, horiz.   .60 .35
625 A182 20fr multi   .65 .35
626 A182 29fr multi, horiz.   .75 .45
   Nos. 624-626 (3)   2.00 1.15
Exist without the Cartor imprint. Value, set
unused $30.

Arrival of
First French
Gendarme
in Tahiti,
150th Anniv.
A183

1993, Oct. 14   *Perf. 13*
627 A183 100fr multicolored   2.50 1.60
Exists without the Cartor imprint. Value,
unused $17.50.

Alain
Gerbault
(1893-1941),
Sailor
A184

1993, Nov. 17   Engr.   *Perf. 13*
628 A184 150fr red, green & blue 4.00 2.75

Paintings
A185

Artists: 40fr, Vaea Sylvain. 70fr, A. Marere,
vert. 80fr, J. Shelsher. 90fr, P.E. Victor, vert.

1993, Dec. 3   Photo.   *Perf. 13*
629 A185 40fr multicolored   1.75 .70
630 A185 70fr multicolored   2.50 1.25
631 A185 80fr multicolored   3.00 1.25
632 A185 90fr multicolored   3.50 1.50
   Nos. 629-632 (4)   10.75 4.70

French School of
the Pacific, 30th
Anniv. — A186

1993, Dec. 7   Litho.   *Perf. 12½*
633 A186 200fr multicolored   5.00 3.50

Whales and
Dolphins — A187

Designs: 25fr, Whale breeching. 68fr, Dolphins. 72fr, Humpback whales, vert.

1994, Jan. 12   Litho.   *Perf. 13½*
634 A187 25fr multi   .75 .45
635 A187 68fr multi   1.75 1.25
636 A187 72fr multi   2.00 1.25
   Nos. 634-636 (3)   4.50 2.80

A188

1994, Feb. 18   Litho.   *Perf. 13½*
637 A188 51fr multicolored   2.25 .95
Hong Kong '94. New Year 1994 (Year of the
Dog).

Sister Germaine
Bruel — A189

1994, Mar. 16
638 A189 180fr multicolored   4.00 3.00
Arrival of Nuns from St. Joseph of Cluny,
150th anniv.

A190

1994, Apr. 30   Litho.   *Perf. 13½*
639 A190 154fr Tahiti temple   3.50 2.75
Church of Jesus Christ of Latter-day Saints
in French Polynesia, 150th Anniv.

Conservatory of Arts and Crafts, Bicent. — A191

1994, May 25   Photo.   Perf. 13
640 A191 316fr multicolored   7.50 5.50
Regional Associated Center of Papeete, 15th anniv.

Internal Self-Government, 10th Anniv. — A192

1994, June 29   Litho.   Perf. 13
641 A192 500fr multicolored   12.00 7.50

Tahitian Academy, 20th Anniv. A193

1994, July 2   Engr.   Perf. 13
642 A193 136fr multicolored   3.00 2.00

Scenes of Old Tahiti A194

1994, Aug. 10   Litho.   Perf. 13
643 A194 22fr Papara   .90 .50
644 A194 26fr Mataiea   1.10 .65
645 A194 51fr Taravao, vert.   1.90 .95
    Nos. 643-645 (3)   3.90 2.10
    See Nos. 673-675.

Faaturuma, by Paul Gauguin (1848-1903) A195

1994, Sept. 14   Litho.   Perf. 13
646 A195 1000fr multicolored   24.00 16.00

Epiphyllum Oxypetalum A196

1994, Oct. 15   Litho.   Perf. 13½
647 A196 51fr multicolored   1.75 .95

Hawaiki Nui Va'a '94 (Canoe Race) — A197

Designs: a, 52fr, Yellow canoe, bow paddler. b, 76fr, Paddlers. c, 80fr, Paddlers, blue canoe. d, 94fr, Stern paddler, yellow canoe.

1994, Nov. 10   Litho.   Perf. 13½x13
648 A197 Strip of 4, #a.-d.   8.00 4.75
    No. 648 is a continuous design.

Paintings of French Polynesia A198

62fr, Young girl, by Michelle Villemin. 78fr, Ocean tide, fish, by Michele Dallet. 102fr, Native carrying bundles of fruit, by Johel Blanchard. 110fr, View of coastline, by Pierre Lacouture.

1994, Dec. 19   Litho.   Perf. 13
649 A198 62fr multi, vert.   1.75 .95
650 A198 78fr multi, vert.   2.00 1.25
651 A198 102fr multi, vert.   2.25 1.60
652 A198 110fr multi   2.75 1.75
    Nos. 649-652 (4)   8.75 5.55

Don Domingo de Boenechea's Tautira Expedition, 220th Anniv. A199

1995, Jan. 1
653 A199 92fr multicolored   2.25 1.25

South Pacific Tourism Year — A200

1995, Jan. 11   Litho.   Perf. 13½
654 A200 92fr multicolored   2.25 1.40

New Year 1995 (Year of the Boar) — A201

1995, Feb. 1   Litho.
655 A201 51fr multicolored   1.75 .80
Portions of the design on No. 655 were applied by a thermographic process producing a shiny, raised effect.
Exists without the Cartor imprint. Value, unused $9.

University Teacher's Training Institute of the Pacific — A202

1995, Mar. 8   Litho.   Perf. 13½
656 A202 59fr multicolored   1.50 .95
See New Caledonia No. 710 and Wallis & Futuna No. C182.

Nature Protection A203

1995, May 4   Litho.   Perf. 13
657 Strip of 3 + 2 labels   4.25 4.25
    a. A203 22fr Head of turtle   .75 .35
    b. A203 29fr Turtle swimming   1.00 .50
    c. A203 91fr Black coral   2.50 1.50

Louis Pasteur (1822-95) A204

1995, May 8
658 A204 290fr dk blue & blue   6.75 4.00

Loti's Marriage, Novel by Julien Viaud (1850-1923) A205

1995, May 19   Photo.   Perf. 13
659 A205 66fr multicolored   2.00 1.10

A206

1995, May 24   Litho.   Perf. 13½
660 A206 150fr multicolored   3.50 2.25
Tahitian Monoi beauty aid.

Birds — A207

1995, June 7
661 A207 22fr Ptilinopus huttoni   .65 .50
662 A207 44fr Ducula galeata   1.40 .75

Tahitian Pearls — A208

1995, June 14
663 A208 66fr shown   1.60 1.10
664 A208 84fr Eight pearls   2.10 1.40
On Nos. 663-664 portions of the design were applied by a thermographic process producing a shiny, raised effect.

Discovery of Marquesas Islands, 400th Anniv. A209

a, Alvaro de Mendana de Neira, sailing ships. b, Pedro Fernandez de Quiros, map of islands.

1995, July 21   Litho.   Perf. 13
665 Pair + label   8.00 6.00
    a. A209 161fr multicolored   3.50 2.75
    b. A209 195fr multicolored   4.50 3.25

A210

1995, Aug. 12   Litho.   Perf. 13
666 A210 83fr multicolored   2.00 1.40
10th South Pacific Games, Tahiti.

Pandanus Plant — A211

No. 667a, Entire plant. b, Flower. c, Fruit. d, Using dry leaves for weaving.

1995, Sept. 1   Perf. 13½x13
667 Strip of 4   8.50 6.00
    a.-d. A211 91fr any single   2.00 1.50
    Singapore '95.

UN, 50th Anniv. A212

1995, Oct. 24   Litho.   Perf. 13
668 A212 420fr multicolored   9.50 6.00

Paintings A213

Designs: 57fr, The Paddler with the Yellow Dog, by Philippe Dubois, vert. 76fr, An Afternoon in Vaitape, by Maui Seaman, vert. 79fr, The Mama with the White Hat, by Simone Testeguide. 100fr, In Front of the Kellum House in Moorea, by Christian Deloffre.

1995, Dec. 6   Photo.   Perf. 13
669 A213 57fr multicolored   1.50 .90
670 A213 76fr multicolored   1.75 1.25
671 A213 79fr multicolored   1.90 1.25
672 A213 100fr multicolored   2.50 1.60
    Nos. 669-672 (4)   7.65 5.00

Scenes of Old Tahiti Type
Designs: 18fr, Fautaua. 30fr, District of Punaauia. 35fr, Tautira.

1996, Jan. 17   Litho.   Perf. 13
673 A194 18fr multi   .65 .45
674 A194 30fr multi   .80 .50
675 A194 35fr multi   .90 .60
    Nos. 673-675 (3)   2.35 1.55

New Year 1996 (Year of the Rat) — A214

1996, Feb. 19   Photo.   Perf. 13
676 A214 51fr multicolored   1.75 .80
Portions of the design on No. 676 were applied by a thermographic process producing a shiny, raised effect.

Paul-Emile Victor (1907-95), Explorer, Writer A215

1996, Mar. 7   Litho.
677 A215 500fr multicolored   12.00 8.00

Queen Pomare IV — A216

1996, Mar. 1   Litho.   Perf. 13
678 A216 (51fr) multicolored   1.50 .80

Serpentine Die Cut 7 Vert.
Self-Adhesive
Size: 17x24mm

678A	A216	(51fr) multicolored	2.00	1.15
b.		Booklet pane of 5	10.00	
		Complete booklet, 2 #678b	20.00	

Sea Shells — A217

10fr, Conus pertusus. 15fr, Cypraea alisonae. 25fr, Vexillum roseotinctum.

1996, Apr. 10　Photo.　Perf. 13½x13

679	A217	10fr multicolored	.45	.25
680	A217	15fr multicolored	.50	.25
681	A217	25fr multicolored	.95	.40
		Nos. 679-681 (3)	1.90	.90

Portions of the designs on Nos. 679-681 were applied by a thermographic process producing a shiny, raised effect.

Return of the Pacific Battalion, 50th Anniv. A218

1996, May 5　Litho.　Perf. 13

682	A218	100fr multicolored	3.00	1.60

CHINA '96, 9th Asian Intl. Philatelic Exhibition — A219

Design: 200fr, Chinese School, Tahiti, 1940.

1996, May 18　　　　Perf. 13x13½

683	A219	50fr multicolored	1.25	.80

Souvenir Sheet
Imperf

684	A219	200fr multicolored	4.50	3.40

Birds — A220

1996, June 12　Litho.　Perf. 13x13½

685	A220	66fr Sula sula	1.50	1.10
686	A220	79fr Fregata minor	2.00	1.25
687	A220	84fr Anous stolidus	2.00	1.40
		Nos. 685-687 (3)	5.50	3.75

Musical Instruments A221

Designs: 5fr, Pahu, ukulele, toere. 9fr, Toere. 14fr, Pu, vivo.

1996, July 10　　　　Perf. 13x13½

688	A221	5fr multicolored	.30	.25
689	A221	9fr multicolored	.40	.25
690	A221	14fr multicolored	.50	.25
		Nos. 688-690 (3)	1.20	.75

Raiateana Oulietea — A222

1996, Aug. 7　Litho.　Perf. 13x13½

691	A222	66fr multicolored	1.75	1.10

Ruahatu, God of the Ocean — A223

1996, Sept. 9　Litho.　Perf. 13

692	A223	70fr multicolored	1.75	1.10

7th Pacific Arts Festival.

A224

Stamp Day: Young Tahitian girl (Type A2), Noho Mercier, taken from photo by Henry Lemasson (1870-1956), postal administrator.

1996, Oct. 16　Engr.　Perf. 13

693	A224	92fr black, red & blue	2.50	1.50

First Representative Assembly, 50th Anniv. — A225

1996, Nov. 7　Litho.　Perf. 13

694	A225	85fr multicolored	2.00	1.10

Paintings of Tahitian Women A226

Designs: 70fr, Woman lounging on Bora Bora Beach, by Titi Bécaud. 85fr, "Woman with Crown of Auti leaves," by Maryse Noguier, vert. 92fr, "Dreamy Woman," by Christine de Dinechin, vert. 96fr, Two working women, by Andrée Lang, vert.

1996, Dec. 4　Litho.　Perf. 13

695	A226	70fr multicolored	2.00	.75
696	A226	85fr multicolored	2.25	.90
697	A226	92fr multicolored	2.50	1.00
698	A226	96fr multicolored	3.00	1.00
		Nos. 695-698 (4)	9.75	3.65

A227

1997, Jan. 2　Litho.　Perf. 13

699	A227	55fr brown	1.25	.55

Society of South Sea Studies, 80th anniv.

A228

1997, Feb. 7　Photo.　Perf. 13½x13

700	A228	13fr multicolored	1.00	.30

New Year 1997 (Year of the Ox). Portions of the design were applied by a thermographic process producing a shiny, raised effect.

Arrival of Evangelists in Tahiti, Bicent. A229

Designs: a, Sailing ship, "Duff." b, Painting, "Transfer of the Matavai District to the L.M.S. Missionaries," by Robert Smirke.

1997, Mar. 5　Litho.　Perf. 13

701	A229	43fr Pair, #a.-b. + label	2.00	1.25

Tifaifai (Tahitian Bedspread) A230

Various leaf and floral patterns.

1997, Apr. 16

702	A230	1fr multicolored	.25	.25
703	A230	5fr multicolored	.25	.25
704	A230	70fr multicolored	1.60	.70
		Nos. 702-704 (3)	2.10	1.20

PACIFIC 97 — A231

Sailing ships carrying mail, passengers between Tahiti and San Francisco: No. 705, Tropic Bird, 1897. No. 706, Papeete/Zélee, 1892.

1997, May 29　Litho.　Perf. 13

705	A231	92fr multicolored	3.25	1.60
706	A231	92fr multicolored	3.25	1.60
a.		Pair, #705-706	6.50	6.50
b.		Souvenir sheet, #705-706	65.00	65.00

No. 706b sold for 400fr.

Island Scenes — A232

No. 707, Flower. No. 708, Rowing canoe, sun behind mountain. No. 709, Throwing spears. No. 710, Aerial view of island. No. 711, Fish. No. 712, Women walking on beach. No. 713, Holding oyster shell with pearls. No. 714, Boat with sail down, sunset across water. No. 715, Snorkeling, sting ray. No. 716, Bananas, pineapples. No. 717, Palm tree, beach. No. 718, Women dancers in costume.

1997, June 25　Litho.　Perf. 13
Booklet Stamps

707	A232	85fr multicolored	14.00	14.00
708	A232	85fr multicolored	14.00	14.00
709	A232	85fr multicolored	14.00	14.00
710	A232	85fr multicolored	14.00	14.00
711	A232	85fr multicolored	14.00	14.00
712	A232	85fr multicolored	14.00	14.00
a.		Bklt. pane of 6, #707-712	90.00	
713	A232	85fr multicolored	14.00	14.00
714	A232	85fr multicolored	14.00	14.00
715	A232	85fr multicolored	14.00	14.00
716	A232	85fr multicolored	14.00	14.00
717	A232	85fr multicolored	14.00	14.00
718	A232	85fr multicolored	14.00	14.00
a.		Bklt. pane of 6, #713-718	90.00	
		Complete booklet, 2 each #712a, #718a	350.00	

Traditional Dance Costumes — A233

Designs: 4fr, Warrior's costume. 9fr, Women's costume. 11fr, Couple.

1997, July 10　Litho.　Perf. 13½x13

719	A233	4fr multicolored	1.00	.30
720	A233	9fr multicolored	1.25	.30
721	A233	11fr multicolored	2.00	.30
		Nos. 719-721 (3)	4.25	.90

Kon-Tiki Expedition, 50th Anniv. A234

1997, Aug. 7　Litho.　Perf. 13

722	A234	88fr multicolored	2.25	.80

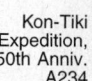

Artists in Tahiti A235

Designs: 85fr, Painting, "The Fruit Carrier," by Monique "Mono" Garnier-Bissol. 96fr, "Revival of Our Resources," mother of pearl painting, by Camélia Maraea. 110fr, "Tahitian Spirit," pottery, by Peter Owen, vert. 126fr, "Monoi," surrealist painting, by Elisabeth Stefanovitch.

1997, Oct. 15　Litho.　Perf. 13

723	A235	85fr multicolored	1.90	.80
724	A235	96fr multicolored	2.00	.90
725	A235	110fr multicolored	2.50	1.00
726	A235	126fr multicolored	3.00	1.10
		Nos. 723-726 (4)	9.40	3.80

Te Arii Vahine, by Paul Gauguin (1848-1903) A236

1997, Nov. 6　Litho.　Perf. 13

727	A236	600fr multicolored	13.00	8.00

Christmas A237

1997, Dec. 3　Litho.　Perf. 13

728	A237	118fr multicolored	3.00	1.10

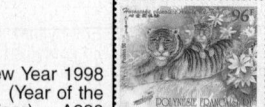

New Year 1998 (Year of the Tiger) — A238

1998, Jan. 28　Photo.　Perf. 13

729	A238	96fr multicolored	2.50	.90

Portions of the design on No. 729 were applied by a thermographic process producing a shiny, raised effect.

Domestic Airline Network — A239

Designs: a, 70fr, Grumman Widgeon, 1950. b, 85fr, DHC 6 Twin-Otter, 1968. c, 70fr, Fairchild FH 227, 1980. d, 85fr, ATR 42-500, 1998.

1998, Apr. 16   Photo.   Perf. 13
730 A239   Strip of 4, #a.-d. + label   6.50 2.90

Orchids — A240

5fr, Dendrobium "Royal King." 20fr, Oncidium "Ramsey." 50fr, Ascodenca "Laksi." 100fr, Cattleya "hybride."

1998, May 14   Photo.   Perf. 13
731 A240   5fr multi   .25   .25
732 A240   20fr multi, vert.   .50   .25
733 A240   50fr multi, vert. 1.25   .45
734 A240   100fr multi   2.25   .95
    Nos. 731-734 (4)   4.25 1.90

On Nos. 731-734 portions of the design were applied by a thermographic process producing a shiny, raised effect.

The Lovers, by Paul Gauguin (1848-1903) A241

1998, June 7   Photo.   Perf. 13x12½
735 A241   1000fr multicolored   22.50 9.00

Printed se-tenant with label.

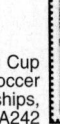

1998 World Cup Soccer Championships, France — A242

1998, June 10
736 A242   85fr multicolored   2.00   .75

For overprint see No. 742.

Tahiti Festival of Flower and Shell Garlands — A243

Women wearing various garlands of flowers or shells.

1998, July 16   Photo.   Perf. 13½
737 A243   55fr multicolored   1.50   .50
738 A243   65fr multicolored   1.75   .60
739 A243   70fr multicolored   2.00   .65
740 A243   80fr multicolored   2.25   .75
    Nos. 737-740 (4)   7.50 2.50

Painting, "Underwater World of Polynesia," by Stanley Haumani — A244

1998, Sept. 10   Photo.   Perf. 12½x13
741 A244   200fr multicolored   4.00 2.00

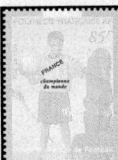

No. 736 Overprinted in Blue & Black

1998, Oct. 28   Photo.   Perf. 13½
742 A242   85fr multicolored   3.00 1.00

No. 742 has blue, white and red margins and No. 736 has white margins.

Autumn Philatelic Fair, Paris A246

Watercolor paintings of Papeete Bay, by René Gillotin (1814-61), 250fr each: a, Beach at left, people. b, Beach at right, people.

1998, Nov. 5   Perf. 13
743 A246   Pair, #a.-b. + label   12.00 5.00
  c.   Souvenir sheet, #a.-b., imperf.   12.00 5.00

Life in Tahiti and the Islands — A247

Paintings by André Deymonaz: 70fr, Return to the Market, vert. 100fr, Bonito Fish Stalls, vert. 102fr, Going Fishing. 110fr, Discussion after Church Services.

1998, Dec. 10   Photo.   Perf. 13
744 A247   70fr multicolored   1.50   .80
745 A247   100fr multicolored   2.00 1.00
746 A247   102fr multicolored   2.25 1.00
747 A247   110fr multicolored   2.50 1.10
    Nos. 744-747 (4)   8.25 3.90

St. Valentine's Day — A248

1999, Feb. 11   Litho.   Perf. 13
748 A248   96fr multicolored   2.50   .90

New Year 1999 (Year of the Rabbit) — A249

1999, Feb. 16
749 A249   118fr Rabbits, flowers   2.50 1.10

Portions of the design of No. 749 were applied by a thermographic process producing a shiny, raised effect.

Marine Life — A250

Designs: 70fr, Ptérois volitans. 85fr, Hippocampus histrix. 90fr, Antennarius pictus. 120fr, Taenianotus triacanthus.

1999, Mar. 18   Photo.   Perf. 13
750 A250   70fr multicolored   1.50   .65
751 A250   85fr multicolored   1.90   .80
752 A250   90fr multicolored   2.00   .80
753 A250   120fr multicolored   2.75 1.10
    Nos. 750-753 (4)   8.15 3.35

Portions of the designs on Nos. 750-753 were applied by a thermographic process producing a shiny, raised effect.

IBRA '99, World Philatelic Exhibition, Nuremberg — A251

Tatooed men of Marquesas Islands, 1804: 90fr, Holding staff, fan. 120fr, Wearing blue cape.

Photo. & Engr.
1999, Apr. 27   Perf. 13¼
754 A251   90fr multicolored   2.00   .90
755 A251   120fr multicolored   2.75 1.25

Mother's Day — A252

1999, May 27   Litho.   Perf. 13¼
756 A252   85fr Children, vert.   1.90   .75
757 A252   120fr shown   2.75 1.00

A253

Island Fruits — A254

No. 758, Breadfruit, vert. 120fr, Coconut. No. 760: a, Papaya. b, Guava (goyave). c, Mombin. d, Rambutan. e, Star apple (pomme-etoile). f, Otaheite gooseberry (seurette). g, Rose apple. h, Star fruit (carambole). i, Spanish lime (quenette). j, Sweetsop (pomme-cannelle). k, Cashew (pomme de cajou). l, Passion fruit.

1999   Litho.   Perf. 13½x13, 13x13½
758 A253   85fr multicolored   1.90   .75
759 A253   120fr multicolored   2.75 1.10
Souvenir Booklet
760   Complete bklt.   32.50
  a.-l.   A254 85fr Any single   2.00 1.40

Issued: No. 758, 120fr, 7/21; No. 760, 7/21. No. 760 sold for 1200fr, and contains two booklet panes, containing Nos. 760a-760f, and Nos. 760g-760l. A second variety of No. 760 exists with selling price on cover as 1020fr. Value, complete booklet, $100.

No. 720, 1856 Letter, 1864 Postmark A255

1999, July 2   Litho.   Perf. 13
761 A255   180fr multicolored   4.00 2.25
  a.   Souvenir sheet of 1   12.00 12.00

150th anniv. of French postage stamps, PhilexFrance 99.
No. 761 issued se-tenant with label. No. 761a sold for 500fr.

Frédéric Chopin (1810-49), Composer A256

1999, July 2   Litho.   Perf. 13
762 A256   250fr multicolored   5.50 2.50

Malardé Medical Research Institute, 50th Anniv. A257

1999, Sept. 27
763 A257   400fr multicolored   8.75 3.75

Nudes — A258

Paintings by: 85fr, J. Sorgniard. 120fr, J. Dubrusk. 180fr, C. Deloffre. 250fr, J. Gandouin.

1999, Oct. 14   Litho.   Perf. 13
764 A258   85fr multi   2.10   .75
765 A258   120fr multi   3.25 1.20
766 A258   180fr multi   4.50 1.60
767 A258   250fr multi   6.00 2.25
    Nos. 764-767 (4)   15.85 5.70

Tahiti on the Eve of the Year 2000 — A259

1999, Nov. 10   Litho.   Perf. 13
768 A259   85fr multi   2.50   .75

5th Marquesas Islands Arts Festival — A260

1999, Dec. 10
769 A260   90fr multi   2.00   .80

Year 2000 — A261

85fr, Hands of adult and infant. 120fr, Eye.

2000, Jan. 3   Perf. 13¼x13, 13x13¼
770 A261 85fr multi, vert.   2.50 .75
771 A261 120fr multi   3.25 1.10

New Year 2000 (Year of the Dragon) — A262

2000, Feb. 5   Litho.   Perf. 13x13¼
772 A262 180fr multi   5.50 1.50

Portions of the design were applied by a thermographic process producing a shiny, raised effect.

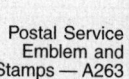

Postal Service Emblem and Stamps — A263

2000, Mar. 15   Litho.   Perf. 13x13¼
773 A263 90fr multi   2.00 .75

First Intl. Tattoo Festival, Raiatea A264

Various tattoos.

2000, Apr. 28   Perf. 13
774 A264 85fr multi   1.90 .70
775 A264 120fr multi   2.75 .95
776 A264 130fr multi   2.90 1.00
777 A264 160fr multi   3.50 1.25
       Nos. 774-777 (4)   11.05 3.90

Beautiful Women of French Polynesia A265

2000, May 30
778 A265 300fr multi   7.50 3.00
a.   Souvenir sheet of 1   12.00 12.00
       No. 778a sold for 500fr.

Traditional Dresses — A266

Denominations: 85fr, 120fr, 160fr, 250fr.

2000, June 21   Litho.   Perf. 13x13¼
779-782 A266   Set of 4   13.50 6.00

Mountains A267

Designs: 90fr, Mts. Aorai and Orohena. 180fr, Mts. Orohena and Aorai.

2000, July 10   Perf. 13x13¼
783-784 A267   Set of 2   6.00 2.60

Traditional Sports — A268

120fr, Fruit carrying. 250fr, Stone lifting, vert.

Perf. 13x13¼, 13¼x13
2000, Sept. 15
785-786 A268   Set of 2   8.25 3.50

Native Woven Crafts — A269

No. 787, Fans. No. 788, Hat.

2000, Oct. 3   Litho.   Perf. 13x13¼
787-788 A269 85fr Set of 2   3.75 1.75

Year of Ancient Tahitian Language Reo Ma'ohi — A270

2000, Nov. 9   Litho.   Perf. 13x13¼
789 A270 120fr multi   2.75 1.20

Portions of the design were applied by a thermographic process producing a shiny, raised effect.

Advent of New Millennium A271

2000, Dec. 28
790 A271 85fr multi   2.50 .90

Central School, Cent. A272

Designs: No. 791, 85fr, Central School. No. 792, 85fr, Paul Gauguin High School.

2001, Jan. 16
791-792 A272   Set of 2   3.75 1.75

New Year 2001 (Year of the Snake) — A273

2001, Jan. 24   Perf. 13¼x13
793 A273 120fr multi   2.75 1.20

Portions of the design were applied by a thermographic process producing a shiny, raised effect.

Landscapes — A274

Designs: 35fr, Vaiharuru Waterfall. 50fr, Vahiria Lake, horiz. 90fr, Hakaui Valley.

Perf. 13¼x13, 13x13¼
2001, Feb. 26   Litho.
794-796 A274   Set of 3   6.00 1.75

Year of the Polynesian Child — A275

2001, Mar. 28   Litho.   Perf. 13x13¼
797 A275 55fr multi   1.25 .55

Polynesian Singers — A276

Designs: 85fr, Eddie Lund. 120fr, Charley Mauu. 130fr, Bimbo. 180fr, Marie Mariteragi and Emma Terangi, horiz.

2001, Apr. 12   Perf. 13¼x13, 13x13¼
798-801 A276   Set of 4   11.50 5.00

Volunteers of the Pacific Batallion, 60th Anniv. — A277

2001, Apr. 21   Perf. 13x13¼
802 A277 85fr multi   2.25 .90

Surfing Waves of Teahupoo A278

2001, May 4
803 A278 120fr multi   2.75 1.20

Internal Autonomy, 17th Anniv. — A279

2001, June 29   Litho.   Perf. 13
804 A279 250fr multi   5.50 2.50
a.   Souvenir sheet of 1   12.00 12.00
       No. 804a sold for 500fr.

Pirogue Racing — A280

Designs: 85fr, Male racers. 120fr, Female racers.

2001, July 12   Perf. 13¼x13
805-806 A280   Set of 2   4.50 2.00
a.   Souvenir sheet, #805-806, imperf. 5.50 5.50
       No. 806a sold for 250fr.

Hardwood Trees — A281

Designs: 90fr, Tou. 130fr, Ati. 180fr, Miro.

2001, Oct. 23   Litho.   Perf. 13x13½
807-809 A281   Set of 3   11.00 8.00

AIDS Prevention A282

2001, Sept. 20 Litho.   Perf. 13x13¼
810 A282 55fr multi   2.75 1.10

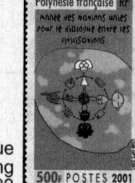

Year of Dialogue Among Civilizations — A283

2001, Oct. 9   Perf. 13
811 A283 500fr multi   11.50 10.00

Perfume Flowers — A284

Designs: 35fr, Gardenia tahitensis. 50fr, Fagraea berteriana. 85fr, Gardenia jasminoides.

2001, Nov. 8   Perf. 13¼x13
812-814 A284   Set of 3   6.00 3.50

Portions of the designs were applied by a thermographic process producing a shiny, raised effect.

Christmas — A285

2001, Dec. 6   Perf. 13x13¼
815 A285 120fr multi   2.75 2.40

New Year 2002 (Year of the Horse) — A286

2002, Feb. 12   Litho.   Perf. 13x13¼
816 A286 130fr multi   3.25 2.60

Portions of the design were applied by a thermographic process producing a shiny, raised effect.

Happy Holidays — A287

Greetings — A288

2002, Feb. 28   Background Colors
817 A287 55fr red   1.25 1.10
818 A288 55fr blue   1.25 1.10
819 A287 85fr blue   1.90 1.75
820 A288 85fr green   1.90 1.75
       Nos. 817-820 (4)   6.30 5.70

10th World Outrigger Canoe Championships A289

Canoe rowers and emblems: 120fr, 180fr.

2002, Mar. 9   Photo.   Perf. 13¼
821-822   A289   Set of 2   6.75 6.25

Sea Urchins — A290

Designs: 35fr, Echinometra sp. 50fr, Heterocentrotus trigonarius. 90fr, Echinothrix calamaris. 120fr, Toxopneustes sp.

2002, Apr. 18   Litho.   Perf. 13x13¼
823-826   A290   Set of 4   6.50 6.25

Blood Donation — A291

2002, May 3   Litho.   Perf. 13¼x13
827   A291   130fr multi   4.00 3.25

2002 World Cup Soccer Championships, Japan and Korea — A292

2002, May 30
828   A292   85fr multi   2.10 1.75

Traditional Sports — A293

Designs: 85fr, Coconut husking. 120fr, Fruit carrying. 250fr, Javelin throwing.

2002, June 27
829-831   A293   Set of 3   10.00 9.00

House of James Norman Hall — A294

2002, July 4   Perf. 13x13¼
832   A294   90fr multi   2.00 1.90

Papeete Market A295

2002, Aug. 30   Litho.   Perf. 13
833   A295   400fr multi   8.75 8.00
a.   Souvenir sheet of 1   11.00 11.00

Amphilex 2002 Stamp Exhibition, Amsterdam (No. 833a). No. 833a sold for 500fr.

Pacific Oceanology Center, Vairoa — A296

Designs: 55fr, Research pond, fish, shrimp, oyster, and flasks. 90fr, Aeriel view of center, fish, shrimp and oyster.

2002, Sept. 26   Photo.   Perf. 13¼
834-835   A296   Set of 2   3.50 2.40

Taapuna Master 2002 Surfing Competition A297

2002, Oct. 21   Litho.   Perf. 13x13¼
836   A297   120fr multi   2.75 2.00

Halophilic Flowers — A298

Designs: 85fr, Hibiscus tiliaceus. 130fr, Scaveola sericea. 180fr, Guettarda speciosa.

2002, Nov. 7
837-839   A298   Set of 3   8.75 6.75

Polynesians at Festivals — A299

Designs: 55fr, Dancers and bus. 120fr, Musicians, vert.

2002, Dec. 5   Perf. 13x13¼, 13¼x13
840-841   A299   Set of 2   3.75 3.00

New Year 2003 (Year of the Ram) — A300

2003, Feb. 1   Litho.   Perf. 13¼x13
842   A300   120fr multi   3.00 2.25

Portions of the design was applied by a thermographic process producing a shiny, raised effect.

Polynesian Women — A301

2003, Mar. 8   Litho.   Perf. 13¼x13
843   A301   55fr multi   1.25 1.00

Waterfalls A302

2003, Apr. 10   Perf. 13
844   A302   330fr multi   7.25 6.00

Old Papeete — A303

Designs: 55fr, Automobiles and buildings, vert. 85fr, Ship in harbor. 90fr, People with bicycles in front of buildings (50x28mm). 120fr, Tree-lined street (50x28mm).

Perf. 13¼x13, 13x13¼, 13
2003, May 15
845-848   A303   Set of 4   7.75 7.00
848a   Souvenir sheet, #845-848   12.00 12.00

No. 848a sold for 550fr.

Fish — A304

2003, June 12   Litho.   Perf. 13
849   A304   460fr multi   9.50 9.50

Portions of the design were applied by a thermographic process producing a shiny, raised effect.

Outrigger Canoes — A305

Designs: No. 850, 85fr, shown. No. 851, 85fr, Three sailors on canoe at sea. No. 852, 85fr, Three sailors on canoe, vert. No. 853, 85fr, Sailor sitting on outrigger, vert.

Perf. 13x13¼, 13¼x13
2003, July 11   Litho.
850-853   A305   Set of 4   7.50 6.50

Firewalkers A306

Orange-banded Cowrie — A307

2003, Aug. 14   Photo.   Perf. 13¼
854   A306   130fr multi   2.50 2.50

Perf. 13x13¼
855   A307   420fr multi   8.50 8.50

Are You Jealous? by Paul Gauguin (1848-1903) A308

2003, Sept. 11   Perf. 13x12¼
856   A308   250fr multi   6.50 3.50

Office of Posts and Telecommunications Emblem — A308a

Type I: "Postes 2003" at right.
Type II: "Postes" only at right.

Serpentine Die Cut 6½ Vert.
2003, Oct. 1   Engr.
Booklet Stamp
Self-Adhesive
856A   A308a   (60fr) blue (type
                II), 2006   10.00 1.00
b.   Booklet pane of 10   100.00
c.   Type I   40.00 24.00
d.   As "c," booklet pane of 10 400.00
e.   As #856A, inscribed
          "Phil@poste"   8.00 1.00
f.   Booklet pane of 10
          #856Ae   80.00

Issued: No. 856Ac, 10/1/03. No. 856A, 2006. No. 856Ae, 2007.
See Nos. 869, 1070-1070B.

French Polynesian Flag — A309

2003, Oct. 1   Litho.   Perf. 13x13¼
857   A309   (60fr) multi   1.50 1.25

Tiki — A310

2003, Oct. 1   Perf. 13¼x13
858   A310   100fr multi   3.00 2.00

Reissued in 2006 on shiny paper with much deeper colors. Values the same.

Flowers — A311

Designs: 90fr, Orchid. 130fr, Rose de porcelain (torch ginger).

2003, Oct. 4   Litho.   Perf. 13x13¼
859-860   A311   Set of 2   6.50 4.50

Portions of the designs were applied by a thermographic process producing a shiny, raised effect.

Bora Bora — A312

Designs: No. 861, 60fr, Painting of Bora Bora by A. Van Der Heyde. No. 862, 60fr, Aerial photograph of Bora Bora.

2003, Nov. 6   Litho.   Perf. 13x13¼
861-862   A312   Set of 2   5.00 2.75

Tiki — A313

2003, Dec. 6   Perf. 13
863   A313   190fr multi   4.00 4.00

Buildings and Palm Trees — A314

2003, Dec. 19   Perf. 13x13¼
864   A314   90fr multi   3.00 1.90

New Year 2004 (Year of the Monkey) — A315

2004, Jan. 22   Litho.   Perf. 13¼x13
865   A315   130fr multi   3.50 3.50

A portion of the design was applied by a thermographic process producing a shiny, raised effect.

Scenes From Everyday Life — A316

Designs: 60fr, Women working with cloth. 90fr, Street scene, vert.

Perf. 13x13¼, 13¼x13

2004, Feb. 13   **Litho.**
866-867 A316   Set of 2   3.25 3.25

Polynesian Woman — A317

2004, Mar. 8   **Perf. 13¼x13**
868 A317 90fr multi   4.00 1.90

Post Emblem Type of 2003
Serpentine Die Cut 6¾ Vert.
2004, Apr. 22   **Engr.**
Booklet Stamp
Self-Adhesive
869 A308a (90fr) red   6.00 2.00
a.   Booklet pane of 10   60.00
b.   As #869, inscribed
    "Phil@poste"   —
c.   Booklet pane of 10 #869b   —
    No. 869 lacks year date.

Polynesian Economic Development — A318

2004, Apr. 23   **Litho.**   **Perf. 13x12¾**
870 A318 500fr multi   11.00 10.00

Arahurahu Marae, Paea A319

2004, Apr. 23
871 A319 500fr multi   11.00 10.00

Vanilla — A320

2004, May 14   **Perf. 13¼x13**
872 A320 90fr multi   2.10 1.90
No. 872 is impregnated with a vanilla scent.

Mobile Snack Bars A321

2004, May 28   **Perf. 13x12¾**
873 A321 300fr multi   6.50 6.25

Handicrafts A322

Designs: No. 874, 60fr, Artisan braiding fibers. No. 875, 60fr, Mother-of-pearl carving. No. 876, 90fr, Artisan carving statue. No. 877, 90fr, Hat.

2004, June 26   **Perf. 13x13¼**
874-877 A322   Set of 4   10.00 6.25
Portion of the designs were applied by a thermographic process producing a shiny, raised effect.

Involvement in South Pacific Area of Office of Posts and Telecommunications A323

Designs: 100fr, Earth, Sun on horizon. 130fr, Satellite dish, building.

2004, July 23   **Photo.**   **Perf. 13¼**
878-879 A323   Set of 2   5.50 4.75

Information Technology and Communications A324

Designs: No. 880, 190fr, Computer keyboard, "@." No. 881, 190fr, Satellite, satellite dish.

2004, Sept. 23   **Litho.**   **Perf. 13¼x13**
880-881 A324   Set of 2   8.00 8.00

Omai, Polynesian Capt. James Cook Brought to England — A325

2004, Oct. 14   **Perf. 13**
882 A325 250fr multi   5.25 5.25

Shell Collectors A326

2004, Nov. 10   **Photo.**   **Perf. 13¼**
883 A326 60fr multi   1.60 1.40
A souvenir sheet of one sold for 250fr. Value $7.

Adenium Obesum — A327

Alpinia Purpurata A328

Ixora Chinensis A329

Gardenia Taitensis — A330

Heliconia Psittacorum A331

Allamanda Blanchetii A332

Otacanthus Caeruleus A333

Hibiscus Rosa-sinensis A334

Euphorba Milii — A335

Asocenda Hybrid of Vanda x Ascocentrum A336

Mussaenda Erythrophylia A337

Bougainvillea Glabra — A338

2004, Nov. 10   **Litho.**   **Perf. 13x13¼**
884   Booklet pane of 6   17.50
a.   A327 90fr multi   2.50 2.50
b.   A328 90fr multi   2.50 2.50
c.   A329 90fr multi   2.50 2.50
d.   A330 90fr multi   2.50 2.50
e.   A331 90fr multi   2.50 2.50
f.   A332 90fr multi   2.50 2.50
885   Booklet pane of 6   17.50 —
a.   A333 90fr multi   2.50 2.50
b.   A334 90fr multi   2.50 2.50
c.   A335 90fr multi   2.50 2.50
d.   A336 90fr multi   2.50 2.50
e.   A337 90fr multi   2.50 2.50
f.   A338 90fr multi   2.50 2.50
   Complete booklet, #884-885   30.00
Complete booklet sold for 1200fr.

Christmas A339

2004, Dec. 17
886 A339 60fr multi   1.60 1.40
A portion of the design was applied by a thermographic process producing a shiny, raised effect.

Bamboo — A340

2005, Feb. 9   **Perf. 13¼x13**
887 A340 130fr multi   3.00 3.00
New Year 2005. A portion of the design was applied by a thermographic process producing a shiny, raised effect.

People and Hut — A341

2005, Feb. 25   **Perf. 13x13¼**
888 A341 90fr multi   2.00 2.00

Polynesian Women — A342

Designs: 60fr, Woman wearing lei. 90fr, Woman wearing flower garland on head and robe.

2005, Mar. 8   **Perf. 13¼x13**
889-890 A342   Set of 2   4.00 3.50

Woman Making Tapa Cloth — A343

2005, Apr. 22   **Perf. 13**
891 A343 250fr multi   5.50 5.50

Tifaifai — A344

2005, Mar. 23   **Litho.**   **Perf. 13x13¼**
892 A344 5fr multi   .25 .25

Angelfish — A345

Designs: No. 893, 90fr, Centropyge bispinosa. No. 894, 90fr, Centropyge loricula. No. 895, 130fr, Centropyge heraldi. No. 896, 130fr, Centropyge flavissima.

2005, May 27   **Litho.**   **Perf. 13x13¼**
893-896 A345   Set of 4   9.50 9.50
896a   Souvenir sheet, #893-896   9.50 9.50
Portions of the designs were applied by a thermographic process producing a shiny, raised effect.

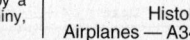

Historic Airplanes — A346

Designs: No. 897, 60fr, TAI DC-8, first jet in Tahiti, 1961. No. 898, 60fr, Pan American Boeing 707, first foreign flight, 1963. No. 899, 100fr, Air France Boeing 707, first Air France flight to Tahiti, 1973. No. 900, 100fr, Air Tahiti Nui Airbus A340-300, first Tahitian airline, 2000.

2005, June 24
897-900 A346 Set of 4   6.50 6.50

Musical Instruments — A347

Designs: No. 901, 130fr, Drum. No. 902, 130fr, Nose flutes, horiz.

2005, July 22   **Perf. 13¼x13, 13x13¼**
901-902 A347 Set of 2   5.50 5.50

Polynesian Landscapes A348

2005, Aug. 26   **Perf. 13**
903 A348 300fr multi   6.25 6.25

Pineapples — A349

Designs: 90fr, Close-up of spines. 130fr, Entire fruit.

2005, Sept. 23 Litho.   **Perf. 13¼x13**
904-905 A349 Set of 2   4.75 4.50

Nos. 904-905 are impregnated with pineapple scent.

Marae A350

Marquesan Tohua A351

2005, Oct. 21   **Perf. 13**
906 A350 500fr multi   10.00 10.00
907 A351 500fr multi   10.00 10.00

Autonomy, 20th Anniv. (in 2004) — A352

2005, Nov. 10   **Perf. 13¼x13**
908 A352 60fr multi   4.00 1.75

No. 908 was printed in France and distributed there in June 2004 but was not sold in French Polynesia until 2005, where it was available from the philatelic bureau upon request, and not through standing orders.

O'Parrey Harbor, Tahiti — A353

2005, Nov. 10 Engr.   **Perf. 13x12½**
909 A353 100fr multi   2.00 2.00

Christmas A354

2005, Dec. 16 Litho.   **Perf. 13x13¼**
910 A354 90fr multi   2.00 2.00

Lotus Flower — A355

Litho. & Silk-screened
2006, Jan. 30   **Perf. 13x13¼**
911 A355 130fr multi   2.60 2.60

A356

Hearts — A357

2006, Feb. 14 Photo.   **Perf. 13**
912 A356 60fr multi   1.25 1.25
913 A357 90fr multi   1.90 1.90

Values are for stamps with surrounding selvage.

Polynesian Women — A358

Woman: 60fr, At water's edge. 90fr, With oil lamp.

2006, Mar. 8 Litho.   **Perf. 13¼x13**
914-915 A358 Set of 2   3.75 3.25

Maupiti A359

2006, Apr. 26 Engr.   **Perf. 13¼x13**
916 A359 500fr multi   11.00 11.00

History of the Marquesas (Washington) Islands — A360

Designs: 60fr, Native man and woman. 130fr, Ships.

2006, May 27 Litho.   **Perf. 13¼x13**
917-918 A360 Set of 2   4.00 4.00
918a   Souvenir sheet, #917-918   4.00 4.00

Diners and Musicians A361

2006, June 6   **Perf. 13**
919 A361 300fr multi   6.50 6.50

Polynesian Ground Dove — A362

Tuamotu Sandpiper A363

2006, June 21   **Perf. 13x13¼**
920 A362 250fr multi   5.25 5.25
921 A363 250fr multi   5.25 5.25

Heiva — A364

Designs: 90fr, Canoe race. 130fr, Stone lifting. 190fr, Dancer.

2006, July 19   **Perf. 13¼x13**
922-924 A364 Set of 3   8.75 8.75

Frangipani Flowers — A365

2006, Aug. 23 Litho.   **Perf. 13x13½**
925 A365 90fr multi   2.25 1.90

No. 925 is impregnated with frangipani scent.

A366

World Tourism Day — A367

Designs: 40fr, Ruins. No. 927, 90fr, Waterfall, woman and child. 130fr, Clothing at open-air market.
No. 929: a, Dancers with yellow skirts. b, Surfer. c, House and palm tree. d, Pearls. e, Fish and coral. f, Islanders in outrigger canoes.
No. 930: a, Woman in hammock. b, Stilt houses. c, Tower and boats. d, Horses and riders. e, Aerial view of island. f, Diver and sting ray.

2006, Sept. 22   **Perf. 13¼x13**
926-928 A366 Set of 3   6.00 6.00

Booklet Stamps
Perf. 13x13¼
929   Booklet pane of 6   15.00 —
a.-f. A367 90fr Any single   2.00 2.00
930   Booklet pane of 6   15.00 —
a.-f. A367 90fr Any single   2.00 2.00
Complete booklet, #929-930   30.00

Complete booklet sold for 1200fr.

Paintings — A368

Designs: 60fr, Javelin Throwing, by Monique Garnier Bissol. 90fr, Market Life, by Albert Luzuy, horiz. 100fr, Island Quay, by Gilbert Chaussoy, horiz. 190fr, Vahine, by Olivier Louzé.

2006, Oct. 25   **Perf. 13**
931-934 A368 Set of 4   9.50 9.50

Engravings by Paul Gauguin (1848-1903) A369

Engravings depicting: 60fr, Women. 130fr, Cow and man carrying items on stick.

2006, Nov. 8 Engr.   **Perf. 13¼**
935-936 A369 Set of 2   4.25 4.25

Children's Art — A370

2006, Dec. 13 Litho.   **Perf. 13x13¼**
937 A370 90fr multi   2.00 2.00

Beach Gear — A371

Designs: 60fr, Flip-flops. 90fr, Surfboards.

Serpentine Die Cut 11x11¼
2007 Photo.   **Self-Adhesive**
938 A371 60fr multicolored   1.25 1.25
a.   Blue tips of die cutting along left side   1.25 1.25
939 A371 90fr multicolored   2.00 2.00
a.   Light blue tips of die cutting along bottom   2.00 2.00

Issued: Nos. 938a, 939a, 1/24; Nos. 938-939, Feb. Nos. 938a and 939a are from the original printing, and are from sheets having adjacent stamps and die cutting that does not extend through the backing paper. Nos. 938-939, which were distributed to the philatelic trade, are from sheets with selvage around each stamp, and with rouletting that extends through the backing paper that allows the stamps to be removed from the sheet more easily.

New Year 2007 (Year of the Pig) — A372

2007, Feb. 19 Litho.   **Perf. 13x13¼**
940 A372 130fr multi   3.50 3.50

Portions of the design were applied by a thermographic process producing a shiny, raised effect.

Painting of Polynesian Woman by Mathius — A373

Photograph of Polynesian Woman by John Stember — A374

2007, Mar. 8   Litho.   Perf. 13¼x13
941 A373 60fr multi   1.50 1.40
        Perf. 13x13¼
942 A374 90fr multi   2.25 2.00

Audit Office, Bicent. — A375

2007, Mar. 17   Engr.   Perf. 13¼x13
943 A375 90fr multi   2.75 2.00

Shells — A376

Designs: 10fr, Lambis crocata pilsbryi. 60fr, Cypraea thomasi. 90fr, Cyrtulus serotinus. 130fr, Chicoreus laqueatus.

2007, Apr. 25   Litho.
944-947 A376 Set of 4   6.75 6.75
947a   Souvenir sheet, #944-947   6.75 6.75

Coconut — A377

2007, May 23   Perf. 13x13¼
948 A377 90fr multi   2.25 2.00
No. 948 is impregnated with a coconut scent.

Ships A378

Designs: No. 949, 250fr, Gunboat Zélée. No. 950, 250fr, Passenger and cargo liner Sagittaire.

2007, June 22   Perf. 13
949-950 A378 Set of 2   12.00 11.50

Heiva Festival — A379

Various women dancers: 65fr, 100fr, 140fr.

2007, July 4   Perf. 13¼x13
951-953 A379 Set of 3   7.50 7.50

Arrival of Kon-Tiki Expedition in Polynesia, 60th Anniv. A380

Litho. & Silk-screened
2007, Aug. 7   Perf. 13
954 A380 300fr multi   7.00 7.00

Arrival of Ship at Papeete Dock A381

2007, Aug. 29   Litho.   Perf. 13
955 A381 190fr multi   4.50 4.50

Old and Modern Photos of Papeete A382

Designs: 65fr, Rue Gauguin, 2007. 100fr, Rue de la Petite-Pologne (now Rue Gauguin), 1907.

2007, Sept. 26
956-957 A382 Set of 2   4.75 4.00

Old Franc and Centime Notes A383

Designs: 65fr, 1919 2-franc Chamber of Commerce note. 140fr, 1942 2-franc note. 500fr, 1943 50-centime note.

2007, Oct. 26   Engr.   Perf. 13
958-960 A383 Set of 3   20.00 17.00

Flowers — A384

Designs: 100fr, Hibiscus. 140fr, Bird-of-paradise (Oiseaux de paradis).

Litho. & Silk-screened
2007, Nov. 8   Perf. 13x13¼
961-962 A384 Set of 2   7.50 7.50

Christmas A385

2007, Dec. 6   Litho.   Perf. 13x13¼
963 A385 100fr multi   2.50 2.50

Marine Life — A386

Designs: 10fr, Himantura fai. 20fr, Tursiops truncatus. 40fr, Megaptera novaeangliae. 65fr, Negaprion acutidens.

2008, Jan. 10
964-967 A386 Set of 4   4.00 4.00

New Year 2008 (Year of the Rat) — A387

2008, Feb. 7   Photo.   Perf. 13¼x13
968 A387 140fr multi   3.75 3.75

Paintings of Women by Bénilde Menghini — A388

Designs: 65fr, Woman picking mangos. 100fr, Women scaling fish.

2008, Mar. 7   Litho.
969-970 A388 Set of 2   4.25 4.25

Paintings by Polynesian Artists — A389

Unnamed paintings depicting: No. 971, 100fr, Boat and reef, by Torea Chan. No. 972, 100fr, Polynesian man, by Raymond Vigor. No. 973, 100fr, Fruit bowl, by Teurarea Prokop, horiz.

2008, Apr. 10   Perf. 13x13¼, 13¼x13
971-973 A389 Set of 3   8.00 8.00

Pouvanaa a Oopa (1895-1977), Politician — A390

2008, May 20   Litho.   Perf. 13
974 A390 500fr multi   13.00 13.00

Island Touring Vehicles — A391

Designs: 65fr, Motor scooter. 100fr, Bus, horiz.

Serpentine Die Cut 11
2008, June 12   Photo.
        Self-Adhesive
975-976 A391 Set of 2   4.50 4.50

Heiva Festival — A392

Designs: 65fr, Woman with floral headdress. 140fr, Tattooed man. 190fr, Girl dancing.

2008, July 16   Litho.   Perf. 13
977-979 A392 Set of 3   11.00 11.00

Sports — A393

Designs: No. 980, 140fr, Table tennis. No. 981, 140fr, Weight lifting.

2008, Aug. 8   Litho.   Perf. 13¼x13
980-981 A393 Set of 2   7.00 7.00

End of Tahiti Nui Expedition, 50th Anniv. A394

2008, Aug. 29   Litho.   Perf. 13
982 A394 190fr multi   4.50 4.50
Eric de Bisschop (1890-1958), expedition leader.

Polynesian Scenes — A395

No. 983: a, Woman crouching. b, Woman under shelter. c, Boat in bay near cliffs. d, Orange flowers. e, Red hibiscus flower. f, Island. g, Woman with headdress. h, White flower. i, Woman with headdress and flower garland. j, Pink flower. k, Islands. l, Bay near mountains.

Serpentine Die Cut 11¼x11
2008, Sept. 8   Self-Adhesive
983   Booklet pane of 12   32.50
a.-d. A395 65fr Any single   1.50 1.50
e.-h. A395 100fr Any single   2.40 2.40
i.-l. A395 140fr Any single   3.25 3.25

Gardenia Taitensis in Bottle of Monoi Oil — A396

2008, Sept. 17   Perf. 13¼x13
984 A396 100fr multi   2.40 2.40
No. 984 is impregnated with a gardenia scent.

Aviation Anniversaries — A397

Designs: No. 985, 250fr, Air service between France and French Polynesia, 50th anniv. No. 986, 250fr, Air Tahiti Nui, 10th anniv.

2008, Oct. 15   Litho.   Perf. 13
985-986 A397 Set of 2   11.00 11.00

French Polynesia Postage Stamps, 50th Anniv. — A398

Designs: 65fr, French Polynesia #185. 100fr, Vignette of French Polynesia #C24. 140fr, French Polynesia #J29.

2008, Nov. 6 Engr. Perf. 13
987-989 A398 Set of 3 6.75 6.75
989a Sheet of 3, #987-989 6.75 6.75

Boater and Dancer — A399

2008, Dec. 5 Litho. Perf. 13x13¼
990 A399 100fr multi 2.25 2.25
Winning design in children's stamp design contest.

Hypolimnas Bolina — A400

Litho. & Silk-screened
2009, Jan. 16 Perf. 13
991 A400 70fr multi 1.50 1.50

Fire Fighters — A401

Designs: 70fr, Fireman on aerial ladder. 140fr, Fireboat.

2009, Feb. 13 Litho. Perf. 13
992-993 A401 Set of 2 4.50 4.50

Paintings of Polynesian Women — A402

Designs: 70fr, Woman, by Myriam Stroken. 100fr, Woman with Guitar, by Stanley Haumani.

2009, Mar. 30 Litho. Perf. 13¼x13
994-995 A402 Set of 2 4.00 4.00

Jacques Brel (1929-78), Singer — A403

Colors: 70fr, Blue. 100fr, Brown.

2009, Apr. 8 Engr.
996-997 A403 Set of 2 4.25 4.25

Pareo Fabric — A404

Pareo in: (70fr), Blue. (100fr), Red. (140fr), Green.

Serpentine Die Cut 11
2009, May 29 Litho.
Self-Adhesive
998-1000 A404 Set of 3 7.25 7.25

Heiva Celebrations of the Past — A405

Various Heiva dancers: 70fr, 100fr, 140fr. 100fr and 140fr are horiz.

Perf. 13¼x13, 13x13¼
2009, June 19
1001-1003 A405 Set of 3 7.50 7.50

First Man on the Moon, 40th Anniv. — A406

2009, July 20 Perf. 13¼
1004 A406 140fr multi 3.50 3.50

Water Activities — A407

Designs: 70fr, Surfing. 100fr, Canoeing (pirogue).

Serpentine Die Cut 11x11¼
2009, Aug. 7 Litho. Self-Adhesive
1005-1006 A407 Set of 2 4.00 4.00

Passion Fruit — A408

2009, Aug. 14 Perf. 13x13¼
1007 A408 100fr multi 2.40 2.40
No. 1007 has a scratch-and-sniff coating on the fruit having a passion fruit scent.

Underwater Scenes — A409

Designs: 70fr, Scuba divers. 100fr, Turtles, horiz. 140fr, Whale, horiz.

Litho. & Silk-screened
Perf. 13¼x13, 13x13¼
2009, Sept. 11
1008-1010 A409 Set of 3 7.75 7.75
1010a Sheet of 3, #1008-1010 7.75 7.75

Fish — A410

No. 1011: a, Chaetodon lunula. b, Chaetodon trichrous. c, Chaetodon ornatissimus. d, Chaetodon pelewensis. e, Pterois antennata. f, Myripristis berndti. g, Priacanthus hamrur. h, Epinephelus polyphekadion. i, Thalassoma lutescens. j, Thalassoma hardwicke. k, Pygoplites diacanthus. l, Coris gaimard.

Serpentine Die Cut 11¼x11
2009, Sept. 11 Self-Adhesive
1011 Booklet pane of 12 31.00
a.-d. A410 70fr Any single 1.75 1.75
e.-h. A410 100fr Any single 2.50 2.50
i.-l. A410 140fr Any single 3.50 3.50

Paintings by Paul Gauguin (1848-1903) A411

Designs: No. 1012, 250fr, Still Life with a Maori Statuette. No. 1013, 250fr, Still Life with Apples, horiz.

2009, Oct. 16 Litho. Perf. 13
1012-1013 A411 Set of 2 12.50 12.50

French Polynesia No. 180 — A412

2009, Nov. 5 Engr.
1014 A412 500fr multi 12.50 12.50

Legend of the Coconut Tree — A413

2009, Dec. 11 Litho. Perf. 13¼x13
1015 A413 190fr multi 4.75 4.75

Papeete Post Office, 150th Anniv. A414

2010, Jan. 20
1016 A414 70fr multi 1.60 1.60

New Year 2010 (Year of the Tiger) — A415

Litho. & Silk-screened
2010, Feb. 15 Perf. 13x13¼
1017 A415 140fr multi 3.25 3.25

Woman and Child — A416

Woman and child: 70fr, Facing forward. 100fr, Facing right.

2010, Mar. 8 Litho. Perf. 13¼x13
1018-1019 A416 Set of 2 4.00 4.00

Tattoos — A417

Tattooed: No. 1020, 250fr, Woman (green background). No. 1021, 250fr, Man (dark red background).

2010, Apr. 6
1020-1021 A417 Set of 2 11.50 11.50

Tiare Apetahi Flower — A418

Litho. & Silk-screened
2010, Apr. 20 Perf. 13x13¼
1022 A418 70fr multi 1.50 1.50

Captain Frederick William Beechey (1796-1856), Explorer — A419

2010, May 5 Litho.
1023 A419 140fr multi 3.00 3.00

Corals — A420

Various corals: 70fr, 100fr, 140fr. 140fr is vert.

Litho. & Silk-screened
2010, June 4 Perf. 13x13¼, 13¼x13
1024-1026 A420 Set of 3 6.50 6.50
1026a Sheet of 3, #1024-1026 6.50 6.50

Heiva Festival — A421

Various festival participants: 100fr, 140fr, 190fr.

2010, July 20 Litho. Perf. 13¼x13
1027-1029 A421 Set of 3 9.50 9.50

Mango — A422

2010, Aug. 8 Perf. 13x13¼
1030 A422 100fr multi 2.25 2.25
No. 1030 has a scratch-and-sniff coating on the fruit having a mango scent.

Phosphate Mining at Makatea, Cent. — A423

Designs: 70fr, Office. 100fr, Train. 140fr, Mining operations.

2010, Aug. 17 Litho. Perf. 13x13¼
1031-1033 A423 Set of 3 6.75 6.75

Honotua Fiber Optic Submarine Cable Project — A424

Serpentine Die Cut 11
2010, Sept. 15   **Photo.**
Self-Adhesive
1034 A424 70fr multi   1.75 1.75

Birds — A425

No. 1035: a, Lori de Kuhl (Kuhl's lorikeet). b, Bécasseau Sanderling (Sanderling). c, Carpophage de la Société (Imperial pigeon). d, Tangara à dos rouge (Crimson-backed tanager). e, Ptilope de Hutton (Rapa fruit dove). f, Sterne huppée (Great crested tern). g, Gygis blanche (White tern). h, Lori Nonnette (Blue lorikeet). i, Chevalier errant (Wandering tattler). j, Martin chasseur des Gambier (Tuamotu kingfisher). k, Fou brun (Brown booby). l, Pluvier fauve (Pacific golden plover).

Litho. & Silk-screened
2010, Sept. 15   **Self-Adhesive**
1035   Booklet pane of 12   28.00
a.-l. A425 100fr Any single   2.25 2.25

Tahiti Faa'a International Airport, 50th Anniv. — A426

2010, Oct. 14   **Litho.**   **Perf. 13**
1036 A426 500fr multi   11.50 11.50

Sphinx Moth — A427

2010, Oct. 14   **Perf. 13x13½**
1037 A427 5fr multi   .25 .25

1948 Air Post Stamps of French Oceania A428

Designs: 70fr, #C17. 100fr, #C18. 140fr, #C19.

2010, Nov. 4   **Engr.**   **Perf. 13**
1038-1040 A428   Set of 3   7.25 7.25

Legend of Moua Puta — A429

2010, Dec. 9   **Litho.**   **Perf. 13x13¼**
1041 A429 70fr multi   1.60 1.60

Crabs — A430

Designs: 20fr, Atergatopsis cf. germanini. 40fr, Zosimus aeneus. 70fr, Carpilius convexus. 100fr, Carpilius maculatus.

2011, Jan. 18
1042-1045 A430   Set of 4   5.25 5.25
1045a   Souvenir sheet of 4, #1042-1045   5.25 5.25

New Year 2011 (Year of the Rabbit) — A431

Litho. & Silk-screened
2011, Feb. 3   **Perf. 13¼x13**
1046 A431 140fr multi   3.25 3.25

Images of Polynesia — A432

No. 1047: a, Canoe race. b, Outrigger canoe. c, Aerial view of islands. d, Fish on reef. e, Pearls. f, Flowers.

Serpentine Die Cut 11¼
2011, Mar. 8   **Litho.**
Self-Adhesive
1047   Booklet pane of 6   14.50
a.-f. A432 100fr Any single   2.40 2.40

Intl. Women's Year — A433

Designs: 70fr, Two women weaving. 100fr, Woman standing.

2011, Mar. 8   **Perf. 13¼x13**
1048-1049 A433   Set of 2   4.00 4.00

Pearl of Tahiti, 50th Anniv. — A434

2011, Apr. 7   **Litho.**
1050 A434 140fr multi   3.50 3.50

Portions of the design were applied by a thermographic process producing a shiny, raised effect.

Transportation of the Past — A435

Designs: 70fr, Truck, 1939. 100fr, Horse-drawn carriages, 1900.

2011, May 17   **Litho.**   **Perf. 13**
1051-1052 A435   Set of 2   4.25 4.25

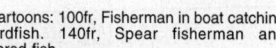

Fishing — A436

Cartoons: 100fr, Fisherman in boat catching swordfish. 140fr, Spear fisherman and speared fish.

Serpentine Die Cut 11
2011, June 22   **Litho.**
Self-Adhesive
1053-1054 A436   Set of 2   5.75 5.75

Carved Items — A437

Designs: 70fr, Coral pestle. 140fr, Basalt tiki. 190fr, Oceania rosewood container with lid, horiz.

2011, July 19   **Perf. 13¼x13, 13x13¼**
1055-1057 A437   Set of 3   9.75 9.75

Orchid — A438

2011, Aug. 17   **Litho.**   **Perf. 13¼x13**
1058 A438 140fr multi   3.25 3.25

No. 1058 is impregnated with an orchid scent.

Islands — A439

Photographs of: 10fr, Rangiroa. 100fr, Ua Pou. 140fr, Bora Bora.

2011, Sept. 27   **Perf. 13x13¼**
1059-1061 A439   Set of 3   5.75 5.75

Marine Birds and Sea Life — A440

No. 1062: a, Birds. b, Bird and whale. c, Dolphin and fish. d, Red striped fish, black and white striped angelfish. e, Blue and yellow striped fish. f, Lionfish, yellow fish. g, Ray. h, Shark. i, Sea turtle, fish, coral. j, Anemonefish, sea anemones. k, Crab. l, Moray eel, coral.

Serpentine Die Cut 11¼x11
2011, Sept. 27   **Self-Adhesive**
1062   Booklet pane of 12   29.00
a.-l. A440 100fr Any single   2.40 2.40

Filming of *Mutiny on the Bounty* in Tahiti, 50th Anniv. A441

2011, Oct. 19   **Perf. 13**
1063 A441 500fr multi   11.50 11.50

Fort Collet, Marquesas Islands — A442

No. 1064 — Engraving of Fort from 1854: a, Buildings without flags. b, Buildings with flags.

2011, Nov. 3   **Engr.**   **Perf. 13**
1064 A442 250fr Horiz. pair, #a-b   11.50 11.50

Ta'aroa, Polynesian God of Creation — A443

2011, Dec. 15   **Litho.**   **Perf. 13¼x13**
1065 A443 70fr multi   1.60 1.60

New Yeart 2012 (Year of the Dragon) — A444

Litho & Silk-screened
2012, Jan. 23   **Perf. 13**
1066 A444 140fr multi   3.25 3.25

Papeete Maritime Station A445

Ships in Papeete Harbor A446

2012, Jan. 27   **Litho.**
1067 A445 70fr multi   1.60 1.60
1068 A446 100fr multi   2.25 2.25

Port of Papeete Authority, 50th anniv.

Food Truck Vendors — A447

Serpentine Die Cut 11
2012, Feb. 22   **Self-Adhesive**
1069 A447 100fr multi   2.25 2.25

Office of Posts and Telecommunications Emblem Type of 2003
Booklet Stamps
Serpentine Die Cut 6¾ Vert.
2012, Feb. 8   **Self-Adhesive**
1070 A308a   5fr red violet   .25 .25
c.   Booklet pane of 10 #1070   1.25
1070A A308a   (75fr) blue, type II   1.75 1.75
d.   Booklet pane of 10 #1070A   17.50
1070B A308a   (100fr) rose   2.25 2.25
e.   Booklet pane of 10 #1070B   22.50
Nos. 1070-1070B (3)   4.25 4.25

Intl. Women's Day — A448

Designs: 70fr, Woman. 100fr, Woman and child.

2012, Mar. 8   **Perf. 13¼x13**
1071-1072 A448   Set of 2   3.75 3.75

Flowers — A449

No. 1073: a, Gingembre à abeilles. b, Reine de Malaisie. c, Opuhi alpinia rose. d, Zedoaire. e, Safran indien. f, Opuhi alpinia orchidée.

2012, Mar. 8   *Serpentine Die Cut 11*
Self-Adhesive
1073   Booklet pane of 6   13.50
  a.-f.   A449 100fr Any single   2.25 2.25

Nudibranchs A450

Designs: 75fr, Glossodoris rufomarginata. 100fr, Elysia ornata. 190fr, Cyerce nigricans.

Litho. & Silk-screened
2012, Apr. 26   *Perf. 13x13¼*
1074-1076   A450   Set of 3   8.00 8.00
1076b   Souvenir sheet of 3,
    #1074-1076   8.00 8.00

Tiurai (1842-1918), Healer — A451

2012, June 18   Litho.   Perf. 13¼x13
1077   A451 75fr multi   1.60 1.60

Tamanu Orange Picking Contest — A452

2012, June 27
1078   A452 75fr multi   1.60 1.60

Heiva Dancer — A453

2012, July 18   *Perf. 13x13¼*
1079   A453 100fr multi   2.10 2.10

Grapefruits A454

2012, Aug. 22
1080   A454 140fr multi   3.00 3.00
  No. 1080 is impregnated with a grapefruit scent.

Airports — A455

  Airport at: 5fr, Bora Bora. 75fr, Tikehau. 100fr, Ua Pou.

2012, Sept. 27
1081-1083   A455   Set of 3   4.00 4.00

Landscapes — A456

No. 1084: a, Moorea. b, Mangareva. c, Rurutu. d, Kauehi. e, Hiva Oa. f, Rapa.

Serpentine Die Cut 11
2012, Sept. 27   **Self-Adhesive**
1084   Booklet pane of 6   13.50
  a.-f.   A456 100fr Any single   2.25 2.25

Turtles in Botanical Gardens, Papeari — A457

Horses and Riders, Marquesas Islands — A458

2012, Oct. 17   *Perf. 13x13¼*
1085   A457 75fr multi   1.60 1.60
1086   A458 100fr multi   2.25 2.25

First Stamps of French Oceania, 120th Anniv. A459

No. 1087: a, "Commerce," horse-drawn carriage, people near shore. b, People on rowboat, "Navigation."

2012, Nov. 8   Engr.   Perf. 13xx13¼
1087   Horiz. pair, #a-b, +
    central label   11.00 11.00
  a.-b.   A459 250fr Either single   5.50 5.50

Season of Matari'i i Ni'a — A460

2012, Nov. 20   Litho.   Perf. 13
1088   A460 75fr multi   1.75 1.75

Matavai Bay — A461

2012, Dec. 13   **Engr.**
1089   A461 500fr blk & gray
    blue   11.00 11.00

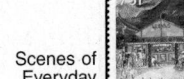

Scenes of Everyday Life — A462

Designs: 75fr, Street scene outside of Quinn's Bar, Papeete. 100fr, Street musicians.

2013, Jan. 2   Litho.   Perf. 13¼x13¼
1090-1091   A462   Set of 2   4.00 4.00

New Year 2013 (Year of the Snake) — A463

Litho. & Silk-screened
2013, Feb. 11   *Perf. 13*
1092   A463 140fr multi   3.00 3.00

Queen Pomare IV (1813-77) — A464

Serpentine Die Cut 11
2013, Feb. 28   **Photo.**
    Self-Adhesive
1093   A464 75fr multi   1.75 1.75

Legend of Tahiri Vahine — A465

  Designs: 75fr, Tahiri Vahine (woman with fan). 100fr, Tahiri Vahine with other women.

2013, Mar. 8   Litho.   Perf. 13¼x13
1094-1095   A465   Set of 2   4.00 4.00
  Intl. Women's Day.

Flora and Fauna — A466

  Designs: 20fr, Lemon (citron). 40fr, Lizard (lézard), horiz. 190fr, Chestnut-breasted mannikin (capuchin).

Litho. & Silk-screened
2013, Apr. 26   Perf. 13¼x13¼, 13x13¼
1096-1098   A466   Set of 3   5.50 5.50
1098a   Souvenir sheet of 3,
    #1096-1098   5.50 5.50

Jacques Brel (1929-78), Singer A467

2013, May 10   Engr.   Perf. 13
1099   A467 500fr multi   11.50 11.50

Fruits — A468

  No. 110: a, Pineapples. b, Mangos. c, Bananas. d, Coconuts. e, Papayas. f, Watermelon.

Litho. & Silk-screened
2013, May 10   Serpentine Die Cut 11
    Self-Adhesive
1100   Booklet pane of 6   13.50
  a.-f.   A468 100fr Any single   2.25 2.25

Marine Life — A469

Designs: 5fr, Starfish. 10fr, Giant clam. 75fr, Sea anemone and clown fish. 100fr, Sea turtle.

Litho. & Silk-screened
2013, June 7   *Perf. 13x13¼*
1101-1104   A469   Set of 4   4.25 4.25
1104a   Souvenir sheet of 4, #1101-
    1104   4.25 4.25

Carousel at Heiva Fairground A470

2013, July 16   Litho.   Perf. 13
1105   A470 100fr multi   2.25 2.25

Jasmine Flowers — A471

2013, Aug. 22   Litho.   Perf. 13x13¼
1106   A471 100fr multi   2.25 2.25
  No. 1106 is impregnated with a jasmine scent.

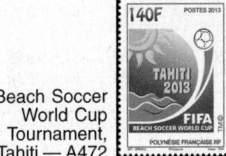

FIFA Beach Soccer World Cup Tournament, Tahiti — A472

2013, Sept. 18   Litho.   Perf. 13¼x13
1107   A472 140fr multi   3.25 3.25

A473   A474

A475   A476

Women
A477   A478

Serpentine Die Cut 11
2013, Sept. 18   **Litho.**
    Self-Adhesive
1108   Booklet pane of 6,
    #1108a-1108f   13.50
  a.   A473 100fr multi   2.25 2.25
  b.   A474 100fr multi   2.25 2.25
  c.   A475 100fr multi   2.25 2.25
  d.   A476 100fr multi   2.25 2.25
  e.   A477 100fr multi   2.25 2.25
  f.   A478 100fr multi   2.25 2.25
  g.   A473 100fr Dated "2015"   1.75 1.75
  h.   A474 100fr Dated "2015"   1.75 1.75
  i.   A475 100fr Dated "2015"   1.75 1.75
  j.   A476 100fr Dated "2015"   1.75 1.75
  k.   A477 100fr Dated "2015"   1.75 1.75

l. A478 100fr Dated "2015" 1.75 1.75
m. Booklet pane of 6, #1180g-1108l 10.50

Issued: Nos. 1108g-1108m, 11/5/15.

Canoes A479

Various canoes: 75fr, 100fr.

2013, Oct. 17 Litho. *Perf. 13*
1109-1110 A479 Set of 2 4.00 4.00

Stock Certificates A480

Stock certificate of: 250fr, Comptoirs Français d'Océanie. 300fr, Compagnie Française de Tahiti.

2013, Nov. 6 Engr. *Perf. 13*
1111-1112 A480 Set of 2 12.50 12.50

Old Automobiles A481

Designs: 75fr, 1915 Ford Model T. 100fr, 1950 Citroen Traction Avant.

2013, Dec. 12 Litho. *Perf. 13*
1113-1114 A481 Set of 2 4.00 4.00

New Banknotes A482

Designs: 10fr, 500-franc banknote. 20fr, 1000-franc banknote. 75fr, 5000-franc banknote. 100fr, 10,000-franc banknote.

Litho. & Silk-Screened

2014, Jan. 20 *Perf. 13*
1115-1118 A482 Set of 4 4.75 4.75
1118a Souvenir sheet of 4, #1115-1118 4.75 4.75

Postal Check Center, 50th Anniv. — A483

2014, Jan. 27 Litho. *Perf. 13x13¼*
1119 A483 75fr multi 1.75 1.75

New Year 2014 (Year of the Horse) — A484

Litho. & Silk-Screened

2014, Jan. 31 *Perf. 13*
1120 A484 140fr multi 3.25 3.25

Intl. Year of Family Farming A485

Designs: 75fr, Woman watering flower garden. 100fr, Farmers, fruits and vegetables.

2014, Feb. 21 Litho. *Perf. 13*
1121-1122 A485 Set of 2 4.00 4.00

Intl. Women's Day — A486

Design: 75fr, Head of woman with floral headdress. 100fr, Woman, vert.

Perf. 13x13¼, 13¼x13

2014, Mar. 7 Litho.
1123-1124 A486 Set of 2 4.00 4.00

Wild Boars — A487

Serpentine Die Cut 11

2014, Apr. 30 Photo.

Self-Adhesive

1125 A487 100fr multi 2.40 2.40

A488

A489

A490

A491

A492

A493

Serpentine Die Cut 11

2014, May 16 Litho.

Self-Adhesive

1126 Booklet pane of 6 13.50
a. A488 100fr multi 2.25 2.25
b. A489 100fr multi 2.25 2.25
c. A490 100fr multi 2.25 2.25
d. A491 100fr multi 2.25 2.25
e. A492 100fr multi 2.25 2.25
f. A493 100fr multi 2.25 2.25

Graffiti art by Enos.

Sharks A494

Designs: 10fr, Carcharhinus melanopterus. 40fr, Sphyrna mokarran. 75fr, Carcharhinus albimarginatus. 190fr, Galeocerdo cuvier.

Litho. & Silk-Screened

2014, June 10 *Perf. 13*
1127-1130 A494 Set of 4 7.25 7.25
1130a Souvenir sheet of 4, #1127-1130 7.25 7.25

Autonomy, 30th Anniv. — A495

2014, June 27 Litho. *Perf. 13¼x13*
1131 A495 75fr multi 1.75 1.75

Woman in Heiva Costume — A496

2014, July 3 Litho. *Perf. 13¼x13*
1132 A496 75fr multi 1.75 1.75

Jar of Honey, Honeybee and Honeycomb A497

2014, Aug. 28 Litho. *Perf. 13x13¼*
1133 A497 100fr multi 2.25 2.25

No. 1133 is impregnated with a honey scent.

Bombardment of Papeete, Cent. — A498

Litho. & Engr.

2014, Sept. 30 *Perf. 13*
1134 A498 300fr multi 6.50 6.50

World War I, cent.

Tiaré Flower — A499

2014, Nov. 6 Litho. *Perf. 13x13¼*
1135 A499 2fr multi .25 .25

Sunset — A500

2014, Nov. 6 Litho. *Perf. 13¼x13*
1136 A500 77fr multi 1.60 1.60

Issuance of French Polynesia No. C30, 50th Anniv. — A501

2014, Nov. 6 Litho. *Perf. 13*
1137 A501 500fr multi 10.50 10.50

Office of Posts and Telecommunications Emblem — A502

Serpentine Die Cut 6¾ Vert.

2014, Nov. 6 Litho.

Booklet Stamps Self-Adhesive

1138 A502 (75fr) deep blue 1.60 1.60
a. Booklet pane of 10 16.00
1139 A502 (100fr) red 2.10 2.10
a. Booklet pane of 10 21.00
b. Dated "2019" 1.90 1.90
c. Booklet pane of 10 #1139b 19.00

Issued: No. 1139b, 11/4/19.

Legend of Pipiri Ma — A503

2014, Dec. 12 Litho. *Perf. 13*
1140 A503 75fr multi 1.50 1.50

Occupations — A504

Designs: 10fr, Underwater spear fisherman. 20fr, Sculptor. 75fr, Masseuse, horiz. 100fr, Seamstress, horiz.

2015, Jan. 29 Litho. *Perf. 13¼x13*
1141 A504 10fr multi .25 .25
1142 A504 20fr multi .40 .40

Perf. 13x13¼

1143 A504 75fr multi 1.50 1.50
1144 A504 100fr multi 1.90 1.90
Nos. 1141-1144 (4) 4.05 4.05

New Year 2015 (Year of the Goat) — A505

Litho. & Silk-Screened

2015, Feb. 19 *Perf. 13*
1145 A505 140fr multi 2.60 2.60

Mama Dolphin at Sea Post Office — A506

2015, Mar. 26 Litho. *Perf. 13x13¼*
1146 A506 75fr multi 1.40 1.40

Translation of Bible Into Tahitian by Henry Nott, 180th Anniv. A507

Discovery of King George Islands by John Byron, 250th Anniv. A508

Litho. & Engr.

2015, May 13 *Perf. 13*
1147 A507 140fr multi 2.60 2.60

Litho.
1148 A508 190fr multi 3.50 3.50
a. Souvenir sheet of 2, #1147-1148 6.25 6.25

Coffee — A509

2015, July 1 Litho. Perf. 13x13¼
1149 A509 100fr multi 1.90 1.90
No. 1149 is impregnated with a coffee scent.

Children's Art — A510

2015, Aug. 1 Litho. Perf. 13¼
1150 A510 1fr multi .25 .25

Orator — A511

2015, Aug. 5 Litho. Perf. 13x13¼
1151 A511 80fr multi 1.50 1.50

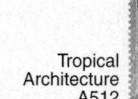

Tropical Architecture A512

Designs: 80fr, Chez Vat Restaurant and Chez Alin Store. 100fr, Houses.

2015, Aug. 14 Litho. Perf. 13x13¼
1152-1153 A512 Set of 2 3.50 3.50

First Flight Between Tahiti and Santiago, Chile, 50th Anniv. — A513

2015, Aug. 31 Litho. Perf. 13x13¼
1154 A513 80fr multi 1.50 1.50

1915 Postcard Depicting Papeete A514

2015, Sept. 29 Litho. Perf. 13¼x13
1155 A514 300fr multi 5.75 5.75

Issuance of Tahiti No. B2, Cent. — A515

Litho. & Engr.
2015, Nov. 5 Perf. 13¼x13
1156 A515 500fr multi 9.00 9.00
a. Souvenir sheet of 1 9.00 9.00

Sponges — A516

No. 1157: a, Clathrina n. sp. b, Dysidea n. sp. c, Haliclona n. sp. d, Ernstia n. sp. e, Stylissa flabelliformis. f, Darwinella n. sp.

Serpentine Die Cut 11
2015, Nov. 5 Litho.
Self-Adhesive
1157 Booklet pane of 6 10.50
a.-f. A516 100fr Any single 1.75 1.75

Papeete Market — A517

Designs: 80fr, Tower and awning. 100fr, Vendors and shoppers, horiz. 140fr, Fish vendors and shoppers, horiz.

2015, Dec. 16 Litho. Perf. 13
1158-1160 A517 Set of 3 6.00 6.00

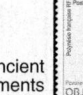

Ancient Adornments A518

Designs: 10fr, Pa'e kea and pavahina. 20fr, Hei ku'a. 80fr, Peue kavi'i.

2016, Jan. 29 Litho. Perf. 13x13¼
1161-1163 A518 Set of 3 2.00 2.00

New Year 2016 (Year of the Monkey) — A519

Litho. & Silk-screened
2016, Feb. 8 Perf. 13
1164 A519 140fr multi 2.60 2.60

Hikers — A520

Serpentine Die Cut 11
2016, Mar. 18 Litho.
Self-Adhesive
1165 A520 100fr multi 1.90 1.90

Ships A521

Designs: 40fr, Queen Elizabeth 2. 80fr, France. 100fr, City of New York.

Litho. & Silk-screened
2016, Apr. 22 Perf. 13
1166-1168 A521 Set of 3 4.25 4.25

Street Art in Papeete by Seth and HTJ — A522

2016, May 27 Litho. Perf. 13
1169 A522 140fr multi 2.60 2.60
World Stamp Show 2016, New York.

Sandalwood A523

2016, June 17 Litho. Perf. 13x13¼
1170 A523 100fr multi 1.90 1.90
No. 1170 is impregnated with a sandalwood scent.

Miss Tahiti Pageant Winners — A524

No. 1171: a, Marie Moua, 1965. b, Moea Amiot, 1975. c, Ruth Manea, 1985. d, Timeri Baudry, 1995. e, Mihimana Sachet, 2005. f, Vaimiti Teiefitu, 2015.

Serpentine Die Cut 11
2016, June 24 Litho.
Self-Adhesive
1171 Booklet pane of 6 11.50
a.-f. A524 100fr Any single 1.90 1.90
Compare type A524 with type A613. See Nos. 1191, 1211, 1230, 1257, 1266.

Famous People Wearing Heiva Costumes — A525

Designs: 80fr, Gilles Hollande. 100fr, Madeleine Moua (1899-1989).

2016, July 11 Litho. Perf. 13¼x13
1172-1173 A525 Set of 2 3.50 3.50

Premna Serratifolia — A526

2016, Aug. 12 Engr. Perf. 13
1174 A526 80fr multi 1.50 1.50

Woman and Plum Blossoms — A527

2016, Oct. 21 Litho. Perf. 13x13¼
1175 A527 300fr multi 5.75 5.75
a. Souvenir sheet of 1 5.75 5.75
PhilaTaipei 2016 International Philatelic Exhibition; Taipei.

Francis Ariioehau Sanford (1912-96), Politician — A528

2016, Nov. 3 Engr. Perf. 13
1176 A528 500fr multi 9.00 9.00

A529

A530

A531

A532

A533

Men — A534

Serpentine Die Cut 11
2016, Nov. 3 Litho.
Self-Adhesive
1177 Booklet pane of 6 10.50
a. A529 100fr multi 1.75 1.75
b. A530 100fr multi 1.75 1.75
c. A531 100fr multi 1.75 1.75
d. A532 100fr multi 1.75 1.75
e. A533 100fr multi 1.75 1.75
f. A534 100fr multi 1.75 1.75

Birds A535

Designs: 80fr, Striated heron (héron strié). 100fr, Southern Marquesan reed warbler (rousserolle des Marquises).

2016, Dec. 9 Litho. Perf. 13
1178-1179 A535 Set of 2 3.25 3.25
1179a Souvenir sheet of 2, #1178-1179 3.25 3.25

Society for Oceania Studies, Cent. — A536

2017, Jan. 2 Litho. Perf. 13¼x13
1180 A536 100fr multi 1.75 1.75

Shells — A537

No. 1181: a, Lentigo lentiginosus. b, Mitra papalis. c, Monoplex aquatilis. d, Conus nussatella. e, Oxymeris maculata. f, Drupa clathrata.

Serpentine Die Cut 11
2017, Jan. 3   Litho.
Self-Adhesive
1181   Booklet pane of 6   10.50
a.-f.   A537 100fr Any single   1.75   1.75

New Year 2017 (Year of the Rooster) — A538

Litho. & Silk-Screened
2017, Jan. 27   Perf. 13
1182 A538 140fr multi   2.60   2.60

Henri Cadousteau (1890-1946), Fighter Pilot, and Salmson 2A2 — A539

Litho. & Silk-Screened
2017, Feb. 17   Perf. 13
1183 A539 80fr multi   1.40   1.40

International Women's Day — A540

Women wearing headdresses: 80fr, 100fr.

2017, Mar. 8   Litho.   Perf. 13¼x13
1184-1185 A540   Set of 2   3.25   3.25

Polynesian Women of the Bounty — A541

2017, Mar. 30   Litho.   Perf. 13
1186 A541 140fr multi   2.50   2.50
See Pitcairn Islands No. 827.

Underwater Scenes — A542

Designs: 10fr, Woman laying on sea floor and ray. 20fr, Diver and school of fish. 80fr, Diver on sea floor and school of fish. 100fr, Woman sitting on sea floor and ray, diff.

2017, May 5   Litho.   Perf. 13x13¼
1187-1190 A542   Set of 4   4.00   4.00
1190a   Souvenir sheet of 4, #1187-1190   4.00   4.00

Miss Tahiti Pageant Winners Type of 2016

No. 1191: a, Sonia Agnieray, 1966. b, Patricia Servonnat, 1976. c, Loana Bohl, 1986. d, Hinerava Hiro, 1996. e, Tehere Pere, 2006. f, Vaea Ferrand, 2016.

Serpentine Die Cut 11
2017, June 23   Litho.
Self-Adhesive
1191   Booklet pane of 6   11.50
a.-f.   A524 100fr Any single   1.90   1.90

Oranges — A543

2017, June 23   Litho.   Perf. 13x13¼
1192 A543 100fr multi   1.90   1.90
No. 1192 is impregnated with an orange scent.

Heiva Celebration Dancers — A544

2017, July 13   Litho.   Perf. 13¼x13
1193 A544 80fr multi   1.60   1.60

Lions Clubs International, Cent. — A545

2017, Aug. 25   Litho.   Perf. 13¼x13
1194 A545 190fr multi   3.75   3.75

Cats and Dogs — A546

No. 1195: a, Cat named Kitty. b, Cat named Gribouille. c, Cat named Caramel. d, Dog named Peanuts. e, Dog named Lolly. f, Dog named Sydney.

Serpentine Die Cut 11
2017, Aug. 25   Litho.
Self-Adhesive
1195   Booklet pane of 6   12.00
a.-f.   A546 100fr Any single   2.00   2.00

Navigators and Boats — A547

Boat and: 40fr, Rodolphe Tuko Harry Williams (1920-86). 100fr, Francis Puara Cowan (1926-2009).

2017, Sept. 27   Engr.   Perf. 13
1196-1197 A547   Set of 2   2.75   2.75

Hina Natua, 2017 Miss Heiva — A548

2017, Oct. 24   Litho.   Perf. 13
1198 A548 300fr multi   6.00   6.00
Brasilia 2017 International Philatelic Exhibition, Brasilia, Brazil.

Halloween A549

Serpentine Die Cut 11
2017, Oct. 27   Litho.
Self-Adhesive
1199 A549 80fr multi   1.60   1.60

Fautaua Waterfall — A550

2017, Nov. 9   Engr.   Perf. 13
1200   A550 500fr turq blue & slate grn   10.00   10.00
Souvenir Sheet
Litho.
Imperf
1200A A550 500fr multi   10.00   10.00
Pierre Loti (1850-1923), writer.

French Polynesia No. 527 — A551

2017, Dec. 15   Litho.   Perf. 13
1201 A551 80fr multi   1.60   1.60

Air Tahiti, 60th Anniv. — A552

Designs: 10fr, Sunderland Bermuda. 20fr, Douglas DC-4. 40fr, ATR 72-500. 80fr, ATR 72-600.

2018, Jan. 11   Litho.   Perf. 13x13¼
1202-1205 A552   Set of 4   3.25   3.25

New Year 2018 (Year fo the Dog) — A553

Litho. & Silk-Screened
2018, Feb. 16   Perf. 13
1206 A553 140fr multi   3.00   3.00
No. 1206 was printed in sheets of 10 + central label.

International Women's Day — A554

2018, Mar. 8   Litho.   Perf. 13¼x13
1207 A554 80fr multi   1.75   1.75

Arrival of Louis-Antoine de Bougainville (1729-1811) in Tahiti, 250th Anniv. — A555

2018, Apr. 6   Engr.   Perf. 12¾x13
1208 A555 250fr mar & dp bluish grn   5.00   5.00

Pointe Vénus Lighthouse, 150th Anniv. — A556

2018, Apr. 23   Litho.   Perf. 13
1209 A556 80fr multi   1.60   1.60

Bird and Kite — A557

Serpentine Die Cut 11
2018, May 25   Litho.
Self-Adhesive
1210 A557 100fr multi   2.00   2.00

Miss Tahiti Pageant Winners Type of 2016

No. 1211: a, Pageant emblem. b, Timia Teriiero, 1977. c, Meari Manoi, 1987. d, Hinano Teanotoga, 1997. e, Taoahere Richmond, 2007. f, Turouru Temorere, 2017.

Serpentine Die Cut 11
2018, June 1   Litho.
Self-Adhesive
1211   Booklet pane of 6   12.00
a.-f.   A524 100fr Any single   2.00   2.00

Basil — A558

2018, June 22   Litho.   Perf. 13¼x13
1212 A558 80fr multi   1.60   1.60
No. 1212 is impregnated with a basil scent.

Polynesian Canoes — A559

2018, July 16   Litho.   Perf. 13x13¼
1213 A559 80fr multi   1.60   1.60

Milan Rastislav Stefánik (1880-1919), Slovak General and His Tahitian Astronomical Observatory
A560

2018, Aug. 17 Litho. Perf. 13
1214 A560 140fr multi 2.75 2.75
Praga 2018 International Philatelic Exhibition, Prague.

Self-portrait with Yellow Christ, by Paul Gauguin (1848-1903) — A561

2018, Sept. 21 Litho. Perf. 13
1215 A561 300fr multi 6.00 6.00
a. Souvenir sheet of 1 ...... 6.00 6.00

Disappearance of Alain Colas (1943-78), Sailboat Racer, 40th Anniv. — A562

2018, Oct. 26 Litho. Perf. 13x13¼
1216 A562 100fr multi 1.90 1.90

Babies — A563

No. 1217 — Names at lower right: a, Tahi. b, Hinarani. c, Nainoa. d, Imianau. e, Tevaihereiti. f, Kihani.

Serpentine Die Cut 11
2018, Oct. 26 Litho.
Booklet Stamps Self-Adhesive
1217 Booklet pane of 6 ...... 11.50
a.-f. A563 100fr Any single .. 1.90 1.90

French Polynesia No. 184 — A564

2018, Nov. 8 Engr. Perf. 13
1218 A564 190fr multi 3.75 3.75
First stamps inscribed "Polynésie Française," 60th anniv.

End of World War I, Cent. — A565

2018, Nov. 8 Engr. Perf. 13
1219 A565 500fr multi 9.50 9.50
a. Souvenir sheet of 1 ...... 9.50 9.50

Taputapuatea UNESCO World Heritage Site — A566

2018, Dec. 14 Litho. Perf. 13x13¼
1220 A566 100fr multi 1.90 1.90

Endangered Birds — A567

Designs: 10fr, Pseudobulweria rostrata. 80fr, Pomarea nigra, vert.

Perf. 13x13¼, 13¼x13
2019, Jan. 25 Litho.
1221-1222 A567 Set of 2 ..... 1.75 1.75

New Year 2019 (Year of the Pig) — A568

Litho. & Silk-Screened
2019, Feb. 5 Perf. 13
1223 A568 140fr multi 2.75 2.75

International Women's Day — A569

Designs: 80fr, Woman and palm trees. 100fr, Woman with flower in hair.

2019, Mar. 8 Litho. Perf. 13¼x13
1224-1225 A569 Set of 2 ..... 3.50 3.50

Tupaia (c. 1725-70), Navigator, Capt. James Cook (1728-79), and Ship, Endeavour
A570

2019, Apr. 12 Engr. Perf. 13
1226 A570 250fr multi 4.75 4.75
Cook's arrival in Tahiti, 250th anniv.

Marine Life in Protected Reserve
A571

2019, May 24 Litho. Perf. 13
1227 A571 100fr multi 1.90 1.90

Campaign Against Obesity — A572

No. 1228: a, Lychee fruit on lollipop stick. b, Mango in ice cream cup. c, Pineapple surrounding soda can. d, Watermelon slice on ice cream stick. e, Peeled banana in candy wrapper. f, Coconut surrounding bottle and straw.

Serpentine Die Cut 11
2019, May 24 Litho.
Booklet Stamps Self-Adhesive
1228 Booklet pane of 6 ...... 11.50
a.-f. A572 100fr Any single .. 1.90 1.90

Office of Posts and Telecommunications Emblem — A573

Serpentine Die Cut 6¾ Vert.
2019 Self-Adhesive Litho.
Booklet Stamp
1229 A573 (80fr) deep ultra .. — —
a. Booklet pane of 10 ...... — —
b. Dated "2020" .... — —
c. Booklet pane of 10 #1229b .. — —
Issued: Nos. 1229b, 1229c, 9/21/20.

Miss Tahiti Pageant Winners Type of 2016

No. 1230: a, Viola Teriitahi, 1968. b, Moeata Schmouker, 1978. c, Teumrre Pater, 1988. d, Mareva Galanter, 1998. e, Hinatea Boosie, 2008. f, Vaimalama Chaves, 2018.

Serpentine Die Cut 11
2019, June 7 Litho.
Self-Adhesive
1230 Booklet pane of 6 ...... 11.50
a.-f. A524 100fr Any single .. 1.90 1.90

Cantaloupe A574

2019, June 7 Litho. Perf. 13x13¼
1231 A574 140fr multi 2.75 2.75
No. 1231 is impregnated with a cantaloupe scent.

Artistic Conservatory of French Polynesia, 40th Anniv. — A575

Serpentine Die Cut 11
2019, July 19 Litho.
Self-Adhesive
1232 A575 80fr multi 1.50 1.50

André Japy (1904-74), Aviator A576

2019, Aug. 23 Litho. Perf. 13
1233 A576 100fr multi 1.90 1.90

General Milan Stefánik (1880-1919), Builder of Astronomical Observatory in French Polynesia — A577

2019, Sept. 6 Litho. Perf. 13
1234 A577 140fr multi 2.60 2.60

Fish — A578

Designs: 40fr, Ruvettus pretiosus. 80fr, Pontinus macrocephalus. 100fr, Etelis carbunculus.

Litho. & Silk-Screened
2019, Oct. 18 Perf. 13x13¼
1235-1237 A578 Set of 3 ..... 4.25 4.25
1237a Souvenir sheet of 3, #1235-1237 ...... 4.25 4.25

Polynesia, the Sky, by Henri Matisse (1869-1954) A579

Polynesia, the Sea, by Matisse A580

2019, Nov. 7 Litho. Perf. 13
1238 A579 100fr multi 1.90 1.90
1239 A580 100fr multi 1.90 1.90

Cargo Vessel Hawaiki Nui A581

Litho. & Engr.
2019, Nov. 7 Perf. 13½x13
1240 A581 500fr multi 9.25 9.25
a. Souvenir sheet of 1 ...... 9.25 9.25
See St. Pierre & Miquelon No. 1084.

Statue of God A'a — A582

2019, Dec. 13 Litho. Perf. 13¼x13
1241 A582 80fr multi 1.50 1.50

New Year 2020 (Year of the Rat) — A583

Litho. & Silk-Screened
2020, Jan. 24 Perf. 13
1242 A583 140fr multi 2.60 2.60

Snails — A584

Designs: 10fr, Partula hyalina. 100fr, Partula nodosa.

2020, Feb. 21 Litho. Perf. 13x13¼
1243-1244 A584 Set of 2 ..... 2.10 2.10
1244a Souvenir sheet of 2, #1243-1244 ...... 2.10 2.10

International Women's Day — A585

Designs: 80fr, Maadi Gobrait (1909-80), Nurse for Free French Forces in World War II.

100fr, Tuianu Le Gayic (1922-95), mayor and founder of women's organizations.

2020, Mar. 6   Litho.   *Perf. 13¼x13*
1245-1246   A585   Set of 2   3.25   3.25

Bearer Certificates
A586

Certificate for: 20fr, French-Czechoslovakian Oceanic Islands Society. 80fr, Agricultural Society of Mopélia.

2020, June 26   Litho.   *Perf. 13x13¼*
1247-1248   A586   Set of 2   1.90   1.90

First day covers of Nos. 1247-1248 have additional cancels with the originally planned day of issue of Apr. 24, 2020, because the issuance of the stamps was delayed because of the coronavirus pandemic.

Island
Scenes — A587

Designs: 5fr, Canoe off of Raivavae. 80fr, Horse on Nuku Hiva. 100fr, Bora Bora.

2020, July 31   Litho.   *Perf. 13x13¼*
1249-1251   A587   Set of 3   3.75   3.75

First day covers of Nos. 1249-1251 have additional cancels with the originally planned day of issue of June 26, 2020, because the issuance of the stamps was delayed because of the coronavirus pandemic.

Women Wearing Protective Face Masks to Prevent Spread of Coronavirus A588

2020, July 31   Litho.   *Perf. 13x13¼*
1252   A588   80fr multi   1.60   1.60

Bananas — A589

2020, Aug. 20   Litho.   *Perf. 13x13¼*
1253   A589   100fr multi   2.00   2.00

First day covers of No. 1253 have an additional cancel with the originally planned day of issue of June 26, 2020, because the issuance of the stamps was delayed because of the coronavirus pandemic. No. 1253 is impregnated with a banana scent.

Joe Dassin (1938-80), Singer — A590

2020, Aug. 20   Litho.   *Perf. 13*
1254   A590   100fr multi   2.00   2.00

Ville d'Amiens, Badge of 1st Free French Division A591

2020, Sept. 2   Litho.   *Perf. 13*
1255   A591   190fr multi   3.75   3.75

Recognition of Free French Forces by French Polynesian governmental authorities, 80th anniv.

Abandoned Hotel
Tahara'a — A592

2020, Oct. 23   Litho.   *Perf. 13¼x13*
1256   A592   90fr multi   1.75   1.75

Miss Tahiti Pageant Winners Type of 2016

No. 1257: a, Dominique Tepava, 1969. b, Thilda Fuller, 1979. c, Myriam Tuheiava, 1989. d, Manoa Fruge, 1999. e, Puahinano Bonno, 2009. f, Matahari Bousquet, 2019.

Serpentine Die Cut 11

2020, Nov. 4   Litho.

Self-Adhesive
1257   Booklet pane of 6   12.00
a.-f.   A524 100fr Any single   2.00   2.00

Ballons Montes (Letters Sent From Paris by Balloons) of the Franco-Prussian War, 150th Anniv. — A593

Litho. & Engr.

2020, Nov. 4   *Perf. 13*
1258   A593   500fr multi   10.00   10.00
a.   Souvenir sheet of 1   10.00   10.00

Tutepoganui
Mask — A594

2020, Dec. 18   Litho.   *Perf. 13¼x13*
1259   A594   100fr multi   2.10   2.10

Arrival of Ferdinand Magellan at the Tuamotu Archipelago, 500th Anniv. A595

Litho. & Engr.

2021, Jan. 22   *Perf. 13*
1260   A595   500fr multi   10.00   10.00
a.   Souvenir sheet of 1   10.00   10.00

New Year 2021 (Year of the Ox) — A596

Litho. & Silk-Screened
2021, Feb. 12   *Perf. 13*
1261   A596   140fr multi   3.00   3.00

International Women's Day — A597

2021, Mar. 8   Litho.   *Perf. 13¼x13*
1262   A597   110fr multi   2.25   2.25

Palm Trees — A598

Designs: 10fr, Pelagodoxa henryana. 110fr, Pritchardia mitiaroana.

2021, Apr. 9   Litho.   *Perf. 13¼x13*
1263-1264   A598   Set of 2   2.50   2.50

Tahiti-Faa'a Airport, 60th Anniv.
A599

2021, May 4   Litho.   *Perf. 13*
1265   A599   100fr multi   2.10   2.10

Miss Tahiti Pageant Winners Type of 2016

No. 1266: a, Teura Teuira, 1960. b, Maire Tehei, 1970. c, Tatiana Teraiamano, 1980. d, Mareva Georges, 1990. e, Vanina Bea, 2000. f, Poehere Hutihuti Wilson, 2010.

Serpentine Die Cut 11

2021, June 4   Litho.

Self-Adhesive
1266   Booklet pane of 6   12.00
a.-f.   A524 100fr Any single   2.00   2.00

Woman and Gardenias — A600

2021, June 25   Litho.   *Perf. 13¼x13*
1267   A600   100fr multi   2.00   2.00

No. 1267 is impregnated with a gardenia scent.

Fire Walkers — A601

2021, July 16   Litho.   *Perf. 13¼x13*
1268   A601   110fr multi   2.25   2.25

Statue of God Rao — A602

2021, Aug. 20   Litho.   *Perf. 13¼x13*
1269   A602   100fr multi   2.00   2.00

Obverse and Reverse of 2021 Coins With New Designs — A603

No. 1270: a, 5-franc coin. b, 10-franc coin. c, 20-franc coin. d, 50-franc coin. e, 100-franc coin. f, 200-franc coin.

Serpentine Die Cut 11

2021, Sept. 1   Litho.

Self-Adhesive
1270   Booklet pane of 6   12.00
a.-f.   A603 100fr Any single   2.00   2.00

Islands — A604

Designs: 30fr, Maupiti. 100fr, Mangareva. 110fr, Fakarava.

2021, Sept. 24   Litho.   *Perf. 13x13¼*
1271-1273   A604   Set of 3   4.75   4.75

Hotel Maeva Beach — A605

2021, Oct. 22   Litho.   *Perf. 13x13¼*
1274   A605   110fr multi   2.25   2.25

Three Tahitians, Painting by Paul Gauguin (1848-1903) — A606

Litho. & Silk-Screened
2021, Nov. 4   *Perf. 13*
1275   A606   500fr multi   9.50   9.50
a.   Souvenir sheet of 1   9.50   9.50

Arrival of Gauguin in Papeete, 130th anniv.

Pomare II (c. 1782-1821), King of Tahiti — A607

2021, Dec. 17   Litho.   *Perf. 13¼x13*
1276   A607   100fr multi   1.90   1.90

Endangered Plants — A608

Designs: 100fr, Pacifigeron rapensis. 130fr, Erythrina tahitensis.

2022, Jan. 28   Litho.   *Perf. 13¼x13*
1277-1278   A608   Set of 2   4.50   4.50

New Year 2022 (Year of the Tiger) — A609

Litho. & Silk-Screened
2022, Feb. 1   *Perf. 13*
1279   A609   140fr multi   2.75   2.75

International Women's Day — A610

Designs: 20fr, Woman with fishing spear and catch. 130fr, Mother and daughter.

2022, Mar. 8   Litho.   *Perf. 13¼x13*
1280-1281   A610   Set of 2   2.75   2.75

Charles Darwin (1809-82), Naturalist A611

Litho. & Silk-Screened
2022, Apr. 19   *Perf. 13x12¾*
1282 A611 500fr multi   9.00 9.00
  a.   Souvenir sheet of 1   9.00 9.00

Polynesian Expedition of Jacob Roggeveen (1659-1729), 300th Anniv. — A612

2022, June 2   **Litho.**   *Perf. 13x13¼*
1283 A612 100fr multi   1.90 1.90

Miss Tahiti Pageant Winners — A613

No. 1284: a, Tahia Piehi, 1961. b, Jeanne Burns, 1971. c, Maimiti Kinnander, 1981. d, Hina Sarciaux, 1991. e, Ravanui Teri-itaumihau, 2001. f, Rauata Temauri, 2011. g, Tumateata Buisson, 2021. h, Pageant emblem.

Serpentine Die Cut 11
2022, June 2   **Litho.**
Self-Adhesive
1284   Booklet pane of 8   15.50
 a.-h.   A613 100fr Any single   1.90 1.90

Compare type A613 with type A524.

Battle of Bir Hakeim, 80th Anniv. — A614

2022, June 10   **Litho.**   *Perf. 13x13¼*
1285 A614 130fr multi   2.25 2.25

Heiva Dancers — A615

Designs: No. 1286, 130fr, Coco Hotahota (1941-2020). No. 1287, 130fr, Louise Kimitete (1940-2020).

2022, July 8   **Litho.**   *Perf. 13x13¼*
1286-1287 A615   Set of 2   4.50 4.50

Lemons — A616

2022, Aug. 26   **Litho.**   *Perf. 13x13¼*
1288 A616 130fr multi   2.25 2.25
No. 1288 is impregnated with a lemon scent.

Cetacean Sanctuary, 20th Anniv. — A617

Flag of French Polynesia and: 10fr, Stenella longirostris. 100fr, Megaptera novaeangliae.

2022, Sept. 23   **Litho.**   *Perf. 13x13¼*
1289-1290 A617   Set of 2   1.90 1.90

SEMI-POSTAL STAMPS

Nos. 55 and 26 Surcharged in Red

1915   **Unwmk.**   *Perf. 14x13½*
B1   A1 10c + 5c red   32.50 32.50
 a.   "e" instead of "c"   87.50 87.50
 b.   Inverted surcharge   225.00 225.00
 c.   Double surcharge   525.00 525.00
B2   A2 10c + 5c rose & org   12.50 12.50
 a.   "e" instead of "c"   65.00 65.00
 b.   "c" inverted   65.00 65.00
 c.   Inverted surcharge   300.00 300.00
 d.   As "a," inverted surcharge   400.00
 e.   As "b," inverted surcharge   400.00

Surcharged in Carmine

B3   A2 10c + 5c rose & org   5.50 5.50
 a.   "e" instead of "c"   45.00 45.00
 b.   Inverted surcharge   200.00 200.00
 c.   Double surcharge   200.00 200.00
 d.   As "a," inverted surcharge   325.00

Surcharged in Carmine

1916
B4   A2 10c + 5c rose & org   5.50 5.50

Curie Issue
Common Design Type
1938   **Engr.**   *Perf. 13*
B5   CD80 1.75fr + 50c brt ultra   20.00 20.00

French Revolution Issue
Common Design Type
1939   **Photo.**
Name and Value Typo. in Black
B6   CD83   45c + 25c grn   17.50 17.50
B7   CD83   70c + 30c brn   17.50 17.50
B8   CD83   90c + 35c red org   17.50 17.50
B9   CD83 1.25fr + 1fr rose pink   17.50 17.50
B10   CD83 2.25fr + 2fr dk grn   17.50 17.50
   Nos. B6-B10 (5)   87.50 87.50
   Set, never hinged   145.00

Catalogue values for unused stamps in this section, from this point to the end of the section, are for Never Hinged items.

Common Design Type and

Marine Officer SP1   "L'Astrolabe" SP2

1941   **Photo.**   *Perf. 13½*
B11   SP1   1fr + 1fr red   3.50
B12   CD86 1.50fr + 3fr maroon   3.50
B12A   SP2   2.50fr + 1fr blue   3.50
   Nos. B11-B12A (3)   10.50

Nos. B11-B12A were issued by the Vichy government in France, and were not placed on sale in French Polynesia.

Nos. 125A-125B Srchd. in Black or Red

1944   **Engr.**   *Perf. 12½x12*
B12B   50c + 1.50fr on 2.50fr dp blue (R)   1.75
B12C   + 2.50fr on 1fr green   1.75
Colonial Development Fund.
Nos. B12B-B12C were issued by the Vichy government in France, but were not placed on sale in French Polynesia.

Red Cross Issue
Common Design Type
1944   **Photo.**   *Perf. 14½x14*
B13   CD90 5fr + 20fr pck blue   2.00 1.60
The surtax was for the French Red Cross and national relief.

Tropical Medicine Issue
Common Design Type
1950, July 17   **Engr.**   *Perf. 13*
B14   CD100 10fr + 2fr dk bl grn & dk grn   10.50 8.00
The surtax was for charitable work.

AIR POST STAMPS

Seaplane in Flight — AP1

Perf. 13½
1934, Nov. 5   **Unwmk.**   **Photo.**
C1   AP1 5fr green   1.25 1.25
For overprint see No. C2.
For Type AP1 without "RF," see Nos. C1A-C1D.

Type of 1934 without "RF" and

Beach Scene — AP1a

Perf. 13½, 13 (#C1E)
1944   **Photo, Engr. (#C1E)**
C1A   AP1   5fr green   .70
C1B   AP1   10fr black   1.00
C1C   AP1   20fr orange   1.10
C1D   AP1   50fr gray blue   1.50
C1E   AP1a 100fr turquoise blue   2.00
   Nos. C1A-C1E (5)   6.30

Nos. C1A-C1E were issued by the Vichy government in France, but were not placed on sale in French Polynesia.

Catalogue values for unused stamps in this section, from this point to the end of the section, are for Never Hinged items.

No. C1 Overprinted in Red

1941
C2   AP1 5fr green   7.25 4.75

Common Design Type
1942   *Perf. 14½x14*
C3   CD87   1fr dark orange   .90 .65
C4   CD87 1.50fr bright red   .95 .70
C5   CD87   5fr brown red   1.25 .95
C6   CD87   10fr black   1.90 1.40
C7   CD87   25fr ultra   2.75 2.10
C8   CD87   50fr dark green   3.00 2.10
C9   CD87 100fr plum   3.00 2.10
   Nos. C3-C9 (7)   13.75 10.00

Victory Issue
Common Design Type
1946, May 8   **Engr.**   *Perf. 12½*
C10   CD92 8fr dark green   2.75 2.00

Chad to Rhine Issue
Common Design Types
1946, June 6
C11   CD93   5fr red orange   2.10 1.60
C12   CD94   10fr dk olive bis   2.10 1.60
C13   CD95   15fr dk yellow grn   2.10 1.60
C14   CD96   20fr carmine   2.75 2.10
C15   CD97   25fr dk rose violet   4.00 3.00
C16   CD98   50fr black   4.50 3.50
   Nos. C11-C16 (6)   17.55 13.40

Shearwater and Moorea Landscape AP2

Fishermen AP3

Shearwater over Maupiti Shoreline AP4

1948, Mar. 1   **Unwmk.**   *Perf. 13*
C17   AP2   50fr red brown   30.00 11.00
C18   AP3 100fr purple   24.00 8.00
C19   AP4 200fr blue green   52.50 17.50
   Nos. C17-C19 (3)   106.50 36.50

UPU Issue
Common Design Type
1949
C20   CD99 10fr deep blue   20.00 15.00

Gauguin's "Nafea faaipoipo" — AP5

1953, Sept. 24
C21   AP5 14fr dk brn, dk gray grn & red   80.00 65.00
50th anniv. of the death of Paul Gauguin.

Liberation Issue
Common Design Type
1954, June 6
C22   CD102 3fr dk grnsh bl & bl grn   10.00 8.00

Bahia Peak, Borabora AP6

1955, Sept. 26   **Unwmk.**   *Perf. 13*
C23   AP6 13fr indigo & blue   10.00 5.50

Mother-of-Pearl Artist — AP7

Designs: 50fr, "Women of Tahiti," Gauguin, horiz. 100fr, "The White Horse," Gauguin. 200fr, Night fishing at Moorea, horiz.

1958, Nov. 3   Engr.   Perf. 13
C24 AP7 13fr multicolored   13.00   4.50
C25 AP7 50fr multicolored   12.00   4.50
C26 AP7 100fr multicolored   20.00   7.25
C27 AP7 200fr lilac & slate   40.00 21.00
      Nos. C24-C27 (4)   85.00 37.25

Airport, Papeete
AP8

1960, Nov. 19
C28 AP8 13fr rose lil, vio, & yel grn   3.50   2.40

Telstar Issue
Common Design Type
1962, Dec. 5   Perf. 13
C29 CD111 50fr red lil, mar & vio bl   11.50   8.00

Tahitian Dancer — AP10

1964, May 14   Photo.   Perf. 13
C30 AP10 15fr multicolored   4.75   2.00

Map of Tahiti and Free French Emblems
AP11

1964, July 10   Unwmk.
C31 AP11 16fr multicolored   15.00   9.00
      Issued to commemorate the rallying of French Polynesia to the Free French cause.

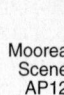
Moorea Scene AP12

1964, Dec. 1   Litho.   Perf. 13
C32 AP12 23fr multicolored   9.50   4.00

ITU Issue
Common Design Type
1965, May 17   Engr.   Perf. 13
C33 CD120 50fr vio, red brn & bl   80.00 52.50

Paul Gauguin AP13

Design: 25fr, Gauguin Museum (stylized). 40fr, Primitive statues at Gauguin Museum.

1965   Engr.   Perf. 13
C34 AP13 25fr olive green   7.50   4.50
C35 AP13 40fr blue green   15.00   8.00
C36 AP13 75fr brt red brown   20.00 15.00
      Nos. C34-C36 (3)   42.50 27.50
      Opening of Gauguin Museum, Papeete.
      Issued: 25fr, 75fr, 6/13. 40fr, 11/7.

Skin Diver with Spear Gun
AP14

1965, Sept. 1   Engr.   Perf. 13
C37 AP14 50fr red brn, dl bl & dk grn   90.00 55.00
      World Championships in Underwater Fishing, Tuamotu Archipelago, Sept. 1965.

Painting from a School Dining Room — AP15

1965, Nov. 29
C38 AP15 80fr brn, bl, dl bl & red   22.50 17.50
      School Canteen Program.

Radio Tower, Globe and Palm — AP16

1965, Dec. 29   Engr.   Perf. 13
C39 AP16 60fr org, grn & dk brn   19.00 15.00
      50th anniversary of the first radio link between Tahiti and France.

French Satellite A-1 Issue
Common Design Type
Designs: 7fr, Diamant Rocket and launching installations. 10fr, A-1 satellite.

1966, Feb. 7
C40 CD121 7fr choc, dp grn & lil   6.75   6.00
C41 CD121 10fr lil, dp grn & dk brn   6.75   6.00
   a.   Pair, #C40-C41 + label   14.00 14.00

French Satellite D-1 Issue
Common Design Type
1966, May 10   Engr.   Perf. 13
C42 CD122 20fr multicolored   7.00   4.75

Papeete Harbor AP17

1966, June 30   Photo.   Perf. 13
C43 AP17 50fr multicolored   15.00 11.00

"Vive Tahiti" by A. Benichou AP18

1966, Nov. 28   Photo.   Perf. 13
C44 AP18 13fr multicolored   11.00   6.50

Explorer's Ship and Canoe AP19

Designs: 60fr, Polynesian costume and ship. 80fr, Louis Antoine de Bougainville, vert.

1968, Apr. 6   Engr.   Perf. 13
C45 AP19 40fr multicolored   8.75   3.25
C46 AP19 60fr multicolored   11.50   6.50
C47 AP19 80fr multicolored   14.50   8.75
   a.   Souv. sheet, #C45-C47   160.00 160.00
      Nos. C45-C47 (3)   34.75 18.50
      200th anniv. of the discovery of Tahiti by Louis Antoine de Bougainville.
      Issued: 40fr, 4/6/68.

The Meal, by Paul Gauguin AP20

1968, July 30   Photo.   Perf. 12x12½
C48 AP20 200fr multicolored   40.00 32.50
      See Nos. C63-C67, C78-C82, C89-C93, C98.

Shot Put — AP21

1968, Oct. 12   Engr.   Perf. 13
C49 AP21 35fr dk car rose & brt grn   16.00   9.00
      19th Olympic Games, Mexico City, 10/12-27.

Concorde Issue
Common Design Type
1969, Apr. 17
C50 CD129 40fr red brn & car rose   55.00 35.00

PATA 1970 Poster — AP22

1969, July 9   Photo.   Perf. 12½x13
C51 AP22 25fr blue & multi   17.50   7.25
      Issued to publicize PATA 1970 (Pacific Area Travel Association Congress), Tahiti.

Underwater Fishing AP23

52fr, Hand holding fish made up of flags, vert.

1969, Aug. 5   Photo.   Perf. 13
C52 AP23 48fr blk, grnsh bl & red lil   35.00 13.50
C53 AP23 52fr bl, blk & red   40.00 22.50
      Issued to publicize the World Underwater Fishing Championships.

Gen. Bonaparte as Commander of the Army in Italy, by Jean Sebastien Rouillard — AP24

1969, Oct. 15   Photo.   Perf. 12½x12
C54 AP24 100fr car & multi   80.00 67.50
      Bicentenary of the birth of Napoleon Bonaparte (1769-1821).

Eiffel Tower, Torii and EXPO Emblem — AP25

Design: 30fr, Mount Fuji, Tower of the Sun and EXPO emblem, horiz.

1970, Sept. 15   Photo.   Perf. 13
C55 AP25 30fr multicolored   20.00   8.00
C56 AP25 50fr multicolored   27.50 12.00
      EXPO '70 International Exposition, Osaka, Japan, Mar. 15-Sept. 13.

Pearl Diver Descending, and Basket — AP26

Designs: 5fr, Diver collecting oysters. 18fr, Implantation into oyster, horiz. 27fr, Open oyster with pearl. 50fr, Woman with mother of pearl jewelry.

1970, Sept. 30   Engr.   Perf. 13
C57 AP26 2fr slate, grnsh bl & red brn   1.50   .90
C58 AP26 5fr grnsh blue, ultra & org   2.75   1.50
C59 AP26 18fr sl, mag & org   3.75   2.75
C60 AP26 27fr brt pink, brn & dl lil   9.25   4.75
C61 AP26 50fr gray, red brn & org   16.00   7.50
      Nos. C57-C61 (5)   33.25 17.40
      Pearl industry of French Polynesia.

The Thinker, by Auguste Rodin and Education Year Emblem AP27

1970, Oct. 15   Engr.   Perf. 13
C62 AP27 50fr bl, ind & fawn   17.00 10.50
      International Education Year.

Painting Type of 1968
Paintings by Artists Living in Polynesia: 20fr, Woman on the Beach, by Yves de Saint-Front. 40fr, Abstract, by Frank Fay. 60fr, Woman and Shells, by Jean Guillois. 80fr, Hut under Palms, by Jean Masson. 100fr, Polynesian Girl, by Jean-Charles Bouloc, vert.

Perf. 12x12½, 12½x12
1970, Dec. 14   Photo.
C63 AP20 20fr brn & multi   8.00   4.00
C64 AP20 40fr brn & multi   12.00   7.50
C65 AP20 60fr brn & multi   16.00 11.00
C66 AP20 80fr brn & multi   20.00 16.00
C67 AP20 100fr brn & multi   26.00 22.50
      Nos. C63-C67 (5)   82.00 61.00

South Pacific Games
Emblem — AP28

1971, Jan. 26   *Perf. 12½*
C68 AP28 20fr ultra & multi   8.00   5.00
  Publicity for 4th South Pacific Games, held
in Papeete, Sept. 8-19, 1971.

Memorial
Flame — AP29

1971, Mar. 19   Photo.   Perf. 12½
C69 AP29 5fr multicolored   8.00   5.00
  In memory of Charles de Gaulle.

Soldier and
Badge
AP30

1971, Apr. 21
C70 AP30 25fr multicolored   11.00   6.75
  30th anniversary of departure of Tahitian
volunteers to serve in World War II.

Water Sports Type

  Designs: 15fr, Surfing, vert. 16fr, Skin diving, vert. 20fr, Water-skiing with kite.

1971, May 11   Photo.   Perf. 13
C71 A44 15fr multicolored   6.50   3.50
C72 A44 16fr multicolored   7.50   3.25
C73 A44 20fr multicolored   11.00   7.75
    Nos. C71-C73 (3)   25.00 14.50

Sailing — AP31

1971, Sept. 8   *Perf. 12½*
C74 AP31 15fr shown   6.50   3.50
C75 AP31 18fr Golf   8.00   4.75
C76 AP31 27fr Archery   12.00   7.25
C77 AP31 53fr Tennis   20.00 13.50
  a.   Souv. sheet, #C74-C77   190.00 190.00
    Nos. C74-C77 (4)   46.50 29.00
  4th So. Pacific Games, Papeete, Sept. 8-19.

Painting Type of 1968

  Paintings by Artists Living in Polynesia: 20fr,
Hut and Palms, by Isabelle Wolf. 40fr, Palms
on Shore, by André Dobrowolski. 60fr, Polyne-
sian Woman, by Françoise Séli, vert. 80fr,
Holy Family, by Pierre Heymann, vert. 100fr,
Crowd, by Nicolai Michoutouchkine.

1971, Dec. 15   Perf. 13
C78 AP20 20fr multicolored   7.50   4.50
C79 AP20 40fr multicolored   11.00   7.50
C80 AP20 60fr multicolored   13.00 10.00
C81 AP20 80fr multicolored   18.00 12.50
C82 AP20 100fr multicolored   30.00 22.50
    Nos. C78-C82 (5)   79.50 57.00

Papeete
Harbor
AP32

1972, Jan. 13
C83 AP32 28fr violet & multi   11.00   8.00
  Free port of Papeete, 10th anniversary.

Figure Skating
and
Dragon — AP33

1972, Jan. 25   Engr.   Perf. 13
C84 AP33 20fr ultra, lake & brt
           grn   9.00   7.00
  11th Winter Olympic Games, Sapporo,
Japan, Feb. 3-13.

South Pacific Commission
Headquarters, Noumea — AP34

1972, Feb. 5   Photo.   Perf. 13
C85 AP34 21fr blue & multi   11.00   5.25
  South Pacific Commission, 25th anniv.

Festival
Emblem — AP35

1972, May 9   Engr.   Perf. 13
C86 AP35 36fr orange, bl & grn   8.00   5.25
  So. Pacific Festival of Arts, Fiji, May 6-20.

Kon Tiki and
Route,
Callao to
Tahiti
AP36

1972, Aug. 18   Photo.   Perf. 13
C87 AP36 16fr dk & lt bl, blk &
           org   10.00   6.50
  25th anniversary of the arrival of the raft Kon
Tiki in Tahiti.

Charles de
Gaulle and
Memorial
AP37

1972, Dec. 9   Engr.   Perf. 13
C88 AP37 100fr slate   62.50 42.50

Painting Type of 1968

  Paintings by Artists Living in Polynesia: 20fr,
Horses, by Georges Bovy. 40fr, Sailboats, by
Ruy Juventin, vert. 60fr, Harbor, by André
Brooke. 80fr, Farmers, by Daniel Adam, vert.
100fr, Dancers, by Aloysius Pilioko, vert.

1972, Dec. 14   Photo.
C89 AP20   20fr gold & multi   9.75   4.25
C90 AP20   40fr gold & multi   12.00   6.75
C91 AP20   60fr gold & multi   21.00   9.50
C92 AP20   80fr dk grn, buff
             & dk brn   27.50 13.00
C93 AP20 100fr gold & multi   32.50 25.00
    Nos. C89-C93 (5)   102.75 58.50

St. Teresa and
Lisieux
Basilica — AP38

1973, Jan. 23   Engr.   Perf. 13
C94 AP38 85fr multicolored   25.00 17.50
  Centenary of the birth of St. Teresa of
Lisieux (1873-1897), Carmelite nun.

Nicolaus
Copernicus
AP39

1973, Mar. 7   Engr.   Perf. 13
C95 AP39 100fr brn, vio bl &
           red lil   30.00 17.50
  Copernicus (1473-1543), Polish astronomer.

Plane over
Tahiti
AP40

1973, Apr. 3   Photo.   Perf. 13
C96 AP40 80fr ultra, gold & lt
           grn   22.50 16.00
  Air France's World Tour via Tahiti.

DC-10 at
Papeete
Airport
AP41

1973, May 18   Engr.   Perf. 13
C97 AP41 20fr bl, ultra & sl
           grn   16.00   9.00
  Start of DC-10 service.

Painting Type of 1968

  Design: 200fr, "Ta Matete" (seated women),
by Paul Gauguin.

1973, June 7   Photo.   Perf. 13
C98 AP20 200fr multicolored   27.50 20.00
  Paul Gauguin (1848-1903), painter.

Pierre Loti
and
Characters
from his
Books
AP42

1973, July 4   Engr.   Perf. 13
C99 AP42 60fr multicolored   40.00 20.00
  Pierre Loti (1850-1923), French naval officer
and writer.

Woman with
Flowers, by Eliane
de
Gennes — AP43

  Paintings by Artists Living in Polynesia: 20fr,
Sun, by Jean Francois Favre. 60fr, Seascape,
by Alain Sidet. 80fr, Crowded Bus, by Francois
Ravello. 100fr, Stylized Boats, by Jackie
Bourdin, horiz.

1973, Dec. 13   Photo.   Perf. 13
C100 AP43 20fr gold & multi   8.00   2.75
C101 AP43 40fr gold & multi   11.50   6.00
C102 AP43 60fr gold & multi   17.00 10.50
C103 AP43 80fr gold & multi   22.50 17.00
C104 AP43 100fr gold & multi   27.50 20.00
    Nos. C100-C104 (5)   86.50 56.25

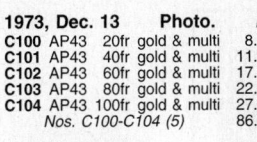

Bird, Fish, Flower and
Water — AP44

1974, June 12   Photo.   Perf. 13
C105 AP44 12fr blue & multi   7.50   5.25
  Nature protection.

Catamaran under
Sail — AP45

1974, July 22   Engr.   Perf. 13
C106 AP45 100fr multicolored   27.50 16.00
  2nd Catamaran World Championships.

Still-life, by
Rosine Temarui-
Masson
AP46

  Paintings by Artists Living in Polynesia: 40fr,
Palms and House on Beach, by Marcel
Chardon. 60fr, Man, by Marie-Françoise Avril.
80fr, Polynesian Woman, by Henriette Robin.
100fr, Lagoon by Moon-light, by David Farsi,
horiz.

1974, Dec. 12   Photo.   Perf. 13
C107 AP46 20fr gold & multi   18.00   8.50
C108 AP46 40fr gold & multi   27.50   9.50
C109 AP46 60fr gold & multi   32.50 12.00
C110 AP46 80fr gold & multi   45.00 16.50
C111 AP46 100fr gold & multi   65.00 27.50
    Nos. C107-C111 (5)   188.00 74.00
    See Nos. C122-C126.

Polynesian
Gods of
Travel
AP47

  Designs: 75fr, Tourville hydroplane, 1929.
100fr, Passengers leaving plane.

1975, Feb. 7   Engr.   Perf. 13
C112 AP47 50fr sep, pur &
             brn   11.00   6.00
C113 AP47 75fr grn, bl & red   16.00   8.00
C114 AP47 100fr grn, sep &
             car   25.00 15.00
    Nos. C112-C114 (3)   52.00 29.00
  Fifty years of Tahitian aviation.

French Ceres Stamp
and Woman — AP48

1975, May 29   Engr.   Perf. 13
C115 AP48 32fr ver, brn & blk   8.00 5.00
ARPHILA 75 International Philatelic Exhibition, Paris, June 6-16.

Shot Put and
Games'
Emblem — AP50

Designs: 30fr, Volleyball. 40fr, Women's swimming.

1975, Aug. 1   Photo.   Perf. 13
C117 AP50 25fr shown   4.75 3.00
C118 AP50 30fr multicolored   7.00 3.75
C119 AP50 40fr multicolored   9.25 5.25
   Nos. C117-C119 (3)   21.00 12.00
5th South Pacific Games, Guam, Aug. 1-10.

Flowers, Athlete, View
of Montreal — AP51

1975, Oct. 15   Engr.   Perf. 13
C120 AP51 44fr brt bl, ver & blk 11.00 6.50
Pre-Olympic Year 1975.

UPU
Emblem, Jet
and Letters
AP52

1975, Nov. 5   Engr.   Perf. 13
C121 AP52 100fr brn, bl & ol 22.50 13.00
World Universal Postal Union Day.

Paintings Type of 1974
Paintings by Artists Living in Polynesia: 20fr, Beach Scene, by R. Marcel Marius, horiz. 40fr, Roofs with TV antennas, by M. Anglade, horiz. 60fr, Street scene with bus, by J. Day, horiz. 80fr, Tropical waters (fish), by J. Steimetz. 100fr, Women, by A. van der Heyde.

1975, Dec. 17   Litho.   Perf. 13
C122 AP46 20fr gold & multi   3.00 1.75
C123 AP46 40fr gold & multi   6.00 3.00
C124 AP46 60fr gold & multi   9.00 4.50
C125 AP46 80fr gold & multi   12.00 7.50
C126 AP46 100fr gold & multi 14.50 12.00
   Nos. C122-C126 (5)   44.50 28.75

Concorde
AP53

1976, Jan. 21   Engr.   Perf. 13
C127 AP53 100fr car, bl & ind 19.00 13.00
First commercial flight of supersonic jet Concorde from Paris to Rio, Jan. 21.

Adm. Rodney, Count de la Perouse, "Barfleur" and "Triomphant" in Battle
AP54

31fr, Count de Grasse and Lord Graves, "Ville de Paris" & "Le Terible" in Chesapeake Bay Battle.

1976, Apr. 15   Engr.   Perf. 13
C128 AP54 24fr grnsh bl, lt brn &
              blk   5.00 2.50
C129 AP54 31fr mag, red & lt brn 5.75 3.50
American Bicentennial.

King Pomaré I — AP55

Portraits: 21fr, King Pomaré II. 26fr, Queen Pomaré IV. 30fr, King Pomaré V.

1976, Apr. 28   Litho.   Perf. 12½
C130 AP55 18fr olive & multi   1.75   .75
C131 AP55 21fr multicolored   2.00 1.10
C132 AP55 26fr gray & multi   2.75 1.25
C133 AP55 30fr plum & multi   3.00 1.90
   Nos. C130-C133 (4)   9.50 5.00
Pomaré Dynasty. See Nos. C141-C144.

Running and
Maple Leaf
AP56

Designs: 34fr, Long jump, vert. 50fr, Olympic flame and flowers.

1976, July 19   Engr.   Perf. 13
C134 AP56 26fr ultra & multi   4.25 2.10
C135 AP56 34fr ultra & multi   6.00 2.75
C136 AP56 50fr ultra & multi   11.50 5.00
   a. Min. sheet, #C134-C136 90.00 90.00
   Nos. C134-C136 (3)   21.75 9.85
21st Olympic Games, Montreal, Canada, July 17-Aug. 1.

The Dream,
by Paul
Gauguin
AP57

1976, Oct. 17   Photo.   Perf. 13
C137 AP57 50fr multicolored 11.00 7.25

Murex
Steeriae — AP58

Sea Shells: 27fr, Conus Gauguini. 35fr, Conus marchionatus.

1977, Mar. 14   Photo.   Perf. 12½x13
C138 AP58 25fr vio bl & multi   4.25 1.25
C139 AP58 27fr ultra & multi   4.25 1.50
C140 AP58 35fr blue & multi   5.00 2.00
   Nos. C138-C140 (3)   13.50 4.75
See Nos. C156-C158.

Royalty Type of 1976
19fr, King Maputeoa, Mangareva. 33fr, King Camatoa V, Raiatea. 39fr, Queen Vaekehu, Marquesas. 43fr, King Teurarii III, Rurutu.

1977, Apr. 19   Litho.   Perf. 12½
C141 AP55 19fr dull red & multi 1.25   .95
C142 AP55 33fr dk blue & multi   1.90 1.25
C143 AP55 39fr ultra & multi   1.90 1.25
C144 AP55 43fr green & multi   2.75 1.90
   Nos. C141-C144 (4)   7.80 5.35
Polynesian rulers.

Pocillopora — AP59

Design: 25fr, Acropora, horiz.

Perf. 13x12½, 12½x13
1977, May 23   Photo.
C145 AP59 25fr multicolored   1.90 1.10
C146 AP59 33fr multicolored   2.75 1.90
3rd Symposium on Coral Reefs, Miami, Fla. See Nos. C162-C163.

De Gaulle
Memorial — AP60

Photogravure and Embossed
1977, June 18   Perf. 13
C147 AP60 40fr gold & multi   7.00 5.00
5th anniversary of dedication of De Gaulle memorial at Colombey-les-Deux-Eglises.

Tahitian
Dancer — AP61

1977, July 14   Litho.   Perf. 12½
C148 AP61 27fr multicolored   4.00 2.50

Charles A.
Lindbergh
and Spirit of
St. Louis
AP62

1977, Aug. 18   Litho.   Perf. 12½
C149 AP62 28fr multicolored   7.00 3.50
Lindbergh's solo transatlantic flight from New York to Paris, 50th anniv.

Mahoe — AP63

1977, Sept. 15   Photo.   Perf. 12½x13
C150 AP63 8fr shown   1.40   .80
C151 AP63 12fr Frangipani   1.75 1.25

Palms on
Shore — AP64

1977, Nov. 8   Photo.   Perf. 12½x13
C152 AP64 32fr multicolored   10.00 4.50
Ecology, protection of trees.

Rubens' Son
Albert — AP65

1977, Nov. 28   Engr.   Perf. 13
C153 AP65 100fr grnsh blk &
              rose cl   11.00 8.00
Peter Paul Rubens (1577-1640), painter, 400th birth anniversary.

Capt. Cook
and
"Discovery"
AP66

Design: 39fr, Capt. Cook and "Resolution."

1978, Jan. 20   Engr.   Perf. 13
C154 AP66 33fr multicolored   2.50 3.00
C155 AP66 39fr multicolored   3.00 3.50
Bicentenary of Capt. James Cook's arrival in Hawaii.
For overprints see Nos. C166-C167.

Shell Type of 1977
Sea Shells: 22fr, Erosaria obvelata. 24fr, Cypraea ventriculus. 31fr, Lambis robusta.

1978, Apr. 13   Photo.   Perf. 13½x13
C156 AP58 22fr brt blue & multi 2.25 1.25
C157 AP58 24fr brt blue & multi 2.25 1.50
C158 AP58 31fr brt blue & multi 3.50 2.50
   Nos. C156-C158 (3)   8.00 5.25

Tahitian Woman
and Boy, by
Gauguin — AP67

1978, May 7   Perf. 13
C159 AP67 50fr multicolored   8.75 5.25
Paul Gauguin (1848-1903).

 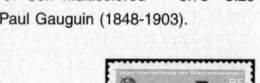

Antenna and ITU
Emblem — AP68

1978, May 17   Litho.   Perf. 13
C160 AP68 80fr gray & multi   6.00 3.25
10th World Telecommunications Day.

Soccer and Argentina '78 Emblem AP69

1978, June 1
C161 AP69 28fr multicolored 3.25 2.10
11th World Cup Soccer Championship, Argentina, June 1-25.

Coral Type of 1977
Designs: 26fr, Fungia, horiz. 34fr, Millepora.

Perf. 13x12½, 12½x13

1978, July 13 Photo.
C162 AP59 26fr multicolored 1.75 1.25
C163 AP59 34fr multicolored 2.25 1.60

Radar Antenna, Polynesian Woman — AP70

1978, Sept. 5 Engr. *Perf. 13*
C164 AP70 50fr blue & black 3.00 1.75
Papenoo earth station.

Bird and Rainbow over Island AP71

1978, Oct. 5 Photo.
C165 AP71 23fr multicolored 6.00 1.75
Nature protection.

Nos. C154-C155 Overprinted

No. C166

No. C167

1979, Feb. 14 Engr. *Perf. 13*
C166 AP66 33fr multi 4.00 2.50
C167 AP66 39fr multi (VBI) 5.00 3.50
Bicentenary of Capt. Cook's death. On No. C167 date is last line of overprint.

Children, Toys and IYC Emblem AP72

1979, May 3 Engr. *Perf. 13*
C168 AP72 150fr multicolored 12.00 7.00
International Year of the Child.

"Do you expect a letter?" by Paul Gauguin AP73

1979, May 20 Photo. *Perf. 13*
C169 AP73 200fr multicolored 16.00 8.00

Shell and Carved Head AP74

1979, June 30 Engr. *Perf. 13*
C170 AP74 44fr multicolored 3.50 2.00
Museum of Tahiti and the Islands.

Conference Emblem over Island — AP75

1979, Oct. 6 Photo. *Perf. 13*
C171 AP75 23fr multicolored 2.25 1.10
19th South Pacific Conf., Tahiti, Oct. 6-12.

Flying Boat "Bermuda" AP76

Planes Used in Polynesia: 40fr, DC-4 over Papeete. 60fr, Britten-Norman "Islander." 80fr, Fairchild F-27A. 120fr, DC-8 over Tahiti.

1979, Dec. 19 Litho. *Perf. 13*
C172 AP76 24fr multicolored 1.00 .50
C173 AP76 40fr multicolored 1.75 1.00
C174 AP76 60fr multicolored 2.75 1.50
C175 AP76 80fr multicolored 3.50 2.25
C176 AP76 120fr multicolored 6.00 3.00
Nos. C172-C176 (5) 15.00 8.25
See Nos. C180-C183.

Window on Tahiti, by Henri Matisse — AP77

1980, Feb. 18 Photo.
C177 AP77 150fr multicolored 8.00 5.00

Marshi Metua No Tehamana, by Gauguin — AP78

1980, Aug. 24 Photo. *Perf. 13*
C178 AP78 500fr multicolored 18.00 13.00

Sydpex '80, Philatelic Exhibition, Sydney Town Hall — AP79

1980, Sept. 29 Photo. *Perf. 13*
C179 AP79 70fr multicolored 8.00 5.25

Aviation Type of 1979
1980, Dec. 15 Litho. *Perf. 13*
C180 AP76 15fr Catalina .75 .55
C181 AP76 26fr Twin Otter 1.00 .70
C182 AP76 30fr CAMS 55 1.25 .90
C183 AP76 50fr DC-6 2.00 1.40
Nos. C180-C183 (4) 5.00 3.55

And The Gold of their Bodies, by Gauguin AP80

1981, Mar. 15 Photo. *Perf. 13*
C184 AP80 100fr multicolored 4.50 2.50

20th Anniv. of Manned Space Flight — AP81

1981, June 15 Litho. *Perf. 12½*
C185 AP81 300fr multicolored 9.00 7.00

First Intl. Pirogue (6-man Canoe) Championship — AP82

1981, July 25 Litho. *Perf. 13x12½*
C186 AP82 200fr multicolored 5.50 4.50

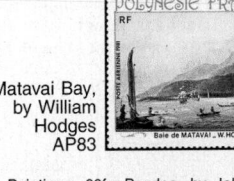

Matavai Bay, by William Hodges AP83

Paintings: 60fr, Poedea, by John Weber, vert. 80fr, Omai, by Joshua Reynolds, vert. 120fr, Point Venus, by George Tobin.

1981, Dec. 10 Photo. *Perf. 13*
C187 AP83 40fr multicolored 1.10 .90
C188 AP83 60fr multicolored 1.75 1.25
C189 AP83 80fr multicolored 2.75 1.75
C190 AP83 120fr multicolored 3.50 2.40
Nos. C187-C190 (4) 9.10 6.30
See Nos. C194-C197, C202-C205.

TB Bacillus Centenary AP84

1982, Mar. 24 Engr. *Perf. 13*
C191 AP84 200fr multicolored 5.00 3.00

1982 World Cup — AP85

1982, May 18 Litho. *Perf. 13*
C192 AP85 250fr multicolored 6.50 4.50

French Overseas Possessions' Week, Sept. 18-25 — AP86

1982, Sept. 17 Engr.
C193 AP86 110fr multicolored 2.75 1.65

Painting Type of 1981
Designs: 50fr, The Tahitian, by M. Radiguet, vert. 70fr, Souvenir of Tahiti, by C. Giraud. 100fr, Beating Cloth Lengths, by Atlas JL the Younger. 160fr, Papeete Harbor, by C.F. Gordon Cumming.

1982, Dec. 15 Photo. *Perf. 13*
C194 AP83 50fr multicolored 1.90 1.00
C195 AP83 70fr multicolored 2.25 1.50
C196 AP83 100fr multicolored 2.75 2.00
C197 AP83 160fr multicolored 4.50 2.75
Nos. C194-C197 (4) 11.40 7.25

Wood Cutter, by Gauguin — AP87

Photo. & Engr.
1983, May 8 *Perf. 12½x13*
C198 AP87 600fr multicolored 16.00 8.00

Voyage of Capt. Bligh AP88

1983, June 9 Litho. *Perf. 13*
C199 AP88 200fr Map, fruit 6.00 3.00

BRASILIANA '83 Intl. Stamp Exhibition, Rio de Janeiro, July 29-Aug. 7 — AP89

1983, July 29 Litho. *Perf. 13x12½*
C200 AP89 100fr multicolored 2.50 1.75
a. Souvenir sheet 3.50 3.50

1983, Aug. 4 Litho. *Perf. 13x12½*
C201 AP89 110fr Bangkok '83 3.00 2.00
a. Souvenir sheet 4.00 4.00

Painting Type of 1981
20th Cent. Paintings: 40fr, View of Moorea, by William Alister MacDonald (1861-1956). 60fr, The Fruit Carrier, by Adrian Herman Gouwe (1875-1965). 80fr, Arrival of the Destroyer Escort, by Nicolas Mordvinoff (1911-1977). 100fr, Women on a Veranda, by Charles Alfred Le Moine (1872-1918).

1983, Dec. 22   Photo.   *Perf. 13*
C202	AP83	40fr multi	1.00	.75
C203	AP83	60fr multi, vert.	1.50	1.00
C204	AP83	80fr multi, vert.	1.60	1.25
C205	AP83	100fr multi	2.00	1.60
	Nos. C202-C205 (4)		6.10	4.60

ESPANA '84 — AP90

Design: Maori canoers.

1984, Apr. 27   Engr.   *Perf. 13*
C206	AP90	80fr brn red & dk bl	2.25	1.50

Souvenir Sheet
C207	AP90	200fr dk bl & dk red	7.25	7.25

Woman with Mango, by Gauguin — AP91

Photo. & Engr.
1984, May 27   *Perf. 12½x13*
C208	AP91	400fr multicolored	11.00	6.00

Ausipex '84 — AP92

Details from Human Sacrifice of the Maori in Tahiti, 18th cent. engraving.

1984, Sept. 5   Litho.   *Perf. 13x12½*
C209	AP92	120fr Worshippers	3.00	2.25
C210	AP92	120fr Preparation	3.00	2.25
a.	Pair, #C209-C210 + label		7.50	7.50

Souvenir Sheet
C211	AP92	200fr Entire	9.50	9.50

Painting by Gaugin (1848-1903) — AP93

Design: Where have we come from? What are we? Where are we going?

1985, Mar. 17   Litho.   *Perf. 13½x13*
C212	AP93	550fr multi	14.00	7.50

4th Pacific Arts Festival Type
Design: Islander, tiki, artifacts.

1985, July 3   Litho.   *Perf. 13*
C213	A95	200fr multicolored	4.50	3.00

Intl. Youth Year AP95

Design: Island youths, frigate bird.

1985, Sept. 18   Litho.
C214	AP95	250fr multi	5.50	3.25

ITALIA '85 — AP96

Designs: Ship sailing into Papeete Harbor, 19th century print.

1985, Oct. 22   Engr.
C215	AP96	130fr multicolored	2.75	2.50

Souvenir Sheet
C216	AP96	240fr multicolored	7.50	7.50

1st Intl. Marlin Fishing Contest, Feb. 27-Mar. 5 — AP97

1986, Feb. 27   Litho.   *Perf. 12½*
C217	AP97	300fr multicolored	6.50	4.00

Arrival of a Boat, c.1880 AP98

1986, June 24   Engr.   *Perf. 13*
C218	AP98	400fr intense blue	8.75	5.25

STOCKHOLMIA '86 — AP99

Design: Dr. Karl Solander and Anders Sparrmann, Swedish scientists who accompanied Capt. Cook, and map of Tahiti.

1986, Aug. 28   Engr.   *Perf. 13*
C219	AP99	150fr multicolored	3.25	2.25

Souvenir Sheet
C220	AP99	210fr multicolored	4.75	4.75

Protestant Churches AP100

1986, Dec. 17   Litho.   *Perf. 13*
C221	AP100	80fr Tiva, 1955	1.75	.90
C222	AP100	200fr Avera, 1880	4.50	2.10
C223	AP100	300fr Papetoai, 1822	6.50	3.25
	Nos. C221-C223 (3)		12.75	6.25

Broche Barracks, 120th Anniv. AP101

1987, Apr. 21   Litho.   *Perf. 12½x12*
C224	AP101	350fr multicolored	7.75	5.00

CAPEX '87 AP102

Design: George Vancouver (1757-1798), English navigator and cartographer, chart and excerpt from ship's log.

1987, June 15   Engr.   *Perf. 13*
C225	AP102	130fr multi	2.90	2.25

Imperf
Size: 143x100mm
C226	AP102	260fr multicolored	5.75	5.75

Soyez Mysterieuses, from a 5-Panel Sculpture by Paul Gauguin, Gauguin Museum — AP103

1987, Nov. 15   *Perf. 13*
C227	AP103	600fr multicolored	14.00	9.50

AIR POST SEMI-POSTAL STAMPS

> Catalogue values for unused stamps in this section are for Never Hinged items.

French Revolution Issue
Common Design Type
Unwmk.
1939, July 5   Photo.   *Perf. 13*
Name and Value Typo. in Orange
CB1	CD83	5fr + 4fr brn blk	35.00	35.00

Mother & Children on Beach — SPAP1

Perf. 12½x13½
1942, June 22   Engr.
CB2	SPAP1	1.50fr + 3.50fr green	2.00	
CB3	SPAP1	2fr + 6fr yel brn	2.00	

Native children's welfare fund. Nos. CB2-CB3 were issued by the Vichy government in France, but were not placed on sale in French Polynesia.

Colonial Education Fund
Common Design Type
1942, June 22
CB4	CD86a	1.20fr + 1.80fr blue & red	2.00	

No. CB4 was issued by the Vichy government in France, but was not placed on sale in French Polynesia.

POSTAGE DUE STAMPS

Postage Due Stamps of French Colonies, 1894-1906, Overprinted

1926-27   Unwmk.   *Perf. 14x13½*
J1	D1	5c light blue	.95	.95
J2	D1	10c brown	.95	.95
J3	D1	20c olive green	1.40	1.40
J4	D1	30c dull red	1.60	1.60
J5	D1	40c rose	3.50	3.50
J6	D1	60c blue green	3.50	3.50
J7	D1	1fr red brown, *straw*	3.75	3.75

J8	D1	3fr magenta ('27)	15.00	15.00

With Additional Surcharge of New Value
J9	D1	2fr on 1fr orange red	4.00	4.75
	Nos. J1-J9 (9)		34.65	35.40

Fautaua Falls, Tahiti — D2   Tahitian Youth — D3

1929   Typo.   *Perf. 13½x14*
J10	D2	5c lt blue & dk brn	.75	.75
J11	D2	10c vermilion & grn	.75	.75
J12	D2	30c dk brn & dk red	1.75	1.75
J13	D2	50c yel grn & dk brn	1.40	1.40
J14	D2	60c dl vio & yel grn	4.00	4.00
J15	D3	1fr Prus bl & red vio	3.50	3.50
J16	D3	2fr brn red & dk brn	2.00	2.10
J17	D3	3fr bl vio & bl grn	2.10	2.40
	Nos. J10-J17 (8)		16.25	16.65

> **Catalogue values for unused stamps in this section, from this point to the end of the section, are for Never Hinged items.**

D4

1948   Engr.   *Perf. 14x13*
J18	D4	10c brt blue grn	.40	.25
J19	D4	30c black brown	.40	.25
J20	D4	50c dk car rose	.50	.30
J21	D4	1fr ultra	.65	.50
J22	D4	2fr dk blue green	.95	.70
J23	D4	3fr red	1.90	1.40
J24	D4	4fr violet	2.00	1.60
J25	D4	5fr lilac rose	3.00	2.10
J26	D4	10fr slate	4.00	3.00
J27	D4	20fr red brown	5.50	4.25
	Nos. J18-J27 (10)		19.30	14.35

Polynesian Club — D5

1958   Unwmk.   *Perf. 14x13*
J28	D5	1fr dk brn & grn	.65	.65
J29	D5	3fr bluish blk & hn brn	.90	.90
J30	D5	5fr brown & ultra	1.10	1.10
	Nos. J28-J30 (3)		2.65	2.65

Tahitian Bowl — D6

Designs: 1fr, Mother-of-pearl fish hook, vert. 5fr, Marquesan fan. 10fr, Lamp stand, vert. 20fr, Wood headrest ('87). 50fr, Wood scoop ('87).

1984-87   Litho.   *Perf. 13*
J31	D6	1fr multicolored	.25	.25
J32	D6	3fr shown	.25	.25
J33	D6	5fr multicolored	.30	.30
J34	D6	10fr multicolored	.55	.55
J35	D6	20fr multicolored	.60	.60
J36	D6	50fr multicolored	1.50	1.50
	Nos. J31-J36 (6)		3.45	3.45

Issued: #J31-34, 3/15; #J35-J36, 8/18.

OFFICIAL STAMPS

> Catalogue values for unused stamps in this section are for Never Hinged items.

Breadfruit — O1

Polynesian Fruits: 2fr, 3fr, 5fr, like 1fr. 7fr, 8fr, 10fr, 15fr, "Vi Tahiti." 19fr, 20fr, 25fr, 35fr, Avocados. 50fr, 100fr, 200fr, Mangos.

1977, June 9   Litho.   Perf. 12½

O1	O1	1fr ultra & multi	.40	.65
O2	O1	2fr ultra & multi	.40	.65
O3	O1	3fr ultra & multi	.40	.65
O4	O1	5fr ultra & multi	.40	.65
O5	O1	7fr red & multi	.65	.95
O6	O1	8fr red & multi	.65	.95
O7	O1	10fr red & multi	.95	1.25
O8	O1	19fr black & multi	1.40	1.60
O9	O1	19fr black & multi	1.60	2.00
O10	O1	20fr black & multi	1.75	2.40
O11	O1	25fr black & multi	2.50	2.75
O12	O1	35fr black & multi	3.25	3.50
O13	O1	50fr black & multi	3.25	3.50
O14	O1	100fr red & multi	7.25	8.00
O15	O1	200fr ultra & multi	14.00	16.00
		Nos. O1-O15 (15)	38.85	45.50

1982-86   Perf. 13

O1a	O1	1fr ultra & multi	.70	1.25
O2a	O1	2fr ultra & multi	.70	1.25
O3a	O1	3fr ultra & multi	.95	1.25
O4a	O1	5fr ultra & multi	2.25	2.40
O5a	O1	7fr red & multi	2.25	2.50
O6a	O1	8fr red & multi	3.25	3.50
O7a	O1	10fr red & multi	3.50	3.50
O8a	O1	15fr red & multi ('84)	3.50	3.50
O10a	O1	20fr black & multi	3.50	3.50
O11a	O1	25fr black & multi ('84)	3.50	3.50
O12a	O1	35fr black & multi ('84)	8.00	10.50
O13a	O1	50fr black & multi ('84)	20.00	22.50
O14a	O1	100fr red & multi ('86)	52.50	60.00
O15a	O1	200fr ultra & multi ('86)	67.50	80.00
		Nos. O1a-O15a (14)	172.10	199.15

Nos. O1-O15 have dull finish (matte) gum.
Nos. O1a-O15a have shiny gum.

Stamps and Postmarks — O2

1fr, French Colonies #5. 2fr, French Colonies #27, #12. 3fr, French Colonies #29, 1884 Papeete postmark. 5fr, Newspaper franked with surcharge of Tahiti #2, 1884 Papeete postmark. 9fr, #176. 10fr, #4, 1894 octagonal postmark. 20fr, #6, #8. 46fr, #48. 51fr, #147-148, Vaiteaua-Makatea Island postmark. 70fr, Visit Tahiti postmark on postal card piece. 85fr, #59 with 1921 manuscript cancel, vert. 100fr, #181. 200fr, #C21, 1st day cancel.

Perf. 13¼, 13¼x13 (#O20), 13x13¼ (#O26)

1993-99   Litho.

O16	O2	1fr multicolored	.25	.40
a.		Perf. 13¼x13 ('98)	8.00	9.50
O17	O2	2fr multicolored	.25	.40
a.		Perf. 13¼x13 ('97)	1.00	1.25
O18	O2	3fr multicolored	.25	.40
a.		Perf. 13¼x13 ('98)	8.00	9.50
O19	O2	5fr multicolored	.30	.55
a.		Perf. 13¼x13 ('97)	1.00	1.25
O20	O2	9fr multicolored	.80	1.25
O21	O2	10fr multicolored	.30	.55
a.		Perf. 13¼x13 ('99)	1.00	.85
O22	O2	20fr multicolored	.65	.95
a.		Perf. 13¼x13 ('99)	8.00	9.50
O23	O2	46fr multicolored	1.40	1.60
O24	O2	51fr multicolored	2.50	3.25
O25	O2	70fr multicolored	2.40	2.75
a.		Perf. 13¼x13 ('97)	4.00	6.50
O26	O2	85fr multicolored	2.50	3.25
O27	O2	100fr multicolored	2.75	3.50
a.		Perf. 13¼x13 ('99)	2.40	1.90
O28	O2	200fr multicolored	5.25	6.50
a.		Perf. 13¼x13 ('97)	5.00	4.50
		Nos. O16-O28 (13)	19.60	25.35

Issued: 51fr, 4/6/94; 9fr, 85fr, 4/21/97; others, 1/13/93.

FRENCH SOUTHERN & ANTARCTIC TERRITORY

ˈfrench ˈsə-thərn and
ˌant-ärk-tik ˈter-ə-ˈtōr-ēs

POP. — 130 staff

Formerly dependencies of Madagascar, these areas, comprising the Kerguelen Archipelago; St. Paul, Amsterdam and Crozet Islands and Adelle

Light-mantled Sooty Albatross — A4

Designs: 40c, Skua, horiz. 12fr, King shag.

1959, Sept. 14   Engr.   Perf. 13

12	A4	30c blue, grn & red brn	.55	.85
13	A4	40c blk, dl red brn & bl	.55	.85
14	A4	12fr lt blue & blk	10.00	8.00
		Nos. 12-14 (3)	11.10	9.70

Land in Antarctica achieved territorial status on August 6, 1955.

100 Centimes = 1 Franc
100 Cents = 1 Euro (2002)

Catalogue values for all unused stamps in this country are for Never Hinged items.

Madagascar No. 289 Ovptd. in Red

Unwmk.

1955, Oct. 28   Engr.   Perf. 13

1	A25	15f dk grn & dp ultra	10.00	27.50

Rockhopper Penguins, Crozet Archipelago A1

New Amsterdam A2

Design: 10fr, 15fr, Elephant seal.

1956, Apr. 25   Engr.   Perf. 13

2	A1	50c dk blue, sepia & yel	.40	1.00
3	A1	1fr ultra, org & gray	.40	1.00
4	A2	5fr blue & dp ultra	2.40	2.50
5	A2	8fr gray vio & dk brn	14.00	17.50
6	A2	10fr indigo	5.00	5.00
7	A2	15fr indigo & brn vio	6.50	6.50
		Nos. 2-7 (6)	28.70	33.50

Polar Observation — A3

1957, Oct. 11

8	A3	5fr black & violet	2.50	4.25
9	A3	10fr rose red	3.50	5.00
10	A3	15fr dark blue	4.00	6.50
		Nos. 8-10 (3)	10.00	15.75

International Geophysical Year, 1957-58.

Imperforates

Most stamps of this French possession exist imperforate in issued and trial colors, and also in small presentation sheets in issued colors.

Flower Issue
Common Design Type

Design: Pringlea, horiz.

1959   Photo.   Perf. 12½x12

11	CD104	10fr sal, grn & yel	8.75	7.50

Common Design Types pictured following the introduction.

Coat of Arms — A5

1959, Sept. 14   Typo.   Perf. 13x14

15	A5	20fr ultra, lt bl & yel	13.50	11.00

Sheathbills — A6

4fr, Sea leopard, horiz. 25fr, Weddell seal at Kerguélen, horiz. 85fr, King penguin.

1960, Dec. 15   Engr.   Perf. 13

16	A6	2fr grnsh bl, gray & choc	2.00	2.50
17	A6	4fr bl, dk brn & dk grn	8.00	7.75
18	A6	25fr sl grn, bis brn & blk	77.50	45.00
19	A6	85fr grnsh bl, org & blk	17.50	17.50
		Nos. 16-19 (4)	105.00	72.75

Yves-Joseph de Kerguélen-Trémarec — A7

1960, Nov. 22

20	A7	25fr red org, dk bl & brn	22.50	21.00

Yves-Joseph de Kerguélen-Trémarec, discoverer of the Kerguélen Archipelago.

Charcot, Compass Rose and "Pourquoi-pas?" A8

1961, Dec. 26   Unwmk.   Perf. 13

21	A8	25fr brn, grn & red	24.00	21.00

25th anniv. of the death of Commander Jean Charcot (1867-1936), Antarctic explorer.

Elephant Seals Fighting — A9

1963, Feb. 11   Engr.   Perf. 13

22	A9	8fr dk blue, blk & claret	10.00	8.00

See No. C4.

Penguins and Camp on Crozet Island — A10

20fr, Research station & IQSY emblem.

1963, Dec. 16   Unwmk.   Perf. 13

23	A10	5fr blk, red brn & Prus bl	55.00	45.00
24	A10	20fr vio, sl & red brn	57.50	52.50

Intl. Quiet Sun Year, 1964-65. See No. C6.

Great Blue Whale A11

Black-browed Albatross A12

10fr, Cape pigeons. 12fr, Phylica trees, Amsterdam Island. 15fr, Killer whale (orca).

1966-69   Engr.   Perf. 13

25	A11	5fr brt bl & indigo	18.50	12.50
26	A12	10fr sl, ind & ol brn	27.50	24.00
27	A11	12fr brt bl, sl grn & lemon	17.50	16.00
27A	A11	15fr ol, dk bl & ind	14.00	9.50
28	A12	20fr slate, ol & org	280.00	225.00
		Nos. 25-28 (5)	357.50	287.00

Issued: 5fr, 12/12; 20fr, 1/3/68; 10fr, 12fr, 1/6/69; 15fr, 12/21/69.

Aurora Australis, Map of Antarctica and Rocket — A13

1967, Mar. 4   Engr.   Perf. 13

29	A13	20fr mag, blue & blk	22.00	20.00

Launching of the 1st space rocket from Adelie Land, Jan., 1967.

Dumont d'Urville — A14

1968, Jan. 20
30 A14 30fr lt ultra, dk bl & dk brn 110.00 75.00

Jules Sébastien César Dumont D'Urville (1790-1842), French naval commander and South Seas explorer.

WHO Anniversary Issue
Common Design Type
1968, May 4 Engr. Perf. 13
31 CD126 30fr red, yel & bl 62.50 47.50

Human Rights Year Issue
Common Design Type
1968, Aug. 10 Engr. Perf. 13
32 CD127 30fr grnsh bl, red & brn 55.00 47.50

Polar Camp with Helicopter, Plane and Snocat Tractor A15

1969, Mar. 17 Engr. Perf. 13
33 A15 25fr Prus bl, lt grnsh bl & brn red 19.00 11.00

20 years of French Polar expeditions.

ILO Issue
Common Design Type
1970, Jan. 1 Engr. Perf. 13
35 CD131 20fr org, dk bl & brn 15.00 10.00

UPU Headquarters Issue
Common Design Type
1970, May 20 Engr. Perf. 13
36 CD133 50fr blue, plum & ol bis 40.00 27.50

Ice Fish — A16

Fish: Nos. 38-43, Antarctic cods, various species. 135fr, Zanchlorhynchus spinifer.

1971 Engr. Perf. 13
37 A16 5fr brt grn, ind & org 2.50 1.25
38 A16 10fr redsh brn & dp vio 3.50 1.50
39 A16 20fr dp cl, brt grn & org 4.75 2.50
40 A16 22fr pur, brn ol & mag 5.00 3.50
41 A16 25fr grn, ind & org 5.75 3.75
42 A16 30fr sep, gray & bl vio 6.00 4.50
43 A16 35fr sl grn, dk brn & ocher 6.25 3.75
44 A16 135fr Prus bl, dp org & ol grn 10.00 5.75
Nos. 37-44 (8) 43.75 26.50
Issued: Nos. 37-39, 41-42, 1/1; Nos. 40, 43-44, 12/22.

Map of Antarctica — A17

1971, Dec. 22
45 A17 75fr red 19.00 19.00

Antarctic Treaty pledging peaceful uses of and scientific cooperation in Antarctica, 10th anniv.

Microzetia Mirabilis — A18

Insects: 15fr, Christiansenia dreuxi. 22fr, Phtirocoris antarcticus. 30fr, Antarctophytosus atriceps. 40fr, Paractora drenxi. 140fr, Pringleophaga Kerguelenensis.

1972
46 A18 15fr cl, org & brn 8.50 5.50
47 A18 22fr vio bl, sl grn & yel 12.00 8.50
48 A18 25fr grn, rose lil & pur 5.25 3.50
49 A18 30fr blue & multi 15.00 9.00
50 A18 40fr dk brn, ocher & blk 7.50 4.25
51 A18 140fr bl, emer & brn 11.00 8.00
Nos. 46-51 (6) 59.25 38.75
Issued: Nos. 48, 50-51, 1/3; Nos. 46-47, 49, 12/16.

De Gaulle Issue
Common Design Type
Designs: 50fr, Gen. de Gaulle, 1940. 100fr, Pres. de Gaulle, 1970.
1972, Feb. 1 Engr. Perf. 13
52 CD134 50fr brt grn & blk 17.50 13.00
53 CD134 100fr brt grn & blk 22.50 16.50

Kerguelen Cabbage — A19

Designs: 61fr, Azorella selago, horiz. 87fr, Acaena ascendens, horiz.

1972-73
54 A19 45fr multicolored 8.00 4.75
55 A19 61fr multicolored 3.00 2.50
56 A19 87fr multicolored 5.00 3.50
Nos. 54-56 (3) 16.00 10.75
Issued: 45fr, 12/18; others, 12/13/73.

Mailship Sapmer and Map of Amsterdam Island A20

1974, Dec. 31 Engr. Perf. 13
57 A20 75fr bl, blk & dk brn 6.00 5.00
25th anniversary of postal service.

Antarctic Tern — A21

Designs: 50c, Antarctic petrel. 90c, Sea lioness. 1fr, Weddell seal. 1.20fr, Kerguelen cormorant, vert. 1.40fr, Gentoo penguin, vert.

1976, Jan. Engr. Perf. 13
58 A21 40c multicolored 4.00 3.00
59 A21 50c multicolored 4.25 3.00
60 A21 90c multicolored 6.25 4.00
61 A21 1fr multicolored 10.00 9.25
62 A21 1.20fr multicolored 12.00 11.00
63 A21 1.40fr multicolored 13.00 11.50
Nos. 58-63 (6) 49.50 41.75

Climbing Mount Ross — A22 | James Clark Ross — A22a

1976, Dec. 16 Engr. Perf. 13
64 A22 30c multicolored 3.75 2.75
65 A22a 3fr multicolored 4.00 2.75
First climbing of Mount Ross, Kerguelen Island, Jan. 5, 1975.

James Cook — A23

1976, Dec. 16
66 A23 70c multicolored 10.00 9.00
Bicentenary of Capt. Cook's voyage past Kerguelen Island. See No. C46.

Commerson's Dolphins — A24

1977, Feb. 1 Engr. Perf. 13
67 A24 1.10fr Blue whale 5.25 3.75
68 A24 1.50fr shown 5.75 4.00

Macrocystis Algae A25

Salmon Hatchery A26

Magga Dan — A27

Designs: 70c, Durvillea algae. 90c, Albatross. 1fr, Underwater sampling and scientists, vert. 1.40fr, Thala Dan and penguins.

1977, Dec. 20 Engr. Perf. 13
69 A25 40c ol brn & bis 1.20 .75
70 A26 50c dk bl & pur 1.25 1.10
71 A25 70c blk, grn & brn 1.40 1.00
72 A26 90c grn, brt bl & brn 1.50 1.10
73 A27 1fr slate 1.25 1.10
74 A27 1.20fr multi 2.50 1.75
75 A27 1.40fr multi 1.75 1.75
Nos. 69-75 (7) 10.85 8.55
See Nos. 77-79.

A28

Explorer with French and Expedition Flags.

1977, Dec. 24
76 A28 1.90fr multicolored 6.25 5.25
French Polar expeditions, 1947-48.

Types of 1977
40c, Forbin, destroyer. 50c, Jeanne d'Arc, helicopter carrier. 1.40fr, Kerguelen cormorant.

1979, Jan. 1 Engr. Perf. 13
77 A27 40c black & blue 1.00 1.00
78 A27 50c black & blue 1.25 1.15
79 A26 1.40fr multicolored 1.25 1.25
Nos. 77-79 (3) 3.50 3.40

Raymond Rallier du Baty — A29

1979, Jan. 1
80 A29 1.20fr citron & indigo 1.10 1.00
See Nos. 97, 100, 111, 117, 129, 135, 188.

French Navigators Monument, Hobart A30

1979, Jan. 1
81 A30 1fr multicolored .80 .75
French navigators and explorers.

Petrel A31

Design: 70c, Rockhopper penguins, vert.
1979 Engr. Perf. 13
82 A31 70c multi .90 .90
83 A31 1fr shown 1.10 1.10

Commandant Bourdais — A32

Design: 1.10fr, Doudart de Lagree, vert.
1979
84 A32 1.10fr multicolored .95 .90
85 A32 1.50fr shown 1.10 1.10

Adm. Antoine d'Entrecasteaux — A33

1979
86 A33 1.20fr multicolored 1.00 1.00

Sebastian de el Cano — A34

Discovery of Amsterdam Island, 1522: 4fr, Victoria, horiz.
1979
87 A34 1.40fr multicolored .85 .75
88 A34 4fr multicolored 1.75 1.40

 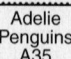

Adelie Penguins A35 | Adelie Penguin A36

Sea Leopard — A37

1980, Dec. 15   Engr.   Perf. 13
89 A35 50c rose violet   1.10 1.00
90 A36 60c multicolored   1.10 1.00
91 A35 1.20fr multicolored   1.75 1.25
92 A37 1.30fr multicolored   1.10 1.00
93 A37 1.80fr multicolored   1.10 1.00
   Nos. 89-93 (5)   6.15 5.25

20th Anniv. of Antarctic Treaty — A38

1981, June 23   Engr.   Perf. 13
94 A38 1.80fr multicolored   3.75 3.75

Alouette II — A39

1981-82   Engr.   Perf. 13
95 A39 55c brown & multi   .50 .45
96 A39 65c blue & multi   .55 .45

Explorer Type of 1979
1981
97 A29 1.40fr Jean Loranchet   .70 .50

Landing Ship Le Gros Ventre, Kerguelen A41

1983, Jan. 3   Engr.   Perf. 13
98 A41 55c multicolored   .80 .60

Our Lady of the Winds Statue and Church, Kerguelen — A42

1983, Jan. 3
99 A42 1.40fr multicolored   .80 .75

Explorer Type of 1979
Design: Martin de Vivies, Navigator.

1983, Jan. 3
100 A29 1.60fr multicolored   .80 .70

Eaton's Ducks — A44

1983, Jan. 3
101 A44 1.50fr multicolored   .75 .55
102 A44 1.80fr multicolored   .80 .75

Trawler Austral A45

1983, Jan. 3
103 A45 2.30fr multicolored   1.25 1.00

Freighter Lady Franklin — A46

1983, Aug. 4   Engr.   Perf. 13
104 A46 5fr multicolored   3.50 2.75

Glaciology A47

Design: Scientists examining glacier, base.

1984, Jan. 1   Engr.   Perf. 13
105 A47 15c multicolored   .30 .25
106 A47 1.70fr multicolored   .70 .60

Crab-eating Seal — A48

Penguins A49

1984, Jan. 1
107 A48 60c multicolored   .50 .50
108 A49 70c multicolored   .40 .40
109 A49 2fr multicolored   1.10 .90
110 A48 5.90fr multicolored   1.75 1.50
   Nos. 107-110 (4)   3.75 3.30

Explorer Type of 1979
1984, Jan. 1
111 A29 1.80fr Alfred Faure   .80 .65

Biomass A51

1985, Jan. 1   Engr.   Perf. 13
112 A51 1.80fr multicolored   .65 .50
113 A51 5.20fr multicolored   1.50 1.25

Emperor Penguins A52

Snowy Petrel A53

1985, Jan. 1   Engr.   Perf. 13
114 A52 1.70fr multicolored   .90 .75
115 A53 2.80fr multicolored   1.10 1.00

Port Martin — A54

1985, Jan. 1   Engr.   Perf. 13
116 A54 2.20fr multicolored   1.10 .75

Explorer Type of 1979
1985, Jan. 1   Engr.   Perf. 13
117 A29 2fr Andre-Frank Liotard .80 .65

Antarctic Fulmar A56

1986, Jan. 1   Engr.   Perf. 13
118 A56 1fr shown   .50 .40
119 A56 1.70fr Giant petrels   .75 .70
   Nos. 118-119,C91 (3)   3.25 2.85

Echinoderms A57

1986, Jan. 1
120 A57 1.90fr shown   .85 .70

Cotula Plumosa — A58

Design: 6.20fr, Lycopodium. saururus.

1986, Jan. 1
121 A58 2.30fr shown   .75 .70
122 A58 6.20fr multicolored   2.00 1.75

Shipping — A59

Designs: 2.10fr, Var research ship. 3fr, Polarbjorn support ship.

1986, Jan. 1
123 A59 2.10fr multicolored   .85 .75
124 A59 3fr multicolored   1.10 1.00

Marine Life — A60

1987, Jan. 1   Engr.   Perf. 13½x13
125 A60 50c dk blue & org   .55 .45

Flora — A61

Designs: 1.80fr, Poa cookii. 6.50fr, Lichen, Neuropogon taylori.

1987, Jan. 1
126 A61 1.80fr multicolored   .65 .45
127 A61 6.50fr multicolored   1.90 1.40

Marret Base, Adelie Land — A62

1987, Jan. 1
128 A62 2fr yel brn, dk ultra & lake .80 .65

Explorer Type of 1979
1987, Jan. 1
129 A29 2.20fr Adm. Mouchez   .85 .65

Reindeer A64

1987, Jan. 1
130 A64 2.50fr black   1.25 1.00

Transport Ship Eure — A65

1987, Jan. 1
131 A65 3.20fr dk ultra, Prus grn & dk grn 1.25 1.00

Macaroni Penguins A66

1987, Jan. 1   Perf. 13x12½
132 A66 4.80fr multicolored   2.50 1.75

Elephant Grass A67

1988, Jan. 1   Engr.   Perf. 13
133 A67 1.70fr Prus grn, emer & olive .75 .60

Rev.-Father Lejay, Explorer — A68

1988, Jan. 1
134 A68 2.20fr vio, ultra & blk .85 .70

Explorer Type of 1979
Design: Robert Gessain (1907-86).

1988, Jan. 1
135 A29 3.40fr gray, dk red & blk 1.25 1.00

Le Gros Ventre, 18th Cent. — A70

1988, Jan. 1
136 A70 3.50fr dp ultra, bl grn & brn 1.25 1.10

Mermaid and B.A.P. Jules Verne, Research Vessel
A71

1988, Jan. 1
137 A71 4.90fr gray & dk blue   2.25 1.60

La Fortune, Early 19th Cent. — A72

1988, Jan. 1
138 A72 5fr blk & dull bl grn   2.00 1.60

Wilson's Petrel
A73

1988, Jan. 1
139 A73 6.80fr blk, sepia & dl bl grn   2.75 2.00
See Nos. 143-144.

Mt. Ross Campaign (in 1987)
A74

Designs: 2.20fr, Volcanic rock cross-sections. 15.10fr, Kerguelen Is.

1988, Jan. 1   Perf. 13x12½
140 A74 2.20fr multi   .75 .60
141 A74 15.10fr multi   4.25 3.50
 a. Pair, #140-141 + label   6.50 6.50

Darrieus System Wind Vane Electric Generator
A75

1988, Jan. 1   Engr.   Perf. 13
142 A75 1fr dark blue & blue   .50 .30

Fauna Type of 1988
1989, Jan. 1   Engr.
143 A73 1.10fr Lithodes   .35 .35
144 A73 3.60fr Blue petrel   1.40 1.10

Fern — A76

Designs: Blechnum penna Marina.

1989, Jan. 1
145 A76 2.80fr multicolored   1.00 .85

Minerals — A77

1989, Jan. 1
146 A77 5.10fr Mesotype   1.90 1.75
147 A77 7.30fr Analcime   2.75 2.75

Henri and Rene Bossiere, Pioneers of the Kerguelen Isls. — A78

1989, Jan. 1
148 A78 2.20fr multicolored   1.10 .65

Kerguelen Is. Sheep
A79

1989, Jan. 1   Perf. 13½x13
149 A79 2fr multicolored   .80 .60

Scuba Diver, Adelie Coast
A80

1989, Jan. 1
150 A80 1.70fr dk olive bis, blue & dk grn   .75 .65

Map of Kerguelen Island, Protozoa and Copepod
A81

1990, Jan. 1   Engr.   Perf. 13
151 A81 1.10fr blk, brt blue & red brn   .90 .50
Study of protista, Kerguelan Is.

Cattle on Farm, Sea Birds — A82

1990, Jan. 1
152 A82 1.70fr Prus blue, grn & brn blk   .80 .65
Rehabilitation of the environment, Amsterdam Is.

Quoy and *Copendium decollata* — A83

1990, Jan. 1   Perf. 13½x13
153 A83 2.20fr brt blue, blk & red brn   .90 .70
Jean Rene C. Quoy (1790-1869), naturalist, navigator.

Dumont d'Urville (1790-1842), Explorer — A84

1990, Jan. 1
154 A84 3.60fr ultra & blk   1.50 1.00

Yellow-billed Albatross
A85

1990, Jan. 1   Perf. 13x12½
155 A85 2.80fr multicolored   1.75 1.00

Aragonite — A86

1990, Jan. 1
156 A86 5.10fr deep ultra & dark yel grn   2.75 2.00

Ranunculus pseudo trullifolius — A87

1990, Jan. 1   Perf. 13
157 A87 8.40fr dp bl, org & emer grn   3.00 2.50

Penguin Type of Airpost 1974
1991, Jan. 1
158 AP18 50c blue grn, bl & blk   .75 .45
Postal Service at Crozet Island, 30th anniv.

Moss
A88

1991, Jan. 1   Perf. 13x12½
159 A88 1.70fr gray, brn & blk   .80 .60

Adm. Max Douguet (1903-1989)
A89

1991, Jan. 1
160 A89 2.30fr org brn, blk & bl   1.25 .90

Lighter L'Aventure
A90

1991, Jan. 1   Engr.   Perf. 13
161 A90 3.20fr brn, grn & bl   1.50 1.10

Sea Lions — A91

1991, Jan. 1   Perf. 13
162 A91 3.60fr blue & ol brn   2.25 1.50

Mordenite
A92

1991, Jan. 1
163 A92 5.20fr blk, grn bl & grn   2.60 1.75

Champsocephalus Gunnari — A93

1991, Jan. 1
164 A93 7.80fr blue & green   3.00 2.50

Antarctic Treaty, 30th Anniv. — A94

1991, Jan. 1
165 A94 9.30fr ol grn & rose red   3.75 3.25

A95

Design: Colobanthus Kerguelensis.

1992, Jan. 1   Engr.   Perf. 13
166 A95 1fr bl grn, grn & brn   .85 .40

Globe Challenge Yacht Race — A96

1992, Jan. 1   Litho.
167 A96 2.20fr multicolored   1.75 1.10

Dissostichus Eleginoides
A97

1992, Jan. 1   Engr.
168 A97 2.30fr blue, ol grn & red brn   1.60 1.10

Paul Tchernia — A98

1992, Jan. 1   Engr.   Perf. 13
169 A98 2.50fr brown & green   .95 .90

Capt. Marion Dufresne
(1724-1772) — A99

1992, Jan. 1   Engr.   Perf. 13
170 A99 3.70fr red, blk & bl   1.60 1.30

Supply Ship
Tottan, 1951
A100

1992, Jan. 1   Engr.   Perf. 13
171 A100 14fr blue grn, brn & bl   5.50 4.50

WOCE
Program
A101

1992, Jan. 1
172 A101 25.40fr multi   11.00 9.50

Coat of Arms — A102

1992-95   Engr.   Perf. 13
173 A102 10c black   .25 .25
174 A102 20c greenish blue   .40 .25
175 A102 30c red   .50 .25
176 A102 40c green   .60 .25
177 A102 50c orange   .60 .25
      Nos. 173-177 (5)   2.35 1.25

Issued: 10c, 1/1/92; 20c, 30c, 1/1/93; 40c, 1/1/94; 50c, 1/2/95.
See Nos. 295-299.

Garnet — A103

1993, Jan. 1   Engr.   Perf. 13
183 A103 1fr multicolored   1.40 .35

See Nos. 194, 203, 212, 222, 235, 244, 259, 279, 300, 330.

Research Ship Marion
Dufresne, 20th
Anniv. — A104

1993, Jan. 1
184 A104 2.20fr multicolored   1.25 .70

Lyallia
Kerguelensis — A105

1993, Jan. 1
185 A105 2.30fr blue & green   1.25 .70

A106

A107

1993, Jan. 1
186 A106 2.50fr Killer whale   1.25 .80
187 A107 2.50fr Skua   6.50 1.50

A108

Design: 2.50fr, Andre Prudhomme (1930-1959), Meteorologist. 22fr, Weather station, Adelie Land.

1993, Jan. 1   Perf. 12½x13
188   2.50fr blue, blk & org   1.00 .75
189   22fr org, blk & bl   7.50 5.25
   a. A108 Pair, #188-189 + label 11.00 11.00

43rd Anniv. of Mètèo France in French Southern & Antarctic Territory.

Centriscops
Obliquus
A109

1993, Jan. 1   Perf. 13
190 A109 3.40fr multicolored   1.50 1.00

Freighter
Italo
Marsano
A110

1993, Jan. 1
191 A110 3.70fr multicolored   1.75 .90

ECOPHY
Program — A111

1993, Jan. 1
192 A111 14fr black, blue & brn 6.25 3.50

L'Astrolabe on
Northeast Route,
1991 — A112

1993, Jan. 1
193 A112 22fr multicolored   9.00 6.25

Mineral Type of 1993
1994, Jan. 1   Engr.   Perf. 13
194 A103 1fr Cordierite   1.25 .70

Felis Catus
A113

1994, Jan. 1
195 A113 2fr green & black   3.50 1.25

A114

1994, Jan. 1   Engr.   Perf. 13
196 A114 2.40fr dk brn, blk & bl 1.50 .65

A115

1994, Jan. 1
197 A115 2.80fr slate blue   1.50 .80

Robert Pommier
(1919-61) — A116

1994, Jan. 1
198 A116 2.80fr multicolored   1.50 .85

A117

Designs: 2.80fr, C.A. Vincendon Dumoulin (1811-58), hydrographer. 23fr, Measuring Earth's magnetic field.

1994, Jan. 1   Perf. 12½x13
199   2.80fr black & blue   1.50 1.00
200   23fr blue & black   7.25 5.00
   a. A117 Pair, #199-200 + label 10.00 10.00

Rascasse
A119

1994, Jan. 1   Perf. 13
201 A119 3.70fr bl grn & red brn 1.40 1.00

Kerguelen of
Tremarec
A120

1994, Jan. 1
202 A120 4.30fr multicolored   1.75 1.25

Mineral Type of 1993
1995, Jan. 2   Engr.   Perf. 13
203 A103 1fr Olivine   1.50 .40

Mancoglosse Antarctique — A121

1995, Jan. 2
204 A121 2.40fr ol brn, vio & bl grn 1.25 1.00

Andree (1903-90) and
Edgar de la Rue
(1901-91) — A122

1995, Jan. 2
205 A122 2.80fr bl, red brn & mag 1.40 .90

SODAR
Station
A123

1995, Jan. 2
206 A123 2.80fr vio, mag & red brn 1.40 1.00

Mont
D'Alsace
A124

1995, Jan. 2
207 A124 3.70fr dk bl, vio, red brn 1.75 1.10

Balaenoptera Acutorostrata — A125

1995, Jan. 2
208 A125 23fr blue, claret & ind 9.75 6.50

Sailing Ship
Tamaris — A126

1995, Jan. 2
209 A126 25.80fr multicolored   10.00 6.75

L'Heroine, Crozet
Islands Mission,
1837 — A127

1995, Jan. 2
210 A127 27.30fr blue   11.00 7.25

Creation of the Territories, 40th
Anniv. — A128

1995, Aug. 7　Litho.　Imperf.
Size: 143x84mm
211　A128　30fr multicolored　15.00　15.00

Mineral Type of 1993
1996, Jan. 1　Engr.　Perf. 13
212　A103　1fr Amazonite　　.90　.30

White-chinned Petrel — A129

1996, Jan. 1
213　A129　2.40fr blue black　1.40　.70

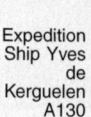

Expedition
Ship Yves
de
Kerguelen
A130

1996, Jan. 1
214　A130　2.80fr multicolored　1.50　.75

Benedict Point
Scientific Research
Station, Amsterdam
Island — A131

1996, Jan. 1
215　A131　2.80fr multicolored　1.50　.75

Paul-Emile Victor (1907-1995), Polar
Explorer — A132

Designs: 2.80fr, Victor crossing Greenland
with sled dogs, 1936. 23fr, Victor, penguins,
Dumont d'Urville Base, Adélie Land.

1996, Jan. 1
216　A132　2.80fr multicolored　1.40　.85
217　A132　23fr multicolored　11.50　7.50
a.　Pair, #216-217 + label　14.00　14.00

Admiral Jacquinot (1796-
1879), Antarctic
Explorer — A133

1996, Jan. 1
218　A133　3.70fr dark blue & blue　1.50　1.00

Trawler
Austral
A134

1996, Jan. 1　Photo. & Engr.
219　A134　4.30fr multicolored　2.25　1.25

Lycopodium Magellanicum — A135

1996, Jan. 1　Engr.
220　A135　7.70fr multicolored　3.00　2.25

Search for Micrometeorites, Cape
Prudhomme — A136

1996, Jan. 1
221　A136　15fr vio, blk & grn bl　8.00　5.00

Mineral Type of 1993
1997, Jan. 1　Engr.　Perf. 13x12½
222　A103　1fr Amethyst　1.25　.40

Storm Petrel
A137

1997, Jan. 1　Perf. 13
223　A137　2.70fr blue & indigo　1.50　.80

Rene Garcia
(1915-95),
Windmill — A138

1997, Jan. 1
224　A138　3fr multicolored　1.60　.90

Research Ship Marion
Dufresne — A139

Photo. & Engr.
1997, Jan. 1　Perf. 13x12½
225　A139　3fr multicolored　1.60　.90

Jean Turquet (1867-
1945) — A140

1997, Jan. 1　Engr.　Perf. 13
226　A140　4fr black & brown　1.60　1.10

A141

1997, Jan. 1
227　A141　5.20fr multicolored　2.40　1.50
Church of Our Lady of Birds, Crozet Island.

Army Health
Service — A142

1997, Jan. 1
228　A142　8fr multicolored　3.75　2.50

Poa
Kerguelensis — A143

1997, Jan. 1
229　A143　29.20fr multi　12.50　8.50

French Polar Expeditions, 50th
Anniv. — A144

Designs: No. 230, Greenland Expedition.
No. 231, Port Martin, 1950-51, Marret Base,
1952, Adélie Land. No. 232, Dumont D'Urville,
1956, Charcot Station, Magnetic Pole, 1957.

Photo. & Engr.
1997, Feb. 28　Perf. 13x12½
230　1fr multicolored　1.10　.70
231　1fr multicolored　1.10　.70
232　1fr multicolored　1.10　.70
a.　A144 Strip of 3, #230-232　8.00　6.00

Yves-Joseph de Kerguelen Trémarec
(1734-97) — A145

3fr, Portrait. 24fr, Cook's landing at Kerguelen Island, Dec. 1776.

1997, Mar. 3　Engr.　Perf. 13
233　3fr multicolored　1.25　.90
234　24fr multicolored　9.00　7.00
a.　A145 Pair, #233-234 + label　14.00　11.00
No. 234 is 37x37mm.

Mineral Type of 1993
1998, Jan. 2　Engr.　Perf. 13
235　A103　1fr Rock crystal　1.25　.40

Fisheries Management — A146

Designs: No. 236, Fishing boats. No. 237,
Examining fish, performing research.

1998, Jan. 2
236　A146　2.60fr multicolored　1.40　.70
237　A146　2.60fr multicolored　1.40　.70
a.　Pair, #236-237 + label　3.50　3.50

Gray-headed Albatross — A147

1998, Jan. 2
238　A147　2.70fr multicolored　1.75　.75

Ecology of
St. Paul
Island
A148

1998, Jan. 2
239　A148　3fr bl, brn & grn　2.25　1.00

Etienne Peau, Antarctic
Explorer — A149

1998, Jan. 2　Perf. 13x13½
240　A149　3fr lilac, blue & black　1.75　.85

Georges Laclavere
(1906-94),
Geographer — A150

1998, Jan. 2
241　A150　4fr lt org, blk & red brn　1.75　1.00

Mole Shark
A151

1998, Jan. 2　Perf. 13
242　A151　27fr multicolored　11.00　6.75

"Le
Cancalais"
A152

1998, Jan. 2
243　A152　29.20fr multicolored　11.50　7.00

Mineral Type of 1993
1999, Jan. 1　Engr.　Perf. 13
244　A103　1fr Epidote, vert.　1.25　.40

Chinstrap
Penguin
A153

1999, Jan. 1
245　A153　2.70fr brn, blk & bl　1.60　.85

Pierre Sicaud (1911-98),
Antarctic Explorer,
Commander of Outpost
at Kerguelen
Islands — A154

1999, Jan. 1
246　A154　3fr black & green　1.25　.80

Penguins
of Crozet
Islands
A155

1999, Jan. 1
247　A155　3fr multicolored　3.00　.85

Jacques-André
Martin (1911-
49) — A156

1999, Jan. 1
248 A156 4fr multicolored   1.75 1.00

Ray
A157

1999, Jan. 1   **Perf. 12½**
249 A157 5.20fr mag, bl & brn   2.25 2.25
Value is for stamp with surrounding rectangular selvage.

F.S.
Floreal
A158

1999, Jan. 1 **Photo.**   **Perf. 13**
250 A158 5.20fr multicolored   2.25 1.75
No. 250 was printed se-tenant with label. Value is for stamp with label attached.

"Pop Cat"
Program,
Kerguelen
Islands
A159

1999, Jan. 1   **Engr.**
251 A159 8fr multicolored   4.75 3.00

Study of
Albatrosses on
Artificial
Nests — A160

1999, Jan. 1
252 A160 16fr olive, grn & blk   6.50 4.25

Amsterdam
Base,
Kerguelen
Base, 50th
Anniv.
A161

Designs: 3fr, Amsterdam Base. 24fr, Kerguelen Base.

1999, Jan. 1
253 A161 3fr multi   4.50 1.00
254 A161 24fr multi   8.50 5.00
a.   Pair, #253-254 + label   15.00 12.00

Festuca
Contracta — A162

1999, Jan. 1
255 A162 24fr dk grn, ol & bl
          grn   9.00 6.00

Geoleta
Program
A163

1999, Jan. 1   **Perf. 13x12½**
256 A163 29.20fr blk, bl & red
           brn   11.00 7.00

Voyage
of
Marion
Dufresne
II
A164

a, Docked, Reunion. b, Passengers in dining salon. c, Penguins, Crozet Island. d, Postal manager of Alfred Faure, Crozet Island, vert. e, Port of France, Kerguelen Island. f, Port Couvreux, Kerguelen Island. g, Offloading stores, Port of France, Kerguelen Island. h, Port Jeanne d'arc, Kerguelen Island. i, St. Paul Island. j, Ruins of lobster cannery, St. Paul Island. k, Martin de Vivies Base, Amsterdam Island. l, Offloading cargo, Amsterdam Island.

1999, May 1 **Litho.**   **Perf. 13**
257 A164 Souv. bklt., #a.-l.   90.00

Nos. 257a-257l are all non-denominated. Stamps are valid for 20 gram international letter rate. Each stamp appears on a separate booklet pane showing an enlarged design of the stamp. Booklet sold for 100fr.
See Nos. 294, 329, 359, 390, 420, 482, 573C.

Souvenir Sheet

PhilexFrance '99, World Philatelic
Exhibition — A165

Antarctic postmarks on stamps: a, Malagasy Republic #280. b, Malagasy Republic #282. c, Malagasy Republic #C42. d, #21.

1999, July 2 Litho. & Engr. Perf. 13
258 A165 5.20fr Sheet of 4, #a.-
           d.   10.00 7.50
Nos. 258b-258c are each 40x52mm.

Mineral Type of 1993
2000, Jan. Engr.   Perf. 12¾x13
259 A103 1fr Mica, *vert.*   1.25 .40

Puffin
A166

2000, Jan.   **Perf. 13x12¾**
260 A166 2.70fr multi   2.00 .80

André Beaugé
(1913-97) — A167

2000, Jan.   **Perf. 12¾x13**
261 A167 3fr multi   1.40 .60

Abby Jane
Morrell — A168

2000, Jan.   **Perf. 13¼x13**
262 A168 4fr multi   1.75 .95

Oceanographic Survey — A169

2000, Jan.   **Perf. 13x12½**
263 A169 4.40fr multi   2.10 1.25

Sled Dog
Hobbs — A170

2000, Jan.   **Perf. 12¾x13**
264 A170 5.20fr multi   2.25 1.25

Sleep
Study
A171

2000, Jan. Photo.   Perf. 13x12½
265 A171 8fr multi + label   3.50 2.25

Ship "La
Perouse"
A172

2000, Jan. Engr.   Perf. 13x12½
266 A172 16fr multi   7.00 4.25

Lantern
Fish
A173

2000, Jan.
267 A173 24fr multi   10.50 6.00

Larose
Bay — A174

2000, Jan.
268 A174 27fr multi   11.00 7.00

Explorers — A175

No. 269, Yves Joseph de Kerguelen-Trémarec (1734-97). No. 270, Jules Sébastien César Dumont D'Urville (1790-1842). No. 271, Raymond Rallier du Baty (1881-1978). No. 272, Paul Emile Victor (1907-95). #273, Edgar Aubert de La Rüe (1901-91). #273, Paul-Emile Victor (1907-95).

2000, Jan.   **Perf. 13**
Booklet Stamps
269 A175 3fr multi   1.60 .75
270 A175 3fr multi   1.60 .75
271 A175 3fr multi   1.60 .75
272 A175 3fr multi   1.60 .75

---

273 A175 3fr multi   1.60 .75
a.   Bklt. pane, #269-273 + 2 labels   9.00
        Complete booklet, #273a   10.00

Souvenir Sheet

The Third Millennium — A176

No. 274: a, Penguins, Crozet Islands. b, Seals, Kerguelen Islands. c, Crustacean, Saint-Paul and Amsterdam Islands. d, Hovering vehicle, Adelie Land.

2000, Jan. Photo.   Perf. 13
274 A176 3fr Sheet of 4, #a.-d.   8.50 5.50

Bird Demographic Studies — A177

Designs: 5.20fr, Bird banding. 8fr, Albatross, graph. 16fr, Emperor penguins, graph.

2000, Jan.   **Perf. 13x13¼**
275 A177 5.20fr multi   2.00 1.00

Size: 50x28mm
276 A177 8fr multi   3.00 1.50
277 A177 16fr multi   6.50 4.00
a.   Horiz. strip, #275-277   15.00 15.00

Relocation of Headquarters to
Reunion — A178

2000, Aug. 6 Litho.   Perf. 13
278 A178 27fr multi   12.00 9.00

Mineral Type of 1993
2001, Jan. 1 Engr.   Perf. 13x12¾
279 A103 1fr Magnetite   1.25 .40

Diving
Petrel
A179

2001, Jan. 1   **Perf. 13x13¼**
280 A179 2.70fr multi   1.50 .60

High Mountain
Military
Group — A180

2001, Jan. 1   **Perf. 13¼x13**
281 A180 3fr multi   1.40 .65

Kerguelen Arch
A181

2001, Jan. 1 — *Perf. 13*
282 A181 3fr blue gray   2.00 .70

Xavier-Charles Richert (1913-92) — A182

2001, Jan. 1
283 A182 3fr multi   1.40 .65

Jean Coulomb — A183

2001, Jan. 1
284 A183 4fr multi   1.75 .85

Memorial to 1874 Astronomical Observation, St. Paul Island — A184

2001, Jan. 1
285 A184 8fr brn & blk   3.50 1.75

Frigate La Fayette A185

2001, Jan. 1 — *Perf. 13x13¼*
286 A185 16fr multi   7.00 3.50

Squid A186

2001, Jan. 1
287 A186 24fr multi   10.50 5.00

Amateur Radio Link Between Space Station Mir and Crozet Island — A187

2001, Jan. 1 — *Litho.* — *Perf. 13*
288 A187 27fr multi   12.00 5.50

Bryum Laevigatum — A188

2001, Jan. 1 — *Engr.* — *Perf. 13x12½*
289 A188 29.20fr multi   13.00 6.00

Souvenir Sheet

Ships A189

No. 290: a, Carmen. b, Austral. c, Ramuntcho. d, Samper 1.

2001, Jan. 1 — *Perf. 13x13½*
290 A189 5.20fr Sheet of 4, #a-d   9.00 4.50

Souvenir Sheet

Wildlife A190

No. 291: a, Albatrosses. b, Emperor penguins, horiz. c, Sea lions, horiz. d, Whales.

2001, Jan. 1 — *Litho.* — *Perf. 13*
291 A190 3fr Sheet of 4, #a-d   10.50 5.00

Antarctic Treaty, 40th Anniv. — A191

2001, June 23 — *Engr.* — *Perf. 13x12¾*
292 A191 5.20fr dark & sky blue   3.25 1.00

Commission for the Conservation of Antarctic Marine Living Resources, 20th Anniv. A192

2001, Oct. 22 — *Litho.* — *Perf. 13*
293 A192 5.20fr multi   5.00 2.00

Voyage Booklet Type of 1999

Adélie Land: a, Boat in pack ice. b, Dumont d'Urville Base. c, Adélie penguin rookery. d, L'Astrolabe Glacier. e, Pointe Géologie Archipelago. f, Release of meteorological balloon. g, Equipment convoy. h, Helicopter transport of fresh supplies. i, Arrival of emperor penguins. j, Telecommunications center. k, Looking towards the Antarctic. l, Cape Prud'homme. m, Ship L'Astrolabe anchored. n, Dispatch of mail.

2001, Oct. 29 — *Perf. 13*
294 A164 Souvenir booklet, 2 each #a-n   95.00

Nos. 294a-294n are all non-denominated. Stamps are valid for 20 gram international letter rate. Each stamp appears on a separate booklet pane showing an enlarged design of the stamp and on one pane with all of the

stamps and four labels found at the center of the booklet. the booklet sold for 196.78fr.

100 Cents = 1 Euro (€)
Arms Type of 1992-95 with Euro Denominations

2002, Jan. 2 — *Engr.* — *Perf. 13*

295	A102	1c black	.25	.25
296	A102	2c greenish blue	.25	.25
297	A102	5c red	.30	.25
298	A102	10c green	.40	.25
299	A102	20c orange	.70	.25
	Nos. 295-299 (5)		1.90	1.25

Mineral Type of 1993 with Euro Denomination

2002, Jan. 2 — *Engr.* — *Perf. 12¾x13*
300 A103 15c Nepheline, vert.   1.00 .40

Albatross — A193

2002, Jan. 2 — *Perf. 13¼x13*
301 A193 41c multi   3.00 .80

Ship "Marion Dufresne" A194

2002, Jan. 2 — *Perf. 13x13¼*
302 A194 46c multi   1.40 .60

1963-83 Telegraph Station, Crozet Island — A195

2002, Jan. 2 — *Litho.* — *Perf. 13*
303 A195 46c multi   1.50 .60

Jacques Dubois (1920-2000) A196

2002, Jan. 2 — *Engr.*
304 A196 61c multi   2.25 .90

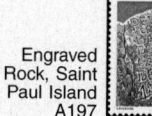

Engraved Rock, Saint Paul Island A197

2002, Jan. 2 — *Perf. 13x13¼*
305 A197 79c multi   2.40 1.25

Kerguelen Cabbage — A198

2002, Jan. 2 — *Perf. 12¼*
306 A198 €1.22 multi   3.50 1.75

Passage of the Ship "Gauss," Cent. A199

2002, Jan. 2 — *Perf. 13x12¼*
307 A199 €2.44 multi   7.25 3.50

Crab A200

2002, Jan. 2 — *Perf. 13x13¼*
308 A200 €3.66 multi   11.00 5.25

Pack Ice Diatoms A201

2002, Jan. 2 — *Litho.* — *Perf. 13*
309 A201 €4.12 multi   12.50 6.00

French Geographic Society Building, Paris — A202

2002, Jan. 2 — *Engr.* — *Perf. 13¼x13*
310 A202 €4.45 multi + label   13.50 8.00

Cartoker Program A203

No. 311: a, 46c, Diagram of plate tectonics. b, €3.66, Geological map of Kerguelen Island.

2002, Jan. 2 — *Perf. 13x12¼*
311 A203 Horiz. pair, #a-b, + central label   12.50 12.50

Souvenir Sheet

Olympic Games for Antarctic Animals A204

No. 312: a, Albatrosses flying marathon. b, Langoustines diving, vert. c, Penguins riding bobsled course, vert. d, Killer whales performing synchronized swimming, vert.

2002, Jan. 2 — *Litho.* — *Perf. 13*
312 A204 46c Sheet of 4, #a-d   6.50 5.50

Souvenir Sheet

Animals and Their Young
A205

No. 313: a, Penguins. b, Sea lions. c, Albatrosses. d, Elephant seals.

2002, Jan. 2
313 A205 79c Sheet of 4, #a-d   10.50 9.50

Introduction of the Euro — A206

2002, Feb. 17
314 A206 46c blue & black   3.50 .60

Mineral Type of 1993
2003, Jan.   Engr.   *Perf. 13¼*
315 A103 15c Apatite, vert.   1.25 .40

Lobster Processing Plant, Saint-Paul
A207

2003, Jan.   *Perf. 13x13¼*
316 A207 41c multi   1.25 .65

Luc Marie Bayle (1914-2000), Painter — A208

2003, Jan.   Litho.   *Perf. 13*
317 A208 46c multi   1.50 .70

Emperor Penguins
A209

2003, Jan.
318 A209 46c multi   2.75 .80

Otice Hydroacoustic Station — A210

2003, Jan.   Engr.   *Perf. 13x13¼*
319 A210 61c multi   1.90 1.00

Restoration of Port Jeanne d'Arc
A211

2003, Jan.   *Perf. 13x12¼*
320 A211 79c multi   2.40 1.25

Phylica
A212

2003, Jan.   *Perf. 13x13¼*
321 A212 €1.22 multi   4.50 2.25

Ship "Bougainville" — A213

2003, Jan.   *Perf. 13¼x13*
322 A213 €2.44 multi   7.25 4.25

Chub
A214

2003, Jan.   Engr.   *Perf. 13x13¼*
323 A214 €3.66 multi   11.00 6.50

Ile aux Pingouins
A215

2003, Jan.   *Perf. 13x12¼*
324 A215 €3.66 black   11.00 6.50

Super Darn Antenna Array
A216

2003, Jan.   *Perf. 13*
325 A216 €4.12 multi   12.50 7.00

Souvenir Sheet

Paintings Revised to Reflect a Less Southerly Antarctica — A217

No. 326: a, Triumph of Venus with fish and lobsters. b, King Louis XV and wife with penguins, vert. c, Jules Dumont d'Urville and wife in a grassy Adélie Land. d, Chevalier Yves de Kerguelin under umbrella, seal in pool, vert.

2003, Jan.
326 A217 46c Sheet of 4, #a-d   6.50 6.50

Protective Clothing — A218

Cold-weather outerwear from: a, 1898. b, 1912. c, 2002. d, 1980, e, 1996.

2003, Jan.   Photo.   *Perf. 13¼x13*
327   Booklet pane of 5   12.00
   a.-e. A218 79c Any single   2.40 1.25
   Booklet, #327   12.00

Voyage of the Ship "Français," Cent. — A219

2003, Aug. 31   Engr.   *Perf. 13x13¼*
328   Horiz. strip of 3   15.00 13.50
   a. A219 79c Capt. J.-B. Charcot   2.50 1.25
   b. A219 €1.22 Ship in ice, horiz.   4.00 2.00
   c. A219 €2.44 Ship in harbor, horiz.   7.50 4.25

Stamp size: Nos. 328b-328c, 49x29mm.

Voyage Booklet Type of 1999

Recipes: a, Truite aus deux citrons (trout and waterfall). b, Veau d'Amsterdam à la savoyarde (cattle). c, Lapin "Volage" à la cannelle (rabbits, penguins). d, Rôti de légine de l'ile de l'est (fish). e, Civet de renne "Volcan du diable," (reindeer). f, Iles antarctiques flottantes. g, Langouste à la mode de Saint-Paul (lobster). h, Gigot de mouflon aux 5 épices et aux pommes (sheep). i, Cabot tropical (fish, ship). j, Tagine d'agneau aux épices de la Réunion (sheep). k, Moules au pastis (mussels). l, Glace à la menthe sauvage d'Amsterdam (mint plant).

2003, Nov. 6   Litho.   *Perf. 13*
329 A164   Souvenir booklet, #a-l   60.00

Nos. 329a-329l are all non-denominated. Stamps are valid for 20 gram international letter rate. Each stamp appears on a separate booklet pane showing an enlarged design of the stamp. The booklet sold for €17.

Mineral Type of 1993
2004, Jan. 1   Engr.   *Perf. 13¼*
330 A103 15c Chalcedony, vert.   1.25 .40

A220

2004, Jan. 1   Engr.   *Perf. 13x13¼*
331 A220 45c multi   1.40 .85

Mario Marret, director of film "Terre Adélie."

Col. Robert Genty (1910-2001) — A221

2004, Jan. 1
332 A221 50c multi   1.75 .95

Albert Faure Base, Crozet Island, 40th Anniv.
A222

2004, Jan. 1   Litho. & Engr.
333 A222 50c multi   1.50 .95

Péron's Dolphins
A223

2004, Jan. 1   Litho.   *Perf. 13*
334 A223 75c multi   3.00 1.50

Twin Otter Flights — A224

2004, Jan. 1   Photo.   *Perf. 12¾*
335 A224 90c multi   2.75 1.75

Values are for stamps with surrounding selvage.

Iceberg
A225

2004, Jan. 1   Engr.   *Perf. 13x13¼*
336 A225 €1.30 multi   4.00 2.40

Grave of Sailors from the Volage — A226

2004, Jan. 1   *Perf. 13¼x13*
337 A226 €2.50 multi   7.50 5.00

Krill
A227

2004, Jan. 1   *Perf. 13x13¼*
338 A227 €4 multi   12.00 8.00

Ship "Dives" A228

2004, Jan. 1
339 A228 €4.50 multi   13.50 9.25

Souvenir Sheet

Hydrological Surveys, Adélie Land — A229

2004, Jan. 1   **Litho.**   *Perf. 13*
340 A229 €4.90 multi   15.00 10.50

Souvenir Sheet

Imaginary "TAAFland" Theme Park — A230

No. 341: a, Whale statue, pyramidal entrance structure. b, Showgirls, seals, vert. c, Boy and girl with ice cream cones, vert. d, Woman in swimsuit, penguins.

2004, Jan. 1
341 A230 50c Sheet of 4, #a-d   8.00 8.00

Souvenir Sheet

Post Offices A231

No. 342: a, Amsterdam Island. b, Crozet Island. c, Kerguelen Island. d, Adélie Land.

2004, Jan. 1
342 A231 90c Sheet of 4, #a-d   12.00 12.00

Penguin and Liberty Cap — A232

2004, June 26   **Engr.**   *Perf. 13¼x13*
343 A232 €4.50 multi   15.00 7.00

Mineral Type of 1993
2005, Jan. 1   **Engr.**   *Perf. 13¼*
344 A103 15c Agate   .80 .50

Albert Bauer (1916-2003), Glaciologist — A233

2005, Jan. 1   *Perf. 13x13¼*
345 A233 45c multi   2.00 1.75

Roger Barberot (1915-2002), Administrator — A234

2005, Jan. 1
346 A234 50c multi   2.00 2.00

Ship "Cap Horn" A235

2005, Jan. 1
347 A235 50c multi   2.00 2.00

Seal Pot — A236

2005, Jan. 1   **Litho.**   *Perf. 13*
348 A236 50c multi   2.25 2.25

Macgillivray's Prion — A237

2005, Jan. 1   **Engr.**   *Perf. 13x13¼*
349 A237 75c multi   2.75 2.75

Studer Valley A238

2005, Jan. 1   *Perf. 13x12½*
350 A238 90c multi   3.00 3.00

Peigne des Néréides — A239

2005, Jan. 1   *Perf. 12¼*
351 A239 €2.50 multi   8.00 7.50

Harpovoluta Charcoti A240

2005, Jan. 1   *Perf. 13x12½*
352 A240 €4 multi   14.00 14.00

Murray's Ray — A241

2005, Jan. 1   **Litho.**   *Perf. 13*
353 A241 €4.50 multi   14.00 14.00

Elephant Seal and Oceanographic Chart — A242

2005, Jan. 1   **Engr.**
354 A242 €4.90 multi   16.00 16.00

Concordia Station — A243

2005, Jan. 3   **Litho.**   *Perf. 13*
355 A243 50c multi   1.75 1.75

Return of the Ship "Français," Cent. — A244

2005, Mar. 4   **Engr.**   *Perf. 13x13¼*
356 A244 €4.50 multi + label   15.00 15.00

Disappearance of Paul-Emile Victor, 10th Anniv. — A245

2005, Mar. 7   **Litho.**   *Perf. 13*
357 A245 50c multi   2.50 2.50

50th Anniversary Coat of Arms — A246

2005, Aug. 6
358 A246 (90c) multi   3.00 3.00
   a.   Booklet pane of 1   4.00 —

No. 358a is found in No. 359.

Voyage Booklet Type of 1999

History: a, Discovery of Amsterdam Island, 1522. b, Discovery of Crozet Island, 1772. c, Discovery of Kerguelen Island, 1772, vert. d, Discovery of Adélie Land, 1840. e, Astronomers viewing 1874 transit of Venus on St. Paul Island. f, Wreck of the Strathmore, 1875. g, Port Jeanne d'Arc, 1908. h, Port-Couvreux, 1925. i, Building of Port-Martin, 1950. j, Antarctic Treaty, 1959. k, Building of fourth base, 1963-64.

2005, Aug. 6   **Litho.**   *Perf. 13*
359 A164   Souvenir booklet, #a-k, 358a   70.00

Nos. 359a-359k are all non-denominated. Stamps are valid for 90c, the 20 gram international letter rate. Each stamp appears on a separate booklet pane showing an enlarged design of the stamp. The booklet sold for €18.

Penguins and No. 1 — A247

2005, Nov. 2
360 A247 90c multi   3.25 3.25
French Southern & Antarctic Territories, 50th anniv.

Souvenir Sheet

Maps A248

Maps of: a, Crozet Archipelago. b, Amsterdam and St. Paul Islands. c, Kerguelen Island. d, Adélie Land.

Litho. & Engr.
2005, Nov. 10   *Perf. 13x13¼*
361 A248 50c Sheet of 4, #a-d   6.50 6.50
French Southern & Antarctic Territories, 50th anniv.

Rutile — A249

2006, Jan. 1   **Engr.**   *Perf. 13x12½*
362 A249 15c multi   .80 .80

Charles Vélain (1845-1925), Geologist — A250

2006, Jan. 1   *Perf. 13x13¼*
363 A250 48c pur & red   1.60 1.60

Albert Seyrolle (1887-1919), Mariner — A251

2006, Jan. 1
364 A251 53c multi   1.60 1.60

Amsterdam Island Garden A252

2006, Jan. 1   **Litho.**   *Perf. 13*
365 A252 53c multi   1.60 1.60

Ship "Osiris" A253

2006, Jan. 1   **Photo.**   *Perf. 13x13¼*
366 A253 90c multi   3.00 3.00

Dumont d'Urville Base, 50th Anniv.
A254

2006, Jan. 1   Engr.   Perf. 13x12½
367 A254 90c multi   2.75 2.75

Virgin of the Seal
Hunters — A255

2006, Jan. 1   Perf. 12½x13
368 A255 €2.50 multi   7.50 7.50

Lagenorhynchus Cruciger — A256

2006, Jan. 1   Perf. 13x13¼
369 A256 €4 multi   12.00 12.00

Keguelen
Hake
A257

2006, Jan. 1
370 A257 €4.53 multi   13.50 13.50

Amsterdam Island Carbon Dioxide
Measurements, 25th Anniv. — A258

2006, Jan. 1
371 A258 €4.90 multi   15.00 15.00

Miniature Sheet

Penguins
A259

No. 372 — Penguin (background color): a,
Emperor penguin (lilac, 22x36mm). b, King
penguin (pale yellow green, 22x36mm). c,
Gentoo penguin (green, 22x27mm). d, Adélie
penguin (pink, 22x27mm). e, Macaroni penguin (orange, 22x27mm). f, Rockhopper penguin (blue, 22x27mm).

Litho. & Engr.
2006, Jan. 1   Perf. 13
372 A259 53c Sheet of 6, #a-f   12.00 12.00

Souvenir Sheet

Albatross
A260

Litho. & Engr.
2006, June 1   Perf. 13
373 A260 €4.53 multi   14.50 14.50

Souvenir Sheet

Albatross
A261

Litho. & Engr.
2006, Nov. 8   Perf. 13
374 A261 90c multi   3.50 3.50

Corundum — A262

2007, Jan. 1   Engr.   Perf. 13¼
375 A262 15c multi   1.25 1.25

A263

2007, Jan. 1   Perf. 13x13¼
376 A263 49c multi   1.50 1.50

Louis-Francois Aleno de Saint Aloüarn
(1738-72), explorer who claimed Australia for
France.

A264

2007, Jan. 1
377 A264 54c multi   1.60 1.60

Marthe Emmanuel (1901-97), assistant to
explorer Jean Charcot.

Cattle,
Amsterdam
Island
A265

2007, Jan. 1   Perf. 13x12½
378 A265 54c multi   1.50 1.50

Ship
Tonkinois
A266

2007, Jan. 1   Perf. 13x13¼
379 A266 90c multi   2.50 2.50

Ile de la
Baleine
A267

2007, Jan. 1   Perf. 13x12½
380 A267 90c multi   2.50 2.50

Archaeology on Saint
Paul Island — A268

2007, Jan. 1   Perf. 12½x13
381 A268 €2.50 multi   7.00 7.00

Lampris Immaculatus — A269

2007, Jan. 1   Perf. 13x12½
382 A269 €4 multi   11.00 11.00

Astonomy
at
Concordia
A270

Litho. & Engr.
2007, Jan. 1   Perf. 13
383 A270 €4.90 multi   14.00 14.00

French
Polar
Expeditions,
60th Anniv.
A271

No. 384: a, Expedition headquarters, Paris,
men shaking hands over globe. b, Expedition
headquarters.

2007, Jan. 1   Engr.   Perf. 13x13¼
384   Horiz. pair + central la-
           bel   13.50 13.50
  a. A271 54c multi   1.75 1.75
  b. A271 €4 multi   11.00 11.00

Miniature Sheet

Albatrosses — A272

No. 385: a, Amsterdam albatross. b, Great
albatross (Grand albatros). c, Black-browed
albatross (Albatros à sourcils noir). d, Yellow-
beaked albatross (Albatros à bec jaune). e,
Sooty albatross (Albatros fuligineux).

Litho. & Engr.
2007, Jan. 1   Perf. 13
385 A272 54c Sheet of 5, #a-e   8.00 8.00

Intl. Polar
Year
A273

No. 386: a, Penguins. b, Map of Antarctica,
French Southern & Antarctic Territories #9.

2007, Mar. 1   Litho.   Perf. 13
386   Horiz. pair + central la-
           bel   15.00 15.00
  a. A273 90c multi   2.75 2.75
  b. A273 €4 multi   12.00 12.00

Audit Office,
Bicent. — A274

2007 Mar. 19   Engr.   Perf. 13¼
387 A274 90c multi   4.50 4.50

Miniature Sheet

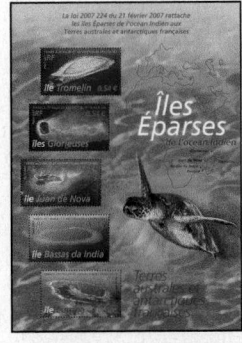

Indian
Ocean
Islands
A275

No. 388: a, Ile Tromelin. b, Iles Glorieuses.
c, Ile Juan de Nova. d, Ile Bassas da India. e,
Ile Europa.

2007, May 10   Photo.   Perf. 13x13¼
388 A275 54c Sheet of 5, #a-e   9.00 9.00

Path of Sun on June 21 Over Dumont
d'Urville Base
A276

2007, June 21
389 A276 90c multi   3.00 3.00

Voyage Booklet Type of 1999

No. 390 — Photographs of land features: a,
Apostle Island, Crozet Archipelago. b, Chamo-
nix Lake, Kerguelen Island. c, Phylicia forest,
Amsterdam Island. d, Gulf of Morbihan, Ker-
guelen Islands. e, Mount Cook, Chamonix
Lake and glacier, Kerguelen Islands. f,
Tourbiéres Plateau, Amsterdam Island. g,
Nuageuses Islands, Kerguelen Islands. h, Cal-
dera, Amsterdam Island. i, Mount Cook, Ker-
guelen Island. j, Central Plateau, Kerguelen
Island. k, Isle of Penguins, Crozet Archipelago.
l, Antonelli Crater, Amsterdam Island. m, Lake
on Possession Island, Crozet Archipelago. n,
Rocks off Apostle Island, Crozet Archipelago.
o, Geographic Society Peninsula, Kerguelen
Island. p, Ronarch Peninsula, Kerguelen
Island.

2007, Nov. 8   Litho.   Perf. 13
390 A164 (90c) Souvenir book-
           let, #a-p   70.00

No. 390 sold for €20, and contains four
panes, consisting of a block of four stamps of
Nos. 390a-390d, 390e-390h, 390i-390l, and
390m-390p.

French Southern and
Antarctic Territories
Flag — A277

2008, Jan. 1   Litho.   *Perf. 13*
Background Color
391 A277 1c black   .25   .25
392 A277 2c blue   .35   .35
393 A277 5c red   .40   .40
394 A277 10c green   .40   .40
395 A277 20c brn orange   .80   .80
  Nos. 391-395 (5)   2.20 2.20

Spinel — A278

2008, Jan. 1   Engr.   *Perf. 13¼*
396 A278 15c multi   .80   .45

Samivel (1907-92),
Writer — A279

2008, Jan. 1   *Perf. 13x13¼*
397 A279 54c grn & brown   1.60 1.60

St. Paul Island — A280

2008, Jan. 1
398 A280 54c blue & dk blue   1.60 1.60

Construction of Port Jeanne d'Arc,
Cent. — A281

2008, Jan. 1   *Perf. 13x12¾*
399 A281 90c multi   2.75 2.75

Rockhopper
Penguins
A282

2008, Jan. 1   *Perf. 13x12½*
400 A282 90c multi   2.75 2.75

Shipwreck
of
L'Esperance
A283

2008, Jan. 1   Litho.   *Perf. 13x12¾*
401 A283 90c multi   2.75 2.75

Macrourus
Carinatus
A284

2008, Jan. 1   Engr.   *Perf. 13x12½*
402 A284 €4 multi   12.00 12.00

Galium
Antarcticum — A285

2008, Jan. 1   *Perf. 12½x13*
403 A285 €4.54 multi   13.50 13.50

Adélie Land
Coastal
Ichthyology
Program — A286

2008, Jan. 1   Litho.   *Perf. 13*
404 A286 €4.90 multi   14.50 14.50

Souvenir Sheet

Kerguelen Fish Biomass Evaluation
Project (POKER) — A287

2008, Jan. 1   Litho. & Engr.
405 A287 €2.50 multi   7.50 7.50

Souvenir Sheet

Elephant
Seals
A288

No. 406: a, Head of adult female. b, Seals
initiating combat. c, Juvenile seal. d, Head of
adult male.

2008, Jan. 1
406 A288 54c Sheet of 4, #a-d   6.50 6.50

Gérard Mégie (1946-
2004), Ozone
Researcher — A289

2008, Feb. 15   Engr.   *Perf. 13x13¼*
407 A289 54c multi   1.75 1.75

Miniature Sheet

Birds
A290

No. 408: a, Sooty tern (Sterne fulgineuse).
b, Red-footed booby (Fou a pieds rouges),
vert. c, Masked booby (Fou masque), vert. d,
Great frigatebird (Fregate du Pacifique), vert.
e, Tropicbird (Paille en queue).
Perf. 13¼x13 (#408a, 408e), 13x13¼
2008, June 1   Litho. & Engr.
408 A290 54c Sheet of 5, #a-e   8.50 8.50

Earth
and
Birds
A291

2008, June 14   Photo.   *Perf. 13*
409 A291 €4.54 multi   14.50 14.50

Ship Marion
Dufresne
A292

2008, Nov. 6   Litho.   *Perf. 13*
410 A292 (55c) multi   1.75 1.75
  Compare with type A194.

Pyrite — A293

2009, Jan. 1   Engr.   *Perf. 13¼*
411 A293 15c multi   .60   .60

A294

2009, Jan. 1   *Perf. 13x13¼*
412 A294 55c multi   1.60 1.60
  Henri Paschal de Rochegude (1741-1834),
naval officer.

A295

2009, Jan. 1   *Perf. 13*
413 A295 55c multi   1.60 1.60
  Charles Gaston Rouillon (1915-2007),
director of French polar scientific expeditions.

Residence
de France
Seal of
Kerguelen
Islands,
Cent.
A296

2009, Jan. 1   Litho.
414 A296 90c multi   2.50 2.50

Shark With
Dorsal
Spines
A297

2009, Jan. 1   Engr.   *Perf. 13x12½*
415 A297 €2.50 multi   7.00 7.00

Ship
Jeanne
d'Arc
A298

2009, Jan. 1
416 A298 €4 multi   11.00 11.00

MACARBI Program
Scallop
Research — A299

2009, Jan. 1   *Perf. 12½x13*
417 A299 €4.55 multi   13.00 13.00

Seaweed
A300

No. 418: a, Himantothallus grandifolius and
iceberg. b, Laminaria pallida and seals.

2009, Jan. 1   *Perf. 13x13¼*
418   Horiz. pair + central
       label   13.50 13.50
  a. A300 90c multi   2.50 2.50
  b. A300 €4 multi   11.00 11.00

Miniature Sheet

Petrels
A301

No. 419: a, Soft-plumaged petrel (Petrel
soyeux). b, Wilson's petrel (Petrel de Wilson).
c, Gray petrel (Petrel gris). d, Diving petrel
(Petrel plongeur). e, Snow petrel (Petrel des
neiges).

Litho. & Engr.
2009, Jan. 1   *Perf. 13¼x13*
419 A301 55c Sheet of 5, #a-e   7.75 7.75

Voyage Booklet Type of 1999
  No. 420 — Photographs: a, Frigatebirds,
Europa Island. b, Beach on north coast of
Europa Island. c, Mangroves, Europa Island.
d, Flagpole, palm trees, Europa Island. e, Turtle on beach, Juan de Nova Island. f, Sand-
banks off Juan de Nova Island. g, Tree, Juan
de Nova Island. h, Grounded ship, Juan de
Nova Island. i, Brown noddies, Glorioso
Islands. j, Flower, Glorioso Islands. k, Pool of
water, Glorioso Islands. l, Tree on islet, Glorioso Islands. m, Birds, Tromelin Island. n,
Meteorological station, Tromelin Island. o,
Coral fossil, Tromelin Island. p, Anchor, Tromelin Island.

2009, Nov. 5   Litho.   *Perf. 13*
420 A164 (90c) Souvenir book-
       let, #a-p   65.00

  No. 420 sold for €21.50, and contains four
panes, consisting of a block of four stamps of
Nos. 420a-420d, 420e-420h, 420i-4290l, and
420m-420p.

 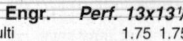

Antarctic
Treaty, 50th
Anniv.
A302

2009, Dec. 1   Engr.   *Perf. 13x13¼*
421 A302 56c multi   1.75 1.75

Tourmaline — A303

2010, Jan. 2   **Engr.**   **Perf. 13¼**
422 A303 28c multi   .80 .80

Dr. Jean Rivolier (1923-2007), Medical Researcher A304

2010, Jan. 2   **Litho.**   **Perf. 13**
423 A304 56c multi   1.60 1.60

Birds on Ile du Lys — A305

2010, Jan. 2   **Engr.**   **Perf. 13x13¼**
424 A305 56c multi   1.60 1.60

Patureau House, Juan de Nova Island A306

2010, Jan. 2
425 A306 56c multi   1.60 1.60

Program Crac-ice A307

2010, Jan. 2
426 A307 90c multi   2.50 2.50

Supply Ship Ile St. Paul A308

2010, Jan. 2
427 A308 €1.35 multi   3.75 3.75

Crozet Orca A309

2010, Jan. 2
428 A309 €2.80 multi   7.75 7.75

Kerguelen Terns A310

2010, Jan. 2
429 A310 €4.30 multi   12.00 12.00

Miniature Sheet

Sea Lions of Amsterdam Island — A311

No. 430: a, Sea lion and ship. b, Two sea lions on rocks, denomination at UR in black, horiz. c, Sea lion, denomination at UL in black, horiz. d, Two sea lions near water, denomination in white at UR, horiz. e, Two sea lions, denomination at LL in black, horiz.

Litho. & Engr.
2010, Jan. 2   **Perf. 13**
430 A311 56c Sheet of 5, #a-e   7.75 7.75

Miniature Sheet

Polar Transportation — A312

No. 431: a, Team of dogs pulling sled. b, Weasel M29C. c, Sno-cat 743. d, HB40-Castor. e, Challenger 65. f, PB 330.

2010, Jan. 2
431 A312 90c Sheet of 6, #a-f   15.00 15.00

Gabriel Pavilion, Paris A313

2010, May 28   **Litho.**   **Perf. 13**
432 A313 56c multi   1.40 1.40

Second Elysée Philatelic Club Show, Paris.

Miniature Sheet

Albatross Protection — A314

No. 433: a, Albatross and chick on nest. b, Albatross facing left. c, Albatross facing right. d, Two juvenile albatrosses.

Litho. & Engr.
2010, June 12   **Perf. 13**
433 A314 56c Sheet of 4, #a-d   5.75 5.75

French Southern & Antarctic Territories Booth at Espace Champerret Stamp Show A315

2010, Nov. 5   **Litho.**   **Perf. 13**
434 A315 56c multi   3.00 3.00

Self-Adhesive
Serpentine Die Cut 11
435 A315 56c multi   3.00 3.00

Astronomical Observatory, Concordia Base, Antarctica and Southern Cross — A316

Litho. & Engr.
2011, Jan. 2   **Perf. 13**
436 A316 56c multi   1.50 1.50

Martin de Viviès Base, Amsterdam Island — A317

2011, Jan. 2   **Engr.**   **Perf. 13x13¼**
437 A317 90c multi   2.40 2.40

Josef Enzensperger (1873-1903), Meteorologist A318

2011, Jan. 2   **Perf. 13¼x13**
438 A318 90c multi   2.40 2.40

André Chastain (1906-62), Botanist — A319

2011, Jan. 2
439 A319 €1.35 multi   3.75 3.75

Sheathbills A320

2011, Jan. 2   **Perf. 13x13¼**
440 A320 €1.35 black & purple   3.75 3.75

Artedidraco Orianae A321

2011, Jan. 2
441 A321 €1.35 multi   3.75 3.75

Cruiser Lapérouse A322

2011, Jan. 2
442 A322 €4.30 multi   11.50 11.50

Zircons A323

No. 443: a, Zircons embedded in rock. b, Cut and polished zircon.

Litho. & Engr.
2011, Jan. 2   **Perf. 13¼**
443 A323 Horiz. pair   1.75 1.75
   a.   28c multi   .75 .75
   b.   34c multi   .90 .90

December 8, 1929 Mail Plane Crash A324

No. 444: a, Farman F190 airplane. b, Map of flight. c, Crew and crash covers.

2011, Jan. 2   **Perf. 13**
444   Horiz. strip of 3   7.75 7.75
   a.   A324 56c multi   1.50 1.50
   b.   A324 90c multi   2.40 2.40
   c.   A324 €1.35 multi   3.75 3.75

Miniature Sheet

Whales A325

No. 445: a, Baleine à bosse (humpback whale). b, Baleine franche australe (southern right whale). c, Cachalot (sperm whale). d, Rorqual de Rudolphi (sei whale).

2011, Jan. 2
445 A325 56c Sheet of 4, #a-d   6.00 6.00

Patrol Boat Osiris A326

2011, Apr. 1   **Litho.**
446 A326 (60c) multi   1.75 1.75

Gentoo Penguins A327

2011, June 15   **Litho.**   **Perf. 13**
447 A327 €1 multi + label   3.00 3.00

Orré House (Prefect's Residence), St. Pierre, Reunion A328

2011, Sept. 19
448 A328 60c multi   1.75 1.75

Souvenir Sheet

Squadron Escort Forbin — A329

2011, Nov. 3   **Litho. & Engr.**
449 A329 €1.10 multi   3.00 3.00

See St. Pierre & Miquelon No. 938.

Adélie Penguins A330

2011, Dec. 2   **Litho.**   **Perf. 13**
450 A330 60c multi   1.60 1.60

Penguin Breeding Grounds, Baie du Marin, Crozet Island A331

Views of Baie du Marin in: No. 451, 60c, 1961. No. 452, 60c, 2011.

2011, Dec. 23   *Perf. 13x13¼*
451-452   A331   Set of 2   3.25   3.25

Ship Marion Dufresne in Mamoudzou Lagoon
A332

Serpentine Die Cut 11

2011, Dec. 31   **Self-Adhesive**
453   A332   60c multi   1.60   1.60

See Mayotte No. 288.

Notodiscus Hookeri
A333

2012, Jan. 2   **Engr.**   *Perf. 13x13¼*
454   A333   60c multi   1.60   1.60

Ship Marius Moutet
A334

2012, Jan. 2
455   A334   60c multi   1.60   1.60

Weddell Seals — A335

2012, Jan. 2   *Perf. 13¼x13*
456   A335   €1 multi   2.60   2.60

Roald Amundsen (1872-1928), Polar Explorer — A336

2012, Jan. 2
457   A336   €1 multi   2.60   2.60

René-Emile Bossière (1857-1941), Kerguelen Island Business Entrepreneur — A337

2012, Jan. 2
458   A337   €1.45 multi   3.75   3.75

Lepidonotothen Larseni — A338

Litho. & Silk-screened
2012, Jan. 2   *Perf. 13*
459   A338   €2.40 multi   6.25   6.25

Diopside
A339

No. 460: a, Crystals. b, Crystal and cut stone.

2012, Jan. 2   **Engr.**   *Perf. 13¼*
460   A339   Horiz. pair   1.75   1.75
   a.   29c red & green   .80   .80
   b.   36c red & green   .95   .95

Point Molloy, Kerguelen Island — A340

No. 461: a, Buildings at Point Molloy. b, Molloy seismological station, 1953-63.

Litho. & Engr.
2012, Jan. 2   *Perf. 13x13¼*
461   Horiz. pair   3.25   3.25
   a.-b.   A340 60c Either single   1.60   1.60

Military Presence in French Southern & Antarctic Territories
A341

No. 462: a, Second Regiment of Marine Infantry Parachutists on Europa Island. b, Detachment of the Mayotte Foreign Legion on the Glorioso Islands.

Litho. & Silk-screened
2012, Jan. 2   *Perf. 13*
462   Horiz. pair   3.25   3.25
   a.-b.   A341 60c Either single   1.60   1.60

Miniature Sheet

Derelict Whaling Station, Port-Jeanne d'Arc, Kerguelen Island — A342

No. 463: a, Eight storage tanks. b, Three boilers, vert. c, Two storage silos. d, House, vert.

2012, Jan. 2   **Photo.**
463   A342   60c Sheet of 4, #a-d   6.25   6.25

Miniature Sheet

Nature Reserve Flora and Fauna
A343

No. 464: a, Gentoo penguin (manchot papou). b, White-chinned petrel (petrel a menton blanc). c, Lyallia kerguelensis. d, Anatalanta aptera.

2012, Jan. 2   **Litho. & Engr.**
464   A343   Sheet of 4   8.50   8.50
   a.   20c multi   .55   .55
   b.   60c multi   1.60   1.60
   c.   €1 multi   2.60   2.60
   d.   €1.45 multi   3.75   3.75

Miniature Sheet

Aircraft Used in Polar Regions
A344

No. 465: a, B-24 Liberator. b, DC-4 Skymaster. c, Nord 2501 Noratlas. d, C-130 Hercules. e, DC-3 Basler BT-67. f, DHC-6 Twin Otter.

2012, Jan. 2
465   A344   €1 Sheet of 6, #a-f   16.00   16.00

Ile Longue, Kerguelen Islands — A345

No. 466: a, 60c, Painting. b, €1, Painting, diff.

2012, Apr. 13   **Litho.**   *Perf. 13x13¼*
466   A345   Pair, #a-b   4.25   4.25
No. 466 was printed in sheets containing two pairs.

Souvenir Sheet

Prince of Monaco Islands
A346

No. 467: a, Giant Antarctic petrel. b, Coastline of Prince of Monaco Islands.

Litho. & Engr.
2012, June 9   *Perf. 13¼*
467   A346   €1 Sheet of 2, #a-b   5.00   5.00

See Monaco No. 2680.

National Space Studies Center (CNES) Projects
A347

No. 468: a, Map of Antarctica. b, Penguin with tracking devices. c, Galileo satellite. d, Scientists deploying weather balloon. e, Pleaides satellite.

2012, June 9   **Photo.**   *Perf. 13*
468   Vert. strip of 5 + 5 labels   12.00   12.00
   a.-b.   A347 60c Either single + label   1.50   1.50
   c.-d.   A347 €1 Either single + label   2.50   2.50
   e.   A347 €1.45 multi + label   3.75   3.75

French Polar Institute, 20th Anniv.
A348

2012, July 12   **Litho.**   *Perf. 13¼x13*
469   A348   60c multi   1.50   1.50

Souvenir Sheet

Bridge for Tracking Adélie Penguins
A349

Litho. & Engr.
2012, Nov. 2   *Perf. 13¼x13*
470   A349   €2 multi   5.25   5.25

Flight of Maryse Hilsz to Juan de Nova Island, 80th Anniv.
A350

No. 471: a, Airplane, map of route. b, Hilsz (1901-46) in airplane.

2012, Nov. 8   **Litho.**   *Perf. 13*
471   A350   Horiz. pair   4.25   4.25
   a.   60c multi   1.60   1.60
   b.   €1 multi   2.60   2.60

Prasiola Crispa and Penguins
A351

2013, Jan. 1   **Engr.**   *Perf. 13x13¼*
472   A351   65c multi   1.75   1.75

Charles Petitjean (1914-88), Pilot — A352

2013, Jan. 1   *Perf. 12½x13*
473   A352   65c multi   1.75   1.75

Lepidonothen Squamifrons — A353

2013, Jan. 1   *Perf. 13x13¼*
474   A353   €1 multi   2.75   2.75

Sailboat "Le Mischief" — A354

2013, Jan. 1   *Perf. 12¼*
475   A354   €1 multi   2.75   2.75

Douglas Mawson (1882-1958), Antarctic Explorer, Huts and Penguins — A355

2013, Jan. 1   Litho. & Engr.   Perf. 13
476 A355 €1.45 multi   4.00 4.00

Bernard-Marie Boudin, Chevalier de Tromelin (1735-1816), Explorer and Colonial Administrator A356

2013, Jan. 13   Litho.
477 A356 €2.40 multi   6.50 6.50

Hematite A357

2013, Jan. 1   Engr.   Perf. 13¼
478 A357 Horiz. pair   2.75 2.75
a.   40c Crystals   1.10 1.10
b.   60c Crystal   1.60 1.60

Miniature Sheet

Eaton's Pintail A358

No. 479: a, Duck in water. b, Heads of two ducks, vert. c, Duck and eggs. d, Head of duck, ducks in flight.

Litho. & Engr.
2013, Jan. 1   Perf. 13
479 A358 Sheet of 4   9.00 9.00
a.   20c multi   .55   .55
b.   60c multi   1.60 1.60
c.   €1 multi   2.75 2.75
d.   €1.45 multi   4.00 4.00

Miniature Sheet

Helicopters — A359

No. 480: a, Sud-Ouest Djinn 1221. b, Bell 47 G2. c, Hiller 360. d, Sud-Est Alouette II 3130. e, Ecureuil AS 350. f, Panther AS 565

2013, Jan. 1
480 A359 €1 Sheet of 6, #a-f 16.00 16.00

Souvenir Sheet

Engravings of Amsterdam and St. Paul Islands — A360

2013, Jan. 1   Litho.
481 A360 €3.40 multi   9.00 9.00

Voyage Booklet Type of 1999

No. 482: a, Ship Astrolabe near Dumont d'Urville Station. b, The Astrolabe, helicopter and Adélie penguins. c, Astrolabe docked near Lion landing strip. d, Four Adélie penguins at Dumont d'Urville station. e, View of Dumon't d'Urville Station taken from the Astrolabe. f, Aerial view of Dumont d'Urville Station. g, Aurora Australis. h, Colony of Emperor penguins. i, Five men and plow at Cap Prudhomme Base. j, Aerial view of Cap Prudhomme Base, island at right. k, View of Cap Prudhomme Base, island at center. l, Two penguins. m, Italian, French and European Union flags at Concordia Base. n, Snow vehicle moving containers. o, Astronomical equipment near Concordia Base. p, Steps leading to containers.

2013, Apr. 5   Litho.   Perf. 13
482 A164 (€1) Souvenir book-
     let, #a-p   65.00

No. 482 sold for €25 and contains four panes, consisting of a block of four stamps of Nos. 482a-482d, 482e-482h, 482i-482l, and 482m-482p.

F.S. Floreal A361

2013, Apr. 5   Litho.   Perf. 13
483 A361 (63c) multi   1.75 1.75

A362

Silhouettes of Emblems — A363

Designs: 1c, Green turtle. 2c, Helicopter. 3c, Penguin. 4c, Ship "Marion Dufresne." 63c, Green turtle, helicopter, penguin, ship, "TAAF."

2013, Apr. 29   Engr.   Perf. 13
484 A362 1c dk bl & bl   .25   .25
485 A362 2c purple   .25   .25
486 A362 3c dk grn & yel grn   .25   .25
487 A362 4c brn org & org   .25   .25

Litho. & Silk-screened
Perf. 13¼
488 A363 63c multi   1.75 1.75
     Nos. 484-488 (5)   2.75 2.75

See Nos. 504-507, 568a.

Souvenir Sheet

Engraver, Map, Penguin — A364

Engr. (Litho. Margin)
2013, May 17   Perf. 13
489 A364 €5 multi   13.50 13.50

Souvenir Sheets

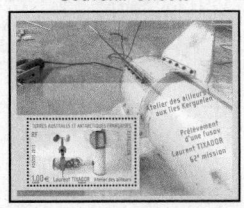

Prélèvement d'une Fusov, by Laurent Tixador — A365

Jours Heureux à l'Ile de la Désolation, by Klavdij Sluban — A366

2013, June 17   Litho.   Perf. 13
490 A365 €1 multi   2.75 2.75
491 A366 €1 black   2.75 2.75

Ateliers des Ailleurs art project.

Souvenir Sheet

Whale and Stock Certificate for Kerguelen Fisheries Society — A367

2013, Nov. 6   Litho.   Perf. 13¼x13
492 A367 €1 multi   2.75 2.75

Louis Jacquinot (1898-1993), Minister of Overseas France — A368

2014, Jan. 2   Engr.   Perf. 13¼x13
493 A368 66c multi   1.90 1.90

Bertrand Imbert (1924-2011), Leader of French Research for International Geophysical Year — A369

2014, Jan. 2   Engr.   Perf. 12¾x13
494 A369 66c multi   1.90 1.90

Tromelin Meteorological Station, 60th Anniv. — A370

2014, Jan. 2   Engr.   Perf. 13x13¼
495 A370 €1.55 multi   4.25 4.25

Rock Carvings of Amsterdam Island A371

2014, Jan. 2   Engr.   Perf. 13x13¼
496 A371 €1.55 multi   4.25 4.25

Supply Ship "Le Malin" A372

2014, Jan. 2   Litho.   Perf. 13
497 A372 €1.55 multi   4.25 4.25

Bren Carrier on Kerguelen Island A373

2014, Jan. 2   Engr.   Perf. 13x13¼
498 A373 €2 multi   5.50 5.50

White Tower (Basalt Columns), Crozet Islands — A374

2014, Jan. 2   Litho.   Perf. 13
499 A374 €2 multi   5.50 5.50

Lepidonotothen Mizops — A375

2014, Jan. 2   Engr.   Perf. 13x13¼
500 A375 €2.40 multi   6.50 6.50

Fluorite A376

No. 501: a, Polished stones. b, Crystal.

2014, Jan. 2   Litho.   Perf. 13
501 A376 Horiz. pair   2.75 2.75
a.   37c multi   1.00 1.00
b.   63c multi   1.75 1.75

Miniature Sheet

Mollusks A377

No. 502: a, Moule de Kerguelen (Kerguelen mussel). b, Volute de Challenger (Challenger volute). c, Moule de Magellan (Magellan mussel), vert. d, Buccin antarctique (Antarctic whelk). e, Laternule antarctique (Antarctic clam).

Litho. & Engr.
2014, Jan. 2   Perf. 13
502 A377 63c Sheet of 5, #a-e 8.75 8.75

Miniature Sheet

BIrds
A378

No. 503: a, Damier du Cap (Cape petrels). b, Manchot royal de Crozet (Crozet Island king penguins). c, Fulmar antarctique (Antarctic fulmars). d, Grand albatros de Crozet (Wandering albatrosses).

2014, Jan. 2		**Engr.**	**Perf. 13x12¾**	
503	A378	Sheet of 4	11.00	11.00
a.-b.		66c Either single	1.90	1.90
c.		€1.05 multi	2.75	2.75
d.		€1.55 multi	4.25	4.25

Silhouette of Emblems Type of 2013 and

Silhouettes of Emblems — A379

A362 designs as before.
€7, Map of District of Crozet, dolphin, penguin, ship, "TAAF."

2014, Mar. 7		**Litho.**	**Perf. 13**	
		Dated "2014"		
504	A362	1c dk bl & bl	.25	.25
a.		Litho. & silk-screened (varnish on silhouette), dated "2015"	.25	.25
b.		As "a," dated "2016"	.25	.25
505	A362	2c purple	.25	.25
a.		Litho. & silk-screened (varnish on silhouette), dated "2015"	.25	.25
b.		As "a," dated "2016"	.25	.25
506	A362	3c dk grn & yel grn	.25	.25
a.		Litho. & silk-screened (varnish on silhouette), dated "2015"	.25	.25
b.		As "a," dated "2016"	.25	.25
c.		Pair, #505b-506b	.25	.25
507	A362	4c brn org & org	.25	.25
a.		Litho. & silk-screened (varnish on silhouette), dated "2015"	.25	.25
b.		As "a," dated "2016"	.25	.25
c.		Pair, #504b, 507b	.25	.25

	Litho. & Silk-Screened			
	Perf. 13¼			
508	A379	€7 multi	19.00	19.00
	Nos. 504-508 (5)		20.00	20.00

Issued: Nos. 504a, 505a, 506a, 507a, 3/19; Nos. 504b, 505b, 506b, 507b, 3/30/16. See No. 568b.

Miniature Sheet

Commerson's Dolphins — A380

No. 509: a, 63c, Dolphin sticking head out of water. b, 66c, Three dolphins underwater. c, 66c, Dolphin breaching surface. d, €1.05, Dolphin above water.

	Litho. & Engr.			
2014, June 26			**Perf. 13¼x13**	
509	A380	Sheet of 4, #a-d	8.25	8.25

Map of Madagascar to Tromelin Flight A381

AAC-1 Toucan A382

AAC-1 Toucan and Stamped Cover from Tromelin A383

2014, Sept. 21		**Litho.**	**Perf. 13**	
510		Horiz. strip of 3	8.50	8.50
a.	A381	66c multi	1.75	1.75
b.	A382	€1.05 multi	2.75	2.75
c.	A383	€1.55 multi	4.00	4.00

First flight between Madagascar and Tromelin, 50th anniv.

Green Turtle — A384

2014, Oct. 9		**Litho.**	**Perf. 13x13¼**	
511	A384	€1.05 multi	2.60	2.60

See Comoro Islands No. , France No. 4695, Malagasy Republic No. 1637, Mauritius No. 1144, Seychelles No. 904.

Gendarmes A385

No. 512 — Gendarme on: a, Iles Eparses. b, Iles Kerguelen.

	Litho. & Silk-Screened			
2014, Oct. 16			**Perf. 13**	
512		Horiz. pair + central label	3.50	3.50
a.-b	A385	66c Either single	1.75	1.75

Souvenir Sheet

Amateur Radio — A386

No. 513: a, QSL card, radio key, amateur radio antenna on Tromelin Island. b, Radio operator, radio and antenna, vert.

	Perf. 13x13¼, 13¼x13			
2014, Nov. 6		**Litho.**		
513	A386	Sheet of 2	2.75	2.75
a.		39c multi	1.00	1.00
b.		66c multi	1.75	1.75

Decauville Hopper Cars on Juan de Nova Island A387

2015, Jan. 1		**Engr.**	**Perf. 13x13¼**	
514	A387	66c multi	1.60	1.60

Euphausia Superba — A388

	Litho. & Engr.			
2015, Jan. 1			**Perf. 13¼**	
515	A388	66c multi	1.60	1.60

Emperor Penguin — A389

2015, Jan. 1		**Litho.**	**Perf. 13**	
516	A389	€1 multi	2.40	2.40

Leopard Seal in Adélie Land A390

2015, Jan. 1		**Engr.**	**Perf. 13¼x13**	
517	A390	€1.05 multi	2.60	2.60

Ship Radioleine — A391

2015, Jan. 1		**Engr.**	**Perf. 13¼x13¼**	
518	A391	€2.40 multi	5.75	5.75

Antarctic Terns A392

	Litho. & Engr.			
2015, Jan. 1			**Perf. 13**	
519	A392	€4.30 multi	10.50	10.50

Insects — A393

Designs: 66c, Amalopteryx maritima. €2, Ectemnorhinus vanhoeffenianus, horiz.

2015, Jan.1		**Litho.**	**Perf. 13¼**	
520-521	A393	Set of 2	6.50	6.50

Beryl A394

No. 522: a, Polihsed gemstones. b, Crystals in matrix.

	Litho. & Engr.			
2015, Jan. 1			**Perf. 13**	
522	A394	Horiz. pair	2.40	2.40
a.		34c multi	.80	.80
b.		66c multi	1.60	1.60

Snowmobile Transport — A395

No. 523: a, Snowmobile pulling cargo. b, Snowmobile without cargo.

2015, Jan. 1		**Litho.**	**Perf. 13¼**	
523		Horiz. pair	4.25	4.25
a.	A395	66c multi	1.60	1.60
b.	A395	€1.05 multi	2.60	2.60

Robert Guillard (1919-2013), Polar Explorations Chief of Operations — A396

No. 524 — Guillard and: a, Ship and penguins, Adélie Land. b, Expedition vehicles, Greenland.

2015, Jan. 1		**Engr.**	**Perf. 13x13¼**	
524		Horiz. pair + central label	4.25	4.25
a.	A396	66c multi	1.60	1.60
b.	A396	€1.05 multi	2.60	2.60

Miniature Sheet

Fish A397

No. 525: a, Chaenodraco wilsoni. b, Chaenodraco myersi. c, Pagetopsis macropterus. d, Pagetopsis maculatus.

2015, Jan. 1		**Engr.**	**Perf. 13**	
525	A397	Sheet of 4	9.75	9.75
a.-b.		66c Either single	1.60	1.60
c.		€1.05 multi	2.60	2.60
d.		€1.55 multi	3.75	3.75

Paul-Emile Victor (1907-95), Polar Explorer A398

2015, Mar. 7		**Engr.**	**Perf. 13x12½**	
526	A398	€1 multi	2.25	2.25

Silhouettes of Saint-Paul & Amsterdam District Emblems — A399

	Litho. & Silk-Screened			
2015, Mar. 19			**Perf. 13¼**	
527	A399	50c multi	1.10	1.10

See No. 568d.

François Tabuteau (1921-2000), Polar Explorer — A400

2015, Apr. 17		**Litho.**	**Perf. 13**	
528	A400	80c multi	1.90	1.90

French Southern and Antarctic Territories, 60th Anniv. A401

No. 529 — Ship and: a, Airplane, seal, bird, turtle. b, Helicopter, birds, fish, killer whales. c, Penguins and birds in flight.

2015, July 14	Litho.	Perf. 13
529	Horiz. strip of 3	5.25 5.25
a.-c.	A401 80c Any single	1.75 1.75

People Stranded Without Supplies on Saint Paul Island, 1930 — A402

2015, Sept. 18	Engr.	Perf. 13
530	A402 €1 multi	2.25 2.25

Ship Marion Dufresne, 20th Anniv. — A403

2015	Litho. & Engr.	Perf. 13
	Denomination Color	
531	A403 80c red	1.90 1.90
532	A403 €1.35 blue	3.00 3.00

Issued: 80c, 10/4; €1.35, 11/5.

Souvenir Sheet

Penguin on Floating Ice — A404

	Litho. & Embossed	
2015, Nov. 5		Perf. 13½x13
533	A404 €1.24 multi	2.75 2.75

Ships — A405

No. 534: a, Croix du Sud I. b, Albius. c, Le Saint-Andre. d, Mascareignes III. e, Ile de la Reunion. f, Cap Horn I. g, Ile Bourbon.

	Litho. & Engr.	
2015, Dec. 3		Perf. 13
534	Booklet pane of 7	19.50
a.-g.	A405 €1.24 Any single	2.75 2.75
	Complete booklet, #534	19.50

Lozère Waterfall — A406

2016, Jan. 2	Engr.	Perf. 13¼x13
535	A406 50c multi	1.10 1.10

Pringleophaga Crozetensis — A407

2016, Jan. 2	Engr.	Perf. 12¼
536	A407 80c black	1.75 1.75

Serge Frolow, Director of Meteorological Service — A408

2016, Jan. 2	Litho.	Perf. 13
537	A408 80c multi	1.75 1.75

Point d'Entrecasteaux — A409

2016, Jan. 2	Engr.	Perf. 13x13¼
538	A409 €1.05 multi	2.40 2.40

Valdivia, Ship From 1898-99 German Deep Sea Expedition — A410

2016, Jan. 2	Engr.	Perf. 13x12½
539	A410 €1.24 multi	2.75 2.75

Jean Volot (1921-2012), Polar Expedition Engineer and Priest — A411

2016, Jan. 2	Engr.	Perf. 12½x13
540	A411 €1.35 multi	3.00 3.00

Diatoms — A412

	Litho. & Silk-Screened	
2016, Jan. 2		Perf. 13
541	A412 €2.80 multi	6.25 6.25

Schooner Rêve and Grave of Raoul Fleurié — A413

2016, Jan. 2	Engr.	Perf. 13x13¼
542	A413 €2.80 multi	6.25 6.25

Sphene — A414

No. 543: a, Polished and cut gemstones. b, Crystal.

	Litho. & Silk-Screened	
2016, Jan. 2		Perf. 13
543	A414 Horiz. pair	2.25 2.25
a.	20c multi	.50 .50
b.	80c multi	1.75 1.75

Kerguelen Island — A415

No. 544: a, Whaling. b, Ships from The Ice Sphinx, by Jules Verne. c, Cormoran-Vert Hostel, Christmas Harbor.

2016, Jan. 2	Litho.	Perf. 13
544	Horiz. strip of 3	7.50 7.50
a.	A415 80c cream & black	1.75 1.75
b.	A415 €1.24 cream & black	2.75 2.75
c.	A415 €1.35 cream & black	3.00 3.00

Souvenir Sheet

Flyovers of the Kerguelen Islands — A416

No. 545: a, RRS Discovery. b, De Havilland Gipsy Moth seaplane.

2016, Jan. 2	Litho.	Perf. 13
545	A416 Sheet of 2	2.75 2.75
a.	44c multi	1.00 1.00
b.	80c multi	1.75 1.75

Miniature Sheet

Fish — A417

No. 546: a, Histiodraco velifer (52x41mm). b, Dolloidraco longedorsalis (60x27mm). c, Pogonophryne phyllopogon (60x27mm). d, Pogonophryne cf. barsukovi (52x31mm).

2016, Jan. 2	Engr.	Perf. 13
546	A417 Sheet of 4	9.00 9.00
a.-b.	80c Either single	1.75 1.75
c.	€1.05 multi	2.40 2.40
d.	€1.35 multi	3.00 3.00

Miniature Sheet

Birds — A418

No. 547: a, Fulmar antarctique (Antarctic fulmar). b, Petrel geant (giant petrel), horiz. c, Damier du cap (cape petrel), horiz. d, Skua, horiz.

	Litho. & Engr.	
2016, Jan. 2		Perf. 13
547	A418 Sheet of 4	9.00 9.00
a.	70c multi	1.50 1.50
b.	80c multi	1.75 1.75
c.	€1.05 multi	2.40 2.40
d.	€1.45 multi	3.25 3.25

Silhouettes of Kerguelen District Emblems — A419

	Litho. & Silk-Screened	
2016, Mar. 31		Perf. 13¼
548	A419 80c multi	1.90 1.90

See No. 568c.

No. 2 and Rockhopper Penguin — A420

2016, May 19	Litho.	Perf. 13
549	A420 €2 multi + label	4.50 4.50

Paris Philex 2016.

Souvenir Sheet

Albatrosses — A421

2016, May 21	Litho.	Perf. 13¼x13
550	A421 €1 multi	2.25 2.25

Bernard Duboys de Lavigerie (1934-2008), Ionosphere Researcher — A422

2016, Oct. 1	Engr.	Perf. 13¼x13
551	A422 80c multi	1.90 1.90

Souvenir Sheet

Fillod Prefabricated Buildings In French Southern & Antarctic Territories, 60th Anniv. — A423

No. 552 — Prefabricated building and: a, Penguins. b, Ferdinand Fillod (1891-1956), building manufacturer.

	Litho. & Embossed	
2016, Nov. 3		Perf. 13
552	A423 Sheet of 2	9.25 9.25
a.	€1.60 blue	3.50 3.50
b.	€2.70 blue	5.75 5.75

Cirque du Château, Kerguelen Island — A424

2016, Nov. 25	Litho.	Perf. 13
553	A424 50c multi	1.10 1.10

Cabins Near the Mortadella, Kerguelen Island — A425

2017, Jan. 2	Litho.	Perf. 13
554	A425 80c multi	1.75 1.75

Halirythus Amphibius — A426

2017, Jan. 2   Litho.   **Perf. 13x13¼**
555   A426   80c multi   1.75   1.75

1696 Landing of Willem de Vlamingh on Saint Paul and Amsterdam Islands A427

2017, Jan. 2   Litho.   **Perf. 13**
556   A427   €1 multi   2.10   2.10

Turborotalita Quinqueloba A428

Photo. & Embossed
2017, Jan. 2   **Perf. 13¼**
557   A428   €1.24 multi   2.60   2.60
Values are for stamps with surrounding selvage.

Challenger 8 Tractor — A429

2017, Jan. 2   Engr.   **Perf. 13x13¼**
558   A429   €1.24 multi   2.60   2.60

RV Ob, Flagship of 1956 Soviet Antarctic Expedition at Kerguelen Island — A430

2017, Jan. 2   Engr.   **Perf. 13x13¼**
559   A430   €1.24 multi   2.60   2.60

Amalopteryx Maritima A431

2017, Jan. 2   Engr.   **Perf. 13x13¼**
560   A431   €1.55 multi   3.25   3.25

Slaves Abandoned on Tromelin Island After 1761 Shipwreck — A432

Litho. & Engr.
2017, Jan. 2   **Perf. 13x13¼**
561   A432   €1.55 multi   3.25   3.25

Pyroxene A433

No. 562: a, Crystal. b, Polished and cut stones.

Litho. & Silk-Screened
2017, Jan. 2   **Perf. 13**
562   A433   Horiz. pair   2.25   2.25
a.   20c multi   .45   .45
b.   80c multi   1.75   1.75

Founders of French Polar Expeditions A434

Polar Expedition Port-Martin Station, Adélie Land A435

2017, Jan. 2   Engr.   **Perf. 13x13¼**
563   Horiz. pair + central label   4.50   4.50
a.   A434 80c multi   1.75   1.75
b.   A435 €1.24 multi   2.60   2.60

Souvenir Sheet

CASA CN-235 Over Island A436

2017, Jan. 2   Litho.   **Perf. 13**
564   A436   €3.90 multi   8.25   8.25

Souvenir Sheet

Tuna Fishing A437

No. 565: a, Albacore tuna. b, Fishing trawler.

Litho. & Engr.
2017, Jan. 2   **Perf. 13**
565   A437   Sheet of 2   2.60   2.60
a.   44c multi   .85   .85
b.   80c multi   1.75   1.75

Miniature Sheet

Gygis Alba A438

No. 566: a, Two terns, blue background, vert. b, Chick, green background. c, Head of tern facing forward, blue background. d, Head of tern facing left, red background.

Litho. & Engr.
2017, Jan. 2   **Perf. 13**
566   A438   Sheet of 4   7.00   7.00
a.-d.   85c Any single   1.75   1.75

Miniature Sheet

Amphipods — A439

No. 567: a, Epimeria robusta. b, Epimeria inermis. c, Échiniphimedia scotti. d, Anchiphimedia dorsalis.

2017, Jan. 2   Engr.   **Perf. 13**
567   A439   Sheet of 4   9.50   9.50
a.-b.   80c Either single   1.75   1.75
c.   €1.24 multi   2.60   2.60
d.   €1.55 multi   3.25   3.25

Silhouettes of Emblems Types of 2013-16
Miniature Sheet
2017, Mar. 9   Litho.   **Perf. 13**
568   Sheet of 4   16.00   16.00
a.   A363 (€1.24) multi   4.00   4.00
b.   A379 (€1.24) multi   4.00   4.00
c.   A419 (€1.24) multi   4.00   4.00
d.   A399 (€1.24) multi   4.00   4.00

No. 568 sold for €7.50. Nos. 568a-568d are each inscribed "Lettre 20g tarif international."

Ship Marion Dufresne A440

Litho. & Engr.
2017, May 12   **Perf. 13**
569   A440   (€1.24) multi   2.75   2.75

Ship L'Astrolabe — A441

2017, Oct. 9   Engr.   **Perf. 13x13¼**
570   A441   €1.30 multi   3.00   3.00

Birds of the Arctic and Antarctic A442

Designs: €1.41, Stercorarius maccormicki. €3.63, Aptenodytes forsteri.
No. 573: a, Like No. 571. b, Like No. 572.

Litho. & Engr.
2017, Oct. 27   **Perf. 13x12¾**
Stamps With Gray Frames
571-572   A442   Set of 2   12.00   12.00
Souvenir Sheet
Stamps Without Gray Frames
573   Sheet of 2 + label   6.00   6.00
a.   A442 €1 multi   2.40   2.40
b.   A442 €1.50 multi   3.50   3.50

See Greenland Nos. 763-765.

Voyage Booklet Type of 1999
No. 573C: d, Morne Rouge, Crozet Island. e, Baie Larose, Kerguelen Island. f, Plateau des Tourbières, Amsterdam Island. g, Ile Saint-Paul. h, Diver observing seaweed off Kerguelen Island. i, Scientist measuring lobster. j, Photo-identification chart of orca dorsal fins. k, Photographer on ship near Kerguelen Island. l, Man uprooting invasive non-native plants, Crozet Island. m, Scientist on bird survey, Kerguelen Island. o, Man inspecting plants, Amsterdam Island. p, Stacks of wooden pathway segments, Crozet Island. q, Freight decontamination at port, Reunion. r, Aerial view of building site, Crozet Island. s, Fence, Kerguelen Island.

2017, Nov. 9   Litho.   **Perf. 13**
573C   A164   (€1.24) Souvenir booklet, #d-s   65.00

No. 573C sold for €27 and contains four panes consisting of a block of four of Nos. 573Cd-573Cg, 573Ch-573Ck, 573Cl-573Co and 573Cp-573Cs.

Miniature Sheet

Birds and Reptiles A443

No. 574: a, Phaéton à bec jaune (yellow-billed tropicbird) (44x43mm). b, Scinque aux

labiales tachetés (skink) (54x54mm diamond). c, Frégate du Pacifique (great frigatebird) (38x38mm). d, Tortue verte (green turtle) (43mm diameter).

Perf. 13, Perf. (#574a, 574d)
2017, Nov. 30   Litho. & Engr.
574   A443   Sheet of 4   10.00   10.00
a.-c.   85c Any single   2.10   2.10
d.   €1.45 multi   3.50   3.50

Adélie Penguins A444

Litho. & Silk-screened
2017, Dec. 8   **Perf. 13**
575   A444   €1 multi   —   —

Myro Jeanneli — A445

2018, Jan. 2   Photo.   **Perf. 13¼**
576   A445   80c brnsh black   2.00   2.00

Cabin in Canyon des Sourcils Noirs, Kerguelen Island — A446

2018, Jan. 2   Litho.   **Perf. 13**
577   A446   85c multi   2.10   2.10

Kubota Snow Vehicle A447

2018, Jan. 2   Litho.   **Perf. 13**
578   A447   85c multi   2.10   2.10

Dr. Jean Sapin-Jaloustre (1917-99), Polar Expedition Physician — A448

2018, Jan. 2   Litho.   **Perf. 13**
579   A448   85c multi   2.10   2.10

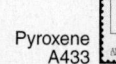

Pierre Etienne de Boynes (1718-83), French Secretary of the Navy A449

2018, Jan. 2   Engr.   **Perf. 13x12¾**
580   A449   85c multi   2.10   2.10

La Quille
Island Near
Saint Paul
Island
A450

2018, Jan. 2 Engr. Perf. 13x13¼
581 A450 €1.05 multi 2.60 2.60

Ectemnorhinus Viridis — A451

2018, Jan. 2 Engr. Perf. 13x13¼
582 A451 €1.55 multi 3.75 3.75

Transport Ship La Grandière — A452

2018, Jan. 2 Engr. Perf. 13x13¼
583 A452 €1.70 multi 4.25 4.25

Ilmenite
A453

No. 584: a, Ilmenite in rock. b, Cut and polished ilmenite.

Litho. & Silk-Screened
2018, Jan. 2 Perf. 13
584 A453 50c Horiz. pair, #a-b 2.40 2.40

Renker Program, 2011-15 Study of Reindeer on Kerguelen Island
A454

No. 585: a, Head of reindeer. b, Herd of reindeer. c, Adult and juvenile reindeer.

2018, Jan. 2 Engr. Perf. 13
585 Horiz. strip of 3 6.50 6.50
a.-c. A454 85c Any single 2.10 2.10

Souvenir Sheet

Map of Antarctica — A455

2018, Jan. 2 Photo. Perf. 13¼
586 A455 85c multi 2.10 2.10

Madrid Protocol on Envrionmental Protection to the Antarctic Treaty, 20th anniv.

Souvenir Sheet

MacGillivray's Prions — A456

2018, Jan. 2 Litho. Perf. 13
587 A456 €1 multi 2.40 2.40

Souvenir Sheet

PBY Catalina, Ship La Pérouse, Map of Forgotten Airfield on Kerguelen Island — A457

2018, Jan. 2 Litho. Perf. 13¼x13
588 A457 €3.90 multi 9.50 9.50

Souvenir Sheet

Echinoderms of Adélie Land — A458

No. 589: a, Lophaster gaini (40x40mm). b, Notocidaris platyacantha (52x40mm). c, Promachocrinus kerguelensis (80x53mm).

2018, Jan. 2 Engr. Perf. 13
589 A458 Sheet of 3 8.50 8.50
a. 80c multi 2.00 2.00
b. €1.05 multi 2.60 2.60
c. €1.55 multi 3.75 3.75

Miniature Sheet

Protected Animals — A459

No. 590: a, Amsterdam albatross. b, Emperor penguin, vert. c, Crozet elephant seal. d, Kerguelen fur seal.

2018, Jan. 2 Engr. Perf. 13
590 A459 Sheet of 4 13.00 13.00
a.-b. 85c Either single 2.10 2.10
c.-d. €1.70 Either single 4.25 4.25

Ship
L'Astrolabe
A460

2018, Apr. 8 Litho. Perf. 13
591 A460 (85c) multi 2.10 2.10

Silhouettes of Adélie Land District Emblems — A461

Litho. & Silk-screened
2018, Apr. 8 Perf. 13¼
592 A461 €1 multi 2.40 2.40

A stamp similar to No. 592, with an inscription of "lettre - 20g tarif international" was issued on Nov. 7, 2019 in a sheet along with a similarly inscribed stamp similar to No. 617. The franking value of each of these stamps was €1.10, but the sheet sold for €5, along with a folder.

Souvenir Sheet

Symphonie Australe, Musical Composition by Julien Gauthier — A462

2018, Apr. 20 Litho. Perf. 13¼
593 A462 €2 multi 5.00 5.00

A463

Penguins
A464

Designs: 10c, Rockhopper penguin (gorfou sauteur). 20c, King penguin (manchot royal). 30c, Gentoo penguin (manchot papou).
No. 597: a, Emperor penguin (manchot empereur, 40mm diameter). b, King penguin (40x30mm). c, Gentoo penguin (40x30mm). d, Rockhopper penguin (40x30mm).

2018, June 7 Litho. Perf. 13
594-596 A463 Set of 3 1.40 1.40
594a Dated "2019" .25 .25
595a Dated "2019" .45 .45
596a Dated "2019" .70 .70
Miniature Sheet
Perf. (#597a), Perf. 13¼ (#597b-597d)
597 A464 Sheet of 4 8.00 8.00
a.-d. 85c Any single 2.00 2.00
Issued: Nos. 594a, 595a, 596a, 3/14/19.

Souvenir Sheet

Alfred Faure (1925-68), Leader of Crozet Island Base — A465

2018, Oct. 17 Litho. Perf. 13
598 A465 95c multi 2.25 2.25

Eudyptes Chrysocome Moseleyi — A466

No. 599: a, Head of penguin and Ile Saint-Paul. b, Penguin and volcano cone.

2018, Oct. 26 Engr. Perf. 13
599 A466 Horiz. pair + central label 5.50 5.50
a. 95c dp bluish grn & blk lil 2.25 2.25
b. €1.35 dp bluish grn & blk lil 3.25 3.25

Souvenir Sheet

Modern Art Exhibition at Dumont d'Urville Station, Antarctica — A467

Photo. & Silk-Screened
2018, Nov. 8 Perf.
600 A467 €2.20 multi 5.00 5.00

Elephant
Seal
Observation
Cabins Near
American
Bay, Crozet
Island
A468

2019, Jan. 2 Litho. Perf. 13
601 A468 95c multi 2.25 2.25

Gygis
Alba and
Tromelin
Island
A469

2019, Jan. 2 Engr. Perf. 13
602 A469 95c multi 2.25 2.25

Yves Vallette (1920-2014), Civil Engineer and Member of 1949-51 French Polar Expeditions — A470

2019, Jan. 2 Engr. Perf. 12½x13
603 A470 95c multi 2.25 2.25

Mario Zucchelli (1944-2003), Director of Italian Antarctic Program — A471

2019, Jan. 2 Engr. Perf. 13
604 A471 €1.35 multi 3.25 3.25

Neomaso
Antarcticus
A472

2019, Jan. 2 Engr. Perf. 13
605 A472 €1.55 multi 3.50 3.50

Zanclorhynchus Spinifer — A473

2019, Jan. 2 Engr. Perf. 13
606 A473 €1.70 multi 4.00 4.00

B2M Champlain A474

2019, Jan. 2   Litho.   Perf. 13
607 A474 €1.90 multi   4.50 4.50

Missile Cruiser Colbert A475

2019, Jan. 2   Litho.   Perf. 13
608 A475 €2.80 multi   6.50 6.50

Sapphirines A476

No. 609: a, Raw sapphirine. b, Three cut and polished sapphirines.

Litho. & Silk-Screened
2019, Jan. 2   Perf. 13
609 A476 50c Horiz. pair, #a-b   2.25 2.25

Laboureur, Kerguelen Island — A477

No. 610: a, Mairie Annexe Cabin (40x26mm). b, Laboureur (81x26mm).

2019, Jan. 2   Engr.   Perf. 13
610   Horiz. pair + central label 5.50 5.50
  a.   A477 95c multi   2.25 2.25
  b.   A477 €1.35 multi   3.25 3.25

Study of Lake Sediment Cores A478

No. 611: a, Workers on barge coring lake sediment. b, Barge on Lac d'Armor. c, Equipment for studying cores.

2019, Jan. 2   Litho.   Perf. 13
611   Horiz. strip of 3   12.00 12.00
  a.   A478 95c multi   2.25 2.25
  b.   A478 €1.35 multi   3.25 3.25
  c.   A478 €2.70 multi   6.25 6.25

Souvenir Sheet

Restoration of Phylica Arborea on Amsterdam Island — A479

2019, Jan. 2   Litho.   Perf. 13
612 A479 95c multi   2.25 2.25

Souvenir Sheet

Flesh-footed Shearwater — A480

2019, Jan. 2   Litho.   Perf. 13
613 A480 €2 multi   4.50 4.50

Souvenir Sheet

Photovoltaic Solar Power Plant on Tromelin Island — A481

No. 614 — Power plant and: a, Bird at UL, sea turtle at LR (40x40mm). b, Bird at UR, sea turtle at LL (40x30mm).

Perf. 13 (#614a), 13x13¼ (#614b)
2019, Jan. 2   Litho.
614 A481   Sheet of 2   4.50 4.50
  a.-b.   95c Either single   2.25 2.25

Souvenir Sheet

Shells of Adélie Land A482

No. 615: a, Falsimargarita gemma (40x40mm). b, Trophonella scotiana (52x40mm). c, Trophonella shackletoni (52x40mm).

2019, Jan. 2   Engr.   Perf. 13
615 A482   Sheet of 3   7.25 7.25
  a.   70c multi   1.60 1.60
  b.   95c multi   2.25 2.25
  c.   €1.35 multi   3.25 3.25

Gentoo Penguins A483

2019, Mar. 16   Litho.   Perf. 13
616 A483 €1 multi   2.25 2.25

Silhouettes of Scattered Islands of the Indian Ocean District Emblems — A484

Litho. & Silk-screened
2019, Mar. 16   Perf. 13¼
617 A484 €1.50 multi   3.50 3.50

A stamp similar to No. 617, with an inscription of "lettre - 20g tarif international" was issued on Nov. 7, 2019 in a sheet along with a similarly inscribed stamp similar to No. 592. The franking value of each of these stamps was €1.10, but the sheet sold for €5, along with a folder.

Oceanographic Ship La Curieuse — A485

2019, June 7   Litho.   Perf. 13
618 A485 €1.35 multi   3.25 3.25

A sheet of two, containing stamps similar to Nos. 592 and 617, but with an inscription of "lettre - 20g tarif international" was issued on Nov. 7, 2019. The franking value of each of these stamps was €1.10, but the sheet sold for €5, along with a folder.

Souvenir Sheet

Aptenodytes Patagonicus — A486

No. 619: a, Three King penguins (40x40mm). b, One King penguin (40x30mm).

Perf. 13 (#619a), 13x13¼ (#619b)
2019, Nov. 28   Litho.
619 A486   Sheet of 2   7.00 7.00
  a.-b.   €1.50 Either single   3.50 3.50

Entrecasteaux Cabins, Amsterdam Island — A487

2020, Jan. 2   Litho.   Perf. 13
620 A487 €1.05 multi   2.40 2.40

Channichthys Velifer — A488

2020, Jan. 2   Engr.   Perf. 13x13¼
621 A488 €1.05 multi   2.40 2.40

Bernard Morlet (1932-2010), Geophysicist — A489

2020, Jan. 2   Engr.   Perf. 13¼x13
622 A489 €1.05 multi   2.40 2.40

Saint Anne's Finger and Larose Bay, Kerguelen Islands A490

2020, Jan. 2   Litho.   Perf. 13
623 A490 €1.45 multi   3.25 3.25

Egretta Dimorpha A491

2020, Jan. 2   Engr.   Perf. 13
624 A491 €1.55 multi   3.50 3.50

Frigate Nivôse A492

2020, Jan. 2   Engr.   Perf. 13
625 A492 €1.55 multi   3.50 3.50

Amethyst A493

No. 626: a, Uncut stone. b, Cut and polished stones.

Litho. & Silk-Screened
2020, Jan. 2   Perf. 13
626 A493   Horiz. pair   2.20 2.20
  a.-b.   50c Either single   1.10 1.10

Robert-Guillard Station — A494

No. 627: a, Station and equipment. b, Map showing location of station.

2020, Jan. 2   Litho.   Perf. 13
627 A494   Horiz. pair   8.75 8.75
  a.   €1.05 multi   2.40 2.40
  b.   €2.80 multi   6.25 6.25

Souvenir Sheet

Great Albatrosses — A495

2020, Jan. 2   Litho.   Perf. 13
628 A495 €1 multi   2.25 2.25

Souvenir Sheet

Penguins and Aurora Australis A496

Litho. & Silk-Screened
2020, Jan. 2   Perf. 13
629 A496 €1.45 multi   3.25 3.25

Souvenir Sheet

Natural Bridge, Crozet Islands A497

2020, Jan. 2   Litho.   Perf. 13x13¼
630   A497   €2.80 multi   6.25 6.25

Souvenir Sheet

Concordia Base Logistics — A498

No. 631: a, DHC-6 Twin Otter over Concordia Base (52x31mm). b, Map showing location of Concordia Base (32x24mm).

Perf. 13 (#631a), 13¼ (#631b)
2020, Jan. 2   Litho.
631   A498   Sheet of 2   4.80 4.80
a.-b.   €1.05 Either single   2.40 2.40

Souvenir Sheet

Commerson's Dolphins — A499

No. 632: a, Commerson's dolphin near Zodiac boat (40x30mm). b, Commerson's dolphin (40x40mm).

Perf. 13 (#632a), 13x13¼ (#632b)
2020, Jan. 2   Litho.
632   A499   Sheet of 2   5.50 5.50
a.   €1.05 multi   2.40 2.40
b.   €1.35 multi   3.00 3.00

Souvenir Sheet

Marine Life Management — A500

No. 633: a, Lobster. b, Marker.

Litho. & Silk-Screened
2020, Jan. 2   Perf. 13¼x13
633   A500   Sheet of 2   7.00 7.00
a.   €1.05 multi   2.40 2.40
b.   €1.95 multi   4.50 4.50

Souvenir Sheet

Cephalopods — A501

No. 634: a, Psychroteuthis glacialis. b, Pareledone turqueti.

2020, Jan. 2   Engr.   Perf. 13
634   A501   Sheet of 2 + label   6.75 6.75
a.   €1.45 multi   3.25 3.25
b.   €1.55 multi   3.50 3.50

Postal Services of the French Southern and Antarctic Territories — A502

No. 635: a, Postage stamps, handstamps and clerk applying cancel. b, Transfer of mail bags.

2020, Oct. 29   Litho.   Perf. 13
635   Horiz. pair + 2 alternat-
            ing labels   4.75 4.75
a.   A502 95c multi + label   2.25 2.25
b.   A502 €1.05 multi + label   2.50 2.50

Map of Scattered Islands of the Indian Ocean, Palm Tree, Bird, Spider and Crab — A503

Map of St. Paul and Amsterdam Islands, Bird, Plants and Helicopter — A504

Map of Crozet Islands, Birds, Ship, Building, Seal and Helicopter — A505

Map of Kerguelen Islands, Penguin, Ship, Flags and Building — A506

Map of Adélie Land, Penguin, Crab, Starfish, Ship, Buildings and Helicopter — A507

2020, Nov. 1   Photo.   Perf. 13
Stamps With White Frames
636   A503   €1.05 multi   2.50 2.50
637   A504   €1.05 multi   2.50 2.50
638   A505   €1.05 multi   2.50 2.50
639   A506   €1.05 multi   2.50 2.50
640   A507   €1.05 multi   2.50 2.50
            Nos. 636-640 (5)   12.50 12.50

French Southern & Antarctic Territories, 65th anniv.

French Southern and Antarctic Territories 65th Anniv. Types of 2020

Miniature Sheet
2020, Dec. 1   Litho.   Perf. 13
Stamps Without White Frames
641   Sheet of 5   19.00 19.00
a.   A503 €1.50 multi   3.75 3.75
b.   A504 €1.50 multi   3.75 3.75
c.   A505 €1.50 multi   3.75 3.75
d.   A506 €1.50 multi   3.75 3.75
e.   A507 €1.50 multi   3.75 3.75

Souvenir Sheet

Paul-Emile Victor (1907-95), Polar Explorer — A508

2020, Nov. 5   Litho.   Perf. 13
642   A508   €1.50 multi   3.75 3.75

Apostle Islets, Crozet Archipelago A509

King Penguins, Larose Bay, Kerguelen Islands A510

Albatross Colony, Cliffs of Entrecasteaux, Amsterdam Island — A511

Pointe des Moines, Possession Island, Crozet Archipelago A512

Birds at Ocean Deeding Zones A513

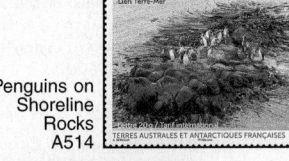

Penguins on Shoreline Rocks A514

Biodiversity of Fish A515

Aerial View of Shoreline A516

Amsterdam Sea Lions, Amsterdam Island A517

Commerson Dolphins, Morbihan Gulf, Kerguelen Islands A518

Amsterdam Albatrosses, Amsterdam Island A519

Black-browed Albatrosses, Kerguelen Islands — A520

2020, Nov. 6   Litho.   Perf. 13
643   Souvenir booklet,
            #643m, 643n, 643o   63.00
a.   A509 (€1.50) multi   5.25 5.25
b.   A510 (€1.50) multi   5.25 5.25
c.   A511 (€1.50) multi   5.25 5.25
d.   A512 (€1.50) multi   5.25 5.25
e.   A513 (€1.50) multi   5.25 5.25
f.   A514 (€1.50) multi   5.25 5.25
g.   A515 (€1.50) multi   5.25 5.25
h.   A516 (€1.50) multi   5.25 5.25
i.   A517 (€1.50) multi   5.25 5.25
j.   A518 (€1.50) multi   5.25 5.25
k.   A519 (€1.50) multi   5.25 5.25
l.   A520 (€1.50) multi   5.25 5.25
m.   Booklet pane of 4, #643e-643h   21.00
n.   Booklet pane of 4, #643a-643d   21.00
o.   Booklet pane of 4, #643i-643l   21.00

French Austral Lands and Seas UNESCO World Heritage Sites. No. 643 sold for €26.

Chalcedony A521

No. 644: a, Unpolished chalcedony rock. b, Three polished and shaped chalcedony stones.

2021, Jan. 2   Litho.   Perf. 13
644   A521   50c Horiz. pair, #a-b   2.50 2.50

Model of the Marion Dufresne in Bottle — A522

Litho. & Silk-Screened
2021, Jan. 2   Perf. 13x13¼
645   A522   €1.05 multi   2.60 2.60

Pierre-François Péron (1769-1846), Captain Marooned on Amsterdam Island — A523

2021, Jan. 2   Engr.   Perf. 12¾x13¼
646   A523   €1.05 multi   2.60 2.60

Cabins at Pointe Basse, Crozet Archipelago A524

2021, Jan. 2   Litho.   Perf. 13
647   A524   €1.10 multi   2.75 2.75

Workers Maintining Relay 26, Kerguelen Islands A525

2021, Jan. 2   **Litho.**   *Perf. 13*
648 A525 €1.20 multi   3.00 3.00

André Lebeau (1932-2013), Geophysicist — A526

2021, Jan. 2   **Engr.**   *Perf. 13*
649 A526 €1.20 multi   3.00 3.00

Ship La Meurthe at Crozet Archipelago, 1887 — A527

2021, Jan. 2   **Engr.**   *Perf. 13x13¼*
650 A527 €1.20 multi   3.00 3.00

Souvenir Sheet

Kerguelen Shag and Crozet Shag — A528

2021, Jan. 2   **Litho.**   *Perf. 13*
651 A528 €1 multi   2.50 2.50

Souvenir Sheet

Apostle Islets, Crozet Archipelago — A529

2021, Jan. 2   **Litho.**   *Perf. 13x13¼*
652 A529 €1.50 multi   3.75 3.75

Souvenir Sheet

Jellyfish A530

No. 653: a, 80c, Calycopsis borchgrevinki (40x40mm). b, €1.20, Periphylla periphylla (53x40mm).

Litho. & Engr.
2021, Jan. 2   *Perf. 13*
653 A530 Sheet of 2, #a-b   5.00 5.00

Souvenir Sheet

Basler BT-67 Airplane A531

No. 654 — Basler BT-67: a, In flight (82x30mm). b, On ground (52x31mm).

Perf. 13¼ (#654a), 13 (#654b)
2021, Jan. 2   **Litho.**
654 A531 €1.50 Sheet of 2, #a-b   7.50 7.50

Souvenir Sheet

Coral Reefs of the Glorioso Islands A532

No. 655 — Various photographs of reef: a, Horizontal stamp. b, Vertical stamp.

Litho. & Engr.
2021, Jan. 2   *Perf. 13*
655 A532 €2 Sheet of 2, #a-b   10.00 10.00

Miniature Sheet

Amsterdam Sea Lions — A533

No. 656: a, €1.05, Sea lion facing right (52x32mm). b, €1.05, Sea lion facing left (52x32mm). c, €1.45, Sea lion facing right, diff. (31x53mm). d, €1.45, Head of sea lion (41x42mm).

Perf. 13x12¾ (#656a-656b), 12¾x13 (#656c), 13 (#656d)
2021, Jan. 2   **Engr.**
656 A533   Sheet of 4, #a-d   12.50 12.50

Miniature Sheet

Crabs A534

No. 657: a. €1.05, Beuroisia duhameli. b, €1.05, Ovalipes trimaculatus. c, €1.45, Chaceon paulensis. d, €1.45, Guinusia chabrus.

2021, Jan. 2   **Engr.**   *Perf. 13*
657 A534   Sheet of 4, #a-d   12.50 12.50

Miniature Sheet

Kerguelen Islands Flora — A535

No. 658: a, Pringlea antiscorbutica. b, Lyallia kerguelensis. c, Blechnum penna-marina. d, Acaena magellanica.

2021, Jan. 2   **Litho.**   *Perf. 13¼x13*
658 A535 €1.50 Sheet of 4, #a-d   15.00 15.00

Souvenir Sheet

Consultative Meeting on the Antarctic Treaty, Paris — A536

Litho., Sheet Margin Litho. & Embossed
2021, June 11   *Perf. 13¼x13*
659 A536 €3 multi   7.25 7.25

Wildlife — A537

Designs: 10c, Orca, Crozet Islands. 20c, Australasian gannets, Saint Paul and Amsterdam Islands, vert. No. 662. 40c, Atlantic yellow-nosed albatross and chicks, Kerguelen Islands, vert. No. 663. 40c, Emperor penguins and chicks, Adélie Land, vert. 50c, Great frigatebird, Scattered Islands.
No. 665: a, Like No. 660. b, Like No. 661. c, Like No. 662. d, Like No. 663. e, Like No. 664.

Perf. 13x13¼, 13¼x13
2021, Nov. 4   **Photo.**
660-664 A537   Set of 5   3.75 3.75
Miniature Sheet
665   A537   Sheet of 5   11.50 11.50
  a.-e.   €1 Any single   2.25 2.25

Claude Pieri (1922-2002), Senior Administrator of French Southern and Antarctic Territories — A538

2022, Jan. 2   **Engr.**   *Perf. 13*
666 A538 €1.10 multi   2.50 2.50

Sunrise on Ile de l'Est — A539

2022, Jan. 2   **Litho.**   *Perf. 13x13¼*
667 A539 €1.10 multi   2.50 2.50

Seabed Near the Scattered Islands — A540

2022, Jan. 2   **Litho.**   *Perf. 13x13¼*
668 A540 €1.10 multi   2.50 2.50

Maintenance on Relay 26, Mt. Fernand, Amsterdam Island A541

2022, Jan. 2   **Litho.**   *Perf. 13*
669 A541 €1.20 multi   2.75 2.75

Shipwreck of Le Meridian Near Amsterdam Island and its Artifacts — A542

2022, Jan. 2   **Litho.**   *Perf. 13x13¼*
670 A542 €1.50 multi   3.50 3.50

Serpentine A543

No. 671: a, One unpolished serpentine rock. b, Three polished serpentine stones.

2022, Jan. 2   **Litho.**   *Perf. 13*
671 A543 50c Horiz. pair, #a-b   2.25 2.25

Souvenir Sheet

Marc-Joseph Marion du Fresne (1724-72), Explorer, Ship, and Ile de la Possession — A544

Litho. & Engr.
2022, Jan. 2   *Perf. 13*
672 A544 €1.10 multi   2.50 2.50

Discovery of Crozet Islands by Marion du Fresne, 250th anniv.

Souvenir Sheet

Ship and Kerguelen Island — A545

Litho. & Engr.
2022, Jan. 2   *Perf. 13*
673 A545 €1.10 multi   2.50 2.50

Discovery of Kerguelen Islands by Yves-Joseph de Kerguelen-Trémarec, 250th anniv.

Souvenir Sheet

Wheeled Robot at Penguin Colony, Adélie Land A546

2022, Jan. 2   **Litho.**   *Perf. 13*
674 A546 €1.50 multi   3.50 3.50

Souvenir Sheet

Restocking of the Marion Dufresne by Helicopter Off Kerguelen Island — A547

2022, Jan. 2   **Litho.**   *Perf. 13*
675 A547 €1.50 multi   3.50 3.50

Souvenir Sheet

White-chinned Petrel — A548

2022, Jan. 2   Litho.   *Perf. 13*
676 A548 €2 multi   4.50 4.50

Souvenir Sheet

Publication of *An Antarctic Mystery*, Novel by Jules Verne (1828-1905), 125th Anniv. — A549

Litho. & Engr.
2022, Jan. 2   *Perf. 13*
677 A549 €3 multi   6.75 6.75

Souvenir Sheet

Bénédicte Ardouin (1935-2016), Scientist — A550

Litho. & Engr.
2022, Jan. 2   *Perf. 13*
678 A550 €3 multi   6.75 6.75

Souvenir Sheet

Icebreakers — A551

No. 679: a, L'Astrolabe. b, Aurora Australis.

2022, Jan. 2 Litho. *Perf. 13¼x13*
679 A551 Sheet of 2   7.00 7.00
a.-b. €1.50 Either single   3.50 3.50

Souvenir Sheet

Amsterdam Island and Its Discoverer, Juan Sebastián Elcano (c. 1486-1526) — A552

2022, June 23 Litho. *Perf. 13*
680 A552 €1.50 multi   3.25 3.25
Discovery of Amsterdam Island, 500th anniv.

Antarctic Explorers — A553

Map of Antarctica and: No. 681, Capt. James Cook (1728-79). No. 682, Jules Dumont d'Urville (1790-1842). No. 683, Jean-Baptiste Charcot (1867-1936). No. 684, Roald Amundsen (1872-1928). No. 685, Robert Falcon Scott (1868-1912). No. 686, Douglas Mawson (1882-1958). No. 687, Ernest Shackleton (1874-1922).

2022, June 25   Engr.   *Perf. 13*
Booklet Stamps
681 A553 €1.50 black   3.25 3.25
682 A553 €1.50 black   3.25 3.25
683 A553 €1.50 black   3.25 3.25
684 A553 €1.50 black   3.25 3.25
685 A553 €1.50 black   3.25 3.25
686 A553 €1.50 black   3.25 3.25
687 A553 €1.50 black   3.25 3.25
a.   Booklet pane of 7, #681-687   23.00 —
      Complete booklet, #687a   23.00
      Nos. 681-687 (7)   22.75 22.75

Souvenir Sheet

Discovery of Tromelin Island By the Crew of the Diane, 300th Anniv. — A554

Litho. & Engr.
2022, Nov. 4   *Perf. 13*
688 A554 €2.20 multi   4.75 4.75

Souvenir Sheet

Prince Albert I of Monaco (1848-1922) — A555

No. 689: a, Prince Albert I, map of Antarctica (52x31mm). b, Pourquoi-Pas, ship from the second Charcot expedition to Antarctica (30x40mm).

Perf. 13 (#689a), 13¼x13 (#689b)
2022, Nov. 24   Litho.
689   A555   Sheet of 2   8.50 8.50
a.-b.   €2 Either single   4.25 4.25

See Monaco No.

AIR POST STAMPS

Emperor Penguins and Map of Antarctica AP1

Unwmk.
1956, Apr. 25   Engr.   *Perf. 13*
C1 AP1 50fr lt ol grn & dk grn   42.50 29.00
C2 AP1 100fr dl bl & indigo   35.00 25.00

Wandering Albatross AP2

1959, Sept. 14
C3 AP2 200fr brn red, bl & blk   40.00 27.50

Adélie Penguins AP3

1963, Feb. 11   Unwmk.   *Perf. 13*
C4 AP3 50fr blk, dk bl & dp cl 42.50 32.50

Telstar Issue
Common Design Type
1962, Dec. 24
C5 CD111 50fr dp bl, ol & grn 29.00 21.00

Radio Towers, Adelie Penguins and IQSY Emblem — AP4

1963, Dec. 16   Engr.
C6 AP4 100fr bl, ver & blk   110.00 87.50
International Quiet Sun Year, 1964-65.

Discovery of Adelie Land — AP5

1965, Jan. 20   Engr.   *Perf. 13*
C7 AP5 50fr blue & indigo   125.00 87.50
125th anniversary of the discovery of Adelie Land by Dumont d'Urville.

ITU Issue
Common Design Type
1965, May 17   Unwmk.   *Perf. 13*
C8 CD120 30fr multi   200.00 160.00

French Satellite A-1 Issue
Common Design Type

Designs: 25fr, Diamant rocket and launching installations. 30fr, A-1 satellite.

1966, Mar. 2   Engr.   *Perf. 13*
C9 CD121 25fr dk grn, choc
              & sl   13.50 10.00
C10 CD121 30fr choc, sl & dk
              grn   13.50 10.00
a.   Pair, #C9-C10 + label   29.00 24.00

French Satellite D-1 Issue
Common Design Type
1966, Mar. 27
C11 CD122 50fr dk pur, lil &
              org   57.50 40.00

Ionospheric Research Pylon, Adelie Land — AP6

1966, Dec. 12
C12 AP6 25fr plum, bl & dk
              brn   32.50 17.50

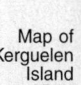

Port aux Français, Emperor Penguin and Explorer AP7

40fr, Aerial view of Saint Paul Island.

1968-69   Engr.   *Perf. 13*
C13 AP7 40fr brt bl & dk
              gray   42.50 27.50
C14 AP7 50fr lt ultra, dk grn
              & blk   175.00 110.00
Issue dates: 50fr, Jan. 21; 40fr, Jan. 5, 1969.

Kerguelen Island and Rocket AP8

Design: 30fr, Adelie Land.

1968, Apr. 22   Engr.   *Perf. 13*
C15 AP8 25fr sl grn, dk brn &
              Prus bl   19.00 14.00
C16 AP8 30fr dk brn, sl grn &
              Prus bl   19.00 14.00
a.   Pair, #C15-C16 + label   40.00 30.00
Space explorations with Dragon rockets, 1967-68.

Eiffel Tower, Antarctic Research Station, Ship from Paris Arms and Albatross — AP9

1969, Jan. 13
C17 AP9 50fr bright blue   45.00 35.00
5th Consultative Meeting of the Antarctic Treaty Powers, Paris, Nov. 18, 1968.

Concorde Issue
Common Design Type
1969, Apr. 17
C18 CD129 85fr indigo & blue 55.00 37.50
Prepared but not issued with 87fr denomination. Value $3,000.

Map of Amsterdam Island — AP10

Map of Kerguelen Island AP11

Coat of Arms — AP12

Designs: 50fr, Possession Island. 200fr, Point Geology Archipelago.

1969-71   Engr.   *Perf. 13*
C19 AP10 30fr brown   19.00 12.50
C20 AP11 50fr sl grn, bl &
              dk red   21.00 14.00
C21 AP11 100fr blue & blk 85.00 40.00
C22 AP10 200fr sl grn, brn
              & Prus bl   70.00 42.50
C23 AP12 500fr pck blue   20.00 15.00
      Nos. C19-C23 (5)   215.00 124.00

30fr for the 20th anniv. of the Amsterdam Island Meteorological Station.
Issued: 100fr, 500fr, 12/21; 30fr, 3/27/70; 50fr, 12/22/70; 200fr, 1/1/71.

Port-aux-Français, 1970 — AP13

Design: 40fr, Port-aux-Français, 1950.

1971, Mar. 9   Engr.   Perf. 13
C24 AP13 40fr bl, ocher & sl
    grn   19.00 12.00
C25 AP13 50fr bl, grn ol & sl
    grn   19.00 12.00
a.   Pair, #C24-C25 + label   40.00 27.50

20th anniversary of Port-aux-Français on
Kerguelen Island.

Marquis de
Castries
Taking
Possession
of Crozet
Island, 1772
AP14

250fr, Fleur-de-lis flag raising on Kerguelen
Is.

1972   Engr.   Perf. 13
C26 AP14 100fr black   45.00 29.00
C27 AP14 250fr blk & dk brn   100.00 45.00

Bicentenary of the discovery of the Crozet
and Kerguelen Islands.
Issue dates: 100fr, Jan. 24; 250fr, Feb. 23.

M. S.
Galliéni
AP15

1973, Jan. 25   Engr.   Perf. 13
C28 AP15 100fr black & blue   25.00 17.50

Exploration voyages of the Galliéni.

"Le
Mascarin,"
1772
AP16

Sailing Ships: 145fr, "L'Astrolabe," 1840.
150fr, "Le Rolland," 1774. 185fr, "La Victoire,"
1522.

1973, Dec. 13   Engr.   Perf. 13
C29 AP16 120fr brown olive   6.75 4.75
C30 AP16 145fr brt ultra   6.75 4.75
C31 AP16 150fr slate   8.00 8.00
C32 AP16 185fr ocher   10.50 8.00
    Nos. C29-C32 (4)   32.00 25.50

Ships used in exploring Antarctica.
See Nos. C37-C38.

Alfred Faure
Base
AP17

Design: Nos. C33-C35 show panoramic
view of Alfred Faure Base.

1974, Jan. 7   Engr.   Perf. 13
C33 AP17 75fr Prus bl, ultra
    & brn   8.00 5.25
C34 AP17 110fr Prus bl, ultra
    & brn   11.00 8.00
C35 AP17 150fr Prus bl, ultra
    & brn   14.00 8.00
a.   Triptych, Nos. C33-C35   37.50 30.00

Alfred Faure Antarctic Base, 10th anniv.

Penguin, Map of
Antarctica,
Letters — AP18

1974, Oct. 9   Engr.   Perf. 13
C36 AP18 150fr multicolored   7.00 5.50
Centenary of Universal Postal Union.

Ship Type of 1973

100fr, "Le Français." 200fr, "Pourquoi-pas?"

1974, Dec. 16   Engr.   Perf. 13
C37 AP16 100fr brt blue   5.50 3.00
C38 AP16 200fr dk car rose   9.00 4.50

Ships used in exploring Antarctica.

Rockets
over
Kerguelen
Islands
AP19

Design: 90fr, Northern lights over map of
northern coast of Russia.

1975, Jan. 26   Engr.   Perf. 13
C39 AP19 45fr purple & multi   7.00 4.00
C40 AP19 90fr purple & multi   9.00 5.25
a.   Pair, #C39-C40 + label   19.00 13.00

Franco-Soviet magnetosphere research.

"La
Curieuse"
AP20

Ships: 2.70fr, Commandant Charcot. 4fr,
Marion-Dufresne.

1976, Jan.   Engr.   Perf. 13
C41 AP20 1.90fr multicolored   3.25 2.00
C42 AP20 2.70fr multicolored   5.00 3.25
C43 AP20 4fr red & multi   9.00 4.25
    Nos. C41-C43 (3)   17.25 9.50

Dumont
d'Urville
Base, 1956
AP21

4fr, Dumont d'Urville Base, 1976, Adelie
Land.

1976, Jan.
C44 AP21 1.20fr multicolored   9.00 4.00
C45 AP21 4fr multicolored   11.00 7.25
a.   Pair, #C44-C45 + label   24.00 16.00

Dumont d'Urville Antarctic Base, 20th anniv.

Capt. Cook's
Ships
Passing
Kerguelen
Island
AP22

1976, Dec. 31   Engr.   Perf. 13
C46 AP22 3.50fr slate & blue   13.00 8.00
Bicentenary of Capt. Cook's voyage past
Kerguelen Island.

Sea Lion and
Cub — AP23

1977-79   Engr.   Perf. 13
C47 AP23 4fr dk blue, grn ('79)   3.00 2.50
C48 AP23 10fr multicolored   10.00 9.00

Satellite
Survey,
Kerguelen
AP24

Designs: 50c, 2.70fr, Satellites, Kerguelen.
70c, Geophysical laboratory. 1.90fr, Satellite
and Kerguelen tracking station. 3fr, Satellites,
Adelie Land.

1977-79   Engr.   Perf. 13
C49 AP24 50c multi ('79)   .90   .70
C50 AP24 70c multi ('79)   .90   .70
C51 AP24 1.90fr multi ('79)   1.60 1.40
C52 AP24 2.70fr multi ('78)   2.75 2.00
C53 AP24 3fr multicolored   4.25 3.25
    Nos. C49-C53 (5)   10.40 8.05

Elephant
Seals — AP25

1979, Jan. 1
C54 AP25 10fr multicolored   5.50 4.50

Challenger
AP26

1979, Jan. 1
C55 AP26 2.70fr black & blue   2.25 1.75
Antarctic expeditions to Crozet and Kergue-
len Islands, 1872-1876.

La
Recherche
and
L'Esperance
AP27

1979
C56 AP27 1.90fr deep blue   1.50 1.10
Arrival of d'Entrecasteaux and Kermadec at
Amsterdam Island, Mar. 28, 1792.

Lion Rock
AP28

1979
C57 AP28 90c multicolored   1.10   .70

Natural
Arch,
Kerguelen
Island, 1840
AP29

1979
C58 AP29 2.70fr multicolored   1.25 1.10

Phylica
Nitida,
Amsterdam
Island
AP30

1979
C59 AP30 10fr multicolored   4.00 3.25

Charles de
Gaulle, 10th
Anniversary of
Death — AP31

1980, Nov. 9   Engr.   Perf. 13
C60 AP31 5.40fr multicolored   11.00 8.00

HB-40
Castor
Truck and
Trailer
AP32

1980, Dec. 15
C61 AP32 2.40fr pur, blue & org   1.25 1.00

Supply Ship
Saint
Marcouf
AP33

Design: 7.30fr, Icebreaker Norsel.

1980, Dec. 15
C62 AP33 3.50fr shown   1.60 1.10
C63 AP33 7.30fr multicolored   2.50 2.00

Glacial
Landscape,
Dumont
d'Urville
Sea — AP34

Chionis
AP35

Adele Dumont
d'Urville (1798-
1842)
AP36

Arcad III
AP37

25th Anniv. of Charcot Station AP38

Antares AP39

1981 Engr. Perf. 13, 12½x13 (2fr)
C64 AP34 1.30fr multicolored .70 .45
C65 AP35 1.50fr black .70 .50
C66 AP36 2fr black & lt brn .90 .85
C67 AP37 3.85fr multicolored 1.60 1.25
C68 AP38 5fr multicolored 1.75 1.50
C69 AP39 8.40fr multicolored 2.75 2.25
Nos. C64-C69 (6) 8.40 6.80

PHILEXFRANCE '82 Stamp Exhibition, Paris, June 11-21 — AP40

1982, June 11 Engr. Perf. 13
C70 AP40 8fr multicolored 5.50 5.25

French Overseas Possessions Week, Sept. 18-25 AP41

1982, Sept. 17 Engr. Perf. 13
C71 AP41 5fr Commandant Charcot 1.75 1.75

Apostle Islands AP42

1983, Jan. 3 Engr. Perf. 13
C72 AP42 65c multicolored .55 .35

Sputnik I, 25th Anniv. of Intl. Geophysical Year AP43

Orange Bay Base, Cape Horn, 1883, Cent. AP44

5.20fr, Scoresby Sound Base, Greenland, 50th anniv.

1983, Jan. 3
C73 AP43 1.50fr multicolored .60 .60
C74 AP44 3.30fr multicolored 1.75 1.75
C75 AP44 5.20fr multicolored 2.00 2.00
a. Strip of 3, #C73-C75 4.50 4.50

AP45

1983, Jan. 3
C76 AP45 4.55fr dark blue 4.00 3.00

Abstract, by G. Mathieu AP46

1983, Jan. 3 Photo. Perf. 13x13½
C77 AP46 25fr multicolored 10.00 8.00

Erebus off Antarctic Ice Cap, 1842 — AP47

Port of Joan of Arc, 1930 — AP48

1984, Jan. 1 Engr. Perf. 13
C78 AP47 2.60fr ultra & dk blue 1.10 1.00
C79 AP48 4.70fr multicolored 1.75 1.75

Aurora Polaris AP49

1984, Jan. 1 Photo.
C80 AP49 3.50fr multicolored 2.00 1.25

Manned Flight Bicentenary (1983) AP50

Various balloons and airships.

1984, Jan. 1 Engr.
C81 AP50 3.50fr multicolored 1.75 1.75
C82 AP50 7.80fr multicolored 2.75 2.75
a. Pair, #C81-C82 + label 5.00 5.00

Patrol Boat Albatros — AP51

1984, July 2 Engr. Perf. 13
C83 AP51 11.30fr multi 4.25 4.25

NORDPOSTA Exhibition — AP52

Design: Scientific Vessel Gauss.

1984, Nov. 3 Engr. Perf. 13
C84 AP52 9fr multicolored 4.50 3.50
Issued se-tenant with label.

Corsican Sheep AP53

Amsterdam Albatross AP54

Designs: 70c, Mouflons. 3.90fr, Diomedia amsterdamensis.

1985, Jan. 1 Engr. Perf. 13
C85 AP53 70c multicolored .70 .40
C86 AP54 3.90fr multicolored 1.60 1.25

La Novara, Frigate — AP55

Design: La Novara at St. Paul.

1985, Jan. 1 Engr. Perf. 13
C87 AP55 12.80fr multi 5.00 4.50

Explorer and Seal, by Tremois AP56

Design: Explorer, seal, names of territories.

1985, Jan. 1 Photo. Perf. 13x12½
C88 AP56 30fr + label 11.00 8.50

Sailing Ships, Ropes, Flora & Fauna AP57

1985, Aug. 6 Engr. Perf. 13
C89 AP57 2fr blk, brt bl & ol grn .70 .55
C90 AP57 12.80fr blk, ol grn & brt bl 3.75 3.75
a. Pair, #C89-C90 + label 5.50 5.50
French Southern & Antarctic Territories, 30th anniv. No. C90a has continuous design with center label.

Bird Type of 1986
1986, Jan. 1 Engr. Perf. 13½x13
C91 A56 4.60fr Sea Gulls 2.00 1.75

Antarctic Atmospheric Research, 10th Anniv. AP58

1986, Jan. 1
C92 AP58 14fr blk, dk red & brt org 5.00 4.00

Jean Charcot (1867-1936), Explorer AP59

Designs: 2.10fr, Ship Pourquoi Pas. 14fr, Ship in storm.

1986, Jan. 1
C93 AP59 2.10fr multicolored .90 .60
C94 AP59 14fr multicolored 4.50 4.25
a. Pair, #C93-C94 + label 6.25 6.25

SPOT Satellite over the Antarctic AP60

1986, May 26 Engr. Perf. 13
C95 AP60 8fr dp ultra, sep & dk ol grn 3.25 2.50

J.B. Charcot — AP61

1987, Jan. 1 Engr. Perf. 13x13½
C96 AP61 14.60fr multi 5.00 4.50

Ocean Drilling Program AP62

1987, Jan. 1 Perf. 13½x13
C97 AP62 16.80fr ol bis, ultra & dk blue 5.50 4.50

INMARSAT AP63

1987, Mar. 2 Engr. Perf. 13
C98 AP63 16.80fr multi 8.00 7.50

French Polar Expeditions, 40th Anniv. AP64

1988, Jan. 1
C99 AP64 20fr lake, ol grn & plum 8.00 6.75

Views of Penguin Is. — AP65

1988, Jan. 1
C100 AP65 3.90fr dk bl & sep 1.75 1.50
C101 AP65 15.10fr dp grn, choc brn & dk bl 5.50 5.00
See Nos. C103, C109.

Founding of Permanent Settlements in the Territories, 40th Anniv. AP66

1989, Jan. 1 Engr. Perf. 13½x13
C102 AP66 15.50fr black 5.00 4.75

Island View Type

1989, Jan. 1
C103 AP65 8.40fr Apostle Islands 2.75 2.50

La Curieuse AP68

1989, Jan. 1 Perf. 13x12½
C104 AP68 2.20fr multicolored .80 .70
C105 AP68 15.50fr multi, diff. 5.00 5.00
 a. Pair, #C104-C105 + label 6.00 6.00

No. C105a label continues the design.

French Revolution, Bicent. AP69

1989, July 14 Engr. Perf. 13x12½
C106 AP69 5fr pink, dark olive grn & dark blue 5.50 3.50

Souvenir Sheet
Perf. 13
C107 Sheet of 4 10.00 10.00
 a. AP69 5fr Prus green, brt ultra & dark red 2.50 2.50

No. C107 for PHILEXFRANCE '89.

15th Antarctic Treaty Summit Conference AP70

1989, Oct. 9 Engr. Perf. 13
C108 AP70 17.70fr multicolored 6.00 5.75

Island View Type

1990, Jan. 1 Engr. Perf. 13
C109 AP65 7.30fr Isle of Pigs, Crozet Isls. 3.00 2.40

L'Astrolabe, Expedition Team AP72

1990, Jan. 1
C110 AP72 15.50fr dk red vio & blk 5.00 5.00

Discovery of Adelie Land by Dumont D'Urville, 150th anniv.

L'Astrolabe, Commanded by Dumont D'Urville, 1840 AP73

1990, Jan. 1
C111 AP73 2.20fr L'Astrolabe, 1988 .80 .75
C112 AP73 15.50fr shown 5.00 5.00
 a. Pair, #C111-C112 + label 6.50 6.50

Bird, by Folon AP74

1990, Jan. 1 Litho. Perf. 12½x13
C113 AP74 30fr multicolored 10.00 9.50

Albatross, Argos Satellite — AP75

1991, Jan. 1
C114 AP75 2.10fr red brn, bl & brn 1.50 .95

Climatological Research — AP76

3.60fr, Weather balloons, instruments. 20fr, Research ship.

1991, Jan. 1 Engr. Perf. 13
C115 AP76 3.60fr multi 1.40 1.40
C116 AP76 20fr multi 7.75 7.75
 a. Pair, #C115-C116 + label 10.00 10.00

Charles de Gaulle (1890-1970) AP77

1991, Jan. 1
C117 AP77 18.80fr blk, red & bl 7.75 7.75

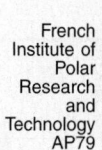

Cape Petrel — AP78

1992, Jan. 1 Engr. Perf. 13
C118 AP78 3.40fr multicolored 2.25 1.40

French Institute of Polar Research and Technology AP79

#C120, Polar bear with man offering flowers.

1991, Dec. 16 Engr. Perf. 13x12
C119 AP79 15fr multicolored 5.75 5.75
C120 AP79 15fr multicolored 5.75 5.75
 a. Strip, #C119-C120 + label 12.00 12.00

Christopher Columbus and Discovery of America AP80

1992, Jan. 1 Perf. 13
C121 AP80 22fr multicolored 9.75 9.75

Mapping Satellite Poseidon AP81

1992, Jan. 1 Engr. Perf. 13
C122 AP81 24.50fr multi 11.00 10.50

Dumont d'Urville Base, Adelie Land AP82

1992, Jan. 1 Litho. Perf. 13x12½
C123 AP82 25.70fr multi 12.00 10.50

Amateur Radio AP83

1993, Jan. 1 Engr. Perf. 13
C124 AP83 2fr multicolored 2.00 .75

New Animal Biology Laboratory, Adelie Land AP84

1993, Jan. 1
C125 AP84 25.40fr multicolored 11.00 6.75

Support Base D10 — AP85

1993, Jan. 1
C126 AP85 25.70fr ol, red & bl 11.00 7.00

Opening of Adelie Land Airfield AP86

1993, Jan. 1
C127 AP86 30fr multicolored 13.00 8.75

Krill — AP87

1994, Jan. 1 Engr. Perf. 13
C128 AP87 15fr black 6.50 4.00

Fishery Management — AP88

1994, Jan. 1
C129 AP88 23fr multicolored 10.00 6.00

Satellite, Ground Station AP89

Design: 27.30fr, Lidar Station.

1994, Jan. 1
C130 AP89 26.70fr multicolored 12.00 7.00
C131 AP89 27.30fr multicolored 12.00 7.25

Arrival of Emperor Penguins AP90

1994, Jan. 1 Perf. 13x12½
C132 AP90 28fr blue & black 13.00 8.00

Erebus Mission AP91

1995, Jan. 2 Engr. Perf. 13
C133 AP91 4.30fr brt bl, brt redsh pur & gray grn 2.25 1.50

Moving of Winter Station, Charcot AP92

1995, Jan. 2 Litho.
C134 AP92 15fr multicolored 6.50 4.25

G. Lesquin (1803-30) — AP93

1995, Jan. 2
C135 AP93 28fr multicolored 12.00 8.00

Map of East Island AP94

1996, Jan. 1 Engr. Perf. 13
C136 AP94 20fr multicolored 8.50 6.00

Expedition to Dome/C AP95

1996, Jan. 1
C137 AP95 23fr dark blue 10.00 7.00

Blue Whale, Southern Whale Sanctuary AP96

1996, Jan. 1
C138 AP96 26.70fr multicolored 12.00 8.00

Port-Couvreux — AP97

1996, Jan. 1
C139 AP97 27.30fr multicolored 12.00 8.50

Jasus Paulensis — AP98

1997, Jan. 1 Engr. Perf. 12½x13
C140 AP98 5.20fr multicolored 3.00 1.75

Racing Yacht Charentes 2 — AP99

1997, Jan. 1 Litho. Perf. 13
C141 AP99 16fr multicolored 8.00 5.50

John Nunn, Shipwrecked 1825-29, Hope Cottage — AP100

1997, Jan. 1 Engr.
C142 AP100 20fr multicolored 8.75 6.25

ICOTA Program AP101

1997, Jan. 1
C143 AP101 24fr multicolored 10.50 7.50

Harpagifer Spinosus AP102

1997, Jan. 1
C144 AP102 27fr multicolored 12.00 8.50

EPICA Program AP103

1998, Jan. 2 Engr. Perf. 13
C145 AP103 5.20fr dk brn & lil 2.50 1.40

First Radio Meteorological Station, Port Aux Francais — AP104

1998, Jan. 2
C146 AP104 8fr black, blue & red 4.25 2.25

King Penguin, Argos Satellite — AP105

1998, Jan. 2 Perf. 12½x13
C147 AP105 16fr multicolored 7.00 4.75

Ranunculas Moseleyi — AP106

1998, Jan. 2
C148 AP106 24fr multicolored 10.50 6.50

Intl. Geophysical Year, 40th Anniv. — AP107

1998, Oct. Engr. Perf. 13x12½
C149 AP107 5.20fr dk bl, blk & brick red 3.00 1.50

FRENCH SUDAN

'french sü-'dan

LOCATION — In northwest Africa, north of French Guinea and Ivory Coast
GOVT. — French Colony
AREA — 590,966 sq. mi.
POP. — 3,794,270 (1941)
CAPITAL — Bamako

In 1899 French Sudan was abolished as a separate colony and was divided among Dahomey, French Guinea, Ivory Coast, Senegal and Senegambia and Niger. Issues for French Sudan were resumed in 1921.
From 1906 to 1921 a part of this territory was known as Upper Senegal and Niger. A part of Upper Volta was added in 1933. See Mali.

100 Centimes = 1 Franc

See French West Africa No. 70 for stamp inscribed "Soudan Francais" and "Afrique Occidentale Francaise."

French Colonies Nos. 58-59 Srchd. in Black

Perf. 14x13½
1894, Apr. 12 Unwmk.
1 A9 15c on 75c car, rose 4,600. 2,300.
2 A9 25c on 1fr brnz grn, straw 5,000. 1,700.

The imperforate stamp like No. 1 was made privately in Paris from a fragment of the lithographic stone which had been used in the Colony for surcharging No. 1.
Counterfeit surcharges exist.

Navigation and Commerce — A2

1894-1900 Typo. Perf. 14x13½
Name of colony in Blue or Carmine
3 A2 1c blk, lil bl 1.60 2.00
4 A2 2c brn, buff 2.40 2.75
5 A2 4c claret, lav 8.00 6.50
6 A2 5c grn, grnsh 12.00 12.00
7 A2 10c blk, lav 24.00 24.00
8 A2 10c red ('00) 8.00 8.00
9 A2 15c blue, quadrille paper 8.00 8.00
10 A2 15c gray, lt gray ('00) 8.00 8.00
11 A2 20c red, grn 40.00 35.00
12 A2 25c blk, rose 32.50 27.50
13 A2 25c blue ('00) 8.00 8.75
14 A2 30c brn, bister 40.00 40.00
15 A2 40c red, straw 40.00 35.00
16 A2 50c car, rose 55.00 65.00
17 A2 50c brn, az ('00) 16.00 16.00
18 A2 75c dp vio, org 55.00 55.00
19 A2 1fr brnz grn, straw 12.00 12.00
Nos. 3-19 (17) 370.50 365.50

Perf. 13½x14 stamps are counterfeits.
Nos. 8, 10, 13, 17 were issued in error. They were accepted for use in the other colonies.

Stamps and Types of Upper Senegal and Niger, 1914-17, Overprinted

1921-30 Perf. 13½x14
21 A4 1c brn vio & vio .25 .40
22 A4 2c dk gray & dl vio .30 .50
23 A4 4c blk & blue .30 .50
24 A4 5c ol brn & dk brn .30 .40
25 A4 10c yel grn & bl grn .90 .55
26 A4 10c red vio & bl ('25) .40 .50
27 A4 15c red brn & org .50 .55
28 A4 15c yel grn & dp ('25) .40 .40
29 A4 15c org brn & vio ('27) 1.60 1.60
30 A4 20c brn vio & blk .50 .55
31 A4 25c blk & bl grn 1.25 .80
a. Booklet pane of 4, 5 #31a 650.00
Complete booklet 16,000.
Complete booklet, overprint omitted on one pane
32 A4 30c red org & rose 1.60 1.60
33 A4 30c bl grn & blk ('26) .80 .70
34 A4 30c dl grn & bl grn ('28) 2.00 2.00
35 A4 35c rose & vio .40 .55
36 A4 40c gray & rose 1.25 1.25
37 A4 45c bl & ol brn 1.25 1.25
38 A4 50c ultra & bl 1.60 1.25
39 A4 50c red org & bl ('26) 1.25 1.25
40 A4 60c vio, pnksh 1.25 1.25
41 A4 65c bis & pale bl ('28) 1.60 1.60
42 A4 75c org & ol brn 1.60 2.00
43 A4 90c brn red & pink ('26) 5.50 5.50
44 A4 1fr dk brn & dl vio 1.60 2.00
45 A4 1.10fr gray lil & red vio ('28) 3.25 4.00
46 A4 1.50fr dp bl & bl ('30) 5.50 5.50
47 A4 2fr grn & bl 2.40 2.75
48 A4 3fr red vio ('30) 12.00 12.00
a. Double overprint 190.00
49 A4 5fr vio & blk 8.00 7.25
Nos. 21-49 (29) 59.55 60.45

Type of 1921 Surcharged

1922, Sept. 28
50 A4 60c on 75c vio, pnksh .80 .80

Stamps and Type of 1921-30 Surcharged

1925-27
51 A4 25c on 45c .80 .80
52 A4 65c on 75c 2.00 2.40
53 A4 85c on 2fr 2.00 2.40
54 A4 85c on 5fr 2.00 2.40
55 A4 90c on 75c brn red & sal pink ('27) 2.40 2.75
56 A4 1.25fr on 1fr dp bl & lt bl (R) ('26) 1.25 1.60
57 A4 1.50fr on 1fr dp bl & ultra ('27) 1.60 2.00
58 A4 3fr on 5fr dl red & brn org ('27) 6.50 5.50
59 A4 10fr on 5fr brn red & bl grn ('27) 24.00 21.00
60 A4 20fr on 5fr vio & ver ('27) 29.00 29.00
Nos. 51-60 (10) 71.55 69.85

Sudanese Woman A4

Entrance to the Residency at Djenné A5

Sudanese Boatman — A6

1931-40 Typo. Perf. 13x14
61 A4 1c dk red & blk .25 .25
62 A4 2c dp blue & org .25 .25
63 A4 3c dk red & blk ('40) .25 .25
64 A4 4c gray lil & rose .25 .25
65 A4 5c indigo & grn .25 .25
66 A4 10c ol grn & rose .25 .25
67 A4 15c blk & brt vio .40 .30
68 A4 20c hn brn & lt bl .40 .30
69 A4 25c red vio & lt red .40 .30
70 A5 30c grn & lt grn .80 .50
71 A5 30c dk bl & red org ('40) .30 .30
72 A5 35c ol grn & grn ('38) .40 .40
73 A5 40c ol grn & pink .40 .30
74 A5 45c dk bl & red org 1.20 .65
75 A5 45c ol grn & grn ('40) .50 .50
76 A5 50c red & black .40 .30
77 A5 55c ultra & car ('38) .40 .40
78 A5 60c brt bl & brn ('40) 1.20 1.20
79 A5 65c brt vio & blk .80 .80
80 A5 70c vio bl & car rose ('40) .80 .80
81 A5 75c brt bl & ol brn 2.40 2.00
82 A5 80c car & brn ('38) .80 .80
83 A5 90c dp red & red org 1.60 .80
84 A5 90c brt vio & sl blk ('39) .90 1.00
85 A5 1fr indigo & grn 8.00 2.40
86 A5 1fr rose red ('38) 5.50 1.60
87 A5 1fr car & brn ('40) .80 .80
88 A6 1.25fr vio & dl vio ('33) .80 .80

89	A6	1.25fr red ('39)	.90	1.00
90	A6	1.40fr brt vio & blk ('40)	.90	.90
91	A6	1.50fr dk bl & ultra	.80	.55
92	A6	1.60fr brn & dp bl ('40)	.90	.90
93	A6	1.75fr dk brn & dp bl ('33)	.80	.80
94	A6	1.75fr vio bl ('38)	.80	.80
95	A6	2fr org brn & grn	.80	.55
96	A6	2.25fr vio bl & ultra ('39)	1.00	1.10
97	A6	2.50fr lt brown ('40)	1.60	1.60
98	A6	3fr Prus grn & brn	.80	.40
99	A6	5fr red & blk	2.00	1.20
100	A6	10fr dull bl & grn	2.40	2.00
101	A6	20fr red vio & brn	3.25	2.40
		Nos. 61-101 (41)	47.65	32.70

For surcharges see Nos. B7-B10.
For 10c and 30c, without "RF," see Nos. 120-121.

Common Design Types
pictured following the introduction.

Colonial Exposition Issue
Common Design Types

1931, Apr. 13   **Engr.**   **Perf. 12½**
Name of Country Printed in Black

102	CD70	40c deep green	4.75	4.75
103	CD71	50c violet	4.75	4.75
104	CD72	90c red orange	4.75	4.75
105	CD73	1.50fr dull blue	4.75	4.75
		Set, never hinged	29.00	

Paris International Exposition Issue
Common Design Types

1937, Apr. 15   **Perf. 13**

106	CD74	20c deep violet	2.00	2.00
107	CD75	30c dark green	2.00	2.00
108	CD76	40c car rose	2.40	2.40
109	CD77	50c dark brown	1.60	1.60
110	CD78	90c red	1.60	1.60
111	CD79	1.50fr ultra	2.40	2.40
		Nos. 106-111 (6)	12.00	12.00
		Set, never hinged	20.25	

Colonial Arts Exhibition Issue
Souvenir Sheet
Common Design Type

1937   **Engr.**   **Imperf.**

112	CD77	3fr magenta & blk	12.00	16.00
		Never hinged	16.00	

Caillie Issue
Common Design Type

1939, Apr. 5   **Perf. 12½x12**

113	CD81	90c org brn & org	.40	.80
114	CD81	1.50fr ultra	.40	1.20
115	CD81	2.25fr ultra & dk bl	.40	1.20
		Nos. 113-115 (3)	1.20	3.20
		Set, never hinged	2.40	

New York World's Fair Issue
Common Design Type

1939, May 10

116	CD82	1.25fr car lake	.80	1.60
117	CD82	2.25fr ultra	.80	1.60
		Set, never hinged	2.40	

Entrance to the Residency at Djenné and Marshal Pétain — A7

1941   **Engr.**   **Perf. 12x12½**

118	A7	1fr green	.40	—
119	A7	2.50fr blue	.40	—
		Set, never hinged	1.60	

For surcharges, see Nos. B14-B15.

Types of 1931-40 without "RF"

1943-44   **Typo.**   **Perf. 13½x14**

120	A4	10c ol green & rose	.65	
121	A5	30c dk bl & red org	.95	
		Set, never hinged	2.00	

Nos. 120-121 were issued by the Vichy government in France, but were not placed on sale in French Sudan.

Stamps of French Sudan were superseded by those of French West Africa.

SEMI-POSTAL STAMPS

Curie Issue
Common Design Type
Unwmk.

1938, Oct. 24   **Engr.**   **Perf. 13**

B1	CD80	1.75fr + 50c brt ultra	12.50	12.50
		Never hinged	21.00	

French Revolution Issue
Common Design Type

1939, July 5   **Photo.**
Name and Value Typo. in Black

B2	CD83	45c + 25c green	10.00	10.00
B3	CD83	70c + 30c brown	10.00	10.00
B4	CD83	90c + 35c red org	10.00	10.00
B5	CD83	1.25fr + 1fr rose pink	10.00	10.00
B6	CD83	2.25fr + 2fr blue	10.00	10.00
		Nos. B2-B6 (5)	50.00	50.00
		Set, never hinged	87.50	

Stamps of 1931-40, Surcharged in Black or Red

1941   **Perf. 13x14**

B7	A5	50c + 1fr red & blk (R)	4.00	4.00
B8	A5	80c + 2fr car & brn	8.00	8.00
B9	A6	1.50fr + 2fr dk bl & ultra	8.00	8.00
B10	A6	2fr + 3fr org brn & grn	8.00	8.00
		Nos. B7-B10 (4)	28.00	28.00
		Set, never hinged	55.00	

Common Design Type and

Native Officer SP1	Aviation Officer SP2

1941   **Photo.**   **Perf. 13½**

B11	SP1	1fr + 1fr red	1.25
B12	CD86	1.50fr + 3fr claret	1.40
B13	SP2	2.50fr + 1fr blue	1.40
		Nos. B11-B13 (3)	4.05
		Set, never hinged	5.50

Surtax for the defense of the colonies. Issued by the Vichy government in France, but not placed on sale in French Sudan.

Petain type of 1941 Surcharged in Black or Red

1944   **Engr.**   **Perf. 12x12½**

B14		50c + 1.50fr on 2.50fr deep blue (R)	.40
B15		+ 2.50fr on 1fr green	.40
		Set, never hinged	1.60

Colonial Development Fund.
Nos. B14-B15 were issued by the Vichy government in France, but were not placed on sale in French Sudan.

AIR POST STAMPS

Common Design Type
Perf. 12½x12

1940, Feb. 8   **Unwmk.**   **Engr.**

C1	CD85	1.90fr ultra	.40	.40
C2	CD85	2.90fr dark red	.40	.40
C3	CD85	4.50fr dk gray green	.80	.80

C4	CD85	4.90fr yellow bister	.80	.80
C5	CD85	6.90fr deep orange	1.60	1.60
		Nos. C1-C5 (5)	4.00	4.00
		Set, never hinged	5.20	

Common Design Types

1942, Oct. 19

C6	CD88	50c carmine & bl	.40
C7	CD88	1fr brown & blk	.40
C8	CD88	2fr dk grn & red brn	.80
C9	CD88	3fr dk blue & scar	.80
C10	CD88	5fr vio & brn red	.80

Frame Engr., Center Typo.

C11	CD89	10fr ultra, ind & gray blk	1.20
C12	CD89	20fr rose car, mag & lt vio	1.60
C13	CD89	50fr yel grn, dl grn & dl bl	2.00
		Nos. C6-C13 (8)	8.00
		Set, never hinged	12.00

There is doubt whether Nos. C7-C12 were officially placed in use.

AIR POST SEMI-POSTAL STAMPS

Types of Dahomey Air Post Semi-Postal Issue
Perf. 13½x12½, 13 (#CB3)
Photo, Engr. (#CB3)

1942, June 22

CB1	SPAP1	1.50fr + 3.50fr grn	.40	5.50
CB2	SPAP2	2fr + 6fr brown	.40	5.50
CB3	SPAP2	3fr + 9fr car red	.40	5.50
		Nos. CB1-CB3 (3)	1.20	16.50
		Set, never hinged	2.40	

Native children's welfare fund.

Colonial Education Fund
Common Design Type
Perf. 12½x13½

1942, June 22   **Engr.**

CB4	CD86a	1.20fr + 1.80fr blue & red	.40	5.50
		Never hinged	.80	

POSTAGE DUE STAMPS

Upper Senegal and Niger Postage Due Stamps Overprinted

Perf. 14x13½

1921, Dec.   **Unwmk.**   **Typo.**

J1	D1	5c green	.40	.40
J2	D1	10c rose	.40	.40
J3	D1	15c gray	.40	.80
J4	D1	20c brown	1.20	1.20
J5	D1	30c blue	1.20	1.20
J6	D1	50c black	2.00	2.40
J7	D1	60c orange	2.40	2.40
J8	D1	1fr violet	2.40	3.25
		Nos. J1-J8 (8)	10.40	12.05

Type of 1921 Issue Surcharged

1927, Oct. 10

J9	D1	2fr on 1fr lilac rose	8.00	8.00
J10	D1	3fr on 1fr org brown	8.00	8.00

D2

1931, Mar. 9

J11	D2	5c green	.25	.30
J12	D2	10c rose	.25	.30
J13	D2	15c gray	.25	.30
J14	D2	20c dark brown	.25	.50
J15	D2	30c dark blue	.40	.55
J16	D2	50c black	.40	.55
J17	D2	60c deep orange	.80	.80
J18	D2	1fr violet	1.20	1.20
J19	D2	2fr lilac rose	1.60	1.60
J20	D2	3fr red brown	1.60	1.60
		Nos. J11-J20 (10)	7.00	7.90

FRENCH WEST AFRICA
'french 'west 'a-fri-kə

LOCATION — Northwestern Africa
GOVT. — French colonial administrative unit
AREA — 1,821,768 sq. mi.
POP. — 18,777,163 (est.)
CAPITAL — Dakar

French West Africa comprised the former colonies of Senegal, French Guinea, Ivory Coast, Dahomey, French Sudan, Mauritania, Niger and Upper Volta.

In 1958, these former colonies became republics, eventually issuing their own stamps. Until the republic issues appeared, stamps of French West Africa continued in use. The Senegal and Sudanese Republics issued stamps jointly as the Federation of Mali, starting in 1959.

> **Catalogue values for all unused stamps in this country are for Never Hinged items.**

Many stamps other than Nos. 65-72 and 77 are inscribed "Afrique Occidentale Francaise" and the name of one of the former colonies. See listings in these colonies for such stamps.

Senegal No. 156 Surcharged in Red

1943   **Unwmk.**   **Perf. 12½x12**

1	A30	1.50fr on 65c dk vio	1.20	.90
2	A30	5.50fr on 65c dk vio	1.60	.80
3	A30	50fr on 65c dk vio	4.00	2.00

Mauritania No. 91 Surcharged in Red

1943   **Perf. 13**

4	A7	3.50fr on 65c dp grn	.80	.40
5	A7	4fr on 65c dp grn	.80	.40
6	A7	5fr on 65c dp grn	1.60	.80
7	A7	10fr on 65c dp grn	1.60	.80
		Nos. 1-7 (7)	11.60	6.10

Senegal No. 143, 148 and 188 Surcharged with New Values in Black and Orange

1944   **Perf. 12½x12**

8	A29	1.50fr on 15c blk (O)	.80	.65
9	A29	4.50fr on 15c blk (O)	1.20	.90
10	A29	5.50fr on 2c brn	2.40	1.60
11	A29	15fr on 15c blk (O)	4.00	1.75
12	CD81	20fr on 90c org brn & org	2.40	1.75
13	CD81	50fr on 90c org brn & org	6.50	3.25

Mauritania No. 109 Surcharged in Black

14	CD81	15fr on 90c org brn & org	2.40	1.60
		Nos. 8-14 (7)	19.70	11.50

Common Design Types pictured following the introduction.

Eboue Issue
Common Design Type

1945   **Engr.**   **Perf. 13**

15	CD91	2fr green	.80	.80
16	CD91	25fr Prussian green	1.60	1.60

Nos. 15 and 16 exist imperforate.

Colonial Soldier — A1

1945		Litho.	Perf. 12½x12, 12	
17	A1	10c indigo & buff	.40	.25
18	A1	30c olive & yel	.40	.25
19	A1	40c blue & buff	.40	.25
20	A1	50c red org & gray	.40	.25
21	A1	60c ol brn & bl	.80	.40
22	A1	70c mag & cit	.80	.40
23	A1	80c bl grn & pale lem	.80	.40
24	A1	1fr brn vio & cit	.80	.40
25	A1	1.20fr gray brn & cit	4.00	2.40
26	A1	1.50fr choc & pink	.80	.40
27	A1	2fr ocher and gray	.80	.40
28	A1	2.40fr red & gray	1.25	.80
29	A1	3fr brn red & yelsh	.80	.40
30	A1	4fr ultra & pink	.80	.40
31	A1	4.50fr org brn & yelsh	.80	.40
32	A1	5fr dk pur & yelsh	.80	.40
33	A1	10fr ol grn & pink	1.60	.80
34	A1	15fr orange & yel	2.40	1.20
35	A1	20fr sl grn & grnsh	2.75	2.00
		Nos. 17-35 (19)	21.60	12.20

Rifle Dance, Mauritania A2

Bamako Dike, French Sudan A3

Trading Canoe, Niger River — A4

Oasis of Bilma, Niger — A5

Shelling Coconuts, Togo — A6

Kouandé Weaving, Dahomey — A7

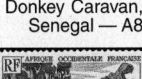

Donkey Caravan, Senegal — A8

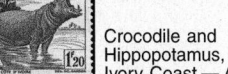

Crocodile and Hippopotamus, Ivory Coast — A9

Gathering Coconuts, French Guinea A10

Bamako Fountain, French Sudan A11

Peul Woman of Dienné A12

Bamako Market A13

Dahomey Laborer A14

Woman of Mauritania A15

Fula Woman, French Guinea A16

Djenné Mosque, French Sudan A17

Monorail Train, Senegal A18

Agni Woman, Ivory Coast A19

Azwa Women at Niger River — A20

1947		Engr. Unwmk.	Perf. 12½	
36	A2	10c blue	.40	.25
37	A3	30c red brn	.40	.25
38	A4	40c gray grn	.40	.25
39	A5	50c red brn	.40	.25
40	A6	60c gray blk	.80	.50
41	A7	80c brown vio	.80	.50
42	A8	1fr maroon	.80	.30
43	A9	1.20fr dk blue grn	2.00	1.40
44	A10	1.50fr ultra	2.00	1.10
45	A11	2fr red orange	.80	.25
46	A12	3fr chocolate	.80	.30
47	A13	3.60fr brown red	1.60	1.40
48	A14	4fr deep blue	.80	.30
49	A15	5fr gray green	.40	.25
50	A16	6fr dark blue	.80	.30
51	A17	10fr brn red	.80	.25
52	A18	15fr sepia	2.40	.30
53	A19	20fr chocolate	1.60	.30
54	A20	25fr grnsh blk	2.40	.50
		Nos. 36-54 (19)	20.40	8.95

Types of 1947

1948			Re-engraved	
55	A6	60c brown olive	1.20	.80
56	A12	3fr chocolate	1.20	.55

Nos. 40 and 46 are inscribed "TOGO" in lower margin. Inscription omitted on Nos. 55 and 56.

Imperforates

Most stamps of French West Africa from 1949 onward exist imperforate in issued and trial colors, and also in small presentation sheets in issued colors.

Military Medal Issue
Common Design Type
Engraved and Typographed

1952, Dec. 1			Perf. 13	
57	CD101	15fr multicolored	8.75	6.50

Treich Laplène and Map — A21

1952, Dec. 1			Engr.	
58	A21	40fr brown lake	2.40	.40

Marcel Treich Laplène, a leading contributor to the development of Ivory Coast.

Medical Laboratory — A22

1953, Nov. 18				
59	A22	15fr brn, dk bl grn & blk brn	1.60	.40

Couple Feeding Antelopes — A23

1954, Sept. 20				
60	A23	25fr multicolored	2.00	.40

Gov. Noel Eugène Ballay — A24

1954, Nov. 29				
61	A24	8fr indigo & brown	2.00	.80

Chimpanzee A25

Giant Pangolin A26

1955, May 2		Unwmk.	Perf. 13	
62	A25	5fr dp vio & dk brn	2.00	.80
63	A26	8fr brn & bl grn	2.00	.80

International Exhibition for Wildlife Protection, Paris, May 1955.

Map, Symbols of Industry, Rotary Emblem — A27

1955, July 4				
64	A27	15fr dark blue	2.40	.80

50th anniv. of the founding of Rotary Intl.

FIDES Issue
Common Design Type

Designs: 1fr, Date grove, Mauritania. 2fr, Milo Bridge, French Guinea. 3fr, Mossi Railroad, Upper Volta. 4fr, Cattle raising, Niger. 15fr, Farm machinery and landscape, Senegal. 17fr, Woman and Niger River, French Sudan. 20fr, Palm oil production, Dahomey. 30fr, Road construction, Ivory Coast.

1956		Engr.	Perf. 13x12½	
65	CD103	1fr dk grn & dk bl grn	1.60	.65
66	CD103	2fr dk bl grn & bl	1.60	.65
67	CD103	3fr dk brn & red brn	1.60	1.00
68	CD103	4fr dk car rose	2.40	1.10
69	CD103	15fr ind & ultra	1.60	.55
70	CD103	17fr dk bl & ind	2.40	.75
71	CD103	20fr rose lake	2.40	.65
72	CD103	30fr dk pur & claret	2.40	1.00
		Nos. 65-72 (8)	16.00	6.35

Coffee — A28a

1956, Oct. 22			Perf. 13	
73	A28a	15fr dk blue green	1.60	.80

Mobile Leprosy Clinic and Maltese Cross — A29

1957, Mar. 11				
74	A29	15fr dk red brn, pur & red	2.40	.80

Issued in honor of the Knights of Malta.

Map of Africa — A30

1958, Feb.		Unwmk.	Perf. 13	
75	A30	20fr multicolored	1.60	.80

6h Intl.Cong. for African Tourism at Dakar.

"Africa" and Communications Symbols — A31

1958, Mar. 15			Engr.	
76	A31	15fr org, ultra & choc	2.00	.80

Stamp Day. See No. 86.

Abidjan Bridge — A32

1958, Mar. 15				
77	A32	20fr dk sl grn & grnsh bl	2.00	.80

Bananas — A33

1958, May 19			Perf. 13	
78	A33	20fr rose lil, dk grn & ol	1.60	.40

Flower Issue
Common Design Type

10fr, Gloriosa. 25fr, Adenopus. 30fr, Cyrtosperma. 40fr, Cistanche. 65fr, Crinum Moorei.

1958-59		Photo.	Perf. 12x12½	
79	CD104	10fr multicolored	1.20	.40
80	CD104	25fr red, yel & grn	1.60	.80
81	CD104	30fr multicolored	2.00	1.20
82	CD104	40fr blk brn, grn & yel	2.40	1.60
83	CD104	65fr multicolored	3.25	1.60
		Nos. 79-83 (5)	10.45	5.60

Issued: 25fr, 40fr, 1/5/59; others, 7/7/58.

Moro Naba Sagha and Map — A34

1958, Nov. 1			Engr.	Perf. 13
84	A34	20fr ol brn, car & vio	1.60	.80

10th anniv. of the reestablishment of the Upper Volta territory.

Human Rights Issue
Common Design Type

1958, Dec. 10				
85	CD105	20fr maroon & dk bl	2.40	2.00

Type of 1958 Redrawn

1959, Mar. 21   Engr.   Perf. 13

86 A31 20fr red, grnsh bl & sl grn 2.75 2.40

Name of country omitted on No. 86; "RF" replaced by "CF," inscribed "Dakar-Abidjan." Stamp Day.

SEMI-POSTAL STAMPS

Red Cross Issue
Common Design Type
Perf. 14½x14

1944, Dec.   Photo.   Unwmk.

B1 CD90 5fr + 20fr plum 6.50 4.75

The surtax was for the French Red Cross and national relief.

Type of France, 1945, Overprinted in Black

1945, Oct. 13   Engr.   Perf. 13

B2 SP150 2fr + 3fr orange red 1.20 .80

Tropical Medicine Issue
Common Design Type

1950, May 15   Perf. 13

B3 CD100 10fr +2fr red brn & sep 9.50 7.25

The surtax was for charitable work.

AIR POST STAMPS

Common Design Type

1945 Photo. Unwmk. Perf. 14½x14

C1 CD87 5.50fr ultra 2.00 1.00
C2 CD87 50fr dark green 3.50 1.40
C3 CD87 100fr plum 4.00 1.50
    Nos. C1-C3 (3) 9.50 3.90

Victory Issue
Common Design Type

1946, May 8   Engr.   Perf. 12½

C4 CD92 8fr violet 1.60 1.20

Chad to Rhine Issue
Common Design Types

1946, June 6

C5 CD93 5fr brown car 2.00 1.60
C6 CD94 10fr deep blue 2.00 1.60
C7 CD95 15fr brt violet 2.40 1.60
C8 CD96 20fr dk slate grn 2.40 2.00
C9 CD97 25fr olive brn 3.25 2.40
C10 CD98 50fr brown 4.00 2.75
    Nos. C5-C10 (6) 16.05 11.95

Antoine de Saint-Exupéry, Map and Natives — AP1

Plane over Dakar AP2

Great White Egrets in Flight AP3

Natives and Phantom Plane AP4

1947, Mar. 24   Engr.

C11 AP1 8fr red brown 1.60 .80
C12 AP2 50fr rose violet 4.00 1.20
C13 AP3 100fr ultra 16.00 4.75
C14 AP4 200fr slate gray 14.00 5.25
    Nos. C11-C14 (4) 35.60 12.00

UPU Issue
Common Design Type

1949, July 4   Perf. 13

C15 CD99 25fr multicolored 12.00 8.75

Vridi Canal, Abidjan AP5

1951, Nov. 5   Unwmk.   Perf. 13

C16 AP5 500fr red org, bl grn & dp ultra 32.50 4.75

Liberation Issue
Common Design Type

1954, June 6

C17 CD102 15fr indigo & ultra 12.00 5.50

Logging AP6

Designs: 100fr, Radiotelephone exchange. 200fr, Baobab trees.

1954, Sept. 20

C18 AP6 50fr ol grn & org brn 4.00 .80
C19 AP6 100fr ind, dk brn & dk grn 6.50 1.20
C20 AP6 200fr bl grn, grnsh blk & brn lake 17.50 2.75
    Nos. C18-C20 (3) 28.00 4.75

Gen. Louis Faidherbé and African Sharpshooter — AP7

1957, July 20   Unwmk.   Perf. 13

C21 AP7 15fr indigo & blue 2.00 1.60

Centenary of French African troops.

Gorée Island and Woman AP8

Designs: 20fr, Map with planes and ships. 25fr, Village and modern city. 40fr, Seat of Council of French West Africa. 50fr, Worker, ship and peanut plant. 100fr, Bay of N'Gor.

1958, Mar. 15   Engr.

C22 AP8 15fr blk brn, grn & vio 1.60 .80
C23 AP8 20fr blk brn, dk bl & red brn 1.60 .80
C24 AP8 25fr blk vio, bis & grn 1.60 1.20
C25 AP8 40fr dk bl, brn & grn 1.60 1.20
C26 AP8 50fr violet, brn & grn 3.25 1.60
C27 AP8 100fr brown, bl & grn 6.50 2.40
  a.   Souvenir sheet of 6, #C22-C27 20.00 16.00
    Nos. C22-C27 (6) 16.15 8.00

Centenary of Dakar.

Woman Playing Native Harp — AP9

1958, Dec. 1   Unwmk.   Perf. 13

C28 AP9 20fr red brn, blk & gray 1.60 .80

Inauguration of Nouakchott as capital of Mauritania.

POSTAGE DUE STAMPS

D1

1947   Engr.   Unwmk.   Perf. 13

J1 D1 10c red .40 .25
J2 D1 30c deep orange .40 .25
J3 D1 50c greenish blk .40 .25
J4 D1 1fr carmine .40 .25
J5 D1 2fr emerald .50 .30
J6 D1 3fr red lilac .90 .65
J7 D1 4fr deep ultra 1.10 .80
J8 D1 5fr red brown 2.25 1.60
J9 D1 10fr peacock blue 2.90 2.25
J10 D1 20fr sepia 5.25 3.75
    Nos. J1-J10 (10) 14.50 10.35

OFFICIAL STAMPS

Mask — O1

Designs: Various masks.

Perf. 14x13

1958, June 2   Typo.   Unwmk.

O1 O1 1fr dk brn red 1.10 1.00
O2 O1 3fr brt green .65 .55
O3 O1 5fr crim rose .65 .50
O4 O1 10fr light ultra .80 .65
O5 O1 20fr bright red 1.60 .80
O6 O1 25fr purple 1.60 .80
O7 O1 30fr green 2.75 1.60
O8 O1 45fr gray black 3.25 1.60
O9 O1 50fr dark red 3.25 1.60
O10 O1 65fr brt ultra 4.50 1.60
O11 O1 100fr olive bister 10.50 2.75
O12 O1 200fr deep green 21.00 5.50
    Nos. O1-O12 (12) 51.65 18.95

FUJEIRA

fü-'jī-rə

LOCATION — Oman Peninsula, Arabia, on Persian Gulf

GOVT. — Sheikdom under British protection

Fujeira is one of six Persian Gulf sheikdoms which proclaimed independence Dec. 2, 1971. See United Arab Emirates.

100 Naye Paise = 1 Rupee

Catalogue values for all unused stamps in this country are for Never Hinged items.

Sheik Hamad bin Mohammed al Sharqi and Grebe — A1

Sheik and: 2np, 50np, Arabian oryx. 3np, 70np, Hoopoe. 4np, 1r, Wild ass. 5np, 1.50r, Herons in flight. 10np, 2r, Arabian horses. 15np, 3r, Leopard. 20np, 5r, Camels. 30np, 10r, Hawks.

Photo. & Litho.

1964   Unwmk.   Perf. 14
Size: 36x24mm

1 A1 1np gold & multi .25 .25
2 A1 2np gold & multi .25 .25
3 A1 3np gold & multi .25 .25
4 A1 4np gold & multi .25 .25
5 A1 5np gold & multi .25 .25
6 A1 10np gold & multi .25 .25
7 A1 15np gold & multi .25 .25
8 A1 20np gold & multi .25 .25
9 A1 30np gold & multi .25 .25

Size: 43x28mm

10 A1 40np gold & multi .35 .25
11 A1 50np gold & multi .40 .25
12 A1 70np gold & multi .45 .25
13 A1 1r gold & multi .65 .25
14 A1 1.50r gold & multi .95 .25
15 A1 2r gold & multi 1.50 .25

Size: 53½x35mm

16 A1 3r gold & multi 2.40 .25
17 A1 5r gold & multi 2.25 .35
18 A1 10r gold & multi 7.50 .50
    Nos. 1-18 (18) 18.70 4.85

Issued: 20np, 30np, 70np, 1.50r, 3r, 10r, Nov. 14; others, Sept. 22.

Exist imperf. Value, set $30.

Sheik Hamad and Shot Put — A2

1964, Dec. 6   Perf. 14
Size: 43x28mm

19 A2 25np shown .25 .25
20 A2 50np Discus .25 .25
21 A2 75np Fencing .25 .25
22 A2 1r Boxing .35 .30
23 A2 1.50r Relay race .50 .35
24 A2 2r Soccer .60 .40

Size: 53½x35mm

25 A2 3r Pole vaulting 1.15 .50
26 A2 5r Hurdling 3.00 .75
27 A2 7.50r Equestrian 4.25 .90
    Nos. 19-27 (9) 10.60 3.95

18th Olympic Games, Tokyo, 10/10-25/64. Exist imperf. Value, set $12.

John F. Kennedy — A3

Kennedy: 10np, As sailor in the Pacific. 15np, As naval lieutenant. 20np, On speaker's rostrum. 25np, Sailing with family. 50np, With crowd of people. 1r, With Mrs. Kennedy, Lyndon B. Johnson. 2r, With Eisenhower on White House porch. 3r, With Mrs. Kennedy & Caroline. 5r, Portrait.

1965, Feb. 23   Photo.   Perf. 13½
Size: 29x44mm
Black Design with Gold Inscriptions

28 A3 5np pale gray .25 .25
29 A3 10np pale yellow .25 .25
30 A3 15np pink .25 .25
31 A3 20np pale greenish gray .25 .25
32 A3 25np pale blue .25 .25
33 A3 50np pale rose .30 .25

Size: 33x51mm

34 A3 1r pale gray .75 .30
35 A3 2r pale green 1.25 .40
36 A3 3r pale gray 2.50 .50
37 A3 5r pale yellow 3.25 .80
    Nos. 28-37 (10) 9.30 3.50

Pres. John F. Kennedy (1917-1963). A souvenir sheet contains 2 29x44mm stamps similar to Nos. 36-37 with pale blue (3r) and pale rose (5r) backgrounds. Value (unused): perf $7; imperf $9.

Nos. 28-37 exist imperf. Value $14.

AIR POST STAMPS

Wild Ass — AP1

Photo. & Litho.
1965, Aug. 16   Unwmk.   Perf. 13½
Size: 43x28mm

C1	AP1	15np Grebe	.25	.25
C2	AP1	25np Arabian oryx	.25	.25
C3	AP1	35np Hoopoe	.35	.25
C4	AP1	50np Wild ass	.40	.25
C5	AP1	75np Herons in flight	.45	.25
C6	AP1	1r Arabian horses	.60	.25

Size: 53½x35mm

C7	AP1	2r Leopard	1.25	.25
C8	AP1	3r Camels	2.50	.25
C9	AP1	5r Hawks	4.50	.50
		Nos. C1-C9 (9)	10.55	2.50

Exist imperf. Value, set $11.

AIR POST OFFICIAL STAMPS

Type of Air Post Issue, 1965
Photo. & Litho.
1965, Nov. 10   Unwmk.   Perf. 13½
Size: 43x28mm

CO1	AP1	75np Arabian horses	.60	.25

Perf. 13
Size: 53½x35mm

CO2	AP1	2r Leopard	1.50	.40
CO3	AP1	3r Camels	2.50	.60
CO4	AP1	5r Hawks	4.50	1.00
		Nos. CO1-CO4 (4)	9.10	2.25

Exist imperf. Values same as perf.

OFFICIAL STAMPS

Type of Air Post Issue, 1965
Photo. & Litho.
1965, Oct. 14   Unwmk.   Perf. 13½
Size: 43x28mm

O1	AP1	25np Grebe	.25	.25
O2	AP1	40np Arabian oryx	.25	.25
O3	AP1	50np Hoopoe	.35	.25
O4	AP1	75np Wild ass	.55	.25
O5	AP1	1r Herons in flight	1.25	.25
		Nos. O1-O5 (5)	2.65	1.25

Exist imperf. Values same as perf.

FUNCHAL

fün-'shäl

LOCATION — A city and administrative district in the Madeira island group in the Atlantic Ocean northwest of Africa
GOVT. — A part of the Republic of Portugal
POP. — 150,574 (1900)

Postage stamps of Funchal were superseded by those of Portugal.

1000 Reis = 1 Milreis

King Carlos — A1

1892-93   Typo.   Unwmk.
Perf. 11½, 12½, 13½

1	A1	5r yellow	4.25	2.00
2	A1	10r red violet	4.25	2.00
3	A1	15r chocolate	5.50	3.75
4	A1	20r lavender	5.50	3.00
5a	A1	25r dark green	8.00	1.75
6	A1	50r ultramarine	10.25	5.00
7	A1	75r carmine	10.25	6.75
8	A1	80r yellow green	20.00	12.00
9	A1	100r brn, *yel* ('93)	13.50	5.50

10	A1	150r car, *rose* ('93)	70.00	31.00
11	A1	200r dk bl, *bl* ('93)	80.00	45.00
12	A1	300r dk bl, *sal* ('93)	80.00	55.00
		Nos. 1-12 (12)	311.50	172.75

Nos. 1-12 were printed on both enamel-surfaced and chalky papers. Values are for the most common varieties. For detailed listings, see the *Scott Classic Specialized Catalogue.*

The reprints of this issue have shiny white gum and clean-cut perforation 13½. The shades differ from those of the originals and the uncolored paper is thin.

King Carlos — A2

Name and Value in Black
except Nos. 25 and 34

1897-1905   Perf. 11¾

13	A2	2½r gray	.60	.60
a.		Name and denomination inverted		275.00
14	A2	5r orange	.60	.60
15	A2	10r light green	.60	.60
16	A2	15r brown	8.00	5.00
17	A2	15r gray grn ('99)	5.50	3.75
18	A2	20r gray vio	2.40	1.20
19	A2	25r sea green	3.75	1.20
20	A2	25r car rose ('99)	2.40	.60
a.		Booklet pane of 6		
21	A2	50r dark blue	9.25	5.00
a.		Perf. 12½	25.00	12.00
22	A2	50r ultra ('05)	2.40	1.20
23	A2	65r slate blue ('98)	1.25	1.20
24	A2	75r rose	2.40	1.20
25	A2	75r brn & red, *yel* ('05)	3.00	1.40
26	A2	80r violet	2.40	1.75
27	A2	100r dark blue, *blue*	2.40	1.75
28	A2	115r org brn, *pink* ('98)	3.50	1.75
29	A2	130r gray brown, *buff* ('98)	3.50	1.75
30	A2	150r lt brn, *buff*	4.25	1.75
31	A2	180r sl, *pnksh* ('98)	3.50	1.75
32	A2	200r red vio, *pale lil*	4.25	2.40
33	A2	300r blue, *rose*	4.25	2.40
34	A2	500r blk & red, *bl*	4.25	2.40
a.		Perf. 12½	17.50	9.00
		Nos. 13-34 (22)	74.45	41.25

INDEX AND IDENTIFIER

All page numbers shown are
those in this Volume 2B.

Postage stamps that do not have
English words on them are shown
in the Illustrated Identifier.

INDEX TO ADVERTISERS
2024 VOLUME 2B

2024
VOLUME 2B
DEALER DIRECTORY
YELLOW PAGE LISTINGS

This section of your Scott Catalogue contains advertisements to help you conveniently find what you need, when you need it....!

Aerophilately

**HENRY GITNER
PHILATELISTS, INC.**
PO Box 3077-S
Middletown, NY 10940
PH: 845-343-5151
PH: 845-947-8267
FAX: 845-343-0068
hgitner@hgitner.com
www.hgitner.com

Appraisals

**DR. ROBERT FRIEDMAN &
SONS STAMP & COIN
BUYING CENTER**
2029 W. 75th St.
Woodridge, IL 60517
PH: 800-588-8100
FAX: 630-985-1588
stampcollections@drbobstamps.com
www.drbobfriedmanstamps.com

Asia

KELLEHER & ROGERS LTD.
22 Shelter Rock Lane, Unit #53
Danbury, CT 06810
PH: 203-830-2500
Toll Free: 800-212-2830
info@kelleherauctions.com
www.kelleherauctions.com

Auctions

DUTCH COUNTRY AUCTIONS
The Stamp Center
4115 Concord Pike
Wilmington, DE 19803
PH: 302-478-8740
FAX: 302-478-8779
auctions@dutchcountryauctions.com
www.dutchcountryauctions.com

KELLEHER & ROGERS LTD.
22 Shelter Rock Lane, Unit #53
Danbury, CT 06810
PH: 203-830-2500
Toll Free: 800-212-2830
info@kelleherauctions.com
www.kelleherauctions.com

British Commonwealth

**ARON R. HALBERSTAM
PHILATELISTS, LTD.**
PO Box 150168
Van Brunt Station
Brooklyn, NY 11215-0168
PH: 718-788-3978
arh@arhstamps.com
www.arhstamps.com

ROY'S STAMPS
PO Box 28001
600 Ontario Street
St. Catharines, ON
CANADA L2N 7P8
Phone: 905-934-8377
Email: roystamp@cogeco.ca
www.roysstamps.com

THE STAMP ACT
PO Box 1136
Belmont, CA 94002
PH: 650-703-2342
thestampact@sbcglobal.net

Buying

**DR. ROBERT FRIEDMAN &
SONS STAMP & COIN
BUYING CENTER**
2029 W. 75th St.
Woodridge, IL 60517
PH: 800-588-8100
FAX: 630-985-1588
stampcollections@drbobstamps.com
www.drbobfriedmanstamps.com

Canada

CANADA STAMP FINDER LLC
2800 N 6th Street, Unit 1-708
St. Augustine, FL 32084
PH: 904-217-2166
Canadian Address:
PO Box 92591
Brampton, ON L6W 4R1
PH: 514-238-5751
Toll Free in North America:
877-412-3106
FAX: 323-315-2635
canadastampfinder@gmail.com
www.canadastampfinder.com

ROY'S STAMPS
PO Box 28001
600 Ontario Street
St. Catharines, ON
CANADA L2N 7P8
Phone: 905-934-8377
Email: roystamp@cogeco.ca
www.roysstamps.com

China

ASIA PHILATELICS
3276 Andora Drive
San Jose, CA 95148
PH: 408-238-0893
Richard@asiaphilatelics.com

KELLEHER & ROGERS LTD.
22 Shelter Rock Lane, Unit #53
Danbury, CT 06810
PH: 203-830-2500
Toll Free: 800-212-2830
info@kelleherauctions.com
www.kelleherauctions.com

THE STAMP ACT
PO Box 1136
Belmont, CA 94002
PH: 650-703-2342
thestampact@sbcglobal.net

Collections

**DR. ROBERT FRIEDMAN &
SONS STAMP & COIN
BUYING CENTER**
2029 W. 75th St.
Woodridge, IL 60517
PH: 800-588-8100
FAX: 630-985-1588
stampcollections@drbobstamps.com
www.drbobfriedmanstamps.com

Ducks

MICHAEL JAFFE
PO Box 61484
Vancouver, WA 98666
PH: 360-695-6161
PH: 800-782-6770
FAX: 360-695-1616
mjaffe@brookmanstamps.com
www.brookmanstamps.com

France & Colonies

E. JOSEPH MCCONNELL, INC.
PO Box 683
Monroe, NY 10949
PH: 845-783-9791
ejstamps@gmail.com
www.EJMcConnell.com

French S. Antarctic

E. JOSEPH MCCONNELL, INC.
PO Box 683
Monroe, NY 10949
PH: 845-783-9791
ejstamps@gmail.com
www.EJMcConnell.com

Japan

KELLEHER & ROGERS LTD.
22 Shelter Rock Lane, Unit #53
Danbury, CT 06810
PH: 203-830-2500
Toll Free: 800-212-2830
info@kelleherauctions.com
www.kelleherauctions.com

Korea

KELLEHER & ROGERS LTD.
22 Shelter Rock Lane, Unit #53
Danbury, CT 06810
PH: 203-830-2500
Toll Free: 800-212-2830
info@kelleherauctions.com
www.kelleherauctions.com

Manchukuo

KELLEHER & ROGERS LTD.
22 Shelter Rock Lane, Unit #53
Danbury, CT 06810
PH: 203-830-2500
Toll Free: 800-212-2830
info@kelleherauctions.com
www.kelleherauctions.com

Middle East - Arab

KELLEHER & ROGERS LTD.
22 Shelter Rock Lane, Unit #53
Danbury, CT 06810
PH: 203-830-2500
Toll Free: 800-212-2830
info@kelleherauctions.com
www.kelleherauctions.com

New Issues

DAVIDSON'S STAMP SERVICE
Personalized Service since 1970
PO Box 36355
Indianapolis, IN 46236-0355
PH: 317-826-2620
ed-davidson@earthlink.net
www.newstampissues.com

Proofs & Essays

**HENRY GITNER
PHILATELISTS, INC.**
PO Box 3077-S
Middletown, NY 10940
PH: 845-343-5151
PH: 800-947-8267
FAX: 845-343-0068
hgitner@hgitner.com
www.hgitner.com

Stamp Stores

Delaware

DUTCH COUNTRY AUCTIONS
The Stamp Center
4115 Concord Pike
Wilmington, DE 19803
PH: 302-478-8740
FAX: 302-478-8779
auctions@dutchcountryauctions.com
www.dutchcountryauctions.com

British Commonwealth

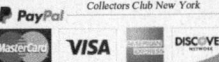

Stamp Stores

Florida

DR. ROBERT FRIEDMAN & SONS STAMP & COIN BUYING CENTER
PH: 800-588-8100
FAX: 630-985-1588
stampcollections@drbobstamps.com
www.drbobfriedmanstamps.com

Illinois

DR. ROBERT FRIEDMAN & SONS STAMP & COIN BUYING CENTER
2029 W. 75th St.
Woodridge, IL 60517
PH: 800-588-8100
FAX: 630-985-1588
stampcollections@drbobstamps.com
www.drbobfriedmanstamps.com

Indiana

KNIGHT STAMP & COIN CO.
237 Main St.
Hobart, IN 46342
PH: 219-942-4341
PH: 800-634-2646
knight@knightcoin.com
www.knightcoin.com

New Jersey

BERGEN STAMPS & COLLECTIBLES
306 Queen Anne Rd.
Teaneck, NJ 07666
PH: 201-836-8987
bergenstamps@gmail.com

TRENTON STAMP & COIN
Thomas DeLuca
Store: Forest Glen Plaza
1800 Highway #33, Suite 103
Hamilton Square, NJ 08690
Mail: PO Box 8574
Trenton, NJ 08650
PH: 609-584-8100
FAX: 609-587-8664
TOMD4TSC@aol.com
www.trentonstampandcoin.com

New York

CHAMPION STAMP CO., INC.
432 West 54th St.
New York, NY 10019
PH: 212-489-8130
FAX: 212-581-8130
championstamp@aol.com
www.championstamp.com

Ohio

HILLTOP STAMP SERVICE
Richard A. Peterson
PO Box 626
Wooster, OH 44691
PH: 330-262-8907 (O)
PH: 330-201-1377 (H)
hilltop@bright.net
hilltopstamps@sssnet.com
www.hilltopstamps.com

Supplies

BROOKLYN GALLERY COIN & STAMP, INC.
8725 4th Ave.
Brooklyn, NY 11209
PH: 718-745-5701
FAX: 718-745-2775
info@brooklyngallery.com
www.brooklyngallery.com

Topicals

E. JOSEPH MCCONNELL, INC.
PO Box 683
Monroe, NY 10949
PH: 845-783-9791
ejstamps@gmail.com
www.EJMcConnell.com

Topicals - Columbus

MR. COLUMBUS
PO Box 1492
Fennville, MI 49408
PH: 269-543-4755
David@MrColumbus1492.com
www.MrColumbus1492.com

United States

ACS STAMP COMPANY
2914 W 135th Ave
Broomfield, Colorado 80020
303-841-8666
www.ACSStamp.com

BROOKMAN STAMP CO.
PO Box 90
Vancouver, WA 98666
PH: 360-695-1391
PH: 800-545-4871
FAX: 360-695-1616
info@brookmanstamps.com
www.brookmanstamps.com

U.S. Classics/Moderns

BARDO STAMPS
PO Box 7437
Buffalo Grove, IL 60089
PH: 847-634-2676
jfb7437@aol.com
www.bardostamps.com

U.S.-Collections Wanted

DUTCH COUNTRY AUCTIONS
The Stamp Center
4115 Concord Pike
Wilmington, DE 19803
PH: 302-478-8740
FAX: 302-478-8779
auctions@dutchcountryauctions.com
www.dutchcountryauctions.com

DR. ROBERT FRIEDMAN & SONS STAMP & COIN BUYING CENTER
2029 W. 75th St.
Woodridge, IL 60517
PH: 800-588-8100
FAX: 630-985-1588
stampcollections@drbobstamps.com
www.drbobfriedmanstamps.com

Wanted - Worldwide Collections

DUTCH COUNTRY AUCTIONS
The Stamp Center
4115 Concord Pike
Wilmington, DE 19803
PH: 302-478-8740
FAX: 302-478-8779
auctions@dutchcountryauctions.com
www.dutchcountryauctions.com

Websites

ACS STAMP COMPANY
2914 W 135th Ave
Broomfield, Colorado 80020
303-841-8666
www.ACSStamp.com

Wholesale

HENRY GITNER PHILATELISTS, INC.
PO Box 3077-S
Middletown, NY 10940
PH: 845-343-5151
PH: 800-947-8267
FAX: 845-343-0068
hgitner@hgitner.com
www.hgitner.com

Worldwide

KELLEHER & ROGERS LTD.
22 Shelter Rock Lane, Unit #53
Danbury, CT 06810
PH: 203-830-2500
Toll Free: 800-212-2830
info@kelleherauctions.com
www.kelleherauctions.com

GUILLERMO JALIL
Maipu 466, local 4
1006 Buenos Aires
Argentina
guillermo@jalilstamps.com
philatino@philatino.com
www.philatino.com (worldwide stamp auctions)
www.jalilstamps.com (direct sale, worldwide stamps)

Worldwide-Collections

DR. ROBERT FRIEDMAN & SONS STAMP & COIN BUYING CENTER
2029 W. 75th St.
Woodridge, IL 60517
PH: 800-588-8100
FAX: 630-985-1588
stampcollections@drbobstamps.com
www.drbobfriedmanstamps.com